RHS Plant Finder 2017

DEVISED BY CHRIS PHILIP AND REALISED BY TONY LORD

EDITOR-IN-CHIEF
JANET CUBEY

RHS EDITORS
JAMES ARMITAGE DAWN EDWARDS KÁLMÁN KÖNYVES
NEIL LANCASTER ROSALYN MARSHALL

COMPILER
JUDITH MERRICK

Sharing the best in Gardening

Published and compiled by
The Royal Horticultural Society
80 Vincent Square
London SW1P 2PE

Reg charity no: 222879/SC038262

First edition 1987

Thirty-first edition 2017

British Library Cataloguing Publication Data
A catalogue record for this book is available from the British Library

ISBN 978-1-907057-77-9

RHS Publisher – Rae Spencer-Jones

RHS Editor – Simon Maughan

RHS Art Editor – Mark Timothy

RHS Head of Editorial – Chris Young

Designer – Peter Cooling

Printed and bound by Wheatons Exeter Ltd, Hennock Road, Marsh Barton, Exeter, Devon EX2 8RP

The compiler and editors of the RHS Plant Finder have taken every care, in the time available, to check all the information supplied to them by the nurseries concerned. Nevertheless, in a work of this kind, containing as it does hundreds of thousands of separate computer encodings, errors and omissions will inevitably occur. The RHS, the Publisher and Editors, cannot accept responsibility for any consequences that may arise from such errors.

If you find any mistakes, we hope that you will let us know so that the matter can be corrected in the next edition.

Front cover photograph: *Prunus* 'Matsumae-hayazaki' (RHS / Jason Ingram)
Back cover: Plant portraits from top to bottom: *Cosmos bipinnatus* 'Antiquity' (RHS / Joanna Kossak)
Harvesting beetroot (RHS / Jason Ingram)
Malus domestica 'Scrumptious' (RHS / Josh Bailey)
Paeonia lactiflora 'Albert Crousse' (RHS / Carol Sheppard)

The Royal Horticultural Society is the UK's leading gardening charity dedicated to advancing horticulture and promoting good gardening. Its charitable work includes providing expert advice and information, training the next generation of gardeners, creating hands-on opportunities for children to grow plants and conducting research into plants, pests and environmental issues affecting gardeners.

For more information visit www.rhs.org.uk or call 020 3176 5800.

Contents

A changing picture of the UK's garden flora

Over three decades, the *Plant Finder* has provided a snapshot of British garden plants and trends. Instrumental in linking plant seekers with suppliers, this directory was the brainchild of a computer-literate gardener and his nomenclatural mentor

Author: **Tony Lord** VMH gardener, photographer and author.

When Chris Philip and his partner Denys Gueroult moved to Whitbourne in Worcestershire in 1984, they could scarcely have guessed that their attempts to stock their new garden would have a profound and long-lasting effect on gardeners across Britain and beyond.

Failing to find the fine plants he and Denys saw in current gardening literature, Chris (1928–98) decided to compile a listing of plant sources.

In 1985, he started to collect plant catalogues, entering every specimen offered onto his computer database. Denys, who died in 2014 aged 87, proof read the printouts, correcting names and standardising spellings. This was when they found their first and biggest problem. Often many different names were given for what appeared to be the same plant, and respected reference sources did not always agree about which was right. Clearly the finished version could contain only one correct name, with important synonyms cross referenced – but which was the most correct?

This was the question Chris and Denys raised on joining the Hardy Plant Society (HPS) in 1986. They generously offered the HPS half of the profits in return for its endorsement of *Plant Finder*. Knowing that I specialised in checking plant names for the National Trust and HPS publications, HPS Chairman Jack Elliott introduced Chris to me.

I gave Chris a list of 450 nurseries from a directory I had compiled in my work, which he added with their plants to the database. I convinced him to style each name according to the codes of nomenclature and to give the database a separate field for each element of the plant name. As a result, in the long term, the name set was much more compatible with the RHS BG-Base plant name database.

To his eternal credit, Chris took great pains to ensure every name was as correct as possible and checked all the cross references. When I received the first printouts to check, I slogged through reference works, such as *Index Kewensis*, and dictated the corrections to Chris. It was printed in late March 1987, and appeared at the Harrogate Spring Show.

The first edition listed 22,000 plants and other countries soon produced similar books. Almost all adopted the *Plant Finder* name set, which ultimately proved a tremendous boon for gardeners seeking information about a plant online. However, independent advice about plant names became harder to find because most nurseries just followed the *Plant Finder* names.

'The finished version could contain only one name – but which one?'

Second edition

More plant groups and cross references appeared in the second edition along with classifications for *Dianthus*, *Narcissus* and *Dahlia*. The third edition contained 40,000 entries; this plateaued at 70,000 in 1997 with new entries roughly equalling deletions. So for all our delight in a fresh edition's new plants, for each of these, an old one has often disappeared from the nursery trade.

The Royal Horticultural Society acquired the copyright for the eighth edition in 1994, with Chris and me working as before until the 1996 edition. The title changed to *RHS Plant Finder* in 1995, the year in which the RHS Advisory Panel on Nomenclature and Taxonomy (now the RHS Nomenclature and Taxonomy Advisory Group) was set up, largely to deal with some of the more imponderable problems arising from *RHS Plant Finder*.

Chris's database was transferred to the RHS BG-Base system. Since 1996, compilers have been Clare Burgh followed by Judith Merrick, while first Niki Simpson and now Richard Sanford have coordinated RHS botanists' plant naming of the edits on to the database. »

FIVE OF MY TOP *RHS PLANT FINDER* PLANTS

Graham Rice

Plantsman and author

✤ I first came across ***Galanthus* 'John Gray'** when I planted these impressive snowdrops – tall and elegant with large flowers beautifully marked and shaped – on the rock garden at the Royal Botanic Gardens, Kew.

✤ Descended from breakthrough breeding by nursery owner Elizabeth Strangman (with whom I wrote a book about hellebores), the exquisite colours, patterns and elegant shape combined with the absence of off-types, make the ***Helleborus* x *hybridus* Ashwood Garden Hybrids** the best on the market.

✤ **x *Heucherella* 'Solar Eclipse'** represents the new golden age of perennial plant breeding. Its reddish-brown, nicely scalloped leaves are edged in lime green and the whole plant develops into an elegant mound.

✤ ***Lathyrus odoratus* 'High Scent'** is a fragrant reminder of working with my wife Judy White on my sweet pea book. New Zealand plant breeder Keith Hammett created this deliciously scented cultivar with cream flowers delicately edged in purple.

✤ In our American garden, ***Physocarpus* Diable D'Or ('Mindia')** has taken -25°C, deluges of snow, hosted birds' nests, flowered in spring, berried in autumn and the exquisite amber shoot tips have matured to rich bronze-purple foliage all summer and autumn – simply indispensible.

Online growth

Following the growth of the internet over the past 10 years, some nurseries feel they do not need to be in *RHS Plant Finder*: provided they publish their catalogue online using *RHS Plant Finder* plant names, they believe online users will find their catalogue. Sales of the printed version have also been affected, but the RHS remains committed to publishing a paperback version.

Many gardeners use this printed directory at home or on garden or nursery visits; for garden designers it offers an indispensable list of ingredients; while horticultural writers use it for reference and scour new editions for novelties and evidence of emerging trends.

Availability is an important criterion for a plant receiving the Award of Garden Merit (AGM 🏆), but now that some nurseries are listing their plants independently online, the *RHS Plant Finder* cannot be relied on for determining whether a plant is available enough to receive the AGM or be included in an RHS Plant Trial.

Furthermore, pot plants, bedding plants and plants raised from seed, which account for 80 or 90 percent of total plant sales, have always been patchily represented. Many are sold by garden centres and supermarkets, but are only available for a few weeks. A handful turn up at the RHS Chelsea Flower Show and are mentioned in the horticultural press, but, apart from Graham Rice's blog, there otherwise seems to be a deafening silence about them. If you can track down a nursery that grows them, it might be reluctant to list them in *RHS Plant Finder* if they are scarce or available only periodically.

The most obvious effect of *RHS Plant Finder* over its first 30 years has been that it is generally far easier to find specific plants. New fads, such as galanthophilia, can rapidly sweep the country, leaving breeders gasping to keep up and the evidence of such trends is seen in successive editions.

Looking to the future

Chris Philip's vision, tempered with realism, and his fierce determination, ably assisted by Denys Gueroult, were rare qualities that came together to produce a publication of lasting worth. And it is so encouraging to find that gardeners now tend to use the same name for a plant wherever they are around the world, a common language instead of confusing synonyms.

So, what of the future? I hope *RHS Plant Finder* continues to thrive for many more decades but we should not take it for granted. It depends on all of us to buy it and support the nurseries it lists. Take a look through this new edition – especially if your last copy is a few years old. You might be surprised how much the British garden flora has changed.

Plant favourites through the decades

Author: **Janet Cubey,** Editor-in-Chief, *RHS Plant Finder.*

With such a rich diversity of plants listed in *RHS Plant Finder* (since it was first published by the Hardy Plant Society in 1987), it seemed fitting to celebrate the 30th anniversary edition with plants centre-stage. I asked a range of different plant-lovers to choose five plants that are special to them.

When you love plants, choosing just five favourites is a tough challenge, so I'm grateful to all who joined the challenge. Selected plants from the full list of plant favourites from the past 30 years will be popping up throughout this celebration year in different ways, including in a display at RHS Garden Wisley.

On these pages, I've selected one plant to represent each year, featured chronologically according to when each plant first appeared in the book. So many entries were chosen from the first *Plant Finder* edition, that I've selected six garden stalwarts – plants that we couldn't imagine gardening without, which all have the Award of Garden Merit (🏆).

Each year, during the editing and proof-reading process, I delight in reading the names of plants that are new to the book, with the joyful anticipation of meeting them later at shows, at nurseries or in the trade; this year is no exception. But there is also sadness when a wonderful plant isn't listed, combined with hope that it will return.

Perhaps you'll spot some of your own favourites in this timeline, as well as making the acquaintance of ones you are less familiar with. As for highlights of the new plants in this 2017 edition? I leave you to choose your own, but feel free to let me know...

1987

Many reliable friends were listed in the first edition, including: ***Dicksonia antarctica*** 🏆 – then listed by one nursery. Dave Root, Kelways Plants, says it brings 'pleasure beyond words.'

1987

1988

1988

***Narcissus* 'Tête-à-tête'** 🏆 was among the bulbs included from 1988 in *Plant Finder*. 'I have clumps of it by paths, smiling at me and my visitors,' says Trehane Nursery owner Jennifer Trehane.

1989

Roses, as well as tender plants, were included from 1989. Garden designer Adam Frost chose ***Rosa* 'Doncasteri'**. 'The single cerise pink flowers really stand out against the beautiful arching foliage and are followed by big bright hips. The blooms are similar to a wild rose and add a natural feel to a border.'

1991

Flowering shrub ***Heptacodium miconioides*** 🏆 with its 'unusual and attractive foliage, scented late summer flowers and colourful calyces that remain after the flowers fall' was the choice of John David, RHS Head of Horticultural Taxonomy.

1989 — 1990 — 1991 — 1992

1990

'Clematis come no better than the Viticella cultivars, and ***Clematis* 'Betty Corning'** is top with its mass of light blue mauve nodding-dancing summer flowers,' says Sarah Wain of West Dean Gardens. 'It is an eye-catcher and good doer, and its light flower colour combines beautifully with selected colour palettes.'

1992

When Sharon McDonald, RHS International Registrar, first saw ***Cornus sanguinea* 'Midwinter Fire'** she remembers how 'the winter colour knocked my socks off.'

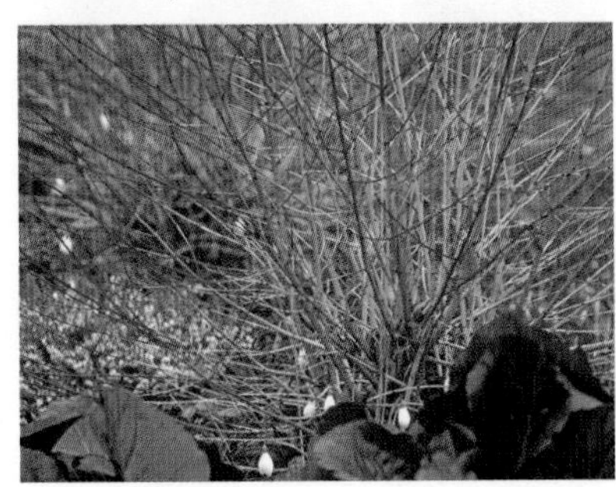

»

1993
This year saw an explosion in the number of Himalayan birch cultivars. Marcus Chilton-Jones, Curator of our new fifth garden, RHS Garden Bridgewater, thinks '***Betula utilis* var. *jacquemontii* 'Grayswood Ghost'** 🏆 steals the show in winter. With striking white stems from an early age, it's hard to take your eyes off these ghostly-looking trees.'

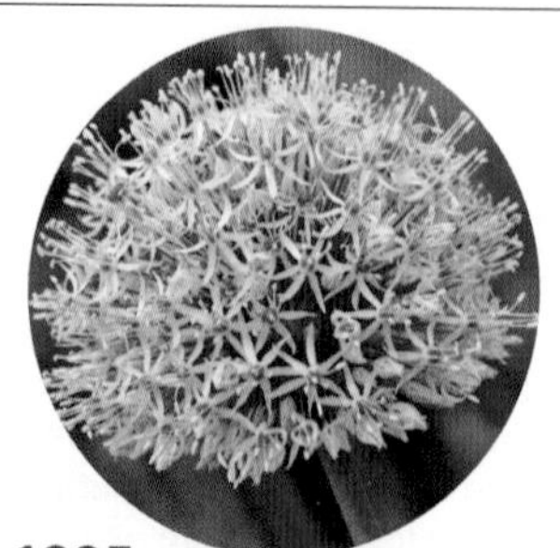

1995
White-flowered ***Allium stipitatum* 'Mount Everest'** is a favourite of Malcolm Berry, Head of Buying, RHS Plant Centres. 'I've never seen so many bees attracted to a single plant.'

1993 **1994** **1995** **1996**

GAP / JOHN GLOVER

1994
Matthew Pottage, Curator of RHS Garden Wisley, selected ***Aloe variegata*** 🏆, because 'My grandma used to have a huge potful of this succulent in her greenhouse. I always loved the leaf markings and how the small offsets appeared alongside larger plants.'

1996
Mike Grant, Editor, *The Plantsman*, says: 'Sea hollies are one of my favourite herbaceous plants, and ***Eryngium* x *zabelii* 'Jos Eijking'**, although seed-raised, is usually a strong metallic blue with finely cut bracts.'

1997

Of ***Rhododendron ochraceum*** 🏆, Peter Cox of Glendoick Gardens says, 'My introduction of this widespread but rare species involved a hard climb in south Sichuan. Growing on top of large boulders, it appreciates good drainage. Its rounded shape and globe-shaped, small, rich red flower trusses make this my favourite introduction.'

GAP / CHRISTINA BOLLEN

1999

This year is noted for the arrival of ***Geranium* ROZANNE ('Gerwat')** 🏆, the most popular favourite on our 30 years list. Peter Chapman, of Perryhill Nurseries, sums it up well. 'Nothing else flowers for so long and is so easy to grow. It's great for a border scrambling through small shrubs or in a stand-alone pot. I love it, customers love it and it is our bestselling new introduction – no new plant has risen to prominence so quickly. It was quite rightly voted RHS Plant of the Centenary in 2013.'

1997 — 1998 — 1999 — 2000

1998

This was the year in which the popularity of hellebores started to escalate.
Nigel Eaton, Head of Harlow Carr Shop & Plant Centre, favours the ***Helleborus* x *hybridus* Harvington hybrids**: 'Ever since I heard about Hugh Nunn's quest to develop and hybridise the hellebore to give us more true colours and forms, I have grown these for their vigour and longer flowering pattern.'

2000

By the new Millennium, dahlias were enjoying a revival. '***Dahlia* 'Sir Alf Ramsey'** is one of the best and most easily grown giant dahlias,' according to Greg Redwood, RHS Tender Ornamental Plant Committee Chairman. 'They remind me of my mother's fabulous 1970s Nelbarden swimming hats.'

»

2001

'***Geum* 'Bell Bank'** excels all other geums in my garden with its profusion of dainty pale pink frilly flowers,' says Robin Pearce, RHS Herbaceous Plant Committee Chairman. 'It was raised by gardener Geoffrey Smith, then disappeared from cultivation for several years before being reintroduced by Dove Cottage Nursery, thank goodness!'

2003

This was the year for fabulous foliage plants from Asia, with the much-selected *Fatsia polycarpa* and ***Tetrapanax papyrifer* 'Rex'**. Of the *Tetrapanax*, Dawn Edwards, RHS Botanist, loves 'its large, architectural and exotic appearance.'

2001 2002 2003 2004

2002

'***Brunnera macrophylla* 'Jack Frost'** 🏆 is a superb perennial with heads of blue spring flowers held above wonderful silvery heart-shaped leaves that last in beauty for much of the year,' says Phil Clayton, Deputy Editor, *The Garden.*

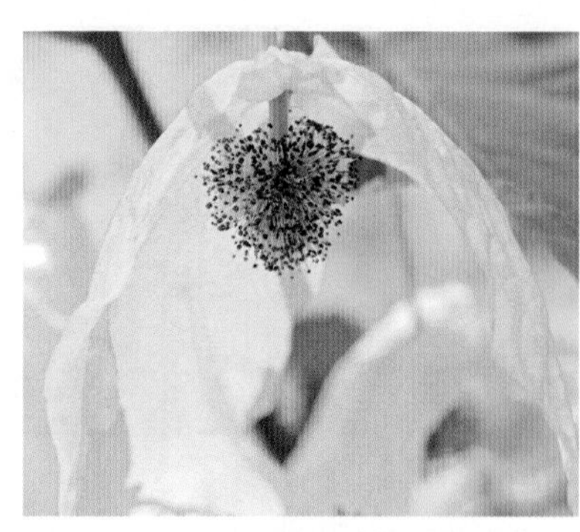

2004

***Davidia involucrata* 'Sonoma'** 'looks amazing in flower,' says Jonathan Webster, Curator, RHS Garden Rosemoor. 'A plus point is that it can flower from the first year of planting – far earlier than the true species – so this is a great addition to our arboretum.'

30 ANNIVERSARY

2005

'*Daphne* x *transatlantica* ETERNAL FRAGRANCE ('Blafra') 🏆 is easy to grow, with a compact habit and beautifully-scented flowers in winter,' says Peter Chapman of Perryhill Nurseries. It's not surprising that this flowering shrub was also chosen by John Winterson, Deputy Plant Buyer, RHS Plant Centres, among others.

2007

'It still seems amazing that when *Plant Finder* started, there lurked in the world, undiscovered, a new genus of temperate conifer that could be grown outdoors in the UK,' says James Armitage, Principal Scientist, Horticultural Taxonomy. '***Wollemia nobilis*** (Wollemi pine) is perhaps the most romantic introduction to modern gardens.'

2006 2008

2005 2007

2006

***Magnolia* 'Lois'** was chosen by Wolfgang Bopp, Director, Sir Harold Hillier Gardens. 'It's covered in cup-shaped flowers of a really good yellow that fully open to a star. I love seeing it every year at work and in a friend's garden; it never fails to delight. This is a plant you quickly fall in love with.'

2008

Neil Lucas of Knoll Gardens fell in love with ***Pennisetum* 'Fairy Tails'** when he saw it in California. 'I knew its fabulous upright habit would bring an extra quality to UK gardens but I wasn't sure if it would survive the transition to our mild, relatively damp climate. But it's proving to be one of the hardier fountain grasses and works well as an informal screen or hedging.'

»

2009

'*Gaura lindheimeri* ROSYJANE ('Harrosy') is a bicoloured gem that dances happily with its neighbours in any perennial border,' says Edward Cannon of Langthorns Plantery, Essex. 'I find it looks particularly effective when mixed with grasses and it is reliably perennial in well-drained borders.'

2011

Laurel Emms, RHS Horticultural Advisor, describes ***Salvia* 'Amistad'** as her 'favourite salvia among the many that I love. A beautiful herbaceous plant it's tall and upright, so ideal anywhere in the border, and has deep, velvety, lilac-purple flowers.'

2010 2012

2009 2011

2010

***Streptocarpus* 'Harlequin Blue'** 🏆 won the first RHS Chelsea Plant of the Year competition with its striking bicolour, blue and yellow flowers and is a favourite of Janet Cubey's who has bought many of these as gifts for friends.

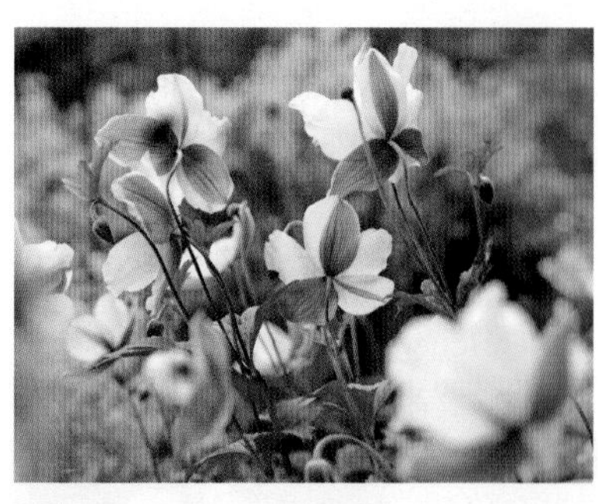

2012

Chris Young, Editor, *The Garden*, says: 'There was real excitement when ***Anemone* WILD SWAN ('Macane001')** won the RHS Chelsea Plant of the Year award in 2011. Its flowers, white in the front, a pale mauve/blue on the reverse, still excite me when I see them coming through during the summer.'

2013

***Hydrangea aspera* HOT CHOCOLATE ('Hpopr012')** was picked by RHS Botanist Neil Lancaster, who favours this pink lacecap hydrangea, with blue and purple inner fertile florets, for its 'velvety foliage with red undersides, purplish in spring.'

2015

Of the English roses that his father bred, David Austin Jnr chose ***Rosa* OLIVIA ROSE AUSTIN ('Ausmixture')** because it is 'an outstanding shrub rose in almost every way. Its beautiful pink flowers bloom exceptionally early in the season, enabling it to flower three times annually. It is named after my daughter, so it had to be something rather special! It's planted *en masse* in my garden, creating a fragrant pathway leading to a bench – a great spot to unwind with a cup of tea.'

GAP

2014

2016

2013

2015

2014

***Rosmarinus officinalis* 'Jekka Blue'** is one of the choices of landscape designer Paul Hervey-Brookes. 'I love this blue-flowered shrub for its short leaves and its upright yet arching habit', he says.

JEKKA MCVICAR

2016

This was the first year in which the *RHS Plant Finder* included a directory of Award of Garden Merit vegetables, including climbing **French bean 'Cobra'** 🏆, a favourite of RHS Horticultural Advisor Anne Adam for its 'high yields of flavoursome beans produced over a long period.'

GAP / FHF GREENMEDIA

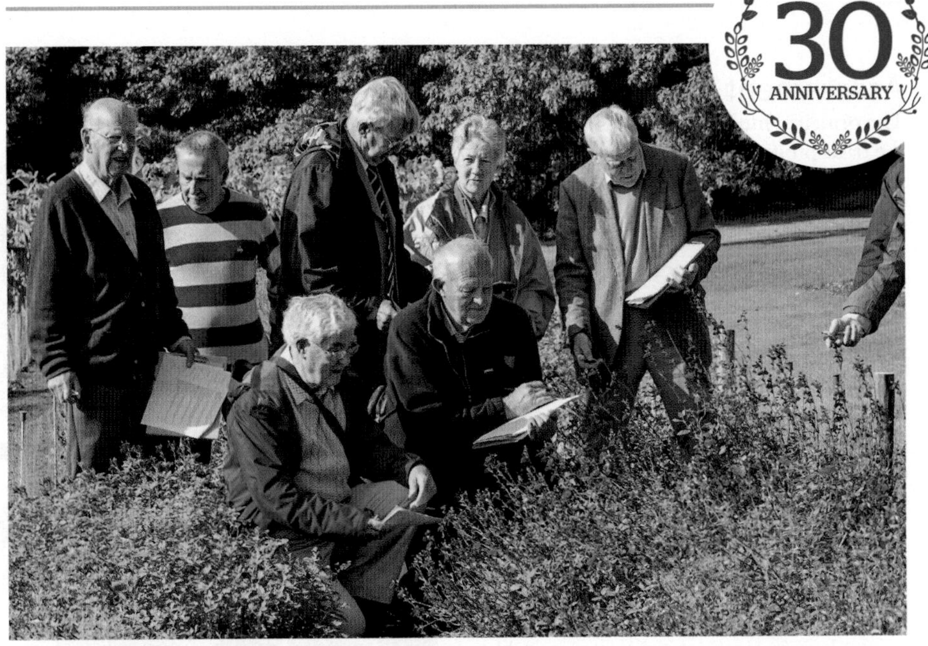

The best plant choice for gardeners

Authors: **Tim Upson**, RHS Director of Horticulture responsible for RHS Plant Trials and Plant Committees, **Mark Heath**, former Trials Development Manager, and **Jim Gardiner**, former RHS Executive Vice-President.

The wealth of cultivated plants available in the UK offers an unrivalled choice for gardeners, but which are the best for garden use? The RHS Award of Garden Merit 🏆 (AGM) is a mark of quality given to garden plants that have demonstrated excellent qualities. It is awarded after a period of assessment and epitomises the society's traditions and endeavour to help provide a practical but rigorous guide for gardeners. Of the 76,000 plants in the *RHS Plant Finder* 2017, almost 6,000 have received the AGM.

To achieve this coveted award, plants are assessed by experts and must be:

- excellent for ordinary use in appropriate conditions
- of good constitution
- essentially stable in form and colour
- reasonably resistant to pests and diseases
- available

RHS AWARD OF GARDEN MERIT

Depending upon the plants assessed, additional criteria are used, such as taste for fruit and vegetables. While information on appropriate conditions such as soil type is readily available, an RHS hardiness rating is now assigned to AGM plants to help gardeners make choices for their locality. In essence an AGM plant will perform well in the right conditions. »

Assessment

The principal means of awarding is through the trials programme. To allow performance to be judged under the appropriate climate conditions, the RHS Gardens (principally Wisley) and regional networks of gardens and nurseries provide suitable sites across the UK. While trials for annuals, tender plants and vegetables take place over a growing season, those for woody and perennial plants last at least three years, allowing performance to be assessed against the prevailing weather.

Garden trials are not possible for every plant group and so the roundtable assessment programme provides a valuable and flexible means to award AGMs. It is particularly suited for trees, which take time to reach maturity; for large plant groups such as *Rhododendron*; or simply to assess new introductions quickly.

Both field trials and roundtables are judged and evaluated by an independent RHS forum. The forums consist of 10 people and are carefully composed of experts, professional and amateur, intentionally representing a broad range of interests to ensure that the trials remain independent and transparent.

In the final assessment an AGM is only awarded if it fulfils all criteria and receives a 3:1 vote in favour from the forum and is subsequently ratified by the appropriate Plant Committee – there are seven of these in total.

The involvement of growers, retailers and breeders is particularly important in helping to source material, new introductions and subsequently to ensure plants are available. It is also an industry mark of quality, readily identified by the cup-shaped trophy (left) and widely used in the nursery trade and retail.

RHS AWARD OF GARDEN MERIT

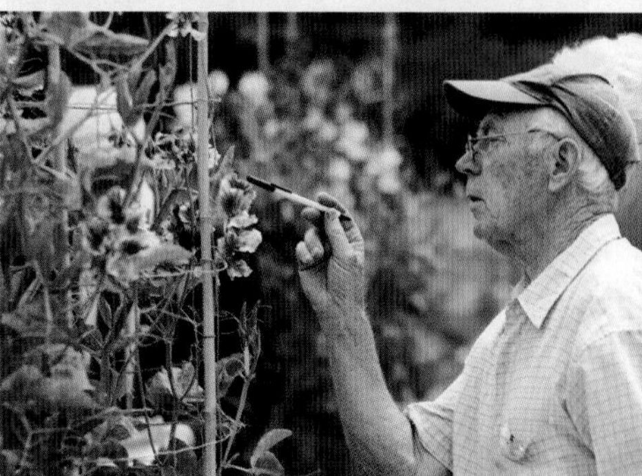

Flowering plants growing *en masse* on the RHS Garden Wisley Trials Field (top); **assessment of the sweet pea trial** (above); ***Zantedeschia*** (above right) **is currently being evaluated.**

Necessary knowledge

The process of awarding AGMs is a constant, ongoing programme, with the RHS plant committees providing the necessary knowledge as to priorities. The current trials of *Agapanthus*, *Zantedeschia* and new hybrids of *Cypripedium* are all examples where many new selections require evaluation.

Trials for woody and perennial plants last at least three years

The committees also provide a key role in reconfirming existing AGMs or rescinding the award if the criteria are no longer met. The last full review was completed in 2013 and a programme of rolling reviews has been instituted alongside the trials and roundtables.

RHS Science also plays a key part in checking the correct identification and name of each entry, and often provides advice on pests and diseases. This ensures users can have confidence in the quality of AGMs and that they are both well-deserved and current.

AGM vegetables, available from featured nurseries, appeared for the first time in the 2016 *RHS Plant Finder*. The naming of vegetables does not always follow convention and new introductions are frequent, so they had not previously fitted well into the *Plant Finder* format, but this is a welcome addition. Equally orchids with their naming issues and great diversity, had not been trialled for »

FOUR OF MY TOP *RHS PLANT FINDER* PLANTS

Roy Lancaster

Author and plantsman

'I have been using *Plant Finder* since the very beginning. In my study it is at my right hand and my preferred first reference before even my iPad.'

✤ Among the many Chinese mahonias I grow, ***Mahonia sheridaniana*** (syn ***M. huiliensis***) is special for its bold autumn golden-yellow flowers displayed in erect spike-like clusters crowning the terminal ruff of spine-toothed, glossy, evergreen leaves. It grows in partial shade or sun.

✤ ***Lysimachia paridiformis* var. *stenophylla*** is a low-growing, hardy perennial whose ascending fleshy stems are crowned with a generous whorl of handsome, glossy leaves. A crowded, fist-sized head of rich, golden-yellow, star-shaped flowers develops to open in July. This plant is ideal for partial shade.

✤ ***Fatsia polycarpa*** rivals well-known *F. japonica* for its larger, long-stalked and more boldly lobed leaves of a paler, matt green. This is a great stand-alone plant for a special place in shade or sun.

✤ ***Calycanthus* x *raulstonii* 'Hartlage Wine'** is one of the best hardy, summer-flowering deciduous shrubs for sun or shade. The striking maroon, scented flowers have a creamy white 'eye' and its large, glossy foliage turns yellow before falling in autumn.

AGMs until recently. Among the first to be assessed are popular *Phalaenopsis* (moth) orchids and those holding the AGM are now available from high street outlets. We are considering including them in a future *RHS Plant Finder* edition.

Visitors enjoyed an explosion of colour from the *Cosmos* trial in 2016 (top left); **newly awarded *Phalaenopsis* 'Kleopatra 4'** (top right); ***Zea mays* (sweetcorn) 'Earlibird'** (above left) **has an AGM; *Sarracenia* forum members** (above).

Grower Guides

The key aim of each plant trial is to award AGMs but they also provide a unique opportunity to understand the plants in cultivation at the time. Information is captured in trials reports, available on the RHS website, and are a key feature of *The Garden* magazine, providing members with the most up to date results. More detailed information was made available through the popular Plant Trials Bulletins, which have now been superseded by Grower Guides, the first featuring *Euphorbia*. These guides aim to bring together information on all AGM plants in the genus, along with additional observations and details gleaned during the trials process.

Since the publication of the first *Plant Finder* 30 years ago, the AGM has evolved, underpinned by its programme of trialling, roundtables and expert assessment. It is the vital complement to the *RHS Plant Finder* in helping gardeners to choose the best-performing garden plants.

C STONE

PLANT HERITAGE

Primula **'Fife Yellow'** (above). **National Plant Collection of *Hosta* (small and miniature) exhibited by Jonathan Hogarth at the 2016 RHS Chelsea Flower Show** (right).

A mission to save at-risk

Thousands of threatened plants are safeguarded in Plant Heritage National Plant

Authors: **Plant Heritage Conservation Team.**

Plant Heritage was founded in 1978 to help address the loss of diversity of cultivated plants in the UK and Ireland. The National Plant Collection scheme, established in 1981, has been highly successful in conserving plants, sparking similar initiatives in other countries. However, these plant conservation collections are only a part of the work undertaken by Plant Heritage.

Cultivated plants are vulnerable to garden fashions, can be difficult to propagate, and are routinely superseded by newer cultivars. The scale of the problem is challenging: according to *RHS Plant Finder* data, almost half of the 110,000 cultivars offered commercially in the UK since 1987 no longer appear to be available. Some plant groups are particularly affected: for example, two-thirds of heather cultivars ever grown are no longer listed.

PLANT HERITAGE NCCPG

In 2009, Plant Heritage launched the Threatened Plants Project, an innovative approach to identify, rescue and conserve cultivars deemed to be most at risk.

The project combines *RHS Plant Finder* data on rarity in the trade, with plant lists from National Plant Collections and hundreds of UK and Irish gardens to find, often, the last known plant.

RHS Plant Finder is the ideal baseline for the project: it is the only comprehensive source of information on the availability of plants in commerce, covers an extensive time

plants

Collections across the UK and Ireland

period and provides a reference for plant names. With so many species and cultivars dropping out of commerce, it would be impossible to conserve them all. The project therefore works with plant experts to record particular attributes of value, such as breeding use, heritage importance and useful traits, to help prioritise what to conserve. Additional information from the *RHS Plant Finder* on awards, or specific traits such as variegation, assists this process.

Thanks to its data-sharing partnership with the RHS, Plant Heritage has been able to identify in excess of 40,000 threatened cultivars to date; more than 850 of these are already being actively conserved. Double primrose *Primula* 'Fife Yellow' was last listed in *RHS Plant Finder 2008*, but in 2013 the project found a record of it growing at RHS Garden Wisley. It was propagated and is now safeguarded in a National Plant Collection of *Primula* in Cornwall.

The *RHS Plant Finder* also benefits from the expertise of Plant Heritage's National Plant Collection holders, who hold many additional plants that they have bred or imported, and verified. Plant Heritage encourages them to add their plants to the *RHS Plant Finder* listings, and to feed back information to the *RHS Plant Finder* team, for example on wrongly named cultivars.

Our priority is to continue to identify plants that have become at risk and this research would not be possible without the historical data provided by the *RHS Plant Finder*. It is a unique resource for gardeners of the present and of the future, and a reference that is admired worldwide.

✤ www.plantheritage.com; 01483 447540

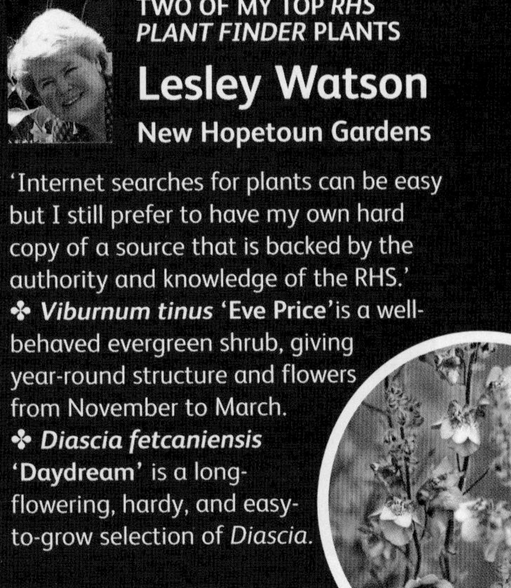

TWO OF MY TOP *RHS PLANT FINDER* PLANTS

Lesley Watson

New Hopetoun Gardens

'Internet searches for plants can be easy but I still prefer to have my own hard copy of a source that is backed by the authority and knowledge of the RHS.'

✤ ***Viburnum tinus* 'Eve Price'** is a well-behaved evergreen shrub, giving year-round structure and flowers from November to March.

✤ ***Diascia fetcaniensis* 'Daydream'** is a long-flowering, hardy, and easy-to-grow selection of *Diascia*.

The sum of many parts

Rare and unusual plants from independent nurseries form the backbone of the *RHS Plant Finder* – and it provides a useful tool for nursery owners too

Author: **Rosy Hardy** founder of Hampshire nursery Hardy's Cottage Garden Plants.

My husband Rob and I have been running Hardy's Cottage Garden Plants for 28 years. It started off as a small enterprise with us growing a selection of plants in our back garden in Camberley, Surrey, which we sold at car boot sales initially. We then moved on to specialist plants sales and eventually the world of flower shows.

It was due to demand from our customers that we came to specialise in herbaceous perennials, both old and newer cultivars, and we now have a broad spectrum of plant genera, species and cultivars in our collection. However, many independent nurseries are highly specialised, although it is difficult to put a true number on them because many operate on a part-time basis.

Keeping up the diversity of plant material is a really important part of the independent nursery world. Some Plant Heritage National Plant Collection holders provide certain nurseries with propagation material, therefore making their plants available in small quantities. Small independent nurseries are essential to maintain plant diversity, which has a direct impact on choice for the consumer. The beauty of the *RHS Plant Finder* is the breadth of listed nurseries it contains – large or small, varied or specialist, located right across Britain and Ireland.

These independents have important skills in propagating and growing their plants, and can also advise about their care. It is the passion of independent nurseries that is missing in most garden centres and large DIY retail units, and without a listing such as the *RHS Plant Finder*, the consumer is unlikely to find these tiny specialist outlets. »

My first recollections of using the *RHS Plant Finder* were as an amateur gardener looking for plants to add to my collection. I first found out about it after travel writer Lindsey Porter visited my sister-in-law Anne Liverman's beautiful National Gardens Scheme (NGS) open garden in Derbyshire. While admiring a gorgeous *Crambe cordifolia* in full bloom, Lindsey told Anne about a book that allowed plant lovers to track down specific plant species. This turned out to be the first *Plant Finder*, and Lindsey sent Anne a free copy. Anne then brought the publication to my attention, as a must-have companion in her car. I've continued this tradition and my copy is very well thumbed.

Hardy's Cottage Garden Plants' impressive stand at the 2016 Wisley Flower Show (above); **owner Rosy Hardy finds the *RHS Plant Finder* indispensable for checking that her nursery's plant labels are correct** (left).

Checking nomenclature

The *RHS Plant Finder* also became a useful asset when preparing my nursery show displays. RHS Shows judging criteria requires all plants to be labelled with the correct nomenclature and in this age of DNA testing, names can quickly change, so an up-to-date reference is essential. Even familiar plant names can sometimes look wrong when you're writing labels, so having a handy reference such as the *RHS Plant Finder* is most helpful.

Our nursery supplies a considerable range of plant cultivars, so being listed in the directory book helps link us with consumers who are looking for a particular species or cultivar. We became listed after about five years of trading, and the publication gave us another platform from which to advertise our plants directly to the plant-buying public. It does take a long time for us to go through all the listings each year because the *RHS Plant Finder* keeps getting larger. Although all our plants are contained in a management

> *'Being listed in the* RHS Plant Finder *links our nursery with consumers'*

software programme on our computer, we still complete our listing in paper form because the digital return system is not currently compatible with our systems.

Annual submission

It takes an enormous amount of work at the end of our season to complete each year's submission, collating the plants we produce and cross referencing with the *RHS Plant Finder* to ascertain whether they are new, widely available or up for re-listing. From this cross referencing we can then focus our submission on our more unusual plants, rather than those that are widely stocked.

We appreciate that the RHS then has to further process all the information they receive, but the success of the *RHS Plant Finder* does depend upon all small nurseries giving commitment to their submissions. »

FOUR OF MY TOP *RHS PLANT FINDER* PLANTS

David Ward

Garden and Nursery Director, The Beth Chatto Gardens

✤ It was pleasing to offer the first variegated *Gaura* in the early 1990s. ***Gaura lindheimeri* 'Corrie's Gold'** was discovered at The Beth Chatto Gardens by a member of our propagating staff, Debbie Allcock and posthumously named after her daughter. It is prolific and long-flowering and makes an ideal container plant.

✤ ***Galanthus elwesii* 'Cedric's Prolific'** came to Beth from Sir Cedric Morris, whose garden at Benton End, Hadleigh, Suffolk, was both an inspiration and a learning ground for Beth during her early years as a gardener and nurserywoman. This snowdrop stood out for Cedric as worthy of naming.

✤ ***Persicaria amplexicaulis* 'Rubie's Pink'** is a long-flowering perennial which grew un-named at the Gardens for many years. A true pink to go alongside the scarlet or white forms, it was named after my granddaughter in 2011.

✤ ***Geranium maculatum* 'Beth Chatto'** was possibly named in Holland but we don't know why, as the plant did not originate from here. I find the naming of plants fascinating and always find time to read the explanation of name changes at the beginning of each new edition of the *RHS Plant Finder*.

Recent nomenclatural changes include *Meconopsis cambrica* (Welsh poppy) becoming *Papaver cambricum* (top left). **Hardy's Cottage Garden Plants is one of only a handful of nurseries to stock *Silene dioica* 'Firefly'** (top right), **and *Francoa sonchifolia* 'Pink Bouquet'** (above left). **Rosy Hardy helps customers at her RHS Secret Sunday stand** (above).

Aiding customers

As a small nursery, we find the *RHS Plant Finder* is incredibly useful for aiding our customers in their plant searches. If we don't supply a certain cultivar, we often use it to recommend another listed nursery who does, and hope that this act is reciprocated!

The directory certainly offers a wonderful resource for plant hunters in all areas of the UK and Ireland, and it encourages more nurseries to list their fabulous plants and ensure that even more cultivars are made available. Additionally, the fact that *RHS Plant Finder* is available both in book format and online (www.rhs.org.uk/findaplant) is great because often while out plant hunting you find yourself in parts of the countryside lacking good internet connection.

The online format is interactive and contains more information than could possibly be included in a book with so many listings. *RHS Plant Finder* is our first port of call when checking nomenclature. Other online lists are available, which are relevant especially for research, but these are not as user friendly for finding a specific plant and its availability.

Without the *RHS Plant Finder* to aid my spelling of plant labels at the RHS Shows, I would have to rely on my phone being fully charged and be dependent on a good internet connection. My preference, however, is always for the book, and my well-thumbed copy is certainly ready for an upgrade! ●

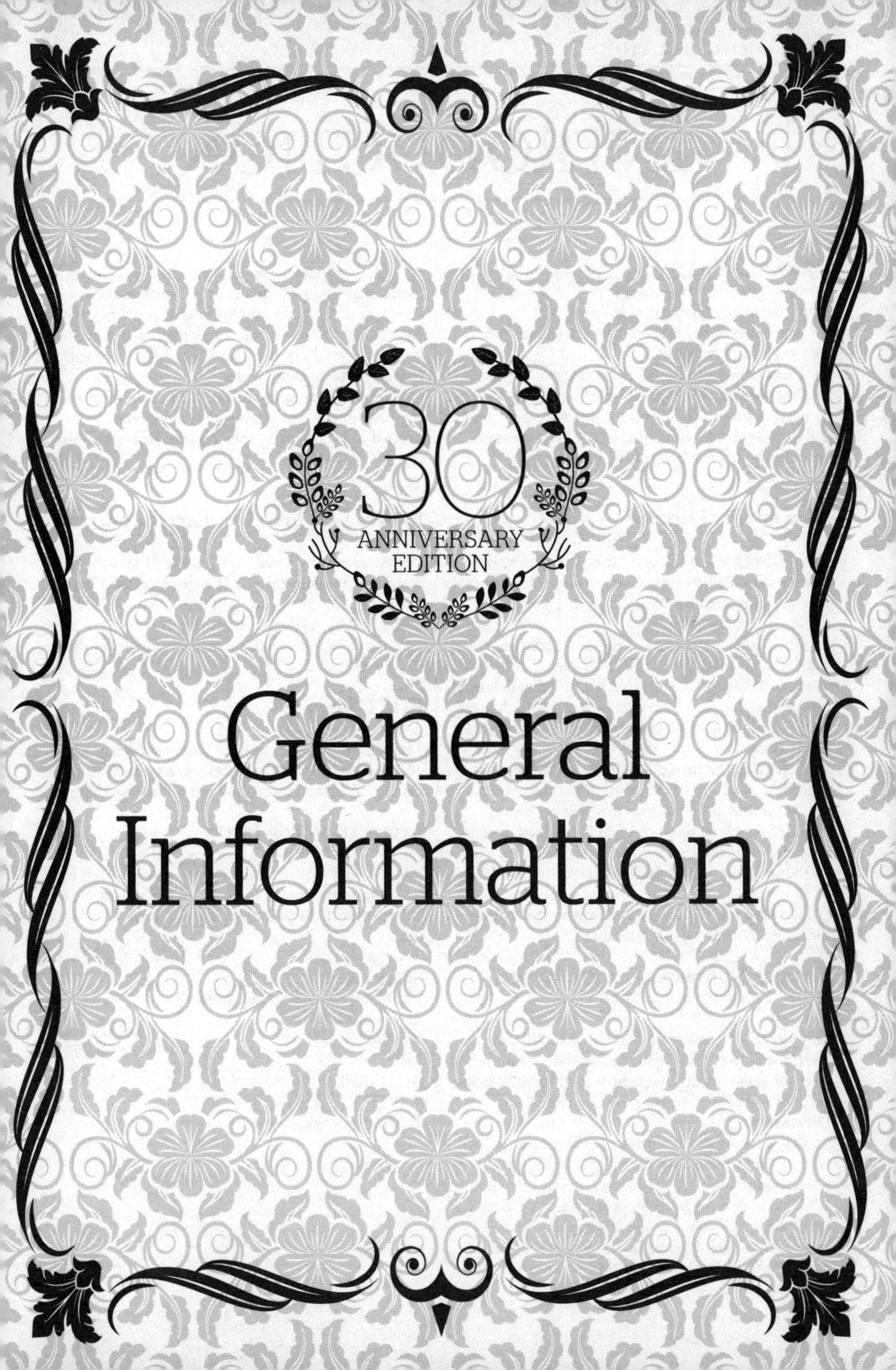

General Information

INTRODUCTION

The *RHS Plant Finder* exists to put enthusiastic gardeners in touch with suppliers of plants. It is comprehensively updated every year.

The book is divided into two related sections: **PLANTS** and **NURSERIES**.

PLANTS includes an A-Z Directory of around 76,000 plant names, against which are listed a series of nursery codes. These codes point the reader to the full nursery details contained in the **NURSERIES** section towards the back of the book.

It is important to remember when ordering plants that many of the nurseries listed in the book are small, family-run businesses that propagate their own material. They cannot, therefore, guarantee to hold large stocks of the plants they list. Some will, however, propagate to order.

Nurseries appearing in the *RHS Plant Finder* for the first time or re-entering after an absence are printed in bold type in the **Nursery Index by Name** (pp.949-953).

NEW IN THIS EDITION

We are delighted to celebrate the 30th Anniversary Edition with the first ever colour section. This includes specially commissioned articles from a range of distinguished contributors.

The plant names used in the 2017 edition reflect the decisions made by the RHS Nomenclature and Taxonomy Advisory Group (NATAG). **Nomenclatural Notes** (p.49) gives a brief overview of these changes made since the compilation of the previous edition of the book.

Following the introduction of a section on vegetables with the RHS Award of Garden Merit (AGM) in the 2016 edition, this year we have included a new section on AGM fruit. Descriptions of these, together with their nursery suppliers, can be found in the handy **AGM Fruit** section (pp.842-853).

We have not included any **Maps** in this edition. Please let us know if you miss them.

LISTS OF NURSERIES FOR PLANTS WITH MORE THAN 30 SUPPLIERS

To prevent the book from becoming too big, we do not print nursery codes where more than 30 nurseries offer the same plant. The plant is then listed as being "widely available". See **How to Use the Plant Directory** (p.55).

A full list of all the nurseries held on file as current suppliers can be found by searching the RHS website Find a Plant facility or can be made available in printed form by post from the Compiler at the address below. For the latter, please ensure you include the full name of the plant (as given in the *RHS Plant Finder*) and enclose a stamped addressed envelope.

PLANTS LAST LISTED IN EARLIER EDITIONS

Plants cease to be listed for a variety of reasons. For more information, turn to **How to Use the Plant Directory** (p.55). A listing of more than 60,000 plants listed in earlier editions but for which we have no current suppliers will be made available on the RHS website.

RHS ONLINE

The plant data from the *RHS Plant Finder* is available on the Royal Horticultural Society's website at www.rhs.org.uk/plants under the Find a Plant section.

APPLICATION FOR ENTRY

If you would like your nursery to be considered for inclusion in the next edition of the *RHS Plant Finder*, please contact the Compiler. Entries to the book are free.

Contact details
The Compiler, *RHS Plant Finder*
RHS Garden Wisley
Woking
Surrey
GU23 6QB
Ⓣ (01483) 224234
Ⓔ plantfinder@rhs.org.uk

ACKNOWLEDGEMENTS

This edition was compiled by Judith Merrick with Lindsay Durrant, assisted by Gill Skilton, Joanne Godden, Jane Rowlands and Anne Young. Richard Sanford managed the editing of the plant names in the database and Rupert Wilson and Julia Barclay administered the RHS Horticultural Database using the BG-Base™ Collection Management Software.

RHS botanists James Armitage, Dawn Edwards, Kálmán Könyves, Neil Lancaster and Rosalyn Marshall undertook the task of editing the new plant names for this edition of the book.

RHS Editor, Rae Spencer-Jones, collated the 30th Anniversary colour section and we acknowledge the contribution of Louise Bowering, Diana Levy, Michelle Housden, Mark Timothy and Marina Jordan-Rugg. Special thanks go to those guest contributors to the 30th Anniversary Edition: John David, Jim Gardiner, Rosie Hardy, Mark Heath, Sophie Leguil, Tony Lord and Tim Upson.

As ever, we are grateful for the professional support of Kerry Walter of BG-Base (UK) Ltd and Max Phillips of Strange Software Ltd. Finally, we are greatly indebted to Peter Cooling for his skill in turning our data into a publishable form.

Our colleagues on the RHS Nomenclature and Taxonomy Advisory Group, along with the RHS International Cultivar Registrars, have all provided valuable guidance and information. Many nurseries have supplied useful details on new plants and have suggested corrections to existing entries. Some of these remain to be checked and will be entered in the next edition, although those that contravene the Codes of Nomenclature may have to be rejected. We appreciate your patience while these checks are made.

We are also grateful to our regular correspondents and to all those readers who have made helpful comments.

Clematis	D.R. Donald, Int. Cultivar Registrar
Chrysanthemum	J. Barker
Conifers	S. McDonald, Int. Cultivar Registrar
Dahlia	S. McDonald, Int. Cultivar Registrar
Dianthus	Dr A.C. Leslie, Int. Cultivar Registrar
Delphinium	M.R. Underwood, Int. Cultivar Registrar
Heathers	Dr E.C. Nelson, Int. Cultivar Registrar (to end 2016)
Ilex	S. Andrews
Lilium	D.R. Donald, Int. Cultivar Registrar
Narcissus	M.R. Underwood, Int. Cultivar Registrar
Nerine	Dr J.C. David
Orchids	J.M.H. Shaw, Int. Cultivar Registrar
Rhododendron	Dr A.C. Leslie, Int. Cultivar Registrar
Sorbus	Dr H. McAllister
Thymus	M. Easter, Int. Cultivar Registrar

Janet Cubey
RHS Editor in Chief
February 2017

Symbols and Abbreviations

Symbols Appearing to the Left of the Name

*	Name not validated. Not listed in the appropriate International Registration Authority checklist nor in works cited in the Bibliography. For fuller discussion see p.37
I	Invalid name. See *International Code of Botanical Nomenclature 2012* and *International Code of Nomenclature for Cultivated Plants 2016*. For fuller discussion see p.37
§	Plant listed elsewhere in the Plant Directory under a synonym
×	Hybrid genus
+	Graft hybrid genus

Symbols Appearing to the Right of the Name

✿	Plant Heritage National Plant Collection® exists for all or part of this genus. Further details can be found by searching the National Plant Collections online or in the Plant Heritage Directory available from www.plantheritage.com or by phone (01483) 447540.
♀H4	The Royal Horticultural Society's Award of Garden Merit, see p.37
(d)	double-flowered
(F)	Fruit
(f)	female
(m)	male
(v)	variegated plant, see p.41
PBR	Plant Breeders' Rights see p.39
new	New plant entry in this edition

For abbreviations relating to individual genera see **Classification of Genera** p.50

For **Collectors' References** see p.45

For symbols used in the **Nurseries** section see p.865

Symbols and Abbreviations used as Part of the Name

×	hybrid species
aff.	affinis (akin to)
agg.	aggregate, a single name used to cover a group of very similar plants, regarded by some as separate species
ambig.	ambiguous, a name used by two authors for different plants and where it is unclear which is being offered
cf.	compare to
cl.	clone
f.	forma (botanical form)
gx	grex
sensu stricto	in the narrow sense
sp.	species
subsp.	subspecies
subvar.	subvarietas (botanical subvariety)
var.	varietas (botanical variety)

It is not within the remit of this book to check that nurseries are applying the right names to the right plants or to ensure nurseries selling plants with Plant Breeders' Rights are licensed to do so.

Please, never use an out of date edition

Extended Glossary

This glossary combines some of the helpful introductory sections from older editions in an alphabetical listing. A fuller, more discursive account of plant names, *Guide to Plant Names*, and a detailed guide to the typography of plant names, *Recommended Style for Printing Plant Names*, are both available as leaflets. To request a copy of either please send an A4 sae to The Compiler at the contact address given on page 34.

Advisory Committee on Nomenclature and Taxonomy

See **Nomenclature and Taxonomy Advisory Group**

Authorities

In order that plant names can be used with precision throughout the scientific world, the name of the person who coined the name of a plant species (its author, or authority) is added to the plant name. Usually this information is of little consequence to gardeners, except in cases where the same name has been given to two different plants or a name is commonly misapplied. Although only one usage is correct, both may be encountered in books, so indicating the author is the only way to be certain about which plant is being referred to. This can happen equally with cultivars. Authors' names, where it is appropriate to cite them, appear in a smaller typeface after the species or cultivar name to which they refer and are abbreviated following Brummitt and Powell's *Authors of Plant Names*.

🏆 Award of Garden Merit

The Award of Garden Merit (AGM) is intended as a practical guide for the gardener and is therefore awarded only after a period of assessment by the RHS Standing and Joint Committees. The AGM is awarded only to plants that are:

- excellent for ordinary use in appropriate conditions
- available
- of good constitution
- essentially stable in form and colour
- reasonably resistant to pests and diseases

The AGM symbol is cited in conjunction with the **hardiness** rating. A full list of AGM plants may be found on the RHS website at www.rhs.org.uk/agmplants.

The AGM list was originally reviewed every ten years, to ensure that every plant still merited the award. The last review took place in 2012; since 2013, the list has been subject to a "rolling review", and AGMs may now be rescinded at any time.

Botanical Names

The aim of the botanical naming system is to provide each different plant with a single, unique, universal name. The basic unit of plant classification is the species. Species that share a number of significant characteristics are grouped together to form a genus (plural **genera**). The name of a species is made up of two elements; the name of the genus followed by the specific epithet, for example, *Narcissus romieuxii*.

Variation within a species can be recognised by division into subspecies (usually abbreviated to subsp.), varietas (or variety abbreviated to var.) and forma (or form abbreviated to f.). Whilst it is unusual for a plant to have all of these, it is possible, as in this example, *Narcissus romieuxii* subsp. *albidus* var. *zaianicus* f. *lutescens*.

The botanical elements are always given in italics, with only the genus taking an initial capital letter. The rank indications are never in italics. In instances where the rank is not known it is necessary to form an invalid construction by quoting a second epithet without a rank. This is an unsatisfactory situation, but requires considerable research to resolve.

In some genera, such as *Hosta*, we list the cultivar names alphabetically with the species or **hybrid** to which they are attributed afterwards in parentheses. For example, *Hosta* 'Reversed' (*sieboldiana*). In other situations where the aim is not to create a list alphabetically by cultivar name we would recommend styling this as *Hosta sieboldiana* 'Reversed'.

Classification of Genera

Genera that include a large number of species or with many cultivars are often subdivided into informal horticultural classifications or more formal Cultivar Groups, each based on a particular characteristic or combination of characteristics. Colour of flower or fruit and shape of flower are common examples and, with fruit, whether a cultivar is grown for culinary or dessert purposes. How such groups are named differs from genus to genus.

To help users of the *RHS Plant Finder* find the plants they want, the classifications used within cultivated genera are listed using codes and plants are marked with the appropriate code in brackets after its name in the Plant Directory. To find the explanation of each code, simply look it up under the genus concerned in the **Classification of Genera** starting on p.50. The codes relating to edible fruits are also listed here, but these apply across several genera.

COLLECTORS' REFERENCES

Abbreviations (usually with numbers) following a plant name refer to the collector(s) of the plant. These abbreviations are expanded, with a collector's name or expedition title, in the section **Collectors' References** starting on p.45.

A collector's reference may indicate a new, as yet unnamed range of variation within a species. The inclusion of collectors' references in the *RHS Plant Finder* supports the book's role in sourcing unusual plants.

The Convention on Biological Diversity calls for conservation of biodiversity, its sustainable use and the fair and equitable sharing of any derived benefits. Since its adoption in 1993, collectors are required to have prior informed consent from the country of origin for the acquisition and commercialisation of collected material.

COMMON NAMES

In a work such as this, it is necessary to refer to plants by their botanical names for the sake of universal comprehension and clarity. However, at the same time we recognise that with fruit and vegetables most people are more familiar with their common names than their botanical ones. Cross-references are therefore given from common to botanical names for fruit, vegetables and the commoner culinary herbs throughout the Plant Directory.

CULTIVAR

Literally meaning cultivated variety, cultivar names are given to denote variation within species and that generated by hybridisation, in cultivation. To make them easily distinguishable from botanical names, they are not printed in italics and are enclosed in single quotation marks. Cultivar names coined since 1959 should follow the rules of the International Code of Nomenclature for Cultivated Plants (**ICNCP**).

DESCRIPTIVE TERMS

Terms that appear after the main part of the plant name are shown in a smaller font to distinguish them. These descriptive elements give extra information about the plant and may include the **collector's reference**, **authority**, or what colour it is. For example, *Clematis henryi* B&SWJ 3402, *Penstemon* 'Sour Grapes' M. Fish, *Akebia quinata* cream-flowered.

FAMILIES

Genera are grouped into larger groups of related plants called families. Most family names, with the exception of eight familiar names, end with the same group of letters, *-aceae*. While it is still acceptable to use these eight exceptions, the modern trend adopted in the *RHS Plant Finder* is to use alternative names with *–aceae* endings. The families concerned are *Compositae* (*Asteraceae*), *Cruciferae* (*Brassicaceae*), *Gramineae* (*Poaceae*), *Guttiferae* (*Clusiaceae*), *Labiatae* (*Lamiaceae*), *Leguminosae* (split here into *Caesalpiniaceae*, *Mimosaceae* and *Papilionaceae*), *Palmae* (*Arecaceae*) and *Umbelliferae* (*Apiaceae*).

Apart from these exceptions we now follow (from 2010) *Mabberley's Plant-book* (3rd edition).

GENUS (plural – GENERA)

Genera used in the *RHS Plant Finder* were originally based on Brummitt's *Vascular Plant Families and Genera* but are now based on a range of sources. For spellings and genders of generic names, Greuter's *Names in Current Use for Extant Plant Genera* has also been consulted. See **Botanical Names**.

GREX

Within orchids, hybrids of the same parentage, regardless of how alike they are, are given a grex name. Individuals can be selected, given cultivar names and propagated vegetatively. For example, *Pleione* Versailles gx 'Bucklebury', where Versailles is the grex name and 'Bucklebury' is a selected **cultivar**.

GROUP

This is a collective name for a group of cultivars within a genus with similar characteristics. The word Group is always included and, where cited with a cultivar name, it is enclosed in brackets, for example, *Actaea simplex* (Atropurpurea Group) 'Brunette', where 'Brunette' is a distinct cultivar in a group of purple-leaved cultivars.

Another example of a Group is *Rhododendron polycladum* Scintillans Group. In this case *Rhododendron scintillans* was a species that is now botanically 'sunk' within *R. polycladum*, but it is still recognised horticulturally as a Group.

Group names are also used for swarms of hybrids with the same parentage, for example, *Rhododendron* Polar Bear Group. These were formerly treated as **grex** names, a term now used only for orchids. A single clone from the Group may be given the same cultivar name, for example, *Rhododendron* 'Polar Bear'.

Hardiness

Hardiness ratings are shown for **Award of Garden Merit** plants. To assist gardeners to determine more clearly which plants are hardy in their local area, the RHS introduced a new, enhanced, hardiness rating scheme in 2013, to coincide with the publication of the new **Award of Garden Merit** plant list. The categories now used are as follows:
Temperature ranges given are intended to be absolute minimum winter temperatures (°C).
H1a = Heated greenhouse – tropical >15
H1b = Heated greenhouse – subtropical 10 to 15
H1c = Heated greenhouse – warm temperate 5 to 10
H2 = Tender – cool or frost-free greenhouse 1 to 5
H3 = Half-hardy – unheated greenhouse/mild winter -5 to 1
H4 = Hardy – average winter -10 to -5
H5 = Hardy – cold winter -15 to -10
H6 = Hardy – very cold winter -20 to -15
H7 = Very hardy <-20

Further definition of these categories can be found on the RHS website, in the Feb 2013 edition of *The Garden* and in the *RHS Plant Finder 2013* essay.

Hybrids

Some species, when grown together, in the wild or in cultivation, are found to interbreed and form hybrids. In some instances a hybrid name is coined, for example hybrids between *Primula hirsuta* and *P. minima* are given the name *Primula* × *forsteri*, the multiplication sign indicating hybrid origin. Hybrid formulae that quote the parentage of the hybrid are used where a unique name has not been coined, for example *Rhododendron auriculatum* × *R. hemsleyanum*. In hybrid formulae you will find parents in alphabetical order, with the male (m) and female (f) parent indicated where known. Hybrids between different genera are also possible, for example × *Mahoberberis* is the name given to hybrids between *Mahonia* and *Berberis*.

There are also a few special-case hybrids called graft hybrids, where the tissues of two plants are physically rather than genetically mixed. These are indicated by an addition rather than a multiplication sign, so *Laburnum* + *Cytisus* becomes + *Laburnocytisus*.

ICNCP

The ICNCP is the International Code of Nomenclature for Cultivated Plants. First published in 1959, the 9th edition was published in 2016.

Cultivar names that do not conform to this Code, and for which there is no valid alternative, are flagged I (for invalid). This code states that the minimum requirement is for a cultivar name to be given in conjunction with the name of the genus. However, in the *RHS Plant Finder* we choose to give as full a name as possible to give the gardener and botanist more information about the plant, following the Recommendation in the Code.

Nomenclature and Taxonomy Advisory Group

This Group advises the RHS on individual problems of nomenclature regarding plants in cultivation and, in particular, use of names in the *RHS Horticultural Database*, reflected in the annual publication of the *RHS Plant Finder*.

The aim is always to make the plant names in the *RHS Plant Finder* as consistent, reliable and stable as possible and acceptable to gardeners and botanists alike, not only in the British Isles but around the world. Recent proposals to change or correct names are examined with the aim of creating a balance between the stability of well-known names and botanical and taxonomic correctness. In some cases the conflicting views on the names of some groups of plants will not easily be resolved. The Group's policy is then to wait and review the situation once a more obvious consensus is reached, rather than rush to rename plants only to have to change them again when opinions have shifted.

As we start 2017, the Group is chaired by Dr John Grimshaw and includes: Susyn Andrews, Chris Brickell, Dr James Compton, Dr Janet Cubey (Vice-Chair), Mike Grant, Dr Stephen Jury, Dr Alan Leslie, Dr Tony Lord, Chris Sanders with Dr Crinan Alexander, Prof David Mabberley, Dr Charles Nelson and Julian Sutton (corresponding members), James Armitage, Dr John David and Julian Shaw (attending RHS staff) and Dr Dawn Edwards as Secretary.

Notes on Nomenclature and Identification

The **Notes on Nomenclature and Identification**, p.49, give further information for names that are complex or may be confusing. See also **Nomenclature and Taxonomy Advisory Group**.

Plant Breeders' Rights

Plants covered by an *active* grant of Plant Breeders' Rights (PBR) are indicated throughout the Plant Directory. Grants indicated are those awarded by both UK and EU Plant Variety Rights offices. Because grants can both come into force and lapse at any time, this book can only aim to represent the situation at one point in time, but it is hoped that this will act as a useful guide to growers and gardeners. UK and EU grants represent the published position as of the end of December 2016. We do not give any indication where PBR grants may be pending.

To obtain PBR protection, a new plant must be registered and pass tests for distinctness, uniformity and stability under an approved name. This approved name, under the rules of the **ICNCP**, established by a legal process, has to be regarded as the cultivar name. Increasingly however, these approved names are a code or "nonsense" name and are therefore often unpronounceable and meaningless, so the plants are given other names designed to attract sales when they are released. These secondary names are often referred to as selling names but are officially termed **trade designations**. We do our best to link PBR names to their trade descriptions but if you spot any we've missed, do let us know.

For further information on UK PBR contact:
Plant Variety Rights Office,
Animal and Plant Health Agency,
Eastbrook,
Shaftesbury Road,
Cambridge CB2 8DR
Ⓣ (0208) 026 5993
Ⓔ pvs.helpdesk@apha.gsi.gov.uk
Ⓦ www.gov.uk/plant-breeders-rights

For details of plants covered by EU Community Rights contact:
Community Plant Variety Office (CPVO)
3 Boulevard Maréchal Foch, CS 10121
49101 Angers Cedex 2, France
Ⓣ 00 33 (02) 41 25 64 00
Ⓔ cpvo@cpvo.europa.eu
Ⓦ www.cpvo.europa.eu

The *RHS Plant Finder* takes no responsibility for ensuring that nurseries selling plants with PBR are licensed to do so.

Reverse Synonyms

It is likely that users of this book will come across names in certain genera that they did not expect to find. This may be because species have been transferred from another genus (or **genera**).

Selling Names

See **Trade Designations**

Series

With seed-raised plants and some popular vegetatively propagated plants, especially bedding plants and pot plants such as *Petunia* or *Verbena*, Series have become increasingly popular. A Series contains a number of similar cultivars, but differs from a **Group** in that it is a marketing device, with cultivars added to create a range of flower colours in plants of similar habit. Individual colour elements within a Series may be represented by slightly different cultivars over the years.

The word Series is always included and, where cited with a cultivar name it is enclosed in brackets, for example *Aquilegia* 'Robin' (Songbird Series). The Series name usually follows the rest of the plant name, but sometimes in this book we list it before the cultivar name in order to group members of a Series together when they occur next to one another on the page.

Species

See under **Botanical Names**

Subspecies

See under **Botanical Names**

Synonyms

Although the ideal is for each species or cultivar to have only one name, anyone dealing with plants soon comes across a situation where one plant has received two or more names, or two plants have received the same name. In each case, only one name and application, for reasons of precision and stability, can be regarded as correct. Additional names are known as synonyms. Further information on synonyms and why plants change names is available in *Guide to Plant Names*. See the introduction to this glossary for details of how to request a copy.

See also **Reverse Synonyms**.

Trade Designations

A **trade designation** is the name used to market a plant when the cultivar name is considered unsuitable for selling purposes. It is distinguished typographically (see below) from a cultivar name, and is not enclosed in single quotation marks.

In the case of **Plant Breeders' Rights** it is a legal requirement for the cultivar name to appear with the trade designation on a label at the point of sale. Most plants are sold under only one trade designation, but some, especially roses, are sold under a number of names, particularly when cultivars are introduced from other countries. Usually, the correct cultivar name is the only way to ensure that the same plant is not bought unwittingly under two or more different trade designations. The *RHS Plant Finder* follows the recommendations of the **ICNCP** when dealing with trade designations and PBR. These are always to quote the cultivar name and trade designation together and to style the trade designation in small capitals, for example *Choisya* × *dewitteana* GOLDFINGERS ('Limo'PBR). Here GOLDFINGERS is the trade designation and 'Limo' is the cultivar name that has been granted **Plant Breeders' Rights**.

TRANSLATIONS

When a cultivar name is translated from the language of first publication, the translation is regarded as a **trade designation** and styled accordingly. We endeavour to recognise the original cultivar name in every case and to give an English translation where it is in general use.

VARIEGATED PLANTS

Following a suggestion from the Variegated Plant Group of the Hardy Plant Society, a (v) is cited after those plants which are "variegated". The dividing line between variegation and less distinct colour marking is necessarily arbitrary and plants with light veins, pale, silver or dark zones, or leaves flushed in paler colours, are not shown as being variegated unless there is an absolutely sharp distinction between paler and darker zones.

For further details of the Variegated Plant Group, please write to:

Brian Dockerill
19 Westfield Road
Glyncoch
Pontypridd
Mid-Glamorgan
CF37 3AG

VARIETY

See under **Botanical Names** and **Cultivar**

CONSERVATION AND THE ENVIRONMENT

Invasive Plants

As the *RHS Plant Finder* demonstrates, gardens in Britain have been greatly enriched by the diversity of plants introduced to cultivation from abroad. While the vast majority of those introduced have enhanced our gardens, a few have proved to be highly invasive and to threaten native habitats. Once such plants are established it is very difficult, costly and potentially damaging to native ecosystems to eradicate or control the invasive "alien" species. Gardeners can help by choosing not to buy or distribute non-native invasive plants and by taking steps to prevent them escaping into the wild and by disposing of them in a responsible way.

Ten of the most serious invasive non-native species are no longer listed in the *RHS Plant Finder*. Any cultivars or varieties of them that are listed are believed to be less invasive than the species. These 10 plants are:

**Azolla filiculoides* – fairy fern
**Crassula helmsii* – New Zealand pygmy weed
Elodea nuttallii – Nuttall's waterweed
Fallopia japonica – Japanese knotweed
Heracleum mantegazzianum – giant hogweed
†**Hydrocotyle ranunculoides* – floating pennywort
Impatiens glandulifera – Himalayan balsam
†*Lagarosiphon major* – curly waterweed
†**Ludwigia grandiflora* – water primrose
†**Myriophyllum aquaticum* – parrot's feather

From April 2014 the five aquatic species indicated by a * above have been banned from sale in the UK. Anyone trading in these species is liable to a fine of up to £5000.

The EU Regulation on Invasive Alien Species, which became law early in 2015, has a provision for a list of species of EU-wide concern. That list has now been published by the EU Commission and became effective from August 2016. Species that are included in the list attract the strictest measures of control, including a ban on keeping, growing or cultivating, transporting or trading, use or exchange, as well as release into the wider environment. These controls will apply to individuals as well as organisations and businesses that own or hold any of these species. There are 14 plants on this list, most of which are of marginal importance to gardeners, or are already banned from sale in the UK (marked with † in the above list), but two widely grown species, *Eichhornia crassipes* (water hyacinth) and *Lysichiton americanus* (skunk cabbage), are included. Although there are transitionary measures allowing businesses to sell off their stock of these species within one year, to minimise potential for confusion, we have taken the step of not listing the species in the 2017 *RHS Plant Finder*. Those species affected are:

Baccharis halmifolia – tree groundsel
Cabomba caroliniana – Carolina fanwort
Eichhornia crassipes – water hyacinth
Ludwigia peploides – water primrose
Lysichiton americanus – American skunk cabbage
Parthenium hysterophorus – parthenium weed
Pueraria montana var. *lobata* – kudzu

Gardeners who already have these species in their gardens are not at risk of prosecution for possession as the Regulation is not retrospective, but will be required to meet the other requirements of the Regulation to ensure that they control the species effectively on their property and do not allow it to spread.

Species control provisions

The UK Government introduced new provisions in the Infrastructure Act (2015) to control invasive non-native species in England and Wales. There are two levels of control: a species control agreement and a species control order. In the former, the owner of land where an invasive non-native species is present, when approached by the relevant environmental authority, agrees to take action to limit or remove the species. If the landowner fails to do so, or does not agree, or where it is not known who the landowner is, then the environment authority can take action to enforce the control of the species. This may involve entry of the property by the authority to carry out the control if the owner fails to comply. In the case of an emergency then a species control order may be issued without going through the previous steps. Only those species listed on Schedule 9 of the Wildlife & Countryside Act can be subject to these control measures. For the purposes of the Act, Defra, Natural England, the Environment Agency and the Forestry Commission are defined as Environmental Authorities in England. For Wales it is Natural Resources Wales.

Bringing plants back from abroad

Travelling can be a great source of inspiration for gardeners and often provides an opportunity to encounter new and interesting plants. Anyone wishing to bring plants back into Britain from overseas must realise, however, that this is a complex matter. Various regulations are in force that apply to amateur gardeners as well as to commercial nurseries. The penalties for breaking these can be serious.

Most countries have regulations concerning the collection of plants from the wild, including seed.

These regulations are likely to ban collection from certain protected places, such as national parks, ban the collection of rare or endangered species, and require permits to collect where special protection measures are not in place. In addition there is likely to be an additional permit to export any collected plant material. Travellers are reminded of regulations in force at airports and other points of entry to a country. Anyone wishing to collect wild plants, for whatever purpose, will need to contact the country concerned well in advance of travel to seek the relevant permits. Breach of the regulations will result, as a minimum, in the confiscation of plant material if discovered. Any such material brought back to the UK is illegal.

The situation with plants in cultivation in another country is less clear and travellers are advised to check with the authorities in the country, particularly with regard to any Access and Benefit Sharing requirements (see **Nagoya Protocol** below), export permits or phytosanitary certificates that might be needed.

Plant Health regulations are in place to control the spread of pests and diseases. Plants are divided into the categories of prohibited, controlled and unrestricted, but there are also limits that vary according to the part of the world you are travelling from.

Ⓦ www.gov.uk/bringing-food-animals-plants-into-uk/plants

The Convention on International Trade in Endangered Species (CITES) affects the transport of animal and plant material across international boundaries. Its aim is to prevent exploitative trade and thereby to prevent harm and the ultimate extinction of wild populations. A tighter regime on trade in species of wild fauna and flora exists in the EU that requires export permits for any plants listed in Appendices A, B & C and import permits for Appendices A & B. There is a further Appendix D for non-CITES listed species that the EU consider to be endangered. A broad range of plants is covered in these Appendices, including *Cactaceae* and *Orchidaceae* and, although species are mentioned in the convention title, the restrictions cover all cultivars and hybrids of listed species too, except for specific exclusions, where there are annotations in the Appendices.

Ⓦ www.gov.uk/cites-imports-and-exports#cites-species

The Convention on Biological Diversity (CBD or the "Rio Convention") recognises the property rights of individual countries in relation to their own biodiversity. It exists to enable access to that biodiversity, but equally to ensure the sharing of any benefit derived from it. In principle it is possible to collect plant material from other countries that have asserted their rights under the CBD, by ensuring that you have obtained documentary evidence of prior informed consent on the basis of mutually agreed terms for any uses that the material will be put to in the future. In practice the legal requirements for collecting plant material vary from country to country and it is advisable to contact the National Focal Point for further information.

Ⓦ www.cbd.int

The **Nagoya Protocol** is a supplementary agreement of the CBD which entered into force in 2015, and provides a framework for Access and Benefit Sharing. In the UK this is implemented by the European Union Regulation which is effective from 12 October 2014, and requires anyone utilising genetic resources from another country which is a signatory of the Nagoya Protocol, collected after 12 October 2014, to carry out due diligence to ensure that the material was collected in accordance with the Protocol and the CBD. While the most likely examples of utilisation are the development of new products or medicines from plants, breeding programmes to raise new plants for horticulture would also be covered. Although the burden to prove legitimate use of the genetic resource lies with the person or organisation utilising the genetic resource, anyone providing the source of the genetic resource (such as wild-collected plants) will need to be able to provide the relevant paperwork, such as a Material Transfer Agreement and Prior Informed Consent.

Ⓦ www.cbd.int/abs/about/

In March 2015 the UK Government put in place the scheme of penalties for failure to comply with the EU Regulation which includes a range of both civil and criminal penalties, with the ultimate sanction of a two-year prison sentence. This legislation also formally appointed Regulatory Delivery (formerly National Measurement and Regulation Office) as the authority to enforce compliance in the UK, effective from June 2015.

Ⓦ www.gov.uk/guidance/abs

European Habitats Directive. The full implementation of this Directive into UK law in 2007 extended protection to all of the European Protected Species (EPS) listed in the Appendices of that Directive (these are Appendices II(b) and IV(b) for plants) whether they are native to the UK or not. This requires a licence for material of any of these species collected in the wild after 1994. These are issued by Natural England (for England), Natural Resources Wales (in Wales) and Scottish Natural Heritage (for Scotland).

Ⓦ www.gov.uk/guidance/wild-plants-sell-them-legally

Contact addresses

The UK authorities issue licences for UK plants. For other EU states a collector would need to contact the relevant national authorities.

Department for Environment, Food & Rural Affairs (Defra)
Nobel House
17 Smith Square
London
SW1P 3JR
For biodiversity queries:
Ⓔ biodiversity@defra.gsi.gov.uk

Plant Health is covered by the Plant Health and Seeds Inspectorate (PHSI) which is part of the Animal and Plant Health Agency.

Animal & Plant Health Agency (APHA)
Centre for International Trade – Bristol
1/17 Temple Quay House
2 The Square
Temple Quay
Bristol
BS1 6EB
Ⓣ 0117 372 8774
Ⓕ 0117 372 8206
Ⓔ wildlife.licensing@apha.gsi.gov.uk
Ⓦ www.gov.uk/plant-health-controls

Natural England
Wildlife Management & Licensing
Horizon House
Deanery Road
Bristol
BS1 5AH
Ⓣ 020 8026 1089
Ⓔ wildlife@naturalengland.org.uk

Non-Native Species Secretariat
Animal and Plant Health Agency
Sand Hutton
York
YO41 1LZ
Ⓦ www.nonnativespecies.org

Regulatory Delivery
Stanton Avenue
Teddington
TW110JZ
Ⓣ 020 8943 7272
Ⓔ info@nmro.gov.uk

SUPPLEMENTARY KEYS TO THE DIRECTORY

COLLECTORS' REFERENCES

Abbreviations following a plant name, refer to the collector(s) of the plant. These abbreviations are expanded below, with a collector's name or expedition title. For a fuller explanation, see p.38.

A&JW Watson, A. & J.
A&L Ala, A. & Lancaster, Roy
AB&S Archibald, James; Blanchard, John W. & Salmon, M.
AC Clark, Alan J.
AC&H Apold, J.; Cox, Peter & Hutchison, Peter
AC&W Albury; Cheese, M. & Watson, J.M.
ACE AGS Expedition to China (1994)
ACL Leslie, Alan C.
AER Robinson, Allan
AGS/ES AGS Expedition to Sikkim (1983)
AGSJ AGS Expedition to Japan (1988)
AH Hoog, A.
AIM Avent, Tony Mexico (1994)
Airth Airth, Murray
Akagi Akagi Botanical Garden
AL&JS Sharman, Joseph L. & Leslie, Alan C.
APA Cox, K.; Hootman, S.; Hudson, T.; et al, Expedition to Arunchal Pradesh (2005)
ARG Argent, G.C.G.
ARGS Alaska Rock Garden Society trip to China
ARJA Ruksans, J. & Siesums, A.
B Blanchard, John
B&F MA Brown, Robert & Fisher, Rif & Middle Atlas (2007)
B L. Beer, Len
B&L Brickell, Christopher D. & Leslie, Alan C.
B&M & BM Brickell, Christopher D. & Mathew, Brian
B&S Bird P. & Salmon M.
B&SWJ Wynn-Jones, Bleddyn & Susan
B&V Burras, K. & Vosa, C.G.
BB Bartholomew, B.
BBJMT Boland, Brownless, Jamieson & McNamara
BC Chudziak, W.
BC&W Beckett; Cheese, M. & Watson, J.M.
Beavis Beavis, Derek S.
Berry Berry, P.
Berry & Brako Berry, P. & Brako, Lois
BKBlount Blount, B.K.
BKN Bis, J., Kupčák, P. & Novak, H.
BL&M University of Bangor Expedition to NE Nepal
BM Mathew, Brian F.
BM&W Binns, David L.; Mason, M. & Wright, A.
BOA Boardman, P.
Breedlove Breedlove, D.
BR Rushbrooke, Ben
BS Smith, Basil
BSBE Bowles Scholarship Botanical Expedition (1963)
BSSS Crûg Expedition, Jordan (1991)
Bu Bubert, S.
Burtt Burtt, Brian L.
BWJ Wynn-Jones, Bleddyn
C Cole, Desmond T.
C&C Cox, P.A. & Cox, K.N.E.
C&Cu Cox, K.N.E. & Cubey, J.
C&H Cox, Peter & Hutchison, Peter
C&K Chamberlain & Knott
C&R Christian & Roderick
C&S Clark, Alan & Sinclair, Ian W.J.
C&V K.N.E. Cox & Vergera, S.
C&W Cheese, M. & Watson, J.M.
CC Chadwell, Christopher
CC&H Chamberlain, David F.; Cox, Peter & Hutchison, P.
CC&McK Chadwell, Christopher & McKelvie, A.
CC&MR Chadwell, Christopher & Ramsay
CCH&H Chamberlain, D.F.; Cox, P.; Hutchison, P. & Hootman, S.
CD&R Compton, J.; D'Arcy, J. & Rix, E.M.
CDB Brickell, Christopher D.
CDC Coode, Mark J.E.; Dockrill, Alexander
CDC&C Compton; D'Arcy; Christopher & Coke
CDPR Compton; D'Arcy; Pope & Rix
CE&H Christian, P.J.; Elliott & Hoog
CEE Chengdu Edinburgh Expedition China (1991)

CGG Glendoick Gardens Expedition to Guizou (2009)
CGV Vosa, Canio
CGW Grey-Wilson, Christopher
CH Christian, P. & Hoog, A.
CH&M Cox, P.; Hutchison, P. & Maxwell-MacDonald, D.
CHP&W Kashmir Botanical Expedition
CL Lovell, Chris
CLD Chungtien, Lijiang & Dali Exped. China (1990)
CM&W Cheese M.; Mitchel J. & Watson, J.
CN&W Clark; Neilson & Wilson
CNDS Nelson, C. & Sayers D.
COLA Costin, J.J. & Lancaster, R., Japan (1990)
Cooper Cooper, R.E.
Cox Cox, Peter A.
CPC Cobblewood Plant Collection
CPN Compton, James
CS Stapleton, Christopher
CSE Cyclamen Society Expedition (1990)
CT Teune, Carla
CW&T Clark, A., Wilson, H. & Taggart, J., North Vietnam
CWJ Colley, Finlay; Wynn-Jones, Bleddyn, Taiwan (2007)
Dahl Dahl, Sally
DBG Denver Botanic Garden, Colorado
DC Cheshire, David
DF Fox, D.
DG Green, D.
DHTU Hinkley, D., Turkey (2000)
DJF Ferguson, Dave
DJH Hinkley, Dan
DJHC Hinkley D., China
DJHS Hinkley, D., Sichuan
DJHV Hinkley, D., Vietnam
DM Millais, David
Doleshy Doleshy, F.L.
DS&T Drake, Sharman J. & Thompson
DWD Rose, D.
DZ Zummell, D.
ECN Nelson, E. Charles
EDHCH Hammond, Eric D.
EGM Millais, T.
EKB Balls, Edward K.
EM East Malling Research Station
EMAK Edinburgh Makalu Expedition (1991)
EMR Rix, E.Martyn
EN Needham, Edward F.
ENF Fuller, E. Nigel
ETE Edinburgh Taiwan Expedition (1993)
ETOT Kirkham, T.S.; Flanagan, Mark
F Forrest, G.
F&M Fernandez & Mendoza, Mexico
F&W Watson, J. & Flores, A.
Farrer Farrer, Reginald
FK Kinmonth, Fergus W.
FMB Bailey, F.M.
FO Otiery, Felix
G Gardner, Martin F.
G&K Gardner, Martin F. & Knees, Sabina G.
G&P Gardner, Martin F. & Page, Christopher N.
GDJ Dumont, Gerard
GG Gusman, G.
GS Sherriff, George
Green Green, D.
Guitt Guittoneau, G.G.
Guiz Guizhou Expedition (1985)
GWJ Goddard, Sally; Wynne-Jones, Bleddyn & Susan
G-W&P Grey-Wilson, Christopher & Phillips
H Huggins, Paul
H&B Hilliard, Olive M. & Burtt, Brian L.
H&D Howick, C. & Darby
H&M Howick, Charles & McNamara, William A.
H&W Hedge, Ian C. & Wendelbo, Per W.
Harry Smith Smith, K.A.Harry
Hartside Hartside Nursery
HCM Heronswood Expedition to Chile (1998)
HECC Hutchison; Evans; Cox, P.; Cox, K.
HEHEHE Zetterlund, H. et al, Gothenburg Botanic Gardens Expedition to northern China
Hird Hird
HH&K Hannay, S & S & Kingsbury, N.
HK Kuenzler, Horst
HLMS Springate, L.S.
HM&S Halliwell, B.; Mason, D. & Smallcombe
HOA Hoog, Anton
HOLUB Holubec, V.
HRS Hers, J.
Hummel Hummel, D.
HW&E Wendelbo, Per; Hedge, I. & Ekberg, L.
HWEL Hirst, J.Michael; Webster, D.
HWJ Crûg Heronswood Joint Expedition
HWJCM Crûg Heronswood Expedition
HWJK Crûg Heronswood Expedition, East Nepal (2002)
HZ Zetterlund, Henrik
ICE Instituto de Investigaciónes Ecológicas Chiloé & RBGE
IDS International Dendrological Society
ISI Int. Succulent Introductions
J&JA Archibald, James & Jennifer
J. Jurasek Jurasek, J.
JCA Archibald, James
JE Jack Elliott
JJ Jackson, J.
JJ&JH Halda, J. & Halda, J.
JJH Halda, Joseph J.
JL Lode, Joel
JLS Sharman, J.L.
JMH Hoog, J. & M.

JM-MK	Mahr, J.; Kammerlander, M.
JMT	Mann Taylor, J.
JN	Nielson, Jens
JR	Russell, J.
JRM	Marr, John
JW	Watson, J.M.
K	Kirkpatrick, George
K&LG	Gillanders, Kenneth & Gillanders, L.
K&Mc	Kirkpatrick, George & McBeath, Ronald J.D.
K&P	Josef Kopec & Milan Prasil
K&T	Kurashige, Y. & Tsukie, S.
KC	Cox, Kenneth
KEKE	Kew/Edinburgh Kanchenjunga Expedition (1989)
KGB	Kunming/Gothenburg Botanical Expedition (1993)
KM	Marsh, K.
KMR	Kupčák, M.
KR	Rushforth, K.D.
KRW	Wooster, K.R. (distributed after his death by Kath Dryden)
KW	Kingdon-Ward, F.
KWJ	Crûg-World of Ferns Joint Expedition, Vietnam (2007)
L	Lancaster, C. Roy
L&S	Ludlow, Francis & Sherriff, George
LA	Long Ashton Research Station clonal selection scheme
LB	Bercht, L. (*Cactaceae*)
LB	Bird P.; Salmon, M.
LEG	Lesotho Edinburgh/Gothenburg Expedition (1997)
Lismore	Lismore Nursery, Breeder's Number
LM&S	Leslie, Mattern & Sharman
LP	Palmer, W.J.L.
LS&E	Ludlow, Frank; Sherriff, George & Elliott, E. E.
LS&H	Ludlow, Frank; Sherriff, George & Hicks, J. H.
LS&T	Ludlow, Frank; Sherriff, George & Taylor, George
LZ	Lutz, Eberhard
M&PS	Mike & Polly Stone
M&T	Mathew & Tomlinson
Mac&W	McPhail & Watson
McB	McBeath, R.J.D.
McLaren	McLaren, H.D.
MDM	Myers, Michael D.
MECC	Scottish Rock Garden Club, Nepal (1997)
MESE	Alpine Garden Society Expedition, Greece (1999)
MF	Foster, Maurice
MH	Heasman, Matthew T.
MK	Kammerlander, Michael
MP	Pavelka, Mojmir
MPF	Frankis, M.P.
MS	Salmon, M.
MS&CL	Salmon, M. & Lovell, C.
MSF	Fillan, M.S.
MUG	Uhlig, M.
NAPE	Expedition to Naglaland and Arunachal Pradesh (2003)
NICE	North India Expedition (1997)
NJM	Macer, N.J.
NMWJ	Taiwan National Museum of Natural Science; Wynn-Jones, B. & S.
NN	Nielsen & Nielsen (2009)
NNS	Ratko, Ron
NS	Turland, Nick
NVD	Expedition to Vietnam
NVFDE	Northern Vietnam First Darwin Expedition
Og	Ogisu, Mikinori
ORO	Oron, Peri
OS	Sonderhousen, O.
P. Bon	Bonavia, P.
P&C	Paterson, David S. & Clarke, Sidney
P&W	Polastri & Watson, J. M.
PAB	Barney, P.A.
PB	Bird, Peter
PBR	Bruggeman, P.
PC&H	Pattison, G.; Catt, P. & Hickson, M.
PD	Davis, Peter H.
PDM	Purdom, William
PF	Furse, Paul
PG	Pichler, G.
PJC	Christian, Paul J.
PJC&AH	P.J. Christian & A. Hogg
PNMK	Nicholls, P.; Kammerlander, M.
Polunin	Polunin, Oleg
Pras	Prasil, M.
PS&W	Polunin, Oleg; Sykes, William & Williams, John
PW	Wharton, Peter
R	Rock, J.F.C.
RB	Brown, R.
RBS	Brown, Ray, Sakharin Island
RCB AM	Brown, Robert, Expedition to Armenia
RCB/Arg	Brown, Robert, Argentina, (2002)
RCB E	Brown, Robert, Expedition to Spain (Andalucia)
RCB/Eq	Brown, Robert, Ecuador, (1988)
RCB RA	Brown, Robert
RCB RL	Brown, Robert, Expedition to Lebanon
RCB/TQ	Brown, Robert, Turkey (2001)
RE	Evans, Ron
RH	Hancock, R.
RJN	Neilsen, R.
RKMP	Ruksans, J.; Krumins, A.; Kitts, M.; Paivel, A.
RM	Ruksans, J. & Kitts, M.
RMRP	Rocky Mountain Rare Plants, Denver, Colorado
RS	Suckow, Reinhart

RSC Richard Somer Cocks
RV Richard Valder
RWJ Crûg Farm-Rickards Ferns Expedition to Taiwan (2003)
S&B Blanchard, J.W. & Salmon, M.
S&F Salmon, M. & Fillan, M.
S&L Sinclair, Ian W.J. & Long, David G.
S&SH Sheilah & Spencer Hannay
Sandham Sandham, John
SB Brack, Steven
SB&L Salmon, Bird & Lovell
SBEC Sino-British Expedition to Cangshan
SBEL Sino-British Lijiang Expedition
SBQE Sino-British Expedition to Quinghai
Sch Schilling, Anthony D.
SD Sashal Dayal
SDR Rankin, Stella & David
SEH Hootman, Steve
SEP Swedish Expedition to Pakistan
SF Forde, P.
SG Salmon, M. & Guy, P.
SH Hannay, Spencer
Sich Simmons, Erskine, Howick & Mcnamara
SJ Johansson, Stellan
SLIZE Swedish-Latvian-Iranian Zagros Expedition to Iran (May 1988)
SOJA Kew/Quarryhill Expedition to Southern Japan
SS&W Stainton, J.D. Adam; Sykes, William & Williams, John
SSNY Sino-Scottish Expedition to NW Yunnan (1992)
T Taylor, Nigel P.
T&K Taylor, Nigel P. & Knees, Sabina
TCM Mitchell, Thomas Carly
TG Thomas, H-P. & Gilmer, K.
TH Hudson, T.
TJR Roberts, Tim
TS&BC Smythe, T. & Cherry, B.
TSS Spring Smyth, T.L.M.
TW Weston, Tony
USDAPI US Department of Agriculture Plant Index Number
USDAPQ US Dept. of Agriculture Plant Quarantine Number
USNA United States National Arboretum
VdL Van de Laar, Harry
VHH Vernon H. Heywood
VV Victor, David
W Wilson, Ernest H.
W&B Watkins, D. & Brown, R., Bulgaria (2012)
WJC Wynn-Jones, B. & S. & Colley, F.
WM McLewin, William
Woods Woods, Patrick J.B.
Wr Wraight, David & Anke
WWJ Wharton, Peter; Wynn-Jones, Bleddyn & Susan
Yu Yu, Tse-tsun
ZE&S Zetterlund, H., Eriksson, A-I. & Strid, A.

NOMENCLATURAL NOTES

The following changes have been made during 2016 to the names used in the *RHS Plant Finder* based on decisions of the RHS Nomenclature and Taxonomy Advisory Group (NATAG). If you have any suggestions for other plant name changes within the *RHS Plant Finder*, then please write, stating your reasons in full to:

The Chairman & Vice-Chairman
Dr John Grimshaw & Dr Janet Cubey
Nomenclature and Taxonomy Advisory Group
Royal Horticultural Society
RHS Garden Wisley
Woking
Surrey
GU23 6QB

- *Artemisia vulgaris* ORIENTAL LIMELIGHT ('Janlim') to *Artemisia* ORIENTAL LIMELIGHT ('Janlim')
- *Dacrydium colensoi* to *Lepidothamnus colensoi*
- Adopting *Goeppertia,* as distinct from *Calathea*
- *Elaeagnus* × *ebbingei* to the earlier name of *E.* × *submacrophylla*
- Transferring *Fagraea* from *Loganiaceae* to *Gentianaceae*
- Incorporating *Amitostigma* and *Ponerorchis* within *Hemipilia*; following this recognition by the RHS Orchid Hybrid Registration Advisory Group
- Separating *Hylotelephium* from *Sedum*
- Including *Iberis pruitii* within *I. violacea*
- Expanding *Kalmia* to include *Loiseleuria* and *Leiophyllum*
- To use *Lupinus* × *regalis* Russell Group for the Russell hybrid lupins
- Correcting *Malus floribunda* to *M.* × *floribunda*; a hybrid between *M. baccata* and *M. sieboldii*
- Including *Podocarpus cunninghamii* and *P. hallii* within *P. laetus*
- *Rosa wichurana* as a synonym of *R. lucieae*
- *Speirantha convallarioides* to *S. gardenii*
- Recognising *Toxicodendron* as distinct from *Rhus*
- *Vinca minor* 'La Grave' to 'Bowles's Variety'
- Changes within *Wisteria* [*Bot. Mag.* Oct 2015, Vol 32]

This is not intended to be an exhaustive list of the changes made to the RHS Horticultural Database, reflected in the *RHS Plant Finder*; many more changes are made during the year by the RHS botanical team. This list is to highlight some of the some of the NATAG changes.

Changes already proposed for the 2018 edition of this book, include:

- Use of the family *Fabaceae* instead of *Caesalpiniaceae, Papilionaceae* and *Mimosaceae*; and splitting of the genus *Caesalpinia*
- A revision of generic boundaries within *Rosaceae*

Discussions are also ongoing around the generic boundaries within *Gesneriaceae* and *Primulaceae*.

CLASSIFICATION OF GENERA

Genera including a large number of species, or with many cultivars, are often subdivided into informal horticultural classifications, or formal cultivar groups in the case of *Clematis* and *Tulipa*. The breeding of new cultivars is sometimes limited to hybrids between closely related species, thus for *Saxifraga* and *Primula*, the cultivars are allocated to the sections given in the infrageneric treatments cited. Please turn to p.37 for a fuller explanation.

ACER

(A) Amoenum Group
(D) Dissectum Group
(Dw) Dwarf Group
(L) Linearilobum Group
(M) Matsumurae Group
(P) Palmatum Group

ACTINIDIA

(s-p) Self-pollinating

BEGONIA

(C) Cane-like
(R) Rex Cultorum
(S) Semperflorens Cultorum
(T) × *tuberhybrida* (Tuberous)

CHRYSANTHEMUM

(By the National Chrysanthemum Society)
(1) Indoor Large (Exhibition)
(2) Indoor Medium (Exhibition)
(3a) Indoor Incurved: Large-flowered
(3b) Indoor Incurved: Medium-flowered
(3c) Indoor Incurved: Small-flowered
(4a) Indoor Reflexed: Large-flowered
(4b) Indoor Reflexed: Medium-flowered
(4c) Indoor Reflexed: Small-flowered
(5a) Indoor Intermediate: Large-flowered
(5b) Indoor Intermediate: Medium-flowered
(5c) Indoor Intermediate: Small-flowered
(6a) Indoor Anemone: Large-flowered
(6b) Indoor Anemone: Medium-flowered
(6c) Indoor Anemone: Small-flowered
(7a) Indoor Single: Large-flowered
(7b) Indoor Single: Medium-flowered
(7c) Indoor Single: Small-flowered
(8a) Indoor True Pompon
(8b) Indoor Semi-pompon
(9a) Indoor Spray: Anemone
(9b) Indoor Spray: Pompon
(9c) Indoor Spray: Reflexed
(9d) Indoor Spray: Single
(9e) Indoor Spray: Intermediate
(9f) Indoor Spray: Spider, Quill, Spoon or Any Other Type
(10a) Indoor, Spider
(10b) Indoor, Quill
(10c) Indoor, Spoon
(11) Any Other Indoor Type
(12a) Indoor, Charm
(12b) Indoor, Cascade
(13a) October-flowering Incurved: Large-flowered
(13b) October-flowering Incurved: Medium-flowered
(13c) October-flowering Incurved: Small-flowered
(14a) October-flowering Reflexed: Large-flowered
(14b) October-flowering Reflexed: Medium-flowered
(14c) October-flowering Reflexed: Small-flowered
(15a) October-flowering Intermediate: Large-flowered
(15b) October-flowering Intermediate: Medium-flowered
(15c) October-flowered Intermediate: Small-flowered
(16) October-flowering Large
(17a) October-flowering Single: Large-flowered
(17b) October-flowering Single: Medium-flowered
(17c) October-flowering Single: Small-flowered
(18a) October-flowering Pompon: True Pompon
(18b) October-flowering Pompon: Semi-pompon
(19a) October-flowering Spray: Anemone
(19b) October-flowering Spray: Pompon
(19c) October-flowering Spray: Reflexed
(19d) October-flowering Spray: Single
(19e) October-flowering Spray: Intermediate
(19f) October-flowering Spray: Spider, Quill, Spoon or Any Other Type
(20) Any Other October-flowering Type
(21a) Korean: Anemone
(21b) Korean: Pompon
(21c) Korean: Reflexed
(21d) Korean: Single
(21e) Korean: Intermediate
(21f) Korean: Spider, Quill, Spoon, or any other type
(22a) Charm: Anemone

(22b) Charm: Pompon
(22c) Charm: Reflexed
(22d) Charm: Single
(22e) Charm: Intermediate
(22f) Charm: Spider, Quill, Spoon or Any Other Type
(23a) Early-flowering Outdoor Incurved: Large-flowered
(23b) Early-flowering Outdoor Incurved: Medium-flowered
(23c) Early-flowering Outdoor Incurved: Small-flowered
(24a) Early-flowering Outdoor Reflexed: Large-flowered
(24b) Early-flowering Outdoor Reflexed: Medium-flowered
(24c) Early-flowering Outdoor Reflexed: Small-flowered
(25a) Early-flowering Outdoor Intermediate: Large-flowered
(25b) Early-flowering Outdoor Intermediate: Medium-flowered
(25c) Early-flowering Outdoor Intermediate: Small-flowered
(26a) Early-flowering Outdoor Anemone: Large-flowered
(26b) Early-flowering Outdoor Anemone: Medium-flowered
(27a) Early-flowering Outdoor Single: Large-flowered
(27b) Early-flowering Outdoor Single:Medium-flowered
(28a) Early-flowering Outdoor Pompon: True Pompon
(28b) Early-flowering Outdoor Pompon: Semi-pompon
(29a) Early-flowering Outdoor Spray: Anemone
(29b) Early-flowering Outdoor Spray: Pompon
(29c) Early-flowering Outdoor Spray: Reflexed
(29d) Early-flowering Outdoor Spray: Single
(29e) Early-flowering Outdoor Spray: Intermediate
(29f) Early-flowering Outdoor Spray: Spider, Quill, Spoon or Any Other Type
(29Rub) Early-flowering Outdoor Spray: Rubellum
(30) Any Other Early-flowering Outdoor Type

CLEMATIS

(Cultivar Groups as per Matthews, V. (2002) *The International Clematis Register & Checklist 2002*, RHS, London.)

(A) Atragene Group
(Ar) Armandii Group
(C) Cirrhosa Group
(EL) Early Large-flowered Group
(F) Flammula Group
(Fo) Forsteri Group
(H) Heracleifolia Group
(I) Integrifolia Group
(LL) Late Large-flowered Group
(M) Montana Group
(T) Texensis Group
(Ta) Tangutica Group
(V) Viorna Group
(Vb) Vitalba Group
(Vt) Viticella Group

DAHLIA

(Classification according to The International Dahlia Register (1969), 22nd Supp. (2012) formed through consultation with national dahlia societies.)

(Sin) 1 Single
(Anem) 2 Anemone-flowered
(Col) 3 Collerette
(WL) 4 Waterlily
(D) 5 Decorative
(Ba) 6 Ball
(Pom) 7 Pompon
(C) 8 Cactus
(S-c) 9 Semi-cactus
(Misc) 10 Miscellaneous
(Fim) 11 Fimbriated
(SinO) 12 Single Orchid (Star)
(DblO) 13 Double Orchid
(P) 14 Peony-flowered
(B) Botanical
(DwB) Dwarf Bedding
(Lil) Lilliput

DIANTHUS

(By the RHS)

(b) Carnation, border
(M) Carnation, Malmaison
(p) Pink
(p,a) Pink, annual
(pf) Carnation, perpetual-flowering
(pt) Carnation, pot

FRUIT

(B) Black (*Vitis*), Blackberry (*Rubus*), Blackcurrant (*Ribes*)
(Ball) Ballerina (*Malus*)
(C) Culinary (*Malus, Prunus, Pyrus, Ribes*)
(Cider) Cider (*Malus*)
(D) Dessert (*Malus, Prunus, Pyrus, Ribes*)
(F) Fruit
(G) Glasshouse (*Vitis*)
(O) Outdoor (*Vitis*)
(P) Pinkcurrant (*Ribes*)
(Perry) Perry (*Pyrus*)

(R) Red (*Vitis*), Redcurrant (*Ribes*)
(S) Seedless (*Citrus, Vitis*)
(s-p) Self-pollinating
(W) White (*Vitis*), Whitecurrant (*Ribes*)

Fuchsia

(E) Encliandra
(T) Variants and hybrids of *F. triphylla*

Gladiolus

(B) Butterfly
(E) Exotic
(G) Giant
(L) Large
(M) Medium
(Min) Miniature
(N) Nanus
(P) Primulinus
(S) Small
(Tub) Tubergenii

Hepatica nobilis

(Adapted from the International Hepatica Society classification for *Hepatica nobilis*)
(1) Hyoujun (normal)
(2) (degenerated anther)
(3) Otome (degenerated stamen)
(4) Henka (petal deformity)
(5/d) Herashibe (semi-double, primitive)
(5A/d) Choji (semi-double, primitive)
(6/d) Nidan (semi-double, advanced)
(7/d) Sandan (double, primitive)
(8/d) Karako (double, advanced)
(9/d) Sene-e (double, completed)

Hydrangea macrophylla

(H) Hortensia
(L) Lacecap

Impatiens

(NG) New Guinea Group

Iris

(Adapted from the American Iris Society Classification)
(AB) Arilbred
(BB) Border Bearded
(Cal-Sib) Series *Californicae* × Series *Sibiricae*
(CH) Californian Hybrid
(DB) Dwarf Bearded (not assigned)
(Dut) Dutch (can be assigned to *I.* × *hollandica*)
(IB) Intermediate Bearded
(J) Juno (subgenus *Scorpiris*)
(La) Louisiana Hybrid
(MDB) Miniature Dwarf Bearded
(MTB) Miniature Tall Bearded
(Rc) Regeliocyclus (Section *Regelia* × Section *Oncocyclus*)
(Reticulata)
(SDB) Standard Dwarf Bearded
(Sib) Siberian
(Sino-Sib) Series *Sibiricae*, chromosome number 2n=40
(SpH) Species Hybrid
(Spuria) Spuria
(TB) Tall Bearded

Lilium

(Classification according to *The International Lily Register* (ed. 4, 2007))
(I) Asiatic hybrids derived from *L. amabile, L. bulbiferum, L. callosum, L. cernuum, L. concolor, L. dauricum, L. davidii, L.* × *hollandicum, L. lancifolium, L. lankongense, L. leichtlinii, L.* × *maculatum* and *L. pumilum, L.* × *scottiae, L. wardii* and *L. wilsonii.*
(II) Martagon hybrids derived from *L. dalhansonii, L. hansonii, L. martagon, L. medeoloides and L. tsingtauense*
(III) Euro-Caucasian hybrids derived from *L. candidum, L. chalcedonicum, L. kesselringianum, L. monadelphum, L. pomponium, L. pyrenaicum* and *L.* × *testaceum.*
(IV) American hybrids derived from *L. bolanderi, L.* × *burbankii, L. canadense, L. columbianum, L. grayi, L. humboldtii, L. kelleyanum, L. kelloggii, L. maritimum, L. michauxii, L. michiganense, L. occidentale, L.* × *pardaboldtii, L. pardalinum, L. parryi, L. parvum, L. philadelphicum, L. pitkinense, L. superbum, L. vollmeri, L. washingtonianum* and *L. wigginsii.*
(V) Longiflorum lilies derived from *L. formosanum, L. longiflorum, L. philippinense and L. wallichianum.*
(VI) Trumpet and Aurelian hybrids derived from *L.* × *aurelianense, L. brownii, L.* × *centigale, L. henryi, L.* × *imperiale, L.* × *kewense, L. leucantheum, L. regale, L. rosthornii, L. sargentiae, L. sulphureum* and *L. sulphurgale* (but excluding hybrids of *L. henryi* with all species listed in Division VII).
(VII) Oriental hybrids derived from *L. auratum, L. japonicum, L. nobilissimum, L.* × *parkmanii, L rubellum* and *L. speciosum* (but excl. all hybrids of these with *L. henryi*).
(VIII) Other hybrids not covered by any of the previous divisions (I-VII)
(IX) Species and cultivars of species
a/ upward-facing flowers
b/ outward-facing flowers
c/ downward-facing flowers

/a trumpet-shaped flowers
/b bowl-shaped flowers
/c flat flowers (or with only tepal tips recurved)
/d recurved flowers

Malus *see* Fruit

Narcissus

(By the RHS, revised 1998)
(1) Trumpet
(2) Large-cupped
(3) Small-cupped
(4) Double
(5) Triandrus
(6) Cyclamineus
(7) Jonquilla and Apodanthus
(8) Tazetta
(9) Poeticus
(10) Bulbocodium
(11a) Split-corona: Collar
(11b) Split-corona: Papillon
(12) Miscellaneous
(13) Species

Nymphaea

(H) Hardy
(D) Day-blooming
(N) Night-blooming
(T) Tropical

Paeonia

(S) Shrubby

Pelargonium

(A) Angel
(C) Coloured Foliage (in combination)
(Ca) Cactus (in combination)
(d) Double (in combination)
(Dec) Decorative
(Dw) Dwarf
(DwI) Dwarf Ivy-leaved
(Fr) Frutetorum
(I) Ivy-leaved
(Min) Miniature
(MinI) Miniature Ivy-leaved
(R) Regal
(Sc) Scented-leaved
(St) Stellar (in combination)
(T) Tulip (in combination)
(U) Unique
(Z) Zonal

Primula

(Classification by Section as per Richards. J. (2002) *Primula* (2nd edition). Batsford, London)
(Ag) *Auganthus*
(Al) *Aleuritia*
(Am) *Amethystinae*
(Ar) *Armerina*
(Au) *Auricula*
  (A) Alpine Auricula
  (B) Border Auricula
  (S) Show Auricula
  (St) Striped Auricula
(Bu) *Bullatae*
(Ca) *Capitatae*
(Cf) *Cordifoliae*
(Ch) *Chartaceae*
(Co) *Cortusoides*
(Cr) *Carolinella*
(Cu) *Cuneifoliae*
(Cy) *Crystallophlomis*
(Da) *Davidii*
(De) *Denticulatae*
(Dr) *Dryadifoliae*
(F) *Fedtschenkoanae*
(G) *Glabrae*
(Ma) *Malvaceae*
(Mi) *Minutissimae*
(Mo) *Monocarpicae*
(Mu) *Muscarioides*
(Ob) *Obconicolisteri*
(Or) *Oreophlomis*
(Pa) *Parryi*
(Pe) *Petiolares*
(Pf) *Proliferae*
(Pi) *Pinnatae*
(Pr) *Primula*
  (Poly) Polyanthus (can be assigned to *P.* × *polyantha*)
  (Prim) Primrose
(Pu) *Pulchellae*
(Py) *Pycnoloba*
(R) *Reinii*
(Si) *Sikkimenses*
(So) *Soldanelloides*
(Sp) *Sphondylia*
(Sr) *Sredinskya*
(Su) *Suffrutescentes*
(Y) *Yunnanenses*

Prunus *see* Fruit

Pyrus *see* Fruit

Rhododendron

(A) Azalea (deciduous, species or unclassified hybrid)
(Ad) Azaleodendron
(EA) Evergreen azalea
(G) Ghent azalea (deciduous)
(K) Knap Hill or Exbury azalea (deciduous)
(M) Mollis azalea (deciduous)
(O) Occidentalis azalea (deciduous)
(R) Rustica azalea (deciduous)

(V) Vireya rhododendron
(Vs) Viscosa azalea (deciduous)

Ribes *see* Fruit

Rosa

(A) Alba
(Bb) Bourbon
(Bs) Boursault
(Ce) Centifolia
(Ch) China
(Cl) Climbing (in combination)
(D) Damask
(DPo) Damask Portland
(F) Floribunda or Cluster-flowered
(G) Gallica
(Ga) Garnette
(GC) Ground Cover
(HM) Hybrid Musk
(HP) Hybrid Perpetual
(HT) Hybrid Tea or Large-flowered
(Min) Miniature
(Mo) Moss (in combination)
(N) Noisette
(Patio) Patio, Miniature Floribunda or Dwarf Cluster-flowered
(Poly) Polyantha
(Ra) Rambler
(RH) Rubiginosa hybrid (Hybrid Sweet Briar)
(Ru) Rugosa
(S) Shrub
(SpH) Spinosissima Hybrid
(T) Tea

Rubus *see* Fruit

Saxifraga

(Classification by Section from Gornall, R.J. (1987). *Botanical Journal of the Linnean Society,* 95(4): 273-292)

(1) *Ciliatae*
(2) *Cymbalaria*
(3) *Merkianae*
(4) *Micranthes*
(5) *Irregulares*
(6) *Heterisia*
(7) *Porphyrion*
(8) *Ligulatae*
(9) *Xanthizoon*
(10) *Trachyphyllum*
(11) *Gymnopera*
(12) *Cotylea*
(13) *Odontophyllae*
(14) *Mesogyne*
(15) *Saxifraga*

Tulipa

(Classification by Cultivar Group from *Classified List and International Register of Tulip Names* by Koninklijke Algemeene Vereniging voor Bloembollencultuur 1996)

(1) Single Early Group
(2) Double Early Group
(3) Triumph Group
(4) Darwin Hybrid Group
(5) Single Late Group (including Darwin Group and Cottage Group)
(6) Lily-flowered Group
(7) Fringed Group
(8) Viridiflora Group
(9) Rembrandt Group
(10) Parrot Group
(11) Double Late Group
(12) Kaufmanniana Group
(13) Fosteriana Group
(14) Greigii Group
(15) Miscellaneous

Verbena

(G) Species and hybrids considered by some botanists to belong to the separate genus *Glandularia* are included in *Glandularia* in this edition for the first time.

Viola

(C) Cornuta Hybrid
(dVt) Double Violet
(ExVa) Exhibition Viola
(FP) Fancy Pansy
(P) Pansy
(PVt) Parma Violet
(SP) Show Pansy
(T) Tricolor
(Va) Viola
(Vt) Violet
(Vtta) Violetta

Vitis *see* Fruit

How to Use the Plant Directory

Nursery Codes

Look up the plant you require in the alphabetical Plant Directory. Against each plant you will find one or more four-letter codes, for example WCru, each code represents one nursery offering that plant. The first letter of each code indicates the main area of the country in which the nursery is situated. For this geographical key, refer to the **Nursery Codes and Symbols** on p.864.

Turn to the **Nursery Details by Code** starting on p.868 where, in alphabetical order of codes, you will find details of each nursery which offers the plant in question. For a fuller explanation of how to use the nursery listings please turn to p.865. **Always check that the nursery you select has the plant in stock before you set out.**

Plants with more than 30 Suppliers

In some cases, against the plant name you will see the term 'Widely available' instead of a nursery code. If we were to include every plant listed by all nurseries, the *RHS Plant Finder* would become unmanageably bulky. We therefore ask nurseries to restrict their entries to those plants that are not already well represented. As a result, if more than 30 nurseries offer any plant the Directory gives no nursery codes and the plant is listed instead as being 'Widely available'.

You should not have difficulty in locating these in local nurseries or garden centres. If, however, you are unable to find such plants, a list of all the current suppliers we have on file is available by post or online. See the Introduction (p.34).

Finding Fruit, Vegetables and Herbs

You will need to search for these by their botanical names. Common names are cross-referenced to their botanical names in the Plant Directory.

If you have Difficulty Finding your Plant

If you cannot immediately find the plant you seek, look through the various species of the genus. You may be using an incomplete name. The problem is most likely to arise in very large genera such as *Phlox* where there are a number of possible species, each with a large number of cultivars. A search through the whole genus may well bring success. For space reasons, we are not able to list in the Plant Directory annuals, orchids or cacti (except hardy terrestrial orchids and hardy cacti), or non-ornamental vegetables. For fruit and vegetables with an RHS Award of Garden Merit please see the relevant sections on p.842 and p.826.

Cross-references

It may be that the plant name you seek is a synonym. Our intention is to list nursery codes only against the correct botanical name. Where you find a synonym you will be cross-referred to the correct name.

Plants Last Listed in Earlier Editions

It may be that the plant you are seeking has no known suppliers and is thus not listed.

The loss of a plant name from the Directory may arise for a number of reasons – the supplier may have gone out of business, or may not have responded to our latest questionnaire and has therefore been removed from the book. Such plants may well be available but we have no knowledge of current suppliers. Alternatively, some plants may have been misnamed by nurseries in previous editions and are now appearing under their correct name.

For further information on plants last listed in earlier editions please see the Introduction (p.34).

Please, never use an out of date edition

Using the Plant Directory

The purpose of the Plant Directory is to help the reader correctly identify the plant they seek and find stockists. Each nursery has a unique code which appears to the right of the plant name. **Nursery Details by Code** (p.868) gives details about each nursery. The first letter in each code denotes its geographical region. Turn to the **Nursery Codes and Symbols** (p.864) to find the correct code for an area.

The Plant Directory provides information about plants through symbols and notes. For example: if a plant has an alternative name; is new to the book; or has received the RHS Award of Garden Merit.

Descriptive term — See p.38.

Symbols to the left of the name — Provides information about the name of the plant. See p.36 for the key.

Symbols to the right of the name — Tells you more about the plant itself, e.g. (v) indicates that the plant is variegated, (F) = fruit. See p.36 for the key.

Abbreviations — To save space a dash indicates that the previous heading is repeated. If written out in full the name would be Abelia × grandiflora 'Kaleidoscope'.

New — Plant new to this edition.

Trade Designation — See p.40.

♀H5 — *This plant has received the RHS Award of Garden Merit. See p.37.*

Cross-references — Directs you to the correct name of the plant and the nursery codes. See p.55.

Widely available — Indicates that more than 30 Plant Finder nurseries supply the plant, and it may be available locally. See p.55.

PBR — Plant Breeders' Rights. See p.39.

Nursery code — A unique code identifying each nursery. Turn to p.868 for details of the nurseries.

Abelia ✿ (*Caprifoliaceae*)

chinensis misapplied	see *A.* × *grandiflora* 'Lake Maggiore'
§ ***chinensis*** R. Br.	CBcs CExl CMCN CMac EBee EHyd ELan EPfP EWTr LRHS MAsh MGil MMuc SEND SPer SRms WGrn
§ ***dielsii***	CBot
'Edward Goucher' ♀H5	Widely available
engleriana	CExl CRos EHyd EPfP LRHS MAsh MBlu MGil NLar SLon
floribunda	see *Vesalea floribunda*
§ × ***grandiflora***	CChe CTho ELan ETMg EWTr LCro LOPS LRHS MJak SRms SWeb WAvo
- 'Aurea'	see *A.* × *grandiflora* 'Gold Spot'
- 'Brockhill Allgold'	EMil EPfP LRHS SPoG
- common clone	see *A.* × *grandiflora* 'Lake Maggiore'
- 'Compacta'	WFar
- CONFETTI ('Conti'PBR) (v)	CBcs CMac CRos CSBt ECrN EHyd ELan EMOT EMil EPfP GMcL LRHS LSRN MAsh MGos MRav NLar SCob SEle SGol SLim SPer SPoG SWvt WFar
§ - 'Francis Mason' (v)	Widely available
§ - 'Gold Spot' (v)	CBot EPfP NLar SPer
- 'Gold Strike'	see *A.* × *grandiflora* 'Gold Spot'
- GOLDEN PANACHE ('Minpan')	MRav
- 'Goldsport'	see *A.* × *grandiflora* 'Gold Spot'
- 'Hopleys'PBR (v) ♀H5	CBcs CMac CRos CSBt CTri EHyd ELan EMil EPfP EWTr LRHS MAsh MGos NLar SCob SEle SGol SLon SRms SWvt WGrn WHar
- 'Kaleidoscope'PBR (v)	CMac CRos CWGN ECrN EHoe ELan EPfP EShb ETMg LCro LRHS LSRN MAsh MGos MJak MPkF NLar NRHS SCob SGol SLim SPer SPoG SRms SWvt WCot WFar
- LADY LIBERTY ('Keylib')	LRHS
§ - 'Lake Maggiore' ♀H5	CBar CBot CMac CSBt CTri EHoe ELan EMOT EPfP MBlu MGil MGos MMuc MRav MSwo SCob SEND SPer SPoG SSta WHar
- LUCKY LOTS ('Wevo2') (v)	LLHF NLar SCob SGol
- 'Panache' (v)	LLHF WCot
- 'Prostrate White'	ECrN LRHS NLar SPoG
- 'Radiance' (v) **new**	NEoE
- 'Semperflorens'	LRHS
- 'Sherwoodii'	ECrN EHoe EPfP LRHS MAsh MGos SGol WRHF
- 'Sparkling Silver' (v)	LRHS
- SUNNY CHARMS ('Mindu01'PBR)	LCro
- 'Sunrise' (v)	NLar

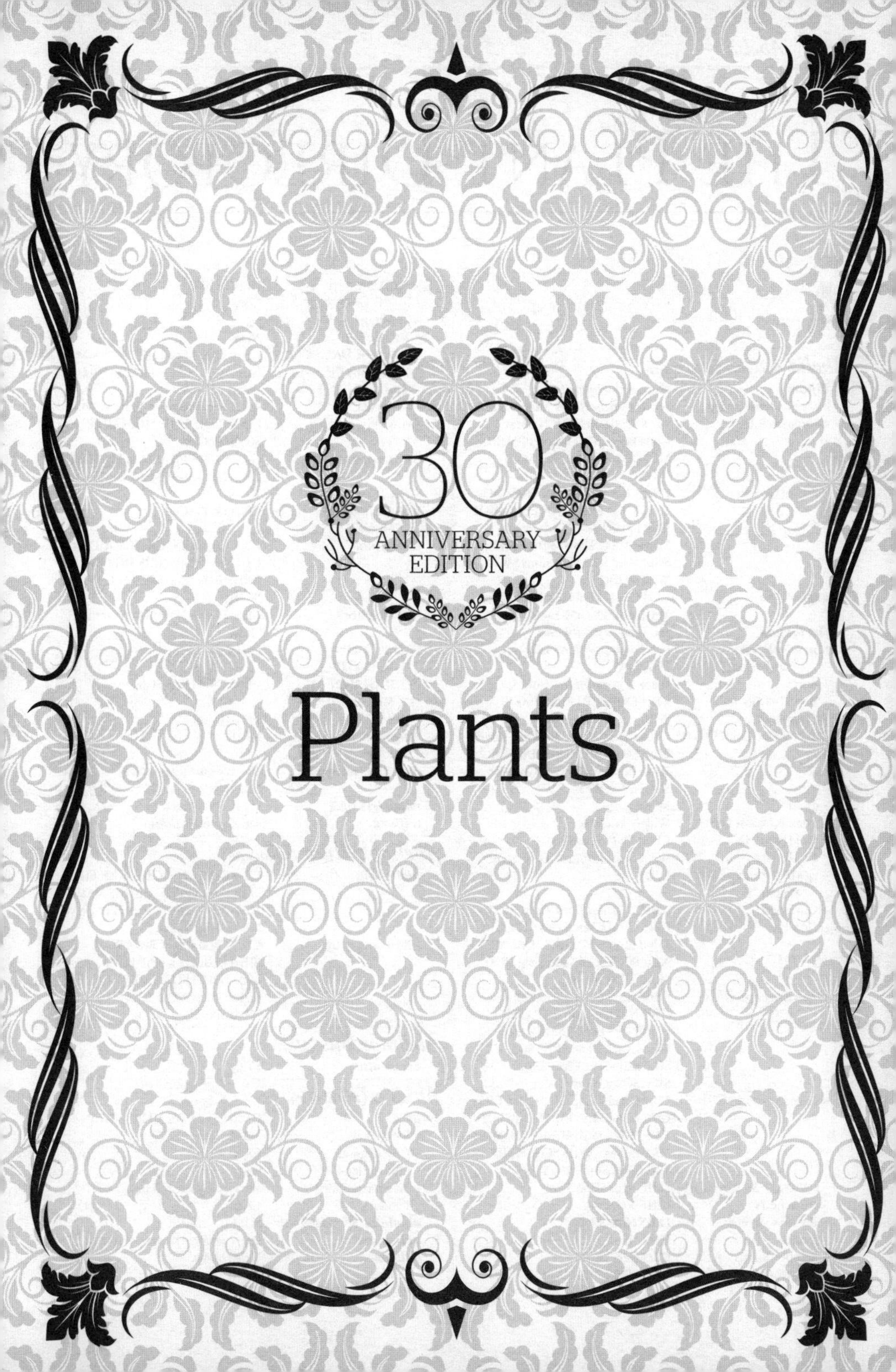

Plants

THE PLANT DIRECTORY

A

Abelia ✿ (*Caprifoliaceae*)

biflora	see *Zabelia biflora*
chinensis misapplied	see *A.* × *grandiflora* 'Lake Maggiore'
§ ***chinensis*** R. Br.	CBcs CExl CKel CMCN CMac CRos EBee EHyd ELan EPfP LRHS MGil MMuc SEND SPer SRms WGrn
'Edward Goucher' ♀H5	CBar CBcs CBod CDul CKel CMac CRos CTsd EBee ECrN ELan EMOT EPfP LRHS LSRN MAsh MGos MMuc MRav MSwo SCob SEND SGbt SGol SPer SPlb SRms SWvt WFar WSHC
engleriana	CExl CRos EHyd ELan EPfP LRHS MAsh MBlu MGil NLar SLon
floribunda	see *Vesalea floribunda*
§ × ***grandiflora*** (common clone)	see *A.* × *grandiflora* 'Lake Maggiore'
- 'Aurea'	see *A.* × *grandiflora* 'Gold Spot'
- 'Brockhill Allgold'	CKel EMil EPfP LRHS SPoG
- 'Compacta'	WFar
- CONFETTI ('Conti'PBR) (v)	CBcs CKel CMac CRos CSBt EHyd ELan EMOT EPfP LRHS LSRN MGos MRav NLar SCob SEle SGol SPer SPoG SWvt WFar
- dwarf	MSwo
§ - 'Francis Mason' (v)	Widely available
§ - 'Gold Spot' (v)	CBod EPfP NLar SPer
- 'Gold Strike'	see *A.* × *grandiflora* 'Gold Spot'
- GOLDEN PANACHE ('Minpan')	MRav
- 'Goldsport'	see *A.* × *grandiflora* 'Gold Spot'
- 'Hopleys'PBR (v) ♀H5	CBcs CDul CMac CRos CSBt CTri EHyd ELan EPfP LRHS MAsh MGos NLar SCob SGol SLon SNig SPoG SRms SWvt WGrn
- 'Kaleidoscope'PBR (v)	CBod CKel CMac CRos CSBt CWGN EHoe ELan EPfP EShb LCro LOPS LRHS LSRN MAsh MGos MJak NLar NRHS SCob SGol SLim SPer SPoG SRms SWvt WCot WFar
§ - 'Lake Maggiore' ♀H5	CBar CBod CChe CKel CMac CRos CSBt CTho ELan EMOT LCro LOPS LRHS MBlu MGil MGos MJak MMuc MRav MSwo NRHS SCob SEND SPer SPoG SRms SSta WAvo
- LUCKY LOTS ('Wevo2') (v)	LLHF NLar SCob SGol
- 'Panache' (v)	LLHF WCot
- 'Prostrate White'	LRHS NLar SPoG
- 'Radiance' (v)	EBee NEoE
- 'Semperflorens'	CKel CPla LRHS
- 'Sherwoodii'	CKel EPfP LRHS MAsh MGil MGos SGol WRHF
- 'Sparkling Silver' (v)	CKel LRHS
- SUNNY CHARMS ('Mindu01'PBR)	CBcs
- 'Sunrise' (v)	NLar
- SUNSHINE DAYDREAM ('Abelops'PBR) (v)	CEnd EBee LCro LLHF LOPS MMrt NLar SCob SGbt SGol SPad SRms
- 'Tanya'	WAvo
- 'Variegata'	see *A.* × *grandiflora* 'Francis Mason'
§ 'Lynn'PBR	EMOT LLHF LRHS MGos MPkF SCob SPoG
mosanensis	CMCN CRos EHyd ELan EPfP LLHF LRHS MBlu MGil NLar SLon WCot WGob
- BRIDAL BOUQUET ('Monia')	CRos LRHS SChF
parvifolia	CBcs CBod CExl CKel CMac CSBt CTri EHyd ELan LRHS MGil NLar NRHS SGbt SLon SPer SPoG SWvt WGrn
- 'Bumblebee'	CRos LCro LOPS MAsh NLar SPoG SRms
PASTEL CHARM ('Minduo2')	LRHS
PETITE GARDEN ('Minedward'PBR)	CBod CKel LRHS SGol
PINKY BELLS	see *A.* 'Lynn'
'Raspberry Profusion'PBR **new**	MPkF
rupestris misapplied	see *A.* × *grandiflora* 'Lake Maggiore'
rupestris Lindl.	see *A. chinensis* R. Br.
triflora	see *Zabelia triflora*

Abeliophyllum (*Oleaceae*)

distichum	CBcs CDul CEnd CRos ECrN EHyd ELan ELon EPfP IDee LRHS MAsh MBlu MSwo NRHS SGol SPer SWvt WCFE WFar WSHC
- Roseum Group	CBcs CBod CExl CRos CWld EHyd ELan ELon EPfP EShb LCro LOPS LRHS MAsh MGil MMuc MRav NQui SGol SLon SMad SPer SPoG WCot

Abelmoschus (*Malvaceae*)

esculentus	SVic

Abies ✿ (*Pinaceae*)

alba	CAco CDul CPer MMuc NWea
- 'Bystricka'	MAsh NLar
- 'Green Spiral'	CAco NLar
- 'Münsterland'	CKen
- 'Nana' misapplied	see *Picea glauca* 'Nana'
- 'Pendula'	CKen
amabilis 'Spreading Star'	SLim
arizonica	see *A. lasiocarpa* var. *arizonica*
balsamea	MAsh MMuc
- 'Cook's Blue'	CKen
- 'Eugene Gold'	NLar

	Name	Suppliers
	- Hudsonia Group	CKen LRHS WIce
	- - 'Nana'	CKen ELan LRHS MGil MJak NEgg
	- 'Jamie'	CKen NEgg
	- 'Kiwi'	NLar
	- 'Le Feber'	CKen
	- 'Little Carleigh'	NLar
	- var. ***phanerolepis*** 'Bear Swamp'	CKen NHol
	- 'Piccolo'	CKen LRHS NLar SAko SLim
	- 'Renswoude'	CKen NLar
	- 'Sky Meadow'	NLar
	- 'Tyler Blue'	CKen
	- 'Verkade's Prostrate'	CKen
	- 'Wisconsin' **new**	NLar
	borisii-regis	CDul
*	- 'Pendula'	CKen
	- 'Spring Delight'	LRHS
	brachyphylla dwarf	see *A. homolepis* 'Prostrata'
	cephalonica	CMCN
	- 'Greg's Broom'	CKen NLar
§	- 'Meyer's Dwarf'	NEgg NLar SLim
	- 'Nana'	see *A. cephalonica* 'Meyer's Dwarf'
	chensiensis	CDul LRHS
	cilicica 'Spring Grove'	CKen
	concolor	CAco CBcs CDul CTho LMaj LPra LRHS MMuc NWea SEND
	- 'Archer's Dwarf'	CKen NEgg NLar SLim
§	- 'Argentea' Niemetz, 1903	SAko
	- 'Aurea'	NLar
	- 'Birthday Broom'	CKen
	- 'Blue Cloak'	CKen
	- 'Blue Sapphire'	CAco CKen
	- 'Bryce Canyon'	NLar
	- 'Candicans'	see *A. concolor* 'Argentea' Niemetz, 1903
§	- 'Compacta' 🏆H7	CKen LRHS MGos NEgg NHol SLim
	- 'Fagerhult'	CKen
	- 'Gable's Weeping'	CKen
	- 'Glauca'	see *A. concolor* 'Violacea'
	- 'Glauca Compacta'	see *A. concolor* 'Compacta'
	- 'Hillier Broom'	see *A. concolor* 'Hillier's Dwarf'
§	- 'Hillier's Dwarf'	CKen
	- 'Husky Pup'	CKen
	- 'La Veta'	CKen SAko
	- (Lowiana Group) 'Creamy'	CKen NLar
	- 'Masonic Broom'	CKen
	- 'Mike Stearn'	CKen
	- 'Mora'	CKen
	- 'Piggelmee'	CKen MAsh NLar
	- 'Pygmy'	CKen
	- 'Scooter'	CKen
	- 'Sherwood's Blue'	CAco NEgg
	- Violacea Group	CKen SLim
§	- - 'Violacea' 🏆H7	WMat
	- - 'Violacea Prostrate' 🏆H7	NHol SAko
	- 'Viona'	NLar
	- 'Wattezii'	CKen
	- 'Wintergold'	CAco CKen LRHS MBlu NEgg NHol NLar SLim
	- 'Wyoming South' **new**	NLar
	delavayi	CDul CMCN EPfP LEdu LRHS NWea SAko WPGP
	- var. ***delavayi***	CExl
	- - Fabri Group	see *A. fabri*
	- 'Major Neishe'	CKen
§	***fabri***	CDul CKen
	fargesii	CKen CMCN NWea
	firma	CDul
	forrestii	CKen
	fraseri	CAco CBcs CDul CPer CTho LRHS MMuc NWea WTSh
	- 'Blue Bonnet'	CKen
	- 'Franklin'	NLar
	- 'Kline's Nest'	SLim
	- 'Palmeri'	NLar
	- 'Piglet's' witches' broom	NLar
	- 'Raul's Dwarf'	CKen
	grandis	CBcs CDul CJun CMCN CPer ELan EPfP LPra MMuc NWea WTSh
	- 'Compacta'	CKen
	- 'Van Dedem's Dwarf'	CKen SLim
	homolepis	CDul CKen
§	- 'Prostrata'	CKen
	koreana 🏆H7	Widely available
	- 'Alpin Star'	CKen MAsh NEgg NLar
	- 'Aurea'	see *A. koreana* 'Flava'
	- 'Blaue Zwo'	CKen LRHS
	- 'Blauer Eskimo' 🏆H7	CKen MAsh NEgg NLar SLim
	- 'Blauer Pfiff'	CAco CKen
	- 'Blinsham Gold'	CKen
	- 'Blue Emperor'	CAco MBlu NEgg NLar
	- 'Blue Magic'	CAco CKen NLar
	- 'Brilliant'	CKen LRHS
	- 'Cis' 🏆H7	CKen LRHS MGil NHol NLar SLim
	- CRYSTAL GLOBE	see *A. koreana* 'Kristallkugel'
	- 'Discus'	NLar
	- 'Doni-tajuso'	CKen
	- 'Eisregen'	CKen SAko
	- 'Festival'	NEgg NHol
§	- 'Flava'	CAco
	- 'Frosty'	SLim
	- 'Gait'	CKen NLar
	- 'Golden Glow'	SLim
	- 'Goldener Traum'	CKen NLar
	- 'Green Carpet'	CKen LRHS NLar
	- 'Green 'n' Cream'	CAco
	- 'Horstmann'	CKen NEgg
	- 'Inge'	NLar
	- 'Inverleith'	CKen
	- 'Kleiner Prinz'	NLar
	- 'Kohout'	CAco CKen
	- 'Kohout's Ice Breaker'PBR 🏆H7	CAco CKen LRHS MAsh MGos NLar SAko SLim
§	- 'Kristallkugel'	CAco CKen MAsh NEgg NLar
	- 'Lippetal'	CKen
	- 'Luminetta'	CAco CKen LRHS NHol
	- 'Nadelkissen'	CKen NHol
	- 'Nisbet'	CAco NHol
	- 'Oberon'	CAco CKen MAsh NEgg NHol NLar
	- 'Piccolo'	CKen
	- 'Pinocchio'	CKen MGil NHol
	- 'Ry'	MGil
	- 'Schillerlocke'	NLar
	- 'Schneestern'	NLar
	- 'Schwedenkönig' **new**	NLar
	- 'Sherwood Compact'	CKen
	- 'Shorty'	CKen NEgg NLar
	- 'Silberkugel'	CAco CKen CMen NEgg NLar SLim
	- 'Silberlocke' 🏆H7	CAco CCVT CDul CKen LRHS MAsh MBlu MGos NEgg NLar NOra NWea SCoo SLim WMat
	- 'Silbermavers'	CKen
	- 'Silberperl'	CKen CMen LRHS NEgg NLar SLim
	- 'Silberschmelze'	NLar
	- 'Silver Show'	CAco CDul LRHS MGil NHol NLar SAko
	- 'Silver Star' **new**	NLar
	- 'Threave'	CKen NHol
	- 'Tundra'	CAco NEgg NLar

	Name	Suppliers
	- 'Wellenseind'	CKen
	lasiocarpa	CDul
	- 'Alpine Beauty'	CKen NLar
§	- var. ***arizonica***	CAco
	- - 'Compacta' Hornibr. ♀H7	CAco CCVT CKen LRHS MAsh MGos NEgg NHol SLim SPoG WMat
	- - 'Kenwith Blue'	CKen NEgg SLim
	- 'Beano Broom'	CKen NLar
	- 'Chikov'	CKen
	- 'Day Creek'	CKen NLar
	- 'Duflon'	CKen NLar
	- 'Elaine'	CKen
	- 'Green Globe'	CKen NLar SLim
	- 'Joe's Alpine'	CKen
	- 'Kyle's Alpine'	CKen
	- 'Logan Pass'	CAco CKen
	- 'Lopalpun'	CKen
	- 'Mulligan's Dwarf'	CKen
	- 'Prickly Pete'	CKen NLar
	- 'Rhumpa' **new**	SAko
	- 'Stevens Blue'	CKen MAsh
	- 'Toenisvorst'	CAco CKen
	- 'Utah'	CKen
	magnifica 'Mount Si'	CKen NLar
I	- 'Nana'	CKen
	- witches' broom	CKen
	marocana	see *A. pinsapo* var. *marocana*
	nebrodensis	CKen
	- 'Sicilian Gold'	NLar
	nephrolepis	CAco
	nobilis	see *A. procera*
	nordmanniana	CAco CCVT CDul CJun CMCN CMac CPer CTho ELan EPfP EWhm LBuc LMaj LPra MJak MMuc NLar NWea SEND SLim SPoG WMou WTSh
	- 'Arne's Dwarf'	CKen
	- 'Barabits' Compact'	LRHS NEgg NLar
	- 'Barabits' Spreader'	CKen
	- 'Dahlheim'	NEgg
	- 'Dobřichovice'	NLar
	- 'Emmanuel' **new**	NLar
	- subsp. ***equi-trojani***	CDul
	- - 'Archer'	CKen
	- - 'Franke'	NEgg NLar
	- 'Filip's Gold Heart'	NLar
	- 'Filip's Perfect Column'	NLar
	- 'Golden Spreader' ♀H7	CAco CKen LRHS MAsh MBlu MGos NEgg NLar SCoo SLim
	- 'Hasselt'	see *A. nordmanniana* 'Pévé Hasselt'
	- 'Jakobsen'	CKen
	- 'Kbng'	NLar
	- 'Midwinter Gold'	NLar
	- 'Münsterland'	NEgg
	- 'Peli'	NLar
	- 'Pendula'	LRHS MBlu MGil SMad
§	- 'Pévé Hasselt'	CKen
	- 'Saerling' **new**	NLar
	- 'Silberspitze'	CKen
	numidica	CKen
	- 'Glauca'	CKen
	pinsapo	CAco CDul WThu
	- 'Atlas'	CKen MAsh NLar
	- 'Aurea' ♀H6	CAco CCVT CKen ELan LRHS MPkF NHol NLar SLim
I	- 'Aurea Nana'	CKen
	- 'Fastigiata'	CAco MPkF SAko SGol
	- 'Fatima' **new**	CAco CKen
	- 'Glauca' ♀H6	CAco CCVT CKen CTho ELan LRHS MBlu NLar SEND SLim
	- 'Hamondii'	CKen
I	- 'Horstmann'	CAco CKen NEgg NHol NLar SLim
§	- var. ***marocana***	CDul
	- 'Marokko'	CKen NLar
	- 'Pendula'	CAco CKen LRHS
	- 'Quicksilver'	CKen
	- 'San Pedro'	CKen
	- 'Ubrique'	NLar
§	***procera***	CBcs CDul CMCN CPer EPfP LPra NWea WTSh
	- 'Aurea'	LRHS
	- 'Bizarro'	NEgg NLar
	- 'Blaue Hexe'	CKen LRHS NEgg SLim
	- 'Delbar Cascade'	CKen
	- Glauca Group	CAco CDul EPfP GKin LPra LRHS MBlu NHol SLim
	- - 'Glauca' ♀H7	CTho LMaj SAko
	- - 'Glauca Prostrata' ♀H7	LRHS MAsh SLim
	- 'Hupp's Dwarf'	CKen NLar
	- 'Jeddeloh' **new**	CKen
	- 'La Graciosa'	NLar
	- 'Pospíšil'	CAco CKen
	- 'Prostrata'	NLar
	- 'Rat Tail'	NLar
	- 'Seattle Mount'	CKen
	- 'Sherwoodii'	CKen NLar SLim
	Rosemoor hybrid	CKen
	sachalinensis	CKen
	sibirica	EPfP NWea
	spectabilis	EPfP
	veitchii	CDul LPra WTSh
	- 'Heddergott'	CKen LRHS NEgg NHol NLar SLim
	- 'Heine'	CKen
	- 'Kramer'	CKen
	- 'Otovenack'	NLar
I	- 'Pendula'	CKen
	- 'Rumburk'	CKen MAsh NLar SLim
	- 'Secrest'	NLar
	- 'Syców'	CKen
	vejarii	LRHS

Abromeitiella see *Deuterocohnia*

Abutilon ✿ (*Malvaceae*)

	Name	Suppliers
	'Ashford Red'	CBcs CCCN ELan GQue LRHS WKif
	'Canary Bird' ♀H2	CBcs CCCN CHll CSde ELan WKif
	'Cannington Carol' (v) ♀H2	CCCN ELan LLHF LSRN SEND
	'Cannington Peter' (v) ♀H2	CCCN LSRN
	'Cloth of Gold'	CMac
	'Cynthia Pike' (v)	CRos EHyd LRHS NRHS
	'Flamenco'	CCCN CWGN
	'Hinton Seedling'	CCCN CRHN
	indicum	EBtc
	'John Thompson'	CBcs CCCN CKel CWGN LSRN WCot
	'Kentish Belle' ♀H3	Widely available
	'Marion' ♀H1b	CCCN CRHN CRos EHyd LRHS LSRN NRHS SPlb
	'Master Michael'	CMac
	megapotamicum ♀H3	CAby CBcs CCCN CChe CHll CKel CMac CRHN CTri ELan ELon EMOT EPfP EUJe LRHS MGos MRav MSCN NAln SCob SEND SEle SGol SLim SPer SPoG SRms WSHC XLum
	- 'Big Bell'	ECre WGob
	- 'Big Bud'	WBor
	- 'Ines'	ELon WPGP
	- 'Pink Charm'	ELon

- 'Variegatum' (v) 🏆H3	CBcs CCCN CKel CMac CRos ELon EPfP EUJe LRHS MGil SEle SLim SLon SNig SPer SPoG SWvt WGob
- 'Wisley Red'	CKel CRHN CTsd ELon LRHS WGob
× ***milleri*** hort. 🏆H3	CCCN CMac CRHN ELon WCot WGob
- 'Variegatum' (v)	CCCN CKel CMac CRos EBee LRHS WCot
'Nabob' 🏆H2	CBcs CCCN CExl CKel CRHN CSde EBee ELan EMOT EPfP EShb EUJe SAko SEND WBor WCot WFar
'Orange Hot Lava'	CBcs CExl EBee SChF WPGP
'Patrick Synge'	CBcs CCCN CHll EBee SChF SPhx WPGP
pictum 'Thompsonii' (v) 🏆H2	CCCN MGil
'Pink Lady'	CCCN
'Red Tiger'	WKif
'Russels Dwarf'	CCCN
'Savitzii' (v) 🏆H2	MSCN
'Silver Belle'	CCCN
'Simcox White'	CCCN
'Souvenir de Bonn' (v) 🏆H2	CCCN CHll EShb WCot
× ***suntense***	CBcs CCCN CHll CPla CRos CSBt EHyd EPfP EUJe GKev LRHS MSCN NPer NRHS WArt
- 'Jermyns' 🏆H4	CExl ELon EPfP LSRN MGos SPoG SWvt
- 'Violetta'	WSpi
'Tango'	CCCN CKel CRos CWGN EUJe LRHS SMad WCot WGob
'Victory'	CCCN CWGN
vitifolium	CBcs CCCN CDTJ CHll EBee MHer SPad SPoG SPtp WArt WFar WKif WSpi
- 'Album'	CBcs CCCN CExl SPer WSpi
- 'Buckland'	CCCN
- 'Chalk Blues' **new**	SPer
- 'Tennant's White' 🏆H4	CCCN CExl CRos EHyd EPfP LRHS NRHS SAko WCot
- 'Veronica Tennant' 🏆H4	CExl EBee EPfP LRHS SChF
'Waltz'	CCCN CRos CWGN EMOT EShb EUJe LLHF LRHS WBor WCot WGob

Acacia (*Mimosaceae*)

acinacea	SPlb
adunca	SPlb
angustissima	SPlb
armata	see *A. paradoxa*
axillaris	SPlb
baileyana 🏆H3	CBcs CCCN CMac CSBt ELan EPfP LRHS LSRN MGos SCoo SPlb SWvt WFar
- var. ***aurea***	SPlb
- 'Purpurea' 🏆H3	CAby CBcs CBod CCCN CEnd CExl CKel CMac CSBt CSpe CTri CTsd EBee ELan EPfP LSRN MGos NOra SChF SCoo SGol SPer SPlb SPoG SWvt WFar WPGP
- 'Songlines'	CRos LRHS MGos NRHS
boormanii	CAbb GBin IDee SPlb WPGP
cultriformis	CTsd ESwi
dealbata 🏆H3	Widely available
- 'Gaulois Astier'	CKel CSBt EPfP LRHS LSRN MGos NRHS SGol SPoG SWvt WCot
- subsp. ***subalpina***	SChF WPGP
'Exeter Hybrid'	CSBt
glaucoptera	SPlb
gregorii	SPlb
jibberdingensis	SPlb
julibrissin	see *Albizia julibrissin*
karroo	see *Vachellia karroo*
longifolia	CDTJ
macradenia	SPlb
mearnsii	CPla
melanoxylon	CBcs CDTJ CMCN SPlb
nanodealbata	SPad
§ ***paradoxa***	MGil
pataczekii	WPGP
pendula	SPlb
podalyriifolia	SPlb
pravissima 🏆H3	CAbb CBcs CBod CChe CDul CExl CHll CMac CRos CTri CTsd ELan EPfP GBin IDee ILea LRHS LSRN SArc SPlb SWvt
retinodes	CBcs CCCN CDTJ CTsd MMuc SEND SPad SWvt
- blue-leaved	CTsd
- 'Lisette'	MGos
riceana	CTsd SVen
rubida	CTsd SPlb
sentis	see *A. victoriae*
spectabilis	SPlb
suaveolens	IDee SPlb
truncata	SPlb
verticillata	CBcs CDTJ CHll EPfP
- riverine form	CCCN CExl EPfP LRHS SEND
§ ***victoriae***	SPlb

Acaena (*Rosaceae*)

adscendens misapplied	see *A. affinis*, *A. saccaticupula* 'Blue Haze'
adscendens ambig. 'Glauca'	NBir
§ ***affinis***	EBee ECha
anserinifolia misapplied	see *A. novae-zelandiae*
§ ***anserinifolia*** (Forst. & Forst. f.) Druce	MMuc
argentea	EBee
buchananii	EBee EHoe EPPr GAbr GBin GKev MBrN MMuc NLar SCob SRms
caerulea hort.	see *A. caesiiglauca*
§ ***caesiiglauca***	CTri EPPr GAbr GMaP GQue
inermis	NWad SPlb
- 'Purpurea'	CSam EBee ECha ECtt EHoe ELan EShb EUJe GAbr GMaP GQue MMuc NDov NHol NHpl NLar NWad SPlb WMoo XLum
magellanica	GAbr GCal GKev
microphylla 🏆H5	CBod CSam GQue MBel MBrN NLar SPlb SRms WMoo
- COPPER CARPET	see *A. microphylla* 'Kupferteppich'
- 'Glauca'	see *A. caesiiglauca*
- 'Grüner Zwerg'	NLar
§ - 'Kupferteppich'	CSam EBou ECtt EHoe ELan EPPr GAbr GBin GCal GCrg GKev GLog GMaP LEdu MHol MRav NBro NLar SCob SMHy SRms WMoo XLum
minor var. ***antarctica***	GBin
myriophylla	EBee
§ ***novae-zelandiae***	CTri EBee GAbr GKev WMoo XLum
ovalifolia	GKev GQue
'Pewter'	see *A. saccaticupula* 'Blue Haze'
poeppigiana	EBee
profundeincisa	see *A. anserinifolia* (Forst. & Forst. f.) Druce
'Purple Carpet'	see *A. microphylla* 'Kupferteppich'
'Purple Haze'	CSpe SCob
saccaticupula	EBee GKev MMuc NAln

§ - 'Blue Haze'	CRos EBee ECha EDAr EHyd LRHS MBrN MRav NRHS SPlb SRms WMoo
sanguisorbae	see *A. anserinifolia* (Forst. & Forst. f.) Druce
tesca	GBin GQue
viridior	see *A. anserinifolia* (Forst. & Forst. f.) Druce

Acalypha (*Euphorbiaceae*)

§ ***herzogiana***	CCCN EShb
pendula misapplied	see *A. herzogiana*

Acanthocalyx see *Morina*

Acantholimon (*Plumbaginaceae*)

androsaceum	see *A. ulicinum*
armenum	XSen
§ ***ulicinum***	XEll

Acanthopanax see *Eleutherococcus*

ricinifolius	see *Kalopanax septemlobus*

Acanthus ✿ (*Acanthaceae*)

sp.	NBir
arboreus	XLum
balcanicus misapplied	see *A. hungaricus*
'Candelabra'	WHil
caroli-alexandri	see *A. spinosus* L.
dioscoridis	GCal IMou WHil
- var. ***perringii***	CDor EBee ECha MNrw NLar WCot WFar WHil XLum
- smooth-leaved	WHil
eminens	WCot
hirsutus	CDor CFis WCot WHil
- JCA 106.700 **new**	WHil
- subsp. ***syriacus***	ECha EHrv GCal SIgm WHil
'Hollande du Nort'	CRos EBee LRHS NAln NRHS XLum
§ ***hungaricus***	CBod CDor CMac CRos EBee ELan EMor ILea LCro LOPS LRHS MBel MMuc MRav NLar NRHS SCob SPer WCot WFar WHil XLum
- AL&JS 90097YU	WHil
- MESE 561	WHil
- 'White Lips'	EBee MAvo MNrw NCou NLar WCot WRHF
longifolius Host	see *A. hungaricus*
mollis	Widely available
- from Turkey	WHil
- 'Fielding Gold'	see *A. mollis* 'Hollard's Gold'
- free-flowering	ESwi GCal MAvo SChr WHil XLum
§ - 'Hollard's Gold'	CBct CDor CExl CMac EBee ECha ECtt EHoe ELan EMor EPPr EPfP EWhm GKin GMaP LRHS MNrw NEgg NGdn NLar NRHS SPoG SRms WAvo WCAu WCot WFar WHil WSHC
- 'Jefalba'	see *A. mollis* (Latifolius Group) 'Rue Ledan'
- Latifolius Group	CDor MRav SRms WHil WHoo
§ - - 'Rue Ledan' ♀H6	CRos EBee ECtt EPPr EWTr GBin LRHS MAvo MBel MNrw NDai NGdn NLar NSti SCob SMHy SPhx WCAu WCot WHil XLum
- - 'Sjaak'	MAvo WHil
- 'Long Spike'	GCal WHil
- 'Tasmanian Angel' (v)	CAbb CBct CDor CWGN ECtt ELan EMor ESwi LCro LOPS MBNS MJak NHpl NPri SCob SMad SPoG WCot WFar XLum
'Morning's Candle'	CBod EBee ECtt EMor MNrw NGdn NLar WFar WHil XLum
sennii	CAby IMou SMad SPhx WCot WHil WSHC XLum
spinosus misapplied	see *A. spinosus* Spinosissimus Group
§ ***spinosus*** L.	Widely available
- Ferguson's form	EBee MAvo WCot XLum
- 'Lady Moore' (v)	CDor NLar WHil XLum
- 'Royal Haughty'	MAvo WHil XLum
§ - Spinosissimus Group	CBct CDor CTsd ECha ELan EMor GBin GCal LEdu LPot MAvo MGos MRav NChi SMad WCot WFar WHil
'Summer Beauty'	EBee ECtt EWes LRHS MAvo MRav WCot WFar WHil XLum
'Whitewater' (v)	CBct CDor CPla CWGN EBee ECtt ELan GEdr GKin NLar NPri NSti NWad SCob SHeu SMad SPad SPer SPoG SRms WCot WHil

Acca (*Myrtaceae*)

sellowiana (F)	CAby CAgr CBcs CCCN CCht CDTJ CDul CExl CKel CMac CRos CTsd ECrN ELan EPfP EShb LMaj LPra LRHS MGos SCob SEle SLim SPer SPlb SVic SWvt WFar
- 'Apollo' (F)	EUJe
- 'Mammoth' (F)	CBcs CCCN
- 'Triumph' (F)	CBcs CCCN SGol
- 'Unique' (F)	EUJe
- 'Variegata' (F/v)	CCCN

Acer ✿ (*Sapindaceae*)

acuminatum	CMCN
albopurpurascens NMWJ 14455 **new**	WCru
amoenum B&SWJ 10916	WCru
- B&SWJ 10977	WCru
- 'Firecracker'	see *A. palmatum* 'Firecracker'
'Ample Surprise'	MBlu SMad
'Asian Queen'	CJun
buergerianum	CDul CLnd CMen CTho ECrN MMuc MPkF NLar SBrt SGol WPGP
- B&SWJ 12676 from South Korea	WCru
- var. ***formosanum*** CWJ 12477	WCru
- 'Integrifolium'	see *A. buergerianum* 'Subintegrum'
- 'Naruto'	CMCN MPkF
§ - 'Subintegrum'	CMCN
campbellii	MBlu
- subsp. ***campbellii*** GWJ 9360	WCru
- - PAB 13.071	LEdu
- - 'Exuberance'	CJun
campestre ♀H6	Widely available
- 'Anny's Globe'	MBlu
- 'Carnival' (v) ♀H6	CCVT CEnd ECrN ELan ELon EMOT MAsh MBlu SCob SGol SPer SPoG SWvt
- 'Elsrijk'	CCVT CLnd EMOT LMaj SCoo SGol
- 'Evelyn'	see *A. campestre* 'Queen Elizabeth'
- 'Evenley Red'	CDul MBlu WPGP
- 'Green Column'	EMOT LRHS
- 'Louisa Red Shine'	CLnd
- 'Nanum'	MBlu
- 'Pendulum'	CEnd
- 'Postelense'	MBlu
- 'Pulverulentum' (v)	NEgg

Plant	Suppliers
§ - 'Queen Elizabeth'	CDul MGos SGol
- 'Red Shine'	EBar EMOT MMuc SGol
- 'Royal Ruby'	MGos
- 'Ruby Glow' ♀H6	CEnd
I - 'Silver Celebration' (v)	CJun
- 'William Caldwell'	CEnd CTho MBlu
capillipes	CBcs CDul CMCN CTho ELan EMOT EWTr GQue LMaj MJak MMuc NWea SCob SPlb WMat WTSh
- 'Antoine'	CJun LRHS MBlu NLar
- 'Candy Stripe'	see *A.* × *conspicuum* 'Candy Stripe'
- 'Honey Dew'	CJun SSta
aff. ***capillipes***	NWea
cappadocicum	CCVT CDul CEnd CMCN ECrN LMaj
- 'Aureum' ♀H6	CBcs CDul CEnd CLnd CMCN CNWT CTho EBee ECrN ELan EMOT EPfP GKin IArd MAsh MBlu MRav NLar NOra SCob SGol SPer SWvt WFar WMat WTSh
§ - subsp. ***lobelii***	LMaj
- var. ***mono***	see *A. pictum*
- 'Rubrum' ♀H6	CArg CBcs CDul CLnd CMCN CNWT EBee ECrN ELan EMOT EPfP GKin LMaj MBlu MMuc MRav NOra SCob SEND SGol SPer WFar WHer WMat
- var. ***tricaudatum***	CExl
carpinifolium	CDul CMCN EBee EPfP IArd LRHS MBlu MMuc NLar WPGP
- B&SWJ 10955	WCru
- B&SWJ 11124	WCru
§ ***caudatifolium*** CWJ 12403	WCru
- NMWJ 14459 new	WCru
- RWJ 9843	WCru
§ ***caudatum*** GWJ 9279	WCru
- GWJ 9317	WCru
- HWJK 2240	WCru
- HWJK 2338	WCru
- subsp. ***ukurunduense***	MPkF
- - B&SWJ 8658	WCru
- - B&SWJ 12602 new	WCru
circinatum	CBcs CCVT CDul CJun CMCN ECrN MBlu MMuc NEgg NLar NWea SEND SPlb
- B&SWJ 9565	WCru
- 'Burgundy Jewel'	CJun LCro LOPS LRHS MPkF
- 'Monroe'	CJun CMCN SGol
- 'Pacific Fire'	CJun NLar
- 'Whitney Broom' new	NLar
cissifolium	CMCN EPfP NLar
- B&SWJ 10801	WCru
§ × ***conspicuum*** 'Candy Stripe'	CJun
- 'Elephant's Ear'	CJun MBlu NLar
- 'Phoenix'	CEnd CJun CMCN EPfP GKin LRHS MBlu NLar SPoG SSta WPGP
- 'Silver Ghost'	SWvt
§ - 'Silver Vein'	CEnd CJun CMCN EPfP NLar SSta SWvt
crataegifolium	CMCN SSta
- B&SWJ 11036	WCru
- B&SWJ 11355	WCru
- 'Ittai-san-nishiki'	SSta
- 'Meuri-no-ōfu' (v)	SSta
- 'Veitchii' (v)	CDul CJun CMCN EBee EPfP LRHS MBlu MPkF SSta
creticum misapplied	see *A. sempervirens*
dasycarpum	see *A. saccharinum*
davidii	CBcs CDul CExl ECrN LCro LOPS MBlu MGos MMuc MRav SCob SGol SSta WCot
§ - 'Canton'	CJun SSta
- 'Cantonspark'	see *A. davidii* 'Canton'
- 'Cascade'	CJun MBlu SSta
- 'Ernest Wilson'	SSta
- 'George Forrest' ♀H5	CBcs CDul CExl CJun CMCN CMac CTho EBee ECrN ELan EPfP GBin MMuc NLar NOra NWea SCob SPoG SSta SWvt WMat
- 'Hagelunie'	SBir SSta
- 'Hansu-suru' (v)	SSta
- 'Karmen'	CBcs CJun EPfP SSta
- 'Purple Bark'	CExl CJun NLar SBir SSta
- 'Rosalie'	CBcs CJun EPfP LRHS MAsh MBlu NLar SBir SSta
- 'Sekka'	SSta
- 'Serpentine'	CBcs CDul CJun CMCN CNWT EPfP IDee MAsh MBlu NEgg NLar SSta
- 'Silver Vein'	see *A.* × *conspicuum* 'Silver Vein'
- VIPER ('Mindavi')	CDul EPfP LRHS MAsh NLar NOra NWea SPer SPoG WHCr WMat
diabolicum	CMCN
duplicatoserratum NMWJ 14599 new	WCru
elegantulum	CExl CJun GBin SPtp
erythranthum	WPGP
- B&SWJ 11733	WCru
- FMWJ 13157	WCru
fabri	CExl
- WWJ 11614	WCru
flabellatum	CJun EBee
- NJM 11.017	WPGP
- var. ***yunnanense***	CBcs CMCN MMuc SPtp
forrestii	CExl CMCN MMuc SPtp
- BWJ 7515	WCru
- 'Alice'	CEnd CJun SSta
- 'Inoense'	SSta
- 'Sirene'	CJun SSta
- 'Sparkling'	CJun
× ***freemanii***	CMCN
- 'Armstrong'	CCVT EMOT LPra MMuc SGol
- AUTUMN BLAZE ('Jeffersred') ♀H6	CBcs CCVT CDul CLnd CMCN CTho EMOT EPfP IArd LMaj LRHS MBlu MGos MMuc NOra SBir SCoo SGol SPer SPoG WMat WMou
- CELEBRATION ('Celzam')	CArg CCVT CDul CTho EBee MGos
- 'Indian Summer'	see *A.* × *freemanii* 'Morgan'
§ - 'Morgan'	CJun
ginnala	see *A. tataricum* subsp. *ginnala*
glabrum B&SWJ 14119 new	WCru
globosum	see *A. platanoides* 'Globosum'
grandidentatum	see *A. saccharum* subsp. *grandidentatum*
griseum ♀H5	Widely available
grosseri	CMCN CTri SGol
- var. ***hersii***	CBcs CDul CLnd CMac EBee EPfP LSRN MMuc MRav NOra NWea SCob SSta SWvt WMat
- 'Leiden'	EPfP LRHS
heldreichii	CMCN
henryi	CBcs CDul EPfP NLar
heptaphlebium B&SWJ 11695	WCru
- B&SWJ 11713	WCru
- FMWJ 13369	WCru
japonicum	CMCN LPra SEWo
- B&SWJ 12847	WCru

- CWJ 12840	WCru
§ - 'Aconitifolium' 🏆H6	Widely available
- 'Aki-hi'	NLar
- 'Ao-jutan'	CJun
- 'Attaryi'	CMen NEgg NLar
- 'Aureum'	see *A. shirasawanum* 'Aureum'
- 'Emmit's Pumpkins'	CJun
- 'Ezo-no-momiji'	see *A. shirasawanum* 'Ezo-no-momiji'
- 'Fairy Lights'	NLar
- 'Filicifolium'	see *A. japonicum* 'Aconitifolium'
- 'Green Cascade' 🏆H6	CAco CEnd CJun CMCN CMac CMen MGos MPkF NLar SGol
- 'King's Copse'	CJun
- 'Laciniatum'	see *A. japonicum* 'Aconitifolium'
- f. ***microphyllum***	see *A. shirasawanum* 'Microphyllum'
- 'Ogurayama'	see *A. shirasawanum* 'Ogurayama'
- 'Ō-taki'	CJun
- 'Vitifolium' 🏆H6	CDul CEnd CJun CMCN CMac CNWT CTho ELan EPfP GBin LRHS MBlu MGos MPkF NEgg NLar NRHS SGol SPer SPoG SSta WCFE WTSh
kawakamii	see *A. caudatifolium*
laevigatum B&SWJ 11684	WCru
- FMWJ 13378	WCru
- FMWJ 13439	WCru
- NJM 10.049	WPGP
§ - var. ***reticulatum*** B&SWJ 11698	WCru
laurinum FMWJ 13412	WCru
- KWJ 12232	WCru
laxiflorum	SSta
lobelii Ten.	see *A. cappadocicum* subsp. *lobelii*
macrophyllum	CMCN EPfP MBlu MMuc
- B&SWJ 13183 **new**	WCru
mandshuricum	LRHS
- B&SWJ 12592	WCru
§ ***maximowiczianum***	MMuc MPkF SGol SSta
maximowiczii	MPkF
micranthum 🏆H6	CDul CMCN EPfP LRHS MBlu NLar
- CWJ 12843 **new**	WCru
miyabei	MPkF
mono	see *A. pictum*
monspessulanum	CDul CMCN LEdu MMuc SEND XSen
- subsp. ***oksalianum***	WMat
morifolium B&SWJ 11473	WCru
morrisonense Hayata	see *A. caudatifolium*
negundo	CAco CDul CMCN ECrN EMOT LPra NWea SCob SWvt
- B&SWJ 14060	WCru
- 'Auratum'	CMCN SGol
- 'Aureomarginatum' (v)	CCVT ECrN SGol
- 'Aureovariegatum' (v)	LPra
§ - 'Elegans' (v)	CEnd CMCN EMOT SCoo
- 'Elegantissimum'	see *A. negundo* 'Elegans'
- 'Flamingo' (v)	CAco CBcs CCVT CDul CEnd CMCN CMac ECrN ELan EMOT EPfP LPra LRHS MAsh NLar NOra NWea SCob SGol SPer SPoG SWvt WMat
- 'Kelly's Gold'	CBcs CCVT CMCN EMOT NLar NWea SCob SGol SPoG WMat
- 'Sensation'	NLar
- 'Variegatum' (v)	ECrN LMaj LPra SGol
- var. ***violaceum*** 🏆H6	CEnd EBee SVen
- 'Winter Lightning' 🏆H6	NLar
nikoense misapplied	see *A. maximowiczianum*
nipponicum	CDul CMCN SPtp

'Norwegian Sunset'	CCVT EBee EMOT
oliverianum	CDul CExl MBlu
- subsp. ***formosanum*** CWJ 12437	WCru
- - NMWJ 14460 **new**	WCru
opalus	CMCN SEND
orientale misapplied	see *A. sempervirens*
ORIENTALIA ('Minorient')	MMrt WFar
orizabense	EBee
PACIFIC SUNSET ('Warrenred')	NLar
palmatum	CAby CBcs CCVT CDul CKel CMCN CMen CSBt CTri EMOT EPfP GKin LCro LMaj LPra MBlu MGos NWea SArc SCob SEWo SGol SPlb SWvt WFar WTSh
- (D)	Widely available
- 'Akane' (P)	CMen MPkF
§ - 'Aka-shigitatsu-sawa' (M)	CBcs CJun CMCN CMac CMen ESMi MGos MPkF NLar SGol SPer
- 'Akegarasu' (M)	CJun CMCN CMen NLar
- 'Alpenweiss' (P)	CJun
- 'Alpine Surprise'	SAko
- 'Amagi-shigure' (M)	CJun LRHS MPkF
- 'Amber Ghost' (M)	CJun NLar
- 'Anne Irene'PBR (P)	LRHS MPkF
- 'Aoba-jo' (Dw)	CJun CMen MPkF
- 'Ao-kanzashi' (P/v)	MPkF NLar
- 'Ao-shidare' (D)	CJun
- 'Aoshime-no-uchi'	see *A. palmatum* 'Shinobuga-oka'
- 'Aoyagi' (P)	CEnd CJun CMCN CMen CRos CTho EMac ESMi GKin LMil LRHS MGos MPkF NEgg NLar NRHS SCoo
- 'Aoyagi-gawa'	CJun
§ - 'Arakawa' (P)	CEnd CMCN CMen ESMi MPkF
- 'Arakawa-ukon'	CJun
- 'Aratama' (Dw)	CJun CMCN CMen EMac ESMi LRHS MJak
- 'Ariadne' (M/v) 🏆H6	CEnd CJun LRHS MGos MPkF NLar SCoo SPoG
- 'Ariake-nomura' (A)	CMen MPkF
- 'Asahi-zuru' (P/v)	CBcs CJun CMCN CMen LRHS MGos NLar NRHS SPer WMat
- 'Atrolineare' (L)	CMen MPkF NLar
- 'Atropurpureum' (A)	Widely available
- 'Atropurpureum Novum'	MPkF NLar SGol
- 'Attraction' (P)	CMac CMen
- 'Aureum' (P)	CAco CMCN CMen CRos CTri ELan EPfP LMil LRHS MAsh MBlu MGos MPkF NLar NRHS SPoG WCFE WFar
- 'Autumn Fire' (D)	CJun
- 'Autumn Glory' (M)	CAco CEnd CJun CMen
- 'Autumn Red' (M)	CMen ESMi
* - 'Autumn Showers'	CEnd CJun
- 'Azuma-murasaki' (M)	CJun CMen MPkF NLar
- 'Baby Lace' (Dw)	CWGN SAko
- 'Baldsmith' (D)	CJun EMac EUJe LRHS MPkF NEgg
- 'Barrie Bergman' (D)	CJun NLar
- 'Beni-chidori' (P)	CMen
- 'Beni-fushigi' (P)	MPkF
- 'Beni-gasa' (M)	CJun MPkF NLar
- 'Beni-hime' (Dw)	MPkF SAko
- 'Beni-hoshi' (Dw)	MPkF
- 'Beni-kagami' (M)	CEnd CJun CMCN MPkF NLar SGol
- 'Beni-kawa' (P)	CJun CMCN CMen MPkF SGol
- 'Beni-komachi' (P)	CAco CEnd CKel CMCN CMen CRos EPfP ESMi LRHS MGos MPkF NLar NRHS SCob SSta
- 'Beni-kosode' (v)	MPkF

	Name	Suppliers
	- 'Beni-maiko' (P) ♀H6	CEnd CJun CMCN CMen CRos EPfP ESMi LRHS MGos MJak MPkF NLar NRHS SCob SCoo SWvt WCFE
	- 'Beni-musume'	MPkF
	- 'Beni-otake' (L)	CBcs CJun CMen ELan EPfP ESMi LRHS MGos MPkF NEgg NLar SAko SCob
	- 'Beni-otome'	MPkF
	- 'Beni-schichi-henge' (P/v)	CBcs CEnd CJun CMCN CMen CRos CWGN ESMi LRHS MAsh MGos MPkF NHol NLar NOra NRHS SAko SCob SCoo SGol SSta WMat
	- 'Beni-shidare' (D)	NLar SCob
	- 'Beni-shidare Tricolor'	see *A. palmatum* 'Toyama-nishiki'
	- 'Beni-shidare Variegated'	see *A. palmatum* 'Toyama-nishiki'
	- 'Beni-shi-en' (P)	CJun MPkF NLar
	- 'Beni-shigitatsu-sawa'	see *A. palmatum* 'Aka-shigitatsu-sawa'
	- 'Beni-tsukasa' (P/v) ♀H6	CEnd CJun CMCN CMen ESMi LMaj LMil NEgg NLar SSta
	- 'Beni-tsuru'	MPkF
	- 'Beni-yubi-gohon' (P)	CJun MPkF
	- 'Berrima Bridge' (D)	CJun
	- 'Berry Broom'	MPkF NLar
	- 'Berry Dwarf' (Dw)	CJun MPkF
	- 'Bewley's Red' (D)	CJun
	- 'Bi Hō' (P)	CJun CRos LCro LOPS LRHS MAsh MGos NLar NRHS SAko SGol
	- 'Black Lace' (M)	LRHS MAsh MGos MPkF NLar NRHS
	- 'Bloodgood' (A) ♀H6	Widely available
	- 'Bonfire' misapplied	see *A. palmatum* 'Seigai'
	- 'Bonfire' ambig.	CJun LRHS
	- 'Bonnie Bergman'	CJun
	- 'Boskoop Glory' (A)	GKin
	- 'Brandt's Dwarf' (Dw)	NLar
	- 'Brocade' (D)	CJun MPkF NLar
	- 'Bronzewing' (D)	CJun
	- 'Burgundy Lace' (M) ♀H6	CAco CBcs CEnd CJun CMCN CMen CRos ELan EMac EPfP ESMi EUJe GKin LMil LRHS LSRN MAsh MGos MJak MPkF NEgg NRHS SCoo SGol SPer SPoG SSta
	- 'Butterfly' (P/v)	CAco CEnd CJun CKel CMCN CMac CMen CWGN ELan ELon EMOT ESMi LCro LOPS LSRN MAsh MBlu MGos NEgg NLar SCob SCoo SGol SPer SWvt WFar
	- 'Calico' (P)	CJun NLar
	- 'Candy Kitchen'	see *A. palmatum* 'Kandy Kitchen'
	- 'Caperci Dwarf' (Dw)	MPkF
	- 'Carminium'	see *A. palmatum* 'Corallinum'
	- 'Caroline' (v) **new**	NLar
	- 'Chantilly Lace' (D)	CJun
	- 'Chikuma-no' (A)	CMen MPkF
	- 'Chirimen-nishiki' (P/v)	MPkF
	- 'Chishio' (P)	CMCN CMen ESMi LMil LRHS MPkF NLar
	- 'Chishio Improved' (P)	CEnd CJun CMCN CMac CMen CTho EPfP LRHS MGos MPkF NHol NLar NRHS SWvt
	- 'Chitose-yama' (M) ♀H6	CEnd CJun CMCN CMen EPfP GKin LMaj LRHS MAsh MGos MPkF NLar NRHS SGol SLim SSta
§	- 'Chiyo-hime'	EPfP LCro LOPS NEgg NPri WFar
	- 'Collingwood Ingram'	SGol
	- 'Coonara Pygmy' (Dw)	CJun CMCN CMac CMen EMac ESMi GKin LRHS MPkF SCoo
	- 'Coral Pink' (Dw)	CJun CMen MPkF SGol SSta
§	- 'Corallinum' (P) ♀H6	CAco CEnd CJun CMCN CMen NEgg NLar SPoG
	- var. ***coreanum*** B&SWJ 8606	WCru
	- 'Crimson Carol' (M)	CJun NLar
	- 'Crimson Prince'	CJun MPkF NLar SCoo
	- 'Crimson Princess' (D)	CBcs CRos EPfP LMaj LRHS MJak MPkF NRHS WMat
	- 'Crimson Queen' (D) ♀H6	CAco CBcs CCVT CDul CEnd CJun CMCN CMac CMen CRos CSBt ELan EMOT EMac EPfP GKin IArd LRHS MAsh MGos NEgg NLar NRHS SGol SPer SSta WCFE WFar WMat
	- 'Crippsii' (D)	CBcs CMac CMen MPkF SCoo SGol
	- 'Deshōjō' (P)	CMCN CMen ESMi LMaj MBlu MGos NLar SCoo SGol WMat
	- 'Diana' (Dw)	CJun CMen SGol
	- 'Dissectum' (D)	CAco CKel CTho CTri EMOT EWTr LBuc LOPS LPra NOra NWea WCFE WFar WTSh
	- 'Dissectum Atropurpureum' (D)	LMil LPra NWea
	- 'Dissectum Flavescens' (D)	CAco CBcs CEnd CJun CMac CMen EMac EUJe MBlu MGos MPkF WMat
§	- 'Dissectum Nigrum' (D)	CAco CJun CMac CMen ESMi MAsh MPkF NEgg
	- 'Dissectum Palmatifidum' (D)	CAco CMen EMac MPkF SCoo SGol SPer
	- 'Dissectum Rubrifolium' (D)	MPkF
§	- 'Dissectum Variegatum' (Dw/v)	CJun MPkF
	- Dissectum Viride Group	CBcs CJun CMCN CMac CMen CRos CSBt ELan EMac EPfP ESMi LCro LMil LPra LRHS MAsh MBlu MGos MJak MSwo NEgg NOra NRHS NWea SLim SPer SSta SWvt WCFE WMat
	- 'Donzuru-bo'	CJun
	- 'Dr Seuss' (L) **new**	NLar
	- 'Dragon's Fire'	CJun
	- 'Dwarf Shishi' (Dw) **new**	NLar
	- 'Earthfire'	MPkF
I	- 'Ebbingei'	CMac
	- 'Eddisbury' (P) ♀H6	CEnd CJun CMen CSBt MBlu NLar SSta
	- 'Edna Bergman' (M)	CJun
	- 'Effegi'	see *A. palmatum* 'Fireglow'
	- 'Eimini' (Dw)	NLar
§	- 'Elegans' (M) ♀H6	CMen CRos EPfP LRHS MPkF NRHS
	- 'Elizabeth' (Dw)	CJun
	- 'Ellen' (D)	CJun MPkF NLar
	- 'Emerald Lace' (D) ♀H6	CJun CRos EBee EMac EUJe GKin LBuc LCro LOPS LRHS MGos MPkF NEgg NLar NRHS SPoG SSta WCFE WFar
§	- 'Emperor 1' (A)	CJun ELan EMac EUJe LMaj MPkF SCob SPer WMat
	- 'Englishtown' (Dw)	NLar
	- 'Enkan' (L)	CEnd CJun CMen CWGN ESMi LRHS MGos MPkF NLar NOra NPri SGol SPoG WMat
	- 'Eono-momiji'	CMen
	- 'Ever Red'	see *A. palmatum* 'Dissectum Nigrum'
	- 'Fairy Hair' (L)	CJun
	- 'Fall's Fire' (P)	CJun
	- 'Fascination' (M)	CJun
	- 'Felice' (D)	CJun MPkF

	Name	Suppliers
	– 'Filigree' (Dw/v)	CAco CJun CMCN CMen EPfP LMil MAsh MGos MPkF NEgg NLar SSta WCFE
	– 'Fior d'Arancio' (M)	CJun MPkF
	– 'Fireball'	CJun
§	– 'Firecracker'^{PBR} (D)	CRos LRHS MAsh MPkF NLar NRHS
§	– 'Fireglow' (A)	CAco CBcs CEnd CJun CKel CMCN CMen CRos CSBt ESMi LMaj LMil LPra LRHS LSRN MGos MJak MPkF NLar NRHS SAko SCob SCoo SGol SPer
	– 'First Ghost' (M/v)	CJun
	– 'Frederici Guglielmi'	see *A. palmatum* 'Dissectum Variegatum'
	– 'Garnet' (D) ♀H6	Widely available
	– 'Garnet Tower' (D)	LRHS MPkF NLar
	– 'Garyū' (Dw)	MPkF
	– 'Geisha' (Dw)	MPkF
	– 'Geisha Gone Wild' (P/v)	CJun NLar
	– 'Gentaku'	CJun
	– 'Germaine's Gyration' (D)	CJun
	– 'Gibbsii'	CMen
I	– 'Globosum' (Dw)	MPkF
	– 'Glowing Embers' (P)	CJun MPkF
	– 'Going Green'	CRos LCro LOPS LRHS MPkF NLar NRHS
	– 'Going Red'	LRHS NLar
	– 'Golden Pond' (A)	CJun
	– 'Goshiki-kotohime' (Dw/v)	CMCN NLar
	– 'Goshiki-shidare'	see *A. palmatum* 'Toyama-nishiki'
	– 'Goten-nomura'	NLar
	– 'Grandma Ghost' (M)	CJun
	– 'Green Fingers' (D) **new**	NLar
	– 'Green Flag'	CJun
	– 'Green Globe' (D)	CJun
	– 'Green Hornet' (D)	CJun NLar
	– 'Green Lace' (D)	CMen LMaj MPkF
	– 'Green Mist' (D)	CJun
	– 'Green Trompenburg' (M)	CJun CMen GBin MPkF NEgg
	– 'Groundcover' (Dw)	MPkF
§	– 'Hagoromo'	CMac CMen ESMi NEgg SCoo
	– 'Hana-matoi'^{PBR} (v)	CMCN
	– 'Hanami-nishiki' (Dw)	CMen MPkF
	– 'Hanzel' (D)	NLar
	– 'Happy Corallinum' (A)	CJun
	– 'Haru-iro'	CJun
	– 'Harusame' (P/v)	MPkF NLar
	– 'Hazeroino' (v)	CMen MPkF
	– 'Heartbeat' (D)	CJun LRHS MPkF NRHS
	– 'Heffner's Red'	CJun
	– var. ***heptalobum***	CMCN
	– 'Heptalobum Elegans Purpureum'	see *A. palmatum* 'Hessei'
	– 'Herbstfeuer' (P)	CJun NLar
§	– 'Hessei' (M)	CEnd CMen MPkF
	– 'Higasa-yama' (P/v)	CAco CEnd CJun CMCN CMen CWGN ESMi LRHS MPkF NLar SGol
	– 'Hino-tori-nishiki'	CMen SGol
	– 'Hōgyoku' (A)	CJun CMCN CMen LRHS MPkF
	– 'Hondoshi' (A)	NLar
	– 'Hōno-o'	MPkF
	– 'Hoshi-kuzu' (Dw)	MPkF
	– 'Hupp's Dwarf' (Dw)	CJun MPkF
	– 'Hupp's Red Willow'	NLar WMat
	– 'Ibo-nishiki' (P)	CMen ESMi MPkF
	– 'Ichigyōji' (A)	CEnd CJun CMen MAsh
	– 'Ightham Gold'	SSta
	– 'Iijima-sunago' (M)	CMen MPkF
	– 'Inaba-shidare' (D) ♀H6	Widely available
	– 'Inazuma' (M)	CAco CBcs CJun CMCN CMen MPkF NLar SCoo SGol SLau
	– 'Irish Lace'	CJun
	– 'Irish Lace' × ***palmatum*** 'Yasemin'	CJun
	– 'Isobel'	NLar
	– 'Iso-chidori' (Dw)	MPkF
	– 'Issai-nishiki'	CMen MPkF
*	– 'Issai-nishiki-kawazu'	MPkF
	– 'Jane'	CJun MPkF
	– 'Japanese Sunrise' (P)	CJun NLar WMat
	– 'Jerre Schwartz' (Dw)	CRos EPfP LCro LOPS LRHS MGos MPkF NLar NRHS
	– 'Jirō-shidare' (P)	CJun MPkF NLar
	– 'JJ'	CJun
	– 'Julia D.'	CJun
	– 'Kaba' (Dw)	CMen MPkF SPoG
	– 'Kagero' (A/v)	MPkF
§	– 'Kagiri-nishiki' (P/v)	CBcs CJun CMCN CMac CMen CWGN MJak MPkF NEgg SPer
	– 'Kamagata' (Dw)	CAco CEnd CJun CMCN CMen ESMi LRHS MAsh MGos MPkF NLar NRHS SCoo
§	– 'Kandy Kitchen' (Dw)	CMen MPkF
	– 'Karaori-nishiki' (P/v)	CMen MPkF NLar
	– 'Karasu-gawa' (P/v)	CJun CMen CWGN MPkF
	– 'Kasagiyama' (M)	CEnd CJun CMen MPkF
	– 'Kasen-nishiki' (P)	CMen MPkF
	– 'Kashima' (Dw)	CEnd CJun CMCN CMen MPkF NEgg NLar
	– 'Kashima-yatsubusa'	MPkF
	– 'Katja'	CJun CMen MPkF
	– 'Katsura' (P) ♀H6	Widely available
	– 'Katsura-nishiki'	MPkF
	– 'Kawahara Rose'	MPkF NLar
I	– 'Kawaii' (D)	CJun
	– 'Ki-hachijō' (M)	CJun CMCN CMen MPkF
	– 'Killarney' (M)	CJun
	– 'Kinky Krinkle' (P)	CJun LRHS NLar
	– 'Kinran' (M)	CAco CMen ESMi MPkF NEgg
	– 'Kinshi' (L) ♀H6	CEnd CJun CMCN CMen EPfP GBin MPkF NLar NOra SAko WMat
	– 'Kiri-nishiki' (D)	CJun CMen MPkF NLar
	– 'Ki-shuzan' (M)	CJun
	– 'Kiyohime' (Dw) ♀H6	CMCN CMen MPkF NEgg
	– 'Koba-shōjō' (M)	MPkF
	– 'Kogane-nishiki' (P)	CMen NLar SGol
	– 'Kogane-sakae' (A)	CJun MPkF
	– 'Kokobunji-nishiki' (v)	MPkF
	– 'Komachi-hime' (Dw)	CJun CMen MPkF
	– 'Komon-nishiki' (P/v)	CJun CMen MPkF NEgg
	– 'Korean Gem' (M)	CAco CJun CMen MPkF NEgg
	– 'Koriba' (P)	CJun MPkF NLar
	– 'Koshibori-nishiki' (P)	MPkF
	– 'Kotohime' (Dw)	CJun CMCN CMen MGos MPkF NLar SCoo SPoG
	– 'Koto-ito-komachi' (Dw)	CJun CMen ESMi MPkF
	– 'Koto-maru' (Dw)	NLar SGol
	– 'Koto-no-ito' (L)	CMCN LBuc LMaj LRHS MAsh MBlu MGos MPkF NLar NRHS SAko SGol SPoG
	– 'Koya-san' (Dw)	CMen MPkF
	– 'Kurabu-yama' (M)	CMen MPkF
	– 'Kurui-jishi' (Dw)	MPkF
	– 'Kyōryū'	MPkF
	– 'Kyra'	CMen MPkF
	– 'Limelight' (P)	NLar
§	– 'Linearilobum' (L)	CBcs CMen EPfP MGos MPkF NLar NOra SCoo SLau WMat

* - 'Lionheart' (D)	CBcs CJun CMen CWGN ESMi EUJe MGos MPkF NEgg NLar SCoo
- 'Little Princess'	see *A. palmatum* 'Chiyo-hime'
- 'Lozita' (P)	NLar
- 'Lutescens' (A)	CMen MPkF NEgg
- 'Lydia'	MPkF
- 'Maiko' (P)	CMen MPkF
- 'Mallet'	NLar
- 'Mama' (P)	CMen
- 'Manyō-no-sato' (P/v)	LCro LRHS MPkF
- 'Mapi-no-machi-hime' (Dw)	CEnd CJun CMCN CMen LRHS MPkF NHol NRHS
- 'Marakumo' (P)	MPkF
- 'Marasaki-yama'	MPkF
- 'Mardi Gras'	CJun
- 'Margaret'	MPkF
- 'Margaret Bee' (A)	CJun NLar
- 'Marjan' (M)	CJun MPkF NLar
- 'Marlo'[PBR] (D)	CRos LCro LOPS LRHS MAsh MGos NLar NRHS
- 'Masamurasaki'	CMen MPkF
- 'Masukagami' (P/v)	CEnd CJun MPkF NLar
- 'Matsu-ga-e' (P/v)	CMen MPkF
- 'Matsukaze'	CJun CMCN CMen
- var. ***matsumurae*** B&SWJ 11100	WCru
- - B&SWJ 11195	WCru
- 'Matsuyoi' (A)	CJun MPkF
- 'Meihō-nishiki'	CJun
- 'Melanie'	CJun
- 'Meoto'	CJun
- 'Midori-no-teiboku' (Dw)	CJun
- 'Mikasa-nishiki' (v)	MPkF
- 'Mikawa-yatsubusa' (Dw)	CJun CMCN CMac CMen EMac ESMi MGos MPkF SAko SGol
- 'Mikazuki' (M/v)	CJun LRHS MPkF
- 'Mimaye'	CJun
- 'Mini Mondo'	MPkF
- 'Mirte' (M)	CJun CMen MPkF NLar SGol
- 'Mizuho-beni' (P)	CJun CMen NLar
- 'Mizu-kuguri' (A)	CJun MPkF
- 'Momoiro-koya-san' (Dw)	CJun LRHS MPkF NLar SGol
- 'Mon Papa' (M)	CJun CMen NLar
- 'Monzukushi' (A)	CJun MPkF
- 'Moonfire' (M)	CJun CMCN EMac EPfP MAsh MPkF NLar SGol
- 'Murasaki-hime' (Dw)	MPkF
- 'Murasaki-kiyohime' (Dw)	CAco CEnd CJun CMCN CMen ESMi MPkF
- 'Mure-hibari' (M)	CJun CMen MPkF
- 'Murogawa' (A)	CJun CMen
- 'Musashino' (M)	CJun SGol
- 'Mutsu-beni-shidare' (D) **new**	NLar
- 'Nakata'	NLar
- 'Nanase-gawa' (A)	MPkF NLar
- 'Nicholsonii' (M)	CMen MPkF NEgg NLar
- 'Nigrum' (A)	CMCN CTri
- 'Nishiki-gasane' (P/v)	CMen MPkF
§ - 'Nishiki-gawa' (P)	CEnd CJun CMen ESMi MPkF NEgg
- 'Nishiki-momiji' (P)	CMen
- 'Nomura'	CJun CMen
- 'Nomura-nishiki' (Dw/v)	CMen
- 'Nomurishidare' misapplied	see *A. palmatum* 'Shōjō-shidare'
- 'Nuresagi' (M)	CEnd CJun MPkF
- 'Octopus' (D)	CJun NLar
- 'Ōgi-nagashi' (P/v)	MPkF NLar
- 'Ōgi-no-sen'	MPkF
- 'Ōgon-sarasa' (A)	CJun MPkF

- 'Ojishi' (Dw)	CMen MPkF
- 'Ō-kagami' (P)	CAco CBcs CEnd CJun CMac CMen EPfP ESMi EUJe LRHS MAsh MGos MPkF NLar SCoo
- 'Okukuji-nishiki' (P)	CJun
- 'Okushimo' (P)	CEnd CJun CMCN CMen MPkF NEgg NLar SSta
- 'Omato' (A)	CJun MPkF
- 'Omure-yama' (M)	CAco CEnd CJun CMCN CMen EPfP ESMi MGos MPkF NEgg SCob SCoo SGol SPer SSta
- 'Orange Dream' (P) 🏆H6	Widely available
- 'Orangeola' (D) 🏆H6	CJun CMen CSBt CTri ESMi EUJe LRHS MAsh MGos MJak MPkF NHol NLar NRHS SCob SCoo SGol SPer SPoG SSta WMat
- 'Oranges and Lemons'	CJun SGol
- 'Oregon Sunset' (M)	CJun MJak MPkF WMat
- 'Oridono-nishiki' (P/v)	CEnd CJun CMCN CMac CMen CWGN ELan ELon EPfP ESMi MBlu MGos MPkF SLim SPoG SSta
- 'Oriental Mystery'	CJun
- 'Ornatum' (D) 🏆H6	CKel CMCN CMen EPfP ESMi LMaj LSRN MAsh MGos MPkF MRav NLar NPri NWea SCob SCoo WCFE
- 'Ōsakazuki' (A) 🏆H6	Widely available
- 'Ōshio-beni' (A)	CJun CMen NEgg
- 'Ōshū-shidare' (M)	CJun CMen MPkF
- 'Oto-hime' (Dw)	CJun CMen MPkF
- 'Otome-zakura' (P)	CJun CMen NEgg
- 'Otto's Dissectum' (D)	CJun
- 'Peaches and Cream' (M/v)	CAco CJun CMen ESMi MPkF NLar SGol SPer
- 'Pendulum Julian' (D)	CMCN MPkF SPer
- 'Pévé Dave'	CKel CRos LRHS MAsh MPkF NLar NRHS
- 'Pévé Multicolor'	CJun
- 'Pévé Ollie'[PBR]	MPkF
- 'Pévé Stanley'	MPkF NLar
- 'Pévé Starfish'	NLar
- 'Phoenix' (P)	CJun EUJe LRHS MGos MPkF NLar NRHS
- 'Pine Bark Maple'	see *A. palmatum* 'Nishiki-gawa'
- 'Pink Ballerina' (Dw/v)	CJun NLar
- 'Pink Filigree' (D)	CJun CMen NLar
- 'Pink Passion' (v)	LSRN NLar
- 'Pixie' (Dw)	CJun CMen CSBt LRHS MGos MPkF NLar NOra SAko SCob WMat
- 'Princetown Gold'	CCVT EUJe IArd NLar
- 'Pung-kil'	LRHS MPkF SAko
- 'Purple Ghost' (M)	CJun NLar
- 'Raraflora' (D)	CJun
- 'Red Autumn Lace' (D)	CJun
- 'Red Baron' (A)	CJun
- 'Red Cloud' (L)	CJun MPkF
- 'Red Dragon' (D)	CJun CMen CWGN ESMi LRHS MAsh MJak MPkF SAko
- RED EMPEROR	see *A. palmatum* 'Emperor 1'
- 'Red Feather' (D)	CJun MPkF
- 'Red Filigree Lace' (D)	CEnd CJun CMCN CMen CWGN MPkF
- 'Red Flame'	NLar
- 'Red Flash' (A)	CJun CMen MPkF NLar
- 'Red Jonas'	MPkF NLar
- 'Red Pygmy' (L) 🏆H6	CAco CBcs CEnd CJun CMCN CMac CMen CRos CWGN EPfP GKin LMil LRHS MAsh MBlu MGos NHol NLar NPri NRHS SAko SCoo SGol SPer SPoG SSta SWvt
- 'Red Select' (D)	MPkF

	Cultivar	Suppliers
	– 'Red Spider' (L)	CJun
	– 'Red Wood' (P)	CJun SGol SLau
	– 'Redwine'PBR (P)	CRos EPfP LRHS MPkF NLar NRHS
	– 'Renjaku-maru'	MPkF
	– 'Reticulatum'	see *A. palmatum* 'Shigi-tatsu-sawa'
	– 'Ribesifolium'	see *A. palmatum* 'Shishi-gashira'
	– 'Rilas Red' (D)	NLar
	– 'Rising Sun'	CJun
	– 'Roseomarginatum'	see *A. palmatum* 'Kagiri-nishiki'
	– 'Rough Bark Maple'	see *A. palmatum* 'Arakawa'
	– 'Rubrum' (A)	CMen
I	– 'Rubrum Kaiser'	CJun
	– 'Ruby Ridge' (M)	CJun
	– 'Ruby Star'	CJun MPkF
	– 'Rufescens' (P)	MPkF
	– 'Ruslyn-in-the-Pink' (Dw) **new**	NLar
	– 'Ryokū-ryū' (P)	CMen MPkF
	– 'Ryusen'	CJun LRHS MBlu NLar
	– 'Ryuzu' (Dw)	CJun MPkF NLar
	– 'Sagara-nishiki' (v)	CAco CEnd CMen MPkF
	– 'Sai-ho'	MPkF
	– 'Saint Jean'	MPkF
	– 'Samidare' (A)	CJun MPkF NLar
	– 'Sandra' (Dw)	CMen MPkF
	– 'Sango-kaku' (P) 🏆H6	Widely available
	– 'Saoshika' (A)	CJun CMen MPkF NLar
	– 'Sa-otome' (P)	CMen MPkF
	– 'Satsuki-beni' (M)	CJun CMen ESMi MPkF
	– 'Sazanami' (M)	CEnd CJun CMen MPkF NLar
	– 'Scolopendriifolium'	see *A. palmatum* 'Linearilobum'
§	– 'Seigai' (M)	CJun
	– 'Seigen' (Dw)	CEnd CJun CMCN CMen MBlu MPkF
	– 'Seiryū' (D) 🏆H6	Widely available
	– 'Seiun-kaku' (P)	CJun CMen MPkF
	– 'Sekimori' (D)	CJun NLar
	– 'Sekka-yatsubusa' (P)	CMCN CMen MPkF NLar
	– 'Semi-no-hane' (M)	CJun
	– 'Senkaki'	see *A. palmatum* 'Sango-kaku'
	– 'Septemlobum Elegans'	see *A. palmatum* 'Elegans'
	– 'Septemlobum Purpureum'	see *A. palmatum* 'Hessei'
	– 'Sessilifolium' dwarf	see *A. palmatum* 'Hagoromo'
	– 'Shaina' (P)	CBcs CEnd CJun CKel CMen CRos CSBt CWGN EBee EPfP LBuc LCro LMaj LOPS LRHS MBlu MGos MJak MPkF NLar NRHS SAko SCob SCoo SGol SLim SPoG SRms
	– 'Sharp's Pygmy' (P)	CJun CMen MPkF SGol
	– 'Sherwood Flame' (M)	CJun CMen LRHS MAsh MBlu MGos MPkF NLar NRHS SCoo SGol
	– 'Shichigosan'	CMen
	– 'Shichihenge' (P)	NLar
	– 'Shidava Gold' (Dw)	CJun EMac MPkF
	– 'Shigarami' (P)	CJun CMen MPkF
§	– 'Shigi-tatsu-sawa' (A/v)	CEnd CJun CMCN CMac CMen LRHS MGos MPkF NEgg NLar NRHS
	– 'Shigure-bato' (M)	CJun MPkF NLar
	– 'Shigurezome' (M)	MPkF
	– 'Shikageori-nishiki' (P)	CJun CMen MPkF
	– 'Shime-no-uchi' (L)	CJun
	– 'Shin Nyo'PBR	MBlu
	– 'Shin-chishio' (P)	CJun
	– 'Shin-deshōjō' (P) 🏆H6	CBcs CEnd CJun CMCN CMac CMen CRos CSBt CWGN EMac EPfP LMil LRHS LSRN MAsh MGos NEgg NLar NPri NRHS SCoo SGol SPer SPoG SSta
§	– 'Shinobuga-oka' (L)	CBcs CJun CMCN CMen LRHS MPkF NLar SGol SLau
	– 'Shinonome' (M)	CJun CMen MPkF NLar
	– 'Shirazz' (P/v)	CRos CWGN EMac ESMi EUJe LMil LRHS LSRN MGos MJak MPkF NEgg NLar NOra NRHS SCob SPer SWvt WMat
§	– 'Shishi-gashira' (P) 🏆H6	CJun CMCN CMac CMen ESMi EUJe LMaj MBlu MGos MPkF NEgg NLar SCoo SGol
	– 'Shishio-hime' (Dw)	MPkF
	– 'Shishi-yatsubusa'	CJun MPkF
	– 'Shōjō' (A)	CJun CMCN
	– 'Shōjō-no-mai' (P)	CJun
	– 'Shōjō-nomura' (A)	CEnd CMen MPkF
§	– 'Shōjō-shidare' (D)	CEnd CJun CMen MPkF NOra WMat
	– 'Shu-shidare' (D)	CJun
	– 'Silhouette'PBR	CJun LCro LOPS LRHS MPkF
	– 'Sister Ghost' (M)	CJun NLar
	– 'Skeeter's Broom' (Dw)	CAco CBcs CJun CMen CRos CSBt EBee ELan EPfP ESMi EUJe IArd LMaj LRHS MGos MPkF NEgg NRHS SCoo SPoG
*	– 'Sode-nishiki' (P)	CJun MPkF
	– 'Spring Delight' (D)	CJun MPkF SAko
	– 'Stanley's Jewel' (Dw) **new**	NLar
	– 'Starfish'PBR	LBuc LRHS MPkF
	– 'Stella Rossa' (D)	CEnd CJun LRHS MPkF NLar NPri
	– 'Suisei' (Dw/v)	MPkF
	– 'Sumi-nagashi' (M)	CBcs CCVT CMen CRos ESMi LRHS MAsh MGos MPkF NLar NOra NRHS SCoo SGol SLau WMat
	– 'Sumi-shidare' (D)	NLar
I	– 'Summer Gold' (P)	CAco CJun CRos LRHS MPkF NLar NRHS SAko SWvt
	– 'Sunset' (D)	CJun MPkF
	– 'Sunshine' (D)	MPkF
	– 'Super Ruby' (L) **new**	NLar
	– 'Susan'	MPkF
	– 'Taiyō-nishiki' (P)	MPkF
	– 'Takao' (P)	CMen
	– 'Tama-hime' (Dw)	CJun CMen ESMi MPkF NEgg
	– 'Tamukeyama' (D)	CAco CJun CMCN CMen ELan ESMi EUJe LRHS MAsh MGos MJak MPkF NEgg NLar NOra SAko SCob SCoo SGol SLau WHor WMat
	– 'Tana' (A)	CJun CMCN CMen MPkF
	– 'Tarō-yama' (Dw)	CJun MPkF
	– 'Tatsuta'	CMen MPkF
	– 'Taylor'PBR (P/v)	CDul CEnd CKel CRos CWGN EPfP LRHS LSRN MAsh MGos MPkF NLar NPri NRHS SCoo SPoG
	– 'Tennyo-no-hoshi' (P)	CMen MPkF NLar
	– 'The Bishop' (A)	NLar
	– 'Tiger Rose' (M)	CJun
	– 'Tiny Tim'	CJun
	– 'Tobiosho' (P)	CJun
§	– 'Toyama-nishiki' (Dw/v)	CJun CMCN CMen CWGN ESMi MPkF
	– 'Trompenburg' (M) 🏆H6	Widely available
	– 'Tsuchigumo' (P)	CJun CMen MPkF NLar
	– 'Tsukuma-no'	MPkF
	– 'Tsukushigata' (A)	MPkF SGol
	– 'Tsuma-gaki' (A)	CAco CJun CMCN CMen EPfP ESMi LRHS MGos MPkF NEgg NLar NRHS
	– 'Tsuri-nishiki' (M)	CJun CMen MPkF
	– 'Twombly's Red Sentinel'	CJun MBlu

- 'Ueno-homare' (P)	CMen EUJe MPkF
- 'Ueno-yama'	CBcs CJun LRHS MPkF SGol SPer
- 'Uki-gumo' (P/v)	CAco CBcs CEnd CJun CMCN CMac CMen ESMi MGos MPkF NHol SCoo SPer SPoG SSta
- 'Umegae' (A)	CJun
- 'Uncle Ghost' (M)	CJun
- 'Usu-midori'	CJun
- 'Utsu-semi' (A)	CJun MPkF
- 'Van der Akker'	CJun
- 'Versicolor' (P/v)	CMCN MPkF
- 'Vic Pink' (D)	CJun
- 'Victoria'	SGol
- 'Villa Taranto' (L) Y^{H6}	CEnd CJun CMCN CMen EPfP ESMi MBlu MGos MPkF NLar NOra SCoo SGol WMat
- 'Volubile' (P)	CMCN CMen MPkF
- 'Wabito' (P)	CJun CMen MPkF
- 'Waka-midori'	CMen
- 'Waka-momiji' (P/v)	CJun
- 'Wakehurst Pink' (M/v)	CMCN MPkF
- 'Waterfall' (D)	CJun CMCN
- 'Watnong' (D)	CJun MPkF
- 'Wendy' (P)	CJun CMen MPkF NLar SGol
- 'Wetumpka Red'	CJun NLar
- 'Whitney Red' (A)	CMen
- 'Wild Goose' (P)	MPkF
- 'Will's Devine'	CJun
- 'Wilson's Pink Dwarf' (Dw)	CAco CEnd CJun CMen CRos CSBt LRHS MAsh MGos MJak MPkF NLar NRHS SAko SCoo SPoG WFar
- 'Winter Flame' (P)	CJun LRHS MPkF NHol
- 'Wou-nishiki'	CMCN CMen MPkF NEgg
- 'Yana-gawa'	CMen
- 'Yasemin' (M)	CJun CMen CWGN LRHS MPkF NLar
- 'Yatsubusa' (Dw)	MPkF
- 'Yezo-nishiki' (A/v)	CMen MBlu MPkF
- 'Yūba-e' (M)	MPkF
- 'Yūgure' (M)	MPkF
- 'Yuri-hime' (Dw)	MPkF
- 'Zaaling' (D)	CAco CMen NEgg
- 'Zoë' **new**	NLar
papilio	see *A. caudatum*
pauciflorum 'Blaze Away'	CJun
pectinatum	MMuc WPGP
- GWJ 9354	WCru
- 'Mozart'	CBcs CJun MBlu SSta
- subsp. ***pectinatum*** HWJ 569	WCru
- - HWJ 944	WCru
pensylvanicum	CBcs CDul CLnd CMCN CTho EBee ECrN EPfP LPra MGos MJak MMuc MRav NEgg NWea SCob SPtp SSta WHor
- 'Erythrocladum'	CBcs CEnd CJun CMCN EPfP MAsh MGos NHol NLar
pentaphyllum	WPGP
§ ***pictum***	CMCN
- B&SWJ 12737 **new**	WCru
- 'Mallet Court'	CMCN
- subsp. ***okamotoanum***	CMCN
- - B&SWJ 12623	WCru
- subsp. ***pictum*** f. ***ambiguum*** B&SWJ 8806	WCru
- 'Shufu-nishiki'	CMCN
platanoides	CAco CBcs CCVT CDul CLnd CMCN CPer CSBt CTri EMOT EPfP GQue LMaj LPra MGos MMuc MSwo NWea SEWo SGol SPer WMat WMou WTSh
- 'Columnare'	CLnd CMCN LMaj LPra SCoo
- 'Crimson King' Y^{H7}	Widely available
- 'Crimson Sentry'	CArg CCVT CDul CEnd CLnd CMac CTri ELan EMOT EUJe LCro LMaj LSRN MAsh MGos MRav SGol SPer SWvt
- 'Deborah'	CDul CTho EPfP LMaj LPra NWea SGol SPer
- 'Dissectum'	CAco IArd
- 'Drummondii' (v)	Widely available
- 'Emerald Queen'	CDul ECrN LMaj LPra NWea
- 'Faassen's Black'	CDul LPra
§ - 'Globosum'	CDul CMCN ECrN LMaj NLar SWvt
- 'Jules' (v)	EMOT
- 'Laciniatum'	CMCN EBtc GBin
- PRINCETON GOLD ('Prigo'^{PBR}) Y^{H7}	CBcs CCVT CDul CLnd CTho EBee ECrN ELan EMOT EUJe GQue LBuc MAsh MGos NOra NWea SCoo SEWo SLim SPer SPoG SWvt WMat
- 'Reitenbachii'	CDul
- 'Royal Red'	CDul EPfP LMaj LPra MRav NLar SCoo SEWo
- 'Schwedleri' Y^{H7}	CMCN LPra NWea WTSh
- SENSATION	see *A. platanoides* 'Ulmer's Sensation'
- subsp. ***turkestanicum***	CMCN SSta
- 'Ulmers Select'	WMat
§ - 'Ulmers Sensation'^{PBR} (v) **new**	SPoG
pseudoplatanus	CBcs CCVT CDul CLnd CMCN CPer CTri ECrN ELan EMOT LPra MGos NWea SGol SPer WMou WTSh
§ - 'Atropurpureum'	CDul LPra NWea SEND SEWo
- 'Brilliantissimum' Y^{H7}	Widely available
- 'Corstorphinense'	CDul
- f. ***erythrocarpum*** 'Erythrocarpum'	CMac
- 'Gadsby'	CDul
- 'Leopoldii' misapplied	see *A. pseudoplatanus* f. *variegatum*
- 'Negenia'	CDul
- 'Prinz Handjéry'	CDul CEnd CMCN CTri MGos NHol NLar NOra NWea SGol WMat
- 'Spaethii' misapplied	see *A. pseudoplatanus* 'Atropurpureum'
§ - f. ***variegatum*** (v)	LPra
- - 'Esk Sunset' (v)	CLnd ELan LSRN MGos SPoG
- - 'Leopoldii' ambig. (v)	CCVT CDul CLnd CMCN ECrN EMOT LPra SEND SWvt
- - 'Leopoldii' Vervaene (v)	SPer
- - 'Simon-Louis Frères' (v)	CBcs CCVT CDul CLnd CMCN ECrN EMOT MAsh MGos NLar SGol SPer SWvt WMat
- 'Worley'	CDul CMCN CMac EMOT MRav NWea SGol SLim SPer
pseudosieboldianum	CMCN LRHS MBlu MPkF
- B&SWJ 8468	WCru
- B&SWJ 8746	WCru
- B&SWJ 8769	WCru
- var. ***microsieboldianum*** B&SWJ 8766	WCru
- subsp. ***takesimense***	MBlu
- - B&SWJ 8500	WCru
- - B&SWJ 8540	WCru
'Red Flamingo' (v)	CBcs CJun CMac CRos EPfP LRHS MBlu MGos MPkF NLar NOra SGol SPoG WMat

Plant	Suppliers
§ 'Red Wings' (*A. palmatum* hybrid)	CJun
reticulatum	see *A. laevigatum* var. *reticulatum*
rubescens CWJ 12438	WCru
- NMWJ 14525 **new**	WCru
rubrum	CAco CAgr CBcs CDul CLnd CMCN CPer CSBt CTri EBee ECrN ELan EMOT EPfP LCro LMaj LOPS LPra MGos MMuc NEgg NWea SCoo SEWo SGol WCFE WMat WTSh
- 'Autumn Flame'	CCVT WHCr WMou
- 'Autumn Spire'	CJun
- 'Brandywine'	CDul CEnd CJun CLnd CTho EBee EMOT EPfP LRHS LSRN MAsh MBlu NLar NOra NWea SBir SCoo SPoG WHCr WMat
- 'Embers'	CJun
- FAIRVIEW FLAME	see *A. rubrum* 'Pete's Fairview'
- 'Firedance'	CJun
- 'Florida Flame' **new**	CMCN
- 'Joseph'	NLar
- 'New World'	SCoo
- 'October Glory' ♀H6	Widely available
§ - 'Pete's Fairview'	CJun MMuc SPer
- 'Red King'	CJun
- RED SUNSET ('Franksred') ♀H6	CAco CBcs CDul CEnd CKel CMCN CTho EBee EMOT EPfP LPra NLar NWea SBir SCoo SGol SLim SPer SPoG
- 'Scanlon'	CBcs CDul CEnd CJun CMCN CTho EPfP LMaj LPra LRHS NOra SLim SPer WHCr
- 'Schlesingeri'	CEnd CJun CLnd CMac EPfP SPer
I - 'Sekka'	MBlu
- 'Somerset'	CDul CJun CTho EBee SCoo WMat
- SUMMER RED ('Hosr')	CDul EBee EMOT EPfP LRHS SCoo WMat
- 'Sun Valley'	CJun CTho EBee MAsh NOra NWea WHCr WMat
- 'Tilford'	CJun SSta
§ ***rufinerve***	CBcs CDul CLnd CMCN CTho CTri EBee ECrN EPfP EWTr LPra MMuc NLar NOra NWea SCoo SGol SPtp SSta SWvt WMat WTSh
- 'Albolimbatum' (v)	CEnd CJun CMCN SSta
- 'Erythrocladum'	CJun MBlu
- 'Ko-fuji-nishiki'	SSta
I - 'Sunshine'	SSta
- 'Winter Gold'	CJun NLar SSta
- 'Yellow Ribbon'	LRHS
§ ***saccharinum***	CBcs CCVT CDul CLnd CMCN CTri EBee ECrN ELan EPfP LPra MGos MMuc NOra NWea SCoo SGol SPer WMat WTSh
- 'Born's Gracious'	CJun
- 'Fastigiatum'	see *A. saccharinum* 'Pyramidale'
- f. ***laciniatum***	EBee LPra MBlu MMuc NWea SGol SPer
- - 'Laciniatum Wieri'	CDul CMCN NLar NWea SGol
- 'Lutescens'	CTho
§ - 'Pyramidale'	CLnd LMaj NWea SPer
saccharum	CAgr CBcs CDul CLnd CMCN CTho EBee ECrN EPfP IArd LMaj LPra LRHS MBlu NEgg NWea WTSh
- 'Fiddlers Creek'	CJun
§ - subsp. ***grandidentatum***	CMCN
§ ***sempervirens***	EBee EPfP IArd LEdu MPkF SEND
'Sensu'	CJun NLar
'Serendipity'	SSta
serrulatum	CMCN
- CWJ 12437	WCru
- NMWJ 14514 **new**	WCru
- NMWJ 14521 **new**	WCru
- hybrid NMWJ 14548 **new**	WCru
shirasawanum	CMCN LRHS
§ - 'Aureum' ♀H6	Widely available
- 'Autumn Moon'	CBcs CJun CMCN CMen CWGN EPfP EUJe MPkF NLar NOra SCob SCoo SGol SPer SPoG WMat
§ - 'Ezo-no-momiji'	CMen MPkF
- 'Gloria'	CJun MPkF SGol
- 'Green Snow Flake' **new**	NLar
- 'Jordan'PBR	CBcs CDul CEnd CMCN CMac CRos CWGN EBee LBuc LRHS LSRN MAsh MGos MPkF NEgg NRHS SPoG SWvt
- 'Kakure-gasa'	CJun
- 'Lovett'	CJun
§ - 'Microphyllum'	NEgg
- MOONRISE ('Munn 001'PBR) **new**	LCro LOPS LRHS MPkF
- 'Mr Sun'	CJun
§ - 'Ogurayama'	CAco CJun CMen
- 'Palmatifolium'	CJun
- 'Red Dawn'	CJun
- 'Susanne'	CJun CMen NLar SGol
- var. ***tenuifolium*** B&SWJ 11073	WCru
sieboldianum ♀H6	CDul CMCN CMen CTho CTri ECrN MAsh MBlu MMuc SEND SGol
- B&SWJ 10849	WCru
- B&SWJ 11049	WCru
- B&SWJ 11090	WCru
- 'Sode-no-uchi'	CJun CMen
- var. ***tsushimense*** B&SWJ 10962	WCru
sikkimense B&SWJ 11689	WCru
- B&SWJ 11703	WCru
- FMWJ 13166 from northern Vietnam	WCru
- WJC 13674 from Sikkim	WCru
- WWJ 11601	WCru
- WWJ 11613	WCru
- WWJ 11853	WCru
'Silver Cardinal' (v)	CEnd CJun CMCN EPfP MBlu MGos NLar SSta
'Silver Vein'	see *A.* × *conspicuum* 'Silver Vein'
sinense	CMCN
spicatum	CMCN NLar
§ ***sterculiaceum***	EBee
- PAB 13.135	LEdu
- subsp. ***franchetii***	CMCN NLar
- subsp. ***sterculiaceum*** NJM 13.087	WPGP
- subsp. ***franchetii*** **new**	WPGP
tataricum	CMCN SPtp
§ - subsp. ***ginnala***	CAco CArg CBcs CDul CLnd CMCN CNWT CTri ECrN LPra MBlu MGos NLar NWea SGol SPer
- - 'Flame'	CCVT CJun EBee ECrN EPfP MGos MMuc NLar NWea SPoG
tegmentosum ♀H5	CDul CJun CMCN EPfP MBlu SMad SSta WHor
- 'Cobhay Ghost' **new**	CJun
- subsp. ***glaucorufinerve***	see *A. rufinerve*
- 'Valley Phantom'	LSvl SSta
tonkinense subsp. ***liquidambarifolium*** DJHV 06173	WCru

trautvetteri CMCN
triflorum ♀H7 CBcs CCVT CJun CMCN EBee EPfP LMaj LRHS MBlu NLar NOra WMat WMou
truncatum CDul MPkF
- 'Akikaze-nishiki' (v) CJun MPkF
tschonoskii GKin
- subsp. ***koreanum*** MPkF
- - B&SWJ 12596 WCru
- - B&SWJ 12603 WCru
turkestanicum from Kyrgyzstan new WPGP
velutinum CMCN
villosum see *A. sterculiaceum*
wardii WPGP
'White Tigress' CBcs CJun EPfP NLar SSta WMat
× ***zoeschense*** CMCN MPkF
- 'Annae' MMuc SGol

Aceriphyllum see *Mukdenia*

Achillea (*Asteraceae*)

ageratifolia ♀H5 CMea GWyn NGdn SRms WSpi XLum XSen
§ ***ageratum*** CBod CCBP CLau ENfk EWhm GPoy LEdu MHer MNHC SRms WFar WGwG WHer WJek WTre XLum XSen
'Alabaster' CRos LRHS NRHS WSpi
ANTHEA ('Anblo'PBR) EBee ECtt EMor LRHS LSRN MCot MRav NRHS SHar SRms SWvt WFar
§ 'Apfelblüte' (Galaxy Series) CAby CBod CRos EBee ECha ECtt ELan EMor EPfP LRHS LSRN MMuc MRav NGdn NHol NQui NRHS NSti SCob SEND SPer SRms WCAu WFar XSen
APPLEBLOSSOM see *A.* 'Apfelblüte'
'Apricot Beauty' ECtt EMor WSpi
'Apricot Delight' (Tutti Frutti Series) CRos EMor IPot LRHS NAst NLar NRHS WTor
argentea misapplied see *A. clavennae*, *A. umbellata*
argentea Lamarck see *Tanacetum argenteum*
argentea ambig. ELan
aurea see *A. chrysocoma*
'Bahama' EPPr GBin GQue
'Belle Epoque' WSpi XSen
biebersteinii XLum
'Breckland Ruby' EWes
'Carmina Burana' CMea
cartilaginea see *A. salicifolia*
§ ***chrysocoma*** WMoo
- 'Grandiflora' ECha MMuc NGdn WBrk
§ ***clavennae*** GKev SRms WAbe WIce
clypeolata Sibth. & Sm. EHyd SPhx SPlb SRms XLum
coarctata NBir XSen
Colorado Group CBod CWCL EHyd LRHS NPol NRHS
'Coronation Gold' ♀H7 CRos CWCL EBee ECtt ELan EPfP LRHS MAsh MHol MRav MWat NChi NDov NRHS SCob SPer SRms SWvt WCAu WCot WSpi XLum XSen
'Credo' ♀H7 CAby CDor CRos CWld EAJP ECha ECtt EMor EPfP EWTr GBin IPot LCro LOPS LRHS MArl MRav NBir NGdn NHol NLar NRHS NSti SMad SPer SSut WCAu WSpi XSen
crithmifolia XLum XSen
decolorans see *A. ageratum*
(Desert Eve Series) DESERT EVE CREAM ('Deseve') EBee
- DESERT EVE DEEP ROSE ('Desderos') EBee MAsh
- DESERT EVE LIGHT YELLOW SRms
- DESERT EVE RED ('Desred'PBR) EBee
- DESERT EVE YELLOW ('Desyel'PBR) EBee
falcata GKev NAln
§ 'Fanal' CAby CBod CCBP CKel CRos CWCL EBee ECha ECtt ELan EMor EPfP GWyn LRHS MAsh MRav MTis NBir NEgg NHol NLar NRHS SPer SWvt WCAu
'Faust' CDor ELon
'Feuerland' CMac CSam EBee ECha ECtt ELon EMor EPfP LRHS MRav NBir NDov NGdn NRHS SAko SPer SPoG WFar WSpi XSen
filipendulina 'Cloth of Gold' ♀H7 Widely available
- 'Gold Plate' ♀H7 Widely available
- 'Hymne' EBee
- 'Parker's Variety' ♀H7 EBee NBre WFar WMoo XLum XSen
'Fleur van Zonneveld' NDov WGoo
FLOWERS OF SULPHUR see *A.* 'Schwefelblüte'
(Forncett Series) 'Forncett Beauty' SWvt
- 'Forncett Bride' EBee
- 'Forncett Citrus' ECtt WFar
- 'Forncett Fletton' CWld ECtt EHrv EPfP GBin MBel MRav NGdn NHol WCAu WFar
- 'Forncett Ivory' MAvo
'Gloria Jean' SHar
'Golden Fleece' GWyn
grandifolia misapplied see *Tanacetum macrophyllum* (Waldst. & Kit.) Sch.Bip.
§ ***grandifolia*** Friv. CSam EMor MArl MHol NBro WFar WMoo WOld
'Great Expectations' see *A.* 'Hoffnung'
'Heidi' ♀H7 MRav XSen
'Heinrich Vogeler' EBee LPla MHol
'Hella Glashoff' ♀H7 CMea CRos EBee ELon LRHS NAln NRHS WGoo
§ 'Hoffnung' CRos CWCL NLar NRHS
× ***huteri*** EBou ECtt EDAr GCrg MMuc NGdn NHpl NRya SEND SIgm SRms SWvt WFar
'Inca Gold' CBcs CSam ECha ECtt EHoe EHrv LRHS MCot MRav NDov NHol NRHS NSti SPer SRms SWvt WFar WGwG WHoo WSpi
× ***kellereri*** EMor XLum XSen
'King Alfred' CBod CMea NCou NHpl SRms
× ***kolbiana*** EWes SRms XSen
§ 'Lachsschönheit' (Galaxy Series) ♀H7 CAby CDor CRos CWCL EBee ECha ECtt ELan EPfP GBin GMaP LRHS MBNS MCot MRav NBir NDov NHol NLar NRHS NSti SCob SPer SRms WCAu WFar
× ***lewisii*** 'King Edward' ♀H5 EBou EDAr GCrg NBir SRms WAbe WFar WIce
'Lucky Break' ♀H7 EBee ECha ECtt EWes LEdu MHol WBrk WCot WRHF
macrophylla MBNS
'Marie Ann' CWCL LSRN NLar
'Marmalade' CDor MRav NDov

	Name	Suppliers
	'Martina' ♀H7	CAby CSam ECtt GBin LRHS MBNS MBel MCot MRav NDov NGdn NHol NRHS WBrk WCot WGwG WHoo
	'McVities'	CWCL ECtt
	millefolium	CHab ENfk GPoy MNHC NGrd NMir NPol SRms SVic WHer WJek WOut WSFF WSpi XLum
	- 'Apricot Seduction'	WFar
	- 'Bloodstone'	ECtt EWes MRav
	- 'Carla Hussey'	WFar
	- 'Cassis'	CBod CRos CSam CSpe EHyd EPfP LRHS MCot NChi NGBl NLar NRHS WBor WFar WOut
§	- 'Cerise Queen'	Widely available
	- 'Chamois'	MNrw
	- 'Cherry King'	NBir
	- 'Circus'	XLum
	- 'Dark Lilac Beauty'	CWCL
	- KIRSCHKÖNIGIN	see *A. millefolium* 'Cerise Queen'
	- 'Lansdorferglut' ♀H7	CRos EBee LRHS NAln NDov NRHS SPhx
	- 'Laura'	CSam CWGN ECtt EPfP MBel MNrw WFar
	- 'Lavender Beauty'	see *A. millefolium* 'Lilac Beauty'
§	- 'Lilac Beauty'	CBod CKel CRos ECha EHrv ELon EPfP EWTr GMaP GWyn LCro LOPS LRHS LSRN MMuc MRav NAln NAst NBir NEgg NLar NRHS SCob SEND SRms WCAu WFar WSpi XLum
*	- 'Lilac Queen'	MArl
	- 'Little Suzie'	CWGN ECtt WFar
	- (New Vintage Series) NEW VINTAGE RED ('Balvinred')	LRHS MHol SCob WHil
	- - NEW VINTAGE ROSE ('Balvinrose')	LRHS SCob WHil
	- - NEW VINTAGE VIOLET ('Balvinviolet')	LRHS
	- 'Old Brocade'	EShb NDov
	- Pastel Shades	WFar
	- 'Peggy Sue'	CWGN EBee ECtt EWes WFar
	- 'Pomegranate' (Tutti Frutti Series)	CRos CWGN IPot LCro LOPS LRHS MBel MNrw NRHS SCob SHar WHil WTor XLum
	- 'Pretty Woman'	CSam CWGN EBee MAsh
	- 'Raspberry Ripple'	GBin GWyn
	- 'Red Beauty'	CWCL EPfP MBNS MBel SRms XLum
	- 'Red Salmon'	EWes
	- 'Red Velvet' ♀H7	Widely available
	- 'Rose Madder'	CWCL ECtt EHoe EPPr EPfP GMaP LRHS MBel MCot MHol MMuc MNrw MPie NBir NChi NGdn NHol NLar NRHS NSti SEND SPer SPoG SWvt WCot WFar WHoo WSpi XLum
	- 'Ruby Port'	WFar
	- 'Salmon Queen'	NHol WFar
	- 'Sammetriese'	EBee ELon MNrw SMad SPhx
	- 'Schneetaler'	MNrw
	- 'Serenade'	ECtt
	- 'Sue's Pink'	CSam
	- (Summer Fruits Series) 'Summer Fruits Carmine'	EBee ELan EMor LRHS
	- - 'Summer Fruits Lemon'	EBee ELan EMor LRHS NRHS WFar WSpi
	- - 'Summer Fruits Salmon'	CWld EBee ELan LRHS
	- 'Summertime'	WFar
	- 'White Beauty'	EWTr WCAu
	- 'White Queen'	EBee
	- 'Wonderful Wampee'	CRos EBee EHyd EWes LRHS MNrw NAst NRHS SCob SPoG
	'Mondpagode' ♀H7	ECtt EPfP EWTr LRHS MBNS MCot MRav NGdn NHol NRHS SPhx SWvt
*	'Moonbeam'	SEND
	'Moonshine' ♀H7	Widely available
	'Moonwalker'	CBod EPfP WCot XLum
	nana	WFar
	nobilis	XSen
	- subsp. ***neilreichii***	CBod EHoe IKil MBNS MMuc NSti SEND SWvt WFar WGwG
*	***odilis***	EWTr
	'Paprika' (Galaxy Series)	Widely available
	'Petra'	EBee ILea MMrt MNrw XLum
	pindicola subsp. ***integrifolia***	EWes
	'Pineapple Mango'PBR	SCob
	'Pink Grapefruit' (Tutti Frutti Series)	CRos EMor GWyn IPot LRHS MAsh NLar NRHS SCob WCAu
	'Pretty Belinda'	CDor CRos EBee ECtt EHyd EPfP EWhm GWyn LRHS LSRN MAsh MBel NRHS NSti SAko SCob SPoG SRms WCAu WFar
	'Prospero'	WCot
	ptarmica	CBod CBre EMor MHer NMir SCob SRms WArt XLum
*	- 'Ballerina'	MBNS NDov NLar
	- 'Nana Compacta'	EHyd LRHS NBir NCGa NRHS SPlb SPoG WCFE WFar
	- 'Noblessa'	MHol
	- 'Perry's White' (d)	CBre ECha MNrw WCot
	- 'Stephanie Cohen'	see *A. sibirica* 'Stephanie Cohen'
	- The Pearl Group seed-raised (d)	CTri ELan GWyn MMuc SGbt SPlb WFar WMoo
	- - 'Boule de Neige' (clonal) (d)	ELan MRav NPer NSti SHar SPer WFar WSpi XLum
	- - 'The Pearl' (clonal) (d)	CBod CMac CRos CSBt EBee ECha EHoe EHyd EPfP LCro LPot LRHS LSRN MBel MRav MWat NBid NBir NBro NHic NLar NRHS SCob SRms WBor WBrk WCAu WCot WFar WJam
	pyrenaica	XLum
	'Rougham Salmon'	CDor
	'Ruby Wine'	SHar WFar
	'Safran'	LRHS NLar NRHS XLum
§	***salicifolia***	WFar
	- 'Silver Spray'	NLar WOut
	'Sally'	EPPr
	SALMON BEAUTY	see *A.* 'Lachsschönheit'
	'Sandra Wagg'	ECtt
	'Sandstone'	see *A.* 'Wesersandstein'
	'Saucy Seduction' (Seduction Series)	CWCL EBee EMor EUJe MHol MTis NAst NBid
§	'Schwefelblüte'	MRav NBir
	'Schwellenburg'	NBre WCot WFar
	sibirica	CBod EBee MBNS MHol MNrw
	subsp. ***camschatica*** 'Love Parade'	SGbt SPtp WArt WFar XLum
§	- 'Stephanie Cohen'	GBee WFar
	'Stephanie'	EWes LSRN
	SUMMER BERRIES MIXED	CRos EHyd LPot LRHS NGrd NHic NRHS SCob WFar WHil
	Summer Pastels Group	CBod CRos EHyd EPfP GKev LRHS NGrd NLar NRHS SRms WFar XLum
	- (Seduction Series) 'Peachy Seduction'PBR	EMor MCot NLar WCAu
	- - 'Strawberry Seduction'	ECtt
	'Summerwine' ♀H7	Widely available

	'Sunbeam'	SHar
	'Sunny Seduction' (Seduction Series)	ECtt ELon EMor IKil MAsh MTis NAst
I	'Taygetea'	ELan GWyn LCro LOPS MBNS SCob SPer SPoG SRkn WCAu WCot WFar WSpi XLum
	'Terracotta'	Widely available
	'The Beacon'	see *A.* 'Fanal'
	'Tissington Old Rose'	MNrw
	tomentosa ♀H5	CTri EBou ECha GPSL WFar
§	- 'Aurea'	CMea NBro SPhx XLum
	- 'Goldie'	SWvt WFar
	- 'Maynard's Gold'	see *A. tomentosa* 'Aurea'
	'Tri-colour'	MBNS MBel NGdn
§	***umbellata***	NSla XSen
	'Velour'	GBin
	'W.B. Childs'	ELan MNrw MRav NDov SHar
	'Walther Funcke'	Widely available
§	'Wesersandstein'	GMaP MNrw NBir SCob SGbt
	'Wilczekii'	SRms
	'Yellowstone'	EWes

× *Achimenantha* (*Gesneriaceae*)

'Aries'	WDib
'Cool Inferno'	WDib
'Golden Jubilee'	WDib
'Himalayan Sunrise'	LAma WDib
'Inferno' ♀H1b	WDib
'Pisces'	WDib
'Texas Blue Bayou'	WDib

Achimenes (*Gesneriaceae*)

'Addano'	WDib
admirabilis	WDib
'Ambroise Verschaffelt' ♀H1c	EShb LAma WDib
'Ami Van Houtte'	WDib
'Apricot Glow'	WDib
'Aquamarine'	WDib
'Aurora Charm'	WDib
'Ballerina'	WDib
'Beautiful Fire'	WDib
'Big Weiss'	WDib
'Blue Sparks'	SDeJ
'Caligula'	WDib
'Cameo Rose'	WDib
'Candy Shop'	WDib
(Cascade Series) 'Cascade Fairy Pink'	WDib
- 'Cascade Fashionable Pink'	WDib
- 'Cascade Rose Red'	WDib
- 'Cascade Violet Night'	WDib
'Cattleya'	LAma
cettoana	WDib
'Charity'	WDib
'Charm'	LAma SDeJ WDib
'Claret'	WDib
'Crackerjack'	WDib
'Crummock Water'	WDib
'Double Picotee Rose' (d)	WDib
'Double Pink Rose' (d)	WDib
erecta	WDib
'Erlkönig'	WDib
'Escheriana'	LAma
'Extravaganza'	WDib
'Firefly'	WDib
'Flamenco'	WDib
'Glory'	WDib
'Golden Butterfly'	WDib
'Harry Williams'	EShb LAma WDib
'Hilda Michelssen' ♀H1c	WDib
(Himalayan Series) 'Himalayan Angel'	LAma
- 'Himalayan Double' (d)	LAma
- 'Himalayan Mandarin'	LAma
'Hugues Aufray'	WDib
'Ice Tea'	WDib
'India'	EShb
(Jay Dee Series) 'Jay Dee Coral'	WDib
- 'Jay Dee Large White'	WDib
- 'Jay Dee Pink'	WDib
- 'Jay Dee Purple'	WDib
'Jennifer Goode'	WDib
'Johanna Michelssen'	WDib
'Just Divine'	WDib
'Kim Blue'	WDib
'Lady in Black'	WDib
'Light Lilac'	WDib
'Little Beauty'	WDib
longiflora 'Major'	WDib
'Maxima'	LAma
'Melon Ice Cream'	WDib
'Menuett'	WDib
mexicana	LAma SDeJ
misera	WDib
'Opal'	WDib
'Orange Delight'	WDib
'Pally'	WDib
'Patens Major'	WDib
'Peach Blossom'	EShb LAma SDeJ WDib
'Peach Glow'	WDib
pedunculata	WDib
'Petite Fadette'	WDib
'Poil de Carotte' **new**	WDib
'Primadonna'	SDeJ WDib
'Pulcherrima'	SDeJ
'Purple King'	WDib
'Purple Queen'	WDib
'Purple Triumph'	WDib
'Queen of Queens'	WDib
'Rai'	WDib
'Rainbow'	WDib
'Rainbow Warrior'	WDib
'Red Hilda Michelssen'	WDib
'Rozi Roza'	WDib
'Santa Claus'	WDib
'Schneewittchen'	WDib
'Serge Saliba'	WDib
'Serge's Fantasy'	WDib
'Show-off'	WDib
'Shy Sun'	WDib
skinneri	WDib
'Snow Princess'	EShb SDeJ
'Stan's Delight' (d) ♀H1c	WDib
'Sterntaler'	WDib
'Sugarland'	WDib
'Sun Wind'	WDib
'Sweet and Sour'	WDib
'Tango'	WDib
'Tarantella'	WDib
'Tetra Himalayan Purple' (Tetra Series)	LAma WDib
'Tiger Eye'	WDib
'Valse Bleu'	WDib
'Violacea Semiplena' (d)	WDib
'Vivid'	LAma WDib
'Weinrot Elfe'	WDib
'Wetterlow's Triumph'	WDib
'Yellow Beauty'	WDib

Achimenes × Smithiantha see *× Achimenantha*

Achlys (*Berberidaceae*)

Name	Suppliers
japonica	WCru
triphylla	WCru
- B&SWJ 13541 new	WCru

Achnatherum see *Stipa*

Achyranthes (*Amaranthaceae*)

Name	Suppliers
bidentata var. ***longifolia*** PAB 8037	LEdu

Acidanthera see *Gladiolus*

Acinos (*Lamiaceae*)

Name	Suppliers
§ ***alpinus***	CMea EBou EDAr GJos LLHF SRms WJek XLum
§ ***corsicus***	WHoo WKif

Aciphylla (*Apiaceae*)

Name	Suppliers
aurea	GBin GCal SPlb
glaucescens	GCal SPlb
montana	CMen
scott-thomsonii	GKev
squarrosa	GKev

Acis (*Amaryllidaceae*)

Name	Suppliers
§ ***autumnalis*** ♀H5	CAby CAvo CBor CBro CElw CTri EAJP ECha EDAr EHyd ELan EPot EWes GKev LRHS MPie NBir NHpl NRHS SBrt SMHy SPhx SRms SRot WAbe WFar WHoo WSHC
- 'Cobb's Variety'	GCal
- var. ***oporantha***	CWCL GKev LAma
- - f. ***dispathacea***	GEdr GKev
- 'September Snow'	ELan GKev LAma
I ***ionica***	GKev
subsp. ***vlorensis*** new	
§ ***longifolia***	GKev
nicaeensis	EHyd EPot GCal GKev LRHS NRHS NWad WAbe WCot WThu
§ ***rosea***	WAbe
§ ***tingitana***	CBro
§ ***trichophylla***	GKev
- f. ***purpurascens***	WCot
§ ***valentina***	SRot WCot

Acmella (*Asteraceae*)

Name	Suppliers
§ ***oleracea***	CLau

Acnistus (*Solanaceae*)

Name	Suppliers
australis	see *Iochroma australe*

Aconitum (*Ranunculaceae*)

Name	Suppliers
sp.	EMor
ACE new	EPPr
'Album'	NPri WSpi
altissimum	see *A. lycoctonum* subsp. *vulparia*
anglicum	see *A. napellus* subsp. *napellus* Anglicum Group
§ ***anthora***	EBee EPfP GKev IKil MHol
arcuatum	see *A. fischeri* var. *arcuatum*
austroyunnanense	WHal WSHC
- BWJ 7902	WCru
autumnale misapplied	see *A. carmichaelii* Wilsonii Group
autumnale Rchb.	see *A. fischeri* Rchb.
× ***bicolor***	see *A. × cammarum* 'Bicolor'
'Blue Lagoon'[PBR]	CWGN EBee NLar WHil
'Blue Opal'	EBee EWes MAvo
'Blue Sceptre'	SRms
'Bressingham Spire' ♀H7	CMac CRos ECtt EHrv EHyd ELan EPfP GAbr GBin GKin GMaP IKil LRHS MAvo MCot MHol NDov NGdn NLar NPer NRHS SCob SPer SRms SSut WFar WSpi
bulbilliferum HWJK 2120	WSHC
× ***cammarum***	NChi
§ - 'Bicolor' ♀H7	Widely available
- 'Eleanora'	CBod ECtt EMor EPPr EPfP GMaP SRms
- 'Grandiflorum Album'	EMor MNrw WGoo
- 'Pink Sensation'[PBR]	GKev NLar
§ ***carmichaelii***	CSam EHyd ELan EPfP GAbr GKin IFro LRHS MMuc MNrw NBro NChi NEgg NGdn NPri NRHS SEND SRms WCot WFar WHoo WSpi
- Arendsii Group	CAby ECtt GKev LEdu SRot WCAu WCFE
- - 'Arendsii' ♀H7	Widely available
- - 'Cloudy'[PBR]	CWGN EBee ECtt ELon EMor LEdu LPla MAvo MBel MHol NGdn NLar NRHS WCot WHil WSpi
- 'Moody Blues'	EBee
- 'Redleaf'	see *A. carmichaelii* 'Royal Flush'
- 'River Finn'	WCot
- 'River Lugg'	WCot
- 'River Medway'	CDor WCot
- 'River Nene'	WCot
- 'River Ouse'	ECtt WCot
- 'River Spey'	WCot
- 'River Teifi'	WCot
- 'River Trent'	WCot
- 'River Welland'	WCot
§ - 'Royal Flush'[PBR]	CDor CWGN EBee ECtt LSun MBNS MCot MHol MNrw NEgg NLar SPad SPoG WCot
- var. ***truppelianum***	WCot
- - HWJ 732	EBee WCot
§ - Wilsonii Group	CMac EBee LEdu MCot MRav NDov NEgg WHoo XLum
- - 'Barker's Variety'	CKno CRos EBee ELon GCal LRHS NGdn NLar NRHS NSti SRms WCot WSpi
- - 'Kelmscott' ♀H7	ELon MCot MRav SMHy WCot WFar WSpi
- - 'Spätlese'	CDor CSam CWGN EBee ECtt ELon GBin GCal GQue LEdu LRHS MCot MHol NBir NGdn NLar SGbt SPer SPoG WCAu WCot WRHF
§ ***chasmanthum***	CRos LRHS NRHS
- GWJ 9393	WCru
chiisanense B&SWJ 4446	WCru
cilicicum	see *Eranthis hyemalis* Cilicica Group
compactum	see *A. napellus* subsp. *vulgare*
confertiflorum	see *A. anthora*
delphinifolium	CExl
elliotii	EBee
elwesii	EBee LEdu
episcopale	WCot WCru
excelsum	see *A. lycoctonum* subsp. *lycoctonum*
ferox	EBee EMor LLHF
- GWJ 9333 from Sikkim	WCru
- GWJ 9403	WCru
fischeri misapplied	see *A. carmichaelii*
§ ***fischeri*** Rchb.	CBod EBee LRHS NBid NLar WCot
- B&SWJ 8809	WCru

§ - var. ***arcuatum*** B&SWJ 774	WCru
formosanum B&SWJ 3057	WCru
fukutomei B&SWJ 337	MRav WCru
gammiei GWJ 9418	WCru
gmelinii	see *A. lycoctonum* subsp. *lycoctonum*
grossedentatum	LPla NLar
- subsp. ***paniculatum***	see *A. variegatum* subsp. *paniculatum*
§ ***hemsleyanum***	CAby CExl CRHN CWGN ECtt EWld GKev GLog MBel NBid WCot WCru
- dark blue-flowered	WSpi
- 'Red Wine'	MHol MSCN WCot
- var. ***unguiculatum*** new	GKev
hyemale	see *Eranthis hyemalis*
'Ivorine'	CRos CSam EBee ECha EHyd ELan EMor EPfP GMaP ILea LEdu LRHS MCot MHol NGdn NLar NRHS NSti SCob SPer WFar WPnP WWtn
jaluense B&SWJ 8741	WCru
japonicum	EBee GCal GQue NLar WCot
- var. ***hakonense***	CExl
- var. ***montanum*** B&SWJ 5507	WCru
§ - subsp. ***napiforme***	EWes
- - B&SWJ 943	EBee ELon WCru
§ - subsp. ***subcuneatum*** B&SWJ 6228	WCru
kitadakense B&SWJ 11173	WCru
'Kleiner Ritter'	EBee
kusnezoffii	WCot
laciniatum GWJ 9254	WCru
- GWJ 9324	WCru
lamarckii	see *A. lycoctonum* subsp. *neapolitanum*
lasianthum	see *A. lycoctonum* subsp. *vulparia*
leucostomum	EBee GCal
loczyanum	GKev WCot
- B&SWJ 11529	WCru WSHC
lycoctonum	NGrd NLar NSti WSpi
- 'Darkeyes'	WCot
§ - subsp. ***lycoctonum***	SRms
§ - subsp. ***moldavicum***	WCot
§ - subsp. ***neapolitanum***	CDor EBee GCal GMaP IMou MMuc NLar SEND WHil WSpi
- 'Russian Yellow'	EWld GCal
§ - subsp. ***vulparia***	CMac LEdu GPoy ILea MNrw MRav NEgg NGdn SRms WWtn
mairei	see *A. vilmorinianum*
moldavicum	see *A. lycoctonum* subsp. *moldavicum*
nagarum	LEdu WCot
- KR 7589	EBee
napellus	CBod CCBP CRos CWld ECtt EPfP GBin GPoy ILea LRHS MBel MCot MHol MMuc MNHC MWat NDai NGrd SEND SPoG SRms WCot WFar WHoo WPnP WShi XLum
- 'Bergfürst'	EBee NDov
- 'Blue Valley'	EBee EPfP EWes
- 'Gletschereis'	CRos EBee LRHS NRHS
§ - subsp. ***napellus*** Anglicum Group	MCot MHol MMuc SEND WCot WWtn
- - - 'Spring Yellow'	WCot
- 'Rubellum'	IMou LRHS MBel NBro NLar
- 'Schneewittchen'	CSpe EWes MBel SAko
§ - subsp. ***vulgare***	GKev
- - 'Albidum'	CBod CRos ELon EPfP EWTr GMaP LEdu LRHS MBel MHol NBid NCGa NHol NLar NRHS SPer SPoG WWtn
- - 'Carneum'	EBee NGrd WHer WOut
- 'William Turner' new	NGrd
napiforme	see *A. japonicum* subsp. *napiforme*
nasutum	WCot
- white-flowered	WCot
neapolitanum	see *A. lycoctonum* subsp. *neapolitanum*
'Newry Blue'	CRos EBee ECtt ELan EMor IMou LRHS MArl MAvo MBNS MRav NBir NEgg NRHS NWad SRms WSpi
orientale misapplied	see *A. lycoctonum* subsp. *vulparia*
paniculatum misapplied	see *A. variegatum* subsp. *paniculatum*
piepunense	EBee GKev
proliferum	WCot
- B&SWJ 4107	WCru
pseudohuiliense	CExl
pseudolaeve var. ***erectum*** B&SWJ 8466	WCru
pubiceps white-flowered	GCal
pyramidale	see *A. napellus* subsp. *vulgare*
pyrenaicum misapplied	see *A. lycoctonum* subsp. *neapolitanum*
ranunculifolium	see *A. lycoctonum* subsp. *neapolitanum*
sachalinense	WCot
- subsp. ***yezoense***	EBee LPla NLar WCot
senanense var. ***incisum*** B&SWJ 11032	SMad WCru
- subsp. ***paludicola*** B&SWJ 10866	WCru
seoulense	EBee
- B&SWJ 694	WCru
- B&SWJ 864	WCru
- BWJ 4107	IMou
septentrionale	see *A. lycoctonum* subsp. *lycoctonum*
'Spark's Variety' ♀H7	Widely available
spicatum GWJ 9394	WCru
'Stainless Steel' ♀H7	Widely available
subcuneatum	see *A. japonicum* subsp. *subcuneatum*
'Surprise'	WCot
× ***tubergenii***	see *Eranthis hyemalis* Tubergenii Group
uchiyamae B&SWJ 1005	WCru
- B&SWJ 1216	ECha ELon WCru
- B&SWJ 4446	NLar
variegatum	EBee GCal
§ - subsp. ***paniculatum***	EBee GCal LPla WCot
- - 'Roseum'	WFar
§ ***vilmorinianum*** BWJ 8055	WCru
violaceum var. ***robustum***	see *A. chasmanthum*
volubile misapplied	see *A. hemsleyanum*
volubile Pall.	EBee
vulparia	see *A. lycoctonum* subsp. *vulparia*
yamazakii	WCru
zigzag var. ***ryohakuense*** B&SWJ 8906	WCru

Aconogonon see *Persicaria*

Acorus ✿ (*Acoraceae*)

calamus	CBen CKno CWat EMor GPoy MNHC NPer WMAq
- subsp. ***angustatus***	GPoy

- 'Argenteostriatus' (v)	CWat ECha MMuc SCob SEND SRms WMAq
* ***christophii***	ELon EPPr
gramineus	GPoy NPer
- 'Golden Delight'	SCob SRms
- 'Golden Edge' (v)	ELon NRHS NWad
- 'Hakuro-nishiki' (v)	GCrg GWyn NBid NWad SCob SRms SWvt WMoo XLum
- 'Kinchinjunga' (v)	IFro
- 'Licorice'	GBin GCal MSCN WBrk WGrn
- 'Masamune' (v)	EWes GBin GCal
- 'Minimus Aureus'	CBre GCal
- 'Oborozuki' misapplied	see *A. gramineus* 'Ōgon'
- 'Oborozuki' (v)	EHoe
§ - 'Ōgon' (v)	Widely available
- var. ***pusillus***	NBro
- 'Variegatus' (v)	Widely available
'Intermedius'	NPer

Acradenia (*Rutaceae*)

frankliniae	CBcs CCCN CMac EBee EPfP LRHS MBlu SEND SPlb WHor WPGP

Actaea (*Ranunculaceae*)

alba misapplied	see *A. pachypoda, A. rubra* f. *neglecta*
arizonica	CRos EBee LPla LRHS NLar NRHS WCru
asiatica B&SWJ 616	WCru
- B&SWJ 6351 from Japan	WCru
- B&SWJ 8694 from Korea	WCru
- BWJ 8174 from China	WCru
biternata B&SWJ 8917	NLar WCru
- B&SWJ 11190	WCru
'Chocoholic'	CBod CWGN EBee ECtt ELan EMor EUJe GEdr ILea IPot LRHS MAsh MAvo MBel MHol MMrt MNrw NPri NRHS WHil
§ ***cimicifuga***	ECha GCal GPoy
aff. ***cimicifuga*** WJC 13720	WCru
§ ***cordifolia***	CFis EBee GBin GMaP LRHS NAln NLar SWvt
- variegated (v)	EBee
dahurica	GBin GQue
- B&SWJ 8426	WCru
- B&SWJ 8573	WCru
- tall	NBid
elata	CPla IMou
erythrocarpa	see *A. rubra*
frigida B&SWJ 2966	WCru
§ ***japonica***	GCal NLar
- B&SWJ 5828	WCru
- B&SWJ 11136	WCru
- B&SWJ 11526	WCru
- from Jejudo, South Korea	EBee GBin IMou IPot MNrw NDov WWtn
- var. ***acutiloba*** B&SWJ 6257	WCru
- 'Cheju-Do'	CBod LPla MBel MMrt WWtn
- compact B&SWJ 8758A	WCot WCru
mairei	CRos IMou LRHS NRHS
- BWJ 7635	WCru
- BWJ 7939	WCru
§ ***matsumurae***	CExl
- B&SWJ 11187	WCru
- B&SWJ 11528	WCru
- 'Elstead Variety' ♀H7	CExl GCal MRav
- 'White Pearl' ♀H7	Widely available
§ ***pachypoda***	CBro CExl EBee EPfP EWTr GCal GLog GPoy MBel NBid NSti WCru
- MISTY BLUE ('Lk05'PBR)	CBod CBro CSpe IPot CWGN EBee ECtt ESwi GEdr LPla MAvo MHol MNrw SCob SMad SPoG WCot WNPC
- f. ***rubrocarpa***	GCal
- 'Silver Leaf' **new**	CSpe
§ ***podocarpa***	EBee SPlb SRms WCru
'Queen of Sheba'PBR	EBee NDov
racemosa ♀H7	CBod CMac CRos EBee ELan EPfP GCal GPoy NBid NGdn NLar NSti SCob SPer SWvt WFar WWtn XLum
§ ***rubra***	CBod CRos CSpe EBee ECha ELan GCal LEdu LRHS MBel MMrt NBid NLar NRHS NWad SMad SPoG WBor WCru
- B&SWJ 9555	WCru
- ***alba***	see *A. pachypoda, A. rubra* f. *neglecta*
§ - f. ***neglecta***	GLog WCot WCru
simplex	CPla EBee GLog WCot
- B&SWJ 8653	WCru
- B&SWJ 8664	WCru
- B&SWJ 10957	WCru
- B&SWJ 11133	WCru
§ - Atropurpurea Group	Widely available
- - 'Black Negligee'	Widely available
- - 'Brunette' ♀H7	Widely available
- - 'Carbonella'	EBee ECtt ELan EWTr MHol MNHC MNrw WFar WHil
- - 'Hillside Black Beauty' ♀H7	CBct CDor EBee ECtt EMor GKin GMaP IKil LRHS MAsh MTis NBir NLar SCob
- - 'James Compton' ♀H7	Widely available
- - 'Mountain Wave'	ECtt MAsh NDov
- 'Pink Spike'	Widely available
§ - 'Prichard's Giant'	GCal LRHS MNrw MRav NHic NLar NRHS WFar
- ***ramosa***	see *A. simplex* 'Prichard's Giant'
- 'Silver Axe'	GCal
- variegated (v)	WCot
spicata	CSpe EMor GBin GPoy LEdu WCru
- PAB 8131	LEdu
- from England	WCru
taiwanensis B&SWJ 3413	WCru
- RWJ 9996	WCru
yesoensis	NLar
- B&SWJ 6355	WCru
- B&SWJ 10860	WCru
yunnanensis	GCal

Actinella see *Tetraneuris*

Actinidia (*Actinidiaceae*)

sp.	CCCN
BWJ 8161 from China	WCru
arguta	CRHN EBee MGil
- (f/F)	CAgr
- B&SWJ 4455 from Jejudo, South Korea	WCru
- B&SWJ 4823 from Japan	WCru
- B&SWJ 8529 from Ulleungdo, South Korea	WCru
- 'Ambrosia' (f/F)	WMat
- 'Ambrosia Grande' (f/F)	NLar
- 'Ananasnaya' (f/F)	CAgr WPGP
- 'Bayern' (f/F)	CAgr CCCN
- 'Geneva 2' (f/F)	CAgr
- 'Honigbeere'	NLar
- 'Issai' (s-p/F)	CAgr CBcs CCCN EPom LBuc LEdu LRHS SVic WPGP

- 'Jumbo' (f/F) CAgr LEdu SVic
- 'Ken's Red' (f/F) CAgr CCCN CFGn IDee LEdu SVic
- 'Kokuwa' (s-p/F) **new** CAgr
- 'Meader' (m) CAgr
- 'Purpurna Sadowa' (f/F) NLar
- SCARLET SEPTEMBER KIWI ('Mirzan') (f/F) **new** CAgr
- 'Shoko' (f/F) WCru
- 'Unchae' (m) WCru
- 'Weiki' (m) CAgr CCCN LEdu SVic

chinensis misapplied see *A. deliciosa*
chinensis Planch. var. ***setosa*** B&SWJ 3563 WCru
coriacea WWJ 11895 **new** WCru
§ ***deliciosa*** CCCN MRav WFar WSHC
- 'Atlas' (m) NLar SDea
- 'Golden Delight' (f/F) CBcs
- 'Hayward' (f/F) CBcs CCCN EPfP LRHS LSRN SCob SDea SWvt WFar
- 'Jenny' (s-p/F) CAgr CEnd CMac CRos CTri ELan EMOT EPfP EPom LBuc LCro LOPS LRHS MGos MJak SCob SDea SPoG SPre SSFr SVic WFar
- 'Oriental Delight' (s-p/F) CRHN
- SOLISSIMO ('Renact'[PBR]) (s-p/F) CRos EHyd LRHS MCoo NRHS WMat
- 'Solo' (s-p/F) CBar CBcs CCCN CMac CRHN CRos ECrN EPfP LRHS LSRN NLar SLim SPer SWvt
- 'Tomuri' (m) CBcs CCCN EBee EPfP LRHS LSRN SWvt

hypoleuca B&SWJ 5942 WCru
'Kiwai Bee' CCCN
kolomikta ♀H5 Widely available
- B&SWJ 4243 LSRN WCru
- (m) MBlu
- 'Doctor Szymanowski' (s-p/F) CAgr WPGP
- 'Sentyabraskaya' (f/F) NLar
- 'Tomoko' (f/F) WCru
- 'Yazuaki' (m) WCru

melanandra SPlb
petelotii FMWJ 13137 WCru
- HWJ 628 WCru
pilosula misapplied see *A. tetramera* var. *maloides*
pilosula (Finet & Gagnep.) Stapf ex Hand.-Mazz. CAby CKel CRos EHyd ELan IArd IDee IMou LRHS NRHS SPoG SRms WKif
polygama CMen GCal
- B&SWJ 5444 WCru
- B&SWJ 8525 from Korea WCru
- B&SWJ 8923 from Japan WCru
- B&SWJ 12564 from Korea WCru

rufa B&SWJ 3525 WCru
strigosa WJC 13662 WCru
- WJC 13807 WCru

aff. ***strigosa*** HWJK 2367 WCru
§ ***tetramera*** var. ***maloides*** ♀H5 CBcs CExl CWGN EBee EUJe GCal MGil NLar SBrt SCoo WBor WCru WPGP WSHC

Adansonia (*Malvaceae*)

grandidieri SPlb
madagascariensis SPlb
rubrostipa SPlb
za SPlb

Adelocaryum see *Lindelofia*

Adenanthos (*Proteaceae*)

sericeus SPlb

Adenium (*Apocynaceae*)

obesum ♀H1a CCCN

Adenocarpus (*Papilionaceae*)

decorticans SPlb

Adenophora (*Campanulaceae*)

sp. MHol
'Afterglow' see *Campanula rapunculoides* 'Afterglow'
asiatica see *Hanabusaya asiatica*
aurita SBrt
bulleyana CRos ELan LRHS NBid NEgg NGdn NLar SPlb WCot WFar
capillaris NLar
subsp. ***leptosepala***
- - BWJ 7986 WCru

coelestis CExl NBid
- B&SWJ 7998 WCru

confusa WSHC
divaricata B&SWJ 11018 WCru
'Gaudi Violet' EMor SEle SPad SPoG WCot WHlf
grandiflora B&SWJ 8555 WCru
khasiana CExl EMor GKev LLHF NLar XLum
lamarkii B&SWJ 8738 WCru
latifolia misapplied see *A. pereskiifolia*
liliifolia CMea EPfP GCal GKev NAln NLar NPer WFar
maximowicziana B&SWJ 11008 WCru
morrisonensis RWJ 10008 WCru
§ ***nikoensis*** EBee EMor GEdr NBid WCot
- B&SWJ 11201 WCru

§ ***pereskiifolia*** EWes SHar SPlb WCot
- 'Alba' SRms

polyantha NLar SRms
polymorpha see *A. nikoensis*
potaninii EBee MMuc SEND WFar WHal
- pale-flowered MAvo WHal

remotiflora EBee
- B&SWJ 8714 WCru
- B&SWJ 11016 WCru

stricta subsp. ***confusa*** GKev NAln
- subsp. ***sessilifolia*** EBee

takedae EBee SBrt
- B&SWJ 11424 WCru

taquetii GEdr
tashiroi EBee GKev NAln XLum
triphylla GKev
- B&SWJ 10916 WCru
- var. ***japonica*** B&SWJ 10933 WCru

uehatae GEdr
- B&SWJ 126 WCru

Adenophora × *Campanula* (*Campanulaceae*)

A. taquetii × ***C. waldensteinia*** **new** EPot

Adenostyles (*Asteraceae*)

alpina SBrt

Adesmia (*Papilionaceae*)

longipes SPlb

Adiantum ✿ (*Pteridaceae*)

	sp.	CMac
	aethiopicum	XBlo
§	***aleuticum*** ♀H6	CAby CKel CLAP NBro NLar SPlb WFib
	- 'Imbricatum'	CBdn CBod CElw CLAP CRos EBee ECha ELon EMor EUJe GEdr ISha LPla LRHS MGos NBid NBro NLar NRHS SPoG SRms WCot WFar WFib XLum
§	- 'Japonicum'	WFar
	- 'Miss Sharples'	CAby CDTJ CLAP CRos ECha GEdr LEdu LPla LRHS MGos NLar NRHS SRms WCot
§	- 'Subpumilum' ♀H5	CLAP NBro WCot WFib
	- 'Tasselatum'	WCot
	bonatianum	CExl
	capillus-veneris	CBdn EBee ISha NBro WFib
	- 'Mairisii'	see *A.* × *mairisii*
	caudatum	ISha
	hispidulum	CBdn CCCN CRos EBee ISha LEdu LRHS NRHS
	- 'Bronze Venus'	CCCN CRos EShb ISha LRHS NRHS SRms
§	× ***mairisii*** ♀H5	CLAP CRos EBee EShb ISha LEdu LRHS NRHS
	pedatum misapplied	see *A. aleuticum*
	pedatum ambig.	EUJe ISha SMad
	pedatum L.	CBcs CBct CDor CLAP ECha EFer ELon GAbr GMaP NAst NBro SPlb WFar
	- Asiatic form	see *A. aleuticum* 'Japonicum'
	- 'Japonicum'	see *A. aleuticum* 'Japonicum'
	- 'Roseum'	see *A. aleuticum* 'Japonicum'
	- var. ***subpumilum***	see *A. aleuticum* 'Subpumilum'
	peruvianum	ISha
	poiretii	WCot
	pubescens	ISha
	raddianum 'Fragrans'	see *A. raddianum* 'Fragrantissimum'
§	- 'Fragrantissimum'	EShb ISha
	- 'Fritz Lüthi' ♀H1c	EShb
	- 'Lady Geneva'	WCot
	- 'Lisa' **new**	EShb
	- 'Monocolor'	ISha
	reniforme	WCot
	tenerum 'Bicolor'	ISha
	× ***tracyi***	ISha
	venustum ♀H7	Widely available

Adlumia (*Papaveraceae*)

	fungosa	CRos CSpe LRHS NRHS

Adonis (*Ranunculaceae*)

	aestivalis	CSpe
	amurensis misapplied	see *A.* 'Fukujukai', *A. multiflora*
	amurensis ambig.	CMea EBee EHrv EPot GEdr GKev LEdu MBel NHpl WPnP
	- 'Pleniflora'	see *A. multiflora* 'Sandanzaki'
	- 'Sakhalin'	EBee
	annua	SPhx
	brevistyla	GEdr
	'Chichibu-beni'	GEdr
§	'Fukujukai'	ECha GEdr XEll
§	***multiflora***	MBel SRot
	- 'Beni-nadeshiko'	GEdr
	- 'Hakuju'	GEdr
	- 'Hanazono' (d)	GEdr
§	- 'Sandanzaki' (d)	EBee EPot GBin GEdr GKev LEdu NLar
	ramosa	GEdr
	'Sado-no-maboroshi' (d)	GEdr
	vernalis	GPoy NLar WCot

Adoxa (*Adoxaceae*)

	moschatellina	CBre EBee EWld LEdu MNrw NRya WHer WSFF WSHC WShi WWtn

Aechmea ✿ (*Bromeliaceae*)

	sp.	XBlo
	fasciata	WSFF XBlo
	ramosa	XBlo
	victoriana	XBlo

Aegle (*Rutaceae*)

	sepiaria	see *Citrus trifoliata*

Aegopodium (*Apiaceae*)

	aff. ***handellii*** PAB 9003	SPhx
	podagraria 'Dangerous' (v)	CNat
	- gold-margined (v)	EPPr
	- 'Variegatum' (v)	CKel CRos EBee ECha ECrN EHoe EPPr EShb GKev GMaP GQue LRHS MBel MRav NBid NRHS NSti SEND SPer WCot WHil WMoo WSHC XLum

Aeonium (*Crassulaceae*)

	arboreum	CDTJ CKno CPbh CPla ELan EShb GCal NCft SEND
	- 'Atropurpureum'	CAbb CCCN CDTJ CPla CSde ELan EShb NCft NPer SEND SPer
I	- 'Magnificum'	EShb ESwi GBin SArc
	- 'Variegatum' (v)	CPbh CPla NPer
	balsamiferum	CCCN CDTJ CPbh EUJe NCft SChr SSim WCot
	'Black Cap'	CCCN
	'Blush'	CKno
	'Blushing Beauty' ♀H1c	CAbb SSim
	canariense	CCCN CDTJ SVen
	- var. ***palmense***	SVen
	castello-paivae	SChr
	ciliatum	SPlb
	'Copper Kettle'	WAvo
	'Cornish Tribute'	CCCN CPbh SSim
	'Cristata Sunburst'	CDTJ CPbh WCot
	cuneatum	CDTJ CPbh CSde SEND
	- blue-leaved **new**	SChr
	'Cyclops'	CPbh NCft
*	***decorum*** 'Variegatum' (v)	WCot
	'Dinner Plate'	CDTJ CPbh
	× ***domesticum***	see *Aichryson* × *aizoides* var. *domesticum*
	'Du Rozzen'	CPbh
*	***escobarii***	SPlb
	glandulosum	SVen
	gomerense	CPla
	goochiae 'Ballerina' (v) **new**	SBch SSim WCot
	haworthii ♀H1c	CDTJ NCft NHpl SAll SEND SSim SVen
	- 'Kiwi'	CCCN SSim
	- 'Variegatum' (v) ♀H1c	CDTJ CPbh EShb SAll SVen
	hierrense	CPbh SPlb
	holochrysum Webb & Berth.	CAbb
	leucoblepharum	EShb
	lindleyi	SChr
	'Logan Rock'	CPbh
	'Merry Maiden'	CPbh

*	***multiflorum*** 'Variegatum' (v)	CDTJ EUJe
	nobile	CBrP
	'Poldark'	CCCN CPbh
	sedifolium	CPbh NCft SAll SSim
	'Simply Misty' **new**	SSim
	'Simply Scarlet' **new**	SSim
	simsii	CDTJ CPbh NCft
	- variegated (v)	EShb
	simsii × 'Zwartkop'	CCCN CPbh CPla ELan GCal MHer SChr
	spathulatum	CDTJ CPbh EDAr WCot
	'Sunburst' (v) ♀H1c	CPbh WCot
	tabuliforme ♀H1c	CCCN CDTJ CPbh SMad SPlb SSim WCot
	'Trewidden'	WCot
	undulatum	SPlb
	urbicum	EShb
	'Velour'	CCCN CDTJ CPbh NCft NPer SSim
	'Voodoo'	GCal SSim WCot
	'Zwartkop' ♀H1c	CAbb CBcs CCCN CCht CHll CKno CPbh CSpe EShb EUJe GBin MCot MSCN NPer SArc SChr SEND SEle SMad SPlb SRot SSim SWvt WAvo WCot WWFP

Aeschynanthus ✿ (*Gesneriaceae*)

	Black Pagoda Group	WDib
	buxifolius KR 7798	WAbe
	'Fire Wheel'	WDib
	'Hot Flash'	WDib
	'Little Tiger'	WDib
	longicalyx	WDib
§	***longicaulis*** ♀H1a	WDib
	marmoratus	see *A. longicaulis*
	radicans ♀H1a	WDib
	'Scooby Doo'	WDib
	speciosus ♀H1a	WDib

Aesculus ✿ (*Sapindaceae*)

	arguta	see *A. glabra* var. *arguta*
	× ***arnoldiana***	CDul
	assamica WWJ 11886	WCru
	'Autumn Splendor'	EPfP
§	× ***bushii***	CDul MBlu
	californica	CDul CMCN EPfP ERod SBrt WPGP
	- 'Blue Haze'	WMat
	- 'Canyon Pink'	CMCN
	× ***carnea***	CDul LPra SGol
	- 'Aureomarginata' (v)	ERod LLHF
	- 'Briotii'	CAco CBcs CCVT CDul CEnd CMac CSBt ECrN ELan EMOT EPfP LMaj LPra LRHS MGos MMuc NLar NWea SCob SEND SEWo SPer WMat WTSh
	- 'Plantierensis'	CDul
*	- 'Variegata' (v)	CDul CMCN
	chinensis	CBcs CMCN
	flava ♀H5	CDul CMCN ELan EPfP EWTr IArd LMaj LPra MMuc SEND
	- f. ***vestita***	CDul EPfP MBlu
	georgiana	see *A. sylvatica*
	glabra	CDul CMCN MMuc
§	- var. ***arguta***	CMCN NLar
	- 'Autumn Blaze'	EPfP
	- 'October Red'	EPfP
	glaucescens	see *A.* × *neglecta*
	hippocastanum	CAco CBcs CCVT CDul CMac CPer CSBt CTri ECrN ELan EMOT LPra MGos MMuc MSwo NLar NOra NWea SCob SEND SEWo SGol SPer WFar WMat WTSh
	- 'Aureomarginata' (v)	CMac
§	- 'Baumannii' (d)	CDul CMCN ECrN ELan LPra MGos MSwo NWea SCob SPer
	- 'Digitata'	CDul CMCN WCot
	- 'Flore Pleno'	see *A. hippocastanum* 'Baumannii'
	- 'Hampton Court Gold'	CDul CMCN CMac
	- f. ***laciniata***	CDul CMCN NLar WCot
	- 'Pyramidalis'	LPra
	- 'Wisselink'	CDul CMCN WCot
	indica	CDul CLnd CMCN ECrN ELan EPfP EWTr LEdu LMaj MMuc SEND SGol WMou WTSh
	- 'Sydney Pearce' ♀H5	CBcs CEnd CJun CMCN EPfP ERod IArd MBlu MGos NLar NOra WMat
	× ***marylandica***	CDul
	× ***mississippiensis***	see *A.* × *bushii*
	× ***mutabilis*** 'Induta'	CDul CMCN EPfP NOra WMat
§	- 'Penduliflora'	CDul
§	× ***neglecta***	CMCN
	- 'Autumn Fire'	EBee EPfP WMat
	- 'Erythroblastos' ♀H5	CBcs CDul CEnd CJun CMCN EPfP ERod MBlu SCoo SMad SPer WCot WMat
	parviflora ♀H5	CBcs CDul CMCN CTri EBee ELan EPfP EWTr GKin IDee LMaj LPra MBlu MGos MMuc MRav NLar NOra NWea SEND SGol SMad SPer SWvt WMat
	pavia	CBcs CMCN EPfP MMuc
	- 'Atrosanguinea'	CEnd CMCN EPfP ERod
	- var. ***discolor*** 'Koehnei'	CMCN EPfP NLar NOra SPoG WMat
	- northern **new**	SBrt
	- 'Penduliflora'	see *A.* × *mutabilis* 'Penduliflora'
	- 'Rosea Nana'	CMCN
§	- Splendens Group	CMCN EPfP
	splendens	see *A. pavia* Splendens Group
§	***sylvatica***	CMCN
	turbinata	CBcs CDul CMCN
	wilsonii	CBcs CDul CExl MBlu

Aethionema (*Brassicaceae*)

I	***antitaurii***	GJos
	armenum	GJos GKev
	capitatum	CPBP GJos SIgm
§	***grandiflorum*** ♀H5	ELan GJos GKev SRms
	- Pulchellum Group ♀H5	CSpe MMuc
*	***kotschyi*** hort.	GJos WAbe
	pulchellum	see *A. grandiflorum*
	schistosum	LLHF SPlb
	subulatum	LLHF
	'Warley Rose' ♀H5	CBor CRos EHyd ELan EPot EWTr GCrg LRHS MAsh MBel NBir NRHS NSla SRms WIce WThu WTor XSen
	'Warley Ruber'	CMea EPot WAbe

Afrocarpus (*Podocarpaceae*)

	falcatus	CBcs

Agapanthus ✿ (*Agapanthaceae*)

	'Adonis'	CPrp IBlr
	'African Moon'	CPrp IBal
	'African Skies'	CAbb CPrp IBal SFai
	africanus misapplied	CElw CExl CTsd EBee EHrv ELan EPfP EUJe GKev ILea ITim LCro LOPS MJak SArc SChr SCob SDeJ SPer SRot SVic WBor XLum XSen
	- 'Albus' misapplied	CBcs CExl CKel CRos EBee ELan EPfP EUJe EWTr GKev IKil ILea

		LCro LOPS LSRN MGos MJak MNHC NAln NRHS SCob SDeJ SEND SPer SRms WSpi XLum XSen
	- TWISTER ('Ambic001')	CBro CKel CPar CPla CSpe IBal LCro LOPS NSti SFai SPad SPoG SRms
	'Aimee'	CBro IBal
	'Alan Street'	IBal
	'Albus' ambig.	GKev GMaP MHer
I	'Albus Nanus'	IBal
I	'Albus Roseus'	IBal
	'Alice Gloucester'	CPrp
	'Allisio'	IBal
	'Amsterdam'	EBee EMor EWTr IBal IMou
	'Angela'	IBal MAvo
	'Ankara'	IBal
	'Anneke'	IBal
	'Antibe'	IBal
	'Aphrodite'	IBlr
	'Aquamarine'	IBal
	'Arctic Star'	CBdn CCCN CExl CKno CMac CPne CPou CPrp EBee ELon IBal LSRN MAvo MNHC NHoy NLar SDys SFai SPoG
	'Ardernei Hybrid'	CExl ECha ECtt EWes GAbr GCal IBal IBlr MAvo WCot WGwG
	'Ascona'	IBal
	'Atlas'	IBlr
	'Aureovittatus' (v)	IBal
	'Autumn Mist'	IBal
	'Avalanche'	EBee IBal SFai WSpi
§	'B in B'[PBR]	CBro CCCN CExl CWCL ECha ELan EPfP EShb IBal MBNS MRav NBid SCob SHyH SMad WCot WFar
	'Baby Blue'	see *A.* 'Blue Baby' Rom.
	'Baby Pete'[PBR]	EBee IBal NHoy
	BACK IN BLACK	see A. 'B in B'
	'Ballerina'	CBdn CPne CPrp IBal
	'Ballyrogan'	IBlr
	'Bangor Blue'	IBlr
	'Barley Blue'	IBal
	'Barnfield Blue'	CBdn CPne CPrp EBee IBal
	'Beatrice'	CPrp
	'Becky'	IBal
	'Beeches Dwarf'	IBal
	'Ben Hope'	CBro IBal IBlr
	'Berlin'	IBal
	'Beth Chatto'	see *A. campanulatus* 'Albovittatus'
	'Bicton Bell'	IBal IBlr
	'Bicton Bride'	IBal
	'Big Ben'	IBal
	'Big Blue'	CBod CCCN CChe CKel CMac CPrp CWCL EBee SEND SLdr SRkn WSpi
	'Big Boy' **new**	MAvo
	'Black Beauty'	CBod CPrp IBal WSpi
	'Black Buddhist'	CCCN CPrp CRos CWCL EBee ECtt EPfP EUJe GKev IBal MAvo NGdn NHoy NSti SPer XSen
	'Black Magic'	CAbb CPar CPrp EBee IBal NHoy NSti SFai SPoG
	'Black Pantha'[PBR]	Widely available
	'Blitzza' **new**	IBal
	'Bloemfontein'	IBal
§	'Blue Baby' Rom.	CCCN CRos EHyd ELan ELon IBal MJak NRHS
	'Blue Bayou'	IBal
	'Blue Bird'	CBdn CPne CRos NRHS
	'Blue Brush'	CPrp EPfP SCoo
	'Blue Cascade'	IBlr
	'Blue Companion'	CPrp IBlr
	'Blue Diamond' ambig.	CMac
	'Blue Dot'	CPrp EMor EPfP LLHF SDys
	'Blue Flare'	IBal
	'Blue Flash'	IBal
	'Blue Formality'	IBal IBlr
	'Blue Giant'	CBro CCCN CChe CDor CKno CPrp EBee ELan IBal MGos SCob WAvo WSpi
	'Blue Globe'	CBod EBee GMaP IBal
	'Blue Gown'	CSam
	'Blue Heaven'[PBR]	CBdn CPne CWGN IBal NHoy SCob
	'Blue Horizons'[PBR] (v)	CCCN IBal
	'Blue Ice'	CAbb CPou CPrp CRos EBee IBal NHoy SAko WTyc
	'Blue Imp'	CBro IBal IBlr
	'Blue Jay'	IBal
	'Blue Magic'	EBee IBal NHoy
	'Blue Moon'	CBro CPrp EBee ECha ECtt IBal IBlr ILea IPot MAvo MHol NLar SEND SHyH SLdr WCot
	'Blue Nile'	CBdn CPne CPrp IBal
	'Blue Pixie'	IBal
	'Blue Prince'	EBee
	'Blue Rinse'	IBal
I	'Blue Skies' Dunlop	IBlr
	'Blue Steel'	IBal
	'Blue Triumphator'	CBod CDor EPfP EWTr GKev GMaP IBal ILea MAvo NHoy SCob WSpi
	'Blue Umbrella'	CDor CPrp ELan SRkn WSpi
	'Blue Yonder'	EBee
	blue-flowered	WAvo WCFE
	BLUESTORM ('Atiblu'[PBR])	CPrp CRos EHyd EPfP IBal LBuc NRHS SArc SCob SEND
	'Bluety'[PBR]	IBal
	'Bray Valley'	CBdn CPne CPrp
	'Bressingham Blue'	CAbb CBro CSam CTri EWes GCal IBal IBlr MAvo MRav NHoy SFai SMHy WSpi
	'Bressingham Bounty'	EBee IBal
	'Bressingham White'	EPfP MRav
	'Bridal Bouquet'	CRos EBee IBal LSRN NHoy NRHS SAko SFai
	'Bright Blue'	IBal
	BRILLIANT BLUE ('Aga0451')	CKno EBee IBal SFai WHoo
	'Bristol'	IBal
	'Broadleigh Babe' **new**	CBro
	'Brody'	CPrp
	'Buckingham Palace'	CBro EBee ECha ELon EWes GAbr IBal IBlr NChi WCot
	'Calimero'	IBal
	'Cally Blue'	GAbr GCal IBal
	'Cally Large White'	GAbr
	'Cally Longstem'	EBee GCal
	'Cally Pale Blue'	IBal
	campanulatus	CMac CPbh CPrp ELan EPfP GKin IBal IBlr MRav NChi NEgg WAvo WFar WKif WSpi
	- var. ***albidus***	CBod CPrp CWCL ECha ELan EPfP GKev GKin IBlr MMuc MWat NBid NGdn NHoy SEND SPer WGwG WHoo WSHC WSpi
§	- 'Albovittatus' (v)	IBal
	- bright blue-flowered	GCal IBal
	- 'Cobalt Blue'	CBod CPrp ELan GKin IBal MAsh MMuc NGdn SSut WHoo
	- 'Oxford Blue'	IBlr
	- subsp. ***patens*** ♀H4	CPrp EPfP IBal MRav

– – deep blue-flowered	IBlr
– 'Profusion'	CBro ECha IBal IBlr NHoy
– 'Ultramarine'	IBal
– variegated (v)	EBee ECha NPer
– 'Wedgwood Blue'	CPrp EBee IBal IBlr
– 'Wendy'	EBee IBal IBlr
– 'White Hope'	IBal IBlr
'Castle of Mey'	CBdn CBod CBro CExl CPne CPrp
	EBee ELon GAbr GCal IBal IBlr
	LCro LOPS MAvo NHoy SFai WCAu
	WSpi
'Catharina'	IBal
§ ***caulescens*** ♀H3	CBdn CPne CPrp IBal IBlr SMHy
– subsp. ***angustifolius***	ELon IBal IBlr MHol SEND
– subsp. ***caulescens***	IBlr
'Cedric Morris'	IBal IBlr SMHy
'Celebration'	CBdn CPne IBal
'Chandra'	IBal IBlr
'Charlotte'PBR	CMac CRos EBee ELan EPfP IBal
	NRHS SFai SPoG
'Cheney's Lane'	SMHy
'Cherbours'	IBal
'Cherry Holley'	ELon IBal WSpi
'Chika's Blue'	EBee IBal MAvo
'Clarence House'	CBro IBal
'Cloudy Days'	IBal
coddii	CExl IBal IBlr MHer WCot
'Columba'	CPrp EBee ELon IBal LAma MAvo
	NBid XSen
comptonii	see *A. praecox* subsp. *minimus*
'Corina'	EBee
'Crystal'	GCal
'Crystal Drop'	CAbb CBdn CExl CPne CPou CPrp
	EBee IBal SFai
DANUBE	see *A.* 'Donau'
'Dart Valley'	CPrp IBal
'Dawn Star'	ECha
'Debbie'	IBal
'Delft'	EBee IBal IBlr
'Delft Blue'	CRos IBal
'Density'	IBlr
'Dnjepr'	CBro EBee IBal
'Dokkum'	IBal
'Dokter Brouwer'	CKno EMor EWTr GKev IKil ILea
	LSRN MCot SHyH
§ 'Donau'	CBro EBee EShb IBal NAln NBir
DOUBLE DIAMOND	CRos EBee EHyd EPfP EPot EWes
('Rfdd'PBR)	IBal LSRN NHoy NRHS SAko SCob
	SFai SPoG WFar WSpi XEll
'Dublin'	IBal
'Duivenbrugge Blue'	IBal
'Duivenbrugge White'	IBal SFai
'Durban'	IBal
dwarf blue **new**	NHoy
dyeri	see *A. inapertus* subsp. *intermedius*
'Early Blue'	EBee IPot
'Eggesford Sky'	CBdn CPne CPrp EBee IBal
'Elaine'	IBal
'Elisa'	IBal
'Elizabeth Salisbury'	IBal
'Ellamae'	IBal
'Enigma'	Widely available
'Enigma Variations'	EBee
'Ethel's Joy'	EBee IBal
'Eve'	IBlr
'Evening Eclipse'	CRos EMor IBal
'Evening Star'	CBdn CPne
'Exmoor'	IBal MAvo
'Findlay's Blue'	SMHy
'Finnline' (v)	SRms

'Flore Pleno' (d)	CExl CMac CPrp EBee ECha ECtt
	EHrv ELan GAbr GKin IBal IBlr
	MHer MHol NGdn NHoy WCot
	WFar WPGP WSHC
'Flower of Love' **new**	CBdn CPne MHol SFai SPoG WHlf
'Fulsome'	IBlr
'Gayle's Lilac'	CBcs CCCN CElw CExl CPrp ECtt
	ELan ELon EMor EPfP EWTr GKin
	MRav NGdn WGwG
'Gem'	CPrp ELon
'Genua'	IBal
'Glacier'	IBal
'Glacier Stream'	CBro CDor IBal IKil XSen
'Glen Avon'	CAbb CCCN CExl CPrp CRos EBee
	EPfP IBal NLar SCoo SFai SLon
'Gold Strike'PBR (v)	CPla IBal NHoy SFai SPoG WCot
'Golden Drop'PBR (v)	CBcs CRos EHyd NHoy NRHS SFai
	SPad SRms
'Golden Rule' (v)	EHoe IBlr
'Gothenburg'	IBal
'Greenfield'	EBee IBal
'Hamar'	IBal
'Hanneke'	IBal
'Hannover'	IBal
'Happy Blue'	IBal
'Harvest Blue'	CBdn CPne IBal
§ Headbourne hybrids	Widely available
– dark blue-flowered	LPot
'Heavenly Blue'	CCCN
'Helen'	IBlr
'Helsinki'	IBal
'His Majesty'	IBal
'Holbrook'	CSam
'Hole Park Blue' **new**	NHoy
'Hoyland Blue'	CPrp IBal NHoy
'Hoyland Chelsea Blue'	NHoy
'Ice Blue Star'	CBro CPrp
'Ice Lolly'	CBro EShb IBal IKil
inapertus	CBro CPbh CPrp EWes SMHy
	WPGP WSHC
– dwarf	IBlr
– subsp. ***hollandii***	IBal IBlr
– – 'Zealot'	IBlr
– 'Ice Cascade'	CCCN CRos EBee IBal
– 'Icicle'	GCal MAvo SPoG
– subsp. ***inapertus***	IBlr
I – – 'Albus'	IBlr
– – 'Cyan'	IBlr
– – 'White'	CPrp IBal
§ – subsp. ***intermedius***	CPrp IBlr NHoy
– – 'Long Tom'	CExl CPrp EBee IBal
– – white-flowered	CPou
– large	IBal
– 'Margaret'	CCCN
– 'Midnight Cascade'	CCCN CExl CPar EBee ECtt ELan
	IBal IPot LEdu NBid NHoy SCob
	SRms WTyc
– subsp. ***parviflorus***	IBlr
– subsp. ***pendulus***	IBal IBlr
– – 'Black Magic'	CBdn CPne IBal
– – 'Graskop'	CBcs CCCN CExl CSam EBee EHyd
	ELan EPfP IBal IBlr MNrw NHoy
	NSti SFai SMHy SRms WTyc
– – 'Violet Dusk'	IBlr
– 'Sapphire Cascade'	LSRN
– 'Tempest'	WPGP
'Indigo Dreams'	CBdn CKno CPne CPrp EBee IBal
	LLHF LPla MAvo NHoy SFai
'Inkspots'	CCCN CMac CRos EHyd EPfP IBal
	LCro LOPS NHoy SFai SPoG WHlf

	'Intermedius' Leichtlin	IBal LEdu
I	'Intermedius' van Tubergen	EBee IBal NBid
	'Isis'	CBro CSam CSde ECha ELon IBal IBlr MAvo
	'Jacaranda'	CMac EBee IBal NHoy SFai
	'Jack Elliott'	MAvo
	'Jack's Blue'	CBro CDor CSam EBee ECtt ELan ELon EMor GMaP IBal LSRN MHol MNrw NGdn NHoy NLar SEND SLdr SMad WCot WFar WSpi
	'Jersey Giant'	CPrp
	'Jodie'	ELon MAvo
	'Johanna'	EBee EMor IBal
	'Johannesburg'	IBal
	Johannesburg hybrids	ECha EPfP
	'Jolanda'	CPrp IBal LAma
	'Jonie'	IBal
	'Jonny's White'	IBal
	'Kalmthout Blue'	IBal
	'Kew White'	SMHy
	'Kilmurry Blue'	IBal IKil
	'Kilmurry White'	IBal IKil
	'Kingston Blue'	IBlr MAvo NBid NHoy WSHC
	'Kobold'	CBro IBal WFar
	'Lady Edith'	IBlr
§	'Lady Grey'	IBlr
	'Lady Moore'	SMHy
	'Lapis'	CAbb CBod CMac CPrp CRos EBee IBal NHoy NPri SFai SHyH SLdr
	'Latent Blue'	IBlr
	'Lavender Haze'	CCCN CMac CRos EBee EHyd EPfP IBal NHoy NRHS SFai WSpi
	'Leanne'	IBal
	'Leicester'	IBal
	'Liam's Lilac'	CBdn CCCN CExl CKno CPou CPrp CRos ELon IBal LCro LOPS MAvo NHoy NLar SFai
	'Lilac Flash'	CBdn CPne IBal
	'Lilac Lullaby'	IBal
	'Lilac Time'	CExl CPrp IBal IBlr
	'Lilliput'	CBcs CBro CCCN CMac CMea CPrp CSpe ECha ECtt ELan ELon EPfP EShb EWTr GKev GMaP IBal MRav NGdn SPer SRms WCFE WFar XEll XSen
	'Lissabon'	IBal
	'Lisse'	IBal
	'Little Dutch Blue'	IBal WCot
	'Little Dutch White'[PBR]	IBal WCot
	'Little Frank' **new**	NHoy
	'Little Sebastian' **new**	NHoy
	'Little White'	IBal
	'Littlecourt'	CBro IBal MAvo
	'Loch Hope' ♀H6	CAby CBro CPrp CSam EBee ECtt ELon EPfP GCal IBal LPla MAvo MHol MRav SLdr SPer WCot WSpi
	'Los Angeles'	IBal
	'Luly'	CBdn CPne CRos IBal MAvo MGos NRHS
	'Luna'	EBee IBal
	'Lydenburg'	EBee IBal IBlr LEdu
	'Lyn Valley'	CBdn CPne CPrp EBee IBal
	'Mabel Grey'	see *A.* 'Lady Grey'
	'Madurodam'	IBal
	'Magnifico'	CPrp IBlr
	'Malaga'	IBal
	'Malmo'	IBal
	'Marchants Cobalt Cracker'	SMHy
	'Marchants Midnight Blue'	SMHy
	'Marcus'	EBee IBal
	'Margaret'	GCal GKev IBal LSRN NAln NHoy
	'Marianne'	IBal
	'Mariëtte'	CBdn CPne EBee
	'Marijke'	IBal
	'Marjorie'	CBdn CPne
	'Marnie'	CBdn CPne
	'Martine'	EBee IBal
	'Maureen'	CBdn CPne CPrp EBee IBal LSRN
	'Maurice'	IBal
	'May Snow' (v)	WCot
	'Medan'	IBal
	'Medusa'	IBal
	'Megan's Mauve'	CBdn CBro CKno CPne CPou CPrp EBee ELon IBal LCro LOPS LSRN NSti SFai SHyH
	'Meibont' (v)	IBal WCot
	'Melbourne'	SPad
	'Mercury'	IBlr
	'Messina'	IBal
	'Mi Casa'	IBal SFai
	'Michelle'	IBal
	'Middleburg'	IBal
	MIDKNIGHT BLUE ('Monmid')	WSHC
	'Midnight'	EWes IBal MAvo
	'Midnight Blue' ambig.	ELan EPfP EShb EUJe IBal MCot SMHy WFar
	'Midnight Blue' P. Wood	GCal IBlr
	'Midnight Dream'	EBee ECtt EMor IBal LEdu NHoy STPC WFar
§	'Midnight Star'	Widely available
	'Mini Blue'	IBal
	'Misty Dawn' (v)	CBcs CWGN EBee ECtt ELon EWhm IBal MHol SEND SHyH SLdr WCot
	'Mole Valley'	IBal
	'Molly Howick'	EBee
	'Monique'	IBal
	'Montreal'	IBal
	'Mood Indigo'	CPrp EBee IBal NHoy
	'Moonlight Star'	EBee IBal IPot MHol NHoy SFai
	'Moonshine'	IBal
I	'Mooreanus' misapplied	EBee EPfP IBal NBid
	'Mooreanus' H.R. Wehrh.	GCal MAvo
	'Morning Star'	IBal
	'Mount Stewart'	IBal IBlr
	'Nana Blue'	SHyH
	'Nancy'	IBal
	'Napoli'	IBal
	'Navy Blue'	see *A.* 'Midnight Star'
	'Newa'	EBee
	'Newcastle'	IBal
	'Nikki'	CBdn CMea CPne CPrp IBal
	'Norman Hadden'	IBlr
	'Northern Light'	IBal LLHF
	'Northern Star'[PBR]	CAbb CBdn CExl CKel CKno CPne CPrp CRos CWGN EBee EHyd EMor EWes IBal LCro LOPS LSRN MHol NHoy NRHS NSti SCob SFai SLon SPoG SRms
	nutans	see *A. caulescens*
	'Nyx'	IBlr
	'Odessa'	IBal
	'Oslo'	CBdn CPne IBal
	'Oxbridge'	IBlr
	'Oxford'	IBal
	'Pacific Blue'[PBR]	CWCL IBal SFai SHyH SLdr
	Palmer's hybrids	see *A.* Headbourne hybrids
	'Patent Blue'	CPrp IBal IBlr
	'Patriot'	EPfP

Name	Suppliers
'Pavlova'	EUJe IBal
'Penelope Palmer'	CPrp IBal IBlr
'Peter Franklin'	CPrp EBee IBal
'Peter Pan' ambig.	Widely available
'Peter Pan American'	GKev NAln NHoy
'Phantom'	CAbb CPrp CRos EBee IBal IBlr IMou MAvo SAko SFai WCot
'Picton Blue'	WFar
'Pinocchio'	EPot GKev IBal IMou SDeJ WCot
'Pirame'	IBal
PITCHOUNE BLUE ('Scrarey09'PBR) **new**	CKel
'Plas Merdyn Blue'	CPrp
'Plas Merdyn White'	IBal IBlr
'Podge Mill'	IBal IBlr
'Polar Ice'	CPrp EBee ELon GBin GKev IBal ILea IPot LAma LSRN MAvo MNrw NCGa NHoy WCAu WSpi
'Polar Star'	EMor IBal
'Porcelain'	IBal IBlr
praecox ♀H2	CPrp GKev IBlr NHoy
- 'Albiflorus' ♀H2	CBcs CBod CBro CPou CPrp CTri GWyn MTin NHoy SEND
- 'Maximus Albus'	CBod CPou IBal IBlr
§ - subsp. ***minimus***	CElw CPou IBal IBlr SEND
- - 'Adelaide'	CPrp IBal
- - white-flowered	CBdn CPne
- 'Neptune'	IBlr
§ - subsp. ***orientalis***	CBro CCCN IBlr
- - 'Full Moon'	IBal SFai
- - 'Royal Velvet' **new**	CBdn CPne
- subsp. ***praecox***	IBlr
- 'Saturn'	IBlr
- Slieve Donard form	IBlr
- 'Storms River'	IBal
- 'Uranus'	IBlr
- 'Venus'	IBlr
'Premier'	IBlr
'Pretty Wendy'	IBal
'Princess Margaret'	CPrp IBal
§ 'Purple Cloud'	Widely available
'Purple Delight'	CPar CPrp CRos EBee IBal LCro LOPS NRHS SAko SFai WFar
'Purple Emperor'	IBal SFai
'Purple Fountain'	IBal SRms
'Purple Haze'	IBal
'Purple Heart' **new**	SFai
'Purple Magic'	IBal
'Purple Ripple'	IBal
'Purple Star'	CCCN CKno
'Queen Anne'	IBal
'Queen Mother'	IBal NRHS WSpi
QUEEN MUM ('Pmn06'PBR)	Widely available
'Queen of the Ocean'	IBal
'Quink Drops'	SMHy
'Radiant Star'	CRos IBal
'Regal Beauty'	CBro CPrp CSBt EBee IBal LSRN NBid SAko SFai
'Rhapsody in Blue'	CBdn CPne CPrp
'Rhone'	CBro IBal IBlr
'Robin'	IBal
'Rosewarne'	CBcs CBod CCCN CExl CPrp IBal IBlr NLar
'Rotterdam'	IBal XSen
'Roxanne'	EBee IBal
'Royal Blue'	CBro CPrp GMaP IBal WCot WSpi
'Royal Knight'	IBal
'Ruan Vean'	CPrp
'Sabang'	IBal
'Sally Anne'	CBdn CPne CPrp
'San Gabriel' (v)	CBdn CPne
'San Remo'	IBal
'Sandringham'	CAbb CBdn CBod CPne CPrp EBee ELon EPfP EWes IBal LSRN MMuc NBid NHoy SFai WFar
'Sandy'PBR	IBal
'Sapphire'	CPrp IBlr
'Sarah'PBR	CCCN CWCL EBee IBal LSRN MTin SEND SFai SHyH SLdr
'Saville Blue'	CPrp MCot
'Sea Coral'	CBdn CCCN CMac CPne CPrp EBee EMor IBal MAvo NEgg NSti
'Sea Foam'	CMac NLar XLum
'Sea Mist'	CBdn CCCN CPne CPrp EBee
'Sea Spray'	CCCN EBee IBal WFar
'Selma Bock'	IBal
'Semarang'	IBal
'Senna'PBR	CCCN CExl EBee GKev IBal
'Septemberhemel'	IBal
'Shooting Stars'	IBal
'Silberpfeil'	IBal
'Silver Anniversary'	IBal NHoy
'Silver Baby'	CAbb CKno CPrp CRos CWGN EBee EHyd EPfP IBal LEdu MHol NHoy NRHS SFai SRms WTyc
'Silver Jubilee'	IBal
'Silver Lining'	CBdn CPne CRos ECtt EMor IBal
'Silver Mist'	CBdn CPne IBal IBlr
SILVER MOON ('Notfred'PBR) (v)	CAbb CBro CCCN EBee EHyd ELan EMor EPfP GKev IBal MGos MJak NAln NHoy NLar NRHS NSti SCob SFai SPoG WCot
'Silver Sceptre'	IBlr
'Silver Stream' **new**	NHoy
'Silver Suzy'	IBal
'Sky'	CAbb CPrp EMor EPfP EWTr IBal IBlr NBid SFai SRms
'Sky Rocket'	CPrp IBal IBlr
'Sky Star'	IBal
'Skyscraper'	IBal
'Slieve Donard'	IBlr
'Snow Cloud'	CAbb CBdn CBro CExl CPne CPrp CRos CTsd EBee EHyd EPfP LCro LOPS NLar NRHS SAko SEND SFai SLdr SLon WSpi
'Snow Crystal' **new**	SFai
'Snow Pixie'	CRos CSpe EBee IBal LSRN NHoy SFai SHyH SLdr WSpi
'Snow Princess'	ELon EPfP IBal
'Snow Shadows'	CBro IBal
'Snowball'	CBcs CExl WSpi
'Snowdrops'	CCCN EBee ELan WFar
'Snowstorm'PBR	EBee EPfP IBal LBuc SArc SPad
'Sofie'PBR	CBod CKel EBee EUJe MJak SCob STPC
'Sorento'	IBal
'Southern Cross'	EBee IBal NHoy SFai
'Southern Star'	IBal
'Star Quality'	CRos EBee IBal LBuc MNrw SFai
'Starburst'	IBlr
'Starburst Blue'	IBal
'Starburst White'	IBal
'Stardust'	CRos IBal LBuc
'Stargazer'	CRos EBee IBal LBuc NRHS
'Stars and Stripes'	IBal
'Stéphanie Charm'	IBal
'Stockholm'	IBal
'Storm Cloud' Reads	see *A.* 'Purple Cloud'
'Storm Cloud' (d)	CBro IBal
'Strawberry Ice'	CBro EBee IBal SFai

'Streamline'	CBcs CBod CElw CKno CMea CRos EAJP EBee ECtt EHyd ELon EMor EPfP EShb GAbr GKin GMaP IBal MRav NAln NHoy NRHS SDys SEND WSHC
'Su Casa'	IBal
'Summer Blue'	IBal
'Summer Clouds'	CPrp ELan
'Summer Days'	CBdn CPne CPrp IBal SFai
'Summer Delight'	IBal
'Summer Skies'	CBdn CPne IBal
'Sunfield'	CDor CKno CPrp CRos EPfP IBal ILea LAma MNrw NLar NPer NRHS
'Super Star'	CBro CPrp IBal
'Susan Elizabeth' **new**	CPrp
'Sweet Surprise'	EBee IBal SFai
'Sylvia'PBR	IBal
'Sylvine'	CPrp IBal
'Tall Boy'	CPrp IBlr
'Tarka'	CBdn CExl CPne CPrp CRos ELon EPfP IBal NHoy NRHS SDys
'Taw Valley'	CAbb CKno CPrp EBee ELon IBal MGos NHoy SHyH SMad
'Thorn'	IBal
'Thumbelina'	CBro CMac CRos EBee IBal NHoy NLar XLum
'Timaru'	CBro CElw CPrp EBee ECha ECtt ELan ELon EPfP GAbr GMaP IBal MHol NGdn SHyH SLdr WCot
'Tinkerbell' (v)	CBcs CBdn CBor CBro CCCN CPne EBee EHoe ELan EPfP EShb IBal MGos MRav NHoy NPer SPoG SRms SWvt
'Titan'	IBlr
'Titch'	IBal
'Tom Thumb'PBR	CExl CKel CPrp CRos ECtt EHyd EPau EPfP GBin IBal MAsh NAln NCou NEgg NHoy NRHS SRkn SRot
'Top Slice' **new**	WCot
'Torbay'	CElw CPrp ECtt ELon EMor EPau EPfP EShb EWTr GAbr GCal GKin IBal MMuc MNrw NCGa NHol WAvo WHoo
'Tornado'	CPrp CRos EBee ECtt ELon IBal ILea SEND STPC
'Triangle'	CPbh
'Tsolo'	IBal
'Twilight Zone'	EBee IBal
umbellatus Redouté	see *A. praecox* subsp. *orientalis*
'Underway'	EWes GCal GKev IBal IBlr
Ventnor hybrid	SVen
'Volendam'	IBal
'Washington'	IBal
'Wavy Navy'	IBal
'Wedding Day'	CBdn CPne EBee IBal
'Wembworthy'	CBdn CPne CPrp EBee IBal
'White Cloud'	IBal
'White Dwarf'	see *A.* white-flowered, dwarf
'White Flash'	IBal
'White Giant'	WSpi
'White Heaven'PBR	CAby CRos CSpe EBee ECtt EHrv ELon EWTr IBal LCro LEdu LOPS LSun MAvo MHol NEgg NHoy NRHS NSti SCob SEND SFai SHyH SLdr WCot WSpi
'White Ice'	CBcs IBal
'White Pixie'	IBal
'White Superior'	CBod EBee EPfP GMaP
'White Swan'	SCob
'White Umbrella'	CKel CRos EHyd ELan NRHS
'White Wings'	IBal
white-flowered	WAvo WCFE
§ white-flowered, dwarf	CBro CKno ECha EPfP EShb IBal MAsh MPie NBir NEgg NGdn NHol
'Whitestorm'	SCob
'Whitney'PBR	IBal IBlr
'Windlebrooke'	CCCN IBal SDeJ WCot
'Windsor Castle'	IBlr
'Windsor Grey'	Widely available
'Winsome'	IBlr
'Winter Sky'	IBal
'Wolga'	CBro EBee IBal
'Wolkberg' Kirstenbosch	IBal IBlr
'Yellow Tips'	IBal
'Yves Klein'	CPrp IBlr
'Zachary'	CPou CPrp EBee ELon
'Zeal Thomas'	IBal
'Zigzag White'	WCot

Agapetes (*Ericaceae*)

'Ludgvan Cross' ♀H2	CBcs CCCN CTsd EBee EShb MGil SPad
serpens ♀H2	CBcs CCCN CHll CTsd SLon
- 'Scarlet Elf'	CCCN CTsd LRHS
smithiana var. ***major***	GGGa

Agastache (*Lamiaceae*)

'After Eight'	CSpe ECtt LRHS MAvo MBel
anethiodora	see *A. foeniculum* (Pursh) Kuntze
anisata	see *A. foeniculum* (Pursh) Kuntze
'Astello Indigo'	MNHC SPhx
aurantiaca	NGBl SPhx WMoo
- 'Apricot Sprite'	CSpe EMor EPfP NGdn NHic NRHS SRkn WKif
- 'Sunset Yellow'	NCGa
'Blackadder'	Widely available
'Blaue Sangria'	LPla NDov WGoo
'Blue Boa'PBR	CBod CDor CPla CWGN EBee ECtt EMor LCro LOPS LRHS MAvo MHol MNHC NCGa NCou NDov NEgg NLar NSti SMad SPoG SRms WCAu WTor
* 'Blue Bonnet' **new**	CSpe
'Blue Fortune' ♀H6	CBcs CBod CKel CRos ECha EHyd EMor EPfP GWyn LCro LOPS LRHS MCot MRav NDov NLar NRHS SAko SCob SMad SPer SPhx SRms SWvt WCAu WSpi XSen
'Bolero'	CSpe LRHS MHol SPhx
breviflora	SPhx
§ ***cana***	SPhx
- 'Heatwave'PBR	EPfP NDov
- 'Purple Pygmy'	EPfP
'Cotton Candy'PBR	ECtt LCro LOPS
'Firebird'	CKel CWGN EBee ECtt ELan EPfP SRms SWvt
'Fleur'	ECtt WGoo
foeniculum misapplied	see *A. rugosa*
§ ***foeniculum*** (Pursh) Kuntze	CCBP EBee ELan ENfk GPoy MCot MHer MNHC SPhx SRms WJek WTre
- 'Alabaster'	CBcs EBee EWes LCro LOPS
- 'Alba'	NBre
- 'Blaustrahl'	SAko
'Globetrotter'	CBod ELan NDai SPhx WArt
GRAPEFRUIT NECTAR (Nectar Series)	SCob
'Kolibri'	ECtt ILea WGoo
(Kudos Series) 'Kudos Ambrosia'PBR	CRos ECtt EMor LRHS NCGa NPri NRHS SPoG

- 'Kudos Coral'[PBR]	CRos IKil LRHS NPri NRHS
- 'Kudos Gold'[PBR]	CKno EMor LRHS NLar NPri SPoG
- 'Kudos Mandarin'[PBR]	CRos EMor IKil LRHS MMrt NCGa NLar NRHS SPoG
- 'Kudos Silver Blue'	CRos ECtt LRHS NEoE NPri NRHS
- 'Kudos Yellow' **new**	IKil
'Linda'	CWGN NDov WCot
mexicana 'Champagne'	NWad
- 'Red Fortune'[PBR]	CWGN EAJP EBee ECtt EHyd EMor IKil ILea LCro LOPS LRHS MHol NRHS SCob SPad SPoG WCot
- 'Rosea'	see *A. cana*
- 'Sangria'	CWGN ILea NGdn SPhx SRms XLum XSen
micrantha	SPhx
nepetoides	EPPr NDov
- 'Green Candles'	WFar
occidentalis	SPhx
ORANGE NECTAR (Nectar Series)	EBee MHol MPie WCot
'Painted Lady'	CSpe ECtt
pallidiflora	SPhx SPlb
var. ***neomexicana***	
- - 'Lavender Haze'	CBod
- - 'Rose Mint'	CSpe NHic
'Pink Pop'	EPfP MHol WHil
'Purple Haze'	LRHS MAvo NDov NRHS
RASPBERRY NECTAR (Nectar Series) **new**	IKil
'Raspberry Summer'[PBR]	CWGN ECtt EMor EPfP LRHS MPie NRHS SCob WAul
§ ***rugosa***	CAby CBod CCBP EBou ECha GPoy LEdu MNHC MWat SPer SPhx SPlb SRms WJek WMoo
- from Korea	IMou
- f. ***albiflora***	WCAu
- - 'Alabaster'	CDor NDov
- - 'Liquorice White'	CBod EBee ECha ELan EPfP GWyn MArl MBel NGBl SPer SPlb SPoG SRms
- 'Golden Jubilee'	CAby CBod CRos CSpe EBee ECha ELan ELon EMor EPfP LRHS MAvo NGdn NLar NRHS NSti SCob SRms SWvt WAul WJek WMoo XLum
- 'Heronswood Mist'	EBee
- 'Korean Zest'	WCru
- 'Liquorice Blue'	CBod CDor CTsd ELan EPfP LRHS MBel MWat NEgg NGBl NGdn SPoG SRms SSut SWvt WMoo
- 'Little Adder'	CBod MHol
rupestris	CSpe SPhx XSen
- 'Apache Sunset'	NHic SPlb XSen
'Serpentine'	ECtt EWes MAvo NDov WGoo
'Spicy'	NDov
'Summer Fiesta'[PBR]	EBee ECtt
'Summer Glow'[PBR]	CDor CKno CSam CWGN ECtt EMor EPfP EUJe LRHS MHol NDov NGBl NRHS SCob SDys SPad SPoG SRkn WCot WRHF
'Summer Love'[PBR]	ECtt
'Summer Sky'[PBR]	ECtt LRHS NDov
'Summer Sunset'[PBR]	CDor CWGN EBee ELan LCro LOPS LPla LRHS MHol NRHS SCob
'Tangerine Dreams' 🏆H3	ECtt ELan EPfP LRHS NCGa NRHS SCoo
'Tango'	MEch NHic SGbt WKif
'Tutti-frutti'	ECtt
urticifolia	WArt
- 'Alba'	WArt
'Violet Vision'[PBR]	CWGN ECtt

Agathaea see *Felicia*

Agathosma (*Rutaceae*)

ovata	CCCN

Agave ✿ (*Asparagaceae*)

albomarginata	CDTJ
americana 🏆H2	CAbb CAco CBcs CBen CBod CKel CPla ELan EPfP EShb EUJe LRHS LSun SArc SChr SCob SEND SPlb SPre SVen SWvt WCot WGrn
- blue-flowered	SPlb
- 'Marginata' (v) 🏆H2	CBrP CDTJ CHll CKel NQui SEND SVen WCot WSFF
- 'Mediopicta' misapplied	see *A. americana* 'Mediopicta Alba'
- 'Mediopicta' (v) 🏆H2	CDTJ SArc WGrn
§ - 'Mediopicta Alba' (v) 🏆H2	CAbb CBrP CCCN CDTJ CJun CPbh ELan EUJe SPlb WCot WGrn
- 'Mediopicta Aurea' (v)	WCot
- var. ***oaxacensis***	WPGP
- subsp. ***protamericana***	CDTJ
- subsp. ***protamericana*** × ***scabra*** F&M 310	WPGP
- 'Striata' (v)	CDTJ EShb WCot
- 'Variegata' (v) 🏆H2	CAbb CAco CBcs CBen CBod CKel CPbh CSde ELan EPfP EShb EUJe LRHS LSun MGos NPer SArc SChr SCob SPlb SWvt WCot
angustifolia	see *A. vivipara* var. *vivipara*
- var. ***marginata*** hort.	WCot
applanata	CJun SPlb WPGP
asperrima	CDTJ
§ - subsp. ***maderensis***	SPlb
atrovirens	SPlb WCot
- var. ***mirabilis***	CDTJ
- - F&M 245	WPGP
attenuata	CAbb CDTJ SPlb
'Bloodspot'	WCot
'Blue Brian' **new**	SArc
boldinghiana	WCot
bracteosa	CCCN CDTJ EUJe WCot
celsii	see *A. mitis* var. *mitis*
cerulata subsp. ***nelsonii***	CDTJ
chrysantha	CAco CCCN CDTJ WCot
- 'Black Canyon'	WCot
chrysoglossa	CDTJ
colimana	see *A. ortgiesiana*
colorata	CCCN CDTJ CJun WCot
'Cornelius'	WCot WGrn
cupreata	CDTJ
decipiens	SPlb
deserti	CAco CDTJ CJun CPbh LRHS WCot
- var. ***simplex***	WCot
difformis	CDTJ
- NJM 05.034	WPGP
durangensis	SPlb
elongata	see *A. vivipara* var. *vivipara*
ensifera	CJun
felgeri	CDTJ
ferdinandi-regis	see *A. victoriae-reginae*
ferox	see *A. salmiana* var. *ferox*
filifera 🏆H2	CCCN CDTJ CJun CPbh SChr SPlb WCot
flexispina	SPlb
garciae-mendozae	CDTJ
geminiflora	CCCN CDTJ CJun CPbh EShb EUJe
gentryi	CDTJ EUJe SPlb WCot
ghiesbreghtii	CPbh
gigantea	see *Furcraea foetida*

guadalajarana	CDTJ CPbh
guttata	WCot
havardiana	CDTJ XSen
horrida	CDTJ CJun
- subsp. ***horrida***	SPlb
- 'Perotensis'	CDTJ EShb
hurteri	CDTJ
impressa	CDTJ WCot
isthmensis	SPlb
kerchovei	WCot
lechuguilla	CDTJ WCot XSen
lophantha	see *A. univittata*
- var. ***caerulescens***	see *A. univittata*
'Macha Mocha'	WCot
macroacantha ♀H1c	CDTJ EUJe
maculosa	WCot
marmorata	CJun WCot
maximilliana	SPlb
mckelveyana	WCot
- DJF 1575 from Bagdad, Arizona	WCot
mitis	CCht
§ - var. ***mitis***	CDTJ SSim
- var. ***mitis*** × ***variegata***	WCot
montana	CCht CDTJ EUJe SArc SChr SPlb SPtp XSen
multifilifera	XSen
§ ***obscura***	CDTJ WCot
oroensis	WCot
§ ***ortgiesiana***	WCot
ovatifolia	CDTJ CJun EUJe SPlb WCot XSen
- NJM 09.002	WPGP
palmeri	CCCN CDTJ SPlb WCot XSen
panamana	see *A. vivipara* var. *vivipara*
parrasana ♀H2	CDTJ EUJe SSim WCot
parryi ♀H2	CDTJ CPbh EUJe GKev SPlb SPtp WCot XSen
- var. ***couesii***	CDTJ XSen
- 'Cream Spike' (v)	CBcs CBod EUJe SPad WArt WCot WGrn
- var. ***huachucensis***	CDTJ WCot
- subsp. ***neomexicana***	CCCN CDTJ EUJe SPlb WCot XSen
- - SB 948 from W of Artesia, New Mexico	WCot
- 'Ohi-kissho-ten-nishiki' (v)	WCot
- subsp. ***parryi***	CDTJ WCot WPGP
- var. ***truncata***	CDTJ EUJe SPlb
- - variegated (v)	WCot
parviflora ♀H2	WCot
polyacantha var. ***xalapensis***	see *A. obscura*
potatorum 'Gary Fisher'	WCot
salmiana	CDTJ SPlb
- subsp. ***crassispina***	SPlb
§ - var. ***ferox***	CDTJ EUJe SArc SChr SPlb
scabra	CCCN WCot
- subsp. ***maderensis***	see *A. asperrima* subsp. *maderensis*
schidigera	EUJe WCot
- 'Shira-ito-no-ohi' (v)	EUJe WCot
schottii	CDTJ WCot
'Sharkskin Shoes'	EUJe WCot
shrevei subsp. ***magna***	SPlb
sileri	WCot
sisalana	CDTJ
stictata	WCot
striata subsp. ***falcata***	WCot
* - 'Rubra'	CDTJ SPlb WCot
stricta ♀H2	CCCN CDTJ EUJe WCot
- 'Nana'	CDTJ SMad
- 'Rubra'	WCot
aff. ***stricta***	WCot
tenuifolia	CPla
titanota ♀H1c	SPlb
toumeyana ♀H2	CPbh SPlb WCot
- var. ***bella***	CDTJ
triangularis	CDTJ
undulata	WCot
- 'Chocolate Chips'	WCot
§ ***univittata***	CDTJ CJun WCot
- 'Quadricolor' (v)	CDTJ EUJe SMad SPlb WCot
utahensis ♀H3	CDTJ SEND SPlb WCot XSen
- DJF 1521from Peach Springs, Arizona	WCot
- var. ***eborispina***	WCot
- subsp. ***kaibabensis***	WCot
variegata	WCot
- B&SWJ 10234	WCru
§ ***victoriae-reginae*** ♀H2	CCCN CDTJ CJun CPbh EUJe SChr SPlb SSim WCot XSen
- dwarf	WCot
virginica	WCot
§ ***vivipara*** var. ***vivipara***	WCot
wocomahi	WCot
xylonacantha	CDTJ SChr SPlb WCot
zebra	CDTJ

Ageratina (*Asteraceae*)

§ ***altissima***	CDor CMac EBee
- 'Braunlaub'	NAln NBir NLar SHar WCAu WPtf WWtn
- 'Chocolate'	Widely available
- LUCKY MELODY ('Allmelody') **new**	LCro LOPS
§ ***aromatica***	MRav SHar
§ ***ligustrina***	CBod CExl CKel CRHN CSde CTri EBee ECha ELan LRHS MBlu SBrt SEND SPer SPoG SRkn SRms WSFF WSHC

Ageratum (*Asteraceae*)

'Blue Champion'	NPri
corymbosum	CHll CSpe EShb
houstonianum 'High Tide Blue'	NPri
petiolatum	LRHS SHar WFar

Aglaonema (*Araceae*)

'Jubilee Compacta'PBR **new**	LCro LOPS

Agrimonia (*Rosaceae*)

eupatoria	CBod CHab CWld ENfk GPoy MHer MNHC NMir SRms WHer WWFP
* - var. ***alba***	NLar
- 'Cambridge Lace' (v)	MAvo WCot
odorata (L.) Mill.	see *A. repens*
§ ***repens***	WMoo

Agropyron (*Poaceae*)

glaucum	see *Elymus hispidus*
magellanicum	see *Elymus magellanicus*
pubiflorum	see *Elymus magellanicus*

Agrostemma (*Caryophyllaceae*)

coronaria	see *Lychnis coronaria*
githago	CHab LCro LOPS MNHC SRms WTre
- 'Ocean Pearl'	CSpe SPhx

Agrostis (*Poaceae*)

calamagrostis	see *Stipa calamagrostis*

capillaris CHab
nebulosa SPhx
- 'Fibre Optics' see *Panicum* 'Fibre Optics'
stolonifera 'Julia Ann' (v) WCot

Aichryson (*Crassulaceae*)

§ × ***aizoides*** var. ***domesticum*** SAll
- - 'Variegatum' (v) ♀H1c CDTJ CPbh EBak SSim WCot

Ailanthus (*Simaroubaceae*)

sp. LPra
§ ***altissima*** CBcs CCVT CDul CExl ECrN EPfP EUJe LPra NWea SPer SPlb SWvt
- 'Purple Dragon' MBlu
- var. ***tanakae*** CWJ 12452 WCru
- - NMWJ 14522 **new** WCru
- - RWJ 9906 WCru
glandulosa see *A. altissima*

Ainsliaea (*Asteraceae*)

apiculata MAsh
- var. ***acerifolia*** B&SWJ 6059 WCru
chapaensis B&SWJ 11720 WCru
- B&SWJ 11732 WCru
latifolia FMWJ 13426 WCru
nervosa B&SWJ 11344 WCru
petelotii FMWJ 13427 WCru
tonkinensis B&SWJ 11819 WCru
uniflora GEdr

Ajania (*Asteraceae*)

§ ***pacifica*** CBor
- 'Silver Edge' XLum
trilobata **new** GKev

Ajuga (*Lamiaceae*)

genevensis GCal GWyn LRHS NHic SIgm SPhx WOut
incisa EWld GCal
- 'Bikun' (v) CBct EBee SPoG WCot WRHF
- 'Blue Enigma' CExl EBee ELon IMou NLar
- 'Blue Ensign' WSHC
'Little Court Pink' see *A. reptans* 'Purple Torch'
lupulina GEdr
'Pink Lightning' (v) CRos ELan LRHS NHpl NRHS SRms WHil
'Pink Spires' WFar
pyramidalis 'Metallica Crispa' CBre EBee ELan EWes NBir NEoE NHol NHpl NLar SRms SWvt WTor XSen
reptans CHab CTri ECtt ENfk GKev GPoy LCro LOPS MBel MHer MNHC SRms WOut XLum
- f. ***albiflora*** CDor WFar
- - 'Alba' CBod CBre EBee ELon MBel MRav NBro SRms WFar WMoo
- 'Arctic Fox' (v) GEdr MRav NBro SWvt
- 'Argentea' see *A. reptans* 'Variegata'
§ - 'Atropurpurea' CRos CTri ECha EHyd ELan EPfP GAbr GWyn LCro LOPS LRHS MGos MMuc NRHS NWad SEND SGol SPlb SRms SWvt WBrk XLum
- BLACK SCALLOP ('Binblasca'PBR) Widely available
- 'Blueberry Muffin' ECtt EWTr LCro LOPS NHpl
- 'Braunherz' CRos CTri ECtt EHoe EHyd ELan EPfP EShb GMaP LRHS MAsh MCot NBir NHpl NLar NPri NRHS NSla SCob SGol SPer SRms SWvt WFar WMoo
- 'Burgundy Glow' (v) Widely available
§ - 'Catlin's Giant' ♀H7 Widely available
- 'Choc Ice' EWTr
- 'Chocolate Chip' see *A. reptans* 'Valfredda'
- 'Ebony' LSRN
- 'Evening Glow' CBod WMoo
- 'Flisteridge' CNat
- 'Golden Beauty' (v) SRms WOut
- 'Golden Glow' (v) CRos LRHS NRHS
- 'Harlequin' (v) SWvt
- 'John Pierpoint' SHar
- 'Jumbo' see *A. reptans* 'Jungle Beauty'
§ - 'Jungle Beauty' EPfP MRav NAln XLum
- 'Macrophylla' see *A. reptans* 'Catlin's Giant'
- 'Mahogany' SRms
§ - 'Multicolor' (v) CBcs CRos ELan LRHS MAsh NPri NRHS SPer SPlb SPoG SRms SWvt WMoo
- PARTY COLORS ('Binparcol'PBR) (v) SCob
- 'Pink Elf' GQue MRav NBro
- 'Pink Surprise' MHer NRya WFar
- 'Purple Brocade' EHoe
§ - 'Purple Torch' MPie NLar SRms SWvt
- 'Purpurea' see *A. reptans* 'Atropurpurea'
- 'Rainbow' see *A. reptans* 'Multicolor'
- 'Rosea' CBod GWyn MBel WMoo XLum
- 'Rowden Amethyst' WHil
- 'Tricolor' see *A. reptans* 'Multicolor'
§ - 'Valfredda' CBod CRos EHyd EPfP GAbr GBin GKev GQue GWyn LRHS MHCG NAln NHpl NLar NRHS SRms SWvt WBrk WMoo
§ - 'Variegata' (v) ECtt EPfP NHpl SPer SPoG SRms WFar WTor
'Rose Glow' NHpl
'Sparkler' (v) EMor NHpl WOut
SUGAR PLUM ('Binsugplu'PBR) (v) ELan

Akebia ✿ (*Lardizabalaceae*)

longeracemosa CRHN EBee SBrt
- B&SWJ 3606 CExl LEdu WCot WCru WPGP
× ***pentaphylla*** CBcs CRHN CRos EBee EHyd ELan EPfP LRHS MAsh MGil MRav SPer
quinata Widely available
- B&SWJ 4425 WCru
- 'Amethyst Glow' CKel CRos CWCL EHyd EMil EPfP EWTr LRHS NLar SEle SPer SPoG
- cream-flowered CCCN CKel CRHN CRos EHyd EPfP EWld LCro LOPS LRHS MGos MRav NLar SPer SRms SSta SWvt WCru WPGP
- 'Shirobana' CBcs CHll CMen CWGN EUJe MBlu MGil NLar WAvo
- 'Silver Bells' LRHS
- variegated (v) LLHF
- 'White Chocolate' ♀H6 ESwi NLar WCru WSHC
trifoliata CBcs CMen CRHN CRos EBee EHyd EPfP LRHS MGil MGos SLon
- B&SWJ 14570 **new** WCru
- B&SWJ 5063 WCru

Alangium (*Cornaceae*)

platanifolium CBcs CExl WPGP
- var. ***macrophyllum*** CCCN EPfP MGil WBor

Albizia (*Mimosaceae*)

	chinensis	EBtc EPfP LRHS
	distachya	see *Paraserianthes lophantha*
§	***julibrissin***	CDTJ EBee EPfP EUJe IDee MGil
	- CHOCOLATE FOUNTAIN ('Ncaj1') new	ELan
	- LEONIDAS	see *A. julibrissin* 'Summer Chocolate'
	- OMBRELLA ('Boubri'PBR)	CBcs EBee ELan NOra WMat WPGP
	- f. ***rosea*** ♀H4	CAco CBcs CDul CExl CKel CLnd CMCN CRos CWGN ELan EPfP LEdu LRHS SArc SEND SLim SPad SPlb SPoG WPGP WSHC
I	- 'Rouge Selection'	CKel EPfP LRHS SPoG
	- 'Shidare'	EBee ELan NOra WMat
§	- 'Summer Chocolate'PBR ♀H3	CBcs CDul CRos CWGN EBee EHyd ELan EPfP IDee LRHS MAsh NOra NRHS SCoo SPer SPoG WMat
	- TROPICAL DREAM ('Pos 1')	EBee
	kalkora	SPlb
	lophantha	see *Paraserianthes lophantha*

Albuca ✿ (*Asparagaceae*)

	JCA 15856	CTca
	angolensis	CPou
	aurea	CTca
	canadensis (L.) F.M. Leight.	CPou WHil
	'Dirk Wallace'	CExl
	glauca	EBee
	humilis	CExl EPot LLHF WAbe WHil
	namaquensis	WHil
	nelsonii	CAvo CPrp EBee LAma SChr WHil
	setosa	CTca
	shawii	CAvo CBod CBor CBro CPou CPrp CTca CWld EAJP EBee EHoe ERCP EWld GKev LPot MHer NSla SChr SPoG SRms WAbe WGwG WHil
	spiralis	GKev WHil
	wakefieldii	WHil

× *Alcalthaea* (*Malvaceae*)

suffrutescens 'Freedom'	CBod ELan LPla MCot WFar
- 'Parkallee' (d)	CBod EBee ECha ECtt ELan ELon GMaP GWyn LRHS MAvo MCot MHol MNrw NLar SPhx WBrk WCot XLum
- 'Parkfrieden' (d)	CSpe ECha ECtt ELon LRHS MAvo MCot MNrw SPhx XLum
- 'Parkrondell' (d)	CBod ECha ECtt ELan ELon LRHS MAvo MNrw SHar SPhx WCot XLum
- 'Poetry'	CBod ECtt ELan ELon LPla LRHS MCot
- white-flowered	IFro

Alcea (*Malvaceae*)

	'Apple Blossom' (d)	EPfP
	'Burgundy Towers'	SEND
	ficifolia	WFar WMoo WSpi
	froloviana new	EBee
	'Las Vegas'	ELon
	nudiflora	GCal
	'Peaches 'n' Dreams'	EPfP
§	***rosea***	WFar
	- 'Blacknight' (Spotlight Series)	EPfP GKev MHer NAln NCGa
	- Chater's Double Group (d)	EPfP SPoG SRms SVic WFar
	- - chamois (d)	EPfP
	- - chestnut-brown-flowered (d)	EPfP
	- - maroon-flowered (d)	EPfP SPoG
	- - pink-flowered (d)	ELan EPfP
	- - red-flowered (d)	ELan EPfP SPoG
	- - salmon-pink-flowered (d)	EPfP
	- - scarlet-flowered (d)	EPfP SPoG
	- - violet-flowered (d)	EPfP
	- - white-flowered (d)	ELan EPfP LCro LOPS SPoG
	- - yellow-flowered (d)	EPfP SPoG SRms
	- 'Crème de Cassis'	ELan EPfP LRHS
	- (Halo Series) 'Halo Apricot'	CRos EHyd EPfP LRHS NRHS SPoG WHoo
	- - 'Halo Blush'	CRos EHyd EPfP LRHS NRHS SPoG WHil
	- - 'Halo Cerise'	CRos EHyd EPfP LRHS NRHS SPoG
	- - 'Halo Cream'	CRos EHyd LRHS NRHS SPoG
	- - 'Halo Red'	CRos EPfP LRHS NRHS SPoG
	- - 'Halo White'	CRos EHyd EPfP LRHS NRHS SPoG
	- 'Mars Magic' (Spotlight Series)	EBee EPfP LRHS MBel MHer NCGa
	- 'Nigra'	CSpe ECtt ELan EPfP LCro LOPS LRHS LSRN MBel MNHC NGdn SPer SRms XEll XSen
	- 'Polarstar' (Spotlight Series)	EBee ELan LRHS MBel NCGa
	- 'Radiant Rose' (Spotlight Series)	ELan LRHS MHer
	- single-flowered	MMuc SEND SRms
	- (Spring Celebrities Series) 'Spring Celebrities Crimson' (d)	LRHS NRHS
	- - 'Spring Celebrities Lemon' (d)	NRHS
	- - 'Spring Celebrities Pink' (d)	LRHS NRHS
	- - 'Spring Celebrities White' (d)	NRHS
	- Summer Carnival Group	SRms
	- 'Sunshine' (Spotlight Series)	EBee EPfP LRHS
§	***rugosa***	EBee EPPr LEdu MCot SHar XSen

Alcea × *Althaea* see × *Alcalthaea*

Alchemilla ✿ (*Rosaceae*)

	abyssinica	EBee
	alpina misapplied	see *A. conjuncta*, *A. plicatula*
	alpina ambig.	LPot MCot SCob
	alpina L.	EBee EHoe ELan EMor EPfP GPoy LEdu LRHS MBel MMuc MRav NAln NChi SEND SRms WMoo WPGP WSHC
§	***conjuncta***	CCBP CDor CMac CSam CSpe EBee ECha EHrv ELan EPfP GAbr GMaP GWyn MHer MRav NBid NGrd NRya NSti SPer SPlb SRms WCAu WHoo
	ellenbeckii	GAbr IMou NChi WTor
	epipsila	EBee ELan EPfP EShb GCal LRHS LSun NLar SPhx WSHC
	erythropoda ♀H7	Widely available
	- (Cepa Group) 'Alma'	EUJe LSun
	- Turkish form	ECha
	faeroensis	WMoo WPtf XLum
	- var. ***pumila***	EBee GKev WTor
	fissa	EBee EPPr
§	***fulgens***	WPGP
	glabra	EBee
	glaucescens	CNat
	hoppeana misapplied	see *A. plicatula*
	hoppeana (Reichenb.) Dalla Torre	EBee

	iniquiformis	EBee
	'Irish Silk'	CBod
	mollis ♀H7	Widely available
I	- 'Auslese'	SWvt
	- 'Robustica'	GQue LSun MMuc SEND SPlb WFar WMoo WPnP
	- 'Thriller'	CBod CRos EHyd EPfP LRHS LSun NRHS WFar
	- 'Variegata' (v)	CNat
	'Mr Poland's Variety'	see *A. venosa*
	pedata	EBee NChi
	peristerica	EBee
§	***plicatula***	NLar
	saxatilis	CRos EBee EBou LRHS NLar NRHS
	sericata 'Gold Strike'	CRos EBee ECtt ELan EMor EPfP GLog IMou LRHS NRHS SHar SWvt
	splendens misapplied	see *A. fulgens*
	straminea	EBee MRav
	valdehirsuta	EBee
§	***venosa***	EBee SHar
	vetteri	CRos EBee LRHS NRHS WHrl
	vulgaris misapplied	see *A. xanthochlora*
§	***xanthochlora***	GPoy NLar SRms WFar WHer

alecost see *Tanacetum balsamita*

Alectorurus see *Comospermum*

Alectryon (*Sapindaceae*)

	excelsus	CBcs

Alisma (*Alismataceae*)

	lanceolatum	XBlo
	plantago-aquatica	CBen CHab MWts NPer WMAq WWtn XBlo
	- var. ***parviflorum***	SPlb WWtn

Allamanda (*Apocynaceae*)

	cathartica	CCCN

Alliaria (*Brassicaceae*)

	petiolata	GPoy WHer WOut WSFF

Allium ✿ (*Alliaceae*)

	RCB AM 21	WCot
	SSSE 250	GEdr
§	***acuminatum***	GKev NBir
I	- 'Album'	LRHS NRHS
	acutiflorum	GKev LAma
	aflatunense misapplied	see *A. hollandicum*
	aflatunense ambig.	CRos LRHS LSRN SCob SDeJ SEND
	albidum	see *A. denudatum*
	albopilosum	see *A. cristophii*
	alexeianum	GKev
	altissimum	LAma
	- 'Goliath'	CRos GKev LRHS NRHS WCot
	amabile	see *A. mairei* var. *amabile*
	'Ambassador' ♀H5	CAvo CMea CRos CTca CWCL ERCP GKev ILea LAma LRHS NRHS WCot
	amethystinum	GKev
	- 'Red Mohican'	CMea CTca EBee ERCP GKev ILea IPot LAma LEdu SDeJ WCot
	ampeloprasum	ECha GKev LAma SPlb WHer WShi
	- var. ***babingtonii***	CAgr CTca GKev GPoy LEdu SRms WHer WPGP WShi
§	- 'Elephant'	LCro LEdu LOPS WCot
	- 'Pink Lady'	GKev
	- 'Purple Mystery'	GKev WCot
	amphibolum	GKev LAma
	amplectens	LAma
	- 'Graceful Beauty'	EBee EPfP EPot ERCP GKev LAma LCro LOPS SCob SDeJ SPer SPhx XEll
§	***angulosum***	CAvo CTca GKev LAma LEdu NHpl WCot
	- 'Sara'	GKev
	aschersonianum	EBee GKev SDeJ WCot
	atropurpureum	CRos EBee ECha ELan EPfP EPot ERCP GBin GKev GWyn LAma LCro LOPS LRHS NRHS SDeJ SMad SPhx WCot
	atropurpureum	LSRN
	atroviolaceum W&B BG A-5	WCot
	auctum	EBee
	azureum	see *A. caeruleum*
	backhousianum	GKev LAma
	'Beau Regard' ♀H7	CRos CTca CWCL EBee ELan ERCP GKev ILea LAma LRHS NLar NRHS
	beesianum misapplied	see *A. cyaneum*
	beesianum W.W. Sm. ♀H5	EBee LLHF NBir NHpl
	'Bizar'	LAma
	blandum	see *A. carolinianum*
	bodeanum	see *A. cristophii*
	'Bolero'	EBee LAma LRHS NRHS
	brevicaule	GKev
	bulgaricum	see *Nectaroscordum siculum* subsp. *bulgaricum*
§	***caeruleum***	CAvo CBor CCBP CDor CRos CTca EBee EPot ERCP GKev LAma LCro LOPS LRHS MGos MNrw NAln NBir NLar NPer NRHS NRya SCob SDeJ SPhx
	- ***azureum***	see *A. caeruleum*
	caesium ♀H5	EBee ERCP GKev WCot
	- 'Pskem's Beauty'	WCot
	callimischon subsp. ***callimischon***	EPot GKev
	- subsp. ***haemostictum***	WCot
	'Caméléon'	CCBP CRos EBee ERCP GKev LAma LCro LOPS LRHS NRHS SCob WCot
	canadense	SHar
	candolleanum	GKev
§	***carinatum***	GKev WHer
§	- subsp. ***pulchellum*** ♀H5	CBro CRos CSpe EBee ECha EPot GKev LAma LRHS MHer MMuc MNrw NRHS SDeJ SPhx WArt WThu
	- - f. ***album*** ♀H5	CBro CSpe EBee ECha GKev LEdu LSun MNrw SPhx
	- - 'Bill Baker'	LEdu
	- - 'Olympic Mist'	GKev
§	***carolinianum***	LAma
	cepa	CBod SVic
	- Aggregatum Group	CLau GPoy SRms
	- 'Kew White'	WCot
	- 'Perutile'	CHby GPoy LEdu MHer
	- Proliferum Group	CAgr EWhm GPoy LEdu MHer MNHC SRms WGwG WHer WJek XLum
	- var. ***viviparum***	GKev LAma
	cernuum	CAvo CBor CBro CDor CMea CRos CTca EBee ECha ELan EPfP EPot ERCP EWhm GKev LAma LCro LEdu LOPS LRHS MCot MNHC MNrw NHpl NRHS SDeJ SPhx SRms WBor XSen
§	- 'Hidcote' ♀H6	CSam EBee EDAr WArt WKif XSen
	- 'Major'	see *A. cernuum* 'Hidcote'
	- pink-flowered	NBir

- 'White Dwarf'	CBor CMea EBee GKev LAma
chinense	CAgr GPoy LEdu
- 'October Mist'	LEdu
cirrhosum	see *A. carinatum* subsp. *pulchellum*
* ***cneorum***	LAma
commutatum	GKev
convallarioides	GKev LAma
cowanii	see *A. neapolitanum* Cowanii Group
crenulatum	LAma
§ ***cristophii*** ♀H5	Widely available
cupanii	GKev
cupuliferum	GKev
curtum RCB RL 13	WCot
§ ***cyaneum*** ♀H5	CRos GEdr GKev LAma LBee LRHS MHer NHpl NRHS NRya WCot
cyathophorum	CBor
§ - var. ***farreri***	CBro CElw CRos EPot GKev LAma LEdu LRHS MHer MNrw MRav NHpl NRHS NRya WCot WThu XEll
cyrilli	GKev
darwasicum	WCot
decipiens	GKev LAma
§ ***denudatum***	GKev
dolichostylum	GKev
§ ***drummondii***	CRos LRHS NRHS
elatum	see *A. macleanii*
'Emir'	GKev
ericetorum	GKev WCot
- PAB 1009	LEdu
'Eros'	CBor EBee GKev LAma LCro LOPS MMrt WRHF
falcifolium	GKev LAma WCot
farreri	see *A. cyathophorum* var. *farreri*
fasciculatum	LAma
'Firmament'	CWCL ECha ERCP GKev LAma LRHS MCot SDeJ SPhx WCot XEll
fistulosum	CAgr CHby EMor ENfk EWhm GKev GPoy LAma MHer MNHC NPri SEND SRms SVic WCot WGwG WJek XLum
fistulosum* × *pskemense	GKev
flavum ♀H5	CBor CBro CRos CTca ECha EPot ERCP LAma LRHS NHpl NRHS NSla SDeJ WGwG WThu
§ - 'Blue Leaf'	NBir
- subsp. ***flavum***	GKev SPhx
- - var. ***minus***	MMuc SEND
- 'Glaucum'	see *A. flavum* 'Blue Leaf'
- var. ***nanum***	EPot
- subsp. ***tauricum***	CSpe GKev SPhx WCot
'Forelock'	CTca EPfP ERCP GBin GKev LAma MNrw SCob WCot XEll
forrestii	NSla WCot
geyeri	EBee GBin
giganteum	Widely available
- 'Twinkling Stars'	ERCP GKev LAma
'Gladiator' ♀H6	CAvo CRos CWCL EBee EPfP ERCP GKev GMaP LAma LCro LOPS LRHS LSun NRHS SCob SDeJ
glaucum	see *A. senescens* subsp. *glaucum*
'Globemaster' ♀H6	CAvo CBro CMea CRos CTca CWCL EBee EHyd ELan EMor EPot ERCP GKev ILea LAma LCro LEdu LOPS LRHS LSRN MJak MMrt NLar NRHS SArc SCob SDeJ SPhx WCot WHoo
'Globus'	EBee GKev LAma
guttatum	GKev
subsp. ***dalmaticum***	
- subsp. ***sardoum***	GKev
haemanthoides	WCot
'Hair'	see *A. vineale* 'Hair'
* ***hirtifolium*** var. ***album***	EBee GKev LAma
'His Excellency'	CRos CWCL EBee ERCP GBin GKev LAma LRHS NRHS SCob
§ ***hollandicum***	CArg CAvo ECha GKev LAma LCro LOPS SPlb WFar
- 'Purple Sensation' ♀H7	Widely available
- 'Purple Surprise' ♀H7	NBir WCot
hookeri	GKev LEdu SPhx
- ACE 2430	LEdu WCot
- var. ***muliense***	GEdr LEdu
- 'Zorami'	CAgr ELan LEdu WPGP
howellii var. ***clokeyi***	GKev
huber-morathii	CBor EBee
humile	GEdr
hyalinum	GKev
- pink-flowered	WCot
'In Orbit' **new**	SMad
inconspicuum	LAma
§ ***insubricum*** ♀H5	CRos CSpe EDAr GBin GEdr LRHS MNrw NBir NHpl NRHS NRya NSla SChF WAbe XEll
'Jackpot'	CWCL EBee ERCP GKev LAma SPhx
jajlae	see *A. rotundum* subsp. *jajlae*
jesdianum	GKev
- 'Akbulak' ♀H5	EBee GKev LAma LRHS NRHS
- 'Early Emperor' ♀H5	CRos CWCL EBee EPfP ERCP GKev LAma LRHS NRHS SCob
- 'Michael Hoog'	see *A. rosenorum* 'Michael H. Hoog'
- 'Purple King'	CRos GKev LAma LRHS NRHS SPhx
- 'White Empress'PBR	CRos EBee LRHS NRHS
kansuense	see *A. sikkimense*
karataviense	CAby CAvo CRos EBee ECha ELan EPot GAbr GKev LAma LCro LOPS LRHS LSun NAln NBir NHpl NLar NRHS SCob SDeJ SWvt WCAu
- subsp. ***henrikii***	LAma WCot
- 'Ivory Queen'	CAby CAvo CRos CTca EBee ECha EMor EPfP ERCP GKev LAma LCro LOPS LRHS LSRN NHpl NLar NRHS SCob SDeJ SPlb
- red- and pink-flowered	GKev
komarovianum	see *A. thunbergii*
komarovii	GKev LAma
ledebourianum	GKev LAma SPhx
lenkoranicum	CAvo LAma WCot
litvinovii	EBee LAma SPhx WCot
loratum	EBee LAma
'Lucy Ball'	CRos EPfP ERCP GKev LAma LRHS NBir NLar NRHS SDeJ
§ ***lusitanicum***	CBor CBro CSpe ECha ERCP GKev GMaP LEdu MHol NBre NDov SPhx SRms WGoo XSen
§ ***macleanii***	CRos EBee EPfP GKev LAma LRHS NRHS
macranthum	CSpe EBee GKev LAma NHpl SBrt WCot
mairei	CRos EHyd LAma LRHS MMuc NRHS NRya
§ - var. ***amabile***	GEdr LEdu NRya NSla WThu
- - dark-flowered **new**	CBor
maximowiczii	GKev NHpl
- white-flowered	LAma
'Mercurius'PBR	CRos EBee GKev LAma LRHS NRHS SDeJ SPhx WCot
'Metallic Shine'	ERCP GKev LAma SPhx
meteoricum	GKev WCot

	'Miami'	CRos EBee ERCP GKev LAma LRHS NRHS SDeJ SPhx WRHF
	'Millennium'	CBod WCot WGoo
	moly	CAgr CWCL GKev GQue LAma LCro LOPS MRav NAln NRya SCob SDeJ SRms XLum
	- 'Jeannine' ♀H6	CRos EBee EPot GBin GKev LAma LRHS NRHS
	'Mont Blanc'	CMea CRos EBee ELan ERCP GBin GKev LAma LRHS NLar NRHS SCob
	moschatum	GKev
	multibulbosum	see *A. nigrum*
	murrayanum misapplied	see *A. unifolium*
	murrayanum Regel	see *A. acuminatum*
	narcissiflorum misapplied	see *A. insubricum*
§	***narcissiflorum*** Vill.	CSpe GCal LEdu MNrw NSla NWad
	neapolitanum	CAgr CRos EPot GKev LAma LRHS NRHS SEND SRms WGwG
§	- Cowanii Group	CRos GKev LCro LOPS LRHS NRHS SDeJ SPhx WCot
§	***neriniflorum***	NSla WAbe
	nevskianum	EPot GKev LAma
§	***nigrum***	CArg CAvo CBro CRos EBee ECha EHrv EPfP EPot ERCP GKev GWyn LAma LCro LOPS LRHS MCot MJak NBir NPer NRHS SCob SDeJ SPhx WCot
	- f. ***roseum***	CBro
	nutans	EWhm GKev LAma LEdu MHer SRms WHal WJek
	- 'Caroline' **new**	WGoo
	- 'Isabelle' **new**	GKev
	nuttallii	see *A. drummondii*
§	***obliquum***	CAvo CBor CBro CSpe ECha ERCP GEdr GKev MNHC SDeJ SPhx WCot
	ochotense	LPla WCot
	odorum L.	see *A. ramosum* L.
	oleraceum	WHer
	olympicum	GKev
§	***oreophilum***	CCBP CRos CSam ECha GJos GKev LAma LCro LOPS LRHS NRHS SRms
	- 'Samur'	WCot
	- 'Zwanenburg' ♀H6	EPot
	orientale	GKev
	oschaninii	LAma
	'Ostara'	ERCP GKev
	ostrowskianum	see *A. oreophilum*
	ovalifolium var. ***leuconeurum***	GEdr WCot
	pallens	CBre NBir
§	***paniculatum***	GKev LAma WCot
*	- var. ***minor***	GKev LAma SPhx
	paradoxum	LEdu NBir
	- var. ***normale***	CBro EPot EWld GKev NBir WCot
	parciflorum	GKev
	pedemontanum	see *A. narcissiflorum* Vill.
	pendulinum	GKev SPhx
	'Pinball Wizard'	CAvo CRos CTca CWCL EBee EHyd EMor ERCP GKev LAma LRHS NRHS
	'Ping Pong'	EBee NLar
	'Pink Jewel'	CAvo EBee ERCP GKev LAma SDeJ WCot
	platycaule	LAma WCot
	plummerae	EBee GKev XEll
	plurifoliatum	LAma
	polyphyllum	see *A. carolinianum*
	'Powder Puff'	CAvo CTca EBee GKev LAma
	prattii	EBee WCot
	przewalskianum	LAma SBch
	pskemense	LAma SPhx WCot
	pulchellum	see *A. carinatum* subsp. *pulchellum*
	'Purple Rain' ♀H5	CAvo CMea CRos CWCL ECha ELan ERCP GKev LAma LRHS NCGa NRHS SDeJ WCot WRHF
	'Purple Suze'	LAma
	pyrenaicum misapplied	see *A. angulosum*
	pyrenaicum ambig.	SEND
	pyrenaicum Costa & Vayr.	XSen
	ramosum Jacq.	see *A. obliquum*
§	***ramosum*** L.	GKev LAma LEdu
	'Red Eye'	SPhx
	'Rien Poortvliet'	GKev LAma
	roborowskianum	GKev
	rosenbachianum misapplied	see *A. stipitatum*
	rosenbachianum Regel	CBro LRHS NRHS
	- 'Album'	CRos EMor EPfP GBin GKev LAma LRHS NRHS WCot
	- 'Michael Hoog'	see *A. rosenorum* 'Michael H. Hoog'
	- 'Shing'	GKev LAma
§	***rosenorum*** 'Michael H. Hoog' ♀H5	CRos EPot GKev LAma LRHS NRHS
	roseum	CMea CRos EAJP GKev LAma LCro LOPS LRHS NAln NRHS SCob SDeJ XLum
	rotundum	GKev
§	- subsp. ***jajlae***	LAma WCot
	'Round and Purple' ♀H5	CRos EMor ERCP GKev LAma LRHS NRHS
	rupestre	GKev
	sativum	ENfk LOPS NPri SPoG SRms
	- 'Elephant'	see *A. ampeloprasum* 'Elephant'
	- var. ***ophioscorodon***	CWld GKev GPoy LAma SPlb
	saxatile	GKev WCot
	- pink-flowered	GKev
	schmitzii	LEdu
	schoenoprasum	Widely available
	- f. ***albiflorum***	CLau ECha EWhm GKev LEdu MHer NBir SRms
	- 'Black Isle Blush'	EBee EMor GPoy LEdu MHer WGoo WPGP
	- 'Cha Cha' **new**	WJek
	- 'Colesbourne Giant'	EBee LEdu
	- 'Corsican White'	LEdu XSen
	- dwarf, white-flowered **new**	CBre
	- 'Elbe'	LEdu
	- fine-leaved	CLau GQue
	- 'Forescate'	CRos ECha EWhm GKev LAma LEdu LRHS MHer MRav NBir NRHS SRms WJek XLum
	- medium-leaved	CLau NPri
	- 'Pink Bere' **new**	LEdu
	- 'Pink Perfection'	GPoy LEdu MHer NDov
	- 'Polar Bere'	LEdu
	- 'Polyphant'	CBre
	- PROFUSION	see *A. schoenoprasum* 'Sterile'
	- 'Rising Star'	XSen
	- 'Shining Silver'	LEdu
	- var. ***sibiricum***	WShi
	- 'Silver Chimes'	CBor EBee EWhm MRav
§	- 'Sterile'	LEdu
	- thick-leaved	CLau SRms
	schubertii	CAvo CBod CRos CSpe CTca CWCL EHyd ELan EPfP EPot ERCP GKev LAma LCro LOPS LRHS MNHC NRHS SCob SDeJ SPer SPhx WCot WFar WWFP
	- 'Magic'	EWhm LAma
	scorodoprasum	LAma

	Name	Suppliers
	- 'Art'	CRos ERCP GKev LAma LRHS NRHS
	- subsp. ***jajlae***	see *A. rotundum* subsp. *jajlae*
	- 'Passion'	CRos EBee ERCP GKev LAma LRHS NRHS
	- 'Purple Caila'	GKev
	senescens ♀H6	CBro CRos CTca CTri EBee EPot GKev IMou LAma LEdu LRHS MBel MRav NRHS SBch SRms WBrk WCAu XLum XSen
§	- subsp. ***glaucum***	CAvo CMea CPBP CRos CSpe EBee ECha EDAr EWTr GKev LEdu LRHS NDov NGdn NLar NRHS NRya SEND WCot WHoo XSen
	- 'Lisa Blue' **new**	GKev
	- subsp. ***senescens***	GKev LEdu WPGP
	serra	WCot
	shelkovnikovii	EPot
	sibthorpianum	see *A. paniculatum*
	siculum	see *Nectaroscordum siculum*
§	***sikkimense***	CBor CRos EBee EDAr GEdr GKev GQue LRHS MHer MMuc NHpl NRHS NSla WAbe WCot
	'Silver Spring'	EPot ERCP IPot MNrw SDeJ
	sphaerocephalon ♀H6	Widely available
	- subsp. ***arvense***	WCot
	'Spider'	CBor CWCL EBee EPot ERCP GKev ILea LAma LRHS SPhx WCot
I	***splendens*** var. ***kurilense***	GEdr
	stamineum W&B BGF-2	WCot
	'Statos'	EBee GKev LAma LRHS NRHS WCot
	stellatum	CRos LRHS NRHS SPhx WGwG
	stellerianum	GKev
	- var. ***kurilense***	NRya WThu
§	***stipitatum***	EMor GKev LAma WCot
	- 'Mars'	CRos EBee GKev LAma LRHS NRHS
	- 'Mount Everest' ♀H5	CAvo CBod CBro CRos CTca EPfP EPot ERCP GBin GKev GMaP GWyn ILea LAma LCro LOPS LRHS LSRN MJak NLar NRHS SDeJ SPer SPhx
	- 'Violet Beauty' ♀H5	CRos CWCL EWhm GKev LAma LCro LOPS LRHS NLar NRHS WCot WRHF
	- 'White Giant'	CRos CWCL EBee ERCP GKev LAma LEdu LRHS NRHS SArc
	stracheyi	WCot
	strictum Ledeb.	see *A. szovitsii*
	strictum Schrad. **new**	ITim
	subhirsutum	GKev XLum
	subvillosum	EPot GKev
	'Summer Beauty'	see *A. lusitanicum*
	'Summer Drummer'	CTca EPfP ERCP GKev LRHS SDeJ SPer SPhx WCot WHoo
	suworowii ♀H5	GKev
	'Sweet Discovery'	LAma
§	***szovitsii***	ITim
	taquetii	see *A. thunbergii*
	texanum	LAma
§	***thunbergii*** ♀H5	LAma MHer NBir NRya SPhx WAbe
	- PAB 3821	LEdu
	- 'Album'	NRya WAbe
	- 'Ozawa'	EBee GEdr SRms WCot
	tibeticum	see *A. sikkimense*
	triquetrum	ELan EPot GKev LAma LEdu NBir SEND WCot WFar WHer WMoo WPnP XLum
	tschimganicum	EBee LAma
	tuberosum	Widely available
	- B&SWJ 8881	WCru
	- purple/mauve-flowered	CHby CLau
	- 'White Dwarf'	SPhx WCot
	tuncelianum	GKev WCot
	tuolumnense **new**	GKev
	umbilicatum	GKev
§	***unifolium*** ♀H5	CAvo EBee EPfP EPot ERCP GKev GWyn LAma LCro LOPS MRav NAln NBir NPer NQui SDeJ SEND SPhx SRms WCot
	ursinum	CHab CHby CWld EMor ENfk EWhm GKev GPoy LAma LEdu MHer MMuc NPri SMad SRms WSFF WShi XLum
	- 'Golden Fleece' **new**	WCot
	validum NNS 06-41	WCot
	victorialis 'Cantabria'	EBee GKev
	vineale	GQue WHer WJek
	- PAB 2763	LEdu
	- 'Dready'	ERCP GKev LAma
§	- 'Hair'	CBor CRos ELan ERCP GKev LAma LRHS MCot NAln NBir NPer NRHS SCob SDeJ
	violaceum	see *A. carinatum*
	virgunculae	CMea CPBP EDAr GEdr
	- f. ***albiflorum***	GEdr
	wallichii	CSpe EBee EWes LEdu LLHF MBNS NBir NChi WCot XLum
	- CLD 1500	NBid
	- PAB 2976	LEdu WPGP
	- PAB 9191	LEdu
	- dark-flowered	LPla WCot WFar
	'White Cloud'	EBee ELan GKev XEll
	winklerianum **new**	GKev
	'World Cup'	LAma
	woronowii	GKev
	zaprjagajevii	WCot
	zebdanense	EBee GKev LAma

almond see *Prunus dulcis*

Alniphyllum (*Styracaceae*)

Name	Suppliers
eberhardtii FMWJ 13121	WCru
fortunei FMWJ 13013	WCru

Alnus ✿ (*Betulaceae*)

Name	Suppliers
cordata ♀H6	Widely available
cremastogyne	EBtc
formosana	IArd
glutinosa	Widely available
- 'Aurea'	CDul CEnd MGos
- 'Imperialis' ♀H7	CCVT CDul CEnd CKel CLnd CTho EBee ELan EMOT EPfP EWTr IDee MBlu MMuc NEgg NLar NOra NWea SCob SGol SMad SPer WMat WMou WTSh
- 'Laciniata'	CCVT CDul CTho ECrN GKev MGos NLar NWea
- 'Pyramidalis'	CDul
incana	CBcs CCVT CDul CLnd CMCN CPer CTho ECrN EMOT LBuc LMaj LPra MGos NLar NWea SCob SGol SPer WMat WTSh
- 'Aurea' ♀H7	Widely available
- 'Laciniata'	ELan NLar NWea SCoo WFar
- 'Pendula'	CDul CTho
japonica	MBlu
maximowiczii from Ulleungdo	WCru
nitida	EBtc
oregana	see *A. rubra*
pendula B&SWJ 10895	WCru

rhombifolia	EBtc
§ ***rubra***	CDul CMCN CPer CTho ELan MCoo NWea WMat WTSh
- f. ***pinnatisecta***	CMCN MBlu
serrulata	CMCN
sieboldiana	GKev LRHS NAln WCru
× ***spaethii***	EWTr LMaj LPra MBlu
subcordata NJM 13.009	EBee WPGP
viridis	CAgr MCoo NWea WTSh
- subsp. ***sinuata***	CAgr

Alocasia (*Araceae*)

× ***amazonica*** ♀H1a	XBlo
- 'Polly'	LCro LOPS
'Calidora'	CDTJ EUJe
cucullata	XBlo
macrorrhiza	CDTJ EUJe
odora	EUJe XBlo
plumbea	XBlo
'Portodora'	CDTJ
wentii	CDTJ

Aloe ✿ (*Asphodelaceae*)

africana	CAbb
arborescens	CDTJ CPbh EShb EUJe SEND
- 'Variegata' (v) ♀H1c	EShb SRms
aristata ♀H3	CBcs CKel EUJe SArc SChr SEND SPad SPlb SSim XLum
- 'Cathedral Peak'	SChr
- 'Green Pearl'PBR	SMad
barbadensis	see *A. vera*
barberae	CCCN CPbh
brevifolia ♀H2	EShb SArc SSim
broomii	CCCN CPbh SPlb
buettneri new	EShb
camperi 'Maculata'	SEND
ciliaris	CHll EShb EUJe SChr
'Cleopatra'	WCot
cooperi	CCCN CDTJ
dichotoma	CAbb SPlb
ecklonis	CCCN SPlb
ferox	CAbb CBod CCCN CDTJ CPbh
fosteri	CDTJ
greatheadii var. ***davyana***	SChr SPlb
humilis	SChr SEND
juvenna	SRms
kedongensis	SEND
maculata	CDTJ
marlothii	CAbb CCCN SPlb
melanacantha	CAbb
microstigma	CCCN
mitriformis	NGBl SChr SEND
mutabilis	SChr SEND
peglerae	SRms
petricola	CAbb
plicatilis ♀H2	CCCN CDTJ EShb
pluridens	CAbb
polyphylla ♀H3	CCCN CDTJ CPbh MHer WPGP
pratensis	CCCN CDTJ
rauhii ♀H1b	CPbh SChr
reitzii	CAbb CPbh SPlb
'Snowflake'	EShb
speciosa	CAbb
× ***spinosissima***	SChr
striata	CBcs CCCN CPbh EShb EUJe SPlb SSim
striatula ♀H3	CAbb CBrP CDTJ CSam CSde CTca EUJe IBlr LEdu SArc SChr SEND SMad SPlb SVen WCot WPGP
- var. ***caesia***	WPGP
succotrina	CAbb
suprafoliata	CAbb
tenuior	EShb
variegata (v) ♀H1c	EShb LSun SSim
§ ***vera*** ♀H1c	CCBP CCCN ELan EUJe GPoy LCro LOPS MHer MNHC NPer NPri SChr SEND SMad SPlb SPre SRms SSim SVic
'White Beauty' new	EShb
wickensii	SPlb
yavellana	SPlb

Aloe × *Haworthia* see × *Alworthia*

Aloinopsis (*Aizoaceae*)

lueckhoffii	SSim
rosulata new	SSim

Aloinopsis × *Nananthus* (*Aizoaceae*)

A. spathulata* × *N. transvaalensis	CPBP

Alonsoa (*Scrophulariaceae*)

'Bright Spark'	CSpe
incisifolia	CCCN CSpe
meridionalis	CCCN
- 'Rebel'	CBod CPla ECtt SRkn
'Pink Beauty'	CPla CSpe
warscewiczii	CCCN
- 'Peachy-keen'	CSpe

Alopecurus (*Poaceae*)

alpinus	see *A. magellanicus*
§ ***magellanicus***	ELan GBin LPot
pratensis	CHab
- 'Aureovariegatus' (v)	CTri EHoe EPPr EShb GMaP NBid SPer SRms
- 'Aureus'	NBro SPlb
- 'No Overtaking' (v)	EPPr

Aloysia (*Verbenaceae*)

chamaedryfolia	EPfP LRHS
citriodora	see *A. citrodora*
§ ***citrodora*** ♀H3	Widely available
- 'Spilsbury Mint'	ELan
gratissima	WJek
triphylla	see *A. citrodora*

Alpinia (*Zingiberaceae*)

japonica	CExl LEdu
- B&SWJ 8889	ESwi WCru
- PAB 6441	LEdu
nutans misapplied	see *A. zerumbet*
speciosa	see *A. zerumbet*
§ ***zerumbet***	XBlo
- 'Variegata' (v)	XBlo

Alsobia see *Episcia*

Alstroemeria ✿ (*Alstroemeriaceae*)

'Adonis'PBR	IKil WViv
'Aimi'	ELan MNrw SWvt WViv
'Alexis'PBR	WViv
'Amarillo'	WViv
'Angelina'	CTsd SWvt
'Anne' (Midi Series)	SPer
'Apollo' ♀H4	CTsd EHyd ELan IKil LRHS MNrw NBre NRHS SWvt WViv
'Athena'	WViv
aurantiaca	see *A. aurea*

§	***aurea***	CPla GWyn MRav NWad SRms XLum
	- 'Apricot'	GCal
	- 'Lutea'	GKev NLar SDeJ SPlb WPav
	- 'Orange King'	ELan EPfP GKev NLar SDeJ
	'Avanti'	EHyd ELan LRHS NRHS WViv
	'Blushing Bride'	CTsd SWvt WViv
	'Bodega'[PBR]	WViv
	'Bolero'	WViv
	'Bonanza'	WViv
	brasiliensis	CTsd GCal SBrt SHar WCot WSHC WViv XLum
	- 'Cally Star' (v)	EBee GCal NLar
	'Candy'	WViv
	'Candy Floss'	EPfP
	'Catherine' (Little Miss Series)	WViv
	'Charm'	CTsd SWvt WSpi WViv
	'Chi Chi'	WCot
	'Chloé' (Mini Series)	SCob
	'Christina'[PBR] (Little Miss Series)	CRos ELan LRHS NRHS SWvt WViv
	'Christine Marsh'	WViv
	'Cindy'	WViv
	'Coronet' ♀H4	WViv
	'Dandy Candy'	CBod ECtt EHyd GAbr LRHS MCot MHol NCou NGdn NLar SPad WBrk WCot
	'Davina'[PBR] (Little Miss Series)	EHyd LRHS NLar NRHS WViv
	'Dayspring Delight' (v)	GCal MNrw
§	DIANA, PRINCESS OF WALES ('Stablaco')	EHyd LRHS NRHS
	Doctor Salter's hybrids	SRms
	'Eleanor'	WViv
	'Elvira'	WViv
	'Emily'[PBR] (Little Miss Series)	WViv
	'Etna'[PBR]	WViv
	'Evening Song'	EHyd LRHS NRHS SWvt WViv
	exserens	WCot
	'Flaming Star'	LSvl WGwG WViv
	'Flirt' **new**	LOPS
	'Frances' (v)	CAvo CBro WFar
	'Freedom'	CBod CNor CWGN ECtt ELon MHol NEgg NLar NSti SCob SHar SMad SPoG WCot
	'Friendship' ♀H5	CTsd EHyd ELan LRHS NBre NRHS SWvt WGwG WViv
	'Gaspard' (Mini Series)	SCob
	'Gina'[PBR] (Little Miss Series) **new**	CRos ELan LRHS NRHS WViv
	'Gloria'	ELan LRHS NRHS SWvt WViv
	'Glory of the Andes' (v)	CWGN NLar
	'Golden Delight'	EHyd ELan LRHS NRHS WViv
§	H.R.H. PRINCESS ALICE ('Staverpi')	CRos LRHS NRHS
I	'Hatch Hybrid'	GCal
	'Hawera'	GBin GCal
	(Inca Series) INCA ADORE ('Koadore')	CExl
	- INCA AVANTI ('Koncavanti'[PBR])	CWGN LBuc SCob WViv
	- INCA AZURE ('Konazur'[PBR])	GBin WViv
	- INCA BANDIT ('Koncaband') **new**	WViv
	- INCA CLASSIC ('Konclassic')	WViv
	- INCA CORAL ('Konocoral')	WViv
	- INCA DEVOTION ('Konevotio'[PBR])	NLar
	- INCA DREAM ('Kodream')	WViv
	- INCA EXOTICA ('Koexotica')	WViv
	- INCA GLOW ('Koglow')	CExl CWGN EHyd ELon GBin LRHS MHol NLar NRHS SDeJ SRms WViv
	- INCA GOAL ('Koncagoal')	CBcs CBod CPla WViv
	- INCA HUSKY ('Koncahusky'[PBR])	CBcs CBod CPla CWGN LRHS MHol SCob WViv
	- INCA ICE ('Koice')	CWGN NLar WViv
	- INCA JOLI ('Koncajoli'[PBR])	LBuc WViv
	- INCA LAKE ('Koncalake')	CWGN LBuc NRHS SCob WViv
	- INCA LOLLY ('Koncalolly'[PBR])	WViv
	- INCA MAMBO ('Koncamambo'[PBR])	NRHS WViv
	- INCA MILK ('Koncamilk')	WViv
	- INCA MOONLIGHT ('Komolight')	NLar
	- INCA NOBLE ('Koncanoble')	WViv
	- INCA OBSESSION ('Koobsion')	WViv
	- INCA PULSE ('Konpulse'[PBR])	CWGN ELon GBin NLar SDeJ SMad WViv
	- INCA SERIN ('Koserin'[PBR])	CWGN WViv
	- INCA SMILE ('Koncasmile'[PBR])	CWGN SCob WViv
	- INCA SWEETY ('Koncasweet'[PBR])	WViv
	- INCA TOTO ('Koncatoto'[PBR])	WViv
	- INCA TROPIC ('Kotrop')	CExl CWGN WViv
	- INCA VITO ('Koncavito'[PBR])	CBcs CBod CWGN EPfP EUJe LRHS MHol NLar SCob SPoG
	- INCA YUKO ('Koncayuko'[PBR])	CBod CWGN LBuc MHol WSpi WViv
	INDIAN SUMMER ('Tesronto'[PBR])	CRos CWGN ECtt EHyd EPfP EUJe IKil LRHS NPri NRHS NSti SPoG SWvt WCot WFar WViv
	(Inticancha Series) INTICANCHA ANTARCTICA ('Tesantarc'[PBR])	WViv
	- INTICANCHA BRYCE ('Tesbryce'[PBR])	NLar WFar WViv
	- INTICANCHA CABANA ('Tescaban')	CBod CRos EHyd NRHS
	- INTICANCHA CREAMY DARK PINK ('Tescreda')	SDeJ WViv
	- INTICANCHA DARK PURPLE ('Tesdarklin'[PBR])	CRos LRHS MHol NLar NRHS WFar WViv
	- INTICANCHA IMALA ('Tesima'[PBR])	CRos EHyd NRHS
	- INTICANCHA INDIGO ('Tesindie')	CBod MHol
	- INTICANCHA KANIKA ('Tesikani')	CRos EHyd NRHS
	- INTICANCHA MACHU ('Tesmach'[PBR])	WFar WViv
	- INTICANCHA MAYA ('Tesmaya'[PBR])	CRos CWGN ECtt EHyd LRHS NRHS WFar WViv
	- INTICANCHA NAVAYO ('Tesnava'[PBR])	ECtt MHol WFar
	- INTICANCHA PASSION ('Tespassion'[PBR])	CRos ECtt EHyd LRHS NRHS WViv
	- INTICANCHA PURPLE ('Tespurplin'[PBR])	CWGN WFar WViv
	- INTICANCHA RED ('Tesrobin'[PBR])	CRos CWGN LRHS NRHS WFar WViv
	- INTICANCHA SUNDAY ('Tessunday'[PBR])	WViv

- INTICANCHA SUNLIGHT ('Tessunlight'PBR)	ECtt NLar WFar WViv
- INTICANCHA SUNSHINE ('Tesshine'PBR)	MHol
- INTICANCHA WHITE PINK BLUSH ('Tesblushin'PBR)	CRos EHyd LRHS NRHS WFar WViv
- INTICANCHA WHITE ('Teswhitin'PBR)	CBod
'Isabel' (Little Miss Series)	LRHS NRHS WFar WViv
ISABELLA ('Stalis')	LSRN
§ ***isabellana***	WCru
'Jessica'PBR (Little Miss Series)	LRHS NRHS WViv
'Laguna'	WViv
LAURA ('Stalauli'PBR)	ECtt SCob
'Leonie' **new**	SPer
ligtu hybrids	CAvo ECha EPfP GKev LCro LOPS MNrw NPer SDeJ SRms SWvt WBrk WHoo XLum
- var. ***ligtu***	SMHy
'Little Eleanor'	EHyd LRHS NRHS WViv
'Louise' (Midi Series)	LSRN
'Lucca'	WViv
'Lucy'PBR (Little Miss Series)	WViv
'Lucinda'	SWvt WViv
'Maestro'PBR	WViv
'Majestic Maze' **new**	WHlf
'Marissa'	GMaP
'Mars' (Planet Series)	EHyd LRHS NRHS
'Mathilde' (Midi Series)	NLar
'Matilda' (Little Miss Series)	WViv
'Mauve Majesty'	ECtt ELon ILea LRHS MHol NLar SPoG WCot WViv
'Miranda' (Little Miss Series)	WViv
'Moulin Rouge'	WViv
'Natalie'PBR (Little Miss Series)	EHyd LRHS NRHS WViv
'Neptune'	LCro LOPS
'Orange Glory' ♀H4	EHyd ELon LRHS MNrw NRHS SWvt WViv
'Orange Supreme'	EHyd LRHS NRHS WViv
'Oriana' ♀H4	IKil SWvt WViv
pallida	SPlb
'Pandora'PBR	LRHS NRHS WViv
patagonica	WAbe
'Perfect Orange'	WViv
philippii	WCot
- F&W 8699 **new**	WCot
'Phoenix' (v) ♀H4	SWvt WViv
'Pink Lady'	WViv
'Pink Perfection'	NLar
'Pink Sensation'	LRHS NRHS WViv
'Polka'	WViv
presliana RB 94103	WCot
(Princess Series) PRINCESS ALICE	see *A.* H.R.H. PRINCESS ALICE
- PRINCESS AMINA ('Zapriamin'PBR)	CBcs SPoG WViv
- PRINCESS ANOUSKA ('Zaprinous'PBR)	NLar WViv
- PRINCESS ARIANE ('Zapriari'PBR)	CBcs WViv
- PRINCESS BEATRIX ('Stadoran')	SChr
- PRINCESS CAMILLA ('Stapricamil')	SPoG
§ - PRINCESS CHARLOTTE ('Staprizsa'PBR)	SPer
- PRINCESS CLAIRE ('Zapriclair'PBR)	CBcs CRos EHyd EPfP LRHS NRHS
- PRINCESS DANIELA ('Stapridani')	SCoo
- PRINCESS DIANA	see *A.* DIANA, PRINCESS OF WALES ('Stablaco'), *A.* (Princess Series) PRINCESS DIANA ('Zapridapal')
§ - PRINCESS DIANA ('Zapridapal'PBR)	WViv
- PRINCESS ELIANE ('Zaprielia'PBR)	CRos EHyd LRHS NRHS WViv
- PRINCESS FABIANA ('Zaprifabi'PBR)	CBcs CRos EHyd LRHS NLar NRHS SPoG WViv
- PRINCESS FREDERIKA ('Stabronza')	MCot
- PRINCESS ISABELLA ('Zapribel'PBR)	CRos EHyd LRHS LSRN NRHS WViv
- PRINCESS IVANA ('Staprivane'PBR)	SPoG
- PRINCESS JULIETA ('Zaprijul'PBR)	NLar
- PRINCESS KATE ('Zaprikate'PBR)	CBcs CRos EHyd EPfP LRHS NRHS
- PRINCESS LETIZIA ('Zaprilet'PBR)	CBcs CRos EHyd EPfP LRHS NRHS SPoG
- PRINCESS LILIAN ('Zaprilian'PBR)	CBcs CRos EHyd LRHS NRHS WViv
- PRINCESS LOUISE ('Zaprilou'PBR)	EHyd LRHS LSRN NRHS WViv
- PRINCESS MARGARET ('Staprimar')	NLar
- PRINCESS MARY ('Zaprimary'PBR)	NLar
- PRINCESS MATHILDE ('Zaprimat'PBR)	WViv
- PRINCESS PAOLA ('Stapripal'PBR)	CBcs CRos EHyd LRHS NRHS SCoo SPoG WViv
- PRINCESS SARA ('Staprisara'PBR)	CBcs CRos EHyd EPfP LRHS NRHS SPoG
- PRINCESS SUSANA ('Staprisusa')	SCoo
- PRINCESS THERESA ('Zapriteres'PBR)	EPfP NLar
- PRINCESS ZAVINA ('Staprivina'PBR)	NLar SPoG
- PRINCESS ZSA ZSA	see *A.* (Princess Series) PRINCESS CHARLOTTE
pseudospathulata	CPla WCot
§ ***psittacina***	CAvo CBro CHll CMea CSam CTsd ECha EHrv ELan EPfP GBin GCal MCot MHer SHar SRms WAvo WFar WGwG WViv XLum
- 'Mona Lisa'	CBod XLum
- 'Royal Star' (v)	CAby CBod CBro CExl CWCL EHyd ELan ELon EPfP EWTr LRHS MPie NRHS SHar SPoG SRms WBrk WCot WFar WHoo WSHC WSpi WWtn XLum
pulchella Sims	see *A. psittacina*
'Purple Rain'	ELan SWvt WViv
'Red Beauty' (v)	see *A.* 'Spitfire'
'Red Beauty'	EHyd ELan GMaP LRHS NRHS SWvt WViv
'Red Elf' ♀H4	SMHy SWvt WViv
'Rhubarb and Custard'	ELan EPfP
ROCK 'N' ROLL ('Alsdun01'PBR) (v)	CDor EBee ELan ELon LCro LOPS MHol MNrw MSCN NEgg SPoG WCot WViv
'Rosanna' (Little Miss Series)	WViv
'Roselind' (Little Miss Series)	CRos ELan LRHS NRHS SWvt WViv
'Rosie' (Mini Series)	SCob
'Saturne' (Planet Series)	EPfP LCro LOPS
'Selina'	CRos EHyd LRHS MNrw NBre NRHS WViv

	'Serenade'	WViv
	'Sirius' (Planet Series) ♀H4	LCro LOPS
	'Sonata' ♀H4	WViv
	'Sophie'PBR (Little Miss Series)	ELan LRHS NEgg SWvt WViv
§	'Spitfire' (v) ♀H4	EHyd EPfP LRHS NRHS SWvt WCot WViv
	'Strawberry Lace'	ELan EPfP
	'Summer Breeze'	CBod CRos ECtt EHyd LRHS NRHS SPoG WViv
	SUMMER PARTY ('Tessumpar') (Summer Paradise Series)	CRos ECtt EHyd LRHS NRHS WFar
	'Summer Saint' new	WViv
	SUMMER SNOW ('Gasumsnow') new	CBod
	'Summertime'	CRos LRHS NRHS WViv
	'Sunstar'	GMaP
	'Sweet Laura'PBR	CBod ECtt ELan ELon LRHS LSRN MHol MNrw MPie NGdn NLar NSti SMad SPoG WCot WSpi WViv
	'Tangerine Tango'	WViv
	'Tanya'	MNrw WViv
	'Tara'PBR (Little Miss Series)	CRos ELan LRHS NLar NRHS SWvt WViv
	'Tessa' ♀H4	EHyd LRHS NBre NRHS WViv
	'Turkish Delight'	EPfP
	'Ventura'	WViv
	'Verona'	IKil
	'Veronica' (Little Miss Series)	WViv
	'Yellow Friendship' ♀H4	MNrw NLar SWvt WViv

Alternanthera (*Amaranthaceae*)

	reineckii	XBlo
	- 'Lilacina'	XBlo
I	- 'Rosaefolia'	XBlo

Althaea (*Malvaceae*)

	armeniaca	EBee GCal WCot
	cannabina	CAby CFis CSam CSpe ECha ELan EPPr GCal IPot MAvo MBel MHer MMuc MNrw NGBl SHar SPhx WBor WCot WHal WOld WSHC
	officinalis	CBod CCBP CHab EBou ELan ENfk EPPr GPoy MAvo MHer MMuc MNHC NLar SRms SVic WHer WJek WSpi XLum XSen
§	- 'Romney Marsh'	MAvo MRav
	rosea	see *Alcea rosea*
	rugosostellulata	see *Alcea rugosa*

Altingia (*Hamamelidaceae*)

	poilanei B&SWJ 11756	WCru

× *Alworthia* (*Asphodelaceae*)

	'Black Gem'	EBee EShb EUJe SRms SSim

Alyogyne (*Malvaceae*)

§	***huegelii***	CCCN CSpe EShb EUJe SEle SPlb
	- 'Santa Cruz'	CCCN CHll CSam
	MAGIC MOMENTS ('Hutwow'PBR)	CCCN CWGN SPoG SRkn

Alyssum (*Brassicaceae*)

	argenteum	GJos
	cuneifolium	GJos
	montanum	ECha GJos SPlb SRms
§	- 'Berggold'	EBou EPfP XLum
	- MOUNTAIN GOLD	see *A. montanum* 'Berggold'
	- 'Tekara'	GJos
	oxycarpum	EPot
	repens	GJos
	saxatile	see *Aurinia saxatilis*
	- 'Summit'	SRms
	spinosum	CPla GKev
	- 'Roseum' ♀H5	CMea CSpe CTri ECha ELan EPot GCrg SIgm WAbe
*	- 'Roseum Variegatum' (v)	GCrg
	- 'Rubrum'	EPot
	'Takara Yellow'	GWyn
	tortuosum	SEND
	wulfenianum	GJos WIce XLum

Amaranthus (*Amaranthaceae*)

	'Autumn Palette'	CSpe
	caudatus	LCro LOPS
	- 'Viridis'	SPhx
	hypochondriacus 'Pygmy Torch' ♀H2	CSpe
	'Red Army'	LCro LOPS
	tricolor	CLau SRms

× *Amarcrinum* (*Amaryllidaceae*)

	'Dorothy Hannibal'	WCot
	memoria-corsii	CPrp
	- 'Howardii'	GKev LEdu SDeJ WCot

× *Amarine* (*Amaryllidaceae*)

	tubergenii	CAvo
	- Belladiva Series	CBro EBee ERCP GKev LAma LCro LOPS LRHS NHoy
	- - 'Anastasia'PBR	ERCP GKev LAma NHoy SMad
	- - 'Aphrodite'PBR	GKev LAma NHoy
	- - 'Elvi'	LAma NHoy
	- - 'Emanuelle'PBR	CBro ERCP GKev NHoy
	- - 'Smilla'	LAma NHoy
	- - 'Tomoka'PBR new	CBro LAma
	- 'Fletcheri'	WCot
	- 'Zwanenburg'	GKev LAma WCot

× *Amarygia* (*Amaryllidaceae*)

§	***bidwillii*** 'Alba'	CAvo CBro CPrp WCot
	- 'Rosea'	WCot

Amaryllis (*Amaryllidaceae*)

§	***belladonna*** ♀H4	CAby CBcs CBro CPrp CTca CTri CTsd EBee EPfP ERCP EShb GKev LAma LCro LOPS MPie SDeJ SEND WCot
	- 'Hathor'	CBro SMHy
	- 'Johannesburg'	CBro WCot
	- 'Major'	SChr
	- 'Parkeri Alba'	see × *Amarygia bidwillii* 'Alba'
	- 'Purpurea'	WCot
	- white-flowered	SDeJ

Amaryllis × *Brunsvigia* see × *Amarygia*

Amaryllis × *Crinum* see × *Amarcrinum*

Amaryllis × *Nerine* see × *Amarine*

Ambrosina (*Araceae*)

	bassii	WCot

Amelanchier ✿ (*Rosaceae*)

	alnifolia	EBtc MGil NEgg NGrd
	- 'Forestburg'	MBlu NLar
	- 'Jb30' (F)	CAgr MCoo
	- 'Martin' (F)	CAgr NOra
	- 'Northline' (F)	CAgr LRHS MCoo NOra

	- 'Obelisk'[PBR]	CAgr CDul CRos EBee EHyd ELan EMOT EPfP EUJe GKin LBuc LLHF LRHS LSRN MAsh MCoo MGos MJak MSwo NLar NOra NPri SCoo SPer SPoG WCot WMat
	- pink-fruited	NLar
§	- var. ***pumila***	MMrt WCot
	- 'Regent' (F)	CAgr NLar
	- 'Smokey'	CAgr CDul LRHS MBlu MCoo NLar NOra SPoG
	- 'Thiessen'	MCoo
§	***arborea***	LPra
	- 'Robin Hill'	see *A.* × *grandiflora* 'Robin Hill'
	- TRADITION ('Trazam')	NLar SAko
	'Autumn Glory'	EPfP
	bartramiana	SSta
	- 'Eskimo'	EMOT NLar
	canadensis K. Koch	see *A. lamarckii*
	canadensis Sieb. & Zucc.	see *A. arborea*
	canadensis ambig.	CAco CDul CFGn CPer CTsd EMOT EUJe LPot MMuc NEgg NOra NPri NWea SCob SEND SEWo SPoG WFar WRHF
	canadensis (L.) Medik.	CAgr CJun CLnd CMac CRos CSBt CTho CTri EBee ECrN ELan EPfP LEdu LRHS MGos MRav MSwo SPer WMat
§	- 'Glenn Form'	CEnd EMOT EPfP LRHS NLar NOra SGol SLim SPer SPoG WMat WMou
	- 'Prince William'	CAgr MCoo SGol
	- RAINBOW PILLAR	see *A. canadensis* 'Glenn Form'
	× ***grandiflora***	SCob
	- 'Autumn Brilliance'	CEnd CJun EPfP MBlu NHol NLar NRHS SGol
	- 'Ballerina'	Widely available
	- 'Cole's Select'	CAby CKel EBee LRHS NLar SWvt
	- 'Forest Prince'	NLar
	- 'Princess Diana' ♀H7	NLar SCoo
§	- 'Robin Hill' ♀H7	Widely available
	- 'Rubescens'	CEnd CJun EBee EUJe NLar SLon SWvt
	'La Paloma' ♀H6	EBee EPfP LRHS LSRN MGos NOra SCoo SLim WMat
	laevis	CBcs CDul CTri EPfP LMaj NLar
	- 'Prince Charles'	NLar
	- 'R.J. Hilton' ♀H7	EBee EPfP LRHS NLar NOra SCoo WMat
	- 'Snow Cloud'	EPfP
	- 'Snowflakes'	CEnd CJun CSBt EBee EMOT EWTr LRHS LSRN MAsh NOra SEWo SLim SPer SPoG SWvt WMat WMou
§	***lamarckii*** ♀H7	Widely available
	ovalis misapplied	see *A. spicata* (Lam.) K. Koch
	ovalis Medik.	SPlb
	- 'Edelweiss'	CJun IArd MRav NLar SCoo
	pumila	see *A. alnifolia* var. *pumila*
	rotundifolia ambig.	CAgr MCoo
	sanguinea 'Chimney Rock'	NLar
§	***spicata*** (Lam.) K. Koch	CAgr MCoo
	stolonifera	CTri

Amelanchier × *Sorbus* see × *Amelasorbus*

× *Amelasorbus* (*Rosaceae*)

raciborskiana	MBlu NLar

Amellus (*Asteraceae*)

asteroides new	MAsh

Amicia (*Papilionaceae*)

zygomeris	CAbb CBcs CDTJ CHll CSpe EBee ELon EPfP EUJe EWes GCal IPot LEdu LRHS MGil SEle SMad SPhx SPoG WCot WPGP WSHC
- 'John's Big Splash' (v)	WCot

Ammi (*Apiaceae*)

majus ♀H6	CBod CSpe LCro LEdu LOPS LRHS MAvo MNHC SPhx WSFF
visnaga	see *Visnaga daucoides*

Ammobium (*Asteraceae*)

calyceroides	GBin

Ammocharis (*Amaryllidaceae*)

coranica	WCot
longifolia	WCot

Ammophila (*Poaceae*)

arenaria	CKel CKno IMou SMea XLum XSen
breviligulata	IMou XLum

Amomum (*Zingiberaceae*)

subulatum	SPre

Amomyrtus (*Myrtaceae*)

§	***luma***	CBcs CDul CTri CTsd EBee ELan ELon IDee LEdu MMuc SEND SPoG WJek WPGP WPav

Amorpha (*Papilionaceae*)

canescens	CRos EBee LRHS MGil NRHS SPhx SPlb
fruticosa	CAco EBtc MBlu MGil MMuc SEND SPlb
nana	XLum
ouachitensis	SMad

Amorphophallus ✿ (*Araceae*)

albus	CDTJ LEdu SPlb WCot
bulbifer	CDTJ CRos ESwi EUJe LAma LRHS NRHS SDeJ SPlb XLum
dunnii	CDTJ LEdu
henryi	WCot
kerrii	CExl WCot
kiusianus B&SWJ 4845	WCru
konjac	CDTJ CExl CSpe EUJe GCal LEdu LRHS NRHS SChF SChr SDeJ SPlb WCot XLum
nepalensis	WCot XLum
stipitatus	LEdu WCot
yuloensis	WCot

Ampelaster (*Asteraceae*)

§	***carolinianus***	XEll

Ampelocalamus (*Poaceae*)

§	***mocrophyllum***	CBdn ERod
	scandens	XCre

Ampelocissus (*Vitaceae*)

sikkimensis HWJK 2066	WCru

Ampelodesmos (*Poaceae*)

mauritanicus ♀H3	CKno CSam CSpe ECha EHoe EShb EWes MAvo SEND SMad SPlb WCot
- white-flowered new	SMHy

Ampelopsis (*Vitaceae*)

aconitifolia	NLar WAvo WCru
- 'Chinese Lace'	EBee EShb EUJe MRav NLar WBor
arborea	WCru
brevipedunculata	ELan MGil MMrt SCoo SLim SPer
- 'Citrulloides'	WCru
- 'Elegans' (v)	CBcs CMac CRos EBee ELan ELon EPfP EShb LRHS MGil MGos MMuc MRav SNig SPer SPoG SWvt WAvo WCot WSHC
delavayana	EShb MGil MMuc
glandulosa var. ***hancei*** B&SWJ 1793	WCru
henryana	see *Parthenocissus henryana*
megalophylla	EShb GCal NLar
sempervirens hort. ex Veitch	see *Cissus striata*
tricuspidata 'Veitchii'	see *Parthenocissus tricuspidata* 'Veitchii'

Amphicome see *Incarvillea*

Amsonia (*Apocynaceae*)

'Blue Ice'	Widely available
ciliata	IPot LEdu MMrt NLar SHar WPGP XLum
§ ***elliptica***	EBee EPPr SPhx
'Ernst Pagels'	EPPr MAvo WCot WGoo
fugatei	EBee
hubrichtii	CBod CKno CRos CSpe EBee ECha EMor EPPr EPfP EWTr IPot LEdu LRHS LSun NRHS SBrt SMHy SMad SPhx SWvt WCAu WPGP WPtf WSHC
illustris	CRos CSpe EPPr GCal LEdu LRHS NEgg NLar NRHS SHar SMHy SPhx WHoo
jonesii	EBee SBrt SMHy SPhx
§ ***orientalis***	CHll CMea CRos CSpe CTri EBee ECha EMor GWyn IPot LEdu LRHS MCot MRav NDov NLar NRHS SPhx SVen SWvt WCot WFar WKif XEll XLum
- from Turkey	SMHy
- 'Cally Dark Stem'	GCal
peeblesii	EBee SPhx
rigida	GEdr
sinensis	see *A. elliptica*
tabernaemontana	Widely available
- 'Montana'	SPer SWvt
- var. ***salicifolia***	CRos EBee IMou IPot LCro LEdu LOPS LPla LRHS NRHS SMad WCAu
- 'Stella Azul'	EBee MNrw
tharpii	SPhx
tomentosa var. ***stenophylla***	EBee SPhx

Amygdalus see *Prunus*

Anacampseros (*Portulacaceae*)

arachnoides new	SCob

Anacamptis (*Orchidaceae*)

coriophora	NLAp
§ ***laxiflora***	NLAp
§ ***morio***	NLAp
papilionacea	NLAp
pyramidalis	NLAp WHer

Anacyclus (*Asteraceae*)

pyrethrum	GPoy
- var. ***depressus*** ♀H4	EBou ELan EPfP GKev MAsh MMuc NAln SPlb SRot
- - 'Garden Gnome'	CTri SRms
- - 'Silberkissen'	CMea EDAr NSla WRHF

Anagallis (*Primulaceae*)

monellii subsp. ***linifolia*** 'Blue Light'	CSpe
- 'Skylover'	CCCN
tenella	LLWG
- 'Studland'	WAbe WIce

Ananas (*Bromeliaceae*)

comosus (F)	CCCN SPre
- 'Champaca' (F) ♀H1a	CCCN LCro LOPS SPre

Anaphalioides (*Asteraceae*)

§ ***bellidioides***	CTri

Anaphalis (*Asteraceae*)

sp.	NGrd
alpicola	EBee
margaritacea	CBcs ECha GMaP NBid NLar SRms WCAu WFar WMoo
§ - 'Neuschnee'	GJos ILea LPla NBre NLar XLum
- NEW SNOW	see *A. margaritacea* 'Neuschnee'
- var. ***yedoensis***	CTri
§ ***nepalensis*** var. ***monocephala***	EBee MCot NSti SRms
nubigena	see *A. nepalensis* var. *monocephala*
transnokoensis	EWes
§ ***trinervis***	CExl LSun XLum
triplinervis ♀H7	CRos EHoe ELan ELon EPfP EShb EWTr EWld GAbr GKev GMaP ILea LRHS MMuc MRav NBid NLar NRHS SPer WCAu WHoo WMoo
- CC 1620	EPPr NBir
- 'Silberregen'	SAko
§ - 'Sommerschnee' ♀H7	CBod CMac CRos EAJP ECha ECtt EPfP GWyn LPot LRHS MCot MHol MRav NEgg NLar NRHS NWad SPer WGwG WWtn
- SUMMER SNOW	see *A. triplinervis* 'Sommerschnee'

Anchusa (*Boraginaceae*)

sp.	CHab
§ ***azurea***	NLar SPhx
- 'Dropmore'	EBee EMor EPfP GQue LCro LOPS LRHS MRav NLar SCob SRms
- 'Feltham Pride'	CDor CRos EBee ELan EPfP LRHS NRHS SRms SWvt WHoo
- 'Little John'	SRms
- 'Loddon Royalist'	Widely available
- 'Opal'	ECtt LRHS NRHS WCAu
capensis	GKev
- 'Blue Angel'	SWvt
cespitosa	ELan EPot EWes LLHF WAbe WIce
italica	see *A. azurea*
laxiflora	see *Borago pygmaea*
myosotidiflora	see *Brunnera macrophylla*
officinalis	MNHC SRms
sempervirens	see *Pentaglottis sempervirens*

Ancylostemon (*Gesneriaceae*)

convexus B&SWJ 6624	WCru
- B&SWJ 7182	WCru

Andrachne (*Phyllanthaceae*)

colchica	see *Leptopus chinensis*

Andromeda (*Ericaceae*)

polifolia 'Alba'	CRos EHyd LRHS MAsh SPer SPlb SWvt WFar
- 'Alisa'	GKev
- 'Blue Ice'	CRos EHyd ELan GBin IDee LRHS LSRN MAsh NLar SPer SPoG WFar
- 'Blue Lagoon'	NLar
- 'Compacta' ♀H6	CBor CRos EHyd GEdr LRHS LSRN MAsh MGil NLar NWad SWvt WFar WGwG
- 'Grandiflora'	GKev
- 'Kirigamine'	CRos LRHS MAsh
- 'Macrophylla' ♀H6	GEdr ITim WAbe WThu
- 'Nana'	EPfP
- 'Nikko'	CMac NLar

Andropogon (*Poaceae*)

gerardii	CKno CRos EBee EHoe LRHS NRHS NWsh XLum
- 'Prairie Sommer'	NDov
- 'Weinheim Burgundy' new	IPot
glomeratus var. ***glaucopsis***	CAco
'JS Purple Konza' new	IPot
scoparius	see *Schizachyrium scoparium*
ternarius	GCal

Androsace (*Primulaceae*)

sp.	MAsh
alpina	WAbe
armeniaca var. ***macrantha***	GKev
* ***bayanharshanensis***	WAbe
brachystegia	GKev
bulleyana	CPla GKev WAbe
cantabrica	EPot
carnea	GKev
- subsp. ***brigantiaca***	GCrg GKev NHpl NRHS NSla WAbe WHoo
- var. ***halleri***	see *A. carnea* subsp. *rosea*
- subsp. ***laggeri*** ♀H5	GCrg GKev LLHF NRHS NSla WAbe
§ - subsp. ***rosea*** ♀H5	GCrg GKev ITim NHpl NSla
carnea × ***pyrenaica***	CPBP ELan EPot LLHF
chamaejasme subsp. ***carinata***	LLHF
'Chris Chadwell' new	GCrg
ciliata	WAbe
cylindrica	CRos EPot ITim LRHS NRHS
cylindrica × ***hirtella***	CRos EHyd EPot LRHS NRHS
delavayi	GKev SPlb WAbe
- ACE 1786	WAbe
elatior	WAbe
flavescens	EPot
foliosa	GKev
geraniifolia	EBee ECha SRms
globifera	GKev WAbe
halleri	see *A. carnea* subsp. *rosea*
hausmannii × ***hirtella***	LLHF
hedraeantha	GCrg NSla WAbe
helvetica hybrid	CPBP
himalaica	CPBP EPot GEdr WAbe
hirtella	ITim LLHF WAbe
idahoensis	WAbe
idahoensis × ***laevigata***	WAbe
jacquemontii	see *A. villosa* var. *jacquemontii*
kosopoljanskii	EPot
lactea	WAbe
laevigata	GCrg ITim WAbe
- 'Gothenburg'	GKev
- var. ***laevigata***	GKev
lanuginosa ♀H5	CBod CMea CPBP CSpe EBou ECtt EDAr EPot GBin GEdr MMuc NHol NHpl SBch SRms SRot WAbe WIce WOld WTor
lehmanniana	WAbe
- 'Gotëborg Yellow'	WAbe
limprichtii	see *A. sarmentosa* var. *watkinsii*
mariae	LLHF
× ***marpensis***	EPot SIgm WAbe
mathildae	LLHF WAbe
microphylla	see *A. mucronifolia* G.Watt
minor	WAbe
montana	WAbe
mucronifolia misapplied	see *A. sempervivoides*
§ ***mucronifolia*** G.Watt	WAbe
mucronifolia G.Watt × ***sempervivoides***	EPot SIgm WAbe
muscoidea	GKev WAbe
- 'Breviscapa'	EPot
- 'Dolpo Lilac'	WAbe
- Schacht's form	EPot WAbe
nivalis	SPlb
- Chumstick form	GKev LLHF
ochotensis	WAbe
× ***pedemontana***	LLHF
primuloides	see *A. studiosorum*
pubescens	CPla CRos EHyd EPot ITim LLHF LRHS NRHS
pyrenaica	CRos EHyd EPot GKev ITim LLHF LRHS NRHS WAbe
rigida	EPot WAbe
robusta subsp. ***purpurea***	WAbe
- - 'Dolpo Dwarf'	EPot WAbe
rotundifolia	GKev
sarmentosa misapplied	see *A. studiosorum*
sarmentosa ambig.	NHpl SPlb XLum
sarmentosa Wall.	EBou GKev SRms WHoo
- from Namche, Nepal	EPot MGil WAbe
- Galmont's form	see *A. studiosorum* 'Salmon's Variety'
- 'Sherriffii'	EPot SIgm SRms WHoo WIce
§ - var. ***watkinsii***	EPot
- var. ***yunnanensis*** misapplied	see *A. studiosorum*
selago	WAbe
- 'Red Eye'	WAbe
§ ***sempervivoides*** ♀H5	CRos EBou EDAr EHyd ELan EPot GBin GCrg GKev GMaP LRHS MBel NHol NRHS NSla SBch SIgm SPlb SRms WIce WOld
- 'Susan Joan'	EPot WAbe WOld
septentrionalis	CSpe
- 'Stardust'	ELan MHol WTor
spinulifera	EPot GKev
stenophylla	MAsh
strigillosa	GKev NHpl WAbe
§ ***studiosorum*** ♀H5	EPot GAbr GKev WAbe
- 'Chumbyi'	EPot LLHF NHpl SIgm SRms WIce WThu
- 'Conwy Gem'	WAbe
- 'Conwy Jewel'	WAbe
- 'Doksa'	CPBP EPot SIgm WAbe WIce
§ - 'Salmon's Variety'	CMea CTri EDAr SIgm
tapete	WAbe
vandellii	ITim NSla WAbe
villosa	NSla WAbe

	- var. ***incana***	GKev
§	- var. ***jacquemontii***	CPBP WThu
	- - lilac-flowered	EPot WAbe
	- - pink-flowered	EPot SIgm WAbe
	vitaliana	see *Vitaliana primuliflora*
	wardii	WAbe
	watkinsii	see *A. sarmentosa* var. *watkinsii*
	yargongensis	GKev WAbe
	zambalensis	WAbe
	- pink-flowered	GKev

Andryala (*Asteraceae*)

	agardhii	GKev
	glandulosa	WCot
	lanata	see *Hieracium lanatum*

Anemanthele (*Poaceae*)

	sp.	NGrd
§	***lessoniana*** ♀H4	Widely available
	- 'Autumn Tints'	EHoe
	- 'Gold Hue'	EHoe ELon
	- 'Sirocco'	CBod CSpe EUJe WCot WFar

Anemarrhena (*Asparagaceae*)

	asphodeloides	WCot

Anemia (*Schizaeaceae*)

	mexicana	ISha WPGP
	tomentosa	CRos ISha LEdu LRHS NRHS

Anemone ✿ (*Ranunculaceae*)

	Chen Yi T49	WCot
	aconitifolia Michx.	see *A. narcissiflora*
	altaica	GKev NLar SRms
	amurensis	CExl
	apennina ♀H6	CAvo GEdr LEdu WShi
	- var. ***albiflora***	EPot MAvo
	- double-flowered (d)	EPot LLHF MAvo
	- 'Petrovac'	CBor EPot GKev LEdu LLHF
	baicalensis	WSHC
	baldensis	EPPr GEdr GKev ITim NAln SRms
	barbulata	CExl CPla EBee EMor EWes GEdr GKev GPSL LEdu
	biflora var. ***petiolulosa***	GKev
	blanda ♀H6	CAby CRos LAma LCro LOPS LRHS NLar NRHS SCob SEND SRms WBor WFar WShi
I	- 'Alba'	CRos EHyd LRHS NRHS
	- blue-flowered	CAvo CCBP CMea CRos CTri EHyd ELan EPfP EPot ERCP GAbr GKev GMaP LCro LOPS LRHS NAln NRHS SCob SDeJ SPer SPhx SPoG SRms WCot
	- 'Charmer'	CCBP CGrW EPot GKev NHpl SDeJ WCot
	- 'Ingramii'	EPot GKev WCot
	- var. ***rosea***	CRos EHyd LAma LRHS NRHS SDeJ SPoG
	- - 'Pink Star'	CAvo ERCP GKev LAma NBir
	- - 'Radar' ♀H6	EPot ERCP GKev LAma MNrw NBir NHpl SDeJ
	- 'Violet Star'	GKev SDeJ
	- 'White Splendour' ♀H6	CAby CAvo CCBP CMea CRos CTri ELan EPfP EPot ERCP GAbr GKev LAma LCro LEdu LOPS LRHS NAln NBir NLar NRHS SDeJ SPhx SPoG SRms WCot WWFP
	- white-flowered	CRos LRHS NRHS
	'Bowles's Mauve'	GEdr MAsh
	caerulea	LEdu
	canadensis	ELon EMor EPPr GEdr LEdu WCot
	caroliniana	GKev
	chapaensis HWJ 631	WCru
	'Cinderella'PBR (Fantasy Series)	CRos EBee EHyd LRHS NRHS
	coelestina	GKev
	var. ***linearis*** **new**	
	coronaria	EPfP SCob SVic
	- De Caen Group	CRos EHyd EPfP GKev LAma LOPS LRHS NRHS SCob SPoG
	- - 'Bicolor'	GKev LAma SDeJ WRHF
	- - blue-flowered	CRos LRHS NRHS
	- - 'Bordeaux'	LCro LOPS SCob
§	- - 'Die Braut'	ERCP EShb GKev LAma LCro LOPS NBir SDeJ
	- - 'His Excellency'	see *A. coronaria* (De Caen Group) 'Hollandia'
§	- - 'Hollandia'	GKev LAma SDeJ
	- - 'Mister Fokker'	CTca ERCP EShb GBin GKev ILea LAma LCro LOPS SDeJ WRHF
	- - pink-flowered	CRos LRHS NRHS
	- - red-flowered	CRos LRHS NRHS
	- - THE BRIDE	see *A. coronaria* (De Caen Group) 'Die Braut'
	- - 'The Governor'	ERCP GKev ILea SDeJ
	- (Harmony Series) 'Harmony Orchid'	CRos EHyd EPfP LRHS NRHS
	- - 'Harmony Pearl'	CRos EHyd LRHS NRHS
	- - 'Harmony Scarlet'	CRos EHyd LRHS NRHS
	- Saint Bridgid Group (d)	CRos EHyd GKev LAma LRHS NRHS
	- - 'Lord Lieutenant' (d)	ERCP GKev NBir SDeJ
	- - 'Mount Everest' (d)	ERCP GKev ILea NBir SDeJ
	- - 'The Admiral' (d)	GKev NBir SDeJ
	- 'Sylphide' (Mona Lisa Series)	ERCP GKev ILea LAma LCro LOPS NBir SDeJ
	crinita	NLar
	cylindrica	EPPr GEdr MHer NDov NLar XEll
	'Dainty Swan'	EBee IPot LRHS MNrw NPri NRHS
	'Danish White'	MNrw WCot
	decapetala	MHer XEll
	demissa var. ***major***	EBee
	'Dreaming Swan'	CWGN EBee EMor GBin IPot LLHF LRHS MBel MHol MNrw MPnt NLar NPri NSti SHar SPoG SWvt WCAu WNPC
	drummondii	CPla GKev
	'Elfin Swan'	LRHS MNrw NLar NRHS SPoG
	fasciculata	see *A. narcissiflora*
	filisecta	CAby EBee MBel MHol MTis WCot WRHF
	flaccida	CAby CBro CRos EHrv EHyd EPPr GEdr LEdu LPla LRHS MAvo MNrw NRHS SHar WCot WHal WSHC
	- 'Futabazuru' (d)	GEdr
	- 'Ginpai' (d)	GEdr WCot
	× ***fulgens*** 'Annulata Grandiflora'	EBee
	globosa	see *A. multifida* Poir.
	'Guernica'	EWes
	'Hatakeyama Double' (d)	GCal LPla WSHC
	'Hatakeyama Single'	LPla
	hepatica L.	see *Hepatica nobilis*
§	***hortensis***	EBee
§	***hupehensis***	CExl CKel EBee EBou GMaP LSun
	- BWJ 8190	WCru
	- NJM 11.068	WPGP
	- f. ***alba***	CExl CSpe IFro
§	- 'Bowles's Pink' ♀H7	CDor CElw CExl LCro LOPS NLar
	- 'Crispa'	see *A.* × *hybrida* 'Lady Gilmour' Wolley-Dod

	- 'Eugenie'	ECtt EPfP LRHS NBir NRHS
	- 'Hadspen Abundance' ♀H7	Widely available
	- var. ***hupehensis***	WFar
§	- var. ***japonica***	CPou SRms XLum
	- - B&SWJ 4886	WCru
	- - PAB 8884	LEdu
	- - 'Bodnant Burgundy'	EBee LRHS SWvt WBrk
§	- - 'Bressingham Glow'	CExl CMac CRos ECtt ELan EPfP EPot EShb GKin ILea LRHS NBir NLar NRHS SPer WBrk WCAu WFar WHil
§	- - 'Pamina' ♀H7	Widely available
	- - 'Pink Saucer'	EBee WFar
	- - PRINCE HENRY	see *A. hupehensis* var. *japonica* 'Prinz Heinrich'
§	- - 'Prinz Heinrich'	Widely available
§	- - 'Rotkäppchen' ♀H7	CDor CRos ECtt GBin GKin GQue LRHS LSun MHol MMuc NHol NLar NRHS NSti SPad SWvt WCot WRHF WSHC
	- - 'Splendens'	CBod CMea CRos EHyd ELan EPfP LCro LOPS LRHS MCot NAst NLar NRHS SCob SPer SPoG SRms SWvt WHal WSpi XLum
	- 'Little Princess'PBR	EBee ECtt MNrw
	- 'Ouvertüre'	ECtt
	- 'Pocahontas'PBR (Fantasy Series)	CRos ECtt EHyd EMor EPfP GBin LRHS MNrw NRHS
	- 'Praecox'	CBod CMea CRos EPfP LRHS MBNS MNHC NBir NEgg NRHS SRms SWvt WCAu
	- 'Red Riding Hood' (Fantasy Series)	CRos LRHS NRHS
	- 'September Charm'	see *A.* × *hybrida* 'September Charm'
	- 'Superba'	WSpi
§	× ***hybrida***	NChi WMoo
	- 'Alba' misapplied (UK)	see *A.* × *hybrida* 'Honorine Jobert'
	- 'Alba Dura'	see *A. tomentosa* 'Albadura'
	- 'Albert Schweitzer'	see *A.* × *hybrida* 'Elegans'
	- 'Andrea Atkinson'	Widely available
	- 'Bowles's Pink'	see *A. hupehensis* 'Bowles's Pink'
	- 'Bressingham Glow'	see *A. hupehensis* var. *japonica* 'Bressingham Glow'
	- 'Carmen' **new**	LPla
	- 'Coupe d'Argent'	EBee ECtt IKil LRHS MBel NLar
§	- 'Elegans' ♀H7	CSam ECtt GMaP LCro LOPS LRHS MMuc NBir SEND SWvt WFar
	- 'Frau Marie Maushardt'	WBrk
§	- 'Géante des Blanches'	LPla
§	- 'Honorine Jobert' ♀H7	Widely available
	- 'Josephine'	WFar
§	- 'Königin Charlotte' ♀H7	Widely available
	- 'Lady Gilmour' misapplied	see *A.* × *hybrida* 'Montrose'
	- 'Lady Gilmour' ambig.	GMaP GWyn XLum
§	- 'Lady Gilmour' Wolley-Dod	CBod CRos CSpe EBee ECtt EPfP LEdu LRHS MRav NBir NChi NRHS SRms WSpi XLum
	- 'Loreley'	CBod EPfP IKil LPla NLar SCob SWvt WCot
	- 'Luise Uhink'	CPou
	- 'Märchenfee'	MNrw
	- 'Margarete' Kayser & Seibert	CExl CRos ECrN ECtt ELan EPfP LRHS MHol NRHS WHil
	- 'Max Vogel'	see *A.* × *hybrida* 'Elegans'
	- 'Monterosa'	see *A.* × *hybrida* 'Montrose'
§	- 'Montrose'	CPou CRos EBee ECha ELan EWes GMaP LCro LOPS LPla LRHS NBir NLar NRHS SRms WCAu
	- 'Nightingale' (Fantasy Series)	EBee
	- 'Pamina'	see *A. hupehensis* var. *japonica* 'Pamina'
	- PINK KISS ('Pkan'PBR)	EBee ELon
	- (Pretty Lady Series) 'Pretty Lady Diana'PBR	ECtt LBuc LCro LRHS NRHS SCob SWvt WHil
	- - 'Pretty Lady Emily'PBR	EPfP LBuc LRHS NLar NRHS SCob SWvt WHil
	- - 'Pretty Lady Julia'PBR	EBee LBuc SCob SHar WHil
	- - 'Pretty Lady Maria'	EBee LRHS NRHS
	- - 'Pretty Lady Susan'	CWGN EBee LBuc LCro LOPS LRHS NLar SCob SHar SWvt WHil
	- PRINCE HENRY	see *A. hupehensis* var. *japonica* 'Prinz Heinrich'
	- 'Profusion'	CRos CTri EBee LBuc LRHS NRHS WHal
	- QUEEN CHARLOTTE	see *A.* × *hybrida* 'Königin Charlotte'
	- 'Richard Ahrens'	CAvo CRos ECtt EPfP EShb GBee GCal GMaP LRHS LSRN MGos NAln NEgg NGdn NLar NRHS SWvt WGwG
§	- 'Robustissima'	CBod CRos EBee EMor EPfP GMaP ILea LRHS LSRN MCot MHol MMuc MNrw NAln NBir NEgg NGdn NLar NRHS NSti SEND SPer SRms SWvt WAvo WCAu WMoo
	- 'Rosea' **new**	CBod
	- 'Rosenschale'	CRos EWes LRHS MNrw NRHS
	- 'Rotkäppchen'	see *A. hupehensis* var. *japonica* 'Rotkäppchen'
§	- 'September Charm' ♀H7	Widely available
	- 'Serenade'	CKel CRos CSam ECtt ELan EMor EPfP LRHS LSRN MRav NBir NLar NRHS SPoG WCAu WMoo XLum
	- TOURBILLON	see *A.* × *hybrida* 'Whirlwind'
§	- 'Whirlwind'	Widely available
	- 'White Queen'	see *A.* × *hybrida* 'Géante des Blanches'
	- WIRBELWIND	see *A.* × *hybrida* 'Whirlwind'
	japonica	see *A. hupehensis*, *A. hupehensis* var. *japonica*, *A.* × *hybrida*
	- 'Crustata'	CMac
§	× ***lesseri***	CSpe ECha ELan GEdr GKev SRms
	leveillei	Widely available
	- BWJ 7919	WCru
§	× ***lipsiensis***	CAby CBro EBee ECtt EHrv EPfP EPot GAbr GEdr GKev GMaP IFro LEdu MAvo MBel MCot MNrw NHpl NLar WCru WFar WHal WHoo WPGP WSHC WSpi
	- 'Pallida' ♀H5	CBor CElw CSam CSpe ELon GEdr GKev LEdu NAln NLar WCot WShi XEll
	- 'Schwefelfeuer'	LEdu MAvo
	- 'Vindobonensis'	EBee GEdr MAvo WCot
	lithophila	GEdr
	lyallii	GKev
	magellanica hort. ex Wehrh.	see *A. multifida* Poir.
	'Majestic' **new**	MHol
	matsudae B&SWJ 1452	WCru
	- NMWJ 14517 **new**	WCru
	multifida misapplied, red-flowered	see *A.* × *lesseri*
§	***multifida*** Poir.	CRos ECha EHyd EPfP GKev ILea LRHS NBir NRHS NSti SPer WFar WHoo
	- Annabella Series	GKev
	- var. ***globosa***	GKev

	- 'Major'	CMea CSpe EPfP GPSL SPhx WIce
	- pink-flowered	LPot
	- 'Rubra'	CBod EHrv EPfP GBin GEdr GKev GWyn ILea LRHS MSCN NAln NBir NEgg NLar NRHS SPoG WBor WHoo
	- yellow-flowered	GEdr NEgg
§	***narcissiflora***	CSpe EBee GKev NBir NChi
	nemorosa	Widely available
	- 'Alba'	CRos LRHS NRHS WFar
	- 'Alba Plena' (d)	CSam ECha ECtt EPPr EPfP GKev MAvo NGdn NLar WFar WSHC
	- 'Allenii' ♀H5	CBor CBro CElw CRos EHrv ELon EPPr EPot GEdr GKev GMaP ITim LRHS MAvo MRav NRHS NRya WFar WShi
	- 'Amy Doncaster'	CLAP
	- 'Apuseni'	LEdu
	- 'Atley'	EBee GEdr GKev MAvo WCot WFar
	- 'Atrocaerulea'	IBlr NLar
	- 'Atrorosea'	EPPr
	- 'Ballyrogan Blue'	MAvo
	- 'Behemoth Blue'	LEdu MAvo
	- 'Bill Baker's Pink'	CLAP LEdu
	- 'Blue Beauty'	EBee ELon GMaP IBlr MAvo
	- 'Blue Bonnet'	CAby EPot ITim LEdu MAvo
	- 'Blue Eyes' (d)	CAby CElw CLAP EBee GAbr GEdr GKev GMaP IBlr ITim LEdu NBir NHpl SMHy WFar WSHC
	- 'Blue Queen'	ELon
	- 'Blush'	LEdu
	- 'Bohemia'	MAvo
	- 'Bowles's Purple'	CAby EBee ELon EMor EPot GEdr GMaP LRHS MAvo MHol NBid NHpl NRya WBor WCot WFar WSHC
	- 'Bracteata'	CAby CBro CTca GEdr GKev MMrt
	- 'Bracteata Pleniflora' (d)	CLAP EBee EHrv EPot GKev GMaP IBlr LEdu MAvo MNrw NBir SDeJ WCot WHal WShi XEll
	- 'Buckland'	EBee EPfP EPot IBlr MAvo
	- 'Caerulea'	EPot GKev ITim
	- 'Cedric's Pink'	EPPr IBlr LLHF MAvo WFar
	- 'Celestial'	EAJP ELan EPPr MAvo
	- 'Dee Day'	EBee LEdu MAvo
	- 'Dell Garden'	EPPr
	- 'Evelyn Meadows'	WSHC
	- 'Flore Pleno' (d)	CAby CPla EBee GAbr IFro NBir WBor WFar
	- 'Flushing'	GEdr GKev MAvo
	- 'Frenzy'	MAvo WCot
	- 'Frühlingsfee'	MAvo
	- 'Frühlingsfest'	EBee
	- 'Gerda Ramusen'	ELan ELon EPot EShb EWes LEdu LLHF
	- 'Gerry'	MAvo
I	- 'Gigantea Rubra'	MAvo WCot
	- 'Good Blue'	MAvo
	- 'Green Dream'	WSHC
	- 'Green Fingers'	EHrv EPPr GEdr GKev GMaP ITim MMrt WSHC XEll
	- 'Hakumane Senjuizaki'	WCot
	- 'Hannah Gubbay'	EPot
	- 'Helsinki'	MAvo
	- 'Hilda'	EBee ECtt GEdr GKev LEdu NBir NRya
	- 'Ice and Fire'	EPot GKev LEdu
	- 'Jack Brownless'	LEdu
	- 'Kentish Pink'	GBin GMaP
	- 'Knightshayes Vestal' (d)	CExl CLAP MAvo MRav WSHC
	- 'La Rochanne'	MAvo MNrw
	- 'Lady Doneraile'	EPot LEdu NBir WFar WSHC
	- 'Latvian Pink'	EPot GEdr GKev LEdu MAvo
	- 'Leeds' Variety'	EPot GKev GMaP LEdu
	- 'Lehna' (d)	MAvo
	- 'Lionel Bacon'	LEdu MAvo
	- 'Lismore Blue'	EBee EPPr EPot GKev
	- 'Lismore Pink'	GEdr LEdu
	- 'Lucia'	EPot GEdr GKev LEdu MAvo WCot WFar
	- 'Lychette'	EHrv EPPr EPot GAbr GEdr GKev IBlr MAvo WSHC
	- 'Marie Rose'	EPot WFar
	- 'Mart's Blue'	EBee EPfP EPot GKev MAvo WCot
	- 'Monstrosa'	EPot GKev MAvo
	- 'Noémie'	XEll
	- 'Parlez Vous'	CExl EHrv EPPr GEdr LEdu MAvo MNrw NHpl SMHy WFar WPnP WSHC XEll
	- 'Pat's Pink'	WShi
	- 'Pentre Pink'	EPot IBlr
	- 'Picos Pink'	EHrv
	- 'Pink Carpet'	GEdr LEdu
	- 'Pink Delight'	LEdu
	- pink-flowered	MMuc
	- 'Robinsoniana' ♀H5	Widely available
	- 'Rosea'	LEdu NLar
	- 'Royal Blue'	CAby CBro CTca EBee ECtt EHrv EPPr EPot ERCP EUJe GAbr GEdr GKev GMaP LAma LEdu MAvo NDov NHpl NLar WCot WFar WPnP
	- 'Salt and Pepper'	LEdu MAvo
	- 'Slack Top Pink'	MAvo
	- 'Slenaken' **new**	MAvo
§	- 'Stammerberg' (d)	EPPr MAvo WSHC
	- 'Stammheim'	see *A. nemorosa* 'Stammerberg'
	- 'Thekla' (d) **new**	MAvo
	- 'Tilo'	MAvo
	- 'Tinney's Blush'	CLAP
	- 'Tomas'	CLAP EAJP ELon EPot GEdr LEdu MAvo NHpl NRya WFar
	- 'Tups'	LEdu
	- 'Vestal' (d) ♀H5	Widely available
	- 'Virescens' ♀H5	CWCL EHrv ELon EMor EPPr EPot GEdr GKev GMaP LEdu MAvo NAln NBir NLar WShi
	- 'Viridiflora'	CExl CLAP EPfP GAbr GBin MAvo MNrw NBir WCot WSHC
	- 'Westwell Pink'	EPPr LLHF MAvo MNrw WCot WFar WSHC WShi
	- white-flowered	CRos LRHS NRHS
	- 'Wilks' White'	ELon EPPr GEdr MAvo
	- 'Wisley Pink'	EPot LEdu MAvo WFar
I	- 'Wisley White Form'	MAvo WHoo
	- 'Wyatt's Pink'	ELon EPot GKev LEdu MAvo
	- 'Yerda Ramusem'	EPPr LEdu MAvo MNrw WSHC
	nemorosa* × *ranunculoides	see *A.* × *lipsiensis*
	obtusiloba	GBin GEdr NHpl WAbe WHal
	- CLD 1549	GEdr
	- 'Alba'	GEdr WAbe
	- 'Large Blue'	EPot GEdr LEdu NSla WAbe
	- 'Pradesh'	GEdr NHpl
I	- 'Sulphurea'	GEdr WAbe
	palmata	GEdr LEdu NSum WKif
	parviflora	GKev LLHF XEll
	patens	see *Pulsatilla patens*
	pavonina	CAby CSpe ECha LPla MHol NBir SLon SMHy SPoG WCot

- lilac-flowered	NBir
- pink-flowered	NBir
polyanthes	CRos EBee EPfP GEdr GKev LLHF LRHS NRHS
prattii	CExl EPPr GEdr LEdu NHpl
pseudoaltaica	LEdu WCru
- 'Yuki-no-sei' (d)	GEdr WCot
pulsatilla	see *Pulsatilla vulgaris*
* ***raddeana*** f. ***rosea***	GEdr
ranunculoides ♀H6	Widely available
- 'Bill Baker'	LEdu MAvo
- 'Crazy Vienna'	MAvo WCot
- 'Ferguson's Fancy'	GCal
- 'Frank Waley'	MAvo WCot
- 'Fuchsis Traum'	LEdu WCot
- 'Grandiflora'	MAvo
* - ***laciniata***	MAvo WCot
- 'Pleniflora' (d) ♀H6	CAvo CRos ECha GKev LRHS MAvo NLar NRHS WFar
- subsp. ***ranunculoides***	GKev
- 'Semi-Plena'	GEdr GKev LEdu
- subsp. ***wockeana***	CSam EBee LEdu MAvo
reflexa	EBee GKev LLHF
riparia	see *A. virginiana* var. *alba*
rivularis	CAvo CPar CRos CSpe CTsd EMor GEdr GKev GPoy ILea IPot ITim LRHS MNrw NBir NLar NRHS SBrt SChF SPer SRms WCru WFar WKif WMoo WSpi XEll
- B&SWJ 13944	WCru
- BWJ 7611	WCru
- CC 4588	CExl
- 'Glacier'	CCBP CWCL EBee MHol WHil
aff. ***rivularis***	WSpi
'Ruffled Swan'	CWGN EMor EWTr GBin IPot LLHF LRHS MNrw NRHS NSti SHar SLon SPoG STPC WTyc
rupicola	GEdr GKev NBir WCot XEll
× ***seemannii***	see *A.* × *lipsiensis*
stellata Lam.	see *A. hortensis*
stolonifera double-flowered (d)	EBee LEdu LPla WCot WSHC
sulphurea misapplied	see *Pulsatilla alpina* subsp. *apiifolia*
sumatrana B&SWJ 11265	WCru
sylvestris	Widely available
- 'Elise Fellmann' (d)	CSpe EBee WHal
- 'Macrantha'	EPfP
- 'Madonna' new	LSun
- 'Snow White'	CBod
tenuifolia new	NHpl
tetrasepala	WCot XEll
§ ***tomentosa***	LRHS NAln NRHS SRms
§ - 'Albadura'	EBee
- 'Robustissima'	see *A.* × *hybrida* 'Robustissima'
trifolia L.	EBee EPPr EPot EWTr GKev LEdu NBid NLar WCot XEll
trullifolia	GBin GCal NHar
- var. ***linearis***	WAbe
udensis	GEdr WCot
vernalis	see *Pulsatilla vernalis*
vesicatoria	SBrt
virginiana	EBee LEdu MNrw NBid WCot WHrl
§ - var. ***alba***	GEdr
vitifolia misapplied	see *A. tomentosa*
vitifolia Buch.-Ham. ex DC. WJC 12743	WCru
WILD SWAN ('Macane001'PBR)	Widely available

Anemonella (*Ranunculaceae*)

thalictroides	CBor CElw EHrv ELon EMor EPot GAbr GEdr GKev ITim LAma MBel NHpl NLar NRya WAbe WFar WPnP WSHC WSpi XLum
- 'Amelia'	GEdr NBro NHpl
- 'Babe'	WCot
- 'Betty Blake' (d)	EBee ELon GBin GEdr GKev LAma LLHF MAvo MMrt NBro NHpl NRya WCot WFar
- 'Blushing Bride' (d) new	NBro
- 'Cameo'	GEdr GKev LAma MNrw NHpl NRya WCot WFar
- 'Charlotte'	GEdr
- 'Dark Pink'	EBee GBin MAvo NHpl
- 'Diamante'	CElw MAvo WCot
- 'Double Diamante' (d)	WCot
- 'Full Double White' (d)	NHpl
- 'Green Hurricane' (d)	GEdr GKev LAma NRya WCot
- 'Hakikomi-fu' (v)	GEdr
- 'Kikuzaki Pink' (d)	GEdr GKev LAma
- 'Kikuzaki White' (d)	GEdr GKev LAma
- 'Nadine A.' (d) new	XEll
- 'Pink Fairy' new	SMHy
- f. ***rosea***	CAby CElw ELan GKev LLHF NLar WAbe
- - 'Oscar Schoaf' (d)	EBee GEdr GKev ITim MAvo NHpl WAbe WCot WFar
- - semi-double pink-flowered (d)	CElw EHrv
- 'Rosea Plena' (d)	EMor LAma
- semi-double white-flowered (d)	CElw WAbe
- 'Snowflakes' (d)	MAvo
- 'Spring Nymph'	SMHy
- 'Tairin'	GEdr GKev LAma NHpl WCot

Anemonopsis (*Ranunculaceae*)

macrophylla	CAby CExl CPBP CSpe EBee EPfP EWes GCal GEdr LEdu MNrw MRav NHpl NLar WCru WFar WOld WPGP WSHC
- double-flowered (d)	GKev WSHC
- 'White Swan'	EWld GEdr WCru WSHC

Anemopsis (*Saururaceae*)

californica	EBee EWat GEdr LCro LLWG LOPS MWts SBrt WCot

Anethum (*Apiaceae*)

graveolens	EMor ENfk GPoy MHer MNHC NPri SRms SVic
- 'Dukat'	CLau LCro LOPS
- 'Vierling'	SPhx

angelica see *Angelica archangelica*

Angelica (*Apiaceae*)

PAB 8986 new	CSpe
acutiloba	WFar
- var. ***iwatensis*** B&SWJ 11197	WCru
anomala B&SWJ 10886	ESwi LEdu WCru
archangelica	Widely available
arguta	EBee
- B&SWJ 14162 new	WCru
atropurpurea	CRos EPfP LRHS MNrw MRav NRHS SWvt
brevicaulis	LEdu WPGP

	breweri B&SWJ 14083	WCru
	cartilaginomarginata B&SWJ 12663	WCru
	cyclocarpa WJC 13658	WCru
	dahurica	NDov SPhx WFar
	decursiva B&SWJ 5746	WCru
	edulis	WHer WPGP
	- B&SWJ 10968	WCru
	genuflexa B&SWJ 14109 **new**	WCru
	gigas	Widely available
	- B&SWJ 4170	WCru
	grayi	SPhx
	hendersoni	SPhx
	hispanica	see *A. pachycarpa*
	japonica B&SWJ 11480	WCru
	montana	see *A. sylvestris*
	morii RWJ 9802	WCru
	nubigena WJC 13763	WCru
§	***pachycarpa***	CRos CSam CSpe EBee EPPr GBin GMaP LRHS MAvo MHer MRav NBir NGBl NLar NRHS WFar
	pubescens	NDov
	- B&SWJ 5593	WCru
	sachalinensis	EBee
	sinensis	GPoy LEdu
	'Summer Delight'	see *Ligusticum scoticum*
§	***sylvestris***	CBre CHab LLWG WHil WOut
	- 'Burgundy'	NGBl
	- 'Ebony' ♀H5	CBct CPla ECtt LEdu LRHS MHer MHol NCGa NSti SCob SPad SPhx SPoG WCot WFar WPGP
*	- 'Purpurea'	CDor CSam CSpe EWes GMaP
	- 'Vicar's Mead'	EBee ECha LEdu LRHS MBel NBir NDai SPhx SWvt WCAu WHil
	taiwaniana	CBre CDTJ CRos EBee ELan ESwi IMou LRHS MMuc NLar NRHS SPhx
	ursina	NGBl WCru

Angelonia (*Plantaginaceae*)

ARCHANGEL DEEP ROSE ('Balarcrose')	CRos EHyd LRHS NRHS

Anigozanthos (*Haemodoraceae*)

(Bush Gems Series) BUSH BONANZA ('Rambubona'PBR)	SEle
- BUSH DIAMOND ('Rambodiam'PBR)	SEle
- BUSH ELEGANCE ('Rambueleg'PBR) **new**	CAbb
- 'Bush Inferno'PBR	SEle
- 'Bush Ranger'	CCCN
- BUSH TENACITY ('Rambocity') **new**	CAbb
flavidus	SPlb
- 'Ember'	CCCN
- 'Illusion'	CCCN
- 'Opal'	CCCN
- 'Pearl'	CCCN
- red-flowered	SPlb
- 'Splendour'	CCCN
- 'Yellow Gem'	CCCN
manglesii	SPlb SVen
rufus	SEle

anise see *Pimpinella anisum*

Anisodontea (*Malvaceae*)

	bryoniifolia	SVen
§	***capensis*** ♀H2	CCCN CRos ELan SChF SEle SLim SPlb SRkn SRms SVen SWvt WTre
	- 'Elegans Princess'	CCCN
	'Crystal Rose'	EPfP MGos XLum
	'El Rayo'	CSde CSpe CWGN ECtt EMor MHol MNrw MPie NCou SDys SMad SPad SPoG SRkn WAvo WBor WBrk WCot WFar WTre XLum
	huegelii	see *Alyogyne huegelii*
	× ***hypomadara*** misapplied	see *A. capensis*
§	× ***hypomadara*** (Sprague) D.M. Bates	SEle
	julii	SVen
	LADY IN PINK ('Nuanilaninp')	NCou
	'Large Magenta'	EBee ELon LRHS SWvt

Anisodus (*Solanaceae*)

carnioliciodes BWJ 7501	WCru

Anisotome (*Apiaceae*)

imbricata var. ***imbricata***	WAbe
lyallii	GKev

Annona (*Annonaceae*)

cherimola (F)	CCCN XBlo
squamosa (F)	SPlb

Anoiganthus see *Cyrtanthus*

Anomalesia see *Gladiolus*

Anomatheca (*Iridaceae*)

cruenta	see *Freesia laxa*

Anopterus (*Escalloniaceae*)

glandulosus	WSHC

Anredera (*Basellaceae*)

§	***cordifolia***	CRHN EShb GKev LEdu

Antennaria (*Asteraceae*)

	aprica	see *A. parvifolia*
	dioica	CPla CTri ECtt GAbr GBin GPoy NSla SPlb SRms WAbe XLum
	- 'Alba'	EHoe
	- 'Alex Duguid'	GPSL NWad
	- 'Aprica'	see *A. parvifolia*
	- 'Minima'	EPot GCrg ITim NBro NRHS NSla WAbe
	- 'Nyewoods Variety'	SRms
	- var. ***rosea***	see *A. rosea*
	- 'Rotes Wunder'	CMea ECha EPot GCrg WAbe
*	- 'Rubra'	ECha ECtt EDAr MBel MMuc SRms WIce XLum
	microphylla 'Pink Pussy Toes' **new**	EBou
§	***parvifolia***	CTri SRms SRot
	- 'Alba'	EDAr
	plantaginifolia	EBee
§	***rosea*** ♀H5	CRos EBou EHyd GKev GMaP LRHS MAsh MHer NAln NRHS NSla SPlb SRms WHal WHoo WIce

Antenoron see *Persicaria*

Anthemis ✿ (*Asteraceae*)

	from Turkey	ECtt EWes
	arvensis	CHab MNHC SRms
§	'Beauty of Grallagh'	WSpi
	'Cally Cream'	ELon GCal GWyn LRHS SMHy SPhx

'Cally White'	GBee GBin GCal WBrk
carpatica	MMuc NBro
- 'Karpatenschnee'	CRos EHyd EPfP LRHS NRHS SAko SRms
cretica subsp. ***leucanthemoides***	WAbe
- subsp. ***tenuiloba***	EWes
frutescens Voss	see *Argyranthemum frutescens*
'Grallagh Gold' misapplied, orange-yellow	see *A.* 'Beauty of Grallagh'
'Grallagh Gold'	ECtt NPer SPhx
§ ***marschalliana***	CRos EBou ECtt EDAr EPot LRHS NHpl NRHS SPlb WAbe WCot
- subsp. ***pectinata***	GCrg
nobilis	see *Chamaemelum nobile*
'Orange Dream' **new**	CBcs
punctata	Widely available
subsp. ***cupaniana*** ♀H4	
- - 'Nana'	NBir NPer SHar WCot
rudolphiana	see *A. marschalliana*
sancti-johannis	CRos EPfP LRHS NPer NRHS SAko SRms
SUSANNA MITCHELL ('Blomit')	CDor CRos EBee ECtt ELon GAbr GMaP LRHS LSRN MAvo MBel MHol MNrw NBir NDov NLar NRHS NWad SWvt WSHC XLum
'Tetworth'	ECha EHrv ELan EPfP GBee GBin LRHS SAko
tinctoria	CBod CHby CMac EBee ENfk GPoy MHer MNHC NPer SRms SWvt WSFF XLum
- 'Alba'	CRos EBee LRHS NRHS NWad WFar
- 'Charme'PBR	CRos LRHS NLar NRHS SPoG SRms SWvt
- 'Compacta'	CBod EWes GCal XLum
- 'E.C. Buxton' ♀H6	Widely available
- 'Eva'	NDov
- 'Hall Farm Frilly'	ECtt ELon
- 'Kelwayi'	CRos CSBt EBou EMor EPfP GLog GWyn LRHS NHic NLar NPer NRHS SPer SRms WFar XLum
- 'Lemon Ice'	EBee EMor GBin GWyn MBel NLar
- 'Lemon Maid'	ECtt ELon
- 'Sauce Hollandaise'	Widely available
- 'Wargrave Variety'	CElw CMac CRos CSam ECha ECtt EHrv ELan EPfP GBin GWyn LRHS MAvo MHol NBir NChi NGdn NRHS NWad SPhx SWvt WCAu WFar WGwG
'Tinpenny Sparkle'	CBod CSam EBee ECtt EMor EWes GWyn MHol MPie NLar WFar WHoo
triumfettii	EBee NDov NPer WGoo
tuberculata	NChi SBch

Anthericum (Asparagaceae)

algeriense	see *A. liliago*
* ***bovei***	CBro
§ ***liliago***	CRos CSpe ELan EWTr EWld GCal GKev GMaP LRHS MCot MPie MRav NDai NLar NRHS SPer WAul WPtf XEll
- 'Major' ♀H5	CAvo CBro ECha EHrv IBlr LEdu SPhx
plumosum	see *Trichopetalum plumosum*
ramosum	CAby CFis CRos CSpe ECha EPPr EPot EWes GCal GKev LEdu LRHS MBrN NBid NBir NLar NRHS NSla SPhx WCot

Antholyza (Iridaceae)

coccinea	see *Crocosmia paniculata*
paniculata	see *Crocosmia paniculata*

Anthoxanthum (Poaceae)

odoratum	CHab GPoy GQue XLum

Anthriscus (Apiaceae)

cerefolium	CHby CLau ENfk GPoy LCro LOPS MHer MNHC SRms SVic WSFF
sylvestris	CBre CHab GQue LCro LOPS LRHS NMir SPhx WFar WOut WSFF
- 'Going for Gold'	CAby CNat EPPr EWes NChi WCot WHil WOut
- 'Kabir'	LRHS SPhx
- 'Ravenswing'	Widely available
- 'Snape Cottage Brown'	CNat
- yellow-leaved **new**	GBin

Anthurium (Araceae)

andraeanum 'Glowing Pink'	XBlo
- 'Red Heart'	XBlo
- 'Tivolo'	XBlo
'Aztec'	XBlo
BALENO ('Anthauf4'PBR)	XBlo
'Caribo'	XBlo
crenatum	XBlo
'Crimson'	XBlo
'Magenta'	XBlo
'Mikra'	XBlo
'Octavia'	XBlo
PICO BELLO ('Anthcupcup'PBR)	XBlo
PINK CHAMPION ('Antinkeles'PBR)	LCro LOPS XBlo
'Porcelaine White'	XBlo
RED CHAMPION ('Anthbnena'PBR)	LCro LOPS XBlo
'Vitara'	XBlo
WHITE CHAMPION ('Anthefaqyr'PBR)	XBlo

Anthyllis (Papilionaceae)

hermanniae	LRHS
- 'Compacta'	see *A. hermanniae* 'Minor'
§ - 'Minor'	ELan EPot ITim WAbe
montana	CPBP XSen
- subsp. ***atropurpurea***	CRos LRHS NRHS
- 'Rubra' ♀H5	CSpe EDAr EPot LLHF NSla SPhx
vulneraria	CHab GJos LRHS NMir NRHS NRya SPhx WSFF WWFP
- var. ***coccinea***	EAJP ELan GJos GKev MBel NRHS NSla SPhx WCFE WOut
- dark red-flowered	CSpe

Antirrhinum (Plantaginaceae)

asarina	see *Asarina procumbens*
australe	GCal
barrelieri	SEND
braun-blanquetii	WCot
charidemi **new**	EBee
glutinosum	see *A. hispanicum* subsp. *hispanicum*
hispanicum 'Avalanche'	ECtt
§ - subsp. ***hispanicum***	CSpe
- subsp. ***mollissimum*** **new**	EPot
latifolium	EBee
majus 'Admiral White'	LCro LOPS

- 'Black Prince'	CSpe ECtt ELan LPla SPhx
- 'Night and Day'	CSpe
- 'Rocket White' (Rocket Series) new	CSpe
- Sonnet Series, formula mixed	NPri
molle	CSpe EBee GKev MCot NAln NPer SChF WAbe
- pink-flowered	MCot
- white-flowered	EBee
PRETTY IN PINK ('Pmoore07'[PBR])	CSBt IPot LCro LOPS LRHS MHol NPri SHar SLon
sempervirens	MHer WAbe
siculum	EBee

añu see *Tropaeolum tuberosum*

Aphelandra (*Acanthaceae*)

squarrosa	EShb
- 'Citrina'	XBlo

Aphyllanthes (*Asparagaceae*)

monspeliensis	SBrt XLum XSen

Apios (*Papilionaceae*)

§	***americana***	EWes LEdu NBir WCot WCru WSHC
	- 'Nutty'	CAgr MCoo
	tuberosa	see *A. americana*

Apium (*Apiaceae*)

graveolens	CHab CLau ENfk GPoy MHer MNHC SRms SVic WJek
- var. ***dulce*** 'Aurora' new	LOPS
- - 'Brydon's Prize Red' new	SVic
- - 'Celebrity' ♀H2	LRHS MCtn NRHS
- - 'Golden Self-blanching' new	SVic
- - 'Victoria' ♀H2	EKin
- 'Giant Pink' - Mammoth Pink ♀H4	NRob
- var. ***rapaceum*** 'Prinz' ♀H4	CHby EKin LCro LOPS MCtn SVic
- (Secalinum Group) 'Par-cel'	MHer SRms

Apium × *Petroselinum* (*Apiaceae*)

hybrid, misapplied	see *A. graveolens* Secalinum Group

Apocynum (*Apocynaceae*)

cannabinum	GPoy

Aponogeton (*Aponogetonaceae*)

desertorum	EWat
distachyos	CBen CWat EWat LCro LLWG LOPS MWts NPer SVic WMAq XLum

apple see *Malus domestica*; also AGM Fruit Section

apricot see *Prunus armeniaca*

Aptenia (*Aizoaceae*)

cordifolia	CCCN NPer SChr SPlb SVen
- 'Variegata' (v)	CCCN

Aquilegia (*Ranunculaceae*)

	akitensis misapplied	see *A. flabellata* var. *pumila*
	'Alaska' (State Series) ♀H5	CRos EBee EMor LRHS NRHS
	alpina	CMea EBee EBou EPfP LRHS MAsh MBel MNHC NGdn NHic SCob SPer SRms WHoo WSpi XEll XLum
	amaliae	see *A. ottonis* subsp. *amaliae*
	'Apple Blossom'	NBir
	aragonensis	see *A. pyrenaica*
§	***atrata***	CPou EBee EMor GKev
	aurea misapplied	see *A. vulgaris* golden-leaved
	aurea Janka	EBee LLHF
	barnebyi	CWCL GKev
	bertolonii ♀H5	CMea CRos EBee EMor EWld GKev LRHS NRHS NSla SIgm SRms WHoo
	Biedermeier Group	CRos EAJP EPfP GJos LRHS NGdn NNor NRHS SRot WHil
	'Blackcurrant'	CWCL
	'Blue Pleats'	CWCL
	'Blue Star' (Star Series)	CRos CWCL ELan EPfP GBin GMaP GWyn LRHS NEgg NRHS SPtp
	'Bluebird' (Songbird Series) ♀H5	LBuc LRHS NBir NPer WFar
	'Bob Hares'	WAvo
	brevistyla	NNor
	buergeriana	CFis GKev SPhx
	- 'Calimero'	CTsd EBee MBNS NCGa NLar
	- var. ***oxysepala***	see *A. oxysepala*
	'Bunting' (Songbird Series) ♀H5	SGbt
	canadensis ♀H5	CSpe EBou ELan GAbr GCrg GKev GLog NBir NBro NHic SPhx SRms WFar WSpi XEll XLum
	- 'Little Lanterns'	EDAr EPPr GKev NHpl NLar WIce
	- 'Nana'	GKev WThu
	- 'Pink Lanterns'	EDAr NEgg
	'Cardinal' (Songbird Series)	LBuc LRHS
	chaplinei	GKev NBir
	chrysantha	EHrv GJos GWyn MCot SIgm SRms SWvt WKif XSen
	- 'Denver Gold'	CSam EShb SPhx WHil
	- 'Yellow Queen' ♀H5	CExl CRos CWCL ELon EMor EPPr EPfP GBin GMaP IKil LCro LOPS LRHS MBel NGdn NRHS SCob SGbt SPhx SWvt WCFE WHil WTor XEll XLum
	clematiflora	see *A. vulgaris* var. *stellata*
	Clementine Series	EPfP
	coerulea ♀H5	GKev NHic NNor SRms
	'Colorado' (State Series)	CRos LRHS NRHS
	'Crimson Star'	CRos CWCL ELan EMor EPfP EShb LRHS MBel NRHS SPoG
	desertorum	GKev
	discolor	GKev LLHF WThu XEll
	'Double Rubies' (d)	ELan WMoo
	'Dove' (Songbird Series) ♀H5	LBuc LRHS MHer SGbt SHar
I	'Dragonfly'	CBcs CRos ELan EPfP LRHS NRHS SPoG
	ecalcarata	see *Semiaquilegia ecalcarata*
	einseleana	LLHF
	elegantula	GKev NAln
	eximia B&SWJ 14053	WCru
	flabellata f. ***alba*** 'White Jewel' (Jewel Series)	GKev
	- 'Blackcurrant Ice'	CWCL
	- Cameo Series	GMaP WFar
	- - 'Cameo Blue and White'	SRms SRot WFar
	- - 'Cameo Rose'	WFar
	- - 'Cameo White'	SRot WFar
	- 'Georgia' (State Series) ♀H5	CRos LRHS NRHS
	- 'Ministar'	CWCL EDAr GCrg GWyn MHol XLum
	- 'Nana Alba'	see *A. flabellata* var. *pumila* f. *alba*

	Name	Suppliers
§	- var. ***pumila*** ♀H5	CRos CWCL EBou ECha EDAr ELon GEdr GKev LRHS LSun NGdn NRHS SRms
§	- - f. ***alba*** ♀H5	CRos ECha GKev LRHS LSun NRHS
	- - 'Atlantis'	MHol
I	- - f. ***kurilensis*** 'Rosea'	WAbe
	- 'Vermont' (State Series)	EBee EMor
	'Florida' (State Series) ♀H5	CRos EMor LRHS NRHS
	formosa	EMor EPPr GQue NChi
	- var. ***formosa*** B&SWJ 13543	WCru
	- var. ***truncata***	SIgm
	- - B&SWJ 14072	WCru
§	***fragrans***	EBee GEdr SGbt SIgm WArt
	'Fruit and Nut Chocolate'	EBee MHol WCot
	glandulosa	GKev GWyn LLHF
	glauca	see *A. fragrans*
	'Golden Guiness'	ELon GPSL MMrt
	'Goldfinch' (Songbird Series)	LBuc LRHS NBir SGbt
	grahamii	WAbe
	'Heavenly Blue'	CDor CRos EBee GWyn LRHS NRHS
	'Hensol Harebell'	SHar SRms WSpi
	'Honeydew'	GWyn
	japonica	see *A. flabellata* var. *pumila*
	jonesii	GKev SPlb
	karelinii	GKev
	'Koralle'	CDor GWyn MMrt WHil
	'Kristall'	CBar EShb EWTr MBel SGbt
*	***kuhistanica***	EBee GKev GWyn
	'Leprechaun Gold' (v)	EMor EPfP MHol NGdn
	'Lime Sorbet'	LEdu LRHS SRms
	longissima	GQue MHer SHar WHoo
	'Louisiana' (State Series) ♀H5	CRos LRHS MHer NRHS SCob
	'Magpie'	see *A. vulgaris* 'William Guiness'
	× ***maruyamana***	EBee
	McKana Group	CRos CTri EAJP ELan ELon EPfP GAbr GJos LRHS MGos MJak NGdn NHol NLar NRHS SCob SPer SPlb SPoG SRms SVic SWvt WFar WMoo XLum
	Mrs Scott-Elliot hybrids	CSBt ECtt EPfP MHol NHic
	Music Series	SRms
	'Nightingale' (Songbird Series)	SGbt
	nigricans	see *A. atrata*
	olympica	LSun
	'Oregon' (State Series)	EMor
	'Origami Rose and White' (Origami Series)	NRHS
§	***ottonis*** subsp. ***amaliae***	CPBP LLHF SIgm WAbe
§	***oxysepala***	CExl GLog MMrt NAln
	- B&SWJ 4775	WCru
	- var. ***kansuensis***	GKev NAln
	Perfumed Garden Group	WFar
§	***pyrenaica***	GKev
	- dwarf	GKev WAbe
	'Red Hobbit'	CRos CSpe CWCL ELan EPfP LRHS MBel MHol NEgg NGdn NHpl NLar NRHS WFar
	'Red Star' (Star Series)	CWCL EAJP EPfP EShb NEgg SHar SPoG WHil
	'Rhubarb and Custard'	EMor
	'Robin' (Songbird Series)	SGbt
	rockii	EBee EWld GKev SBrt
	'Roman Bronze'	see *Aquilegia* × *Semiaquilegia* 'Roman Bronze'
	'Rose Queen'	CDor CWCL EPfP EShb GWyn NNor SPtp WFar WHoo
	saximontana	EPot GEdr GKev NSla
§	'Schneekönigin'	CWCL EBee LRHS NRHS WCFE
	scopulorum	GKev LLHF SIgm
	sibirica	EBee GKev LLHF
	'Silver Queen'	ELan EWTr GBin
	skinneri	CExl ELan EMor GLog NWad
	- 'Tequila Sunrise'	CRos CSpe CWCL ELan EMor LRHS MHer NNor NRHS
	SNOW QUEEN	see *A.* 'Schneekönigin'
	Spring Magic Series	NPri
	- SPRING MAGIC BLUE AND WHITE	LRHS SCob
	- SPRING MAGIC WHITE	NRHS SCob
	stellata	see *A. vulgaris* var. *stellata*
	'Sunburst Ruby'	CWCL WMoo
	(Swan Series) 'Swan Lavender'	NHic
	- 'Swan Pink and Yellow'	CBod NHic
	- 'Swan Red and White'	CBod NHic WFar
	triternata	GWyn NNor
	'Virginia' (State Series)	CBod CRos EMor LRHS NRHS
	viridiflora	CBor EBee EMor GCal LRHS SIgm SPhx WAbe WCot XEll
	- var. ***atropurpurea***	LEdu
	- 'Chocolate Soldier'	CCBP CSpe
	'Volcano!' (mixed)	WHil
	vulgaris	CHab CWld EPfP GKev GPoy GQue GWyn LCro LOPS LRHS MHer MNHC NBro NGdn NHic SPlb WCAu WMoo WShi XSen
	- 'Adelaide Addison'	ECha WAvo WHoo
	- var. ***alba***	CMea CRos EPfP LRHS MMuc NDov NRHS SCob
	- 'Altrosa'	GWyn
	- 'Aureovariegata'	see *A. vulgaris* Vervaeneana Group
	- 'Blackbird' (Songbird Series) (d)	CWCL
	- ***clematiflora***	see *A. vulgaris* var. *stellata*
	- (Clementine Series) 'Clementine Blue' (d)	CRos EPfP LRHS NRHS SPoG WCot
	- - 'Clementine Dark Purple' (d)	CRos EPfP LRHS NRHS SPoG
	- - 'Clementine Red' (d)	CRos EPfP LRHS NRHS
	- - 'Clementine Rose' (d)	CRos LRHS NRHS SPoG
	- - 'Clementine Salmon Rose' (d)	CRos CWCL EPfP LRHS NRHS SPoG
	- - 'Clementine White' (d)	CRos CWCL EPfP LRHS NRHS SPoG WSpi
	- 'Crystal Star'	CRos EPfP LRHS NRHS
	- 'Eyecatcher'	WCot
	- var. ***flore-pleno*** black-flowered (d)	MMuc SEND WCot
	- - 'Dorothy Rose' (Dorothy Series) (d)	SPtp
	- - 'Double Pleat' (d)	EPfP
	- - 'Double Pleat' pink/white-flowered (d)	CWCL
	- - 'Jane Hollow' (d)	CPou
	- - pink-flowered (d)	CWCL
	- - 'Strawberry Ice Cream' (d)	NBro NNor
*	- - 'White Bonnet' (d)	CWCL
§	- golden-leaved	GKev
	- 'Heidi'	GWyn MMuc SEND
	- 'Mellow Yellow'	CRos CTsd EHoe ELon LRHS NRHS WMoo
	- MUNSTEAD WHITE	see *A. vulgaris* 'Nivea'
§	- 'Nivea' ♀H7	CDor CPou CSpe EBee ECha ELan EPfP LCro LOPS NChi SEND SPoG SPtp WArt WCot WSpi
	- Pom Pom Series	WSpi

- - 'Pom Pom Crimson' NBro WCot
§ - var. ***stellata*** CDor CTsd ELan EMor GAbr GKev GWyn NBir NBro NNor
- - (Barlow Series) 'Black Barlow' (d) Widely available
- - - 'Blue Barlow' (d) CAvo CBod CDor CRos CSpe EBee ECtt EMor EPfP GMaP ILea LCro LOPS LRHS LSRN MJak NPri NRHS SCob SPer SPhx SWvt WCot WSpi XLum
- - - 'Bordeaux Barlow' (d) CRos LRHS NRHS STPC
- - - 'Christa Barlow' (d) CRos EBee EMor EPfP LRHS MBel NLar NRHS SHar
- - - 'Nora Barlow' (d) Widely available
- - - 'Rose Barlow' (d) CCBP CRos EPfP LRHS LSRN NRHS WSpi
- - - 'White Barlow' (d) CDor CRos EPfP GMaP ILea LCro LOPS LRHS MBel NPri NRHS SPer SWvt
- - blue-flowered MMuc NBir SEND
- - 'Greenapples' (d) CDor CRos CWCL EMor EPfP EWhm GAbr GKev LRHS NAln NRHS SCob WHoo
* - - 'Iceberg' WSpi
- - 'Royal Purple' (d) NBro NNor WMoo
- - 'Ruby Port' (d) Widely available
- - white-flowered CSpe NBir NBro
- variegated foliage see *A. vulgaris* Vervaeneana Group
§ - Vervaeneana Group (v) CDor CSpe CWCL EMor EPfP GAbr LRHS NBir NPer SPlb SRms WHoo WMoo
- - 'Woodside Blue' (v) NWad
- - 'Woodside White' (v) NBir WBrk
§ - 'William Guiness' Widely available
- 'William Guiness Doubles' (d) CAvo GWyn WMoo
'White Star' (Star Series) CDor CWCL EBee ELan EPfP GMaP LRHS SPoG
white-flowered NRHS
Winky Series ELan GJos NNor SWvt WFar
- 'Winky Blue-White' CRos GBin LRHS NLar NRHS WCFE
- 'Winky Double Dark-Blue-White' (d) **new** NCGa WHlf
- 'Winky Double Red-White' (d) NCGa WHlf
- 'Winky Purple-White' CRos LRHS NRHS
- 'Winky Red-White' CRos LRHS NRHS SWvt
- 'Winky Rose-Rose' CRos LRHS NRHS
yabeana GKev SPhx
'Yellow Star' (Star Series) 🏆H5 CDor ECtt EPfP LRHS NRHS

Aquilegia × *Semiaquilegia* (*Ranunculaceae*)

blue-flowered NGdn
§ 'Roman Bronze' WMoo

Arabis (*Brassicaceae*)

albida see *A. alpina* subsp. *caucasica*
allionii EDAr
alpina MAsh SPlb
§ - subsp. ***caucasica*** GKev XSen
- - 'Arctic Joy' (v) WCot
- - 'Corfe Castle' ECtt
- - 'Douler Angevine' (v) CBod CKel ELon NHpl SPoG SRms WIce
- - 'Flore Pleno' (d) 🏆H6 CElw CFis CSpe CTri ECtt ELan EWld GAbr GJos GMaP SBch SIgm SRms WBrk WHoo XLum
- - 'Hedi' MJak
- - 'Little Treasure White' GWyn
- - 'Lotti Deep Rose' CBod MHol
- - 'Lotti White' **new** MHol
- - 'Pink Pearl' WFar
- - 'Pixie Cream' ECtt MHol MMuc NGdn WRHF
- - 'Rosea' GJos LRHS NBir SRms
§ - - 'Schneehaube' 🏆H6 CPla CTri EPfP GMaP GWyn LRHS MBel NBir NGdn SPoG SRms
- - SNOWCAP see *A. alpina* subsp. *caucasica* 'Schneehaube'
- - 'Snowdrop' WFar
- - 'Variegata' (v) ELan GMaP SPoG SRms
androsacea CPla GKev SRms
× ***arendsii*** 'Compinkie' GJos SPlb SRms WHil
- 'La Fraicheur' GJos
aubrietoides ITim
blepharophylla MHol NEgg NPri
§ - 'Frühlingszauber' 🏆H5 CTri EAJP ELan EPfP GJos MAsh MMuc NBir NGdn SPoG SRms WCot
- 'Rose Delight' LRHS NRHS
- 'Rote Sensation' ELan NGdn
- SPRING CHARM see *A. blepharophylla* 'Frühlingszauber'
carduchorum XLum
caucasica see *A. alpina* subsp. *caucasica*
ferdinandi-coburgi NHol SRms
- 'Aureovariegata' (v) CMea CTri ECtt ELan SWvt
- 'Old Gold' EBou EHoe EPfP GWyn LPot MAsh MHer MJak NHol NRya SPoG SRms SRot SWvt WCFE WFar WJam WRHF
- 'Variegata' see *A. procurrens* 'Variegata'
procurrens WCot XLum XSen
- 'Glacier' GJos
§ - 'Variegata' (v) 🏆H6 CTri ECtt EHoe ELan EPfP EWes GAbr GKev GPSL MAsh MBrN MHer MJak SPlb SRms SRot WCot WFar
pumila GKev
SNOW CAP see *A. alpina* subsp. *caucasica* 'Schneehaube'

Arachniodes (*Dryopteridaceae*)

davalliaeformis CLAP CRos EBee ISha LRHS NRHS WPGP
miqueliana ISha
rhomboidea CBdn CLAP
simplicior CBdn CCCN CKel CLAP CRos EBee EShb EUJe ISha LBuc LEdu LRHS NRHS SCob SPlb WCot WPGP
standishii CLAP CRos EBee EShb ISha LEdu LRHS NRHS WCot WPGP

Araiostegia (*Davalliaceae*)

faberiana CExl
hymenophylloides WCot
parvipinnata see *A. perdurans*
§ ***perdurans*** LEdu WPGP
- B&SWJ 1608 EBee WCru
pulchra HWJ 1007 WCru

Aralia ✿ (*Araliaceae*)

apioides IMou LEdu
- EDHCH 9720 SBrt WCru
armata B&SWJ 6916 WCru
bipinnata Blanco CWJ 12407 WCru
- RWJ 10101 WCru
cachemirica CDTJ EWld GCal NBid SMad SPlb WCru WHal WMoo

californica CSam EBee GCal GPoy LEdu NLar WCru
castanopsidicola CWJ 12411 WCru
chapaensis B&SWJ 11812 WCru
- HWJ 1013 WCru
chinensis misapplied see *A. elata*
chinensis L. BWJ 8102 WCru
continentalis LEdu MPie NLar WHoo
- B&SWJ 8437 WCru
- B&SWJ 8524 WCru
§ **cordata** Thunb. CAgr GCal LEdu
- B&SWJ 5596 WCru
- var. **sachalinensis** NLar
- - B&SWJ 4773 WCru
- 'Sun King' CAby CBct CBod CCht EBee ECtt EPfP ESwi EUJe LCro LOPS LRHS MHol MNrw MPie NBid NEoE NLar NSti SCob SPad SPoG SWvt WFar WHil WMoo
dasyphylla LEdu
decaisneana B&SWJ 6794 WCru
- NMWJ 14531 new WCru
- NMWJ 14542 new WCru
- RWJ 9910 WCru
§ **elata** CAby CBcs CDul CExl CKel CMac CRos CTsd EBee ELan EPfP EUJe LRHS LSRN MBlu MGil MGos MMuc SArc SCob SGol SPer SPoG SWvt WFar WSpi
- B&SWJ 5480 WCru
- 'Albomarginata' see *A. elata* 'Variegata'
- 'Aureo-marginata' (v) WSpi
- 'Aureovariegata' (v) ♀H5 CBcs EWes NLar SCob
- 'Golden Umbrella' (v) NLar
- 'Silver Umbrella' (v) NLar WSpi
§ - 'Variegata' (v) ♀H5 CBcs CDul NLar SCob SWvt
foliolosa B&SWJ 8360 WCru
- NJM 13.033 WPGP
- NJM 13.061 WPGP
kansuensis BWJ 7650 WCru
- CD&R 2289 WCru
leschenaultii B&SWJ 9515 WCru
- B&SWJ 11789 WCru
nudicaulis Blume see *A. cordata*
nudicaulis L. GPoy
papyrifera see *Tetrapanax papyrifer*
racemosa CBod GPoy LEdu SRms WJek
- B&SWJ 9570 WCru
searelliana B&SWJ 11736 WCru
sieboldii see *Fatsia japonica*
spinosa L. EBtc GQue MBlu NChi NEgg SPlb
subcordata HWJK 2385 WCru
verticillata B&SWJ 11797 WCru
vietnamensis B&SWJ 12349E WCru

Araucaria (*Araucariaceae*)

angustifolia CDTJ WPGP
angustifolia × araucana CBrP NEgg
§ **araucana** Widely available
bidwillii MMuc SEND
excelsa misapplied see *A. heterophylla*
§ **heterophylla** ♀H2 CCCN SEND
imbricata see *A. araucana*

Araujia (*Apocynaceae*)

sericifera CBcs CHll CKel CMac ECre LRHS SVen WSHC

Arbutus ✿ (*Ericaceae*)

andrachne IDee LRHS SMad WSpi
× **andrachnoides** ♀H4 CBcs CJun CKel CRos CTho ELan EPfP LEdu LRHS LSRN MAsh MRav NRHS SPer SPoG WPGP WSpi
× **androsterilis** new WPGP
menziesii MBlu
× **reyorum** 'Marina' CJun CRos ELan EPfP LRHS MAsh MBlu SPoG WPGP
× **thuretiana** new WPGP
unedo Widely available
- 'Atlantic' ♀H5 CCCN CJun CRos ECrN EPfP LRHS LSRN MAsh MGos SAko SGbt SGol SWvt
- 'Compacta' CBcs CCCN CRos ELan EPfP EUJe LRHS MAsh NLar SGol SLon SWvt WFar
- 'Elfin King' CRos ELan EPfP LRHS MAsh SLon SPoG SWvt
- 'Quercifolia' CCCN CDul CHll CJun EBee ELan LEdu LLHF LRHS MAsh NLar WHor
- ROSELILY ('Minlily'PBR) CKel EBee EMil LRHS MPkF SMad
- f. **rubra** ♀H5 CAgr CBcs CCCN CDul CJun CKel CMac CRos CSBt ELan EPfP LRHS LSRN MAsh MBlu MMuc MRav NLar NRHS SEND SGol SPer SPoG SSta SWvt WMat WPGP
xalapensis SPlb

Archontophoenix (*Arecaceae*)

cunninghamiana XBlo

Arctanthemum (*Asteraceae*)

§ **arcticum** ECha MMuc NLar XLum
- 'Polarstern' WFar
- 'Roseum' EBee ELon WFar
- 'Schwefelglanz' EBee WFar

Arcterica see *Pieris*

Arctium (*Asteraceae*)

lappa GPoy SRms SVic WHer WSFF

Arctostaphylos (*Ericaceae*)

uva-ursi CKel GPoy NLar SPlb
- 'Snowcap' MAsh
- 'Vancouver Jade' CMac CRos EBee ELan GKin LRHS LSRN MAsh NRHS SCoo SLon SPer SPoG SSta SWvt

Arctotheca (*Asteraceae*)

calendula EBee WSHC

Arctotis (*Asteraceae*)

§ HANNAH ('Archnah'PBR) (The Ravers Series) CAby CCht CPla ECtt MBNS
§ HAYLEY ('Archley'PBR) (The Ravers Series) CCCN ECtt MBNS
'Heidi' CCht MBNS
'Holly' CCht
× **hybrida** hort. 'Apricot' CCCN ECtt
- 'Flame' ♀H2 CAby CCCN ECtt MBNS SCoo
- 'Red Devil' CCCN MBNS SCoo
- 'Wine' CCCN CCht MBNS SCoo SRkn
PINK SUGAR (The Ravers Series) new WHlf
PUMPKIN PIE (The Ravers Series) see *A.* HANNAH
SUNSPOT (The Ravers Series) see *A.* HAYLEY

Ardisia (*Primulaceae*)

PAB 7988 from Mizoram, India — LEdu
japonica — WCot
- B&SWJ 1032 — SMad WCru
- var. ***angusta*** — WCot
- 'Ito Fukurin' (v) — EBee WPGP
- var. ***minor*** — GEdr
- - B&SWJ 1841 — WCru
- - B&SWJ 3809 — WCru

Areca (*Arecaceae*)

triandra — XBlo

Arecastrum see *Syagrus*

Arenaria (*Caryophyllaceae*)

§ ***alfacarensis*** — EPot NLar SPlb WAbe WOld
balearica — EWes GKev LLWG MAsh NRHS NSla SPlb SRms
capillaris — CTri
festucoides — CPBP GKev WAbe
grandiflora — GKev XLum
hookeri subsp. ***desertorum*** — WAbe
kansuensis — NLar
ledebouriana — NLar SBrt
montana ♀H5 — CAby CMea CRos CTri ECha EDAr EPfP GMaP LRHS MBel MGos NRHS NSla SPlb SRms SRot WAbe WFar WIce WKif
- 'Avalanche' — ECtt LSun MHol
pulvinata — see *A. alfacarensis*
purpurascens — CPla EPot EWes GKev LLHF NLar SRms WAbe
* ***scopolina*** — EWes
tetraquetra — SIgm
- subsp. ***amabilis*** — EPot
'The Pearl' — CBod

Arenga (*Arecaceae*)

micrantha — WCot

Argania (*Sapotaceae*)

spinosa — WPGP

Argemone (*Papaveraceae*)

grandiflora — CSpe EPPr
mexicana — IMou LRHS SPhx

Argyranthemum ✿ (*Asteraceae*)

'Bridesmaid' — MHom
broussonetii — MHom
canariense hort. — see *A. frutescens* subsp. *canariae*
CHERRY HARMONY ('Supa532') (Daisy Crazy Series) (d) — MCot
CHERRY LOVE ('Supacher') (Daisy Crazy Series) (d) ♀H2 — CCCN
'Citronelle' — CBcs
'Cornish Gold' ♀H2 — CBcs CCCN ECtt
double pink-flowered (d) — SVen
'Everest' — CRos LRHS NRHS SPoG
'Flamingo' — see *Rhodanthemum gayanum*
foeniculaceum misapplied pink-flowered — see *A.* 'Petite Pink'
§ ***foeniculaceum*** (Willd.) Webb & Sch.Bip. — MCot
- 'Royal Haze' ♀H2 — CCCN CHll NPer
§ ***frutescens*** — LCro LOPS SEND WKif
§ - subsp. ***canariae*** ♀H2 — CCCN MHom
'Gill's Pink' — MHom
gracile — CHll
- 'Chelsea Girl' ♀H2 — CCCN CSpe MBNS MCot MHom WKif
GranDaisy Series **new** — NPri
'Guernsey Pink' — MHom
GYPSY ROSE ('M9/18d') — CCCN
'Jamaica Primrose' ♀H2 — CSpe CTri ECtt
'Jamaica Snowstorm' — see *A.* 'Snow Storm'
LARITA BANANA SPLIT ('Kleaf10067') (LaRita Series) ♀H2 — CRos LRHS NRHS SPoG
'Levada Cream' ♀H2 — CSpe MHom
(Madeira Series) MADEIRA CRESTED IVORY ('Bonmadcivy') (d) — SPoG
- MADEIRA CRESTED PINK ('Bonmadcink'PBR) — MCot SPoG
- MADEIRA CRESTED YELLOW ('Bonmadcrel'PBR) — SPoG
- MADEIRA RED ('Bonmadre'PBR) — SPoG
- MADEIRA WHITE IMPROVED ('Bonmadwitim'PBR) — SPoG
§ ***maderense*** ♀H2 — CHll MHom
'Mary Wootton' (d) — ECtt MHom
mawii — see *Rhodanthemum gayanum*
METEOR RED ('Supa742') (Daisy Crazy Series) — CBcs CWGN MBNS
MOLIMBA XL PASTEL YELLOW ('Argyrayesi'PBR) (Molimba Series) **new** — SPoG
ochroleucum — see *A. maderense*
PACIFIC GOLD ('Pacargone'PBR) (d) — CBcs CWGN
§ 'Petite Pink' ♀H2 — CCCN
PING-PONG ('Innping'PBR) (d) — CCCN
'Pink Australian' (d) — MHom
'Pink Delight' — see *A.* 'Petite Pink'
'Powder Puff' (d) — ECtt
'Raspberry Ruffles' (d) **new** — CBcs
'Shirley's Yellow' — MHom
§ 'Snow Storm' ♀H2 — MHom
SOLE MIO ('Supa3047') (d) — CWCL
'Starlight' ♀H2 — MCot MHom
'Sugar and Ice' (d) — CCCN
'Sugar Baby' (d) — CCCN
'Summer Cloud' — MCot
'Summer Melody' (d) — CBcs CCCN
'Summer Pink' — CCCN
'Vancouver' (d) ♀H2 — CCCN ECtt
'Vera' — CCCN
'Weymouth Pink' — MHom
'White Spider' — CCCN ELan

Argyrocytisus (*Papilionaceae*)

battandieri — Widely available
- 'Yellow Tail' ♀H5 — CDul CEnd CKel ELan EPfP EUJe LRHS MGos NLar NOra NPri SPoG SSta WMat

Arisaema (*Araceae*)

CC 4904 — CExl
CC 5511 — CExl
album — XLum
amurense — CElw LAma LLHF WThu

§ - subsp. ***robustum***	WBor
angustatum	WCru
var. ***peninsulae*** B&SWJ 8639	
auriculatum	GKev LAma
brachyspathum	see *A. heterophyllum*
brevipes	CExl
candidissimum ♀H4	CDor CElw CRos CSpe ECha EHrv ELon EPPr EPfP EPot GEdr GKev LAma LRHS MRav NLar NRHS NSla SDeJ WBor WCot WHal WPnP
- pink-flowered	MAvo
- white-flowered	GEdr LAma
ciliatum ♀H4	CPla EBee GEdr LAma MAvo NLar SRot
- var. ***liubaense***	CWCL EPfP GKev ITim WCot
- - CT 369	CExl EPfP SDys
- - GG 97091	WCot
aff. ***ciliatum***	CPla
concinnum	EUJe GBin GEdr GKev LAma WPnP XLum
consanguineum	CAby CBcs CExl EBee EPfP EUJe GBin GCal GEdr GKev LAma MAvo MBel WCot WFar WPGP WPnP XLum
- from Burma	GCal
- subsp. ***kelung-insulare*** B&SWJ 256	WCru
- 'The Perfect Wave'	CAby WCot
- variegated (v)	WCot
costatum	CCCN EPfP EPot GKev LAma WCot WFar WPGP XLum
dracontium	EUJe XLum
ehimense	LAma
engleri	GKev
erubescens	XEll
exappendiculatum	CExl LAma
fargesii	CExl EPot EUJe GKev XLum
flavum	CWCL EBee EPfP ESwi GBin GCal GKev LAma MAvo SPlb WHil
- CC 6303	ITim
- subsp. ***abbreviatum***	GBin MBel
- - CC 6300	ITim
formosanum B&SWJ 280	WCru
§ ***franchetianum***	CExl GKev
galeatum	GKev LAma WCot XLum
grapsospadix B&SWJ 7000	WCru
§ ***griffithii***	EMor EUJe GBin GEdr GKev LAma NBid NLar SDeJ XLum
- var. ***pradhanii***	CAby GBin GEdr GKev LAma XLum
- - WJC 13660	WCru
helleborifolium	see *A. tortuosum*
§ ***heterophyllum***	GKev ITim LAma
intermedium	LAma MNrw XLum
iyoanum	LAma
subsp. ***nakaianum***	
jacquemontii	CAby GEdr GKev GLog LAma NLar XLum
- CC 5184	ITim
japonicum Blume	see *A. serratum* var. *mayebarae*
japonicum Komarov	see *A. serratum*
jinshajiangense	CExl
kishidae	GEdr LAma
kiushianum	GKev LAma WCot
- 'Kikkou-fu'	GEdr
lichiangense	GKev
§ ***lobatum***	CExl
maximowiczii	GEdr LAma
§ ***nepenthoides***	CAby EPot EUJe GBin GEdr GKev LAma WPnP XLum
ochraceum	see *A. nepenthoides*
onoticum	see *A. lobatum*
petelotii B&SWJ 9706	WCru
propinquum	GKev LAma XLum
purpureogaleatum	see *A. franchetianum*
ringens misapplied	see *A. amurense* subsp. *robustum*
ringens ambig.	CDTJ EPfP GEdr GKev
ringens (Thunberg) Schott	LAma LEdu
- green-flowered **new**	GKev
- f. ***sieboldii*** B&SWJ 551	WCru
aff. ***ringens***	NHpl
robustum	see *A. amurense* subsp. *robustum*
sazensoo	GEdr LAma
§ ***serratum***	GKev LAma
- B&SWJ 14607 **new**	WCru
§ - var. ***mayebarae***	GEdr GKev LAma
- var. ***serratum***	LAma
sikokianum	EPot GEdr GKev LAma LLHF LRHS NHpl NLar WPnP WTyc
- variegated (v)	GEdr NHpl
speciosum	CExl GEdr GKev LAma MSCN SDeJ SPlb WCot WPnP XLum
* - var. ***magnificum***	CAby CBcs GEdr GKev LAma NLar XLum
- var. ***mirabile***	GKev LAma XLum
taiwanense	GEdr
- B&SWJ 269	WCru
- NMWJ 14541 **new**	WCru
- f. ***cinereum*** NMWJ 14530 **new**	WCru
tashiroi	LAma
ternatipartitum	LAma
thunbergii	GEdr LAma WBor
- subsp. ***autumnale*** B&SWJ 1425	WCru
- subsp. ***urashima***	GKev LAma
§ ***tortuosum***	CExl ECha EPfP EUJe GKev LAma LEdu NLar WFar WPnP XLum
- var. ***helleborifolium***	NBid XLum
tosaense	LAma
triphyllum	CElw CExl EMor EUJe GKev GPoy LAma NLar SPlb
§ ***utile***	EPot EUJe GBin GEdr GKev LAma XLum
verrucosum	see *A. griffithii*
- var. ***utile***	see *A. utile*
yamatense subsp. ***sugimotoi***	LAma

Arisarum (*Araceae*)

proboscideum	Widely available
vulgare	GKev

Aristea (*Iridaceae*)

§ ***capitata***	CHll
ecklonii	CBcs CExl CPou CPrp CTsd EBee EShb GBin MHer SBrt
- GWJ 9469	WCru
ensifolia	ELan
thyrsiflora	see *A. capitata*

Aristolochia (*Aristolochiaceae*)

baetica	CExl SBrt
- B&SWJ 14001 **new**	WCru
californica	LEdu SBrt
chilensis	CCCN SPlb
clematitis	GPoy LEdu
cucurbitifolia B&SWJ 7043	WCru
debilis	SBrt

durior	see *A. macrophylla*
fimbriata	CPla SBrt
- B&SWJ 13612	WCru
gigantea ♀H1b	CCCN CHll
grandiflora	CCCN
griffithii B&SWJ 2118	WCru
- Mabiluo Strain	GCal
kaempferi	CCCN
- B&SWJ 293	WCru
- B&SWJ 14674 new	WCru
- NMWJ 14565 new	WCru
kanukuensis NMWJ 14577 new	WCru
× ***kewensis***	CCCN
§ ***macrophylla***	CBcs CCCN CMac MRav SBrt WSpi
manshuriensis	EBee
- B&SWJ 12557	WCru
paucinervis	EWld
sempervirens	LEdu SBrt WCru WSHC
- B&SWJ 13600	WCru
serpentaria	SBrt
sipho	see *A. macrophylla*
trilobata	SBrt

Aristotelia (*Elaeocarpaceae*)

§ ***chilensis***	LEdu WPav
- 'Variegata' (v)	CCCN CMCN CMac
macqui	see *A. chilensis*
peduncularis	CExl
serrata	GBin MGil SVen

Armeria (*Plumbaginaceae*)

§ ***alliacea*** (Cav.) Hoffmanns. & Link	ECha GKev SPhx
- f. ***leucantha***	SPhx SRms WMoo
alpina	GJos
'Avalanche'	MHol
'Brutus'	MAvo MHCG
caespitosa	see *A. juniperifolia*
- 'Bevan's Variety'	see *A. juniperifolia* 'Bevan's Variety'
curvifolia	GAbr GKev
§ ***girardii***	EPot
Joystick Series	MMuc
- 'Joystick Lilac Shades'	CRos EBee ELan EPfP LRHS NRHS SPoG
- 'Joystick Red'	CRos ELan EPfP EShb LRHS NRHS SPoG
- 'Joystick White'	CRos ELan EPfP LRHS NRHS SPoG
§ ***juniperifolia*** ♀H5	CRos ELan EPfP GCrg GJos LRHS MAsh MHer NRHS NSla SPlb SRms WIce XLum
- 'Alba'	CMea ELan EPfP EPot GBin GCrg GJos GKev GMaP ITim MHer MMuc NHpl SRms SRot WAbe WHoo WThu
- 'Beechwood'	GCrg
§ - 'Bevan's Variety' ♀H5	CMea EBou ECha ELan ELon EPfP GEdr GJos GMaP MMuc NLar NRya SPoG SRms SRot WHoo
- dark-flowered	WAbe
- 'New Zealand Form'	see *A. juniperifolia* 'Sugar Baby'
- rose-flowered	ITim
§ - 'Sugar Baby'	SRms
juniperifolia × ***maritima***	SRms
§ ***maritima***	CHab CRos ECtt ELan EPfP GJos LPot LRHS MBel NAln NEgg NRHS SWvt WBrk WCFE WMoo
§ - 'A Little in the Red'	EPot GEdr
- 'Alba'	CAby CBcs CTri ECha ELan EPfP GJos GMaP LPot LSun MAsh MBel MCot MHol MMuc NHpl NRHS NRya SEND SPlb SPoG SRms WBrk WCFE WJam WMoo
- 'Armada Rose'	CRos EPfP GKev LRHS NRHS SRms
- 'Bloodstone'	CTri ELan
- 'Corsica'	CMea CTri ECha MMuc NBir
- DÜSSELDORF PRIDE	see *A. maritima* 'Düsseldorfer Stolz'
§ - 'Düsseldorfer Stolz'	CBod CElw CKel CRos EBou ECha ECtt EDAr ELan EPfP EPot GCrg GJos GKev GMaP LRHS NRHS SPoG SWvt WIce XLum
- 'Glory of Holland'	EPot
§ - 'In the Red'	Widely available
- 'Laucheana'	WHoo WMoo
- 'Ministicks Rose'	CRos LRHS
- 'Ministicks White'	CRos LRHS
- 'Morning Star White'	CBod
- 'Nifty Thrifty' (v)	CTri EBou ECtt EHoe MHer MHol NEgg SPoG SRms
- 'Rubrifolia'	see *A. maritima* 'In the Red'
- 'Rubrifolia Compacta'	see *A. maritima* 'A Little in the Red'
- 'Ruby Glow'	CTri
- 'Schöne von Fellbach'	XLum
- 'Splendens'	CBcs CRos CTri EDAr EPfP GMaP LRHS MAsh MHer MHol MJak MMuc NHpl NMir NRHS NRya SPhx SPoG SSut WMoo XLum
- 'Splendens Alba'	XLum
- 'Vindictive' ♀H5	CMea EPfP
plantaginea misapplied	see *A. alliacea* (Cav.) Hoffmanns. & Link
pseudarmeria	ELan EPfP LPot MHol XLum
- (Ballerina Series) 'Ballerina'	NBir NHic
- - 'Ballerina Lilac'	CBod CRos LRHS NRHS WFar
- - 'Ballerina Red'	CRos LRHS NRHS SRms WFar WTor
- - 'Ballerina White'	CRos LPot LRHS NRHS WFar
setacea	see *A. girardii*
splendens 'Perfecta'	CRos LRHS NRHS
'Vesuvius'	XLum
vulgaris	see *A. maritima*
welwitschii	SBrt

Armoracia (*Brassicaceae*)

§ ***rusticana***	CBod CCBP CFGn CHby CTri EBou EMor ENfk GPoy LOPS MHer MMuc MNHC NPer SPoG SRms SVic WHer WHrl WSpi
- 'Horwood'	LCro
- 'Variegata' (v)	EBee ELan GCal LEdu NSti SMad SRms WHer

Arnebia (*Boraginaceae*)

echioides	see *A. pulchra*
longiflora	see *A. pulchra*
§ ***pulchra***	LLHF

Arnica (*Asteraceae*)

angustifolia	EBee EMor
subsp. ***alpina***	
- subsp. ***iljinii***	NBir
chamissonis Less.	CBod CHby EBee ENfk MNHC NLar SRms
montana	GPoy MHer MNHC SRms

Arnoglossum (*Asteraceae*)

§ ***plantagineum***	SPhx

Aronia ✿ (*Rosaceae*)

arbutifolia	CAco EPfP LSRN MBlu MMuc SGol SLon SPlb
- 'Erecta'	CCVT CDul CKel CRos CTho EBee ELan EPfP EWTr LRHS MBlu MGil MMuc NEgg SPoG SRms SWvt WCFE
melanocarpa	CCVT CDul CMCN CPla CRos CSpe CTsd ELan EPfP EWTr EWld GKin LRHS MAsh MMuc NRHS NWea WGrn
- var. ***grandifolia***	CJun
- 'Hugin'	CAgr CJun IDee LEdu MCoo MMuc MPkF NEgg NLar SVic WPGP
× ***prunifolia***	WGrn
- 'Aron' (F)	CAgr CJun MCoo
- 'Autumn Magic'	CBcs CJun CRos CTho EBee ELan LRHS MAsh
- 'Brilliant'	CBcs CDul CKel CRos CTri EBee ELan EPfP LRHS MGil MMuc SGol SPer WAvo WMat
- 'Karhumäki' (F)	NLar
- 'Nero' (F)	CAgr CBcs CBod GBin LEdu MCoo NLar WMat WPGP
- 'Serina' (F)	CJun
- 'Viking' (F)	CAgr CDul CFGn CJun CTho ECrN EPfP EPom EWTr GBin IDee LBuc LCro LEdu LOPS LRHS MBlu MMuc NLar SGol WFar WPGP

Aronia × *Sorbus* see × *Sorbaronia*

Arrhenatherum (*Poaceae*)

elatius	CHab
- var. ***bulbosum*** 'Variegatum' (v)	EBee EHoe ELan EPPr GBin GKev GMaP GQue MMuc NBid NWad SEND WMoo

Artedia (*Apiaceae*)

squamata	SPhx

Artemisia ✿ (*Asteraceae*)

RBS 0207	CExl
from Taiwan	WHer
§ ***abrotanum***	Widely available
- 'Courson'	ECha XSen
absinthium	CBod CEls CHab ELan ENfk GPoy MHer MNHC NLar SRms SVic WHer WTre XSen
- 'Lambrook Giant'	CEls
- 'Lambrook Mist'	CEls CFis CKel CMac CRos ECtt ELan EPfP GQue LRHS MBel MRav NRHS WCAu XLum
- 'Lambrook Silver'	CEls CExl CRos EBee ECha EHrv ELan EPfP GMaP LRHS LSRN MHer MMuc MRav NBro NRHS SCob SPer SRms SWvt
- 'Silver Ghost'	CEls
afra	CEls XSen
§ ***alba***	CBod CEls GPoy SRms WJek XSen
§ - 'Canescens' ♀H5	CEls CSam EBee ECha ELan EPfP GMaP MAsh MHer MRav NLar SBrt WCFE XSen
annua	CEls
anomala	CEls
§ ***arborescens*** ♀H4	CEls GAbr SPer
- 'Brass Band'	see *A.* 'Powis Castle'
- 'Faith Raven' ♀H3	CEls GBin MBNS NLar
- 'Porquerolles'	CEls
arbuscula	CEls
argentea misapplied	see *A. arborescens*
argentea L'Hér.	CEls
argyi	CEls
§ ***armeniaca***	CEls WHer
assoana	see *A. caucasica*
atrata	CEls
barrelieri	CEls
caerulescens subsp. ***cretacea***	CEls WCot
- subsp. ***gallica***	CEls
californica	CEls WHer
- 'Canyon Gray'	CEls
- 'Montara'	CEls
campestris	XLum XSen
- subsp. ***borealis***	CEls
- subsp. ***campestris***	CEls
- subsp. ***maritima***	CEls
- - from Wales	CEls
camphorata	see *A. alba*
cana	CEls
canariensis	see *A. thuscula*
canescens misapplied	see *A. alba* 'Canescens'
canescens Willd.	see *A. armeniaca*
capillaris	CEls XLum
carruthii	CEls
§ ***caucasica*** ♀H7	CEls EWes MHer SPhx SRms SRot
- var. ***caucasica*** **new**	EBou
chamaemelifolia	CBod CEls SRms XSen
cretacea	see *A. nutans*
discolor Dougl. ex Besser	see *A. michauxiana*
douglasiana	CEls
- 'Valerie Finnis'	see *A. ludoviciana* 'Valerie Finnis'
dracunculus	ECha EWTr MJak MNHC MRav SPlb SRms SVic WBrk XSen
- French	CBod CCBP CEls CHby CLau CTsd EBou ENfk EWhm GPoy LEdu MHer NGrd NPri SEND WGwG WJek XLum
- Russian	CEls EBou ENfk LCro LOPS SVic
- 'Thüringen'	IMou
ferganensis	CEls
filifolia	CEls
fragrans	CEls
frigida ♀H5	CEls
genipi	CEls
glacialis	CEls
gmelinii	CEls
gnaphalodes	see *A. ludoviciana*
gorgonum	CEls SEND
'Hausserman'	XLum
herba-alba	CEls XSen
indica var. ***momiyamae***	CEls EBee ECha WCot
japonica	CEls
kitadakensis 'Guizhou'	see *A. lactiflora* Guizhou Group
laciniata	CEls
lactiflora ♀H7	CEls CRos EBee ECha ELan GMaP MRav NDov NGdn SPer SRms WMoo WWtn XLum
- NJM 11.010	WPGP
- 'Elfenbein'	CEls EBee EPPr GCal IMou MNrw MRav SMHy
§ - Guizhou Group	Widely available
- - 'Dark Delight'	CEls CMea EBee ECtt EWes LEdu SPhx
- 'Jim Russell'	CDor CEls CElw EBee EWes LEdu MPie SPhx
- ***purpurea***	see *A. lactiflora* Guizhou Group
- 'Weisse Dame' **new**	MNrw
- 'Weisses Wunder'	CEls EBee

	lanata Willd.	see *A. caucasica*
	lanata Lam.	XSen
	laxa	see *A. umbelliformis*
	'Little Mice'	CEls NLar
	longifolia	XSen
§	***ludoviciana***	CEls GBee NLar NPer SRms WCFE WFar XLum
	- subsp. ***ludoviciana*** var. ***incompta***	CEls
	- - var. ***latiloba***	CEls EHoe NBro SWvt
	- subsp. ***mexicana*** var. ***albula***	CEls
	- 'Silver Queen'	Widely available
	- 'Valerie Finnis' 🏆H6	Widely available
	maritima 'Coca-Cola'	EBee SRms XSen
	- var. ***maritima***	CEls
	mauiensis	CEls
§	***michauxiana***	CEls EBee
	molinieri	CEls XSen
	mutellina	see *A. umbelliformis*
	niitakayamensis	CEls
	nova	CEls
§	***nutans***	CEls MRav
	ORIENTAL LIMELIGHT ('Janlim') (v)	CBod CEls EBee EHoe GAbr NBir NEgg NLar SWvt WHrl WOut WPnP
	palmeri hort.	see *A. ludoviciana*
	aff. ***parviflora*** CLD 1531	CEls
	pedemontana	see *A. caucasica*
	pontica	CBod CEls EBee EHoe ELan GMaP GPoy LEdu MNHC MRav NBro NSti SEND SPer SRms WFar WHoo WPGP XSen
§	'Powis Castle' 🏆H3	Widely available
	princeps	CEls EBee GPoy LEdu
	procera Willd.	see *A. abrotanum*
	purshiana	see *A. ludoviciana*
	pycnocephala	CEls
	- 'David's Choice'	CEls
	ramosa	CEls
	'Rosenschleier'	CEls EPPr GCal GQue SHar WWtn
	schmidtiana 🏆H5	CEls ECha SRms
	- 'Nana' 🏆H5	CBcs CEls CMea CRos EBee ECtt ELan EPfP EPot EUJe EWTr GMaP LRHS MAsh MCot MHer MRav MSwo NLar NRHS SIgm SPer SPlb SPoG SRms SRot WCFE XLum XSen
	- 'Nana Attraction'	NLar SRot
	selengensis	CEls
	splendens misapplied	see *A. alba* 'Canescens'
	splendens Willd. var. ***brachyphylla***	MAsh
	stelleriana	CEls CTri ECha GBee GKev MAvo NBro NLar SRms
	- RBS 0207	CEls
	- from Alaska	WCot
	- 'Boughton Silver'	CDor CEls CRos EBee ECtt ELan EPfP EShb GMaP IKil LRHS MAsh MBel MHer MRav NEgg NLar NRHS NSti SRms SWvt
	- 'Mori'	see *A. stelleriana* 'Boughton Silver'
	- 'Nana'	CEls SWvt
	- 'Prostrata'	see *A. stelleriana* 'Boughton Silver'
	- 'Shemya'	CEls
	- 'Silver Brocade'	see *A. stelleriana* 'Boughton Silver'
	suksdorfii	CEls
	taurica	CEls
§	***thuscula***	CEls
	tridentata	EBee WHer
	- subsp. ***tridentata***	CEls
	- subsp. ***wyomingensis***	CEls
§	***umbelliformis***	CEls EBee
	vallesiaca	CEls
	verlotiorum	CEls
	vulgaris	CBod CEls GJos GPoy MNHC WHer
	- 'Variegata' (v)	CEls ELan SRms WMoo XLum
	× ***wurzellii***	CEls

Arthropodium (*Asparagaceae*)

	candidum	MPie
	- 'Capri'	LPot
	- 'Little Lilia' (v)	MHol WCot
	- 'Maculatum'	LEdu NHpl SPlb
	- 'Purpureum'	GEdr IKil NWsh
	cirratum	CSpe CTsd GKev IKil MHer MPie
	- 'Matapouri Bay'	CBcs SEND
	milleflorum	SBrt
	minus	CExl

artichoke, globe see *Cynara cardunculus* Scolymus Group

artichoke, Jerusalem see *Helianthus tuberosus*

Arum (*Araceae*)

	byzantinum	GKev
	'Chameleon' 🏆H7	CDor LEdu NBir NLar SEND SMad SPer WBrk WCot WRHF
§	***concinnatum***	GKev
	- 'Mount Ida'	LEdu
	cornutum	see *Sauromatum venosum*
	creticum	CBro EBee EPot GCal MAvo MNrw WArt WBor
	- 'Karpathos'	CExl GKev WCot
	- 'Marmaris White'	EBee MAvo WCot
	- white-flowered	CMea
	- white-spotted	EWes
	cyrenaicum	GKev
	dioscoridis	GKev
	- JCA 195.197	WCot
	- var. ***cyprium***	GKev
	- var. ***syriacum***	GKev
	dracunculus	see *Dracunculus vulgaris*
	euxinum	GKev
	gratum **new**	GKev
	hygrophilum	LEdu WCot
	italicum	CTri GBin GWyn LAma LCro LOPS MHol MSCN NAln SDeJ WCot WShi
	- 'Angelique'	WCot
	- 'Edward Dougal'	MAvo WCot WFar
	- 'Green Marble'	MAvo WFar
	- subsp. ***italicum***	GKev MHer WBrk
§	- - 'Marmoratum' 🏆H6	Widely available
	- - 'Spotted Jack'	WCot
	- - 'Tiny'	CExl GCal SMHy SWvt WRHF
	- - 'Uniquity'	WCot
§	- - 'White Winter' 🏆H6	LEdu WBrk WCot
	- subsp. ***neglectum***	SChr
	- - 'Miss Janay Hall' (v)	EHoe WCot
	- 'Pictum'	see *A. italicum* subsp. *italicum* 'Marmoratum'
	- 'Sandy McNabb' **new**	WCot
	- 'Yarnells' **new**	LEdu WCot
	italicum × ***maculatum***	EHrv WHer
	italicum × ***lucanum***	GKev
	korolkowii	WCot
	maculatum	EPot GKev GPoy LAma MHer MRav NLar WHer WShi

- 'Painted Lady' (v) WCot
- 'Pleddel' MRav
- Tar Spot Group SEND
nickelii see *A. concinnatum*
§ ***nigrum*** GKev LEdu LLHF SBrt
petteri misapplied see *A. nigrum*
pictum CExl CMac EWes GKev LEdu
- 'Taff's Form' see *A. italicum* subsp. *italicum* 'White Winter'
purpureospathum GKev LEdu
rupicola var. ***rupicola*** GKev
- var. ***virescens*** LEdu
sintenisii GKev
'Streaked Spectre' LEdu

Aruncus ✿ (*Rosaceae*)

aethusifolius ♀H7 Widely available
- 'Filigran' new EBee
- 'Little Gem' WCru
- 'Porzellan' new EBee
asiaticus B&SWJ 8624 WCru
'Bastei' IMou
dioicus Widely available
§ - (m) ♀H6 CBar CBen CMac EHoe ELan MBNS MRav MWts NBro NSti SMad SPer SRms WHil WMoo
- CHILD OF TWO WORLDS see *A. dioicus* 'Zweiweltenkind'
- 'Glasnevin' ECtt MRav NHol WFar
- var. ***kamtschaticus*** EWes NLar NWad WHrl
- - RBS 0208 NGdn
- 'Kneiffii' Widely available
- 'Whirlwind' CBar EWhm LPla
§ - 'Zweiweltenkind' EWTr GAbr LPla LRHS NLar SMad WCot XLum
'Guinea Fowl' CBod ECtt ELon LEdu LLWG MBel MHol NBid NGdn NLar SCob WCAu WWtn
'Horatio' Widely available
'Johannifest' EBee ECtt IMou IPot WCot
'Misty Lace' CSpe EBee ECtt GBin NGdn NLar SAko
'Netzwerk' IMou
'Noble Spirit' LSun MBel NGdn NLar
'Perlehuhn' EBee IMou
plumosus see *A. dioicus*
* ***sinensis*** NBre
sylvestris see *A. dioicus*
- 'Sommeranfang' IMou
'Ulf' new MAvo
'Woldemar Meier' IMou MAvo MCot NLar SAko WCot

Arundinaria (*Poaceae*)

anceps see *Yushania anceps*
angustifolia see *Pleioblastus chino* 'Murakamianus'
auricoma see *Pleioblastus viridistriatus*
disticha see *Pleioblastus pygmaeus* 'Distichus'
fargesii see *Bashania fargesii*
fastuosa see *Semiarundinaria fastuosa*
fortunei see *Pleioblastus variegatus*
§ ***gigantea*** CDTJ XCre
- subsp. ***tecta*** CBcs
hindsii see *Pleioblastus hindsii*
hookeriana misapplied see *Himalayacalamus falconeri* 'Damarapa'
hookeriana Munro see *Himalayacalamus hookerianus*
japonica see *Pseudosasa japonica*
jaunsarensis see *Yushania anceps*
maling see *Yushania maling*
marmorea see *Chimonobambusa marmorea*
murielae see *Fargesia murielae*
nitida see *Fargesia nitida*
oedogonata see *Oligostachyum oedogonatum*
palmata see *Sasa palmata*
pumila see *Pleioblastus argenteostriatus* f. *pumilus*
pygmaea see *Pleioblastus pygmaeus*
quadrangularis see *Chimonobambusa quadrangularis*
simonii see *Pleioblastus simonii*
spathiflora see *Thamnocalamus spathiflorus*
tessellata see *Bergbambos tessellata*
vagans see *Sasaella ramosa*
variegata see *Pleioblastus variegatus*
veitchii see *Sasa veitchii*
viridistriata see *Pleioblastus viridistriatus*
'Wang Tsai' see *Bambusa multiplex* 'Floribunda'

Arundo (*Poaceae*)

donax CAbb CKno CPla ELan ELon EUJe EWes GMaP IDee MAvo MBlu MNrw MRav SArc SCob SEND SMad SPlb SPoG SSut WHal
- 'Golden Chain' (v) CBcs CKel CKno EPPr EWes LRHS SMad
- 'Macrophylla' CExl CKno LEdu WPGP
- 'Peppermint Stick' (v) SMad
- 'Variegata' see *A. donax* var. *versicolor*
§ - var. ***versicolor*** (v) CAbb CBcs CKno CPla CRos CTsd ELan ELon EUJe EWes LLWG LRHS MRav NRHS NWsh SArc SCob SEND SMad SPer SPlb SPoG SSta WAvo XLum
I - - 'Aureovariegata' (v) CBod CDTJ SEND
formosana CKno EPPr
- 'Golden Showers' ESwi EUJe

Asarina (*Plantaginaceae*)

barclayana see *Maurandya barclayana*
erubescens see *Lophospermum erubescens*
lophantha see *Lophospermum scandens*
lophospermum see *Lophospermum scandens*
§ ***procumbens*** CTri CWld EBou GKev NBir NRya SChF SPhx SRms WBrk WKif
scandens see *Maurandya scandens*

Asarum (*Aristolochiaceae*)

arifolium EBee EHrv EPPr GKev
- 'The Giant' EBee NLar
- white-flowered EBee
canadense CDor EBee EMor GEdr GKev GPoy LEdu NLar
caudatum EBee ECha EMor GEdr GKev LEdu LPla NBro NLar SMad SRms WCot WCru WSpi
- 'Little Murphy' WCot
caulescens EPPr
delavayi NLar WCot
- giant EBee XEll
epigynum CDor EBee EUJe LEdu MNrw NLar WCot
- 'Silver Web' WCot
europaeum ♀H6 Widely available
- PAB 4377 LEdu WPGP
lemmonii LEdu
longirhizomatosum GEdr WCru

maculatum B&SWJ 1114	WCru
maximum	CBor GKev LAma
– 'Silver Panda'	CAby CBct CBod CExl EMor ESwi EUJe MNrw NGBl SMad WCot WMoo
sieboldii	WCru
splendens	CAby CBct CBod CBor CBro EHrv ELan EMor EPfP EUJe GKev ILea LAma LEdu MHol MNrw MRav NLar NSti SPlb SPoG WCot WFar XLum
wulingense	CExl

Asclepias ✿ (*Apocynaceae*)

curassavica	CCCN EShb LLWG SRkn XLum
exaltata	EBee SBrt SPhx
fruticosa	see *Gomphocarpus fruticosus*
hallii	EBee
incarnata	CRos LRHS MRav NEgg NRHS SBrt SPhx SPlb WOld XLum
– 'Ice Ballet'	CBod NLar SPer WHlf
– 'Soulmate'	CBod EBee EPfP EWTr LPot SPer WHlf
latifolia	SPhx
physocarpa	see *Gomphocarpus physocarpus*
purpurascens	EBee
speciosa	EBee MMuc NBre SBrt
sullivantii	IMou SPhx
syriaca	EBee LPla MBel MMuc XLum
tuberosa	CBcs CBod CBor CKel CSpe EBee EMor EShb EUJe GPoy LRHS MBel MHer MNHC MSCN NDov NRHS SCob SPad SPer SPhx SPoG WGwG XLum XSen
– Gay Butterflies Group	NHic
– subsp. ***interior***	EPPr MHol

Asimina (*Annonaceae*)

triloba (F)	CAby CBcs CCCN CDTJ EBee IBal MBlu NLar SGol SPlb
– 'Sunflowers'	CCCN SAko

asparagus see AGM Vegetables Section

Asparagus (*Asparagaceae*)

acutifolius	XSen
asparagoides ♀H3	EShb
densiflorus new	WCot
– 'Mazeppa'	EShb
– 'Myersii' ♀H1c	EShb SEND
– 'Myriocladus' new	EShb
– Sprengeri Group ♀H1c	EShb LCro LOPS NGBl SEND
falcatus	EShb SEND
filicinus	XBlo
– NJM 12.024	WPGP
– var. ***giraldii***	WCot
aff. ***meioclados*** B&SWJ 8309	WCot WCru
plumosus	see *A. setaceus*
pseudoscaber 'Spitzenschleier'	EBee WCot
retrofractus	WCot
scandens	EShb WCot
schoberioides	LEdu
– B&SWJ 8814	WCru
§ ***setaceus*** ♀H2	EShb LCro LOPS
– 'Pyramidalis' ♀H1c	XBlo
tenuifolius	WPGP
umbellatus new	SEND
virgatus	EShb SPlb WPGP

Asperula (*Rubiaceae*)

§ ***arcadiensis*** ♀H3	EPot SIgm
aristata subsp. ***scabra***	CSpe ECha MMuc WCot WSHC
– subsp. ***thessala***	see *A. sintenisii*
boissieri	SIgm SPlb WAbe
daphneola	ELan EWes LLHF
gussonei	EPot LLHF SIgm WAbe WHoo WOld
lilaciflora var. ***caespitosa***	see *A. lilaciflora* subsp. *lilaciflora*
§ – subsp. ***lilaciflora***	EBou
nitida	WIce
– subsp. ***puberula***	see *A. sintenisii*
odorata	see *Galium odoratum*
§ ***sintenisii***	CMea CPBP EPot LLHF WAbe WHoo
suberosa misapplied	see *A. arcadiensis*
taurina	WPtf
– subsp. ***caucasica***	NLar WBor
tinctoria	GPoy MHer SRms

Asphodeline (*Asphodelaceae*)

§ ***brevicaulis***	XSen
liburnica	CBro CPla CSam ECha ELan IMou LCro LOPS MMuc SEND SPhx XSen
§ ***lutea***	Widely available
§ – 'Gelbkerze'	EBee
– YELLOW CANDLE	see *A. lutea* 'Gelbkerze'
taurica	EBee MBNS SMHy XSen

Asphodelus (*Asphodelaceae*)

acaulis	LLHF WCot WWFP
§ ***aestivus***	EBee EWes MBel WCot
– Cally Spear strain	NCGa
albus	CAvo CBro CSam CSpe ECha EPPr EPfP GAbr LSun NBid NDai NGBl SPlb SRms XLum XSen
brevicaulis	see *Asphodeline brevicaulis*
cerasiferus	see *A. ramosus*
fistulosus	CBro LEdu SVen XSen
lusitanicus	see *A. ramosus*
luteus	see *Asphodeline lutea*
microcarpus	see *A. aestivus*
§ ***ramosus***	CPar GCal LPla MCot WCot

Aspidistra (*Asparagaceae*)

B&SWJ 6645 from Thailand	WCru
Chen Yi 135	WCot
attenuata	IMou
– B&SWJ 377	WCru
– B&SWJ 2001 new	WCru
– B&SWJ 3727 new	WCru
– 'Dungpu Dazzler'	WCru
– 'Small 'n' Smart' new	WCru
– 'Xitou Starlet'	WCru
caespitosa 'Jade Ribbons'	see *A. hainanensis* 'Jade Ribbons'
'China Star'	ESwi WCot
daibuensis B&SWJ 1949 new	WCru
– B&SWJ 312b	ESwi WCru
– B&SWJ 3236 new	WCru
– B&SWJ 6863	WCru
– B&SWJ 6866 new	WCru
– 'Taiwan Stars'	WCru
– 'Tidy Trim'	ESwi WCru
– 'Totally Dotty' (v)	WCru
– 'Yuli Yummy'	WCru
elatior ♀H3	CBct CTsd EBak EBee EShb ESwi LCro LEdu LOPS MRav SAko SEND SMad WCot
– 'Akebono' (v)	WCot

- 'Asahi' (v) WCot
- 'Hoshi-zora' (v) WCot
- 'Lennon's Song' (v) WCot
- 'Milky Way' (v) EBee EShb ESwi SAko SEND XLum
- 'Okame' (v) WCot
- 'Variegata' (v) ♀H3 EShb NBir
- 'Variegata Exotica' (v) XBlo

aff. ***geastrum*** B&SWJ 6563 new WCru
- 'Opium Hit' new WCru

§ ***hainanensis*** 'Jade Ribbons' WCot WCru

linearifolia 'Leopard' ESwi WCot
- 'Skinny Dippin'' new WCru

lurida EShb
- 'Ginga' see *A. sichuanensis* 'Ginga'
- 'Ginga Giant' (v) WCot

minutiflora WCot
- 'Spangled Ribbons' new WCru

mushaensis WCru
B&SWJ 315 new
- B&SWJ 1953 new WCru
- 'Purple Picket' new WCru
- 'Wushe Wacky' new WCru

aff. ***mushaensis*** 'Spotty Dotty' (v) ESwi WCru

omeiensis WCot

saxicola 'Uan Fat Lady' see *A. zongbayi* 'Uan Fat Lady'

§ ***sichuanensis*** 'Ginga' (v) WCot

subrotata B&SWJ 5252 new WCru
- 'Chiang-dao Chace' new WCru

sutepensis B&SWJ 5216 WCru
- B&SWJ 6645 new WCru
- 'Pha-Hom Pok-adot' new WCru

tonkinensis WCot WCru

typica 'China Sun' WCot

zongbayi WCot

§ - 'Uan Fat Lady' EBee ESwi WCot WCru

Asplenium ✿ (*Aspleniaceae*)

antiquum EShb
- 'Osaka' CRos LRHS NRHS

bulbiferum misapplied see *A. × lucrosum*

bulbiferum Forst.f. EShb ESwi GBin

§ ***ceterach*** CLAP EUJe ISha WCot WHer XLum

daucifolium NWad WCot

× ***ebenoides*** ♀H4 CBdn EMor ISha LEdu

§ × ***lucrosum*** ♀H1c EShb ESwi

lyallii CBdn

'Maori Princess' GBin WFib

nidus ♀H1b LCro LOPS XBlo
- 'Crispy Wave'PBR EShb

§ ***scolopendrium*** ♀H6 Widely available
- 'Angustatum' ♀H6 Widely available
- Crispum Group ♀H6 CLAP EFer ELan NBid SRms SRot WAbe WFar WFib
- - 'Crispum Bolton's Nobile' WFib
- - 'Golden Queen' CDor MAvo
- Crispum Cristatum Group MMuc SCob
- Crispum Fimbriatum Group CLAP
- - 'Drummondiae' CLAP
- Cristatum Group CAby CBdn CDor CLAP CRos CWCL EBee ECtt EHrv ELan ELon EMor EPfP EUJe LRHS MGos MRav NBro NEgg NLar NRHS SPer SRms SRot WFib WHoo WMoo
- Fimbriatum Group CRos LRHS NRHS
- 'Fimbriatum Cristatum' new CLAP
- 'Furcatum' CBdn CDTJ EBee ELan ELon EMor EUJe GCal MMuc NLar SPad
- 'Kaye's Lacerated' ♀H5 EFer WFib
- Marginatum Group CBdn EFer
- 'Muricatum' ELan MRav NBid WFib WHoo
- 'Sagittatocristatum' CLAP
- 'Sagittatoprojectum Sclater' WFib
- Undulatum Group CDTJ CRos EBee ECha EPfP GEdr GQue LRHS MMuc NBir NLar NRHS SRms WCot WFar WGwG WMoo XLum

trichomanes ♀H6 Widely available
- Cristatum Group CLAP CRos LRHS NRHS
- Incisum Group ♀H6 CLAP EFer WAbe
- 'Ramocristatum' WAbe

Astelia (*Asteliaceae*)

banksii CBcs CKel CPla CRos EUJe IBal LRHS LSRN MGos NRHS SCoo WCot

§ ***chathamica*** ♀H3 CAbb CAby CBcs CRos CSpe CTsd ELan EPfP EUJe IBlr LRHS LSRN MGos MHol MJak NSti SAko SArc SCob SCoo SEND SPer SPlb SPoG SWvt WCot WSpi
- 'Silver Spear' see *A. chathamica*

cunninghamii see *A. solandri*

fragrans CBcs IBlr LEdu

graminea GCal

grandis IBlr LEdu WPGP

nervosa IBlr LSRN SArc
- 'Alpine Ruby' IBlr
- 'Bronze Giant' IBlr
- 'Silver Sabre' IBlr
- 'Westland' CBcs CBod CKel CPla CRos CSpe CTsd ELan EShb EUJe GAbr GBin GCal GWyn ILea LEdu LRHS LSRN MGos NRHS SCob SEND SWvt

nivicola 'Golden Gem' IBlr
- 'Red Gem' LEdu

'Red Devil' CBcs CBct CBod CPla CSpe GBin GWyn MGos MHol MJak NDai SPoG WHer WPav

'Red Shadow' SPad

'Silver Mound' EPfP SCob

'Silver Shadow'PBR CBcs CBod CRos EPfP LCro LOPS LRHS MJak MMrt NRHS SPad SWvt WCot WFar WSpi

§ ***solandri*** IBlr

Aster ✿ (*Asteraceae*)

acris see *Galatella sedifolia*

'Afternoon Delight' new EBee

ageratoides see *A. trifoliatus* subsp. *ageratoides*

§ ***albescens*** WJC 13657 WCru

alpinus ♀H5 EBou EPfP GKev MAsh MHol SIgm SRms WFar
- var. ***albus*** EDAr EPfP GKev WArt WCot
- 'Antje' IPot MNrw
- DARK BEAUTY see *A. alpinus* 'Dunkle Schöne'
- var. ***dolomiticus*** NSla

§ - 'Dunkle Schöne' EAJP EBou EDAr MBel SRms WArt WFar XSen
- 'Goliath' EDAr ELan EPfP SPlb
- 'Happy End' CRos EPfP LRHS NHic NRHS SRms WCAu XLum XSen
- 'Pinkie' EAJP EBou EDAr EPfP WArt

- 'Trimix'	LPot NBir NHic SRms
amelloides	see *Felicia amelloides*
amellus	CPla ELon
- 'Blue King'	ECtt EWes NWsh SWvt WSpi
- 'Breslau'	EBee ELon
- 'Brilliant'	CBod CRos ECha ECtt ELon EPPr LRHS MBNS MRav NEgg NLar NRHS NWsh SAko SEND SPer SRms WCAu WHoo WOld WSpi
- 'Butzemann'	ELon WCot
- 'Danzig'	XLum
- 'Doktor Otto Petschek'	ELon NLar WCot
- EMPRESS	see *A. amellus* 'Glücksfund'
- 'Forncett Flourish' ♀H7	ECtt MAvo MHCG SMHy WCot WHoo WOld
- 'Framfieldii' ♀H7	SMHy WCot WFar WOld
§ - 'Glücksfund'	SAko XSen
- 'Gründer'	IMou IPot MAvo MHCG WCot WOld
- 'Jacqueline Genebrier' ♀H7	MHCG NDov WOld
- 'King George' ♀H7	Widely available
- 'Kobold' ♀H7	WOld
- 'Lac de Genève'	WCot XLum
- 'Lady Hindlip'	CSam ECtt IMou WCot
- 'Louise'	MBrN MHCG
- 'Mira'	EBee ELon IPot SAko SPtp
- 'Moerheim Gem'	ECtt IMou WCot WOld
- 'Mrs Ralph Woods'	WOld
- 'Nocturne'	ELon WCot WOld
- 'Peach Blossom'	WOld
- PINK ZENITH	see *A. amellus* 'Rosa Erfüllung'
§ - 'Rosa Erfüllung' ♀H7	CBod CDor CMac CRos EBee ECtt ELan ELon EPPr EPfP EWes GMaP IPot LRHS MNrw MRav NAln NLar NRHS SCob SPhx SPoG SWvt WCAu WOld WSpi
- 'Rotfeuer'	ELon WSpi
- 'Rudolph Goethe'	CRos EBee ECtt ELan ELon EMil EPPr EPfP IKil LRHS NLar NRHS SCob WOld WSpi
- 'September Glow'	WOld
- 'Silbersee' ♀H7	CSam IMou SAko
- 'Sonia'	CRos EBee ECtt ELon LRHS NRHS SWvt WOld
- 'Sonora' ♀H7	CMea MAsh MAvo MNrw SHar SPhx WKif WOld
- 'Sternkugel'	EBee ELon WOld
- 'Ultramarine'	WOld
- 'Vanity'	WOld
§ - 'Veilchenkönigin' ♀H7	Widely available
- VIOLET QUEEN	see *A. amellus* 'Veilchenkönigin'
- 'Weltfriede'	ECtt WOld
× ***amethystinus***	see *Symphyotrichum* × *amethystinum*
'Anita Pfeiffer'	CRos LRHS NRHS
asperulus misapplied	see *A. peduncularis*
'Beauté du Nord'	WCot
'Betel Nut'	ECha
'Blue Autumn'	EBee
'Bright and Breezy' **new**	MAvo
capensis 'Variegatus'	see *Felicia amelloides* variegated
carolinianus	see *Ampelaster carolinianus*
'Cassandra'	NCGa
'Cheavers'	CRos LRHS NRHS
'Chilly Fingers'	MAvo MNrw MTis
ciliolatus	see *Symphyotrichum ciliolatum*
'Climax' misapplied	see *Symphyotrichum laeve* 'Arcturus', *S. laeve* 'Calliope'
coelestis	see *Felicia amelloides*
coloradoensis	see *Xanthisma coloradoense*
'Connecticut Snow Flurry'	see *Symphyotrichum ericoides* f. *prostratum* 'Snow Flurry'
cordifolius	see *Symphyotrichum cordifolium*
corymbosus	see *Eurybia divaricata*
'Cotswold Gem'	ECtt MHCG MNrw WCot WOld
diffusus	see *Symphyotrichum lateriflorum*
diplostephioides	CRos EPPr EWhm GBee GEdr GKev GLog LRHS MBNS MMrt NRHS SPlb WOld
divaricatus	see *Eurybia divaricata*
dumosus	see *Symphyotrichum dumosum*
'Dwarf Barbados'	CRos EPfP LRHS NRHS
'Eleven Purple'PBR	MNrw
ericoides	see *Symphyotrichum ericoides*
falcatus	see *Symphyotrichum falcatum*
'Fanny's Fall'	see *Symphyotrichum oblongifolium* 'Fanny's'
'Fingers and Thumbs' **new**	MAvo
× ***frikartii***	CMac EPfP MRav SWvt WSHC
- 'Eiger'	WOld
- 'Flora's Delight'	CMea CRos EBee ECtt ELon EMor GCal LPla LRHS MArl MRav NLar NRHS SPoG SRms WCAu WHoo WOld WSpi
- 'Jungfrau'	CBod CRos CWGN EBee EPPr GMaP IKil LRHS MRav NLar NRHS SPhx SRms WMoo WOld
- 'Mönch' ♀H7	Widely available
- WONDER OF STAFA	see *A.* × *frikartii* 'Wunder von Stäfa'
§ - 'Wunder von Stäfa' ♀H7	CBod CEnd CExl CKno CRos EBee ECtt ELan ELon EPPr EPfP GMaP IPot LCro LOPS LRHS MBNS MBel MCot MHol MWat NBir NLar NRHS SWvt WCAu WCot WOld WSpi XLum
furcatus	see *Eurybia furcata*
glehnii	WCAu
- 'Aglenii'	IMou MNrw NDov SMad
greatae	see *Symphyotrichum greatae*
× ***herveyi***	see *Eurybia* × *herveyi*
himalaicus	NSla
hybridus luteus	see *Solidago* × *luteus*
'Ice Cool Pink'	SMHy
'Ivy House'	ECtt
* ***kotarimus***	XLum
laevis	see *Symphyotrichum laeve*
lanceolatus Willd.	see *Symphyotrichum lanceolatum*
lateriflorus	see *Symphyotrichum lateriflorum*
laterifolius 'Snow Flurry'	see *Symphyotrichum ericoides* f. *prostratum* 'Snow Flurry'
limonifolius	GKev
linosyris	see *Galatella linosyris*
maackii	WCot
macrophyllus	see *Eurybia macrophylla*
mongolicus	see *Kalimeris mongolica*
'Moody Blue' **new**	MAvo
'Mrs Dean'	ECtt
natalensis	see *Felicia rosulata*
'Natasha'	LSRN
novae-angliae	see *Symphyotrichum novae-angliae*
novi-belgii	see *Symphyotrichum novi-belgii*
oblongifolius	see *Symphyotrichum oblongifolium*
OCTOBERLIGHT	see *Symphyotrichum* 'Oktoberlicht'
oolentangiensis	see *Symphyotrichum oolentangiense*
pappei	see *Felicia amoena*
§ ***peduncularis***	CKno CPou EBee EMor EPPr GBee IMou LEdu MAvo MHol MMuc MPie

	MTis NCou NRHS NSti WCot WFar WOld
petiolatus	see *Felicia petiolata*
pilosus	see *Symphyotrichum pilosum*
ptarmicoides	see *Solidago ptarmicoides*
puniceus	see *Symphyotrichum puniceum*
pyrenaeus 'Lutetia'	CBod CKno CMea CSam ECha EPPr EWTr GCal GMaP LRHS MAvo MNrw MPie MWat NLar NRHS SPtp SRms WCAu WCot WKif WOld XLum
radula	see *Eurybia radula*
'Rose Queen'	MMrt MNrw MPie NWsh SRms
rotundifolius 'Variegatus'	see *Felicia amelloides* variegated
rugulosus 'Asrugo'	CKno
× ***salignus***	see *Symphyotrichum* × *salignum*
§ ***scaber***	GCal WCot
scandens	see *A. carolinianus*
schreberi	see *Eurybia schreberi*
sedifolius	see *Galatella sedifolia*
sericeus	see *Symphyotrichum sericeum*
sibiricus	see *Eurybia sibirica*
'Small-Ness'	EShb GKev NAln NWad
'Snow Flurry'	see *Symphyotrichum ericoides* f. *prostratum* 'Snow Flurry'
souliei	CPBP GKev
spathulifolius	WCot XLum
spectabilis	see *Eurybia spectabilis*
stracheyi	GKev
subcaeruleus	see *A. tongolensis*
tataricus 'Jindai'	EBee WCAu
thomsonii	GBin SHar WCot WOld
- 'Nanus'	CAby EBee GBin GMaP ILea LRHS MCot MRav SPhx SPoG WOld WSHC WSpi
§ ***tongolensis***	GKev NHpl
- 'Berggarten'	CRos CWCL IPot LRHS MHol MNrw NRHS WOld
- 'Napsbury'	CRos LRHS NRHS
- 'Wartburgstern'	EMor EPfP LRHS SGbt XLum
tradescantii misapplied	see *Symphyotrichum pilosum* var. *pringlei*
tradescantii L.	see *Symphyotrichum tradescantii*
§ ***trifoliatus*** subsp. ***ageratoides***	CPou WCot WOld
- - 'Ashvi'	CBod CKno CMil ECtt LSun MAvo MBel MHol MTis NSti SPoG WCAu WCot WFar WOld WRHF
- - 'Asran'	EBee ECtt EHoe EPPr EWes EWhm GCal IMou LEdu MMuc MPie NLar SEND WBor WBrk WCot WFar WOld XLum
- - 'Blaukuppel' **new**	MAvo
- - 'Ezo Murasaki'	CSpe IPot MAvo NDov SAko SPoG WCot XLum
- - var. ***firmus***	WPGP
- - 'Harry Smith'	CBod CMil MAvo MHol MTis NAln NDov NSti SAko SPoG WBrk WCot WFar WRHF
- - 'Little Theo'	CKno EBee
- - 'Stardust'	WOld
- - 'Starshine'[PBR]	CBcs CBod CKno CWGN EBee ECtt EPfP LEdu MTis WCot WRHF
trinervius var. ***harae***	ELon WFar WOld
tripolium	see *Tripolium pannonicum*
'Triumph'	WCot
turbinellus ambig.	see *Symphyotrichum turbinellum*
vahlii	CPla GAbr WHil
vimineus Lam.	see *Symphyotrichum lateriflorum*
- 'Ptarmicoides'	see *Solidago ptarmicoides*
'Yvonne'	CBre

Asteranthera (*Gesneriaceae*)

ovata	CExl GGGa SLon WAbe WPGP WSHC

Asteriscus (*Asteraceae*)

'Gold Coin'	see *Pallenis maritima*
maritimus	see *Pallenis maritima*

Asteromoea (*Asteraceae*)

mongolica	see *Kalimeris mongolica*
pinnatifida	see *Kalimeris pinnatifida*

Asteropyrum (*Ranunculaceae*)

cavaleriei	GEdr
peltatum	GEdr

Asterotrichion (*Malvaceae*)

discolor	SPlb SVen

Astilbe ✿ (*Saxifragaceae*)

CC 5201	CExl
'Alive and Kicking'	SCob
'Amerika' (× *arendsii*)	CSBt SRms
'Amethyst' (× *arendsii*)	CMac CRos ELon EPfP LRHS MBel MRav NBir NHol NRHS SPer WArt WFar WMoo
'Angel Wings' (× *arendsii*)	NEoE
'Anita Pfeifer' (× *arendsii*)	ELon NLar XLum
'Aphrodite' (*simplicifolia* hybrid)	CBcs GCal XLum
× ***arendsii***	EPfP LBuc NBre WMoo XLum
(Astary Series) 'Astary Light Rose' (× *arendsii*) **new**	NHic
- 'Astary Pink' (× *arendsii*)	CRos LRHS NHic NRHS
- 'Astary Red' (× *arendsii*)	CRos LRHS NHic NRHS
- 'Astary Rose' (× *arendsii*)	NHic NRHS
- 'Astary White' (× *arendsii*)	CRos LRHS NHic NRHS
astilboides	SWvt
'Avalanche'	CAby CTsd NEoE NHol WSpi
§ 'Beauty of Ernst' (× *arendsii*)	CAbb CBod CMea EBee ELon EMor EPfP LRHS SRms WMoo
§ 'Beauty of Lisse' (× *arendsii*)	CBod ELon
'Betsy Cuperus' (*thunbergii* hybrid)	NBre WCAu
'Bonn' (*japonica* hybrid)	CWCL CWat NEgg NLar SCob SCoo SRms
§ 'Brautschleier' (× *arendsii*) ♀H7	CBod CExl CMac CRos ECtt EPfP GBin GKev GWyn LCro LOPS LRHS LSRN MHol NEgg NGdn NLar NQui NRHS WPnP XLum
'Bressingham Beauty' (× *arendsii*) ♀H7	CAby CBod CExl CRos CWCL EBee ECtt ELan EPfP GBin GKev GMaP ILea LCro LOPS LRHS MHol MJak MRav NEgg NEoE NHol NRHS SRms SWvt WMoo
BRIDAL VEIL (× *arendsii*)	see *A.* 'Brautschleier'
§ 'Bronce Elegans' (*simplicifolia* hybrid) ♀H7	ECha ELon GLog GMaP GWyn NHol NLar SCob SRms WMoo WSpi
'Bronze Sprite' (*simplicifolia* hybrid)	WFar
* ***bumalda*** 'Bronze Pygmy'	NHol
'Bumalda' (× *arendsii*)	CRos CSBt ELon GBin GLog GMaP LRHS NChi NEoE NGdn NRHS SPlb WMoo WWtn
'Bunter Zauber' (× *arendsii*)	XLum
'Burgunderrot' (× *arendsii*)	MNrw NLar SRms
'Cappuccino' (× *arendsii*)	CBod EMor GAbr ILea MAsh MBel SPad

	Name	Suppliers
*	'Carmine King'	MMuc
	'Catherine Deneuve'	see *A.* 'Federsee'
	'Cattleya' (× *arendsii*)	CRos CSam GBin GWyn LRHS NLar NRHS SAko WMoo WSpi XLum
	'Cherry Ripe'	see *A.* 'Feuer'
	chinensis	CRos GBin LRHS NRHS WSHC
	- B&SWJ 8178	WCru
	- from Russia	GCal
	- 'Brokat'	GBin
	- var. ***davidii***	XLum
	- - B&SWJ 8583	WCru
	- - B&SWJ 8645	WCru
	- 'Diamonds and Pearls'[PBR]	CWGN ECtt IKil LLWG SCob WFar WSpi
	- 'Finale'	ELon NHol WOut
	- 'Intermezzo'	GBin GCal GMaP NEoE NLar
	- 'Little Vision in Pink'[PBR]	EPfP WFar
	- 'Milk and Honey'[PBR]	CWGN ECtt ELon EWTr MBNS WFar WSpi
§	- var. ***pumila*** 🏆H7	Widely available
	- - 'Serenade'	CMac CRos LRHS NGdn NRHS
I	- - 'Tiny Form'	GCrg
	- 'Purple Glory'	ECtt IKil
	- var. ***taquetii***	CMac ELan EPfP LRHS NSti SRms XLum
	- - PURPLE LANCE	see *A. chinensis* var. *taquetii* 'Purpurlanze'
§	- - 'Purpurlanze' 🏆H7	CKno CRos CSam EBee ECha ECtt ELon EMor EShb GMaP LRHS LSRN MRav NBir NBro NChi NDov NGdn NHol NLar NRHS SCob SPoG SWvt WBor WFar WHoo WMoo WSpi WWtn
§	- - 'Superba' 🏆H7	CMac CRos ECha LRHS NAln NBro NRHS NWad SPer SRms WMoo
	- 'Troll'	GBin
	- 'Veronika Klose'	GBin NLar
	- 'Vision in Pink'[PBR]	CWCL ELan EPfP MBNS MHol MNrw NDov WFar WMoo
	- 'Vision in Red'[PBR]	CBod CWCL CWat ECtt ELan EPfP MBNS MHol MNrw NDov NEgg NLar SAko SGbt SPoG WAul WCAu WFar WMoo
	- 'Vision in White'	EPfP NEoE SAko SPoG WFar WMoo
	- 'Visions'	CMac CRos EPfP LRHS MBNS NBro NEoE NGdn NRHS SCob WMoo
	- 'White Cloud' **new**	NQui
	'Chocolate Shogun'	CAby CBcs CKno CWGN EBee ECtt EMor MAvo MNrw SCob SMad SPad SPoG WCot WFar
	'Close Harmony' **new**	CRos LRHS NRHS
	COLOGNE	see *A.* 'Köln'
	COLOR FLASH	see *A.* 'Beauty of Ernst'
	COLOR FLASH LIME	see *A.* 'Beauty of Lisse'
	'Country and Western'[PBR] (× *arendsii*)	NEoE SCob
	'Crimson Feather'	see *A.* 'Gloria Purpurea'
	× ***crispa*** 'Lilliput'	ECtt GBee NBir NEoE NLar NRya NWad SCob SMad
§	- 'Perkeo' 🏆H5	CBcs CRos ECtt ELan EPfP GMaP LRHS NBir NEoE NHpl NLar NRHS SRms WFar WMoo
	- 'Peter Pan'	see *A.* × *crispa* 'Perkeo'
	- 'Red Rog'	NEoE
	- 'Snow Queen'	NBir NEoE
	'Darwin's Dream'	MHol MNrw NEoE NLar WFar
	'Darwin's Favourite' (× *arendsii*)	CWCL
	'Delft Lace'	CAbb CBod CRos EBee LBuc LRHS MBel NRHS SRms WMoo
	'Deutschland' (*japonica* hybrid) 🏆H7	Widely available
§	'Diamant' (× *arendsii*)	IKil LSRN MMuc MNrw NBir NGdn NHol SEND WFar
	DIAMOND	see *A.* 'Diamant'
	'Drayton Glory' (× *arendsii*)	see *A.* × *rosea* 'Peach Blossom'
	'Drum and Bass'[PBR]	NLar
	'Dunkelachs' (*simplicifolia* hybrid)	EBee
	'Dusseldorf' (*japonica* hybrid)	CRos CWCL EBee LRHS NRHS
	'Eden's Odysseus'	NHol NWad
	'Eden's Phoenix'	CBod
	'Eden's Twinkle'	CBod EBee WWtn
	'Elegans' (*simplicifolia* hybrid)	CMac
	'Elisabeth' van Veen (× *arendsii*)	IKil NBir
	ELIZABETH BLOOM ('Eliblo'[PBR]) (× *arendsii*)	CRos ELon GAbr LLWG LRHS MHol MRav NDov NGdn NHol NRHS WMoo
	'Ellie' (× *arendsii*)	CMac CRos CWCL EPfP EShb GBee LLWG LRHS LSRN MBNS MBel NCGa NGdn NHol NLar NRHS SPoG WFar
	'Else Schluck' (× *arendsii*)	ECha
	'Erica' (× *arendsii*)	CAby CExl CTri CTsd GBin GLog NEoE NLar WMoo
	'Etna' (*japonica* hybrid)	CBcs CSam ECtt LRHS NGdn NLar NRHS SRms WFar WHoo
	'Europa' (*japonica* hybrid)	CMac CRos ECtt EMor GWyn LRHS MGos NEgg NGdn NLar NRHS SPoG WCAu WMoo
	'Fanal' (× *arendsii*) 🏆H7	Widely available
§	'Federsee' (× *arendsii*)	CBcs CRos CWCL EBee ECha ECtt ELan LRHS MBNS NBro NEoE NGdn NRHS SPer WFar WWtn XLum
§	'Feuer' (× *arendsii*)	CMac ECtt ELan NEgg NEoE NGdn NHol NLar WMoo
	FIRE	see *A.* 'Feuer'
	'Fireberry'[PBR] (Short 'n' Sweet Series)	EBee NLar
	'Flamingo'[PBR] (× *arendsii*)	ECtt MBNS MBel
§	***formosa*** B&SWJ 10946	WCru
	'Freya' (× *arendsii*) **new**	CBod MAsh
	'Gertrud Brix' (× *arendsii*)	CWat MMuc NBir NGdn SEND XLum
§	***glaberrima***	NBid
§	- var. ***saxatilis*** 🏆H5	GBin GCrg GEdr IFro WAbe WHal
	- - 'Candy Floss'	NEoE
	- ***saxosa***	see *A. glaberrima* var. *saxatilis*
§	'Gloria Purpurea' (× *arendsii*)	ELon IKil NQui WMoo
	'Gloria' (× *arendsii*)	CMac CTri ECtt MRav
	GLOW	see *A.* 'Glut'
§	'Glut' (× *arendsii*)	CRos CWCL ECtt LRHS MMuc NGdn NHol NRHS SAko SEND SRms WFar WWtn
	'Granat' (× *arendsii*)	CMac NBir NDov NEgg NGdn NHol NLar WMoo
*	Grande Group (× *arendsii*)	NBre
	grandis	WHer
	- BWJ 8076A	NLar
	'Grete Püngel' (× *arendsii*)	ECha SRms WFar
	'Heart and Soul'[PBR]	CWGN EPfP SAko
	'Hennie Graafland' (*simplicifolia* hybrid)	CBcs CWCL NLar WFar
	'Henry Noblett'	LRHS NRHS
	'Hip Hop'	MAsh

'Holden Clough' (*japonica* hybrid) NHol
HYACINTH see *A.* 'Hyazinth'
§ 'Hyazinth' (× *arendsii*) CExl CRos EBee GMaP IKil LLWG LRHS NBir NHol NRHS
'Icecream' (× *arendsii*) CBod
'Inshriach Pink' (*simplicifolia* hybrid) CBcs CRos ECtt EHoe ELan GBee GBin LRHS NBir NHol NLar NRHS SBch SRms WHal
'Irrlicht' (× *arendsii*) CMac CMea CRos EBee ELan EPfP EShb LRHS NRHS NWad SPer SRms WHoo WPnP WWtn
'Isa Hall' NEoE NWad
japonica CExl
* - 'Catherine Gladstone' **new** LRHS NRHS
* - 'Pumila' NBir NEgg NGdn
- var. ***terrestris*** see *A. glaberrima*
'Jo Ophorst' (*davidii* hybrid) CRos LRHS NGdn NLar NRHS
'Jump and Jive'PBR MAsh WFar
'Juno' XLum
'Key West' (*simplicifolia* hybrid) CPla
§ 'Köln' (*japonica* hybrid) CRos CWat ELon LRHS NRHS
'König Albert' (*davidii* hybrid) GCal
koreana WCot
- B&SWJ 8611 WCru
- B&SWJ 8680 WCru
'Kvële' (× *arendsii*) CRos LRHS NRHS WMoo
'Lilli Goos' (× *arendsii*) GBin GCal
'Little Vision in Purple'PBR CBod
'Lollipop' ECtt GBin MBNS NEoE SRms
longicarpa B&SWJ 6711 WCru
'Look at Me'PBR (× *arendsii*) CBod LCro LLWG LOPS MAsh MBel MHol SPoG
'Maggie Daley' EWTr NBro NEoE SRms WMoo
'Mainz' (*japonica* hybrid) CKel CRos EBee ECtt LRHS NRHS
microphylla B&SWJ 11085 WCru
'Mighty Chocolate Cherry' LCro LOPS WWtn
'Mighty Pip' (× *arendsii*) CBod
'Moerheim Glory' (× *arendsii*) GBin NBre NGdn NLar
'Montgomery' (*japonica* hybrid) ♀H7 CBod CRos CWCL EBee ELon EMor EPfP EShb GAbr IKil ILea LLWG LRHS LSRN MBNS MBel MNrw NCGa NGdn NHol NRHS SPoG
'Nemo' CBod
'New Wave' LLWG
'Nikki' NEoE NLar
§ ***okuyamae*** B&SWJ 10975 WCru
OSTRICH PLUME see *A.* 'Straussenfeder'
'Peaches and Cream' NBro NLar
'Peter Barrow' (*glaberrima* hybrid) GBin SRms
'Pink Lightning'PBR (*simplicifolia* hybrid) CWCL ECtt EShb GAbr LLWG MBNS NLar SPad WFar
PINK PEARL (× *arendsii*) see *A.* 'Rosa Perle'
'Poschka' NEoE
'Professor van der Wielen' (*thunbergii* hybrid) CRos EBee ECha LRHS NAln NHol NLar NRHS NWad SAko SRms WSpi
pumila see *A. chinensis* var. *pumila*
'Purple Rain'PBR (× *arendsii*) ILea
'Radius' CBod ELon NGdn NLar WPnP
'Red Baron' CAby CTsd NEoE SPad
RED LIGHT see *A.* 'Rotlicht'
'Red Sentinel' (*japonica* hybrid) CBcs CBod CRos CWCL CWat EBee ELon EMor EPfP GBin GMaP GWyn LRHS LSun MHol NBro NEgg NEoE NGdn NHol NLar NRHS NWad WMoo WWtn
'Rheinland' (*japonica* hybrid) ♀H7 CBcs CKel CRos CWCL ELon GBin GWyn LRHS MBel MMuc NGdn NLar NRHS SCob SEND SRot WPnP
'Rhythm and Blues'PBR ECtt NLar
rivularis IKil WCot
- CC 5201 GKev
- CC 6857 **new** NWad
- GWJ 9366 WCru
- PAB 7353 LEdu
- PAB 9763 LEdu
I - 'Grandiflora' GBin
§ - var. ***myriantha*** EBee WMoo WPGP
- - BWJ 8076a WCru
- - SICH 757 CExl
'Robinson's Pink' NGdn
'Rock and Roll'PBR CAby LSRN NEoE
§ 'Rosa Perle' (× *arendsii*) NHol NWad
§ × ***rosea*** 'Peach Blossom' CBcs CRos ELon EMor ILea LRHS NBir NEoE NGdn NRHS SGbt SPoG SWvt WHoo WMoo
- 'Queen Alexandra' XLum
'Rosea' (*simplicifolia* hybrid) NHol
§ 'Rotlicht' (× *arendsii*) CMac CRos GBin LLWG LRHS NEgg NEoE NGdn NHol NLar NRHS
'Salland' CRos LRHS NRHS
'Saxosa' see *A. glaberrima* var. *saxatilis*
'Sheila Haxton' (*chinensis*) CRos LRHS NRHS
Showstar Group (× *arendsii*) SRms WWtn
simplicifolia ♀H5 CAby CFis WFar
- BRONZE ELEGANCE see *A.* 'Bronce Elegans'
- 'Darwin's Snow Sprite' CMac GBin NHol NLar WFar
- 'Jacqueline' NHol
* - 'Nana Alba' NEoE
- 'Rose of Cimarron' NEoE NWad
- 'White Sensation'PBR CRos EBee GQue LRHS NLar NRHS SAko
'Snowdrift' (× *arendsii*) CRos CWat GMaP IKil LLWG LRHS MAsh MBNS MBel MMuc NBir NEoE NRHS SEND
'Spartan' (× *arendsii*) see *A.* 'Rotlicht'
'Spinell' (× *arendsii*) NBre WMoo WPnP
'Spotlight'PBR GBin NCGa
'Sprite' (*simplicifolia* hybrid) ♀H7 Widely available
'Stand and Deliver'PBR ECtt
§ 'Straussenfeder' (*thunbergii* hybrid) ♀H7 CAby CMac CRos EBee ECtt EPfP GBin GMaP GQue LRHS NAln NBir NBro NEgg NGdn NHol NLar NRHS SPer SPoG SRms WCAu WMoo WWtn
'Sugar Plum' (*simplicifolia* hybrid) NGdn
'Sugarberry'PBR (Short 'n' Sweet Series) NLar
'Superba' see *A. chinensis* var. *taquetii* 'Superba'
thunbergii CExl CRos LRHS NRHS
- var. ***congesta*** B&SWJ 10961 WCru
- var. ***formosa*** see *A. formosa*
- var. ***hachijoensis*** EBee
- - B&SWJ 5622 WCru
- var. ***okuyamae*** see *A. okuyamae*
- var. ***sikokumontanum*** B&SWJ 11164 WCru
- - B&SWJ 11534 WCru
- var. ***terrestris*** B&SWJ 6125 WCru

	'Thunder and Lightning' (*chinensis* hybrid)	NEoE
	'To Have and To Hold'	MNrw
	'Venus' (× *arendsii*)	ECtt GMaP MBNS MCot MMuc NGdn NHol SEND WFar WMoo
	'Vesuvius' (*japonica* hybrid)	CBcs ECtt NBro NLar
	virescens	see *A. rivularis* var. *myriantha*
	'Vision Inferno'PBR (× *arendsii*) **new**	CBod
	'Walter Bitner'	GBin LRHS MBNS NBre NHol NRHS
	'Washington' (*japonica* hybrid)	CKel EMor LRHS NBre NGdn WPnP
§	'Weisse Gloria' (× *arendsii*)	CMac CRos ECha EMor LRHS NBro NEoE NHol NRHS SCoo WCAu WMoo WWtn
	'White Diamond' (× *arendsii*)	WFar
	WHITE GLORIA	see *A.* 'Weisse Gloria'
	'Whiteberry' (Short 'n' Sweet Series) **new**	LCro LOPS
	'William Reeves' (× *arendsii*)	NHol NWad
	'Willie Buchanan' (*simplicifolia* hybrid)	CBcs CRos EHoe GAbr GBin GCrg GKev GMaP LRHS NEgg NHol NHpl NRHS NWad SPer SRms WAbe WCFE WFar WGwG WHoo WMoo WOut
	YOUNIQUE CERISE ('Verscerise'PBR)	ILea
	YOUNIQUE SILVERY PINK ('Versilverypink'PBR)	WFar
	'Zuster Theresa' (× *arendsii*)	CRos EBee ELon LRHS MBNS MNrw NRHS

Astilboides (*Saxifragaceae*)

§	***tabularis***	Widely available

Astragalus (*Papilionaceae*)

	arnotianus	CPBP
	canadensis	CRos EBee LRHS NRHS
	crassicarpus	SPhx
	glycyphyllos	GJos GKev SPhx WCot
	neglectus	SPhx
	odoratus	EBee

Astrantia (*Apiaceae*)

	bavarica	GCal GKev
	'Berendien Stam'	CElw GLet MAvo MNrw STPC
	'Bloody Mary'	CWCL EBee GLet MAvo MNrw NGdn NLar
	'Bradfield Rose'	EHrv
	'Buckland'	Widely available
	'Bury Court'	NDov
	carniolica major	see *A. major*
	- 'Rubra'	CBcs GKev GMaP NAln WMoo WSpi
	- 'Variegata'	see *A. major* 'Sunningdale Variegated'
	'Clear Pink'	NDov
	'Dark Shiny Eyes'	CExl CWCL ECtt GLet ILea LLHF MTis NLar NSti SWvt
	'Good Pink'	LRHS MAvo NRHS
	'Hadspen Blood'	Widely available
	'Harvington Adrian's Choice Pink'	CRos LRHS NRHS
	'Harvington Selected Red'	CRos LRHS NRHS
	'Helen'	NLar
	helleborifolia	see *A. maxima*
	'Larch Cottage Clear Pink'	NLar WFar
	'Madeleine'	see *A. major* 'Madeleine van Bennekom'
§	***major***	Widely available
	- 'Abbey Road'PBR	CExl CWCL ECtt EMor EWTr IKil IPot LRHS MBel MHol MPnt NAln NLar NRHS SAko SCob SMad SRkn SRms
I	- 'Alba'	CBcs EBee EHrv GKev GLet IKil LRHS MCot MRav NBir NGdn NPer WMoo WPnP WSpi
	- 'April Love' **new**	NCGa
	- 'Berdien'	EBee
	- subsp. ***biebersteinii***	CRos EBee LRHS NBir NRHS
	- 'Bo-Ann'	NLar WFar
	- 'Can Candy'	MAvo MNrw
	- 'Celtic Star'	SWvt
	- 'Claret'	Widely available
	- 'Côte d'Azur'	WSpi
	- 'Cottage Herbery'	MNrw
	- 'Dark Desire'	GLet LEdu NDov
	- 'Elaine's Pink'	WHoo
	- 'Elmblut'	IMou MAvo
	- 'Florence'PBR	CBct CBor CKno CNor CRos CWCL CWGN EBee ECtt EMor EPfP EWTr GLet LRHS MNrw NDov NLar NPri NRHS SAko SPoG SWvt WSpi
	- Gill Richardson Group	Widely available
	- 'Gracilis'	CBod EBee EMor NDov
	- 'Green Tapestry' (v)	WCot
	- 'Greenfingers'	EWes
	- 'Gwaun Valley'	WFar
	- subsp. ***involucrata***	CRos LRHS NRHS WGoo
	- - 'Avondale'	MAvo
	- - 'Barrister'	CSam NLar
	- - 'Canneman'	EBee MNrw NLar SMHy WCot
	- - 'Jumble Hole'	EBee MAvo NDov WGoo
	- - 'Margery Fish'	see *A. major* subsp. *involucrata* 'Shaggy'
	- - 'Moira Reid'	CExl CSam CWCL ECtt GCal GLet GMaP LSRN MAvo MRav SHar WGoo
	- - 'Orlando'	MAvo MNrw
§	- - 'Shaggy' 🏆H7	Widely available
	- - 'Snape Cottage'	EBee MAvo
	- 'Jade Lady'	WFar
	- 'Jitse'	GBin MAvo
	- 'Large White'	LCro LOPS
	- 'Lars'	CExl CWCL ECtt ELon GLet LRHS MHol MNrw NAln NBid NGdn NLar SPer SPoG SRms SWvt WCAu
	- 'Little Snowstar'	CWCL
	- 'Lola'	CDor EBee GLet MTis NLar SPad WWtn
§	- 'Madeleine van Bennekom'	CNor CWCL EBee ECha ECtt GLet
	- 'Midnight Owl'	ECtt MAsh MHol NSti
	- 'Penny's Pink'	CWCL EBee EWhm GLet LCro LOPS MNrw NCGa WSpi
	- 'Pink Crush'	CRos EBee EPfP LRHS NRHS
	- 'Pink Pride'	CWCL GLet GWyn MHol MTis WCAu WFar WHil
	- 'Pink Sensation'	EBee GLet
	- 'Pink Surprise'	GLet MAvo MNrw NLar
	- 'Primadonna'	CRos EBee GLet GMaP LRHS MHol MTis NLar NRHS SPlb SRms WMoo
	- 'Princesse Sturdza'	CWCL EBee EWTr
	- 'Red Joyce'	CBod SPad
	- 'Rosa Lee'	CWCL WGoo
	- var. ***rosea***	CBod CRos CWCL EHrv EPfP EWTr GKev GLet GWyn LRHS MRav NAln NGdn NRHS SHar WCAu WFar WMoo
	- - George's form	CWCL EPPr LSRN

	- 'Rosensinfonie'	CWCL EBee GLet GMaP GWyn NBro WPnP
§	- 'Rubra'	CBod CRos CWCL EMor EPfP GKev GKin LCro LOPS LPot LRHS MCot MGos MHol NBir NChi NPer NRHS SCob SRms WBor WCAu WHal
	- 'Ruby Cloud'	CBod CWCL EBee ECtt ELan ELon EMor EWTr GLet NBro NGdn NLar NRHS SRot WFar WMoo WSpi WWtn
	- 'Ruby Giant'	EBee EWTr GKin SHar
	- 'Ruby Wedding'	Widely available
	- 'Silver Glow'	EBee ECtt
	- 'Star of Beauty' PBR	CKno CRos CWCL ECtt ELan EMor GLet GWyn LRHS NCGa NLar NPri NRHS NSti SAko SCob SPoG SRms SWvt WSpi
	- 'Star of Billion' PBR	CBod CRos EBee ECtt ELan GLet IKil LRHS LSun MHol MNrw NLar NPri NRHS SCob SPoG SWvt WCAu WCot
	- 'Star of Fire' PBR	CWGN EBee ECtt GLet LRHS MAsh MBel MNrw NCGa SCob WFar WHil
	- 'Star of Magic' PBR (v)	LRHS MAvo MNrw SPoG WCAu
	- 'Star of Royals' PBR	CRos CWCL ECtt GLet IPot LRHS NRHS SPoG WFar
	- 'Star of Summer'	EBee
	- 'Starburst'	EBee MNrw
	- 'Sue Barnes' (v)	MNrw
§	- 'Sunningdale Variegated' (v) ♀H7	Widely available
	- 'Titoki Point'	WCot
	- 'Venice' PBR	CBct CBor CDor CKno CRos CWCL CWGN EBee ECtt EMor LRHS MAsh MAvo MHol MNrw NEoE NLar NRHS SPoG SRms SWvt WCAu WCot WFar WHil WPnP WSpi WTyc
§	***maxima*** ♀H7	Widely available
	- 'Mark Fenwick'	MNrw NBir
I	- 'Rosea'	CDor ECtt MNrw MTis NBir NGdn
	minor	EBee LRHS WCru
	'Moulin Rouge' PBR	Widely available
§	'Mrs MacGregor'	MAvo MNrw
	'Old Warwickshire Pink'	see *A.* 'Mrs MacGregor'
	'Queen's Children'	CDor GLet
	'Rainbow'	NLar
	'Roma' PBR ♀H7	Widely available
	rubra	see *A. major* 'Rubra'
	'Ruby Bere'	LEdu
	'Ruby Star' PBR ♀H7	Widely available
	'Sheila's Red'	LSRN MNrw NDov
	'Snow Star' PBR	CRos CWCL EBee EHrv EPfP GLet IKil LRHS MBNS MNrw NLar NPri NRHS STPC
	'Sparkling Stars Pink' **new**	CBod NGrd SMad
	'Star of Heaven'	NLar
	'Star of Passion' PBR	EBee ECtt ELan GLet NLar NRHS SCob
	'Star of Treasure' PBR	EBee ELan EMor GLet NLar NRHS
	'Superstar' PBR	CAvo CBod CDor CWCL EBee ECtt ELon EMor EPfP EWhm GLet IPot LCro LOPS LRHS MAvo MBNS MHol MNrw MRav NDov NEgg NLar NSti SPer SWvt WCot WHoo WSpi XEll
	'Warren Hills'	EBee GMaP MAvo MNrw NLar
	'Washfield'	CWCL MTis NDov NEoE

Astrodaucus (*Apiaceae*)

	littoralis **new**	SPhx

Astrolepis (*Pteridaceae*)

	sinuata	ISha SPlb

Asyneuma (*Campanulaceae*)

	campanuloides	SBch SIgm
	canescens	CRos LRHS NRHS
	pulvinatum	CPBP NSla WAbe

Asystasia (*Acanthaceae*)

	bella	see *Mackaya bella*

Athamanta (*Apiaceae*)

	cretensis	SPhx
	turbith	CPla CSpe MNrw SBrt SIgm
	- subsp. ***haynaldii***	SPhx
	vestina	LRHS SBrt SIgm SPhx

Athanasia (*Asteraceae*)

§	***parviflora***	SPlb

Atherosperma (*Atherospermataceae*)

	moschatum	CHll

Athrotaxis (*Cupressaceae*)

	cupressoides	CBcs CKen WThu
	laxifolia	CKen LRHS
	selaginoides	CAco

Athyrium ✿ (*Woodsiaceae*)

	auriculatum	CBdn
	'Branford Beauty'	CCCN CLAP CRos ISha LEdu LRHS NRHS
	'Branford Rambler'	CBdn CLAP EBee ISha LEdu
	filix-femina ♀H6	Widely available
§	- subsp. ***angustum*** ♀H6	CRos EMor LRHS MRav NGdn NRHS WMoo
	- - f. ***rubellum*** 'Lady in Red' ♀H6	CAby CBdn CBod CCCN CKel CLAP CRos CWCL EBee ELan EPfP ESwi EUJe GBin IBal ISha LCro LRHS LSRN MGos NLar NRHS SCob SPoG WCot WMoo
	- 'Clarissimum Jones' **new**	WCot
	- 'Crispum Grandiceps Kaye'	NGdn
	- Cristatum Group	CLAP EFer ELan LSRN NGdn WCot WFib
	- 'Dre's Dagger'	CBdn CLAP EBee EMor LEdu NAst SCob SPoG WPGP
	- 'Fieldii'	CLAP EFer
	- 'Frizelliae' ♀H6	Widely available
	- 'Frizelliae Capitatum'	CLAP WFib
	- 'Frizelliae Cristatum'	CLAP
	- 'Howardii' **new**	NBro
	- 'Lady-in-Lace' ♀H6	EBee LLHF
	- 'Minutissimum'	CRos EBee ELan ISha LRHS NRHS WCot
	- Plumosum Group	EShb MRav WFib XLum
	- 'Plumosum Axminster'	CLAP EFer EShb WFar
	- 'Plumosum Druery'	EFer
	- RED STEM	see *A. filix-femina* 'Rotstiel'
§	- 'Rotstiel'	CDTJ CLAP EBee EMor NBro WMoo WPnP
	- 'Rotstiel Grandiceps' **new**	ISha
	- 'Setigerum Cristatum'	WFar
	- 'Vernoniae' ♀H6	CLAP ISha MRav
	- 'Vernoniae Cristatum'	CLAP WFib
	- 'Victoriae'	CAby CBdn CCCN CDTJ CKel CRos CWCL EBee ECtt EFer ELan EPfP GBin GMaP IBal ISha LLWG LRHS

	NBid NLar NRHS WMoo WSpi XLum
- aff. 'Victoriae'	CKel CLAP EWTr WFar
- aff. Victoriae Group	see *A. filix-femina* subsp. *angustum*
'Ghost' ♀H5	CBdn CCCN CLAP CRos EBee EMor ESwi ISha LEdu LRHS MGos NBro NLar NRHS NSti SPlb SPoG WCot
goeringianum 'Pictum'	see *A. niponicum* var. *pictum*
minimum	CAby CBdn CLAP EMor LLHF NBro WCot WPGP
niponicum	CLAP CRos LRHS MJak NRHS WHal
- 'Godzilla'	CBdn CLAP EBee ISha
- f. ***metallicum***	see *A. niponicum* var. *pictum*
§ - var. ***pictum*** ♀H5	Widely available
- - 'Apple Court'	CBdn CCCN CLAP CRos EBee ESwi ISha LEdu LRHS NRHS
- - 'Burgundy Lace'	CBdn CLAP EBee ECtt ESwi EUJe MPnt NAst NBro NLar WCot
* - - 'Cristatoflabellatum'	CLAP CRos EBee LRHS NRHS
- - 'Pearly White'	CBdn
- - 'Pewter Lace'	CBdn CLAP EBee ECtt EMor NAst NBro NLar
- - 'Red Beauty'	CAby CBcs CBod CDTJ CRos CSpe ECha ECtt ELan EMOT EMor EPfP EUJe GBin GEdr IBal LRHS LSRN MMuc NLar NRHS SRkn WCot WFar WMoo
- - 'Regal Red'	CBdn CRos EBee ISha LRHS NRHS
- - 'Silver Falls' ♀H5	CBcs CLAP CRos EBee EShb ESwi LRHS NRHS SPoG WCot
- - 'Soul Mate'	CLAP
- - 'Ursula's Red'	CBod CLAP EBee ELan ELon EMor EShb LCro LLWG LOPS LRHS LSRN MHol NBid NHpl NLar SPoG WCot WFar WPGP
'Ocean's Fury'	CAby CBdn CLAP EBee ECtt EFer EShb ESwi GBin LPla SPoG WCot
otophorum ♀H4	ISha MRav NBid WPGP
- var. ***okanum*** ♀H4	Widely available
vidalii	CBdn CBod CLAP CRos EBee EMor IBal ISha LLWG LRHS MSCN NBro NLar NRHS WCot WFar WFib XLum
wardii	CBdn

Atractylodes (*Asteraceae*)

japonica	GEdr LEdu

Atragene see *Clematis*

Atriplex (*Amaranthaceae*)

canescens	CAgr XSen
halimus	CAgr CBcs CFGn CLau CSde EBee ECha EHoe EPPr MRav NLar SLon SPer SPlb WCot
- 'Cascais'	WCot
- 'Limelight' (v)	EPPr
hortensis	ENfk
- var. ***rubra***	CSpe ELan MNHC SRms
portulacoides	see *Halimione portulacoides*

Atropa (*Solanaceae*)

belladonna	GPoy MMuc SEND
mandragora	see *Mandragora officinarum*

aubergine see AGM Vegetables Section

Aubrieta (*Brassicaceae*)

'Agnetta'	ECtt GCrg
'Alba'	see *A.* 'Fiona'
albomarginata	see *A.* 'Argenteovariegata'
'Alix Brett'	CMea
'Ann Kendall'	ECtt
§ 'Argenteovariegata' (v) ♀H6	CRos ELan LRHS MJak NRHS
'Astolat' (v)	EBou GCrg
'Audrey Blue' (Audrey Series)	GWyn
§ 'Aureovariegata' (v) ♀H6	CMea NPer XLum
(Axcent Series) AXCENT BLUE WITH EYE (Audelbley'PBR)	LBuc LRHS
- AXCENT DARK RED ('Audeldare')	CRos LRHS NRHS
- AXCENT DEEP RED ('Abrz0001'PBR) **new**	NHic
- AXCENT DEEP PURPLE ('Audelpur'PBR)	LBuc LRHS
- AXCENT LIGHT BLUE ('Abrz0002'PBR)	CRos EPfP LRHS NRHS
- AXCENT LILAC ('Audelip'PBR)	CRos LRHS NRHS
- AXCENT MAGENTA ('Audelmag'PBR)	LRHS
bicoloured	CMea
BLAUE SCHÖNHEIT	see *A.* 'Blue Beauty'
'Blaumeise'	EBou LRHS MHol
§ 'Blue Beauty'	CBod CMea EBou ECtt EPfP GBin GKev GMaP NHpl NLar WHoo
'Blue Emperor'	ECtt
'Blue Whale'	CBod CPla ECtt GAbr MHol NLar SRms SRot SWvt
§ 'Bob Saunders' (d)	CMea ECtt
'Boundary Haze' **new**	EBou
'Boundary Purple' **new**	EBou
'Bressingham Pink' (d) ♀H6	ECtt SRms
'Bressingham Red'	EBou ECtt ELan EPfP GCrg GMaP SRms
'Bubble Purple'	EPfP
canescens	CPBP GKev
Cascade Series	SPoG
- 'Blue Cascade'	CTri EBou GMaP MBNS MBel MJak SPlb SPoG SRms WCAu
- 'Lilac Cascade'	SPoG SRms
- 'Purple Cascade'	CTri EBou LCro LOPS LSRN MAsh MBNS MBel MJak NSla SPlb SPoG SRms WCAu WRHF
- 'Red Cascade' ♀H6	CTri EBou ECtt LSRN MBNS MJak NSla SPlb SPoG
× ***cultorum***	SVic XSen
deltoidea	WCFE
- Variegata Group (v)	ECtt MAsh MHol WFar
- - 'Golden Variegata' (v) **new**	EBou
- - 'Nana Variegata' (v)	CMea EPot SIgm
'Doctor Mules' ♀H6	ECtt SRms
'Doctor Mules Variegata' (v)	ECtt EHoe ELan ELon EPfP GCrg GMaP GWyn MHer NLar SPoG SRot SWvt WHoo WIce
double pink-flowered (d)	CBod ELan GAbr GMaP MHol MJak
Double Stock-flowered Group pink-flowered (d)	CRos
'Downers Variegata' (v)	ECtt EPot NWad
'Elsa Lancaster'	NHpl NSla
§ 'Fiona'	ECtt EWes
glabrescens	CMea NHpl SIgm WAbe WTor
'Gloria'	CBod CMea EBou ECtt NHpl NLar SRot WIce
'Golden Emperor'	MHer
'Golden King'	see *A.* 'Aureovariegata'
gracilis 'Kitte Rose'	CRos LBuc LRHS MHol NRHS

'Greencourt Purple' ♀H6 EBou ECtt MHer
'Hamburger Stadtpark' CWCL ECtt ELan ELon EPfP GCrg GMaP SRms SRot
'Hemswell Purity' see *A.* 'Snow Maiden'
'Ida' ECtt WIce
'Kati' GMaP LRHS
'Kitte' CSma EBou ECtt ELan EPfP LRHS MHer NLar SPoG SRms
'Kitte Blue' CRos EPfP LBuc LRHS MHol NPri NRHS SPoG SRms WIce
'Kitte Purple' ELan EPfP SPoG
'Kitte White' CRos LRHS MHer NRHS
'Leichtlinii' XLum
'Lime Variegated' (v) NHpl
macedonica EPot
'Oakington Lavender' ECtt
pinardii CPBP
'Pink Beauty' ECtt
'Purple Charm' SRms
'Red Carpet' EBou ELan EPot MAsh MHer SRms
'Rose Queen' CMea ECtt
(Royal Series) 'Royal Blue' CTri ELan EPfP MJak NLar SRms SRot WFar WMoo
- 'Royal Lilac' CTri WFar
- 'Royal Red' CTri ELan EPfP GBin GWyn SRms WMoo
- 'Royal Violet' ELan EPfP WFar WMoo
'Schofield's Double' see *A.* 'Bob Saunders'
'Shobden' (v) WIce
'Silberrand' (v) ECha
§ 'Snow Maiden'PBR NHpl
'Somerfield Silver' ELan EPfP
'Somerford Lime' (v) ELan EPfP SRms WIce
'Swan Red' (v) CBod CPla EBou ECtt EHoe ELon EPot NHpl NSla SRot WTor
'Valerie' (v) EWes
'Westacre Gold' (v) CBod ECtt EWes MAsh MHol
'Whitewell Gem' WMoo XLum
'Winterberg' ECtt

Aucuba ✿ (*Garryaceae*)

chlorascens B&SWJ 11815 WCru
himalaica SBrt
var. ***dolichophylla***
- - Og 95038 WCru
japonica CAco CCVT CDul NLar SCob SEWo WCru WFar
- var. ***borealis*** (f) CWJ 12898 WCru
- 'Clent Wortley Hall' (m) WCFE
- 'Crassifolia' (m) EBtc ELon SArc
- 'Crotonifolia' (f/v) ♀H5 Widely available
- 'Crotonifolia' (m/v) CMac EBou MAsh SGol SRms
- 'Dentata' (f) WAvo WCru
- 'Golden Girl' (v) CRos LRHS MAsh NRHS SLon
- 'Golden King' (m/v) ♀H5 CKel CMac CRos ELan ELon EMOT EPfP LRHS MAsh MGos NLar NRHS SCob SGol SLim WFar
- 'Golden Spangles' (f/v) CBcs CKel EBee EMil EPfP LRHS SWvt
- 'Hillieri' (f) EBtc
- 'Leucocarpa' (f) SPer
- f. ***longifolia*** CMac EPfP NLar SArc WCru
- - 'Salicifolia' (f) ♀H5 EBee ESwi MRav NLar SCob WCru WFar WPGP
- 'Maculata' misapplied see *A. japonica* 'Variegata'
- 'Marmorata' (v) CRos LRHS MAsh NRHS
- 'Mr Goldstrike' (m/v) CKel CRos EPfP LRHS MAsh NEgg
- PEPPER POT ('Shilpot') (m/v) ♀H5 CRos CTsd EPfP LRHS MAsh MJak SLon
- 'Pepperspot'PBR (m/v) MJak WMoo
- 'Picturata' (m/v) CDul CMac CRos CSBt ELan ELon LRHS MAsh MJak MMuc NLar NRHS SEND WFar
- 'Rozannie' (f/m) ♀H5 Widely available
- 'Sulphurea Marginata' (f/v) CKel CMac CRos CTri EBee EShb ESwi LRHS NLar NRHS SPer WFar
§ - 'Variegata' (f/v) Widely available
- 'Variegata' white-flowered (m/v) SGbt
omeiensis CBcs CDTJ CExl
- B&SWJ 2864 ESwi WCru
- BWJ 8048 WCru
- L 614 WPGP

Aulax (*Proteaceae*)

cancellata CCCN CKel SPlb

Aurinia (*Brassicaceae*)

§ ***saxatilis*** ♀H5 ELan EPfP MMuc SPlb WFar XSen
- 'Citrina' ♀H5 ECha ECtt SRms
- 'Compacta' ECtt GJos WIce
- 'Dudley Nevill' WFar
- 'Dudley Nevill Variegated' (v) ECha EWes
- GOLD BALL see *A. saxatilis* 'Goldkugel'
- 'Gold Dust' SRms WRHF
§ - 'Goldkugel' CBod CMea EPfP GJos GWyn MHol SPoG SRms WFar
- 'Variegata' (v) SPoG SRms

Austrocedrus (*Cupressaceae*)

§ ***chilensis*** CKen SLim

Avena (*Poaceae*)

candida see *Helictotrichon sempervirens*

Avenula see *Helictotrichon*

Averrhoa (*Oxalidaceae*)

carambola (F) CCCN

avocado see *Persea americana*

Azalea see *Rhododendron*

Azara ✿ (*Salicaceae*)

dentata CBcs CHll CMac WFar WPav
- 'Variegata' see *A. integrifolia* 'Variegata'
integrifolia CCCN MGil WPav
- 'Uarie' CCCN
§ - 'Variegata' (v) CCCN LRHS
lanceolata CBcs CExl CTri CTsd EBee LEdu NSti WPav
microphylla ♀H4 CBcs CCCN CDul CExl CKel CMac CRos CTri EBee ELan ELon EPfP EUJe LRHS LSRN MAsh MGil MGos MMuc MNHC NQui SArc SEND SPer SPlb WFar WPGP WPav WSpi
* - 'Albovariegata' (v) CTri WPav
- 'Gold Edge' (v) CBcs WFar WPav
- 'Variegata' (v) CBcs CBct CExl CKel CMac CRos CTsd EBee EHoe ELan EPfP LRHS MAsh MGil MMuc NLar SEND SPoG WAvo WFar WPav
* ***patagonica*** MBlu WPav
petiolaris CTri MGil WPav
serrata ♀H4 CBcs CCCN CDul CEnd CKel CRos CTsd ELan EPfP EShb EUJe GBin LRHS MGil NLar SEND SGol SPer

	SPoG SRms SVen WBor WFar WKif WPav WSHC WSpi
- 'Maurice Mason'	EBee
uruguayensis	CBcs CCCN CExl CTsd WPav

Azorella (*Apiaceae*)

glebaria misapplied	see *A. trifurcata*
glebaria A. Gray	see *Bolax gummifer*
gummifer	see *Bolax gummifer*
lycopodioides	EPot WAbe
patagonica	EPot SPlb
§ ***trifurcata***	CPar CSpe CTri GAbr GCrg GKev MMuc NBir SIgm SPlb WAbe
- 'Nana'	GEdr GMaP XLum

Azorina (*Campanulaceae*)

§ ***vidalii***	EShb NWad SPlb

B

Babiana (*Iridaceae*)

nana	CTca GKev
- 'Claudia'	GKev
patersoniae	SPlb
stricta ♀H2	CCCN GKev SDeJ
- Kew hybrids	GKev
- 'Purple Star'	CBor CExl
thunbergii	CPbh
'Zwanenburg's Glory'	CPrp

Baccharis (*Asteraceae*)

genistelloides	MPkF
patagonica	CRos EHyd LRHS MMuc SArc SVen

Backhousia (*Myrtaceae*)

citriodora	GPoy MHer

Bacopa (*Plantaginaceae*)

sp.	SWvt
'Snowflake'	see *Chaenostoma cordatum* 'Snowflake'

Baeckea (*Myrtaceae*)

gunniana	CExl
linifolia	SPlb
virgata	SPlb

Balbisia (*Ledocarpaceae*)

peduncularis	CCCN WCot

Baldellia (*Alismataceae*)

ranunculoides	EWat WMAq
- f. ***repens***	LLWG

Ballota (*Lamiaceae*)

acetabulosa	ECha EWes WCot
'All Hallow's Green'	see *Marrubium bourgaei* var. *bourgaei* 'All Hallows Green'
hirsuta	XSen
nigra	GPoy NMir SRms
pseudodictamnus ♀H4	CBcs CBod CMac CRos EBee ECha EHoe EHyd ELan EPfP GMaP LRHS LSRN MRav NPer NRHS NSti SCob SEND SLon SPer WAvo XLum XSen
- B&M 8119	WCot WPGP
- from Crete	ECha
- compact	CBct
rupestris 'Frogswell Carolyn' (v)	IFro XSen

Baloskion (*Restionaceae*)

§ ***tetraphyllum***	CPbh GBin GCal LRHS SPlb SPoG
§ - 'Cornish Gold' (v)	CPbh

Balsamita see *Tanacetum*

Bambusa (*Poaceae*)

glaucescens	see *B. multiplex*
§ ***multiplex***	XBlo
- 'Elegans'	see *B. multiplex* 'Floribunda'
- 'Fernleaf'	see *B. multiplex* 'Floribunda'
§ - 'Floribunda'	EShb XBlo XCre
- 'Golden Goddess'	XBlo
- 'Silverstripe'	see *B. multiplex* 'Variegata'
§ - 'Variegata' (v)	XBlo
- 'Wang Tsai'	see *B. multiplex* 'Floribunda'
oldhamii	XCre
pubescens	see *Dendrocalamus strictus*
tuldoides	XCre
ventricosa	XBlo XCre
- 'Striata' **new**	XCre
vulgaris	XBlo
- 'Vittata'	ERod XBlo

banana see *Ensete*, *Musa*

Banksia ✿ (*Proteaceae*)

baxteri	CKel
burdettii	CKel
canei	SPlb
coccinea	CKel
ericifolia	CKel CPbh
- var. ***ericifolia***	CCCN
- var. ***macrantha***	SPlb
grandis	CCCN CPbh
integrifolia	CBcs CCCN CDTJ CKel CPbh SPlb
marginata	CTsd LRHS SPlb
media	SPlb
menziesii	CKel
oblongifolia	SPlb
occidentalis	CKel
paludosa	SPlb
praemorsa	CCCN CKel
- yellow-flowered	CCCN
prionotes	CCCN CKel
robur	CBcs CCCN CPbh SPlb
serrata	CCCN CKel SPlb
speciosa	SPlb
spinulosa	CPbh
- 'Birthday Candles'	CKel CPbh
- var. ***collina***	SPlb
- var. ***spinulosa***	CCCN
violacea	SPlb

Baptisia (*Papilionaceae*)

§ ***alba***	EBee ILea LPla MBel MNrw SPhx WHil
- var. ***alba***	IPot NLar WCAu
- - 'Wayne's World'	EBee
§ - var. ***macrophylla***	CRos EHyd EWes LRHS MNrw NRHS SPhx
australis ♀H7	Widely available
- 'Blueberry Sundae'	EBee EWTr ILea SPer
- 'Caspian Blue'	CExl GMaP LEdu WHil
- 'Exaltata' ♀H7	EBee ECtt EPau LPla MBNS MHer MHol NCou NLar WCot WRHF
- var. ***minor***	CSpe MMrt SPhx

	- 'Nelson's Navy'	LEdu
	× ***bicolor*** 'Starlite' (Prairieblues Series)	MAvo MNrw
	bracteata var. ***leucophaea***	SPhx
	'Carolina Moonlight'	EBee ECtt EWes IPot MMrt MNrw NDai NSti SHar SPer
	'Cherries Jubilee'	EBee ILea WHil
	'Chocolate Chip'	MCot NCGa SHar
	'Dutch Chocolate' (Decadence Series)	CBcs CWGN EBee ECtt EMor EWTr EWes ILea IPot LCro LOPS LRHS MAvo NSti SPer SPoG WHil XEll
	'Indigo Spires'	EBee ILea MBel
	lactea	see *B. alba* var. *macrophylla*
	'Lemon Meringue'	EBee MAvo SPoG WHil
	leucantha	see *B. alba* var. *macrophylla*
	pendula	see *B. alba*
	'Pink Truffles' (Decadence Series) **new**	NSti
	'Purple Smoke'	CExl CSpe EBee ECtt ILea IPot LCro LEdu LOPS LRHS MAvo MBel MCot MHol MNrw NCGa SMHy SPhx WAul
	'Solar Flare' (Prairieblues Series)	ILea
	'Sparkling Sapphires' (Decadence Series) **new**	IPot
	sphaerocarpa	SPhx SPlb
	tinctoria	SPhx
	'Vanilla Cream'	IPot MBel
	× ***variicolor*** 'Twilite' (Prairieblues Series)	EBee EPfP LRHS MMrt NDov

Barbarea (*Brassicaceae*)

	praecox	see *B. verna*
	rupicola 'Sunnyola'	CBor
§	***verna***	GPoy MHer SRms SVic
	vulgaris 'Variegata' (v)	NBro WMoo

Barleria (*Acanthaceae*)

	oenotheroides	CCCN
	suberecta	see *Dicliptera sericea*

Barnardia (*Asparagaceae*)

	japonica	WCot

Barosma see *Agathosma*

Bartlettina (*Asteraceae*)

§	***sordida***	CCCN EUJe

Basella (*Basellaceae*)

	rubra	CLau SPre SVic

Bashania (*Poaceae*)

§	***fargesii***	ENBC ERod MMuc MRav MWht SEND XCre
I	***qingchengshanensis***	ERod MWht XCre

basil see *Ocimum basilicum*; also AGM Vegetables section

Bauhinia (*Caesalpiniaceae*)

	alba	see *B. variegata*
*	***lutea***	CCCN
	natalensis	SPlb
	purpurea L.	CCCN SPlb
	tomentosa	CAco CCCN
§	***variegata***	CAco
	'White Lady'	CCCN
	yunnanensis	SBrt SPlb

bay see *Laurus nobilis*

beans see AGM Vegetables Section

Beaucarnea (*Asparagaceae*)

	recurvata ♀^{H1c}	LCro LOPS SPlb

Beaufortia (*Myrtaceae*)

	sparsa	CTsd
	squarrosa	SPlb

Beckmannia (*Poaceae*)

	eruciformis	XLum

Bedfordia (*Asteraceae*)

	linearis	SPlb

Beesia (*Ranunculaceae*)

§	***calthifolia***	CBct CDTJ CDor CSpe EBee EHrv EPfP EWld GEdr IMou LEdu LLHF SChF SMad WCot WCru WPGP WSHC
	- DJHC 98447	CExl
	deltophylla misapplied	see *B. calthifolia*

beetroot see AGM Vegetables Section

Begonia ✿ (*Begoniaceae*)

	from Taiwan	GCal
	'Abel Carrière' (R)	WDib
	aconitifolia (C)	EShb
	albopicta (C)	EBak
	- 'Rosea' (C)	EShb WDib
	'Angela Jane' (T)	WFib
	aff. ***angularis***	SPlb
§	***annulata*** ♀^{H1b}	LEdu
	- HWJK 2424	ESwi WCru
	'Apricot Delight' (Fragrant Falls Improved Series) (T)	WFib
	'Apricot Nectar' (Fragrant Falls Improved Series) (T)	CRos EHyd LRHS NRHS
I	'Apricot Shades Improved'	SDeJ
	'Argentea' (R)	EBak
	'Argenteo-guttata'	EShb
	'Aya' (C)	WDib
	balansana	CBct
	'Benitochiba' (R) ♀^{H1b}	CAvo CBcs CBct CExl CHll CSpe ECtt ESwi EUJe GBin MHol NLar SPoG WCot WDib WGrn
	'Beryl Rhodes' (T)	WFib
	'Bethlehem Star'	NWad WDib
	'Billy Langdon' (T)	WFib
	'Black Fang' ♀^{H1b}	WDib
	'Black Knight' (R)	WDib
	'Blackberry Swirl' (R)	WDib
	'Blazing Star' (T)	LCro LOPS
	'Blushing Star' (T)	CPla LCro LOPS
	'Bokit' × ***imperialis***	WDib
	boliviensis (T)	ESwi
	- 'Firecracker'	WDib
	BONFIRE ('Nzcone'[PBR]) ♀^{H1b}	SPoG
	'Bouton de Rose' (T)	SDeJ
	'Buffey'[PBR] (T)	NPri
	'Buttermilk' (T)	WFib
	'Can-can' (T)	WFib
	'Candy Floss'	WCru
	carolineifolia ♀^{H1b}	WDib
	'Cascade Florence'	SDeJ
	'Cascade Sunray'	SDeJ

	'Casey Corwin' (R)	WDib
	cathayana	EBee GCal
	'Champagne'	LCro LOPS
	'Chantilly Lace'	NWad
I	***chapaensis*** HWJ 642	WCru
	'China Curl' (R) ♀H1b	WDib
	chitoensis B&SWJ 1954	GCal WCru
	'Cleopatra' ♀H1b	WDib
	coccinea (C)	WPav
	'Comte de Lesseps' (C)	WDib
	'Connee Boswell' ♀H1b	CHll WDib
§	***corallina*** (C)	EBak
	cucullata var. ***arenosicola*** (S)	ECtt ESwi
	'Curly Fireflush' (R) ♀H1b	WDib
	'David Blais' (R) ♀H1b	WDib
	'Dawnal Meyer' (C)	WDib
I	'De Elegans'	WDib
	DEVOTION ('Yadev'PBR) (Million Kisses Series) ♀H1b	NPri
	'Dewdrop' (R) ♀H1b	WDib
	'Dibleys Pink Showers' ♀H1b	WDib
	discolor	see *B. grandis* subsp. *evansiana*
	'Don Miller' (C)	WDib
	'Down Home' (C) **new**	WDib
	DRAGON WING RED ('Bepared'PBR) ♀H1b	EShb
§	***dregei*** (T) ♀H1b	CSpe EShb
	ELEGANCE ('Yagance'PBR) (Million Kisses Series) ♀H1b	NPri
	emeiensis	CSpe EBee WPGP
	'Emerald Giant' (R)	WDib
	'Erythrophylla' ♀H1b	EShb
	'Escargot' (R) ♀H1b	SMad WDib
	'Fairy Lights' (T)	WFib
	Fimbriata Group (T)	SDeJ
	'Fireworks' (R) ♀H1b	WDib
	'Flamenco' (T/d) **new**	NPri
	'Flo'Belle Moseley' (C)	WDib
§	***foliosa*** var. ***miniata*** ♀H1b	CHll CTsd EBak EShb MArl WCot WDib
	- - pink-flowered	CCCN WCot
	Fragrant Falls Improved Series	SPoG
	fuchsioides	see *B. foliosa* var. *miniata*
	'Funky Pink' (Funky Series) (T/d) **new**	NPri
	fusca	WPGP
	'Garden Angel Blush' (Garden Angel Series)	CAbb CBct EUJe WCot
	'Gay Gordon' (T)	WFib
	'Glowing Embers' ♀H1b	ECtt LBuc NWad SPoG
	grandis (T)	IDee XLum
§	- subsp. ***evansiana*** ♀H2	CAby CBct CHll CKel CTsd EPPr EShb EUJe GCal LEdu SEND SPlb WCot WCru WFar WMoo
	- - B&SWJ 11188	WCru
	- - var. ***alba*** hort. ♀H2	CAby CSpe EBee EPPr EShb ESwi EWld GCal LEdu SBch WCot WMoo WPGP XLum
	- - 'Claret Jug'	CExl EBee ECtt ESwi WGrn
	- - 'Pink Parasol'	ESwi WCru
	- - pink-flowered	WFar
	- - 'Simsii'	EBee WFar
	- - 'Sublime'	LEdu
	- 'Sapporo'	EBee ESwi GCal SChr WCru
	- silver-spotted	GCal
§	- subsp. ***sinensis*** (T)	EBee NWad
I	- - 'Red Undies'	ESwi WCru
	- - 'Snowpop'	WPGP
	- aff. subsp. ***sinensis*** (T) BWJ 8133	WCru
	'Green Gold' (R) ♀H1b	WDib
	'Green Valleyleaf' **new**	NWad
	griffithii	see *B. annulata*
	haageana hort. ex W. Watson	see *B. scharffii*
	hatacoa	LEdu
	- silver-leaved	WDib
	'Helen Teupel' (R)	WDib
	'Helena Hall' (T)	WFib
	'Hilo Holiday' (R) ♀H1b	WDib
	homonyma	see *B. dregei*
	(Illumination Series) 'Illumination Apricot' (T/d)	SCoo
	- 'Illumination Rose' (T/d)	SCoo
	- 'Illumination Salmon Pink' (T/d) ♀H2	SCoo
	- 'Illumination White' (T/d)	SCoo
	× ***intermedia*** 'Bertinii' (T)	LCro LOPS SDeJ
	'Jennifer Wilson' (T)	WFib
	'Jessie Cruickshank' (T)	WFib
	'John Smith' (T)	WFib
	'La Paloma' (C)	WDib
	Large-flowered Double Group (T/d)	SDeJ
	'Lianne' (T)	WFib
	'Lime Green'	GCal
	'Lime Swirl'	WDib
	'Limeade' ♀H1b	WDib
	'Linda Jackson' (T)	WFib
	listada ♀H1b	WDib
	'Little Brother Montgomery' ♀H1b	EShb NWad WDib
	'Lois Burks' (C)	WDib
	'Looking Glass' (C)	WDib
	'Lucerna' (C)	EBak ELan EShb WDib
	luxurians ♀H1b	CAbb CBct CBod CHll CSpe EBee ECtt ELan ESwi EUJe GBin GCal MNrw MPie SMad SPlb WCot WGrn WPGP
	macduffieana	see *B. corallina*
	maculata 'Wightii' (C)	CSpe WDib
	'Madame Butterfly' (C)	NWad
	'Majesty' (T)	WFib
	Marginata Group (T)	SDeJ
*	'Marginata Crispa White'	SDeJ
	'Marmaduke' ♀H1b	WDib
	'Marmorata' (T)	SDeJ
	'Martin Johnson' (R) ♀H1b	WDib
	masoniana ♀H1b	ESwi GCal WDib WSFF
I	'Matador' (T)	WFib
	'Matisse' (Impressionist Series)	CRos EHyd LRHS NRHS
	'Melissa' (T)	WFib
	'Merry Christmas' (R)	WDib
	'Metallic Mist'PBR	ESwi
	'Midnight Magic' (R) ♀H1b	WDib
	Million Kisses Series	LBuc NPri
	'Mishmi Silver'	CBct GCal LEdu NSti WPGP
	'Monet' (Impressionist Series)	CRos EHyd LRHS NRHS
	'Mother's Day' (T)	LCro LOPS
	'Mrs E. McLaughlan' (T)	WFib
	'Mrs Peters' (T)	WFib
	'Munchkin' ♀H1b	WDib
	'My Best Friend'	WDib
	'Namur' (R) ♀H1b	WDib
	natalensis	see *B. dregei*

'Nick Woodfield'	WFib
Nonstop Series (T/d)	SDeJ
- 'Nonstop Pink' (T/d)	SDeJ
- 'Nonstop Red' (T/d)	SDeJ
- 'Nonstop Salmon' (T/d)	SDeJ
- 'Nonstop White' (T/d)	SDeJ
- 'Nonstop Yellow' (T/d)	SDeJ
'Northern Lights Scarlet Burst' (T) **new**	NPri
'Odorosa'	SDeJ
'Ollykey' (T)	WFib
'Orange Rubra' (C)	WDib
'Orangeade' (c)	NWad
palmata	CBct CDTJ CExl GCal
panchtharensis	SPlb
- B&SWJ 2692	WCru
partita	see *B. dregei*
'Peardrop'PBR	NPri
pedatifida DJHC 98473	ESwi EWld WCru
Pendula Group (T)	SDeJ
- 'Pink Giant' (T)	LCro LOPS
- 'Red Giant' (T)	LCro LOPS
- 'White Giant' (T)	LCro LOPS
'Picasso' (Impressionist Series)	CRos EHyd LRHS NRHS
'Picotee' (T)	SDeJ
'Pink Cascade'	SDeJ
'Pink Champagne' (R) ♀H1b	WDib
'Pink Flamingo' (T)	LCro LOPS
'Pink Twist'	WDib
'Pollux' ♀H1b	WDib
'Powder Puff' (T)	WFib
'Président Carnot' (C) ♀H1b	NWad
'Princess Alice' (T)	WFib
'Princess of Hanover' (R) ♀H1b	WDib
putii B&SWJ 7245	WCru
'Queen Olympus'	WDib
'Quinebaug'	CPla
'Raspberry Swirl' (R)	WDib
ravenii (T)	EBee
'Ray Peters'	WFib
'Red Admiral' (T)	WFib
'Red Glory' (T)	LCro LOPS
'Red Robin' (R) ♀H1b	WDib
'Red Tempest'	WDib
'Red Undies' (*grandis*)	see *B. grandis* subsp. *sinensis* 'Red Undies'
'Regal Minuet' (R) ♀H1b	WDib
'Renoir' (Impressionist Series)	CRos EHyd LRHS NRHS
'Richmondensis' (S)	EShb
'Rocheart' (R) ♀H1b	WDib
'Rosy Jewel' (R) **new**	WDib
'Roy Hartley' (T/d)	WFib
'Ruby Slippers'PBR (R) **new**	ELan
'Sal's Comet' (R) ♀H1b	WDib
'Sandra Haynes' (T)	WFib
'Satin Starburst' (R) **new**	WDib
'Sceptre' (T)	WFib
'Sceptre Cross' (T)	WFib
§ ***scharffii***	EBak
'Scherzo'	WDib
'Sea Urchin'	WDib
serratipetala ♀H1b	EBak WDib
'Shamus'	WDib
* ***shepherdii***	WDib
sikkimensis	ESwi GCal
silletensis	WCot
- subsp. ***mengyangensis***	GCal
'Silver Cloud' (R) ♀H1b	WDib
'Silver Jewell' ♀H1b	WDib
'Silver Lace'	WDib
'Silver Spirit' (R) **new**	WDib
'Silver Splendor'	CSpe ECtt ESwi XEll
sinensis	see *B. grandis* subsp. *sinensis*
sizemoreae	GCal WDib WPGP
'Snow Storm'	WDib
I 'Snowcap' (C) ♀H1b	EShb WDib
solananthera A. DC. ♀H1b	WDib
'Solid Silver' (R)	WDib
soli-mutata	WDib
sonderiana (T)	GCal
'Stained Glass'	WDib
'Star Bright'	WDib
'Star Light'	WDib
'Sugar Candy' (T/d)	WFib
'Sugar Plum'	MAsh
(Summerwings Series) SUMMERWINGS DARK ELEGANCE ('Insumdaele'PBR)	CSpe SPoG
- SUMMERWINGS WHITE ('Innbolwhi'PBR)	ESwi
'Sunset Yellow Champagne'	LCro LOPS
'Susan' (T)	WFib
sutherlandii (T) ♀H2	CAvo CCCN CExl EBak EBee EShb ESwi EWld NPer SAdn SBch WCot WDib WGrn WPGP
- 'Papaya' (T)	CSpe
'Sweet Dreams' (T/d)	WFib
SWEET SPICE CITRUS	NPri
SWEET SPICE ENGLISH ROSE	NPri
'Switzerland' (T)	SDeJ
'Tahiti' (T)	WFib
taliensis EDHCH 042	WCot WCru
'Tapestry'	NWad
'Tessa Robinson' (T)	WFib
'Thurstonii' ♀H1b	EShb
'Tiger Paws' ♀H1b	EShb
'Tiny Gem'	WDib
* ***tripartita*** (T)	WDib
'Two Face'	WDib
'Tye Dye'	GCal
'Van Gogh' (Impressionist Series)	CRos EHyd LRHS NRHS
'Vera Coates' (T)	WFib
'Vesuvius' (R)	WDib
'Vibrant Star' (T)	LCro LOPS
'Wavy Green'	CBct EBee GCal WPGP
'Whispers' (T)	WFib
'Wild Swan'	WCru
* ***wynn-jonesiae*** 'Pink Lady'	WCru
'Ziggy' (T)	WFib

Belamcanda see *Iris*

chinensis	see *Iris domestica*

Bellevalia (*Asparagaceae*)

atroviolacea	GKev
'Cream Pearl'	WCot
desertorum JCA 0.227.690	WCot
dubia	GKev WCot
forniculata	GKev WCot
hyacinthoides	WCot
§ ***paradoxa***	CAby CMea ERCP GBin GKev MNrw SDeJ WCot
pycnantha misapplied	see *B. paradoxa*
pycnantha ambig.	SDeJ SIgm

pycnantha (K. Koch) Losinsk. 'Green Pearl'	CAby ERCP GKev SDeJ
romana	ERCP GKev SDeJ WCot
tabriziana	WCot

Bellis (*Asteraceae*)

§ ***caerulescens***	ECtt GAbr
perennis	GQue
- 'Alice'	ECtt GAbr WHer
- 'Big Bob' (d)	ECtt WCot
- 'Dresden China'	WCot WHer
- HEN AND CHICKENS	see *B. perennis* 'Prolifera' single-flowered
- 'Hula'	CNat
- 'Miss Mason'	WCot WHer
- old strain	WCot
- 'Prolifera' double-flowered (d)	WHer
§ - 'Prolifera' single-flowered	CFis ECtt WCot
- 'Single Blue'	see *B. caerulescens*
- 'Stafford Pink'	WHer
- 'The Pearl'	GAbr WCot
- 'Upper Seagry'	CNat
rotundifolia 'Caerulescens'	see *B. caerulescens*
sylvestris	WCot

Bellium (*Asteraceae*)

bellidioides	GQue

Belloa (*Asteraceae*)

chilensis	SPlb

Beloperone see *Justicia*

Bensoniella (*Saxifragaceae*)

oregona	CExl

Benthamiella (*Solanaceae*)

patagonica	SPlb WAbe
- F&W 9345	ITim WAbe
- white-flowered	WAbe
- yellow-flowered	WAbe

Berberidopsis (*Berberidopsidaceae*)

corallina	CBcs CKel CMac CRHN CRos ELan EPfP EUJe IArd IDee IMou LRHS MGil MGos MRav NLar SLim SPer SPoG SWvt WPav WSHC

Berberis (*Berberidaceae*)

CC 4730	CExl
CC 7810 **new**	CMCN
aggregata	NBir SRms
amurensis var. ***latifolia*** B&SWJ 8539	WCru
aquifolium	see *Mahonia aquifolium*
- 'Fascicularis'	see *Mahonia* × *wagneri* 'Pinnacle'
aristata misapplied	see *B. glaucocarpa*
asiatica	CExl GPoy WPGP
bealei	see *Mahonia bealei*
'Boughton Red'	WHor
buxifolia 'Nana' misapplied	see *B. microphylla* 'Pygmaea'
calliantha	WFar
candidula C.K. Schneid.	CDul LRHS MMuc MSwo NLar SCob SEND SPer
- 'Jytte'	see *B.* 'Jytte'
× ***carminea*** 'Buccaneer'	WSpi
- 'Pirate King'	CKel CRos CSBt EBee EHyd EPfP LRHS MAsh SPer SPoG SWvt
chilensis	WPav
darwinii ♀H5	Widely available
I - 'Compacta'	CKel CMac CRos CSBt EBee ELan EMOT EPfP LBuc LRHS MAsh MGos NEgg NLar NRHS SCob SLim SPoG SWvt WCot WFar WPav
aff. ***densa*** B&SWJ 14880 **new**	WCru
dictyophylla	CDul CKel EBee ELan EPfP LRHS MMuc NLar SCob SPer WSpi
dulcis 'Nana'	see *B. microphylla* 'Pygmaea'
empetrifolia	LEdu WPav WSpi
× ***frikartii*** 'Amstelveen' ♀H5	CCVT ELan EPfP MBNS MMuc MRav SCob SEND
- 'Telstar'	CKel EMOT SCob
gagnepainii misapplied	see *B. gagnepainii* var. *lanceifolia*
gagnepainii C.K. Schneid.	CDul CMac SCob
§ - var. ***lanceifolia***	MMuc NWea SEND SGol
- - 'Fernspray'	EPfP MRav SRms
- - 'Robin Hood'	see *B.* × *hybridogagnepainii* 'Robin Hood'
- 'Purpurea'	see *B.* × *interposita* 'Wallich's Purple'
'Georgei' ♀H6	EPfP SPtp
§ ***glaucocarpa***	SPtp
'Goldilocks'	CDul CKel EMil EPfP MBlu SCob SPoG
goudotii B&SWJ 10769	WCru
- B&SWJ 14721 **new**	WCru
- B&SWJ 14892 **new**	WCru
haematocarpa	SIgm
hamiltoniana H&M 1919	GKev
heterophylla	GKev
× ***hybridogagnepainii*** 'Chenault'	ELan
§ - 'Robin Hood'	NEgg
hypokerina	CMac IDee SPtp
insignis	IDee
- subsp. ***insignis*** var. ***insignis***	ELon LLHF
- - - B&SWJ 2432	WCru
§ × ***interposita*** 'Wallich's Purple'	CBod CCVT CRos EPfP LRHS MRav MSwo SGol SPer
jamesiana	LLHF SPtp WCFE
julianae	CAco CArg CBcs CDul CMac ELan EPfP MGos MJak MMuc MSwo NEgg NWea SCob SEND SGol SPer SRms SWvt WFar WSHC WSpi
§ 'Jytte'	EBee
koehneana	SPtp
koreana	EPfP NLar
linearifolia 'Orange King'	see *B. trigona* 'Orange King'
'Little Favourite'	see *B. thunbergii* f. *atropurpurea* 'Atropurpurea Nana'
× ***lologensis*** 'Apricot Queen' ♀H5	CBcs CMac EPfP MAsh MGos NLar SCob SPer SPoG SWvt
- 'Mystery Fire'	IArd MAsh MGos NEgg NLar SGol SWvt WRHF
- 'Stapehill'	CMac CRos EHyd ELan EPfP MAsh SPoG
× ***media*** 'Dual Jewel'PBR	NLar
- PARK JEWEL	see *B.* × *media* 'Parkjuweel'
§ - 'Parkjuweel'	CMac IArd MRav SCob SRms
- 'Red Jewel' ♀H6	CKel CMac CRos EPfP LRHS MAsh MGos MMuc MRav NEgg SCob SEND SPer SPoG WCFE WFar
microphylla	EPfP GKev WCFE
- SDR 7027	GKev
§ - 'Pygmaea'	CKel CRos EHyd EPfP LRHS MGos MMuc MRav SCob SLim SPer WPav
mitifolia	NLar
montana	WPGP

× ***ottawensis*** 'Auricoma' SGol SWvt
- f. ***purpurea*** CCVT CMac
§ - - 'Silver Miles' (v) EHoe MRav WFar
§ - - 'Superba' CBar CBcs CBod CDul CSBt CTri EBee ECrN EHoe ELan ELon EMOT EPfP MGos MJak MMuc MRav MSwo NWea SCob SEND SLim SPer SRms SWvt WFar WMoo
panlanensis 'Cally Rose' EBee GCal SMad WPGP
poiretii CExl
polyantha var. ***polyantha*** CTri
pruinosa GKev
'Red Tears' MAsh MRav SPer WFar
× ***rubrostilla*** 'Cherry Ripe' CMac
- 'Wisley' CRos EBee EHyd LRHS
sieboldii LEdu LLHF MAsh MRav WCFE WPav WSpi
§ ***soulieana*** CKel EPfP NWea
stenophylla Hance see *B. soulieana*
× ***stenophylla*** Lindl. ♀H5 CCVT CDul CMac CSBt CTri EPfP LBuc MMuc MRav SGol SPer SRms
- 'Claret Cascade' EBee MRav NLar SPer SPoG
- 'Compacta' NEgg
- 'Corallina Compacta' ♀H5 CKel CMac CMea CRos EHyd ELan EPfP EPot GCrg LRHS MAsh MHer SCob SIgm SPer SPoG SRms
- 'Cornish Cream' see *B.* × *stenophylla* 'Lemon Queen'
- 'Crawley Gem' GAbr NLar NWea
- 'Cream Showers' see *B.* × *stenophylla* 'Lemon Queen'
- 'Etna' CRos EHyd ELan LRHS MAsh SCoo SPoG
- 'Irwinii' CKel CMac LRHS
- 'Lemon Queen' WSpi
- 'Nana' CRos EHyd LRHS
subacuminata FMWJ 13290 WCru
- NJM 09.165 WPGP
sublevis PAB 8943 LEdu
taliensis CExl
temolaica ♀H5 EPfP EWes IDee MGos NLar NPri NWea SCob SPer WPGP WSpi
thunbergii CArg CBcs CDul CKel CMac CPer EMOT EPfP LBuc LPra MJak NHic NWea SCob SPer SWvt WFar
- f. ***atropurpurea*** CAco CBcs CCVT CKel CMac CSBt CTri EBee ECrN ELan EPfP LBuc MGos MMuc MRav MSwo NEgg NLar SCob SGol SPer SPlb SRms WAvo WMoo WMou WTSh
- - 'Admiration'[PBR] ♀H7 Widely available
§ - - 'Atropurpurea Nana' ♀H7 Widely available
- - 'Bagatelle' CKel CRos ELan EPfP IArd LRHS LSRN MAsh MGos MRav NLar SCob SLim SPer SWvt WCFE WMoo
- - 'Concorde' ♀H7 CRos EHyd ELan EPfP LRHS MAsh NRHS SCob
- - 'Dart's Red Lady' ♀H7 CExl CKel CRos CSBt EHoe EHyd ELan EPfP LRHS MAsh NLar NRHS SCob SPer SWvt WAvo WFar
- - 'Golden Ring' (v) ♀H7 CAco CBcs CDul CMac CRos EHoe EHyd ELan EMOT EPfP LRHS MAsh MGos MRav NEgg NRHS SCob SGbt SPer SPoG SWvt WAvo WFar WMoo
- - 'Harlequin' (v) ♀H7 CChe CKel CRos EHyd ELan EPfP LCro LOPS LRHS LSRN MAsh MGos NEgg NRHS SCob SEle SGol SPer SPoG SRms SWvt WFar
- - 'Helmond Pillar' Widely available
- - 'Pink Queen' (v) CDul CKel CPer ELan EPfP LRHS MAsh SCob WFar
- - 'Red Chief' CBcs CKel CMac CRos EHoe ELan EMOT EPfP LRHS MAsh MGos MJak MSwo NEgg NRHS SCob SGol SLim SLon SPer SPoG SRms SWvt WFar
- - 'Red Pillar' CChe CKel CMac EHoe ELan EMOT EPfP MAsh MGos NEgg SWvt WFar WRHF
- - 'Red Rocket' CRos EBee ELan EPfP EUJe LRHS NEgg NLar NRHS SCob SCoo SPer
- - 'Rose Glow' (v) ♀H7 Widely available
- - 'Rosy Rocket'[PBR] (v) CKel CWGN EBee ELan EMOT EMil EPfP LRHS MRav NHol NLar SPad SPer SPoG WFar
- 'Atropurpurea Superba' see *B.* × *ottawensis* f. *purpurea* 'Superba'
- 'Aurea' CBcs CDul CMac CRos EHoe EHyd ELan EMOT EPfP LRHS LSRN MBlu MGos MRav NLar NRHS SCob SLim SPlb SRms SWvt
- BONANZA GOLD ('Bogozam'[PBR]) CBcs CRos EBee EHyd ELan EPfP LRHS MAsh MRav NLar SCob SLim SPer
- 'Crimson Pygmy' see *B. thunbergii* f. *atropurpurea* 'Atropurpurea Nana'
- 'Diabolic' CRos EHyd LRHS MAsh NHol NRHS SPer SPoG
- 'Erecta' CMac EPfP MRav SPer WCFE
- 'Fireball'[PBR] ♀H7 CRos EHyd EPfP LRHS MAsh
- FLAMINGO ('Hoho 1') SGol
- 'Golden Dream'[PBR] EMOT
- 'Golden Rocket'[PBR] CRos EBee EHyd ELan EPfP LLHF LRHS MAsh MGos MJak MRav NEgg NLar NRHS SCoo SPer SPoG WFar
- 'Golden Torch' CKel CRos CSBt EHyd ELan EMOT EPfP LRHS MAsh MRav NEgg NHol NRHS SLim SWvt
- 'Green Carpet' CKel CMac EUJe LRHS MBlu NLar SGol SPoG SWvt
- 'Green Mantle' see *B. thunbergii* 'Kelleriis'
- 'Green Marble' see *B. thunbergii* 'Kelleriis'
- 'Green Ornament' NHol
§ - 'Kelleriis' (v) CRos EHyd LRHS MRav
- 'Kobold' CMac CRos EHyd EPfP LRHS MGos NEgg SCob SPer WMoo
- 'Maria'[PBR] ♀H7 CRos CWGN EHoe EHyd ELon EMOT EPfP LLHF LRHS MGos MJak NLar NRHS SCob SGol SPoG WGrn WMoo
- 'Orange Dream'[PBR] EBee EMOT
- 'Orange Rocket'[PBR] CBod CRos EBee EHyd ELan EMOT EPfP LRHS MAsh MGos MRav NEgg NHol NRHS SCoo SEle SPer SPoG WFar
- 'Orange Sunrise' (v) **new** LCro LOPS
- 'Pow-wow' CKel CRos EHyd ELan EMOT LRHS MGos NLar NRHS SCob SCoo SGol SLim SPoG SWvt
- 'Redtorch'[PBR] CKel CRos EHyd LRHS NRHS
- 'Silver Beauty' (v) EHoe
- 'Silver Mile' see *B.* × *ottawensis* f. *purpurea* 'Silver Miles'
- 'Smaragd' **new** WFar
- 'Somerset' CMac
- 'Starburst'[PBR] (v) CBcs CBod CDul CKel CRos CSBt EBee EHyd EMOT EPfP LRHS LSRN MGos MJak NEgg NHol NRHS SCoo SLim SLon SRms SWvt

– 'Tiny Gold'[PBR]	CRos EHyd ELan LCro LOPS LRHS MAsh MGos NEgg SCob SLim SLon SWvt WFar
* – 'Tricolor' (v)	CMac MRav WFar
§ ***trigona*** 'Orange King'	CBcs CMac CTri ELan EPfP MAsh MGos NEgg NLar SCob SPer SPoG
valdiviana ♀[H5]	CBcs CExl CJun EBee EPfP GBin IArd IDee IMou SChF SMad WPGP
verruculosa ♀[H5]	CBcs CDul CKel CRos EPfP LRHS MBlu MGos NWea SCob SPer SRms SWvt WFar
aff. ***verticillata*** B&SWJ 10672	WCru
virescens B&SWJ 2646D	WCru
vulgaris	CAgr CNat GPoy MCoo NWea
– 'Wiltshire Wonder' (v)	CNat
wilsoniae	CBcs CDul CMac CTri ELan ELon EPfP GLog MMuc NWea SCob SPer SRms WAvo WFar WSpi
– blue-leaved	WFar
– var. ***guhtzunica***	EWes
xanthoclada NJM 11.007	WPGP

Berberis × *Mahonia* see × *Mahoberberis*

Berchemia (*Rhamnaceae*)

racemosa	NLar

bergamot see *Citrus* × *limon* Bergamot Group

Bergbambos (*Poaceae*)

§ ***tessellata***	ERod MMuc MWht SEND

Bergenia ✿ (*Saxifragaceae*)

'Abendglocken'	CMac ECha ECtt EPfP MWat NSti WCot WFar
§ 'Abendglut'	Widely available
'Admiral'	CBct CMac ECha WCot
afghanica	XLum
* ***agavifolia***	CBct XLum
'Andrea'	WCot
'Angel Kiss' (Dragonfly Series)	CWCL ECtt GBin MNrw NLar WCot
'Apple Blossom'	CRos EHyd EPfP LRHS NRHS
'Apple Court White'	CBct
'Autumn Magic'	CBct CBod CKel CRos ELon EPfP LRHS NAst NCou WFar
'Baby Doll'	Widely available
'Bach'	CBct CBod CDor CRos EBee ECtt EHyd EPfP LPla LRHS LSun MBel MCot MMuc NEgg NGBl NLar NRHS NSti SCob SWvt WCAu WCot WFar WMoo WWtn
§ 'Ballawley' clonal	CRos ECha EHyd GCal IMou LRHS MRav NRHS WCot XLum
'Ballawley Guardsman'	CBct
§ Ballawley hybrids	CMac WSpi
'Ballawley' seed-raised	see *B.* Ballawley hybrids
'Bartók'	CBct EBee ECtt ESwi EUJe GAbr IKil NEgg NRHS WCAu WCot WMoo
beesiana	see *B. purpurascens*
'Beethoven'	CBct ECha GBin MRav NBir WCAu WCot
BELL TOWER	see *B.* 'Glockenturm'
'Biedermeier' ♀[H7]	ECha
'Bizet'	CBct XLum
'Borodin'	CBct
'Brahms'	CBct WCot
'Bressingham Bountiful'	CBct
'Bressingham Ruby'[PBR]	CBct CBod CRos CWCL EBee ECha ECtt ELon EPfP GBin LRHS LSRN MBel MGos MHol MRav NBir NRHS SCob SPer SWvt WCAu WCot WHoo WSpi
'Bressingham Salmon'	CBct EBee ECha ECtt ELon GMaP MRav NLar SRms WCot WMoo
'Bressingham White' ♀[H6]	Widely available
'Britten' ♀[H7]	CBct CMac GBin IMou WCot
ciliata	CBct CDor CMac ECha EHrv EShb EUJe GEdr GMaP LEdu LRHS MRav NHol NLar SPer WFar WPGP WSHC WSpi XLum
– 'Dumbo'	CAbb CBct GBin LEdu NLar WCAu
– f. ***ligulata***	see *B. pacumbis*
– 'Wilton'	CBct EWld LEdu MAvo SHar WCot WSHC
ciliata × ***crassifolia***	see *B.* × *schmidtii*
'Claire Maxine' ♀[H7]	CBct ECtt EPPr EUJe GBin GCal GQue LRHS MPie NLar NWad SHar SPad WCAu WCot WSHC
cordifolia	Widely available
– 'Flore Pleno' (d)	CBct
– 'Jelle'	CBct EBee GBin WCAu
– 'Lunar Glow'	EBee ECtt ELan EPfP ESwi SRms WFar
– 'Purpurea'	CBcs CBod CMac CRos CWCL EBee ECha EHyd ELan EPfP GBin LBuc LCro LOPS LRHS MRav NBir NRHS SCob SPer SRms SWvt WFar XLum
– 'Rosa Schwester'	CBct ECha
– 'Rosa Zeiten' ♀[H7]	CBct GBin IMou
– 'Tubby Andrews' (v)	CBct CMac ECha EShb GEdr LEdu LRHS MAvo MBel MBrN NEgg NEoE NLar SRms WHil WHrl
– 'Vinterglöd'	CBod CRos EBee ELan ELon EPfP EUJe GMaP LRHS LSun MBel MGos NLar SWvt XLum
crassifolia	EPfP NAln SRms XLum
– DF 90028	CBct GBin
– 'Autumn Red'	CBct ECha
– 'Orbicularis'	see *B.* × *schmidtii*
I – var. ***pacifica***	XLum
– – 'Cally Gem'	GCal
'Croesus'	GBin
* ***cyanea***	WCot
'Dark Damsel'	CBct IBal
'David'	CBct EBee ECha EWes GBin
'Delbees'	see *B.* 'Ballawley' clonal
'Diamond Drops'	IBal
'Doppelgänger'	EBee
'Eden's Dark Margin'	CBct CBod ECtt ELan ELon GBin IKil MHol MNrw NLar WCot WHoo
'Eden's Magic Giant' ♀[H7]	CBct ECtt ELan ELon EUJe GBin GQue IKil LRHS MPie NEgg NLar SRms WCot WMoo XSen
emeiensis	CBct CDor GCal IMou LEdu WCot WPGP WSHC
– hybrid	MWat
'Eric Smith' ♀[H7]	ECha GCal SWvt WCAu
'Eroica' ♀[H7]	Widely available
'Evening Glow'	see *B.* 'Abendglut'
'Flower Joy'	GBin
§ 'Glockenturm'	CBct GBin
'Godfrey Owen'	EBee
'Harzkristall'	CBct CBod CDor CKel CMac CMea CPla CRos EHyd EPfP GBin GWyn LRHS NCou NRHS SHar SPoG STPC SWvt WSpi

	'Hellen Dillon'	see *B. purpurascens* 'Irish Crimson'
	'Herbstblute'	EPfP GBin WCAu
	'Ice Queen'	CBct CKel CMil EBee ELan EWTr GBin LLHF LPla MBel NLar SWvt WCAu WCot
	'Jo Watanabe'	CBct ECha MRav
	'Kashmir'	XLum
	'Lambrook'	see *B.* 'Margery Fish'
	'Little Pine'	WCot
§	'Margery Fish'	CBct CFis ECha SPer
	milesii	see *B. stracheyi*
§	'Morgenröte' ♀H6	CBcs CBct CBod CMac CRos ECha ELon EPfP GMaP LRHS LSRN MRav NHol NLar NSti SAko SCob SPer SRms SWvt WCAu WCFE WCot XSen
	'Morning Light'	ECtt
	MORNING RED	see *B.* 'Morgenröte'
	'Mrs Crawford'	ECha
	'Oeschberg'	CBct GBin GCal
	'Opal'	CBct EBee GBin
	'Overture'	Widely available
§	***pacumbis***	EBee GCal NBid NSti
	- B&SWJ 2693	WCru
	- CC 1793	SBch WCot
	- CC 3616	CBct
	'Pink Dragonfly'	CBct CMac CRos ECtt EHyd ELon EPfP LPla LRHS NAst NLar NRHS SCob SWvt WCAu WCot WFar
	'Pink Ice'	CBct CDor EBee WSHC
	'Pinneberg'	CBct EBee GBin
	'Pugsley's Pink' ♀H7	CBct ECha
§	***purpurascens*** ♀H5	CMac EBee EPfP GMaP LPot SPer WSpi
	- SDR 4548	GKev
	- var. ***delavayi*** ♀H5	CRos CWCL EHyd LRHS NLar NRHS SRms
§	- 'Irish Crimson' ♀H7	CBct ECha WCot
	aff. ***purpurascens***	NGdn
	'Purpurglocken'	ECtt GCal WCAu
	'Red Beauty'	CPla EPfP
	'Red Rush'	EBee
	'Rietheim'	CBct EBee GBin
	'Rosenkristall'	CRos EHyd LRHS NRHS
	'Rosi Klose'	CBct CDor CRos EBee ECha ECtt EHoe EHyd ELon EWes GBin LRHS MHol MRav NGdn NRHS WCot WFar
	'Rosi Ruffles'	EBee
	'Rotblum'	CBct EHoe ELon EPfP GMaP LBuc NBir NGdn NGrd NRHS SCob SRkn
	'Sakura' (Dragonfly Series)	CWCL EBee GBin MNrw
§	× ***schmidtii***	CBct CMac GBin MRav NBir NLar
	'Schneekissen'	CBct CMac ECtt EHyd LRHS MCot NRHS WCAu WGwG
§	'Schneekoenigin'	CBct ECha GBin GCal SWvt WCot
§	'Silberlicht' ♀H6	Widely available
	SILVERLIGHT	see *B.* 'Silberlicht'
	'Simply Sweet'	WCot
	SNOW QUEEN	see *B.* 'Schneekoenigin'
	'Spring Fling'	GBin
§	***stracheyi***	CBct CExl ECha GBin GCal GKev NBid NLar WCot
	- Alba Group	ECha GCal
	'Sunningdale' ♀H7	CBcs CBct CBod CMac ECha EHyd ELan EPfP GMaP LRHS MRav NBir NGdn NRHS SWvt WAvo WCAu
	'Tim'	EBee
	'Walter Kienli'	GBin
	WINTER FAIRY TALES	see *B.* 'Wintermärchen'
§	'Wintermärchen' ♀H7	CBct CBod CChe CRos ECha ELan ELon EPfP EShb GWyn LRHS MMuc MRav NHol NRHS SCob SEND SPoG SRms SWvt WCot WMoo
	'XXL'	WCot

Bergenia × *Mukdenia* see × *Mukgenia*

Bergera (*Rutaceae*)

§	***koenigii***	EOHP SCit SPre SVen WSFF

Bergeranthus (*Aizoaceae*)

vespertinus	XLum

Berkheya (*Asteraceae*)

cirsiifolia	EBee SMad SPhx
'Helios'	GCal
macrocephala	SPlb
multijuga	CRos EHyd LRHS NRHS
- 'Golden Spike'	WHil
purpurea	CAby CBcs CDor CRos CSpe ECha EHyd ELon EPfP LRHS MHol MNrw NRHS SPlb WCot WHer WKif WTor
- 'Silver Spike'	EPfP NGdn
- 'Zulu Warrior'	CMac
radula	EBee GCal

Berlandiera (*Asteraceae*)

lyrata	CBod CRos EHyd GEdr LRHS NRHS

Berneuxia (*Diapensiaceae*)

thibetica	IBlr

Berula (*Apiaceae*)

erecta	NPer

Berzelia (*Bruniaceae*)

galpinii	SPlb
intermedia	LRHS
lanuginosa new	CKel

Beschorneria (*Asparagaceae*)

albiflora	EBee WCot
calcicola	WCot
'Red Bells'	WCot
rigida	WCot
septentrionalis	CAby CBod CDTJ CRos ESwi EUJe IKil LRHS LSun MBNS MHol NGBl SPad WCot WGrn
- variegated (v)	WCot
tubiflora	CDTJ
wrightii	WCot
yuccoides ♀H3	CAbb CBcs CExl CPla SEND SPlb
- 'Quicksilver'	CBcs CCCN CEnd CExl ELan EPfP LRHS SPoG WGrn WPav

Bessera (*Asparagaceae*)

elegans	CAby CAvo CGrW EPot GKev LAma SDeJ WCot

Besseya (*Plantaginaceae*)

alpina	LLHF
wyomingensis	GKev

Beta (*Amaranthaceae*)

vulgaris	WHer
- subsp. ***maritima***	CAgr CFGn

Betonica see *Stachys*

Betula ✿ (*Betulaceae*)

alba	see *B. pendula*, *B. pubescens*
albosinensis misapplied	see *B. utilis*
albosinensis Burkill	CBrP CLnd CMCN EMOT EPfP MMuc SEND
- 'Bowling Green'	CExl CJun MBlu WPGP
§ - 'China Rose' 🏆H7	CJun EBee EPfP WMat WPGP
- 'China Ruby' K.Ashburner	see *B. albosinensis* 'China Rose'
- 'China Ruby' ambig.	CJun CLnd EPfP
- 'China Ruby' B. Humphrey 🏆H7	CBcs
- 'Chinese Garden'	CJun EBee MBlu WPGP
- 'Chris Lane'	CJun WPGP
- clone F	see *B. albosinensis* 'Ness'
- hybrid	CDul
- 'Joseph Rock'	CJun
- 'K.Ashburner'	CJun CTho
§ - 'Ness'	CJun CTho
- 'Pink Champagne'	CBcs CJun EBee EPfP MBlu WPGP
- 'Red Panda' 🏆H7	CJun EBee LRHS WMat WPGP
- 'Rhinegold'	MBlu
- 'Sable'	SLim
- var. ***septentrionalis***	CBcs CCVT CDul CEnd CLnd CMac CTho EBee ECrN ELan ELon EPfP GBin MBlu MGos MMuc MRav MSwo NWea SCob SGol SLim SPer WMou WPGP WSpi
- - PDM 752	WPGP
- - 'Kansu'	CEnd CJun CTsd EBee MBlu NOra WMat
- - 'Purdom'	CJun CLnd
cf. ***albosinensis*** Burkill new	EWTr
§ ***alleghaniensis***	CBcs CCVT CDul CMCN EPfP MMuc NLar SEND WCru
ashburneri	GKev
- S&L 5297	GKev
bomiensis new	GKev
chichibuensis	CJun CMCN GKev MMrt SPtp
chinensis	CMCN
'Conyngham'	CJun CTho MBlu SLau
costata misapplied	see *B. ermanii* 'Grayswood Hill'
costata ambig.	CMCN LMaj SGol
costata Trautv.	EBee MSwo
- 'Daleside'	EBee NDal NOra WMat
- 'Fincham Cream'	see *B. ermanii* 'Fincham Cream'
'Crimson Frost'	CKel EBee GBin
cylindrostachya	WPGP
dahurica Pall.	CBrP
- 'Maurice Foster'	CJun EBee MBlu WPGP
- 'Stone Farm'	CJun
ermanii	CBcs CCVT CDul CLnd CMCN CMac CNWT ECrN ELan EMOT GBin LMaj LPra MBlu MGos MMuc MRav NWea SCob SGol
- B&SWJ 8801 from South Korea	WCru
- B&SWJ 10852 from Aomori, Japan	WCru
- B&SWJ 12600 from South Korea	WCru
- 'Blush'	CJun EPfP MBlu SCoo
§ - 'Fincham Cream'	CJun
§ - 'Grayswood Hill' 🏆H7	CEnd CJun CLnd CMCN CSBt CTho EBee EPfP GBin LRHS MBlu SCoo SWvt WPGP
- 'Hakkoda Orange'	CJun CTho EMOT SCoo WPGP
- 'Holland'	IArd LMaj
- 'Kwanak Weeping'	CJun LLHF MBlu NWea SBir
- 'Mount Zao'	CJun EBee WPGP
- 'Polar Bear'	CJun CLnd EPfP MAsh MBlu NLar SCoo WMat
- 'Zao Purple'	CDul
'Fascination' 🏆H6	CBcs CCVT CDul CJun CLnd CMCN CNWT EBar EBee EPfP IArd LMaj LPra MBlu MGos NOra NWea SCob SCoo SLim SPer SSta WHCr WMat WSpi
'Fetisowii'	CDul CJun MBlu NOra WMat
fruticosa	see *B. humilis*
globispica	CJun
gmelinii	see *B. ovalifolia*
grossa	IDee
'Haywood'	WMat
'Hergest' 🏆H6	CJun EBee ECrN EPfP MGos NOra SLau WHCr WMat
§ ***humilis***	EBee
insignis	CJun EBee WPGP
- subsp. ***fansipanensis***	IArd IDee SAko
- - B&SWJ 11751	WCru
- - FMWJ 13149	WCru
'Inverleith'	see *B. utilis* var. *jacquemontii* 'Inverleith'
jacquemontii	see *B. utilis* var. *jacquemontii*
kamtschatica H. Buek	see *B. humilis*
lenta	CDul CMCN IArd IDee MBlu MMuc
luminifera	CJun EBee EBtc IArd WPGP
lutea	see *B. alleghaniensis*
maximowicziana	CDul CMCN EMOT MBlu NLar SGol WSpi
medwediewii	CDul CJun CMCN EBee EPfP GKev NLar WPGP
- 'Gold Bark' 🏆H7	CJun CMCN EPfP MBlu
megrelica	GKev
michauxii	EBee GKev NLar WCru
'Mount Apoi'	CJun
nana	CDul MRav NWea
- 'Glengarry'	EPot GCrg GEdr
nigra	CBcs CCVT CDul CEnd CMCN CNWT EBee ELan LMaj LPra MMuc NLar SCob SEWo SGol WMou WTSh
- 'Black Star'	CDul NOra WMat
§ - 'Cully'	CCVT CDul CLnd CMCN EBee ECrN LMaj LRHS NOra NWea SGol WHCr WMat
- HERITAGE	see *B. nigra* 'Cully'
- 'Little King'	CMCN
- 'Peter Collinson'	CJun
- 'Shiloh Splash'	SSta
- 'Summer Cascade' PBR	EBee LSRN MAsh NOra SLon WMat
- TECUMSEH COMPACT ('Studetec')	SGol
- Wakehurst form	EPfP SPer SPoG WPGP WSpi
§ ***ovalifolia*** MF 357	GKev
papyrifera	CAco CCVT CDul CLnd CMCN CMac CPer CTri EBee ECrN ELan EMOT EPfP LBuc MGos MMuc MSwo NOra NWea SCob SEND SGol SPer WMat WTSh
- 'Belle Vue'	EBee
- var. ***cordifolia*** 'Clarenville'	CJun
- var. ***papyrifera***	EBee
- 'Saint George'	CJun CTho EBee WHCr WMat
- 'Vancouver'	CTho
§ ***pendula***	Widely available
- 'Black Prince'	WHCr
- f. ***crispa***	see *B. pendula* 'Laciniata'
- 'Dalecarlica' misapplied	see *B. pendula* 'Laciniata'

	- 'Dalecarlica' ambig.	CBcs ECrN EMOT LPra LRHS MRav NOra SWvt WFar WHCr WMat WTSh
	- 'Fastigiata'	CCVT CDul CJun CLnd CSBt CTho EBee ECrN ELan EMOT LPra LRHS MGos SCoo SGol SPer
	- FASTIGIATA JOES ('Jolep1') **new**	SPoG
	- 'Golden Beauty'	CDul CMac EMOT EUJe MAsh MGos MJak NOra NWea SGol SLim WMat
	- 'Golden Cloud'	MJak
§	- 'Laciniata' ♀H7	CDul CMCN CMac EBee ELan LMaj MAsh MBlu MGos MSwo SCob SCoo SGol SPer WCFE WMou WTSh
	- 'Long Trunk'	CDul LLHF MBlu SGol SLim
	- 'Purpurea'	CCVT CDul CMCN CMac CSBt ECrN ELan EMOT GKin IDee LPra LSRN MGos MSwo NWea SCoo SGol SMad SPer WFar WTSh
	- 'Silver Grace'	CJun ECrN LSRN MBlu
§	- 'Spider Alley'PBR	CKel EBee EUJe GBin LRHS SLon WMat
	- 'Swiss Glory'	LMaj
	- 'Tristis' ♀H7	CBcs CCVT CDul CEnd CKel CLnd CMCN CMac CTho CTri EBee ECrN EMOT EPfP LMaj LPra LRHS LSRN MGos MRav MSwo NOra NWea SCob SGol SLim SPer WFar WMat WMou
	- 'Youngii'	Widely available
	- 'Zwitsers Glorie'	CDul CJun NLar
	platyphylla misapplied	see *B. platyphylla* subsp. *mandshurica*
	platyphylla Sukaczev DAKOTA PINNACLE ('Fargo')	CDul EBee NLar NOra SCoo WMat
§	- subsp. ***mandshurica***	MMuc
	populifolia	EBtc
	- 'Whitespire'	CDul
	potaninii	GKev
§	***pubescens***	CAco CCVT CDul CHab CPer CTho CTri EBee LMaj MMuc NWea SCob SEND WTSh
	- 'Armenian Gold'	CLnd
	raddeana	EBtc GKev
	'Royal Frost'	CBcs CDul EBee EUJe GQue LSRN MBlu NEgg NLar NWea SGol WMat
	'Silver Trestles'	see *B. pendula* 'Spider Alley'
	szechuanica 'Liuba White'	CJun MBlu
	tianschanica	CAco
§	***utilis***	CDul CMCN ECrN LMaj LPra NWea SSta
	- GWJ 9259	WCru
	- HWJK 2250	WCru
	- HWJK 2345	WCru
	- Sch 2168	EBee
	- S&L from Nepal	CDul
	- 'Bhutan Sienna'	CJun EBee WPGP
	- 'Buckland'	EBee
	- 'Buddha'	CJun EBee MBlu WPGP
	- 'China Bronze'	WPGP
	- 'Cobhay Amber'	CJun
	- 'Cobhay Sentinel'	CJun
	- 'Dark-Ness'	CJun EBee MBlu NOra SLon WHCr WMat WPGP
*	- 'Fastigiata'	CJun CLnd SSta
	- 'Forest Blush' ♀H7	CDul CJun EBee EPfP WPGP
	- 'Himalayan Pink'	CJun WSpi
§	- var. ***jacquemontii***	Widely available
	- - Polunin	WPGP
§	- - 'Doorenbos' ♀H7	Widely available
	- - 'Grayswood Ghost' ♀H7	CBcs CDul CEnd CJun CLnd CMCN CTho CTri ECrN ELan EPfP LCro LOPS LRHS MBlu NLar NOra SBir SLau SLim SPer SSta WHor WMat WPGP WSpi
§	- - 'Inverleith'	CDul CJun SCoo WPGP
	- - 'Jermyns' ♀H7	CBcs CDul CEnd CJun CLnd EPfP LRHS LSRN MBlu NOra SCoo SLau SLim SPer SSta SWvt WHCr WMat WPGP
	- - 'McBeath'	SLau
	- - 'Moonbeam'	CDul CJun CLnd CSBt EBee EHyd MAsh NWea SCoo SEWo SLim SPoG WHCr WMat
	- - 'Silver Shadow' ♀H7	CDul CEnd CJun CLnd CMCN CTho EBee EPfP LRHS LSRN MAsh MBlu NLar NOra NRHS NWea SCoo SLau SLim SPer SPoG SSta WHCr WMat WSpi
	- - 'Snow Leopard'	CJun WPGP
	- - 'Snow Queen'	see *B. utilis* var. *jacquemontii* 'Doorenbos'
	- - 'Trinity College'	CDul CJun LRHS MAsh MSwo SCoo WHCr WMat WPGP
	- 'Jim Russell' **new**	WPGP
	- 'Knightshayes'	CJun CTho EBee WPGP
	- 'Mount Luoji'	CJun EBee WPGP
	- 'Nepalese Orange'	CJun EBee EPfP WPGP
	- var. ***occidentalis*** 'Kyelang'	CJun
	- 'Park Wood' ♀H7	CJun EPfP WPGP
	- 'Polar Bear'	MBlu
	- var. ***prattii***	CJun CTho MBlu
	- 'Ramdana River'	CJun MBlu WPGP
	- 'Schilling'	CJun
	- 'Sichuan Red'	CJun
	- 'Silver Queen'	WSpi
	- subsp. ***utilis*** 'Edinburgh'	CJun LRHS WMat
	- 'Wakehurst Place Chocolate' ♀H7	CJun CSBt EBee GBin MBlu NWea SCoo SLim WSpi
	- 'White-Ness' **new**	MBlu
	cf. ***utilis***	CTri SGol
	verrucosa	see *B. pendula*

Biarum ✿ (*Araceae*)

S&L 604	WCot
SB&L 597	WCot
carratracense from Spain	WCot
davisii	LAma WCot
dispar SB&L 294	WCot
ditschianum from Turkey	WCot
marmarisense	EPot GKev WCot
rhopalospadix **new**	GKev
tenuifolium	WCot
- LB 295	WCot
- PB 357	WCot
- S&L 174	WCot
- subsp. ***abbreviatum*** MS 974	WCot
- subsp. ***arundanum***	GKev WCot
- subsp. ***galianii*** PB 435	WCot
- subsp. ***tenuifolium***	GKev
- subsp. ***zelebori***	WCot
- - CRL 502	WCot
- - LB 300	WCot
- - PB 224	WCot
- - PB 334	WCot

Bidens (*Asteraceae*)

	atrosanguinea	see *Cosmos atrosanguineus*
§	***aurea***	CCBP CFis EAJP ECtt EMor EPPr EWes LEdu MHol NPer WBor WFar WPGP XLum
	- cream-flowered	MNrw
	- 'Hannay's Lemon Drop'	CAby CFis CKno EAJP ECtt ELan ELon EMor EPPr EPfP ILea LEdu LPot MNrw SGbt SPoG SPtp SRms WBor WFar WMoo WPGP
*	- 'Lemon Queen'	SMad
	- 'Mellow Yellow'	WCot
	- 'Rising Sun'	ECtt EWes
	- 'Super Nova'	EPPr GCal
	- white-flowered	EBee ELon EMor EPPr GCal NSti WFar
	ferulifolia	NPer
	- 'Bee Alive' **new**	NPri
	- BEEDANCE PAINTED RED ('Sunbidevb 2')	SPoG
	- BEEDANCE PAINTED YELLOW ('Sunbidevb4') **new**	SPoG
	- 'Golden Eye'	ECtt SPoG
	- 'Golden Glory'	NPri
	- SUN DROP ('Danbid7346') **new**	NPri
	'Firelight' **new**	NPri
	heterophylla Ortega	see *B. aurea*
	heterophylla misapplied	CAby CRos ECtt MAsh MCot MHol MMuc MRav MWat WFar WHal WMoo XLum
	integrifolia	SMad
	'Pirate's Treasure'	ECtt
	'Rockstar'	CPla

Bignonia (*Bignoniaceae*)

capreolata	CCCN CRHN ECre WSHC
lindleyana	see *Clytostoma calystegioides*
tweedieana	see *Dolichandra unguis-cati*
unguis-cati	see *Dolichandra unguis-cati*

Bilderdykia see *Fallopia*

Billardiera (*Pittosporaceae*)

cymosa	CTsd
longiflora ♀H3	CBcs CMac CRos CSBt CTri EBee EHyd ELan EPfP EUJe GKev IArd ITim LRHS MAsh MGil MGos MMuc MRav SLim SPer SPoG SWvt
- 'Cherry Berry'	CBcs CFlo CRos EHyd ELan EPfP EUJe LRHS SMad SPer SPoG SRms SWvt
- 'Fructu-albo'	CBcs CFlo CRos EHyd ELan EPfP EWes LRHS NLar SLon SPer SPoG SWvt

Billbergia ✿ (*Bromeliaceae*)

	nutans	CCCN CHll EBak EShb ESwi EUJe LEdu NGBl SChr SEND SPlb WSFF
	- var. ***schimperiana***	EShb
*	- 'Variegata' (v)	CCCN CHll CPla EShb EUJe SChr WCot
	pyramidalis	XBlo
	'Santa Barbara' (v)	SChr
	× ***windii*** ♀H1b	EBak

Bismarckia (*Arecaceae*)

nobilis	CCCN

Bistorta see *Persicaria*

blackberry see *Rubus fruticosus*; also AGM Fruit Section

blackcurrant see *Ribes nigrum*; also AGM Fruit Section

Blechnum ✿ (*Blechnaceae*)

	alpinum	see *B. penna-marina* subsp. *alpinum*
	brasiliense ♀H1a	EShb ESwi ISha SPlb
	- 'Volcano'	CBcs CBdn EUJe IBal LBuc LCro LLWG LOPS LRHS SCob SPad SPoG WPGP
§	***chilense*** ♀H4	CBdn CDTJ CKel CLAP CRos EBee EHyd EPfP EShb EWes GAbr GBin GCal IBal IBlr ITim LEdu LRHS NBro NRHS SArc SPlb SRms WCru WMoo
	discolor	GCal
	fluviatile	CDTJ
	gibbum	CKel EShb ISha SPlb
	- 'Silver Lady'	ISha
	magellanicum misapplied	see *B. chilense*
	magellanicum (Desv.) Mett.	SPlb
	minus	CBdn
	nudum	CBdn CDTJ CKel ITim
	penna-marina	Widely available
§	- subsp. ***alpinum***	EBee ECha EPfP GEdr GKev NWad SBrt SHar WMoo
	- - BR 68	GEdr
	- 'Cristatum'	CLAP GAbr GEdr GWyn NWad
	spicant ♀H6	Widely available
	- ***incisum***	see *B. spicant* 'Rickard's Serrate'
§	- 'Rickard's Serrate'	CLAP
	tabulare misapplied	see *B. chilense*
	tabulare (Thunb.) Kuhn	CBcs CBdn CDTJ CKel EPfP WCot
	wattsii	EBee

Blepharocalyx (*Myrtaceae*)

§	***cruckshanksii***	CCCN CExl CRos CSde ELon IDee LRHS MGil SEND SVen WPGP
	- 'Heaven Scent'	see *B. cruckshanksii*

Blephilia (*Lamiaceae*)

ciliata	SPhx

Bletilla (*Orchidaceae*)

	sp.	NDav
	Brigantes gx	NLAp
	Coritani gx	NLAp
*	***formosana alba***	CBod
	hyacinthina	see *B. striata*
	Laneside Amos gx **new**	NLAp
	Laneside Sally gx **new**	NLAp
	Laneside Thea gx **new**	NLAp
	ochracea	CExl LAma NLAp
	Penway Dragon gx	CBod NLAp
	Penway Paris gx	NLAp
	Penway Sunset gx	NLAp
	sinensis	CExl
§	***striata*** ♀H4	CAby CBct CExl CTri EBee EPot GAbr GKev LAma LCro LEdu LOPS LRHS MHer MNrw MSCN NLAp NRHS SDeJ SPer WCot WFar WPGP XLum
	- ***alba***	see *B. striata* f. *gebina*
	- 'Albostriata'	CBct CExl ELan LAma WCot XLum

	- BLUE DRAGON	see *B. striata* 'Soryu'
	- blue-flowered	GKev
§	- f. ***gebina***	CExl CTri EBee GKev LCro LEdu LOPS LRHS NLAp NRHS SDeJ SPer WCot WPGP
	- - variegated (v)	EBee GKev LEdu NLAp WHlf
	- 'Junpaku'	NLAp
	- 'Kuchi-beni'	EBee LAma NLAp WHlf
	- 'Lips'	GKev NLAp
	- purple-flowered	GKev
	- 'Shi-ran'	CBod EBee WHlf
§	- 'Soryu'	GKev LAma MHol NLAp
	- variegated (v)	GKev
	- yellow-flowered	GKev NLAp

blueberry see *Vaccinium corymbosum*; also AGM Fruit Section

Blumea (*Asteraceae*)

balsamifera	CHab

Bocconia (*Papaveraceae*)

cordata	see *Macleaya cordata* (Willd.) R. Br.
frutescens B&SWJ 10654	WCru
microcarpa	see *Macleaya microcarpa*

Boehmeria (*Urticaceae*)

nivea	WCot
platanifolia	IMou
sieboldiana	EBee EPPr SBrt WFar
tricuspis	IMou

Boenninghausenia (*Rutaceae*)

albiflora B&SWJ 1479	WCru
- pink-flowered B&SWJ 3112	WCru

Bolax (*Apiaceae*)

	glebaria	see *B. gummifer*
§	***gummifer***	EPot GEdr GKev WAbe WFar

Bolboschoenus (*Cyperaceae*)

§	***maritimus***	SMea

Boltonia (*Asteraceae*)

asteroides	GQue MMuc NGrd NWsh SPer XLum
- var. ***latisquama***	GMaP MHol MRav NCGa NLar SHar WBor WHal
- - JIM CROCKETT ('Masbolimket'PBR)	EBee LRHS
- - 'Nana'	LPla NChi
- - 'Snowbank'	ELan WCAu WGoo
decurrens	CBod EBee EPPr IMou WBor
incisa	see *Kalimeris incisa*

Bomarea (*Alstroemeriaceae*)

	acuminata	see *B. andreana*
	acutifolia	WCot
	- B&SWJ 14291 **new**	WCru
	- F&M 104	WPGP
§	***andreana*** B&SWJ 14310	WCru
	- B&SWJ 14376	WCru
	aff. ***andreana*** B&SWJ 10617	WCru
	boliviensis misapplied	see *Alstroemeria isabellana*
	boliviensis Baker	WCot
	aff. ***bredemeyerana*** B&SWJ 14706 **new**	WCru
	caldasii	see *B. multiflora*
	costaricensis	EBee GCal
	- B&SWJ 10467	WCru
	distichifolia	CExl WCru
§	***edulis*** ♀H3	CAvo CHll CRHN EWld MGil SBrt WCot WPav
	- B&SWJ 9017	WCru
	- F&M 104	CExl
	'Fiesta'	WCot
	frondea	see *B. multiflora*
	aff. ***frondea*** B&SWJ 10681	WCru
	hirsuta B&SWJ 14442	WCru
	- B&SWJ 14902	WCru
	hirtella	see *B. edulis*
§	***multiflora*** ♀H2	CBcs CCCN CExl CPbh EBee GCal WCru WSHC
	- B&SWJ 14347 **new**	WCru
	- B&SWJ 14354 **new**	WCru
	- B&SWJ 14406 **new**	WCru
	- B&SWJ 14419	WCru
	- B&SWJ 14847 **new**	WCru
	aff. ***multiflora*** B&SWJ 14730 **new**	WCru
	'Orange Sunset'	WCot
	patacocensis JCA 13987	WCot
	patinii B&SWJ 14310 **new**	WCru
	- B&SWJ 14895 **new**	WCru
	puracensis B&SWJ 14705 **new**	WCru
	salsilla ♀H3	CAvo CCCN CPla SBrt
	setacea B&SWJ 14875 **new**	WCru

Bombax (*Malvaceae*)

ceiba	SPlb

Bongardia (*Berberidaceae*)

chrysogonum	CAvo CRos EHyd EPot GKev LLHF LRHS NRHS

Bonia (*Poaceae*)

§	***solida***	ERod MMuc MWht SEND XCre

Boquila (*Lardizabalaceae*)

trifoliolata	WCru

borage see *Borago officinalis*

Borago (*Boraginaceae*)

	laxiflora	see *B. pygmaea*
	officinalis	CCBP CHby CLau ENfk EPfP GPoy LCro LOPS MHer MNHC NBir NPri SRms SVic
	- 'Alba'	CBre CLau ENfk SRms WJek
	- 'Bill Archer' (v)	CNat
§	***pygmaea***	CExl CSpe ELan GCal LEdu MHer MNrw NBir NChi NSti SPhx SRms WHer WJek WMoo

borecole see AGM Vegetables Section

Borinda (*Poaceae*)

KR 4558	ERod
KR 5287	MWht
KR 5600	MWht
KR 5950	ERod
KR 6438	MWht
KR 6439	MWht
KR 7346	MWht
KR 7613	MWht
KR 7662	MWht
albocerea ♀H4	EPfP ERod MWht
- Yunnan 1	ERod
- Yunnan 2	CDTJ ERod

- Yunnan 3a	CDTJ ERod
- Yunnan 3b	ERod
- Yunnan 4	see *B. lushuiensis* Yunnan 4
angustissima	CDTJ CExl EPfP ERod MMuc MWht XCre
boliana	SSut
frigida	CDTJ
- KR 4059	ERod MWht
fungosa	XCre
grossa	CDTJ
- KR 5931	MWht
§ ***lushuiensis*** Yunnan 4	CDTJ MWht
macclureana KR 5051	MWht
- KR 5177 from Gyala, Nepal	ERod ESwi MWht
- KR 5602	ERod
- KR 5950	ERod
- KR 6236	ESwi
- KR 6243	ERod
- KR 6400 from Show La	ESwi
- KR 6438 from Pasm Tso	ESwi
aff. ***macclureana*** KR 6900	MWht
nujiangensis	CBct CDTJ
papyrifera	ERod WPGP XCre
- CS 1046	CBdn CJun MWht
scabrida	*Fargesia scabrida*
Yunnan 4	see *B. lushuiensis* Yunnan 4

Boronia (*Rutaceae*)

crenulata	CBcs CCCN
heterophylla	CAbb CBcs CCCN CSde CTsd EBee EPfP IDee LRHS MPkF SEle WCot
- 'Ice Charlotte'	CCCN SEle

Bossiaea (*Papilionaceae*)

riparia	SPlb
scolopendria	SPlb

Bothriochloa (*Poaceae*)

§ ***bladhii***	CKno EPPr SRms
caucasica	see *B. bladhii*

Bougainvillea (*Nyctaginaceae*)

'Alexandra'	CCCN SPre
'Brilliant' misapplied	see *B.* × *buttiana* 'Raspberry Ice'
§ × ***buttiana*** 'Raspberry Ice' (v)	EShb
glabra ♀H2	EShb SPre
§ - 'Sanderiana'	EUJe
'Sanderiana'	see *B. glabra* 'Sanderiana'
'Sentimento'	CCCN
'Tropical Rainbow'	see *B.* × *buttiana* 'Raspberry Ice'
Vera Series	CCCN

Boussingaultia (*Basellaceae*)

baselloides Hook.	see *Anredera cordifolia*

Bouteloua (*Poaceae*)

curtipendula	CBod
§ ***gracilis***	CAby CRos EBee EHoe EHyd LRHS MBel NRHS SMad SMea XSen

Bouvardia (*Rubiaceae*)

× ***domestica***	EShb
ternifolia	CWGN EBee ESwi SMad WCot

Bowiea (*Asparagaceae*)

volubilis	GKev

Bowkeria (*Stilbaceae*)

sp.	CCCN
cymosa	SPlb SVen
verticillata	CBcs

Boykinia (*Saxifragaceae*)

aconitifolia	CElw CMac GEdr GKev GLog IMou MRav NRya SMad WCru WMoo WSHC
elata	see *B. occidentalis*
heucheriformis	see *B. jamesii*
§ ***jamesii***	GKev
lycoctonifolia	LEdu NLar
major	EBee
§ ***occidentalis***	WCru WMoo WPtf XLum
rotundifolia	NBir WCru WMoo
tellimoides	see *Peltoboykinia tellimoides*

boysenberry see *Rubus* 'Boysenberry'

Brachychilum see *Hedychium*

Brachychiton (*Malvaceae*)

acerifolius	SPlb
populneus	CBcs SPlb
§ ***rupestris***	EShb

Brachyglottis (*Asteraceae*)

§ ***bidwillii***	WCot
- 'Basil Fox'	WAbe
§ ***compacta***	CRos EHyd ELan EPfP LRHS MAsh SPer
'County Park'	SCob
(Dunedin Group) 'Drysdale'	CKel CRos EBee EHyd ELan EPfP LRHS NRHS SLon SWvt
§ - 'Moira Reid' (v)	CExl CTsd
§ - 'Sunshine' ♀H4	CAgr CBar CBod CDul CKel CRos CSBt CTri EBee EHyd ELan EPfP LCro LOPS LRHS MGos MJak MMuc MRav MSwo NPer NRHS SCob SEND SLim SPer SPlb SRms SWvt
'Frosty'	MJak
greyi misapplied	see *B.* (Dunedin Group) 'Sunshine'
§ ***greyi*** (Hook. f.) B. Nord.	CMac SGol
huntii	SVen
huntii × ***stewartii***	SEND
laxifolia misapplied	see *B.* (Dunedin Group) 'Sunshine'
§ ***monroi***	CBcs CMac CRos CSBt CTsd EHoe EHyd ELan EPfP LRHS MAsh MRav SGol SLon SVen WFar
repanda 'Purpurea'	CBcs
- var. ***rangiora***	CTsd
§ ***rotundifolia***	CCCN EBee ELan
'Silver Waves'	CCht
I 'Sunshine Improved'	CBcs EHoe MAsh
'Sunshine Variegated'	see *B.* (Dunedin Group) 'Moira Reid'
WALBERTON'S SILVER DORMOUSE ('Walbrach'PBR) ♀H4	CBct CKel CRos CSBt EBee EHyd EPfP GBin LRHS MGos MRav NEgg NRHS SCob SPoG SWvt

Brachypodium (*Poaceae*)

pinnatum	EPPr
sylvaticum	CHab MMuc SEND

Brachyscome (*Asteraceae*)

rigidula	CPBP
'Royal Blue' **new**	NPri

Brachystachyum (*Poaceae*)

densiflorum	ERod XCre

Bracteantha see *Xerochrysum*

Brahea (*Arecaceae*)

armata ♀H1c	CBrP CDTJ CPHo EPfP EShb EUJe SPlb WCot
edulis	CCCN CPHo SChr
'Super Silver'	WCot

Brassaia see *Schefflera*

Brassica (*Brassicaceae*)

japonica	see *B. juncea* var. *crispifolia*
juncea	SVic
§ - var. ***crispifolia***	MNHC
- 'Red Giant'	LCro LOPS
oleracea	CAgr SVic WHer
- var. ***ramosa***	LEdu NGrd
- - 'Cotswold Cream' (v)	WCot
- - 'D'Aubenton Panaché' (v)	WCot
rapa	LCro LOPS
* - var. ***japonica***	MNHC
- subsp. ***nipposinica*** var. ***laciniata***	SVic

× *Brigandra* (*Gesneriaceae*)

calliantha	WAbe

Briggsia × *Opithandra* see × *Brigandra*

Brighamia (*Campanulaceae*)

insignis	CCCN

Brillantaisia (*Acanthaceae*)

kirungae	CCCN
owariensis	CSpe

Brimeura (*Asparagaceae*)

§ ***amethystina*** ♀H5	CExl GBin LEdu NAln SBrt SDeJ SPhx WPGP WThu
- 'Alba'	NAln SDeJ SPhx

Briza (*Poaceae*)

maxima	EHoe IKil LPot NGdn NSti NWad SHar SPhx
media	Widely available
- 'Golden Bee'	CKno CRos CWCL EHoe EHyd ELon EPPr EPfP EWes LEdu LRHS MMrt NDov NLar NRHS SMad SPhx WPGP
- 'Limouzi'	CElw CKno CRos EHoe EHyd ELon EPPr EUJe GCal LEdu LRHS MAvo NAln NDai NRHS NSti NWsh SMad SMea SPoG WPGP XLum
- 'Romany Silver'	LEdu
- 'Russells'[PBR]	CBod CKno CRos EBee EHoe EHyd ELan EPfP LEdu LPot LRHS MGos NAln NRHS NWsh SCob SMea SPer SPoG SRms SWvt
subaristata	EPPr
triloba	CRos EAJP EHyd LRHS NRHS NWsh SMea SPhx

broccoli see AGM Vegetables Section

Brodiaea (*Asparagaceae*)

§ ***californica***	CSpe EBee ERCP GKev WCot
- NNS 00-109	WCot
- 'Babylon'	ERCP GKev
'Corrina'	see *Triteleia* 'Corrina'
ida-maia	see *Dichelostemma ida-maia*
laxa	see *Triteleia laxa*
peduncularis	see *Triteleia peduncularis*

Bromus (*Poaceae*)

erectus	CHab
- W&B BG B-5	WCot
inermis 'Skinner's Gold' (v)	EBee EHoe EPPr NLar SMea WCot

Broussonetia (*Moraceae*)

kazinoki	EBee
papyrifera	CBcs CDul CMCN CTsd EBtc ELan ESwi MGil SPer WAvo WBor WCot
- 'Billardii'	NLar
- 'Laciniata'	EBee IDee SMad

Browallia (*Solanaceae*)

from Sikkim	CSpe
americana	SPhx

Bruckenthalia see *Erica*

Brugmansia (*Solanaceae*)

'Angel's Sunbeam'	ELan
§ ***arborea***	CBcs CDTJ IDee
§ - 'Knightii' (d) ♀H1c	CDTJ
- 'Rosea' variegated (v)	ELan
- variegated (v)	ELan
aurea	CCCN SAdn
'Baby Doll' (d) **new**	CHll
× ***candida***	CCCN
§ - 'Grand Marnier' ♀H1c	CHll CSam
- 'Plena'	see *B. arborea* 'Knightii'
§ - 'Variegata' (v)	CCCN CDTJ CHll CSam
double orange-flowered (d) **new**	CHll
'Flowerdream' (d)	EUJe
§ × ***insignis***	CHll
§ - pink-flowered	SEND
§ ***sanguinea***	CCCN EUJe GCal SEND SPlb
- 'Rosea'	see *B.* × *insignis* pink-flowered
§ ***suaveolens*** ♀H1c	CBcs CHll EUJe
- 'Flore Pleno' (d)	EUJe
- ***rosea***	see *B.* × *insignis* pink-flowered
- 'Variegata' (v)	EShb
- yellow-flowered	EShb
suaveolens × ***versicolor***	see *B.* × *insignis*
'Variegata Sunset'	see *B.* × *candida* 'Variegata'
versicolor misapplied	see *B. arborea*
§ ***versicolor*** Lagerh.	CCCN
* 'Yellow Trumpet'	ELan

Brunfelsia (*Solanaceae*)

americana	CCCN WFib
australis	WFib
calycina	see *B. pauciflora*
lactea	CCCN
§ ***pauciflora*** ♀H1c	CCCN ELan EShb

Brunia (*Bruniaceae*)

albiflora	CKel SPlb
noduliflora 'Bubbles' **new**	CKel

Brunnera ✿ (*Boraginaceae*)

§ ***macrophylla***	Widely available
- 'Agnes Amez'	IMou
- 'Aimee Angus'	EPPr
- 'Alba'	see *B. macrophylla* 'Betty Bowring'

- 'Alexanders Great'[PBR] CAby CBod CPla CSpe EBee ECtt ELan EMor EUJe GBin IMou MAvo MBel MNrw MPnt NBid NCou NEgg NLar NSti SCob SHeu SPad SPoG WCot WFar WSpi
§ - 'Betty Bowring' Widely available
- 'Blaukuppel' EWes GCal NBir
- 'Dawson's White' (v) CBcs CDor CRos CWCL ECha ECtt ELan ELon EMor EPfP GKev GMaP IKil LRHS NAln NBid NBir NHpl NLar NRHS SCob SPer SRms SWvt WBor WCAu WCot WFar
- 'Diane's Gold'[PBR] CBcs EBee ECha ECtt MGos MHol MNrw MPnt NLar SCob SHeu
- 'Emerald Mist'[PBR] (v) CBod EBee ECtt EMor GBin MGos MTin NLar SWvt WSpi
- 'Golden Jack Frost' MPnt
- 'Gordano Gold' (v) EHoe NBir WCot
- 'Green Gold' (v) EMor IMou WFar
- 'Hadspen Cream' (v) ♀H6 Widely available
- 'Henry's Eyes' EBee ECtt EPfP
- 'Jack Frost'[PBR] ♀H6 Widely available
- 'Jack's Gold' **new** MBel SMad
- 'Jennifer' MBel WCAu
- 'Joanna' **new** NSum
- 'King's Ransom'[PBR] (v) CBct CNor CWGN ECtt GPSL NLar NSti WFar
- 'Langford Hewitt' (v) MNrw
- 'Langtrees' CBct CMac EBee ECha EHyd GAbr GBin GCal LRHS MCot MHol MMuc NBir NEgg NGdn NRHS SEND WCFE WSpi
- 'Little Jack' (v) CRos EBee EHyd EMor LRHS NRHS SPoG
- 'Looking Glass'[PBR] ♀H6 Widely available
- 'Marley's White' ELan SCob SGbt
§ - 'Mister Morse'[PBR] (v) ♀H6 Widely available
- 'Sea Heart'[PBR] CKel CMea EBee ECtt EWTr GBin IPot NLar SCob SHeu
- 'Silver Heart'[PBR] CWGN ECtt EMor LSun MCot MTis SCob SHeu SPad WBor WPnP
- 'Silver Spear' EBee MHol NGBl WCot WHoo WRHF
- 'Silver Wings' CBod CElw CRos CWCL EBee ECtt EHyd EMor EPfP GEdr GKev LRHS MBel MGos NAln NBir NGdn NLar NRHS NSti NWad WCAu WFar
- 'Spring Yellow' ECtt WCAu
- 'Starry Eyes' MSCN MTis SCob

'Mrs Morse' see *B. macrophylla* 'Mister Morse'
sibirica CElw EBee EPPr EWes NBid

Brunsvigia (*Amaryllidaceae*)

bosmaniae WCot
- white-flowered WCot

elandsmontana WCot
grandiflora WCot
gregaria WCot
josephinae WCot
- LAV 30394 WCot

litoralis WCot
marginata WCot
multiflora see *B. orientalis*
§ ***orientalis*** WCot
pulchra WCot
radulosa WCot
rosea 'Minor' see *Amaryllis belladonna*

Brussels sprouts see AGM Vegetables Section

Bryonia (*Cucurbitaceae*)

dioica GPoy NMir

Bryophyllum see *Kalanchoe*

Buddleja ✿ (*Scrophulariaceae*)

agathosma CExl SLon WKif WLav WSHC
albiflora SLon WLav
alternifolia ♀H6 Widely available
- KR 4881 GKev
- 'Argentea' CBcs CKel CRos EHyd ELan EPfP LRHS MBNS MRav NLar SPer SPoG SWvt WCot WLav
- UNIQUE ('Pmoore12') LCro LOPS SLon SPoG

asiatica ♀H3 CSde EShb SLon WLav
- B&SWJ 11278 WCru

asiatica* × *lindleyana WSpi
auriculata CBcs CExl CHll CMCN CRos CSde EBee ELan EPfP IArd IDee LRHS MGil NSti SLon SPlb SVen WGwG WLav
'Bel Argent' EBee WPGP
'Blue Chip'[PBR] (Lo and Behold Series) CKel CRos EHyd EPfP LBuc LRHS MAsh MGos MJak NLar NRHS SCob SGol SLim SLon SRms SWvt WCot WFar WLav
'Blue Chip Junior' (Lo and Behold Series) **new** SPoG
* 'Blue Trerice' CExl
caryopteridifolia EBtc SEND SLon
colvilei CAby CBcs CCCN CDul CKel ELan EPfP GBin GCal GKin IArd IDee LRHS SBrt SLon SWvt WBor WHer WSpi
- B&SWJ 2121 WCru
- GWJ 9399 WCru
- WJC 13760 WCru
- 'Kewensis' CExl CRHN CWld EPfP EWes GCal MGil NEgg NLar SLon SVen WCFE WCru WLav WSHC
- large-leaved **new** SBrt
- pink-flowered MGil NLar

cordata SLon
- B&SWJ 10433 WCru

coriacea SLon
CRAN RAZZ ('Boscranz') **new** WTyc
§ ***crispa*** CBcs CBct CExl CKel CRos CSpe EBee ECha EHyd ELan EPfP LRHS SLon SPer SRkn SVen SWvt WFar WKif WPGP WSHC WSpi
- var. ***farreri*** EUJe MGil SLon SPoG
- 'Stone House Cottage' WSHC

crotonoides subsp. ***amplexicaulis*** SLon
davidii CCVT CPer NAln NPol NWea SCob WTSh
- B&SWJ 8083 WCru
- ADONIS BLUE ('Adokeep'[PBR]) CBcs CRos CSBt EHyd EMOT LBuc LRHS MAsh SLon SPoG WLav
- 'African Queen' SLon WLav
§ - 'Autumn Beauty' CAni SLon WLav
- 'Autumn Delight' SLon
- 'Bath Beauty' CAni
- 'Beijing' see *B. davidii* 'Autumn Beauty'
- 'Bishop's Velvet' CAni
- 'Black Knight' ♀H6 Widely available
- 'Blue Eyes' WLav
- 'Blue Horizon' ♀H6 CAni SLon WCot WLav WMoo WRHF
- 'Border Beauty' CAni NHic SCob SLon WLav

	- 'Brown's Beauty'	CAni
	- 'Butterfly Heaven'PBR	WLav
	- Buzz Series	LBuc NHol SLon
	- - BUZZ CANDY PINK ('Tobudsopin')	CRos EHyd LRHS NRHS SPoG
	- - BUZZ HOT RASPBERRY **new**	CNor NPer
	- - BUZZ INDIGO	CBod CRos EHyd ELan LRHS NRHS
	- - BUZZ IVORY ('Tobudivory'PBR)	CEnd CMac CRos EBee EHyd ELan ELon EMOT EPfP ESwi LRHS LSRN MGos MJak NHol NLar NRHS SLim SLon SPer SPoG WCot WLav WSpi
	- - BUZZ LILAC	ELan MGos NHol SCob SLon
	- - BUZZ MAGENTA ('Tobudpipur'PBR)	CChe CEnd CKel CMac CMea CRos EHyd ELan ELon EMOT LRHS LSRN MGos MJak NEgg NHol NLar NPri NRHS SCob SLon SPad SPoG SRms SWvt WFar WLav WSpi
	- - BUZZ SKY BLUE ('Tobudskybl'PBR)	CKel CMac CRos EHyd EPfP LRHS MGos NEgg NHol NLar NPri NRHS SPad SPoG SRms WFar WHil WLav
	- - BUZZ VELVET ('Tobudvelve'PBR)	CBod CRos LRHS NRHS SPad SPer
	- - BUZZ VIOLET ('Tobudviole')	CKel CRos EHyd ELan ELon LRHS MGos NEgg NHol NLar NPri NRHS SLim SLon SPer SPoG SWvt WHil WLav
	- CAMBERWELL BEAUTY ('Camkeep') (English Butterfly Series) ♀H6	CHll LSRN SLon WGwG WLav
	- 'Car Wash'	CAni
	- 'Castle Blue'	SLon
	- 'Castle School'	CAni CSam WLav
§	- 'Charming'	CDul WMoo
	- 'Clive Farrell'	see *B. davidii* 'Autumn Beauty'
	- 'Corinne Tremaine'	WHer
	- 'Cotswold Blue'	WLav
	- 'Darent Valley' ♀H6	SLon
	- 'Dartmoor' ♀H6	Widely available
	- 'Dart's Ornamental White'	MRav SLon WLav
	- 'Dart's Papillon Blue'	CAni SLon WLav
	- 'Dart's Purple Rain'	CAni SLon WLav
	- 'Dubonnet'	CAni SLon WLav
	- 'Dudley's Compact Lavender'	CAni
	- 'Ecolonia'	CAni SLon WLav
	- 'Empire Blue'	CAni CBcs CDul CKel CRos CSBt ECtt EHyd EPfP GKin LRHS LSRN MGos NBir NPer NRHS NWea SCob SEND SPer SPlb SPoG SRms SWvt WMoo XSen
	- 'Fair Lady'	WLav
	- 'Fascinating'	CAni GCal MRav NBir SLon WLav
	- 'Flaming Violet'	CAni SLon WLav
	- 'Florence'	LSRN NEgg NLar SLon WFar WMoo
	- 'Fortune'	CAni
	- 'Foxtail'	WLav
	- 'Glasnevin Hybrid'	CAni NLar SLon WLav
	- 'Gonglepod'	CAni SLon WLav
	- 'Greenway's River Dart'	CAni SLon
	- 'Grey Dawn'	WLav
	- 'Griffin Blue'	MAsh WLav
	- 'Gulliver'PBR	CRos EHyd EMOT LRHS NEgg NLar NRHS SGol SLon WFar WLav
	- 'Harlequin' (v)	Widely available
	- 'Île de France'	CAni NLar NWea SLon SRms WLav
	- 'Leela Kapila'	SLon
	- 'Les Kneale'	CAni SLon WLav
	- 'Lilac Moon'	WLav
	- 'Lyme Bay'	CAni

	- MARBLED WHITE ('Markeep'PBR) (English Butterfly Series)	CRos CSBt EHyd EShb LRHS NEoE NRHS SLon WLav
	- MASQUERADE ('Notbud') (v)	MRav SLon
	- MOONSHINE ('Buddma'PBR)	MTin NEgg NEoE WFar
§	- NANHO BLUE ('Mongo')	CAni CBcs CMac CRos CSBt EBee ECrN EPfP GBin GKev GKin LRHS MAsh MGos MJak MRav MSwo NAln NBir NLar NRHS SCob SGol SLim WMoo WSpi XSen
	- 'Nanho Petite Indigo'	see *B. davidii* NANHO BLUE
	- 'Nanho Petite Plum'	see *B. davidii* NANHO PURPLE
	- 'Nanho Petite Purple'	see *B. davidii* NANHO PURPLE
§	- NANHO PURPLE ('Monum') ♀H6	CBcs CMac CRos CTri EPfP LRHS LSRN MGos MRav NLar NRHS SCob SGol SLim SLon SPer SPlb SRms XSen
	- NANHO WHITE ('Monite') ♀H6	CMac CRos EPfP LRHS SCob SGol SLon SRms XSen
	- var. ***nanhoensis***	CAni CDul SEND SGol WFar WLav
	- - blue-flowered	EPfP NWad SLon SPer
	- 'Orchid Beauty'	CAni SLon WLav
	- 'Orpheus'	CAni SLon WLav
	- 'Panache'	CRos EHyd EPfP LRHS MAsh NRHS SLon WLav
	- 'Peace'	CMac CTri CWCL LSRN MRav NLar SLon SPoG WLav
	- PEACOCK ('Peakeep'PBR) (English Butterfly Series)	CSBt MAsh MJak NEgg SCob WLav
	- 'Persephone'	SLon WLav
	- 'Petite Indigo'	see *B. davidii* NANHO BLUE
	- 'Pink Beauty'	LSRN MBlu WFar
	- 'Pink Charming'	see *B. davidii* 'Charming'
	- 'Pink Pearl'	CAni SEND SLon WLav
	- 'Pink Spreader'	CAni SLon WLav
	- 'Pixie Blue'	CAni CRos LRHS MAsh NLar WLav
	- 'Pixie Red'	CAni CRos LBuc LRHS MAsh NLar SEND WLav
	- 'Pixie White'	LBuc MAsh NLar SEND SGol WLav
	- PURPLE EMPEROR ('Pyrkeep') (English Butterfly Series)	NBir NEgg SLon WLav
	- 'Purple Friend'	CAni SLon WLav
	- 'Purple Prince'	CAni
	- 'Red Admiral'	CAni LLHF SLon
	- RÊVE DE PAPILLON BLUE ('Minpap3')	WLav
	- RÊVE DE PAPILLON ('Minpap')	CRos EHyd LRHS MAsh NRHS WLav
	- 'Royal Purple'	CAni SLim SWvt
	- 'Royal Red' ♀H6	Widely available
	- 'Saith Ffynnon Early'	WSFF
	- 'Santana' (v)	Widely available
	- 'Shapcott Blue'	CAni
	- 'Shire Blue'	WLav
	- 'Southcombe Splendour'	CAni
	- 'Summer Beauty'	CAni CDul MBlu SLon WLav
	- 'Summer House Blue'	SLon WLav
	- 'Twotones'	WLav
	- 'Variegata' (v)	CAni MAsh SLon SWvt WLav
	- 'White Ball'	ELan NLar SLon WLav
	- 'White Bouquet'	CAni CCVT CSBt EPfP GKin MSwo NLar NWea SCob SEND SPer SWvt WLav XSen
	- 'White Cloud'	CAni EPfP SRms WGwG
	- 'White Harlequin' (v)	SLon WCFE
	- 'White Profusion' ♀H6	Widely available
	- 'White Wings'	SLon WLav
	- 'Widecombe'	CAni

Name	Suppliers
- 'Wisteria Lane' new	LCro LOPS LRHS
davidii* × *fallowiana	WSpi
§ ***delavayi***	CExl ECre GBin SEND WCru
DREAMING LAVENDER ('Hinebud1'PBR) new	WHlf
DREAMING ORANGE new	WTyc
DREAMING PURPLE ('Hinebud4') new	WHlf
DREAMING WHITE ('Hinebud3'PBR) new	WHlf WNPC
'Ellen's Blue'	CExl NLar WLav
fallowiana misapplied	see *B.* 'West Hill'
fallowiana Balf.f. & W.W.Sm.	CRos EHyd ELan LRHS WLav
- ACE 2481	LRHS
- BWJ 7803	WCru
- var. ***alba*** ♀H5	CMac CRos ECrN EHyd ELan EPfP LRHS MRav NLar NRHS SLon SPer
- 'Bishop's Violet'	CTsd
'Flower Power'	see *B.* × *weyeriana* 'Bicolor'
(Flutterby Flow Series)	LCro LOPS
FLUTTERBY FLOW LAVENDER ('Podaras 12'PBR)	
- FLUTTERBY LAVENDER ('Podaras 11'PBR)	CSBt
- FLUTTERBY PEACE ('Podaras 6'PBR)	CSBt NEgg
- FLUTTERBY PETITE BLUE HEAVEN ('Podaras 8'PBR)	CMea LCro LOPS MThu NLar
- FLUTTERBY PETITE DARK PINK ('Podaras 10'PBR)	LCro LOPS NLar SNig
- FLUTTERBY PETITE SNOW WHITE ('Podaras 15'PBR)	LCro LOPS
- FLUTTERBY PETITE TUTTI FRUITTI PINK ('Podaras 13'PBR)	LBuc LCro LOPS SRms
- FLUTTERBY PINK ('Podaras 9'PBR)	CCht CSBt
forrestii	WCru
- BWJ 8020	EBee WCru
globosa ♀H5	Widely available
- RCB/Arg C-11	WCot
- 'Cally Orange'	GCal WGwG
- cream-flowered HCM 98.017 new	WPGP
- 'Lemon Ball'	MBlu NPer SLon WLav
glomerata	EShb MGil SLon SPlb
- 'Silver Service'	CBod CKel LRHS
heliophila	see *B. delavayi*
'Ice Chip'PBR (Lo and Behold Series)	EPfP
indica	SLon WLav
INSPIRED PINK	see *B.* × *weyeriana* 'Pink Pagoda'
japonica	NEgg SLon
- B&SWJ 8912	WCru
× ***lewisiana*** 'Margaret Pike'	SLon
'Lilac Chip' (Lo and Behold Series)	LRHS NLar NRHS SGol
limitanea	CMCN SLon
- from Cangshan, Yunnan, China	SBrt
lindleyana	Widely available
- 'Little Treasure' new	NEoE SLon
aff. ***lindleyana***	EWTr GWyn WSpi
- B&SWJ 11478	WCru
'Lochinch' ♀H5	Widely available
longifolia	SLon
'Longstock Gem'	SLon
'Longstock Silver'	SLon

Name	Suppliers
loricata	CExl CKel CMCN CRos CTsd CWld EBee EHyd EPfP GBin GCal GWyn IDee LRHS MGil SLon SPlb WLav WSpi
macrostachya HWJ 602	WCru
- PAB 4198	LEdu
- WWJ 12016	WCru
§ ***madagascariensis*** ♀H2	CRHN EShb NLar SLon SPlb SVen
'Malvern Blue'	CAni
megalocephala B&SWJ 9106	WCru WPGP
'Miss Ruby'PBR ♀H5	CRos EBee EMOT EPfP LBuc LRHS LSRN MAsh NRHS SGol WLav
§ 'Morning Mist'PBR	CExl CKel CMac CRos CSBt CWGN EPfP LCro LOPS LRHS LSRN NHol NLar NRHS SCob SGol SLon SRms SWvt WCot WFar
myriantha	CExl EBee SLon WPGP
nappii	SLon
nicodemia	see *B. madagascariensis*
nivea	CExl MGil SLon WLav XSen
- B&SWJ 2679	WCru
- pink-flowered	SLon
aff. ***nivea***	WSpi
officinalis ♀H3	CExl CSde SLon WLav
paniculata	SLon WPGP
- GWJ 9286 from Sikkim	WCru
parvifolia	SLon
- MPF 148	WLav
× ***pikei*** 'Hever'	SRms XSen
'Pink Delight' ♀H5	Widely available
'Pink Micro Chip' (Lo and Behold Series) new	SPoG
'Pink Perfection'	CAni WFar
'Pride of Hever'	SDys
'Pride of Longstock'	SLon SPoG
pterocaulis	EBee
'Purple Chip' (Lo and Behold Series)	LRHS NRHS
'Red Chip' (Lo and Behold Series)	SGol
saligna	SLon
'Salmon Spheres'	SLon WLav
salviifolia	CBcs CBct CExl CMac CRos CSde CTsd CWCL EBee ELan IDee LRHS MBlu MGil NLar SBrt SEND SPlb SVen WGwG WHer WLav WPGP
- white-flowered	EBee SLon WPGP
SILVER ANNIVERSARY	see *B.* 'Morning Mist'
speciosissima new	WPGP
stachyoides	WLav
stenostachya	CExl SLon
sterniana	see *B. crispa*
SUGAR PLUM ('Lonplum'PBR)	CKel CRos CSBt EHyd EMil EPfP LBuc LCro LOPS LRHS MAsh NEgg NEoE NRHS SLon SPoG
tibetica	see *B. crispa*
tubiflora	SLon WLav
venenifera	SLon
- B&SWJ 895	WCru
- B&SWJ 6036	WCru
× ***wardii*** KR 4881	EBee WPGP
§ 'West Hill' ♀H5	CRos EHyd LRHS NRHS SLon WLav
× ***weyeriana***	CDul ECtt EWTr MBNS MGil MMuc MNrw MSwo NBir SPad SPlb SWvt WAvo WOut
§ - 'Bicolor'	EBee EPPr EPfP IDee LCro LLHF LOPS LSRN MNrw NLar NQui SCob SLon SRms WLav
- 'Boy Blue'	SLon WLav

	- 'Golden Glow'	CTri GBin GWyn LSRN NLar SLon SWvt WLav WSFF
	- 'Honeycomb'	EShb MGos NLar
	- 'Lady de Ramsey'	SEND
	- 'Moonlight'	CBcs CExl CRos ELan EPPr GBin GWyn SLon SPer WCot WLav WSpi
§	- 'Pink Pagoda'PBR	EPfP SLon SPoG
	- 'Sungold' ♀H6	Widely available
	'White Chip' (Lo and Behold Series)	LRHS NRHS SGol
	'Winter Sun'	SLon
	yunnanensis	CBcs GCal NLar SBrt SLon
	- B&SWJ 8146	WCru

Buglossoides (*Boraginaceae*)

§	***purpurocaerulea***	CHll CSpe ECha ELan EWld LPla MNrw NBid NChi SPhx WCot WFar WSHC XLum

Bukiniczia (*Plumbaginaceae*)

	cabulica	GKev XEll

Bulbine (*Asphodelaceae*)

	annua misapplied	see *B. semibarbata*
	bulbosa misapplied	see *B. semibarbata*
	caulescens	see *B. frutescens*
§	***frutescens***	CBod CHll MHer NChi SRms SVen
	- 'Hallmark'	CCCN
	latifolia	CCCN EBee
§	***semibarbata***	CCCN

Bulbinella (*Asphodelaceae*)

	angustifolia	GKev MHer
	hookeri	CExl CRos EBee EHyd GBee GBin GEdr GKev ITim LRHS NAln NRHS SRms WCot WHal WThu
	latifolia subsp. ***latifolia***	IBlr
	nutans	EBee

Bulbinopsis see *Bulbine*

Bulbocodium (*Colchicaceae*)

	vernum	EPot GKev LAma LLHF SDeJ

bullace see *Prunus insititia*

Bunias (*Brassicaceae*)

	orientalis	CAgr LEdu

Bunium (*Apiaceae*)

	bulbocastanum	CAgr IMou LEdu LRHS SPhx WHil WPGP
	ferulaceum	MHol
	- W&B BG B-10	WCot

Buphthalmum (*Asteraceae*)

	salicifolium	EBee ELan EMor EPfP MMuc NBro NGdn SPer SRms WCot WFar XLum
	- 'Alpengold'	CSam ECha GMaP NLar
	- 'Dora'	ECtt WCot WFar
	- 'Sunwheel'	CBod MHol SRms
	speciosum	see *Telekia speciosa*

Bupleurum (*Apiaceae*)

	angulosum	NBir
	- copper-leaved	see *B. longifolium*
	candollei	WSHC
	falcatum	CSpe ECha LPla LRHS NDov SPhx WCot
	fruticescens	XSen
	fruticosum	CBcs CCCN CCht CRos CSpe EBee ECre EHyd ELan EPfP EWes GBin LRHS NRHS SCob SEND SLon SMad SPer SPoG SPtp WCot WCru XSen
	- bronze-leaved	LRHS
	gibraltaricum	XSen
§	***longifolium***	CElw CFis CSpe EBee ECre EWes LEdu LRHS MNrw NBir NChi SBrt SMad WBor WFar WPGP
	- subsp. ***aureum***	LPla LRHS SPhx
	- 'Bronze Beauty'	GEdr SPtp
	ranunculoides	LPla SPhx XLum
	rotundifolium	CSpe IMou LEdu SPhx WCot
	- 'Copper'	NDov

Bursaria (*Pittosporaceae*)

	spinosa	CCCN

Butia (*Arecaceae*)

	capitata ♀H1c	CCCN CDTJ CPHo EUJe SArc
§	- var. ***odorata***	SPlb
	eriospatha	CPHo
	odorata	see *B. capitata* var. *odorata*

Butomus (*Butomaceae*)

	umbellatus	CBen CSpe CWat ECha EWat GBin MNrw MRav MWts NBir NPer WMAq WWtn XLum
	- 'Rosenrot'	EWat LLWG
	- 'Schneeweisschen'	EWat LLWG MWts

butternut see *Juglans cinerea*

butternut squash see AGM Vegetables Section (under squashes)

Buxus (*Buxaceae*)

	sp.	LPra
	aurea 'Marginata'	see *B. sempervirens* 'Marginata'
	balearica	WSpi
	'Green Gem'	NWad
	harlandii misapplied	CMen SRiv
	japonica 'Nana'	see *B. microphylla*
	macrophylla	WSpi
§	***microphylla***	NWad NWea SGol
	- 'Asiatic Winter'	see *B. microphylla* var. *japonica* 'Winter Gem'
§	- 'Compacta'	CMen LLHF MHer SRiv WCot
	- 'Curly Locks'	NWad
	- 'Faulkner' ♀H6	CCVT ELan EPfP LBuc LMaj MGos SCob SGol SPer SRiv SRms WSpi
	- 'Golden Triumph'PBR	NLar
	- 'Green Pillow'	MHer SRiv WSpi
	- 'Herrenhausen'	WSpi
	- var. ***japonica***	SGol
	- - 'National'	WSpi
§	- - 'Winter Gem'	MRav
	- 'John Baldwin'	SRiv
	- var. ***sinica***	WSpi
	sempervirens	Widely available
§	- 'Angustifolia'	MRav NWad SMad
	- 'Arborescens'	CNWT
	- 'Argenteo-variegata' (v)	MJak SGol WFar
	- 'Aurea'	see *B. sempervirens* 'Aureovariegata'
	- 'Aurea Maculata'	see *B. sempervirens* 'Aureovariegata'
	- 'Aurea Marginata'	see *B. sempervirens* 'Marginata'
§	- 'Aureovariegata' (v)	EPfP EShb MGos MRav NLar NWad SRiv SRms
	- 'Bentley Blue'	NWea

- 'Blauer Heinz'	ELan GQue MHer MRav NWea SRiv WSpi
- 'Bowles's Blue'	EWes WCFE
- clipped ball	EPfP LSRN MGos NLar SGol SRiv SRms
- clipped bird	SRiv
- clipped cone	LSRN SGol SRiv SRms
- clipped pyramid	EPfP LSRN MGos NLar SGol SRiv SRms
- clipped spiral	LSRN NLar SGol SRiv SRms
§ - 'Elegantissima' (v) ♀H6	CDul CExl CJun CTri ECrN ELan EPfP EShb LPot LSRN MAsh MGos MHer MMuc MRav NLar NPri NWea SCob SEND SGol SPer SPoG SRiv SRms WAvo WCFE WSpi
- 'Fiesta'	SRms
- 'Gold Tip'	see *B. sempervirens* 'Notata'
§ - 'Graham Blandy' ♀H6	MHer SAko SGol SRiv WSpi
- 'Green Balloon'	EPfP LBuc
- 'Greenpeace'	see *B. sempervirens* 'Graham Blandy'
- 'Handsworthensis'	CTri NWea SEND SRms WCFE WSpi
- 'Ickworth Giant'	WSpi
- 'Japonica Aurea'	see *B. sempervirens* 'Latifolia Maculata'
- 'Kensington Gardens'	WSpi
- 'King Midas'	SAko
- 'Kingsville'	see *B. microphylla* 'Compacta'
- 'Kingsville Dwarf'	see *B. microphylla* 'Compacta'
§ - 'Latifolia Maculata' (v) ♀H6	CKel CRos EPfP LRHS MMuc NPer SEND SPoG SRiv WRHF WSpi
- 'Longifolia'	see *B. sempervirens* 'Angustifolia'
§ - 'Marginata' (v)	SGol WSpi
- 'Memorial'	NWad SRiv WSpi
- 'Myosotidifolia'	SRiv WCot WSpi
- 'Myrtifolia'	WSpi
§ - 'Notata' (v)	WSpi
- 'Pendula'	WSpi
- 'Prostrata'	WSpi
- 'Pylewell'	WSpi
- 'Raket'	NWea
- 'Rosmarinifolia'	MRav
- 'Rotundifolia'	ELan MMuc SEND WSpi
- 'Silver Variegated'	see *B. sempervirens* 'Elegantissima'
- 'Suffruticosa'	CArg CBcs CSBt CTri ECrN ELan EPfP EShb GPoy LSRN MAsh MGos MHed MRav MSwo NEgg NHol NLar NWea SCob SEND SEWo SGol SPer SRiv SRms SWvt WCFE WSpi
- 'Suffruticosa Variegata' (v)	SRms SWvt
- 'Twisty'	WFar
- 'Vardar Valley'	NWad SRiv WSpi
* - 'Variegata' (v)	CPla MSwo NHic SArc
- 'Wisley Blue'	WSpi
***sinica* var. *insularis* 'Filigree'**	NWad WSpi
- - 'Justin Brouwers'	LPla MHer SRiv WSpi
- - 'Tide Hill'	MHer SRiv WFar WSpi

C

cabbage see AGM Vegetables Section

Cacalia (*Asteraceae*)

plantaginea	see *Arnoglossum plantagineum*
suaveolens	see *Hasteola suaveolens*

Cachrys (*Apiaceae*)

alpina	LEdu SBrt SPhx

Caesalpinia (*Caesalpiniaceae*)

gilliesii ♀H3	CBcs CSpe EBee LRHS SPlb WCot
pulcherrima ♀H3	CCCN
spinosa	SPlb WPav

Caiophora (*Loasaceae*)

coronata	GEdr

calabrese see AGM Vegetables Section

Caladium (*Araceae*)

'Candidum' (v)	SDeJ
'Carolyn Whorton'	SDeJ
'Florida Cardinal' (v)	SDeJ
'Frieda Hempel'	SDeJ
praetermissum 'Hilo Beauty'	XBlo
'White Christmas' (v)	SDeJ

Calamagrostis (*Poaceae*)

× ***acutiflora***	XLum
- 'Avalanche'	CKno CRos EBou ECha ECtt EHoe EHyd EPPr EPfP EShb EWes GCal GQue GWyn IMou LRHS MAsh MAvo MTis NDov NRHS NWsh SPoG WPtf
- 'Eldorado' (v)	CKno ECha MAvo MMuc WCot
- 'England' (v)	EPPr GBin MNrw
- 'Karl Foerster'	Widely available
- 'Overdam' (v)	Widely available
- 'Stricta'	EPPr
- 'Waldenbuch'	CKno EMor
argentea	see *Stipa calamagrostis*
arundinacea	CElw CExl CMac SPlb WMoo XSen
§ ***brachytricha*** ♀H6	Widely available
- 'Mona'	NDov
emodensis	CAby CMea CSam CSpe EAJP EBee ECha GCal NBid SPhx WGrn WMoo
epigejos	CKno LEdu WHrl WPGP
'Glenorchy Fireworks'	EPPr
ophitidis new	SPlb
splendens misapplied	see *Stipa calamagrostis*
splendens Trin.	LPla
varia	CKno EHoe ELon EMor GBin LPla WHrl

Calamintha (*Lamiaceae*)

alpina	see *Acinos alpinus*
§ ***ascendens***	EBee WMoo
clinopodium	see *Clinopodium vulgare*
cretica	SPhx
§ ***grandiflora***	CBod CCBP ECha ELan GJos GPoy MNHC MNrw MRav NBir NLar NPer SPer SPlb SRms WCAu WMoo XSen
- 'Elfin Purple'	EBee EPfP
- 'Variegata' (v)	EBee ELan ENfk EPfP MPie SRms WCAu
'Harrogate'	WGoo
§ ***nepeta***	CBod CCBP CHab CKel CMea CRos EBou ECha EHyd EMor ENfk GBin LRHS MHer MNHC NBro NRHS SCob SEND SPhx SPlb SPoG SRms WCAu WHer WMoo WOut XSen
- subsp. ***glandulosa***	WMoo
- - ACL 1050/90	EBee WHoo

- - 'White Cloud' CFis EBee ECtt EHrv ELan MBel MRav NBir SRms WCAu WMoo
- 'Gottfried Kuehn' LPla MRav
§ - subsp. ***nepeta*** ELan ELon EPfP GMaP IMou MHer MMuc MRav NDov SPer WFar WHal XLum
- - 'Blue Cloud' CCBP CSam CSpe EBee EBou ECha ECtt EHrv EMor EPfP GMaP GWyn MBel MRav NBir NDov SPhx SPoG SPtp SRms WArt WCAu WFar WMoo
- 'Triumphator' **new** IPot WGoo
- 'Weisse Riese' CMea EBee NDov
nepetoides see *C. nepeta* subsp. *nepeta*
officinalis misapplied see *C. ascendens*
sylvatica see *Clinopodium menthifolium*
vulgaris see *Clinopodium vulgare*

calamondin see *Citrus* × *microcarpa*

Calandrinia (*Portulacaceae*)

sibirica see *Claytonia sibirica*
umbellata EDAr MAsh WIce
- 'Ruby Tuesday' XLum

Calanthe (*Orchidaceae*)

aristulifera GKev LAma
bicolor see *C. striata*
discolor EBee GKev LAma NLAp
- var. ***flava*** see *C. striata*
hancockii × ***striata*** **new** NLAp
Higo gx **new** NLAp
Ishizuchi gx **new** NLAp
Kozu gx GKev LEdu NLAp WPGP
nipponica GKev LAma
reflexa GKev LAma
sieboldii see *C. striata*
sieboldii × ***yueana*** **new** NLAp
§ ***striata*** EBee GKev LAma NLAp
Takane gx NLAp
Takane gx × ***yueana*** **new** NLAp
tricarinata LAma NLAp

Calathea (*Marantaceae*)

argyrophylla see *Goeppertia argyrophylla*
crocata see *Goeppertia crocata*
louisae see *Goeppertia louisae*
majestica see *Goeppertia majestica*
makoyana see *Goeppertia makoyana*
picturata see *Goeppertia picturata*
roseopicta see *Goeppertia roseopicta*
rufibarba see *Goeppertia rufibarba*
stromata see *Ctenanthe burle-marxii*
zebrina see *Goeppertia zebrina*

Calceolaria (*Calceolariaceae*)

andina EDAr
arachnoidea EDAr EWes GEdr SPlb WPav
§ ***biflora*** EDAr EWes GAbr GCrg GKev NAln
- 'Goldcap' EBou
- 'Goldcrest Amber' SPlb
'Camden Hero' CBcs CBod
cavanillesii SPlb
corymbosa EBee GKev GLog
- subsp. ***floccosa*** **new** GKev
falklandica EWld GKev
filicaulis GKev
- subsp. ***luxurians*** GKev
fothergillii GAbr GLog WAbe
'Goldcrest' EWld LRHS
integrifolia ♀H2 CAbb CBcs CBod CDTJ CExl CFis CTri ECtt ELan EShb MGil MSCN SAdn SEND SPer SPoG SRms WBor WHer
- bronze-flowered MSCN SPer
- 'Gaines' Yellow' GCal
'John Innes' EWld
'Kentish Hero' EDAr GCal MGil MHer SDys WAbe
meyeniana subsp. ***nahuelbutae*** GCal
mollissima GKev
pavonii MGil SBrt
aff. ***pavonii*** CRHN
plantaginea see *C. biflora*
rugosa see *C. integrifolia*
tenella NSla WAbe
uniflora var. ***darwinii*** NHpl WAbe
'Walter Shrimpton' EPot GCrg WAbe

Calendula ✿ (*Asteraceae*)

arvensis CCCN
'Bronze Beauty' CSpe
officinalis CCBP CLau EBou ENfk GPoy LCro LOPS MHer MNHC SRms SVic SWvt WSFF
- 'Indian Prince' (Prince Series) LCro LOPS SPhx
'Tarifa' SEND
(Winter Creepers Series) WINTER CREEPERS ORANGES & ICE ('20123-107d') **new** NPri
- WINTER CREEPERS SUN & FLURRIES **new** NPri
(Winter Wonders Series) WINTER WONDERS BANANA BLIZZARD ('2012357d') NPri
- WINTER WONDERS GOLDEN GLAZE ('2012329d') NPri

Calibrachoa (*Solanaceae*)

(Cabaret Series) CABARET BRIGHT RED ('Balcabrite'PBR) NPri
- CABARET DEEP BLUE ('Balcabdebu'PBR) NPri
- CABARET DEEP YELLOW ('Balcabdepy'PBR) NPri
- CABARET HOT PINK ('Balcabhopi'PBR) NPri
- CABARET WHITE ('Balcabwit') NPri
(Can-can Series) CAN-CAN APRICOT ('Balcanapt') NPri
- CAN-CAN DOUBLE MAGENTA NPri
NOA VIOLET GLINT **new** NPri
'Starlight Blue' NPri
'Starlight Pink' NPri
(Superbells Series) SUPERBELLS BLUEBERRY PUNCH **new** NPri
- SUPERBELLS CHERRY BLOSSOM ('Uscali212-1') **new** NPri
- SUPERBELLS GRAPE PUNCH ('Uscal84704') NPri

- SUPERBELLS POMEGRANATE PUNCH ('Uscal08501'PBR) NPri
- SUPERBELLS STRAWBERRY PINK ('Uscali47') CPla
- SUPERBELLS STRAWBERRY PUNCH ('Uscal58205') **new** NPri

Calla (*Araceae*)

sp. NRHS
aethiopica see *Zantedeschia aethiopica*
palustris CBod CWat EWat LLWG NPer SRms WMAq

Calliandra (*Mimosaceae*)

'Dixie Pink' CCCN
portoricensis CCCN
surinamensis CCCN
tweediei ♀H1b CCCN

Callianthemum (*Ranunculaceae*)

anemonoides EPot GEdr WAbe WCot
coriandrifolium GEdr
kernerianum GEdr WAbe

Callicarpa (*Lamiaceae*)

CW&T 6228 CMCN
americana CExl
- var. ***lactea*** CMCN
bodinieri CHll
- var. ***giraldii*** LMaj MRav NLar SGol
- - 'Profusion' ♀H6 Widely available
- 'Imperial Pearl' ECrN LRHS
'Cardinal' CJun
cathayana NLar
dichotoma CBcs CExl LRHS NLar SCob
- 'Issai' CKel EBee EPfP EUJe LRHS MBlu
japonica CExl CMen NLar SBrt SMad
- B&SWJ 12621 WCru
- f. ***albibacca*** LRHS NLar
- 'Heavy Berry' NLar
- 'Koshima-no-homate' NLar
- 'Leucocarpa' CBcs CExl CMac EBee ELan EPfP EWTr MRav NLar SPer SPoG WGob
- var. ***luxurians*** B&SWJ 8521 WCru
kwangtungensis CBcs NLar
mollis CExl
psilocalyx NJM 13.057 WPGP
shikokiana NLar
× ***shirasawana*** NLar
aff. ***tikusikensis*** B&SWJ 7127 WCru
Van den Broek selection NLar
yunnanensis NLar

Callirhoe (*Malvaceae*)

bushii EBee WSHC
involucrata LPla WHrl WSHC XLum
- var. ***tenuissima*** EBee GCal

Callisia (*Commelinaceae*)

elegans EShb
fragrans EOHP EShb
- 'Melnickoff' (v) **new** EShb
§ ***navicularis*** SSim
repens EShb

Callistemon (*Myrtaceae*)

acuminatus CCCN
brachyandrus SVen
citrinus CBcs CHll CTri EPfP SEle SPlb WGrn
- 'Albus' see *C. citrinus* 'White Anzac'
- 'Firebrand' CRos LRHS
- 'Splendens' ♀H3 Widely available
§ - 'White Anzac' CHll CKel CMac CSBt CSde CTsd ELan EMil EPfP LRHS SEND SPoG
comboynensis CCCN
glaucus see *C. speciosus*
'Inferno' CAbb SPad
laevis hort. see *C. rugulosus*
linearifolius LSRN
linearis ♀H2 CAby CKel CMac CRos CSde CTri ELan EPfP LRHS LSRN MGos MHer SEND SLim SLon SPlb SWvt WSHC
macropunctatus SPlb SVen
'Masotti'PBR CRos EHyd MPkF SPoG
'Mauve Mist' CAbb CCCN CKel CRos ELan EPfP EWTr LRHS SAko SPad SPoG SVen WGrn
pallidus CBcs CCCN CKel CMCN CMac CRos CTsd EHyd ELan EPfP EWTr LRHS MMuc MRav NRHS SAko SEND SEle SPer SPlb SVen
paludosus see *C. sieberi* DC.
'Perth Pink' CAbb CBcs CCCN CKel CSBt CSde ELan EPfP LRHS SPad SVen WGrn
pinifolius SPlb SVen
§ ***pityoides*** CExl NLar SEle SVen
'Red Clusters' CBcs CKel CMac CRos ELan EMOT EPfP LRHS MAsh MJak SWvt WFar
rigidus CBcs CBod CChe CHll CRos CTri CTsd EHyd ELan EMOT EPfP IArd LRHS LSRN MGos MMuc MRav NLar NRHS SAko SEle SPer SVen SWvt
§ ***rugulosus*** CCCN CKel EUJe LRHS SVen SWvt
salignus ♀H2 CBcs CCCN CCht CDul CKel CMac CTri EMOT EPfP MHer MRav NLar SEle SLim SPer SVen
sieberi misapplied see *C. pityoides*
§ ***sieberi*** DC. CBcs CBod CKel CMCN EBee ELan EPfP LRHS MGil MMuc NLar SLim SPlb
§ ***speciosus*** CDul NLar SEND SPlb
subulatus SArc SPlb
- 'Crimson Tail' MGil MMuc SPtp
viminalis CCCN CMCN SPlb
- 'Captain Cook' CMac ECrN EMOT LRHS LSRN SVen SWvt WFar
- 'Endeavour' CCCN
- 'Hannah Ray' EMOT NEgg WFar
- HOT PINK ('Kkho1'PBR) LRHS MGos MPkF SLim
- 'Little John' CBcs LSRN SEND SPad SWvt
'Violaceus' NLar SPlb SVen
viridiflorus CMCN CTsd MMuc SEND SPlb SPtp WGwG
'White Anzac' see *C. citrinus* 'White Anzac'

Callistephus (*Asteraceae*)

chinensis SVic

Callitriche (*Plantaginaceae*)

sp. WSFF
brutia subsp. ***hamulata*** LLWG

§ ***palustris***	CBen MWts
stagnalis	WMAq
verna	see *C. palustris*

Callitris (*Cupressaceae*)

endlicheri	CBrP
rhomboidea	WPav

Callitropsis see *Chamaecyparis*

× ***leylandii***	see × *Cuprocyparis leylandii*
nootkatensis	see *Xanthocyparis nootkatensis*

Calluna ✿ (*Ericaceae*)

vulgaris	SWhi WOut
- 'Adrie'	CFst SWhi
- 'Alba Elongata'	see *C. vulgaris* 'Mair's Variety'
§ - 'Alba Plena' (d)	GPer
§ - 'Alba Rigida'	CFst GPer
- 'Alex Warwick'	GPer
- 'Alexandra'PBR (Garden Girls Series)	CFst SCoo SPoG
- 'Alicia'PBR (Garden Girls Series) ♀H7	CFst SCoo SPoG
- 'Allegro'	GPer MMuc SCoo
- 'Alportii'	GPer
- 'Amethyst'PBR (Garden Girls Series)	MJak MMuc SPoG SWhi
- 'Amilto'	CFst
- 'Anette'PBR (Garden Girls Series)	CFst MJak SCoo
- 'Angie'	CFst SWhi
- 'Annabel' (d)	CFst SWhi
- 'Annegret'	see *C. vulgaris* 'Marlies'
- 'Annemarie' (d) ♀H7	CFst CSBt GPer SCoo SPlb SWhi
- 'Anne's Goldzwerg'	CFst
- 'Anne's Zwerg'	CFst
- 'Aphrodite'PBR (Garden Girls Series)	CFst
- 'Apollo'	CFst
- 'Arabella'PBR	SWhi
- 'Arina'	GPer SCoo
- 'Athene'PBR (Garden Girls Series)	CFst SWhi
- 'Atholl Gold'	CFst
- 'August Beauty'	GPer
- 'Aurea'	MJak
- 'Baby Ben'	CFst
- 'Beoley Crimson'	GPer SCoo
- 'Beoley Gold' ♀H7	CSBt CTri GPer MAsh NHol SCoo
- 'Beoley Silver'	SCoo SWhi
- 'Blazeaway'	CTri GPer MAsh MJak SCoo
- 'Bonfire Brilliance'	CSBt GPer NHol
- 'Bonita'PBR (Garden Girls Series)	CFst
- 'Boskoop'	CFst GPer MAsh NHol SWhi
- 'C.W. Nix'	CSBt GPer
- 'Caerketton White'	GPer
- 'Carmen'	CFst
- 'Con Brio'	CFst CSBt GPer SCoo SWhi
- 'Connemara Colleen'	CFst
- 'Corrie's White'	GJos GPer
- 'Cottswood Gold'	GPer SCoo
- 'County Wicklow' (d) ♀H7	CFst CTri ELan GPer MMuc NHol SCoo SWhi
- 'Cramond' (d)	GPer
- 'Cuprea'	MJak SCoo SWhi
- 'Dark Beauty'PBR (d) ♀H7	CBcs CFst CKel CSBt ELan LCro LOPS MAsh NHol SCoo SWhi
- 'Dark Star' (d) ♀H7	CFst CSBt GJos MAsh NHol SCoo SWhi
- 'Darkness' ♀H7	CBcs CFst CTri GPer MAsh MJak SCoo SWhi
- 'David Eason'	CFst
- 'David Hagenaars'	CFst SWhi
- 'Dirry'	CFst
- 'Disco Queen'	CFst GPer SWhi
- 'Drum-ra'	GPer
- 'Dunnet Lime'	SPlb
- 'Easter-bonfire'	CFst MJak SCoo
- 'Eckart Miessner'	SWhi
- 'Elsie Purnell' (d) ♀H7	CFst ELan GPer MAsh NHol SCoo SPlb
- 'Feuerwerk'	SCoo
- 'Firefly' ♀H7	CFst CSBt GPer MJak NHol SCoo SPer SWhi
- 'Flamingo'	GPer SCoo
- 'Forest Fire'	CFst
- 'Foxii Nana'	CFst NHol SWhi
- 'Fred J. Chapple'	GPer SWhi
- 'Galaxy'PBR	CFst
- 'Gina'PBR	SWhi
- 'Glenfiddich'	CKel CSBt GPer MAsh
- 'Gold Flame'	GPer
- 'Gold Haze'	CTri MAsh NHol SCoo
- 'Gold Knight'	ELan SCoo
- 'Gold Mist'	MJak
- 'Gold Spronk'	CFst SWhi
- 'Golden Angie'	CFst SWhi
- 'Golden Carpet'	CFst GJos GPer MAsh NHol
- 'Golden Fleece'	CFst
- 'Grey Carpet'	CFst
- 'Guinea Gold'	CFst GPer SWhi
§ - 'H.E. Beale' (d)	CTri GPer MAsh MJak NHol SCoo
- 'Hammondii Aureifolia'	GPer MJak SPlb
- 'Hammondii Rubrifolia'	SWhi
- 'Hannover'	CFst
- 'Heidesinfonie'	CFst
- 'Heike' (d)	CFst
- 'Helena'	CFst
- 'Hera'PBR	SWhi
- 'Highland Rose'	CFst SPlb
- 'Hilda'PBR	CFst
§ - 'Hugh Nicholson'	GPer
- 'J.H. Hamilton' (d)	CTri ELan GPer MAsh NHol SCoo SWhi
- 'Jan Dekker'	GPer
- 'Jana' (d)	CFst
- 'Jette' (Garden Girls Series) **new**	CFst
- 'Jimmy Dyce' (d)	CFst
- 'Johnson's Variety'	SCoo
- 'Josefine'	CFst SWhi
- 'Joy Vanstone'	GPer
- 'Julia'	CFst SWhi
- 'Juliette' (Garden Girls Series) **new**	CFst
- 'Kerstin' ♀H7	CFst GPer NHol SCoo SPlb SWhi
- 'Kinlochruel' (d) ♀H7	CBcs CFst CTri GPer MAsh NHol SPlb SWhi
- 'Kiran' **new**	CFst
- 'Kirby White'	MAsh SPlb SWhi
- 'Klaudine'PBR (Garden Girls Series)	CFst
- 'Larissa'PBR (Garden Girls Series)	CFst
- 'Lemon Queen'	CFst
- 'Leprechaun'	CFst
- 'Leslie Slinger'	SCoo
- 'Liliane'PBR (Garden Girls Series) **new**	CFst

- 'Lilli'PBR	SWhi
- 'Little John'	LSRN
- 'Llanbedrog Pride' (d)	CFst
- 'Loch Turret'	GPer
- 'Loki'PBR	SWhi
- 'Long White'	SWhi
- 'Luisa'PBR (Garden Girls Series) **new**	CFst
- 'Madonna'PBR (Garden Girls Series)	CFst
§ - 'Mair's Variety'	GPer SCoo SWhi
- 'Marcelita' (d) **new**	CFst
- 'Marleen'	CSBt MJak
§ - 'Marlies'	CFst
- 'Melanie' (Garden Girls Series)	CFst CSBt NHol SCoo SWhi
- 'Mickkle-Dickkle'	SWhi
- 'Molecule'	CFst
- 'Mrs Pat'	MAsh
- 'Multicolor'	MAsh NHol
§ - 'My Dream' (d)	CSBt SCoo
- 'Nana Compacta'	CFst GPer
- 'Nora'	SWhi
- 'October White'	CFst
- 'Olympic Gold'	CFst
- 'Orange Max'	GPer
- 'Orange Queen'	CSBt
- 'Pennyacre Lemon'	CFst
- 'Pepper and Salt'	see *C. vulgaris* 'Hugh Nicholson'
- 'Peter Sparkes' (d) ♀H7	CBcs CFst CSBt GPer MAsh MMuc NHol SCoo
- 'Pewter Plate'	CFst
- 'Pink Alicia'PBR (Garden Girls Series)	CFst
- 'Pink Beale'	see *C. vulgaris* 'H.E. Beale'
- 'Purple Passion'	ELan SCoo
- 'Radnor' (d)	CSBt GPer
- 'Ralph Purnell'	ELan SCoo
- 'Red Beauty'	CBcs CFst SWhi
- 'Red Favorit' (d)	CFst GPer SWhi
- 'Red Fred'	SCoo
- 'Red Haze'	GPer NHol SCoo
- 'Red Pimpernel'	CFst ELan SCoo SWhi
- 'Red Star' (d)	CFst NHol
- 'Redbud'	CFst SWhi
- 'Rigida Prostrata'	see *C. vulgaris* 'Alba Rigida'
- 'Robert Chapman' ♀H7	CFst CSBt CTri MAsh NHol SWhi
- 'Roma'	CFst
- 'Rosalind, Underwood's'	NHol
- 'Rosita'PBR	CFst
- 'Roswitha'	CFst
- 'Roter Oktober'	CFst
- 'Ruby Slinger'	NHol
- 'Ruth Sparkes' (d)	NHol
- 'Salmon Leap'	GPer
- 'Sandy'PBR (Garden Girls Series)	CFst SPoG SWhi
- 'Schneewittchen' **new**	CFst
- 'Serlei Aurea'	CSBt
- 'Sesam'	CFst
- 'Silvana'PBR	CFst SWhi
- 'Silver Fox'	CBcs CFst
- 'Silver King'	CFst
- 'Silver Knight'	CSBt ELan GJos GPer MAsh MJak NHol SCoo SPlb SWhi
- 'Silver Queen' ♀H7	CFst GPer MAsh MJak NHol SWhi
- 'Sir John Charrington'	CFst GPer MAsh NHol SWhi
- 'Sister Anne' ♀H7	CFst CSBt GPer MJak MMuc SCoo
- 'Snow White'	CFst SWhi
- 'Snowball'	see *C. vulgaris* 'My Dream'
- 'Spitfire'	CFst GPer MAsh
- 'Spring Cream' ♀H7	CBcs CFst GPer MAsh MMuc NHol SCoo SWhi
- 'Spring Torch'	CBcs CFst CSBt GPer MAsh MJak NHol SCoo SWhi
- 'Stefanie'	SWhi
- 'Strawberry Delight' (d)	ELan SCoo
- 'Summer Orange'	GJos GPer
- 'Sun Sprinkles'	CFst
- 'Sunset'	CFst GPer
- 'Susanne' (Garden Girls Series) **new**	CFst
- 'Theresa' (Garden Girls Series)	CFst SWhi
- 'Tib' (d) ♀H7	CSBt GPer MAsh SWhi
- 'Tom Thumb'	CFst
- 'Tricolorifolia'	SCoo
- 'Trinklet'	SWhi
- 'Velvet Fascination' ♀H7	CFst GPer SCoo SWhi
- 'White Angie'	SWhi
- 'White Bouquet'	see *C. vulgaris* 'Alba Plena'
- 'White Coral' (d) ♀H7	CFst ELan SCoo
- 'White Lawn'	CFst GPer MMuc NHol
- 'Wickwar Flame' ♀H7	CBcs CFst CKel CSBt ELan GPer MAsh MJak NHol SCoo SPlb SWhi
- 'Winter Chocolate'	CFst CSBt MAsh NHol SCoo
- 'Yellow Basket'	CFst
- 'Yellow Beauty'PBR	CFst
- 'Yvette's Gold'	CFst
- 'Yvette's Silver'	CFst
- 'Zeta'PBR (Garden Girls Series) **new**	CFst

Calocedrus (*Cupressaceae*)

§ ***decurrens*** ♀H7	CAco CBcs CDul CLnd CMac CTho EPfP EUJe LMaj LPra MBlu MGil NWea SLim WTSh
- 'Aureovariegata' (v) ♀H7	CBcs NEgg
- 'Berrima Gold' ♀H7	NLar
§ - 'Depressa'	CKen
- 'Nana'	see *C. decurrens* 'Depressa'
- 'Pillar'	CKen

Calocephalus (*Asteraceae*)

brownii	see *Leucophyta brownii*

Calochortus (*Liliaceae*)

'Cupido'PBR	CExl EPot GKev LAma SDeJ
luteus 'Golden Orb'PBR	CExl SDeJ
splendens 'Violet Queen'	SDeJ
superbus	SDeJ
'Symphony'PBR	CExl SDeJ
venustus	SDeJ
- 'Burgundy'	SDeJ

Calomeria (*Asteraceae*)

§ ***amaranthoides***	WJek

Calonyction see *Ipomoea*

Calopogon (*Orchidaceae*)

tuberosus	NLAp
- f. ***albiflorus*** **new**	NLAp

Caloscordum see *Allium*

Calothamnus (*Myrtaceae*)

quadrifidus	CKel
validus	SPlb
villosus	SPlb

Calpurnia (*Papilionaceae*)

aurea	SPlb

Caltha ✿ (*Ranunculaceae*)

howellii	see *C. leptosepala* subsp. *howellii*
laeta	see *C. palustris* var. *palustris*
leptosepala	EBee EMor EWat GEdr GKev GMaP LLWG NLar
- SDR 8134	GKev
§ - subsp. ***howellii*** NNS 07-87	GKev
natans	LLWG
palustris	Widely available
- var. ***alba***	Widely available
- 'Auengold'	LLWG
- 'Auenwald'	LLWG
- var. ***barthei***	GEdr
- 'Flore Pleno' (d) ♀H7	Widely available
- 'Girls Eyes'	MNrw
- 'Himalayan Snow'	EBee ECtt LLWG WFar
- 'Honeydew'	CAby ELon EWat LLWG MNrw WCot WSHC
§ - var. ***major***	CAby
- 'Marilyn'	LLWG
- 'Multiplex' (d)	CDor ECtt EMor NAln SRot
- Newlake hybrid	LLWG
- 'Pallida Plena' (d)	SCob
§ - var. ***palustris***	CBen CBre ECha ELan EUJe EWat GCal LLWG WWtn
- - 'Plena' (d)	CRos CSam CWat EHyd EWat LRHS NRHS SGol WGwG
- var. ***radicans***	EWat GEdr
- - 'Flore Pleno' (d)	WWtn
- 'Stagnalis'	MWts
polypetala misapplied	see *C. palustris* var. *major*
polypetala Hochst. ex Lorent	CWat GCal MSCN NPer SMad WMAq
sagittata	WSHC
scaposa	GKev

Calycanthus (*Calycanthaceae*)

'Aphrodite'	CMCN
chinensis	CBcs CCCN CHll CJun CMCN CRos EBee EHyd EPfP LRHS MBlu MGil MPkF NLar WHor
fertilis	see *C. floridus* var. *glaucus*
floridus	Widely available
- 'Athens'	CBcs CJun WCot WPGP
§ - var. ***glaucus***	EPfP
- - 'Purpureus'	CBcs CJun MBlu NLar
- var. ***laevigatus***	see *C. floridus* var. *glaucus*
- 'Michael Lindsay'	CJun NLar WPGP
mohrii	NLar
occidentalis	CBcs CDul CMCN MAsh MBlu MGil SBrt WCFE
× ***raulstonii*** 'Hartlage Wine' ♀H5	CBcs CJun CMCN CRos EHyd ELan EPfP EUJe GKin IArd IDee LCro LLHF LOPS LRHS MAsh MBlu MGos NLar SMad SPoG WKif
'Venus'	CBcs CJun CMCN ECrN EPfP IArd LCro LOPS MAsh MBlu NLar SMad

Calystegia (*Convolvulaceae*)

§ ***hederacea*** 'Flore Pleno' (d)	SMad
japonica 'Flore Pleno'	see *C. hederacea* 'Flore Pleno'
soldanella NNS 99-85	WCot

Calytrix (*Myrtaceae*)

tetragona	SPlb

Camassia ✿ (*Asparagaceae*)

'Blue Candle'	CTca EPfP EPot GKev LAma NHsp SPhx
'Blue Heaven'	CAvo CMea CRos EPfP ERCP GKev LAma LRHS LSun NHsp NRHS SDeJ SPhx
Broadleigh Belle Group **new**	CBro
cusickii	CAby CBod CBro CExl CRos CTca CTri EBee ECtt EHyd ELan EPfP EPot ERCP EWTr EWhm GBin GKev IFro LAma LCro LOPS LRHS MCot NBir NLar NRHS SDeJ WPnP
- white-flowered	CBod
- 'Zwanenburg'	CRos CTca EHyd ERCP GKev IPot LRHS NHpl NHsp NRHS WCot
esculenta Lindl.	see *C. quamash*
'John Treasure' (d)	GCal MAvo
leichtlinii misapplied	see *C. leichtlinii* subsp. *suksdorfii*
leichtlinii (Baker) S.Watson	MArl
- 'Alba' misapplied	see *C. leichtlinii* subsp. *leichtlinii*
* - 'Alba Plena'	LSun MNrw NBir NHpl
- BLUE DANUBE	see *C. leichtlinii* subsp. *suksdorfii* 'Blauwe Donau'
- 'Blue Wave'	NWad
- 'Harlequin' (v)	NHsp
§ - subsp. ***leichtlinii***	Widely available
- 'Magdalen'	MAvo
- pale pink-flowered	GKev IPot
- 'Plena' (d)	ECha
- 'Sacajawea' (v)	CAvo CMea CRos ECha EHyd EPfP ERCP GKev LAma LRHS MAvo NHsp NRHS SDeJ SMHy WCot WTor
- 'Semiplena' (d)	CAvo CBro CMea CRos CTca EBee ECtt EHyd EPfP EPot ERCP GKev LAma LRHS MBel MNrw NRHS NSti SPhx WBor WCot WPnP WShi
§ - subsp. ***suksdorfii***	LCro LOPS WCot
- - 'Alba'	CAby CAvo CRos EHyd EPot GBin GMaP ITim LCro LOPS LRHS NRHS NSti SCob SPtp
§ - - 'Blauwe Donau'	ILea
- - Caerulea Group	Widely available
- - - 'Maybelle'	CAvo CMea GKev NPri
- - 'Electra'	CAvo ECha MAvo SMHy WCot
- - 'Lady Eve Price'	MAvo WCot
§ ***quamash***	CAvo CBro CCBP CRos CTca CWCL EBee ECha EHyd ELan EPot ERCP GKev LAma LEdu LRHS NBir NRHS SCob SDeJ SRms WFar WPnP WShi XLum
- 'Blue Melody' (v)	CBro CRos CSam CTca EBee EHyd EPot GKev GMaP LAma LEdu LRHS NHsp NRHS SDeJ WRHF
- 'Orion'	CBro CRos EBee EHyd GKev LRHS NHsp NRHS WCot
- var. ***quamash***	CBcs

Camellia ✿ (*Theaceae*)

'Adorable' (*pitardii* hybrid)	LRHS LSRN
'April Blush'	WFar
'Auburn White'	see *C. japonica* 'Mrs Bertha A. Harms'
'Baby Bear'	MPkF
'Barbara Clark' (*reticulata* × *saluenensis*)	LRHS LSRN MAsh NRHS SCog
'Bertha Harms Blush'	see *C. japonica* 'Mrs Bertha A. Harms'
'Black Lace' ♀H5	CBcs CKel CRos CSgt CTrh CTri EPfP LCro LOPS LRHS LSRN MAsh MMuc NPri NRHS SArc SEND SWvt
'Blissful Dawn'	CBcs CTrh

	Name	Suppliers
	'Bonnie Marie'	CBcs SCam SCog
	'Canterbury'	MPkF
	'Christmas Daffodil' (*japonica* hybrid)	CBcs LRHS MPkF
	'Cinnamon Cindy'	LRHS MPkF SCam SCog
	'Congratulations'	CSBt LSRN
	'Contessa Lavinia Maggi'	see *C. japonica* 'Lavinia Maggi'
	'Cornish Snow' (*cuspidata* × *saluenensis*) 🏆H4	CBcs CMac CSBt CTri EPfP SCam SWvt WFar
	'Cornish Spring' (*cuspidata* × *japonica*) 🏆H4	CBcs CCCN CSBt CTrh CTsd LRHS NRHS SCam
	'Crimson Candles' 🏆H5	LRHS
	'Czar'	see *C. japonica* 'The Czar'
	'Delia Williams'	see *C.* × *williamsii* 'Citation'
	'Diamond Head' (*japonica* × *reticulata*)	CBcs LSRN
	'Doctor Clifford Parks' (*japonica* × *reticulata*) 🏆H4	CBcs
	'Donckelaeri'	see *C. japonica* 'Masayoshi'
	'Extravaganza' (*japonica* hybrid) 🏆H5	CTrh IArd SCoo
	'Fairy Blush'	LRHS MPkF
	'Fairy Wand'	MPkF
	'Fascination'	SWvt
	'Faustina Lechi'	see *C. japonica* 'Faustina'
	'Felice Harris' (*reticulata* × *sasanqua*)	SCoo
	'Fiesta Grande'	MPkF
	forrestii	IDee
	'Forty-niner' (*japonica* × *reticulata*)	CSgt LRHS NRHS
	'Fragrant Pink'	CBcs SCam
	'Francie L' 🏆H4	CBcs CMac EPfP
	'Frau Minna Seidel'	see *C. japonica* subsp. *rusticana* 'Otome'
	'Free Spirit'	CTrh
	'Freedom Bell' 🏆H5	CSgt CTrh EPfP GKin LRHS NPri NRHS SCam
	'Frosted Star'	LRHS
	'Gay Baby'	MPkF
	'Golden Anniversary'	see *C. japonica* 'Dahlohnega'
	grijsii	CBcs CExl CTrh LRHS
	handelii	CExl
	'Happy Anniversary'	CSBt LSRN SWvt
§	***hiemalis*** 'Bonanza'	CSgt CTrh LRHS MPkF SCam
	- 'Chansonette'	CSgt ELon
§	- 'Dazzler'	LRHS NRHS SCam
	- 'Elfin Rose'	LRHS
	- 'Interlude'	MPkF
	- 'Kanjirō'	SCam
	- 'Shishigashira'	CTrh
	- 'Shōwa-no-sakae'	MPkF
	'Hooker'	CSgt LRHS MAsh NRHS
	'Imbricata Rubra'	see *C. japonica* 'Imbricata'
	'Innovation'	CSgt
	'Inspiration' (*reticulata* × *saluenensis*) 🏆H5	CMac CSgt CTrh EPfP LRHS LSRN MGos NLar SCam
	japonica	CAco LMaj LPra LRHS SEWo SPre
	- 'Aaron's Ruby'	CBcs ELon LRHS NRHS SCam
	- 'Ace of Hearts'	SCoo
	- 'Ada Pieper'	CTrh
	- 'Adelina Patti' 🏆H5	CBcs CSgt CTrh SCam
	- 'Adeyaka'	CSgt LRHS NRHS
	- 'Adolphe Audusson' 🏆H5	Widely available
§	- 'Akashigata' 🏆H5	CBcs ELon EPfP LRHS LSRN NRHS SCam SSta
	- 'Alba Plena' (d) 🏆H5	CSBt CTrh ELan LRHS SWvt
	- 'Alba Simplex'	CMac CSgt CTrh EPfP LMaj NPri SCam SCob SCog SSta
	- 'Alexander Hunter' 🏆H5	CSgt LRHS NRHS SCam SCog
§	- 'Althaeiflora'	CBcs ELon LRHS NRHS SCam
	- 'Anemoniflora'	CBcs CTsd EPfP LRHS NRHS
	- 'Angel'	LSRN WBor
	- 'Angello'	CSgt LRHS NRHS
	- 'Ann Sothern'	CBcs
	- 'Annie Wylam' 🏆H5	CTrh SCoo
	- 'Apollo' ambig.	CBcs CKel LRHS MAsh NRHS
	- 'Apollo' Paul, 1911	MSwo SCam
§	- 'Apple Blossom'	CBcs CTrh CTsd LRHS NRHS
	- 'April Blush'	CSgt
	- 'April Kiss'	CSgt NEgg
	- 'April Remembered'	NEgg NRHS WFar
	- 'April Rose'	CSgt WFar
	- 'Arajishi' misapplied	see *C. japonica* subsp. *rusticana* 'Beni-arajishi'
	- 'Augustine Supreme'	CMac
	- 'Ave Maria' 🏆H5	CSgt CTrh LRHS MGos NRHS
	- 'Baby Pearl'	LSRN SCam
	- 'Baby Sis'	LRHS NRHS
	- 'Ballet Dancer' 🏆H5	ELon LSRN SCam
	- 'Baron Gomer'	see *C. japonica* 'Comte de Gomer'
	- 'Baronne Leguay'	SCam
	- 'Beau Harp'	LRHS NRHS SCam
	- 'Bella Lambertii'	CKel
	- 'Bella Romana'	SCam
	- 'Berenice Boddy' 🏆H5	LRHS NRHS
	- 'Betty Foy Sanders'	CTrh
	- 'Betty Robinson'	LRHS NRHS
	- 'Betty Sheffield'	LRHS MAsh NRHS
	- 'Betty Sheffield Pink'	LRHS NRHS SCam
	- 'Betty Sheffield Supreme'	CBcs SCam
	- 'Black Magic'	CSgt CTrh LRHS MAsh NRHS SCam
	- 'Black Tie'	CBcs CTrh ELon LRHS MAsh MGos NEgg NRHS SCog WFar
	- 'Blackburnia'	see *C. japonica* 'Althaeiflora'
§	- 'Blood of China'	CBcs CKel CSBt CSgt EUJe LRHS LSRN MGos NLar NRHS SCam SCoo SWvt
	- 'Blush Tinsie'	LRHS NRHS
	- 'Bob Hope' 🏆H5	CBcs CTrh CTri LRHS NRHS SCam
	- 'Bob's Tinsie' 🏆H5	CBcs CSBt CTsd ECre ELon EPfP LRHS LSRN MGos NRHS SPoG
§	- 'Bokuhan' 🏆H5	MPkF SCam
	- 'Bright Buoy'	LRHS NRHS
	- 'Brushfield's Yellow'	CBcs CKel CRos CSBt CSgt CTrh CTsd ELan ELon EPfP IArd LRHS LSRN MAsh MGos NLar NRHS SCam SCog SCoo SPer SSta WSpi
	- 'Bush Hill Beauty'	see *C. japonica* 'Lady de Saumarez'
§	- 'C.M. Hovey' 🏆H5	CMac CSgt LRHS MAsh NRHS
	- 'C.M. Wilson'	CMac
	- 'Campsii Alba'	CSgt CTsd SCam SCoo
	- 'Can Can'	ELon
	- 'Candy Apple'	CTrh
	- 'Cara Mia'	CTsd LRHS NRHS SCam SCoo
	- 'Carolyn Tuttle'	CSgt LRHS NRHS
	- 'Carter's Sunburst' 🏆H5	CBcs ELon EPfP
	- 'Cassandra' 🏆H5	EPfP
	- 'Chandleri Elegans'	see *C. japonica* 'Elegans'
	- 'Charlotte de Rothschild'	CTrh CTri
	- 'Cinderella'	LRHS NRHS
	- CLASSIQUE ('Kerguelen'[PBR]) (v)	CKel LRHS MAsh MPkF NEgg WFar
	- 'Colonel Firey'	see *C. japonica* 'C.M. Hovey'
	- 'Commander Mulroy' 🏆H5	CBcs SCoo
§	- 'Comte de Gomer'	ELon EPfP LRHS NPri NRHS SCam
	- 'Conspicua'	CBcs
	- 'Contessa Woronzoff' **new**	CKel
§	- 'Coquettii' 🏆H5	CSgt LRHS MAsh NRHS

	- 'Curly Lady'[PBR]	MJak NPri WFar
§	- 'Dahlohnega'	CBcs CKel CRos CSBt CSgt CTrh ELon LMil LRHS LSRN MAsh MGos MPkF NRHS SCog WFar
	- 'Daikagura'	CBcs
	- 'Dainty'	CBcs
	- 'Daitairin'	see *C. japonica* 'Dewatairin'
	- 'Daphne du Maurier'	LRHS NRHS
	- 'Dark of the Moon'	LRHS NRHS
	- 'Dear Jenny'	CBcs CSgt
	- 'Debutante'	CBcs CMac ELon SCam
	- 'Deep Secret' 🏆H5	SCog
	- 'Desire' 🏆H5	CBcs CKel CPla CSBt CSgt CTrh CTsd LCro LMil LOPS LRHS LSRN MAsh MGos MJak MPkF NEgg NRHS SCam SCog SPoG WFar
	- 'Devonia'	CBcs
§	- 'Dewatairin' (Higo)	CBcs SCam SCog
	- 'Diddy's Pink Organdie'	LRHS NRHS
	- 'Dixie Knight'	LRHS NRHS SCam
	- 'Dobreei'	CMac
	- 'Doctor Burnside'	CBcs CTrh LMaj LRHS SCam SCog
	- 'Doctor King'	CSgt EPfP LRHS MAsh NEgg NPri NRHS SCoo SPoG WFar
	- 'Doctor Tinsley' 🏆H5	CRos CSgt EPfP LRHS MAsh NPri NRHS SCam
	- 'Dona Herzilia de Freitas Magalhães'	CBcs
	- 'Donckelaeri'	see *C. japonica* 'Masayoshi'
	- 'Donnan's Dream'	CBcs CTrh
	- 'Drama Girl' 🏆H5	CBcs CTsd LMaj LRHS NRHS SCam
	- 'Dream Time'	CBcs
	- 'Duchesse Decazes'	CBcs
	- 'Edelweiss'	ELon SCam
§	- 'Elegans'	CBcs CKel ELon EPfP LCro LMil LOPS LRHS MGos NEgg NRHS SCam SCog SLim SPer SPoG SWvt
	- 'Elegans Champagne'	CSgt
	- 'Elegans Supreme'	SCog
	- 'Elisabeth'	LRHS NRHS
	- 'Elizabeth Arden'	CTsd
	- 'Elizabeth Cooper'	CTrh LSRN
	- 'Elizabeth Hawkins'	CSgt CTrh EUJe LRHS MAsh NRHS SCam
	- 'Emmett Pfingstl'	SCam
	- 'Emperor of Russia'	CBcs LRHS NRHS
	- 'Eric Baker'	SCam
	- 'Eugène Lizé'	SCam
	- 'Eximia'	LRHS NRHS
	- 'Faith'	CBcs
	- 'Fanny'	CSgt
§	- 'Faustina'	LRHS MAsh NRHS
	- 'Finlandia Variegated' (v)	ELon SCam
	- 'Firebird'	CBcs CTsd
	- 'Flashlight'	EPfP LRHS NRHS
§	- 'Fleur Dipater'	CBcs CRos CSgt LRHS NRHS SCam SCog
	- 'Flowerwood'	SCam SCog
	- 'Forest Green'	SCog
	- 'Francesco Ferruccio' **new**	CKel
	- 'Frans van Damme'	CBcs
	- 'Fred Sander'	LRHS NRHS SCam
	- 'Galileo' **new**	CKel
	- 'Giardino Santarelli' **new**	CKel
	- 'Giardino Schmitz' **new**	CKel
§	- 'Gigantea'	ELon LRHS NRHS SCam
	- 'Giuditta Rosani'	LRHS NRHS
	- 'Glen 40'	see *C. japonica* 'Coquettii'
	- 'Gloire de Nantes' 🏆H5	CTrh SCam SCog
	- 'Gold Tone'	ELon SCam
	- 'Grace Bunton'	CBcs ELon
	- 'Grand Prix' 🏆H5	ELon LSRN NLar SCam
	- 'Grand Slam' 🏆H5	MAsh SCam
	- 'Guest of Honor'	CSgt EUJe LRHS NRHS
	- 'Guilio Nuccio' 🏆H5	CBcs CTri ELon EPfP LRHS LSRN NPri NRHS SCam SLim
	- 'Gus Menard'	SCam
	- 'Gwenneth Morey'	CBcs
	- 'H.A. Downing'	SCam
§	- 'Hagoromo' 🏆H5	CBcs CSBt CTrh CTsd LRHS NRHS
§	- 'Hakurakuten' 🏆H5	CTrh CTri SCam SCog SCoo
	- 'Hanafūki'	LRHS MAsh NRHS SCam SCog
	- 'Happy Birthday'	LSRN
	- 'Happy Higo' **new**	SCam
	- 'Haru-no-utena'	CTrh
	- 'Hatsuzakura'	see *C. japonica* 'Dewatairin'
	- 'Hawaii'	CMac CTrh ELon LRHS NRHS SCam
	- HERME	see *C. japonica* 'Hikarugenji'
	- 'High Hat'	CBcs SCam
§	- 'Hikarugenji'	LRHS NRHS SCog
	- 'Hinomaru'	CMac
	- 'Holly Bright'	CTrh LRHS MPkF
§	- 'Imbricata'	CSgt CTrh LRHS MAsh NRHS
	- 'Imperator'	SCam
	- 'Incarnata'	SCam
	- 'Isabella Orsini' **new**	CKel
	- 'Italiana Vera'	CSgt LRHS MAsh NRHS
	- 'J.J. Whitfield'	CMac
§	- 'Japonica Variegata' (v)	LRHS NRHS
	- 'Joseph Pfingstl' 🏆H5	CSgt CTri EPfP LRHS MAsh MMuc NLar NRHS SCam
	- 'Jovey Carlyon'	CBcs CSgt LRHS NRHS
	- 'Joy Sander'	see *C. japonica* 'Apple Blossom'
	- 'Jubilee Gem'	CTsd
	- 'Juno'	CBcs LRHS NRHS
	- 'Jupiter' Paul, 1904 🏆H5	CKel CMac CSgt CTri EPfP LSRN MAsh SCam SCog
§	- 'K. Sawada'	SCam
	- 'Kellingtoniana'	see *C. japonica* 'Gigantea'
	- 'Kentucky'	LRHS NRHS
	- 'Kick-off'	CBcs CTrh LRHS SCam
	- 'Kimberley'	CTsd EUJe LSRN SCam
	- 'King's Ransom'	CSgt LRHS NRHS
	- 'Kingyoba-shiro-wabisuke'	SCam
	- 'Kingyo-tsubaki'	SCam SSta
	- 'Kitty Berry'	CTrh
	- 'Kokinran'	SCam
§	- 'Konronkoku' 🏆H5	CSgt LRHS NRHS
	- 'Kouron-jura'	see *C. japonica* 'Konronkoku'
	- 'Kramer's Supreme' 🏆H5	CBcs CCCN CKel CSgt ELon LRHS LSRN MAsh MGos NRHS SCam SCoo SGol
§	- 'Kumasaka'	CSgt CTri LRHS MAsh NRHS
	- 'La Pace Rubra'	SCam
	- 'Lady Campbell'	CPla CTri EPfP LRHS NPri SCam SCoo WFar
	- 'Lady Clare'	see *C. japonica* 'Akashigata'
§	- 'Lady de Saumarez'	CBcs CMac CTsd
	- 'Lady Kay' **new**	LRHS
	- 'Lady Loch'	CTrh SCam
	- 'Lady Marion'	see *C. japonica* 'Kumasaka'
	- 'Lady McCulloch'	LRHS NRHS
	- 'Lady Vansittart'	CKel CRos CSgt CTrh EPfP LMil LOPS LRHS LSRN MAsh MGos NEgg NRHS SCam SCog SLim SPer SPoG SSta
§	- 'Lady Vansittart Pink'	CMac
	- 'Lady Vansittart Red'	see *C. japonica* 'Lady Vansittart Pink'
	- 'Lady Vansittart Shell'	see *C. japonica* 'Yours Truly'
	- 'Latifolia'	SCam

	Name	Suppliers
	- 'Laura's Red'	CTsd
	- 'Laurie Bray'	SCog SCoo
§	- 'Lavinia Maggi' ♀H5	CBcs CSgt CTri ELon EPfP LRHS LSRN MAsh MGos NPri NRHS SCam SCoo SPoG SRms SSta
	- 'Lavinia Maggi Rosea'	LMaj
	- 'L'Avvenire'	CKel
	- 'Lemon Drop'	CBcs CTrh
	- 'Leonora Novick'	SCog
	- 'Lily Pons'	CTrh LRHS
	- 'Lipstick'	LRHS
	- 'Little Bit'	ELon SCam SSta
	- 'Little Man'	LRHS NRHS
	- 'Lovelight' ♀H5	CSgt CTrh LRHS NRHS
	- 'Ludgvan Red'	LRHS NRHS
	- 'Lulu Belle'	CBcs
	- 'Mabel Blackwell'	ELon SCam
	- 'Madame de Strekaloff'	CMac CSBt SCam
	- 'Madame Lebois'	SCam
	- 'Madge Miller'	CSgt LRHS MAsh NRHS
	- 'Magnoliiflora'	see *C. japonica* 'Hagoromo'
	- 'Maiden's Blush'	CMac
	- 'Marchesa Margherita Serra' **new**	CKel
	- 'Margaret Davis' ♀H5	CCCN CKel CRos CSBt CSgt ELan ELon EPfP LCro LOPS LRHS LSRN MAsh MGos NRHS SCam SCoo SGol SLim WFar
	- 'Margaret Davis Picotee'	CBcs CTrh SCog SPer
	- 'Margaret Rose'	SCam
	- 'Margaret Short'	CTsd
	- 'Margherita Coleoni'	CBcs
	- 'Marguérite Gouillon' Drouard-Gouillon	SSta
	- 'Maria Antonietta' **new**	CKel
	- 'Marian Mitchell'	SCam
	- 'Mariana'	ELon
	- 'Mariottii Rubra'	CMac
	- 'Marjorie Magnificent'	CSgt LRHS MAsh
	- 'Mark Alan'	LSRN SCam
	- 'Maroon and Gold'	CSgt LRHS NRHS
	- 'Mars' ♀H5	CBcs SCam
	- 'Marshmallow'	LRHS
	- 'Mary Costa'	CTrh SCam
	- 'Mary J. Wheeler'	LSRN
§	- 'Masayoshi' ♀H5	CBcs CSBt LRHS NRHS
	- 'Mathotiana Alba'	CMac CTri CTsd EPfP LSRN MGos SCam WSpi
§	- 'Mathotiana Rosea'	CBcs CMac NLar
	- 'Mathotiana Supreme'	SCam SCog
	- 'Matilija Poppy'	CTrh SCam
	- 'Matterhorn'	CTrh
	- 'Mattie Cole'	SCam
	- 'Mercury' ♀H5	CKel CMac EPfP GGGa
	- 'Mermaid'	LRHS NRHS SCam
	- 'Midnight'	CBcs CTsd LRHS MAsh NRHS
	- 'Midnight Magic'	CBcs CSgt CTrh CTri LRHS NRHS
	- 'Midnight Serenade'	LRHS NRHS
	- 'Midnight Variegated' (v)	MPkF
	- 'Midsummer's Day'	CBcs
§	- 'Mikenjaku'	CBcs CKel CSgt EPfP LRHS NRHS SCog
	- 'Miriam Stevenson'	SCam
	- 'Miss Charleston'	CBcs
	- 'Monstruosa Rubra'	see *C. japonica* 'Gigantea'
	- 'Monte Carlo'	SCam
	- 'Moshe Dayan'	CCht CKel CSgt CTsd LRHS MAsh NRHS SCam
§	- 'Mrs Bertha A. Harms'	LRHS NRHS SCam
	- 'Mrs Charles Cobb'	LRHS
	- 'Mrs D.W. Davis'	CBcs EPfP
	- 'Mrs William Thompson'	LRHS NRHS SCam
	- 'Myorenji'	SCam
	- 'Nagasaki'	see *C. japonica* 'Mikenjaku'
	- 'Nancy Bird'	SCam
	- 'Nigra'	see *C. japonica* 'Konronkoku'
	- 'Nina Avery'	SCam
	- 'Niobé'	CKel
	- 'Nobilissima' ♀H5	CBcs CKel CMac CSgt CTrh CTri LCro LMil LOPS MAsh MBlu MJak MMuc NEgg SCam SCog SPer SPoG WFar
	- 'Nokogiriba-tsubaki'	MPkF
	- 'Nuccio's Cameo' ♀H5	CBcs CSgt CTrh EPfP LRHS MAsh NPri NRHS
	- 'Nuccio's Gem' ♀H5	CBcs CSgt EPfP LRHS NRHS SGol
	- 'Nuccio's Jewel' ♀H5	CSBt CSgt EPfP LRHS LSRN MAsh NRHS SCam
	- 'Nuccio's Pearl' ♀H5	CBcs CSgt EPfP LMaj LRHS LSRN NPri NRHS SArc SCam SCog
	- 'Nuccio's Pink Lace'	CBcs CSgt CTri LRHS MAsh NRHS
	- 'Onetia Holland'	CBcs CKel LSRN SCam SCog SLim WFar
	- 'Oo-La-La'	CTrh
	- 'Optima'	CBcs ELon LRHS NRHS SCam
	- 'Orandakō'	LRHS SCob
	- 'Patricia Ann'	LSRN
	- 'Paulette Goddard'	SCam
	- 'Paul's Apollo'	see *C. japonica* 'Apollo' Paul, 1911
	- 'Peachblossom'	see *C. japonica* 'Fleur Dipater'
	- 'Pearl Harbor'	SCam
	- 'Pink Chiffon'	CSgt LRHS NRHS
	- 'Pink Perfection'	see *C. japonica* subsp. *rusticana* 'Otome'
	- 'Pope John Paul XXIII'	SCam
	- 'Pride of Descanso'	see *C. japonica* 'Yukibotan'
	- 'Primavera'	CTrh SCam
	- 'Prince Murat'	LRHS NRHS
	- 'Princess Baciocchi'	SCam
	- 'Princess du Mahe'	CMac
	- 'Princesse Baciocchi' **new**	CBcs
	- 'R.L. Wheeler' ♀H5	CBcs CKel CSBt CSgt CTri EPfP LMaj LRHS LSRN MGos NPri NRHS SCam SCog SCoo
	- 'Raspberry Ripple'	MPkF
	- 'Red Dandy'	CSgt SCam
	- 'Red Red Rose'	LRHS NRHS SCam
	- 'Roger Hall'	CBcs CSgt CTrh LRHS LSRN MAsh NRHS SPoG
	- 'Rōgetsu'	CBcs
	- 'Rosa Baroveira Nella'	NLar
	- 'Rosa Mundi'	LPra
	- 'Rosa Perfecta' **new**	LPra
	- 'Rosularis'	ELon
	- 'Royal Velvet'	CTrh
	- 'Rubescens Major'	CBcs
	- 'Ruddigore'	CTrh
	- subsp. ***rusticana*** 'Arajishi' misapplied	see *C. japonica* subsp. *rusticana* 'Beni-arajishi'
	- - 'Arajishi' Ko'emon	SCam
§	- - 'Beni-arajishi'	LRHS NRHS SCam SCog
§	- - 'Otome'	SCam
	- - 'Reigyoku' (v)	CBcs
	- 'Sabiniana'	LRHS NRHS
	- 'Sacco Nova'	LMaj
	- 'Saint André'	CMac CSgt LRHS MAsh NRHS
	- 'San Dimas' ♀H5	CTrh ELon LRHS MPkF NRHS SCam
	- 'Saturnia'	CKel CRos CSgt ELon LRHS MAsh MJak NRHS
	- 'Sawada's Dream'	SCam SCog

	Name	Suppliers
	- 'Scentsation' ♀H5	CTri LRHS NRHS
	- 'Sea Foam'	LRHS NRHS SCam
	- 'Sea Gull'	SCam
	- 'Shikibu'	CTrh SCam
	- 'Shiragiku'	CBcs LMaj
	- 'Shiro Chan'	ELon SCam
	- 'Shirobotan'	CSgt ELon LRHS NRHS SCam
	- 'Silver Anniversary' ♀H5	CBcs CKel CSBt CSgt CTri ELon EPfP LCro LMil LOPS LRHS LSRN MAsh MGos MJak NEgg NLar NPri NRHS SCam SCoo SLim SPer SPoG SWvt WFar
	- 'Silver Moon'	see *C. japonica* 'K. Sawada'
	- 'Silver Ruffles'	CTrh ELon LRHS NRHS SCam
	- 'Something Beautiful'	SCam
	- 'Souvenir de Bahuaud-Litou' ♀H5	CBcs SCam SCog
	- 'Spencer's Pink'	CBcs
	- 'Splendens Carlyon'	CSgt LRHS MAsh NRHS
	- 'Spring Fever'	SCam
	- 'Spring Fling'	CTrh SPoG
	- 'Spring Formal'	CTrh
	- 'Spring Frill'	SCam
	- 'Stacy Susan'	MPkF
	- 'Strawberry Swirl'	CBcs
	- 'Sugar Babe'	CTrh LRHS NRHS SCam
	- 'Sylva' ♀H5	EUJe GGGa
	- 'Sylvia'	CMac
	- 'Takanini'	CBcs CTrh LRHS MPkF SCam
	- 'Tama-no-ura'	SCam
	- 'Tammia'	CSgt LRHS NRHS
	- 'Teresa Ragland'	SCam
§	- 'The Czar'	CBcs
	- 'The Mikado'	CSgt LRHS NRHS
	- 'Tickled Pink'	SCam
	- 'Tiffany'	CBcs ELon LRHS NRHS SCam SCog
	- 'Tiki'	SCoo
	- 'Tinker Bell'	ELon SCam
	- 'Tinker Toy'	CTrh
	- 'Tom Thumb' ♀H5	CTrh ELon LRHS NRHS SRms
	- 'Tomorrow'	SCam
	- 'Tomorrow Park Hill'	SCog
	- 'Tomorrow's Dawn'	SCam
	- 'Touchdown'	SCam
	- 'Tregye'	CBcs
	- 'Trewithen White'	CSgt LRHS MAsh NRHS
§	- 'Tricolor' ♀H5	CBcs CKel CMac CSBt CTrh ELon LRHS MGos MMuc NRHS SCam SCog
	- 'Tricolor Red'	see *C. japonica* 'Lady de Saumarez'
	- 'Trinket'	SCam
	- 'Victor Emmanuel'	see *C. japonica* 'Blood of China'
	- 'Ville de Nantes'	LRHS NRHS
	- 'Virginia Carlyon'	CBcs
	- 'Virginia Franco' **new**	CKel
	- 'Virginia Robinson'	SCam
	- 'Visconti Nova'	LRHS NRHS
	- 'Vittorio Emanuele II'	CSgt CTrh LRHS NRHS
	- 'Volunteer'	LCro LOPS
	- 'Warrior'	SCam
	- 'Wheel of Fortune'	LRHS NRHS
	- 'White Nun'	CBcs SCog
	- 'White Swan'	CMac CSBt CSgt LRHS NRHS
	- 'Wildfire'	LRHS NRHS
	- 'William Bartlett'	CTrh SCoo
	- 'William Honey'	CTrh
	- 'Wisley White'	see *C. japonica* 'Hakurakuten'
	- 'Witman Yellow'	CTrh
§	- 'Yours Truly'	CMac CRos CSgt CTrh CTsd LRHS LSRN NRHS
§	- 'Yukibotan'	CBcs
	'Jury's Yellow'	see *C. × williamsii* 'Jury's Yellow'
	'Lasca Beauty' (*japonica* × *reticulata*)	CBcs
	'Lavender Queen'	see *C. sasanqua* 'Lavender Queen'
	'Leonard Messel' (*reticulata* × (× *williamsii*)) ♀H5	CKel CMac CTrh CTri CTsd EPfP LRHS MGos MPkF NLar NRHS SCam SCog SPer WHor
	'Liz Henslowe'	CTsd
	lutchuensis	LRHS MPkF
	'Magic Mum'	LSRN
	'Maud Messel' (*reticulata* × (× *williamsii*))	SCam
	'Nicky Crisp' (*japonica* × *pitardii*)	CSgt CTrh LRHS NRHS SPoG
	oleifera	CExl CTrh
	'Pink Goddess' (*hiemalis* hybrid)	LRHS MPkF
	'Pink Icicle' (*oleifera* hybrid)	CBcs ELon SCam
	'Pink Spangles'	see *C. japonica* 'Mathotiana Rosea'
	pitardii WWJ 11925 from Vietnam	WCru
	'Polar Ice'	CBcs
	'Portuense'	see *C. japonica* 'Japonica Variegata'
	'Quintessence' (*japonica* × *lutchuensis*)	CTrh LRHS
	reticulata 'Les Jury'	SCog
	- 'Mary Williams'	SPoG
	- 'Mouchang'	CBcs
	- 'William Hertrich'	CBcs
	rosthorniana CUPIDO	see *C. rosthorniana* 'Elina'
§	- 'Elina'PBR	ELan LCro LOPS LRHS NRHS SPoG
	'Royalty' (*japonica* × *reticulata*) ♀H5	CBcs
I	***sasanqua*** 'Alba'	CMac CSgt CTri
	- 'Baronesa de Soutelinho'	ELon SCam
	- 'Bonanza'	see *C. hiemalis* 'Bonanza'
	- 'Cleopatra'	EPfP SCob
	- 'Cotton Candy'	SCam
	- 'Crimson King' ♀H4	CSgt CTrh LRHS NRHS
	- 'Dazzler'	see *C. hiemalis* 'Dazzler'
	- 'Dwarf Shishi'	CTrh
	- 'Early Pearly'	SCam
	- 'Flamingo'	see *C. sasanqua* 'Fukuzutsumi'
	- 'Fragrans'	ELon SCam
	- 'Fuji-no-mine'	ELon SCam
§	- 'Fukuzutsumi'	CSBt
	- 'Gay Border'	LRHS
	- 'Gay Sue'	CTrh SCam
	- 'Hinode-gumo'	SEWo
	- 'Hiryū'	CSgt LRHS NRHS SCam SCog
	- 'Hugh Evans' ♀H4	CBcs CTrh ELan ELon EPfP LRHS NRHS SCam SSta
	- 'Jean May' ♀H4	CSgt ELon EPfP LRHS NRHS SCam WCot
	- 'Jennifer Susan' **new**	CTri
	- 'Kenkyō'	ELon SCam SSta
§	- 'Lavender Queen'	SCam
	- 'Maiden's Blush'	LRHS NRHS SCam SCog WCot
	- 'Mignonne'	CTrh
	- 'Narumigata' ♀H4	CBcs CKel CMac CSgt CTrh CTsd EPfP LCro LOPS LRHS MBlu MGos NRHS SCam SPoG SSta WSHC
	- 'New Dawn'	SCam
	- 'Nyewoods'	CMac
	- 'Papaver'	SCam
	- 'Paradise Audrey'	LMil LRHS LSRN SPoG
	- 'Paradise Belinda'	EPfP LMil LRHS SPoG
	- 'Paradise Blush'	CBcs LRHS NRHS
	- 'Paradise Glow'	CBcs LMil

- 'Paradise Helen'	LRHS LSRN
- 'Paradise Hilda'	LRHS
- 'Paradise Pearl'	CBcs EPfP LMil LRHS NRHS
- 'Paradise Venessa'	CTsd EPfP SCam
- 'Plantation Pink'	CKel CSgt CTrh LCro LOPS LRHS NRHS SRkn WCot
- 'Rainbow'	CBcs CSgt CTrh ELan ELon EPfP LRHS MPkF NRHS SCog SCoo SSta
- 'Rosea'	CMac CSgt ELon LRHS NRHS SCam SCog
- 'Sasanqua Rubra'	CMac SCam
- 'Sasanqua Variegata' (v)	CTrh ELon MPkF SCam
- 'Sekiyō'	LRHS
- 'Snowflake'	SCam SSta
- 'Sparkling Burgundy'	see *C.* 'Sparkling Burgundy'
- 'Tanya'	CTrh SCam
- 'Versicolor'	CSgt EPfP LRHS NRHS
- 'Winter's Joy'	CBcs SCam
- 'Winter's Snowman'	LCro LOPS LRHS NRHS SCam
'Scented Sun'	CTrh
'Scentuous' (*japonica* × *lutchuensis*)	CBcs
'Show Girl' (*reticulata* × *sasanqua*) ♀H4	SCam SCog
§ ***sinensis***	CBcs CCCN CSgt CTrh CTsd GPoy LRHS NLar NRHS SCam SPlb SPre SWvt
- var. ***assamica***	CCCN SPre
- var. ***sinensis***	CCCN
'Snow Flurry'	CBcs CSgt CTrh LRHS NRHS
§ 'Sparkling Burgundy' ♀H4	LRHS MGos NRHS SCam SCog
'Spring Festival' (*cuspidata* hybrid) ♀H4	CBcs CSBt CSgt CTrh EPfP LCro LMil LOPS LRHS MGos NPri NRHS SCam
'Spring Mist' (*japonica* × *lutchuensis*)	CTrh
'Sugar Dream'	CTrh SCam
'Superscent'	CTrh
'Swan Lake'	EPfP LRHS NPri NRHS
'Sweet Emily Kate' (*japonica* × *lutchuensis*)	MPkF
'Sweet Jane'	LRHS MPkF SCam
'Tarōkaja' (wabisuke)	SCam
thea	see *C. sinensis*
'Tinsie'	see *C. japonica* 'Bokuhan'
'Tiny Princess' (*fraterna* × *japonica*)	CBcs
'Tom Knudsen' (*japonica* × *reticulata*) ♀H4	CTrh LRHS NRHS SCam
transnokoensis ♀H4	CExl CTrh LRHS MPkF
'Tricolor Sieboldii'	see *C. japonica* 'Tricolor'
'Tristrem Carlyon' (*reticulata* hybrid)	CCht CKel CSgt CTri CTsd EPfP LRHS MAsh NPri NRHS
tsaii	LRHS
'Usu-ōtome'	see *C. japonica* subsp. *rusticana* 'Otome'
× ***vernalis*** 'Yuletide'	CTrh LCro LOPS LRHS LSRN MPkF NRHS SCam SCob
× ***williamsii*** 'Angel Wings'	LRHS NRHS
- 'Anticipation' ♀H5	CBcs CCht CDul CKel CMac CSBt CSgt CTrh ELan EPfP GGGa GKin LCro LMil LOPS LRHS MAsh MGos MSwo NRHS SCob SCog SLim SPer SPoG SWvt WFar WHor
- 'Anticipation Variegated' (v)	CBcs LRHS NRHS
- 'Ballet Queen'	CBcs CSBt SCam
- 'Ballet Queen Variegated' (v)	ELon
- 'Bartley Number Five'	CMac
- 'Beatrice Michael'	CBcs CMac
- 'Blue Danube'	CBcs SCoo
- 'Bow Bells'	CDul CTri
- 'Bowen Bryant' ♀H5	CSgt CTrh EPfP LRHS NRHS
- 'Brigadoon' ♀H5	CBcs CSgt CTri EPfP GGGa LRHS MAsh NRHS SCam
- 'Buttons 'n' Bows'	MPkF
- 'C.F. Coates'	SCam
- 'Caerhays'	CBcs
- 'Carolyn Williams'	CBcs
- 'Celebration'	CBcs CSBt LSRN
- 'Charles Colbert'	LRHS SCam
- 'Charles Michael'	CBcs
- 'China Clay' ♀H5	EPfP LRHS LSRN NRHS
§ - 'Citation'	CBcs CMac
- 'Contribution'	CTrh
- 'Coral Delight'	MPkF
- 'Crinkles'	SCam
- 'Debbie' ♀H5	Widely available
- 'Debbie's Carnation'	LRHS NRHS SCam
- 'Deloraine'	CTsd
- 'Donation' ♀H5	Widely available
- 'Dream Boat'	CBcs
- 'E.G. Waterhouse'	CKel CSBt CSgt CTrh CTri ELan GKin LRHS MAsh MGos NRHS SCam SSta WFar
- 'E.T.R. Carlyon' ♀H5	CBcs CSgt CTrh CTri EPfP LMil LRHS MAsh MGos NLar NRHS SLim
- 'Elegant Beauty' ♀H5	CSgt CTrh ELon LRHS MAsh NLar NRHS SCam SCog
- 'Elizabeth Anderson'	CTrh CTsd
- 'Ellamine'	CBcs
- 'Elsie Jury' ♀H5	CBcs CMac CSgt CTri ELan ELon GKin LRHS MAsh MGos NLar NRHS SCam SCog SGol
- 'Exaltation'	SCam
- 'Fiona Colville'	SCam
- 'Francis Hanger'	CTrh LRHS NRHS SCam SPer
- 'Galaxie'	CBcs SCam
- 'Gay Time'	LRHS NRHS
- 'George Blandford' ♀H5	CBcs CMac
- 'Glenn's Orbit' ♀H5	NLar SCam
- 'Golden Spangles' (v)	CMac ELan EPfP LRHS MGos MMuc NRHS SCam SCog SEND SPer SPoG WHor
- 'Grand Jury'	ELon LRHS NRHS
- 'Gwavas'	CBcs CCCN CSgt CTrh LRHS NRHS SCam
- 'Hilo'	SCam
- 'J.C. Williams' ♀H5	CBcs CMac CTri LRHS SCog
- 'Jenefer Carlyon'	CBcs
- 'Jill Totty'	CTrh
- 'John Pickthorn'	CBcs
- 'Julia Hamiter' ♀H5	CBcs CSgt LRHS NRHS
§ - 'Jury's Yellow' ♀H5	CBcs CCCN CRos CSBt CSgt CTrh CTri ELan EPfP GGGa LCro LMil LOPS LRHS LSRN MAsh MGos NEgg NPri SCam SCog SLim SPer SPoG SSta SWvt
- 'Lady's Maid'	SCam
- 'Laura Boscawen'	CBcs CTrh SCam
- 'Les Jury' ♀H5	CBcs CSBt CTrh LMil LRHS LSRN MGos NRHS SCog SLim WFar
- 'Lucky Star' (d)	LRHS
- 'Margaret Waterhouse'	CBcs SCam SCog
- 'Marjorie Waldegrave'	CSgt LRHS NRHS
- 'Mary Jobson'	CBcs
- 'Mary Larcom'	CBcs
- 'Mary Phoebe Taylor' ♀H5	CBcs CKel LMaj NLar SCam SLim
- 'Mirage'	CTrh

- 'Monica Dance'	CBcs
- 'Muskoka' ♀H5	CBcs EPfP
- 'Night Rider'	MPkF SCam WPGP
- 'November Pink'	CBcs SCam
- 'Philippa Forward'	CMac
- 'Pink Wave'	CSgt LRHS NRHS
- 'Rendezvous'	CTrh SCam
- 'Rose Parade'	CSgt
- 'Rose Quartz'	CSgt
- 'Rosemary Williams'	CBcs CMac
- 'Ruby Wedding' (d) ♀H5	CBcs CKel CRos CSBt CSgt CTrh CTsd EPfP LMil LRHS LSRN MAsh MGos MJak NEgg NPri NRHS SCam SCog SCoo SLim SPer SPoG SWvt WFar
- 'Saint Ewe' ♀H5	CSBt CSgt CTrh CTri EPfP LRHS MGos NRHS SCam
- 'Saint Michael'	CBcs
- 'Sayonara'	LMaj
- 'Senorita' ♀H5	CSgt CTrh ELon LRHS MAsh NLar NRHS SCam
- 'Shocking Pink'	CSgt LRHS NRHS
- 'The Duchess of Cornwall'	LRHS NRHS SCam
- 'Tiptoe'	CTrh SCoo
- 'Toni Finlay's Fragrant'	CTrh
- 'Twinkle Star'	CSgt LRHS NRHS
- 'Water Lily' ♀H5	CBcs CTri ELon LRHS NLar NRHS SCam
- 'Wilber Foss'	LRHS NRHS SCam
- 'William Carlyon'	CSgt LRHS NRHS
- 'Winter Gem'	LRHS
'Winter's Charm'	CBcs CSgt LRHS NRHS
'Winter's Dream'	CBcs
'Winter's Interlude'	LRHS NRHS
'Winter's Toughie'	CBcs CSgt LRHS NRHS SCam
'Winton' (*cuspidata* × *saluenensis*)	CBcs
'Yoimachi' (*fraterna* × *sasanqua*)	CTrh LRHS

Camissonia (Onagraceae)

bistorta 'Sunflakes'	CSpe

Campanula ✿ (*Campanulaceae*)

RCBAM 13	WCot
alata	WHil XLum
'Albert Kirkham'	EBee WCot
§ ***alliariifolia***	Widely available
- DHTU 0126	WCru
- 'Ivory Bells'	see *C. alliariifolia*
- 'Ivory Towers' new	EBee
alpina	GJos
alsinoides	GEdr
americana	WFar XLum
ardonensis	GEdr
argaea	GKev
armena	GJos
arvatica	CRos EACa EHyd EPot LRHS NRHS NSla SRms WAbe WIce
aucheri	see *C. bellidifolia* subsp. *aucheri*
'Barbara Valentine'	EBee EWTr SCob WCAu
barbata	EACa EBee EMor EPfP GKev
bayerniana	GKev
'Belinda'	CPBP EPot SIgm
bellidifolia	CPla LLHF NSla
§ - subsp. ***aucheri***	GEdr GKev
- subsp. ***saxifraga***	GEdr
bellidifolia* × *tridentata	GKev
§ ***betulifolia*** ♀H5	EACa GCrg GEdr GKev NSla WCot
biebersteiniana	GEdr LLHF NSla
'Birch Hybrid'	CRos EACa ECtt EHyd ELan ELon GBee GCrg LRHS MMuc NRHS SAko SEND SIgm SRms XLum
'Blue Octopus'	CRos CWGN EHyd ELon EMor IPot LRHS MPnt NCGa NRHS SCob SRms
'Blue Pearl'	WAbe
bononiensis	SRms
'Burghaltii'	NLar SHar WArt
* ***campanulata*** new	MCot
'Cantata'	WAbe
carpatica ♀H5	CPla EPfP NBro NGdn SPlb SRms WFar XLum
- f. ***alba***	CRos EHyd LRHS NGdn NRHS SPlb XLum
§ - - 'Weisse Clips'	CBar CRos ECtt EHyd ELan EPfP GMaP LCro LOPS LRHS MAsh MJak NEgg NGdn NHol NRHS SCob SPer SPoG SRms SWvt WFar
§ - 'Blaue Clips'	CBar CBcs CRos ECtt EHyd ELan EPfP GMaP IPot LCro LRHS MAsh MGos MJak NEgg NGdn NHic NRHS SCob SPer SPoG SRms SWvt WFar
- BLUE CLIPS	see *C. carpatica* 'Blaue Clips'
- 'Blue Moonlight'	CRos EACa EHyd LRHS NRHS
- blue-flowered	ECrN
- 'Chewton Joy'	CRos EACa EHyd LRHS NRHS
- dwarf	EPot
- 'Kathy'	EPot GCrg
- 'Pearl White'	MHol
- 'Rapido Blue'	MHol
- var. ***turbinata***	SRms
- - 'Foerster'	CRos EACa EHyd GCrg LRHS NRHS XLum
- - 'Isabel'	CRos EACa EHyd LRHS NRHS XLum
- - 'Jewel'	CRos EACa EHyd EPot LRHS NRHS
- WHITE CLIPS	see *C. carpatica* f. *alba* 'Weisse Clips'
§ ***cashmeriana***	GKev WAbe
- white-flowered	GKev
cephallenica	see *C. garganica* subsp. *cephallenica*
cervicaria	GJos
§ ***chamissonis***	EPot GEdr LLHF NWad
- 'Major'	EWes
- 'Oyobeni'	EACa
§ - 'Superba' ♀H5	EACa NHpl SIgm WAbe WIce
'Chloe'	EBee EWTr WHil
choruhensis	EWes GEdr GKev LLHF SPlb
ciliata	GEdr
§ ***cochlearifolia*** ♀H5	CRos CSpe EBee EBou EHyd EPfP GAbr GJos GMaP LRHS MAsh MMuc NHpl NRHS NWad SEND SPoG WFar WHoo XLum
- var. ***alba***	CSpe CTri EBou EDAr ELan MHer MMuc NHpl NRya SEND SIgm SRms WFar XLum
- - 'White Baby' (Baby Series)	CRos EACa EHyd EPfP EPot LRHS NRHS NWad SPoG SRms XLum
- 'Bavaria Blue'	NHol XLum
- 'Bells Blue'	MHol NEgg
- 'Blue Baby' (Baby Series)	ECtt EPfP LRHS NHpl SPoG SRms SRot
- 'Blue Wonder'	ECtt GCrg
- 'Elizabeth Oliver' (d) ♀H5	CBod CMea CRos EACa ECtt EDAr EHyd ELan EPot GCrg GEdr GMaP LRHS MHer MHol NBir NHpl NRHS SPlb SRms WAbe WFar WHoo WIce

	- 'Flore Pleno' (d)	WFar
	- 'R.B. Loder' (d)	CRos EHyd LRHS MHer NRHS
	- 'Tubby'	CRos EACa EHyd EPot LLHF LRHS MHer NRHS SBch SRms
	- 'Warleyensis'	see *C.* × *haylodgensis* W. Brockbank 'Warley White'
	collina	CRos EACa EBee EHyd LLHF LRHS NRHS XLum
	'Constellation'	EACa
	'Covadonga'	CMea CRos EACa EHyd LRHS NRHS WAbe WThu
	cretica	MHol
	'Crystal'	CFis ECtt MAvo MCot NLar WCot WFar
	cymbalaria	GKev
	dasyantha	see *C. chamissonis*
	divaricata	LPla
	dolomitica	CPla EACa LLHF
	'E.K. Toogood'	CElw CPBP EACa EBou ECtt EPot SRms XLum
	'Faichem Lilac'	WCot
	fenestrellata	EACa XLum
§	- subsp. ***istriaca***	GKev
	finitima	see *C. betulifolia*
	garganica ♀H5	CRos EACa EBou EDAr EHyd EPfP GMaP GWyn LRHS MAsh MMuc MRav NRHS SRms SVic SWvt WFar WMoo XLum
	- 'Aurea'	see *C. garganica* 'Dickson's Gold'
	- 'Blue Diamond'	EACa EBou ELon NLar
§	- subsp. ***cephallenica***	EACa NBro
§	- 'Dickson's Gold'	Widely available
	- 'Erinus Major'	EACa XLum
	- 'Filigree'	WBrk WCot
	- subsp. ***istriaca***	see *C. fenestrellata* subsp. *istriaca*
	- 'Major'	SPoG
	- 'Mrs Resholt'	CTri ECtt EPau MHer NBir NLar SRms SWvt WIce
	- 'Senior'	EWTr
	- 'W.H. Paine' ♀H5	EACa ECtt NLar NSla WAbe WBrk WFar WHoo
	'Glandore'	EACa SAko XLum
	glomerata	CBod CExl CWld GAbr GJos LSRN MHer NAln NBir NBro NEgg NGBl NMir WArt WFar
	- var. ***acaulis*** hort.	EPfP NEgg NGrd NLar SRms WFar XLum
	- var. ***alba***	CBcs CBod CNor CRos CSpe EACa ECtt EHyd ELan EMor EPfP GBin GJos GMaP LRHS MBel NRHS SCob SPer SPlb SPoG WCAu WGwG
§	- - 'Schneekrone'	ECha LCro LOPS WFar
	- 'Caroline' ♀H7	Widely available
	- CROWN OF SNOW	see *C. glomerata* var. *alba* 'Schneekrone'
	- var. ***dahurica***	CRos EAJP EBee EHyd EMor LRHS NLar NRHS SHar XLum
	- 'Emerald'	CBod CRos EACa EBee EHyd EPfP LRHS MHer MSCN NLar NRHS SPad SRms WFar XSen
	- 'Freya' PBR ♀H7	EACa EBee ECtt EPfP LPla LSun MHol MNrw SCob SPad WCot WFar WHil
	- (Genti Series) GENTI BLUE ('Allgentibl' PBR)	NPri WFar
	- - GENTI TWISTERBELL ('Allgentitwist' PBR)	CRos EMor LSun MHol MSCN NEoE WHil
	- - GENTI WHITE ('Allgentiw' PBR)	CWGN NLar NPri WFar
	- 'Joan Elliott'	CSam EBee ECha ECtt LEdu WGwG XSen
	- 'Purple Pixie'	LRHS SRms
	- 'Superba' ♀H7	Widely available
	grossekii	CRos EBee EHyd LLHF LRHS NRHS
	'Hannah'	CRos EACa EHyd LRHS NRHS
	× ***haylodgensis*** misapplied	see *C.* × *haylodgensis* 'Plena'
§	× ***haylodgensis*** W. Brockbank 'Marion Fisher' (d)	EPot WAbe WHoo
§	- 'Plena' (d)	CRos EACa ECtt EHyd EPot LRHS NRHS SRms WAbe WKif
§	- 'Warley White' (d)	XLum
	- 'Yvonne'	ECtt EPot GCrg NHpl WHil
	hercegovina	CPBP SIgm
	- 'Nana'	CPBP EPot SIgm WAbe
	'Hilltop Snow'	EPot
	hofmannii	CTsd GJos GKev NWad
	hypopolia	WAbe
§	***incurva***	EACa GJos GKev NAln WAbe
	IRIDESCENT BELLS ('Iribella' PBR)	CWGN EACa EBee EMor EWTr EWes LCro LRHS MBel NCGa NEgg NSti SPad SPer WCAu WHil WPnP WTyc
	isophylla ♀H2	EPot
	- 'Alba' ♀H2	EPot
	- 'Pamela'	EPot
	JENNY ('Harjen' PBR)	CWGN IPot SHar
	'Joe Elliott'	WAbe
	kemulariae	EDAr LLHF WCot XLum
	'Kent Belle' ♀H7	Widely available
	kirpicznikovii	GEdr GKev
	komarovii	WCot
	lactiflora	CAby CCBP CElw CFGn CMac CPla CSpe EACa EBee ECha EHyd EPfP GAbr LRHS MCot MNrw NRHS SPer WCAu WFar WMoo WSpi WWtn XLum
	- ***alba***	see *C. lactiflora* white-flowered
	- 'Alba' ♀H7	CAby EBee ECha EPfP GBin GMaP ILea MAvo MBel MHol MMuc SCob WBrk WCot WSpi
	- 'Assendon Pearl' ♀H7	EACa LPla SPhx WCot
	- AVALANCHE ('Camblo')	EACa EBee ECtt LCro LOPS MBNS MTis NCGa WCAu
	- 'Blue Cross'	EBee
	- 'Border Blues'	EBee ECtt ELon EPfP MHol MNrw NAst WFar
	- 'Dixter Presence'	LPla SMHy
	- dwarf pink-flowered	EACa EAJP EBee EPfP
	- 'Favourite' ♀H7	ECtt NGdn
	- 'Lidie's Choice'	CSam
	- 'Loddon Anna' ♀H7	Widely available
	- 'Moorland Rose'	WMoo
	- 'Platinum'	EACa LPla SMHy
	- 'Pouffe'	CRos EACa EBee ECtt EHyd EPfP GMaP GWyn LRHS MHol MNrw MRav NBro NGdn NLar NRHS SGbt SPer SWvt
	- 'Prichard's Variety' ♀H7	Widely available
	- 'Superba' ♀H7	EACa ECtt
	- 'Violet'	WSpi
	- 'White Pouffe'	CBod CRos EACa ECtt EHyd EPfP EWTr GMaP LRHS NChi NLar NRHS SGbt SPer SPoG WFar WGwG
§	- white-flowered	ECha NBir SPer WCAu
	latifolia	EACa GJos MCot NBid NChi NMir SPer SRms WCAu WMoo WShi WSpi
	- var. ***alba***	CRos EBee EHyd EPfP GJos GWyn LRHS MBel MMuc MSCN NGdn NRHS SEND SPer SRms WHal WSpi
*	- 'Amethyst'	WSpi

	Name	Suppliers
	– blue-flowered	SEND
	– 'Brantwood'	CDor CRos EHyd EPfP GAbr LRHS MRav NLar NRHS WSpi
	– 'Gloaming'	CRos EBee ECtt EHyd LRHS NCGa NRHS WSpi
	– var. ***macrantha***	CDor CMea CRos EBee EHyd ELan EPfP GMaP LRHS MBel NEgg NRHS NSti SWvt WMoo
	– – 'Alba'	CMea CRos ECtt GLog GMaP MHol MRav NLar WCAu WMoo
	latiloba	WCot WKif
§	– 'Alba'	EBee GCal MCot MNrw NEgg NLar NWad WBrk
	– 'Hidcote Amethyst'	CDor CRos CWGN ECtt EHyd ELan ELon GCal LRHS MCot MHol MMuc NBid NBir NCGa NGdn NLar NRHS SEND SPer WCAu WCot WKif WSpi
	– 'Highcliffe Variety' ♀H7	EACa EBee ECtt EHyd ELan EPfP LRHS MPie MRav NEgg NLar NRHS SPer SPoG WCAu WCot WRHF WSpi WWtn
	– 'Percy Piper' ♀H7	CRos EACa EBee EHyd LRHS MRav NCGa NLar NRHS WCAu WSpi
	– 'Splash'	MNrw
	'Linda'	IPot
	'Lynchmere'	CMea EPot NWad WAbe
	makaschvilii	CAby EACa EWhm GKev GWyn ILea MHer MMuc WOut
	– pink-flowered	GKev
	makaschvilii* × *trachelium	WCot
	'Margaret Brine'	WAbe
	'Marion Fisher'	see *C.* × *baylodgensis* W. Brockbank 'Marion Fisher'
§	***medium*** var. ***calycanthema*** hort.	WSpi
	– 'Cup and Saucer'	see *C. medium* var. *calycanthema* hort.
	'Mevr. V. Vollenhove'	CSpe EBee ECtt MAvo MHol NSti
	'Misty Dawn' ♀H7	MAvo NLar WCot
	modesta	GJos
	moesiaca	GKev NAln
	muralis	see *C. portenschlagiana*
	nitida	see *C. persicifolia* var. *planiflora*
	'Norman Grove'	EPot
	ochroleuca	CMea EBee GBin IMou WCFE WCot
I	– 'Nana'	GEdr
	odontosepala	WFar
	– from Iran	EMor EPPr NLar
	'Oliver's Choice'	WHrl
	olympica misapplied	see *C. rotundifolia* 'Olympica'
	orphanidea	IMou
	ossetica	EBee ECtt WBor
	pallida subsp. ***tibetica***	see *C. cashmeriana*
	patula	EACa WKif XLum
	'Paul Furse'	ECtt NCGa NSti SHar WCot WHrl
	'Pearlescent Pink'	EWes
	'Pearlescent White'	EWes
	pendula	GJos LSun SRot
	persicifolia	Widely available
	– var. ***alba***	Widely available
§	– 'Alba Coronata' (d)	GAbr SRms
	– 'Alba Plena'	see *C. persicifolia* 'Alba Coronata'
	– 'Azure Beauty'	CSpe EBee ECtt NLar WCot WSpi XSen
	– 'Beau Belle'	NLar
§	– 'Bennett's Blue' (d)	EPfP MRav
	– blue and white-flowered	SRms
	– 'Blue Bell'	GWyn
	– 'Blue Bloomers' (d)	CDor CRos EACa ECtt EHyd EWes IKil LRHS MBel MRav MSCN NQui NRHS NWad SRms WCFE WCot WHal WJam XLum
	– blue cup-in-cup (d)	WPtf
	– 'Blue-eyed Blonde'[PBR] (v)	NLar
	– blue-flowered	SPlb SRms
	– 'Boule de Neige' (d)	CDor WSpi
§	– 'Chettle Charm'[PBR]	CDor CRos CTri CWCL ECtt EHrv EHyd ELan EPfP EShb GAbr LRHS MRav NBir NLar NRHS SCob SRms SWvt WCot WFar WJam WPnP WTyc
	– 'Cornish Mist'	CExl CRos EACa EBee ECtt ELan EPfP GBin MHol MPie NLar WCAu WSpi
	– 'Fleur de Neige' (d)	MRav
	– 'Frances' (d)	WCot
	– 'Gawen'	CMac EACa ECtt EHyd LRHS NBre NRHS SGbt WCAu WCot
	– 'George Chiswell'	see *C. persicifolia* 'Chettle Charm'
	– 'Grandiflora'	CDor GBin
	– 'Grandiflora Alba'	EAJP GBin NLar NWad
	– 'Hampstead White' (d)	GCal WSpi
	– 'Kelly's Gold'	MHol MJak NBir SRms
	– 'La Belle' (d)	CRos EBee EHyd LRHS MNrw NLar NRHS WPnP
	– 'La Bello'[PBR]	CRos EBee EHyd LRHS MNrw NRHS WPnP
	– 'La Bonne Amie' (d)	EBee EPfP MNrw NLar SPoG XEll
	– 'Moerheimii' (d)	EPfP WSpi
	– 'Perry's Boy Blue'	NPer
§	– var. ***planiflora***	CPBP WAbe
	– – f. ***alba***	CPBP NHpl WAbe WCot
	– 'Powder Puff' (d)	EPfP GWyn MHol NEgg XEll
	– 'Pride of Exmouth' (d) ♀H7	CDor MHer MRav WSpi
	– subsp. ***sessiliflora*** 'Alba'	see *C. latiloba* 'Alba'
	– 'Snowdrift'	SRms
	– (Takion Series) 'Takion Blue'	CRos EHyd ELan GWyn LRHS NEgg NRHS SPoG SRms
	– – 'Takion White'	CRos EHyd ELan EPfP GWyn LRHS NEgg NRHS SPoG SRms
	– 'Telham Beauty' ambig.	CBod MCot NDai NEgg NGBl SCob SWvt WPtf WSpi XLum
	– 'Telham Beauty' misapplied	CRos CSBt EBee EHyd ELan EPfP LRHS MRav NRHS SPer SRms SWvt
	– 'Telham Beauty' D. Thurston	NLar
	– 'Tinpenny Blue'	WCot
	– 'Wortham Belle' misapplied	see *C. persicifolia* 'Bennett's Blue'
	– 'Wortham Belle' ambig.	CBod LPot MAsh MRav WCAu WHoo
	– 'Wortham Belle' Blooms	CRos ECtt EHyd GBin LRHS MBNS NEgg NRHS WGwG
	'Peter Nix'	EACa
	petrophila	WAbe
	pilosa	see *C. chamissonis*
	– 'Superba'	see *C. chamissonis* 'Superba'
	'Pink Octopus'[PBR]	CAby CBor CRos CWGN ECtt EHrv EHyd ELan ELon EMor EPfP EUJe LPot LRHS MBNS MHol MSCN MTis NCGa NGdn NLar NRHS SCob SEle SPad SPoG SRkn SRms WSpi XLum
	planiflora	see *C. persicifolia* var. *planiflora*
	pollinensis new	WCot
§	***portenschlagiana*** ♀H5	Widely available
	– 'Biokovo'	XLum
	– 'Catharina'	CRos EACa ECtt EHyd EPPr EShb LRHS MHol NRHS SPoG SRms

- 'Lieselotte' CElw CMea CPBP EACa ECtt EPot SAko
- 'Major' CBod EACa NCou WGwG WMoo
- 'Resholdt's Variety' CBar CMea CRos CSam CTri EACa EAJP EBou ECtt EDAr EHyd ELan EPfP GKev GMaP LRHS MHol MRav NRHS SAko SRms WCot WMoo XLum XSen
- 'Sago' **new** MHol

poscharskyana Widely available
- 'Blauranke' EACa EWes SAko XLum
- 'Blue Gown' EACa ECtt GCrg NCGa SAko XLum
- 'Blue Rivulet'PBR ECtt
- BLUE WATERFALL ('Camgood'PBR) CWCL CWGN EACa ECtt LSun MBNS NDov SPoG WBrk WCot XLum
- 'E.H. Frost' CBre CElw EACa ECtt ELan EPPr EPfP EWTr GKev GMaP LPot MCot MMuc NAln NLar NRya SAko SEND SPer SRms SWvt WBrk WMoo WSpi XLum
- 'Erich G.Arends' SAko
- I - 'Freya' EACa SAko XLum
- 'Frühlingszauber' WCot
- 'Garden Star' **new** CBod
- 'Hirsch Blue' EPfP SRms
- 'Lilacina' EACa EPPr
- 'Lisduggan Variety' CBre CElw EACa EBee ECtt EPPr EWes GMaP MHer NLar SAko SRms WBrk WFar WIce WJam WMoo XLum
- 'Nana Alba' EACa EPPr SAko WBrk
- 'Pinkins'PBR CBod CSma EACa ECtt WIce
- 'Schneeranke' XSen
- 'Silberregen' SAko
- 'Stella' ♀H5 CRos ECha ECtt EHyd ELan EPPr EPfP IPot LRHS LSRN MRav NBro NDov NRHS SAko SPer SWvt WBrk WCot WHoo WJam WMoo XLum
- 'Trollkind' EACa EPPr SAko XLum
- variegated (v) EBee EHoe EPPr
- white-flowered CTri ELan WFar

× ***pseudoraineri*** hort. CRos EACa EHyd EWes LRHS NRHS

pulla CRos EACa EBou ECtt EHyd ELan EPot GCrg GEdr LRHS NHpl NRHS NSla SCob SPoG SRms SRot WAbe WIce
- 'Alba' CRos EACa EHyd EPot LRHS NRHS NSla WAbe

× ***pulloides*** hort. 'G.F.Wilson' ♀H5 EACa ECtt EPot GMaP NLar SIgm SRkn
- 'Jelly Bells'PBR IPot NLar

punctata GJos MCot NBro NSti WFar WGwG WMoo
- f. ***albiflora*** WFar
- 'Alina's Double' (d) NLar
- dwarf CPBP
- 'Folies Bergère' **new** CBor
- var. ***hondoensis*** GKev
- hose-in-hose (d) MMrt WGwG
- 'Hot Lips' CMac MHol
- * - var. ***howozana*** GKev NAln
- 'Kurokawa' WFar
- var. ***microdonta*** B&SWJ 5553 WCru
- 'Milky Way' EMor NEoE
- * - 'Nana' WFar
- 'Pantaloons' (d) CMac CWGN EACa EWes NLar SCob SRms
- 'Pink Chimes' CDor MBNS MHol NAln NEgg NLar SEle
- 'Plum Wine' NWad
- purple-flowered EHyd ELan LRHS
- f. ***rubriflora*** CDor CRos CSpe EBee EBou ECtt EHrv EHyd ELan EMor EPfP LRHS MBel MCot MHol MNrw NEgg NRHS SCob SPer SRms WCAu WGwG
- - 'Beetroot' EBee EMor GBee GKev GWyn IKil MHer NLar WFar
- - 'Bowl of Cherries' CRos ECtt EHyd EPfP LRHS MMrt NRHS SRms SRot
- - 'Cherry Bells' CDor CRos ECtt EHyd LRHS LSRN NRHS
- - 'Vienna Festival' CSBt
- - 'Wine 'n' Rubies' EBee ECtt MHol
- I - 'Silver Bells' CBod CRos EACa EBee ECtt EHyd EMor EPfP LRHS NRHS NSti SPad SRms WFar
- 'Wedding Bells' CDor CWCL EACa EAJP EBou EHrv EHyd EMor EPfP LPot LRHS LSRN MBel MHer MHol MTis NEgg NRHS SCob SRkn SRms WHil
- white hose-in-hose (d) XLum

'Purple Sensation'PBR CSpe CWGN EBee EPfP MBel MHol MNrw MSCN NCGa NLar WCot

pusilla see *C. cochleariifolia*

pyramidalis CCBP CSpe EACa EBee ELan EPfP GJos MMuc MSCN NGBl SEND SPlb XLum
- 'Alba' CSpe EACa ELan EPfP GJos NGBl SPlb XLum

raddeana CPla EACa SBrt WBrk

raineri EPot NRHS NSla WAbe
- * - 'Alba' EPot
- 'Nettleton Gold' CRos EACa EHyd LRHS NRHS

§ ***rapunculoides*** GKev WArt WCFE XLum
- § - 'Afterglow' WFar
- 'Alba' MAvo WFar XLum

rapunculus MNHC WOut XLum

recurva see *C. incurva*

rhomboidalis Gorter see *C. rapunculoides*

rhomboidalis L. WCot XLum

rigidipila GJos WHer

(Ringsabell Series) 'Ringsabell Indigo Blue' EBee ELan EMor SPoG WTor
- 'Ringsabell Mulberry Rose' ELan WTor
- 'Ringsabell Opal White' **new** ELan

rotundifolia CMac CWld EACa EBou EHyd ELan EMor EPfP GAbr GEdr GJos GLog LCro LOPS MCot MHer MNHC SPhx SPlb SRms WBrk
- var. ***albiflora*** CElw EWes
- 'Jotunheimen' EACa WAbe
- § - 'Olympica' EACa EBee ECtt WHoo
- 'White Gem' CBod CRos EACa EBee EHyd EMor EPfP LRHS NBre NRHS WHoo

'Royal Wave' EBee ECtt EPot IPot MBel MHol NLar SCob

rupestris LLHF

rupicola CPBP

'Samantha' EACa EBee ECtt ELon GKev LRHS LSRN MCot NAln NHpl SHar WBrk WTor XEll

'Sarastro' Widely available

sarmatica EACa EBee EMor EPfP NAln SBch SRms WFar

- 'Hemelstraling'	IPot MAvo MCot NAln
- 'Sky Radiator' **new**	IPot
sartorii	SIgm
scheuchzeri	WAbe
'Senior'	EACa ECtt EPPr MHol SAko WBrk WCot WGoo WRHF
speciosa	EBee
'Spring Bell White'	MHol
'Stansfieldii'	CRos EACa EHyd EPot LLHF LRHS NRHS
stevenii	see *C. stevenii* subsp. *beauverdiana*
§ - subsp. ***beauverdiana***	SBrt
suanetica	GMaP
subramulosa	see *C. cochlearifolia*
'Summer Pearl'	CBod ECtt NEgg
'Summertime Blues'PBR	CRos EBee ECtt EHyd ELan EMor LRHS NCGa NRHS WCot
§ 'Swannables'	CPou CRos EACa EHyd LRHS MAvo MRav NCGa NRHS WFar WOut
takesimana	CRos CSpe ECtt EHyd ELan EPfP GKev GKin LEdu LRHS NAln NEgg NGrd NRHS SPer SRms SWvt XLum
- B&SWJ 8499	WCru
I - 'Alba'	EMor WFar
- 'Elizabeth'	Widely available
- 'Elizabeth II' (d)	EPPr WFar
- 'Feenrock JP'	XLum
- purple-flowered	WWtn
thyrsoides	CSpe EBee GJos GKev
'Timsbury Chimes'	WAbe
'Timsbury Perfection'	GCrg WAbe
tommasiniana ♀H6	LLHF SBrt WAbe
topaliana	CPBP
- subsp. ***delphica*** SDR 8254	GKev
trachelium	CRos CWld EACa EBee EHyd ELon GJos GKev LRHS MHer MNHC MRav NAln NMir NRHS WCot WFar WHer WOut WShi WSpi XLum
- f. ***alba***	CRos EBee EHyd GJos IFro IMou LRHS NLar NRHS SGbt WCot WFar WMoo
- - 'Alba Flore Pleno' (d)	LEdu SMHy
- 'Bernice' (d)	CBod CDor EACa EBee ECtt ELan ELon EPfP GMaP IKil LRHS MBel MHol MNrw NLar NSti SCob SPer WBor WCAu WCot WFar WHil WSpi XSen
- 'Purple Break'	EBee MHol WCot
- 'Snowball'	CMac LSRN
tridentata	GEdr
troegerae	EACa GKev
'Van-Houttei'	CDor EBee NLar WCot
versicolor	CPBP SRms
vidalii	see *Azorina vidalii*
'Viking'PBR	CRos ECtt EHyd LRHS NRHS SRms
waldsteiniana	WAbe
wanneri	EDAr GJos
'Warley White'	see *C.* × *haylodgensis* W. Brockbank 'Warley White'
'Warleyensis'	see *C.* × *haylodgensis* W. Brockbank 'Warley White'
'White Octopus'	ECtt GPSL SCob SEle
× ***wockei*** 'Puck'	CPBP CRos EACa ECtt EHyd EPot GCrg LRHS NRHS SIgm WAbe WOld
zangezura	EACa EBee EBou EDAr GJos GKev NAln SGbt XLum
zoysii	WAbe

Campanula × *Symphyandra* see *Campanula*

Campanumoea see *Codonopsis*

Campsis (*Bignoniaceae*)

grandiflora	CBcs CFlo CKel CRos CWGN EHyd ELan EPfP LRHS LSRN SPer SWvt WCFE
radicans	CBcs CBod CMac CRHN CRos CWCL ECrN EHyd ELan EPfP LRHS MGil MJak MSwo NEgg NRHS SLon SNig SPer SPlb
- 'Atrosanguinea'	SVen
- 'Flamenco'	CBcs CKel CMac CRos CWCL EBee EHyd ELan EPfP LRHS LSRN MGil SAdn SCoo SLim SNig SPoG SVen SWvt
§ - f. ***flava*** ♀H4	CBcs CFlo CMac CRos CTri CWCL EBee EHyd ELan EPfP LRHS MBlu MGil MGos MJak NRHS SLim SPer SPoG SVen SWvt
- 'Stromboli'	CAco EBee EPfP
- 'Yellow Trumpet'	see *C. radicans* f. *flava*
× ***tagliabuana*** DANCING FLAME ('Huidan'PBR)	CRos CWCL CWGN EHyd LRHS
- INDIAN SUMMER ('Kudian'PBR)	CBcs CFlo CKel CRos CWCL CWGN EHyd ELon EMOT EPfP EUJe LRHS LSRN MGil MGos NRHS SCoo
- 'Madame Galen' ♀H4	Widely available
- (Summer Jazz Series) 'Takarazuka Yellow'	CRos EHyd LRHS NRHS
- - 'Takarazuka Zujin'	CRos EHyd LRHS NRHS
- 'Tarantella'PBR **new**	EUJe

Camptosorus see *Asplenium*

Campylandra see *Tupistra*

Campylotropis (*Papilionaceae*)

macrocarpa	WSHC

Canarina (*Campanulaceae*)

canariensis ♀H2	CCCN CMCN CTsd SBrt SVen
- from Anaga Mountains, Tenerife	WCot
- from Los Silos, Tenerife	WCot

Candollea see *Hibbertia*

Canna ✿ (*Cannaceae*)

'Adam's Orange'	XBlo
'Alberich'	SHaC
altensteinii	CDTJ SHaC SPlb XBlo
'Ambassador'	LAma SDeJ
'Ambassadour'	SHaC
'Annaeei' ♀H3	SHaC SPlb
'Anthony and Cleopatra' (v)	WCot
'Aphrodite' van Klaveren **new**	CBod
'Argentina'	SHaC
'Assaut'	SHaC
'Atlantis'	XBlo
'Australia'	CDTJ EUJe SHaC XBlo
'Baron Seguier'	XLum
'Bird of Paradise'	SHaC
'Black Knight'	LAma LSvl SDeJ SHaC XBlo
'Bonfire'	CDTJ
brasiliensis	CPla CTsd SHaC XBlo
'Brillant'	LAma SDeJ SHaC
'Burbank'	CDTJ
'Caballero'	SHaC XLum

	Name	Suppliers
	'Calimèro'	SHaC
	'Canary'	XBlo
	Cannova Series	SHaC
	- 'Cannova Lemon'	SHaC
	- 'Cannova Mango'	SHaC
	- 'Cannova Orange Shades'	SHaC
	- 'Cannova Red Shades'	SHaC
	- 'Cannova Rose'	SHaC
	- 'Cannova Scarlet'	SHaC
	- 'Cannova Yellow'	SHaC
	'Carnaval'	EUJe SHaC
	'Centenaire de Rozain-Boucharlat'	SDeJ SHaC XLum
	'Champion'	SHaC
	'Chocolate Sunrise'	LCro LOPS
	'Chouchou'	SHaC
I	'Citrina'	XBlo
§	'City of Portland'	LAma SDeJ
§	'Cleopatra'	CCCN EUJe LAma SDeJ SHaC XBlo
	coccinea	SArc
	compacta	SHaC
	'Corrida'	XLum
	'Creamy White'	XBlo
	'Di Bartolo'	XBlo
	'Durban' Hiley, orange-flowered	see *C.* 'Phasion'
	'Durban' ambig.	CCht CWGN LAma SArc SHaC
	'E. Neubert'	ELan EUJe SHaC
	edulis	CDTJ
§	× ***ehemanii*** ♀H3	CAvo CDTJ SBrt SHaC
	'Emblème'	SHaC
	'En Avant'	SHaC SPlb
	'Endeavour'	EUJe SHaC
	'Erebus' ♀H3	EUJe SHaC
	'Ermine'	EUJe SHaC
	'Étoile du Feu'	XBlo
	'Extase'	SHaC
	'Fatamorgana'	SHaC
	'Feuerzauber'	SHaC
	'Fiesta'	SHaC
	FIREBIRD	see *C.* 'Oiseau de Feu'
	'Firebird' **new**	SHaC
	flaccida	SHaC
	'Flame'	XBlo
	'General Eisenhower' ♀H3	EUJe SHaC
	generalis indica	SHaC
	glauca	SHaC
	'Gnom'	SDeJ SHaC
	'Golden Lucifer'	LAma SDeJ
	'Golden Orb'	SHaC
	'Grand Duc'	SHaC
	'Grande'	SHaC SPlb XLum
	'Grandiose'	SHaC
	'Happy Carmen' (CannaSol Series) **new**	SHaC
	'Happy Cleo' (CannaSol Series) **new**	SHaC
	'Happy Emily' (CannaSol Series) **new**	SHaC
	'Happy Isabel' (CannaSol Series) **new**	SHaC
	'Happy Julia' (CannaSol Series) **new**	SHaC
	'Happy Wilma' (CannaSol Series) **new**	SHaC
	Henlade hybrids	CDTJ
	'Herman'	SHaC
	'Hossegor'	XLum
	'Indiana'	SHaC
	indica	CAbb CDTJ CPla SArc SHaC SMHy SPlb
	- 'Purpurea'	CDTJ SHaC SPlb
	- 'Red King Rupert'	CCCN
	- 'Russian Red' ♀H3	SHaC
	- TROPICANNA GOLD ('Mactro'PBR)	CCCN CPla ELan LCro LOPS
	'Intrigue'	EUJe SHaC
	iridiflora misapplied	see *C.* × *ehemanii*
	iridiflora Ruiz & Pav.	CDTJ CSpe SArc
	'Italia'	CDTJ
	jacobiniflora	SHaC
	jaegeriana	SHaC
	'Jivago'	SHaC
	'Kalimpong'	CDTJ
I	'King Humbert' (blood-red)	CBcs CDTJ SDeJ XBlo
	KING HUMBERT (orange-red)	see *C.* 'Roi Humbert'
	'King Midas'	see *C.* 'Richard Wallace'
§	'Königin Charlotte'	SDeJ SHaC
	latifolia	SHaC
	'Lesotho Lil'	SHaC
	'Libération'	XLum
	'Liberté'	see *C.* 'Wyoming'
	'Lion Rouge'	XLum
	'Lolita'	SHaC
	'Louis Cayeux' ♀H3	LAma SHaC
	'Louis Cottin'	CBcs CCCN CDTJ LAma
	'Lucifer'	CCCN LAma NPer SDeJ XLum
	lutea	SHaC XBlo
	'Madame Angèle Martin'	XBlo
	'Madame Paul Casaneuve'	SHaC
	'Madeira' (Island Series)	EUJe SHaC
	'Malawiensis Variegata'	see *C.* 'Striata'
	'Marlena'	SHaC
	'Marshmallow'	SHaC
	'Mirizia'	SHaC
	'Montaigne'	SHaC
	'Moonshine'	CCCN LCro LOPS
	'Mrs Oklahoma'	SDeJ
	'Musifolia' ♀H3	CDTJ EUJe EWes SHaC XBlo
	'Mystique' ♀H3	SHaC
	'Ointment Pink'	XBlo
§	'Oiseau de Feu'	XLum
	'Oiseau d'Or'	SHaC XLum
	'Orange Chocolate'	SHaC
	'Orange Punch'	SHaC
	'Orchid'	see *C.* 'City of Portland'
	'Panache'	CDTJ SHaC
	'Panama'	SHaC
	paniculata	SHaC
	'Peach Pink'	XBlo
	'Pearlescent Pink'	XBlo
	'Perkeo'	SHaC
§	'Phasion' (v) ♀H3	CAbb CCCN CHll CSpe ELan EUJe EWes LCro LOPS NPer SHaC SPoG WCot XBlo
	'Picasso' ♀H3	CBcs CCCN CDTJ CExl LAma SHaC XBlo
	'Pink Champagne'	XBlo
	'Pink Futurity' (Futurity Series)	CCCN
	'Pink Perfection'	SHaC
	'Plaster Pink'	XBlo
	'President'	LAma SDeJ SHaC XBlo XLum
	'Pretoria'	see *C.* 'Striata'
	'Pretoria Variegata'	see *C.* 'Striata'
	'Prince Charmant'	SHaC
	'Pringle Bay' (v)	XBlo
	'Professor Lorentz'	see *C.* 'Wyoming'
	'Puck'	SHaC

'Queen Charlotte'	see *C.*'Königin Charlotte'
'Ra' ♀H3	EUJe SHaC
'Red Cherry'	SDeJ
§ 'Richard Wallace'	CExl EUJe SDeJ SHaC SPlb XBlo
'Robert Kemp'	SHaC
§ 'Roi Humbert'	CBod SHaC
'Roi Soleil'	SHaC XLum
'Roma'	SHaC
'Rosemond Coles'	SDeJ SHaC XBlo
'Saladin'	SHaC XLum
'Salsa'	SHaC
'Sémaphore'	EUJe SHaC WCot XBlo
'Shenandoah' ♀H3	SHaC
'Singapore Girl'	SHaC
'Snow-white'	XBlo
'Society Belle' ♀H3	SHaC
'Soudan'	CDTJ
'South Pacific'	SHaC
speciosa	CDTJ SPlb XBlo
'Strasbourg'	NPer XLum
'Strawberry Pink'	XBlo
'Striata' misapplied	see *C.*'Stuttgart'
§ 'Striata' (v) ♀H3	CCCN CCht CDTJ CWGN EUJe SEND SHaC WCot XBlo
'Striped Beauty' (v)	CCCN CDTJ EUJe LAma
§ 'Stuttgart' (v)	CDTJ CSpe ESwi EWes SHaC
'Summer Gold'	XBlo
'Sunset'	WCot
'Tali'	SHaC
'Talisman'	XBlo
'Taney'	EUJe SHaC
'Taroudant'	SHaC XLum
'Triomphe'	SHaC
(Tropical Series) 'Tropical Bronze Scarlet'	SHaC
- 'Tropical Red'	SHaC
- 'Tropical Rose'	SHaC
- 'Tropical Salmon'	SHaC
- 'Tropical White'	SHaC
- 'Tropical Yellow'	SHaC
TROPICANNA	see *C.*'Phasion'
TROPICANNA BLACK ('Lon01'PBR)	CAbb CPla EPfP LCro LOPS SPoG
tuerckheimii	SHaC
'Valentine'	WCot
'Vanilla Cream'	SDeJ
'Vanilla Pink'	XBlo
'Verdi' ♀H3	IPot LAma SHaC
warscewiczii	CDTJ CExl SHaC
'Weymouth'	CDTJ
'Whithelm Pride' ♀H3	SDeJ SHaC
'Wintzer's Colossal'	SHaC
'Woodbridge Pink'	XBlo
§ 'Wyoming' ♀H3	CBcs CBod CCCN CDTJ EUJe LAma LCro LOPS SDeJ SEND SHaC XBlo
'Yara'	SDeJ SHaC
'Yellow Humbert' misapplied	see *C.*'Cleopatra', *C.*'Richard Wallace'
'Yellow Humbert'	SDeJ

Cannomois (*Restionaceae*)

grandis	CPbh SPlb

Cantua (*Polemoniaceae*)

buxifolia ♀H3	CBcs CBod CCCN CExl CHll ECre EShb LRHS MGil
- 'Alba'	CBcs CBod CCCN EShb WWFP
- 'Dancing Oaks'	SVen

Cape gooseberry see *Physalis peruviana*

Capeochloa (*Poaceae*)

§ ***cincta***	WCot

Capnoides see *Corydalis*

Capparis (*Capparaceae*)

spinosa	CCCN WJek
- subsp. ***rupestris***	SPlb

Capsicum (*Solanaceae*)

annuum	CCCN SVic
- 'Ancho'	SVic
- var. ***annuum*** 'Blondy' **new**	LRHS NRHS
- - (Cerasiforme Group) 'Piccante Calabresé'	SVic
- - (Conioides Group) 'Super Chili' ♀H1c	SPre SVic
- - (Grossum Group) 'Almapaprika' **new**	SVic
- - - 'Bell Boy'	LCro LOPS LRHS NRHS
- - - 'Corno di Toro Rosso' ♀H1c	CHby
- - - 'Mini Bell Red' **new**	SVic
- - - 'Mini Bell Yellow' **new**	SVic
- - - 'Mohawk' ♀H1c	CRos EHyd EKin LRHS NRHS
- - - 'Redskin' ♀H1c	CRos EHyd EKin LRHS NRHS
- - - 'Thor' **new**	LRHS
- - (Longum Group) 'Bolivian Rainbow' ♀H1c	SVic
- - - cayenne	CCCN
- - - 'Filius Blue' ♀H1c	NRob
- - - 'Fish'	SVic
- - - 'Golden Cayenne'	SVic
- - - 'Hot Thai' ♀H1c	CRos EHyd LRHS NRHS
- - - jalapeño	EHyd LCro LOPS LRHS NRHS SVic
- - - 'Joe's Long Cayenne'	SVic
- - - 'Loco' ♀H1c	CRos EHyd LRHS NRHS
- - - 'Ring of Fire'	SVic
- - - 'Serrano'	SVic
- - - 'Tokyo Hot'	SVic
- - 'Marconi Rosso'	LOPS SVic
- - 'Prairie Fire' ♀H1c	CCCN CRos EHyd LRHS NRHS NRob SVic
- - 'Purple Mavros' **new**	LRHS NRHS
- 'Apache' ♀H1c	CCCN CRos EHyd EKin LRHS NPri NRHS NRob SPre
- 'Basket of Fire' ♀H1c	CRos EHyd EKin LRHS NRHS SPre SVic
- 'Britney' **new**	LRHS
- 'Bulgarian Carrot'	SVic
- 'Cayenne Red'	SPre SVic
- 'Cayenne Sweet' **new**	SVic
- 'Cheyenne'	CRos EHyd LRHS NRHS
- 'Cow Horn' **new**	SVic
- 'Demon Red' ♀H1c	CRos EHyd EKin LRHS MCtn NRHS SPre SVic
- 'Etna' ♀H1c	CRos EHyd LRHS MCtn NRHS
- 'Explosive Ember' **new**	SVic
- 'Fresno' ♀H1c	LRHS NRHS
- var. ***glabriusculum***	SVic
- 'Holy Mole' **new**	SVic
- 'Hungarian Hot Wax' ♀H1c	CHby EKin LCro LOPS MCtn NRob SVic
- 'Hungarian Yellow Wax' **new**	SVic
- 'Jalapeno Fooled You' **new**	SVic
- 'Jericho' **new**	CRos EHyd LRHS NRHS
- 'Krakatoa' ♀H1c	CRos EHyd LRHS NRHS

- 'Las Cruces Cayenne'	SVic
- 'Masquerade'	CRos EHyd LRHS NRHS
- 'Medina' new	LRHS
- 'Medusa'	CRos EHyd LRHS NRHS
- 'Nosferatu'	SVic
- 'Numex Big Jim'	SVic
- 'Numex Garnet'	SVic
- 'Numex Piñata'	SVic
- 'Numex Primavera'	SVic
- 'Numex Twilight'	CRos EHyd LRHS NRHS SPre SVic
- 'Padron'	LCro LOPS SVic
- 'Paper Lantern' new	CRos EHyd LRHS NRHS
- 'Pasilla Bajio' new	SVic
- 'Peter Pepper'	SVic
- 'Pinocchio's Nose'	SVic
- 'Pot Black' ♀H1c	SVic
- 'Razzamatazz' new	CRos EHyd LRHS NRHS
- 'Tricolor Variegatum' ♀H1c	NRob
- 'Trinidad Perfume' new	LRHS
- 'Vampire'	SVic
- 'Zimbabwe Black' new	LRHS
baccatum 'Aji Limon'	SVic
- 'Aji Omnicolor'	SVic
- 'Brazilian Starfish' new	SVic
- 'Christmas Bell'	SVic
- 'Lemon Drop'	SPre
chinense 'Bhut Jolokia' new	SVic
- 'Carolina Reaper' new	SVic
- 'Cheiro Roxa' new	SVic
- Habanero Group ♀H1c	EKin NRob
- - 'Habanero Caribbean Red'	SVic
- - 'Naga Morrich'	SVic
- - 'Caribbean Antillais' ♀H1c	SVic
- 'Hot Paper Lantern' new	SVic
- 'Numex Suave Orange'	SVic
- 'Numex Suave Red'	SVic
- 'Peito de Moca' new	SVic
- 'Scotch Bonnet'	CRos EHyd LRHS NRHS SPre
- 'Seven Poa Brain Strain Yellow' new	SVic
- 'Trinidad Moruga Scorpion' new	LRHS SVic
frutescens Tabasco Group	SVic
'Rodeo'	SVic

Caputia (*Asteraceae*)

§ ***tomentosa*** ♀H1c	EShb

Caragana (*Papilionaceae*)

CC 3945	CExl
arborescens	CAgr CDul CMCN EBee ELan EPfP NLar NWea SCob SPer SPlb
- PAB 13.376	LEdu
- 'Lorbergii'	CEnd MBlu NLar SPer
- 'Pendula'	CAco CMac ELan GBin MAsh MBlu NLar SCoo SPer
- 'Walker'	CDul CEnd ELan MAsh MBlu MGos NHol NLar NWea SCoo SPer
aurantiaca	NLar
pygmaea	NLar

carambola see *Averrhoa carambola*

caraway see *Carum carvi*

Cardamine (*Brassicaceae*)

asarifolia misapplied	see *Pachyphragma macrophyllum*
bipinnata	WCot
bulbifera	EBee ELon EPPr GBin GEdr LEdu MAvo NRya WCru
californica	EBee EPPr LEdu MAvo NRya WCru
concatenata	WCru
digitata	EBee EMor
diphylla	CAby EBee LEdu WCot WCru
- 'American Sweetheart'	CExl
- 'Eco Cut Leaf'	CAby CExl EBee MAvo WCru
- 'Eco Moonlight'	WCru
enneaphylla	EWld GWyn NBid NLar
glanduligera	CElw EBee ECha ELon EPPr GEdr LEdu MAvo MNrw NSum SBrt WCot WCru WFar
§ ***heptaphylla***	CAby ECha ELon GBin GEdr GQue ILea LLHF NSum WCru WSHC
- MDM 03008 new	GEdr
- from the Pyrenees	GCal NLar
- 'Big White'	EBee EPPr GCal MNrw NCGa NLar WFar WPnP
- Guincho form	EPPr MAvo WCot
§ ***kitaibelii***	CAby EMor EPPr GCal LEdu MNrw NLar SBrt WCot WCru WFar
latifolia Vahl	see *C. raphanifolia*
macrophylla	EBee GBin GEdr LEdu WCot WSHC
- 'Bright and Bronzy'	CExl EPPr IMou MAvo WCru
maxima	MAvo SHar WCru
microphylla	GKev
pentaphylla ♀H5	CSpe ELon EPPr GAbr GBin GKev GMaP IFro LEdu MCot NAln NHpl NSum SPhx WCru WSHC
pratensis	CBre CDor CWat GJos LCro LOPS MHer MNHC NMir NRHS SPhx SRms WHer WMoo WSFF WShi
- 'Diane's Petticoat'	MAvo
- 'Flore Pleno' (d)	CBre CDor CSpe ECha GCal GQue IFro LEdu MHer MNrw NBid NBir NBro NCGa NLar NRHS SHar WBor WSFF
- 'Flore Pleno' white-flowered (d)	LEdu
- white-flowered	CDor
- 'William' (d)	LEdu
quinquefolia	CAby CElw CMea CRos ECha EHrv EHyd ELon ILea LEdu LRHS MAvo MBel MNrw MPie NLar NRHS NSum SDys WBrk WCot WCru WFar WPnP
- PAB 9992	LEdu
§ ***raphanifolia***	CBre CExl EBee GAbr GBin GCal IFro IMou LLWG MAvo NBid NBro NRya NSti NSum SHar WBor WMoo
- PAB 204	LEdu
trifolia	CAby CElw CMac EBee ECha EHrv ELon EMor EPPr EWld GBin GCal GEdr GMaP IFro ILea IMou LEdu MAvo MNrw MRav NBir NBro NLar NRya NSum WCot WCru WFar WMoo
waldsteinii	CElw CExl EBee EHrv EPPr GCal GEdr ILea LEdu NCGa NLar SMHy WCru WFar WPGP WSHC
yezoensis	GBin
- B&SWJ 4659	EBee EPPr WCru

cardamon see *Elettaria cardamomum*

Cardiandra (*Hydrangeaceae*)

alternifolia B&SWJ 5719	WCru
- B&SWJ 5845	WCru
- B&SWJ 6177	WCru

– B&SWJ 6354	WCru
– subsp. ***moellendorffii***	CExl WPGP
– 'Pink Geisha'	WCru
amamiohshimensis	WCru
formosana	CExl IArd WPGP
– B&SWJ 2005	WCru
– 'Crûg's Abundant'	WCru
– 'Hsitou'	WCru
– 'Hsitou Splendour'	WCru

Cardiocrinum ✿ (*Liliaceae*)

cathayanum	GKev
cordatum	GKev
– B&SWJ 2812	WCru
– B&SWJ 4841	WCru
– B&SWJ 5427	WCru
– B&SWJ 6336	WCru
– B&SWJ 11069	WCru
– var. ***glehnii***	CCCN GEdr
– – B&SWJ 10827	WCru
– – B&SWJ 10843	WCru
– red-veined	SBrt
giganteum	CAby CBcs CBor CCCN CPla CRos EHyd GAbr GBin GEdr GKev LAma LRHS MNrw NAln NBid NEgg NHpl NLar NRHS SMad WCru WPnP
– B&SWJ 2419	WCru
– GWJ 9219 from Sikkim	WCru
– HWJK 2158 from Nepal	WCru
– WJC 13661 from Sikkim	WCru
– WJC 13698 from Sikkim	WCru
– pure white-flowered	GKev
– var. ***yunnanense***	EBee EPfP GEdr ITim NBid WCru WPGP
– – PAB 8347	LEdu
– – NJM 11.023 from Guizhou	WPGP
aff. ***giganteum*** NJM 12.060 from Nagaland, India	WPGP

cardoon see *Cynara cardunculus*

Carduus (*Asteraceae*)

defloratus aff. subsp. ***argemone***	SBrt
– subsp. ***defloratus***	SBrt

Carex (*Cyperaceae*)

	from Kyoto, Japan	EBee EPPr
	acuta	CHab
	– 'Aureovariegata' (v)	WMoo
	– 'Variegata' (v)	CBen CMac CWat EShb GMaP LLWG NBro WMoo
	alba	CKno WCot
	'Amazon Mist'	CRos EUJe LRHS NRHS SRms WFar
	arenaria	CKno
§	***atrata*** subsp. ***pullata*** KEKE 494	EBee
	aurea	GWyn
	baccans	CExl GCal SBrt
	berggrenii	CSde SPlb
	brizoides	IMou
	brunnea	CMac
	– 'Jenneke' (v)	CRos EHyd LRHS NRHS SWvt
	– 'Jubilo'PBR	EBee
	– 'Variegata' (v)	WHoo
	buchananii	Widely available
	– 'Firefox'	CBod
	– 'Green Twist'	CRos EHyd EShb LRHS NRHS
	– 'Red Rooster'	LBuc NWsh SCob
	– 'Viridis'	XLum
	chathamica	CPla LRHS SVen WCot
	ciliatomarginata 'Treasure Island' (v)	EBee
	colchica	XLum
	comans	EPfP NBro
	– 'Bronze Perfection'	CBod SMea
	– bronze-leaved	Widely available
	– 'Bronzita'	WFar
	– 'Copper Green'	SMea
	– 'Dancing Flame'	CWCL ELon
	– 'Frosted Curls'	Widely available
	– 'Hot Chocolate'	CBod
	– red-leaved	NLar SRms
	– 'Small Red'	see *C. comans* 'Taranaki'
§	– 'Taranaki'	MBNS SCoo
	conica 'Hime-kan-suge'	see *C. conica* 'Snowline'
§	– 'Snowline' (v)	CMac EHoe ELan EShb GMaP LEdu NBro NLar NWsh SGol SWvt XLum
	dallii	WHrl
	davalliana	EBee
	depauperata	EHoe
	dioica	LLWG
	dipsacea	CKno CMac CRos CWCL EHoe EHyd EShb GMaP LRHS MAsh NLar NRHS NWad NWsh WHal
	– 'Dark Horse'	CPla EHoe MMuc SMea WPtf
	divulsa	CKno
	– subsp. ***leersii***	EPPr
§	***dolichostachya*** 'Kaga-nishiki' (v)	LEdu LRHS SLim
	duthiei	see *C. atrata* subsp. *pullata*
§	***elata*** 'Aurea' ♀H6	Widely available
	– 'Bowles's Golden'	see *C. elata* 'Aurea'
	– 'Knightshayes'	CKno WCot
	elongata	CHab
	'Evergold'	see *C. oshimensis* 'Evergold'
	'Feather Falls' (v) **new**	CKno
	firma 'Variegata' (v)	EPot GEdr
	flacca	CHab CKno EPPr GBin WBor XLum XSen
	– 'Blue Zinger'	CBod CKno WMoo
§	– subsp. ***flacca***	EBee NSti SMea
	flagellifera	CBcs CBod CMac CRos CSde CSpe CTri CWCL EBee EHoe EHyd ELan ELon EPfP EShb EUJe GCal GMaP LRHS MMuc NBir NRHS NWsh SCob SEND SPlb SPoG
	– 'Auburn Cascade'	ELan SPtp
	– 'Kiwi'	EHyd NRHS NWsh
	– red-leaved	SCob
	flava ſ	EHoe
	folliculata	EPPr
	fraseri	see *Cymophyllus fraserianus*
	fraserianus	see *Cymophyllus fraserianus*
	glauca Scop.	see *C. flacca* subsp. *flacca*
	'Gold Fountains'	see *C. dolichostachya* 'Kaga-nishiki'
	grayi	CAby CRos CWCL EHoe EHyd GBin LEdu LLWG LRHS MBlu NLar NRHS SPlb WBor WPGP
	'Ice Dance' (v)	Widely available
	kaloides	EHoe XLum
	laxiculmis 'Bunny Blue'PBR	NLar
*	***leformeri***	XLum
	limosa	LLWG
	lupulina	GBin
	lurida	EPfP XLum
	melanocephala	EBee
	mertensii NNS 07-98	ELon
	MILK CHOCOLATE ('Milchoc'PBR) (v)	CBod ECtt ELan EPfP SCob SRms

	morrowii misapplied	see *C. oshimensis*
I	- 'Fisher's Form' (v)	CTri ELan EPPr MRav SCob SWvt WAvo WGrn
	- 'Gilt' (v)	EHoe EPPr MBNS NWad
	- 'Nana Variegata' (v)	CTri
	- 'Pinkie'	CPla WPtf
	- var. ***temnolepis***	IMou
	- VANILLA ICE ('Vanice') (v) **new**	CKno
	- 'Variegata' (v)	CBod ELan EPPr EUJe GCal GMaP MJak MMuc NBir NSti SRms WAvo XLum
	muskingumensis	CExl CKno CWCL EHoe ELan EPPr EPfP EShb GBin GCal LEdu LLWG NBro NLar SLim SMad WMoo WPnP
	- 'Little Midge'	CKno CMac EShb GBin GCal LEdu NLar
	- 'Oehme' (v)	CKno CRos CWCL EBee EHyd EPPr EShb LEdu LLWG LRHS NBid NHol NRHS NWad
	- 'Silberstreif' (v)	CKno EBee EPPr EShb GBin LEdu MMuc XLum
	nigra (L.) Reichard	WAvo XLum
§	- 'On-line' (v)	EPPr WMoo
	- 'Variegata'	see *C. nigra* 'On-line'
	No 4, Nanking (Greg's thin leaf)	EPPr
	obnupta	CKno
	ornithopoda 'Aurea'	see *C. ornithopoda* 'Variegata'
§	- 'Variegata' (v)	EBee GBin NHol NRHS NWsh WMoo
§	***oshimensis***	EPPr WCot
	- EVERCREAM ('Ficre') (v) **new**	CKno
	- EVEREST ('Fiwhite'PBR) (v)	CBcs CBod CKel CKno CSBt EBee EHoe EPfP EShb GBin GWyn LLWG LRHS LSRN LSun MAsh MBel NEoE NWad NWsh SArc SCob SEND SPoG SRms WCot WMoo WSHC
§	- 'Evergold' (v) ♀H7	Widely available
	- 'Everillo'PBR	CBcs CBct CBod CKno EBee EHoe EMor ESwi EUJe GBin LBuc LRHS MAsh NGBl NLar NWad NWsh SPoG SRms WCot
	- 'Everlime'PBR	CBct CKel CKno EMor LLWG LRHS
	- 'Everoro' (v)	CKno LSun WCot WRHF
	- 'Eversheen'	LRHS
	- 'J.S. Greenwell'	EBee
	- 'Variegata' (v)	NBir
	otrubae	CHab XLum
	panicea	CKno CWCL EBee EHoe EPPr EShb LLWG WMoo
	paniculata	XLum
	parviflora	SMea
	pendula	CBcs CBen CHab CKno CTri EBou ECha EHoe ELan EPfP GAbr GMaP MJak MMuc MRav NBid NBir NBro NLar SCob SEND SLim SMad WMoo XLum XSen
	- 'Cool Jazz' (v)	EPPr
	- 'Moonraker' (v)	EHoe ESwi NWad WCot
	petriei	ECha ELon XLum
	phyllocephala	EShb
	- 'Sparkler' (v)	ELon EPfP LRHS SPad SPoG SWvt XLum
	plantaginea	EBee EHoe EPPr EShb GBin LEdu WPGP
	praegracilis	CKno
	Pritchard's selection (v)	IFro
	pseudocyperus	GBin MWts NPer NWsh WMoo WPnP
	punctata	XLum
	remota	CKno EPPr EShb LPla SMea
	riparia	CHab MMuc MWts NPer SMea WShi
	- 'Bowles's Golden'	see *C. elata* 'Aurea'
	sabynensis	see *C. umbrosa* subsp. *sabynensis*
	scaposa KWJ 12304	LEdu WCru
	secta	CKno CRos EHyd EPPr EPfP GMaP IMou LRHS NRHS SAko SRms WMoo
	- from Dunedin, New Zealand	EPPr
	siderosticta	WSHC
	- 'Banana Boat'	see *C. siderosticta* 'Golden Falls'
§	- 'Golden Falls' (v)	SMad
	- 'Kisokaido' (v)	EShb
	- 'Shima-nishiki' (v)	EBee EPfP LRHS
	- 'Variegata' (v)	CTri CTsd EBee EHoe ELan ELon EShb GCal LEdu NBir NLar NSti NWsh SLim WBor
	'Silver Sceptre' (v)	CBod CRos EHyd EMor EShb GKev GMaP LRHS MBNS MGos NRHS NSti NWad NWsh SLim SPlb SWvt WBrk WMoo
	solandri	CKno NRHS XLum
	spicata	CHab
	spissa	MNrw
	stricta Gooden. 'Bowles's Golden'	see *C. elata* 'Aurea'
	stricta Lam.	MMuc SEND
	sylvatica	CHab EHoe WOut
	tenuiculmis	CBod CRos CWCL EBee EHyd LRHS NRHS NSti NWad SPtp WCot XLum
	testacea	Widely available
	- dark-leaved	EPfP
	- 'Limeshine'	EWes GBin WFar
	- 'Old Gold'	EWes SMad SPlb WMoo
	- 'Prairie Fire'	CRos CSpe EBou EPfP EUJe GMaP LRHS NLar NRHS SCob SPtp SRms WGrn
	texensis	EPPr
	'The Beatles'	EHoe NBir
	trifida	CKno
	- 'Chatham Blue'	CBod GBin MMuc SEND
*	- 'Glauca'	CWCL
	- 'Rekohu Sunrise'PBR (v)	CKno EBee ELon EPfP LRHS MMuc NEoE NSti SEND SLon WCot
	umbrosa	EBee EShb
	subsp. ***sabynensis*** 'Thinny Thin' (v)	

Carica (*Caricaceae*)

	papaya (F)	XBlo
	- 'Babaco'	CCCN
	pubescens	see *Vasconcellea pubescens*

Carissa (*Apocynaceae*)

	grandiflora	see *C. macrocarpa*
§	***macrocarpa*** (F)	CCCN

Carlina (*Asteraceae*)

	acanthifolia	SPhx
	acaulis	ELan SPlb
	- subsp. ***acaulis***	GPoy
I	- 'Bronze Form'	SMad
	- var. ***caulescens***	see *C. acaulis* subsp. *simplex*
§	- subsp. ***simplex***	ECha EHyd ELon LRHS NRHS
	- - bronze-leaved	SPhx
	vulgaris	GKev
	- 'Silver Star'	SPhx

Carmichaelia (*Papilionaceae*)

odorata CExl
petriei SMad
stevensonii CBcs CCCN EBee ELan MBlu SBrt WPGP WThu

× *Carmispartium* see *Carmichaelia*

Carpenteria (*Hydrangeaceae*)

californica CCCN CRos CSBt CTri EBee EHyd ELan EPfP ESwi EWTr GBin IDee LCro LOPS LRHS MGil MGos NRHS SCob SPer SWvt WFar WSpi
- 'Bodnant' ♀H4 CBcs CDul CKel CRos EBee EHyd ELan LRHS LSRN MAsh MGos NLar NRHS SEle SPer SWvt WFar WGob WPGP WSpi
- 'Elizabeth' ♀H4 CRos CSBt CWGN EPfP LRHS LSRN MAsh NLar SPoG SSta
- 'Eskimo' CBcs CKel EMil LRHS SWvt
- 'Ladhams' Variety' CBcs CDul CKel CMac CRos EHyd EPfP LRHS MRav NLar SMad SPer SRkn SWvt WKif WSpi

Carpinus ✿ (*Betulaceae*)

sp. LPra
betulus ♀H7 Widely available
* - 'A. Beeckman' CLnd SGol
- 'Columnaris' CDul CLnd CTho
* - 'Columnaris Nana' LLHF MPkF WCot
§ - 'Fastigiata' ♀H7 Widely available
- 'Frans Fontaine' CCVT CDul CEnd CLnd CMCN CMac CTho EBee EMOT EPfP IArd LMaj LPra MBlu MGos NLar NOra NWea SCoo SEWo SGol SLim SPer SPoG WMat
- 'Globus' MBlu
- 'Lucas' CCVT EBee EMOT MBlu NOra SBir SGol WMat
- 'Monument' MPkF
- 'Pendula' CDul CEnd CTho EBee LLHF LMaj MBlu SWvt WMou
- 'Purpurea' CDul CEnd CLnd MBlu
- 'Pyramidalis' see *C. betulus* 'Fastigiata'
- 'Quercifolia' CDul LPra
- 'Rockhampton Red' MBlu WMou
- 'Stegemanns Primus' PBR EBee WMat
caroliniana CDul CLnd CMCN EPfP SBir
- 'Red Fall' EPfP LRHS MBlu
- 'Sentinel Dries' LRHS MBlu
cordata CDul MBlu SSta
coreana CMCN SBir SMad
fangiana CBcs CEnd CExl CJun CLnd CMCN CTho EBee EPfP LLHF MBlu WPGP
fargesiana EBee SMad WPGP
- KR 8780 WPGP
fargesii see *C. viminea*
henryana CExl CMen EBtc SBir
- var. **simplicidentata** CMCN MBlu
japonica ♀H6 CBcs CDul CEnd CLnd CMCN CMen CTho EPfP MBlu NOra SAko SBir SCoo SEWo SMad SSta WMat WMou
- B&SWJ 10803 WCru
- B&SWJ 11072 WCru
- 'Chinese Lantern' SGol
kawakamii CMCN
- CWJ 12412 WCru
- CWJ 12449 WCru
laxiflora CExl CMen
- B&SWJ 10809 WCru
- B&SWJ 11035 WCru
- var. **longispica** B&SWJ 8772 WCru
- var. **macrostachya** see *C. viminea*
omeiensis EBee
- KR 280 WPGP
orientalis CMCN SBir
polyneura EBee SBir SSta WPGP
pubescens EBee WPGP
- 'Abbotsbury' SSta
rankanensis SSta
- RWJ 9839 WCru
× **schuschaensis** EBtc LRHS
shensiensis CDul EBee WPGP
tschonoskii EBee
- B&SWJ 10800 WCru
- BBJMT 297 WPGP
turczaninowii CDul CMCN CMen MBlu NLar SBir SSta
§ **viminea** CEnd CExl CMCN SSta WCot

Carpobrotus (*Aizoaceae*)

acinaciformis SVen
§ **edulis** CCCN CDTJ SArc SEND SVen WHer XLum
- 'Gugh Dawn' (v) SVen
- var. **rubescens** CCCN
muirii CCCN SVen
sauerae CCCN

Carrierea (*Salicaceae*)

calycina CBcs EBee IArd WPGP

carrot see *Daucus carota* for species; also AGM Vegetables Section for cultivars

Carthamus (*Asteraceae*)

dianius SBrt
mitissimus GEdr
tinctorius MNHC SRms SVen

Carum (*Apiaceae*)

carvi CBod EBou EMor ENfk GPoy MHer MJak MNHC SRms SVic WJek
petroselinum see *Petroselinum crispum*

Carya ✿ (*Juglandaceae*)

cordiformis MBlu
glabra CBcs CMCN
illinoinensis (F) CAgr CBcs CDul CLnd CMCN MBlu
- 'Carlson No 3' seedling (F) CAgr
- 'Colby' seedling (F) CAgr
- 'Cornfield' (F) CAgr
- 'Lucas' (F) CAgr
laciniosa (F) CMCN EPfP
- 'Henry' (F) CAgr
- 'Keystone' seedling (F) CAgr
ovata (F) CAgr CBcs CDul CMCN EPfP MBlu WPGP
- 'Grainger' seedling (F) CAgr
- 'Neilson' seedling (F) CAgr
- 'Weschcke' seedling (F) CAgr
- 'Yoder No 1' seedling (F) CAgr
tomentosa CMCN EPfP NLar WPGP

Caryophyllus see *Syzygium*

Caryopteris (*Lamiaceae*)

× ***clandonensis***	CAco CMac ECtt MGil NBir
- 'Arthur Simmonds' 🏆H4	ECha SCob
- BLUE BALLOON ('Korball') new	SGol
- 'Dark Knight'	CBod CKel CRos CTsd EBee ECtt EHyd ELan EMOT EPfP LBuc LCro LOPS LRHS MAsh MCot NRHS SCob SEle SPer SPoG SWvt WFar WHil WHoo
- 'Ferndown'	EWTr NLar SEND SRms
- 'First Choice' 🏆H4	CMac CRos ECrN EHyd ELan EPfP LRHS LSRN MAsh MGos NRHS SCob SLim SPer SRkn SWvt
- 'Gold Giant'	CRos EHyd EPfP LRHS MAsh NRHS
- GRAND BLEU ('Inoveris'PBR)	CDul CMac CRos CSBt EBee EHyd ELan EPfP LRHS LSRN MGos NLar NRHS SAko SCob SGbt SGol SWvt
- 'Heavenly Baby' 🏆H4	CRos EHyd EPfP LRHS MAsh SLon
- 'Heavenly Blue'	Widely available
- 'Hint of Blue'	SGol
- HINT OF GOLD ('Lisaura'PBR) 🏆H4	CRos CSBt EHyd ELan EMOT EPfP LCro LOPS LRHS MAsh MCot NLar NRHS
- 'Kew Blue'	CBcs CDul CKel CMac CRos CSBt EBee EHyd ELan EMOT EPfP EShb LRHS LSRN MAsh MGos MHer MSwo NLar NRHS SCob SCoo SGol SLim SLon SPer SRms SSta SWvt XSen
- 'Longwood Blue'	EPfP
- 'Pershore'	WAvo
- PETIT BLEU ('Minbleu'PBR)	EBee LRHS MPkF
- PINK PERFECTION ('Lisspin')	CRos EHyd ELan LRHS NRHS SEle SPoG
- STEPHI ('Lissteph')	CRos EHyd LRHS NRHS SPoG
- STERLING SILVER ('Lissilv'PBR) 🏆H4	CKel CMac CRos EBee EHyd EPfP LRHS LSRN MAsh NEgg NEoE NRHS SCob SPer SPoG SRms SSta
- 'Summer Gold'	CMac MAsh
- 'Summer Sorbet'PBR (v) 🏆H4	CBod CKel CMac CRos CWGN EBee ECrN EHoe ELan EPfP EWes LRHS MAsh MGos MJak NLar SCob SCoo SEND SGbt SGol SLim SNig SPer SRms SWvt WFar WHil
- weeping	ELan EPPr WFar
- 'White Surprise'PBR	CKel CMac CRos CWGN EHyd ELan EMOT EMil EPfP LRHS MGos NRHS SCob SGol SPer SPoG WFar WHil
- 'Worcester Gold' 🏆H4	Widely available
divaricata	CMCN LPla SBrt WHil
- 'Electrum'	WCot WFar WSHC
- 'Jade Shades'	WSHC
§ ***incana***	XSen
- 'Blue Cascade'	CKel EBtc ELan LRHS MRav NLar SRms WAvo WGrn
- 'Delft Blue'	CKel EBee LRHS
§ - 'Jason'PBR	EMOT NLar SCob SPoG WFar
- SUNSHINE BLUE	see *C. incana* 'Jason'
mastacanthus	see *C. incana*

Caryota (*Arecaceae*)

mitis	CCCN

Cassandra see *Chamaedaphne*

Cassia (*Caesalpiniaceae*)

corymbosa Lam.	see *Senna corymbosa*
marilandica	see *Senna marilandica*
nemophila	SPlb

Cassinia (*Asteraceae*)

fulvida	CBcs SVen
leptophylla	CBcs
vauvilliersii	SEle SVen
'Ward Silver'	EHoe

Cassinia × *Helichrysum* (*Asteraceae*)

hybrid	WKif

Cassiope ✿ (*Ericaceae*)

'Askival Snowbird'	ITim NWad
'Askival Snow-wreath'	see *C.* Snow-wreath Group
'Askival Stormbird'	ITim NWad
'Badenoch'	GKev
'Edinburgh' 🏆H6	EPot GBin ITim NWad WThu
lycopodioides 🏆H6	ITim
- 'Beatrice Lilley'	EPot GKev WThu
- 'Jim Lever'	ITim WAbe
- 'Rokujō'	ITim
mertensiana	NWad WThu
subsp. ***californica***	
- var. ***gracilis***	ITim NWad WThu
'Muirhead' 🏆H6	WThu
'Randle Cooke' 🏆H6	EPot GBin WThu
selaginoides LS&E 13284	EPot WAbe WThu
§ Snow-wreath Group	ITim
tetragona	ITim
wardii	EPot

Castanea ✿ (*Fagaceae*)

'Bouche de Bétizac' (F)	CAgr
crenata	CAgr
dentata	CBcs
henryi	CMCN
'Maraval' (F)	CAgr CTho WMat
'Maridonne' (F)	CAgr
'Marigoule' (F)	CAgr EPom SPer WMat
'Marsol' (F)	CAgr CFGn ECrN WMat
mollissima	CBcs
'Précoce Migoule' (F)	CAgr
sativa	Widely available
§ - 'Albomarginata' (v) 🏆H6	CDul CEnd EPfP NOra SPoG WMat
- 'Anny's Summer Red'	CDul SPer
- 'Argenteovariegata'	see *C. sativa* 'Albomarginata'
- 'Aspleniifolia'	CDul
- 'Aureomarginata'	see *C. sativa* 'Variegata'
- 'Belle Epine' (F)	CAgr
- 'Bournette' (F)	CAgr
* - 'Doré de Lyon'	CAgr
- 'Marlhac' (F)	CAgr CFGn NOra WMat
- 'Marron Comballe' (F)	CAgr
- 'Marron de Goujounac' (F)	CAgr
- 'Marron de Lyon' (F)	CAgr CDul CEnd CFGn CHab CTho EPfP EPom SVic
- 'Regal' (F)	EPom
§ - 'Variegata' (v)	CMCN ELan SPer
seguinii	WPGP

Castanopsis (*Fagaceae*)

sieboldii	CBcs

Castilleja (*Orobanchaceae*)

integra	SPlb
latifolia new	GKev

miniata	SPlb WAbe
scabrida	GKev
sessiliflora	SPlb

Casuarina (*Casuarinaceae*)

cunninghamiana	SPlb

Catalpa ✿ (*Bignoniaceae*)

sp.	LPra
bignonioides ♀H6	Widely available
- 'Aurea' ♀H6	Widely available
* - 'Aurea Nana'	LPra
- 'Nana'	ELan LPra
- 'Purpurea'	see *C.* × *erubescens* 'Purpurea'
- 'Variegata' (v)	EBee EBtc ELon EPfP
bungei	CCVT CMCN MBlu SArc SGol
- 'Purpurea'	EMOT
§ × ***erubescens*** 'Purpurea' ♀H6	CBcs CCVT CDul CEnd CKel CMCN CMac CTho ELan ELon EPfP EUJe LMaj MBlu MGil MRav MSwo NLar NOra SCob SMad SPer SPoG SWvt WMat WMou WPGP
fargesii f. ***duclouxii*** ♀H6	CBcs CDul CEnd EBee EPfP MBlu NLar SAko SChF WPGP
ovata	CMCN SPad
speciosa ♀H6	CDul CMCN GBin SVen
- 'Frederik'	NLar
- 'Pulverulenta' (v)	CDul EBee LLHF MBlu SMad

Catalpa × *Chilopsis* see × *Chitalpa*

Catananche (*Asteraceae*)

caerulea	CBod CMea CRos CSBt CSpe CTri EBee ECha EHyd ELan EPfP EShb LRHS MBel MNHC NDai NEgg NRHS SCob SPer SPhx SPoG SWvt WArt WCAu WHoo WMoo WSHC XSen
- 'Alba'	CBod CCBP CRos CSpe EAJP EBee ECha EHyd ELan EPfP GQue LRHS MBel MNrw NEgg NRHS SCob SPer SPoG SWvt WArt WCAu
- 'Amor Blue'	CRos EHyd EPfP LRHS NRHS SPoG
- 'Major' ♀H5	CRos EHyd EWTr LRHS NRHS SRms

Catha (*Celastraceae*)

edulis	GPoy

Cathcartia (*Papaveraceae*)

§ ***villosa***	GGGa

Catopsis (*Bromeliaceae*)

morreniana	NCft

cauliflower see AGM Vegetables Section

Caulokaempferia (*Zingiberaceae*)

petelotii B&SWJ 11818	LEdu WCru
- HWJ 541	WCru

Caulophyllum (*Berberidaceae*)

thalictroides	CAby EMor EPPr GKev IMou LEdu SRot WCru WHil WPGP WPnP WSHC
- subsp. ***robustum***	EBee WCru

Cautleya ✿ (*Zingiberaceae*)

cathcartii	CExl LEdu
- 'Tenzing's Gold'	EBee GCal LEdu WCru WPGP WSHC
§ ***gracilis***	CAby CBod CDTJ CExl EBee EUJe GCal IBlr WHlf
- BWJ 7843	WCru
- from Manipur, India	WPGP
- 'Crûg Gold'	WCru WPGP
- 'Dzoukou'	LEdu
lutea	see *C. gracilis*
spicata	CAby CBct CCCN CDTJ CSpe CTsd EUJe GKev IBlr MPie
- CC 3676	CExl
- 'Arun Flame'	CBct ESwi GCal LEdu MNrw WCru WPGP
- 'Bleddyn's Beacon'	ESwi WCru
- 'Crûg Canary'	LEdu MAvo WCru WPGP
- 'Crûg Compact'	WCru
* - var. ***lutea***	CBct LEdu WBor WPGP
- 'Robusta'	CAvo CBcs CExl EBee EPfP GCal IBlr LEdu MNrw SMad WBor WCot WCru WPGP

Cayratia (*Vitaceae*)

japonica B&SWJ 6636	WCru
§ ***thomsonii***	SDea
- BWJ 8123	EPPr WCru

Ceanothus ✿ (*Rhamnaceae*)

'A.T. Johnson'	SGol SRms
arboreus	SArc
- 'Trewithen Blue' ♀H4	Widely available
'Autumnal Blue' ♀H4	Widely available
'Blue Cushion'	CRos CTri EPfP LRHS MAsh MGos MJak NLar NRHS SLon SWvt
'Blue Diamond'PBR	LSRN
'Blue Jeans'	CKel MMuc NLar
'Blue Mound' ♀H4	Widely available
'Blue Sapphire'PBR	CWGN ELan EPfP LRHS LSRN MAsh MGos NLar SPoG SRms SWvt WTyc
'Blue Sensation'	NLar
'Burkwoodii' ♀H4	CBcs CKel CRos CSBt EMOT EPfP LRHS MAsh MGos MRav NEgg SCob SPer SRms SWvt
'Cascade' ♀H4	CBcs LSRN SPer SPlb WAvo
'Concha' ♀H4	Widely available
'Cynthia Postan'	CBod CRos EHyd EPfP LRHS MHer NLar SCob
'Dark Star' ♀H4	CBcs CRos CSBt CTri CWGN EHyd ELan ELon EPfP EUJe LRHS LSRN MAsh MGos NHol NRHS SCob SNig SPoG SSta SWvt
'Delight'	CBcs
× ***delileanus*** 'Gloire de Versailles' ♀H4	CBcs CDul CKel CTri ELan EMOT EPfP EWTr MGos MRav MSwo NLar SCob SCoo SGol SPer SPoG SWvt WKif WSHC
- 'Henri Desfossé'	CKel ELan EPfP LSRN MRav MSwo NLar SCob SPer SPoG WKif
- 'Topaze' ♀H4	CKel EPfP LRHS MRav NLar SGol SLon WKif
dentatus Torr. & A. Gray	SPlb
'Diamond Heights'	see *C. griseus* var. *horizontalis* 'Diamond Heights'
'Edinburgh'	NEgg
EL DORADO ('Perado') (v)	CKel CSBt ELan MJak SCob SGol WAvo
gloriosus 'Emily Brown'	CBcs CBod CKel ELan MRav NLar
§ ***griseus*** var. ***horizontalis*** 'Diamond Heights' (v)	CBcs LSRN MAsh NLar SPer

- - 'Silver Surprise'PBR (v)	LBuc LSRN NLar NPri SRms
- - 'Yankee Point'	CBar CBcs CBod CKel CMac CRos CSBt EHyd EPfP EShb LRHS LSRN MGos MRav MSwo NLar NRHS SCoo SEND SGol SLim SPlb SPoG SWvt
impressus	CTri EPfP MAsh SWvt WFar
'Italian Skies'	CBcs CKel CRos CSBt ECrN EHyd ELan EMOT EPfP LRHS LSRN MAsh MGos MSwo NEgg NLar NRHS SCob SCoo SGol SLim SLon SPer SPlb SPoG SWvt
'Julia Phelps'	SGol WAvo
'Lemon and Lime'PBR	CKel EMil LBuc LRHS NRHS
'Madagascar'	EMOT SCoo SPoG
MARIE-ROSE ('Minmarose')	CKel
× ***pallidus*** 'Marie Simon'	CRos EHyd ELan EPfP EWTr LRHS LSRN MAsh MGos SCob SGol SPer SPoG SRms SWvt WCFE WKif
- 'Perle Rose' ♀H4	CBcs EMOT EPfP MGos SPer WKif WSHC
papillosus	IArd WPav
§ 'Pershore Zanzibar'PBR (v)	CBcs CBod CChe CMac CRos CTri EHoe EHyd EPfP EShb LRHS MGos MRav MSwo NEgg NRHS SGol SPer SPoG SRms WAvo
'Pin Cushion'	CRos EHyd EPfP LRHS MAsh WAvo
'Point Millerton'	see *C. thyrsiflorus* 'Millerton Point'
'Popcorn'	LRHS
prostratus	CKel SMad
'Puget Blue' ♀H4	Widely available
'Puget Blue' × ***thyrsiflorus*** var. ***repens***	LOPS
pumilus **new**	NSla
'Ray Hartman'	NLar
repens	see *C. thyrsiflorus* var. *repens*
'Skylark' ♀H4	CBar CBcs CBod CChe CDul CKel CMac CRos EHyd ELan EMOT EPfP GBin GWyn LCro LOPS LRHS LSRN MAsh MGos NHic NRHS SEND SEle SGol SLim SPer WAvo WFar
'Snow Flurries'	see *C. thyrsiflorus* 'Snow Flurry'
'Snow Showers'	CBcs
'Southmead' ♀H4	CKel CRos CTri ECrN EHyd ELan EPfP LRHS MGos MSwo NHic NRHS
thyrsiflorus	CTri SRms SWvt WAvo
- 'Cool Blue' **new**	LCro LOPS
§ - 'Millerton Point'	CCCN CRos ELan EPfP LRHS NLar SGol
- 'Mystery Blue' ♀H4	CRos EHyd EPfP LRHS NEgg NRHS SWvt
§ - var. ***repens*** ♀H4	Widely available
§ - 'Snow Flurry'	CKel ELan MSwo SGol
'Tilden Park'	CRos EHyd LRHS
'Tuxedo'PBR	LRHS MAsh MRav NLar SGol
× ***veitchianus***	CRos CSBt EPfP LRHS NRHS SEND SPer
'Victoria'	CEnd EBee LRHS LSRN MSwo NEgg NLar SGol SRms
'Zanzibar'	see *C.* 'Pershore Zanzibar'

Cedrela (*Meliaceae*)

sinensis	see *Toona sinensis*

Cedronella (*Lamiaceae*)

§ ***canariensis***	CBod ENfk GPoy MNHC SRms WJek WOut
triphylla	see *C. canariensis*

Cedrus (*Pinaceae*)

sp.	LPra
atlantica	CAco CDul CMac LMaj LPra NWea SEND SGol WMat WTSh
- 'Aurea' ♀H6	CKel LRHS MJak NLar SSta
- 'Fastigiata'	CDul LRHS NEgg NLar
- Glauca Group	CAco CCVT CDul CLnd CMac CMen CTho ECrN ELan EPfP EWTr LPra LRHS MBlu MGos MJak NEgg NLar SEWo SGol SLim SMad SPer SPlb SPoG SSta WBor WMat WMou
- - 'Glauca' ♀H6	CAco CKel EMOT LMaj MAsh NWea SAko WTSh
- - 'Glauca Pendula' ♀H6	CAco CCVT CDul CKel LRHS MBlu MGos NEgg NLar NWea SGol SLim SSta WMat
- - 'Silberspitz'	CKen NLar
- 'Pendula'	CAco MAsh
- 'Pyramidalis'	LMaj
- 'Sapphire Nymph'	CKen MAsh NEgg SLim
brevifolia	EBtc LRHS NLar
- 'Hillier Compact'	CKen
- 'Jade Medusa'	LRHS
- 'Kenwith'	CKen NLar
deodara ♀H6	Widely available
- 'Albospica' (v)	SWvt
- 'Aurea' ♀H6	CAco CCVT CKen EPfP LMaj MGos NEgg NHol NOra SGol WFar WMat
I - 'Aurea Pendula'	CAco
- 'Blue Dwarf'	CKen
* - 'Blue Mountain Broom'	CKen
- 'Blue Snake'	CKen
- 'Blue Surprise'	CAco
- 'Bush's Electra'	LRHS MBlu NLar
- 'Devinely Blue'	CKen
- 'Eisregen'	LRHS
- 'Feelin' Blue' ♀H6	CAco CKel CKen ELan EWTr LMaj LRHS MAsh MJak NLar SMad SWvt WFar
- FEELIN' SUNNY ('Monkinn')	NLar
- 'Golden Horizon'	CAco CKen CMen ELan LRHS MAsh NEgg SPoG WFar
- 'Golden Jubilee'	SGol
- 'Karl Fuchs'	LRHS NLar
- 'Klondyke'	CAco MAsh
- 'Lime Glow'	CKen NEgg
- 'Mr Blue'	SPoG
- 'Nana'	CKen
- 'Pendula' ♀H6	CKen NWea
- 'Pygmy'	CKen
- 'Robusta'	LMaj LPra WPGP
- 'Roman Candle'	CAco NEgg
- 'Scott'	CKen NEgg
- 'Silver Mist'	CKen
- 'Silver Spring'	CAco
libani ♀H6	CAco CCVT CDul CLnd CMCN CPer CTho ECrN ELan EMOT EPfP EWTr LMaj LPra LRHS MBlu MMuc NLar NOra NWea SEND SGol SPlb SWvt WFar WTSh
- 'Alibaba'	NLar
- 'Blue Angel'	SLim
- 'Blue Fountain'	NLar
- 'Comte de Dijon'	LRHS NLar
- 'Fontaine'	NLar
- 'Glauca'	CAco
- 'Green Prince'	NLar
- 'Hedgehog'	CKen NLar

- 'Home Park' CKen NLar
- 'Italie' NLar
- 'May' LRHS NLar
- 'Minitaur' new NLar
- Nana Group CAco CKen ELan NEgg
- 'Pendula' CAco NLar
- 'Sargentii' LRHS MBlu NEgg NLar

Ceiba (*Malvaceae*)

pentandra SPlb

Celastrus (*Celastraceae*)

dependens CWJ 12478 WCru
- NMWJ 14556 new WCru
flagellaris B&SWJ 8572 WCru
hookeri B&SWJ 11667 WCru
kusanoi CWJ 12445 WCru
orbiculatus CBcs MRav SLon SPer WHer
- 'Diana' (f) CMac
- 'Hercules' (m) CMac
- Hermaphrodite Group ♀H6 MGil MMuc
- var. ***papillosus*** B&SWJ 591 WCru
- var. ***punctatus*** CWJ 12439 WCru
scandens CMac SPhx SPlb
stephanotiifolius B&SWJ 4727 WCru
stylosus WJC 13746 WCru

celeriac see *Apium graveolens* var. *rapaceum*; also AGM Vegetables Section

celery *Apium graveolens* var. *dulce*; also AGM Vegetables Section

Celmisia (*Asteraceae*)

allanii GKev WAbe
angustifolia ♀H5 GKev NAln WAbe
argentea WAbe
bellidioides EPot GAbr ITim NSla WAbe
coriacea misapplied see *C. semicordata*
densiflora GKev
discolor WAbe
'Eggleston Silver' NBir
gracilenta GKev ITim NSla WAbe
haastii* × *viscosa NSla
hectorii ITim WAbe
longifolia IBlr
ramulosa ITim WAbe
- var. ***tuberculata*** NSla
§ ***semicordata*** IBlr ITim NHpl
- subsp. ***stricta*** IBlr
sessiliflora WAbe
traversii GKev

Celosia (*Amaranthaceae*)

argentea var. ***cristata*** (Plumosa Group) Kimono Series SPoG

Celsia see *Verbascum*

× *Celsioverbascum* see *Verbascum*

Celtica see *Stipa*

Celtis (*Cannabaceae*)

australis CBcs CDul CMCN EBee EBtc LEdu MBlu
biondii NLar
choseniana B&SWJ 12774 WCru
occidentalis CDul EBtc EWTr
sinensis CMen

Cenolophium (*Apiaceae*)

denudatum ♀H6 CSam CSpe EBee EMor EPPr EWes GAbr GBin LCro LEdu LOPS LPla LRHS MAvo MBel MHol MMuc MPie NChi NDov SPhx SPtp WArt WBor WCAu WCot WHil WPGP WSHC WSpi

Centaurea ✿ (*Asteraceae*)

HH&K 271 NBid
RCB AM 6 WCot
W&B BGB-1 WCot
affinis GKev
alpestris NLar SPhx
'Amethyst on Ice' LBuc LRHS NRHS SRms
§ ***atropurpurea*** CBod CRos CSpe EBee EHyd EPfP EWes LPot LRHS MHol NBid NGBl NLar NRHS NSti SBrt SHar SPhx SPlb WCot WHil
babylonica RCB/TQ 18 new WCot
bagadensis GKev
bella CBod CRos EBee ECtt EHyd ELon GCal LRHS MBel MRav NBro NGrd NRHS NSti SMHy SPhx WFar WGwG WKif XLum XSen
benoistii misapplied see *C. atropurpurea*
benoistii ambig. MRav
benoistii ambig. × ***orientalis*** SPhx
'Big Purple' new WCot
cana see *C. triumfettii* subsp. *cana*
candidissima misapplied see *C. cineraria*
'Caramia' CBod CRos EBee ECtt EHyd ELan EMor EPfP LEdu LRHS MHol MNrw NBid NHpl NRHS WCAu WHil
carniolica NAln
- SDR 5443 EBee
cheiranthifolia CFis CMea EPPr MHol MNrw NBid NBir NLar SHar
§ ***cineraria*** ECre WSpi
- subsp. ***cineraria*** ♀H3 SEND WCot
clementei EBee
cyanoides LRHS SPhx
cyanus CHab CSpe LCro LOPS MHer MNHC NPri SVic
- 'Black Ball' CSpe LCro LOPS LRHS MNHC SPhx
- 'Blue Ball' CSpe
- 'Blue Boy' LRHS
- 'Blue Diadem' new SPhx
- 'Florence Blue' (d) new LRHS SPhx
- 'Pinkie' (d) MNHC SPhx
- 'Snowman' SPhx
cynaroides Link see *Rhaponticum centaureoides*
dealbata CBod CMac CRos EAJP EBee EHyd ELon EMor EPfP LRHS MBel MHol MMuc NBro NGrd NLar NMir NRHS SCob SEND SRms WHlf XLum
- 'Steenbergii' CMac EPPr GCal MBel NBid NBir NGdn NPer NSti SPer SPoG WCAu WCot
declinata RCB UA 18 WCot
glastifolia EBee
grinensis WOut
gymnocarpa see *C. cineraria*

	jacea	CSam GAbr GWyn LEdu NBid NLar SPhx WCot WOut WPGP
	- PAB 8821	LEdu
	'John Coutts'	Widely available
	'Jordy'	Widely available
	karabaghensis	EBee GCal GKev
	macrocephala	CBod CRos ECha ECtt EHyd ELan ELon EMor EPfP GAbr ITim LEdu LRHS MBel MHol NBid NBro NChi NEgg NGBl NLar NRHS SMad SPer SPoG SRms WCAu WMoo WPtf XLum
	microptilon	LEdu
	mollis	NBid
	montana	Widely available
	- 'Alba'	Widely available
	- 'Amethyst Dream'PBR	CRos EBee EHyd EMor EPfP LRHS MNrw NLar NRHS SPoG WCAu
	- 'Amethyst in Snow'	CBod CElw CRos EAJP EBee ECtt EHyd EMor EPfP LEdu LRHS MHol NAst NHol NLar NRHS NWad SCob SPoG WBor WMoo WTor
	- 'Black Sprite'	CAby CElw CRos CSpe CWGN EAJP EBee ECtt EHyd ELon EPfP ILea LRHS MNrw NLar NRHS NSti SPoG WBor WBrk WFar WTyc
	- 'Blewit'	CElw EBee ECtt ELon NLar WBor WCAu
§	- 'Carnea'	CElw CSam ELon EPPr GMaP LRHS MCot NAln NBir NChi NLar SHar SPhx WBrk WCAu WFar WMoo WOut
	- 'Coerulea'	NAln
	- 'Elworthy Glacier'	CElw
	- 'Gold Bullion'	CRos CSpe EBee ECtt EHyd EWes GMaP LRHS MHol MRav NBid NLar NRHS WSHC
	- 'Grandiflora'	CCBP EBee ELon MJak MPie
	- 'Joyce'	CElw MTis NBid NLar SHar WBor WCAu WSHC
	- 'Lady Flora Hastings'	CElw CRos CSam CSpe EBee ELon EPPr LRHS MMuc NBid NRHS WBor WBrk
	- 'Lavender Mist'	MHol NRHS
	- lilac-flowered	NBid NLar
	- 'Ochroleuca'	CElw NBid
	- 'Parham'	CElw CRos ECtt EHyd ELon GAbr GCal GQue LRHS MNrw MRav NLar NRHS NSti SPlb WMoo WSHC
	- 'Purple Heart'	CAby CBod CRos CWGN EBee ECtt ELon EPfP EWTr LCro LOPS LSun MBNS MBel MCot MHer MMuc MNrw NGBl NLar SPad SPer SRms WCAu WCot WHlf WMoo
	- 'Purple Prose'	CElw EPPr LPla
	- 'Purpurea'	CElw WBor
	- 'Rosea'	see *C. montana* 'Carnea'
I	- 'Violacea'	NBid
	- 'Violetta'	CElw ELon MAvo NBid NBir WBrk WCAu WMoo
	nervosa	NBid NBro XLum
	nigra	CBod CDor CHab ELan EPfP GJos NLar NMir SPhx SRms WMoo WOut WSFF
	- var. ***alba***	CBre NBid WOut
	- 'Mardi Gras' (v)	ECtt
	- subsp. ***rivularis***	NBid XLum
	nogmovii	MAvo
	orientalis	CBod CSpe EHyd EWes LRHS MBel MHol NGBl NRHS SPhx WHoo
	pannonica	EPPr
	- subsp. ***pannonica*** HH&K 259	NBid
	pestalozzae	GKev
	phrygia	MMuc NLar SEND SPhx
	pulcherrima	EMor MNrw SCob WHil
	'Pulchra Major'	see *Rhaponticum centaureoides*
	pullata	CRos EHyd LRHS NRHS
	rupestris	EBee EPfP SPhx
	ruthenica	CBod CDor CFis SCob SPer SPhx SPlb WGoo
	salicifolia	NBir
	salonitana RCBAM 1	WCot
	scabiosa	CBre CCBP CDor CHab CWld LCro LOPS MHer MNHC NBid NBir NMir SPhx SRms
	'Silver Feather'	CKno CRos EBee EHyd LRHS MHol NRHS NSti SPoG SRms WNPC
	simplicicaulis	CSam ELon MAsh NBir NChi NHpl SHar SRms WHoo WSHC XSen
	thracica	EBee WCot
I	***triumfettii*** subsp. ***cana*** 'Rosea'	WBrk
	- 'Hoar Frost'	EBee ELon NDov
	uniflora	EBee

Centaurium (*Gentianaceae*)

	erythraea	GPoy WOut
	scilloides	EBou GCrg NRHS NSla WAbe

Centella (*Apiaceae*)

§	***asiatica***	GPoy LEdu WJek

Centradenia (*Melastomataceae*)

	inaequilateralis	CCCN

Centranthus (*Caprifoliaceae*)

§	***lecoqii***	ECha ECtt EPPr EWes LRHS MBel SPhx WCot WGoo
	macrosiphon	CMac
§	***ruber***	Widely available
*	- 'Alba Pura'	GAbr
§	- 'Albus'	Widely available
	- 'Atrococcineus'	ECha MMuc
	- var. ***coccineus***	CBcs CBod CRos EAJP EBee EHyd ELan EPfP EWTr GAbr GBin GKin GMaP LPot LRHS LSun MJak MRav NAln NRHS SCob SEND SPer SPhx SRot WCot WFar WGwG WHlf XSen
	- mauve-flowered misapplied	see *C. lecoqii*
	- mauve-flowered	NBir
	- 'Roseus'	CRos EHyd EPfP LRHS NRHS WMoo
	- 'Rosy Red'	CBod
	- 'Snowcloud'	CWld EBee ECtt EHyd ENfk EPfP MNHC SRms WHil
	'White Cloud'	SPad

Centropogon (*Campanulaceae*)

	costaricae B&SWJ 10455	WCru
	ferrugineus B&SWJ 10665	WCru
	hirsutus B&SWJ 10657	WCru

Cephalanthus (*Rubiaceae*)

	'Magical Moonlight'	LRHS
	occidentalis	CDul EBee LRHS MAsh MBNS MBlu NLar NQui SLim SPoG WCFE
	- SUGAR SHACK ('Smcoss') **new**	LRHS

Cephalaria (*Caprifoliaceae*)

§ ***alpina***	CBod CRos EHyd EMor EPPr EPfP LRHS MAsh MNrw NDai NRHS SHar SPhx SRms WBrk WFar XLum
caucasica	see *C. gigantea*
dipsacoides	LRHS SPhx SRms WGoo WMoo
§ ***flava***	CRos EHyd LRHS NRHS
galpiniana	SPlb
§ ***gigantea***	Widely available
graeca	see *C. flava*
leucantha	CFis EMor MMuc NLar SEND SPhx WBrk
litvinovii	SPhx
radiata	NDov SPhx
tatarica hort.	see *C. gigantea*
tchihatchewii	ILea IMou NLar WCot
transsylvanica	SPhx
- W&B BGJ-1	WCot

Cephalotaxus (*Taxaceae*)

fortunei	CAco CDul LEdu WCru
harringtonia	CMCN LEdu
- var. ***drupacea***	CAco NWea
- 'Fastigiata'	CAco CDul IArd LRHS MAsh MGos NWea SLim SPoG
- 'Gimborn's Pillow'	MAsh NLar
- 'Korean Gold'	LRHS SLim
sinensis	CAco

Cephalotus (*Cephalotaceae*)

follicularis 🏆[H2]	SHmp

Cerastium (*Caryophyllaceae*)

alpinum	SRms
- var. ***lanatum***	EWes GKev XLum
biebersteinii	MBel XLum
candidissimum	EWes
fontanum	CHab
tomentosum	CBar CBod CSBt CTri ELan EPfP GWyn MHol MMuc NEgg SEND SPer SPlb SPoG WFar
- var. ***columnae***	ECha EWes GMaP WIce XLum XSen

Ceratonia (*Caesalpiniaceae*)

siliqua	SEND SPlb SVic

Ceratophyllum (*Ceratophyllaceae*)

demersum	CBen CWat EWat LCro LOPS MWts WMAq WSFF XBlo
submersum	LLWG

Ceratostigma (*Plumbaginaceae*)

abyssinicum	CBcs CHll ELan EMor ESwi LEdu
asperrimum B&SWJ 7260	WCru
'Autumn Blue'	EPfP LRHS
capensis	CMac
griffithii	Widely available
§ ***plumbaginoides*** 🏆[H5]	Widely available
willmottianum 🏆[H4]	Widely available
- BWJ 8140	WCru
- DESERT SKIES ('Palmgold'[PBR])	CMac EPfP NLar SCob SLim SWvt
- FOREST BLUE ('Lice'[PBR]) 🏆[H4]	CKel CMac CRos CSBt EHyd ELan EPfP LCro LOPS LRHS LSRN MAsh MGos MRav NLar NPri NRHS SAko SCob SCoo SEle SLim SPer SPoG SSta SWvt WHil
- SAPPHIRE RING ('Lissbrill'[PBR])	CBcs CKel CRos EBee EHyd ELan EPfP LRHS LSRN MAsh NRHS SCoo SPoG WFar WHil

Cercidiphyllum ✿ (*Cercidiphyllaceae*)

japonicum 🏆[H5]	Widely available
- 'Boyd's Dwarf'	CJun CRos EHyd ELan EPfP LLHF LRHS MBlu NLar SPoG SSta WAbe
- 'Chameleon' (v)	MBlu NLar
- GLOWBALL ('Jww4'[PBR])	LRHS MBlu
- 'Herkenrode Dwarf'	MBlu
- 'Heronswood Globe' 🏆[H5]	CJun CMCN EPfP MBlu NLar SSta
- 'Kreukenberg Dwarf'	CJun NLar SSta
- 'Morioka Weeping'	CJun CTho EBee MPkF NLar SChF SMad SSta
- 'Peach'	CJun NLar
§ - f. ***pendulum*** 🏆[H5]	Widely available
- - 'Amazing Grace'	CTho MBlu NLar SSta
- 'Raspberry'	CJun MBlu NLar
- RED FOX	see *C. japonicum* 'Rotfuchs'
§ - 'Rotfuchs'	CBcs CEnd CJun CMCN CMac CRos CTho EBee EHyd ELan EMOT EPfP EWTr LRHS MBlu MGos MPkF NLar SAko SChF SCob SPoG SSta WFar WMat
- 'Ruby'	CJun EBee MBlu NLar
- 'Strawberry'	CBcs CJun MBlu NLar SSta
- 'Tidal Wave'	CJun LRHS MBlu NLar SSta
- 'Titania'	NLar SSta
magnificum	CBcs CDul CEnd CExl CLnd CMCN MBlu NLar
- f. ***pendulum***	see *C. japonicum* f. *pendulum*

Cercis ✿ (*Caesalpiniaceae*)

canadensis	CAco CAgr CDul CMCN CWGN LMaj MGil MGos MMuc NEgg NLar NWea SCob XSen
- f. ***alba***	CBcs CMCN LSRN
- - 'Royal White'	EPfP MBlu SPer
- 'Alley Cat' (v) **new**	NTre
- 'Appalachian Red'	CJun CTho MBlu MGos
- CAROLINA SWEETHEART ('Nccc1') **new**	NTre
- 'Cascading Hearts'	CRos EHyd LRHS NRHS NTre
- 'Flame'	CJun NLar SSta
- 'Forest Pansy' 🏆[H5]	Widely available
- 'Hearts of Gold'[PBR]	CWGN EBee EMOT LRHS MGos MRav NOra SLon SMad SPoG WMat
- LAVENDER TWIST ('Covey')	CDul CMac CRos EBee EHyd ELan EPfP LCro LOPS LRHS LSRN MBlu MGos NLar NOra NRHS NTre SCob SGol SLon SPer SPoG WMat WMou
- LITTLE WOODY ('Litwo'[PBR])	MGos SGol
- 'Melon Beauty'	MBlu NLar SMad
- 'Merlot'	ELan EMOT ESwi MGos NTre NWea WMat
- 'Pauline Lily'	ESwi NLar
- 'Pink Heartbreaker'	SGol
- 'Pink Pom Poms'	LRHS NPri NTre
- RED FORCE ('Minrouge3'[PBR])	WCot
- 'Ruby Falls'[PBR] 🏆[H5]	CBcs CMac CRos EBee EHyd ELan EMOT EUJe EWTr LCro LOPS LRHS MGos NOra NRHS NTre SCob SPoG WMat
- 'Rubye Atkinson'	NLar
- 'Silver Lining' (v)	EBee
- 'Tennessee Pink'	SCob
- var. ***texensis*** 'Oklahoma'	CJun EBee ESwi LRHS MGos NTre WMat WPGP

- - 'Texas White'	CEnd CMac CTho EBee EPfP LRHS NLar SCob WMat
- - 'Traveller'	ESwi NTre SGol
- 'The Rising Sun'	MGos NTre
- 'Vanilla Twist'	EBee NTre SPoG
- 'Whitewater' (v)	NTre
chinensis	EWTr LEdu NLar SPer WMou
- B&SWJ 12665	WCru
- NJM 11.047	WPGP
- f. ***alba***	CTho MGos
- 'Avondale' ♀H5	Widely available
- 'Diane' **new**	SSta
- 'Don Egolf' ♀H5	CJun MBlu MGos NLar SGol
- 'Shirobana'	NTre WMat
chingii	CExl
gigantea	NLar WPGP
griffithii	CMCN LEdu NLar SSta WPGP
occidentalis	LEdu SSta
racemosa	CExl WPGP
siliquastrum	Widely available
- f. ***albida***	CBcs CRos CTho EHyd ELan EPfP EWes LRHS SSta
- 'Bodnant' ♀H5	CMac CTho EPfP EWes IArd LLHF LRHS LSRN MBlu MGos NLar NOra SCob SSta WMat
- 'White Swan'	CJun CTho

Cerinthe (*Boraginaceae*)

major	SWvt
- 'Kiwi Blue'	CHll
- 'Purpurascens'	CSpe ELan EPfP LCro LOPS MNHC SPer SPhx SPoG WKif
minor	CSpe

Ceropegia (*Apocynaceae*)

§ ***linearis*** subsp. ***woodii*** ♀H1c	EShb
sandersonii ♀H1c	CCCN EShb
woodii	see *C. linearis* subsp. *woodii*

Cestrum (*Solanaceae*)

aurantiacum	EShb SEND
buxifolium B&SWJ 14395	WCru
× ***cultum***	CHll
- 'Cretan Pink'	CCCN
- 'Cretan Purple'	CBcs CCCN CHll CKel CRos EHyd ELan ELon EPfP EShb IDee LRHS MGil SEND SWvt WKif
diurnum × ***nocturnum***	EShb
§ ***elegans***	CAby CExl CHll CKel EBee ELon EPfP EWTr EWld LRHS MGil NQui SEND SLon SPad SWvt WCFE
'Newellii' ♀H3	CBcs CCCN CExl CKel CRos EBak EBee EHyd ELan ELon EPfP EUJe LRHS SEND SPlb SVen SWvt WKif
nocturnum	CBcs CCCN CHll EBak EShb GCal WCFE
parqui ♀H3	CAbb CBcs CCCN CHll CKel CMCN CTsd EBee ELan EPfP EUJe IDee MGil SEND SLon SMad SWvt WKif WSHC
- purple-tinged **new**	SBrt
psittacinum	CExl
purpureum (Lindl.) Standl.	see *C. elegans*
roseum	CExl
- B&SWJ 10255 from Oaxaca State, Mexico	WCru
- 'Ilnacullin'	CCCN

Ceterach see *Asplenium*

officinarum	see *Asplenium ceterach*

Chaenomeles (*Rosaceae*)

cathayensis	CAgr CDul LEdu NLar SBrt WCru WHer WPGP
§ ***japonica***	CAco CCCN MMuc SEND
- 'Chojubai'	CMen
- 'Cido'	CAgr LEdu MCoo
- 'Orange Beauty'	CRos LRHS NHol SPer
- 'Rising Sun'	NLar
- 'Sargentii'	ELan MBlu NLar SGol
lagenaria	see *C. speciosa*
MADAME BUTTERFLY ('Whitice')	CRos EBee EHyd ELan EPfP LRHS LSRN MAsh MMuc MRav NEgg NRHS SCob SEND SGol SLim SPer SPoG SRms
maulei	see *C. japonica*
'Orange Star'	CEnd
'Red Kimono'	LRHS NLar SGol
sinensis	see *Pseudocydonia sinensis*
§ ***speciosa***	NWea
- 'Apple Blossom'	see *C. speciosa* 'Moerloosei'
- 'Contorta'	LRHS MAsh WFar
- 'Eximia'	LRHS
- 'Falconnet Charlet' (d)	CRos EHyd LRHS MRav NRHS SRms
- 'Flocon Rose'	EPfP LRHS SGol
- 'Friesdorfer'	LRHS
- 'Geisha Girl' (d) ♀H6	CBcs CEnd CKel CMac CRos CSBt EBee EHyd ELan EPfP LCro LOPS LRHS LSRN MAsh MGos MRav MSwo NRHS SCob SGbt SGol SLim SPer SPoG SRms SWvt WFar
- HOT FIRE ('Minvesu')	EPfP LRHS WCot
- 'Kinshiden'	CKel EMil EPfP LRHS LSRN NLar SGol
§ - 'Moerloosei' ♀H6	Widely available
- 'Nivalis'	Widely available
- 'Orange Storm'PBR	LCro LOPS LRHS LSRN SGol
- 'Pink Storm'	LCro LOPS SGol
- 'Rubra Grandiflora'	LRHS
- 'Scarlet Storm'PBR	LRHS SGol
- 'Simonii' (d)	CBcs MRav NWea SPer
- 'Snow'	MAsh MSwo SRms
- 'Umbilicata'	MBlu SPer SRms
- 'Yukigotan' (d)	CRos LEdu LLHF LRHS NEgg NLar SCob SGol SWvt
× ***superba*** 'Boule de Feu'	CTri MCoo
- 'Cameo' (d)	CEnd ELon EPfP LEdu LRHS MBNS MRav NLar SGol SRms WCot WFar
- 'Coquelicot'	NLar
- 'Crimson and Gold' ♀H6	Widely available
- 'Elly Mossel'	CMac NLar SRms WFar
- 'Ernst Finken'	NLar
- 'Etna'	WFar
- 'Fire Dance'	CDul CHll CTsd EUJe MSwo NLar SGol SNig SPer WCot WRHF
- 'Fusion'	CAgr
- 'Hollandia'	SRms
- 'Issai White'	MRav
- 'Jet Trail'	CBcs CKel CMac CRos CSBt EHyd ELan EPfP LRHS LSRN MAsh MGos MJak MRav MSwo NEgg NHic NLar NRHS SCob SGol SLim SRms SWvt WFar
- 'Knap Hill Scarlet'	CBod CDul CKel CRos EBee EHyd ELan EPfP LRHS MAsh MGos NRHS SCob SEND SLim SNig SPer SPoG SRms SWvt WCot

	Name	Suppliers
	- 'Lemon and Lime'	CBcs ELan EWTr LRHS MAsh MGos MRav NLar SLon SRms
	- 'Nicoline' ♀H6	CBcs CDul CRos LRHS MGos SCob
	- 'Pink Lady' ♀H6	Widely available
	- 'Pink Trail'	NLar SRms
	- 'Red Joy'	CKel EBee EPfP LRHS MRav NLar SRms
	- 'Red Trail'	MRav
	- 'Rowallane' ♀H6	CBod CHll ELan MRav
	- 'Salmon Horizon'	IArd NLar
	- 'Texas Scarlet'	SRms
	- 'Tortuosa'	LRHS MBNS NLar WCot WGrn
	'Toyo-nishiki'	MBlu

Chaenorhinum (*Plantaginaceae*)

	Name	Suppliers
	glareosum	ITim NHpl
§	***origanifolium***	CBod SPlb
	- 'Blue Dream'	CSpe EBou EPfP EWTr GKev MAsh SCob SPoG SWvt WFar WHoo WIce WMoo
	- 'Dreamcatcher'	EPfP WFar

Chaenostoma (*Scrophulariaceae*)

	Name	Suppliers
§	(Abunda Series) ABUNDA COLOSSAL WHITE ('Balabowite'PBR)	NPri
§	(Copia Series) COPIA GULLIVER WHITE ('Dangul14'PBR)	NPri
	cordatum 'Olympic Gold' (v)	SCoo
§	- 'Snowflake'	NPer SCoo SPoG SWvt
§	***neglectum***	WPGP
§	(Scopia Series) SCOPIA GOLDEN LEAVES WHITE ('Dancop15')	NPri
	- SCOPIA GREAT REGAL BLUE ('Dancop30')	NPri
	- SCOPIA GULLIVER DYNAMIC WHITE ('Dancop40'PBR) **new**	MCot

Chaerophyllum (*Apiaceae*)

	Name	Suppliers
	azoricum	LEdu LPla SIgm WOut WPGP
	hirsutum	IMou
	- 'Roseum'	Widely available

Chamaebatiaria (*Rosaceae*)

	Name	Suppliers
	millefolium	SBrt

Chamaecyparis ✿ (*Cupressaceae*)

	Name	Suppliers
	funebris	see *Cupressus funebris*
	lawsoniana	CACo CDul CPer LMaj LPra NWea WMou WTSh
	- 'Allumii Aurea'	see *C. lawsoniana* 'Alumigold'
I	- 'Allumii Green'	CACo
	- 'Allumii Magnificent'	MAsh
§	- 'Alumigold'	LRHS MAsh MJak
	- 'Alumii'	CACo LPra MJak NWea
	- 'Aurea'	CDul
	- 'Aurea Densa' ♀H6	CKen CSBt CTri MGos
	- 'Bleu Nantais' ♀H6	CACo CKen EMOT EPfP LBee LRHS MGos SCoo SLim SPoG WCFE
	- 'Blom'	CKen
	- 'Blue Surprise'	CKen
	- 'Brégéon'	CKen NLar
	- 'Broomhill Gold' ♀H6	CSBt EMOT LBee MGos NEgg SCoo SLim SPoG
	- 'Caudata'	CKen
§	- 'Chilworth Silver' ♀H6	CSBt LBee LRHS MAsh
	- 'Columnaris'	CACo EMOT EPfP LBee LPra MJak NEgg SCoo SPoG
	- 'Columnaris Glauca'	CMac MGos NEgg NWea SCoo SPer
	- 'Cream Crackers'	EMOT
	- 'Cream Glow'	CKen CSBt LRHS
	- 'Dik's Weeping' ♀H6	CACo NLar NWea SLim
	- 'Drooping Solo' **new**	CKen NLar
	- 'Duncanii'	EMOT
	- 'Dutch Gold'	MAsh
	- 'Eclipse'	CKen
	- 'Elegantissima' ambig.	CMac SLim
	- 'Ellwoodii' ♀H6	CACo CBod CDul CMac CSBt CTri ELan EMOT EPfP LRHS MAsh MGil MGos NEgg NPri SCoo SLim SPer
I	- 'Ellwoodii Glauca'	SPlb
	- 'Ellwood's Gold' ♀H6	CACo CBcs CKel CMac CSBt ELan EMOT EPfP LBee LRHS MAsh MGos MJak NPri NWea SPer SPlb SPoG
	- 'Ellwood's Gold Pillar' ♀H6	LBee LRHS MAsh NHol SLim
§	- 'Ellwood's Nymph'	CKen MAsh
	- ELLWOOD'S PILLAR ('Flolar') ♀H6	CACo CMac EMOT LBee LRHS MAsh MGos NLar SCoo SLim
	- 'Ellwood's Pygmy'	CMac
	- 'Ellwood's Silver'	MAsh
	- 'Ellwood's Silver Threads'	CMac LBee NEgg
	- 'Ellwood's Variegata'	see *C. lawsoniana* 'Ellwood's White'
§	- 'Ellwood's White' (v)	CACo CMac EMOT NEgg SPoG
	- 'Emerald Spire'	MAsh
	- 'Erecta Viridis'	MJak NWea
	- 'Filip's Golden Tears'	ELan MAsh NLar SLim
	- 'Fleckellwood'	MAsh
	- 'Fletcheri' ♀H6	CMac NWea
	- 'Fletcheri Aurea'	see *C. lawsoniana* 'Yellow Transparent'
	- 'Forsteckensis'	NLar NWea
	- 'Fraseri'	NWea
	- 'Gimbornii' ♀H6	CDul NLar
	- 'Glauca'	CDul
	- 'Glauca Pendula' **new**	CACo
	- 'Gnome'	CKen CMac EMOT NEgg NHol SCoo SPoG
§	- 'Golden Pot'	CSBt LBee
	- 'Golden Wonder' ♀H6	CACo EMOT MAsh NWea SCoo
	- 'Grayswood Feather' ♀H6	LBee SPlb
	- 'Green Globe' ♀H6	CKen CMen CSBt LBee LRHS MGil
§	- 'Green Hedger'	CSBt NWea
§	- 'Green Pillar'	CACo CDul EMOT LBee NWea
	- 'Green Spire'	see *C. lawsoniana* 'Green Pillar'
	- 'Hillieri'	CACo
	- 'Imbricata Pendula' ♀H6	CACo CKen IDee MBlu NLar SMad WPGP
	- 'Ivonne' ♀H6	CACo CDul EMOT EPfP LRHS MGos SLim SPoG
	- 'Jackman's Green Hedger'	see *C. lawsoniana* 'Green Hedger'
	- 'Jackman's Variety'	see *C. lawsoniana* 'Green Pillar'
	- 'Jeanette'	CKen
	- 'Kilmacurragh' ♀H6	CACo CMac WCFE
	- 'Kilworth Column'	LRHS NLar NWea
	- 'Knowefieldensis'	CMac EMOT
	- 'Lane' misapplied	see *C. lawsoniana* 'Lanei Aurea'
	- 'Lane' den Ouden	EMOT MJak
§	- 'Lanei Aurea' ♀H6	LMaj
	- 'Lemon Queen'	CDul
	- 'Little Spire' ♀H6	EUJe LRHS NLar
§	- 'Lutea Nana'	CMac
§	- 'Lutea Smithii'	CACo
	- 'Luteocompacta'	LBee
	- 'Magnifica Aurea'	LRHS
	- 'Minima Argentea'	see *C. lawsoniana* 'Nana Argentea'

- 'Minima Aurea' ♀H6	CBod CKen CMac CSBt EMOT EPfP LBee LRHS MAsh MGil MGos MJak NEgg SLim SPoG WCFE
- 'Minima Glauca' ♀H6	CAco CMac EMOT MJak NEgg NWea SCoo SLim WFar
- 'Moonsprite' ♀H6	CAco CKen EMOT NLar SCoo SLim SPoG
- 'Nana Albospica' (v)	EMOT LBee
§ - 'Nana Argentea'	CKen CMac EMOT EPfP SPoG
- 'Nana Lutea'	see *C. lawsoniana* 'Lutea Nana'
- 'Nicole'	EMOT MAsh NWea SCoo
- 'Nyewoods'	see *C. lawsoniana* 'Chilworth Silver'
- 'Nymph'	see *C. lawsoniana* 'Ellwood's Nymph'
- 'Pearly Swirls' (v)	LRHS NLar SPoG
§ - 'Pelt's Blue'	CAco CBcs CDul CSBt MJak NLar
- 'Pembury Blue' ♀H6	CCVT CDul CKel EMOT EPfP LBee LPra LRHS MGos MJak NEgg NLar NWea SCoo SLim SPoG
- 'Pina Colada'PBR	LRHS
- POT OF GOLD	see *C. lawsoniana* 'Golden Pot'
- 'Pottenii'	LBee NLar NWea
- 'Pygmaea Argentea' (v) ♀H6	CKen CMac CSBt ELan EMOT MAsh MGos NEgg NWea SLim SPoG
- 'Pygmy'	CMen NEgg NWea
- 'Rijnhof'	LBee
- 'Rimpelaar'	CKen NWad
- 'Silver Queen' (v)	CKen
- 'Silver Threads' (v)	CAco ELan EMOT LBee LRHS SPoG
- 'Silver Tip' (v)	EMOT
- 'Smithii'	see *C. lawsoniana* 'Lutea Smithii'
- 'Snow Flurry' (v)	CKen
- 'Snow White'PBR (v) ♀H6	CAco EMOT LBee LRHS MAsh MGos NHol SCoo SPoG
- 'Springtime'PBR	CSBt LBee LRHS
- 'Stardust' ♀H6	CBcs CDul CKel CSBt ELan LPra LRHS MAsh MGos MJak NEgg NPri
- 'Stewartii'	CDul LPra NEgg
- 'Summer Snow' (v) ♀H6	CAco EMOT EPfP NEgg NHol SCoo
- 'Sunkist'	CKel
- 'Tamariscifolia'	WCFE
- 'Treasure' (v)	CDul MAsh
- 'Van Pelt'	see *C. lawsoniana* 'Pelt's Blue'
- 'Waterfall'	CAco
- 'White Spot' (v)	CKel EMOT
- 'Wisselii' ♀H6	CKel CKen CMac EMOT MGos NEgg NLar NWea SLim WCFE
- 'Wisselii Nana'	CKen
- 'Wissel's Saguaro' ♀H6	CKen NLar
- 'Witzeliana'	NLar
- 'Yellow Spire'	NLar
§ - 'Yellow Transparent'	CMac
× *leylandii*	see × *Cuprocyparis leylandii*
nootkatensis	see *Xanthocyparis nootkatensis*
obtusa	LPra
- 'Albovariegata' (v)	CKen
- 'Arneson's Compact'	CKen
- 'Aurora' ♀H7	CKen ELan EMOT LRHS SLim SPoG
- 'Bambi'	CKen CMen WAbe
- 'Barkenny'	CKen
- 'Bartley'	CKen
- 'Bassett'	CKen
- 'Bess'	CKen
- 'Blizzard' (v) **new**	NLar
- 'Brigitt'	CKen
- 'Bronze Pygmy'	LRHS
- 'Butterball'	CKen CMen LRHS NEgg
- 'Caespitosa'	WAbe
- 'Chilworth'	CKen NWad
- 'Chima-anihiba'	CKen
- 'Chirimen'	CKen CMen NLar SAko
- 'Clarke's Seedling'	CKen LRHS
- 'Confucius'	EUJe
- 'Corley Gold'	EUJe
§ - 'Crippsii' ♀H7	CMac LPra
- 'Crippsii Aurea'	see *C. obtusa* 'Crippsii'
- 'Dainty Doll'	CKen NHol NWad
- 'Densa'	see *C. obtusa* 'Nana Densa'
- 'Draht'	CAco CKel LRHS NLar
- 'Draht Hexe'	CKen
- 'Elf'	CKen NLar
- 'Ellie B'	CKen CMen NEgg
- 'Ericoides'	CKen
- 'Fernspray Gold' ♀H7	CCVT CDul CKen CTri EMOT EPfP LRHS MGos NEgg NLar SCoo SPoG
- 'Flabelliformis'	CKen NWad
- 'Gemstone'	NLar
- 'Gitte'	SLim
- 'Gnome'	CKen CMen
- 'Gold Fern'	CKen
- 'Golden Brigitt' **new**	NLar
- 'Golden Fairy'	CKen
- 'Golden Filament' (v)	CKen
- 'Golden Nymph'	CKen
- 'Golden Sprite'	CKen WAbe
- 'Gracilis'	NEgg
- 'Gracilis Aurea'	CKen CMac CMen
- 'Graciosa'	see *C. obtusa* 'Loenik'
- 'Green Cushion'	CKen NLar
- 'Green Diamond'	CKen
- 'Hage'	CKen
- 'Hannah'	NLar
- 'Hypnoides Nana'	CKen
- 'Intermedia'	CKen WAbe
- 'Ivan's Column'	CKen
- 'Junior'	CKen
- 'Juniperoides'	CKen
- 'Juniperoides Compacta'	WAbe
- 'Kamarachiba' ♀H7	CAco CKen CSBt EMOT LBee NEgg NLar SCoo SLim SPoG
- 'Kerdalo'	CAco LRHS NLar
- 'Kosteri' ♀H7	CKen CMac ELan EMOT LBee NHol SCoo
- 'Kyoto Creeper'	CKen
- 'Leprechaun'	WAbe
- 'Limerick'	CKen
- 'Little Markey'	CKen CMen
§ - 'Loenik'	EMOT
- 'Lucas'PBR	CAco LRHS NLar
- 'Lutea Nova'	CAco
- 'Marian'	CKen NLar
§ - 'Mariesii' (v)	CKen LRHS
- 'Melody'	CKen NLar
- 'Meroke'	MGil NLar
- 'Minima'	CKen
- 'Nana' ♀H7	CAco CKen CMac CMen LBee NEgg NHol NWad
- 'Nana Aurea' ♀H7	CMac CSBt EMOT EPfP LRHS NHol
§ - 'Nana Densa'	CKen CMac LRHS
- 'Nana Gracilis' ♀H7	CAco CKen CMen CSBt ELan EMOT EPfP LRHS MAsh MGos NWad NWea SCoo SLim SPoG
I - 'Nana Gracilis Aurea'	CAco CMen
I - 'Nana Lutea' ♀H7	CAco CKen CMen ELan EMOT LBee LRHS MAsh MGos NEgg NHol NWad NWea SLim
- 'Nana Rigida'	see *C. obtusa* 'Rigid Dwarf'

	– 'Nana Variegata'	see *C. obtusa* 'Mariesii'
	– 'Oregon Crested' **new**	MGil NLar
	– 'Pillnitz' **new**	NLar
	– 'Pygmaea'	CSBt EMOT NEgg SCoo SLim
	– 'Rashahiba'	LRHS
	– 'Reis Dwarf'	EUJe NEgg
	– 'Rezek Dwarf'	CAco CKen CMen
§	– 'Rigid Dwarf'	CKen LBee LRHS SLim
	– 'Saffron Spray'	CAco LRHS NLar
	– 'Slim Jim'	NLar
	– 'Snowflake' (v)	CKen ELan LRHS NWad
	– 'Snowkist' (v)	CKen
	– 'Southern Lights'	NLar
	– 'Sparkles'	NLar
	– 'Spiralis'	CKen
	– 'Split Rock'	NLar
	– 'Stoneham'	CAco CKen CMen NEgg
	– 'Strangman'	CKen
	– 'Tempelhof'	CAco CKen NLar SCoo
	– 'Tetragona Aurea'	CMac NWad
	– 'Timothy'	CMac
	– 'Tonia' (v)	CKen MAsh
	– 'Tsatsumi'	NLar
	– 'Tsatsumi Gold' ♀H7	CAco CKen CMen ELan EPfP LRHS MPkF NLar SCoo SLim SPoG
	– 'Verdon'	CKen
	– 'Wiels Baby'	NLar
	– 'Wyckoff'	CKen
	– 'Yellowtip' (v)	CAco CKen EPfP MAsh NEgg
	pisifera	CAco
	– 'Aurea Nana' misapplied	see *C. pisifera* 'Strathmore'
	– 'Baby Blue'	ELan EPfP LRHS NEgg SCoo SLim SPoG
	– 'Blue Globe'	CKen
	– 'Boulevard' ♀H7	CAco CBcs CBod CDul CKel CMac CSBt ELan EMOT EPfP LBee LRHS MAsh MGos MJak NEgg NWea SLim SPer WBor
	– 'Compacta'	LRHS
	– 'Curly Top' ♀H7	CAco CSBt EMOT EPfP NHol SCoo SLim SPoG
	– 'Devon Cream'	NEgg
	– 'Filifera'	CMac CSBt
	– 'Filifera Aurea' ♀H7	CAco CKen CMac ELan EMOT EPfP LBee LMaj LRHS MAsh MGos NEgg NHol NWea SCoo
	– 'Filifera Aurea Nana' **new**	CAco
	– 'Filifera Nana'	CAco ELan LRHS SLim
	– 'Filifera Nana Aurea'	see *C. pisifera* 'Golden Mop'
	– 'Filifera Sungold'	see *C. pisifera* 'Sungold'
	– 'Fuiri-tsukomo'	CKen
	– 'Gold Cushion'	CKen
	– 'Gold Dust'	see *C. pisifera* 'Plumosa Aurea'
	– 'Gold Spangle'	CKen
§	– 'Golden Mop'	CAco CKen NLar
	– 'Green Pincushion'	CKen CMen
	– 'Hime-himuro'	CKen
	– 'Hime-sawara'	CKen CMen
	– 'Iceberg'	NLar
	– 'Lime Pie' **new**	CKen
	– 'Nana'	CKen CMen EMOT NHol
	– 'Nana Aurea'	NRya
	– 'Nana Aureovariegata' (v)	CSBt LBee NEgg
I	– 'Nana Compacta'	CMac
	– 'Nana Variegata' (v)	CMac LBee
I	– 'Parslorii'	CKen
	– 'Pici'	CKen
§	– 'Plumosa Aurea'	CKen MAsh
	– 'Plumosa Aurea Compacta'	CKen NWad
	– 'Plumosa Aurea Nana'	MAsh
I	– 'Plumosa Aurea Nana Compacta'	CMac
	– 'Plumosa Aurescens'	CMac
§	– 'Plumosa Compressa' ♀H7	CKen NWad
	– 'Plumosa Densa'	see *C. pisifera* 'Plumosa Compressa'
I	– 'Plumosa Juniperoides'	CKen
I	– 'Pygmaea Tsukumo'	NLar
	– 'Silver Lode' (v)	CKen
	– 'Snow' (v)	CKen
	– 'Snowflake'	CKen
	– 'Spaan's Cannon Ball'	CKen CMen NEgg NLar
	– 'Squarrosa Dumosa'	CKen
I	– 'Squarrosa Lombarts'	CMac CSBt
	– 'Squarrosa Lutea'	CKen
	– 'Squarrosa Sulphurea'	CAco CSBt ELan
§	– 'Strathmore'	CAco
§	– 'Sungold' ♀H7	CKen CSBt ELan LRHS MAsh MGos NWea SCoo SLim SPoG SRms
	– 'Tama-himuro'	CKen
	– 'Teddy Bear'	CAco NEgg NLar
	– 'True Blue'	CAco ELan
	– 'White Beauty' (v)	EMOT
	thyoides 'Andelyensis'	CMac CSBt EMOT
	– 'Conica'	MAsh
	– 'Ericoides'	CKen CTri EMOT LBee SPlb
	– 'Little Jamie'	CKen
	– 'Red Star'	see *C. thyoides* 'Rubicon'
§	– 'Rubicon'	CMac CSBt EMOT EPfP LBee LRHS MAsh SLim SPoG
	– 'Top Point'	LBee MAsh SCoo SPoG

Chamaedaphne (*Ericaceae*)

	calyculata	CBcs

Chamaedorea (*Arecaceae*)

	metallica misapplied	see *C. microspadix*
§	***microspadix*** ♀H1a	CPHo
	radicalis	CBrP CPHo

Chamaemelum (*Asteraceae*)

§	***nobile***	CBod CHby CLau CTri EBou ENfk EPfP GPoy LCro LOPS MEch MHer MMuc MNHC NGdn NPri SEND SPlb SRms SVic WArt WSpi WTre
	– dwarf	SMor SVic
	– dwarf, double-flowered (d)	LEdu
	– 'Flore Pleno' (d)	CBod CBre CElw CLau CMea CPrp CTri ECha ENfk EPfP GPoy MHer MHol MNHC MRav NBro NGdn NGrd SBch SPer SRms WHal WJek WTre
	– 'Treneague'	CBod CBre CCBP CPrp CTri EBou ECha EHyd ELan ENfk EPfP EWhm GPoy GQue LRHS MCot MHer MNHC MRav NRHS SMor SPer SPlb SRms WFar WHal WHer WJek WTre

Chamaenerion (*Onagraceae*)

§	***angustifolium***	WSFF
§	– 'Album'	Widely available
	– 'Hullavington Fire' **new**	CNat
	– 'Isobel'	MRav WCot
	– 'Stahl Rose'	CAby CMea EPfP EWes LEdu MBel NSti SGbt SMad SPhx WCot WHrl WSHC
§	***dodonaei***	CFis EWes IMou SMHy SPhx WCot WSHC
§	***fleischeri***	CPla

Chamaepericlymenum see *Cornus*

Chamaerops (*Arecaceae*)

excelsa misapplied	see *Trachycarpus fortunei*
excelsa Thunb.	see *Rhapis excelsa*
humilis ♀H4	CAbb CAco CBcs CBrP CKel CTsd ELan EPfP EUJe LRHS MGos SArc SChr SEND SPlb SPoG STrG
§ - var. ***argentea***	CBrP CDTJ CPHo MGos SChr SPlb WCot
- var. ***cerifera***	see *C. humilis* var. *argentea*
- 'Vulcano'	CDTJ EUJe LRHS SChr

Chamaespartium see *Genista*

Chamaesphacos (*Lamiaceae*)

ilicifolius misapplied	see *Siphocranion macranthum*

Chamelaucium (*Myrtaceae*)

uncinatum	CCCN EShb
- 'Snowflake'	CCCN EBee

Chamerion see *Chamaenerion*

chard see AGM Vegetables Section

Charybdis (*Asparagaceae*)

§ ***maritima***	EMor LAma WCot

Chasmanthe (*Iridaceae*)

aethiopica	CPbh SChr
bicolor	CExl CPrp CTca EWld
floribunda	CPrp GKev SDeJ WOut
- var. ***duckittii***	CPla CPrp GKev SDeJ
- - 'Golden Wave'	CPrp GKev
- 'Saturnus'	GKev

Chasmanthium (*Poaceae*)

§ ***latifolium***	CBod CKno CRos CSde CSpe ECha EHoe EHyd ELan ELon EPPr EPfP EShb EUJe LEdu LRHS MMuc NRHS NWsh SCob SGol SMad SPad SPoG SRms WCot XLum
- 'Little Tickler'	SMad
- 'River Mist' (v)	EBee ELan MMrt SCob SPoG
laxum	SMea

Chasmatophyllum (*Aizoaceae*)

sp.	EDAr

Cheilanthes ✿ (*Pteridaceae*)

argentea	ISha
eatonii	WAbe
***ecklonian*a**	WAbe
grisea	WCot
lanosa	CCCN CCht CRos CSpe EAJP EBee EHyd EMor EWes LBuc LRHS MAvo MJak MPie NRHS SPlb SPoG WCot
lindheimeri	WAbe WCot
microphylla	ISha
myriophylla	WAbe WCot
sieberi	ISha
tomentosa	CAby CCCN CRos EBee EHyd ISha LRHS NRHS WAbe
wootonii	SPlb WAbe

Cheiranthus see *Erysimum*

Cheirolophus (*Asteraceae*)

benoistii misapplied	see *Centaurea atropurpurea*
benoistii (Humb.) Holub	CSpe MRav WSHC

Chelidonium (*Papaveraceae*)

hylomeconoides	GEdr
japonicum	see *Hylomecon japonica*
majus	GPSL GPoy NMir WHer WHil WSFF
- 'Flore Pleno' (d)	CBre GJos NBid NBro
- var. ***laciniatum***	WCot

Chelone (*Plantaginaceae*)

barbata	see *Penstemon barbatus*
§ ***glabra***	CBod CMac CRos EBee ECha ELan EMor EPfP GMaP GWyn LRHS MMuc NBid NBro NEgg NGdn NHol NLar SPer SPlb SRms WFar WMoo WPnP WSHC WWtn
lyonii	EBee NLar WShi
- 'Hot Lips'	CKel WHil WPnP
- 'Pink Temptation'	EBee GEdr NAst
obliqua	Widely available
- var. ***alba***	see *C. glabra*
- 'Ieniemienie'	CBod EBee
- 'Pink Sensation'	WFar
- PINK TURTLE ('Arturtle'PBR)	GBin

Chelonopsis (*Lamiaceae*)

moschata	EBee EMor EWld GEdr LEdu MBel MHer SMad SPlb WHil WMoo
yagiharana	CAby CMea NBid SHar WFar WMoo

Chengiopanax (*Araliaceae*)

sciadophylloides	WCru

Chenopodium (*Amaranthaceae*)

bonus-henricus	CAgr CFGn CHab CHby ENfk EWhm GPoy GQue MCoo MHer MNHC SRms SVic WHer WJek WTre
capitatum	CSpe SVic
giganteum	CLau GJos MNHC SRms WJek

cherimoya see *Annona cherimola*

cherry, Duke see *Prunus* × *gondouinii*

cherry, sour or morello see *Prunus cerasus*; also AGM Fruit Section

cherry, sweet see *Prunus avium*; also AGM Fruit Section

chervil see *Anthriscus cerefolium*

chestnut, sweet see *Castanea sativa*

Chiastophyllum see *Umbilicus*

simplicifolium	see *Umbilicus oppositifolius*

chicory see *Cichorium intybus*; also AGM Vegetables Section

Chiliotrichum (*Asteraceae*)

diffusum	CCCN GAbr MMuc
- 'Siska'	CBcs

chilli pepper see *Capsicum*; also AGM Vegetables Section

Chimonanthus ✿ (*Calycanthaceae*)

fragrans	see *C. praecox*

nitens	CBcs CMCN NLar
§ ***praecox***	Widely available
- 'Brockhill Goldleaf'	NLar
- 'Grandiflorus' ♀H5	CEnd CJun CRos EHyd ELan EPfP LRHS MAsh SPer SPoG WCot
- 'Luteus' ♀H5	CEnd CJun CRos EHyd ELan EPfP LEdu LRHS MAsh MGos NLar SChF SPoG WCot
- 'Sunburst'	CJun
- 'Trenython' ♀H5	CEnd CJun

Chimonobambusa (*Poaceae*)

KR 7592	MWht
hookeriana misapplied	see *Himalayacalamus falconeri* 'Damarapa'
macrophylla f. ***intermedia***	XCre
§ ***marmorea***	CDTJ ERod MMuc XCre
- 'Variegata' (v)	CDTJ ERod ESwi XCre
§ ***quadrangularis***	CBcs CDTJ EPfP ERod ESwi IMou MWht XCre
- 'Nagaminei' (v)	ERod XCre
- 'Suow' (v)	CDTJ XCre
- 'Tatejima'	ERod
sichuanensis	XCre
tumidissinoda	CBcs CDTJ ERod ESwi IMou MWht WFar XCre

Chinese cabbage see AGM Vegetables Section

Chinese chives see *Allium tuberosum*

Chiogenes see *Gaultheria*

Chionanthus (*Oleaceae*)

retusus	CBcs CCCN CDul CRos EBee EHyd EPfP EWTr LRHS MPkF NLar SAko SPer
- 'Arnold's Pride'	WPGP
virginicus	CBcs CCCN CDul CMCN CRos EHyd ELan EPfP EWTr GBin LRHS MBlu MGil MMuc MRav NEgg NLar SPer SPlb WSpi

Chionochloa (*Poaceae*)

conspicua	CAby CBod EAJP EBee EPfP GAbr GBee GBin GCal GKev MAvo NBid NBir SMea WPGP
- subsp. ***conspicua***	WCot
- 'Rubra'	see *C. rubra*
flavescens	EBee EHoe EMor EPfP MAvo WPGP
flavicans	CSpe GBin IMou SMea
rigida	MAvo
§ ***rubra*** ♀H7	CCht CElw CSpe EBee EHoe ELan EWes GBin GCal IMou MRav SMad WCot WMoo WPGP
- PAB 67	CRos EHyd LEdu LRHS NRHS
- subsp. ***cuprea***	CAby GKev

Chionodoxa ✿ (*Asparagaceae*)

§ ***forbesii***	CRos EHyd EPfP EPot GKev LAma LRHS MJak NAln NBir NHpl NRHS SCob SDeJ SRms WShi
- 'Blue Giant'	CAvo ELan EMor EPot ERCP GKev LRHS SCob WCot
- 'Violet Beauty'	GKev SDeJ
gigantea	see *C. luciliae* Gigantea Group
luciliae misapplied	see *C. forbesii*
luciliae ambig.	CAvo CRos EHyd GWyn LCro LOPS LRHS NAln NRHS SEND
luciliae Boiss. ♀H6	CAby EPfP LAma SDeJ SPer
- 'Alba'	CRos EHyd LAma LRHS NAln NHpl NRHS SDeJ SPer
§ - Gigantea Group	GKev
- - 'Alba'	EPot GKev SCob
- 'Rosy Queen'	GKev LAma
'Pink Giant'	CAvo CRos EHyd ELan EMor EPfP EPot ERCP GKev LAma LRHS NRHS SCob SDeJ WBor XLum
sardensis ♀H6	CAby CRos EHyd EPot ERCP GKev LAma LRHS NAln NRHS SDeJ SPhx SRms WShi
siehei 'Rosea'	EMor GKev LAma NHpl
'Valentine Day'	EPot

Chionodoxa × *Scilla* see × *Chionoscilla*

Chionographis (*Melanthiaceae*)

japonica	GEdr

Chionohebe (*Plantaginaceae*)

§ ***densifolia***	EPot
pulvinaris	NSla WAbe
'Vera Cox'	WAbe

× *Chionoscilla* (*Asparagaceae*)

§ ***allenii***	SPhx

Chiranthodendron (*Malvaceae*)

pentadactylon	SPlb

Chirita (*Gesneriaceae*)

'Aiko'	WDib
'Candy'	WDib
'Chastity'	WDib
'Diane Marie'	WDib
'Erika'	WDib
flavimaculata	WDib
heterotricha	WDib
'Keiko'	WDib
linearifolia	WDib
linearifolia × ***sinensis***	WDib
longgangensis	WDib
'New York'	WDib
sinensis ♀H1c	WDib
- 'Hisako'	WCot WDib
speciosa 'Crûg Cornetto'	WCru
'Stardust'	WDib
'Sweet Dreams'	WDib
tamiana	WDib

Chironia (*Gentianaceae*)

baccifera	SPlb

× *Chitalpa* (*Bignoniaceae*)

tashkentensis	CBcs CEnd EPfP ESwi EUJe MMrt SBrt
- 'Morning Cloud'	MBlu
- 'Pink Dawn'	CBcs ESwi MBlu
- SUMMER BELLS ('Minsum')	CCCN CSpe EBee ELan ELon WCot

chives see *Allium schoenoprasum*

Chlidanthus (*Amaryllidaceae*)

fragrans	CCCN GKev SDeJ SEND

Chloranthus (*Chloranthaceae*)

fortunei	ESwi SCob WCot
glaber B&SWJ 11102	WCru

henryi GEdr WCot
japonicus GEdr WCru
oldhamii WPGP
- B&SWJ 2019 GEdr LEdu WCru
serratus GEdr WCru
sessilifolius 'Domino' ESwi WCot

Chloris (*Poaceae*)

distichophylla see *Eustachys distichophylla*

Chlorogalum (*Asparagaceae*)

pomeridianum 'Berkeley Hills' SBrt
- tall, from Siskiyou Mountains, Oregon SBrt

Chlorophytum (*Asparagaceae*)

'Bonnie'PBR (v) **new** EShb
comosum EShb SEND SVic
- 'Aureomarginata' (v) SEND
- 'Variegatum' (v) ♀H2 CTsd EShb LOPS NGBl SEND SPre
- 'Vittatum' (v) ♀H2 EShb NGBl
graminifolium EBee
krookianum WCot
macrophyllum EShb
nepalense WPGP
- B&SWJ 2528 WCru
- PAB 13.034 LEdu
saundersiae CExl

Choisya (*Rutaceae*)

× ***dewitteana*** APPLE BLOSSOM ('Pmoore09') CBcs CSBt LCro LOPS SLon SPad SPoG
- 'Aztec Gold'PBR CBcs CRos EPfP LRHS MAsh MGos NLar NRHS SCob WFar
- 'Aztec Pearl' ♀H4 Widely available
- GOLDFINGERS ('Limo'PBR) Widely available
- SNOW FLURRIES ('Lisflurry'PBR) CRos EHyd ELan EPfP LLHF LRHS MAsh MRav NRHS SPoG
- WHITE DAZZLER ('Londaz'PBR) ♀H4 Widely available
ROYAL LACE ('Pmoore06') LRHS SLon
ternata ♀H4 Widely available
- MOONSHINE ('Walcho'PBR) CBcs EBee NLar
- MOONSLEEPER see *C. ternata* SUNDANCE
§ - SUNDANCE ('Lich') ♀H4 Widely available

Chondrosum (*Poaceae*)

gracile see *Bouteloua gracilis*

Chordospartium see *Carmichaelia*

Chorisia (*Malvaceae*)

speciosa CCCN SPlb

Chorizema (*Papilionaceae*)

cordatum ♀H2 SVen
dicksonii SPlb

Chronanthus see *Cytisus*

Chrysalidocarpus see *Dypsis*

Chrysanthemopsis see *Rhodanthemum*

Chrysanthemum ✿ (*Asteraceae*)

E.H.Wilson s.n. EWes MHCG MNrw NWad WCot
'Action Bronze' (22) NWsh
'Action Yellow' (22) ♀H3 WFar
'Agnes Ann' (21d) MNrw
'Ahlemer Rote' (21) MNrw NWad
'Alan Brown' (25a) MCms
'Alan Foxall Yellow' (3b) MCms
'Alec Bedser' (25a) NHal
'Alex Young' (25b) MCms
'Alfredo Mauve' (12) **new** MCms
'Alfredo Orange' (12) **new** MCms
'Alice Jones' (24b) **new** MCms
'Aline' (21) MHCG
'Alison' (29c) ELon MNrw WFar
'Alison's Dad' MNrw
'Allouise' (25b) ♀H3 NHal
'Allouise Orange' (25b) MCms NHal
'Allouise Pink' (25b) MCms
'Allyson Peace' (14a) MCms NHal
alpinum see *Leucanthemopsis alpina*
'Alyece Shaw' (29d) NHal
'Amber Matlock' (24b) MCms
'American Beauty Lemon' (5b) MCms
'American Beauty Snowball' (5b) MCms
'American Beauty White' (5b) MCms
'Anastasia' ambig. SAko
'Anastasia' (21c) CRos EBee ELon GCal LRHS MNrw MRav NRHS NSti SRms
'Anderton' (6b) MCms
'Angela Blundell' (19b) MNrw WCot WFar
'Angelic' (21b) ♀H4 EBee ELon WBrk
'Ann Dickson' (25a) **new** MCms
'Anne Ratsey' (21) CSam MNrw WBrk WFar
'Anne, Lady Brocket' (21d) ECtt MNrw
'Anthony Peace' (25b) MCms
'Antigua'PBR MCms
'Apollo' H. Shoesmith MNrw WCot
'Apollo' (21) MHCG SPhx WFar WHoo
'Apricot' see *C.* 'Cottage Apricot'
'Apricot Chessington' (25a) MCms
'Apricot Courtier' (24a) MCms NHal
'Apricot Enbee Wedding' see *C.* 'Bronze Enbee Wedding'
'Apricot Mundial' (6b) MCms
'Arctic Beauty' (4b) MCms
'Arctic Cream' (29b) **new** MCms
'Arctic Queen'PBR (23a) MCms
'Arctic Queen Yellow' (23) MCms
'Arctic White' (9c) **new** MCms
'Arctic Yellow' (9c) **new** MCms
arcticum L. see *Arctanthemum arcticum*
argenteum see *Tanacetum argenteum*
'Arthur Ellis' (25b) MCms
'Astro' (25b) MCms NHal
'Aunt Millicent' (21d) ♀H4 MHCG NHal WCot
'Balcombe Perfection' (5a) MCms NHal
balsamita see *Tanacetum balsamita*
BARBARA ('Yobarbara') (22) NHal
'Barca' MCms
'Beacon' (5a) ♀H2 MCms NHal
'Beechcroft' (29Rub) MNrw SPhx WFar
'Belle' (21d) EShb MHCG MNrw
'Beppie Bronze' (29e) MCms
'Beppie Purple' (29e) MCms
'Beppie Red' (29e) MCms
'Beppie Rose' (29e) MCms
'Beppie Yellow' (29e) MCms
'Best Man' (29d) MCms
'Bienchen' SAko
'Bill Holden' (14a) MCms NHal
'Bill Wade' (25a) MCms NHal
'Billy Bell' (15a) MCms NHal

Name	Suppliers
'Blanche Poitevene' (5b)	EMal MCms NHal
'Bob Green' (13b)	MCms
'Bobby Swinburn' (13b)	MCms
boreale	WCot
'Boulou Pink' (12)	MCms
'Boulou White' (12)	MCms
'Boulou Yellow' (12) **new**	MCms
BRAVO ('Yobra') (22c) ♀H3	NHal
* 'Breitner's Supreme'	ECtt MHCG MNrw WFar
'Brennpunkt'	MNrw NWad
'Bretforton Road'	ECtt MHCG MNrw WBrk WCot WFar WOld
'Brierton Violet' (17b)	NHal
'Brightness' (21)	MNrw
'Bronze Cassandra' (5b) ♀H2	MCms NHal
'Bronze Dee Gem' (29c)	MCms NHal
§ 'Bronze Elegance' (21b) ♀H4	CDor CRos CTri ECtt EPPr LRHS MNrw NBir NGdn NRHS NSti NWsh SHar SRms WBor WBrk
§ 'Bronze Enbee Wedding' (29d) ♀H3	MCms NHal
'Bronze Gigantic' (1)	NHal
'Bronze Matlock' (24b)	MCms NHal
'Bronze Max Riley' (23b) ♀H3	MCms NHal
'Bronze Mayford Perfection' (5a) ♀H2	MCms
'Bronze Mei-kyo'	see *C.* 'Bronze Elegance'
'Bronze Talbot Parade' (29c) ♀H3	MCms
'Bronze William Florentine' (15a)	MCms
'Brooke Farm Red'	NWsh
'Brown Eyes' (21b) ♀H4	MNrw
'Bryony Wade' (13b)	MCms NHal
'Bryony Wade White' (13b) **new**	MCms
'Buff William Florentine' (15a)	MCms
'Bunty' (28)	SMad
burnt orange-flowered	CAby CDor CFis MNrw WFar
'Burntwood Belle' (3b)	MCms
'Buxton Ruby'	EWTr
'Candy John Wingfield' (14b)	MCms
'Capel Manor'	EBee MHCG MNrw WCot
'Capella' (10a)	MCms
'Cardinal Red'	LRHS
'Carlene Welby' (25b)	MCms
'Carmine Blush' (21d) ♀H4	GAbr MHCG MNrw WBrk WCot WFar
'Casablanca' (25a)	NHal
'Cassandra' (5b) ♀H2	MCms NHal
'Cawthorne' (29d)	WFar
'Cerisa' (29d) **new**	NHal
'Charles Tandy' (5a)	MCms
'Charles Tandy Primrose' (15a)	MCms
'Charles Tandy Yellow' (15b)	MCms
'Charlie' (24b)	MCms
'Chatsworth' (29c)	NHal
'Chelsea Physic Garden'	CAby EBee ELon GAbr MHCG MNrw SPhx WCot WFar
'Chempak Rose' (14b)	MCms
'Cherry Chessington' (25a)	MCms NHal
'Cherry Tracey Waller' (24b) **new**	MCms
'Chesapeake Primrose' (10a)	MCms
CHESAPEAKE ('Yochesapeake'PBR) (10a)	GBin MCms NHal
'Chessington' (25a)	MCms
'Chessington Oyster' (25a)	MCms
'Chestnut Talbot Maid' (29c)	MCms
'Chestnut Talbot Parade' (29c) ♀H3	MCms WFar
'Chloe Ball' (13b)	MCms
'Christmas'	MNrw NWad
'Christopher Lawson' (24b)	MCms NHal
cinerariifolium	see *Tanacetum cinerariifolium*
'Citronella'	MNrw
'Clapham Delight' (23a)	MCms NHal
'Clara Curtis' (21d)	CAby CBod CDor CMac CRos ECha ECtt ELan EPfP GMaP IKil LRHS MNrw MPie MRav NCGa NEgg NPer NRHS NWsh SPer SPoG SRms WAul WBor WCAu WFar WJam WSHC XLum
'Clare Louise' (24b)	MCms
'Clarksdale' (15b)	MCms NHal
coccineum	see *Tanacetum coccineum*
'Colsterworth'	MNrw NWad WFar
'Coral Reef' (10b)	MCms NHal
'Coral Rynoon' (9d) **new**	MCms
'Corinna' (21d)	GBin MNrw NWad
'Cornetto' (25b)	MCms NHal
'Corsair' (9b) **new**	MCms
corymbosum	see *Tanacetum corymbosum*
§ 'Cottage Apricot' (21)	CDor CRos EBee EPfP LRHS MBNS MRav NRHS SMHy SRms WFar
'Cottage Bronze'	MNrw NWad
'Cottage Lemon'	MNrw NWad WBrk WFar
'Cottage Pink'	see *C.* 'Emperor of China'
'Courtier' (24a)	NHal
'Cousin Joan' (21d) ♀H4	EBee ELon MHCG MNrw WCot WFar WOld
'Cream Dorridge Crystal' (24a)	MCms
'Cream Elegance' (9c)	NHal
'Cream John Hughes' (3b)	MCms
'Cream Patricia Millar' (14b)	NHal
'Cream Ryski' (9d) **new**	MCms
'Cream Talbot Maid' (29c)	MCms
'Cream Talbot Parade' (29c) ♀H3	MCms
'Cream West Bromwich' (14a)	MCms
'Crème Brulée' **new**	MNrw
'Cricket' (25b)	MCms
'Crimson Purple Glow' (5a)	MCms
DANA ('Yodana') (25b) ♀H3	NHal
DANCE ('Fidance'PBR) (9f)	MCms
'Dance Red' (9f)	MCms
DANCE SALMON ('Fidancesal') (9f)	GBin MCms
'Dance Sunny' (9f)	MCms
'Dance White' (9f)	MCms
'Daniel Cooper' (21d) ♀H4	EBee MNrw SBch WFar
'Daphne Davis' (29d)	NHal
'Darren Pugh' (3b)	MCms NHal
'Darren Pugh Primrose' (3b)	MCms
'David Shoesmith' (25a)	MCms
'Dawn Charlton' (14a)	MCms
'Dee Gem' (29c) ♀H3	MCms NHal WFar
'Delta' (5b)	NHal
'Delta Copper Bronze' (9d)	NHal
'Delta Crimson' (29d)	NHal
'Delta Yellow' (29)	NHal

	'Denise Oatridge' (5a)	MCms
	'Dernier Soleil'	EBee MNrw XLum
	'Deva Glow' (25a)	NHal
	'Disco Club'	MCms
	'Dixter Orange'	EBee EWes GCal MHCG SMad SPhx
§	'Doctor Tom Parr' (21c)	CExl ELan MNrw
	'Domingo' (14b)	MCms
	'Doreen Hall' (15a)	NHal
	'Doreen Statham' (4b)	MCms NHal
	'Doris Ozols' (25a)	MCms NHal
	'Dorothy Stone' (25b)	NHal
	'Dorridge Crystal' (24a)	MCms NHal
	'Dorridge King' (4b)	MCms
	'Downpour' (10a)	MCms
	'Dublin' (9f)	MCms
	'Duchess of Edinburgh' (21d)	CRos EBee ECtt ELan ELon EPfP LRHS NRHS SPhx WCAu WFar XLum
	'Dulwich Pink' (21d) 🏆H4	MHCG MNrw NWad WCot WOld
	'Early Yellow'	EBee ELon MNrw WCot WFar
	'Edelweiss' (21)	CAby EShb MNrw NWad
	'Edina' (29d)	NHal
	'Edmund Brown'	MNrw WBrk WCot WFar
	'Egret' (23b)	MCms NHal
	'Elaine's Hardy White'	MNrw WCot WFar
	'Elegance' (9c)	NHal
	'Eliška' **new**	MNrw
	'Elizabeth Lawson' (5b)	NHal
§	'Emperor of China' (21)	CAby CDor ECtt MHer MNrw MRav NHal SMad SPhx SRms WBor WFar XLum
	'Enbee Wedding' (29d) 🏆H3	MCms NHal
	'Energy'PBR (9)	MCms
	'Esther' (21d)	EBee ELon MHCG MHer MNrw NCGa SMad WFar
	'Etta Dakin' (25b) **new**	MCms
	'Fairweather' (3b)	MCms NHal
	'Fairweather Cream' (3b)	MCms
	'Fairweather Peach' (3b)	MCms
	'Fanfare Cherry'	LRHS
	'Fanfare Claret'	ELan LRHS
	'Fanfare Flame'	ELan LRHS
	'Fanfare Glowing Embers'	LRHS
	'Fanfare Orange'	LRHS
	'Fanfare Pink Blush'	LRHS NRHS
	'Fanfare Pink Pastel'	LRHS
	'Fanfare Rosetta'	LRHS
	'Fanfare Ruby'	LRHS
	'Fanfare Sunset'	LRHS
	'Feeling Green Dark'PBR	MCms
	'Feeling Sunny'PBR	MCms
	'Fleur de Lis' (10a)	MCms
	foeniculaceum (Willd.) Desf.	see *Argyranthemum foeniculaceum* (Willd.) Webb & Sch. Bip.
	'Folk Song' (4b)	MNrw
	'Fondant'	NHal
	'Fred's Yellow' **new**	NWad
	'French Rose'	WFar
	'Froggy'PBR (9)	MCms
	frutescens	see *Argyranthemum frutescens*
	'Gala Burgundy'	CRos
	'Gambit' (24a)	MCms NHal
	'Geoff Amos' (3b)	MCms
	'Geoff Brady' (5a)	MCms NHal
	'George Griffiths' (24b) 🏆H3	MCms NHal
	'Gillette' (23b)	MCms
	'Ginger Nut' (25b)	MCms
	'Ginger Nut Yellow' (25b)	MCms
I	'Gladys' (12a)	NHal
	'Gladys Emerson' (3b)	MCms NHal
	'Gold Enbee Wedding' (29d) 🏆H3	MCms
	'Gold Mundial' (6b) 🏆H2	MCms
	'Golden Cassandra' (5b) 🏆H2	MCms NHal
	'Golden Chalice' (12a)	NHal
	'Golden Courtier' (24a)	MCms NHal
	'Golden Masons' (7b)	MCms
	'Golden Mayford Perfection' (5a) 🏆H2	MCms
	'Golden Rain' (10a) 🏆H2	MCms NHal
	'Golden Roy Coopland' (5b)	MCms
	'Golden Seal' (7b)	MCms
	'Golden Shoesmith Salmon' (4a)	MCms
	'Golden Splendour' (10a)	MCms
	'Golden Wedding' (21)	MNrw
	'Golden William Florentine' (15a)	MCms
	'Golden Woolman's Glory' (7a)	NHal
	'Goldengreenheart' (21d) 🏆H4	EBee ECtt ELon EPPr EShb MHCG MNrw SPhx SRms WBrk WFar WHoo
	'Goldmarianne' (21)	GBin WFar XLum
	'Goodlife Sombrero' (29a) 🏆H3	MCms
	'Goshu Penta' (10a)	MCms
	'Grace Riley' (24a)	MCms
	'Grand Cherry'	MCms
	'Grand Pink'	MCms
	'Grand Salmon'	MCms
	'Grandchild' (21c) 🏆H4	MNrw NHal
	'Green Goddess' (2)	MCms
	'Hanenburg' (25b)	MCms NHal
	haradjanii	see *Tanacetum haradjanii*
	'Harold Lawson' (5a)	NHal
*	'Harry Lawson'	MCms
	'Harry Woolman' (13b)	MCms
	'Heather James' (3b)	MCms NHal
	'Hebe' (21d)	EBee MNrw
	'Heda' **new**	MNrw
	'Heide' (29c) 🏆H3	NHal
	'Helen Louise' (25b)	MCms NHal
	'Helen Ward' **new**	MNrw
	'Herbie McCauley' (24b)	NHal
	'Herbstbrokat'	GBin WFar XLum
	'Herbstfeuer' (21)	MNrw NWad
	'Hillfield Apricot'	EShb
	'Hillside Apricot'	ECtt
	'Hoagy' (29d)	MCms NHal
	'Holly Elizabeth' (14a)	MCms
	HOLLY ('Yoholly') (22b) 🏆H3	NHal
	'Honey Enbee Wedding' (29d)	MCms NHal
	hosmariense	see *Rhodanthemum hosmariense*
	indicum	SVic
	'Innocence' (21d) 🏆H4	CDor CFis CSam ECtt ELan ELon MNrw MRav NCGa NGdn SHar WFar WHoo
	'Jan Wardle' (5a)	MCms
	'Janet South'	MNrw NWad
	'Jante Wells' (21b) 🏆H4	MNrw
	'Jenny Wren' (12a)	NHal
	'Jessie Cooper' misapplied	see *C.* 'Mrs Jessie Cooper' (21d)
	'Jimmy Tranter' (14b)	NHal
	'John Harrison' (25b)	MCms NHal
	'John Hughes' (3b)	MCms NHal

'John Lowry' (24a)	NHal
'John Riley' (14a)	NHal
'John Wingfield' (14b)	MCms NHal
'John Wingfield Honey' (14b)	MCms
'John Wingfield Pearl' (14b)	MCms
'Jolie Rose'	WCot WFar
'Joyce Fountain' (24a)	MCms NHal
'Joyce Frieda' (13b)	MCms NHal
'Julia' (28)	EPfP MNrw
'Julia Arnold'	WHoo
'Julia Peterson'	MHCG MHer MNrw SRms WCot WFar WHoo
'Julie Lagravère' (28)	MHCG MNrw WFar XLum
'Karen Taylor' (29c) ♀H3	NHal
'Kath Stephenson' (7b)	MCms NHal
'Kath Stephenson Honey' (7b)	MCms
'Kath Stephenson Peach' (7b)	MCms
'Kath Stephenson Primrose' (7b)	MCms NHal
'Kath Stephenson Rose' (7b)	MCms NHal
'Kath Stephenson Salmon' (7b)	MCms
'Kay Woolman' (13b)	MCms NHal
'Kay Woolman Cream' (13b)	MCms
'Kay Woolman Primrose' (13b)	MCms
'Kay Woolman Yellow' (13b)	MCms
'Killerton Tangerine'	MNrw WFar
'Kimberley Marie' (15b)	MCms NHal
'Kiyomi-no-meisui'	MCms NHal
'Kleiner Bernstein'	MNrw
'Königssohn'	WCot
'La Damoiselle'	WCot
§ 'Lady in Pink' (21)	MNrw MPie
'Lakelanders' (3b)	MCms NHal
'Laura Jayne' (25a)	MCms
'Lava' (10a)	MCms
'Leo' (21b) ♀H4	EBee
leucanthemum	see *Leucanthemum vulgare*
'Lexy' PBR (9)	GBin MCms
'Lexy Red' PBR (9)	GBin MCms
'Lighthouse'	NHal
'Lilac Chessington' (25a)	MCms
'Lilian Shoesmith' (5b)	MCms
LINDA ('Lindayo') (22c) ♀H3	NHal
'L'Innocence' (21)	CAby
'Liverpool Festival' (23b)	MCms
'Lollipop' PBR (9e)	GBin MCms
LOLLIPOP PURPLE ('Filollipop Purple' PBR) (9e)	MCms
'Lorna Wood' (13b)	MCms NHal
'Lucy' (29a)	MCms NHal
'Lynn Johnson' (15a)	MCms
LYNN ('Yolynn') (22c) ♀H3	NHal
macrophyllum	see *Tanacetum macrophyllum* (Waldst. & Kit.) Sch.Bip.
'Malcolm Perkins' (25a)	NHal
'Mancetta Comet' (29a)	MCms NHal
'Mancetta Symbol' (5a)	MCms
'Mandarin' (5b)	SAko
I 'Mandarin' **new**	MNrw
'Manito' **new**	MNrw
maresii	see *Rhodanthemum hosmariense*
'Margaret Dear' (25a)	MCms
'Margaret Lawson' (14b)	NHal
'Margery Fish'	MNrw
'Marion' (25a)	MNrw WCot WFar
'Martin Bell' (29d)	WFar
'Martina' (24b)	MCms
'Mary' (21f)	MHCG NHal
'Mary Stoker' (21d)	CAby CDor CRos CSam CTri EBee ECtt ELan LRHS MNrw MPie MRav NHal NLar NRHS NWsh WAul WCAu XLum
'Mason's Bronze' (7b)	MCms
'Matlock' (24b)	NHal
'Mauve Gem' (21f) ♀H3	MNrw NHal
'Mavis' (21) ♀H3	MHCG MNrw
'Mavis Smith' **new**	MNrw
mawii	see *Rhodanthemum gayanum*
'Max Riley' (23b) ♀H3	MCms NHal
maximum misapplied	see *Leucanthemum × superbum*
maximum Ramond	see *Leucanthemum maximum* (Ramond) DC.
'Maxine Charlton' (24b)	NHal
'Maxine Johnson' (25b)	MCms
'May Shoesmith' (5a) ♀H2	MCms NHal
'Mayford Perfection' (5a) ♀H2	MCms
'Mei-Kyō' (28b) ♀H4	CDor CFis CMea CRos CTri ECtt EPPr LRHS MNrw MPie NRHS SRms WBor WBrk WCAu WFar
'Membury' (24b)	MCms NHal
'Mezzo Bronze Red' (Poppins Series) **new**	MCms
'Mezzo Gold' (Poppins Series) **new**	MCms
'Mezzo Magenta' (Poppins Series) **new**	MCms
'Mezzo Pink' (Poppins Series) **new**	MCms
'Michelle Preston' (13b)	NHal
'Millennium' (25b) ♀H3	MCms NHal
'Misty Cream' (25b)	MCms
'Misty Golden' (25b)	MCms
'Misty Lemon' (25b)	MCms
'Moonlight' (29d/K)	MNrw MRav NWad
'Morning Star' (12a)	NHal
'Mount Fuji' (10b)	MCms
§ 'Mrs Jessie Cooper' (21d) ♀H4	CAby EBee ELon EPPr GQue MNrw NCGa NLar SDys SRms WCot WFar WHoo WPtf
'Mrs Jessie Cooper No 1'	SBch
'Mrs Jessie Cooper No 2'	MNrw
'Mundial' (6)	MCms
'Mundial Peach' (6b/9a)	MCms
'Mundial Rose' (6b)	MCms
'Mundial Ruby' (6b)	MCms
'Muriel Odell' (7b)	MCms
'Music' (23b)	MCms NHal
'Muxton Sable' (10a)	GBin MCms
'Myss Debbie' (29e)	NHal
'Myss Dorothy' (29c)	MCms NHal
'Myss Eliza' (29c)	MCms
'Myss Goldie' (29c)	MCms
'Myss Rihanna' (29c)	MCms NHal
'Myss Saffron' (29c) ♀H3	MCms NHal
'Nancy Perry' (21d)	CSam MRav XLum
'Nantyderry Sunshine' (28b) ♀H4	CDor CRos ELon LRHS MHCG MNrw MPie NRHS NWsh SPhx SRms WCot WFar WOld
'Naru' (9c)	NHal
'Naru Crimson' (9c)	NHal
'Natalie Sarah' (29d) ♀H3	NHal
'Nell Gwynn' (21d)	MNrw NHal
'New Stylist' (24b)	MCms

NICOLE ('Yonicole') (22c) ♀H3	NHal
nipponicum	see *Nipponanthemum nipponicum*
'Nora Brook' (25b)	MCms
'Nutcracker' (23b)	MCms
'Orange Enbee Wedding' (29d)	NHal
'Orchid Helen' **new**	MNrw
'Pacific Lady' (29d) **new**	NHal
pacificum	see *Ajania pacifica*
'Paloma Redeye' (29d)	NHal
'Paloma Regent' (29d)	NHal
'Paloma Sands' (29d)	NHal
parthenium	see *Tanacetum parthenium*
'Pat Bahn' (29c)	NHal
'Patricia Millar' (14b)	MCms NHal
'Patricia Millar Cerise' (14b)	MCms
'Patricia Millar Coral' (14b)	MCms
'Patricia Millar Orange' (14b)	MCms
'Patricia Millar Yellow' (14b)	MCms NHal
'Paul Boissier' (30Rub)	CAby CDor CFis ECtt MNrw NSti SPhx WFar
'Pauline White' (15a)	MCms
'Peach Courtier' (24a)	NHal
'Peach Enbee Wedding' (29d) ♀H3	MCms NHal
'Peach John Wingfield' (14b)	MCms NHal
'Peach Patricia Millar' (14b)	MCms
'Peach Rynoon' (9d) **new**	MCms
'Peach Southway Sheeba' (29d)	NHal
'Pearl Celebration' (24a)	MCms
'Pearl Enbee Wedding' (29d)	MCms
'Pennine Bullion'	NHal
'Pennine Gambol' (29a)	MCms
'Pennine Jude' (29a)	MCms
'Pennine Marie' (29a) ♀H3	MCms
'Pennine Oriel' (29a) ♀H3	MCms NHal
'Pennine Point' (19c)	NHal
'Pennine Polo' (29d) ♀H3	NHal
'Pennine Swan' (29c)	MCms NHal
'Penny's Yellow'	WBrk
'Percy Salter' (24b)	NHal
'Perry's Peach' (21d) ♀H4	ELon MHCG MNrw NCGa NHal NPer SPhx
'Peter Jolley' (25b)	MCms
'Peter Rowe' (23b)	MCms NHal
'Peterkin'	CMac CRos EBee ECtt ELon LRHS NRHS XLum
'Picasso'	EShb MHCG MNrw WCot WFar
'Pink John Wingfield' (14b)	NHal
'Pink Progression'	see *C.* 'Lady in Pink'
'Pocahontas' (10a)	MCms
'Poesie'	MNrw SAko WCot WFar
'Polar Gem' (3a)	MCms NHal
'Pomander' (25b)	MCms
'Pot Black' (14b)	MCms
'Prelude Apricot' (Poppins Series) **new**	MCms
'Prelude Autumn Bronze' (Poppins Series) **new**	MCms
'Prelude Popcorn' (Poppins Series) **new**	MCms
'Prelude Rose Pink' (Poppins Series) **new**	MCms
'Prelude White' (Poppins Series) **new**	MCms
'President Osaka'	MNrw NWad

'Primrose Allouise' (24b) ♀H3	MCms NHal
'Primrose Chessington' (25a)	MCms
'Primrose Courtier'	see *C.* 'Yellow Courtier'
'Primrose Cricket' (25b)	MCms
'Primrose Dorothy Stone' (25b)	NHal
'Primrose Dorridge Crystal' (24a)	MCms
'Primrose Egret' (23b)	MCms
'Primrose Enbee Wedding' (29d) ♀H3	MCms NHal
'Primrose Fairweather' (3b)	MCms
'Primrose John Hughes' (3b)	MCms
'Primrose Mayford Perfection' (5a) ♀H2	MCms
'Primrose Pauline White' (15a)	MCms
'Primrose Pennine Oriel' (29a)	MCms
'Primrose West Bromwich' (14a)	MCms
'Princess' (21d)	MNrw
'Promise' (25a)	MCms NHal
'Purleigh White' (28b)	CRos ECtt ELon EPPr MNrw NSti WFar
'Purple Chempak Rose' (14b)	MCms
'Purple Dee Gem' (29c)	NHal
'Purple Glow' (5a)	MCms
'Quinty' (19)	GBin
'Raquel' (21)	MNrw
'Ray's Red'	MNrw
'Red Balcombe Perfection' (5a)	MCms NHal
'Red Chempak Rose' (14b)	MCms
'Red Goodlife Sombrero' (29a)	MCms
'Red Mayford Perfection' (5a)	MCms
'Red Pennine Gift' (29c)	NHal
'Red Regal Mist' (25b)	MCms NHal
'Red Shirley Model' (3a)	MCms NHal
'Redbreast' (12a)	NHal
'Regal Mist' (25b)	NHal
'Regal Mist Purple' (25b)	MCms
'Regent' (5b)	MCms
'Rejoyce'	GBin
I 'Rhumba'	MNrw WCot
'Rihanna'	MCms
'Riley's Dynasty' (14a)	MCms
'Ringdove' (12a)	NHal
'Rita Fox' (25b)	MCms
'Rita McMahon' (29d) ♀H3	NHal
'Robeam' (9c) ♀H2	MCms
ROBIN ('Yorobi') (22c)	NHal
'Roblush' (9c) **new**	MCms
'Roen Sarah' (29c)	NHal
'Romantica'	MNrw NWad WOld
'Roscene' (9c) **new**	MCms
'Rose Enbee Wedding' (29d)	MCms NHal
'Rose Madder'	GAbr MNrw WCot WFar
'Rose Mayford Perfection' (5a) ♀H2	MCms
'Rose Patricia Millar' (14b)	MCms NHal
'Rose Talbot Parade' (29c)	MCms
'Rosetta'	MHCG MNrw
roseum	see *Tanacetum coccineum*

'Rosie Lyttle' (29c) new	NHal
'Roter Spray'	MNrw NWad
'Roy Bevan' (29d)	MCms
'Roy Coopland' (5b) ♀H2	MCms
'Royal Command' (21a)	MHCG MNrw WCot WHoo
'Royal Sport'	MNrw
rubellum	see *C. zawadzkii*
'Ruby Enbee Wedding' (29d) ♀H3	MCms NHal WFar
'Ruby Glow' (7b)	MCms
'Ruby Mound' (21c) ♀H3	MHCG MNrw NHal SDys SHar SPhx WBrk WCot WFar
'Ruby Raynor' (21c) ♀H4	MNrw NHal WFar
'Rumpelstilzchen' (21d)	CFis CMea ECtt MHer MNrw NWsh
'Ryflare' (9c)	MCms
'Ryflash' (9d)	MCms
'Rynoon' (9d)	MCms
'Ryski' (9d) new	MCms
'Salhouse Dream' (10a)	MCms NHal
'Salhouse Joy' (10a)	MCms NHal
'Salmon Allouise' (25b)	MCms NHal
'Salmon Enbee Wedding' (29d) ♀H3	NHal
'Salmon Fairweather' (3b)	MCms
'Salmon John Wingfield' (24b)	MCms
'Salmon Patricia Millar' (14b)	MCms
'Salmon Pauline White' (15a)	MCms
'Salmon Talbot Maid' (29c)	MCms
'Salmon Talbot Parade' (29c) ♀H3	MCms WFar
'Salmon Tracey Waller' (24b) new	MCms
'Salmon Venice' (24b)	MCms
'Sam Vinter' (5a)	NHal
'Samba'	WCot WFar
'Samson' new	MCms
'Samson Bronze' new	MCms
'Samson Orange' new	MCms
'Samson Purple' new	MCms
'Sarah Louise' (25b)	NHal
'Savanna Charlton' (25a)	MCms NHal
'Schaffhausen'	WFar
'Sea Urchin' (21f) ♀H3	NHal SDys
'Seaton's Galaxy' (10a)	MCms NHal
'Senkyo Karyu' (10a)	MCms
'Senkyo Kenshin' (10a)	GBin MCms NHal
'Shamrock' (10b)	MCms
'Sheffield'	XLum
'Sheila Coles' (7b)	NHal
'Sheila Harris' (3b)	MCms
'Shining Light' (21f)	WCot WFar
'Shoesmith Salmon' (4a)	MCms
'Shoesmith Salmon Bright Bronze' (4a)	MCms
'Shoesmith Salmon Crimson' (4b)	MCms
'Shoesmith Salmon Purple' (4a)	MCms
'Skomer' (9f) new	MCms
'Skomer Pink' (9f) new	MCms
'Skomer Yellow' (9f) new	MCms
'Soir d'Orient'	WFar
'Sonya' (21)	MNrw
'Sound' (9d)	MCms
'Southway Semtex' (29d)	MCms
'Southway Sheba' (29d) ♀H3	MCms NHal

'Southway Sheba Bronze' (29d)	MCms NHal
'Southway Shimmer' (29d)	MCms NHal WFar
'Southway Shiraz' (29d)	MCms WFar
'Southway Sloe' (29d)	MCms NHal
'Southway Spectacular' (29d)	MCms
'Southway Spritzer' (29d)	MCms NHal
'Southway Strontium' (29d)	MCms NHal
'Southway Sunbeam' (29d)	MCms
'Spartan Display'	EWes MNrw
'Spartan Seagull' (21d)	MNrw
'Spencer's Cottage' (13b)	MCms
'Stallion'PBR (9)	GBin MCms
'Stallion Yellow'	MCms
'Starlet' (21f) ♀H4	NHal
'Steve Packham' (23b)	NHal
'Stockton' (3b) ♀H2	MCms
'Stratford Pink' (21d)	MNrw NWad
'Suffolk Pink'	ECtt EShb MNrw NWsh
'Sunny John Wingfield' (14b)	MCms
'Super-Bronze Shoesmith Salmon' (4a)	MCms
'Susan Kate' (25b)	MCms
'Swan Cream'	MCms
SWAN ('Fiswan'PBR) (9)	MCms
'Swan Sunny'	MCms
'Sweetheart Pink'	MHCG MNrw
'Syllabub' (21f) ♀H3	ECtt MNrw
'Symphony' (10a)	MCms NHal
'Talbot Maid' (29c)	MCms
'Talbot Parade' (29c) ♀H3	MCms
'Talbot Parade Pink' (29c)	MCms
'Tapestry Rose' (21d)	CMea MNrw NCGa NWsh SPhx SRms WBrk WFar WHoo
'Terry Brook' (29e)	NHal
'Thoroughbred' (24a)	NHal
'Tickle Pink' (29f/K)	MNrw NWad
'Tom Parr'	see *C.* 'Doctor Tom Parr'
'Tom Snowball' (3b)	MCms
'Topsy' (21d) ♀H4	MHCG
'Tracey Waller' (24b)	MCms
TRIUMPH ('Yotri') (22)	NHal
uliginosum	see *Leucanthemella serotina*
'Uri'	CAby CFis EBee ELon MHCG MNrw SPhx WFar
'Vagabond Prince'	ELon MHCG MNrw SRms WBor WBrk WFar WHoo WOld
'Venice' (24b)	MCms NHal
'Venice Peach' (24b)	MCms
'Venice Rose' (24b)	MCms
'Venus' (21)	NWad WCot
'Venus One'	ECtt MNrw NHal
'Vibrant' (9c) ♀H2	NHal
'Viking' (9)	MCms
'Vysočina' new	MNrw
'Wedding Day' (29k)	MNrw
'Wedding Sunshine' (21)	MNrw NWad WFar
welwitschii	see *Glebionis segetum*
'Wembley' (24b)	MCms
'Wendy Tench' (21d)	EBee ECtt MNrw NWsh
'West Bromwich' (14a)	MCms
weyrichii	CRos CTri EBou GPSL IKil LEdu LRHS MNrw NHpl NRHS SBch SRms WIce
'White Allouise' (25b) ♀H3	MCms NHal
'White Beppie' (29e)	MCms WFar
'White Cassandra' (5b)	MCms NHal

'White Denise Oatridge' (5a)	MCms
'White Enbee Wedding' (29d)	MCms NHal
'White Fairweather' (3b)	MCms NHal
'White Gem' (21f)	NHal
'White Gloss' (21e)	MNrw SPhx
'White Pearl Celebration' (24a)	MCms
'White Tower' (27)	MNrw MPie NWad
'Wilder Charms'	MNrw NWad
'William Florentine' (15a)	MCms NHal
'Wills Wonderful' (21d) ♀H4	MHCG
'Win' (9c)	NHal
'Wind Dancer' (10a)	MCms
'Winning's Red' (21)	MHCG NCGa SMad WCot WFar
'Winter Queen' (5b)	MCms
'Winter Queen Yellow' (5b)	MCms
'Woolley Globe' (15b)	MCms
'Woolman's Glory' (7a)	MCms NHal
'Woolman's Glory Red' (7a)	MCms
'Woolman's Star' (3a)	MCms NHal
'Woolman's Venture' (14b)	MCms NHal
'Woolman's Venture Red' (14b)	MCms
'Xiang'	MNrw NWad
'Yellow Allouise' (25b)	MCms
'Yellow American Beauty' (5b) ♀H2	MCms
'Yellow Billy Bell' (15a)	NHal
'Yellow Chessington' (25a) **new**	MCms
'Yellow Clapham Delight' (23a)	MCms NHal
§ 'Yellow Courtier' (24a)	MCms NHal
'Yellow Duke of Kent' (1)	NHal
'Yellow Egret' (23b)	MCms
'Yellow Enbee Wedding' (29d)	MCms NHal
'Yellow Goodlife Sombrero' (29a)	MCms
'Yellow Heide' (29c) ♀H3	NHal
'Yellow Jewel' (Poppins Series) **new**	MCms
'Yellow John Harrison' (25b)	MCms
'Yellow John Hughes' (3b) ♀H2	MCms NHal
'Yellow John Wingfield' (14b)	MCms NHal
'Yellow May Shoesmith' (5a)	NHal
'Yellow Mayford Perfection' (5a) ♀H2	MCms
'Yellow Pennine Oriel' (29a) ♀H4	MCms NHal
'Yellow Ryski' (9d) **new**	MCms
'Yellow Spider' (10a)	MCms
'Yellow Talbot Parade' (29c)	MCms
'Yellow Woolman's Glory' (7a)	MCms
yezoense	CDor MNrw SRms
- B&SWJ 10872	WCru
- 'Roseum'	ECtt
'Yvonne's Rot-Goldene'	SAko
§ ***zawadzkii***	CMac SRms WFar

Chrysogonum (*Asteraceae*)

australe	CRos LRHS NRHS
virginianum	CKel CMea EBee EWes SPer WFar
- 'Golden Acres'	ECtt

Chrysopogon (*Poaceae*)

gryllus	EBee WPGP

Chrysosplenium (*Saxifragaceae*)

alternifolium	EBee GEdr
davidianum	CBre CSam EBee EPot EWld GCal GJos GKev ILea IMou NAln NHpl NLar NRHS WBor WCru WMoo WSHC
- SBEC 233	CExl
aff. ***hebetatum*** B&SWJ 9835 **new**	NWad
lanuginosum var. ***formosanum***	GEdr
- - B&SWJ 6979	ESwi WCru
macrophyllum	CExl EPPr EWld GBin GCal GKev GMaP IMou LEdu MAvo MNrw MPie NLar SHar WBor WCot WCru WSHC
oppositifolium	ECha WMoo WSFF WShi

Chusquea (*Poaceae*)

breviglumis misapplied	see *C. culeou* 'Tenuis'
culeou ♀H4	CAbb CBcs CRos EPfP LEdu MAvo MGos MWht SPlb SSta XCre
- 'Breviglumis'	see *C. culeou* 'Tenuis'
- 'Purple Splendour'	CDTJ
§ - 'Tenuis'	ERod XCre
- weeping	CDTJ
delicatula from Machu Picchu, Peru	CExl
gigantea ♀H3	CBcs CDTJ CExl EPfP ERod ESwi MAvo MWht WPGP XCre
macrostachya	XCre
montana	CDTJ
mulleri F&M 104A from Mexico	CExl

Cicerbita (*Asteraceae*)

§ ***alpina***	GAbr GBee NBid SPlb
bourgaei	CFis MMuc
macrorhiza CC 6912	EBee
plumieri	GAbr SBrt WCot WFar WMoo WSHC
- 'Blott' (v)	WCot

Cichorium (*Asteraceae*)

endivia 'Pancalieri' ♀H3	CHby EKin MCtn
intybus	CHby CLau CSpe CWld ELan ENfk GAbr GPoy LSun MBel MCot MHer MNHC NBir NGBl NMir SPer SPlb SPoG SRms WFar WHrl WMoo WSHC WTre
- f. ***album***	ECha ECtt LRHS MBel MPie NRHS SPer
- 'Brussels Witloof' **new**	SVic
- 'Indigo' ♀H5	LRHS NRHS
- 'Palla Rossa' ♀H5	CHby MCtn SRms
- 'Pan di Zucchero' ♀H5	CHby MCtn
- 'Red Rib'	SRms
- 'Roseum'	CBod CRos ECha ECtt ELan LRHS MBel MPie NEgg NRHS SPer SPoG

Cimicifuga see *Actaea*

acerina	see *Actaea japonica*
americana	see *Actaea podocarpa*
cordifolia (DC.) Torrey & A.Gray	see *Actaea cordifolia*

cordifolia Pursh	see *Actaea podocarpa*
foetida	see *Actaea cimicifuga*
racemosa var. ***cordifolia***	see *Actaea cordifolia*
- 'Purpurea'	see *Actaea simplex* Atropurpurea Group
ramosa	see *Actaea simplex* 'Prichard's Giant'
rubifolia	see *Actaea cordifolia*
simplex var. ***matsumurae***	see *Actaea matsumurae*

Cineraria (*Asteraceae*)

× ***hybrida***	see *Pericallis* × *hybrida*
maritima	see *Jacobaea maritima*

Cinnamomum (*Lauraceae*)

camphora	CExl IArd SPlb

Circaea (*Onagraceae*)

alpina	EBee
lutetiana	WHer
- 'Caveat Emptor' (v)	NBid WCot

Cirsium (*Asteraceae*)

arvense	WSFF
canum	CSpe GQue
diacantha	see *Ptilostemon diacantha*
eriophoroides	GEdr
helenioides	see *C. heterophyllum*
§ ***heterophyllum***	CDor EBee EWld LEdu LRHS MAvo NChi NLar SHar
- PAB 067	LEdu WPGP
- 'Pink Blush'	EMor GBin LCro LOPS MPnt NPri NSti WNPC
japonicum 'Pink Beauty'	EMor NHic
- 'Rose Beauty'	SCob WSpi
'Mount Etna'	CBod CFis CSam EBee ELan EPfP GCal GKin LRHS MBNS MBel MMuc MPie NDov NGdn NRHS SEND WCAu WGwG
oleraceum	EBee LEdu NBid NLar SBrt
purpuratum	MHer
rivulare 'Atropurpureum' ♀H7	Widely available
- FROSTED MAGIC ('Lowcir')	CKno IPot LBuc LCro LOPS LRHS MBel NPri NSti SHar SMad WHil WNPC
- 'Trevor's Blue Wonder'	Widely available
tuberosum	CAby LEdu LPla LRHS SPhx WCot
vulgare	WSFF

Cissus (*Vitaceae*)

antarctica ♀H1c	CCCN EShb SEND
pedata B&SWJ 2371	WCru
rhombifolia ♀H1c	EOHP EShb
- 'Ellen Danica' ♀H1c	EShb LCro LOPS
§ ***striata***	CBcs CKel CMac CRos CWCL EBee ELon EShb LRHS MGil MRav NChi SBrt SEND SLim SNig SWvt WSHC
trifoliata new	CRos

Cistus ✿ (*Cistaceae*)

acutifolius misapplied	see *C.* × *pulverulentus*
× ***aguilarii***	CTri MRav
- 'Maculatus' ♀H4	CAby CBcs CBod CDul CExl CKel CRos CSBt CSam ELan EPfP LRHS LSRN MMuc NLar SEle SPer SPoG SWvt WKif WPGP WSpi
albidus	WSpi XSen
algarvensis	see *Halimium ocymoides*
'Anne Palmer'	see *C.* × *fernandesiae* 'Anne Palmer'
× ***argenteus*** 'Blushing Peggy Sammons'	CAby CRos ELan EPfP EWTr LRHS NLar NRHS SWvt WAvo XSen
- 'Paper Moon'	CBod EWTr LSRN NLar
§ - 'Peggy Sammons'	CBod CDul CRos ECha ELan EPfP EWTr LRHS LSRN MAsh MGos NLar SAko SCob SEND SLim SPer SWvt XSen
- 'Silver Ghost'	CAby CKel LRHS SWvt
- 'Silver Pink' misapplied	see *C.* × *lenis* 'Grayswood Pink'
- 'Silver Pink' ambig.	Widely available
atriplicifolius	see *Halimium atriplicifolium*
'Blanche'	see *C. ladanifer* 'Blanche'
× ***bornetianus*** 'Jester' ♀H4	CBod CKel CRos CSBt ELan EPfP EWTr LRHS MAsh NLar NRHS SWvt
× ***canescens*** f. ***albus***	XSen
clusii subsp. ***multiflorus***	XSen
× ***corbariensis***	see *C.* × *hybridus*
creticus	CAby CBcs CExl CKel CPla CRos CSam GPoy LRHS MAsh MGos NEgg SLon SPoG SRms SWvt WKif WSpi
- subsp. ***corsicus***	XSen
§ - subsp. ***creticus***	EBee ELan EPfP MRav SCoo SPer
- subsp. ***eriocephalus***	CBod
§ - subsp. ***incanus***	WCot
§ × ***crispatus*** 'Warley Rose'	GMaP SIgm WKif XLum
crispus misapplied	see *C.* × *pulverulentus*, *C.* × *purpureus*
§ ***crispus*** L.	ELan SEND SGol XSen
- 'Prostratus'	see *C. crispus* L.
- 'Sunset'	see *C.* × *pulverulentus* 'Sunset'
§ × ***cyprius*** ♀H4	CDul CRos EBee ELan EPfP LRHS NRHS SEND SPer SRms SWvt WKif WSpi
§ - var. ***ellipticus*** 'Elma' ♀H4	CRos ELan EPfP LRHS MAsh NLar NRHS SPer WAvo WCot
§ × ***dansereaui***	CKel CMac CSBt LRHS SWvt WSpi
- 'Decumbens' ♀H4	CBod CDul CRos CSde CTri CTsd EBee ELan EPau EPfP EUJe LRHS MAsh MBNS MJak MRav MSwo NEgg NLar NRHS SArc SCoo SGbt SPer SPhx SPoG SWvt WFar WPGP WSpi
- 'Jenkyn Place' ♀H4	CBod EBee ELan GMaP LSRN MBNS MMuc NLar SPer SPoG WKif
'Elma'	see *C.* × *cyprius* var. *ellipticus* 'Elma'
§ × ***fernandesiae*** 'Anne Palmer'	CRos EBee LLHF LRHS MAsh
× ***florentinus*** misapplied	see × *Halimiocistus* 'Ingwersenii'
× ***florentinus*** ambig.	WSpi XLum
§ × ***florentinus*** Lam.	GMaP XSen
* - 'Tramontane'	XSen
× ***gardianus***	XSen
'Gordon Cooper' ♀H4	LSRN MMrt MMuc NLar SCob SPoG WSpi
× ***heterocalyx*** 'Chelsea Bonnet'	CBod EUJe GMaP MBNS MNHC NLar SCoo SPoG
'Highlights'	MAsh
§ × ***hybridus***	Widely available
- 'Coral Tears' new	CKel
- 'Gold Prize' (v)	CWGN NLar SWvt WGrn
- LITTLE MISS SUNSHINE ('Dunnecis'PBR) (v)	MAsh MGos NHol NLar SRms SWvt
- ROSPICO ('Rencis'PBR) (v)	EPfP LRHS NLar
incanus	see *C. creticus* subsp. *incanus*
ingwerseniana	see × *Halimiocistus* 'Ingwersenii'
'Jessamy Beauty'	WAvo
'Jessamy Charm'	SPhx
ladanifer misapplied	see *C.* × *cyprius*

	ladanifer ambig.	CMac ECha WKif
	ladanifer L.	CBcs CKel CSBt CSde CTri ELan EPfP GPoy LRHS MRav MSwo SWvt WSpi XSen
§	- 'Blanche'	EPfP LLHF LSRN NLar SEND SPer SWvt WKif WSpi
	- var. ***maculatus***	CBod
§	- 'Paladin'	EUJe
	- Palhinhae Group	see *C. ladanifer* var. *sulcatus*
	- 'Pat'	CRos ELan EPfP LRHS LSRN MAsh NLar NRHS SPoG SWvt
	- var. ***petiolatus*** 'Bennett's White'	WAvo
§	- var. ***sulcatus***	CRos CTsd ELan LRHS
	lasianthus	see *Halimium lasianthum*
	laurifolius	CKel EPfP LRHS MGos SCob SWvt WSpi XSen
	- subsp. ***atlanticus***	XSen
	× ***laxus*** 'Snow White' ♀H4	CWGN EBee EPfP LRHS MGos NLar NPer SAko SLon
§	× ***lenis*** 'Grayswood Pink' ♀H4	CBod CExl CKel CRos CTri EBee ECrN ELan EPfP EUJe LRHS LSRN MAsh MGos MMuc MSwo NEgg NLar SAko SEND SIgm SLim SPer SPhx SPlb SPoG SWvt XLum XSen
	× ***loretii*** misapplied	see *C.* × *dansereaui*
	× ***lusitanicus*** Maund	see *C.* × *dansereaui*
	'McGuire's Gold' **new**	ELan
	'Merrist Wood Cream'	see × *Halimiocistus wintonensis* 'Merrist Wood Cream'
	'Mickie' (v) **new**	ELan
	monspeliensis	CMac CRos EPfP GKev LRHS MAsh MBNS MMuc SLon SPer SPoG XSen
	- 'Vicar's Mead'	CCCN CRos LRHS MBNS
	monspeliensis* × *salviifolius	see *C.* × *florentinus* Lam.
	× ***oblongifolius***	SWvt XSen
	× ***obtusifolius*** ambig.	CKel EBou ELan LRHS NHic
	× ***obtusifolius*** Sweet	WPGP XSen
§	- 'Thrive' ♀H4	CRos EPfP LRHS MGos NRHS SCoo
	ocymoides	see *Halimium ocymoides*
	'Paladin'	see *C. ladanifer* 'Paladin'
	palhinhae	see *C. ladanifer* var. *sulcatus*
	parviflorus misapplied	see *C.* × *lenis* 'Grayswood Pink'
	parviflorus Lam.	WSHC
	'Peggy Sammons'	see *C.* × *argenteus* 'Peggy Sammons'
	× ***platysepalus***	SPhx
	populifolius	CMac CRos ECha EPfP LLHF LRHS NLar SGol SPer SWvt
	- var. ***lasiocalyx***	see *C. populifolius* subsp. *major*
§	- subsp. ***major***	CRos LRHS LSRN WPGP WSpi
§	× ***pulverulentus***	CExl CTri ECha WSHC XSen
§	- 'Sunset' ♀H4	Widely available
	- 'Warley Rose'	see *C.* × *crispatus* 'Warley Rose'
§	× ***purpureus*** ♀H4	Widely available
	- 'Alan Fradd'	CBcs CBod CKel CMac CRos ECrN ELan EPfP LCro LOPS LRHS LSRN MAsh MCot MGos MMuc MSwo NEgg NRHS SCob SCoo SEND SEle SGol SLim SPoG SWvt WFar XLum XSen
	- 'Betty Taudevin'	see *C.* × *purpureus*
	- f. ***stictus***	LRHS WAvo
	× ***rodiaei*** 'Jessabel'	CRos EPfP LRHS MAsh MRav NLar SPer SWvt WPGP
	'Ruby Cluster'	CBod CCCN LRHS MMuc NLar
	sahucii	see × *Halimiocistus sahucii*
	salviifolius	CCCN XSen
	- 'Avalanche'	WAbe
	- 'Gold Star'	NLar
	- 'May Snow'	EHoe LRHS MAsh
	- 'Prostratus'	CAby CKel CRos CSde ELan EPfP LRHS SWvt WSpi
	× ***skanbergii***	CBod CMac CSam CTri ELan EPfP MGos MHol MMuc MRav NBir NLar SCob SEND SPer WCFE WSpi XLum XSen
	'Snow Fire' ♀H4	CAby CCCN CKel CRos EBee ELan EPfP LRHS LSRN MAsh MGos MMuc NEgg NLar SAko SCoo SWvt WAvo WGrn
	symphytifolius	GKev NAln
	'Thrive'	see *C.* × *obtusifolius* 'Thrive'
	× ***verguinii***	XSen
	villosus	see *C. creticus* subsp. *creticus*
	wintonensis	see × *Halimiocistus wintonensis*

Cistus × *Halimium* see × *Halimiocistus*

Citharexylum (*Verbenaceae*)

	quadrangulare Jacq.	see *C. spinosum*
	spicatum	CExl WBor
§	***spinosum***	CHll EBee

citrandarin see *Citrus reticulata* × *C. trifoliata*

citrange see *Citrus* × *insitorum*

citrangequat see *Citrus* × *georgiana*

× *Citrofortunella* see *Citrus*

	mitis	see *Citrus* × *microcarpa*

citron see *Citrus medica*

Citronella (*Icacinaceae*)

§	***gongonha***	SVen
	mucronata	see *C. gongonha*

Citrullus (*Cucurbitaceae*)

	lanatus 'Charleston Gray'	SVic

Citrus (*Rutaceae*)

§	× ***aurantiifolia*** (F)	CCCN EPfP SCit SPre
	- key lime	see *C.* × *aurantiifolia*
§	× ***aurantium*** (F)	SCit
	- 'Aber's Narrowleaf' (F)	SCit
	- subsp. ***bergamia***	see *C.* × *limon*
	- 'Bouquet de Fleurs'	see *C.* × *aurantium* (Sour Orange Group) 'Bouquet'
	- 'Gou-tou Cheng' (F)	SCit
§	- Grapefruit Group (F)	CCCN EUJe SPre SVic
	- - 'Foster' (F)	SCit
	- - 'Golden Special' (F)	SCit
	- - 'Marsh' (F)	SCit
	- - 'Oroblanco' (F)	SCit
	- - 'Red Blush' (F/S)	SCit
	- - 'Star Ruby' (F/S)	CCCN SCit SPre SVic
	- - 'Wheeny'	see *C. maxima* 'Wheeny'
	- var. ***myrtifolia***	see *C.* × *aurantium*
	- 'Pursha' (F)	SPre
	- 'Robinson' (F)	SCit
§	- (Sour Orange Group) 'Bouquet' (F)	SCit
	- - 'Bouquetier de Nice' (F)	SCit
	- - 'Chinotto' (F)	SCit SPre
	- - 'Seville' (F)	LSRN SCit SPre
	- - 'Smooth Flat Seville' (F)	SCit

§	- Sweet Orange Group (F)	CCCN EUJe SCit SPre SVic
§	- - 'Baia' (F/S)	SCit
	- - 'Embiguo' (F)	SCit
	- - 'Fukumoto' (F)	CCCN
	- - 'Jaffa'	see *C.* × *aurantium* (Sweet Orange Group) 'Shamouti'
	- - 'Lane Late' (F)	CCCN SCit SPre
§	- - 'Malta Blood' (F)	SCit
	- - 'Maltaise Sanguine'	see *C.* × *aurantium* (Sweet Orange Group) 'Malta Blood'
	- - 'Navelate' (F)	SCit
	- - 'Navelina' (F/S)	CCCN SCit SPre SVic
	- - 'Newhall' (F/S)	NLar SCit
	- - 'Salustiana' (F/S)	SCit
§	- - 'Sanguinelli' (F)	CCCN SCit SPre SVic
§	- - 'Shamouti' (F)	SCit
	- - 'Spanish Sanguinelli'	see *C.* × *aurantium* (Sweet Orange Group) 'Sanguinelli'
	- - 'Succari' (F)	SCit
	- - 'Tarocco' (F)	SCit
	- - 'Valencia' (F)	CCCN SCit SPre
	- - 'Washington'	see *C.* × *aurantium* (Sweet Orange Group) 'Baia'
	- - 'Washington Navel'	see *C.* × *aurantium* (Sweet Orange Group) 'Baia'
§	- (Tangelo Group) 'Minneola' (F)	SCit
§	- - 'Nova' (F/S)	CCCN SCit SVic
	- - 'Orlando' (F)	SCit
	- - 'Seminole' (F)	SCit
	- - 'Ugli' misapplied	see *C.* × *aurantium* 'Minneola'
	- - 'Ugli' (F)	SCit
	- (Tangor Group) 'Dweet' (F)	SCit
	- - 'Ellendale' (F)	SCit
	- - 'Murcott' (F)	SCit
	australasica (F)	SCit SPre SVic
	bergamia	see *C.* × *limon*
	- bergamot	see *C.* × *limon* Bergamot Group
	- 'Castagnaro' (F)	SCit
	'Buddha's Hand'	see *C. medica* 'Fingered'
	calamondin	see *C.* × *microcarpa*
§	***cavaleriei*** (F)	WPGP
	citrandarin	see *C. reticulata* × *trifoliata*
	deliciosa	see *C. reticulata* 'Willowleaf'
	× ***floridana*** 'Eustis' (F)	SCit SPre
	- 'Lakeland' (F)	SCit SPre
	× ***georgiana*** 'Thomasville' (F)	SCit
§	***hystrix***	CCCN ELan LSRN NLar SCit SPre
	Ichang lemon	see *C. cavaleriei*
	ichangensis	see *C. cavaleriei*
	× ***insitorum*** 'C-35' (F)	SCit
	- 'Carrizo' (F)	SCit
	- 'Citromon' (F)	SCit
	- 'Curafora' (F)	SCit
	- 'Swingle' (F)	SCit
	- 'Us119' (F)	SCit
	- 'Venasca' (F)	SCit
	jambhiri	see *C.* × *taitensis*
§	***japonica*** (F) ♀H1c	CBcs ELan EPfP SCit SPre SVic
	- Hong Kong kumquat (F)	SCit
	- 'Nagami' (F)	SPre
	- 'Reale'[PBR] (F)	SPre
§	× ***junos***	SCit SPre
	kinokuni	see *C. japonica*
	kotokan	see *C.* × *aurantium*
	'Kucle' (F)	SCit SPre
	'Kulci' (F)	CCCN
	kumquat	see *C. japonica*
	'La Valette' (F)	CCCN LSRN SPre
	× ***latifolia*** (F/S)	CCCN EPfP EUJe SCit SPre
	- 'Bearss' (F)	SCit SVic
	- variegated (F/v)	SPre
	latipes Hook. f. & Thomson ex Hook. f.	see *C. hystrix*
	limetta (F)	CCCN SPre SVic
	limettioides (F)	SCit SPre
§	× ***limon*** (F)	EUJe LSRN SCit SVic
§	- Bergamot Group (F)	SPre
	- - 'Fantastico' (F)	SCit
	- 'Eureka'	see *C.* × *limon* 'Garey's Eureka'
	- 'Eureka Variegated' (F/v)	SCit
	- 'Fino' (F)	CCCN SCit
	- 'Four Seasons'	see *C.* × *limon* 'Garey's Eureka'
§	- 'Garey's Eureka' (F)	CCCN ELan EPfP LCro LOPS LSRN NLar SCit SPre SVic
	- 'Imperial' (F)	SCit SPre
	- 'Improved Meyer'	see *C.* × *limon* 'Meyer'
	- 'Lemonade' (F)	SCit
	- 'Lisbon' (F)	SCit
	- 'Lunario' (F)	SCit SPre
§	- 'Meyer' (F) ♀H2	CBcs CCCN CHll CTri ELan EPfP LSRN NLar SCit SPre
	- 'Ponderosa' (F)	SCit
	- 'Quatre Saisons'	see *C.* × *limon* 'Garey's Eureka'
	- 'Rangpur' (F)	SCit
	- 'Romana' (F)	SCit
	- 'Sfusato d'Amalfi' (F)	SCit
	- 'Siracusano' (F)	SCit
	- 'Variegata' (F/v) ♀H2	CCCN SCit SPre
	- 'Verna' (F)	CCCN SCit
	- 'Villa Franca' (F)	SCit
	- 'Yen Ben' (F)	SCit
	- 'Zagara Bianco' (F)	SCit
	× ***limonia***	see *C.* × *limon*
	'Lipo' (F)	CCCN SCit SPre
	macrophylla (F)	SCit
	madurensis	see *C. japonica*
§	***maxima*** 'Wheeny' (F)	SCit
	medica 'Cedra' (F)	SPre
	- 'Cidro Digitado'	see *C. medica* 'Fingered'
	- var. ***digitata***	see *C. medica* 'Fingered'
	- 'Ethrog' (F)	SCit SPre
§	- 'Fingered' (F)	EUJe SCit SPre
*	- 'Rubra'	SPre
	- var. ***sarcodactylis***	see *C. medica* 'Fingered'
	× ***meyeri***	see *C.* × *limon*
§	× ***microcarpa*** (F) ♀H3	CCCN NLar SCit SPre
	- Philippine lime	see *C.* × *microcarpa*
§	- 'Tiger' (F/v)	SCit SPre
	- 'Variegata'	see *C.* × *microcarpa* 'Tiger'
	× ***mitis***	see *C.* × *microcarpa*
	natsudaidai	see *C.* × *aurantium*
	'Nippon'	SCit
	× ***nobilis*** Lour.	see *C. reticulata* 'Willowleaf'
	- var. ***inermis***	see *C. japonica*
	- Ortanique Group	see *C.* × *aurantium* Sweet Orange Group
	× ***obovata*** (F)	SPre
	- 'Fukushu' (F)	CCCN SCit
	× ***paradisi***	see *C.* × *aurantium* Grapefruit Group
	- 'Wheeny'	see *C. maxima* 'Wheeny'
	'Pursta' (F)	CCCN
	reshni	see *C.* × *aurantium*
§	***reticulata*** (F)	CCCN SCit SPre
	- 'Clausellina' (F/S)	SCit
	- var. ***deliciosa***	see *C. reticulata* 'Willowleaf'
	- 'Fina' (F/S)	SCit
	- 'Hashimoto' (F/S)	SCit
	- 'Hernandina' (F)	CCCN

- Mandarin Group (F)	EPfP EUJe SPre
- - 'Clementine' (F)	EPfP SPre
- - 'Encore' (F)	SCit
- - 'Esbal' (F)	CCCN
- - 'Fortune' (F)	SCit
- - 'Fremont' (F)	SCit
- - 'Nules' (F/S)	CCCN SCit
- 'Marisol' (F/S)	SCit
- 'Miyagawa' (F)	CCCN SCit
- 'Nour' (F)	SCit
- 'Nova'	see *C.* × *aurantium* (Tangelo Group) 'Nova'
- 'Okitsu' (F/S)	CCCN SCit
- 'Owari' (F/S)	SCit
- Satsuma Group	see *C. reticulata*
- (Tangerine Group) 'Dancy' (F)	SCit
§ - 'Willowleaf' (F)	SCit
§ ***reticulata*** × ***trifoliata***	SCit
sinensis	see *C.* × *aurantium* Sweet Orange Group
- 'Jaffa'	see *C.* × *aurantium* (Sweet Orange Group) 'Shamouti'
- 'Washington'	see *C.* × *aurantium* (Sweet Orange Group) 'Baia'
§ × ***taitensis*** (F)	SCit SPre
- 'Otaheite' (F)	CCCN SCit
§ - rough lemon (F)	SCit
- Schaub rough lemon	see *C.* × *taitensis* rough lemon
§ ***trifoliata***	CAgr CBcs CCCN CDul EBee ELan ELon EPfP IDee LRHS MBlu MGil MMuc MRav SCit SMad SPer SPlb WFar WSHC
- 'Flying Dragon'	LEdu SCit
unshiu	see *C. reticulata*
volkameriana	see *C.* × *limon*
wilsonii	see *C.* × *junos*

Cladium (*Cyperaceae*)

mariscus	XLum

Cladrastis (*Papilionaceae*)

§ ***kentukea***	CBcs CDul CLnd CMCN CTho EBee ELan EPfP ESwi EUJe EWTr LMaj MBlu MRav NLar NOra WMat WPGP
§ - 'Perkins Pink'	MBlu
- 'Rosea'	see *C. kentukea* 'Perkins Pink'
lutea	see *C. kentukea*
sinensis	CExl EBee EPfP MBlu WPGP
wilsonii	WPGP

Claytonia (*Portulacaceae*)

alsinoides	see *C. sibirica*
caroliniana	GKev
§ ***perfoliata***	GPoy MNHC WHer
§ ***sibirica***	CAgr IMou XLum
- f. ***albiflora***	EWld MPie WCot WMoo
virginica	EBee EPot GKev LAma MPie WFar WMoo WPnP

Clematis ✿ (*Ranunculaceae*)

BWJ 7630 from China	WCru
CC 711	CExl
CC 4710	CExl
SDR 6151	GKev
SDR 7835	GKev
'Abigail' (Vt)	NHaw
ABILENE ('Evipo027'PBR) (EL)	CFlo CKel CRos CWGN ELan EPfP LRHS MAsh NRHS SNig SPoG
'Abundance' (Vt) 🏆H6	CArg CBcs CFlo CKel CRHN CWCL ELan EPfP LCro LRHS LSRN MAsh NHol SNig WFar
ACROPOLIS ('Evipo078') (Boulevard Series)	CWGN
addisonii	NHaw WSHC
'Advent Bells' (C)	CWGN LCro LOPS
akebioides	NHaw
akoensis	NHaw
ALABAST ('Poulala'PBR) (EL) 🏆H6	LRHS SCoo
ALAINA ('Evipo056'PBR) (EL)	CKel CRos LRHS NRHS SLon SPoG
'Alba Luxurians' (Vt)	CBcs CFlo CKel CRHN CRos CTri CWCL ELan EPfP EShb LCro LOPS LRHS LSRN MAsh MGos NHol NRHS SCob SLim SPer SPoG
'Albatross' (EL)	LSRN
'Albina Plena' (A/d)	EPfP
'Aleksandrit' (EL)	NHaw
'Alice Fisk' (EL)	CKel LSRN MSwo
'Aliide' (LL)	NHaw
'Alionushka' (I) 🏆H6	CKel CRHN CRos CWCL ELan EPfP LRHS LSRN NLar
ALITA ('Evipo070'PBR) (Vt)	CRos CWCL EBee LRHS MMrt NRHS SNig
'Allanah' (LL)	CWCL LRHS LSRN NHaw SCoo SNig SPet
alpina	GKev GLog LCro LOPS LRHS LSRN MAsh MRav NPer SCob SEWo SPlb SPre SWvt WFar
- 'Albiflora'	see *C. sibirica*
- 'Columbine White'	see *C.* 'White Columbine'
§ - 'Pamela Jackman' (A) 🏆H6	CKel CMac CRos CWCL ELan LRHS LSRN MAsh MMuc NEgg NRHS SCoo SLim SPer SPoG SRkn SWvt WFar
- pink-flowered	GKev
- 'Stolwijk Gold' (A)	CWGN EBee MBlu SRms
alternata	CWGN EBee NHaw
'Amethyst Beauty' (A)	EPfP LRHS
AMETHYST BEAUTY ('Evipo043'PBR) (LL)	CRos MAsh SLon SPoG
'Andante' (I)	CWGN
'Andromeda' (EL)	CRos EBee LRHS NHaw NLar NRHS
ANETA ('Evipo055'PBR) (Vt)	CFlo CWGN
ANGELA ('Zoang'PBR) (EL)	LSRN
ANGELIQUE ('Evipo017') (EL)	CFlo CKel CRos CWGN ELan EPfP LRHS MAsh MGos NRHS SCoo SLon SNig SPer
'Anissa' (V)	NHaw
'Anita' (Ta)	CFlo EBee EPfP LSRN NHaw
ANNA LOUISE ('Evithree'PBR) (EL) 🏆H6	CRos CWCL EPfP LRHS LSRN MGos SCoo SLim SLon SNig
'Annabel' (EL)	LSRN MAsh
ANNABELLA ('Zo08169') (V) **new**	CFlo IPot
ANNIVERSARY ('Pynot') (EL)	LSRN SCoo
'Aotearoa' (LL)	IPot NHaw
'Aphrodite' (I)	MAsh
'Aphrodite Elegafumina' (I)	CRHN CRos CWGN LRHS NHaw
'Apollonia'	CWGN
'Apple Blossom' (Ar) 🏆H4	CBcs CFlo CKel CRos CTri CWCL ELan EMOT EPfP EUJe IPot LBuc LCro LOPS LRHS LSRN MAsh MGos MJak MRav MSwo NLar NRHS SCob SLim SPer SPoG SRkn SRms SWvt
'Arabella' (I) 🏆H6	CFlo CKel CRHN CRos CWCL CWGN ELan ELon EPfP EShb LRHS

	LSRN MAsh MGos NEgg NLar NRHS SLim SNig SPer SRkn SWvt WBor WFar
§ ARCTIC QUEEN ('Evitwo'[PBR]) (EL) ♀H6	CFlo CKel CRos EPfP LBuc LCro LOPS LRHS LSRN MAsh NPri NRHS SCoo SLon SPoG
armandii	Widely available
- 'Enham Star' (Ar)	CRos EPfP LRHS MGos NRHS
§ - 'Little White Charm' (Ar)	CKel CRos EBee ELan EPfP LBuc LRHS NRHS
- 'Meyeniana'	see *C. armandii* 'Little White Charm'
§ - 'Snowdrift' (Ar)	CBcs CFlo CKel CRos EBee ELan EPfP LCro LOPS LRHS LSRN MAsh MGos MSwo NLar NRHS SCob SEle SPer SPoG SRms
× ***aromatica***	CFlo CKel CRos CWGN EBee ELan EPfP IPot LRHS MMrt
'Asao' (EL)	CArg CRos EPfP LRHS SCoo SPoG WFar
'Ascotiensis' (LL) ♀H6	CRHN CRos EBee EPfP LRHS NHaw SCoo SLon SNig
'Ashva' (LL)	CWGN
ASTRA NOVA ('Zo09085') (Vt)	CFlo CWGN IPot
AVANT-GARDE ('Evipo033'[PBR]) (Vt)	CFlo CKel CRos CWCL CWGN ELan EPfP EUJe LRHS SLon
§ AZTEK ('Daihelios') (Ta)	CKel CRos LRHS SNig
BABY DOLL ('Zobadol'[PBR]) (EL)	CKel CWGN EBee
'Baby Pink' (I)	NHaw
BABY STAR ('Zobast'[PBR]) (EL)	CKel CWGN
§ 'Bagatelle' (LL)	CRos LRHS NHaw SNig
'Bal Maiden' (Vt)	CRHN NHaw
'Barbara' (LL)	LSRN
'Barbara Dibley' (EL)	CFlo CKel CRos CTri CWCL LRHS MAsh NHaw SCoo SNig SPet
'Barbara Harrington'[PBR] (LL)	CRos LRHS LSRN SNig
'Barbara Jackman' (EL)	CArg CKel CRos CWCL LRHS LSRN MAsh MGos MSwo NEgg SCoo SLon SNig
'Beata' (LL)	CWCL NHaw SNig
'Beautiful Bride'[PBR] (EL)	LCro LOPS
'Beauty of Worcester' (EL)	CKel CRos CWCL ELan ELon EPfP LRHS LSRN MAsh MSwo NEgg NHaw SCoo SLim SNig SPer SPet
'Bees' Jubilee' (EL)	CArg CBcs CKel CMac CRos CWCL EBee ELan EPfP LCro LOPS LRHS LSRN MAsh MGos MSwo NEgg NLar SLim SNig SPer SPoG SWvt
'Bella' (EL)	LSRN
'Belle Nantaise' (EL)	CRos LRHS NRHS SCoo SRms
'Belle of Woking' (EL)	CRos CWCL ELan ELon LRHS LSRN NEgg SCoo SWvt
'Ben's Beauty' (A)	CFlo CKel
BERNADINE ('Evipo 061'[PBR]) (EL)	CFlo CPla CRos CWGN LRHS NRHS
'Berry Red' (A)	CWGN
'Best Wishes'	CKel CRos LRHS LSRN NRHS SNig
§ 'Beth Currie' (EL)	CRos EPfP LRHS SNig
'Betty Corning' (Vt)	CFlo CKel CRHN CRos CWGN EBee ELan EPfP LRHS LSRN MGos NRHS SCoo SLon SNig SPoG SRms SWvt
BIJOU	see *C.* THUMBELINA
'Bill MacKenzie' (Ta) ♀H6	CArg CFlo CKel CMac CRos CSam CTri ELan EPfP GKev IPot LRHS LSRN MGos MRav NAln NHol NPri NRHS SCob SLim SNig SPer SPoG SRms SWvt WSHC
'Black Prince' (Vt)	CFlo CKel CRHN CRos CWGN ELan EPfP IPot LCro LRHS LSRN NHaw NLar NRHS SLim SLon SNig SPer SPoG SRms
'Black Tea' (LL)	CKel CRos EPfP IPot LRHS LSRN NHaw NRHS SLim SLon SNig
§ 'Błękitny Anioł' (LL) ♀H6	CFlo CKel CRHN CRos CWCL CWGN EBee ELan ELon LRHS MAsh NLar NRHS SCob SCoo SNig SPer SPoG WBor
BLUE ANGEL	see *C.* 'Błękitny Anioł'
'Blue Belle' (Vt)	CRHN ELan IPot LRHS NLar SLon WFar
'Blue Bird' (A/d)	CArg CBcs CWCL EBee ELan LRHS NAln SRms
BLUE BLOOD	see *C.* 'Königskind'
'Blue Boy' (EL)	see *C.* 'Elsa Späth'
'Blue Boy' (I)	see *C.* × *diversifolia* 'Blue Boy'
'Blue Dancer' (A)	CBcs CKel CRos EPfP LRHS MGos NLar SNig
'Blue Eclipse' (A)	CFlo CKel CRos CWGN LRHS NHaw NHol NRHS SPoG
'Blue Eyes' (EL)	LSRN NLar
§ 'Blue Light'[PBR] (EL/d)	CFlo CRos CWGN ELan LRHS NLar
BLUE MOON ('Evirin'[PBR]) (EL)	CRos CWCL LRHS LSRN NLar SCoo SLon SNig
BLUE OCEAN ('Zo09045') (I)	EBee IPot
BLUE PIROUETTE ('Zobluepi'[PBR]) (I)	CWCL ELan IPot MJak
BLUE RAIN	see *C.* 'Sinii Dozhd'
'Blue Ravine' (EL)	CRos EPfP LRHS NLar SCoo
BLUE RIVER ('Zoblueriver'[PBR])	CWCL CWGN ELan
'Bolam Belle' (Vt)	NHaw
BONANZA ('Evipo031'[PBR]) (Vt)	CRos EPfP LRHS NLar SCoo SLon SNig SPoG
× ***bonstedtii*** 'Crépuscule' (H)	ECtt GCal MCot
BOURBON ('Evipo018'[PBR]) (EL)	CRos ELan EPfP LRHS SCoo SLon SNig
'Brianna' (Vt)	NHaw
'Brocade' (Vt)	CRHN NHaw
'Broughton Bride' (A)	CFlo CKel CRos CWCL CWGN EPfP LRHS NHol NLar NRHS SRms
'Broughton Star' (M/d) ♀H5	CArg CFlo CKel CMac CRHN CRos CSBt CWCL EBee EBou ELan EPfP LRHS LSRN MBlu MGos MRav MSwo NAln NHol NRHS SCob SLim SLon SNig SPoG SRkn SRms SWvt
'Brunette' (A)	CFlo CKel CRos ELan EPfP LRHS NLar SLon SNig
buchananiana Finet & Gagnep.	see *C. rehderiana*
'Buckland Beauty' (V)	CFlo CWGN NHaw
'Buckland Pixie' (Vt)	NHaw
'Burford Bell' (V)	NHaw
'Burford Princess' (Vt)	CRHN NHaw
'Burford White' (A)	NLar
'Burma Star' (EL)	CFlo CKel CWCL CWGN EPfP SNig
CADDICK'S CASCADE	see *C.* 'Semu'
calycina	see *C. cirrhosa* var. *balearica*
§ ***campaniflora***	GCal NHaw
campestris	GKev
'Candy Stripe'	CRos LRHS SCoo SPoG
'Capitaine Thuilleaux'	see *C.* 'Souvenir du Capitaine Thuilleaux'
'Carlotta' (Vt)	NHaw

'Carmencita' (Vt)	CRHN EBee LRHS LSRN NHaw SCoo SLon
'Carnaby' (EL)	CArg CKel CRos CWCL ELan EPfP LRHS LSRN MAsh NEgg SCoo SNig SWvt
'Carol Klein' (I)	NHaw
'Carol Leeds' (Vt)	NHaw
'Caroline' (LL)	CWGN LSRN
× ***cartmanii*** 'Avalanche'^{PBR} (Fo/m)	CFlo CKel CRos ELan EPfP LRHS MGos NLar NPri NRHS SCoo SLon SNig SPoG SWvt
- 'Joe' (Fo/m) Υ^{H4}	CBcs CFlo CKel CRos CTsd CWCL ELan EPfP EWes ITim LRHS LSRN NRHS SCob SCoo SPoG SWvt WIce
- 'Joe' × ***marmoraria*** (Fo)	MAsh
- 'Joe' × 'Sharon'	LSRN
- MICHIKO ('Evipo044'^{PBR}) (Fo)	CRos EBee EPfP LRHS NRHS SNig SPoG
- 'White Abundance'^{PBR} (Fo/f)	CRos LRHS NLar
CASSIS ('Evipo020'^{PBR})	CKel CRos LRHS LSRN MAsh SCoo SLon SNig SPer
'Catherine Clanwilliam' (T)	CWGN
'Catherine Penny' (VT)	NHaw
'Celebration'^{PBR} Godfrey (EL)	CFlo
CEZANNE ('Evipo023'^{PBR}) (EL)	CFlo CKel CRos CWCL ELan EPfP LRHS MAsh MGos NLar NRHS SCoo SLon SNig
'Chacewater' (Vt)	CRHN
'Chalcedony' (EL)	CWGN
CHANTILLY ('Evipo021'^{PBR}) (EL)	CFlo CKel CRos ELan EPfP LRHS LSRN NRHS SCoo SLon SNig
'Charissima' (EL)	CRos CWGN LRHS NLar SCoo
'Charlie Brown' (LL)	CRHN NHaw
'Charlotte' (EL)	CFlo
CHARMAINE ('Evipo022'^{PBR}) (EL)	CFlo CKel CRos CWGN LRHS NRHS SPoG
'Chatsworth' (Vt)	CRHN CWGN NHaw SLon
CHELSEA ('Evipo100')	CRos EPfP LRHS NRHS SLon
CHEROKEE	see *C.* OOH LA LA
CHEVALIER ('Evipo040'^{PBR}) (EL)	CRos ELan EPfP LRHS MAsh NRHS SLon SNig SPoG
chinensis misapplied	see *C. terniflora*
CHINOOK ('Evipo013'^{PBR})	CRos LRHS SRms
chrysantha	see *C. tangutica*
chrysocoma misapplied	see *C. spooneri*
chrysocoma Franch.	WSpi
'Cicciolina' (Vt)	CRHN NHaw
cirrhosa	CRos CTri LRHS MAsh SArc SCob
§ - var. ***balearica***	CBcs CFlo CKel CMac CRos CTri CWCL ELan EPfP LCro LOPS LRHS LSRN MAsh MGos MRav MSwo SCob SEND SLim SNig SPer SPoG SWvt
- 'Jingle Bells' (C)	CFlo CKel CMac CRos CWCL EBee ELan EPfP LCro LOPS LRHS LSRN MAsh MGos NLar NRHS SCob SCoo SLim SLon SNig SRms
- 'Ourika Valley' (C)	CWGN EBee ELon MAsh NLar
- var. ***purpurascens*** 'Freckles' (C) Υ^{H4}	Widely available
- - 'Lansdowne Gem' (C)	CFlo CKel CMac CRos CWCL CWGN LBuc LRHS NLar SNig SPoG SWvt WSpi
- 'Winter Parasol' (C)	EBee LBuc
- 'Wisley Cream' (C) Υ^{H4}	CBcs CFlo CKel CMac CRos CWCL EBee ELan EPfP LCro LOPS LRHS LSRN MAsh MSwo NLar NRHS SCob SCoo SEND SLim SNig SPer SPoG SRms SWvt WFar
clarkeana misapplied	see *C. urophylla* 'Winter Beauty'
coactilis	NHaw SBrt
columbiana	GKev
§ - var. ***tenuiloba***	LLHF
- - 'Ylva' (A)	WAbe
'Columbine' (A)	CRos EBee EPfP LRHS MSwo SNig SPer
'Columella' (A)	EBee NLar
'Comtesse de Bouchaud' (LL) Υ^{H6}	CArg CFlo CKel CRos CTri CWCL EBee ELan EPfP EShb LCro LOPS LRHS LSRN MAsh MGos MRav NPri NRHS SLim SNig SPer SPoG WBor
CONFETTI ('Evipo036'^{PBR}) (Vt)	CFlo CRos EPfP LRHS LSRN SLon
'Congratulations' (EL)	CRos LRHS LSRN NRHS SNig SPoG
aff. ***connata*** HWJK 2176 from Nepal	WCru
'Constance' (A) Υ^{H6}	CArg CFlo CKel CRos CWCL EBee EPfP LRHS LSRN NEgg NLar NRHS SCoo SNig SPre SRms WFar
'Continuity' (M)	CWGN
'Cora' (I)	CWGN
CORINNE ('Evipo063'^{PBR}) (EL)	CFlo CRos LRHS NRHS SNig SPoG
'Cornish Spirit' (Vt)	CRHN
'Corona' (EL)	EPfP LRHS SCoo
'Côte d'Azur' (H)	CExl CKel GCal LRHS MNrw NLar
'Countess of Lovelace' (EL)	CBcs ELan EPfP LRHS LSRN SCoo
COUNTRY ROSE ('Zocoro'^{PBR}) (A)	CFlo EPfP
'Cragside' (A)	CFlo CKel CRos LRHS NRHS
§ 'Crimson King' (LL)	NLar
'Crinkle'^{PBR} (M)	CCCN
§ ***crispa***	CWGN NHaw
§ CRYSTAL FOUNTAIN ('Evipo038'^{PBR}) (EL)	CFlo CKel CRos CWCL CWGN ELan EPfP LBuc LCro LOPS LRHS LSRN MGos SCoo SLon SNig SPoG SRms
'Danae' (Vt)	NHaw
DANCING KING ('Zodaki'^{PBR}) (EL)	CKel
DANCING SMILE ('Zodasmi'^{PBR}) (EL)	CKel EBee
'Daniel Deronda' (EL) Υ^{H6}	CArg CFlo CKel CRos CWCL CWGN EBee ELan IPot LRHS LSRN MAsh NRHS SCoo SLim SNig SPet SPoG
'Dark Eyes' (Vt)	CKel CWGN IPot LOPS
'Dark Secret' (A)	NHol
dasyandra NJM 11.075	WPGP
'Dawn' (EL)	CCCN CFlo CRos CWCL LRHS LSRN SCoo
'Dazzle' (EL) **new**	LCro LOPS
'De Vijfhoeven' (Vt)	NHaw
'Débutante' (EL)	NHaw
'Denny's Double' (EL/d)	CKel CWCL CWGN LRHS SNig
'Destiny' (EL)	CWGN
DIAMANTINA ('Evipo039'^{PBR}) (EL)	CFlo CKel CRos CWCL EBee EPfP LRHS NRHS SLon SNig
'Diamond Anniversary' (A)	CWCL EPfP
'Diana' (LL)	LSRN NHaw
DIANA'S DELIGHT ('Evipo026'^{PBR}) (EL)	CKel CRos CWCL EPfP LRHS LSRN MAsh NRHS SLon SPoG
dioscoreifolia	see *C. terniflora*
§ × ***diversifolia***	CRHN LRHS NHaw SWvt WCot
- 'Benedikt' (I)	CWGN
§ - 'Blue Boy' (I)	CRHN NHaw
- 'Heather Herschell' (I)	CFlo CRHN CTsd NHaw

§	– 'Hendersonii' (I)	CFlo CRos CWCL ELan EMor LRHS LSRN MRav SMHy SPer SWvt WCot
§	– 'Olgae' (I)	CExl NHaw
	'Doctor Mary' (V)	NHaw
	'Doctor Ruppel' (EL)	CArg CFlo CKel CMac CRos CWCL ELon LRHS LSRN MAsh MSwo NRHS SCob SLim SNig SPer SPet WFar
	'Dominika' (LL)	NHaw
	'Dorath'	CKel CRos CWGN EPfP LRHS NHaw SNig
	'Dorothy Walton'	see *C.* 'Bagatelle'
	'Double Delight' (M)	CFlo CWGN
	'Duchess of Albany' (1897) (T)	CArg CFlo CKel CRos CTri CWCL ELan EPfP LRHS LSRN MAsh MGos NEgg NHol SNig SPer SRkn
	'Duchess of Edinburgh' (EL)	CBcs CKel CMac CWCL ELan EPfP LRHS LSRN MAsh MGos MSwo NEgg NHol NRHS SLim SNig SPoG SWvt
	× ***durandii*** ♀H6	CBcs CFlo CKel CRHN CRos CSpe CWCL ELan EPfP LRHS LSRN MAsh MGos MRav NRHS SCoo SPer SPoG SWvt WSpi
	'Dutch Sky' (LL)	CWGN
	'Early Sensation' (Fo/f)	CBcs CFlo CKel CRos CTri CWCL ELan ELon EPfP LCro LOPS LRHS LSRN MAsh NRHS SCob SCoo SLim SPer SPoG SPre SWvt
	EAST RIVER ('Zoeastri'PBR) (I)	ELan
	'Eclipse' (H)	CRos LRHS
	EDDA ('Evipo074'PBR) (Boulevard Series) (EL)	CFlo CRos EPfP LRHS MAsh NRHS SNig
	'Edith' (EL) ♀H6	CWCL LSRN NHaw NLar SNig
	'Édouard Desfossé' (EL)	LRHS
	'Edward Prichard'	CFlo CKel EPfP SNig
	'Eetika' (LL)	CRHN NHaw
	'Effie Dewey' (LL)	NHaw
	'Ekstra' (LL)	NHaw
	'Eleanor' (Fo/f)	GEdr
	'Elf' (Vt)	CWGN
	'Elgar'	see *C.* 'Sir Edward Elgar'
	'Elizabeth' (M) ♀H5	Widely available
§	'Elsa Späth' (EL)	CArg CExl CKel CMac CRos CTri ELan EMOT EPfP LRHS LSRN MAsh NEgg NRHS SNig SPer SPoG SWvt
	'Elten' (M)	CKel
	'Elvan' (Vt)	CRHN NHaw NLar SNig
	'Ember' (I)	CWGN
	'Emerald Dream'PBR (Fo)	ELan LRHS
	'Emilia Plater' (Vt)	CRHN EPfP NHaw SLon
	'Emma' (EL)	CFlo
	'Empress Amy Lai'	CWCL NHaw
	EMPRESS ('Evipo011'PBR) (EL)	CFlo CRos ELan EPfP LRHS SLon SNig
	ENDELLION ('Evipo076') (EL)	CRos LRHS NRHS SNig
	'Entel' (Vt)	CRHN EBee NHaw SNig
	× ***eriostemon***	see *C.* × *diversifolia*
	'Ernest Markham' (LL) ♀H6	CKel CMac CRos CWCL ELan EPfP LRHS LSRN MAsh MGos MJak MSwo NEgg NPri NRHS SLim SNig SPer SPoG SWvt
	ESME ('Evipo048'PBR)	CWGN SNig
	'Esperanto' (LL)	NHaw
	ESTHER ('Zo09143') (EL)	IPot
	'Étoile Rose' (Vt)	CMac CRHN CRos CTri CWCL EBee ELan EPfP IPot LRHS LSRN MAsh NEgg NHaw NHol SCoo SLim SLon SNig SPer WBor
	'Étoile Violette' (Vt) ♀H6	Widely available
	EVENING STAR ('Evista') (EL)	EPfP
	'Everett' (V)	WSHC
	'Fair Rosamond' (EL)	NLar
	FAIRY BLUE	see *C.* CRYSTAL FOUNTAIN
	'Fairydust' (Vt)	NHaw
	fargesii var. ***souliei***	see *C. potaninii* var. *potaninii*
	× ***fargesioides***	see *C.* 'Paul Farges'
	fasciculiflora KWJ 12160	WCru
	– L 657	EPfP WCru WPGP
	'Fascination'PBR (I)	CFlo CWCL CWGN WCot
	'Fay' (Vt)	NHaw
	FILIGREE ('Evipo029'PBR) (EL)	CFlo CRos LBuc LRHS MAsh MGos NRHS SNig
	'Filomae' (Vt)	NHaw
	finetiana misapplied	see *C. paniculata* J.G. Gmel.
	'Fireworks' (EL)	CArg CFlo CKel CRos CWCL CWGN EPfP LRHS LSRN MAsh MRav NEgg NLar SLim SNig SPer SPoG
	flammula	CArg CFlo CKel CRos ELan EPfP LCro LOPS LRHS LSRN MAsh MBlu MRav NLar NRHS SPoG SRms SWvt WSpi XSen
	– 'Rubra Marginata'	see *C.* × *triternata* 'Rubromarginata'
	FLEURI ('Evipo042'PBR) (Boulevard Series) (EL)	CFlo CKel CRos CWCL EPfP LRHS LSRN NRHS SCoo SLon SNig SPoG
	florida	CWGN SWvt
	– 'Bicolor'	see *C. florida* var. *florida* 'Sieboldiana'
	– var. ***flore-pleno*** 'Plena' (d)	CCCN CFlo CRos CWCL ELan EPfP IPot LRHS LSRN MAsh NEgg NRHS SNig SPoG
§	– var. ***florida*** 'Sieboldiana' (d)	CBcs CFlo CKel CRos CWCL CWGN ELan EPfP LCro LOPS LRHS LSRN MAsh NEgg NRHS SNig SPoG SWvt WFar
	– var. ***normalis*** PISTACHIO ('Evirida'PBR) (LL)	CCCN CFlo CKel CRos CWGN ELan EPfP LRHS MAsh MGos NLar SLon SNig SPoG
	'Floris V' (I)	GKev MCot NHaw NLar
	'Fluffy Duck' (Vt/d)	NHaw
	'Fond Memories' (EL)	CFlo CKel CRos CWCL CWGN EPfP IPot LCro LOPS LRHS LSRN NHaw NLar NRHS SLon
	FOREVER FRIENDS ('Zofofri'PBR) (LL)	CRos CWGN EPfP IPot LRHS NRHS SLon
	'Forget-me-not NLP1'	LSRN NLar
	forrestii	see *C. napaulensis*
§	***forsteri***	IDee WSHC
	'Foxtrot' (Vt)	CRHN
	'Foxy' (A) ♀H6	CFlo LRHS NLar SLon
	FRAGRANT OBERON ('Hutbron'PBR) (Fo)	CFlo LCro LOPS SWvt
	'Fragrant Spring' (M)	CKel CRos CSBt CWGN EPfP LRHS NLar NRHS SLim SNig SPet
	'Frances Rivis' (A) ♀H6	CArg CFlo CKel CMac CRos CWCL ELan EPfP GBin LCro LOPS LRHS LSRN MAsh MBlu MRav MSwo NLar NWea SPer SPoG SRms
	'Francesca' (A)	LSRN
	'Frankie' (A) ♀H6	CFlo CKel CRos ELan EPfP LCro LOPS LRHS LSRN MAsh MGos SCoo
	FRANZISKA MARIA ('Evipo008') (EL)	CFlo CRos EPfP LRHS MAsh MGos SCoo SLon
	'Freda' (M) ♀H6	CKel CRHN CRos CTri CWGN ELan EPfP LCro LOPS LRHS LSRN MAsh

		MBlu MRav NHol SLim SNig SPer SRms
	FREEDOM ('Zo06128') (EL)	CFlo IPot
	fremontii	NHaw
	'Fryderyk Chopin' (EL)	NLar SNig SPet
	'Fudō' (V)	NHaw
	'Fujimusume' (EL) ♀[H6]	CFlo CKel CRos CWGN EPfP IPot LRHS MAsh NHaw NRHS SPoG
	'Fukuzono'	CRos LRHS LSRN NHaw NRHS
	fusca misapplied	see *C. japonica*
	fusca Turcz. dwarf	CWGN
§	- var. ***fusca***	WSHC
	- var. ***kamtschatica***	see *C. fusca* Turcz. var. *fusca*
	- large-flowered B&SWJ 8431	WCru
	'Fusca Peveril' (V)	NHaw
	'Gabrielle' ambig.	LSRN
	GALORE	see *C.* VESUVIUS
	'Garnet' (V)	NHaw
	GAZELLE ('Evipo014'[PBR]) (I)	CRos LRHS MAsh SRms
	'General Sikorski' (EL)	CBcs CFlo CKel CMac CRos CWCL ELan EPfP LRHS LSRN MAsh MGos NRHS SCoo SLim SNig SPer SWvt
	gentianoides	SBrt
	'Geoffrey Tolver' (LL)	CWGN NHaw SNig
	'Georg Ots' (LL)	NHaw
	GIANT STAR ('Gistar'[PBR]) (M)	CKel CRos LRHS NLar NPer NRHS SLim SPoG SRkn
	'Gillian Blades' (EL) ♀[H6]	CFlo CKel CRos EBee ELan EPfP LBuc LRHS LSRN MAsh MGos NHaw NRHS SCoo SNig SPoG SWvt
	'Ginny' (V)	NHaw
§	'Gipsy Queen' (LL) ♀[H6]	CArg CBcs CMac CRos CWCL ELan ELon EPfP LRHS LSRN MAsh MGos NEgg SLim SNig SPer SPoG SWvt
	GISELLE ('Evipo051'[PBR])	CFlo CRos EPfP LRHS MAsh NRHS SLon SPoG
	'Gladys Picard' (EL)	NHaw
	glauca Turcz.	see *C. intricata*
	glauca ambig.	SBrt
	glaucophylla	NHaw SBrt WSHC
	'Golden Harvest' (Ta)	LSRN NLar
	GOLDEN TIARA ('Kugotia'[PBR]) (Ta) ♀[H6]	CKel CWGN LSRN NLar SRms WCot
	'Grace' (Ta)	EPfP NHaw NLar
	gracilifolia BWJ 8002	WCru
	grandiflora	LBuc SRms
I	'Grandiflora' (F)	WFar
	'Grandiflora Sanguinea' (Vt)	NHaw
	grata misapplied	see *C.* × *jouiniana*
	'Gravetye Beauty' (T)	CFlo CKel CRHN CRos CWCL EBee ELan EPfP LRHS LSRN MAsh MGos NHol SLon SNig SPoG SRms SWvt
	GREEN PASSION ('Zo11050') (EL/d) **new**	CFlo LCro LOPS
	'Guernsey Cream' (EL)	CFlo CRos CWCL EPfP LCro LOPS LRHS LSRN MAsh MGos NLar SCoo SNig SRkn
	GUIDING PROMISE ('Evipo053'[PBR])	SLon SNig
	'H.F. Young' (EL)	CFlo CKel CRos ELan EPfP LRHS LSRN MAsh MGos NLar SCoo SNig SPer SPet SWvt
	'Hågelby Pink' (Vt) ♀[H6]	CRHN CWGN NHaw
	'Hagley Hybrid' (LL)	CArg CMac CRos CWCL EBee ELan EPfP LRHS LSRN MAsh MGos MJak MRav NEgg NLar NRHS SCob SLim SNig SPer SPet SPoG SRms SWvt
	'Hakuōkan' (EL)	CRos EPfP LRHS LSRN NLar SCoo
	'Hakuree' ambig.	CKel
	'Hanaguruma' (EL)	CKel LSRN SNig SPet
	'Happy Anniversary' (EL)	LBuc LCro LOPS LSRN NLar
§	HAPPY BIRTHDAY ('Zohapbi'[PBR]) (LL) ♀[H6]	LCro LOPS LSRN
	HARLOW CARR ('Evipo004'[PBR])	CMac CRos EPfP LRHS NRHS SCoo SRms
	'Hayate'	CWGN
	'Helios'	see *C.* AZTEK
	'Helsingborg' (A) ♀[H6]	CFlo CKel CRos ELan EPfP LRHS MAsh NPri SCoo SNig SPoG SRms
I	'Hendersonii' (I)	CFlo CKel LSRN
	hendersonii Koch	see *C.* × *diversifolia* 'Hendersonii'
	hendersonii Stand.	see *C.* × *diversifolia*
I	'Hendersonii Rubra' (Ar)	LRHS
	'Hendryetta'[PBR] (I)	CRos EMOT LRHS NEgg SWvt
	henryi	EShb LSRN MAsh SNig SPet
	- B&SWJ 3402	WCru
	- var. ***morii*** B&SWJ 1668	WCru
	'Henryi' (EL)	CFlo CKel CMac CRos CTri CWCL EBee ELan EPfP LCro LOPS LRHS LSRN MRav MSwo NRHS SPer SPoG
	heracleifolia	CBod CMac CPou CRos ECtt GLog LRHS NLar WBor WHlf WOld
	- ALAN BLOOM	see *C. tubulosa* ALAN BLOOM
	- 'Blue Dwarf' (H)	CWGN WAbe
	- 'Cassandra' (H)	CFlo CRos CSpe CWGN ECtt ELon EPfP GLog LRHS LSRN MCot NCGa NRHS
	- 'China Purple' (H)	CBod CExl CPou ECtt EUJe GBin ILea LRHS MCot MHol NLar SNig
	- 'Pink Dwarf' (H)	CWGN NLar WAbe
	'Herbert Johnson' (EL)	NHaw
	hexapetala Forster	see *C. forsteri*
	hexasepala	see *C. forsteri*
	hirsutissima	GKev SPhx
	- var. ***scottii***	GKev
	'Honora' (LL)	CFlo CRos CWGN LRHS MAsh NRHS SCoo SNig
	'Horn of Plenty' (EL)	CRos LRHS NHaw
	'Hoshi-no-flamenco' (T)	CWGN IPot
	huchouensis	NHaw
	HUDSON RIVER ('Zo06137'[PBR]) (I)	IPot
	'Huldine' (LL) ♀[H6]	CBcs CKel CRHN CRos CWCL ELan EPfP LRHS LSRN MAsh MRav SLon SPer SWvt
	'Huvi' (LL)	CWGN NHaw
	'Hybrida Sieboldii' (EL)	SCoo
	HYDE HALL ('Evipo009'[PBR]) (EL)	CFlo CKel CMac CRos CWGN ELan EPfP LRHS MAsh MGos NRHS SCoo SLon SRms
	'Hythe Egret' (Fo)	LLHF WIce
	I AM A LITTLE BEAUTY ('Zolibe') (Vt)	CRHN EBee NHaw
	I AM HAPPY ('Zoiamha') (Vt)	CWGN SCob
	I AM LADY J ('Zoiamlj') (Vt)	NHaw SCob
	I AM LADY Q ('Zoiamladyq'[PBR]) (Vt)	CWGN EBee LRHS NHaw SCob
	I AM RED ROBIN ('Zorero'[PBR]) (A)	CWGN
	ianthina 'Josie's Midnight Blue' (V)	NHaw
	- var. ***kuripoensis***	NHaw
	- - B&SWJ 700	WCru
	'Ibi' (EL)	CWGN
	ICE BLUE ('Evipo003'[PBR]) (Prairie Series) (EL)	CRos ELan EPfP LRHS MAsh SCoo SLon
	'Ice Queen' (EL)	MAsh
	'Ilka' (EL)	NHaw
	indivisa Willd.	see *C. paniculata* J.G. Gmel.

INES ('Evipo059'PBR) (Boulevard Series) CRos LRHS NRHS SNig
'Ingrid Biedenkopf' (Vt) NHaw
INSPIRATION ('Zoin'PBR) (I) ELan NLar SCoo
integrifolia CExl CFis ELan EMor EPfP GKev IPot LRHS MCot NChi NLar NPer SRms WArt WHil WHoo
I - 'Alba' (I) CFlo CRos ECtt GKev LRHS LSRN NHaw NLar SCoo SRms
- 'Baby Blue' (I) **new** NHaw
- 'Blue Ribbons' (I) CSpe MMrt NCGa NLar SPhx WHoo
- dark blue-flowered GKev
- 'Hendersonii' Koch see *C.* × *diversifolia* 'Hendersonii'
- MONGOLIAN BELLS ('Psharlan') (I) **new** CSpe NCGa
- 'Olgae' see *C.* × *diversifolia* 'Olgae'
- 'Ozawa's Blue' (I) CWGN MBNS
- violet-flowered GKev
- white-flowered see *C. integrifolia* 'Alba'
§ ***intricata*** CExl
ispahanica NHaw
'Iubileinyi-70' (LL) NHaw
'Ivan Olsson' (EL) CWCL
'Jackmanii' (LL) ♀H6 CArg CBcs CKel CMac CRos CTri EBee EPfP LCro LOPS LRHS LSRN MAsh MGos MJak NAln NWea SCoo SLim SNig SPoG SWvt
'Jackmanii Alba' (EL) CRos CWCL ELan ELon EPfP LRHS LSRN MAsh SCoo SLim SNig SPoG
'Jackmanii Superba' misapplied see *C.* 'Gipsy Queen'
'Jackmanii Superba' ambig. (LL) CDul CFlo CKel CMac CRos CWCL ELan EPfP LCro LOPS LRHS MAsh MGos MRav MSwo NPer NPri NWea SCob SLim SNig SPer SPoG
'Jacqueline du Pré' (A) ♀H6 CBcs CFlo CKel EBee ELan EPfP LRHS SNig
'Jacqui' (M/d) CKel
'James Mason' (EL) LSRN SNig
'Jan Fopma'PBR (I) CWGN
'Jan Lindmark' (A/d) CRos EPfP LRHS MAsh NAln NLar NRHS SCoo SNig SPoG SPre
§ 'Jan Paweł II' (EL) CRos ELan LRHS SCoo SPet
'Jane Ashdown' (M) NHaw
§ ***japonica*** NHaw
'Jean Caldwell' (Vt) NHaw
'Jean Cumpston' (C) NHaw
'Jeanne's Pink' (EL) CWCL EBee LCro LOPS
I 'Jenny' (Cedergren) (LL) NHaw
'Jenny' (M/d) CFlo CKel CRos CWCL LRHS LSRN SPoG
'Jenny Caddick' (Vt) NHaw
JESSICA ('Evipo012'PBR) (I) CRos LRHS
JEWEL OF MERK see *C.* HAPPY BIRTHDAY
JOHN HOWELLS ('Zojohnhowells'PBR) (Vt) CFlo CWCL CWGN LSRN SLon
'John Huxtable' (LL) CFlo CKel CRos LRHS SNig
JOHN PAUL II see *C.* 'Jan Paweł II'
'John Treasure' (Vt) CRHN NHaw NLar
'John Warren' (EL) CRos LRHS MAsh NHaw NRHS SCoo
'Jolly Jake' (Vt) CFlo
JOSEPHINE ('Evijohill'PBR) (EL) CFlo CKel CRos CWCL CWGN EPfP LCro LOPS LRHS LSRN MAsh MGos NLar NRHS SCoo SLim SNig SPer SPoG SRkn SWvt
§ × ***jouiniana*** MRav NHaw SEND SHar SWvt WSHC
'Julka' (EL) CFlo CWCL NHaw
'Justa' (Vt) NHaw
'Juuli' (I) LSRN
'Kaaru' (LL) CRHN
'Kacper' (EL) NHaw
'Kaiu' (V) CFlo CKel CRos CWCL CWGN LRHS NHaw
§ 'Kakio' (EL) CRos CWCL EPfP LRHS LSRN MAsh MGos SNig SPer SPet
I 'Kamilla' (EL) CWGN
§ 'Kasmu' (Vt) NHaw
'Kathleen Dunford' (EL) LSRN SCoo
'Kathryn Chapman' (Vt) CRHN NHaw
'Kaunitar' (LL) NHaw
'Ken Donson' (EL) ♀H6 LRHS SCoo
'Ken Pyne' (LL) CFlo
'Kermesina' (Vt) ♀H6 CKel CRHN CRos EBee ELan EPfP LCro LOPS LRHS MAsh MJak NAln SCoo SLim SNig SPer SPoG SRms WBor
'Ketu Õde' (LL) NHaw
'Kiev' (Vt) NHaw
'Killifreth' (Vt) CRHN NHaw
KIMIKO ('Evipo066'PBR) (Boulevard Series) **new** CRos LRHS NRHS SPoG
'King Edward VII' (EL) LRHS NHaw
KINGFISHER ('Evipo037'PBR) (EL) CFlo CKel CRos ELan EPfP LRHS SCoo SLon SPoG
'Kinju Atarashi' (LL) CWCL
'Kiri Te Kanawa' (EL) CKel CWCL ELon EPfP LRHS LSRN NLar
kirilowii NHaw
'Kirsi' (LL) NHaw
KITTY ('Evipo097') **new** CFlo CRos LRHS NRHS SPoG
'Kommerei' (LL) NHaw
§ 'Königskind' (EL) NLar
'Korean Beauty' (Ta) WHil
koreana CPla LRHS MAsh WCru
- AMBER ('Wit141205') (A) **new** CRos LCro LOPS NRHS WHlf
- var. ***carunculosa*** WSHC
- - B&SWJ 12725 WCru
- - 'Lemon Bells' (A) CRos EBee ELan EPfP LRHS MAsh SCoo SLon SPoG
- - 'Love Child' (A) ELan
'Krakowiak'PBR (Vt) NHaw
'Külli' (LL) NHaw
ladakhiana NHaw
'Lady Betty Balfour' (LL) CMac CRos LRHS SCoo SNig SWvt
'Lady Bird Johnson' (T) CFlo CRos CWCL LRHS LSRN SCoo
'Lady Caroline Nevill' (EL) CRos LRHS NRHS
'Lady Londesborough' (EL) NHaw SCoo
'Lady Northcliffe' (EL) CKel CRos CTri CWCL EPfP LRHS MAsh SNig
'Lambton Park' (Ta) ♀H6 CKel CRHN CWCL NHaw NLar
lasiandra NHaw
'Last Dance' (Ta) CRHN EBee
'Lasurstern' (EL) ♀H6 CArg CBcs CExl CFlo CKel CMac CRos CTri EBee ELan EPfP LCro LOPS LRHS LSRN MAsh NEgg SNig SPer SPet SPoG SWvt WFar
'Lavender Twirl' (Vt) CRHN
'Lawsoniana' (EL) LRHS SNig
'Lemon Chiffon' (EL) CRos LRHS
LIANNE ('Evipo064') (EL) SNig
LIBERATION ('Evifive'PBR) (EL) CRos LRHS NLar SCoo SLon SNig
LIBERTY ('Zo08095') (EL) IPot
ligusticifolia NHaw
'Lily the Pink' (Vt) NHaw
'Lincoln Star' (EL) CArg CMac CRos ELon LRHS MAsh NEgg SLim SNig SPer SWvt
'Lisboa' (Vt) NHaw

	'Little Bas' (Vt)	CRHN CWGN IPot NHaw NLar SLon
	'Little Butterfly' (Vt)	CRHN NHaw
	'Little Mermaid' (EL)	CFlo CWCL
	'Little Nell' (Vt)	CCCN CRHN EBee ELan EPfP LRHS LSRN MAsh SCoo SLon SNig WFar
I	'Longiflora'	CFlo
	'Lord Herschell'	CFlo CKel CWCL CWGN NHaw
	'Lord Nevill' (EL)	CRos EPfP LRHS
	'Louise Rowe' (EL)	CFlo CRos CWCL ELan LRHS LSRN NHaw SNig
	'Love Jewelry' (EL)	SNig
	LUCKY CHARM ('Zo09067') (LL)	CFlo CWGN IPot LCro LOPS
	LULA ('Evipo057'^{PBR}) (Boulevard Series)	CWGN
	'Lunar Lass' (Fo/f)	CFlo EBee LRHS NRHS
	'Lunar Lass Variegata' (Fo/v)	LLHF
	'Luther Burbank' (LL)	SNig
	'Luxuriant Blue' (Vt)	CRHN NHaw
	'M. Koster' (Vt)	CRHN LRHS NHaw SLon SRms
	macropetala (d)	CBcs CRos ELan EPfP GKev LRHS MAsh MGos MMuc MRav NRHS SNig SPer
	- 'Blue Lagoon'	see *C. macropetala* 'Lagoon' Jackman 1959
	- 'Lagoon' Jackman 1956	see *C. macropetala* 'Maidwell Hall' Jackman
	- 'Lagoon' ambig.	LSRN
§	- 'Lagoon' Jackman 1959 (A/d) 🏆^{H6}	CRos LCro LOPS LRHS LSRN MAsh MSwo NAln NHol NRHS SCoo
	- 'Maidwell Hall' ambig. (A)	NAln SCob
§	- 'Maidwell Hall' Jackman (A/d)	CTri EPfP LSRN MAsh WSHC
	- 'Wesselton' (A/d) 🏆^{H6}	CFlo CKel CRos CTri CWCL EPfP LCro LOPS LRHS MAsh NAln NLar NRHS SPoG SPre SRms
	- 'White Moth'	see *C.* 'White Moth'
	'Madame Baron-Veillard' (LL)	CRos LRHS SCoo SNig
	'Madame Edouard André' (LL)	CRos CWCL EPfP LRHS MAsh NRHS SCoo SNig SPet
	'Madame Grangé' (LL)	CRos LRHS NHaw SCoo
	'Madame Julia Correvon' (Vt) 🏆^{H6}	CFlo CKel CRHN CRos CTri CWCL EBee ELan ELon EPfP LCro LOPS LRHS LSRN MAsh MGos MJak NEgg NLar NPri NRHS SLim SLon SNig SPer SPoG SRkn SSta SWvt WBor
	'Madame le Coultre'	see *C.* 'Mevrouw Le Coultre'
	'Majojo' (Fo)	GEdr LLHF
	mandschurica	EBee GBin GCal GKev NHaw NLar XEll
	MANON ('Evipo054'^{PBR}) (Boulevard Series) **new**	CFlo CRos LRHS NRHS
	marata	WThu
	'Margaret Hunt' (LL)	LSRN NHaw SNig
	'Mari' (LL)	NHaw
	'Maria' Kivistik (LL)	NHaw
	'Maria Cornelia'^{PBR} (Vt)	CWGN LCro LOPS SLon
	'Marie Boisselot' (EL) 🏆^{H6}	CArg CBcs CFlo CKel CMac CRos CTri CWCL ELan EPfP LRHS LSRN MAsh MGos MSwo NAln NLar NPri SNig SPer SPet SPoG SWvt
	'Marinka'	CWGN
	'Marjorie' (M/d)	CArg CBcs CKel CRos CTri CWCL ELan EPfP GKin LRHS LSRN MAsh MGos MRav NEgg NRHS SLim SNig SPer SPoG SRms WFar
	'Markham's Pink' (A/d) 🏆^{H6}	CArg CFlo CKel CRos CTri CWCL ELan EPfP LCro LOPS LRHS LSRN MAsh MGos MRav MSwo NAln NEgg NHol NLar NRHS SCob SLim SNig SPer SPoG SRms SWvt WFar WSHC
	marmoraria	CRos EPot LRHS NRHS SPlb SRms
	- 'Timpany Treasure'	ITim
	'Marmori' (LL)	CWGN NHaw
	MARTA ('Evipo071'^{PBR}) (Garland Series)	SNig
	'Mary Habberley' (Vt)	NHaw
	'Mary Rose'	see *C. viticella* 'Flore Pleno'
	'Mary-Claire' (EL/d)	SNig
	maximowicziana	see *C. terniflora*
	'Mayleen' (M) 🏆^{H4}	CRos CSam CTri EPfP LRHS MAsh MRav NAln NEgg NRHS SCoo SLim SNig SPer SPoG SRms SWvt WFar
	'Meeli' (LL)	NHaw
I	'Melodie' (Vt)	NHaw
§	'Mevrouw Le Coultre' (EL)	MJak
	MIENIE BELLE ('Zomibel'^{PBR}) (T)	CWGN IPot NHaw
	'Mikelite' (Vt)	NHaw
	'Miniseelik' (LL)	NHaw
	'Minuet' (Vt) 🏆^{H6}	CRHN CRos EBee EPfP LCro LOPS LRHS MAsh MGos SCob SCoo SLon SNig SPer SPoG SWvt
	MIRABELLE ('Evipo072'^{PBR}) (Boulevard Series)	CRos LRHS NRHS
	MIRANDA ('Floclemi'^{PBR}) (I)	CWGN
	'Miss Bateman' (EL)	CFlo CKel CMac CRos CTri CWCL EBee ELan EPfP LCro LOPS LRHS LSRN MAsh MGos MJak NEgg NRHS SLim SNig SPer SPet SPoG WBor
	'Miss Christine' (M)	CFlo CSam ELan LCro LOPS LSRN SPoG SWvt
	MISSISSIPPI RIVER ('Zomisri') (I)	IPot
	'Mister Hans Horn' (Vt)	NHaw
	MON AMOUR ('Zomoa'^{PBR}) (EL)	CWGN
	MON CHERRY ('Zomonch') (EL)	CWGN IPot
	'Moniuszko' (EL)	CWGN
	montana	CExl CPla CSBt MAsh SCob SEWo
	- WJC 13713 from the Himalaya	WCru
	- var. ***alba***	see *C. montana* var. *montana*
	- 'Alexander' (M)	CRos EPfP LRHS NRHS SPoG
	- 'Da Yun' (M)	CWGN EBee
	- var. ***grandiflora*** (M) 🏆^{H5}	CArg CChe CDul CKel CMac CRos CWCL ELan EPfP GKin LBuc LCro LOPS LRHS MJak MMuc NPri NRHS SCob SEND SLim SNig SPer SPoG SRms SWvt
§	- var. ***montana***	CBar CBcs CBod LCro LOPS LRHS MAsh SCob SPer SPoG WFar
	- var. ***rubens*** misapplied	see *C. montana* var. *montana*
	- var. ***rubens*** E.H. Wilson	CRos CSBt CTri ELan EPfP LRHS NHol NRHS SNig SPlb
I	- - 'Odorata' (M)	EPfP GKin LRHS MRav SCoo
	- - 'Pink Perfection' (M)	CKel CMac CRHN CRos ELan EPfP GKin LCro LOPS LRHS LSRN MAsh NAln NRHS SCob SCoo SLim SNig SPer SPoG SWvt WFar
	- - 'Tetrarose' (M) 🏆^{H5}	Widely available
I	- 'Rubens Superba' (M)	CTri ECtt GKin NEgg NWea SRms WFar
	- var. ***sericea***	see *C. spooneri*

- var. ***wilsonii*** CFlo CKel CRos CWCL ECtt ELan EPfP GKin GLog LRHS LSRN MRav MSwo SNig SPer SPet SPoG SRms SWvt
'Monte Cassino' (EL) CWGN SNig SPet
'Moonbeam' (Fo) EPot GEdr ITim WIce
§ 'Moonlight' (EL) LRHS MAsh
'Moonman' (Fo) LLHF
MORNING CLOUD see *C.* 'Yukikomachi'
'Morning Heaven' (Vt) NHaw
MORNING STAR ('Zoklako'[PBR]) (EL) CWGN LRHS
MORNING YELLOW ('Cadmy'[PBR]) (M) CCCN CFlo EUJe LRHS
'Mrs Cholmondeley' (EL) ♀[H6] CKel CRos CWCL ELan EPfP LRHS LSRN MAsh MGos MSwo NPri SCob SLim SNig SPer SPet SPoG
'Mrs George Jackman' (EL) ♀[H6] CFlo CRos CWCL EBee LRHS NLar SCoo
'Mrs James Mason' (EL) EBee
'Mrs N.Thompson' (EL) CArg CKel CMac CRos CTri CWCL EBee ELan ELon LRHS LSRN MAsh MGos NEgg NHol NPer SLim SNig SPer
'Mrs P.B.Truax' (EL) CRos EPfP LRHS
'Mrs Robert Brydon' (H) CWCL ECtt NLar SRms
'Mrs T. Lundell' (Vt) CRHN NHaw
'Multi Blue' (EL) CArg CBcs CFlo CKel CRos CWCL ELan ELon EPfP EUJe LRHS LSRN MAsh MGos SLim SNig SPer SPoG SRkn SRms
'My Angel'[PBR] (Ta) ELan IPot NHaw NLar SCob
'Myōjō' (EL) LRHS
'Nadezhda' (LL) NHaw
§ ***napaulensis*** CFlo CWCL ELan EMor EPfP LCro LOPS MNrw NHaw WCru WSHC
I 'Natacha' (EL) EBee NHaw SCoo
'Natascha' (EL) CWCL LRHS LSRN SNig SPet SWvt
'Negritianka' (LL) CRos LRHS LSRN NHaw
'Negus' (LL) NHaw
'Nelly Moser' (EL) ♀[H6] Widely available
NEVA ('Evipo050'[PBR]) (Boulevard Series) (EL) CRos LRHS NRHS SNig
'New Love'[PBR] (H) CWGN LSRN NLar SPad SPoG
'Night Veil' (Vt) NHaw SLon
NINON ('Evipo052'[PBR]) (Boulevard Series) CWGN SNig
'Niobe' (EL) ♀[H6] CArg CBcs CKel CMac CRos CWCL EBee ELan EPfP EShb EUJe LCro LOPS LRHS LSRN MAsh MGos MSwo NEgg NHol NLar NRHS SCob SLim SNig SPer SPoG SRms WFar
'North Star' (EL) CKel EPfP
NORTH STAR (LL) see *C.* 'Põhjanael'
NUBIA ('Evipo079') (Boulevard Series) CWGN EUJe
nutans var. ***thyrsoidea*** see *C. rehderiana*, *C. veitchiana*
'Oberek' (Vt) CRHN NHaw
'Ocean Pearl' (A) CFlo LSRN NLar
ochotensis LLHF
ochroleuca NHaw
OCTOPUS ('Zooct'[PBR]) (A) CFlo CWGN
'Odoriba' (V) CRHN CWGN NHaw
'Olimpiada-80' (EL) NHaw
'Omoshiro' (EL) CWCL CWGN IPot LRHS NHaw
§ OOH LA LA ('Evipo041'[PBR]) (Boulevard Series) (EL) CFlo CKel CRos CWCL EPfP LRHS MAsh NRHS SCoo SNig SPer SPoG
orientalis misapplied see *C. tibetana* subsp. *vernayi*
orientalis ambig. SRms
orientalis L. EBee EPfP SCoo SWvt
- PAB 13.731 LEdu
- from Kyrgyzstan WPGP
- 'Orange Peel' see *C. tibetana* subsp. *vernayi* var. *vernayi* 'Orange Peel'
- 'Sherriffii' see *C.* 'Sherriffii'
- var. ***tenuiloba*** see *C. columbiana* var. *tenuiloba*
orientalis* × *tangutica SWvt
'Oshikiri' (V) NHaw
otophora NHaw
'Ovation'[PBR] (Fo) IBal
'Paala' (EL) NHaw
'Pagoda' (Vt) CRHN EPfP LRHS SCoo SLon SRms
PALETTE ('Evipo034'[PBR]) (Vt) IPot SLon
PALETTE ('Zo08111') (EL) **new** CFlo
'Pamela' (F) NHaw
'Pamela Jackman' (A) see *C. alpina* 'Pamela Jackman'
'Pamela Jackman' (Vt) NEgg
'Pamiat Serdtsa' (I) ELon NHaw
'Pangbourne Pink' (I) ♀[H6] CFlo CKel CRos CWCL EPfP LRHS NHaw NRHS SCoo
paniculata Thunb. see *C. terniflora*
§ ***paniculata*** J.G.Gmel. MNrw
'Paradise Queen' (EL) LBuc NLar
PARADISO ('Zo11154') (EL) **new** LCro LOPS
PARISIENNE ('Evipo019'[PBR]) (Boulevard Series) (EL) CFlo CRos CWCL CWGN ELon EPfP EUJe LRHS MAsh NRHS SCoo SLon SNig SPoG
parviflora DC. see *C. campaniflora*
parviloba var. ***bartlettii*** B&SWJ 6788 WCru
'Pat Coleman' (EL) CWCL
patens 'Korean Moon' (EL) WCru
§ - 'Manshuu Ki' (EL) CFlo CRos CWCL LRHS SNig
- 'Yukiokoshi' (EL) EBee
§ 'Paul Farges' (Vb) ♀[H6] CArg CKel CWGN EShb GLog MNrw NHaw NLar
'Pauline' (A/d) ♀[H6] CBcs CRos LRHS LSRN NRHS SCoo
'Peggy West' (LL) NHaw
'Pendragon' (Vt) CRHN NHaw
'Pennell's Purity' (LL) CFlo
PEPPERMINT ('Evipo005'[PBR]) (d) CFlo ELan EPfP LRHS SCoo SLon SNig
'Perida' (LL) CWGN
'Perle d'Azur' (LL) ♀[H6] CBcs CKel CMac CRHN CRos CTri CWCL EBee ELan EPfP LCro LOPS LRHS LSRN MAsh MGos MSwo NEgg SCob SLim SPer SPoG SRms WFar WSpi
'Perrin's Pride' (Vt) CRos EBee LRHS MGos NHaw NLar SCoo
PETIT FAUCON ('Evisix'[PBR]) (I) ♀[H6] CFlo CRos CWCL EPfP LRHS LSRN MGos MMrt NAln NLar SCob SCoo SNig SPer SRms SWvt
petriei WThu
'Peveril Pristine' (Vt) CWGN NHaw
PICARDY ('Evipo024'[PBR]) (EL) CFlo CRos EPfP LRHS MAsh NRHS SCoo SNig SPoG
PICOTEE ('Zo09124') (EL) CFlo IPot
I 'Picton's Variety' (M) CTri
'Piilu' (EL) CArg CKel CRos CWCL CWGN EBee ELan LRHS LSRN MAsh MBNS NHaw NLar SCob SCoo SNig SPet SRkn
'Pille' (LL) NHaw
PINK CHAMPAGNE see *C.* 'Kakio'
'Pink Fantasy' (LL) CFlo CRHN CRos CTri LRHS MAsh NLar SCob SCoo SRkn

Name	Suppliers
'Pink Flamingo' (A) ♀H6	CRos CWCL ELan EPfP LRHS MGos NRHS SCoo SNig SPoG
'Pink Ice' (I)	CKel CWCL NHaw
'Pirko' (Vt)	NHaw
§ ***pitcheri***	CWGN NHaw WSHC
'Pixie' (Fo/m)	CFlo CKel EBee ELan ELon EPfP ITim LRHS MGos NLar SCoo SPoG
pogonandra	NHaw
§ 'Põhjanael' (LL)	NLar
POLAR BEAR	see *C.* ARCTIC QUEEN
'Poldice' (Vt) ♀H6	CRHN
'Polish Spirit' (LL) ♀H6	CArg CBar CBcs CFlo CKel CMac CRHN CRos CTri CWCL ELan EPfP LCro LOPS LRHS LSRN MGos NHol NRHS SCob SLon SNig SPer SPoG SRkn SWvt WBor WFar
'Polonez' (Vt)	NHaw
§ ***potaninii*** var. ***potaninii***	WSHC
- var. ***souliei***	see *C. potaninii* var. *potaninii*
- 'Summer Snow'	see *C.* 'Paul Farges'
'Praecox' (H) ♀H6	CBod CRHN CRos CWCL EBee ELan EPfP LRHS MCot NQui NSti WCot
PRETTY IN BLUE ('Zopre'PBR) (F)	EBee SCob SWvt
'Primrose Star'	see *C.* 'Star'
'Prince Charles' (LL) ♀H6	CFlo CKel CRHN CTri CWCL ELan EPfP EShb LRHS LSRN MAsh MJak NHaw NLar SCoo SLim SNig SPer SWvt
'Prince George' (LL)	CWCL EPfP LCro LOPS LSRN NLar
'Princess Charlotte' (EL)	LCro LOPS
§ 'Princess Diana' (T) ♀H5	CBcs CFlo CKel CRHN CTri CWGN EBee ELan IPot LBuc LCro LOPS LRHS LSRN MAsh MBlu MSwo NAln NHol SCob SCoo SLim SNig SPer SPoG SRms SWvt
PRINCESS KATE ('Zoprika'PBR) (T)	CFlo CRos CWGN EBee EPfP IPot LCro LOPS LRHS MAsh MBlu NRHS SPoG WBor WCot
§ 'Princess of Wales' (1875) (EL)	CWCL LSRN NLar SLon SWvt
'Propertius' (A)	CArg CFlo CKel CRos CWCL CWGN EPfP GEdr LRHS MGos NAln SPoG
'Prosperity' (M)	CRHN
'Proteus' (EL)	CRos ELan EPfP LRHS MAsh MGos SCoo SNig
psilandra CWJ 12377	WCru
'Purple Haze' (Vt)	CRHN NHaw
'Purple Princess' (H)	SPoG
'Purple Spider' (A/d)	CFlo CWCL EPfP LRHS MAsh MBlu NLar SCoo
'Purpurea Plena Elegans' (Vt/d) ♀H6	CBcs CKel CMac CRHN CRos CTri CWCL EBee ELan EPfP IPot LCro LOPS LRHS LSRN MAsh MSwo NEgg NHol NRHS SLim SPer SPoG SWvt WBor
quadribracteolata	NHaw
QUEEN MOTHER ('Zoqum') (Vt)	CWGN EPfP LRHS
'Radiance'	CWGN
'Ramona' (LL)	CRos LRHS LSRN NHaw
ranunculoides	NHaw
'Rasputin' (LL)	CWCL
REBECCA ('Evipo016'PBR) (EL)	CFlo CKel CRos CWCL CWGN ELan EPfP EUJe LCro LOPS LRHS LSRN MAsh NRHS SCob SCoo SLon SPer SPoG
recta	CWCL ECtt MNrw NLar
- PAB 9005	LEdu
- 'Purpurea' (F)	CDor CFlo CRos EHoe ELan EMor EPfP GKev GWyn ILea IPot LRHS MMrt MNrw NChi SEND SPer SPtp WArt XLum
- 'Velvet Night' (F)	ECtt IPot LRHS MHol NCGa NEgg NLar NSti WCot
'Red Ballon' (Ta)	IPot
'Red Cooler'	see *C.* 'Crimson King'
'Red Pearl' (EL)	CFlo CRos CWCL LRHS LSRN
REFLECTIONS ('Evipo035') (LL)	CRos EPfP LRHS MAsh SLon
§ ***rehderiana*** ♀H5	CKel CRHN CWCL EBee ELan EPfP IMou MBlu NAln SWvt WCot WPGP WSHC
'Reiman' (LL)	NHaw
'Remembrance' (LL) ♀H6	CFlo CWCL EPfP LSRN NAln NHaw
'Reverie' (T)	NHaw
'Rhapsody' ambig.	EPfP LBuc MAsh MGos SCoo SNig
'Rhapsody' B. Fretwell (EL)	CRos LRHS LSRN NHaw
'Ribble Red' (V)	NHaw
'Richard Pennell' (EL) ♀H6	CRos LRHS SNig SPet
'Richard's Picotee' (Vt)	NHaw
'Rising Star'	NHaw SNig
'Ristimägi' (LL)	NHaw
'Rituaal' (LL)	NHaw
'Robud'PBR (M/d)	NPer
'Roelie' (Vt)	NHaw
'Roko-Kolla' (LL) ♀H6	NHaw
'Romantika' (LL)	CFlo CRos ELan ELon LCro LRHS LSRN MAsh NHaw NRHS SCoo SNig XEll
'Rooguchi' (I)	CFlo CWCL CWGN LRHS NHaw
'Rooran' (EL)	CWCL
'Rosa Königskind' (EL)	NLar
ROSALYN ('Zo09087') (Vt)	CWGN IPot
I 'Rosea' (I)	CWCL EPfP GKev LRHS LSRN WHoo
I 'Rosea' Westphal. (Vt)	NHaw
ROSEMOOR ('Evipo002'PBR) (EL)	CFlo CKel CRos CWCL CWGN EPfP LRHS MAsh NRHS SCoo SLon SNig SWvt
'Rosy O'Grady' (A) ♀H6	MAsh NLar SRms
'Rosy Pagoda' (A)	CRos ELan LRHS NLar
'Rouge Cardinal' (LL)	CArg CBcs CFlo CMac CRos EBee ELan ELon EPfP LRHS LSRN MAsh MGos MJak NEgg NRHS SCob SLim SNig SPer SPet SPoG SRms
'Royal Velours' (Vt)	CFlo CKel CRHN CRos CTri CWCL ELan EPfP IPot LCro LOPS LRHS LSRN MAsh MGos NHol NLar NRHS SCob SCoo SLim SNig SPer SPoG
ROYAL VELVET ('Evifour'PBR) (EL)	CRos LRHS LSRN SCoo
'Royalty' (EL)	CRos CWCL ELan EPfP LRHS LSRN MAsh SCoo
'Rubens Superba'	see *C. montana* 'Rubens Superba'
'Ruby' (A)	CRos CWCL ELan EPfP LRHS LSRN MAsh NEgg SCoo SNig SPer SRms WFar
'Ruby Glow' (EL)	CRos EPfP LRHS LSRN SCoo SNig
'Ruby Tuesday' (V)	NHaw
'Ruby Wedding' Fretwell (T)	CFlo CWCL CWGN EPfP LBuc LCro LOPS LSRN NAln SWvt
'Rüütel' (EL)	CFlo CKel CRos CWCL ELon LRHS MAsh NHaw SCoo SNig
'Saalomon' (LL)	NHaw
SACHA ('Evipo060')	CRos LRHS NRHS SPoG

SALLY ('Evipo077') (EL) — CFlo CRos ELan EPfP LRHS MAsh NRHS SNig SPoG
'Sally Cadge' (EL) — NHaw
SAMARITAN JO ('Evipo075') — CFlo CRos EPfP LRHS MAsh NRHS SNig SPoG
'Sanssouci' (M) — EBee
SAVANNAH ('Evipo015'PBR) (Vt) — MAsh
'Scartho Gem' (EL) — CRos LRHS SCoo SNig
SEA BREEZE ('Zo09063') (Vt) new — CFlo IPot LCro LOPS
'Sealand Gem' (EL) — NHaw
§ 'Semu' (LL) — CWGN NHaw
serratifolia — CBcs CRHN ECtt GAbr GLog SBrt SPlb
- B&SWJ 8458 from Korea — WCru
I 'Sherriffii' (Ta) — SWvt
'Shikoo' (EL) — CWCL LSRN
SHIMMER ('Evipo028'PBR) (LL) — CKel CRos EPfP LRHS MAsh NRHS SLon
'Shirayukihime' (EL) — NLar
'Sialia' (A/d) — CFlo CKel
§ ***sibirica*** — CRos EPfP LRHS NRHS
- var. ***tianschanica*** — NHaw
'Signe' (Vt) — see *C.* 'Kasmu'
'Siirus' (EL) — NHaw
'Silmakivi' (EL) — NHaw
'Silver Moon' (EL) — CFlo CWCL EPfP LRHS MAsh NLar SCoo
simensis — LEdu
simsii Small — see *C. pitcheri*
simsii Sweet — see *C. crispa*
'Sinee Plamia' (LL) — NHaw
§ 'Sinii Dozhd' (I) — CWCL NHaw
§ 'Sir Edward Elgar' (A) — CRos LRHS NRHS
'Sir Eric Savill' (M) — LSvl
'Sir Trevor Lawrence' (T) — CRos LRHS NHaw
'Sireen' (LL) — NHaw
smilacifolia NJM 10.094 — WPGP
'Snow Queen' (EL) — CFlo CKel CRos CWCL ELon EPfP LRHS SNig SRms
'Snowbird' (A/d) — CFlo CKel CRos LRHS SNig SPer SPoG
'Snowdrift' — see *C. armandii* 'Snowdrift'
socialis — NHaw
'Södertälje' (Vt) — CRHN EPfP NHaw SCoo
'Sokojiro' (EL) — CRos LRHS NRHS
'Solina' (Vt) — NHaw
songarica — NHaw
'Sonnette' (V) — CFlo CRHN CWGN IPot NHaw
'Sophie' (V) — NHaw
SORBET ('Zosor'PBR) (A) — CFlo
§ 'Souvenir du Capitaine Thuilleaux' (EL) — CKel ELon SNig
'Special Occasion' (EL) — CRos CWGN EPfP LRHS LSRN NLar SCoo SNig
SPIKY ('Zospi'PBR) (A/d) — CFlo
§ ***spooneri*** — EPfP LRHS SCoo SWvt
SPRING JOY ('Zo12053') (M) — CFlo
'Sputnik' (I) — NHaw
stans — CExl CPou CRos IFro LLHF LRHS NLar
- B&SWJ 5073 — WCru
- B&SWJ 6345 — WCru
§ 'Star'PBR (M/d) — CRos EPfP LRHS MSwo NLar SPer
'Star of India' (LL) — CKel CRos CWCL EPfP LRHS MGos SCoo SNig SPer
STAR OF PAKISTAN ('Zostapa') — CWGN
STAR RIVER ('Zostarri'PBR) (I) — ELan IPot
I 'Starfish' (EL) — NHaw
'Starlight' (M) — CKel CWCL ELon SNig
'Stasik' (LL) — NHaw
'Stephanie' (A) — CFlo CKel
'Strawberry Kiss' (V) — NHaw
'Sue Reade' (V) new — NHaw
SUGAR CANDY ('Evione'PBR) (EL) — LRHS MAsh SCoo SNig
SUMMER SNOW — see *C.* 'Paul Farges'
'Sundance' (Ta) — NHaw
SUNNY SKY ('Zosusk'PBR) (Vt) — CFlo CKel NHaw
'Sunrise' (M/d) — EBee EPfP MSwo NLar
'Sunset' (EL) ♀H6 — CArg CRos CWCL ELon LRHS LSRN MGos NEgg NLar SCoo SNig
SUPER NOVA ('Zo09088') (Vt) — CFlo IPot
'Swedish Bells' (I) — CWGN
'Sweet Scentsation' (F) — CFlo EPfP NHaw NLar
'Sweet Summer Love'PBR (F) — CWGN IPot NHaw
SWEETHEART ('Witswe'PBR) (I) — ELan EPfP
'Sylvia Denny' (EL) — CArg EPfP MAsh
'Syrena' (LL) — NHaw
szuyuanensis CWJ 12455 — WCru
'Tae' — see *C.* 'Toltae'
'Tage Lundell' (A) — CFlo EPfP LRHS NLar
'Taiga'PBR (d) new — ELan LCro LOPS
'Tamakazura' (V) — NHaw
'Tango' (Vt) — CRHN NHaw
§ ***tangutica*** — Widely available
'Tapestry' (I) — NHaw
'Tartu' (EL) — NHaw
tashiroi 'Yellow Peril' — WCru
TEKLA ('Evipo069'PBR) (LL) — CRos CWCL LRHS NRHS SNig SPoG
'Teksa' (LL) — NHaw
tenuiloba — see *C. columbiana* var. *tenuiloba*
§ ***terniflora*** — EPfP NHaw SPtp
- B&SWJ 5751 — WCru
'Teshio' (EL) — IPot
texensis — NHaw WSHC
- 'The Princess of Wales' — see *C.* 'Princess Diana'
- 'Wellmax'PBR — NHaw
'The Bride' (EL) — CWCL CWGN LRHS LSRN
THE COUNTESS OF WESSEX ('Evipo073') (EL) — CRos EPfP LRHS MAsh NRHS SPoG
'The First Lady' (EL) — CWCL SNig
'The President' (EL) ♀H6 — CArg CKel CMac CRos CTri CWCL ELan EPfP LCro LOPS LRHS LSRN MGos MSwo NAln NEgg NLar NPri NRHS SCob SLim SNig SPer SPet SPoG SRms WFar
'The Princess of Wales' (EL) — see *C.* 'Princess of Wales' (1875) (EL)
'The Princess of Wales' (T) — see *C.* 'Princess Diana'
'The Vagabond' (EL) — CRos CWCL CWGN ELan EPfP LRHS LSRN MAsh NHaw NLar SCoo SNig SPet
'The Velvet' (EL) — SNig
§ THUMBELINA ('Evipo030'PBR) (EL) — CKel CRos CWCL EPfP LRHS NRHS SNig SPoG
thunbergii misapplied — see *C. terniflora*
'Thyrislund' (EL) — CKel SNig
'Tibetan Mix' (Ta) — NHaw
tibetana — NHaw
- CC 7447 — GKev

	Name	Suppliers
	- 'Black Tibet' (Ta)	NHaw
§	- subsp. ***vernayi***	LLHF
	- - 'Glasnevin Dusk' (Ta)	WSHC
§	- - var. ***vernayi*** 'Orange Peel' LS&E 13342 (Ta)	LRHS
	'Tie Dye' (LL)	CWGN EBee ELan EPfP NHaw SPoG SRms
	'Tiiu' (LL)	NHaw
	'Tim's Passion' (Vt)	CRHN
	'Titipu' (V)	NHaw
	'Together' (I)	NHaw
	'Toki' (EL)	CWGN
§	'Toltae'[PBR] (EL)	CFlo CRos CWGN LRHS NRHS
	tongluensis	WPGP
	- HWJK 2368	WCru
	tosaensis f. ***cremea***	NHaw
	'Tranquility'	CWGN
	'Triinu' (Vt)	NHaw
§	× ***triternata*** 'Rubromarginata'	CFlo CKel CMac CRHN CRos CWCL CWGN ELan EPfP LRHS LSRN MAsh MGos MMrt MRav NAln NLar NRHS SCob SLim SLon SNig SPer SPoG SRms
	'Tsunami Child' (M)	IMou
§	***tubulosa*** ALAN BLOOM ('Alblo'[PBR]) (H)	CRos LRHS NRHS
	- 'Wyevale' (H)	CFlo CMac CRos ELan ELon EPfP LRHS MCot MRav NLar NRHS SCoo SPer WAul WHil
	'Tuchka' (EL)	NHaw
	'Twilight' (EL)	CFlo CKel CRos EPfP LRHS MAsh
	TWINKLE ('Zotwi') (I)	CWGN
	'Uno Kivistik'[PBR] (LL)	NHaw
	urophylla	SPhx
§	- 'Winter Beauty'	CFlo CWCL ELan LCro LOPS LSRN SCoo SPoG WPGP WSHC
	urticifolia B&SWJ 8651	WCru
	- B&SWJ 8852	WCru
	'Utopia' (EL)	CWGN
	'Valge Daam' (LL)	CWGN NHaw
	'Valle' (LL)	NHaw
	'Van Gogh' (M)	CWGN
	'Vanessa' (LL)	CRHN NHaw
	'Vanso'	see *C.* 'Blue Light'
§	***veitchiana***	EWld NHaw
	'Venosa Violacea' (Vt) ♀H6	CFlo CKel CRHN CRos ELan EPfP LRHS LSRN MAsh NHaw NHol SCoo SNig SPer SPoG SRms
	'Vera' (M)	EPfP LRHS LSRN SCoo
	vernayi	see *C. tibetana* subsp. *vernayi*
	'Veronica's Choice' (EL)	CFlo CWCL ELan NHaw SNig
	VERSAILLES ('Evipo025'[PBR]) (EL)	CRos EPfP LRHS SNig
§	VESUVIUS ('Evipo032'[PBR]) (Vt)	CRos LRHS SCoo SLon
	'Vetka'[PBR] (LL)	NHaw
	VICTOR HUGO ('Evipo007'[PBR]) (LL)	CFlo CRos LRHS NLar SCoo SNig
	'Victoria' (LL)	CRos LRHS LSRN NHaw SCoo
	VIENNETTA ('Evipo006'[PBR]) (d)	CFlo CKel CRos CWCL CWGN EPfP LRHS MGos SCoo SLon SNig SRms
	'Vihma' (LL)	NHaw
	'Ville de Lyon' (LL)	CBcs CFlo CKel CRHN CWCL ELan EPfP LRHS LSRN MAsh MGos NEgg NRHS SLim SNig SPer SPet SPoG
	vinacea	NHaw
	'Vince Denny' (Ta)	EBee NHaw SNig
	VINO ('Poulvo'[PBR]) (EL)	CRos LRHS NHaw SCoo
	'Viola' (LL)	CFlo CWGN ELon LSRN NHaw
	'Violet Charm' (EL)	NEgg
	viorna	CWGN NHaw WSHC
	virginiana misapplied	see *C. vitalba*
§	***vitalba***	CPer CWld ECrN GKev NHaw NWea WHer WSFF WSpi
	- SDR 6610	GKev
	viticella	CRHN GKev NHaw SMHy WSHC
	- f. ***albiflora*** **new**	GKev
	- subsp. ***campaniflora***	see *C. campaniflora*
§	- 'Flore Pleno' (Vt/d)	CFlo CKel CRHN CRos ELan EPfP IPot LCro LOPS LRHS LSRN NHaw NRHS SLon SNig SPoG
	- 'Hågelby Blue' (Vt)	NHaw
	- 'Hågelby White' (Vt)	CRHN CWGN NHaw
	- 'Hanna' (Vt)	CRHN LSRN NHaw
	- 'Mary Rose'	see *C. viticella* 'Flore Pleno'
	'Vivienne'	see *C.* 'Beth Currie'
	'Voluceau' (Vt)	CRHN CRos CWCL ELan EPfP LRHS LSRN SNig SRms
	VOLUNTEER ('Evipo080')	CRos LRHS NRHS
	'Vostok' (LL)	NHaw
	'Vyvyan Pennell' (EL)	CArg CBcs CFlo CKel CMac CRos CTri CWCL ELan EPfP LRHS LSRN MAsh MSwo NEgg NLar SLim SNig SPer SPet SPoG SWvt WFar
	'W.E. Gladstone' (EL)	CRos LRHS
	WADA'S PRIMROSE	see *C. patens* 'Manshuu Ki'
	'Walenburg' (Vt) ♀H6	CKel CRHN CWGN NHaw SLon
	'Walter Pennell' (EL)	CBcs CRos LRHS SCoo
	'Warsaw' (Ta)	NLar
	'Warszawska Nike' (EL) ♀H6	CMac CRHN CRos CWCL ELan EPfP LCro LOPS LRHS MAsh MGos SCob SCoo SNig SPoG
	'Warwickshire Rose' (M)	CFlo CKel CMac CRHN CRos CTri CWGN EBee ELan LRHS LSRN MAsh NEgg SLim SNig SPoG
	'Wedding Day' (EL)	CFlo EPfP LCro LOPS LSRN NAln NLar
	'Wee Willie Winkie' (M)	SRms
	'Westerplatte' (EL)	CFlo CKel CRos CWCL CWGN EPfP LRHS MGos NHaw SNig SPoG
§	'White Columbine' (A) ♀H6	ELan LRHS SNig SPer
	'White Heart' (Vt)	NHaw
§	'White Moth' (A/d)	LSRN MAsh NHol
	'White Prince Charles' (LL)	NHaw
	'White Satin' (A)	CRos EPfP LRHS SRms
	'White Swan' (A/d)	MAsh NHol NLar SCoo
	'White Wings' (A/d)	CFlo LSRN
	'Will Goodwin' (EL) ♀H6	CBcs CRos CWCL ELan EPfP LRHS SNig SRms
	'William Kennett' (EL)	CWCL ELan LRHS
	'Willy' (A)	CArg CRos ELan EPfP LRHS MAsh MGos NLar NRHS SPer SRms WFar
	WISLEY ('Evipo001'[PBR]) (Vt) ♀H6	CKel EPfP MGos NLar SLon
	WONDERFUL ('Zo09073') (Vt) **new**	LCro LOPS
	'Xerxes' misapplied	see *C.* 'Elsa Späth'
	XIU ('Evipo065') (Boulevard Series) **new**	LRHS
	'Yatsuhashi' ambig.	SNig
	'Yellow Queen' Holland	see *C. patens* 'Manshuu Ki'
	'Yellow Queen' Lundell/ Treasures	see *C.* 'Moonlight'
§	'Yukikomachi' (EL)	NHaw
	yunnanensis	WPGP
	ZARA ('Evipo062'[PBR]) (EL)	ELan MAsh SLon
	'Zephyr' (Vt)	NHaw

Clematopsis see *Clematis*

Clementsia see *Rhodiola*

Cleome (*Cleomaceae*)

hassleriana 'Helen Campbell' 🏆H2	CSpe
- 'Violet Queen'	LCro LOPS
SEÑORITA BLANCA ('Inclesbimp') **new**	CSpe NPri
SEÑORITA CAROLINA ('Inclesrcar'PBR) **new**	NPri
SEÑORITA ROSALITA ('Inncleosr'PBR)	CSpe NPri

Clerodendrum (*Lamiaceae*)

CW&T 6506	CMCN
bungei	Widely available
- PAB 8953	LEdu
- 'Diamond'	SGol
- 'Pink Diamond' (v)	CCCN CKel CWGN ELan EPfP EWes LRHS LSRN MGos NLar SPer SPoG SWvt
§ ***chinense*** var. ***chinense*** (d) 🏆H1b	CCCN CHll
- 'Pleniflorum'	see *C. chinense* var. *chinense*
colebrookianum B&SWJ 6651	WCru
- PAB 7794	LEdu
fragrans var. ***pleniflorum***	see *C. chinense* var. *chinense*
myricoides 'Ugandense'	see *Rotheca myricoides* 'Ugandense'
philippinum	see *C. chinense* var. *chinense*
× ***speciosum***	CHll
aff. ***subscaposum*** WWJ 11735	WCru
thomsoniae 🏆H1b	EShb WSFF
trichotomum	CAby CBcs CEnd CExl CMCN CRos CSam CSpe CTho CTri EPfP IArd LRHS NLar SLim SLon SPer WBor WHor WMat
- var. ***fargesii*** 🏆H5	Widely available
- - 'Carnival' (v) 🏆H5	CBod CCCN CExl CKel CMac CRos EBee ELan EPfP EUJe EWes LRHS MAsh NLar SEle SMad SPer SPoG SWvt WAvo WCot
- 'Purple Blaze'	CJun EBee
- 'Purple Haze'	NLar
- 'Shiro'	WCru
wallichii	EShb

Clethra ✿ (*Clethraceae*)

CW&T 6497	CMCN
alnifolia	CBcs CBod CDul CExl CTsd SPer SRms WCot WFar
- 'Anne Bidwell'	MBlu NLar
- 'Creel's Calico' (v)	NLar
- 'Fern Valley Pink'	CCCN CKel CMac EBee ELon EPfP LLHF LRHS NLar SRms WFar
- 'Hokie Pink'	NLar
- 'Hummingbird' 🏆H5	CCCN CEnd CExl CMac CRos ECrN ELan EPfP LRHS MAsh MBlu NEgg NLar SChF SEle SPad SPoG SWvt WFar
- 'Paniculata'	CRos ELon LRHS MGil MMuc WBor
- 'Pink Spice'	CRos LRHS
- 'Pink Spires'	CAco CBcs CExl CWld ECrN GKin LEdu MMuc MRav NEgg NHic NLar SCob SCoo SEle SPer WBor
- 'Rosea'	CTri GKin
- 'Ruby Spice' 🏆H5	CBcs CCCN CEnd CExl CJun CMac CRos ELan ELon EWTr GBin GGGa GKin IDee LRHS LSRN MAsh MBlu NLar NQui SEle SPad SPer SPoG SWvt
- 'September Beauty'	CJun NLar
- 'Sixteen Candles'	GGGa LRHS MPkF NLar
- VANILLA SPICE ('Caleb')	CBcs NLar
arborea	CBcs MGil
barbinervis 🏆H5	CBcs CExl CRos CTho EPfP GGGa IDee LRHS MBlu MGil NLar SPer WFar WPGP
- B&SWJ 11562	WCru
- GREAT STAR ('Minbarb')	EPfP LRHS WPGP
- 'White Star'	CKel EBee EPfP LRHS
delavayi Franch.	CBcs CCCN CMCN EBee GCal GGGa IDee LLHF MGil WPGP
- SBEC 1513	CExl
fabri B&SWJ 11702	WCru
- FMWJ 13037	WCru
fargesii	CExl EPfP IDee IMou NLar SPtp WPGP
kaipoensis NJM 11.020	WPGP
- NJM 11.058	WPGP
- PAB 8571	LEdu
monostachya	CExl EBee GGGa MGil NLar WPGP
petelotii FMWJ 13401 **new**	WCru
pringlei	CBcs EBee NLar WPGP WSHC
tomentosa 'Cottondale'	CJun NLar

Cleyera (*Pentaphylacaceae*)

fortunei	see *C. japonica* 'Fortunei'
- 'Variegata'	see *C. japonica* 'Fortunei'
§ ***japonica*** 'Fortunei' (v)	CCCN CMac EBee SSta
- var. ***japonica***	EBee WPGP
- 'Tricolor' (v)	CBcs IDee SAko
- var. ***wallichii***	WPGP

Clianthus ✿ (*Papilionaceae*)

maximus	CTsd GDun
- 'Kaka King'	EWes GDun
* ***pauciflorus*** **new**	CCCN
§ ***puniceus*** 🏆H3	CAbb CBcs CCht CExl CHll CKel CRos CSpe CTsd EBee EPfP EUJe GDun LRHS MGil NRHS SEle SGbt SIgm SPer SPlb SPoG SWvt WSHC
§ - 'Albus' 🏆H3	CAby CBcs CCCN CExl CKel CRos CSpe EBee EPfP GDun LRHS MGil NRHS SPer SPoG SWvt
- 'Flamingo'	see *C. puniceus* 'Roseus'
- 'Red Admiral'	see *C. puniceus*
- 'Red Cardinal'	see *C. puniceus*
§ - 'Roseus' 🏆H3	CBcs CCCN CExl CKel CPla CRos EPfP GDun LRHS NRHS SMad SPer SPoG
- 'White Heron'	see *C. puniceus* 'Albus'

Clinanthus (*Amaryllidaceae*)

§ ***variegatus***	WCot
- yellow-flowered	WCot

Clinopodium (*Lamiaceae*)

ascendens	see *Calamintha ascendens*
calamintha	see *Calamintha nepeta*
grandiflorum	see *Calamintha grandiflora*
§ ***menthifolium***	NBre NLar XSen
§ ***vulgare***	CHab EBee GPSL LRHS MHer MNHC NMir NRHS SRms WMoo WOut
- PAB 7562	LEdu

Clintonia (*Liliaceae*)

umbellulata	GCal

Clivia ✿ (*Amaryllidaceae*)

caulescens	NHoy WCot
- pink-flowered	NHoy WCot
× ***cyrtanthiflora***	NHoy
gardenii	NHoy WCot
miniata ♀H1c	CAbb CBcs CCCN CTca CTsd LCro LOPS NHoy SAdn SEND SPlb WCot
- 'Anshan Variegated' (v)	WCot
- 'Arturo's Yellow'	NHoy WCot
- 'Ato-Shan'	WCot
- 'Aurea'	CSpe
- Belgian hybrids	NHoy WCot
- - improved strain **new**	NHoy
- 'Beverley's Delight'	NHoy WCot
- broad-leaved, variegated (v)	NHoy WCot
- 'Chubb's Peach' × 'Vico Yellow' **new**	NHoy
- var. ***citrina*** ♀H1c	CTca LAma NHoy
- - variegated (v)	NHoy WCot
- 'Connemara Flame' **new**	NHoy
- 'Dancing Sisters' × 'Terracotta Green Throat'	NHoy WCot
- Daruma Group	WCot
- fragrant yellow-flowered **new**	NHoy
- 'Florid White Lips' **new**	NHoy
- green-centred	NHoy WCot
- - orange-flowered **new**	NHoy
- historical clone **new**	NHoy
- 'Hot Number One' **new**	NHoy
- large strawberry-orange-flowered **new**	NHoy
- 'Light of Buddha' (v)	NHoy WCot
- 'Mitsuhashi Multipetal'	WCot
- 'Mrs P. Lofus' **new**	NHoy
- Nakamura yellow-flowered **new**	NHoy
- 'Pale Majesty' **new**	NHoy
- pale yellow-flowered **new**	NHoy
- pastel shades	NHoy WCot
- 'Pink Perfection'	NHoy WCot
- 'Queen of the Strawberries' **new**	NHoy
- 'Red Dawn'	WCot
- 'Strawberry Giant' **new**	NHoy
- 'Striata' (v)	NHoy WCot
- 'Terracotta Treasure' (v)	NHoy WCot
- 'Vico Shima'	WCot
- 'Wide Leaf Monk'	WCot
nobilis ♀H1c	NHoy SPlb WCot
robusta	NHoy WCot
'San Marcus Yellow' × 'Solomone Yellow'	WCot
'Sweet Undress'	NHoy WCot

Clusia (*Clusiaceae*)

rosea	CCCN

Clytostoma (*Bignoniaceae*)

§ ***calystegioides***	CCCN CHll CRHN

Cnidium (*Apiaceae*)

officinale	GPoy LEdu
silaifolium **new**	LEdu

Cobaea (*Polemoniaceae*)

pringlei	CRHN EBee WPGP WSHC
- CD&R 1323	SBrt
scandens ♀H2	CCCN CDTJ CSpe EShb SPer
- f. ***alba***	CSpe EShb LCro LOPS SPer

cobnut see *Corylus avellana*; also AGM Fruit Section (under hazelnut)

Cocculus (*Menispermaceae*)

laurifolius	EUJe IArd
§ ***orbiculatus***	CExl
- B&SWJ 535	WCru
trilobus	see *C. orbiculatus*

Cochlearia (*Brassicaceae*)

armoracia	see *Armoracia rusticana*
officinalis	GJos WHer

Cochliasanthus (*Papilionaceae*)

§ ***caracalla***	CCCN

Cocos (*Arecaceae*)

plumosa	see *Syagrus romanzoffiana*

Codonanthe (*Gesneriaceae*)

gracilis	WDib
'Paula'	WDib

Codonanthe × *Nematanthus* see × *Codonatanthus*

× *Codonatanthus* (*Gesneriaceae*)

'Golden Tambourine'	WDib
'Sunset'	WDib
'Tambourine'	WDib

Codonopsis ✿ (*Campanulaceae*)

HWJK 2105 from Nepal	WCru
affinis	EBee
- HWJCM 70	WCru
- HWJK 2151	WCru
benthamii GWJ 9352	WCru
bhutanica	WSHC
cardiophylla	EBee GCal
clematidea	CDor CSpe EBee EBou ECha EPfP EWld GAbr GCal GKev MNrw NAln NEgg NLar SPlb SWvt WSHC
convolvulacea misapplied	see *C. grey-wilsonii*
- 'Alba'	see *C. grey-wilsonii* 'Himal Snow'
- Forrest's form	see *C. forrestii* Diels
'Dangshen'	see *C. pilosula*
aff. ***deltoidea*** SSSE 86	EBee EWld
dicentrifolia	NLar
foetens subsp. ***nervosa*** from Minshan, Sichuan, China **new**	SBrt
forrestii misapplied	see *C. grey-wilsonii*
§ ***forrestii*** Diels	EBee EWld GKev WCot
- BWJ 7847	WCru
§ ***grey-wilsonii*** ♀H5	CAby CBro EWld GEdr GKev WCot
- B&SWJ 7532	WCru
§ - 'Himal Snow'	CAby EWld GEdr WCru
inflata GWJ 9442	WCru
kawakamii	EBee EWld
- B&SWJ 1592	WCru
- RWJ 10007	WCru
§ ***lanceolata***	CAby CPla EWld SBrt
- B&SWJ 562	WCru

	nepalensis Grey-Wilson	see *C. grey-wilsonii*
	obtusa	EBee
	ovata	EBee EWld NBro NLar
§	***pilosula***	CDor EBee EWld GKev GPoy NAln SBrt
	- var. ***modesta***	EBee
	pinifolia	GKev
§	***rotundifolia***	EBee GKev SBrt WCru
	var. ***angustifolia***	
	- var. ***grandiflora***	EBee WSHC
	silvestris	see *C. pilosula*
	tangshen misapplied	see *C. rotundifolia* var. *angustifolia*
	ussuriensis	see *C. lanceolata*
	vinciflora	EWld
	viridis HWJK 2435	WCru

Coffea (*Rubiaceae*)

	arabica	CCCN SPre

coffee see *Coffea*

Colchicum ✿ (*Colchicaceae*)

	agrippinum ♀H4	CAvo ECha EPot GKev LAma MRav NBir WAbe WCot WHoo WThu
	'Antares'	ECha
	asteranthum	GKev
	atropurpureum	GKev LAma
	'Autumn Herald'	LAma
§	***autumnale***	CAvo CHab EPot GKev GPoy GQue IFro LAma NRya SDeJ SEND WShi
	- 'Alboplenum'	ERCP GKev LAma NBir SDeJ
	- 'Album'	CAvo CTca ELan EPot GKev LAma LCro LOPS NBir WShi
	- var. ***major*** hort.	see *C. byzantinum* Ker Gawl.
	- var. ***minor*** hort.	see *C. autumnale*
§	- 'Nancy Lindsay' ♀H5	EPot GKev WShi XEll
	- 'Pannonicum'	see *C. autumnale* 'Nancy Lindsay'
§	- 'Pleniflorum' (d)	GKev LAma
	- 'Roseum Plenum'	see *C. autumnale* 'Pleniflorum'
§	***bivonae***	EPot
	- 'Apollo'	GKev
	- 'Mount Giona'	GKev
	- 'Vesta'	GKev
§	***boissieri***	GKev
	bornmuelleri misapplied	see *C. speciosum* var. *bornmuelleri* hort.
	bornmuelleri Freyn	GKev LAma
	bowlesianum	see *C. bivonae*
	byzantinum ambig.	GKev
§	***byzantinum*** Ker Gawl. ♀H5	ELan LAma NAln SDeJ WShi
	- ***album***	see *C. byzantinum* 'Innocence'
§	- 'Innocence'	WCot
	cilicicum	LAma NAln
	- 'Purpureum'	CTca EPot GKev LAma
	corsicum	GKev WThu
	cupanii AH 9707	GKev
	- var. ***pulverulentum***	GKev
	davisii	GEdr GKev
	'Dick Trotter'	EPot GKev LAma NAln SDeJ WFar WOld
	'Disraeli'	EPot GKev
§	***giganteum***	GKev LAma
	graecum	GKev
	'Hannibal'	GKev
	'Harlekijn'	ERCP GKev LAma
	hungaricum	EPot GKev
	- f. ***albiflorum***	GKev
	- 'Valentine'	GKev
	- 'Velebit Star'	GKev
	illyricum	see *C. giganteum*
	laetum misapplied	see *C. parnassicum*
	'Lilac Bedder'	GKev
	'Lilac Wonder'	ELan GKev LAma MRav SDeJ WCot WHoo
	longifolium	see *C. neapolitanum*
	lusitanum	LAma
	'Lysimachus'	GKev
	macrophyllum	GKev LAma WCot
§	***neapolitanum***	GKev
	'Oktoberfest'	EPot
	parlatoris	GKev
§	***parnassicum***	ECha GKev WThu
	'Pink Goblet' ♀H5	LAma
	'Poseidon'	GKev
	procurrens	see *C. boissieri*
	psaridis	GKev
	'Rosy Dawn' ♀H5	ECha GKev WOld
	'Rosy Wonder'	LAma
	sibthorpii	see *C. bivonae*
	'Spartacus'	GKev
	speciosum ♀H5	CAvo ELan EPot GBin GKev LAma NAln NBir WShi
	- 'Album' ♀H5	CAvo ECha EPfP EPot ERCP GAbr GKev LAma LEdu NAln NBir SDeJ
	- 'Atrorubens' ♀H5	ECha EPot LAma
I	- var. ***bornmuelleri*** hort.	WHoo WOld
	- var. ***illyricum*** hort.	see *C. giganteum*
	szovitsii 'Snow White'	GKev
	tenorei ♀H4	EPot GKev LAma NBir
	'The Giant'	EPfP EPot GKev LAma NAln SCob SDeJ WFar
	triphyllum	GKev
	'Violet Queen'	EPot ERCP GAbr GKev LAma SDeJ
	'Waterlily' (d) ♀H5	CAvo CTca ELan EPfP EPot ERCP GKev LAma LCro LOPS NAln NBir SCob SDeJ WCot WFar WHoo
	'Zephyr'	LAma

Coleonema (*Rutaceae*)

§	***pulchellum***	CCCN CSpe SVen
§	- 'Pink Fountain'	CAbb CBod CCht CRos ELan EPfP LRHS MPkF NRHS SEle SPoG WCot
	pulchrum misapplied	see *C. pulchellum*
§	'Sunset Gold'	CAbb CBod CCCN CCht CPbh CRos CSBt CSpe ELan EPfP LRHS MPkF NRHS SCoo SEle SPlb SPoG

Coleus see *Solenostemon, Plectranthus*

Colignonia (*Nyctaginaceae*)

	ovalifolia B&SWJ 10644	WCru

Colletia (*Rhamnaceae*)

	armata	see *C. hystrix*
	cruciata	see *C. paradoxa*
§	***hystrix***	CBcs CMac CTri CTsd ELon MGil NLar WPav
	- RCB RA S3 new	WCot
	- 'Rosea'	CMac GCal MBlu SArc WPav WSHC
§	***paradoxa***	CBcs CCCN CMCN ELan EPfP IArd IDee SArc SMad SPlb SPoG WFar WPav
	paradoxa × ***spinosissima***	SMad
	spinosissima	WPav
	ulicina	SVen

Collinsonia (*Lamiaceae*)

	canadensis	LEdu

Collomia (Polemoniaceae)

	grandiflora	WCot

Colocasia (Araceae)

	antiquorum	see *C. esculenta*
§	***esculenta*** ♀H1b	CDTJ EUJe LCro LOPS SPlb XBlo
	- 'Black Coral'	CAbb EUJe SPad
	- 'Black Magic'	CBct CDTJ CRos EUJe IPot LAma LRHS NRHS XBlo
	- 'Blue Hawaii'	CAbb CPla
	- burgundy-stemmed	CDTJ EUJe LAma
	- 'Fontanesii'	CBct CDTJ EUJe MPkF
	- 'Hawaiian Punch' new	CAbb
	- 'Illustris'	CAbb CDTJ EUJe
	- 'Mammoth'	EUJe
	- 'Pink China'	MPkF
	- 'Purple Stem'	EUJe
	- 'Ruffles'	EUJe
	- 'Sangria'	EUJe
	fallax	EUJe
	formosana B&SWJ 6909	ESwi WCru
	gaoligongensis	CBct CPHo SPlb
	gigantea	EUJe
	'Kachhu'	LAma

Colquhounia (Lamiaceae)

	coccinea	CBod CCCN CHll CRos CSde EShb ESwi LRHS MBlu MGil MRav NLar NQui SChF SLon SPoG WCot
	- Sch 2458	EPfP WPGP
§	- var. ***mollis*** B&SWJ 7222	WCru
	- var. ***vestita*** misapplied	see *C. coccinea* var. *mollis*
	- var. ***vestita*** ambig.	CBcs CKel CTsd EBee EPfP LRHS MBNS SEND SMad

Columnea (Gesneriaceae)

	'Aladdin's Lamp'	WDib
	× ***banksii*** ♀H1c	WDib
§	'Broget Stavanger' (v) ♀H1c	WDib
	'Chanticleer' ♀H1a	WDib
I	'Firedragon'	WDib
	'Gavin Brown'	WDib
	gloriosa	EBak
	'Inferno'	WDib
	'Katsura'	WDib
	'Merkur'	WDib
I	'Midnight Lantern'	WDib
	'Rising Sun'	WDib
	schiedeana	WDib
	'Sherbert'	WDib
	'Stavanger' ♀H1a	WDib
	'Stavanger Variegated'	see *C.* 'Broget Stavanger'

Coluria (Rosaceae)

	geoides	WCot

Colutea (Papilionaceae)

	arborescens	CAgr CBcs CExl CRos ELan ESwi EWTr LRHS MBlu MGil MGos MMuc NWea SCob SEND SPer SPlb
	× ***media***	CTsd EWld
	- 'Copper Beauty'	CBcs ELan MMrt NLar SCob SPer
	orientalis	CCCN CSde EBee SMad

Colvillea (Caesalpiniaceae)

	racemosa	SPlb

Comarum see *Potentilla*

Combretum (Combretaceae)

	fruticosum	CCCN

Commelina (Commelinaceae)

	benghalensis	XBlo
	coelestis	see *C. tuberosa* Coelestis Group
	dianthifolia	CRos EBee GCal GEdr LEdu LRHS NHpl NRHS SBrt WHil WPtf
	- 'Electric Blue'	ELan SVic
	robusta	WCot WFar
	tuberosa	GKev NWad
	- B&SWJ 10353	SBrt WCru
	- blue-flowered	SDeJ
§	- Coelestis Group	CAby CCBP CSpe ECha SDys WKif WSHC

Comospermum (Asparagaceae)

	yedoense 'Kikuzaki White' new	GKev
	- var. ***platypetalus***	EBee GEdr

Comptonia (Myricaceae)

	peregrina	EBee WPGP

Conandron (Gesneriaceae)

	ramondoides B&SWJ 8929	WCru

Conicosia (Aizoaceae)

	pugioniformis	SVen

Coniogramme (Pteridaceae)

	emeiensis	WCot
	japonica	WFib
	- 'Flavomaculata' ♀H4	EBee EUJe WCot WFar

Conoclinium (Asteraceae)

§	***coelestinum***	CBod CFis CRos EBee LRHS NRHS SBrt WArt XLum

Conopodium (Apiaceae)

	majus	CEls WOut WShi

Consolida (Ranunculaceae)

§	***ajacis***	CSpe LRHS
	- Giant Imperial Series	SVic
	ambigua	see *C. ajacis*

Convallaria ✿ (Asparagaceae)

	japonica	see *Ophiopogon jaburan*
	keiskei	EPPr MAvo WFar
I	- 'Marginata' (v)	WCot
	- 'Shiro-shima-fu' (v)	GEdr WFar
	majalis ♀H7	Widely available
	- 'Alan's Gold Leaf' new	WFar
	- 'Albostriata' (v)	CBct CRos CWCL EHoe EHrv ELan EPPr EUJe GKev GMaP LEdu LRHS MAvo MBel MHer MHol MNrw MRav NBir NEgg NRHS WCot WFar WHer WHil WHoo WPnP
	- 'Aurea' new	WFar
	- 'Berlin Giant'	EPPr MAvo NRya SDeJ WFar
	- 'Blush'	CAvo WFar
	- 'Bordeaux'	CBre CBro CExl CWCL CWld EBee EMor EPPr GKev GPSL MBel NLar WCot
	- 'Bridal Choice'	EBee ELan EPot GKev NLar WFar XEll
	- 'Crème de Mint' (v) new	WFar
	- 'Dorien'	CBct EMor EPPr IMou WFar

	- 'Fernwood's Golden Slippers'	CAvo GEdr LLHF WCot WFar
	- 'Flore Pleno' (d)	GEdr WFar
	- 'Géant de Fortin' ♀H7	CAvo CBct CBro CExl EPot GCal GEdr MRav NBir NLar WCot WFar
	- 'Gerard Debureaux'	see *C. majalis* 'Green Tapestry'
	- 'Golden Jubilee'	CBct LEdu MAvo MNrw WCot WFar
	- 'Grandiflora' **new**	WFar
§	- 'Green Tapestry' (v)	CBct MAvo WCot WFar
	- 'Haldon Grange' (v)	CAby EPPr MAvo WFar
	- 'Hardwick Hall' (v)	CBct CDor CExl CWCL EBee EHoe EHrv EUJe GEdr GKev LEdu MAvo MBel WAul WCot WFar XEll
	- 'Heitmann' **new**	CWCL WFar
	- 'Hitschberger Riesenperle'	WFar XLum
	- 'Hofheim' (v)	CAby CAvo CBct GEdr GKev LEdu MAvo WCot WFar WHal
	- 'Landgraaf' (v)	MAvo WFar
	- 'Lineata' (v) **new**	WFar
	- 'Marcel' (v)	WFar
	- 'Mary Brooks' **new**	WFar
	- 'Polish Beauty' (v) **new**	WFar
	- 'Polish Spirit' **new**	WFar
	- 'Prolificans'	CBct CBod CWCL EBee ECtt EHrv EPPr EPfP EPot GEdr GKev ILea LAma LCro LOPS MAvo MRav NBir NLar NSti WCot WFar WPnP
	- var. ***rosea***	Widely available
	- 'Silbercconfolis' (v)	WCot WFar
	- 'Variegata' (v)	CPla EMor GCal SMad WFar WThu
	- 'Vic Pawlowski's Gold' (v)	CAby CBct CBro CExl CMac EPPr GEdr LEdu MAvo WFar WPGP WSHC
	- 'Vierländer Glockenspiel' **new**	WFar
	- 'Viktor' **new**	WFar
*	- 'Viridistriatus' **new**	WFar
	transcaucasica	GKev MAvo

Convolvulus (*Convolvulaceae*)

	althaeoides	CFis ELan
§	- subsp. ***tenuissimus***	EWes WCot
§	***boissieri***	WAbe XEll
	cantabrica	CRos LRHS NRHS SPhx XLum
	chilensis	CCCN
	cneorum ♀H4	Widely available
	- 'Snow Angel'	CRos LRHS SWvt
	elegantissimus	see *C. althaeoides* subsp. *tenuissimus*
	lineatus	EWes
	mauritanicus	see *C. sabatius*
	nitidus	see *C. boissieri*
§	***sabatius*** ♀H3	CCCN CCht CKel CSam CSpe CTri EBee EBou ECtt ELan EPfP EPot EShb MCot SEND SPer SPlb SPoG SVen SWvt WCFE WSHC XLum
	- dark-flowered	CCCN
	- 'Moroccan Beauty'PBR	ECtt
	- white-flowered	CCCN

× *Cooperanthes* see *Zephyranthes*

Cooperia see *Zephyranthes*

Coprosma (*Rubiaceae*)

	baueri misapplied	see *C. repens*
	'Beatson's Gold' (f/v)	CBcs CDTJ CExl CHll ELan EShb LRHS SEND SWvt WGrn
	'Black Cloud'	ELon SEND
	brunnea (f)	WThu
	- (m)	WThu
	'Cappuccino'	EShb SEle
	'Coppershine'	CExl
	cunninghamii macrocarpa (m)	CCoa
	depressa	WThu
	'Evening Glow'PBR (f/v)	CBod CCCN CDTJ CRos CSBt EUJe LRHS MGos NRHS SEle SLim SRms
	'Fire Burst'PBR (f/v)	CAbb CBcs CCCN CRos LRHS MGos SEle SLim SRms
	'Green Globe'	CHll
	'Inferno'PBR	CAbb CBcs CKel SEle SPad
	'Karo Red'PBR (v)	SRms
I	× ***kirkii*** 'Kirkii' (f)	CHll
	- 'Variegata' (f/v)	CKel CSde CTsd EPfP EShb GBin LRHS
	'Lemon and Lime'PBR (v)	CBod CKel CRos EBee EUJe LRHS MGos NRHS SEle SPoG SRms
	petriei	GAbr WThu
	- 'White Pearls'	WThu
	'Rainbow Surprise'PBR (v)	CCCN CExl CRos CSBt LRHS MGos SRms WFar
§	***repens***	CExl EShb SPlb SVen
	- 'County Park Plum' (v)	CBcs
	- 'Marble Queen' (m/v) ♀H3	EShb
	- 'Midnight Martini' (v)	CKel CRos LRHS NRHS
	- PACIFIC DAWN ('Copdawbucb30') (m/v) **new**	CSBt
	- PACIFIC NIGHT ('Hutpac'PBR) (m)	CCht CKel CRos CSBt EUJe LRHS MGos SLon
	- PACIFIC SUNSET ('Jwncopps') (m/v)	EBee SEle
	- 'Painter's Palette' (m)	SVen
	- 'Picturata' (m/v) ♀H3	EShb
	- 'Pina Colada'PBR (v)	CAbb CRos CSBt LRHS NRHS SEle SPoG
	- 'Tequila Sunrise'	CAbb CCht CKel CRos CSBt EBee LRHS MTin NRHS SEle
	'Roy's Red' (m)	CBod CCht CMac EShb LSRN
	rugosa (f)	CExl
	'Scarlet O'Hara'	CCht SEle SPoG
	'Walter Brockie'	CCoa CHll CSde

Coptis (*Ranunculaceae*)

	chinensis B&SWJ 12865	WCru
	japonica	GPoy WCru
	- var. ***dissecta***	WCru
	- var. ***major***	EBee WCru WSHC
	laciniata B&SWJ 12863	WCru
	omeiensis	WCru
	quinquefolia B&SWJ 1677	WCru
	ramosa B&SWJ 6000	WCru
	- B&SWJ 6030	WCru
	trifolia	WCru

Corallospartium see *Carmichaelia*

Cordyline ✿ (*Asparagaceae*)

	australis ♀H3	Widely available
	- 'Albertii' (v) ♀H3	CCCN SArc
	- 'Atlantic Green'	CRos LRHS NRHS
	- 'Atropurpurea'	CCCN
	- 'Black Night'	CCCN
	- CHARLIE BOY ('Ric01'PBR) (v)	SPad
	- 'Claret'	CBcs
	- 'Karo Kiri'	CCCN
	- 'Olive Fountain'	CCCN
	- 'Peko'PBR	CCCN

- 'Purple Heart'	CCCN MSwo
- Purpurea Group	CBcs CDTJ ELan MGos MMuc SEND SPlb WFar
- 'Red Comet'	SPad
- 'Red Sensation'	CCCN SWvt
- 'Salsa'	CRos NRHS
- 'Sparkler'	CCCN CRos EPfP SCob
- 'Torbay Dazzler' (v) ♀H3	CAbb CBcs CBod CEnd CKel CMac CPla CRos CSBt ELan EMOT EPfP EUJe LRHS LSRN MAsh MGos NPri NRHS SCob SLim SPoG SWvt WFar
- 'Torbay Sunset'	CCCN SCob
'Autumn'	CCCN
'Can Can' PBR	CKel NEgg SEND
'Cardinal' PBR	CBcs
'Cha Cha' PBR	CCCN EUJe MJak SEND WAvo WCot
'Cherry Sensation' (v)	CRos EPfP LBuc LRHS NRHS WFar
'Coffee Cream'	CCCN
'Dark Star'	CCCN CDTJ
'Eurostar'	CCCN
FESTIVAL GRASS ('Jurred')	EUJe
'Firecracker'	CCCN
fruticosa 'Kiwi'	CRos LRHS NRHS
- 'Red Edge' ♀H1b	XBlo
§ ***indivisa***	CCCN CDTJ CPbh CTsd SArc SChr SPlb WPGP
'Jive' PBR (v) **new**	LCro LOPS NEgg
kaspar	CCCN
mauritiana	WCot
obtecta	CCCN
'Pink Champagne'	CCCN CRos EMOT LRHS MPkF MSwo SCob
PINK PASSION ('Seipin' PBR)	CCCN CPla CRos ELan EPfP EUJe LBuc LRHS SCob SPoG
'Pink Stripe' (v)	CCCN LSRN SLim SWvt
'Purple Sensation'	CBcs CCCN
'Red Bush'	XBlo
'Red Heart'	CCCN
'Red Star'	CAbb CBcs CBod CCCN CChe CEnd CKel CRos CSBt EMOT EPfP EUJe LCro LOPS LRHS MSwo NPer NRHS SCob SPoG SWvt WFar
'Salsa' PBR **new**	NEgg
'Southern Splendour'	CBcs CCCN CKel CPla CRos ELan LRHS NPri NRHS SPoG
'Sundance' ♀H3	CBcs CRos EMOT EPfP LRHS MGos MSwo NPer SCob SLim SPoG SRms SWvt WFar
'Sunrise' (v)	CPla CRos LRHS NRHS
terminalis	see *C. fruticosa*
'Torbay Red' ♀H3	CCCN CMac CPla CRos CTsd EPfP LRHS LSRN MAsh NPri SPer SPoG SWvt

Coreopsis (*Asteraceae*)

'Astolat'	CBod MRav
auriculata CUTTING GOLD	see *C.* 'Schnittgold'
- 'Elfin Gold'	EBou ELan EPfP NHic
- 'Nana'	MNrw NBre
- 'Superba'	MRav
- 'Zamphir'	CDor EBee EPfP MNrw WCot
'Baby Gold'	see *C. lanceolata* 'Sonnenkind' (unblotched)
BABY SUN	see *C.* 'Sonnenkind' (red-blotched)
'Buttermilk' **new**	NCGa
'Calypso' (v)	SPoG XLum
'Center Stage' **new**	ELan
'Cha Cha Cha'	SEle
'Cherry Pie' PBR (Pie Series)	SCob
'Citrine' PBR (Hardy Jewel Series)	CWGN IKil NHic
'Cosmic Evolution' (Big Bang Series)	EBee ELan EMor LRHS SPoG
'Cosmic Eye' (Big Bang Series)	EBee ELan NRHS SPoG WFar
'Cranberry Ice'	LRHS NRHS
'Daybreak' (Li'l Bang Series)	CRos NRHS
'Desert Coral' PBR (Hardy Jewel Series)	NHic
'Dream'	SRkn
'Enchanted Eve' (Li'l Bang Series)	CRos MHol NRHS WFar
'Firefly' PBR **new**	NCGa
'Fool's Gold'	EBee
'Full Moon' PBR (Big Bang Series)	CRos EBee ELan IKil LRHS NRHS SPoG STPC WFar XLum
'Galaxy' (Big Bang Series)	CRos EBee ELan LRHS NRHS WFar
'Garnet' PBR (Hardy Jewel Series)	NHic NPri
gigantea	SPlb
grandiflora	CBod NEgg
- 'Bernwode' (v)	CMac EBee SWvt
- 'Domino'	EBee LSun NHic
- 'Early Sunrise' ♀H5	CRos CSBt EAJP EBee EPfP LRHS MNHC NBir NGBl NPer NRHS SCob SGbt SPoG SWvt WFar XLum
- FLYING SAUCERS ('Walcoreop' PBR)	CRos EPfP LRHS NRHS SCoo SPoG
- 'Illico'	EBee
- 'Mayfield Giant'	CBod CSBt EBee ELan EPfP SPer SRms SWvt WHrl WPtf
- 'Presto' (d)	EMor NGBl WFar
- 'Rising Sun'	ELan
- 'Sunburst'	EPfP NBre XLum
- 'Sunfire'	CRos LRHS NRHS WFar
- 'Sunkiss' **new**	NPri
- 'Sunray'	CBcs CChe CRos CSBt ECtt EMor EPfP LRHS MAsh NGdn NRHS SPlb SPoG SRms SWvt XLum
- 'Tetra Riesen'	NBre
'Imperial Sun' PBR **new**	ELan
'Jethro Tull' PBR	EBee
'Jive' PBR (Coloropsis Series)	CWGN SCob SEle
'Ladybird' **new**	MAvo NCGa
lanceolata	NBre
- 'Goldfink'	MRav SRms
- 'Goldteppich'	CRos EPfP LRHS NRHS
- 'Little Sundial'	IKil
§ - 'Sonnenkind' (unblotched)	GMaP XLum
- 'Walter'	EBee NDov NEgg SPoG WCot WFar WGwG XLum XSen
'Limbo' (Coloropsis Series)	SCob
'Limerock Passion' PBR	CRos EPfP LRHS NRHS SRkn
'Limerock Ruby' PBR	CRos GMaP LRHS NRHS SCob SPer SPoG SRkn SWvt WFar XLum
major	EBee WFar
'Mambo' (Coloropsis Series)	SEle
'Mango Punch' (Punch Series)	EBee WFar
maximiliani	see *Helianthus maximiliani*
'Mercury Rising' PBR (Big Bang Series)	CRos EBee EMor IKil LPla LRHS NRHS SHar
'Moonlight' PBR	NPri
palmata	SPhx
'Pineapple Pie' PBR (Pie Series)	SCob
'Pink Sapphire' PBR	NCGa
'Polaris' (Big Bang Series)	CBod WFar
pubescens 'Sunshine Superman'	EBee ELan NHic

'Pumpkin Pie'[PBR] (Pie Series)	SCob
'Red Elf' (Li'l Bang Series)	CRos NRHS
'Red Satin' (Permathread Series)	WTor
'Redshift'	CRos EBee EMor IKil ILea LRHS NRHS SPoG
rosea	NGBl
- 'American Dream'	CBod CRos ELan EPfP GMaP LRHS NBir NGdn NRHS SPer SPlb SRms SWvt WArt WFar WGwG XLum
- 'Heaven's Gate'[PBR]	CSBt LRHS MHol SCob WFar
- 'Nana'	XLum
'Route 66'[PBR]	EBee WCAu WFar
'Ruby Frost' (Hardy Jewel Series)	EBee NHic NPri SPoG
'Salsa' (Coloropsis Series)	SEle
§ 'Schnittgold'	CRos LRHS NBre NRHS SHar
'Show Stopper'[PBR] **new**	ELan
'Sienna Sunset' **new**	CRos EBee ELan LRHS NRHS
'Snowberry'	LRHS NCGa NRHS
SOLANNA GOLDEN SPHERE	EPfP MHol NPri SPoG
'Solar Dance'	EWTr WFar WHlf
I 'Sonnenkind' (red-blotched)	CRos EBee LRHS NBre NRHS
'Star Cluster' (Big Bang Series)	CWGN EBee ELan EMor IKil MHol NRHS SPoG WFar
'Starlight' (Li'l Bang Series)	CRos NRHS WFar
'Sterntaler'	CRos EBee ELon EPfP GWyn LPot LRHS NCou NRHS SEle SPad SWvt WHrl XLum
SUN CHILD	see *C.* 'Sonnenkind' (red-blotched)
SUNNY DAY ('Balcorsunay')	WFar
'Sweet Marmalade'[PBR]	NLar
tinctoria	MNHC SRms
tripteris	ELan EPPr EPfP SMad XLum
- 'Mostenveld'	EBee
- 'Red November'	MNrw
(UpTick Series) UPTICK CREAM ('Balupteam') **new**	CBod
- UPTICK GOLD AND BRONZE ('Baluptgonz') **new**	CBod MHol
verticillata	CMac CTri EBee ECha GCal MBel MBrN MHer NLar NPer SRms WCAu WHal WOld
- 'Bengal Tiger'[PBR]	CMea ELan NCGa
- CRÈME BRÛLÉE ('Crembru'[PBR])	CRos ECtt LRHS MJak NLar NRHS SCoo SRkn
I - 'Golden Gain'	ECtt MArl NGdn WFar
- 'Golden Shower'	see *C. verticillata* 'Grandiflora'
§ - 'Grandiflora' ♀H5	CBcs CBod CRos ELan ELon EMor EPfP GMaP LRHS MArl MAvo MRav NGdn NHol NRHS NWad SHar SPer WFar XLum
- 'Limerock Dream'[PBR]	CRos EBee LRHS NRHS SCob
- 'Moonbeam'	Widely available
- 'Ruby Red'	CRos EBee EWTr LRHS NRHS
- 'Sunbeam'	ELon SCob
- 'Tweety'[PBR]	WFar
- 'Zagreb' ♀H5	Widely available

coriander see *Coriandrum sativum*; also AGM Vegetables Section

Coriandrum (*Apiaceae*)

sativum	CLau ENfk EWhm GPoy MHer MNHC NPri SPoG SRms
- 'Calypso'[PBR] ♀H2	EKin MCtn
- 'Confetti' ♀H2	EKin MCtn
- 'Leisure'	LCro LOPS SVic
- 'Slobolt'	SPhx

Coriaria ✿ (*Coriariaceae*)

intermedia B&SWJ 019	WCru
japonica	ESwi NLar SVen WCru
- B&SWJ 2833	WCru
- subsp. ***intermedia*** B&SWJ 3877	WCru
kingiana	WCru
§ ***microphylla***	GCal WCru
- B&SWJ 8999	WCru
- B&SWJ 14702 **new**	WCru
myrtifolia	WCru
- B&SWJ 14003	WCru
nepalensis	NLar WCru
- BWJ 7755	WCru
pteridoides	WCru
ruscifolia	WCru
- HCM 98178	WCru
sarmentosa	WCru
terminalis f. ***fructu-rubro***	WCru
- var. ***xanthocarpa***	GCal SBrt WCru
- - GWJ 9204	WCru
- - HWJK 2112c	WCru
thymifolia	see *C. microphylla*

Cornus ✿ (*Cornaceae*)

NJM 12.048	WPGP
alba L.	CArg CCVT CDul CLnd ECrN EMOT EWTr MRav NWea SCob SEWo SRms WMou WTSh
- 'Alleman's Compact'	LRHS
- 'Argenteovariegata'	see *C. alba* 'Variegata'
- 'Aurea' ♀H7	Widely available
- BATON ROUGE ('Minbat'[PBR])	CAby CKel CRos EBee ELon EPfP LRHS LSRN MAsh NRHS SPoG SWvt WFar
- 'Cream Cracker'[PBR] (v)	MRav
- 'Elegantissima' (v) ♀H7	Widely available
- 'Gouchaultii' (v)	CKel CMac CRos EPfP GKin LRHS MGos MJak MRav NEgg NLar NRHS SGol SPer SRms WFar WMoo
- 'Hessei' misapplied	see *C. sanguinea* 'Compressa'
- IVORY HALO ('Bailhalo'[PBR])	CKel EMil EPfP LRHS LSRN MAsh MRav NLar SPer
- 'Kesselringii'	Widely available
- RED GNOME ('Regnzam')	ELon EPfP LLHF MAsh
- 'Siberian Pearls'	CBcs CRos ELan GKin LRHS MBlu NHic NLar NRHS SPoG
§ - 'Sibirica' ♀H7	Widely available
- 'Sibirica Variegata' (v) ♀H7	CDul CKel CRos EBee ELon EPfP GKin LPot LRHS LSRN MAsh MBlu MGos NEgg NRHS SCob SLim SPer SWvt WMoo
- 'Spaethii' (v) ♀H7	Widely available
§ - 'Variegata' (v)	WFar
- 'Westonbirt'	see *C. alba* 'Sibirica'
alternifolia	CCVT CMCN CTho LPra SSta
§ - 'Argentea' (v) ♀H6	Widely available
- 'Brunette'	CJun MBlu
- GOLDEN SHADOWS ('Wstackman'[PBR]) (v)	CKel CWGN IArd MMrt SMad WHor
- 'Golden Surprise'	CJun
- 'Goldfinch' (v)	CJun MBlu
- 'Illusion' (v) **new**	CJun
- 'Moonlight' (v)	CJun
- PINKY SPOT ('Minpinky')	LSRN NLar
- 'Silver Giant' (v)	CJun NEgg NLar WSpi
- 'Variegata'	see *C. alternifolia* 'Argentea'
- 'Yellow Spring'	CJun NLar

	Name	Suppliers
	amomum	EBtc NLar
	- 'Blue Cloud'	CBcs CBod EBtc EPfP MBlu MMuc
	- 'Lady Jane'	NLar
	'Ascona'	CBcs CEnd CJun CLnd EWTr NLar SPer SSta WGob
	canadensis	Widely available
	candidissima Marshall	see *C. foemina* Mill.
	capitata	CAby CBcs CDul CJun CLnd CMac CPla CRos CTsd EPfP ESwi GKev IArd IDee IMou LRHS MGos MMuc NRHS SAko SEND SGol SMad SPoG WCru WFar WPGP
	- subsp. ***emeiensis***	CJun
	- 'Foreness Fog' (v)	SEND
	- 'Kilmacurragh Rose'	IArd IDee IMou
	aff. ***capitata*** NJM 13.046 **new**	WPGP
	'Celestial Shadow'	CKel MPkF SGol
	chinensis	SSta SWvt
	controversa	CAco CBcs CCVT CDul CMCN CNWT CTri ELan EPfP EWTr LCro LMaj LOPS LPra MBlu MGil NLar SEND SEWo SGol SSta SWvt
I	- 'Aurea'	LRHS MAsh
	- 'Candlelight'	MBlu NLar SSta
	- 'Carpe Diem'	LRHS
§	- 'Frans Type' (v)	CJun
	- 'Green Carpet'	NLar SSta
	- 'Laska'	CJun LMaj NLar
	- 'Lucia'	CJun NLar
I	- 'Marginata Nord'	NLar
	- 'Pagoda'	CJun MBlu NLar
	- 'Troya Dwarf'	CJun NLar
	- 'Variegata' (v) ♀H5	Widely available
	- 'Variegata' Frans type	see *C. controversa* 'Frans Type'
	'Dorothy'	CJun
	'Eddie's White Wonder' ♀H5	Widely available
	elliptica 'First Choice' **new**	CJun
	- 'Full Moon'	CJun
	× ***elwinortonii*** VENUS ('Kn30 8'PBR) (Jersey Star Series)	CWGN EBee EPfP LCro LOPS LRHS MAsh MBlu MPkF NLar SLon SSta WPGP
	excelsa F&M 57	WPGP
	florida	CAco CBcs CDul CMCN CRos CTho ESwi EWTr LCro LPra MMuc NOra NWea SPer WMat WMou WTSh
	- 'Appalachian Spring'	CJun
	- 'Apple Blossom'	CMen GQue
	- 'Autumn Gold'	SSta
	- CHEROKEE BRAVE ('Comco No 1')	CBcs CJun CMen CRos LMil LRHS MAsh NRHS SGol SPoG SSta WGob
	- 'Cherokee Chief'	CBcs CDul CEnd CJun CMen CRos CTho CTri EWTr LRHS LSRN NRHS SGol SPer WSpi
	- 'Cherokee Daybreak'	see *C. florida* 'Daybreak'
	- 'Cherokee Princess'	CJun CRos EWTr LRHS MAsh NOra SGol SSta WMat
	- 'Cherokee Sunset'	see *C. florida* 'Sunset'
	- 'Cloud Nine'	CBcs CMen CTho EWTr GKin NLar WGob
§	- 'Daybreak' (v) ♀H5	CBcs CKel CRos LRHS LSRN MAsh NOra NRHS SPoG WMat
	- 'Eternal Dogwood' (d)	SGol
	- 'First Lady' (v)	CMen WGob
	- 'Fragrant Cloud'	SWvt
	- 'Granary Gold'	SSta
	- 'Junior Miss'	CEnd
	- 'Pink Flame' (v)	SSta
	- 'Purple Glory'	CJun

	Name	Suppliers
	- 'Rainbow' (v) ♀H5	CBcs CJun CRos LRHS MAsh NOra NRHS NWea SGol SPoG WMat
	- f. ***rubra***	CDul ELan GKin LCro LOPS LRHS MGil MMrt MRav NEgg SPer SPoG WGob WMat
	- - 'Red Giant'	CBcs EWTr MPkF
	- - 'Spring Song'	CJun CMac CMen NEgg WGob
	- 'Spring Day'	CMac CMen WGob
	- 'Springtime'	CJun
	- 'Stoke's Pink'	CEnd CJun CMen WGob
§	- 'Sunset' (v)	CEnd CMen CRos ELan LCro LOPS LRHS MAsh NRHS SSta SWvt WGob WMat
	- 'Sweetwater'	CJun SAko WGob
	- subsp. ***urbiniana***	WPGP
	- 'Variegata' (v)	GKin
	- 'White Cloud'	CJun EWTr NOra WMat
	- yellow-leaved	SPer
§	***foemina*** Mill.	SBrt
	'Gloria Birkett'	CJun CRos LMil LRHS MAsh WGob
	'Gold Splash' (v)	NEgg
	hessei misapplied	see *C. sanguinea* 'Compressa'
	hongkongensis	LRHS NLar WPGP
	- B&SWJ 11700	WCru
	- HWJ 1033	EPfP WPGP
	- PAB 8237	LEdu
	- subsp. ***gigantea*** KWJ 12225	WCru
	- subsp. ***melanotricha***	EBee
	- subsp. ***tonkinensis*** B&SWJ 11791	WCru
	'Jerry Mundy'	CMac
	'Kelsey Dwarf'	see *C. sericea* 'Kelseyi'
	'Kenwyn Clapp'	CJun
	kousa	CBcs CCVT CMCN CMac CTho ELan EPfP GKev GKin LMaj LPra MJak NEgg NLar SCob SGol SPer SPlb WFar
	- B&SWJ 12610 from Korea	WCru
	- 'Akabana'	CJun
	- 'Akatsuki' (v)	CJun MPkF SSta
	- 'All Summer'	CJun
	- 'Autumn Rose'	CJun IArd NLar
	- 'Beni-fuji'	CRos EWTr LRHS MBlu MPkF NLar NRHS SMad WPGP
	- 'Big Apple'	CJun CRos EPfP LLHF LMil LRHS MAsh NLar SBir WGob
	- 'Blue Shadow'	CBcs CJun LRHS MBlu NLar SSta
	- 'Bultinck's Beauty'	LRHS NLar
	- 'Bultinck's Giant'	LRHS MBlu WGob
	- 'Cappuccino'	CJun EWTr LRHS MPkF NRHS SMad
	- 'Cherokee'	CJun LRHS NLar
	- 'China Dawn' (v)	CJun SSta
	- var. ***chinensis***	Widely available
	- - 'Barmstedt'	SAko
	- - 'Bodnant Form'	CAby CEnd CJun CTho EPfP ESwi EUJe NLar SChF SSta WBor WGob
	- - 'China Girl' ♀H5	Widely available
	- - 'Claudia'	EPfP IArd LRHS SSta
	- - 'Great Star'	LRHS LSRN MAsh
	- - 'Greta's Gold' (v)	CJun SSta
	- - 'Ikone'	SAko
	- - 'PVG'	CJun
	- - 'Snowflake'	CJun
	- - 'Spinners'	CJun NEgg
	- - 'Summer Stars'	CJun
	- - 'Tri-Splendor'	NLar
	- - 'White Dusted' (v)	CJun MBlu NLar SMad
	- - 'White Fountain'	EPfP LSRN MPkF MPnt NLar NOra WMat

	Name	Suppliers
	- - 'Wieting's Select'	CJun EWTr MBlu MPkF SAko
	- - 'Wisley Queen' ♀H5	CJun CRos EPfP LMil LRHS MAsh SPoG SSta WPGP
	- - 'Xanthocarpa'	CBcs IArd
	- 'Claudine'	CJun
	- 'Copacabana'	MBlu MPkF
	- 'Daybreak'	SGol
	- 'Doctor Bump'	CJun
	- 'Doubloon'	CJun
	- 'Dwarf Pink'	CJun LRHS
	- 'Ed Mezitt'	CJun LRHS NLar
	- 'Elizabeth Lustgarten'	CJun MBlu MPkF SSta
	- 'Eurostar'	ELan LRHS MBlu
	- 'Fanfare'	CJun
	- 'Fernie's Favourite'	CJun
	- GALILEAN ('Galzam')	CJun MPkF WGob
	- 'Gay Head'	CJun
	- giant-flowered	MPkF
I	- 'Girard's Nana'	CJun
	- 'Gold Cup' (v)	CJun SSta
	- 'Gold Star' (v)	CBcs CEnd CJun CMCN CRos ELan LMil MAsh MBlu NEgg NLar SChF SGol SPoG SSta WGob
	- 'Greensleeves'	CJun CRos EPfP GKev LLHF LMil LRHS MAsh SSta WGob
	- 'Heart Throb'	CJun NLar SGol WGob
	- 'Highland'	CJun
	- 'John Slocock' ♀H5	CJun IArd NLar WGob
	- 'Koree'	NLar
	- 'Kreutzdame'	CJun MBlu
	- 'Laura'	CWGN MBlu SGol SSta
	- 'Little Beauty'	CJun
	- 'Lizzie P'	NLar
	- 'Lustgarten Weeping'	CJun
	- 'Madame Butterfly'	CJun CRos LRHS MBlu NLar SPoG
	- 'Marwood Dawn'	SSta
	- 'Melanie'PBR	WMat
	- 'Milky Way'	CBod CJun CLnd CMCN CTho EPfP EWTr LMaj LRHS LSRN MAsh MBlu MGos MPkF MRav NEgg NLar SGol WGob WSpi
	- 'Milky Way Select'	CBcs CJun CRos LRHS NRHS
	- 'Miss Petty'	CJun NLar
	- 'Miss Satomi' ♀H5	Widely available
	- 'Moonbeam'	CJun EWTr NLar
	- 'Mount Fuji'	CJun MBlu NLar SSta
	- 'National'	CJun LMaj LMil LRHS MAsh NLar SSta WGob
	- 'Nicole'	LRHS WGob
	- 'Ohkan'	CJun
	- 'Pévé Foggy'	LRHS
	- 'Pévé Limbo' (v)	CJun
	- 'Pévé Satomi Compact'	CJun NLar
	- 'Polywood'	CJun NLar
	- RADIANT ROSE ('Hanros')	CJun NLar SBir SSta WGob
	- 'Rasen'	CJun NLar
	- 'Rel Whirlwind'	CJun NLar
*	- 'Robert'	NLar
	- 'Rosea'	CJun
	- 'Rosemoor Pink'	CJun
	- SAMARATIN ('Samzam') (v)	CBcs CEnd CJun LRHS LSRN SGol SSta
	- 'Schmetterling'	CJun EWTr LRHS MBlu NLar
	- 'Sluis Slim' **new**	MBlu
	- 'Snowbird'	CJun LRHS
	- 'Snowboy' (v)	CDul CEnd CLnd MBlu SMad
	- 'Snowflurries'	CJun
	- 'Southern Cross'	CJun WGob
	- 'Square Dance'	CJun
	- 'Steeple'	CJun NEgg
	- 'Summer Fun' ♀H5	CJun CRos LMil LRHS SPoG SSta
	- 'Summer Majesty'	CJun
	- 'Sunsplash' (v)	CJun LRHS SPoG SSta
	- 'Temple Jewel' (v)	CJun
	- 'Teresa'	LRHS
	- 'Teutonia' ♀H5	CJun ELan IArd MGos NLar SAko SSta WGob
	- 'Trinity Star'	CJun
	- 'Triple Crown'	CJun
	- 'Tsukubanomine'	CJun CLnd NLar
	- 'Weaver's Weeping'	CJun MPkF NLar
	- 'Weisse Fontäne'	CJun LRHS MBlu NLar
	- 'White Dream'	CJun LRHS NLar
	- 'White Giant'	CJun SPer
	- 'Willy Boy'	WHor
	- 'Wolf Eyes' (v) ♀H5	CBcs CJun ELan EPfP LMil LRHS MAsh MBlu NLar SGol SPoG SSta
	macrophylla Wall.	CMCN IDee WCru WPGP
	- var. ***macrophylla*** **new**	SSta
	mas	Widely available
	- 'Aurea' (v) ♀H6	CBcs CJun EPfP LRHS MAsh MBlu MRav NEgg NLar SGol SSta
§	- 'Aureoelegantissima' (v)	CJun CMac CRos LRHS WCot
	- 'Elegant' (F)	CAgr
	- 'Elegantissima'	see *C. mas* 'Aureoelegantissima'
	- 'Golden Glory' ♀H6	CJun CLnd EPfP NLar WHor
	- 'Gourmet' (F)	CAgr
	- 'Hillier's Upright'	CJun
	- 'Jolico' (F) ♀H6	CAgr CJun LEdu MBlu NLar WMat
	- 'Kasanlaker' (F)	CAgr LEdu NLar
	- 'Pancharevo' (F)	CAgr
	- 'Pioneer' (F)	CJun NLar
	- 'Redstone' (F)	CJun
	- 'Shan' (F)	CAgr
	- 'Shumen' (F)	CAgr NLar
	- 'Spring Glow'	CJun NLar
	- 'Variegata' (v) ♀H6	CBcs CDul CJun CMCN CMac CRos CTho EPfP LRHS MAsh MBlu MGos NLar SGol SPer
	- 'Vraća Kaštel' (F)	CAgr
	- 'Xanthocarpa' (F)	CAgr CJun
	mas* × *officinalis	CJun
	'Norman Hadden' ♀H5	Widely available
	nuttallii	CDul CLnd ELan EPfP EWTr LPra SPer SWvt
	- 'Colrigo Giant'	CJun
	- 'Gold Spot' (v)	CJun
	- 'Monarch'	CJun EWTr SPer
	- 'North Star'	CDul CJun NLar
	- 'Portlemouth'	CEnd CJun NLar
	- 'Zurico'	CJun
	oblonga	CExl EBee LEdu WPGP
	officinalis	CAgr CBcs CDul CJun CKel CMCN CRos EBee EPfP IMou LRHS MBlu MMuc NLar SWvt WSpi
	- 'Kintoki' ♀H6	NLar
	'Ormonde' ♀H5	CJun EPfP NEgg NLar SMad SSta WGob WPGP
	'Pink Blush'	CJun
	'Porlock' ♀H5	CJun CMCN CRos EPfP ITim LRHS NLar NRHS SWvt WGob WHor
	pumila	NLar
	racemosa	EBtc NLar
	rugosa	EBtc NLar
	× ***rutgersensis***	LRHS
	- (Stellar Series) AURORA ('Rutban')	CJun MBlu NLar SGol
§	- - CELESTIAL ('Rutdan')	CBcs CJun CRos LMil LRHS NLar NRHS SGol WGob

- - CONSTELLATION ('Rutcan')	CJun LMil SGol
- - RUTH ELLEN ('Rutlan')	CJun NLar
- - STARDUST ('Rutfan')	CJun
- - STELLAR PINK ('Rutgan')	CBcs CJun CRos EBee EWTr LRHS MGos NLar NRHS SAko SGol WGob WPGP
× ***rutgersiensis*** GALAXY	see *C.* × *rutgersensis* CELESTIAL
sanguinea	CBcs CCVT CDul CHab CKel CLnd CMac CPer CTho CTri ECrN EPfP LBuc LPra MMuc MRav MSwo NWea SCob SEWo SGol SPer SVic WMat WMou WTSh
§ - 'Anny'	CJun MBlu
- 'Anny's Winter Orange' ♀H6	CJun CRos ELon EShb LRHS LSvl MAsh NRHS SGol SPoG WAvo WCot
§ - 'Compressa'	MBlu MGil MRav NLar WAvo
- 'Magic Flame' ♀H6	CJun CRos ELon EPfP LRHS MAsh NLar NRHS SPoG SWvt WCot
- 'Midwinter Fire'	Widely available
- 'Variegata' (v) **new**	LPot
- 'Winter Beauty'	CJun CSBt EBee EPfP EUJe MBlu NLar NWea SLon SWvt WAvo WCFE
- 'Winter Flame'	see *C. sanguinea* 'Anny'
§ ***sericea***	LPra
- 'Bud's Yellow'	CRos ELon EPfP LRHS MBlu NLar NRHS
- 'Cardinal'	CDul CRos EBee ELon EPfP LRHS MAsh MGos NLar NRHS
- 'Flaviramea' ♀H7	Widely available
- 'Hedgerows Gold' (v) ♀H7	CKel CRos EBee ELan ELon EMil EPfP LRHS MAsh MGos NEoE NRHS SCob SPoG WFar
§ - 'Kelseyi'	CMac CRos EBee ELan EPfP MRav NLar SCob SPoG WMoo
- KELSEY'S GOLD ('Rosco')	CRos LRHS MAsh NRHS SPoG
- subsp. ***occidentalis*** 'Sunshine'	ELon EPfP NEoE NLar
§ - 'White Gold' (v)	CBod CKel EBee EHoe ELon EPfP MRav NLar SPer SPoG SRms WFar WMoo
- 'White Spot'	see *C. sericea* 'White Gold'
stolonifera	see *C. sericea*
stricta	see *C. foemina* Mill.
× ***unalaschkensis***	LLHF
walteri	EBtc
- B&SWJ 8776	WCru
wilsoniana	WPGP
'Winter Orange'	CJun CKel NLar WHor

Corokia ✿ (*Argyrophyllaceae*)

buddlejoides	CBcs CSde CTsd EBee GBin NLar SEND WFar
'Coppershine'	CCoa
cotoneaster	CBcs CDul CMac CRos CSBt CSde CTri EBee ELan EPfP EUJe LRHS MGil MGos NLar SCob SEle SIgm SPer SPoG SWvt WAvo WCot WFar WGrn WSHC
× ***virgata***	CBod CChe CRos CTri CTsd ELan EPfP LRHS NLar SArc SWvt WKif WSHC
- 'Bronze King'	CKel CRos LRHS SPer SVen
- 'Frosted Chocolate'	CCoa CKel CRos CSde CTsd EBee ELan EPfP LLHF LRHS SEND SLim SPoG SSta SVen SWvt WAvo WFar WGrn
- 'Geenty's Green'	CCoa CRos LRHS WGrn
- 'Pink Delight'	CCht EPfP MRav
- 'Red Wonder'	CKel CMac CRos ELan EPfP LRHS SEND SPoG SVen WAvo WGrn
- 'Sunsplash' (v)	CBod CCht CCoa CKel CMac CRos CTsd EBee ELan EPfP LLHF LRHS NLar SEND SEle SPoG SSta SWvt WFar WGrn
- 'Yellow Wonder'	CBcs CKel CRos ELan LRHS NLar SEND SWvt

Coronilla (*Papilionaceae*)

cappadocica	see *C. orientalis*
comosa	see *Hippocrepis comosa*
coronata	CRos LRHS NRHS
emerus	see *Hippocrepis emerus*
glauca	see *C. valentina* subsp. *glauca*
minima	WAbe
'Nan Hicks'	EWld
§ ***orientalis***	CAby CPBP EPPr
valentina	CRHN MGil
- 'Cotswold Cream' (v)	SPoG WCot
§ - subsp. ***glauca*** ♀H4	CDul CKel CMac CSBt CSde CTri EBee ELan EPfP LRHS LSRN MGil MMuc MNHC SEND SPer SRms SVen SWvt WOut XSen
- - 'Brockhill Blue'	CAby CKel EPfP LRHS SAko WCot
- - 'Citrina' ♀H4	Widely available
- - 'Lauren Stevenson' **new**	MHol WCot
* - - 'Pygmaea'	LRHS SEle SRms WAbe WCot
- - 'Variegata' (v)	CBcs CBod CKel CMac CRos CTri EBee ELan EPfP IDee LRHS MAsh MCot MGil MRav NQui SEle SLim SLon SNig SPer SPoG SRms SVen WCot
- - 'XXS' **new**	WCot
varia	see *Securigera varia*

Correa ✿ (*Rutaceae*)

alba	CCCN CExl EPfP
- 'Pinkie' ♀H3	CCCN CExl CSde CTsd
alba × ***backhouseana***	SEle
backhouseana ♀H3	CAbb CBcs CCCN CExl CHll CKel CRos CSde CTri CTsd ELan EPfP GCal IDee LRHS MGil NLar SBrt SEle SVen WAvo WSHC
- 'Peaches and Cream'	CCCN SEle SRkn
'Dusky Bells' ♀H3	CAbb CBcs CCCN CCht CHll CKel CRos CSde CTri CTsd ELan EPfP LRHS MAsh MGil SEle SPlb SPoG SRkn SVen WAvo
'Dusky Maid'	CCCN CExl
'Federation Belle'	CCCN SVen
glabra	SEle WAvo
'Harrisii'	see *C.* 'Mannii'
'Ivory Bells'	LRHS
lawrenceana	CExl CTsd LRHS SEND WPGP
- var. ***grampiana***	SVen
§ 'Mannii' ♀H3	CBcs CCCN CExl CTsd ELan EPfP LRHS MGil WSHC
'Marian's Marvel' ♀H3	CBcs CCCN CExl CKel CSde ELan EPfP IDee MAsh SEND SEle SRkn SVen
'Peachy Cream'	CAbb CCCN CSBt LRHS
'Poorinda Mary'	CCCN CKel SEle
pulchella ♀H3	CExl CMac CTri MGil SEle WAvo
- orange-flowered	WAbe
- 'Pink Mist'	WCot
reflexa ♀H3	CExl
- var. ***nummulariifolia***	MAsh MGil WAbe WCot WPGP
- var. ***reflexa***	CExl

*	- ***virens***	CExl
	schlechtendalii	CCCN CTsd MGil SEle SVen

Cortaderia ✿ (*Poaceae*)

	argentea	see *C. selloana*
	fulvida misapplied	see *C. richardii* (Endl.) Zotov
§	***fulvida*** (Buchanan) Zotov ♀H5	EUJe EWes IArd WCot
	richardii misapplied	see *C. fulvida* (Buchanan) Zotov
	richardii ambig.	CBod CChe CExl CPla EHoe IMou MMuc NBir SMad SPtp SWvt WHrl
§	***richardii*** (Endl.) Zotov ♀H5	CAby CBcs CKno CRos EWes IMou LRHS MAvo NRHS SArc SRms WPGP
	- Brown's strain	WCot
	rudiuscula	EBee
§	***selloana***	CAco CBcs CBod CTsd EMOT MGos MJak NBir NGrd SCob SGol SPlb
§	- 'Albolineata' (v)	CBcs ELon MWht SEND SWvt
§	- 'Aureolineata' (v) ♀H6	CBcs CKel CMac CRos CSde ELan EPfP GMaP LRHS MWht NRHS SCob SEND SPer SPoG SWvt
	- 'Evita'PBR ♀H6	ECtt ELan MAvo NLar SPoG SWvt WCot WFar
	- 'Gold Band'	see *C. selloana* 'Aureolineata'
	- 'Golden Goblin'PBR	CKel CKno EHoe NDai NLar SCob
	- 'Icalma'	CSde EPPr
	- 'Monstrosa' ♀H6	SEND SMad
	- 'Patagonia' ♀H6	EPPr
	- 'Pink Feather'	ELan EPfP MAsh SEND SPer WFar
	- 'Pink Phantom' new	LRHS NRHS
	- 'Pointe du Raz'	CKel EBee ELan SWvt
	- 'Pumila' ♀H6	Widely available
	- 'Rendatleri'	CBcs SCoo SLim SWvt
	- 'Rosea'	CBod CDul EMOT EPfP MJak NLar SCob SGol WFar
	- 'Senior'	NLar
	- SILVER FEATHER ('Notcort') (v) ♀H6	SCob
	- 'Silver Fountain' (v)	CRos ELan EPfP LRHS MAsh NRHS SPer SPoG
	- 'Silver Stripe'	see *C. selloana* 'Albolineata'
	- 'Splendid Star'PBR (v)	CBcs CRos EHoe LRHS MAsh MGos MJak NLar NRHS SPoG SWvt
	- 'Sunningdale Silver' ♀H6	CBcs CDul CKel CMac CRos ECha ELan ELon EPfP EUJe LRHS LSRN MGos NRHS SCob SEND SMad SPer SPoG SWvt
*	- 'White Feather'	CBod NLar SCob SPer WFar
	Toe Toe	see *C. richardii* (Endl.) Zotov

Cortusa (*Primulaceae*)

	brotheri	EBee
*	***caucasica***	GKev
	matthioli	GKev GPSL NHpl WFar
	- 'Alba'	GKev NAln NLar
	- subsp. ***pekinensis***	MPnt NBid NLar WSHC
	- - var. ***sachalinensis***	EBee GKev
	turkestanica	LLHF NWad

Corydalis ✿ (*Papaveraceae*)

	ambigua misapplied	see *C. fumariifolia*
	angustifolia	WCot
	anthriscifolia	EWes IFro LEdu MMrt
	'Blackberry Wine'	CExl CWCL EBee ECtt EMor LEdu MPnt SPoG WTor
	BLUE LINE ('Couriblue')	CWGN EMor LLHF SPoG
	'Blue Panda'	see *C. flexuosa* 'Blue Panda'
	'Bronze Beauty'	WMoo
	brunneovaginata	WCot
	bulbosa misapplied	see *C. cava*
	bulbosa (L.) DC.	see *C. solida*
	buschii	CAby EBee ELon GEdr GKev NRya
	calycosa	MAvo
	'Canary Feathers'PBR	ECtt LRHS MBNS NHpl NRHS
	cashmeriana	CRos GKev LRHS NBid NRHS WAbe WHal
	- 'Kailash'	CRos EBee LRHS NRHS
	cashmeriana* × *flexuosa	CBro WAbe
	caucasica var. ***alba*** misapplied	see *C. malkensis*
§	***cava***	EBee EMor GKev LAma NHpl WShi
	chaerophylla	EWld
	cheilanthifolia	CExl EPfP EPot EWld IMou LEdu SRms
	- 'Pinyin' new	NCGa
	'Craigton Blue'	EBee EPPr EWld GEdr GKev IMou MNrw NHar NSti WFar
	curviflora	WAbe
	- subsp. ***rosthornii***	CExl
	- - 'Blue Heron'	CBct CBod CRos CWCL CWGN ECtt EMor EWld GEdr LRHS MBNS MHol MPnt NCGa NLar NRHS SPad WFar WSHC
	davidii	CExl
	decipiens Schott, Nyman & Kotschy	see *C. solida* subsp. *incisa*
	decipiens misapplied	EPot GKev
	densiflora	GKev
	elata	CBod CRos CSpe EPot EWes GAbr GWyn IFro LRHS MArl MBel MCot MMuc MNrw NBid NBir NChi NRHS NSla SPoG SPtp WCru WHal WOut WSHC
	- 'Blue Summit'	CRos ECtt EMor EPPr IMou LRHS MBel MPnt NRHS WFar
	elata* × *flexuosa	IMou
	elata* × *flexuosa clone 1	CExl GEdr
	flexuosa ♀H5	CSpe EPfP GWyn MArl MNrw WSHC XLum
	- CD&R 528	IFro NRya
	- 'Balang Mist'	CExl
	- 'Blue Dragon'	see *C. flexuosa* 'Purple Leaf'
§	- 'Blue Panda'	CExl EPPr EWTr EWes GMaP MPnt NLar WCru
	- 'Blue Skies'	MHol
	- 'China Blue'	Widely available
	- 'Golden Panda' (v)	ITim NHpl
	- 'Hale Cat'	ECtt EMor EPPr
	- 'Nightshade'	CExl EWld LLHF NBid WCot
I	- 'Norman's Seedling'	EPPr
	- 'Père David'	CDor CMac CRos CSBt CSam CSpe CWCL EBee ECha ELan EMor EPPr EPfP GKev GWyn ITim LRHS MHer NBir NCGa NEgg SPlb SPoG SRms SWvt WCru WPnP XLum
§	- 'Purple Leaf'	Widely available
§	***fumariifolia***	GKev
	glauca	see *C. sempervirens*
	'Heavenly Blue'	GKev
	henrikii	GEdr
	heterocarpa	IMou
	incisa	LAma
	integra	GKev
	'Kingfisher'	CAby CBor CSma GEdr LEdu NLar NSla WAbe WSHC
	leucanthema DJHC 752	CExl
	- 'Silver Spectre' (v)	CExl ECha
	linstowiana	ELan
	- CD&R 605	CExl

§ ***lutea***	CBcs EPfP IFro MMuc NBir NPer NWad SEND SRms WCot WMoo
§ ***malkensis*** ♀H5	CPla CWCL EBee EHrv EMor EPot GKev LLHF MAvo NRya WThu
'Maya' (v)	XLum
moorcroftiana	CExl
nobilis	GKev LLHF MAvo SPhx
ochotensis	CRos IMou LRHS NRHS
§ ***ochroleuca***	CSpe EPot GCal NLar
omeiana	EPPr SPtp WCot WFar
ophiocarpa	EHoe ELan GCal WMoo
pachycentra	CExl WAbe
paczoskii	CRos GKev LRHS NRHS
pseudofumaria alba	see *C. ochroleuca*
'Rainier Blue'	WFar
'Rukšāns Red'	CWCL
'Sapphire'	CBro
scandens	see *Dactylicapnos scandens*
scouleri	NBir
§ ***sempervirens***	GWyn
- 'Alba'	WArt
shimienensis 'Berry Exciting'PBR	CAby CBcs CDor CKel EBee ECtt EMor MBNS MHol MPnt NCGa NPer SPoG
siamensis	IMou
- B&SWJ 7200	WCru
§ ***solida***	CAvo CElw CPla CRos EBee ECtt EMor EPfP EPot GKev LAma LEdu LRHS MPie MRav NLar NRHS NRya SDeJ SPhx WBrk WCot WShi
- 'Advocet'	GEdr
- 'Evening Shade'	GEdr
- 'Fire Bird'	GEdr GKev
- 'Firecracker'	CBor CRos GKev LLHF LRHS NRHS SPhx
- 'Frodo'	LAma
- 'Gaviota'	GEdr
§ - subsp. ***incisa*** ♀H5	EPot SDeJ SPhx
- - 'Giona' **new**	GKev
- 'Lucky Bird'	GKev
- 'Purple Beauty'	CBor GEdr GKev SPhx WTor
- 'Purple Bird'	GKev LAma LLHF SDeJ WFar
- 'Pussy'	EBee EMor
- RAINBOW (mixed)	GKev
- 'Red Giant'	GKev
§ - subsp. ***solida***	EPot GKev NBir NRya SPhx WArt WCot
- - 'Alba'	NSla
- - 'Beth Evans'	CBro CWCL ECha ELon EMor EPot ERCP GEdr GKev IFro LAma LEdu LLHF MHer MNrw NBir NHpl NLar NWad SDeJ SPhx WCot WFar
- - 'Blushing Girl'	GEdr LAma WFar
- - 'Dieter Schacht' ♀H5	EPot GEdr LAma NLar
- - 'Evening Shade'	GEdr LAma
- - 'George Baker' ♀H5	Widely available
- - 'Nettleton Pink'	GKev
- - Prasil Group	CBor GEdr GKev NHpl SPhx
- - 'White Knight'	GKev LAma NHpl WCot
- f. ***transsylvanica***	see *C. solida* subsp. *solida*
- 'Turaco'	GKev
- 'White King'	WCot
- 'White Swallow'	CBor EPot GEdr GKev SDeJ WFar
- 'Zwanenberg'	GKev
'Spinners'	CAby CDor CElw CFis EBee ECtt ELon EMor EPPr GKev GLog GPSL IMou NAln NQui WFar WPnP WSHC WTyc XLum
stipulata B&SWJ 2951	WCru
'Sylvia's Castle Haven'	MPie
taliensis	CExl EMor GCal GKev GLog
tauricola	GEdr
temulifolia 'Chocolate Stars'	CBcs CSpe CWGN EBee ECtt EMor EWTr EWld ILea LRHS MBNS MHol MPie NCGa SCob SPoG WCot WGrn WSHC
tomentella	GKev
'Tory MP'	CDor CExl CRos CSam EBee EPPr GEdr IFro LEdu LRHS MNrw MPie NBid NCGa NChi NRHS WFar WPGP XEll
transsylvanica hort.	see *C. solida* subsp. *solida*
vivipara	EPPr
'Wildside Blue'	EPPr EWld WSHC
wilsonii	CExl GKev

Corylopsis (*Hamamelidaceae*)

SDR 7921	GKev
glabrescens	CJun CRos EPfP LRHS NLar WCFE
- var. ***gotoana***	CJun CRos EPfP LRHS MAsh NLar
- - 'Chollipo'	CBcs CJun CRos LRHS NLar SSta
- 'Lemon Drop'	CJun IArd NLar
glandulifera	CJun
pauciflora ♀H5	CBcs CBod CDul CEnd CJun CRos CTho CTri CWld EBee ELan EPfP IDee LCro LOPS LRHS LSRN MAsh MGil MMuc MRav NLar NPri SCob SGol SLim SPer SPoG WPGP
platypetala	see *C. sinensis* var. *calvescens*
- var. ***laevis***	see *C. sinensis* var. *calvescens*
sinensis	CBcs EBee EPfP GKev
§ - var. ***calvescens***	CBcs CJun CTho EPfP NLar
§ - - f. ***veitchiana*** ♀H5	CJun CRos EPfP IMou LRHS MAsh NLar WCFE
§ - var. ***sinensis*** ♀H5	CCCN CDul CJun CMCN CRos CTho EBee ELon EPfP LRHS MAsh NLar SGol SLon WSpi
- - 'Spring Purple'	CBcs CEnd CJun CMac CRos EBee EPfP IDee LRHS MGos NLar NRHS SChF SPoG WPGP
- 'Veitch's Purple'	CJun NLar
spicata	CBcs CDul CJun CMCN IArd IDee LRHS MBlu MGil MMuc MRav NLar SCob SGol SLim WHor
- 'Golden Spring'	NLar
- 'Red Eye'	CJun NLar
veitchiana	see *C. sinensis* var. *calvescens* f. *veitchiana*
willmottiae	see *C. sinensis* var. *sinensis*

Corylus ✿ (*Betulaceae*)

avellana (F)	Widely available
- 'Anaconda' **new**	MBlu
- 'Anny's Purple Dream'PBR	IDee MBlu NLar
- 'Aurea'	CBcs CDul CEnd CTri ELan EPfP EUJe MAsh MBlu MGos NLar NWea SCob SLim SPer SPoG SSta SWvt WFar
- 'Bollwylle'	see *C. maxima* 'Halle'sche Riesennuss'
§ - 'Butler' (F)	CAgr CDul CMac CTri EMOT MJak SDea SRms
- 'Casina' (F)	CAgr
- 'Contorta' ♀H6	Widely available
- 'Corabel' (F)	CAgr NOra SKee SRms WMat
- 'Cosford' (F)	CAgr CCVT CDul CFGn CMac CSBt CTho CTri ECrN EPom IArd LBuc MBlu MGos NLar NOra NWea SDea SEWo SGol SKee SPer SRms SWvt WMat

– Emoa Series	WMat
§ – 'Ennis' (F)	CAgr CDul EMOT NOra SDea
– 'Feriale' (F)	CAgr
§ – 'Fuscorubra' (F)	EPom EShb MRav NLar SPoG SWvt WFar
– 'Gustav's Zeller' (F)	NOra WMat
§ – 'Heterophylla'	CDul EBee SSta
– 'Laciniata'	see *C. avellana* 'Heterophylla'
§ – 'Lang Tidlig Zeller' (F)	CAgr NOra NWea WMat
– 'Lewis' (F)	CAgr
– 'Merveille de Bollwyller'	see *C. maxima* 'Halle'sche Riesennuss'
– 'Nottingham Prolific'	see *C. avellana* 'Pearson's Prolific'
– 'Pauetet' (F)	CAgr
§ – 'Pearson's Prolific' (F)	CAgr CFGn CSBt EMOT LBuc SDea SGol SSFr
– 'Pendula'	MBlu SCoo SRms WCot
– 'Princess' (F)	SVic
– 'Purpurea'	see *C. avellana* 'Fuscorubra'
– 'Red Majestic'[PBR] ♀H6	Widely available
– 'Rouge de Zeller' (F)	SGol
– 'Tonda di Giffoni' (F)	NOra SKee WMat
– 'Webb's Prize Cob' (F)	CAgr CDul CTri ECrN ELan IArd MBlu MJak NLar NWea SDea SEND SGol SKee SSFr SVic
chinensis	EBee WPGP
colurna ♀H6	CAgr CCVT CDul CLnd CMCN EBee ECrN ELan EPfP EWTr IArd LMaj LPra MBlu MGos NLar NOra NPri NWea SCoo SGol SPer SRms WMat WMou WPGP
× ***colurnoides*** 'Chinoka' (F)	CAgr WMat
– 'Freeoka' (F)	CAgr WMat
EARLY LONG ZELLER	see *C. avellana* 'Lang Tidlig Zeller'
fargesii	WPGP
ferox	CJun
maxima (F)	CLnd CTri EPom LPra MSwo NWea SDea
– 'Butler'	see *C. avellana* 'Butler'
– 'Ennis'	see *C. avellana* 'Ennis'
– 'Fertile de Coutard'	see *C. maxima* 'White Filbert'
– 'Frühe van Frauendorf'	see *C. maxima* 'Red Filbert'
– 'Grote Lambertsnoot'	see *C. maxima* 'Kentish Cob'
– 'Gunslebert' (F) ♀H6	CCVT CDul CMac CTri ECrN EMOT NOra SDea SPoG SRms SSFr WMat
– HALLE GIANT	see *C. maxima* 'Halle'sche Riesennuss'
§ – 'Halle'sche Riesennuss' (F)	CAgr ECrN ELan EMOT MMuc NLar NOra SDea SEND SKee SSFr WMat
§ – 'Kentish Cob' (F) ♀H6	CAgr CBcs CDul CMac CSBt CTho CTri ECrN ELan EMOT EPfP EPom IArd LBuc LRHS MGos NLar SDea SEWo SKee SLim SPer SPoG SRms SSFr SVic SWvt WMat WMou
– 'Lambert's Filbert'	see *C. maxima* 'Kentish Cob'
– 'Longue d'Espagne'	see *C. maxima* 'Kentish Cob'
– 'Monsieur de Bouweller'	see *C. maxima* 'Halle'sche Riesennuss'
– 'Nottingham Cobnut' (F)	SVic
– 'Purple Filbert'	see *C. maxima* 'Purpurea'
§ – 'Purpurea' (F)	Widely available
§ – 'Red Filbert' (F) ♀H6	CDul CEnd CHab CTho EMOT EPom IArd MBlu NLar NOra SCoo SGol SKee SLim SRms SSta WCot
– 'Red Zellernut'	see *C. maxima* 'Red Filbert'
– 'Spanish White'	see *C. maxima* 'White Filbert'
§ – 'White Filbert' (F)	CHab
– 'White Spanish Filbert'	see *C. maxima* 'White Filbert'
– 'Witpit Lambertsnoot'	see *C. maxima* 'White Filbert'
'Nottingham Early' (F)	NLar
sieboldiana B&SWJ 11056	WCru
– var. ***mandshurica***	MBlu
'Te Terra Red'	CDul CMCN EPfP MAsh MBlu SLon SRms WMat WMou
tibetica	LEdu WPGP

Corymbia (*Myrtaceae*)

§ ***citriodora***	MHer SKin SPlb
§ ***eximia***	SPlb
– 'Nana' **new**	SPlb
§ ***ficifolia***	CDTJ IDee

Corynabutilon see *Abutilon*

Corynephorus (*Poaceae*)

canescens	NBir
– 'Spiky Blue'	CBod

Cosmos (*Asteraceae*)

§ ***atrosanguineus***	CBcs CMea CPla CSpe CWGN ECtt ELan EPfP LCro LOPS LSRN MRav NLar SCob SDeJ SPer SPoG SWvt WHoo
– CHOCAMOCHA ('Thomocha'[PBR])	CBcs CBod CCCN CChe CDor CPla CRos CSpe CWGN ECtt EPfP GMaP LCro LOPS LRHS MGos NLar NPri NRHS NSti SCob SEle SPer SPoG SRot WBor
– 'Spellbound'	ECtt
bipinnatus 'Antiquity'	NPri SPhx
– (Casanova Series) 'Casanova Pink' **new**	SPoG
– – 'Casanova Red' **new**	SPoG
– – 'Casanova Violet' **new**	SPoG
– – 'Casanova White' **new**	SPoG
– 'Dazzler'	LCro LOPS SPhx
– (Double Click Series) 'Double Click Cranberries' (d)	CSpe SPhx
– – 'Double Click Snow Puff' (d)	SPhx
– 'Purity'	CSpe LCro LOPS LRHS SPhx
– 'Rubenza' ♀H3	LCro LOPS SPhx
– 'Sensation Picotee' (Sensation Series)	LCro LOPS
– Sonata Series	SEle
– – 'Sonata Carmine'	EPfP NPri
– – 'Sonata Pink'	EPfP NPri
– – 'Sonata White'	CSpe EPfP NPri
– 'Sweet Sixteen'	SPhx
– 'Xanthos'	CSpe LCro LOPS NPri
caudatus	WJek
peucedanifolius	CSpe
– 'Flamingo'	CGrW EPfP ERCP SDeJ
'Razzmatazz Pink'	NPri
sulphureus 'Bunte Lichter'	CSpe
– LADYBIRD MIXED **new**	SVic
'Yellow Garden'	SPhx

Cosmos × *Dahlia* (*Asteraceae*)

'Mexican Black'	see *Dahlia* 'Mexican Black'

costmary see *Tanacetum balsamita*

Costus (*Costaceae*)

pulverulentus	LRHS

Cotinus ✿ (*Anacardiaceae*)

americanus	see *C. obovatus*
'Candy Floss'	CRos EPfP LRHS NRHS
§ ***coggygria***	CAco CBcs CMCN CMac ECrN ELan EPfP MRav MSwo NLar NWea SCob SEND SGol SPer SRms SWvt WFar XSen
- GOLDEN SPIRIT ('Ancot'PBR) ♀H5	Widely available
- GREEN FOUNTAIN ('Kolcot'PBR)	EBee LRHS
- 'Kanari'	NLar
- 'Lilla'PBR	LRHS MBlu NRHS
- 'Notcutt's Variety'	MRav
- 'Old Fashioned'PBR	MPkF NEoE NLar
- 'Pink Champagne'	NLar SSta
- Purpureus Group	EPfP SGol SRms
- 'Red Beauty'	NLar
- RED SPIRIT ('Firstpur')	NLar
- 'Royal Purple' ♀H5	Widely available
- Rubrifolius Group	CBcs CDul EPfP SEND SGol SPer SWvt
- SMOKEY JOE ('Lisjo'PBR)	CBcs CBod CRos EPfP LRHS MAsh SLon SPoG SSta SWvt
- 'Velvet Cloak'	CRos EPfP LRHS MGos MPkF NLar SLon SPer SWvt
- 'Well Spotted' new	CKel EMil
- 'Westonbirt Orange'	NLar
- 'Young Lady'PBR ♀H5	CBcs CKel CMac CRos CSBt ECrN ELon EPfP EUJe EWes GBin LRHS MAsh MBlu MJak MPkF MRav NLar SCob SCoo SGol SPer SRms SWvt WFar
DUSKY MAIDEN ('Londus'PBR)	CKel CRos CSBt CTsd ELan ELon EPfP LRHS MGos NEgg NLar NRHS SCob SLon WFar
'Flame' ♀H5	CBcs CDul CKel CRos CTho EBee ECrN ELan ELon EPfP EUJe EWTr LRHS MAsh MGos MRav NLar NRHS SCob SGbt SPer SPoG SWvt WAvo WFar
'Grace'	Widely available
§ ***obovatus***	CMCN ELon EPfP IArd LRHS MBlu MPkF MRav NLar SSta WPGP
'Ruby Glow'	CRos EPfP LCro LOPS LRHS MGos NRHS

Cotoneaster ✿ (*Rosaceae*)

acuminatus	SRms
acutifolius* var. *laetevirens	see *C. laetevirens*
adpressus	CAco SCob
§ - 'Little Gem'	NHar NLar
- var. ***praecox***	see *C. nanshan*
- 'Tangstedt'	SGol
- 'Tom Thumb'	see *C. adpressus* 'Little Gem'
affinis	SPtp SRms
albokermesinus	SRms
ambiguus Rehder & E.H.Wilson	NLar
amoenus	NLar SRms
- ACE 1028 new	SPtp
§ ***apiculatus***	NLar SRms
§ ***ascendens***	SRms
assamensis	SRms
§ ***astrophoros***	CMac MBlu NLar
atropurpureus	NLar SRms
§ - 'Variegatus' (v) ♀H6	CBcs CDul CKel CMac CRos EHoe ELan ELon EPfP LRHS MAsh MGos MJak MMuc NLar NPer NRHS SCob SCoo SEND SLim SPer SPoG SRms SWvt WAvo WFar
aurantiacus	NLar SPtp
beimashanensis	SPtp
boisianus	NLar SPtp SRms
bradyi	GBin GKev SRms
brickellii	NLar
§ ***bullatus***	CDul CTri EPfP MMuc NLar SPer SRms
- 'Firebird'	see *C. ignescens*
- f. ***floribundus***	see *C. bullatus*
- var. ***macrophyllus***	see *C. rehderi*
bumthangensis	NLar SRms
buxifolius blue-leaved	see *C. lidjiangensis*
- 'Brno'	see *C. marginatus* 'Brno'
- f. ***vellaeus***	see *C. astrophoros*
camilli-schneideri	NLar SRms
canescens	NLar SRms
chadwelli	NLar
chuanus	NLar
chungtiensis	NLar
cinnabarinus	SRms
§ ***cochleatus***	SPtp SRms
§ ***congestus***	CDul CSBt MSwo NLar SPer SPlb SRms XLum
- 'Nanus'	CBor GCrg GEdr
conspicuus	CBcs SPtp SRms
- 'Decorus' ♀H6	CKel CRos CSBt EPfP LRHS MGos MJak MMuc MSwo NWea SCob SGol SLim SNig SPer SPlb SPoG SWvt WMoo
- 'Leicester Gem'	SRms
- 'Red Glory'	CMac
- 'Winter Jewel'	see *C.* × *suecicus* 'Winter Jewel'
cooperi	SRms
* 'Coral'	ECrN
cordifolius	MBlu NLar SRms
- KW 13363 new	SPtp
cornifolius	SRms
- Og 93330 new	SPtp
§ 'Cornubia' ♀H6	Widely available
crispii	NLar
cuspidatus	MBlu NLar
dammeri	Widely available
§ - 'Major'	CBar CDul LBuc WFar
§ - 'Mooncreeper'	MMuc SCob
- 'Oakwood'	see *C. radicans*
- var. ***radicans*** misapplied	see *C. dammeri* 'Major'
- var. ***radicans*** (Dammer ex C.K.Schneid.) C.K.Schneid.	see *C. radicans*
dielsianus	NLar NWea SRms
divaricatus	EPfP NLar NWea SPer SRms
duthieanus	NLar
- 'Boer'	see *C. apiculatus*
elatus	SRms
elegans	SPtp SRms
emeiensis	NLar SRms
encavei	NLar
- KEKE 1239 new	SPtp
'Erlinda'	see *C.* × *suecicus* 'Erlinda'
'Exburiensis'	CBcs CBod CCVT CDul CKel EBee ECrN EMOT EPfP MGos MMuc MRav NOra SCob SEND SGol SPer WFar WMat
falconeri	SRms
fastigiatus	SRms
flinckii	NLar SRms
floccosus	IArd SEND SPtp

floridus	SRms
forrestii	GKev NLar SRms
franchetii	Widely available
cf. ***franchetii***	CKel
frigidus	CMCN CTho EWTr SPtp SRms
§ - 'Pershore Coral'	WAvo
froebelii	SPtp
fulvidus	NLar
gamblei	SRms
- KR 1576 new	SPtp
ganghobaensis	CMCN GKev NLar SPtp SRms
- B&L 12234	WCru
glabratus	SRms
- KR 232 new	SPtp
glacialis	CPla SRms
glaucophyllus	IArd SRms
§ ***glomerulatus***	NLar SRms
gonggashanensis	NLar
gracilis	SRms
granatensis	NLar SRms
'Green Fan' new	SPtp
harrovianus	SRms
harrysmithii	NLar
hebephyllus	NLar
hedegaardii new	SPtp
I - 'Fructu Luteo'	SPtp SRms
henryanus	SRms
- 'Corina'	SRms
'Herbstfeuer'	see *C. salicifolius* 'Herbstfeuer'
'Highlight'	see *C. pluriflorus*
hillieri	NLar SPtp
§ ***hjelmqvistii***	LBuc NLar SPtp SRms
- 'Robustus'	see *C. hjelmqvistii*
- 'Rotundifolius'	see *C. hjelmqvistii*
hodjingensis	SRms
horizontalis	Widely available
- 'Variegatus'	see *C. atropurpureus* 'Variegatus'
- var. ***wilsonii***	see *C. ascendens*
huahongdongensis new	SPtp
hualiensis	NLar SRms
- B&SWJ 3143	WCru
humifusus	see *C. dammeri*
hummelii	SRms
hupehensis	NLar
§ 'Hybridus Pendulus'	CBcs CCVT CDul CMac CTri EBee ECrN EMOT LCro LSRN MGos MJak MRav NEgg NLar NOra NPri NWea SLim SPer SPoG SRms SWvt WJas WMat
§ ***hylmoei***	NLar SPtp SRms
hypocarpus	SRms
ignavus	SRms
§ ***ignescens***	NLar NWea SRms
ignotus	SRms
incanus	NLar
induratus	SRms
insculptus	SPtp SRms
insolitus	NLar SPtp
integerrimus	SRms
§ ***integrifolius***	NLar SRms WMoo
kangdingensis	SRms
kingdonii	NLar
kitaibelii	NLar
konishii	NLar
kuanensis SICH 56A new	SPtp
kweitschoviensis	NLar
lacteus ♀H6	Widely available
- F 10419 new	SPtp
- 'Milkmaid' (v)	NLar
§ ***laetevirens***	NLar
lancasteri	NLar SRms
langei	SRms
laxiflorus	SRms
§ ***lidjiangensis***	NLar SRms
lucidus	SRms
ludlowii	SRms
magnificus	SRms
§ ***mairei***	NLar SPtp SRms
marginatus Lindl. ex Loudon	SRms
§ - 'Blazovice'	NLar SRms
§ - 'Brno'	SRms
marquandii	NLar SRms
§ ***meiophyllus***	MBlu NLar
melanocarpus	NLar
meuselii	NLar SRms
- TSS 13864 new	SPtp
meyeri	NLar
microphyllus misapplied	see *C. purpurascens*
microphyllus ambig.	CBcs CKel EBee GKev NWea SCob
microphyllus Wall. ex Lindl.	CDul CRos CTri LRHS MGos SPer WMoo
- NICE 004	WCFE
- var. ***cochleatus*** (Franch.) Rehder & E.H.Wilson	see *C. cochleatus*
- var. ***cochleatus*** ambig.	EPot NSla
- 'Donard Gem'	see *C. astrophoros*
- 'Teulon Porter'	see *C. astrophoros*
- var. ***thymifolius*** (Lindl.) Koehne	see *C. integrifolius*
- var. ***thymifolius*** ambig.	CRos LRHS MMuc
milkedandaensis	SRms
miniatus	SRms
mirabilis	NLar SRms
monopyrenus	SRms
- F 11422	GKev
'Mooncreeper'	see *C. dammeri* 'Mooncreeper'
morrisonensis	SRms
moupinensis	SRms
- BWJ 8167	WCru
mucronatus	NLar SPtp SRms
'My Pet'	GAbr
§ ***nanshan***	NWea SRms WAvo
- 'Boer'	see *C. apiculatus*
naoujanensis	EPfP NLar
- 'Berried Treasure'	CRos EPfP LRHS NEgg NRHS
nepalensis	NLar
newryensis	SRms
nitens	NLar SRms
nitidifolius	see *C. glomerulatus*
nohelii	NLar SRms
notabilis	SRms
nummularioides	SRms
nummularius Fisch. & C.A.Mey.	SRms
obscurus	SRms
obtusus Wall. ex Lindl.	NLar SRms
ogisui	GBin LEdu NAln
- Og 95105	GKev
omissus	NLar
pangiensis	SRms
pannosus	SRms
paradoxus	SRms
parkeri	NLar SRms
pekinensis	SRms
permutatus	see *C. pluriflorus*
perpusillus	SRms
'Pershore Coral'	see *C. frigidus* 'Pershore Coral'
§ ***pluriflorus***	SRms
poluninii	NLar SPtp SRms

polycarpus	SRms
praecox 'Boer'	see *C. apiculatus*
procumbens	SRms
- 'Needham' **new**	NLar
- 'Queen of Carpets' ♀H6	CBod CKel CRos EBee ELan EPfP LRHS LSRN MAsh MGos MMuc MRav NEgg NLar NRHS SCoo SLim SPoG SRms SWvt WMoo
- 'Streib's Findling'	see *C.* 'Streib's Findling'
prostratus	SRms
- 'Arnold Forster'	SPtp
przewalskii	SRms
pseudo-obscurus	SRms
§ ***purpurascens***	CRos CSBt LRHS NLar NRHS
pyrenaicus misapplied	see *C. congestus*
qungbixiensis	NLar SRms
raboutensis	NLar
racemiflorus	SRms
§ ***radicans***	CKel CMCN
§ ***rehderi***	NLar SPtp SRms
reticulatus	NLar
rhytidophyllus	GKev SPtp
- Og 95102 **new**	SPtp
rokujodaisanensis	NLar
roseus	NLar SRms
'Rothschildianus' ♀H6	Widely available
rubens W.W.Sm.	NLar
rugosus E.Pritz. ex Diels	NLar SPtp SRms
'Saint Monica'	MBlu
salicifolius	CTri MMuc MSwo NLar NWea SPtp SRms WFar
- AUTUMN FIRE	see *C. salicifolius* 'Herbstfeuer'
§ - 'Avonbank'	CEnd NLar WAvo
- 'Brno Orangeade'	SRms
- 'Brockhill Carpet' **new**	CKel
- 'Emerald Carpet'	SEND
- 'Fructuluteo' **new**	SPtp
- 'Gnom' ♀H6	CChe CDul CKel CMac CRos ELan EPfP LRHS MAsh MGos MRav NBir NEgg SCob SLim SPer SPoG SRms WAvo
§ - 'Herbstfeuer'	MRav MSwo SRms
- 'Pendulus'	see *C.* 'Hybridus Pendulus'
- 'Pink Champagne' ♀H6	CMac MRav
- 'Repens'	EPfP NOra SCob SGol SLim SPer SPoG SRms WMat
- var. ***rugosus***	see *C. hylmoei*
salwinensis	NLar SPtp SRms
sandakphuensis	SRms
scandinavicus	SRms
schantungensis	NLar SRms
schlechtendalii 'Blazovice'	see *C. marginatus* 'Blazovice'
- 'Brno'	see *C. marginatus* 'Brno'
schubertii	SRms
* ***sengorensis***	NLar
serotinus misapplied	see *C. meiophyllus*
serotinus Hutch.	SRms
shannanensis	SPtp SRms
shansiensis	NLar SPtp SRms
sherriffii	NLar SRms
sikangensis	GBin NLar SRms
simonsii	CCVT CDul CKel CLnd CMac CPer CRos EBee ECrN ELan EPfP LBuc LRHS MGos MMuc NHol NLar NWad NWea SCob SGol SRms
soczavianus	NLar
§ ***splendens***	GKev SPtp SRms
- 'Sabrina'	see *C. splendens*
spongbergii	NLar SRms
staintonii	SRms
sternianus ♀H6	EPfP NLar SPtp SRms
- ACE 2200	MSwo
aff. ***sternianus*** Yu 15716 **new**	SPtp
§ 'Streib's Findling'	CKel CRos LRHS MAsh NRHS SCob SGol
suavis	SRms
subacutus	SRms
subadpressus	SRms
submultiflorus	NLar
× ***suecicus*** 'Coral Beauty' ♀H6	Widely available
§ - 'Erlinda' (v)	SPoG SRms
- 'Ifor'	SRms
- 'Juliette' (v) ♀H6	CMac CRos EHoe EMOT EShb LRHS LSRN MAsh MJak MMrt MMuc MRav NEgg NLar NRHS SCob SCoo SLim SPer SPoG WMat
- 'Skogholm'	CBcs CRos ELan EPfP LRHS MGos MMuc NWea SCob SPer SRms
§ - 'Winter Jewel'	CKel
svenhedinii	NLar
taoensis	SRms
tardiflorus	NLar SPtp SRms
tauricus	SRms
teijiashanensis	NLar SPtp SRms
tengyuehensis	SRms
thimphuensis	NLar SRms
tomentellus	WCFE
tomentosus	SRms
transcaucasicus	NLar
trinervis	GKev
turbinatus	NLar SPtp SRms
'Valkenburg'	SRms
vandelaarii	NLar SPtp SRms
veitchii	NLar SRms
verruculosus	SRms
vestitus	NLar
villosulus	SRms
vilmorinianus	SPtp SRms
wardii misapplied	see *C. mairei*
wardii W.W.Sm.	SRms
× ***watereri***	CBod CCVT ECrN ELon EMOT EPfP MJak MSwo NWea WJas
- 'Avonbank'	see *C. salicifolius* 'Avonbank'
- 'Cornubia'	see *C.* 'Cornubia'
- 'John Waterer'	EPfP SPer SPoG
- 'Pendulus'	see *C.* 'Hybridus Pendulus'
wilsonii	NLar SRms
yalungensis	SRms
yinchangensis	SRms
zabelii	SRms

Cotula (Asteraceae)

coronopifolia	CBen CWat NPer
hispida ambig.	CPla EBou ECtt EWld GKev MBel SIgm
§ ***hispida*** (DC.) Harv.	CTri CWCL EDAr EHoe GMaP MAsh MHer NPer NRya SPoG SRms WIce XLum
lineariloba (DC.) Hilliard	ECha EWes
minor	see *Leptinella minor*
pectinata	see *Leptinella pectinata*
'Platt's Black'	see *Leptinella squalida* 'Platt's Black'
potentilloides	see *Leptinella potentillina*
pyrethrifolia	see *Leptinella pyrethrifolia*
reptans	see *Leptinella scariosa*
scariosa	see *Leptinella scariosa*
squalida	see *Leptinella squalida*

Cotyledon (*Crassulaceae*)

chrysantha see *Rosularia chrysantha*
oppositifolia see *Umbilicus oppositifolius*
orbiculata CPbh SPlb WCot
- var. **oblonga** EShb WCot
- 'Silver Waves' MCot
simplicifolia see *Umbilicus oppositifolius*
tomentosa subsp. **ladismithensis** ♀H1c SAll

courgette see AGM Vegetables Section

Crambe (*Brassicaceae*)

abyssinica SPhx
cordifolia ♀H5 Widely available
maritima Widely available
- 'Lilywhite' CAgr LEdu SVic
tatarica GJos

cranberry see *Vaccinium macrocarpon*, *V. oxycoccos*

Crassula ✿ (*Crassulaceae*)

anomala see *C. atropurpurea* var. *anomala*
arborescens EShb EUJe SChr SSim
argentea see *C. ovata*
§ **atropurpurea** var. **anomala** SChr
- subsp. **arborescens** 'Blue Mist' SAll SEND
'Buddha's Temple' SSim
coccinea CPbh EShb SPlb WCot
* **coralloides** new CPBP
cordata new EShb
lycopodioides variegata see *C. muscosa* 'Variegata'
multicava CSBt SEND
muscosa EShb SChr SPlb SRot
§ - 'Variegata' (v) EShb SSim
obtusa SRot
§ **ovata** ♀H2 EBak NCft NGBl NPer SAll SChr SEND SPlb SPre SSim SVen WThu
- 'Gollum' ♀H2 EShb NCft SAll SEND
- 'Hummel's Sunset' (v) ♀H2 EShb SAll
- 'Minima' SAll
* - **nana** SEND
- 'Undulata' WCot
- 'Variegata' (v) EBak EShb SAll WCot
pellucida EShb
subsp. **marginalis** f. **rubra**
* - - 'Variegata' (v) SSim
perfoliata EShb SEND SRot WCot
var. **falcata** ♀H2
perforata 'Variegata' (v) EShb EUJe NWad SRot SSim
portulacea see *C. ovata*
rupestris ♀H2 SAll SSim
§ **sarcocaulis** ♀H3 CBcs CMea CPla CTri EBou ELon GCrg GMaP MAsh NHpl SBrt SIgm SPlb SPoG SRms SRot SVen WAbe WHoo WIce WSHC
I - 'Alba' NHpl
sedifolia see *C. setulosa* 'Milfordiae'
sediformis see *C. setulosa* 'Milfordiae'
setulosa SPlb
§ - 'Milfordiae' CTri NBir NHpl NRya WAbe
socialis LLHF
tetragona SAll SEND
* **tomentosa** 'Variegata' (v) EShb
trachysantha SEND

+ *Crataegomespilus* (*Rosaceae*)

'Jules d'Asnières' NLar

× *Crataegosorbus* (*Rosaceae*)

miczurinii 'Ivan's Belle' CAgr

Crataegus (*Rosaceae*)

sp. LPra SWvt
arnoldiana CAgr CDul CLnd CTri EBee ECrN MAsh MCoo MMuc NLar NWea SEND SPer SPoG WMat
'Autumn Glory' CEnd CLnd EBee ECrN
azarolus CDul
§ **coccinea** L. CAgr CDul CLnd CNWT EBee LMaj LPra NWea WMat
cordata see *C. phaenopyrum*
crus-galli misapplied see *C. persimilis* 'Prunifolia'
crus-galli L. CCVT CDul CLnd CNWT ECrN EPfP LPra MAsh NWea SPer WJas
douglasii EBtc
× **durobrivensis** CAgr CDul CLnd EPfP MBlu
ellwangeriana CAgr ECrN WCot
- 'Fire Ball' MBlu
eriocarpa CLnd
gemmosa CAgr
× **grignonensis** ♀H7 CBcs CDul CLnd CTho ECrN ELan MAsh MMuc SPer WJas
harbisonii IArd
jonesiae EPfP
laciniata misapplied see *C. orientalis*
§ **laevigata** CCVT LPra NWea SCob
- 'Coccinea Plena' see *C. laevigata* 'Paul's Scarlet'
- 'Crimson Cloud' see *C. laevigata* 'Punicea'
- 'Gireoudii' CBod EMOT WJas
- 'Mutabilis' CTri SGol
§ - 'Paul's Scarlet' (d) ♀H7 Widely available
- 'Pink Corkscrew' EPfP LLHF MAsh MBlu WCot
- 'Plena' (d) CDul CKel CLnd CMac CSBt CTri EBee ECrN ELan EMOT EPfP MGos MRav MSwo NOra NWea SEWo SGol SLim SPer SWvt WMat
§ - 'Punicea' ♀H7 Widely available
- 'Rosea' GKin
- 'Rosea Flore Pleno' (d) ♀H7 Widely available
× **lavalleei** CCVT CDul CLnd CMCN CTri ECrN ELan EMOT MMuc MRav MSwo SCoo SLon WTSh
- 'Aurora' NLar
- 'Carrierei' ♀H7 CDul CMac CNWT CTho EPfP LMaj LPra LSRN NWea SCoo SEND SEWo SPoG WMat WMou
mexicana see *C. pubescens* f. *stipulacea*
mollis CAgr ECrN EPfP WSpi
monogyna Widely available
§ - 'Biflora' CDul CEnd CTho CTri MAsh MCoo MGos SLim WMat WSpi
- 'Compacta' LLHF LPra MAsh MBlu WCot
- 'Praecox' see *C. monogyna* 'Biflora'
- 'Stricta' CCVT CDul CLnd CSBt ECrN EPfP IDee LMaj LPra MMuc SGol SPer
- 'Variegata' (v) ECrN
× **mordenensis** 'Toba' (d) CDul CLnd LRHS SGol
nigra CDul
§ **orientalis** ♀H6 CCVT CDul CEnd CLnd CMCN CTho CTri ECrN ELan EMOT EPfP EWTr IArd IMou MAsh MCoo MGos NLar NWea SCoo SLim WJas WMat WMou WSpi
oxyacantha misapplied see *C. laevigata*

	pedicellata	see *C. coccinea* L.
	persimilis	LMaj
§	- 'Prunifolia' ♀H7	Widely available
	- 'Prunifolia Splendens'	CAgr CCVT EBar EBee EWTr LBuc LMaj NOra WMat
§	***phaenopyrum***	CDul CLnd CTho EBee EPfP SPtp
	pinnatifida var. ***major***	CDul CEnd ECrN EPfP LEdu MCoo
	- - 'Big Golden Star'	CAgr CFGn CLnd CTho EBee EMOT EPfP MBlu MCoo NOra NWea WMat
	'Praecox'	see *C. monogyna* 'Biflora'
	prunifolia	see *C. persimilis* 'Prunifolia'
§	***pubescens*** f. ***stipulacea***	CDul CTho ECrN EPfP
	punctata	EPfP
	- f. ***aurea***	EPfP MBlu
	sanguinea	EPfP
	schraderiana	CAgr CDul CLnd CTho EBee EBtc EPfP EWTr NLar WMat
	submollis	CLnd
	succulenta 'Jubilee'PBR	CAgr EBee MCoo NOra WMat
	- var. ***macracantha***	CMCN
	tanacetifolia	CAgr CDul CTho EPfP MBlu
	viridis 'Winter King'	CAgr EPfP
	wattiana	CDul CLnd EBee

Crataegus × *Mespilus* see × *Crataemespilus*

Crataegus + *Sorbus* see + *Crataegomespilus*

Crataegus × *Sorbus* see × *Crataegosorbus*

× *Crataemespilus* (*Rosaceae*)

grandiflora	CDul CLnd

Craterocapsa (*Campanulaceae*)

congesta	CPBP

Cremanthodium (*Asteraceae*)

SDR 7968	GKev
arnicoides	EBee GKev
decaisnei	GKev

Crenularia see *Aethionema*

Crepis (*Asteraceae*)

aurea	CPla
incana ♀H5	CBor CPla ECtt EWld GBin GCrg NChi NRHS NSla SRms WAbe
rubra	CSpe

Crinitaria see *Aster*

Crinodendron (*Elaeocarpaceae*)

hookerianum ♀H4	Widely available
- 'Ada Hoffmann'	CBcs CBod CCCN CEnd CExl CMac CPla CRos CTsd ELon EPfP GCal GKin LRHS MBlu MGil MGos MJak MPkF NLar SCob SEle SGol SLim SWvt WFar WPav WSHC
patagua	CBcs CCCN CDul CExl CMac CPla CRos CTsd EBee ELan ELon EPfP ESwi GBin LRHS MGil NLar SEND SEle SPlb SVen WPav

Crinum (*Amaryllidaceae*)

	amoenum	CCCN EShb GKev
	asiaticum	EUJe
§	***bulbispermum***	CPrp
	capense	see *C. bulbispermum*
	'Carolina Beauty'	WCot
	'Cintho Alpha'	GKev SDeJ SPer
	'Elizabeth Traub'	WCot
	'Ellen Bosanquet'	CCCN CRos ELan GKev LAma LRHS NRHS WCot
	'Emma Jones'	WCot
	'Hanibal's Dwarf'	WPGP
	mauritianum new	WHil
	moorei	CBro CTca LEdu SChr WPGP
	- f. ***album***	CCCN CTca EBee GKev LAma
	'Ollene'	WCot
§	× ***powellii***	CAby CBcs CBod CBro CExl CPrp CRos CTca EBak ECha ELan ELon EPfP EShb GCal GKev LAma LEdu LRHS MAvo MNrw MRav NRHS NWad SDeJ SEND SMad SPer SRms WCot
	- 'Album'	Widely available
	- 'Bak-madder'	EBee
	- 'Harlemense'	EBee
	- 'Krelagei'	EBee
	- 'Longifolium'	see *C. bulbispermum*
	- 'Roseum'	see *C.* × *powellii*
	'Sangria'	EUJe WCot
	'Summer Nocturne'	WCot
	'White Queen'	WCot
	yemense misapplied	GKev

Criogenes see *Cypripedium*

Crithmum (*Apiaceae*)

maritimum	CEls EBou GPoy LRHS MNHC SPhx SPlb SRms WJek

Crocosmia (*Iridaceae*)

'Abundant Joy' new	EBee
'African Beauty'	ECtt IBal
'Anna Marie'	CTca EBee ECtt ELan GKev LAma MAvo WFar
'Anniversary'	IBlr
'Apricot'	ECrc IBal
'Apricot Surprise'	ECtt IBal
aurea misapplied	see *C.* × *crocosmiiflora* 'George Davison' Davison
aurea ambig.	CPrp CRos EShb GCal LRHS NRHS
aurea (Pappe ex Hook.f.) Planch.	CPou ECrc IBal IBlr LEdu
- from Swaziland	GCal IBal
- subsp. ***aurea***	CTca ECrc GKev IBlr
- - 'Maculata'	IBlr
- 'Golden Ballerina'PBR	CAbb EBee ECtt EWes IBal MHol MWat NCGa SCob SPoG
- subsp. ***pauciflora***	IBlr
- 'Zomba'	GCal
'Auricorn'	IBal IBlr IKil LEdu
'Auriol'	IBlr
'Aurora'	NGdn
'Ballyrogan Sundown'	CTca IBlr
'Baywalker'	MAvo
'Beth Chatto'	CTca ECrc IBal
'Big Top'	IBal
'Blaze'	IBal
'Bowland Blaze'	IBal MAvo
BRESSINGHAM BEACON ('Blos')	CRos IBlr LRHS NRHS
'Bressingham Blaze'	CBre CPrp CRos CTca IBal IBlr LRHS NGdn NHol NRHS
Bridgemere hybrid	ECrc
BRIGHT EYES ('Walbreyes'PBR)	CRos EPfP LRHS MAvo NRHS
'Buttercups'	CMea WCAu WSpi

	'Cadenza'	IBal IBlr NWad
	'Caistor Sunset'	IBal
	'Carnival'	IBlr
	'Cascade'	IBal IBlr
	'Chinatown'	IBal IBlr
	'Chrome'	CSam
	'Chrome Spray'	CTca IBlr
	'Citronella' misapplied	see *C.* × *crocosmiiflora* 'Honey Angels'
	'Comet' Knutty	CRos CTca IBal IBlr LRHS MAvo NRHS WMoo
	'Cornish Copper'	CTca SMad
	× ***crocosmiiflora***	CTca CTri IBlr LCro LOPS SPlb SRms WBrk WMoo WShi
	- 'A.J. Hogan'	CPrp IBal IBlr NHol
	- 'African Glow'	EBee ECrc IBal
	- 'Amberglow'	CElw CExl GWyn IBal IBlr NHol NPer
	- 'Apricot Queen'	IBlr NHol
	- 'Autumn Gold'	ECrc IBlr
	- 'Baby Barnaby'	CBre EBee WFar
	- 'Babylon' ♀H4	Widely available
	- 'Best of British'	ECtt
	- 'Bicolor'	CElw CTca IBlr
	- 'Burford Bronze'	IBal NHol
	- 'Burnt Umber'	IBal
	- 'Butterball'	NAln
	- 'Buttercup'	CDor CRos CSam CTca ECrc ECtt EPfP IBal IKil LAma LRHS MAvo NHol NRHS SMad SRkn WFar WMoo WSpi
	- 'Canary Bird'	CBro CSam ECrc ECtt IBal NGdn NHol WBrk WSpi
§	- 'Carmin Brillant' ♀H4	Widely available
	- 'Challa'	ECrc ECtt IBal
	- 'Citrina'	MNrw
	- 'Citronella' J.E. Fitt	CBro CExl CRos CSam EBee ECrc EPfP GMaP LRHS MBel NGdn NHol NRHS
§	- 'Coleton Fishacre'	CExl CNor CRos CSam CTca CWCL ECha ECrc ECtt ELan EPfP GMaP IBlr LRHS MMuc MNrw NAln NBid NChi NHol NRHS SEND SMad SPer SPtp WCot WFar WHoo WMoo WOld
§	- 'Columbus'	CAvo CBod CKel CPrp CRos CSam CTca ECrc EPfP EWhm GKev IBal ILea LAma LRHS MAvo MTis NHol NRHS SMad SPer SRms WFar WMoo WWtn
	- 'Colwall'	IBal IBlr NWad
	- 'Comet'	EBee IBal
	- 'Constance'	CBro CDor CRos CSam CTca ECtt IBal LAma LRHS MAvo NBid NGdn NHol NRHS WBrk
	- 'Corona'	CPrp IBal IBlr MAvo NHol
	- 'Corten'	IBlr
§	- 'Croesus'	IBal IBlr
	- 'Custard Cream'	CPrp CRos ECrc LRHS NHol NRHS
	- 'D.H. Houghton'	IBlr
	- 'Daisy Hill'	IBlr
	- 'David Fitt'	MAvo WFar
	- 'Debutante'	CPrp CTca EBee ECrc IBal IBlr NHol SHar WHoo WSHC
§	- 'Diadème'	CWCL IBal
	- 'Dusky Maiden'	CMac ECtt ELon GKin GMaP IBal MMuc MSwo NHol SRms SWvt WMoo
	- 'Dwarf Gold'	IBal
§	- 'E.A. Bowles'	CPou ECrc
	- 'Eastern Promise'	CBre IBal MAvo
	- 'Elegans'	ECrc ECtt IBal
§	- 'Emily McKenzie'	Widely available
	- 'Fantasie'	ECrc IBal
	- 'Fire Jumper'	CTca EBee EMor GWyn IBal MAvo
	- 'Fireglow' PBR	CRos EBee ECtt GKev IBal LAma LRHS NRHS
	- 'George Davison' misapplied	see *C.* × *crocosmiiflora* 'Golden Glory' ambig., *C.* 'Sulphurea'
§	- 'George Davison' Davison	Widely available
	- 'Gillian'	IBal
	- 'Gloria'	ECrc IBal MAvo SMad
	- 'Golden Glory' misapplied	see *C.* × *crocosmiiflora* 'Diadème'
§	- 'Golden Glory' ambig.	CBod CDor CExl CWCL ELan ELon EMor EShb GKev GWyn IBal MSwo NBir SCob SPer SRms WJam
	- 'Goldfinch'	CPrp EBee ECrc
	- 'Goldie'	WFar
	- 'Hades'	IBal IBlr
	- 'Harlequin'	CBod CElw CKel CPrp CTca EBee ECrc EMor IBal ILea LLHF LRHS MAsh MAvo MBNS MHer MSCN MTis SPoG SWvt WFar WTor
	- 'Harvest Sun'	IBlr
	- 'His Majesty'	CBro CPrp ECrc IBal IBlr NHol WFar WMoo
	- 'Hoey Joey'	ECrc
§	- 'Honey Angels'	Widely available
	- 'Honey Bells'	ECrc WBrk WJam WOld
	- 'Irish Dawn'	ECrc IBal IBlr IKil MAvo NHol NWad
§	- 'Jackanapes'	CBor CMea CRos ECtt ELon GCal IBal IBlr IKil LRHS MNrw MSCN SRms
	- 'Jackanapes VI'	IBal
	- 'James Coey' misapplied	see *C.* × *crocosmiiflora* 'Carmin Brillant'
	- 'James Coey' J.E. Fitt	ECha EPfP GKin IBal NDov NGdn NLar SPoG WMoo
§	- 'Jessie'	CElw
	- 'Judith'	IBal
	- 'Kiautschou'	CWCL IBal IBlr NHol
	- 'Lady Hamilton'	CExl CRos CTca ECtt GCal IBal IBlr LRHS MAvo NHol NRHS WMoo WOut
	- 'Lady McKenzie'	see *C.* × *crocosmiiflora* 'Emily McKenzie'
	- 'Lady Oxford'	IBal NHol
	- 'Lady Wilson'	CRos LRHS NRHS
	- 'Lambrook Gold'	CAvo ECrc IBal
	- 'Lord Nelson'	CExl IBal NHol
	- 'Loweswater'	ECrc IBal
	- 'Lutea'	ECrc ECtt IBal
	- 'Marjorie'	IBal
	- 'Mars'	ECrc EWes IBal NGdn
	- 'Mephistopheles'	CBor CPrp CTca IBlr MAvo NHol WFar
	- 'Merryman'	ECrc IBal MAvo
	- 'Météore'	CRos ECtt EPfP LRHS MBNS NRHS WFar
	- 'Morgenlicht'	ECrc IBal NHol WFar
	- 'Mount Usher'	CPrp CTca ECrc ECtt GCal IBal MNrw NHol
§	- 'Mrs Geoffrey Howard'	CRos IBal LRHS NCGa NHol NRHS SHar SRms WCru
	- 'Mrs Morrison'	see *C.* × *crocosmiiflora* 'Mrs Geoffrey Howard'
	- 'Newry Seedling'	see *C.* × *crocosmiiflora* 'Prometheus'

- 'Nimbus'	CPrp IBal
§ - 'Norwich Canary'	CRos CTca ECha ECtt IBal LAma LRHS MRav NBir NGdn NHol NRHS SPer WMoo WSpi
- 'Olympic Fire'	NHol
- 'Pepper'	IBlr
- 'Ping Pong'	CTca
- 'Plaisir'	IBal IBlr NBid NHol
- 'Polo'	CRos CSam CWCL ECrc ECtt IBal LRHS NRHS
- 'Princess'	see *C. pottsii* 'Princess'
- 'Prolificans'	ECrc IBal
§ - 'Prometheus'	CRos CTca IBal IBlr LRHS NHol NRHS
§ - 'Queen Alexandra' J.E. Fitt	EBee ECha EWes IBlr WHal WMoo
- 'Queen Charlotte'	IBal IBlr
- 'Queen Mary II'	see *C.* × *crocosmiiflora* 'Columbus'
- 'Queen of Spain'	EBee IBal
- 'Rayon d'Or'	ECrc IBal
- 'Red King'	CBro CDor CKel CRos CWld EBee EPfP GKev IBal LRHS NLar NPri NRHS WBrk WFar WMoo WRHF
- 'Red Knight'	IBal
- 'Rheingold' misapplied	see *C.* × *crocosmiiflora* 'Diadème'
- 'Saint Clements'	IBal IBlr NHol
- 'Saracen' Y^{H4}	CBcs CBro CMac CTca CWCL EBee ECtt ELon EMor EShb GBin GCal GKin IBal LEdu LRHS MAvo MBNS MHol MNrw NLar NRHS NSti SPoG WAul WCot WFar WMoo
- 'Severn Seas'	ECtt
- 'Sir Mathew Wilson'	IBal
- 'Solfatare' Y^{H4}	Widely available
- 'Solfatare Coleton Fishacre'	see *C.* × *crocosmiiflora* 'Coleton Fishacre'
- 'Star of the East' Y^{H4}	Widely available
- 'Sultan'	CExl WFar WMoo
- 'Sunglow'	CBod CPla CWld EBee ECtt EPfP ERCP GKev IBal LAma LRHS MNrw NPri NWsh SHar SPad WHil WOut
- 'Twilight Fairy Gold'	CAvo CBod CPou CTca EBee ECha ECtt EMor IBal MBNS MHol NCou NHpl SMad SPer WCot WSpi
- 'Venus'	CBre CDor CKel ECtt GPSL IBal MHer NHol WMoo
- 'Vesuvius'	ECrc GCal IBal WSHC
- 'Vic's Yellow'	IBal
- 'Voyager'	CRos ECtt ERCP GKev IBal IKil LRHS NHol NLar NRHS SDeJ
- Wasdale strain	ECrc IBal
- 'Zeal Tan'	CBod CExl CPrp CSam CTca CWCL EBee ECtt ELan ELon EMor EPot EWhm GBin IBal LEdu LLWG LRHS MBNS MNrw NLar NRHS NSti SPoG WAul WCAu WCot WFar WHoo WMoo
× ***crocosmioides*** 'Castle Ward Late'	CBod CPrp ECtt EPfP GCal IBal IBlr LEdu LRHS MAvo NEgg NHol NLar NRHS SRms WCot WFar WMoo
§ - 'Vulcan' Leichtlin	CTca IBlr WHil
'Darkleaf Apricot'	see *C.* × *crocosmiiflora* 'Coleton Fishacre'
'Doctor Marion Wood'	IBal
'Eldorado'	see *C.* × *crocosmiiflora* 'E.A. Bowles'
'Elegance'	IBlr
'Ellenbank Canary'	IBal MAvo
'Ellenbank Firecrest' Y^{H4}	CTca EBee ECrc IBal IPot MAvo MHCG NCGa
'Ellenbank Goldcrest'	WSHC
'Ellenbank Skylark'	IBal MAvo
'Emberglow'	Widely available
'Fandango'	IBal IBlr NHol
'Fernhill'	ECrc IBal IBlr
'Fire King' misapplied	see *C.* × *crocosmiiflora* 'Jackanapes'
'Fire King' ambig.	CRos IBal LAma LRHS NLar NRHS NSti SWvt
'Fire Sprite'	IBlr
'Firebird'	CRos ECtt ELon IBal IBlr LRHS MHol NHol NRHS SRms WCot
'Firecracker'	IBlr
'Firefly'	CRos EBee ECtt EPfP GKev IBlr LRHS MAsh NRHS
'Flaire'	IBlr
'Fleuve Jaune'	IBal
'Forest Fire'	IBal LLHF
fucata	CTca
- 'Jupiter'	see *C.* 'Jupiter'
fucata × ***paniculata***	IBal
'Fugue'	CTca IBal IBlr SMad
'Gold Sprite'	IBlr
'Golden Dew'	ECtt IBal MBNS NCGa WCot WFar WMoo
GOLDEN FLEECE *sensu* Lemoine	see *C.* × *crocosmiiflora* 'Coleton Fishacre'
'Hellfire' Y^{H5}	Widely available
'Highlight'	ECrc IBal IBlr MAvo NHol NWad
'Jennine'	IBal
JENNY BLOOM ('Blacro'^{PBR})	CRos EBee IBal LRHS NRHS
'John Boots'	ECtt ELon IBal LAma LRHS MCot NBid NLar SMad SRms
§ 'Jupiter'	CDor CKel CRos CSam CTca CWCL EBee GCal IBal LRHS MAvo MNrw NChi NHol NLar WHil
'Karin'	CRos CTca EBee ECrc GKev LRHS MAsh NRHS WFar
'Kathleen'	ECrc
'Kilmurry Orange' **new**	IKil
'Krakatoa'	CHll CPrp EBee ECrc IBal LLHF MBel MHer SWvt WFar WMoo
'Lady Ann'	EBee ECrc GKev MAsh
'Lady Jane'	CRos CTca EBee ECrc EPfP GKev LRHS NRHS
'Lady Wilson' misapplied	see *C.* × *crocosmiiflora* 'Norwich Canary'
'Lana de Savary'	CPrp CTca EBee ECtt EWes GCal IBal IBlr MNrw NBid NHol NWad SMad WCot
'Late Cornish'	see *C.* × *crocosmiiflora* 'Queen Alexandra' J.E. Fitt
'Late Lucifer'	CTri GCal IBal IBlr MNrw
'Late Yellow'	IBal
'Lemon Spray'	CTca IBal IBlr
'Limpopo'	Widely available
'Lincolnshire Gold'	ECrc
'Lucifer' Y^{H5}	Widely available
LUCIFER'S CHILDREN	ELan EPfP
'Malahide Castle Red'	SMad WMoo
'Mandarin'	IBlr
'Marcotijn'	IBal
masoniorum Y^{H4}	Widely available
- from Satan's Nek, South Africa	IBal
- 'African Dawn'	CTca EBee ECrc ECtt
- 'Amber'	IBlr
- 'Dixter Flame'	IBlr SMHy WOut
- 'Flamenco'	IBlr
- 'Golden Swan'	SRms
- Holehird strain	ECtt
- hybrid	ECrc

	Name	Suppliers
	- 'Kiaora'	IBlr
	- 'Moira Reid'	ECtt IBal
	- red-flowered	IBlr
	- 'Rowallane Apricot'	IBlr
	- 'Rowallane Orange'	GBin IBal IBlr IKil
	- 'Rowallane Yellow' ♀H4	CRos CTca EBee GCal IBal IBlr IKil IMou LRHS MNrw NCGa NHol NRHS SMHy WSHC
	- 'Sherbert Orange'	IBal MAvo
	- Slieve Donard selection	IBal
	- 'Sunflare'	IBlr
	- 'Tropicana'	IBlr
	mathewsiana	CTca
	'Mex'	IBal LEdu SMad
	'Ministar'	CRos CTca EBee ECrc GKev LRHS MAsh NRHS WFar
	'Minotaur'	IBal IBlr
	'Miss Scarlet'	CRos EPfP LRHS NRHS SAko SCob
	'Mistral'	CCCN CRos CTca ECtt EPfP GAbr GKev IBal IBlr LAma LEdu LRHS NHol NLar NRHS SCob WFar WMoo
	'Moorland Blaze'	WMoo
	'Moorland Sunset'	IBal WMoo
	'Mount Stewart'	see *C.* × *crocosmiiflora* 'Jessie'
	'Mr Bedford'	see *C.* × *crocosmiiflora* 'Croesus'
	'Okavango'PBR	CBcs CBor CBre CBro CMac CPrp CTca ECtt ELon EMor EPfP EPot GBin IBal LPla LSun MAvo MBNS MHol MNrw NEgg NLar NSti WCAu WCot WFar
	OLD HAT	see *C.* 'Walberton Red'
	'Orange Devil'	CBre ECtt EUJe GKin IBal LLHF LRHS MBNS NRHS WGoo
	ORANGE PEKOE ('Pek Or')	EBee IBal LCro LOPS NSti SMad WHil
	'Orange River'	WCot WFar
	'Orangeade'	CTca ECtt IBal NHol SRms
	'Pageant'	IBal
§	***paniculata***	CMac CPou CTca ECtt GAbr LEdu NBid SCob WBrk WMoo WOut WShi
	- brown/orange-flowered	IBlr
	- 'Cally Greyleaf'	EBee GBin GCal IBal MAvo MNrw SMHy WCot
	- 'Cally Sword'	GCal IBal MAvo
	- 'Major'	CTri IBlr
	- 'Natal'	CPrp CTca ECtt IBal NHol
	- red-flowered	IBal IBlr SWvt
	- triploid	IBlr
	aff. ***paniculata***	IBlr
	'Paul's Best Yellow' ♀H4	Widely available
	'Peach Spray'	CTca
	'Peach Sunrise'	IBal
	pearsei	IBlr
	'Phillipa Browne'	CSde ECtt EHoe EPot IBal MNrw NLar SCob WCot WMoo
	'Plancheon'	IBal
	pottsii	CRos CTca EBee GWyn LEdu LRHS NRHS WPtf
	- CD&R 109	CPou
	- 'Culzean Pink'	CElw CExl CPrp CTca EBee EPPr EWhm GAbr GBin GCal IBal IBlr LPla MNrw NBid NBir NHol WFar WOut
	- deep pink-flowered	IBlr WMoo
	- 'Grandiflora'	IBal
§	- 'Princess'	CRos EBee ECtt GKev IBal LAma LRHS NRHS
	- tall	IBal SBrt
	'Pride of Plantion'	CTca ECrc ILea
	'Prince of Orange'	CBod CRos EBee EPfP ERCP GKev LAma LLHF LRHS NRHS SDeJ WFar WWtn
	'Queen Alexandria'	CRos LRHS NRHS
	'R.W. Wallace'	IBal
	'Raspberry Spray'	IBlr
	'Red Star'	IBal
	rosea	see *Tritonia disticha* subsp. *rubrolucens*
	'Rowden Bronze'	see *C.* × *crocosmiiflora* 'Coleton Fishacre'
	'Rowden Chrome'	see *C.* × *crocosmiiflora* 'George Davison' Davison
	'Ruby Velvet'	IBlr
	'Saffron Queen'	IBlr
	'Sampford Yellow'	IBal
	'Saturn'	see *C.* 'Jupiter'
	'Scarlatti'	CRos CTca EBee ECtt GAbr GKev IBal IBlr LRHS NHol
	'Scarlet Wonder'	CTca
	'Severn Sunrise' ♀H5	Widely available
	'Shocking'	IBal IBlr MAvo
	'Sonate'	ECrc
	'Sorento'	IBlr
	'Spitfire'	CExl CPrp CSam CTca ECtt ELan GAbr GQue IBal IBlr MArl MAvo MRav NHol SWvt WFar WOld
§	'Sulphurea'	CExl CPou CRos CSam ECtt EPfP IBal IBlr LRHS NHol
	'Sun Flare'	CTca
	'Sunzest'	ECrc ECtt WHoo
	'Suzanna'	EBee ECrc ECtt LAma
	'Tamar Double Red'	CTca SMad
	'Tamar Glow'	CTca WOld
	'Tamar Gold' **new**	CTca
	'Tamar Golden Ring'	CTca
	'Tamar New Dawn'	CTca
	'Tamar Peace'	CTca SMad
	'Tangerine Dream'	IBlr
	'Tangerine Queen'	GAbr IBal IBlr NHol NWad WMoo
	'Tangerine Spray'	IBlr
	'Tiger'	CElw CTca
	'Toccata'	IBlr
	'Twilight Fairy Crimson'	CTca CWGN EBee ECrc ECtt EMor GBin LEdu NHpl
I	'Vulcan' A. Bloom	CTca IBal IBlr MAvo
	'Vulcan' Leichtlin	see *C.* × *crocosmioides* 'Vulcan' Leichtlin
§	'Walberton Red'	CSam CTca EBee EWes IBal MAvo NCGa NWad SMad
	WALBERTON YELLOW ('Walcroy'PBR)	CRos EPfP LRHS NRHS SMad
	'Zambesi'PBR	CBro CMac ECtt ELon IBal MBNS MNrw MTis WCot
	'Zeal Giant' ♀H4	CTca ECtt IBal IBlr MAvo NHol
	'Zeal Unnamed'	CPrp CTca ECrc ECtt IBal NHol

Crocus ✿ (*Iridaceae*)

	Name	Suppliers
	adanensis	EPot
	'Advance'	EMor ERCP GKev LAma SDeJ
§	***albiflorus***	GKev WShi
	- blue-flowered	GKev
	- purple apex	GKev
	ancyrensis	EPot GKev SDeJ
	- 'Golden Bunch'	CRos LRHS NRHS SDeJ WShi
§	***angustifolius*** ♀H6	EPot GKev SDeJ WShi
	- 'Berlin Gold'	GKev
	- bronze-flowered	GKev
	- 'Minor'	EPot

	Name	Suppliers
	antalyensis yellow-flowered	GKev
	'Ard Schenk'	CRos GKev LAma LRHS NRHS
	asturicus	see *C. serotinus* subsp. *salzmannii*
	asumaniae	EPot GKev
	'Aubade'	EPot GKev LAma
	aureus	see *C. flavus* subsp. *flavus*
	banaticus ♀H6	EPot GKev LLHF NHar NHpl
	- 'Snowdrift'	GKev NHar
	biflorus 'Blue Pearl' ♀H6	CAvo EMor EPfP EPot ERCP GKev LCro LOPS MJak NBir SCob SDeJ SPer SPhx WCot WShi
	- subsp. ***melantherus***	GKev
	- 'Miss Vain'	EPot ERCP GKev LAma
	- subsp. ***pulchricolor***	GKev
	- 'Serevan'	EPot
	- subsp. ***stridii***	EPot GKev
	- subsp. ***tauri***	EPot
	- subsp. ***weldenii*** 'Albus'	EPot GKev LAma
	- - 'Fairy'	GKev LAma
	'Blue Bird'	EPot
	blue-flowered	CRos LRHS NRHS
	boryi	CRos GKev LRHS NRHS
	cancellatus	SDeJ
§	- subsp. ***cancellatus***	EPot GKev LAma
	- var. ***cilicicus***	see *C. cancellatus* subsp. *cancellatus*
	- subsp. ***lycius***	EPot
	candidus var. ***subflavus***	see *C. olivieri* subsp. *olivieri*
	cartwrightianus ♀H6	CRos LRHS NRHS WShi
	- 'Albus' misapplied	see *C. hadriaticus*
	- 'Albus' Tubergen ♀H6	EPot GKev SDeJ
	- 'Marcel'	GKev
	chrysanthus ♀H6	CHab
	- 'Blue Peter'	EPot
	- 'Constellation'	EPot
	- 'Cream Beauty' ♀H6	CAvo CRos EPfP EPot ERCP GKev LAma LCro LOPS LRHS MJak NBir NRHS SCob SDeJ WShi
	- 'E.A. Bowles' misapplied	see *C. chrysanthus* 'E.P. Bowles'
§	- 'E.P. Bowles' ♀H6	LAma
	- var. ***fuscotinctus***	EPot GKev LAma LCro LOPS MJak SDeJ
	- 'Goldene Sonne'	EPot
	- 'Zwanenburg Bronze' ♀H6	SDeJ
	'Cloth of Gold'	see *C. angustifolius*
	clusii	see *C. serotinus* subsp. *clusii*
	corsicus ♀H6	EPot GKev
	dalmaticus	EPot
	- 'Petrovac'	GKev
	'Dorothy'	EPot GKev MJak WShi
	'Dutch Yellow'	see *C.* × *luteus* 'Golden Yellow'
	'Early Gold'	GKev
	etruscus 'Rosalind'	GKev
	- 'Zwanenburg'	CRos EPot GKev LAma LRHS NRHS SDeJ
	'Fantasy'	GKev WShi
§	***flavus*** subsp. ***flavus*** ♀H6	EPot GKev LAma WShi
	fleischeri	EPot GKev LAma
	'Flower Record'	CAby CArg GKev LAma LRHS NBir SDeJ
	gilanicus	GKev
	'Gipsy Girl'	CAvo EMor EPfP EPot ERCP GKev LAma LCro LOPS SCob
	'Golden Mammoth'	see *C.* × *luteus* 'Golden Yellow'
	'Goldilocks' ♀H6	GKev LAma SDeJ
	goulimyi ♀H6	CAvo CRos EPot LAma LRHS NRHS SDeJ WCot
	- 'Albus'	see *C. goulimyi* subsp. *goulimyi* 'Mani White'
§	- subsp. ***goulimyi*** 'Mani White' ♀H4	EPot
	- subsp. ***leucanthus***	GKev
	'Grand Maître'	CAvo GKev LAma SDeJ
	'Haarlem Gem'	GKev
§	***hadriaticus*** ♀H6	CRos GKev LAma LRHS NRHS
	- 'Alepohori'	GKev
	- 'Annabelle'	GKev
	- var. ***chrysobelonicus***	see *C. hadriaticus*
	- subsp. ***hadriaticus*** f. ***lilacinus***	GKev
	- 'Jumbo'	GKev
	'Herald'	CAvo GKev LAma SDeJ
	heuffelianus subsp. ***heuffelianus***	GKev WShi
§	- subsp. ***scepusiensis***	GKev
	imperati subsp. ***suaveolens***	EPot
	- - 'De Jager'	CAvo ERCP GKev LAma SDeJ
	'Jeanne d'Arc'	CAby CArg CAvo EPot GKev LAma LCro LOPS LRHS NBir SDeJ WShi
	'Jeannine'	GKev SDeJ
	karduchorum	EPot GKev LAma
	'Karin'	EPot
	'King of the Striped'	GKev LAma SDeJ SPer
	korolkowii	GKev LAma
	- 'January Gold'	GKev
	- 'Kiss of Spring'	EPot GKev
	kosaninii	GKev
	- 'April View'	GKev LAma
	kotschyanus ♀H6	GKev SDeJ
	- 'Albus'	GKev SDeJ
§	- subsp. ***kotschyanus***	EPot GKev SDeJ
	- 'Reliance'	GKev
	'Ladykiller'	EMor EPot GKev LAma SPhx WShi
	laevigatus ♀H4	GKev
	- CE&H 612	EPot
	- 'Fontenayi'	EPot ERCP GKev
	large-flowered blue **new**	MJak
	'Large Yellow'	see *C.* × *luteus* 'Golden Yellow'
§	***ligusticus*** ♀H6	EPot GKev LAma
	longiflorus ♀H6	CRos EPot LRHS NRHS
§	× ***luteus*** 'Golden Yellow' ♀H6	CArg CAvo EPot LAma LCro LOPS LRHS WShi
§	- 'Stellaris' ♀H6	EPot
	malyi ♀H6	GKev
	- 'Sveti Roc'	GKev LAma
	mathewii	EPot GKev NHpl
	- 'Dream Dancer'	EPot GKev
	medius	see *C. ligusticus*
	minimus	EPot ERCP GKev LAma LLHF
	- 'Bavella' **new**	CAvo
	- 'Spring Beauty'	EMor EPfP ERCP GKev SDeJ
	'Negro Boy'	EPot
	niveus	CRos EPot GKev LAma LRHS NRHS
	nudiflorus	EPot GKev LAma
	ochroleucus	EPot GKev SDeJ
	olivieri AH 0156	GKev
§	- subsp. ***balansae*** 'Orange Monarch'	EPfP ERCP GKev LAma LLHF SCob
	- - 'Zwanenburg'	EPot
§	- subsp. ***olivieri***	GKev
	- - 'Little Tiger'	GKev
	'Orange Monarch'	see *C. olivieri* subsp. *balansae* 'Orange Monarch'
	pallasii VV KR.75	GKev
	- subsp. ***turcicus***	GKev
	paschei	EPot

pestalozzae GKev
- var. ***caeruleus*** GKev
'Pickwick' CAby CArg CAvo GKev LAma LCro LOPS LRHS MJak NBir SDeJ WShi
'Prins Claus' CRos EPfP EPot ERCP GKev LAma LCro LOPS LRHS NBir NRHS SDeJ
pulchellus ♀H6 CAvo GKev LAma SDeJ WCot
- 'Albus' EPot
- 'Inspiration' GKev
'Purple Heart' GKev
purple-striped **new** MJak
'Purpureus' see *C.* 'Purpureus Grandiflorus'
§ 'Purpureus Grandiflorus' SDeJ
'Queen of the Blues' EPot SDeJ
'Rainbow Gold' GKev
'Remembrance' CArg CAvo EPot GKev LAma LCro LOPS LRHS NBir SDeJ WShi
reticulatus EPot GKev
'Romance' CRos EPot GKev LAma LRHS NBir NRHS SDeJ
'Ruby Giant' CAvo CRos EMor EPfP EPot ERCP GKev LAma LCro LOPS LRHS MJak NBir NRHS SCob SDeJ SPer SPhx WShi
rujanensis EPot
salzmannii see *C. serotinus* subsp. *salzmannii*
sativus CAvo CBod CTca ELan EPot ERCP GAbr GKev GPoy ILea LAma LCro LOPS NBir SCob SDeJ SVic WFar
'Saturnus' EPot LAma
scepusiensis see *C. heuffelianus* subsp. *scepusiensis*
§ ***serotinus*** subsp. ***clusii*** LAma
- - 'Poseidon' GKev
§ - subsp. ***salzmannii*** GKev LAma
- - 'Atropurpureus' WCot
- - 'Erectophyllus' GKev
sibiricus see *C. sieberi*
§ ***sieberi*** EPot
- 'Albus' see *C. sieberi* 'Bowles's White'
- subsp. ***atticus*** 'Amfiklia' GKev
- - 'Firefly' CRos EPfP EPot ERCP GKev LAma LRHS NRHS SDeJ
§ - 'Bowles's White' ♀H6 EPot SDeJ
- 'Hubert Edelsten' ♀H6 EPot GKev LAma
- 'Ronald Ginns' EPot
- subsp. ***sublimis*** 'Tricolor' ♀H6 CArg CAvo CRos CTca EPfP EPot GKev LAma LCro LOPS LRHS NBir NRHS SDeJ WOld
- 'Violet Queen' LAma
'Snow Bunting' ♀H6 CAvo CTca ELan EPfP EPot GKev LAma LCro LOPS NBir SCob SDeJ SPer WShi
speciosus ♀H6 CAvo EPfP LAma LCro LOPS NBir SDeJ WShi
- 'Aino' GKev
- 'Aitchisonii' CRos GKev LRHS NRHS
- 'Albus' ♀H6 CAvo EPot ERCP GKev LCro LOPS SDeJ WShi
- 'Artabir' CRos GKev LRHS NRHS SDeJ
- 'Cassiope' CRos GKev LAma LRHS NRHS SDeJ
- 'Conqueror' CRos ELan EPfP ERCP GKev LAma LCro LOPS LRHS NRHS SDeJ
- 'Oxonian' CRos ELan EPot GKev LAma LRHS MCot NRHS WOld
- subsp. ***speciosus*** EPot GKev NBir SDeJ
- subsp. ***xantholaimos*** GKev
× ***stellaris*** see *C.* × *luteus* 'Stellaris'
susianus see *C. angustifolius*
suterianus see *C. olivieri* subsp. *olivieri*
thomasii EPot GKev
tommasinianus ♀H6 CArg CAvo CGrW CHab CTca ELan EPot LAma LCro LOPS MRav NBir SDeJ SPhx SRms WShi
- 'Albus' EPot GKev LAma WShi
- 'Barr's Purple' CRos EPot GKev LAma LCro LOPS LRHS NBir NRHS SDeJ
- 'Eric Smith' EPot
- 'Lilac Beauty' EPot GKev LAma
- 'Pictus' EPot GKev LAma LLHF WShi
- 'Roseus' EPot ERCP GKev LAma SDeJ SPhx WCot WShi
- 'Rubinetta' GKev
- 'Whitewell Purple' CAvo CRos EPot ERCP GKev LAma LCro LOPS LRHS NBir NRHS SDeJ WCot WShi
tournefortii ♀H4 CAvo CRos EPot GKev LRHS NRHS
'Twinborn' EPot
vallicola EPot GKev
'Vanguard' ♀H6 EPot GKev LAma LCro LOPS SDeJ WCot
vernus GKev
- subsp. ***albiflorus*** see *C. albiflorus*
- 'Drina Marvel' GKev
- 'Graecus' EPot GKev
- 'Krasno Polje' GKev
- 'Michael's Purple' GKev
- Uklin strain GKev
- subsp. ***vernus*** 'Grandiflorus' see *C.* 'Purpureus Grandiflorus'
versicolor JMH 8215 GKev
- 'Picturatus' EPot GKev LAma LLHF SDeJ WShi
vitellinus EPot GKev
'Yalta' CAvo ERCP GKev SPhx WCot
'Yellow Giant' SDeJ
'Yellow Mammoth' see *C.* × *luteus* 'Golden Yellow'
'Zenith' EPot
'Zephyr' ♀H6 GKev SDeJ WOld
zonatus see *C. kotschyanus* subsp. *kotschyanus*

Croomia (*Stemonaceae*)

heterosepala WCru

Crossandra (*Acanthaceae*)

infundibuliformis ♀H1a EShb

Crossyne (*Amaryllidaceae*)

flava WCot

Crotalaria (*Papilionaceae*)

laburnifolia ♀H2 CCCN

Crowea (*Rutaceae*)

exalata × ***saligna*** CExl

Crucianella (*Rubiaceae*)

stylosa see *Phuopsis stylosa*

Cruciata (*Rubiaceae*)

§ ***laevipes*** NMir

Crusea (*Rubiaceae*)

coccinea CSpe SBrt WCot
- 'Crûg Crimson' CAby WCru WSHC

Cryptanthus × *Billbergia* see × *Cryptbergia*

× *Cryptbergia* (*Bromeliaceae*)

'Rubra' SChr

Cryptocarya (*Lauraceae*)

alba GBin SVen

Cryptocoryne (*Araceae*)

× ***willisii*** XBlo

Cryptogramma (*Pteridaceae*)

crispa WHer

Cryptomeria ✿ (*Cupressaceae*)

fortunei see *C. japonica*
§ ***japonica*** CAco CMen CPer CTho EPfP LPra MAsh MBlu MMuc NWea SEND SPer SWvt WMou WTSh
- 'Antique Gold' LRHS
- Araucarioides Group NEgg SLim
- 'Atawai' NLar
- 'Bandai-sugi' 🏆H6 CKen CMac CMen EPfP IArd MGos NHol NLar SRms
- 'Barabits Gold' LRHS
- 'Birodo' CKen
- 'Black Dragon' SLim
- 'Blue Diamond' CAco
- 'Compressa' CKen EMOT EPfP LBee LRHS MAsh NLar NWad SRms
§ - 'Cristata' CAco CMac ELan LRHS MGos MPkF NEgg SRms
- 'Dacrydioides' LRHS NLar
- 'Dinger' CAco CKen NLar
- Elegans Group CBcs CDul CMac CSBt ELan EMOT EPfP LRHS MGos NEgg NLar NOra SCoo SEND SLim SPer SPoG SRms WFar WMat
- - 'Elegans' 🏆H6 CAco CKel MGil NWea
- 'Elegans Aurea' CCVT ELan LRHS NEgg SPoG SWvt WFar
- 'Elegans Compacta' 🏆H6 CMac CSBt ELan GBin LBee LRHS MAsh MMuc NLar NWea SRms SWvt
- 'Elegans Nana' MGil SRms
- 'Elegans Viridis' 🏆H6 LRHS MGil NOra SLim WMat
I - 'Elegantissima' CCVT
- 'Filip's Winter Magic' NLar
- 'Globosa Nana' 🏆H6 CAco CDul CKel EMOT EPfP LBee MGos NEgg NHol SArc SCoo SPoG
- 'Golden Promise' 🏆H6 CAco CBcs CBod MAsh NHol NRya NWad SLim SPer SWvt
- 'Jindai-sugi' NLar
- 'Kilmacurragh' CKen NWea
- 'Kohui-yatsubusa' CKen
- 'Koshiji-yatsubusa' NLar
- 'Koshyi' CKen
- 'Little Champion' CKen LRHS SLim
- 'Little Diamond' CKen NEgg
- 'Little Sonja' CAco CKen SLim
- 'Little Yoko' CKen NLar
- 'Littleworth Dwarf' see *C. japonica* 'Littleworth Gnom'
§ - 'Littleworth Gnom' LRHS
- 'Lobbii' CAco
- 'Lobbii Nana' hort. see *C. japonica* 'Nana'
- 'Majiro-sugi' **new** NLar
- 'Midare' CAco NLar
- 'Monstrosa' NLar
- 'Mushroom' SLim
§ - 'Nana' SRms
- 'Osaka-tama' CKen
- 'Pipo' CKen
- 'Pygmaea' NHol NLar NWad SRms
- 'Rasen-sugi' IDee NLar SMad
- 'Sekkan-sugi' 🏆H6 CAco CBcs CBod CCVT CDul CMac EPfP ESwi GBin GKin IArd LBee LRHS MAsh MGos NEgg NLar SCoo SLim SMad SPoG SWvt
- 'Sekka-sugi' see *C. japonica* 'Cristata'
§ - 'Spiralis' 🏆H6 CAco CKen ELan EPfP LBee LRHS MAsh MGos NEgg NHol NLar NWea SAko SCoo SLim SPoG SRms SWvt
§ - 'Spiraliter Falcata' NLar
§ - 'Tansu' CAco CKen LRHS MGil
- 'Tenzan-yatsubusa' **new** CMen
- 'Tenzan-sugi' 🏆H6 CKen NHol NLar
- 'Tilford Gold' EMOT NHol
- 'Toda' CKen
- 'Twinkle Toes' **new** CKen
- 'Vilmorin Gold' NHol
- 'Vilmoriniana' 🏆H6 CKen CMen CTri ELan EPfP GKin LRHS MAsh MGil MGos NEgg NHol NLar SCoo SEND SLim SPoG SWvt
- 'Winter Bronze' CKen
- 'Yatsubusa' see *C. japonica* 'Tansu'
- 'Yellow Twig' NLar
- 'Yore-sugi' see *C. japonica* 'Spiralis', 'Spiraliter Falcata'
- 'Yoshino' CKen NEgg SLim
sinensis see *C. japonica*

Cryptostegia (*Apocynaceae*)

grandiflora CCCN

Cryptotaenia (*Apiaceae*)

japonica CAgr CHby CLau CPou GPoy LEdu MNHC SRms WHer WJek
- f. ***atropurpurea*** CDor CSpe EBee EHoe EWhm LEdu LPla MNrw WBor WPGP

Ctenanthe (*Marantaceae*)

§ ***burle-marxii*** XBlo
lubbersiana 🏆H1b XBlo
oppenheimiana XBlo

Cucubalus (*Caryophyllaceae*)

baccifer NLar

cucumber see AGM Vegetables Section

Cudrania see *Maclura*

cumin see *Cuminum cyminum*

Cuminum (*Apiaceae*)

cyminum SRms SVic

Cunninghamia (*Cupressaceae*)

konishii CExl
§ ***lanceolata*** CAco CBcs CDul CKen CMCN CMac CTho EPfP IDee LRHS MGil SSta WPGP
- 'Glauca' CAco CExl CJun
sinensis see *C. lanceolata*
unicaniculata see *C. lanceolata*

Cunonia (*Cunoniaceae*)

capensis CExl

Cuphea (*Lythraceae*)

cyanea CSpe LSvl
hyssopifolia 🏆H2 CTsd EShb SWvt WHil
- 'Alba' CCCN CLau CPbh EShb SWvt

	- pink-flowered	CCCN CPbh
	- red-flowered	CCCN
	- 'Rosea'	SWvt
§	***ignea*** ♀H2	CTsd
	- 'Matchless'	SVic
	'Lilac Belle'	CSpe
§	***llavea*** 'Georgia Scarlet'	CCCN
	- 'Tiny Mice'	see *C. llavea* 'Georgia Scarlet'
I	***macrophylla*** hort.	CHII
	maculata	CCCN
	platycentra	see *C. ignea*
	viscosissima	CSpe ELan MCot

× *Cupressocyparis* see × *Cuprocyparis*

Cupressus (*Cupressaceae*)

	arizonica 'Conica Glauca'	CAco
	- var. ***glabra*** 'Aurea'	MAsh SGol
	- - 'Blue Ice'	CAco CMac CTho MAsh MGos NEgg SLim SWvt
	- - 'Compacta'	CKen
I	- - 'Fastigiata'	CCVT ECrN EPfP
*	- - 'Lutea'	NEgg
	- 'Pyramidalis' ♀H5	SEND SGol
	cashmeriana ♀H3	CAco
	- KR 8688A **new**	WPGP
	dupreziana var. ***atlantica***	CAco WPav
§	***funebris***	CAco CDul
	× ***leylandii***	see × *Cuprocyparis leylandii*
	lusitanica 'Brice's Weeping'	CAco CKen NEgg SLim
	- 'Pygmy'	CKen
	macnabiana	GLog
	macrocarpa	CBcs CBod CCVT CDul CPer CTho SEND
	- 'Compacta'	CKen
	- 'Gold Spread'	SLim
	- 'Goldcrest' ♀H4	CBcs CBod CCVT CDul CKel CMac ECrN ELan EMOT LRHS MGos NBir NPri SEWo SGol SLim SWvt
	- 'Golden Pillar'	SWvt
	- 'Lohbrunner'	CKen
	- 'Pygmaea'	CKen
	- 'Sulphur Cushion'	CKen
	- 'Wilma' ♀H4	CKel CSBt ELan EMOT LBee LRHS MAsh MGos SCoo SEND SGol SLim SPoG SWvt
	- 'Woking'	CKen
	nootkatensis	see *Xanthocyparis nootkatensis*
	sempervirens	EUJe LPra LRHS SPlb
	- 'Agrimed'	CCVT
	- 'Bolgheri'	LSRN
	- 'Green Pencil'	CKen
	- 'Pyramidalis'	see *C. sempervirens* Stricta Group
	- var. ***sempervirens***	see *C. sempervirens* Stricta Group
§	- Stricta Group	CAco CBcs CCVT CDul CTho LMaj LPra LRHS NLar SArc SEND SEWo SGol WCFE
	- 'Swane's Gold'	CBcs CKen MAsh NEgg
	- 'Totem Pole'	CAco CCVT CKel CKen CSBt CTho CTri ELan EMOT EPfP EUJe LBee LRHS MAsh MGos SCoo SEND SPoG SWvt
	torulosa	CAco CMCN

Cupressus × *Xanthocyparis* see × *Cuprocyparis*

× *Cuprocyparis* ✿ (*Cupressaceae*)

§	***leylandii***	Widely available
I	- '2001'	CBod CCVT SGol
	- 'Blue Jeans'[PBR]	SEND
§	- 'Castlewellan'	CBcs CCVT CDul CKel CMac CSBt CTri EMOT EPfP LBuc LPra LSRN MAsh MGos MJak MMuc NPri NWea SCob SEND SGol SLim SPer SPoG SWvt WAvo WFar WTSh
	- EXCALIBUR GOLD ('Drabb'[PBR])	CPer
	- 'Ferngold'	MAsh
	- 'Galway Gold'	see × *C. leylandii* 'Castlewellan'
	- 'Gold Rider' ♀H6	CBod CKel CMac ELan MAsh MGos MMuc NEgg NWea SCob SCoo SEND SGol SPer SPoG SWvt
§	- 'Harlequin' (v)	CMac SEND SWvt
	- 'Leighton Green'	WTSh
	- 'Naylor's Blue'	CMac SEND
	- 'Olive's Green'	SWvt
	- 'Robinson's Gold'	CMac NWea SGol
	- 'Silver Dust' (v)	WAvo
	- 'Variegata'	see × *C. leylandii* 'Harlequin'
	- 'Winter Sun'	WCFE

Curculigo (*Hypoxidaceae*)

	capitulata	XBlo
	crassifolia B&SWJ 2318	WCru
	- HWJ 683 from Vietnam	WCru
	- NJM 10.123 **new**	WPGP

Curcuma ✿ (*Zingiberaceae*)

	alismatifolia	SDeJ
	longa	GPoy SPlb SPre
	roscoeana	SDeJ
	zedoaria 'Bicolor Wonder'	CCCN
	- 'Pink Wonder'	CCCN
	- 'White Wonder'	CCCN SDeJ

Curio (*Asteraceae*)

§	***articulata***	EShb SEND
§	***ficoides***	EShb
§	***repens***	EShb SSim
§	***rowleyanus***	EBak EShb SSim
	talinoides subsp. ***mandraliscae*** 'Blue Finger'	WCot

Curtonus see *Crocosmia*

Cussonia ✿ (*Araliaceae*)

	gamtoosensis	WCot
	natalensis	WCot
	paniculata	CDTJ CWGN
	sphaerocephala	WCot
	spicata	CDTJ SPlb
	zuluensis	WCot

custard apple see *Annona cherimola*

Cyananthus (*Campanulaceae*)

	incanus	GEdr GKev
	integer misapplied	see *C. microphyllus*
	lobatus ♀H5	GKev LLHF
	- 'Albus'	NHar WAbe
	- giant	GEdr NHar WAbe
	lobatus × ***microphyllus***	EWld GCrg GEdr WAbe
	longiflorus	GKev
	macrocalyx	NHar
§	***microphyllus*** ♀H5	GCrg GEdr GKev NHar NSla WAbe
	microphyllus × 'Sherriff's Variety'	NHar

	sherriffii	WAbe
	spathulifolius	EPot WAbe

Cyanastrum (*Tecophilaeaceae*)

	cordifolium	GKev

Cyanotis (*Commelinaceae*)

	beddomei ♀H1b	EShb
	somaliensis ♀H1b	EShb

Cyathea ✿ (*Cyatheaceae*)

	australis	CBct CBdn CDTJ CKel IDee SPlb
	brownii	CKel
	cooperi	CAbb CBcs CBct CBdn CDTJ CKel ESwi EUJe ISha WFib
*	- 'Brentwood'	EBee ESwi ISha
	cunninghamii	CKel
	dealbata	CBdn CDTJ CKel GBin
	dregei	SPlb
	medullaris	CBdn CKel
	robusta	CKel
	smithii	CDTJ CKel
	tomentosissima	CDTJ CKel

Cyathodes (*Ericaceae*)

	colensoi	see *Leucopogon colensoi*
	fraseri	see *Leucopogon fraseri*

Cycas (*Cycadaceae*)

	panzhihuaensis	CBrP SPlb
	revoluta ♀H2	CAbb CBcs CBrP CCCN CKel EPfP EShb EUJe LCro LOPS SArc SChr SEND SMad SPlb XBlo
	revoluta* × *taitungensis	CBrP
§	***rumphii***	CBrP
	taitungensis	CBrP
	thouarsii	see *C. rumphii*

Cyclamen ✿ (*Primulaceae*)

	abchasicum	see *C. coum* subsp. *caucasicum*
	africanum	CBro CRos GKev LRHS MAsh NRHS XEll
§	***alpinum***	CRos EPot GKev LAma LRHS MAsh NRHS SDeJ XEll
	- 'Nettleton White'	MAsh
	balearicum	CRos EPot GKev LAma LRHS MAsh NRHS
	cilicium ♀H3	CAby CBro CRos EPot ERCP GJos GKev LAma LCro LOPS LRHS MAsh NHpl NRHS NSla WHoo WShi XEll
	- f. ***album***	CRos EPot GKev LAma LLHF LRHS MAsh NRHS XEll
	colchicum	MAsh
	confusum	GKev
§	***coum*** ♀H5	Widely available
	- var. ***abchasicum***	see *C. coum* subsp. *caucasicum*
	- 'Ashwood Snowflake'	MAsh
§	- subsp. ***caucasicum***	MAsh
	- subsp. ***coum***	CBro
	- - f. ***albissimum*** 'George Bisson'	MAsh
	- - - 'Golan Heights'	MAsh
	- - - 'Lake Effect'	MAsh
	- - f. ***coum*** Nymans Group	MAsh
	- - - Pewter Group ♀H5	GEdr GKev NAln WCot XEll
	- - - - 'Maurice Dryden' ♀H5	CBro CRos EPot GKev LAma LRHS MAsh NRHS WHoo
	- - - - 'Tilebarn Elizabeth'	MAsh NBir WHoo
	- - - 'Roseum'	CAvo GKev
	- - - Silver Group	CBro CRos EPot GKev LRHS NRHS NRya WHoo
	- - - - red-flowered	WHoo
	- - magenta-flowered	WHoo
	- - f. ***pallidum*** 'Album'	CAvo CWCL EMor EWhm GEdr GKev GMaP GWyn LAma LCro LOPS SDeJ SPer WHoo WPnP WShi
	- dark pink-flowered	CAvo WHoo
	- hybrid	ERCP
	- marble-leaved	WHoo
	- 'Marianne' **new**	SAko
	- 'Meaden's Crimson'	LAma
I	- 'Rubrum'	GKev GWyn LCro LOPS
	- silver speckled leaf	CAvo EHrv
	creticum	MAsh
	cyprium	CRos GKev LAma LRHS MAsh NRHS XEll
	- 'E.S.'	MAsh WThu
	- 'Galaxy'	MAsh
	× ***drydeniae***	MAsh
	elegans	MAsh
	europaeum	see *C. purpurascens*
	graecum	CBro CRos EPot GKev LAma LLHF LRHS MAsh NRHS WThu XEll
	- subsp. ***candicum***	MAsh
	- subsp. ***graecum*** f. ***album***	CBro CRos GKev LAma LRHS MAsh NRHS XEll
	- - f. ***graecum*** 'Glyfada'	GKev LAma MAsh XEll
§	***hederifolium*** ♀H5	Widely available
	- S&L 175/1	WCot XLum
	- 'Amaze Me'	ECtt MAvo MHol WCot
	- var. ***hederifolium*** f. ***albiflorum*** ♀H5	CAby CAvo CBro EBou EMor GKev LAma LCro LEdu LOPS NWad SCob SDeJ WHoo WPnP XLum
	- - - 'Album'	CWCL EHrv SDeJ WShi
	- - - Bowles's Apollo Group	NWad
	- - - 'Discovery'	WCot
	- - - 'Nettleton Silver'	see *C. hederifolium* var. *hederifolium* f. *albiflorum* 'White Cloud'
	- - - 'Perlenteppich'	GMaP
	- - - silver-leaved	SDys
§	- - - 'White Cloud' ♀H5	MAsh NHpl WHoo
	- - f. ***hederifolium*** 'Fairy Rings'	MAsh
	- - - 'Rosenteppich'	CAby
	- - - 'Ruby Glow'	CRos CWCL LRHS MAsh NBir NRHS WThu
	- - - Silver Cloud Group ♀H5	CAby CBro EHrv MAsh NBir WHoo
	- - - 'Silver Shield'	MAsh
	- - - 'Stargazer'	MAsh
	- island scented strain	WCot
	- 'Lysander'	GKev MAsh
	- 'Pewter Mist'	LAma
	- 'Red Sky'	CBro LAma NWad
	- 'Rose Pearls'	SRot
	- 'Silver Leaf'	see *C. hederifolium* Silver-leaved Group
§	- Silver-leaved Group	CRos EPot GEdr GKev LRHS NRHS NSla SRot WBor XEll
	- - 'Silver Leaf Pink'	GMaP NWad
	- - 'Silver Leaf Red'	NWad
	- - 'Silver Leaf White'	GMaP NWad
	× ***hildebrandii***	LLHF
	ibericum	see *C. coum* subsp. *caucasicum*
	intaminatum	CBro CRos EPot GKev LAma LLHF LRHS MAsh NRHS WHoo XEll
	- plain-leaved	WThu

latifolium	see *C. persicum*
libanoticum	CBro CRos GKev LAma LRHS MAsh NRHS XEll
maritimum	XEll
mirabile ♀H4	CBro CRos EPot GKev LAma LLHF LRHS MAsh NHpl NRHS NSla SDeJ WThu
- 'Alba'	GKev LAma SDeJ XEll
- f. ***mirabile*** 'Tilebarn Anne'	MAsh
- - 'Tilebarn Nicholas'	MAsh
- f. ***niveum***	SDeJ
- - 'Tilebarn Jan'	MAsh
neapolitanum	see *C. hederifolium*
orbiculatum	see *C. coum*
parviflorum	MAsh
§ ***persicum***	CRos CWCL GKev LRHS MAsh NRHS WCot
- f. ***albidum***	MAsh
- Ashwood silver-leaved	MAsh
pseudibericum ♀H4	CBro CRos EPot GKev LAma LLHF LRHS MAsh NRHS SDeJ WCot
- AC&W 664	NWad
- f. ***roseum***	MAsh
§ ***purpurascens***	CAby CBro GKev LLHF MAsh NHpl NSla WHoo WThu
- 'Lake Garda'	MAsh
repandum	CAby CAvo CBro CRos EPot GKev LAma LRHS MAsh NRHS WHer
- 'Pelops' misapplied	see *C. rhodium* subsp. *peloponnesiacum*
rhodium	GKev MAsh
§ - subsp. ***peloponnesiacum***	GKev MAsh
- subsp. ***vividum***	MAsh
rohlfsianum	CRos GKev LRHS MAsh NRHS WThu XEll
× ***schwarzii***	MAsh
'Trena'	SDeJ
trochopteranthum	see *C. alpinum*
× ***wellensiekii***	MAsh
× ***whiteae***	LLHF

Cyclea (*Menispermaceae*)

polypetala KWJ 12157	WCru

Cyclosorus ✿ (*Thelypteridaceae*)

tottoides	CBdn WPGP

Cydonia ✿ (*Rosaceae*)

japonica	see *Chaenomeles japonica*
oblonga 'Agvambari' (F)	SKee
- 'Aromatnaya' (F)	MCoo NOra SKee WMat
- 'Champion' (F)	CAgr CHab EMOT EPom LBuc MCoo NEgg NOra SKee SVic WMat
- 'Early Prolific' (F)	ECrN SEND
- 'Ekme[illegible] (F)	SKee
- 'Gam[illegible]a' (F)	SKee
- 'Iranian' (F)	CAgr
- 'Isfahan' (F)	SKee WMat
- 'Krymsk' (F)	CAgr WWct
- 'Leskovac' (F)	CAgr EPom LMaj NLar NOra WWct
§ - 'Lusitanica' (F)	CAgr CHab ELan EMOT EPom LRHS NLar SPer SSFr WMat
- 'Meech's Prolific' (F) ♀H5	CAgr CDul CHab CLnd CTri ECrN EPom LRHS MAsh MGos MRav NLar NOra NWea SDea SKee SLim SPer SSFT SSFr WMat WWct
- pear-shaped (F)	CHab NEgg SPer
- PORTUGAL	see *C. oblonga* 'Lusitanica'
- 'Rea's Mammoth' (F)	CHab NLar
- 'Seibosa' (F)	SKee
- 'Serbian Gold' (F)	CDul CMac CTho ECrN EMOT EPom GQue LRHS MAsh NLar NOra SKee SSFT WMat
- 'Smyrna' (F)	NLar NOra SKee WMat
- 'Sobu' (F)	SKee
- 'Vranja' ambig. (F)	CBcs EMOT MAsh SPoG
- 'Vranja' Nenadovic (F) ♀H5	Widely available

Cydonia + *Pyrus* see + *Pyrocydonia*

Cydonia × *Pyrus* see × *Pyronia*

Cylindropuntia (*Cactaceae*)

imbricata	SPlb XLum XSen
leptocaulis	XSen
§ ***spinosior***	XLum
versicolor	XSen

Cymbalaria (*Plantaginaceae*)

aequitriloba 'Alba'	GAbr GEdr NRya
§ ***hepaticifolia***	CSma SBrt SPlb
§ ***muralis***	ECtt GAbr GEdr GJos MHer WArt WHer WTor
- 'Albiflora'	see *C. muralis* 'Pallidior'
- 'Kenilworth White'	GJos WArt WCot WMoo
- 'Nana Alba'	ECtt GCrg WIce
§ - 'Pallidior'	SPhx
- 'Snow Wave'	ECtt MHol MSCN WCot WFar
§ ***pallida***	CPBP CSma MAsh MMuc SBch SEND SPlb WMoo
- 'Alba'	WMoo
§ ***pilosa***	ECtt NLar

Cymbopogon (*Poaceae*)

citratus	CBod CCCN CTsd EMor ENfk GPoy MNHC SPlb SPre SRms SVic
flexuosus	CCCN MHer SRms WJek
nardus	GPoy

Cymophyllus (*Cyperaceae*)

§ ***fraserianus***	EBee GCal

Cynanchum (*Apocynaceae*)

ascyrifolium	EBee LEdu

Cynara (*Asteraceae*)

cardunculus ♀H5	Widely available
- from Chelsea Physic Garden	MAvo
- 'Bianco Avorio'	SVic
- subsp. ***flavescens***	SBrt
I - 'Florist Cardy'	NLar
- 'Gobbo di Nizza'	SRms
- 'Porto Spineless'	CAgr
§ - Scolymus Group	CBcs CMea CRos EPfP EWTr EWes GPoy LCro LOPS LRHS LSRN MNHC MRav NRHS SEND SPhx SPoG WHer
- - 'Bere'	LEdu
- - 'Gros Camus de Bretagne'	MAvo WCot
- - 'Gros Vert de Lâon' ♀H5	CBcs CLau CRos ELan LRHS WCot
- - 'Monica Lynden-Bell'	WCot
- - 'Purple Globe'	LEdu SRms
- - 'Romanesco'	CLau LCro LOPS SRms SVic
- - 'Rouge d'Alger'	CAgr
- - 'Tavor'	CLau SVic
- - 'Vert Globe'	CLau ENfk LCro LEdu LOPS NLar NPer SPad SRms SVic SWvt WHil

- - 'Violet de Provence'	CSBt MHer SPad SRms
- - 'Violetto di Chioggia' ♀H4	CLau WHil
cornigera new	SPhx
* ***gomerensis***	WCot
humilis white-flowered	SBrt
scolymus	see *C. cardunculus* Scolymus Group
syriaca	SPhx

Cynodon (*Poaceae*)

aethiopicus	EPPr

Cynoglossum (*Boraginaceae*)

grande	SBrt
nervosum	CBod CCBP EBee ELan EPPr MBel MMrt MMuc SEND SPer WCAu WCot

Cynosurus (*Poaceae*)

cristatus	CHab NMir

Cypella (*Iridaceae*)

aquatilis	EWat
§ ***coelestis***	XEll
plumbea	see *C. coelestis*

Cyperus (*Cyperaceae*)

§ ***albostriatus***	CCCN EShb
alternifolius misapplied	see *C. involucratus*
alternifolius L.	CBen CCCN EPfP SArc WMAq WMoo XBlo
- 'Compactus'	see *C. involucratus* 'Nanus'
'Chira'	NWsh
diffusus misapplied	see *C. albostriatus*
§ ***eragrostis***	EHoe EPPr GCal LPot MWts NSti SPlb WGrn WMAq WMoo
esculentus	CAgr EShb
fuscus	WMoo
haspan misapplied	see *C. papyrus* 'Nanus'
haspan L.	WCot
§ ***involucratus*** ♀H1c	EShb EWat MWts SEND WMoo
§ - 'Nanus'	EShb
longus	CBen CWat EHoe EWat MMuc MWts NPer SEND SMad SPlb WMAq WWtn XLum
papyrus ♀H1c	CCCN CDTJ CKel EShb EUJe LCro LOPS LRHS LSun MHer SPlb XBlo
§ - 'Nanus' ♀H1c	XBlo
- 'Perkamentus'PBR	CCCN
prolifer	EShb
vegetus	see *C. eragrostis*
'Zumila'	EShb

Cyphomandra see *Solanum*

Cyphostemma (*Vitaceae*)

mappia	SPlb

Cypripedium (*Orchidaceae*)

Achim gx	GEdr XFro
Aki gx	GEdr XFro
- 'Pastel'	GEdr XFro
Anna gx	GEdr NLAp XFro
Annette gx	GEdr
Bärbel Schmidt gx	GEdr NLAp
× ***barbeyi***	see *C.* × *ventricosum*
Barry Phillips gx	GEdr LAma NLAp
Bernd gx	GEdr NLAp
- white-flowered new	NLAp
Bill gx	GEdr
Birgit gx pastel-flowered	GEdr XFro
§ **Boots gx**	GEdr LAma NLAp
calceolus	GKev LAma NLAp XEll
calceolus × ***henryii***	LAma
calceolus × ***montanum***	see *C.* Boots gx
californicum	LAma NLAp
Carol Ilene gx	GEdr
Carolin gx	NLAp
Chauncey gx	GEdr XFro
Cleo Pinkepank gx	GEdr NLAp XFro
× ***columbianum***	NLAp
cordigerum	NLAp
corrugatum	see *C. tibeticum*
Dawn Edwards gx	GEdr
debile	LAma
Dietrich gx ♀H5	GEdr XFro
Emil gx	GEdr XFro
Erika gx new	NLAp
Eurasia gx	NLAp XFro
fargesii	NLAp
fasciolatum	GEdr LAma LRHS NLAp NRHS
flavum	GEdr GKev LAma NLAp
- white-flowered	GKev
- white-flowered × ***reginae***	LAma
formosanum ♀H3	GEdr GKev LAma NLAp
'Frosch's Noble Geisha' new	NLAp
Gabriela gx ♀H5	NLAp
- 'Kentucky Maxi'	GKev LAma NHpl
Gisela gx	CAvo GEdr NLAp XFro
- 'Pastel'	GEdr
GPH Petite Delight gx new	NLAp
guttatum	NLAp
Hank Small gx ♀H5	GEdr NLAp XFro
Hans Erni gx	GEdr NLAp XFro
henryi	LAma NLAp
Inge gx	GEdr XFro
Ingrid gx	GEdr NLAp XFro
Irene gx	GEdr XEll
Ivory gx	GEdr LAma NLAp
James Armitage gx	GEdr
Jens gx	GEdr
Judith Merrick gx	GEdr
Julia Barclay gx	GEdr
Karl Heinz gx	NLAp
Kathleen Anne Green gx	GEdr
kentuckiense ♀H5	CCCN GEdr GKev LAma LRHS NHpl NLAp NRHS XEll
- **Lady Dorine gx**	LAma NLAp
kentuckiense × ***macranthos*** var. ***rebunense*** new	NLAp
'Kentucky Pink'	see *C.* Philipp gx 'Kentucky Pink'
Kristi Lyn gx	GEdr NLAp XFro
lichiangense	NLAp
Lothar Pinkepank gx	GEdr
Lucy Pinkepank gx	GEdr NLAp XFro
- 'Kentucky Pink Blush'	LAma LRHS NHpl NRHS
Lukas gx new	NLAp
macranthos	GEdr GKev NLAp
- 'Album' new	GKev
- 'Hotei'	GEdr
- var. ***hotei-atsumorianum*** Sadovsky	GEdr
- John Hagger Group	XFro
- var. ***rebunense***	NLAp
- var. ***speciosum***	GEdr
macranthos × ***henryii***	see *C.* Michael gx
Maria gx	GEdr XFro

Memoria Gerd Kohls gx	GEdr
Memoriam Shawna Austin gx	GEdr NLAp
§ **Michael gx** ♀H5	GEdr LAma NLAp XFro
- 'Pastel'	GEdr NLAp
Monto gx	NLAp XFro
Mops gx new	XFro
Neil Lancaster gx	GEdr
Otto gx	GEdr
parviflorum	GEdr GKev
- var. ***parviflorum***	LAma NLAp
§ - var. ***pubescens***	GEdr GKev LAma NLAp
- - 'Minnesota' new	NLAp
'Parville'	LRHS NHpl
Paul gx	GEdr NLAp XFro
Peter gx	GEdr XFro
Philipp gx ♀H5	GEdr XFro
§ - 'Kentucky Pink'	GKev LAma NHpl
Piccolo gx	GKev
Pixi gx	GEdr
Pluto gx	GEdr XFro
pubescens	see *C. parviflorum* var. *pubescens*
'Pueblo'	LRHS NHpl
Rascal gx	GEdr NLAp
reginae ♀H5	CCCN GEdr GKev LAma LRHS NHpl NLAp XEll
- from Newfoundland, Canada new	NLAp
- f. ***albolabium***	NHpl
- f. ***album***	GEdr GKev LAma LRHS NLAp XEll
Renate gx	GEdr
- pastel-flowered	XFro
Rhodopoxis gx	GEdr
Robin Lee gx new	NLAp
Sabine gx ♀H5	GEdr NLAp XFro
- pastel-flowered	GEdr XFro
Schoko gx	NLAp
Sebastian gx	XFro
- 'Frosch's Mountain King'	NLAp XFro
- 'Multiflower White'	LAma NHpl
segawae	LAma NLAp
Selston High School gx	GEdr
Siggi gx	GEdr
Sunny gx	GEdr NLAp XFro
§ ***tibeticum***	GEdr LAma NLAp
Tilman gx	GEdr LAma NLAp XFro
Tower Hill gx	GEdr
Ulla Silkens gx ♀H5	GEdr GKev LAma XEll XFro
Ursel gx	GEdr NLAp XFro
§ × ***ventricosum***	EBee GEdr GKev LAma NLAp XFro
- 'Frosch's Queen of the Mist' new	NLAp XFro
- 'Pastel'	XFro
- white-flowered	GKev
Victoria gx	GEdr NLAp XFro
Werner Frosch gx	GEdr NLAp

Cyrilla (*Cyrillaceae*)

racemiflora	CMac

Cyrtanthus (*Amaryllidaceae*)

§ ***brachyscyphus***	EShb
breviflorus	CPbh WCot WPGP
'Edwina'	CCCN
§ ***elatus*** ♀H2	CSam EShb GKev LEdu NSti SPtp WCot
'Elizabeth'	CCCN
epiphyticus	WCot
falcatus ♀H2	WCot
mackenii	EShb WPGP
- var. ***cooperi***	CAby
- cream-white-flowered	CCCN GKev
- 'Himalayan Pink'	CCCN GKev
- orange-flowered	GKev
- pink-flowered	GKev
- red-flowered	CCCN GKev
- yellow-flowered	GKev
montanus	WCot
parviflorus	see *C. brachyscyphus*
purpureus	see *C. elatus*
sanguineus	WCot
speciosus	see *C. elatus*
suaveolens	WCot

Cyrtomium ✿ (*Dryopteridaceae*)

§ ***caryotideum***	CLAP ISha
devexiscapulae	CAby CBdn CLAP EUJe LLWG MJak WPGP
§ ***falcatum*** ♀H3	CAby CBod CKel CLAP CPla CRos EFer ELon EMor EPfP EUJe GBin GMaP LEdu LRHS NLar NRHS SEND SPlb SPoG SRms SRot WCot WMoo XBlo XLum
- 'Maritimum' new	CBdn
- 'Rochfordianum'	CCCN CRos GBin ISha LEdu LRHS MRav NRHS WFib
§ ***fortunei*** ♀H3	Widely available
- var. ***clivicola***	CBdn CKel CRos EAJP EBee EMor EPfP EShb ISha LRHS MGos MRav NBro NGrd NLar NRHS SPad SPtp WCot XLum
macrophyllum	CLAP CRos EBee LEdu LRHS NRHS
tukusicola	EBee

Cystopteris ✿ (*Woodsiaceae*)

bulbifera	WCot
dickieana	WFib
fragilis	EFer GKev LEdu WFib
moupinensis B&SWJ 6767	WCot WCru

Cytisus (*Papilionaceae*)

'Andreanus'	see *C. scoparius* f. *andreanus*
× ***beanii*** ♀H5	CRos ELan EPfP LRHS MAsh NLar SLon
'Boskoop Glory'	NLar
× ***boskoopii*** 'Apricot Gem'	CKel CSBt ELan NLar
- 'Boskoop Ruby' ♀H5	CKel CMac CRos CSBt ECrN ELan EPfP GKin LCro LOPS LRHS LSRN MAsh MJak NEgg NHol NRHS SCob SWvt
- 'Dukaat'	NLar
- 'Hollandia' ♀H5	CBcs CSBt ELan EPfP GKin MMuc MRav SCob SGol
- 'La Coquette'	CKel EPfP NEgg SPlb
- 'Windlesham Ruby'	CExl CRos ELan EPfP LRHS LSRN NEgg NLar NRHS SLim SPer WFar
- 'Zeelandia' ♀H5	CMac CRos EBee ELan EPfP EWTr LRHS NHol SCob SPer WFar
'Burkwoodii' ♀H5	CBcs CDul CKel CRos ELan ELon EPfP EUJe LRHS LSRN MSwo NEgg NRHS SPoG WFar
canariensis	see *Genista canariensis*
'Daisy Hill'	CBod WRHF
§ ***decumbens***	MAsh
demissus ♀H5	WAbe
'Dorothy Walpole'	WFar
'Golden Cascade'	CBcs CRos ELan LRHS MAsh NEgg NRHS SLim
'Goldfinch'	CRos CSBt ELan LRHS MJak MSwo NEgg NHol NLar NRHS SCob WFar

§ ***hirsutus*** CExl SBrt
'Johnson's Crimson' new NHic
× ***kewensis*** ♀H5 CRos ELan EPfP LRHS MAsh MGos MRav NLar NRHS SPer SRms
- 'Niki' EPfP MAsh MMuc NLar WRHF
'Killiney Red' ELan
'Killiney Salmon' CKel EMil GKin LSRN MRav
'Lena' ♀H5 CKel CMac CRos CSBt ECrN ELan EPfP GKin LRHS LSRN MGos NBir NEgg NHol NLar NRHS SCob SGol SLim SPoG WFar
'Luna' EPfP NEgg
'Maria Burkwood' NLar
'Minstead' EBee SPer
'Moyclare Pink' LCro LOPS
'Mrs Norman Henry' NLar
'Newry Seedling' CMac
nigricans 'Cyni' ♀H5 CRos ELan IArd LRHS MAsh MMuc SPer SPoG
'Porlock' see *Genista* 'Porlock'
× ***praecox*** CMac CRos ELon EPfP LRHS MAsh NEgg NRHS NWea SGol SPlb SPoG WFar
- 'Albus' CBcs CDul CMac CRos ELan EPfP LRHS LSRN MAsh MGos MJak MMuc MRav NHol NRHS SCob SEND SGol SPer WFar
- 'Allgold' ♀H5 Widely available
- 'Frisia' WFar
- 'Lilac Lady' CRos LRHS SBrt
- 'Warminster' ♀H5 EPfP GKin MRav SEND SPer SRms
proliferus CExl
purpureus EBee EPfP LRHS MMrt MRav SBrt WCot WSHC
- 'Atropurpureus' EPfP
racemosus see *Genista* × *spachiana*
'Red Wings' MMuc SGol
scoparius CDul CPer NWea WTSh
§ - f. ***andreanus*** CTri EPfP
- - 'Splendens' SPer
- 'Cornish Cream' CSBt ELan EPfP NEgg
- 'Firefly' CBcs CMac
- 'Fulgens' EPfP
- 'Golden Sunlight' CSBt MSwo
§ - subsp. ***maritimus*** CMac
- var. ***prostratus*** see *C. scoparius* subsp. *maritimus*
× ***spachianus*** see *Genista* × *spachiana*
supinus see *C. hirsutus*
'White Lion' CMac

D

Daboecia ✿ (*Ericaceae*)

cantabrica MMuc
§ - f. ***alba*** CSBt NWad SWhi
- - 'Alba Globosa' GPer
- - 'Creeping White' CFst
- - 'David Moss' MMuc
- 'Alberta White' CFst SWhi
- 'Amelie'PBR CFst SWhi
- 'Andrea' CFst SWhi
- 'Angelina'PBR new CFst
- 'Arielle' CFst SWhi
- 'Atropurpurea' CFst CSBt NWad SWhi
- 'Bicolor' CFst
- f. ***blumii*** 'Pink Blum' CFst
- - 'Pinky Perky' new CFst
- - 'Purple Blum' CFst
- - 'White Blum' CFst SWhi
- 'Bubbles' CFst
- 'Celtic Star' CFst
- 'Chaldon' CFst
- 'Charles Nelson' (d) CFst
- 'Cinderella' CFst
- 'Covadonga' CFst
- 'Cupido' SWhi
§ - 'Donard Pink' GPer
- 'Glamour' CFst
I - 'Globosa Pink' CFst NWad SWhi
- 'Heather Yates' CFst
- 'Hookstone Purple' NWad
- 'Lilac Osmond' CFst
- 'Pink' see *D. cantabrica* 'Donard Pink'
- 'Pink Lips' new CFst
§ - 'Polifolia' CFst
- 'Rainbow' (v) CFst
- 'Rodeo' CFst
- 'Romantic Muxoll' CFst
- 'Rosella'PBR new CFst
- subsp. ***scotica*** 'Ben' CFst
- - 'Cora' CFst
- - 'Ellen Norris' CFst
- - 'Golden Imp' CFst SWhi
- - 'Goscote' CFst MGos SWhi
- - 'Jack Drake' CFst
- - 'Katherine's Choice' CBcs CFst
- - 'Red Imp' CFst
- - 'Robin' CFst
- - 'Silverwells' ♀H5 CBcs MAsh SWhi
- - 'Thumbelina' new CFst
- - 'William Buchanan' ♀H5 CFst GAbr GPer MAsh NWad SCoo SWhi
- - 'William Buchanan Gold' (v) CFst
- 'Stardust Muxoll' CFst
- 'Sun Seeker' new CFst
- 'Tinkerbell' CFst SWhi
- 'Vanessa'PBR CFst SWhi
- 'Waley's Red' ♀H5 NWad SWhi

Dacrycarpus ✿ (*Podocarpaceae*)

§ ***dacrydioides*** CBrP LEdu

Dacrydium ✿ (*Podocarpaceae*)

araucarioides new CAco
cupressinum SPlb WThu
franklinii see *Lagarostrobos franklinii*

Dactylicapnos (*Papaveraceae*)

macrocapnos CBcs CSpe GKev IDee IFro WBor WCru
platycarpa WPGP
§ ***scandens*** CAby CRHN GEdr IRos MSCN SBrt
- GWJ 9438 WCru
- WJC 13793 WCru
- 'Shirley Clemo' CExl
§ ***ventii*** GWJ 9376 WCru
- WJC 13786 WCru

Dactylis (*Poaceae*)

glomerata CHab SVic WSFF
- 'Variegata' (v) MMuc NBid SEND

Dactylorhiza (*Orchidaceae*)

baltica LAma
× ***braunii*** EHrv
§ ***elata*** ♀H5 GBee GKev LAma

	- 'Glasnevin'	GCal
	Estella gx	WCot
	Foliorella gx	GBin NLAp
§	***foliosa*** ♀H4	CCCN ECha MAvo NChi
§	***fuchsii***	CCCN CMil EMor EPot GKev LEdu MNrw NLAp NRya WHer WSFF
	- 'Bressingham Bonus'	GKev
	× ***grandis***	IBlr
	- Blackthorn hybrid	CJun IBlr
	'Harold Esslemont'	GKev
	hybrid	LEdu NRya
	incarnata	LAma NBid NLAp
§	***maculata***	CRos EHrv GKev LAma LRHS NLAp NRHS WBor
	maderensis	see *D. foliosa*
§	***majalis***	EMor GKev LAma NLAp WSFF XEll
	- subsp. ***sphagnicola***	GKev
	mascula	see *Orchis mascula*
	praetermissa	CCCN GKev LRHS NLAp NRHS
	- subsp. ***junialis*** var. ***junialis***	NLAp
	purpurella	EPot GAbr GJos GKev NLAp NRya
I	**Sissinghurst Hybrid gx** new	NLAp
	viridis	NLAp

Dahlia ✿ (*Asteraceae*)

	'A la Mode' (D)	CWGr
	'Abba' (D)	ECtt
	'Abbie' (D)	NHal
	'Abingdon Ace' (D)	SGbt
	'Abridge Ben' (D)	CWGr
	'Abridge Taffy' (D)	CWGr GRid
I	'Acapulco' (S-c)	ERCP
	'Ace Summer Emotions'PBR (D)	SDeJ
	'Addison June' (Ba)	ERCP
	'Adelaide Fontane' (D)	CWGr
	'Admiral Rawlings' (D)	CWGr
	'Aitara Caress' (C)	SGbt
	'Aitara Majesty' (S-c)	GRid
	'Akita' (Misc)	CWGr ELan LCro LOPS SGbt
	'Aladdin's Lamp' (WL)	NJRG
	'Alauna Clair-Obscur' (Fim)	CWGr ERCP LCro LOPS
	'Albert Schweitzer' (S-c)	CWGr SGbt
	'Alden Regal' (C)	CWGr
	'Alfred C' (S-c)	CWGr
	'Alfred Grille' (S-c)	LCro LOPS SDeJ SGbt
	'Alf's Mascot' (D)	NJRG
	'Alison Shingler' (S-c)	CWGr
	'Aljo' (S-c)	CWGr
	'Allan Snowfire' (S-c)	NHal
	'Allan Sparkes' (WL) ♀H3	CWGr MCot
	'Alloway Candy' (Misc)	ERCP
	'Alloway Cottage' (D)	CWGr NHal SGbt
	'Alltami Apollo' (S-c)	CWGr
	'Alltami Cherry' (Ba)	CWGr
	'Alltami Classic' (D)	CWGr
	'Alltami Corsair' (S-c)	CWGr
	'Alltami Ruby' (S-c)	CWGr
	'Almand's Climax' (D) ♀H3	CWGr GRid SGbt
	'Alpen Beauty' (Col)	CWGr
	'Alpen Fern' (Fim)	CWGr
	'Alpen Flame' (C)	CWGr
	'Alpen Fury' (Anem)	NJRG
	'Alpen Mildred' (S-c)	CWGr
	'Alpen Sun' (S-c)	CWGr
	'Alstergruss' (Col)	SDeJ
	'Alva's Doris' (S-c) ♀H3	CWGr LAyl
	'Alva's Lilac' (D)	CWGr
	'Alva's Supreme' (D) ♀H3	CWGr GRid LAyl NHal
	'Amaran Guard' (D)	CWGr
	'Amaran Relish' (D)	CWGr GRid SGbt
	'Amaran Return' (D)	CWGr
	'Amaran Royale' (D)	CWGr
	'Amaran Troy' (WL)	CWGr
I	'Amazone' (Sin/DwB)	LRHS SPoG
	'Amazonia' (C)	CWGr
	'Amber Banker' (C)	CWGr SGbt
	'Amber Festival' (D)	GRid
	'Amberglow' (Ba)	CWGr
	'Amberley Joan' (D)	CWGr
	'Amberley Victoria' (D)	CWGr
	'Ambition' (S-c)	CAvo CWGr ERCP LCro LOPS
	'Amelia's Surprise' (D)	CWGr
	'American Copper' (D)	CWGr
	'American Dawn' (D)	ERCP LCro LOPS SPer
	'American Moon' (D)	LOPS
	AMERICAN PIE ('Vdtg26'PBR) (Dark Angel Series) (Sin)	SDeJ
	'American Sun' (D)	ERCP
	'Amethyst' (D)	CWGr
	'Amgard Coronet' (D)	CWGr GRid
	'Amgard Delicate' (D)	CWGr SGbt
	'Amgard Rosie' (D)	CWGr
	'Amira' (Ba)	CWGr GRid
	'Amorangi Joy' (C)	CWGr
	'Amy Cave' (Ba)	GRid NHal
	'Amy Madison' (S-c)	CWGr
	'Andrea Clark' (D)	GRid NHal
	'Andrea Lawson' (Ba)	GRid
	'Andrew Mitchell' (S-c)	CWGr GRid NHal
	'Andries' Amber' (S-c)	CWGr
	'Andries' Orange' (C)	ECtt
	'Andries' Orange As' (S-c)	CWGr
	'Andy Murray' (Sin)	CWGr
	'Angora' (Fim)	SGbt
	'Angus McInns Walls' (S-c) new	CWGr
	'Anita Summerhayes' (Misc)	CWGr
	'Ann Breckenfelder' (Col) ♀H3	CWGr ECtt ERCP EUJe GRid NHal NJRG
	'Anna Lindh' (WL)	GRid
	'Annika' (Sin)	LCro LOPS SDeJ
	'Anniversary Ball' (Ba)	CWGr
	'Another Pet'	see *D.* 'Mystic Enchantment'
	'Antique'PBR (Sin)	LRHS NPri
	'Apache' (Fim)	CWGr ERCP SDeJ SGbt SPer
	'Apache Blauw' (Fim)	ERCP
	'Apopa Sky' (Sin)	NJRG
	'Apple Blossom' (C)	SGbt
I	'Appleblossom' (Col)	CWGr
	'Apricot Desire' (WL) new	ERCP
	'Apricot Honeymoon Dress' (D)	CWGr
	'Apricot Jewel' (D)	CWGr
I	'Apricot Parfait' (Fim)	CWGr
	'April Dawn' (D)	CWGr
	'April Heather' (Col) ♀H3	NHal
	'Arabian Night' (D)	CAby CAvo CBcs CWCL CWGr EBee ECtt EHrv ELan EPfP ERCP LAyl LCro LOPS LRHS LSRN LSun MHol NLar SDeJ SEND SGbt WBrk WCot WSpi
	'Arbatax' (D) new	ERCP
	'Arc de Triomphe' (D)	CWGr
	'Arlequin' (D)	SGbt
	'Arnhem' (D)	CWGr
	'Arthur Godfrey' (D)	CWGr
	'Arthur Hankin' (D)	CWGr

	Name	Suppliers
	'Arthur's Delight' (D)	CWGr
	'Asahi Chohje' (Anem) ♀H3	CWGr
	'Askwith Minnie' (D)	NHal
	'Atilla' (D)	CWGr
I	'Atlanta' (D)	SGbt
	atropurpurea	CWGr
	'Audacity' (D)	CWGr LAyl SGbt
	'Aurora's Kiss' (Ba)	CWGr ERCP NHal SGbt
I	'Aurore' (C)	CWGr
	'Aurwen's Violet' (Pom)	NHal
	australis	CSpe EBee
	– B&SWJ 10389	WCru
I	'Autumn Fairy' (S-c)	ERCP SCob SDeJ
	'Autumn Lustre' (WL)	CWGr
	'Avignon' (D)	SDeJ
	'Avoca Amanda' (D)	NHal
	'Avoca Comanche' (S-c)	GRid NHal
	'Avoca Salmon' (D)	GRid
	'B.J. Beauty' (D)	GRid NHal NJRG
	'Babette' (S-c)	GRid
	'Baby Fonteneau' (S-c)	CWGr
	'Babylon' (D)	LRHS SGbt
§	'Babylon Brons' (D)	ERCP LRHS SGbt
	'Babylon Bronze'	see *D.* 'Babylon Brons'
	'Babylon Lila' (D)	SGbt
§	'Babylon Paars' (D)	ECtt LRHS SDeJ SGbt
	'Babylon Purple'	see *D.* 'Babylon Paars'
	'Babylon Rose' (D)	LRHS SGbt
	'Bacardi' (D)	ERCP
	'Badger Twinkle' (S-c)	CWGr GRid
	'Bahama Lemon'	see *D.* 'Lemon Cane'
	'Balham' (Sin)	WCot
	'Ballego's Glory' (D)	CWGr SGbt
	'Bambino' (Lil)	CWGr
	'Banker' (C)	CWGr
	'Bantling' (Pom)	CWGr ERCP SGbt
	'Barbara Schell' (D)	CWGr
	'Barbara's Pastelle' (S-c)	CWGr NJRG SGbt
	'Barbara's Yellow' (S-c)	NJRG
	'Barbarossa' (D)	CWGr
	'Barbarry Ball' (Ba)	CWGr
	'Barbarry Banker' (D)	CWGr LAyl
	'Barbarry Bluebird' (D)	SGbt
	'Barbarry Carousel' (Ba)	CWGr
	'Barbarry Civic' (D)	GRid
	'Barbarry Cosmos' (D)	CWGr
	'Barbarry Dominion' (D)	CWGr
	'Barbarry Drifter' (D)	CWGr
	'Barbarry Flag' (D)	CWGr
	'Barbarry Gem' (Ba)	CWGr
	'Barbarry Maverick' (D)	GRid
	'Barbarry Melody' (D)	NHal
	'Barbarry Monitor' (Ba)	CWGr SGbt
	'Barbarry Olympic' (Ba)	CWGr
	'Barbarry Oracle' (D)	CWGr
	'Barbarry Pinky' (D)	CWGr
	'Barbarry Pip' (D)	GRid NHal
	'Barbarry Red Devil' (Dec)	GRid
	'Barbarry Sultan' (D)	NHal
	'Barbarry Token' (D)	GRid
	'Barbarry Triumph' (D)	CWGr
	'Barbarry Vintage' (D)	GRid
	'Barbetta' (D)	SPer
	'Barbette' (D)	CWGr
	'Bareham's Beauty' (D)	CWGr
	'Baret Joy' (S-c)	CWGr GRid
	'Bargaly Blush' (D)	GRid NHal
	'Baron Ray' (D)	CWGr
	'Barry Williams' (D)	SGbt
	'Bart' (D)	CWGr
	'Barton Memory' (S-c)	GRid
	'Bassingbourne Beauty' (D)	CWGr
	'Bayou'[PBR] (Anem)	CAby CWGr ERCP LCro LOPS NHal NJRG SGbt
	'Bedford Sally' (D)	CWGr
	'Bednall Beauty' (Misc/DwB) ♀H3	CHll CRos CWGr ECtt EHrv ELan EUJe LRHS NJRG WSpi
	'Belinda Appleyard' (Ba) **new**	CWGr
	'Bell Boy' (Ba)	SGbt
	'Belle Epoque' (C)	CWGr
	'Ben Huston' (D)	GRid
	'Bengale' (D)	CWGr
	'Berger's Rekord' (S-c)	CWGr
	'Berliner Orange' (D)	ERCP
	'Bernice Sunset' (S-c)	CWGr
	'Berolina' (D)	CWGr
	'Berwick Banker' (Ba)	CWGr
	'Berwick Wood' (D)	CWGr GRid NHal SGbt
	'Bess Painter' (D)	CWGr
	'Best Bett'	see *D.* MYSTIC SPIRIT
	'Beth's Chaplet' (Sin)	WCot
	'Betty Ann' (Pom)	CWGr
	'Biddenham Fairy' (D)	CWGr
	'Biddenham Strawberry' (D)	CWGr SGbt
	'Bilbao'[PBR] (Jumbo Collection) (D)	SDeJ
	'Bill Holmberg' (D)	CWGr GRid SGbt
	'Bingo' (D)	SGbt
	'Birkenshaw Garden Friends' (Col) **new**	NJRG
	'Bishop of Auckland'[PBR] (Misc)	CAby CAvo CRos CWGN CWGr ECtt EPfP ERCP LAma LCro LOPS LRHS MGos NJRG NRHS SDeJ SGbt WCot
	'Bishop of Canterbury'[PBR] (P)	CRos CWGr ECtt ELan EPfP LAma LCro LOPS LRHS MGos NHal NRHS SDeJ SGbt SPer SPoG
	'Bishop of Dover' (Sin)	CWGr EPfP LAma LCro LOPS LRHS SDeJ SGbt WBrk
	'Bishop of Lancaster' (Misc)	LAma LCro LOPS NLar
	'Bishop of Leicester' (Misc)	CWGr ECtt ELan EPfP LAma LCro LOPS LRHS NLar NRHS SDeJ SGbt SHar
	'Bishop of Llandaff' (P) ♀H3	Widely available
	'Bishop of Oxford' (Misc)	CAby CRos CWGr ELan EPfP ERCP LAma LCro LOPS LRHS MGos NJRG NRHS SDeJ SGbt SPoG
	'Bishop of York' (Misc)	CAby CAvo CRos CWGr ECtt ELan EPfP LAma LAyl LCro LOPS LRHS MGos NGdn NRHS SDeJ SGbt SPer SPoG
	'Bishop Peter Price' (Sin)	CWGr
	'Bista' (Ba)	GRid
	'Black Fire' (D)	CWGr ECtt
	'Black Jack' (D)	CAby ERCP NHal NJRG
	'Black Monarch' (D)	CWGr NHal SGbt
	'Black Narcissus' (C)	CWGr SGbt
I	'Black R Jack'	NJRG
	'Black Spider' (S-c)	CWGr
	'Black Star' (Sin)	EPfP
	'Black Touch' (Fim)	CWGr ERCP
	'Blackberry Ripple' (S-c)	CWGr
	'Blaisdon Red' (D)	CWGr
	'Blaze' (D)	CWGr
	'Blithe Spirit' (D)	CWGr
	'Bloemfontein' (D)	CWGr
	'Bloodstone' (D)	CWGr SGbt
	'Bloody Mary' (D)	ERCP
	'Bloom's Graham' (S-c)	CWGr

	'Bloom's Kenn' (D)	CWGr SGbt
	'Blue Beard' (S-c)	CWGr
	'Blue Bell' (D)	ERCP SPer
	'Blue Boy' (D)	CWGr ERCP LCro LOPS
	'Blue Record' (S-c/DwB)	ERCP
	'Blue Wish' (WL)	ERCP GRid LCro LOPS NJRG
	'Blueberry Hill' (Col) **new**	LAyl
	'Blyton Everest' (D)	NHal
	'Blyton Golden Girl' (D)	GRid NHal
	'Blyton Lady in Red' (D)	GRid LAyl NHal
	'Blyton Romance' (D)	NHal
	'Blyton Royal Velvet' (D)	GRid
	'Blyton Softer Gleam' (D) ♀H3	CWGr GRid NHal NJRG SGbt
	'Blyton Valentine' (D)	NHal
	'Bob's Bonaventure' (D)	GRid NHal
	'Bokay' (WL)	CWGr
	'Bonesta' (D)	CWGr
	'Bonny Blue' (Ba)	CWGr
	'Boogie Woogie' (Anem)	CWGr SDeJ
	'Boom Boom White' (Ba)	ERCP
	'Boom Boom Yellow' (Ba)	ERCP SDeJ
	'Bora Bora' (S-c)	CWGr
	'Border Princess' (C/DwB)	SGbt
	'Boy Scout' (Ba)	CWGr
	'Bracken Lorelei' (WL)	NJRG
	'Brackenridge Ballerina' (WL)	CWGr GRid NHal NJRG SGbt
	'Brandaris' (S-c)	CWGr SGbt
	'Brandon James' (D)	SDeJ
	'Brandysnap' (D)	CWGr SGbt
	'Brantwood' (Sin)	CWGr
	'Brasilia' (D)	CWGr
	BRAVEHEART ('Vdtg67'PBR) (Dark Angel Series) (Sin)	LCro LOPS SDeJ
	'Brian's Dream' (D)	LAyl NHal
	'Bride's Bouquet' (Col)	ERCP LRHS
	'Bridge View Aloha' (S-c) ♀H3	CWGr SGbt
	'Bright Diamond' (D)	SDeJ
	'Bright Eyes' (Sin)	ERCP
	'Brindisii' (Anem)	SDeJ
	'Bristol Petite' (D)	CWGr
	'Brookfield Delight' (Sin/Lil) ♀H3	CWGr
	'Brookfield Rachel' (Ba)	CWGr
	'Brookfield Rene' (D)	CWGr
	'Brookfield Snowball' (Ba)	CWGr
	'Brookfield Sweetie' (Misc/DwB)	CWGr
	'Brookside Cheri' (C)	CWGr
	'Brookside Snowball' (Ba)	CWGr
	'Bryce B. Morrison' (D)	CWGr
	'Bryn Terfel' (D)	CWGr GRid GWyn NHal SGbt
	'Bull's Pride' (D)	CWGr
	'Burlesca' (Ba)	ERCP
	'Butch' (D)	CWGr
	'Butterball' (D/DwB)	SDeJ
*	'Buttercup' (Pom)	CWGr
	'By George' (D)	CWGr
	'Caballero' (WL)	CWGr GRid
	'Café au Lait' (D)	CAby CWGr ELan EPfP ERCP IPot LAyl LCro LOPS LRHS MSCN NHal SDeJ SGbt SPer WSpi
	'Calgary' (D)	CWGr
	'California Sunset' (Misc)	CAby
	'Calin' (WL)	CWGr
	'Camano Ariel' (C)	CWGr
	'Camano Passion' (S-c)	CWGr
	'Camano Poppet' (Ba)	CWGr
	'Camano Regal' (S-c)	CWGr
I	'Cameo' (WL)	ELan LAyl NHal NJRG SGbt
	campanulata	CWGr
	'Campos Billy M' (S-c)	CWGr
	'Campos Hush' (S-c)	CWGr
	'Campos Philip M' (D)	CWGr
	'Canary Fubuki' (Fim)	CWGr ERCP SDeJ SGbt SPer
I	'Candlelight' (D)	GRid
	'Candy Cane CZ' (D)	CWGr
	'Candy Cupid' (Ba)	CWGr
	CANDY EYES	see *D.* 'Zone Ten'
	'Candy Hamilton Lillian' (D)	CWGr
	'Candy Keene' (S-c)	CWGr GRid NHal
	'Caprice' (D)	CWGr
	'Captain Bruce Bairnsfather' (C) **new**	CWGr
	'Careless' (D)	CWGr
	'Caribbean Fantasy' (D)	CWGr
	'Carola' (S-c) **new**	CWGr
	'Carole Chamberlain' (Col)	NJRG
	'Carolina Moon' (D)	CWGr GRid GWyn NHal SGbt
	'Carol's Spanish Dancer' (C)	LAyl NHal NJRG
	'Carstone Firebox' (Col)	LAyl
	'Carstone Ruby' (D)	NHal
	'Carstone Sunbeam' (D)	CWGr
	'Carstone Suntan' (C)	CWGr GRid
	'Carstone Valiant' (Ba)	NHal
	'Cartouche' (D)	CWGr ERCP
	'Catherine Deneuve' (Misc)	CWGN CWGr NJRG SGbt
	'Catherine Ireland' (D)	CWGr
	'Cerise Prefect' (S-c)	CWGr
	'Cha Cha' (S-c)	CWGr SGbt
	'Challenger' (D)	GWyn
	'Charles de Coster' (D)	CWGr
	'Charles Dickens' (Ba)	CWGr
	'Charlie Briggs' (Ba)	NHal
	'Charlie Dimmock' (WL) ♀H3	CWGr GRid NHal NJRG SGbt
	'Charlie Two' (D)	CWGr GRid NHal
I	'Charlotte' (Sin)	CWGr
	'Charlotte Bateson' (Ba)	CWGr
	'Chat Noir' (S-c) ♀H3	CWGr ERCP IPot LAyl LCro LOPS LRHS SGbt
	'Chee' (WL)	CWGr
	'Cheerio' (S-c)	ECtt LRHS NRHS
	'Cherokee Beauty' (D)	CWGr
	'Cherry Wine' (D)	CWGr
	'Cherrywood Millfield' (S-c)	CWGr
	'Cherrywood Turnpike' (D)	CWGr
	'Cherrywood Wilderness' (D)	CWGr
	'Cherubino' (Col)	CWGr
	'Cherwell Goldcrest' (S-c)	CWGr GRid NHal SGbt
	'Cherwell Lapwing' (S-c)	GRid
	'Cherwell Linnet' (Ba)	GRid NHal
	'Cherwell Skylark' (S-c)	GRid
	'Cherwell Waxwing' (D)	GRid
	'Chessy' (Sin/Lil) ♀H3	CWGr
	'Chic Red' (Misc)	NRHS
	'Chilson's Pride' (D)	CWGr SGbt
	'Chiltern Amber' (D)	CWGr
	'Chiltern Sylvia' (S-c)	CWGr
	'Chimacum Topaz' (S-c)	CWGr GRid
	'Chimborazo' (Col)	CWGr EUJe EWes LAyl SGbt
	'Chinese Lantern' (D)	CWGr
	'Chloe's Keene' (S-c)	CWGr
	'Chorus Girl' (D)	CWGr
	'Christie Snowy' **new**	GRid
	'Christine' (D)	CWGr
I	'Christine' (WL)	SGbt

	Name	Suppliers
	'Christmas Carol' (Col)	CWGr ECtt GRid GWyn NHal NJRG
	'Christopher Nickerson' (S-c)	CWGr SGbt
	'Christopher Taylor' (WL)	NHal SGbt SHar
	'City of Leiden' (S-c)	LCro LOPS NHal
	'Clair de Lune' (Col) ♀^{H3}	CWGr ECtt ERCP GRid LRHS NHal NJRG SGbt WCot WSpi
	'Claire Diane' (D)	CWGr
	'Clara May' (Fim)	CWGr
	'Clarion' (S-c)	CRos LRHS NRHS
I	'Clarion' (Sin)	CWGr
	'Classic A. 1' (C)	CWGr
	'Classic Poème'^{PBR} (Misc)	ERCP
	'Classic Rosamunde'^{PBR} (Misc) ♀^{H3}	ERCP NHal
	'Classic Summertime' (Misc)	CWGr
§	'Classic Swanlake'^{PBR} (Misc)	CWGr EPfP ERCP LCro LRHS NJRG
	'Claudette' (D)	MHol
	'Clayt's Candy' (S-c)	GRid NHal
	'Clearview Arlene' (S-c)	GRid
	'Clearview Daniel' (Ba) ♀^{H3} **new**	NHal
	'Clearview Edie' (DblO)	GRid NHal
	'Clearview Irene' (S-c)	GRid NHal
	'Clearview Louise' (S-c)	NHal
	'Clearview Sundance' (C)	GRid NHal
	'Cleo Laine' (S-c)	CWGr NHal
	'Cloverdale' (D)	CWGr
	coccinea	CExl CSpe CWGr MCot SGbt SMHy WPGP
	- NJM 05.072	WPGP
	- hybrids	NSti
	- orange-flowered	CWGr
	- var. ***palmeri***	CAvo WPGP XEll
	- yellow-flowered	CWGr
	'Cocktail' (S-c)	CWGr
	'Color Spectacle' (S-c)	CWGr LRHS
	'Coltness Gem' (Sin/DwB)	CWGr
	'Comet' (Anem)	CWGr
	'Como Polly' (D)	CWGr
	'Contessa' (D)	CWGr SDeJ
	'Coral Jupiter' (S-c)	CWGr GRid
	'Coral Strand' (D)	CWGr
	'Cornel' (Ba)	CWGr ERCP NHal NJRG SGbt
	'Cornel Brons' (Ba)	ERCP
	'Cornell' (D)	GRid
	'Cornish Ruby' (Sin)	EBee EPfP
I	'Corona' (S-c/DwB)	SDeJ
	'Coronella' (D)	CWGr SGbt
	'Cortez Silver' (D)	CWGr
	'Cortez Sovereign' (S-c)	CWGr
	'Corton Bess' (D)	CWGr
	'Corton Olympic' (D)	CWGr GRid
	'Corydon' (D)	CWGr
	'Cottontail' (Col)	CWGr
	'Country Boy' (S-c)	CWGr GRid
	'Coupe de Soleil' (D)	CWGr LCro LOPS
	'Craigowan' (S-c)	GRid NHal
	'Crazy Legs' (DblO)	SGbt
	'Crazy Love' (D)	LCro LOPS SPer
	'Cream Alva's' (D) ♀^{H3}	CWGr GRid
I	'Cream Beauty' (WL)	CWGr
	'Cream Capella' (D)	GRid
	'Cream Klankstad' (C)	CWGr
	'Cream Linda' (D)	CWGr
	'Cream Moonlight' (S-c)	CWGr GRid NJRG SGbt
	'Cream Reliance' (D)	CWGr
	'Crème de Cassis' (D)	CAvo CWGr ERCP LCro LOPS NHal
	'Crève Coeur' (D)	CWGr GRid
	'Crichton Cherry' (D)	CWGr

	Name	Suppliers
	'Croesus' (S-c)	CWGr
	'Crossfield Anne' (D)	CWGr
	'Crossfield Festival' (D)	CWGr GRid
	'Croydon Ace' (D)	CWGr
	'Croydon Jumbo' (D)	CWGr
	'Croydon Snotop' (D)	CWGr
	'Croydon Superior' (D)	SGbt
	'Cryfield Harmony' (Ba)	CWGr
	'Cryfield Jane' (Ba)	CWGr
	'Cryfield Keene' (S-c)	CWGr
	'Cryfield Max' (C)	CWGr
	'Cryfield Rosie' (Ba)	CWGr
	'Culdrose' (D)	SGbt
	'Curate' (Misc)	CWGr
	'Curiosity' (Col)	GRid NJRG
	'Currant Cream' (Ba)	CWGr SGbt
	cuspidata	EBee
	'Cyclone' (D)	CWGr
	'Cycloop' (S-c)	CWGr
	'Cynthia Chalwin' (Ba)	CWGr
	'Cynthia Louise' (D)	CWGr
	'Czar Willo' (Pom)	CWGr
	'Czardas' (C)	GCal
	DAHLIETTA BECKY (Dahlietta Surprise Series) (Col)	CWGr
	DAHLIETTA EMILY ('Daparos'^{PBR}) (Dahlietta Select Series) (Misc) **new**	CWGr
	DAHLIETTA JENNY	see *D.* 'Jenny'
	DAHLIETTA LEANNE ('Dapacher') (Dahlietta Surprise Series) (Misc) **new**	CWGr
	'Daily Mail' (D)	CWGr
	'Daisy Duke' (D)	ERCP
	DALAYA SHIVA ('Kledh13033'^{PBR})	NPri
	DALAYA YOGI ('Kledh11031'^{PBR})	NPri
	'Daleko Gold' (D)	CWGr
	'Daleko Jupiter' (S-c)	CWGr GRid NHal
	'Daleko National' (D)	CWGr
	'Daleko Tangerine' (D)	CWGr
	'Dame Deidre' (S-c)	CWGr
	'Dana Audrey' (C)	CWGr
	'Dana Dream' (S-c)	CWGr
	'Dana Iris' (S-c)	CWGr
	'Dana Sunset' (C)	CWGr
I	'Dandy' (Col)	SVic
	'Danjo Doc' (D)	SGbt
	'Dannevirke' (Sin)	CWGr
	'Danum Belle' (D)	CWGr
	'Danum Fancy' (D)	CWGr
	'Danum Gail' (D)	CWGr GRid
	'Danum Hero' (D)	CWGr
	'Danum Meteor' (S-c)	CWGr
	'Danum Rebel' (S-c)	CWGr
	'Danum Rhoda' (D)	CWGr
	'Danum Salmon' (S-c)	CWGr
	'Danum Torch' (Col)	CWGr ECtt SGbt
	'Dark Butterfly' (D)	CWGr ERCP LCro LOPS
	'Dark Desire' (Sin/DwB)	CWGr
	'Dark Fubuki' (Fim)	ERCP
§	'Dark Side Of The Sun'^{PBR} (Sin)	CRos LRHS NRHS SPoG
	'Dark Spirit' (D)	ECtt SDeJ SGbt
	'Dark Stranger' (C)	CWGr
	'Darlington Diamond' (S-c)	CWGr
	'Darlington Jubilation' (S-c)	CWGr

'Davenport Anita' (D)	CWGr
'Davenport Honey' (D)	CWGr GRid
'Davenport Lesley' (D)	CWGr
'Davenport Sunlight' (S-c)	CWGr
'Dave's Choice' (Ba)	GRid NJRG
'Dave's Snip' (D)	CWGr
'David Digweed' (D)	CWGr SGbt
'David Howard' (D) ♀H3	CAby CRos CWGr ECtt EHrv ELan EPfP ERCP EUJe GRid LAyl LCro LOPS LRHS LSun NHal NJRG NRHS SGbt SPer SWvt WBrk WCot WFar WGwG WSpi
'David Wright' (S-c)	CWGr
'David's Choice' (D)	CWGr
'Dawn Chorus' (D)	CWGr
'Dawn Sky' (D)	LAyl
'Dazzler' (D/DwB)	CWGr
'Debora Renae' (WL) **new**	ERCP
'Deborah's Kiwi' (C)	CWGr GRid NHal SGbt
'Debra Anne Craven' (S-c)	CWGr GRid NHal
'Decorette' (D/DwB)	CWGr SGbt
'Deepest Yellow' (Ba)	CWGr SDeJ SGbt
'De-la-Haye' (S-c)	NHal
'Demi Schneider' (Col)	CWGr
'Dentelle de Venise' (C)	CWGr
'Deuil du Roi Albert' (D)	CWGr
'Deutschland' (D)	CWGr
'Devon Elegance' (S-c)	CWGr
'Devon Liam' (S-c)	CWGr
'Devon Temptation' (C)	CWGr
'Diamond Rose' (Anem/ DwB)	CWGr
'Diamond Wedding' (D)	SGbt
'Diamond Years' (D)	SGbt
'Diana Gregory' (Pom)	CWGr SGbt
'Diana's Memory' (D)	LCro LOPS
'Dikara Jodie' (D)	NHal
'Dikara Moon' (D)	NHal
'Dikara Superb' (D)	CWGr GRid NHal
'Dilys Ayling' (Col)	NHal
'Dinah Shore' (S-c)	CWGr
I 'Disneyland' (Col)	SGbt
dissecta	CExl CWGr EBee
'Diva US' (D)	ERCP SDeJ
'Doc van Horn' (S-c)	CWGr
'Doktor Hans Ricken' (D)	CWGr
'Don Hill' (Col) ♀H3	GRid NJRG
'Doris Bacon' (Ba)	CWGr
'Doris Day' (C)	CWGr NHal SGbt
'Doris Knight' (C)	LSvl
'Doris Muldoon' (WL) **new**	CWGr
'Doris Rollins' (C)	CWGr
'Dorothy Rose' (D)	NHal
'Dottie D.' (Ba)	CWGr
'Double Dream Fantasy' (Dreamy Series) (Misc)	CRos EPfP LRHS NRHS
'Dovegrove' (Sin) ♀H3	CWGr
'Downham Royal' (Ba)	CWGr ERCP LCro LOPS
'Dr Caroline Rabbit' (D)	CWGr SGbt
DRACULA ('Vdtg17'[PBR]) (Dark Angel Series) (Sin)	ERCP
DRAGON BALL ('Vdtg31'[PBR]) (Dark Angel Series) (Sin)	SDeJ
(Dreamy Series) DREAMY BLUSH WHITE (Misc)	CRos NRHS
- DREAMY EYES (Misc)	NLar
- DREAMY FANTASY (Misc)	CBod CPla CWGr ELan
- DREAMY FUSION (Sin)	CWGr
- DREAMY INSPIRE (Misc)	CRos LRHS NLar NRHS
- DREAMY KISS (P)	CRos CWGr LRHS NLar NRHS
- DREAMY LIPS (P)	CBod NLar
- DREAMY MOONLIGHT (Sin)	CRos LRHS NRHS
- DREAMY NIGHTS (Misc)	CBod CRos EUJe LRHS NRHS
- DREAMY PASSION (Sin)	CRos LRHS NRHS
'Drummer Boy' (D)	CWGr GRid
'Duddon Grace' (WL)	NHal
'Duet' (D)	CWGr ELan SGbt
'Dusky Harmony' (WL)	SGbt
'Dutch Boy' (D)	CWGr
'Dutch Explosion' (S-c)	ELan
'Earl Haig' (D)	CWGr
'Earl Marc' (C)	CWGr
'Early Bird' (D)	CWGr
'Early Harvest' (D)	SGbt
'East Anglian' (D)	CWGr
'Easter Sunday' (Col)	CWGr
'Eastwood Moonlight' (S-c)	CWGr GRid NHal SGbt
'Eastwood Star' (S-c)	CWGr
'Ebbw Vale Festival' (D)	CWGr
'Edge of Gold' (D)	CWGr
'Edge of Joy' (D)	EPfP LCro LOPS
'Edgeway Joyce' (Ba)	CWGr GRid
'Edinburgh' (D)	CWGr ERCP GRid GWyn NHal SDeJ SGbt
'Edith Jones' (Col)	CWGr NJRG
'Edith Mueller' (Pom)	CWGr
'Edmund' (Sin)	WCot
'Edna C' (D)	CWGr
'Edwin's Sunset' (WL) ♀H3	GRid NHal
'Eileen Denny' (S-c)	CWGr GRid
'El Cid' (D)	CWGr
'El Paso' (D)	CWGr SDeJ
'Elaine Beedle' (D)	CWGr
'Elga-Bergerhoff' (C)	ERCP LRHS
'Elgico Leanne' (C)	CWGr SGbt
'Elizabeth Snowden' (Col)	GRid
'Ella Britton' (D)	LRHS NRHS
'Ellen Huston' (Misc/ DwB) ♀H3	CWGr ECtt ERCP GRid NHal SCob SGbt
'Elma E' (D)	CWGr ERCP GRid NHal
'Elmbrook Chieftain' (D)	CWGr
'Elmbrook Rebel' (S-c)	CWGr GRid
'Elmdon Superb' (Ba)	GRid
'Elsie Merina' (D)	CWGr
I 'Embrace' (C)	NHal NJRG
'Emma's Coronet' (D)	CWGr GRid
'Emmaus' (Fim)	CWGr
'Emmie Lou' (D)	CWGr
'Emory Paul' (D)	CWGr ERCP
'Emperor' (D)	CWGr
I 'Encore' (Fim)	CWGr ERCP
'Engadin' (D)	CWGr
'Engelhardts Matador' (D)	EBee ECtt ERCP EUJe LRHS MCot MHol MJak NJRG SGbt WBrk WCot
'Enid Adams' (D)	CWGr
'Epping Forest' (D)	CWGr
'Eric's Choice' (D)	CWGr
'Esau' (D)	CWGr
'Essex Chronicle' (D)	CWGr
'Esther' (Col)	SDeJ
'Esther Chamberlain' (Col)	NJRG
'Etheral' (Sin)	CWGr
'Eunice Arrigo' (S-c)	CWGr
I 'Eurydice' (Fim)	CWGr
'Eveline' (D)	CAby CWGr ERCP LCro LOPS SDeJ SGbt
'Evelyn Foster' (D)	CWGr GRid
'Evelyn Rumbold' (D)	CWGr SGbt
'Evelyn Taylor' (S-c)	NJRG
'Evening Breeze' (D) **new**	ERCP

	'Evening Lady' (D)	CWGr
	'Evening Mail' (S-c)	GRid
I	'Evita' (Anem)	NJRG
	excelsa (B)	CHll NJRG
	- 'Penelope Sky' (Sin)	WCru
	'Excentrique' (Misc)	CWGr ERCP NJRG
	'Exotic Dwarf' (Sin/ Lil) ♀H3	NJRG
	'Explosion' (S-c)	CWGr
	'Extase' (S-c)	CWGr
	'Eye Candy' (Sin)	CRos LRHS NJRG NRHS
	'Fabula' (Col)	CWGr
	'Fairway Pilot' (D)	CWGr NHal
	'Fairway Spur' (D)	CWGr GRid NHal
	'Fairy Queen' (C)	CWGr SGbt
§	'Famoso' (Col)	ERCP
	'Fantasie du Cap' (Fim) **new**	ERCP
	'Fantastico' (Col)	CWGr ERCP
	'Fascination' (P) ♀H3	CAby CBcs CRos CWGr ECtt ERCP LAyl LRHS LSRN MCot MSCN NLar NRHS SCob SDeJ SGbt WHoo WSpi
	'Fashion Monger' (Col)	CAby CWGr ECtt EHrv ERCP GRid NHal NJRG SGbt
	'Fata Morgana' (Anem)	CWGr NJRG SGbt
	'Fern Irene' (WL)	CWGr
	'Fern Ridge Painted Lady' (D)	GRid
	'Ferncliff Illusion' (D)	CWGr ERCP SGbt
	'Ferncliff Inspiration' (S-c)	ERCP
	'Fernhill Champion' (D)	CWGr
	'Festivo' (Col)	CWGr
	'Feu Céleste' (Col)	CWGr
	'Fidalgo Blacky' (D)	CWGr
	'Fidalgo Bounce' (D)	CWGr
	'Fidalgo Climax' (Fim)	CWGr
	'Fidalgo Magic' (D)	CWGr
	'Fidalgo Snowman' (S-c)	CWGr
	'Fidalgo Supreme' (D)	GRid LAyl
I	'Fiesta' (Pom)	SDeJ
	Figaro Series (Misc/DwB)	NPri
	'Figurine' (WL) ♀H3	GRid NJRG SHar
	'Fille du Diable' (S-c)	CWGr SGbt
	'Finchcocks' (WL) ♀H3	CWGr LAyl
	'Fiona Stewart' (Ba)	CWGr GRid
	'Fire and Ice' (Misc)	CWGr SDeJ
	'Fire Magic' (S-c)	CWGr
	'Fire Mountain' (D)	GRid LAyl NHal NJRG
	'Firebird' (Sin)	CWGr
	'Firebird' (S-c)	see *D.* 'Vuurvogel'
	'Firebrand' ambig. (S-c)	CWGr SGbt
	'Firepot' (D)	ERCP MSCN SGbt SPer
	'First Lady' (D)	CWGr
	'Flavien' (D)	ERCP
	'Fleur'	see *D.* 'Fleurel'
	'Fleur Mountjoy' (Col)	CWGr
§	'Fleurel' PBR (Fim)	ERCP SDeJ
	'Floorinoor' (Anem)	ERCP GWyn LCro LOPS SGbt
	'Florence Vernon' (Ba)	CWGr
	'Flutterby' (WL)	CWGr
	'Fontmell Kaz' (Col)	NJRG SGbt
	'Formby Art' (D)	LAyl NHal
	'Formby Perfection' (D)	GRid
	'Formby Supreme' (D)	CWGr SGbt
	'Forrestal' (S-c)	CWGr
	'Fortuna' (Col/DwB)	CWGr ERCP
	'Frank Holmes' (Pom)	CWGr GRid
	'Frank Hornsey' (D)	CWGr
	'Frank Lovell' (S-c)	CWGr
	'Franz Kafka' (Pom)	CAvo CWGr ERCP GRid NHal NJRG SDeJ

	'Fred Wallace' (C)	CWGr
	'Freelancer' (C)	CWGr SGbt
	'Freestyle' (C)	CWGr GRid NJRG
§	'Freya's Paso Doble' (Anem) ♀H3	CWGr LAyl SGbt
	'Freya's Thalia' (Sin/Lil)	CWGr
	'Friendship' (C)	CWGr
	'Frigoulet' (C)	CWGr ERCP SGbt
	'Fripon' (C)	CWGr
	'Funfair' (D)	CWGr
	'Fusion' (D) ♀H3	CWGr SGbt SHar WCot
	'G.F. Hemerik' (Sin)	CWGr
	'G.I. Joe' (D)	SGbt
	'Gale Lane' (Pom)	CWGr GRid
	(Gallery Series) 'Gallery Art Deco' PBR (D) ♀H3	CRos CWGr ERCP LRHS NHal NRHS SGbt
	- 'Gallery Art Fair' PBR (D) ♀H3	Ros CWGr ERCP LCro LOPS LRHS NRHS SDeJ
	- 'Gallery Art Nouveau' PBR (D) ♀H3	CRos CWGr ERCP GBin LRHS NHal NRHS SDeJ WFar
	- 'Gallery Bellini' PBR (D)	CRos LRHS NRHS SDeJ
	- 'Gallery Cézanne' PBR (D)	CRos CWGr LRHS NRHS SDeJ SGbt
	- 'Gallery Cobra' PBR (D)	ERCP
	- 'Gallery La Tour' PBR (D) ♀H3	SDeJ
	- 'Gallery Leonardo' PBR (D) ♀H3	CWGr LCro LOPS SDeJ
	- 'Gallery Pablo' PBR (D) ♀H3	CWGr SGbt
	- 'Gallery Pinto' PBR (D)	CRos CWGr LRHS NRHS
	- 'Gallery Rembrandt' PBR (D) ♀H3	CWGr LCro LOPS
	- 'Gallery Renoir' PBR (D) ♀H3	CRos CWGr LRHS NRHS
	- 'Gallery Rivera' PBR (D)	CRos LRHS NRHS SCob SDeJ
	- 'Gallery Salvador' PBR (D)	ERCP SGbt
	- 'Gallery Serenade' PBR (D)	ERCP
	- 'Gallery Singer' PBR (D)	CWGr SDeJ
	- 'Gallery Valentin' PBR (D)	CRos LRHS NRHS WFar
	- 'Gallery Vermeer' PBR (D)	CWGr SGbt
	- 'Gallery Vincent' PBR (D) ♀H3	CWGr
	'Gardaia' (Anem)	CWGr
	'Garden Festival' (WL)	CWGr ERCP GRid
	'Garden Miracle' (D)	NJRG
	'Garden Princess' (C/DwB)	SGbt
	'Garden Wonder' (D)	CWGr SDeJ SPer
	'Gargantuan' (S-c)	CWGr
	GATESHEAD FESTIVAL	see *D.* 'Peach Melba'
	'Gay Mini' (D)	CWGr
	'Gay Princess' (WL)	CWGr
	'Gay Triumph' (S-c)	CWGr
	'Geerlings Babette' (Ba)	ERCP
	'Geerlings Beatrice' (Ba)	CWGr
	'Geerlings Cupido' (WL)	SGbt
	'Geerlings Indian Summer' (S-c)	CWGr NHal
	'Geerlings Moonlight' (D)	CWGr
§	'Geerlings Sorbet' (S-c)	CAby NHal SGbt
	'Geerlings Yellow' (S-c)	CWGr
	'Gelber Vulkan' (S-c)	SGbt
	'Gemma Darling' (D)	CWGr GRid
	'Genova' (Ba)	CAvo ERCP SDeJ SGbt
	'Geoffrey Kent' (D) ♀H3	GRid
	'Gerald Grace' (S-c)	CWGr
	'Gerlos' (D)	CWGr
I	'Geronimo' (S-c)	CWGr
	'Gerrie Hoek' (WL)	CWGr ERCP LRHS NJRG NRHS SDeJ SGbt WSpi
	'Gill's Pastelle' (S-c)	GRid

	Name	Suppliers
	'Gilt Edge' (D)	CWGr
	'Gilwood Terry G' (C)	GRid
	'Gina Lombaert' (S-c)	CWGr SEND
	'Ginger Willo' (Pom)	CWGr
	'Gipsy Boy' (D)	CWGr LAyl
	'Gipsy Night' (Ba)	ERCP SDeJ
	'Giraffe' (DblO)	CWGr ERCP SGbt
	'Gitty' (Ba)	CWGr
	'Glamour Girl' (S-c) **new**	ERCP
	'Glen Afton' (Pom)	CWGr GRid
	'Glen Gharry' (Col)	CWGr
	'Glenbank Honeycomb' (Pom)	GRid
	'Glenbank Paleface' (Pom)	CWGr
	'Glenbank Twinkle' (C)	CWGr
	'Globular' (Ba)	CWGr
	'Glorie van Heemstede' (WL) ♀H3	CWGr ERCP LAyl LCro LOPS NHal NJRG SDeJ SGbt
	'Glorie van Naardwijk' (D)	CWGr
	'Glorie van Noordwijk' (S-c)	ERCP SDeJ SGbt
	'Glow Orange' (Ba)	CWGr
	'Go American' (D)	CWGr NHal
	'Gold Crown' (S-c)	SDeJ
	'Goldean' (D)	CWGr
I	'Golden Emblem' (D)	CWGr ECtt SDeJ
	'Golden Fizz' (Ba)	CWGr
	'Golden Heart' (S-c)	CWGr
	'Golden Horn' (S-c)	CWGr
	'Golden Impact' (S-c)	CWGr GRid
	'Golden Scepter' (D)	CWGr ERCP SDeJ SGbt
	'Golden Symbol' (S-c)	CWGr
	'Golden Turban' (D)	CWGr
	'Goldfield' (D)	CWGr
	'Goldie Gull' (Anem)	NJRG
	'Goldilocks' (S-c)	CWGr
	'Goldorange' (S-c)	CWGr
	'Good Earth' (C)	CWGr SDeJ
I	'Good Hope' (D)	CWGr
	'Good Intent' (Ba)	CWGr
	'Goshen Beauty' (WL)	CWGr
	'Goya's Venus' (S-c)	CWGr
	'Grace Kendall' (D)	GRid
	'Gracie S' (C)	CWGr GRid NHal NJRG
	'Gramma's Lemon Pie' (D)	CWGr
	'Grand Finale' (S-c)	SDeJ
	'Grand Prix' (D)	CWGr ERCP SDeJ SGbt
	'Greenway Zoe' (S-c) **new**	NHal
	'Grenadier' (D) ♀H3	CWGr ECtt ERCP LRHS NJRG NLar SGbt WCot
	'Grenidor Pastelle' (S-c)	CWGr GRid NJRG
	'Gretchen Heine' (D)	CWGr
	'Grock' (Pom)	CWGr
	'Gryson's Yellow Spider' (C) ♀H3	ERCP
	'Gunyuu' (D)	CWGr
	'Gurtla Twilight' (Pom)	GRid NHal NJRG
	'Gute Laune' (C)	CWGr
	'Gwyneth' (WL)	GRid NHal NJRG
	'Gypsy Girl' (D)	CWGr SGbt
	'Hadrian's Midnight' (Sin) **new**	NHal
	'Hadrian's Sunlight' (Sin) ♀H3	NHal
	'Hadrian's Sunset' (Sin)	NHal
	'Hallmark' (Pom)	GRid GWyn NJRG
	'Hallwood Coppernob' (D)	CWGr
	'Hallwood Satin' (D)	CWGr
	'Hallwood Tiptop' (D)	CWGr
	'Hamari Accord' (S-c) ♀H3	CWGr LAyl
	'Hamari Bride' (S-c) ♀H3	CWGr

	Name	Suppliers
	'Hamari Girl' (D)	CWGr GRid SGbt
	'Hamari Gold' (D) ♀H3	CWGr GRid NHal SGbt
	'Hamari Katrina' (S-c)	CWGr
	'Hamari Rosé' (Ba) ♀H3	CWGr GRid NHal SGbt SHar
	'Hamari Sunshine' (D)	SGbt
	'Hamilton Amanda' (D)	CWGr
	'Hamilton Lillian' (D) ♀H3	CWGr
	'Hans Ricken' (D)	CWGr
	'Hapet Charmant' (WL)	NJRG
	'Hapet Ideal' (S-c)	GRid
*	'Happy Birthday' (S-c)	CWGr
	'Happy Boy' (S-c)	GRid
	'Happy Caroline' (D)	CWGr
	HAPPY DAYS LEMON ('Hdle105'PBR) (Sin)	ERCP
	HAPPY DAYS PINK ('Hdpi117'PBR) (Sin) ♀H3 **new**	ERCP WFar
	HAPPY DAYS PURPLE ('Hdpu165'PBR) (Sin) ♀H3	ERCP
	HAPPY DAYS RED FLAME ('Hdrf155'PBR) (Sin)	EPfP
	'Happy Go Lucky' (D)	SDeJ
	'Happy Halloween' (D)	CWGr
	(Happy Single Series) HAPPY SINGLE DATE ('HS Date'PBR) (Sin)	CWGr ERCP LRHS SDeJ
	- HAPPY SINGLE FIRST LOVE ('HS First Love'PBR) (Sin)	CWGr ERCP LRHS SDeJ
	- HAPPY SINGLE FLAME ('HS Flame'PBR) (Sin) ♀H3	CAvo CWGr ERCP LRHS NJRG
	- HAPPY SINGLE JULIET ('HS Juliet'PBR) (Sin)	CWGr ERCP LRHS SDeJ
	- HAPPY SINGLE KISS ('HS Kiss'PBR) (Sin)	CAvo CWGr LRHS
	- HAPPY SINGLE PARTY ('HS Party'PBR) (Sin)	CWGr SDeJ
	- HAPPY SINGLE PRINCESS ('HS Princess'PBR) (Sin) ♀H3	CRos CWGr ERCP LRHS SDeJ
	- HAPPY SINGLE ROMEO ('HS Romeo'PBR) (Sin)	CWGr LRHS SDeJ WFar
	- HAPPY SINGLE WINK ('HS Wink'PBR) (Sin) ♀H3	CWGr ERCP GRid LCro LOPS LRHS SDeJ
	'Haresbrook' (Sin)	SHar WSpi
	'Harriet G' (WL)	NJRG
	'Hartenaas' (Col/DwB)	SDeJ
	'Hart's Dr McMurray' (D) **new**	SPer
	'Harvest' (Fim)	CWGr
§	'Harvest Samantha' (Sin/Lil) ♀H3	CWGr NHal
	'Haseley Goldicote' (D)	CWGr
	'Haseley Triumph' (D)	CWGr
	'Hawai'PBR	CWGr
	'Hawaiian Dreams'PBR (Sin)	LRHS NPri
	'Hayley Jayne' (C)	CWGr ERCP NHal NJRG SGbt
	'Heather Huston' (D)	CWGr
	'Heather Jean' (Col)	NJRG
	'Heather Linford' (Fim)	CWGr NHal
	'Helma Rost' (S-c)	CWGr
	'Hemera' (Sin)	CWGr
	'Henriette' (C)	CWGr
	'Herbert Smith' (S-c)	CWGr
	'Hexton Copper' (Ba)	CWGr SGbt
	'Highgate Torch' (S-c)	CWGr
	'Highness' (S-c)	CWGr

'Highwarden Cliff' (S-c) **new**	GRid
'Hilary's Honour' (Fim) **new**	CWGr
'Hilda Clare' (Col)	CWGr
'Hildepuppe' (Pom)	CWGr
'Hillcrest Albino' (S-c)	CWGr
'Hillcrest Amour' (D)	CWGr GRid SGbt
'Hillcrest Aura' (D)	GRid
'Hillcrest Bobbin' (Ba)	CWGr
'Hillcrest Camelot' (S-c)	CWGr
'Hillcrest Candy' (S-c) ♀H3	CWGr GRid NHal NJRG SGbt
'Hillcrest Carmen' (D)	GRid
'Hillcrest Chelsey' (D)	GRid
'Hillcrest Contessa' (Ba)	CWGr
'Hillcrest Delight' (D)	GRid NHal SGbt
'Hillcrest Desire' (C) ♀H3	GRid
'Hillcrest Divine' (D)	GRid
'Hillcrest Duncan Edwards' (S-c)	NHal
'Hillcrest Embers' (D)	GRid
'Hillcrest Fiesta' (S-c)	CWGr
'Hillcrest Firecrest' (D)	GRid NHal
'Hillcrest Hannah' (D)	GRid
'Hillcrest Harvest' (D)	GRid
'Hillcrest Heights' (S-c)	CWGr
'Hillcrest Hillton' (S-c)	GRid
'Hillcrest Jake' (S-c)	GRid NHal
'Hillcrest Jersie' (S-c)	GRid NHal NJRG
'Hillcrest Jessica J' (C)	GRid
'Hillcrest Kismet' (D)	GRid NHal NJRG
'Hillcrest Liam' (S-c)	GRid
'Hillcrest Margaret' (D)	GRid
'Hillcrest Matt' (D)	GRid
'Hillcrest Millennium' (S-c)	GRid
'Hillcrest Pearl' (D)	CWGr
'Hillcrest Regal' (Col) ♀H3	CWGr GRid SGbt
'Hillcrest Royal' (C) ♀H3	CAvo CWGr LAyl NHal SGbt
'Hillcrest Suffusion' (D)	CWGr GRid NJRG
'Hillcrest Thomas J' (D)	GRid
'Hillcrest Ultra' (D)	GRid
'Hill's Delight' (S-c)	CWGr
'Hindu Star' (Ba)	CWGr
'Hockley Maroon' (D)	CWGr
'Hockley Nymph' (WL)	CWGr
'Holbrook Honey' (Sin)	CSam
'Holbrook Lilac' (Sin)	CSam
'Holbrook Magenta' (Sin)	CSam
'Holland Festival' (D)	CWGr GRid SGbt
'Hollyhill Big Pink' (S-c)	SGbt
'Hollyhill Spiderwoman' (Misc) **new**	CAby ERCP SPer
'Home Run' (Sin)	CWGr
'Homer T' (S-c)	CWGr
'Honest John' (C)	CWGr
'Honey' (Anem/DwB)	CWGr SDeJ
'Honeypot' (Ba)	SGbt
'Honka' (SinO) ♀H3	CRos CWGr ECtt ERCP LAyl LCro LOPS LRHS NHal NJRG SDeJ WCot
'Honka Fragile' (SinO)	CAby ERCP IPot LCro LOPS SDeJ
'Honka Orange' (SinO)	ERCP NJRG
'Honka Pink Edge' (SinO)	NJRG
'Honka Red' (SinO)	CAby CWGr ERCP LCro LOPS SDeJ
'Honka Rose' (SinO)	ERCP NJRG SDeJ
'Honka Surprise' (SinO)	CAby CWGr EBee ECtt ERCP EUJe LCro LOPS NJRG SDeJ WCot
'Honka White' (SinO)	CWGr ERCP
'Honor Francis' (Misc)	WCot
'Hootenanny - Swan Island' (Col) ♀H3	NJRG
'Hot Chocolate' (D)	CWGr NJRG SGbt

'Hugh Mather' (WL)	CWGr GRid
'Hulin's Carnival' (D)	CWGr
'Hy Clown' (D)	CWGr
'Hy Fire' (Ba)	CWGr
'Hy Totem' (D)	GRid
'Ian Hislop' (Sin)	CWGr
'Ice Crystal' (Fim)	ERCP SPer
'Ice Cube' (D)	ERCP SDeJ
'Ice Queen' (WL)	CWGr
I 'Idylle' (S-c)	CWGr
'Ieda' (Sin)	NJRG
'Ike' (Fim)	CWGr
imperialis (B)	CDTJ CHll CWGr ERCP EWes ILea LEdu LRHS NJRG SChr SGbt
- B&SWJ 8997	WCru
- B&SWJ 14341	WCru
- 'Alba' (B)	CWGr
- pink double-flowered (B)	CExl
aff. ***imperialis***	CWGr XLum
'Impression Famosa'	see *D.* 'Famoso'
'Inca' (Anem)	SDeJ
'Inca Dambuster' (S-c)	CWGr NHal SGbt
'Inca Glamour' (D)	CWGr
'Inca Matchless' (D)	CWGr
'Inca Metropolitan' (D)	CWGr
'Inca Panorama' (D)	CWGr
'Inca Spectrum' (S-c)	CWGr
'Inca Vanguard' (D)	CWGr
'Inca Vulcan' (S-c)	CWGr
'Independence' (D)	SGbt
'Inglebrook Jill' (Col)	CWGr NJRG
'Inland Dynasty' (S-c)	CWGr GRid
'Inn's Gerrie Hoek' (D)	CWGr
'Irene Ellen' (D)	GRid
'Irene van der Zwet' (Sin)	CWGr
'Irene's Pride' (S-c)	GRid
'Iris' (Pom)	CWGr GRid GWyn
'Islander' (D)	ERCP
'Ivanetti' (Ba)	CWGr ERCP GRid NHal SGbt
'Ivy Della' (D)	CWGr
'J Boy' (Ba)	GRid
'J.R.G.' (Misc) ♀H3	NJRG
'Jack Hood' (D)	CWGr SGbt
'Jackie Magson' (S-c)	CWGr
'Jacqueline Tivey' (D)	CWGr
'Jake's Pastelle' (S-c)	GRid
'Jaldec Jerry' (S-c)	CWGr
'Jaldec Jolly' (C)	CWGr
'Jamaica' (D)	CWGr SGbt
'Jamie' (S-c)	CWGr
'Jan Lennon' (S-c)	CWGr
'Jan van Schaffelaar' (Pom)	ERCP SDeJ
'Janal Amy' (S-c)	CWGr GRid NHal SGbt
'Jane Cowl' (D)	CWGr
'Jane Horton' (Col)	CWGr GRid SGbt
'Janet Beckett' (C)	CWGr
'Japanese Waterlily' (WL)	CWGr
'Jazzy' (Col)	CWGr
'Je Maintiendrai' (D)	CWGr
'Jean Fairs' (WL) ♀H3	CWGr SGbt
'Jean Marie'PBR (D)	CWGr ERCP
'Jean Melville' (D)	CWGr
'Jean Shaw' (D)	GRid NHal
'Jeanne d'Arc' (C)	CWGr
'Jeannie Leroux' (Fim)	CWGr
'Jean's Carol' (Pom)	CWGr
I 'Jennie' (Fim)	CWGr GRid
§ 'Jenny' (Dahlietta Select Series) (Misc)	SGbt
'Jersey Beauty' (D)	CWGr

	'Jescot India' (D)	CWGr
	'Jescot Jess' (D)	CWGr
	'Jescot Jim' (D)	CWGr
	'Jescot Julie' (DblO)	CWGr ERCP LAyl LCro LOPS NJRG
	'Jescot Lingold' (D)	CWGr SGbt
	'Jescot Redun' (D)	CWGr
	'Jessica' (S-c)	CWGr
	'Jessie G' (Ba)	CWGr ERCP
	'Jessie Ross' (D/DwB)	CWGr
	'Jet' (S-c)	CWGr
I	'Jet Fire' (D)	GRid
	'Jill Day' (C)	CWGr
	'Jill Doc' (D)	CWGr
	'Jill's Delight' (D)	CWGr
	'Jim Branigan' (S-c)	CWGr NHal
	'Jive' (Anem)	ELan ERCP SDeJ
	'Joan Beecham' (D)	GRid
	'Joan Walker' (D)	GRid
	'Jocondo' (D)	CWGr GRid NHal SGbt
	'Jodie Wilkinson' (Ba) ♀H3	NHal
	'Joe Swift' (Sin)	CWGr
	'Johann' (Pom)	CWGr GRid NHal
	'John Hill' (D)	GRid NHal
	'John Prior' (D)	CWGr
	'John Street' (WL)	CWGr WSpi
	'John's Champion' (D)	CWGr
	'Jomanda' (Ba) ♀H3	CWGr GRid NHal NJRG SGbt
	'Jorja' (S-c)	GRid
	'Jo's Choice' (D)	CWGr
	'Josie Gott' (Ba) ♀H3	NJRG SGbt
	'Josudi Hercules' (S-c) **new**	NHal
	'Josudi Telstar' (C) **new**	NHal
	'Jowey Gipsy' (D) **new**	WFar
	'Jowey Ingrid' (D)	GRid
	'Jowey Linda' (Ba)	ERCP
	'Jowey Winnie' (Ba)	ERCP
	'Joy Donaldson' (C)	CWGr
	'Joyce Green' (S-c)	CWGr GRid SGbt
	'Joyce Margaret Cunliffe' (D)	CWGr
	'Juanita' (S-c)	CWGr
	'Jules Dyson' (Misc)	SDys
	'Julie One' (DblO)	CWGr ECtt SGbt
	'Julie's Delight' (S-c)	CWGr
	'Julio' (Ba)	CWGr
	'Jura' (S-c)	CWGr
	'Kaftan' (D)	CWGr
	'Kaga-komachi' (D)	LRHS NRHS
	'Kaiser Wilhelm' (Ba)	CWGr
	'Kaisha Lea' (D)	ERCP
	'Karen G' (Col)	NJRG
	'Karenglen' (D) ♀H3	GRid NHal NJRG SGbt
	'Kari Quill' (C)	CWGr
	'Karma Amanda'PBR (D)	CWGr
	'Karma Bon Bini'PBR (C)	CAby SGbt
	'Karma Choc'PBR (D) ♀H3	CAby CRos CSpe CWGr EBee EPfP ERCP EWes LCro LOPS LRHS MHol NRHS SEND SGbt SPer WBor WCot WFar WHoo
	'Karma Corona'PBR (C)	CAvo CWGr SGbt
	'Karma Fiesta'PBR (D)	ERCP
	'Karma Fuchsiana' (D)	CWGr ERCP LCro LOPS SGbt
	'Karma Irene'PBR (D)	CWGr ERCP
	'Karma Lagoon'PBR (D)	CRos CWGr ERCP LRHS NRHS SGbt
	'Karma Maarten Zwaan'PBR (WL)	CWGr ERCP
	'Karma Naomi'PBR (D)	ERCP SGbt
	'Karma Pink Corona'PBR (C)	LCro LOPS
	'Karma Prospero'PBR (D)	ERCP LCro LOPS

	'Karma Red Corona'PBR (C)	SDeJ SGbt
	'Karma Sangria'PBR (C)	CWGr LCro LOPS SDeJ SGbt
	'Karma Serena'PBR (D)	SDeJ
	'Karma Yin Yang' (D)	LRHS SGbt
	'Karras 150' (S-c)	CWGr
	'Kasasagi' (Pom)	CWGr
	'Kate Mountjoy' (Col)	CWGr SGbt
	'Katie's Velvet' (Col) **new**	NHal
	'Katisha' (D)	CWGr
	'Kayleigh Spiller' (Col)	SGbt
	'Kea Magic' (D)	GRid
	'Keith's Choice' (D)	GRid NHal SGbt
	'Kelsea Carla' (S-c) ♀H3	CWGr
	'Kelsey Annie Joy' (Col)	NJRG
	'Kelvin Floodlight' (D)	CBod CWGr NRHS SDeJ SGbt
	'Kennemerland' (S-c)	LCro LOPS SDeJ SGbt
	'Kenora Challenger' (S-c)	CWGr GRid NHal NJRG SGbt
	'Kenora Clyde' (S-c)	CWGr
	'Kenora Fireball' (Ba)	CWGr GRid
	'Kenora Frills' (Fim)	NHal
	'Kenora Jubilee' (S-c)	GRid GWyn SGbt
	'Kenora Lisa' (D)	CWGr
	'Kenora Macop-B' (Fim)	CWGr ECtt ERCP NHal SPer
	'Kenora Moonbeam' (D)	CWGr GRid
	'Kenora Ontario' (S-c)	CWGr
	'Kenora Sunset' (S-c) ♀H3	CWGr GRid NHal SGbt
	'Kenora Superb' (S-c)	CWGr GRid SGbt
	'Kenora Valentine' (D) ♀H3	CWGr NHal SGbt
	'Kenora Wildfire' (D)	CWGr GRid
	'Kenora Wow' (S-c)	NHal
	'Ken's Choice' (Ba)	GRid
	'Ken's Coral' (WL)	CWGr
	'Ken's Flame' (WL)	CWGr SGbt
	'Ken's Rarity' (WL)	NHal NJRG SGbt
	'Kidd's Climax' (D) ♀H3	CWGr GRid
	'Kiev' (Jumbo Collection) (D)	LCro LOPS
	'Kikoski' (C)	SGbt
	'Kilburn Fiesta' (S-c)	GRid NHal
	'Kilburn Glow' (WL)	LAyl NHal NJRG
	'Kilburn Rose' (WL) ♀H3	NJRG
	'Kilmorie' (S-c)	GRid NHal
	'Kingston' (D)	CWGr SGbt
	'Kirsty G' (Col)	NJRG
	'Kismet' (Ba)	CWGr
	'Kit Kat' (C)	CWGr
	'Kiwi Brother' (S-c)	CWGr
	'Kiwi Gloria' (C)	CWGr GRid NHal NJRG
	'Kiwi Sister' (S-c)	CWGr
	'Klondike' (S-c)	CWGr ERCP NJRG
I	'Knockout'PBR (Sin) ♀H3	CAby CBcs CRos CWGr EPfP ERCP LRHS LSRN NRHS SPoG
	'Kochelsee' (Ba)	CWGr
	'Kogane Fubuki' (Fim)	CWGr
	'Kotare Jackpot' (S-c)	CWGr
	'Kung Fu' (D)	CWGr
	'Kym Willo' (Pom)	CWGr
I	'Kyoto' (WL)	CWGr SGbt
	'L.A.T.E.' (Ba)	CWGr GRid NHal SGbt
	'La Cierva' (Col)	CWGr
	'La Gioconda' (Col)	CWGr GRid
	'La Recoleta' (D)	CWGr ERCP
	'Labyrinth' (D)	ERCP
	'Lady Darlene' (D)	CWGr ERCP
	'Lady Kate' (D)	LCro LOPS
	'Lady Kerkrade' (C)	CWGr
	'Lady Liberty' (D)	ERCP
	'Lady Linda' (D)	CWGr GRid SGbt
	'Lady Orpah' (D)	CWGr
	'Lady Sunshine' (S-c)	CWGr
	'Laguna Beach' (Ba)	CWGr

	'Lake Carey' (D)	LCro LOPS
	'Lakeland Polly' (Pom)	GRid NHal NJRG
	'Lambada' (Anem)	ELan ERCP
	'L'Ancresse' (Ba)	GRid LAyl NHal NJRG
	'Larkford' (D)	CWGr
	'Last Dance' (D)	CWGr
	'Laura's Choice' (D)	CWGr
	'Lavendale' (D)	CWGr
	'Lavender Chiffon' (S-c)	CWGr
	'Lavender Freestyle' (C)	CWGr
	'Lavender Leycett' (D)	CWGr
	'Lavender Line' (S-c)	GRid NHal
	'Lavender Nunton Harvest' (D)	CWGr
	'Lavender Perfection' (D)	CWGr SDeJ
	'Lavengro' (D)	CWGr GRid
	'Le Baron' (D)	ERCP MCot
	'Le Castel' (WL) ♀H3	CWGr SDeJ WFar
	'Le Feu du Soleil' (Fim)	NHal
	'Le Patineur' (D)	CWGr
	'Le Vonné Splinter' (S-c)	CWGr GRid
	'Leander' (S-c)	CWGr
	'Lee Marshall' (C)	CWGr
	'Leila Savanna Rose' (S-c)	ERCP
§	'Lemon Cane' (D)	CWGr ECtt
	'Lemon Elegans' (S-c) ♀H3	CWGr GRid NHal NJRG
	'Lemon Meringue' (D)	CWGr ECtt SGbt
	'Lemon Puff' (Anem)	CWGr
	'Lemon Symbol' (S-c)	CWGr
	'Lemon Zing' (Ba)	GRid LAyl NHal SGbt
	'Leopold Chloe' (D)	GRid NHal
	'Leopold Sophie' (D)	GRid
	'Leslie's Willo' (Pom)	GRid
	'Lexington' (Pom)	CWGr
	'Leycett' (D)	CWGr
	'Libretto' (Col)	CWGr
	'Life Force' (D)	CWGr SGbt
	'Life Style' (Anem)	GWyn
	'Lifesize' (D)	GRid
	'Light Music' (S-c)	CWGr
	'Lilac Athalie' (C)	CWGr
	'Lilac Bull' (D)	LRHS
	'Lilac Marston' (D) ♀H3	NHal
	'Lilac Pathfinder' (Sin)	NJRG
	'Lilac Shadow' (S-c)	CWGr
	'Lilac Taratahi' (C) ♀H3	CSam CWGr
I	'Lilac Time' (D)	CWGr ERCP SDeJ SGbt
	'Lilac Willo' (Pom)	CWGr
	lilac-flowered B&SWJ 14942 from Colombia **new**	WCru
	'Lilian Alice' (Col)	GRid
	'Lilian Marston' (D)	GRid
	'Lilianna W' (Sin/Dw.B.)	NJRG
	'Linda's Baby' (Ba)	ERCP
	'Linda's Chester' (C)	CWGr
	'Linda's Diane' (D)	CWGr
	'Linda's Polly' (Pom)	NJRG
	'Lindsay' (WL)	GRid
	'Lismore Carol' (Pom)	CWGr GWyn NHal
	'Lismore Chaffinch' (D)	GRid
	'Lismore Moonlight' (Pom)	CWGr GRid NHal
	'Lismore Robin' (D)	GRid NHal
	'Lismore Sunset' (Pom)	CWGr GRid SGbt
	'Lismore Willie' (WL) ♀H3	CWGr GRid NJRG
	'Little Beeswing' (C)	ERCP
	'Little Dorrit' (Sin/Lil)	CWGr NJRG
	'Little Lamb' (S-c)	CWGr
	'Little Laura' (Ba)	CWGr
	'Little Matthew' (Pom)	CWGr SGbt
	'Little Reggie' (S-c)	CWGr
	'Little Robert' (D)	CWGr ERCP SGbt
	'Little Sally' (Pom)	CWGr SGbt
	'Little Scottie' (Pom)	CWGr
	'Little Shona' (D)	CWGr
	'Little Snowdrop' (Pom)	CWGr SGbt
	'Little Tiger' (D)	CWGr SCob WFar
	'Little Willem' (Pom)	SDeJ SGbt
	'Lloyd Huston' (S-c)	CWGr
	'Lois Walcher' (D)	CWGr
	'Loraine Mitchell' (WL)	NJRG
	'Loretta' (Ba)	GRid
	'Lorona Dawn' (SinO)	ERCP LAyl
	'Loud Applause' (C)	CWGr
	'Louie Meggos' (D)	NHal
	'Louis V' (Fim)	SGbt
*	'Louis Walchen' (D)	CWGr
	'Louise Bailey' (D)	CWGr
	'Louise'PBR (Dahlietta Surprise Series) (D/DwB)	CWGr
	'Lovelife'PBR (D)	ERCP SPer
	'Lucky Devil' (WL)	CWGr
	'Lucky Number' (D)	CWGr ERCP
	'Ludwig Helfert' (S-c)	CWGr
	'Luka Johanna' (WL)	ERCP
	'Lula Pattie' (D)	GRid
	'Lupin Dixie' (C)	CWGr
	'Lyn Mayo' (D)	CWGr
	'Lynn T' (Col) **new**	GRid
	'Mabel Ann' (D)	CWGr GRid LAyl
	'Madaline Ann' (D)	CWGr
	'Madame Simone Stappers' (WL)	CWGr ECtt EUJe LAyl LRHS NRHS WSpi
	'Madame Vera' (D)	CWGr
	'Maddie Grace' (D)	CWGr
	'Magenta Magenta' (D)	LAyl SGbt
	'Magenta Magic' (Sin/DwB)	NHal
	'Magenta Star' (Sin) ♀H3	CWGr ERCP SGbt
I	'Magic Moment' (S-c)	CWGr
	'Magnificat' (D)	CWGr
	'Maisha' (D) **new**	CWGr
	'Maisie' (D)	CWGr
	'Maisie Mooney' (D)	CWGr
	'Majestic Kerkrade' (C)	CWGr
	'Majjas Symbol' (S-c)	CWGr
	'Maldiva' (D)	ERCP
	'Malham Portia' (WL)	CWGr
	'Malvern Martha' (D)	GRid
I	'Mambo' (Anem)	SDeJ
	'Manhattan Island' (D)	CWGr ERCP SDeJ
	'Manuel' (D)	CWGr
	'Marble Ball' (D)	CWGr ERCP SDeJ SGbt SPer
	'Marcanti' (S-c) **new**	SPer
	'Margaret Anne' (D)	CWGr
	'Margaret Brookes' (D)	CWGr
	'Marie' (D)	CWGr
	'Marie Schnugg' (SinO) ♀H3	CWGr NJRG SGbt
	'Marissa' (WL)	GRid
	'Mark Damp' (S-c)	CWGr
	'Mark Hardwick' (D)	CWGr GRid
	'Mark Lockwood' (Pom)	CWGr
	'Market Joy' (S-c)	CWGr
	'Marla Lu' (C)	CWGr
	'Marlene Joy' (Fim)	CWGr SGbt
	'Marrakech' (WL)	CWGr
I	'Mars' (Col)	CWGr SGbt
	'Marston George' (Ba)	CWGr GRid NHal NJRG
	'Marston Suzanne' (D)	GRid NHal
	'Martina' (D)	GRid
	'Martin's Yellow' (Pom)	GRid NHal
	'Mary Anna Rosa' (S-c) **new**	CWGr

'Mary Crichton' (D) GRid
I 'Mary Eveline' (Col) ECtt NHal
'Mary Evelyn' (C) ERCP SGbt
'Mary Hammett' (D) WSpi
'Mary Layton' (Col) CWGr
'Mary McLelland' (Col) GRid
'Mary Pitt' (D) CWGr SGbt
'Mary Richards' (D) CWGr
'Mary's Jomanda' (Ba) Υ^{H3} CWGr GRid GWyn NHal NJRG SGbt
'MAS Robert' (Fim) **new** CWGr
'MAS Sixty' (D) **new** CWGr
'Mascot Maya' (D) NJRG
'Master Michael' (Pom) CWGr
'Match' (S-c) CWGr GRid
'Matchless' (C) CWGr
'Matilda Huston' (S-c) CWGr LAyl NHal
'Matt Armour' (Sin) CWGr
'Maureen Hardwick' (D) CWGr SGbt
'Maureen Jones' (Col) NJRG
'Maxime' (D) ERCP
'Maxine Bailey' (D) CWGr
'Mayan Blood' (DblO) CWGr
'Mayan Pearl' (DblO) Υ^{H3} CWGr LAyl NHal SGbt
'Mayan Swan' (S-c) Υ^{H3} SGbt
'Mayan Warrior' (S-c) NJRG
'Mediterrannee' (D) ERCP
'Megan Dean' (Ba) GRid NHal
'Meiro' (D) CWGr
'Melanie Jane' (S-c) CWGr
'Melody Allegro'^{PBR} (D) ERCP LRHS MHol NRHS WFar
'Melody Bolero'^{PBR} (D) CWGr SDeJ WFar
'Melody Dixie'^{PBR} (D) CWGr ERCP WFar
'Melody Dora'^{PBR} (D) CWGr GRid LCro LOPS LRHS
'Melody Fanfare'^{PBR} (D) ERCP SDeJ
'Melody Gipsy'^{PBR} (S-c) CWGr ERCP LRHS
'Melody Harmony'^{PBR} (D) Υ^{H3} ERCP
'Melody Latin'^{PBR} (D) CWGr
'Melody Lizza'^{PBR} (D) LRHS NRHS
'Melody Pink Allegro' (D) ERCP
'Melody Swing'^{PBR} (D) CWGr ERCP
'Mel's Orange Marmalade' (Fim) ERCP LCro LOPS
'Menorca' (D) **new** ERCP
merckii CExl CHll CRos CSpe CWGr ECha EUJe EWes LRHS MCot MMrt MNrw MRav NRHS SHar
- 'Alba' (B) CExl CSpe
- dark-flowered WPGP
'Mevrouw Clement Andries' (Fim) ERCP
§ 'Mexican Black' (Misc) CWGr EBee ECtt ERCP IPot NJRG WPGP
'Mexico Mogul' (D) SGbt
'Mi Wong' (Pom) GRid
'Miami' (D) CWGr
'Michael Haynes' (D) **new** CWGr
'Michael J' (D) CWGr
'Michigan' (D) CWGr
'Mick' (C) CWGr
'Mick's Peppermint' (S-c) CAby CWGr SGbt
'Midas' (S-c) CWGr
'Midnight' (Pom) SGbt
'Midnight Star' (SinO) NJRG
'Mies' (Sin) CWGr
'Milk Shake' (D) CWGr NRHS
'Mingus Alex' (S-c) CWGr
'Mingus Arthur K' (Fim) GRid
'Mingus Erik' (Fim) GRid
'Mingus Gregory' (S-c) CWGr ERCP SDeJ
'Mingus Heather' (WL) GRid
'Mingus Julie' (C) GRid
'Mingus Kyle D' (D) CWGr
* 'Mingus Max' ERCP
'Mingus Nichole' (D) CWGr
'Mingus Toni' (D) ERCP
'Mingus Tracy Lynn' (S-c) CWGr GRid
'Mingus Whitney' (S-c) GRid
'Mini Red' (S-c) CWGr
'Minley Carol' (Pom) CWGr GRid NHal NJRG
'Minnesota Migrant' (S-c) CWGr
'Miramar' (D) CWGr
'Mish-Mash' (Fim) GRid
'Miss Ellen' (Misc) Υ^{H3} CWGr
'Miss Rose Fletcher' (S-c) CWGr
'Miss Sophie' (S-c) **new** ERCP
'Miss Swiss' (D) CWGr
'Mister Frans' (D) **new** ERCP
'Misterton' (D) CWGr SGbt
'Mistill Beauty' (C) CWGr
'Mistill Delight' (D) CWGr
'Mom's Special' (D) CWGr ERCP
'Monet Mystique' (WL) SGbt
'Monet Sunlight' (WL) SGbt
'Monk Marc' (C) CWGr
'Monkstown Diane' (C) CWGr
'Monrovia' (Ba) CWGr
§ 'Moonfire' (Sin) Υ^{H3} CAby CBcs CRos CWCL CWGN CWGr ECtt EHrv ELan EPfP ERCP EUJe LAyl LCro LOPS LRHS NHal NJRG NLar NRHS SGbt SPer WCot WHoo WSpi
'Moonglow' (S-c) CWGr ERCP LRHS
'Moor Place' (Pom) CWGr GRid NHal NJRG SGbt
moorei WPGP
'Moray Susan' (WL) CWGr
'Moret' (S-c) CWGr
'Morley Lady' (D) CWGr
'Morna Whitlock' (S-c) CWGr
'Morning Dew' (WL) CWGr
'Motto' (D) CWGr
'Moulin Rouge' (C) SPer
'Mount Noddy' (Sin) CWGr
'Mr Sandman' (Fim) MSCN
'Mrs A. Woods' (D) CWGr
'Mrs Black' (Pom) CWGr
'Mrs Eileen' (D) ERCP SDeJ SGbt
'Mrs H. Brown' (Col) SGbt
'Mrs McDonald Quill' (D) CWGr GRid SGbt
'Mrs Silverston' (D) CWGr
'Ms Kennedy' (Ba) NHal
'München' (D) SDeJ SGbt
'Murdoch' ambig. (D) EBee ECtt LRHS LSun MHol WBrk WCot WSpi
'Murillo' ambig. (Sin) LAyl
'Murray May' (WL) CWGr
'Murray Petite' (S-c) CWGr
'Musette' (D) SGbt
'Musson's Silverback' (Fim) **new** CWGr
'My Irene' (WL) NJRG
'My Joy' (Pom) CWGr
'My Love' (S-c) CWGr ECtt ERCP LCro LOPS SEND SGbt
'My Neddy' (D) SGbt
I 'My Pride' (D) GRid
'Myama Fubuki' (Fim) ELan ERCP
'My-nute Blend' (Misc) Υ^{H3} CWGr
'Myrtle's Folly' (Fim) ERCP SDeJ

	Name	Suppliers
	'Mystère' (Anem)	CWGr
	'Mystery Day' (D)	CWGr
	MYSTIC DESIRE	see *D.* 'Scarlet Fern'
	MYSTIC DREAMER	see *D.* 'Zone Ten'
§	'Mystic Enchantment'PBR (Sin)	CRos ELan LRHS NRHS SPoG
	'Mystic Haze'	see *D.* 'Dark Side Of The Sun'
	MYSTIC ILLUSION	see *D.* 'Knockout' (Sin)
	MYSTIC MARS	see *D.* 'Scarlet Fern'
§	MYSTIC SPIRIT ('Hamspirit'PBR) (Sin)	ELan LRHS NRHS
	'Mystic Wonder' (Sin)	CRos ELan LRHS NRHS WAvo
	'Nadia Ruth' (Fim)	ERCP
	'Nagano' (D)	CWGr SDeJ
	'Nancy H' (Ba)	CWGr
	'Nancy Margaret' (S-c)	GRid
	'Nargold' (Fim)	CWGr LAyl
	'Narrow's Tricia' (S-c)	GRid NJRG
	'Natal' (Ba)	CAvo ECtt SDeJ
	'Natalie G' (D)	EPfP ERCP NJRG
	'Nathalie's Wedding' (WL)	ERCP
	'Nationwide' (D)	CWGr
	'Neal Gillson' (D)	CWGr
	'Nelly Geerlings' (Sin)	CWGr
	'Nenekazi' (Fim)	CWGr GRid LAyl NJRG
	'Néo' (D)	CWGr
	'Nepos' (WL)	CWGr GRid GWyn NJRG SGbt
	'Nescio' (Pom)	CWGr ERCP SDeJ
I	'New Baby' (Ba)	CWGr ERCP LCro LOPS SGbt
	'Newby' (D)	CWGr
	'Newquay' (Sin)	CWGr
	'Newsham Wonder' (D)	CWGr
	'Nicholas' (D)	ERCP SPer
	'Nicola' (S-c)	CWGr
	'Nicolette' (D)	CWGr
	'Nienke' (D)	NJRG
	'Night Butterfly' (Col)	CAby ERCP
	'Night Editor' (D)	CWGr
I	'Night Queen' (Ba)	EPfP ERCP
	'Nijinsky' (Ba)	CWGr
	'Nina Chester' (D)	CWGr GRid
	'Nippon' (Sin)	EPfP LRHS
	'Nogent' (D)	CWGr
	'Nonette' (WL)	CWGr EBee ECtt SGbt WBrk WCot
	'Norbeck Dusky' (S-c)	CWGr
	'Noreen' (Pom)	CWGr GRid NHal NJRG
	'Norman Lockwood' (Pom)	CWGr
	'Normandie Wedding Day' (Fim)	NHal
	'Northland Primrose' (C)	CWGr
§	'Nuit d'Eté' (S-c)	CAby CAvo CWGr ELan ERCP LCro LOPS LRHS SDeJ SGbt
	'Nuland's Josephine' (Ba)	LAyl NHal NJRG
	'Nunton Form' (D)	CWGr
	'Nunton Harvest' (D)	CWGr GRid
	'Nymphenburg' (WL)	CWGr
	'Oakwood Belle' (C)	CWGr
	'Oakwood Bridesmaid' (C)	CWGr
	'Oakwood Christina' (Ba) **new**	CWGr
	'Oakwood Dazzle' (D)	CWGr
	'Oakwood Diamond' (Ba)	CWGr
	'Oakwood Duchess' (D) **new**	CWGr
	'Oakwood Fire' (S-c)	CWGr
	'Oakwood Firelight' (S-c)	CWGr
	'Oakwood Goldcrest' (S-c)	GRid NHal
	'Oakwood Heather' (Ba)	CWGr
	'Oakwood Katie' (S-c)	CWGr
	'Oakwood Kim' (D) **new**	CWGr
	'Oakwood Lyndon S' (S-c) **new**	CWGr
	'Oakwood Marian S' (D)	CWGr
	'Oakwood Naranga' (D) ♀H3	CWGr
	'Oakwood Natasha' (Pom)	CWGr
	'Oakwood Royale' (D)	CWGr
	'Oakwood Tulisa' (D) **new**	CWGr
	'Oakwood Vivian S' (S-c) **new**	CWGr
	'Ocean Bird'PBR (D) ♀H3	ERCP
	'Offshore Dream' (D)	ERCP
I	'Old Gold' (D)	CWGr SGbt
I	'Olivia' (Col)	CWGr GRid NJRG
	'Olivia Mari' (WL)	GRid NHal
	'Omo' (Sin/Lil) ♀H3	NJRG
	'Onesta' (D)	CWGr ERCP SDeJ
	'Only Love' (S-c)	CWGr
	'Onslow Michele' (D)	CWGr
	'Onslow Renown' (S-c)	CWGr
	'Opal' (Ba)	CWGr
	'Optic Illusion' (D)	CWGr ERCP
	'Opus' (D)	CWGr SGbt
	'Orange Chum' (D)	CWGr
	'Orange Cushion' (D)	CWGr
	'Orange Explosion' (Misc)	CWGr SGbt
	'Orange Fire' (S-c)	CWGr
	'Orange Fubuki' (D)	ERCP
	'Orange Keith's Choice' (D)	CWGr GRid
	'Orange Kiss' (Col)	NJRG
	'Orange Mullett' (D/DwB)	CWGr
	'Orange Nugget' (Ba)	CWGr SDeJ
	'Orange Pathfinder' (Misc)	CWGr NJRG
I	'Orange Queen' (C)	CWGr SGbt
	'Orange Sun' (D)	CWGr
	'Orchid Lace' (C)	CWGr
	'Orchid Princess' (S-c)	ERCP
	'Orel' (Col)	GRid SGbt
	'Oreti Bliss' (C)	GRid LAyl NHal
	'Oreti Classic' (D)	NHal
	'Oreti Duke' (Pom)	CWGr
	'Oreti Stacey' (Fim)	GRid
	'Orfeo' (C)	CWGr ERCP LCro LOPS MNrw SDeJ SGbt
I	'Orion' (D)	CWGr
	'Ornamental Rays' (C)	CWGr
	'Osaka' (D)	CWGr
	'Osirium' (D)	ERCP
	'Ossie Latham' (Sin)	CWGr SGbt
	'Othello' (S-c)	CWGr GRid
	'Otto's Thrill' (D) ♀H3	ERCP MSCN
	'Pacific Ocean' (WL)	ERCP
	'Paint Box' (S-c)	CWGr
	'Painted Girl' (D)	ERCP
	'Paisley Gem' (Sin)	CWGr
	'Palomino' (D)	CWGr
	'Pam Howden' (WL)	NHal NJRG SGbt
	'Pamela' (D)	CWGr
	'Paradise City' (D)	ERCP
	'Pari Taha Sunrise' (S-c)	CWGr
	'Park Princess' (C/DwB)	CWGr LAyl NHal NRHS SDeJ SGbt
	'Park Record' (S-c)	LCro LOPS
	'Parkland Rave' (S-c)	CWGr NHal
	'Paroa Gillian' (C)	CWGr
	'Paso Doble' misapplied	see *D.* 'Freya's Paso Doble'
	'Passion' (D)	CWGr
	'Pat Knight' (Col)	CWGr NHal NJRG
	'Pat Mark' (S-c)	CWGr
	'Pat 'n' Dee' (D)	CWGr
	'Pat 'n' Perc' (Col)	NJRG SGbt

	'Pat Seed' (D)	CWGr
	'Paul Chester' (C)	CWGr
	'Paul Critchley' (C)	CWGr
	'Paul Smith' (Ba)	CWGr
	'Peace Pact' (WL)	CWGr
	'Peach Athalie' (C)	CWGr
	'Peach Delight' (S-c)	SGbt
§	'Peach Melba' (D)	GRid NHal
I	'Peaches' (Ba)	ERCP
	'Peaches and Cream'PBR (D)	CWGr ECtt
	'Peachette' (Misc/Lil)	CWGr
	'Pearl Hornsey' (D)	CWGr
	'Pearl of Heemstede' (D) ♀H3	CWGr LAyl NHal NJRG
	'Pearl Sharowean' (S-c)	CWGr
	'Pearson's Ben' (S-c)	CWGr GRid NHal NJRG
	'Pearson's Melanie' (C)	CWGr
	'Pearson's Patrick' (S-c)	CWGr
	'Pembroke Levenna' (Ba)	LAyl
	'Pembroke Pattie' (Pom)	GRid
	'Penhill Autumn Shade' (S-c)	GRid NJRG SGbt
	'Penhill Dark Monarch' (D)	ERCP
	'Penhill Watermelon' (D)	ERCP SDeJ
	'Pennsclout' (D)	CWGr
	'Penny Lane' (D)	ERCP
	'Pensford Marion' (Pom)	CWGr GRid
I	'Perfect' (D)	CWGr
	'Perfect Partner' (Sin)	CWGr
	'Perfectos' (C)	CWGr
	'Peter' (D)	CWGr SGbt
	'Petit Byoux' (Col/DwB)	CWGr
	'Petite Harvest' (Misc/DwB)	NJRG
	'Petite Sunrise' (Sin)	NJRG
	'Petite Sunset' (Misc/Lil)	NJRG
	'Petra's Wedding' (Ba)	CWGr ERCP
	'Pfitzer's Joker' (C)	CAby
	'Philadelphia' (D) **new**	CWGr
	'Pianella' (S-c)	CWGr SGbt
	'Pineapple Lollipop' (Ba)	CWGr
	'Pinelands Pam' (Fim)	CWGr GRid
	'Pinelands Princess' (Fim)	ERCP EUJe SGbt
	'Pink Attraction' (D)	CWGr
	'Pink Breckland Joy' (D)	CWGr
	'Pink Carol' (Pom)	CWGr GRid NJRG
	'Pink Giraffe' (DblO) ♀H3	CWGr ERCP SGbt
	'Pink Isa'PBR (D)	CWGr ERCP
	'Pink Jean Fairs' (WL)	CWGr
	'Pink Jupiter' (S-c)	CWGr GRid NHal SGbt
	'Pink Katisha' (D)	CWGr
	'Pink Kerkrade' (C)	CWGr
	'Pink Leycett' (D)	CWGr
	'Pink Loveliness' (WL)	CWGr
	'Pink Pastelle' (S-c) ♀H3	GRid SGbt
	'Pink Pat and Perc' (Col)	GRid NHal NJRG
	'Pink Preference' (S-c)	CWGr
	'Pink Risca Miner' (Ba)	CWGr
	'Pink Robin Hood' (Ba)	CWGr
	'Pink Runner' (D) **new**	ERCP
	'Pink Sensation' (C) ♀H3	CWGr
	'Pink Shirley Alliance' (C)	CWGr
	'Pink Silk' (D) **new**	ERCP
	'Pink Skin' (D)	ECtt LRHS SDeJ
	'Pink Spur' (D)	GRid
	'Pink Suffusion' (D)	GRid
	'Pink Sylvia' (D)	CWGr
	'Pink Worton Ann' (D)	CWGr
	'Pinkie Swear' (S-c) **new**	ERCP
	pinnata B&SWJ 10240	WCru
	- B&SWJ 14901 from Colombia **new**	WCru
	'Piperoo' (C)	CWGr SGbt
	'Piper's Pink' (S-c/DwB)	CWGr ECtt GRid LRHS NRHS SGbt
I	'Pippa' (WL)	CWGr
I	'Pippi' (D)	CWGr
	'Pitchoun' (Sin)	CWGr
	'Platinum Blonde' (Anem) **new**	ERCP
	'Playa Blanca' (C/DwB)	SCob SGbt
	'Playboy' (D)	CWGr
	'Plum Surprise' (Pom)	CWGr
	'Polar Sight' (C)	CWGr
I	'Polka' (Anem)	NJRG SDeJ SGbt
	'Polly Peachum' (D)	CWGr
	'Polventon Kristobel' (D) **new**	NHal
	'Polventon Supreme' (Ba)	CWGr
	'Pontiac' (C)	CWGr SGbt
	'Pooh' (Col)	see *D.* 'Pooh - Swan Island'
§	'Pooh - Swan Island' (Col) ♀H3	CAby CWGr EBee ECtt ERCP EUJe GRid LAyl MSCN NCou NHal NJRG SPer WCot
	'Pop Willo' (Pom)	GRid NJRG
I	'Poppet' (Pom)	CWGr
	'Poppyscotland' (Sin)	CWGr
	'Popular Guest' (Fim)	CWGr
	'Porcelain' (WL)	WSpi
	'Pot Black' (Ba)	CWGr
	'Potgeiter' (Ba)	CWGr
	'Prefect' (S-c)	CWGr
	'Prefere' (Sin)	CWGr
	'Preference' (C)	CWGr ERCP SDeJ SGbt
	'Preston Park' (Sin/DwB) ♀H3	CWGr LAyl NHal
	PRETTY WOMAN ('Vdtg43'PBR) (Dark Angel Series) (Sin) ♀H3	ERCP LCro LOPS
	'Priceless Pink' (Misc)	ERCP
	PRIDE OF BERLIN	see *D.* 'Stolz von Berlin'
	'Prime Minister' (D)	CWGr
	'Primrose Diane' (D)	GRid
	'Primrose Pastelle' (S-c)	GRid NHal
	'Primrose Rustig' (D)	CWGr
	'Prince Valiant' (D)	CWGr
I	'Princess' (Col)	SDeJ
	'Princess Beatrix' (D)	CWGr
	'Princess Marie José' (Sin)	CWGr
	'Princesse Elisabeth' (D)	ERCP
	'Princesse Gracia' (D)	ERCP
	'Princesse Laetitia' (D)	ERCP
	'Procyon' (D)	CWGr SGbt
	'Prom' (Pom)	CWGr
	'Promise' (Fim)	CWGr ECtt ERCP SDeJ
	pteropoda	CWGr
	aff. ***pteropoda***	CWGr
	- F&M 312	WPGP
	'Puerto Rico' (Fim)	ERCP
	PULP FICTION ('Vdtg61'PBR) (Dark Angel Series) (Sin)	ERCP
	'Punky' (Pom)	CWGr
	'Purbeck Lydia' (S-c)	CWGr
	'Purity' (S-c)	CWGr
	'Purpinca' (Anem)	CWGr
	'Purple Cottesmore' (WL)	CWGr
	'Purple Flame'PBR (D)	CAvo ERCP
	'Purple Fox'PBR (Ba)	ERCP
	'Purple Gem' (S-c)	CWGr ERCP EUJe LCro LOPS SDeJ SGbt SPer
	'Purple Haze' (Misc)	ERCP LCro LOPS LSRN
	'Purple Pearl' (D)	ERCP NHal
	'Purple Petite' (Sin)	NJRG

'Purple Puff' (Anem) LAyl NHal NJRG
'Purple Sensation' (S-c) CWGr
'Purple Splash' (WL) CWGr
'Purple Taiheyō' (D) CWGr
purpusii CWGr
aff. ***purpusii*** B&SWJ 10321 WCru
'Pussycat' (D) CWGr
'Quel Diable' (S-c) CWGr
'R Mona' (WL) **new** NHal
'Rachel de Thame' (Sin) CWGr
'Rachel's Place' (Pom) CWGr
'Radiance' (C) CWGr
I 'Radjah' (Pom) NRHS
'Ragged Robin' (Misc) CSpe CWGr ECtt ERCP LRHS
'Raspberry Valiant' (B) NHal
* 'Raymond Guernsey' ECtt
'Razzle Dazzle' (D) ERCP
'Rebecca Lynn' (D) CWGr
'Rebecca's World' (D) ECtt EPfP ERCP LCro LOPS SPer
'Red and White' (D) CWGr SGbt
'Red Arrows' (D) CWGr
'Red Cap' (D) CWGr
'Red Carol' (Pom) CWGr GRid
'Red Diamond' (D) NHal
'Red Emperor' (D) GRid
'Red Fox'PBR (Ba) LCro LOPS
'Red Fubuki' (D) SDeJ
'Red Highlight' (S-c) CWGr
'Red Majorette' (S-c) CWGr SDeJ
'Red Pathfinder' (Sin) NJRG
'Red Pimpernel' (D) CWGr
'Red Pygmy' (S-c) CWGr SCob SDeJ
'Red Riding Hood' (Sin) CWGr
'Red Rock' (D) ERCP
'Red Schwieter's' (D) CWGr
'Red Sun' (D) CWGr
'Red Velvet' (WL) CWGr GRid
'Red Warrior' (Pom) CWGr
'Reddy' (Sin/Lil) CWGr
'Reedly' (D) CWGr
'Rees' Dream' (D) CWGr GRid
'Reginald Keene' (S-c) CWGr GRid NHal
'Reliance' (Ba) CWGr
'Reputation' (C) CWGr SGbt
'Requiem' (D) CWGr ECtt ERCP NJRG
'Reverend P. Holian' (S-c) CWGr SGbt
'Revive' (Misc) CWGr
'Rhanna Tammy' (D) GRid
'Rhonda' (Pom) GRid NHal
'Rhonda Suzanne' (Pom) ♀H3 GRid
'Richard Marc' (C) CWGr
'Richard S' (S-c) NHal
'Riisa' (Ba) CWGr
'Rip City' (S-c) CAvo CWGr ERCP LCro LOPS LRHS MCot
'Risca Miner' (Ba) CWGr
'Rita Easterbrook' (D) CWGr
'Rita Rosina' (D) **new** CWGr
'Rita Shrimpton' (Misc) CWGr
'Roan' (D) CWGr
'Robann Regal' (D) CWGr
'Robann Royal' (Ba) CWGr
'Robert Too' (D) CWGr
'Rocco' (Ba) ERCP LCro LOPS SGbt
'Rockcliffe Billy' (S-c) NJRG
'Rockcliffe Gold' (S-c) CWGr
'Roger Turrell' (D) **new** NHal
'Rokewood Opal' (C) CWGr
'Romance' (C) CWGr
'Ron's Dark Ember' (Fim) GRid
'Rosalinde' (S-c) CWGr
'Rose Jupiter' (S-c) CWGr GRid NHal
'Rose Tendre' (S-c) CWGr
'Rosella' (D) CWGr SDeJ SGbt
'Rosemary Webb' (D) CWGr SGbt
I 'Rosita' (Col) CWGr
'Rossendale Flamenco' (D) NHal
'Rossendale Heide' (D) NHal
'Rossendale Izzy' (D) GRid
'Rossendale Joshua' (D) GRid
'Rossendale Lewis' (D) GRid
'Rossendale Lottie' (D) GRid
'Rossendale Luke' (D) CWGr GRid
'Rossendale Mollie' (D) NHal
'Rossendale Natasha' (Ba) NHal SGbt
'Rossendale Parky' (D) GRid NHal
'Rossendale Peach' (D) GRid
'Rossendale Stephanie' (D) GRid NHal
'Rossendale Tara' (D) GRid
'Rosy Cloud' (D) CWGr
'Rothesay Castle' (D/DwB) CWGr
'Rothesay Herald' (D/DwB) CWGr
'Rothesay Reveller' (D) CWGr
'Rothesay Robin' (D) CWGr GRid
'Rothesay Rose' (WL) CWGr GRid
'Rothesay Superb' (Ba) CWGr
I 'Roxy' (Sin/DwB) CAby CBcs CRos CWGr EBee ECtt EHrv ELan EPfP ERCP LAyl LRHS LSRN NCou NJRG NRHS SGbt WCot WSpi
'Royal Amethyst' (D) CWGr
'Royal Mail' (D) SGbt
'Royal Visit' (D) CWGr SGbt
'Royal Wedding' (S-c) CWGr
'Ruby' (D) GRid
'Ruby Puff' (Anem) CWGr
'Ruby Red' (Ba) CWGr
'Ruby Wedding' (D) CWGr SGbt
rudis CExl EBee WPGP
'Ruskin Amanda' (S-c) GRid
'Ruskin Andrea' (S-c) GRid NHal
'Ruskin Avenger' (S-c) NJRG
'Ruskin Belle' (S-c) CWGr
'Ruskin Bride' (S-c) GRid
'Ruskin Buttercup' (D) CWGr SGbt
'Ruskin Charlotte' (S-c) CWGr GRid
'Ruskin Diane' (D) CWGr GRid NHal NJRG
'Ruskin Dynasty' (D) CWGr
'Ruskin Emile' (S-c) CWGr
'Ruskin Gypsy' (Ba) CWGr
I 'Ruskin Harmony' (S-c) CWGr GRid NHal
'Ruskin Impact' (D) GRid
'Ruskin Lilactime' (Ba) GRid
'Ruskin Limelight' (C) NHal
'Ruskin Marigold' (S-c) CWGr GRid NHal
'Ruskin Mars' (D) GRid GWyn
'Ruskin Michelle' (S-c) GRid NHal
'Ruskin Myra' (S-c) CWGr GRid NHal
'Ruskin Respectable' (S-c) NJRG
'Ruskin Sensation' (S-c) NHal
'Ruskin Splendour' (S-c) GRid
'Ruskin Sunshine' (S-c) GRid
'Ruskin Tangerine' (Ba) NHal SGbt
'Russell Turner' (S-c) CWGr
'Rustig' (D) CWGr
I 'Rusty' (Sin) CWGr
I 'Ruth Ann' (Ba) NHal
'Ruth Parker' (Col) **new** CWGr
'Ryecroft Brenda T' (D) GRid NHal NJRG

	'Ryecroft Claire' (D)	NHal
	'Ryecroft Gem' (Ba)	GRid
	'Ryecroft Helen' (S-c)	NHal
	'Ryecroft Ice' (D)	GRid SGbt
	'Ryecroft Isobel' (D)	GRid
	'Ryecroft Jan' (Ba) ♀H3	GRid NHal NJRG
	'Ryecroft Jim' (Anem)	LAyl NHal
	'Ryecroft Laura' (Ba)	NHal
	'Ryecroft Pixie' (C)	GRid NHal
	'Ryecroft Rebel' (D)	GRid
	'Ryecroft Sparkler' (C)	SGbt
	'Ryecroft Yellow Orb' (Ba)	NHal
	'Ryecroft Zoe' (S-c)	NHal
	'Ryedale Pinky' (D)	CWGr
	'Ryedale Prince' (D)	CWGr
	'Ryedale Rebecca' (S-c)	CWGr GRid
	'Ryedale Ria' (D)	GRid
	'Safe Shot' (D)	CWGr
	'Sailor' (Fim)	CWGr
	'Saint Giles 150' (Misc)	GRid
	'Saint Martin' (WL) **new**	ERCP
	'Saint-Saëns' (S-c)	ERCP SDeJ
	'Sakura Fubuki' (Fim)	CWGr ERCP
	'Salmon Carpet' (D)	CWGr
	'Salmon Hornsey' (D)	CWGr
	'Salmon Keene' (S-c)	GRid
	'Sam Hopkins' (D)	ERCP LAyl NHal
	'Sam Huston' (D)	CWGr SGbt
	'Samantha'	see *D.* 'Harvest Samantha'
	'Sandia Melody' (WL) ♀H3	GRid
	'Sandia Serenity' (WL) **new**	NHal
	'Sandra' (D)	ERCP LCro LOPS
	'Sans Souci' (C)	CWGr
	'Santa Claus US' (D)	CWGr SGbt
	'Sarabande' (S-c)	CWGr
	'Sarah' (S-c)	CWGr ECtt EUJe LRHS NRHS
	'Sarah Bryant' (D) **new**	NHal
	'Sarah G' (S-c)	CWGr
	'Sarah Louise' (WL)	CWGr
	'Sarah Thomas' (Col)	CWGr
	'Sarum Aurora' (D)	CWGr
	'Sascha' (WL) ♀H3	GRid NHal
	'Sassy' (D)	SGbt
	'Satellite' (S-c)	CWGr
	'Scarborough Ace' (D)	CWGr
	'Scarlet Comet' (Anem)	CWGr
§	'Scarlet Fern' (Sin)	CRos CWGr LRHS NRHS
	'Scarlet Kokarde' (D)	CWGr
	'Scarlet O'Hara' (D)	NJRG
	'Scarlet Rotterdam' (S-c)	CWGr
	'Scarlet Star' (S-c)	CWGr
	'Scarlett Claire' (Col)	CWGr
	'Scaur Blaze' (D)	GRid
	'Scaur Christine' (D)	GRid
	'Scaur Glen' (Pom)	GRid
	'Scaur Promise' (D)	GRid
	'Scaur Queen' (D)	GRid
	'Scaur Ruby' (D)	GRid
	'Scaur Saffron' (D)	GRid
	'Scaur Sunrise' (D)	NJRG
	'Scaur Sunset' (D)	GRid
	'Scaur Swinton' (D)	CWGr GRid NHal SGbt
	'Scaur Tango' (D)	GRid
	'Scaur Topper' (Ba)	GRid
	'Scaur Vale' (D)	GRid
	'Scaur Whisper' (D)	GRid
	'Schneeflocke' (Ba)	CWGr
	'Schweitzer's Kokarde' (D)	CWGr
	'Scottish Rhapsody' (S-c)	CWGr GRid
	'Scura' (Sin)	CWGr
	'Seattle' (D)	CWGr
	'Seduction' (D)	CAvo ERCP
	'Sefton Silvertop' (D) **new**	NHal
	'Seirō' (S-c)	SGbt
	'Senior Ball' (Ba)	CWGr
	'Senzoe Ursula' (D)	CWGr GRid
	'Shandy' (S-c)	CWGr LAyl SHar
	'Shannon' (D)	CWGr
I	'Sheila' (Ba)	GRid
	'Sheila Mooney' (D)	CWGr GRid
	'Shep's Memory' (WL) ♀H3	NJRG
	sherffii	CWGr NJRG
	'Sherwood Monarch' (S-c)	CWGr
	'Sherwood Sunrise' (D)	CWGr
	'Sherwood Titan' (D)	CWGr
	'Sherwood's Peach' (D)	CWGr
	'Sheval Megan' (D)	NHal
	'Shining Star' (C)	CWGr
	'Shirley' (D)	CWGr
	'Shirley Pillman' (Misc)	CWGr
	'Shirwell George' (D)	GRid
	'Shirwell Greta' (D)	GRid NHal
	'Shooting Star' (S-c)	CWGr
	'Show 'n' Tell' (Fim)	CWGr SGbt
	'Shy Princess' (C)	CWGr
	'Siedlerstolz' (D)	CWGr
	'Siesta' (Sin)	CWGr
	'Silver City' (D)	CWGr NHal SGbt
	'Silver Years' (D)	CWGr
	'Silvie's Queen' (D)	SDeJ
	'Sir Alf Ramsey' (D)	CWGr GRid LAyl NHal SGbt
	'Skipper Rock' (D)	CWGr
	'Small World' (Pom) ♀H3	CWGr GRid LAyl NHal
	'Smokey' (D)	CWGr
	'Smoots' (Fim)	CWGr
	'Sneezy' (Sin/DwB)	CWGr
	'Snoho Peggy' (Ba)	GRid
	'Snoho Tammie' (Ba)	CWGr
	'Snow Cap' (S-c)	CWGr SDeJ
	'Snow Fairy' (C)	CWGr
	'Snow White' (Sin/DwB)	CWGr
	'Snowbound' (D)	GRid SGbt
I	'Snowflake' (Pom)	ERCP SDeJ
I	'Snowstorm' (D)	CWGr LRHS SGbt
	'Snowy' (Ba)	CWGr
	'So Dainty' (S-c) ♀H3	CWGr
I	'Sofia' (WL)	CWGr
	'Soheim'	GRid
	'Sonia Henie' (Ba)	CWGr
	'Sophie Taylor' (SinO)	NJRG
	'Sorbet' (DwB)	LAyl
I	'Sorbet' (D)	NHal
	'Sorbet' (S-c)	see *D.* 'Geerlings Sorbet' (S-c)
	sorensenii	CWGr
	'Sorrento Flush' (D)	NJRG
	'Soulman' (Anem)	CWGr ERCP NJRG SGbt SPer
	'Souvenir d'Eté' (Pom)	CWGr SDeJ
	'Spanish Conquest' (D)	CWGr NHal SGbt
I	'Sparkler' (S-c)	ERCP
	'Spartacus' (D)	CWGr ERCP NHal
	'Spassmacher' (S-c)	CWGr
	spectabilis	CWGr
	'Spectacular' (D)	CWGr SGbt
	'Spencer' (D)	CWGr
	'Spennythorn Aristocrat' (Ba)	GRid
I	'Spike' (S-c)	SGbt
	'Spikey Symbol' (S-c)	CWGr
	'Sprinter' (C)	CWGr
	'Staleen Condesa' (S-c) ♀H3	GRid SGbt

	'Stan's Nirvana' (WL)	CWGr
	'Star Child' (SinO)	CWGr
	'Star Elite' (C)	CWGr
	'Star Surprise' (C)	SDeJ
	STAR WARS ('Vdtg14'[PBR]) (Dark Angel Series) (Sin)	ERCP LCro LOPS SDeJ SPer
	'Starlight Keene' (S-c)	CWGr
	'Starry Night' (S-c)	CWGr
	'Star's Favourite' (C)	ERCP SDeJ
	'Star's Lady' (C)	CWGr
	'Stephanie' (S-c)	CWGr
	'Stevie D' (D) 🏆H3	CWGr SGbt
§	'Stolz von Berlin' (Ba)	CWGr ERCP SDeJ SGbt
	'Stoneleigh Joyce' (Pom)	CWGr
	'Storm Warning' (D)	CWGr
	'Storrs Julie' (Pom)	NJRG
	'Streets Ahead' (D)	GRid
	'Strike a Light' (C)	CWGr
	'Striped Ambition' (Fim) **new**	CWGr ERCP
	'Striped Vulcan' (S-c)	CAby
	'Sue Mountjoy' (Col)	CWGr
	'Sue Willo' (Pom)	CWGr
	'Sue's Kilmorie' (S-c)	NHal
	'Suffolk Fantasy' (D)	CWGr
	'Suffolk Punch' (D)	CWGr ELan LAyl
	'Sugar Diamond' (C)	EPfP ERCP SPer
	'Suitzus Julie' (Misc)	CWGr NJRG
	'Summer Festival' (D)	CWGr SGbt
	'Summer Gold' (D)	GRid
	'Summer Night' (S-c)	see *D.* 'Nuit d'Eté'
	'Summer Nights' (Misc)	NJRG
	'Sunlight' (Ba)	CWGr
	'Sunlight Pastelle' (S-c)	CWGr GRid
	'Sunny Boy' (Ba)	SDeJ
	'Sunray Silk' (S-c)	CWGr
	'Sunshine'	see *D.* 'Moonfire'
	'Sunshine Girl' (Col)	NHal NJRG
	'Super Trouper' (D)	CWGr
	'Superfine' (C)	CWGr
	'Sure Thing' (C)	CWGr
	'Susan Gilbert' (Col) 🏆H3	NHal NJRG
	'Susan Gilliott' (S-c)	GRid NHal
	'Susan Willo' (Pom)	CWGr
	'Sutton Gem' (Ba)	GRid
I	'Suzanne' (Col)	NJRG
	'Suzette' (D/DwB)	SGbt
	'Swallow Falls' (D)	CWGr
	'Swan Lake'	see *D.* 'Classic Swanlake'
	'Swanvale' (D)	CWGr GRid SGbt
	'Sweet Content' (D)	CWGr SGbt
	'Sweet Love' (D)	ERCP
	'Sweet Surprise' (D)	ERCP
	'Sweetheart' (D)	CWGr NJRG SDeJ
	'Swiss Miss' (Ba)	CWGr
I	'Sylvia' (Ba)	CWGr ERCP LCro LOPS
	'Sylvia's Desire' (C)	CWGr
	'Symbol' (S-c)	CWGr
	'Sympathy' (WL)	CWGr GRid
	'Syston Harlequin' (D)	CWGr
	'Syston Sophia' (Ba)	CWGr
	'Tahiti Sunrise' (S-c)	CWGr EPfP
	'Tahoma Moonshot' (SinO)	CWGr
	'Tahoma Star' (SinO)	LCro
	'Take Off' (Anem)	SDeJ
	'Tally Ho' (Sin) 🏆H3	CRos CWGr ECtt EHrv EPfP LRHS NJRG NRHS SDys WCot
	'Tally Ho Double' (P) **new**	CWGr
	'Tam Tam' (Ba)	CWGr SPer
	'Tamburo' (S-c)	EPfP ERCP
	'Tangerine Pathfinder' (Misc)	NJRG
I	'Tapestry' (Sin)	CWGr SGbt
	'Taratahi Ruby' (WL) 🏆H3	CWGr ERCP GRid NHal NJRG
	'Tartan' (D)	CWGr
	'Tartarus' (P)	CWGr
	TAXI DRIVER ('Vdtg57'[PBR]) (Dark Angel Series) (Sin)	ERCP
	'Teesbrooke Audrey' (Col)	CAby CWGr ECtt GRid LCro LOPS NHal NJRG
	'Teesbrooke Red Eye' (Col)	CWGr ERCP NJRG SGbt
	'Temptress' (S-c)	CWGr
	'Tender Moon' (D)	CWGr
	tenuicaulis	CDTJ CExl
	aff. ***tenuicaulis***	CWGr
	'Terracotta' (Misc/DwB)	NJRG
	'Terrie Bandey' (Fim)	LAyl NHal
	'Thais' (Col)	NJRG
	'Thames Valley' (D)	CWGr
	'That's It!' (D)	CWGr
	'The Baron' (D)	CWGr
	'The Phantom' (Anem)	ERCP NJRG SDeJ
I	'The Queen' (S-c)	CWGr
	'Thelma Clements' (D)	CWGr
	'Thelma Joyce' (D)	GRid
	'Theo Sprengers' (D)	CWGr
	'Thomas A. Edison' (D)	CAvo CWGr ERCP LCro LOPS MSCN SDeJ SGbt
	'Thoresby Jewel' (D)	CWGr
I	'Tiara' (D)	CWGr
	'Tiffany Lynn' (SinO)	CWGr
I	'Tiger' (Sin/DwB)	CWGr
	'Tiger Eye' (D)	SGbt
	'Tiger Tiv' (D)	CWGr
	'Timeless' (D)	SPer
	'Timmo' (D)	ERCP
	'Tinker's White' (D)	CWGr
	'Tioga Chantilly' (Fim)	GRid
	'Tioga Dawn' (Fim)	GRid
	'Tioga Seahawk' (Fim)	GRid
	'Tioga Spice' (Fim)	CWGr GRid
	'Tip Toe' (D)	GRid
	'Toga' (WL)	CWGr
	'Tohsuikyoh' (Misc)	CWGr SGbt
	'Tom McLelland' (S-c)	NHal
	'Tommy Doc' (S-c)	CWGr
	'Tommy Keith' (Ba)	CWGr
	'Tomo' (D)	LAyl NHal
	'Tom's August Bride' (S-c) **new**	CWGr
	'Top Affair' (S-c)	CWGr
	'Top Choice' (S-c)	CWGr
	'Top Totty' (D)	GRid NHal
I	'Topaz Puff' (Anem)	CWGr
	'Topmix' (Sin/DwB)	SDeJ
	'Topmix Mama' (Sin)	NJRG
	'Topmix Orange' (Sin)	NJRG SDeJ
	'Topmix Pink' (Sin/DwB)	CWGr SDeJ
	'Topmix Purple' (Sin)	NJRG
	'Topmix Red' (Sin/DwB)	NJRG SDeJ
	'Topmix Reddy' (Sin)	NJRG
I	'Topmix Rose' (Sin)	NJRG
	'Topmix Salmon' (Sin)	ERCP
	'Topmix White' (Sin/DwB)	ERCP SDeJ
	'Topmix Yellow' (Sin/DwB)	SDeJ
	'Totally Tangerine' (Anem)	CWGr ERCP
	'Toto' (Anem)	ERCP SDeJ
	'Tour du Monde' (WL)	CWGr
	'Towneley Class' (D)	CWGr
	'Tramar' (C)	CWGr

	'Trelawny' (D)	CWGr
	'Trelissick Purple'	CWGr LSvl
	'Trelyn Daisy' (Col) ♀H3	CWGr
	'Trelyn Kiwi' (S-c) ♀H3	CWGr GRid NHal NJRG SGbt
	'Trelyn Seren' (SinO)	GRid LAyl NHal
	'Trendy' (D)	CWGr
	'Trengrove Autumn' (D)	CWGr SGbt
	'Trengrove Jill' (D)	CWGr
	'Trengrove Millennium' (D)	CWGr GRid NHal NJRG SGbt
I	'Trevor' (Col)	CWGr ECtt SGbt
	'Tricolor' ambig.	MSCN
	'Trooper Dan' (S-c)	GRid
	'Trotter's Jo-Anne' (S-c)	CWGr
	'Troy Dyson' (Misc)	SDys
	'Truly Scrumptious' (S-c)	SGbt
	'Tsuki-yori-no-shisha' (Fim)	LCro LOPS
	tubulata	EBee
	'Tudor 1' (Misc/DwB)	NHal
	'Tui Avis' (C)	CWGr NJRG
	'Tui Connie' (D)	GRid
	'Tui Orange' (S-c)	CWGr
	'Tula Rosa' (Pom)	CWGr
	'Tutankhamun' (Pom)	CWGr
	'Tu-tu' (S-c)	CWGr SGbt
	'Twiggy' (WL)	CWGr SGbt
	'Twilight Time' (D)	CWGr SDeJ
	'Twilite' (Anem) **new**	CWGr
*	'Twinkle Stars'	SDeJ
	'Twyning's After Eight' (Sin) ♀H3	CAby CAvo CBod CExl CRos CSpe CWGN CWGr ECtt EHrv ELan EPfP ERCP IPot LAyl LCro LOPS LRHS MJak NHal NJRG NRHS NSti SDys SGbt SPer WBor WCot WHoo
	'Twyning's Aniseed' (Sin)	CWGr
	'Twyning's Black Cherry' (D)	CWGr ECtt
	'Twyning's Candy' (Sin)	CWGr
	'Twyning's Chocolate' (Sin)	CWGr
	'Twyning's Peppermint' (Sin)	CWGr
	'Twyning's Purple Cherry' (D)	CWGr
	'Twyning's Revel' (Sin) ♀H3	CWGr
	'Twyning's Smartie' (Sin)	CAby CWGr EBee ECtt LCro LOPS SPer
	'Twyning's Velvet' (Sin)	CWGr
	'Twyning's White Chocolate' (Sin)	CWGr ERCP
	'Uchuu' (D)	CWGr
	'Uncle Hankey' (D)	ERCP
	'Union Jack' (Sin)	CWGr
	'Uniquity' **new**	WCot
	'United' (D)	CWGr
	'Urchin' (C)	CWGr
	'Usugesho' (D)	CWGr
	'Vader Abraham' (D)	CWGr
I	'Valentino' (WL/DwB)	CWGr
	'Valerie Moody' (D) **new**	CWGr
	'Val's Candy' (S-c)	GRid NHal
	'Vancouver' (Misc)	CBod CWGr ERCP LCro LOPS SDeJ WFar
	'Variace' (Ba)	CWGr
	'Vassio Meggos' (D)	ERCP GRid NHal
	'Vera's Elma' (D)	CWGr
	'Veritable' (S-c)	LCro LOPS
	'Verrone's Obsidian' (SinO)	CAby ERCP LCro LOPS WBrk
	'Verwer's Heatwave' (D) **new**	ERCP
	'Victory Day' (C)	CWGr
	'Vigor' (WL)	CWGr
	'Viking' (Pom)	CWGr
	'Vino' (Pom)	CWGr
	'Violet Davies' (S-c)	CWGr
	'Vivex' (Pom)	CWGr
	'Vivian Russell' (WL)	NHal NJRG
	'Volkskanzler' (Sin)	CWGr
	'Vulcan' (S-c)	CWGr ERCP SGbt
§	'Vuurvogel' (S-c)	CWGr ERCP SDeJ
	'Walter Hardisty' (D)	CWGr GRid
	'Walter James' (D)	CWGr
	'Waltzing Mathilda' (Misc) ♀H3	CWGr ERCP LCro LOPS
	'Wanborough Gem' (Ba)	CWGr
	'Wanda's Aurora' (D)	GRid
	'Wanda's Capella' (D)	CWGr GRid
	'Wanda's Moonlight' (D)	CWGr
	'Wandy' (Pom)	CWGr
	'War of the Roses' (D)	CWGr EWes WHer
	'Warkton Willo' (Pom)	CWGr
I	'Waterlily' (Sin)	CRos LRHS NRHS
I	'Welcome Guest' (S-c)	CWGr
I	'Wendy' (Ba)	CWGr
	'Wendy's Place' (Pom)	GRid
	'Westerton Folly' (Ba) ♀H3	NHal
	'Westerton Harry' (D)	GRid NHal
	'Westerton J.W.H.' (D)	NHal
	'Westerton Lilian' (D)	GRid NHal
	'Westerton Southside' (D)	NHal
	'Weston Aramac' (S-c)	CWGr
	'Weston Buccaneer' (C)	NHal
	'Weston Corsair' (C)	NJRG
	'Weston Cream' (C)	GRid
	'Weston Forge' (C)	CWGr
	'Weston Kelpie' (C)	NJRG
	'Weston Melody' (S-c)	GRid
	'Weston Miss' (S-c)	CWGr GRid GWyn NJRG
	'Weston Nugget' (C)	CWGr
	'Weston Pirate' (C) ♀H3	CWGr GRid LAyl NHal NJRG
	'Weston Spanish Dancer' (C) ♀H3	CWGr ERCP NHal NJRG SGbt
	'Weston Stardust' (C) ♀H3	GRid NJRG
	'Weston Tea-time' (C)	CWGr
	'Wheels' (Col)	GRid NJRG
	'White Alva's' (D) ♀H3	CWGr GRid LAyl NHal SGbt
	'White Aster' (Pom)	CWGr ERCP
	'White Ballerina' (WL)	NHal SGbt
	'White Ballet' (D) ♀H3	CWGr LAyl SGbt
	'White Cameo' (WL)	CWGr
	'White Charlie Two' (D)	GRid NHal
	'White Hallelujah' (Sin)	CWGr
	'White Hunter' (D)	CWGr
	'White Klankstad' (C)	CWGr
	'White Knight' (D)	GRid NHal
	'White Lace' (Fim)	GRid
	'White Linda' (D)	CWGr GRid
	'White Magenta Star' (Sin)	CWGr
	'White Moonlight' (S-c)	CWGr GRid NHal
	'White Nettie' (Ba)	CWGr SGbt
	'White Onesta' (D)	ERCP SDeJ
	'White Pastelle' (S-c)	CWGr GRid
	'White Perfection' (D)	CWGr ECtt ERCP SDeJ WSpi
	'White Rustig' (D)	CWGr
	'White Seedling' (Sin)	CWGr
	'White Star' (S-c)	CWGr ERCP LCro LOPS LRHS SDeJ
	'White Swallow' (S-c)	NHal
	white-flowered B&SWJ 14340 from Colombia	WCru
	'Who Dun It' (D)	CWGr ERCP
	'Wicky Woo' (D)	CWGr
	'Wildwood Marie' (WL)	CWGr NJRG

'William B' (D) CWGr
'William John' (Pom) CWGr
'Williamsburg' (S-c) CWGr
'Willo's Borealis' (Pom) CWGr GRid NHal
'Willo's Flecks' (Pom) CWGr
'Willo's Night' (Pom) CWGr
'Willo's Place' (Pom) GRid
'Willo's Surprise' (Pom) CWGr GRid NHal SGbt
'Willo's Violet' (Pom) CWGr GRid NHal NJRG SGbt
'Willowfield Matthew' (D) GRid
'Willowfield Mick' (D) CWGr
'Will's Ringwood Rosie' (Pom) GRid
'Wilma McCulloch' GWyn
'Wine & Roses' (WL) SGbt
'Winholme Diane' (D) GRid NHal
'Winkie Colonel' (D) CWGr GRid
'Winkie Lambrusco' (Pom) NHal NJRG
'Winnie' (Pom) CWGr
'Winsome' (WL) CWGr
'Winston Churchill' (WL) CWGr WSpi
'Winter Springs' (S-c) ERCP
'Wise Guy' (D) CWGr
'Wishes n Dreams' (Sin) NJRG
'Wisk' (Pom) CWGr
'Wittem' (D) CWGr
'Witteman's Best' (S-c) CWGr ERCP MCot SGbt
'Witteman's Superba' (S-c) ♀H3 CWGr NHal
'Wizard of Oz' (Ba) ERCP LCro LOPS
'Woodbridge' (Sin) CWGr SGbt
'Woodside Finale' (D) NHal
'Wootton Carnival' (C) CWGr
'Wootton Cupid' (Ba) ♀H3 CWGr
'Wootton Impact' (S-c) ♀H3 GRid NHal
'Wootton Phebe' (D) CWGr
'Wootton Tempest' (S-c) CWGr
'Wootton Windmill' (Col) CWGr
'Worton Blue Streak' (S-c) CWGr ERCP SGbt
'Worton Revival' (D) CWGr
'Worton Superb' (D) CWGr
'Wyndal Horizon' (S-c) CWGr
'XXL Grand Central' (D) CWGr
'Yamabiraki' (D) CWGr
I 'Yellow Bird' (Col) CWGr
'Yellow Bulldog' (Sin) CWGr
'Yellow Galator' (C) SGbt
'Yellow Hammer' (Sin/DwB) ♀H3 CWGr NHal NJRG SGbt
'Yellow Lakeland Sunset' (C) GRid
'Yellow Linda's Chester' (C) CWGr
'Yellow Pages' (D) CWGr
'Yellow Passions' (D) ERCP
'Yellow Perception' (WL) SDeJ
'Yellow Pet' (D) CWGr
'Yellow Present' (D) GRid
'Yellow Sneezy' (Sin/Lil) SDeJ
'Yellow Spiky' (S-c) CWGr
'Yellow Star' (S-c) CWGr ERCP EUJe SDeJ
'Yellow Vulcan' (S-c) CWGr
'Yelno Enchantment' (WL) CWGr
'Yelno Petite Glory' (D) CWGr
'York and Lancaster' (D) CWGr EBee SGbt WAvo WBrk
'Yukino' (Col) CWGr
'Zagato' (D) CWGr
'Zakuro-hime' (D) CWGr
I 'Zelda' (D) CWGr GRid
'Zest' (D) CWGr
'Zingaro' (D) LCro LOPS
'Zippity Do Da' (Pom) **new** ERCP
'Zirconia' (D) ERCP
§ 'Zone Ten'PBR (Sin/DwB) CAby CRos CWGr EPfP LRHS NPri NRHS SPoG WBor
'Zorro' (D) ♀H3 CWGr ERCP GRid NHal SGbt
'Zundert Mystery Fox'PBR (Ba) ERCP
'Zurich' (S-c) CWGr

Daiswa see *Paris*

Dalea (*Papilionaceae*)

gattingeri SBrt
purpurea EBee

damson see *Prunus insititia*; also AGM Fruit Section

Danae (*Asparagaceae*)

§ ***racemosa*** ♀H5 CBcs CMac CTri EBee EPfP EWes LEdu MGil MGos MMuc MRav SEND SPer SRms SWvt WCot WCru WPGP WSpi

Daphne ✿ (*Thymelaeaceae*)

acutiloba GKev WSpi
– 'Fragrant Cloud' CExl CJun EWes SChF WPGP
albowiana CBcs CJun GKev LCro LOPS LRHS WSpi
alpina GKev WThu XEll
altaica CJun
arbuscula ♀H5 EPot SIgm
arisanensis B&SWJ 6983 WCru
aurantiaca EPot
– 'Gang-ho-ba' CJun
bholua CJun GKev LRHS
– B&SWJ 8275 from Fansipan, Vietnam WCru
– GWJ 9436 from India WCru
– NJM 13.115 WPGP
I – 'Alba' EPfP GKev SSta WPGP WSpi
– 'Cobhay Debut' **new** CJun
– 'Cobhay Snow' CJun
– 'Darjeeling' CCCN CExl CJun CTho EBee GKev LSRN WPGP WSpi
– 'Garden House Enchantress' WPGP
– 'Garden House Ghost' WPGP
– 'Garden House Red Stem' WPGP
– 'Garden House Sentinel' WPGP
– var. ***glacialis*** 'Gurkha' ♀H4 CExl CJun WPGP
– – 'Gurkha' × ***mezereum*** WSpi
– 'Hazel Edwards' LRHS
– 'Heale House' WPGP
– 'Jacqueline Postill' ♀H4 CExl CJun CRos CTri EPfP GKev LBuc LCro LOPS LRHS LSRN MBlu MGos NRHS SChF SCob SSta WPGP WSpi
– 'Limpsfield' CJun LRHS SChF SSta WPGP
– 'Penwood' CJun
– 'Peter Smithers' CExl CJun SSta WPGP
blagayana GKev NBir SRms
– 'Brenda Anderson' CJun EPot WAbe
'Bramdean' see *D.* × ***napolitana*** 'Bramdean'
× ***burkwoodii*** CMea LSRN SCob
– 'Albert Burkwood' CJun
– 'Astrid' (v) CBcs LCro LOPS LRHS MGil SCob SGol
§ – 'Carol Mackie' (v) CJun
– 'G.K.Argles' (v) CJun
I – 'Gold Sport' CJun

	- 'Golden Treasure'	CJun LRHS
	- 'Lavenirii'	CJun
	- 'Marjolein'[PBR] **new**	LRHS
	- 'Somerset' 🏆H4	CBcs CJun ELan ESwi LCro LOPS LRHS MGil MGos MSwo NWea SCob WSpi
§	- 'Somerset Gold Edge' (v)	CJun
§	- 'Somerset Variegated' (v)	EPot
	- 'Variegata' broad cream edge	see *D.* × *burkwoodii* 'Somerset Variegated'
	- 'Variegata' broad gold edge	see *D.* × *burkwoodii* 'Somerset Gold Edge'
	- 'Variegata' narrow gold edge	see *D.* × *burkwoodii* 'Carol Mackie'
	caucasica	CJun
	circassica	SChF
	cneorum	CBcs ELon GKev MGil WHor
	- 'Major'	EPot
	- var. ***pygmaea***	EPot
	- 'Variegata' (v)	EWes GEdr
	- var. ***verlotii***	EPot
	collina	see *D. sericea* Collina Group
	domini	GKev
	× ***eschmannii*** 'Jacob Eschmann'	CJun
§	***gemmata***	CBcs LCro LOPS LRHS NLar
	- 'Royal Crown'	CCCN
	genkwa	CJun LRHS
	giraldii	GKev
	aff. ***giraldii***	WSpi
	gnidium	CMCN
	- PAB 8371	LEdu
	'Guardsman'	CJun LRHS
	× ***hendersonii*** 'Aymon Correvon'	WThu
	- 'Bonnie Glen'	EPot
	- 'Ernst Hauser'	WIce WThu
	- 'Fritz Kummert'	WAbe WThu
	- 'Jeanette Brickell'	WThu
	- 'Kath Dryden'	EPot GEdr
	- 'Marion White'	EPot SIgm XEll
	- 'Rosebud'	EPot WThu
	- 'Solferino'	WAbe
	'Hinton'	CJun
	× ***houtteana***	CJun
	japonica 'Striata'	see *D. odora* 'Aureomarginata'
	jasminea upright	EPot
	'Kilmeston Beauty'	CJun
	kosaninii	GKev
	kurdica	CPBP
	× ***latymeri*** 'Spring Sonnet'	SChF
	laureola	CJun EPfP GKev GPoy MMrt NBid NBir NLar NPer SChr WHor WSpi
	- 'Margaret Mathew'	EPot NLar SChF WSpi
	- subsp. ***philippi***	CBcs CCCN CJun CMac EBee EPfP EWes LCro LOPS LRHS MAsh MBlu MGil MGos NLar WCot WPGP WSpi
	longilobata	GKev
	× ***mantensiana*** 'Audrey Vockins'	CJun
	- 'Manten'	CJun
	× ***mauerbachii*** 'Perfume of Spring'	CJun
	'Meon'	see *D.* × *napolitana* 'Meon'
	mezereum	GKev GMaP GPoy LRHS MAsh MGos NChi NWea SChF SCob SGol SWvt WCot WFar WPGP
	- f. ***alba***	CJun GAbr GKev GLog MAsh MGos NChi SRms SWvt WSpi
	- - 'Bowles's Variety'	CJun EPot
I	- var. ***alpina*** hort.	GKev
	- 'Rosea'	MAsh SRms
	- var. ***rubra***	CBcs CCCN CJun ELan GKin LRHS MGil MGos MJak MRav MSwo NWea SPer WFar WSpi
	modesta	XEll
	× ***napolitana*** 🏆H4	CJun
§	- 'Bramdean'	CJun
§	- 'Meon'	CJun ELan EPot GEdr LRHS SChF WThu
	odora	CBcs CCCN CJun CKel CRos EPfP LCro LOPS LRHS MSwo NRHS SCob SEle SGol WPGP WSpi
§	- f. ***alba***	CBcs CCCN LRHS
	- - 'Sakiwaka'	CCCN CExl
§	- 'Aureomarginata' (v)	Widely available
I	- 'Aureomarginata Alba' (v)	SEle WSpi
	- 'Double Cream' (v)	CJun
	- 'Geisha Girl' (v)	LRHS
	- var. ***leucantha***	see *D. odora* f. *alba*
	- 'Mae-jima' (v)	CBcs CExl CRos EPfP LRHS MAsh MGos SLon
	- 'Marginata'	see *D. odora* 'Aureomarginata'
	- MARIANNI ('Rogbret') (v)	CBcs CCCN LRHS MGil MJak SGol SPer SWvt
	- REBECCA ('Hewreb') (v)	CBct CMea CRos EBee ELan EPfP LBuc LRHS LSRN MAsh MBNS MGos NRHS SLon SPoG WSpi
	- var. ***rubra***	CCCN CMac GKev LRHS SGol
	- 'Sweet Amethyst'	LCro LOPS
	- 'Walberton' (v)	CRos EPfP LRHS MNHC NRHS
	oleoides	GKev
	- var. ***buxifolia***	GKev
	papyracea	CExl
	PERFUME PRINCESS ('Dapjur01')	CBcs CCCN GBin LRHS MThu NRHS
	petraea	WAbe XEll
	pontica	CBcs CJun CMac CMea CRos EPfP LRHS NLar NRHS SChF SPoG WPGP WSpi
	retusa	see *D. tangutica* Retusa Group
	'Richard's Choice'	CJun
	× ***rollsdorfii*** 'Arnold Cihlarz'	CJun SChF WAbe
	- 'Wilhelm Schacht' 🏆H5	CJun EPot MAsh SChF WThu
	'Rosy Wave'	CJun
	× ***schlyteri*** 'July Glow'	EPot GEdr SChF
	- 'Lovisa Maria'	EPot GEdr
	sericea	CJun XEll
§	- Collina Group	SChF WIce
	'Spring Beauty'	CJun LRHS SChF WPGP
	'Spring Herald'	CJun WPGP
	× ***suendermannii*** 'Franz Suendermann'	WOld
	× ***susannae*** 'Anton Fahndrich'	GKev WSpi WThu
	- 'Cheriton' 🏆H5	CJun ELan EPot SChF WCot WThu
	- 'Tichborne'	EPot SChF WIce WThu
	tangutica 🏆H5	CBcs CBor CExl CJun CSpe CTri ELan EPfP GKev LCro LOPS LRHS LSRN MAsh MGos NHol NLar SRkn SRms WHor WKif WOld WPGP WSpi
§	- Retusa Group 🏆H5	CExl CJun EPot EWes EWld GBin GEdr GKev SIgm SRms WSpi
	× ***transatlantica*** 'Beulah Cross' (v)	CJun SChF
	- ETERNAL FRAGRANCE ('Blafra'[PBR]) 🏆H5	Widely available

§ - PINK FRAGRANCE ('Blapink'[PBR]) — CBcs CRos EBee ELan EPfP GBin GKev LCro LOPS LRHS MAsh MMrt NRHS SGol SPer SPoG WSpi XEll
- SPRING PINK ETERNAL FRAGRANCE — see *D.* × *transatlantica* PINK FRAGRANCE
- 'Summer Ice' (v) — SChF
'Valerie Hillier' — CJun GKev WSpi
velenovskyi 'Weber's Findling' — SChF
'White Queen' — LCro LOPS LRHS
× ***whiteorum*** 'Beauworth' — EPot WAbe WOld
wolongensis new — GKev
- 'Kevock Star' — CExl GKev

Daphniphyllum (*Daphniphyllaceae*)

aff. ***angustifolium*** B&SWJ 8225 — WCru
- B&SWJ 11804 — WCru
- WWJ 12020 — WCru
chartaceum KWJ 12244 — WCru
- KWJ 12313 — WCru
glaucescens — WCru
subsp. ***oldhamii*** var. ***kengii*** B&SWJ 6872
- - - B&SWJ 7119 — WCru
- - var. ***oldhamii*** B&SWJ 7056 — WCru
- - - CWJ 12351 — WCru
himalaense — IDee
humile — see *D. macropodum* var. *humile*
aff. ***longeracemosum*** B&SWJ 11788 — WCru
- NJM 10.147 — WPGP
macropodum — CBcs CBct CCCN EBee EPfP IArd IMou LRHS NLar SArc SPer SVen WCru WHor WPGP
- B&SWJ 581 — WCru
- B&SWJ 2898 — WCru
- B&SWJ 6809 from Taiwan — WCru
- B&SWJ 8507 from Ulleungdo, South Korea — WCru
- B&SWJ 8763 from Jejudo, South Korea — WCru
- B&SWJ 11489 from Yakushima, Japan — WCru
- B&SWJ 12691 — WCru
- dwarf — WCru
§ - var. ***humile*** B&SWJ 11232 — WCru
majus B&SWJ 11744 — WCru
paxianum B&SWJ 9755 — WCru
pentandrum B&SWJ 6888 — WCru
- B&SWJ 7056 — WCru
- CWJ 12393 — WCru
- RWJ 9836 — WCru
teysmannii B&SWJ 11110 from Japan — WCru
- B&SWJ 11112 — WCru
- B&SWJ 11358 from Japan — WCru
- B&SWJ 14626 from Japan new — WCru
aff. ***teysmannii*** CWJ 12350 from Taiwan — WCru

Darlingtonia (*Sarraceniaceae*)

californica ♀H3 — SHmp SPlb WSSs

Darmera (*Saxifragaceae*)

peltata ♀H6 — Widely available
- 'Nana' — EBee ECha ELan EPfP GCal NBid NHol NLar WFar WMoo

Dasylirion (*Asparagaceae*)

§ ***acrotrichum*** — CDTJ CExl EShb SArc
berlandieri — CExl
cedrosanum — CDTJ CJun SPlb
glaucophyllum — CCht CJun
gracile Planchon — see *D. acrotrichum*
leiophyllum — XSen
longissimum — CCCN EShb XSen
miquihuanense — CCht XSen
quadrangulatum — SPlb
wheeleri ♀H2 — CBrP SIgm SPlb XSen

Dasyphyllum (*Asteraceae*)

diacanthoides — EBee WPGP

date see *Phoenix dactylifera*

Datisca (*Datiscaceae*)

cannabina — CDTJ CSpe ECha GCal IMou LEdu LRHS SBrt SMad WHer WMoo WSHC

Datura (*Solanaceae*)

arborea — see *Brugmansia arborea*
cornigera — see *Brugmansia arborea*
rosea — see *Brugmansia* × *insignis* pink-flowered
rosei — see *Brugmansia sanguinea*
sanguinea — see *Brugmansia sanguinea*
stramonium — EBtc
suaveolens — see *Brugmansia suaveolens*
versicolor — see *Brugmansia versicolor* Lagerh.
- 'Grand Marnier' — see *Brugmansia* × *candida* 'Grand Marnier'

Daucus (*Apiaceae*)

aureus new — SPhx
carota — CHab LRHS SPhx SRms SVic WHer WHil WSFF

Davallia ✿ (*Davalliaceae*)

canariensis ♀H1c — CMen
mariesii ♀H2 — ISha
tasmanii — CMen
trichomanoides — CLAP CMen
- f. ***barbata*** — CMen

Davidia (*Nyssaceae*)

involucrata ♀H5 — Widely available
- 'Iseli Fastigiate' new — WHor
- 'Sonoma' — CDul CLnd LRHS MBlu NLar SMad WHor
- var. ***vilmoriniana*** ♀H5 — CBcs CDul CRos ELan EPfP LMaj LRHS MAsh MBlu MGos SLim SPtp

Daviesia (*Papilionaceae*)

cordata — SPlb
* ***ovalifolia*** — SPlb
pectinata — SPlb

Debregeasia (*Urticaceae*)

longifolia — SVen
- WWJ 11686 — ESwi WCru

Decaisnea (*Lardizabalaceae*)

fargesii — Widely available
- B&SWJ 8070 — WCru
insignis WJC 13740 — WCru

Decodon (*Lythraceae*)

verticillatus LLWG

Decumaria (*Hydrangeaceae*)

barbara CMac MMuc NLar WCru WSHC
- 'Vicki' NBro NLar
sinensis CRos EBee EPfP LRHS MMuc NRHS SLon SPoG WCru WSHC

Degenia (*Brassicaceae*)

velebitica GKev WAbe WOld

Deinanthe ✿ (*Hydrangeaceae*)

bifida CBct CExl CMil CRos EBee EPfP EWes GEdr LRHS MMrt NRHS WCru WPGP
- B&SWJ 5436 WCru
- B&SWJ 5551 WCru
- B&SWJ 5655 LEdu NLar
- 'Pink-Kii' WCru
- 'Pink-Shi' CMil IPot WCru WSHC
bifida × caerulea WCru
'Blue Blush' WCru
caerulea CMil GEdr GKev IMou LEdu LRHS MMrt NLar WCru WHlf WSHC
- 'Blue Wonder' CExl IPot LLHF MNrw
- white-flowered IMou

Delairea (*Asteraceae*)

§ **odorata** CCCN CExl EShb WPGP

Delonix (*Caesalpiniaceae*)

sp. SPlb
decaryi SPlb
regia SPlb

Delosperma (*Aizoaceae*)

from Graaf Reinet, South Africa EPot NRHS NSla XLum XSen
from Ouberg Pass, South Africa CPBP
§ **aberdeenense** ♀H3 SAko XLum XSen
alpinum see *Ectotropis alpina*
ashtonii CCCN EWes NSla WThu XLum
basuticum MAsh NHpl NRHS NSla
'Beaufort West' CRos EDAr EPot EWes LRHS NRHS NSla WIce XLum
congestum misapplied see *Malotigena frantiskae-niederlovae*
cooperi CCCN CRos CTri ECtt EPfP EPot EUJe GBin GKev ITim LRHS MHer NHpl NRHS SChr SIgm SPlb SRot SSim SVen WIce XLum XSen
- (Jewel of Desert Series) GRENADE ('Dsaa13-1') **new** LCro LOPS SPad
- - 'Jewel of Desert Garnet'PBR CAbb CCCN CRos ECtt EWTr LCro LOPS LRHS NHpl NRHS SPad SPoG
- - 'Jewel of Desert Moon Stone'PBR CCCN CRos ECtt LRHS NHpl NRHS WIce
- - 'Jewel of Desert Peridott'PBR CCCN CRos CWGN ECtt LRHS NHpl NRHS SPad SPoG WIce
- - 'Jewel of Desert Rosequartz' CCCN CRos LRHS NRHS SPoG
- - 'Jewel of Desert Ruby'PBR CCCN CWGN LRHS NHpl WIce
- - 'Jewel of Desert Topaz'PBR CAbb CCCN CRos CWGN ECtt EWTr LRHS NHpl NRHS SPad SPoG WIce
- (Wheels of Wonder Series) GOLDEN WONDER ('Wowd20111'PBR) CCCN LCro LOPS SPoG
- - HOT PINK WONDER ('Wowdry1'PBR) LCro LOPS
- - ORANGE WONDER ('Wowdoy3'PBR) CCCN SPoG
- - VIOLET WONDER ('Wowdrw5'PBR) CCCN NPri SPoG
- - WHITE WONDER ('Wowdw7'PBR) CCCN LCro LOPS NPri SPoG
dyeri RED MOUNTAIN ('Psdold') CRos EDAr LRHS NRHS SAko WIce XLum
ecklonis GKev NAln
FIRE SPINNER ('P001s') EDAr WIce XLum
floribundum SEQUINS ('Balosquin') CAbb
- 'Starburst' MHol SSim
- 'Stardust' EWes
jansei NSla
§ 'John Proffitt' CCCN EDAr GKev SAko SPlb XLum
lavisiae ELon NSla SPlb
'Lesotho Pink' EWes
lineare XLum XSen
'Magenta Falls' CSma
MESA VERDE ('Kelaidis') ECtt SAko XLum
nubigenum CSma CTri EBou ECtt EPot EUJe GAbr GCrg GKev NAln NHpl SPlb
'Ruby Coral' CRos ECtt EPot LRHS NRHS
sphalmanthoides CPBP EPot GEdr NHpl NSla SPlb SSim
sutherlandii ♀H3 CCCN CSma EDAr EUJe GBin NHpl SRot XLum
- 'Peach Star' CCCN EDAr NHpl SSim WIce
TABLE MOUNTAIN see *D.* 'John Proffitt'

Delphinium ✿ (*Ranunculaceae*)

'After Midnight' LHom
'Alice Artindale' (d) EWes LHom WCot
ambiguum see *Consolida ajacis*
'Ann Woodfield' CNMi LHom
'Apollo' WSpi
'Ariel' ambig. LRHS
Astolat Group CBcs CRos CTri CWCL ELan EMor EPfP GMaP LCro LOPS LRHS MGos MHol NHol NLar NRHS SPer SPoG SWvt WCAu
'Atholl' ♀H5 CNMi
'Bambi' CNMi
Belladonna Group ELan EPfP
- 'Atlantis' CRos ECha LRHS NLar NRHS WCot WSpi
- 'Bellamosum' EPfP GMaP LRHS MNrw SPer WSpi
- 'Casa Blanca' EPfP GMaP LRHS MBel NLar WSpi
- 'Cliveden Beauty' EPfP GMaP LRHS NLar WSpi
- 'Gute Nacht' LRHS
§ - 'Janny Arrow' LRHS
- 'Moerheimii' WSpi
- 'Piccolo' ECha NLar
- 'Pink Sensation' see *D.* × *ruysii* 'Pink Sensation'
- 'Völkerfrieden' LRHS MCot MNrw NLar WCot WSpi
'Berghimmel' LRHS
'Beryl Burton' CNMi
Black Knight Group Widely available
'Black Pearl' ECtt
'Black-eyed Angels' (New Millennium Series) CRos ELan IPot LRHS NRHS SCob SGbt
'Black-eyed Beauty' MHol
'Blauwal' LRHS WSpi

Name	Suppliers
'Blue Arrow'	see *D.* (Belladonna Group) 'Janny Arrow', *D.* 'Blue Max Arrow', *D.* 'Kings Blue Arrow'
Blue Bird Group	CBcs CRos CTri ELan EMor EPfP GMaP LRHS MGos MJak MWat NRHS SGbt SPer SPoG WCAu
'Blue Butterfly'	see *D. grandiflorum* 'Blue Butterfly'
'Blue Dawn' ♀H5	CNMi LHom
Blue Fountains Group	EPfP LSRN SPoG SRms
'Blue Jay'	EPfP LSRN NAln WSpi
I 'Blue Lace' (New Millennium Series)	CRos ECtt EPfP LCro LOPS LRHS MHer NAln NCou NLar NRHS WSpi
§ 'Blue Max Arrow'	LRHS
'Blue Nile' ♀H5	CNMi LHom LRHS NRHS SPoG
'Blue Oasis'	CNMi
Blue Springs Group	NGdn
'Blue Tit'	CNMi ECtt LHom NAln
'Bolero'	CBcs CRos ECtt LRHS NPri NRHS SCob SPoG WCot
'Boudicca'	CNMi
'Bruce' ♀H5	CNMi LHom NAln
'Butterball'	CNMi LHom WSpi
Cameliard Group	CBcs CRos ELan EPfP LCro LOPS LRHS NLar NRHS SPer SPoG
'Cameliard' (Pacific Hybrid Series)	NAln
carolinianum	SBrt
cashmerianum	EBee
'Cassius'	LHom
caucasicum	see *D. speciosum*
'Centurion White' (Centurion Series)	LCro LOPS
'Cha Cha'	CBcs CRos EBee LRHS NLar NPri NRHS SCob SPad WCot WTor
'Chelsea Star'	LHom LRHS
'Cher'	CNMi
'Cherry Blossom'	CBod EPfP EWTr NLar
'Cherub' ♀H5	CRos LRHS NRHS
chinense	see *D. grandiflorum*
'Christel'	LRHS LSRN NAln NLar
'Claire'	CNMi
'Clifford Sky' ♀H5	CRos LRHS NRHS
confusum **new**	EBee
'Constance Rivett'	LHom
'Cranberry Delight'	CNMi
'Crown Jewel'	EWes LRHS NAln
'Cupid'	LHom
'Dark Blue Black Bee' (Excalibur Series)	SPoG
'Dark Blue Black' (Excalibur Series)	EPfP
'Dark Blue White Bee' (Excalibur Series)	CWCL EMor LRHS SPoG
'Darling Sue'	CNMi LHom
'Darwin's Pink Indulgence' PBR	CBcs
'Diamant' PBR	IKil LRHS
'Dreaming Spires'	SRms
'Dunsden Green'	CNMi LHom
Dusky Maidens Group	ELan LCro LOPS LRHS MHol NAln NLar SGbt SPoG
elatum	GCal
- 'Dasante Blue'	LRHS MHol
- (New Millennium Series) 'Blushing Brides'	EBee LRHS SPoG
- - 'Double Innocence' (d)	CPla ECtt ELan IPot LRHS MHol NAln NLar NRHS
- - 'Morning Lights'	ECtt EPfP IPot LRHS MHol NLar NRHS SPoG
- - 'Sweethearts' ♀H5	EBee ECtt EPfP
'Elizabeth Cook' ♀H5	CNMi LHom
'Elmfreude'	LRHS WSpi
'Emily Hawkins' ♀H5	CNMi LHom
exaltatum	CSpe LPla
'Fanfare'	LHom
'Faust' ♀H5	CNMi CRos IKil LHom LRHS MCot NRHS SPoG WSpi
'Fenella' ♀H5	CNMi CRos LHom LRHS NRHS
'Finsteraarhorn'	LRHS MAvo MCot WSpi
'Flamenco'	CBcs CRos EBee ECtt LRHS NLar NPri NRHS SCob SPad SPoG WCAu WCot
'Foxhill Nina' ♀H5	LHom
Galahad Group	CBcs CWCL ECtt ELan EMor EPfP GMaP LRHS MJak MWat NGdn NHol NRHS SPer SPlb SPoG WCAu WGwG
'Galahad' (Pacific Hybrid Series)	LCro LOPS LSun MGos MHol NAln NLar WJam
'Galileo' ♀H5	CNMi
'Gemini'	CNMi LHom
'Gemma'	CNMi LHom
'Gillian Dallas'	LHom LRHS NAln
glaciale HWJK 2299	WCru
glaucum	EBee
'Gordon Forsyth'	LHom
'Gossamer'	CNMi ECtt NLar
§ ***grandiflorum***	CPla EBee GKev
§ - 'Blue Butterfly'	CMea CRos CSpe EPfP LRHS NRHS SPlb SPoG WSHC
- 'Blue Pygmy' **new**	NHic
- Delfix Series	LRHS
- - 'Delfix Rose'	EPfP
- (Summer Series) 'Summer Blues'	LRHS SRot
- - 'Summer Nights'	CRos EPfP NRHS SPoG
- 'White Butterfly'	CRos LRHS NRHS
'Green Twist' (New Millennium Series)	CRos ECtt EPfP LRHS NDai NRHS SCob
Guardian Series	WFar
- 'Guardian Blue'	CRos LRHS MHol NRHS SPoG
- 'Guardian Lavender'	CRos LRHS MHol NRHS SPoG
- 'Guardian White'	CRos LRHS NRHS SPoG
Guinevere Group	CBcs CWCL ECtt EMor EPfP MBel NAln SPer SPoG
'Guy Langdon'	CNMi
'Highlander Blueberry Pie'	ECtt IKil LPla LRHS SPad SPoG WCot WSpi
'Highlander Crystal Delight'	CRos ECtt LPla LRHS MHol NLar NPri NRHS SPad SPoG WCot
'Highlander Morning Sunrise'	IKil SPoG WCot
himalayae	GKev
hotulae	EBee
I 'Independence'	IKil LRHS
'Innocence'	LRHS SCob WSpi
ithaburense	SPhx
'Jenny Agutter'	CNMi
'Jill Curley' ♀H5	CRos LRHS NRHS
'Kathleen Cooke'	CNMi
'Kennington Classic' ♀H5	LHom
'Kestrel' ♀H5	CNMi LHom
King Arthur Group	CBcs CWCL ELan EMor EPfP LCro LOPS LSRN LSun MBel MGos MHol MNHC MWat NAln SHar SPer SPoG
§ 'Kings Blue Arrow' PBR	LRHS
'La Bohème'	NDai WSpi
'Langdon's Orpheus'	LHom
§ 'Langdon's Royal Flush'	CRos LRHS NRHS

'Lanzenträger'	LRHS
'Leonora'	CNMi
'Light Blue' (Excalibur Series)	EPfP
'Light Blue White Bee' (Excalibur Series) **new**	SPoG
'Lillian Basset'	LHom
'Loch Leven'	CNMi NAln
'Loch Nevis'	LHom
'Lord Butler' ♀H5	CNMi EBee EWes LRHS
'Lucia Sahin' ♀H5	CNMi LHom
maackianum	GCal WCot
Magic Fountains Series	CRos LRHS NAln SPlb SPoG SVic
- 'Magic Fountains Blue/ White Bee'	CBod
- 'Magic Fountains Cherry Blossom'	CWCL EPfP SPoG
- 'Magic Fountains Dark Blue'	EAJP EPfP GMaP LSRN NEgg NLar SPoG WFar
- 'Magic Fountains Lavender'	EAJP EPfP NAln NLar NRHS
- 'Magic Fountains Lilac Pink'	EPfP SPoG WFar
- 'Magic Fountains Lilac Rose'	CRos EAJP LRHS NRHS
- 'Magic Fountains Pure White'	CBod CRos EAJP EPfP LRHS NEgg NRHS WFar
- 'Magic Fountains Sky Blue'	EPfP EUJe MHol SPoG WFar
- 'Magic Fountains White Pixie' **new**	CWCL
'Margaret' ♀H5	LHom
'Marilyn Clarrissa'	CNMi
'Melanie Avery'	LHom
'Merlin' ambig.	LRHS
'Michael Ayres' ♀H5	CNMi LHom
'Mighty Atom'	CNMi IKil LHom LRHS NAln
'Min' ♀H5	CNMi LHom
'Misty Mauves' (New Millennium Series) (d)	CRos LRHS NRHS WSpi
'Molly Buchanan'	CNMi NLar
'Moon Light'PBR (Highlander Series) (d)	CRos ECtt EPfP IKil LBuc LRHS MHer MHol NAst NPri SPoG WCot WSpi
'Moonbeam'	LRHS NRHS SPoG
'Moonlight Blues' (New Millennium Series)	LPla LRHS SGbt
'Morgentau'	LRHS NLar
'Morning Sunrise'PBR	LPla SCob
'Mrs Newton Lees'	LRHS NAln
'Mydark'	LHom
New Zealand hybrids **new**	WFar
nudicaule	GKev SPlb
- 'Laurin'	LRHS
'Olive Poppleton' ♀H5	LHom
'Oliver' ♀H5	LHom
'Our Deb' ♀H5	LHom
'Ouvertüre'	LRHS
Pacific hybrids	EPfP LCro LOPS LSRN MHer SRms SWvt
'Pagan Purples' (New Millennium Series) (d)	CRos ECtt EPfP LCro LOPS LRHS MHer NCou NRHS WSpi
'Patricia Johnson'	CNMi
Percival Group	EPfP
'Pericles'	CNMi LHom
'Pink' (Excalibur Series)	EPfP SPoG
'Pink Punch' (New Millennium Series)	ELan EPfP LRHS SCob
'Pink Ruffles'	CNMi LHom
'Plagu Blue'PBR	NLar WSpi
PRINCESS CAROLINE ('Odabar'PBR)	CBcs
'Pure White' (Excalibur Series) **new**	SPoG
'Purple Passion' (New Millennium Series)	ELan EPfP LRHS NLar SCob SPoG
'Raymond Lister' ♀H5	MAvo
'Red Caroline'	CBcs
requienii	CBgR CCBP CSpe NSti SPhx WGoo WKif
'Rose Butterfly' (d)	CRos LRHS NRHS
'Rosemary Brock' ♀H5	LHom
'Royal Aspirations' (New Millennium Series)	ELan LRHS SCob SGbt SPoG
'Royal Flush'	see *D.* 'Langdon's Royal Flush'
'Ruby'	CNMi
'Ruby Tuesday'	CNMi
'Ruby Wedding'	CNMi LHom
§ × ***ruysii*** 'Pink Sensation'	LRHS NLar WSpi
'Sandpiper'	CNMi LHom
'Schildknappe'	LRHS
'Schönbuch'	LRHS
'Secret'PBR	LRHS WCot
'Shieldbearer'	LRHS
'Silver Jubilee'	CNMi
'Sky Sensation'	LRHS
'Snow Queen Arrow'	LRHS
'Sommerabend'	LRHS
'Sooty'	CNMi
§ ***speciosum***	EBee
'Spindrift' ♀H5	CNMi CRos LHom LRHS NRHS
staphisagria	WArt
'Starlight'PBR	LRHS WSpi
'Strawberry Fair'	LRHS NLar NRHS SPoG
Summer Skies Group	CBcs CCBP CWCL ELan EMor EPfP LCro LOPS LRHS MGos MMrt MWat NAln NRHS SPer SPoG WCAu WGwG
'Summerfield Diana'	CNMi
'Summerfield Oberon'	LHom WCot
'Sungleam' ♀H5	ECtt EWes LHom LRHS NAln NRHS WSpi
'Sunkissed' ♀H5	CNMi LHom
'Sunny Skies' (New Millennium Series)	ELan LRHS
sutchuenense	EWld
'Sweet Sensation'PBR (Highlander Series) (d)	CRos ECtt EPfP IKil LPla LRHS NLar NRHS SPoG WCot WSpi WTor
'Sweetheart'	CRos LRHS NRHS
'Templegong' **new**	NAln
'Tiger Eye'	CNMi LHom
'Titania'	LHom
tricorne	MAvo
'Trudy'	CNMi
'Turkish Delight'	LHom
uliginosum	SPlb
'Vanessa Mae'	CNMi LHom
vestitum	EWTr
'Walton Benjamin'	LHom
'Walton Gemstone' ♀H5	LHom
'White Swan'	EPfP
'Wishful Thinking'PBR	CBcs MHol NDai
'Yvonne'	LRHS
'Zauberflöte'	LRHS

Dendranthema see *Chrysanthemum*

pacificum	see *Ajania pacifica*

Dendriopoterium see *Sanguisorba*

Dendrobenthamia see *Cornus*

Dendrocalamus (*Poaceae*)

asper	XBlo
giganteus	XBlo
§ ***strictus***	XBlo

Dendromecon (*Papaveraceae*)

rigida	CRos LRHS SMad WPGP

Dendropanax ✿ (*Araliaceae*)

cf. ***kwangsiensis*** FMWJ 13274	WCru
trifidus	WPGP
- B&SWJ 11230	WCru

Dendroseris (*Asteraceae*)

litoralis	CCCN

Dennstaedtia ✿ (*Dennstaedtiaceae*)

punctilobula	CRos LRHS NRHS

Dentaria see *Cardamine*

pinnata	see *Cardamine heptaphylla*
polyphylla	see *Cardamine kitaibelii*

Dermatobotrys (*Scrophulariaceae*)

saundersii	ECre WCot

Derwentia see *Parahebe*

Deschampsia ✿ (*Poaceae*)

cespitosa	CBod CKno CNat EPPr EPfP GKev LCro LOPS LRHS SCob SPhx SPlb WCot WMoo XLum XSen
- BRONZE VEIL	see *D. cespitosa* 'Bronzeschleier'
§ - 'Bronzeschleier'	CBod CDor CRos CWCL EBee EHoe ELan ELon EMor EPPr EPfP GBin GMaP GWyn LRHS MAsh NGdn NRHS NWsh SCob SPer SPhx SRms SWvt WMoo WPtf XLum
- 'Cabana Buta'	LEdu SPhx
- 'Coral Cloud'	GQue
- 'Fairy's Joke'	see *D. cespitosa* var. *vivipara*
- 'Garnet Schist'	GQue LEdu LRHS SPhx
- GOLD DUST	see *D. cespitosa* 'Goldstaub'
- GOLDEN DEW	see *D. cespitosa* 'Goldtau'
- GOLDEN PENDANT	see *D. cespitosa* 'Goldgehänge'
- GOLDEN SHOWER	see *D. cespitosa* 'Goldgehänge'
- GOLDEN VEIL	see *D. cespitosa* 'Goldschleier'
§ - 'Goldgehänge'	CSam EHoe NBir XLum
§ - 'Goldschleier' 🏆H6	CBar CBod CRos CSam EBee ECha ELon EMor EPPr EPfP GBin GMaP LRHS NGdn NRHS NWsh SCob SPhx SWvt WMoo XLum
§ - 'Goldstaub'	EPPr
§ - 'Goldtau'	Widely available
- 'Mill End'	CKno LEdu
- 'Morning Dew'	WFar
- 'Northern Lights' (v)	CSBt ELan EPfP LRHS MBel SLim SPer SPoG SRms SWvt XLum
- 'Pixie Fountain'	GQue LRHS NWsh
- 'Schottland'	CKno EBee ECha ELon EPPr GBin LEdu MAvo
- 'Tardiflora'	CKno EBee EPPr
- 'Tauträger'	CKno EBee ELon EPPr GQue SMHy XLum
§ - var. ***vivipara***	EHoe EPPr GBin NBro
- 'Waldschatt'	CKno EBee ECha EPPr
- 'Willow Green'	GCal SCoo
- 'Yunnan' new	EPPr
flexuosa	CKno CRos EHoe LRHS NBir NRHS NWsh SPhx
- 'Tatra Gold' 🏆H6	CBod CRos CWCL ECha ECtt EHoe ELan ELon EMor GMaP LRHS MAsh MBel MRav NBir NBro NGdn NRHS NSti SCob SLim SPer SPoG SRot SWvt

Desfontainia (*Loganiaceae*)

§ ***spinosa*** 🏆H4	CAbb CAby CBcs CDul CMac CPla CRos CTri EBee ELan ELon EPfP EUJe GAbr GKin IArd LRHS MAsh MBlu MGil NLar SLim SPer SPoG SRms WFar WPav WSHC
- 'Harold Comber'	CMac NLar WHor
- f. ***hookeri***	see *D. spinosa*
- Treseder form	CTsd

Desmodium (*Papilionaceae*)

callianthum	CMac CRos LRHS SBrt WSHC
canadense	EBee IMou MNrw NLar SBrt SPhx
§ ***elegans***	CBcs CExl CRos EBee ELan EPfP LRHS NLar SBrt SChF SPhx SVen WPGP WSHC
- dark-flowered	WPGP
glutinosum	EBee
praestans	see *D. yunnanense*
tiliifolium	see *D. elegans*
§ ***yunnanense***	CExl WSHC

Deuterocohnia (*Bromeliaceae*)

brevifolia 🏆H2	WCot WPGP
lotteae	WCot

Deutzia ✿ (*Hydrangeaceae*)

CC 4548	CExl
CC 4550	CExl
SDR 7953	GKev
bhutanensis HWJK 2180	WCru
'Bright Eyes'	WPGP
calycosa BWJ 8007	WCru
- 'Dali'	CExl IArd NLar SDys
chunii	see *D. ningpoensis*
compacta	CBcs CMCN SLon WPGP
- 'Lavender Time'	CExl CKel CMac EBee EPfP LRHS MAsh NLar SWvt
cordatula B&SWJ 3720	WCru
- B&SWJ 6917	WCru
corymbosa	MRav
- GWJ 9202	WCru
- GWJ 9203	WCru
- GWJ 9339	WCru
- var. ***corymbosa***	WSpi
crenata B&SWJ 8886	WCru
- B&SWJ 8896	WCru
- B&SWJ 8924	WCru
- 'Flore Pleno'	see *D. scabra* 'Plena'
- var. ***heterotricha*** B&SWJ 5805	WCru
- - B&SWJ 8879	WCru
- var. ***nakaiana***	SBrt
- - B&SWJ 11184	WCru
- - 'Nikko'	see *D. gracilis* 'Nikko'
§ - 'Pride of Rochester' (d) 🏆H5	CAco CBcs CKel CMCN ECrN GKin LRHS MBlu MGil MMuc MRav NLar SCob SEND SEle SGol SPoG SWvt WGrn
'Dark Eyes'	CExl SAko
discolor 'Major'	CExl WCru WPGP
× ***elegantissima***	SRms

	- 'Fasciculata'	CBod CKel CRos ELan EPfP LRHS MGil NLar SPer SWvt WBor WSpi
	- 'Rosealind' ♀H5	CBcs CCCN CDul CExl CKel CMac CRos CTri EBee ELan EPfP GKin IArd LRHS LSRN MGil MRav SPer SRms SWvt WCFE WKif WSHC WSpi
	glabrata B&SWJ 617	WCru
	- B&SWJ 8427	WCru
	glomeruliflora BWJ 7742	WCru
	gracilis	CBod CKel CSBt ELan EPfP EWTr GKin LRHS MAsh MGil MGos MRav MSwo NLar SPer WFar WSpi
	- B&SWJ 8927	WCru
	- 'Aurea'	CMac EPfP LRHS
	- 'Carminea'	see *D.* × *rosea* 'Carminea'
§	- 'Nikko' ♀H5	CBcs CExl CKel CMCN CMac CRos EBee ELan EPfP EShb EWes GKin LRHS MGos MHer MMuc MRav MSwo NGdn NLar SEND SGol SPad SPlb SRms SWvt WFar WKif
	- var. ***ogatae*** B&SWJ 8911	WCru
	- 'Rosea'	see *D.* × *rosea*
	grandiflora	WPGP
	hookeriana	CKel CRos EBee EPfP LBuc LLHF LRHS NRHS SWvt
	× ***hybrida*** 'Contraste' ♀H5	CMac
	- 'Iris Alford'	CExl CRos EPfP LRHS MGos NRHS SChF SLon WFar WPGP
	- 'Joconde' ♀H5	CExl WFar
	- 'Magicien' misapplied	see *D.* × *hybrida* 'Strawberry Fields'
	- 'Magicien' ambig.	CPla SMad WSpi
	- 'Magicien' Lemoine	CDul CExl CKel CMac CRos CSBt EBee ECrN ELan ELon EPfP EShb LRHS MAsh MRav MSwo NBir NEgg SLon SPer SRms SWvt WFar WKif WSHC WSpi
	- 'Mont Rose' ♀H5	Widely available
	- 'Perle Rose'	CKel
§	- 'Strawberry Fields' ♀H5	Widely available
	× ***kalmiiflora***	CBod CExl CMac CSBt CTri EBee GKin MAsh MGil MJak MMrt MRav NLar SChF SPer SRms WFar
	× ***lemoinei***	EPfP MJak NGdn
	longifolia	CMCN WPGP
	- 'Veitchii'	CDul CSBt EPfP MGil MRav
	- 'Vilmoriniae'	MRav
	× ***magnifica***	CDul MMrt NLar SGbt SRms
	- 'Rubra'	see *D.* × *hybrida* 'Strawberry Fields'
	maximowicziana B&SWJ 11567	WCru
	monbeigii ♀H5	CExl CKel EPfP LLHF LRHS MRav SWvt WKif
	- BWJ 7728	WCru
	multiradiata	CExl EBee WPGP
§	***ningpoensis***	CExl CRos CTsd EBee EPfP MGil NLar SMad WCFE WPGP WSpi
	paniculata B&SWJ 8592	WCru
	parviflora var. ***barbinervis*** B&SWJ 8478	WCru
	'Pink Pompon'	see *D.* 'Rosea Plena'
	prunifolia B&SWJ 8588	WCru
	pulchra	CAby CBcs CDul CKel CMCN CRos EBee ELan EPfP EWTr IDee LRHS MGil MRav SBrt SLon SPer SPoG WPGP WSpi
	- B&SWJ 1738	WCru
	- B&SWJ 3870	WCru
	- B&SWJ 3948 from the Philippines	WCru
	- B&SWJ 6908	WCru
	- pink-tinged	WPGP
	purpurascens	GKev
	- BWJ 7859	WCru
§	× ***rosea***	CDul CRos EPfP LRHS MAsh NHic NRHS SRms WKif
	- 'Campanulata'	CExl MSwo
§	- 'Carminea'	MGil SPlb SRms WFar
§	'Rosea Plena' (d)	CExl CKel CMac CRos CSBt ELan EPfP GKin LBuc LRHS MAsh MGos MMuc NLar NRHS SEle SLim SPoG SRms SWvt WFar
	× ***rosea*** YUKI CHERRY BLOSSOM ('Ncdx2')	LCro LOPS LRHS WHlf
	- YUKI SNOWFLAKE ('Ncdx1')	LRHS
	rubens	LLHF
	scabra	CTri
	- B&SWJ 11127	WCru
	- B&SWJ 11168	WCru
	- B&SWJ 11178	WCru
§	- 'Candidissima' (d) ♀H5	CDul MGil MMuc MRav SCob SEND SPer
	- 'Codsall Pink' ♀H5	MRav
§	- 'Plena' (d)	CExl ECrN EPfP GKin NHic NLar SPer SPoG WCFE
	- 'Pride of Rochester'	see *D. crenata* 'Pride of Rochester'
	- 'Punctata' (v)	EHoe MAsh MMuc SEND SRms
	- 'Robert Fortune'	SPlb
	- 'Variegata' (v)	CDul CMac
	setchuenensis	CMac MRav WCFE WSHC
	- PAB 7449	LEdu
	- var. ***corymbiflora*** ♀H5	CBcs CDul CExl CKel CMCN CRos CTri EBee ECre ELan EPfP IDee LRHS MMuc MSwo NLar SAko SChF SEle SPoG SWvt WFar WKif WPGP WSpi
	- - NJM 11.096	WPGP
	- - 'Kiftsgate'	WPGP
	taiwanensis	EPfP SGol WPGP
	- B&SWJ 6858	WCru
	- CWJ 12443	WCru
	- CWJ 12459	WCru
	× ***wellsii***	see *D. scabra* 'Candidissima'
	× ***wilsonii***	SRms

Dianella ✿ (*Hemerocallidaceae*)

	caerulea	CBcs CJun CMac EBee IMou NBir NLar
	- CASSA BLUE ('Dbb03'PBR)	CHll LRHS NRHS SPer
	- LITTLE JESS ('Dcmp01'PBR)	CExl EBee
	- 'Variegata'	see *D. tasmanica* 'Variegata'
	ensifolia	LEdu
	nigra	CBcs CExl IMou LEdu
	- 'Margaret Pringle' (v)	CExl
	revoluta	CBor
§	- 'Allyn Citation'PBR	EBee LRHS
	- 'Blue Stream'	EBee
	- COOLVISTA	see *D. revoluta* 'Allyn Citation'
	- LITTLE REV ('Dr5000'PBR)	CCht EBee EPfP SEle WSHC
	'Silver Streak' (v)	LRHS NRHS
	'Streetscape'	EBee
	tasmanica	CAbb CBcs CBor CElw CExl CKno CMac CTri CTsd ECre ELan EPfP EShb EUJe GBin LEdu SEle SMad SRms WSHC
	- from Logan	GCal

	- DESTINY ('Tas100') **new**	CBct CCht EUJe
	- 'Emerald Arch'	LEdu SPer
	- 'Splice'	CDTJ MJak
	- TASRED ('Tr20'PBR)	CBod CExl ELan EPfP EUJe MBNS SPer
§	- 'Variegata' (v)	CCCN CDTJ CExl ELan NLar

Dianthus ✿ (*Caryophyllaceae*)

	'Alan Titchmarsh' (p)	ECtt EPfP LRHS LSRN MGos NEgg NRHS SPoG SWvt
	'Albert Hill' (p)	SAll
	'Albus Plenus' (p)	MJak
	'Aldridge Yellow' (b)	SAll
	'Alfred Galbally' (b)	SAll
	'Alice' (p)	LSRN SAll
	'Alice Forbes' (b)	SAll
	'Alice Lever' (p)	WAbe
§	'Allen's Maria' (p)	SAll
	'Allspice' (p)	CFis MRav WHoo
	Allwoodii Group (p)	NNor
	- (Cocktails Series) CHERRY DAIQUIRI ('Wp15 Pie42') (p)	CRos LRHS MTis NRHS
	- - SHIRLEY TEMPLE ('Wp15 Pie44') (p)	CRos LRHS MTis NRHS
	- - TEQUILA SUNRISE ('Wp15 Pie45') (p)	CRos LRHS MTis NRHS
	- 'Doris' (p) ♀H6	CBcs CRos EAJP ECtt EPfP GJos GMaP LCro LOPS LRHS LSRN MAvo MGos MHer MRav MTis NEgg NGdn NNor NRHS SAll SCob SEND SPer SPlb SPoG SWvt WCFE
	Allwoodii Alpinus Group (p)	NGdn SRms XLum
	'Allwood's Celebration' (p)	SAll
	'Allwood's Crimson' (pf)	SAll
	'Allwood's Delight' (p)	SAll
	alpinus ♀H6	GCrg GJos MMuc NRHS NSla
	- 'Albus' (p)	GCrg GKev NWad SIgm
	- 'Darcie's Love' (p) **new**	EDAr
	- 'Joan's Blood' (p) ♀H6	GCrg GKev LSRN NHpl
	- red-flowered (p) **new**	NSla
	'Alyson' (p)	SAll
	amurensis	EPPr GCal NNor SPhx WArt WSHC XLum
	- 'Andrey' (p)	NNor
	- 'Siberian Blue' (p)	EPPr
	anatolicus	CRos EBou EDAr GJos LRHS MHer NGdn NRHS XLum
	'Anders Fay Seagrave' (p)	SAll
	'Anders Irene Ann' (pf)	CNMi
	'Anders Melody' (p)	SAll
	'Anders Patricia Griffiths' (p)	CNMi SAll
	'Anders Supernova' (p) **new**	CTri
	'Angela Carol' (pf)	CNMi
	'Annabelle' (p)	SAll
	'Annette' (p)	CMea CRos EDAr GCrg GKev LRHS LSRN MAsh NGdn NHol NRHS SWvt
	'Annie Claybourne' (pf)	CNMi
	'Apricot Sue' (pf)	SAll
	ARCTIC STAR	see *D.* 'Devon Arctic Star'
	arenarius	GKev LEdu NGdn SAll SPlb WWFP XLum
	- 'Little Maiden' (p)	CSpe EDAr GJos GWyn MMuc NGdn WIce
	- 'Snow Flurries' (p)	ITim
	'Argus' (p)	SAll
	'Aristocrat'	SAll
*	'Arlene' (b)	SAll
	armeria	CBgR CFis WHer WOut
	arpadianus var. ***pumilus***	EPot
§	× ***arvernensis*** (p) ♀H6	ECha SBch
	'Ashley Reay' (p)	CNMi
	'Audrey Robinson' (pf)	CNMi
	'Aurora' (b)	SAll
	'Auvergne'	see *D.* × *arvernensis*
	'Averiensis'	see *D.* 'Berlin Snow'
	'Badenia' (p)	ECha
	'Bailey's Celebration' (p)	MTis
	barbatus	NPri
	- 'Black Adder' (p,a)	CSpe
	- 'Dash Series' (p,a) **new**	CBod
	- - 'Dash Crimson' (p,a)	MHol
	- - 'Dash Magician' (p,a)	MHol
	- GREEN TRICK ('Temarisou'PBR) (p,a)	CSpe WNPC
	- 'Heart Attack' (p,a)	WCot
	- Messenger Group (p,a) **new**	SVic
	- Midget Group (p,a)	GJos
	- 'Monksilver Black' (p,a)	CSpe CWld EBee ECtt MAvo MBNS MBel MHol MPie NCou NSti SPad WCot
	- Nigrescens Group (p,a) ♀H7	CBre CSpe SPhx WHil
	- - 'Sooty' (p,a)	CWld GJos GWyn WCFE WFar WHer
	- 'Oeschberg' (p,a)	GWyn SAko
	- 'Red Romance' (p,a) **new**	CPla
*	- 'Roseus' (p,a)	GWyn
	- 'Tuxedo Black' (p,a)	WMoo
	basuticus	CPbh
§	'Bat's Double Red' (p)	SAll
	'Becky Robinson' (p) ♀H6	CNMi SAll
	'Belmont Duchess' (p)	SAll
§	'Berlin Snow' (p)	CPBP CRos EBou EPot GCrg ITim LRHS NRHS
	'Betsy' (pf)	SAll
	'Betty Miller' (b)	SAll
	'Betty Morton' (p) ♀H6	CRos LRHS NRHS WKif
	'Betty's Choice' (pf)	CNMi
	'Bill Smith' (pf)	CNMi
	'Binsey Red' (p)	SBch
	'Blue Hills' (p)	GKev
	'Blue Ice' (b)	SAll
	'Blush'	see *D.* 'Souvenir de la Malmaison'
	'Bobby' (p)	SAll
	'Bob's Highlight' (pf)	CNMi
	'Bombardier' (p)	ECtt
	'Bookham Gleam' (b)	SAll
	'Bookham Grand' (b)	SAll
	'Bookham Heroine' (b)	SAll
	'Bookham Lad' (b)	SAll
	'Border Special' (b)	SAll
	'Bouquet Purple' (p)	CSpe
	'Bovey Belle' (p)	SAll
	'Bramdean' (pf)	CNMi
	brevicaulis subsp. ***brevicaulis***	LLHF
	'Brian Tumbler' (b) ♀H6	SAll
	'Bridal Veil' (p)	SAll SBch WHer
	'Brilliance' (p)	WMoo
	'Brilliant'	see *D. deltoides* 'Brilliant'
	'Brilliant Star' (p) ♀H6	CRos ECtt LRHS NRHS SEND SWvt WIce
	'Brockenhurst' (pf)	CNMi
	'Brympton Red' (p)	CFis ECha SAll
	'Bryony Lisa' (b) ♀H6	SAll
	caesius	see *D. gratianopolitanus*

	Name	Suppliers
	callizonus	LLHF NSla
	'Calypso Star' (p)	ECtt SPoG
	'Can-can' (pf)	ECtt MHol
	'Candy Clove' (b)	SAll
	CANDY FLOSS	see *D.* 'Devon Flavia'
	'Candy Spice' (p)	MRav
	capitatus subsp. ***andrzejowskianus***	EPPr
§	'Carmine Letitia Wyatt'[PBR] (p) ♀H6	CRos ECtt LRHS NRHS SPoG
	carthusianorum	Widely available
	- W&B BGL-1	WCot
I	- 'Rupert's Pink' (p)	CKno EBee NGdn SWvt
	caryophyllus	ENfk SVic WSFF
	CASSANDRA ('Bardranasca'[PBR]) (pf)	SAll
	'Casser's Pink' (p)	NWad
	'Castleroyal Sceptre' (p)	SAll
	'Charles' (p)	SAll
	'Charles Edward' (p)	SAll
	'Charles Musgrave'	see *D.* 'Musgrave's Pink'
	'Chastity' (p)	ECtt LLHF SAll WHoo
	Cheddar pink	see *D. gratianopolitanus*
	'Cherly'	LSRN
	'Cherry Clove' (b)	SAll
	'Cheryl'	see *D.* 'Houndspool Cheryl'
	'Chesswood Barbara Arif' (b) ♀H6	SAll
	'Chesswood Dorothy Cottam' (b)	SAll
	'Chetwyn Ruth Gillies' (pf)	CNMi
	CHILI	see *D.* CRACKER
	chinensis 'Black and White' (p,a)	CSpe
	'Chris Crew' (b) ♀H6	SAll
	'Christopher' (p)	SAll
	'Clare' (p)	ECtt SAll
	'Claret Joy' (p) ♀H6	ECtt MMuc SAll SEND
	'Cleopatra' (pf)	EMal
	'Clifford Pipperoo' (pf)	SAll WCot
	'Clunie' (b)	SAll
§	'Cockenzie Pink' (p)	SAll SBch WHer
	COCONUT SUNDAE ('Wp 05 Yves'[PBR]) (Scent First Series) (p)	CRos ECtt ELan ELon LRHS LSRN MCot NNor NRHS SEND SRot WTor
	'Constance' (p)	SAll
	'Constance Finnis'	see *D.* 'Fair Folly'
	'Consul' (b)	SAll
	'Conwy Silver' (p)	WAbe
	'Conwy Star' (p)	WAbe
	'Coral Reef'[PBR] (Scent First Series) (p)	CRos ECtt ELan LRHS NNor NRHS SPoG
	'Corona Iceberry Magic' (p,a)	CRos NRHS
	'Coronation Ruby' (p) ♀H6	SAll
	corsicus	XSen
	COSMOPOLITAN ('Wp15 Pie43') (p)	CRos LRHS MTis NRHS
	'Coste Budde' (p)	WSHC
§	CRACKER ('Wp10 Sab06'[PBR]) (Early Bird Series) (p)	CRos LRHS NRHS
	'Cranberry Crush' (pf)	CNMi
	'Cranmere Pool' (p) ♀H6	CBcs CRos ECtt ELan EPfP LCro LOPS LRHS NNor NRHS SEND SPoG SWvt WBrk WCAu WTor
	'Crimson Chance' (p)	NSla
	'Crimson Warrior' (pf)	CNMi
	'Crock of Gold' (b)	SAll
	'Crompton Classic' (pf)	CNMi
	'Crompton Princess' (pf)	CNMi
	cruentus	CAby CFis CPla CSpe EBee EDAr ELan EPPr EWTr EWes GCal LCro LEdu LOPS LRHS MBel MCot NDov SHar SPhx SPtp SWvt WCAu
	'Cumbria' (pf)	CNMi
	'D.D.R.'	see *D.* 'Berlin Snow'
	'Dad's Favourite' (p)	SAll
	'Dainty Dame' (p) ♀H4	CRos CSpe CTri ECtt EPfP LRHS MNHC NRHS SAll SBch SIgm
	'Dancing Geisha' **new**	EDAr
§	'Dancing Queen'[PBR] (p)	NNor
	'Daphne' (p)	SAll
	'David' (p)	LSRN SAll SCob
	'David Russell' (b) ♀H6	SAll
	'Dawn' (b)	SAll
	'Dawn's Delight' (pf)	CNMi
	'Dedham Beauty' (p)	MPie SEND WCot
	deltoides ♀H6	CPbh CWld ECha ENfk EPfP EWld LEdu MAsh MBel MMuc MNHC SIgm SPlb SRms WFar
	- 'Albus' (p)	ECha EPfP GBin GWyn NGdn WMoo
	- 'Arctic Fire' (p)	EPfP GWyn MBel MHol NGdn NHol NSla WFar WMoo
§	- 'Brilliant' (p)	CChe GJos GWyn NGdn NHol SAll SRms WHoo
	- 'Dark Eyes' (p)	EWes
	- 'Erectus' (p)	EPfP
	- FLASHING LIGHT	see *D. deltoides* 'Leuchtfunk'
§	- 'Leuchtfunk' (p)	CCBP GPSL NHic NNor NRHS NSla SPoG WFar WMoo WTor
I	- 'Luneburg Heath Maiden Pink' (p)	NGdn
	- Microchips Group (p)	WMoo
	- 'Nelli' (p)	NGdn WMoo
	- red-flowered (p)	SVic
	- 'Roseus' (p) **new**	GJos
	- 'Shrimp' (p)	ECtt NGdn
	- 'Zing Rose' (p) **new**	GJos
	'Dennis' (p)	LSRN SAll
	'Desert Song' (b)	SAll
	'Desmond'	EPfP
§	'Devon Arctic Star' (Early Bird Series) (p)	CMea CRos CTri ELan GMaP LRHS NRHS SPoG SRot SWvt
	'Devon Cream'[PBR] (p)	ECtt ELan LRHS NEgg
	'Devon Dove'[PBR] (p) ♀H6	CRos CTri ECtt ELan EPfP LRHS MBel MRav MTis NDov NEgg NRHS
	'Devon Esther'	see *D.* POP STAR
	'Devon Fatima'	see *D.* ICED GEM
§	'Devon Flavia'[PBR] (Scent First Series) (p) ♀H6	CRos LRHS MTis NRHS SPoG
	'Devon Flores'	see *D.* SHOOTING STAR
	'Devon General'[PBR] (p)	MWat
	'Devon Glow' (p)	EPfP
	'Devon Magic'[PBR] (p)	ECtt
	'Devon Opal'	see *D.* LADY MADONNA
	'Devon Sapphire'	see *D.* MYSTIC STAR
	'Devon Verity'	see *D.* 'Dancing Queen'
§	'Devon Winnie'[PBR] (p)	MTis
	'Devon Wizard'[PBR] (p) ♀H6	CRos CSBt ECtt EPfP LCro LOPS LRHS MBel MRav MTis NDov NEgg NNor NRHS WCAu
§	'Devon Xera' (p) ♀H6	GJos MTis SEND
§	'Devon Yolande'[PBR] (Scent First Series) (p)	CRos ECtt EPfP LRHS LSRN NRHS SEND SPoG
	'Dewdrop' (p)	CMea EWTr MAsh MHer MMuc NBir NGdn SAll SEND WHal
	'Dian Cape' (b)	SAll
	'Diana'	see *D.* DONA

'Diana Lavender Picotee' (p,a) CRos LRHS NRHS
'Diane' (p) ♀H6 EAJP ECtt EPfP NEgg SAll SPoG SWvt
DIANTICA DARK RED PINK EYE (pt) CRos NRHS
DIANTICA WHITE WITH EYE ('Kledg11116') (pt) CRos NRHS
'Diplomat' (b) SAll
§ DONA ('Brecas') (pf) LSRN
'Dora' (p) CRos LRHS NRHS
'Doreen Hodgson' (p) ECtt SAll
'Doris Allwood' (pf) CNMi EMal SAll
'Doris Elite' (p) SAll
'Doris Galbally' (b) SAll
'Doris Majestic' (p) SAll
'Doris Ruby' see *D.* 'Houndspool Ruby'
'Doris Supreme' (p) SAll
'Double Lace' (b) ECtt
'Double North' (p) CTri
DUBAI ('Bardibua'PBR) (pf) SAll
'Dubarry' (p) ECtt
'Duchess of Roxburghe' (pf) EMal SAll
'Duchess of Westminster' (M) EMal SAll
'Duke of Norfolk' (pf) EMal SAll
'Dunkirk Spirit' (pf) CNMi
'Dusky Janelle' (pf) CNMi
'Earl Kelso' (pf) EMal
'Earl of Essex' (p) SAll
'Edenside Scarlet' (b) SAll
'Edenside White' (b) SAll
'Edna' (p) SAll
'Edward Allwood' (pf) SAll
'Edwin Cross' (b) SAll
'Eileen' (p) SAll
'Eileen Lever' (p) CPBP EPot GCrg SIgm WAbe
'Eileen O'Connor' (b) ♀H6 SAll
'Eira Wen' (p) WAbe
'Eleanor Parker' (p) WAbe
'Eleanor's Old Irish' (p) ECtt ELon LRHS MBel MHol MPie SEND WBrk WCot WHoo
'Elizabeth Nelson' (b) SAll
'Elizabethan' (p) CFis CSpe EWTr MCot MHCG SDys SRms WTor
* 'Elizabethan Pink' (p) SAll
'Elsie Ketchen' (pf) CNMi
'Emile Paré' (p) CFis
'Emjay' (b) SAll
'Emmeline Pankhurst' (pf) CNMi
'Emperor' see *D.* 'Bat's Double Red'
erinaceus EPot GCrg GJos SIgm
- var. ***alpinus*** EPot NSla
- Duguid's WAbe
'Erycina' (b) SAll
'Ethel Hurford' (p) WHoo
'Eva Humphries' (b) SAll
'Evelyn Berry' (p) CNMi
'Evening Star' (p) ♀H6 CBod CRos CTri LRHS NRHS SPoG SWvt WIce
'Eve's Holly' (pf) CNMi
'Exquisite' (b) SAll
§ 'Fair Folly' (p) SAll WHer
'Farnham Rose' (p) SAll
ferrugineus EPPr SBrt SPhx
'Fettes Mount' (p) WAvo WBrk WCot
'Feuerhexe' (p) ECtt GCrg XLum
'Fimbriatus' (p) WHoo
'Fiona' (p) SAll
FIRE STAR see *D.* 'Devon Xera'
'Firestar' (p) CRos CTri ELan GMaP LRHS MAsh NRHS SRot SWvt
'First Lady' (b) SAll
FIZZY ('Wp08 Ver03'PBR) (Early Bird Series) (p) CRos ELan LRHS MHol MWat NRHS
'Flanders' (b) ♀H6 SAll
'Flashdance' (pf) CNMi
'Fleur' (p) SAll
'Florence Franklin' (pf) CNMi
'Floristan Mix' (p,a) NNor
'Forest Glow' (b) SAll
'Forest Princess' (b) SAll
'Forest Sprite' (b) SAll
'Forest Treasure' (b) SAll
'Forge Pink' LLHF
'Fortuna' (p) SAll
'Fragrant Ann' (pf) ♀H6 EMal SAll
'Frances Isabel' (p) SAll
'Freda' (p) SAll
'Freda Woodliffe' (p) ECtt GCrg SBch WAbe WHoo
freynii EPot EWes GKev
* - var. ***nana*** GKev
FRILLY ('Wp08 Ulr03'PBR) (Early Bird Series) (p) CRos LRHS NRHS
fringed pink see *D. superbus*
furcatus SIgm
'Fusilier' (p) CRos CTri EBou ECtt EPfP GCrg GMaP LRHS MAsh NRHS SAll SHar SRot SWvt WIce WRHF
'Gail Graham' (b) SAll
'Gail Tilsley' (b) SAll
'Garland' (p) CMea
'Gaydena' (b) SAll
giganteus SPhx
'Gingham Gown' (p) ECtt EPot NBir SAll
* ***glacialis elegans*** GKev
'Gold Dust' (p) ECtt EPot EWTr SAll SBch
'Gold Embrace' (pf) CNMi
'Grace's Scarlet Clove' (b) SAll
'Grandma Calvert' (p) SAll
'Gran's Favourite' (p) ♀H6 CBcs CRos CSBt EAJP ECtt ELan EPfP GJos LCro LOPS LRHS LSRN MCot MGos MHol MMuc MTis MWat NEgg NGdn NNor NRHS SAll SEND SPer SPlb SPoG SWvt WGwG WHer
§ ***gratianopolitanus*** ♀H6 CBod CTri EDAr ENfk EPfP GQue LEdu MHer MNHC MRav NBid SAll
- 'Albus' (p) EPot MHer
- 'Babi Lom' (p) GCrg
- dwarf SIgm WAbe
* - 'Karlik' (p) GQue
§ - 'Tiny Rubies' (p) EDAr LLHF SDys WAbe
'Greensides' (p) SAll
'Gypsy Star' (p) SPoG
haematocalyx GJos NSla
- 'Alpinus' see *D. haematocalyx* subsp. *pindicola*
§ - subsp. ***pindicola*** CPBP LLHF NSla WAbe
'Hamish Berry' (p) CNMi
'Hampshire' (pf) CNMi
'Hannah Gertsen' (p) SAll
'Harkell Special' (b) SAll
'Harmony' (b) SAll
'Hayden' (pf) CNMi
'Hayley's Choice' (b) SAll
HAYTOR see *D.* 'Haytor White'
'Haytor Rock' (p) ♀H6 ELan EPfP MTis NNor WGwG
§ 'Haytor White' (p) ♀H6 CBcs CTri EAJP EPfP LCro LOPS SAll SCob

'Heath' (p)	SAll
'Heaven Scent' (p)	SAll
'Helen' (p)	ELon LSRN SAll
'Helena Allwood' (pf)	EMal
'Helena Hitchcock' (p)	SAll
'Herbert's Pink' (p)	ECtt SPhx
'Hercules' (pf)	CNMi
'Hereford Butter Market' (p)	EBee
'Hidcote' (p)	CRos CTri LLHF LRHS NRHS SIgm
Highland Group (p)	SGbt
'Highland Fraser' (p)	WKif
'Hope' Allwood, 1946 (p)	SAll
'Hot Spice' (p)	SPoG
§ 'Houndspool Cheryl' (p) ♀^{H6}	CBcs CRos ECtt EPfP GJos LRHS NRHS SAll WCAu
§ 'Houndspool Ruby' (p) ♀^{H6}	CBcs EPfP GQue LSRN SAll
hyssopifolius	EDAr GJos GKev WOut
'Ian' (p)	LSRN SAll
§ ICED GEM ('Wp06 Fatima'^{PBR}) (Scent First Series) (p)	CBod CRos ELan ELon LRHS LSRN MTis NNor NRHS SPoG SRot
'Icomb' (p)	WHoo
'Inchmery' (p)	LRHS SAll WHer
'India Star'^{PBR} (p) ♀^{H6}	CRos CTri EPfP LRHS MTis NEgg NRHS NWad SRot WIce
'Inshriach Dazzler' (p) ♀^{H6}	CPBP CPla ECtt EPot GCrg GMaP LLHF MAsh MHer NEgg NHol NSla SRot WAbe WHal WTor
'Inshriach Startler' (p)	CMea
'Irene Della-Torré' (b) ♀^{H6}	SAll
'James Muir' (M) **new**	EMal
'Janelle Welch' (pf)	CNMi
'Janet Walker' (p)	GMaP
'Jess Hewins' (pf)	CNMi SAll
'Joan Schofield' (p)	CPBP
'Joanne' (pf)	CNMi
'Joanne's Highlight' (pf)	CNMi
'Joy' (p) ♀^{H6}	EPfP SAll SPoG
'Julian' (p)	SAll
'Julie Ann Davis' (b)	SAll
'Julie Martin' (pf)	CNMi
'Just Jodie' (pf)	CNMi
'Kathleen Hitchcock' (b) ♀^{H6}	SAll
'Kelly's Kiss' (p)	CNMi
'Kent' (pf)	CNMi
'Kesteven Kirkstead' (p) ♀^{H6}	MNrw SAll
'Kim' (p)	NDov
knappii	EDAr GWyn LRHS SHar SPhx WHer WSHC XLum
- 'Yellow Harmony' (p,a)	GQue SAll
'La Bourboule' (p) ♀^{H6}	CBod CMea CRos EBou ECtt GAbr GCrg GMaP LRHS NRHS NSla
'La Bourboule Alba' (p) ♀^{H6}	CTri ECtt GCrg MAsh
'Laced Joy' (p)	SAll
'Laced Monarch' (p)	CBcs CRos CSBt ECtt ELan EPfP LRHS MCot MMuc NEgg NNor NRHS SAll SEND SPlb SPoG WGwG WHer
'Laced Mrs Sinkins' (p)	SAll WHer
'Laced Prudence'	see *D.* 'Prudence'
'Laced Romeo' (p)	SAll
'Laced Treasure' (p)	SAll
'Lady Granville' (p)	SAll
LADY IN RED ('Wp04 Xanthe'^{PBR}) (p)	CRos ECtt ELan EPfP LRHS MTis NBir NNor NRHS
§ LADY MADONNA ('Wp04 Opal'^{PBR}) (p) ♀^{H6}	ELan
'Lady Windermere' (M)	EMal SAll
'Lancing Supreme' (p)	SAll WHer
'Langford Manor' (pf)	CNMi
'Langport Lady' (pt)	CNMi
'Laura' (p)	SAll
'Layla Jane' (p)	CNMi
'Leatham Pastel' (pf)	CNMi
'Lemsii' (p) ♀^{H6}	NGdn
'Len Hutton' (p)	SBch
'Letitia Wyatt' (p) ♀^{H6}	CRos EPfP LRHS MWat NRHS SPoG
'Leuchtkugel' (p)	CPBP WAbe
'Lily Lesurf' (b)	SAll
LILY THE PINK ('Wp05 Idare'^{PBR}) (p) ♀^{H6}	CRos ELan LRHS NRHS
'Lime Crush' (pf)	CNMi
'Linfield Annie's Fancy' (pf)	CNMi
'Linfield Doreen Ashmore' (p)	SAll
'Linfield Dorothy Perry' (p) ♀^{H6}	SAll
'Linfield Isobel Croft' (p)	SAll
'Linfield Julie' (p)	SAll
'Linfield Kathy Booker' (p) ♀^{H6}	SAll
'Linfield Pink Margaret' (p)	CNMi SAll
'Little Ben' (p)	SAll
'Little Jock' (p)	CRos ECtt EPot GCrg LRHS MAsh NRHS SAll SPlb
'Liz Rigby' (b)	SAll
'London Brocade' (p)	SAll
'London Glow' (p)	SAll
'London Lovely' (p)	SAll
'London Poppet' (p)	ECtt SAll
'Lord Nuffield' (b)	SAll
lumnitzeri	XLum
'Lustre' (b)	SAll
'Maggie' (p)	LSRN MAvo MBel
'Maisie Neal' (b) ♀^{H6}	SAll
'Mandy' (p)	SAll
'Manon des Sources' (pf)	CNMi
'Margaret Taylor' (p)	SAll
'Maria'	see *D.* 'Allen's Maria'
'Marian Allwood' (pf)	EMal
'Marilyn's Highlight' (pf)	CNMi
'Marjery Breeze' (p)	SAll
'Marmion' (M)	EMal SAll
'Ma's Choice' (p)	SAll
'Matthew' (p)	WHoo
'Maudie Hinds' (b)	SAll
'Maxine' (pf)	CNMi
'Maybole' (b)	SAll
'Maybush' (pf)	CNMi
MEMORIES ('WP11 Gwe04'^{PBR}) (Scent First Series) (p)	CRos EBee ELan EPfP LBuc LRHS LSun MCot MHol MTis MWat NCou NRHS SPoG WCot WWFP
MENDLESHAM MINX ('Russmin'^{PBR}) (p)	CRos ELan EPfP LRHS NRHS SAll SWvt
'Messines Pink' (p)	SAll WHer
microlepis	EDAr EPot LLHF NGdn NSla
- f. ***albus***	NSla
- ED 791562	NGdn
- 'Rivendell' (p)	WAbe
'Mike Briggs' (b)	SAll
'Miss Farrow' (p)	EWes LRHS SCob SPhx
'Miss Sinkins' (p)	CTri
MOJÁCAR ('Barjamocar'^{PBR}) (pf)	SAll
MOJITO ('Wp15 Pie41') (p)	CRos LRHS MTis NPri NRHS
'Monica Wyatt' (p) ♀^{H6}	CBcs CRos ECtt ELan EPfP LRHS NEgg NRHS SPoG
'Montrose Pink'	see *D.* 'Cockenzie Pink'

	Name	Suppliers
	'Monty Allwood' (p)	ECtt SAll
	'Monty's Pink' (pf)	EMal
	'Moor Editha' (p)	CNMi
	'Moor Simply Red' (b)	SAll
	MORNING STAR	see *D.* 'Devon Winnie'
	'Morrissey' (pf)	CNMi
	MOTHER OF PEARL ('Wp10 Ele04'[PBR]) (Perfume Pinks Series) (p)	ELan
	'Mottisfont Pink'	NWad
	'Moulin Rouge' (p) 🏆H6	CRos CTri ECtt ELan EPfP LCro LOPS LRHS MTis NRHS SPoG
	'Mrs Macbride' (p)	SAll
	'Mrs Sinkins' (p)	Widely available
	'Musgrave's Pink' (p)	CFis ECha MRav SAll WHer
	'Musgrave's White'	see *D.* 'Musgrave's Pink'
	myrtinervius	EDAr GPSL NGdn WAvo
	'Mystic Dawn' (b)	SAll
§	MYSTIC STAR ('WP 05 Saphire') (p) 🏆H6	CMea ELan MTis WIce
	'Mystic Sunset' (b)	SAll
	'Napoleon III' (p)	SAll
	nardiformis	XLum
	'Natalie Saunders' (b) 🏆H6	SAll
	'Nautilus' (b)	SAll
	neglectus misapplied	see *D. pavonius*
	'Neon Star'[PBR] (p) 🏆H6	CRos CTri ELan GKev LRHS MTis NRHS SPoG SRot
	'Night Star' (p) 🏆H6	CPla CRos ELan EPfP GBin GKev GMaP GWyn LPot LRHS MHol NEgg NRHS NSla SEND SRot WPtf
	noeanus	see *D. petraeus* subsp. *noeanus*
	'Nomie' (pf)	CNMi
	'Northland' (pf)	CNMi EMal SAll
	'Nyewoods Cream' (p)	CMea EPot GCrg GMaP MHer NGdn NWad SBch
	'Oakwood Erin Mitchell' (p)	CNMi
	'Oakwood Sweetheart' (p)	SAll
	'Odessa Red' (Odessa Series) (pt)	SRms
	'Old Blush'	see *D.* 'Souvenir de la Malmaison'
	'Old Clove Red' (b)	WHoo
	'Old Dutch Pink' (p)	NWad
	'Old French Red' (pf)	EMal
	'Old Fringed White' (p)	EWTr
	'Old Man's Head' (p)	SBch
	'Old Mother Hubbard' (p)	SBch
	'Old Red Clove' (p)	ECtt GAbr GBee MBel MHol MPie NCou SPer WCot
	'Old Rose' (pf)	EMal
§	'Old Square Eyes' (p)	MNrw SAll SHar WHer
	'Old Velvet' (p)	SAll WHoo
	'Oliver' (p)	SAll
	'Owston Third Avenue' (p)	SAll
	'Oxford Magic' (p)	SAll
	'Painted Lady' (p)	SAll
	'Paisley Gem' (p)	SAll
	PASSION ('Wp Passion'[PBR]) (Scent First Series) (p)	CRos EBee ECtt ELan EPfP LRHS MBel MHol MTis NCou NNor NRHS SAko SEND SMad SPoG WCot
§	***pavonius***	CRos EDAr EWes LRHS NGdn NRHS NSla SIgm
	'Peach' (p)	SEND
	'Pendle Doris Delight' (p)	SAll
	'Pennine Reflections' (b)	SAll
	'Peter Wood' (b) 🏆H6	SAll
§	***petraeus***	EWes NGdn
§	- subsp. ***noeanus***	LLHF MMuc WHal
	'Petticoat Lace' (p)	SAll

	Name	Suppliers
	'Pheasant's Eye' (p)	SAll WHer
*	'Picton's Propeller' (p)	GCal NWad WSHC
	PIERROT ('Kobusa') (pf)	CNMi
	'Pike's Pink' (p) 🏆H6	CRos CSpe CTri ELan EPfP EPot EWTr GCrg LRHS MAsh MMuc NBir NGdn NRHS SAll SEND
	PINBALL WIZARD ('Wp15mow08') (p)	CRos LRHS MTis NRHS
	pindicola	see *D. haematocalyx* subsp. *pindicola*
	pinifolius	CWld EDAr SBrt
	'Pink Doris' (pf)	CNMi
	'Pink Fantasy' (b)	SAll
	PINK FIZZ ('Wp10 Xav04'[PBR]) (Scent First Series) (p)	CRos LRHS NRHS
	'Pink Jewel' (p)	CMea CPBP EBou ECha EPot GKev MAsh MNHC SAll XLum
	PINK KISSES ('Kledg12163') (pt)	CRos LRHS NRHS SPoG
	'Pink Mrs Sinkins' (p)	SAll
	'Pink Pearl' (b)	SAll
	'Pixie' (b)	CPBP EPot
	'Pixie Star'[PBR] (p) 🏆H6	EPfP SPoG SRot WIce
	plumarius	SAll XLum
	- 'Albiflorus' (p)	XLum
	- subsp. ***praecox***	CPBP
§	POP STAR ('Wp04 Esther'[PBR]) (p)	MTis SGbt WIce
	'Pretty' (p)	ECtt SAll
	PRETTY FLAMINGO	see *D.* 'Carmine Letitia Wyatt'
	'Prince Charming' (p)	MAsh
	'Princess of Wales' (M)	EMal SAll
	'Priory Pink' (p)	SAll
§	'Prudence' (p)	SAll
	'Pudsey Prize' (p)	CPBP EPot WAbe
	'Purple Frosted' (pf)	EMal
	'Purple Jenny' (p)	ECtt SAll
	pygmaeus	WCru
	NMWJ 14561 **new**	
	'Queen of Hearts' (p)	SEND
§	'Queen of Henri' (p)	CRos EBou LRHS NRHS
	'Queen of Sheba' (p)	SAll WHer WKif
	'Rachel' (p)	SAll
	'Rainbow Loveliness' (p,a)	SAll WOut
	RASPBERRY SUNDAE	see *D.* 'Devon Yolande'
	REBEKAH ('Wp09 Mar05'[PBR]) (Early Bird Series) (p)	CBod CMea CPla CRos ELan LRHS NRHS
	'Red Dwarf'	see *D.* 'Red Star'
§	'Red Star'[PBR] (p) 🏆H6	CRos ELan GJos LRHS NRHS SRot WIce WTor
	'Reine de Henri'	see *D.* 'Queen of Henri'
	repens	GKev
	'Richard Pollak' (b)	SAll
	'Ringwood Belle' (pf)	CNMi
	'Rizalene' (p)	CNMi
	'Robert Allwood' (pf)	EMal SAll
	'Robert Smith' (b)	SAll
	'Robin Ritchie' (p)	WHoo
	'Robin Thain' (b)	SAll
	ROMANCE ('Wp09 Wen04'[PBR]) (Scent First Series) (p)	CRos ELan LRHS MTis NRHS
	'Romsey' (pf)	CNMi
	'Roodkapje' (p)	XLum
	'Rose de Mai' (p)	CFis CNMi CSam SAll WHer WHoo
	'Rose Joy' (p) 🏆H6	EPfP
	ROSEBUD ('Wp08 Ros03'[PBR]) (Early Bird Series) (p)	CRos LRHS NRHS
	'Rötkappchen' (p)	ELon
	'Royal Crimson' (pf)	EMal

'Royal Fragrance' (pf) EMal
'Royal Salmon' (pf) EMal
'Ruby' see *D.* 'Houndspool Ruby'
'Ruby Doris' see *D.* 'Houndspool Ruby'
'Ruby Wedding' (p) LSRN
rupicola WCot
'Saint Nicholas' (p) WThu
'Sam Barlow' (p) SAll
'Santa Claus' (b) SAll
'Seraphina' (pf) CNMi
'Seren Wen' (p) WAbe
serotinus EPot WCot
SHERBET ('Wp08 Nik03'[PBR]) (Early Bird Series) (p) ELan
§ SHOOTING STAR ('Wp04 Flores'[PBR]) (p) ELan MTis SRms
'Shot Silk' (pf) EMal SAll
'Show Aristocrat' (p) SAll
'Show Beauty' (p) SAll
SHOW GIRL ('Hilshow') (pt) CRos LRHS NRHS
'Show Glory' (p) SAll
'Show Harlequin' (p) SAll
'Show Satin' (p) SAll
SHOWGIRL ('Wp08 Uni02'[PBR]) (Scent First Series) (p) ELan
SILVER STAR ('Wp10 Hel01'[PBR]) (p) CRos CTri LRHS NRHS SEND
* 'Six Hills' (p) NWad
SLAP 'N' TICKLE ('Wp 05 Pp 22'[PBR]) (Scent First Series) (p) CRos ECtt ELon LRHS LSRN NRHS SPoG SRot
'Snowshill Manor' (p) ECtt
'Solomon' (p) SAll
'Somerset' (pf) CNMi
'Sops-in-wine' (p) CFis CSam ECha ECtt SAll
§ 'Souvenir de la Malmaison' (M) EMal SAll
'Spangle' (b) SAll
spiculifolius EPot MMuc
'Spinfield Joy' (b) ♀H6 SAll
'Spring Star' (p) ECtt SRot
'Square Eyes' see *D.* 'Old Square Eyes'
squarrosus CPBP EPot
- 'Nanus' see *D.*'Berlin Snow'
'Starburst'[PBR] (p) CMea MTis
STARGAZER ('Wp13 Gil05'[PBR]) (Whetman Stars Series) (p) MTis MWat
'Starlette'[PBR] (Star Double Series) (p) **new** CRos LRHS NRHS
STARLIGHT ('Hilstar') (pf) CMea SRms
'Starry Eyes' (p) ♀H6 CRos CSam ELan GCrg GMaP LRHS NRHS SRms SRot SWvt WIce WTor
'Storm' (pf) EMal SAll
'Strawberries and Cream' (p) ECtt NEgg SPoG
strictus WCot
* - subsp. ***pulchellus*** GEdr NSla
subacaulis EDAr NSla XLum
- subsp. ***brachyanthus*** GJos
- - 'Murray Lyon' (p) WThu
suendermannii see *D. petraeus*
SUGAR PLUM ('Wp08 Ian04'[PBR]) (Scent First Series) (p) CRos EBee ECtt ELan LRHS MTis NRHS
'Summerfield Adam' (p) SAll
'Summerfield Amy Francesca' (p) SAll
'Summerfield Blaze' (p) SAll
'Summerfield Blush' (p) SAll
'Summerfield Daniel' (b) SAll
'Summerfield Debbie' (p) SAll
'Summerfield Emma Louise' (p) SAll
'Summerfield Jo' (p) CFis SAll
'Summerfield Rebecca' (p) SAll
SUNFLOR CHARMY ('Hilcharm') (Sunflor Series) (pt) **new** LRHS
'Sunray' (b) SAll
§ ***superbus*** EPPr LRHS NNor SBrt SIgm SPhx WHer WMoo WWFP
- 'Crimsonia' (p) WOut
SUPERNOVA ('Wp11 Tyr04'[PBR]) (pf) MTis
'Susan' (p) SAll
'Susannah' (p) SAll
* 'Susan's Seedling' (p) SAll
'Sweet Cecille' (pf) CNMi
'Sweet Sue' (b) SAll
sylvestris GJos WOut
'Tamsin Fifield' (b) ♀H6 SAll
'Tatra' (pf) NQui
'Tatra Blush' (p) EPPr GCal
'Tatra Fragrance' (p) GCal SAll
'Tatra Ghost' (p) SAll SDys
'Tayside Red' (M) EMal SAll
THE WESSEX PINK ('Wp15val11') (p) ECtt EPfP LRHS MTis MWat NRHS
'Thora' (M) EMal SAll
'Thunderstorm' (pf) CNMi
tianschanicus **new** GKev SPhx
TICKLED PINK ('Devon Pp 11'[PBR]) (Scent First Series) (p) CRos CTri ECtt ELan ELon LRHS LSRN NRHS SPoG
'Tiny Rubies' see *D. gratianopolitanus* 'Tiny Rubies'
'Tony's Choice' (pf) CNMi
'Treasure' (p) SAll
'Trevor' (p) SAll
tristis XLum
'Tropic Butterfly' (p) LPot
'Tudor' ELon MHCG MNrw
'Tudor Rose' (b) MNrw
turkestanicus NNor WPtf
'Uncle Teddy' (b) ♀H6 SAll
'Unique' (p) SAll
'Valda Wyatt' (p) ♀H6 CBcs ELan EPfP NEgg NNor SAll SEND SPoG SWvt WFar WGwG
'Velvet Pelargonium' (pf) EMal
'Vic Masters' (p) SBch
'Violet Clove' (b) SAll
'Violet Yates' (pf) CNMi
'W.A. Musgrave' see *D.* 'Musgrave's Pink'
'Waithman Beauty' (p) CFis ECtt SAll WHoo
'Waithman's Jubilee' (p) ECtt SAll SBch WAvo
'Warden Hybrid' (p) CMea CRos CTri ECtt EPfP GCrg LRHS MNHC NRHS NWad SPoG SWvt WAbe
'Waterloo Sunset'[PBR] (p) MTis
'Weetwood Double' (p) SBch WAvo
'Welton Raspberry Ice' (p) SAll
'Wessex' (pf) CNMi CRos LRHS NRHS
weyrichii EPot
'Whatfield Anona' (p) SAll
'Whatfield Beauty' (p) ECtt
'Whatfield Cancan' (p) ♀H6 CBod CMea CRos ECtt ELan EPfP EPot GMaP LRHS MHol MNHC NEgg NGdn NHol NRHS NRya NSla SAll SPoG SWvt WCAu
'Whatfield Cyclops' (p) SAll

'Whatfield Dorothy Mann' (p)	SAll
'Whatfield Fuchsia Floss' (p)	SAll
'Whatfield Gem' (p)	CFis CPla EBou ECtt ELan ELon EPfP GCrg MNHC NGdn SAll SIgm SWvt
'Whatfield Joy' (p)	CRos ECtt ELan EPfP GCrg GPSL LRHS NGdn NRHS SAll
'Whatfield Magenta' (p) ♀H6	CRos CSam ECtt ELan EPot EWTr GCrg LRHS NRHS SAll SPoG WAbe
'Whatfield Mini' (p)	SAll
'Whatfield Miss' (p)	SAll
'Whatfield Misty Morn' (p)	ECtt SAll
'Whatfield Peach' (p)	SAll
'Whatfield Ruby' (p)	ECtt SAll
'Whatfield White' (p)	ECtt SAll
'Whatfield Wisp' (p)	CPBP EPfP EPot MRav NBir
'White and Crimson' (p)	SAll
'White Joy' PBR (p) ♀H6	MRav
'White Ladies' (p)	MRav SAll
'Widecombe Fair' (p) ♀H6	ELan EPfP MTis SAll SPoG
'Zebra' (b)	SAll

Diarrhena (*Poaceae*)

japonica	MAvo
obovata	EBee EPPr

Diascia (*Scrophulariaceae*)

'Andrew'	SBch
'Aurora Apricot' (Aurora Series) **new**	CRos ELan LRHS NRHS
barberae 'Belmore Beauty' (v)	EWes
- 'Blackthorn Apricot' ♀H4	CRos EBee ECha ELan EPfP GWyn LRHS LSRN NDov NLar NRHS SPer SPlb SPoG SRms SWvt XEll
§ - 'Ruby Field' ♀H4	CRos EBee ECha EPfP LRHS LSRN NRHS SPer SPoG SRms SWvt
Blue Bonnet ('Hecbon')	SWvt
'Bluebelle' (Maritana Series)	NDov NLar
'Blush'	see *D. integerrima* 'Blush'
(Breezee Series) Breezee Apple Blossom	NLar WHlf
- Breezee Apricot ('Diaspritwo' PBR)	NLar
- Breezee Orange **new**	WHlf
- Breezee Plus Pink **new**	NPri
- Breezee Red	NLar WHlf
- Breezee Snow ('Inndiabzsno' PBR)	NLar
'Coldham'	LPla WGoo
Coral Belle ('Hecbel' PBR) ♀H3	CRos LRHS NRHS
cordata ambig.	WFar
'Denim Blue'	EDAr
elegans misapplied	see *D. fetcaniensis*, *D. vigilis*
'Emma'	LPla NDov SMHy SWvt WGoo
felthamii	see *D. fetcaniensis*
§ ***fetcaniensis***	CKel CMea CPrp CRos EBee EPfP LPla LRHS MCot MHer MMuc NEgg NLar WHal WSHC
- 'Daydream'	LBuc MNrw MPie SBch WCFE WHrl
flanaganii misapplied	see *D. vigilis*
(Flying Colours Series) Flying Colours Antique Rose ('Diastu' PBR)	SPoG
- Flying Colours Appleblossom ('Diastara')	SPoG
- Flying Colours Apricot ('Diastina')	SPoG
- Flying Colours Deep Salmon Improved ('Dala Depsam' PBR)	SPoG
- Flying Colours Red ('Diastonia')	SPoG
'Hector Harrison'	see *D.* 'Salmon Supreme'
§ 'Hopleys'	CRos EPPr EWes LRHS MAvo MHCG MPie MSCN NCGa NRHS SMHy WAvo WFar WOut WWtn
Ice Cracker ('Hecrack')	CMea CRos ELan LRHS NRHS SRms
Iceberg ('Hecice')	NDov SWvt
§ ***integerrima*** ♀H4	ECha MCot MHer SIgm
- 'Alba'	see *D. integerrima* 'Blush'
§ - 'Blush'	CSpe EBee NDov WGoo
- 'Ivory Angel'	see *D. integerrima* 'Blush'
integrifolia	see *D. integerrima*
'Jacqueline's Joy'	CMea NPer
'Joyce's Choice' ♀H3	CRos LRHS NRHS SRms
'Katherine Sharman' (v)	EWes
'Lilac Belle' ♀H3	CRos EDAr ELan LRHS NBir NEgg NRHS SPlb SPoG SRms
'Lilac Mist' ♀H3	NPer
Little Dancer ('Pendan' PBR)	ELan NLar
Little Dreamer ('Pender' PBR)	NLar
Little Drifter ('Pendrif' PBR)	NLar
Little Maiden ('Penmaid' PBR)	NLar
Little Tango ('Pentang' PBR)	NLar SRms
personata	CBar CHll CMea CPrp CSam CSpe EBee ECtt EHoe ELan EMor EPfP EShb EWhm GBin GMaP IMou LLHF LRHS MCot MHer MHol MMuc MNrw NDov SPhx WCot WFar WSHC WWFP
- 'Hopleys'	see *D.* 'Hopleys'
'Peter'	NDov WGoo
Pink Panther ('Penther')	SWvt
Red Ace ('Hecrace' PBR)	EPfP NPer SWvt
Redstart ('Hecstart')	SWvt
rigescens ♀H3	CBod CRos CSpe CWCL ECtt ELan EPfP GBin GWyn ILea LRHS NLar NPer SChF SPer SPlb SPoG SWvt WAbe WAvo WCFE WSpi
§ - 'Anne Rennie'	LRHS SWvt
- pale-flowered	see *D. rigescens* 'Anne Rennie'
'Ruby Field'	see *D. barberae* 'Ruby Field'
'Rupert Lambert' ♀H3	NDov
§ 'Salmon Supreme'	CRos LRHS NPer NRHS SPoG SRms
(Sundiascia Series) Sundiascia Blush Pink ('Sunjodipi' PBR)	CBod
- Sundiascia Orange ('Sunjodiora' PBR)	CBod LCro LOPS
- Sundiascia Rose Pink ('Sunjodiropi' PBR)	CBod
'Twinkle' ♀H3	CRos LRHS NBir NPer NRHS SRms
§ ***vigilis*** ♀H3	CExl CMea CRos EBee EMor EPot LRHS MHol NBro NCGa NRHS SIgm SRms WHal

Dicentra ✿ (*Papaveraceae*)

CC 4452	CExl
'Adrian Bloom'	CExl ECtt EPfP GLet SPer SWvt WFar WMoo

(Amore Series) 'Amore Pink'	CWGN EMor LPla NLar WHil
- 'Amore Rose'[PBR]	CWGN GBin NHpl NLar WHil
'Aurora'	CBod CMac CRos EBee ECtt ELon EMor EPfP GMaP GWyn LCro LOPS LRHS MRav NGdn NLar NRHS NSti SCob SPer SPoG SWvt WCAu WJam WMoo
'Boothman's Variety'	see *D.* 'Stuart Boothman'
'Bountiful'	CMac EBee ECtt GLet LRHS MRav NGdn NRHS SWvt WGwG
'Burning Hearts'[PBR]	CBod CWCL CWGN ECtt EPot GEdr IKil LRHS MPnt SCob SPer SPoG WCAu WHil
canadensis	CAby EBee GKev LEdu MAvo MNrw NLar WAbe WFar WHal
'Candy Hearts'[PBR]	EBee ECtt ELan MHol SCob SGol WHil
cucullaria	CAby CElw CRos CWCL EBee ELon EMor EPPr EPot GAbr GEdr GKev GLet ITim LEdu LRHS MNrw MRav NHpl NLar NRHS WAbe WFar XEll
- 'Pink Punk'	CWCL EBee ELon EMor EPPr EPot LEdu MNrw NLar WFar
- 'Pittsburg'	CAby EBee EPPr LEdu MNrw WSpi
eximia misapplied	see *D. formosa*
eximia ambig.	CMac CPla GPSL MHol WFar
eximia (Ker Gawl.) Torr. 'Alba'	see *D. eximia* (Ker Gawl.) Torr. 'Snowdrift'
§ - 'Snowdrift'	CBod SRms WFar WMoo
'Filigree'	CSpe ECha
'Firecracker'	ECtt MPnt
§ ***formosa***	CBcs CRos CTri ECha EHrv ELan EPfP GKev IFro LRHS NBro NGdn NRHS SPlb SRms WCAu WMoo
- f. ***alba***	CTri GAbr GLet GLog NBir SRms WCru WFar WKif
- 'Bacchanal' 🏆H5	Widely available
- 'Cox's Dark Red'	CExl EHrv EWes GBin GKev GLet IMou LLHF NAln NHpl
- 'Langtrees' 🏆H5	CMac CRos CSam ECha EPfP GKev LEdu LRHS MRav NBro NLar NRHS SRms SSut SWvt WCru WFar WMoo WSpi
- subsp. ***oregana***	EPPr NChi WHal
- - 'Rosea'	EPPr
- SNOWFLAKES ('Fusd')	EWes MRav
- 'Spring Gold'	CRos ECha ELon EPPr LRHS NLar NRHS SPad WMoo
- 'Spring Magic'	CRos ECtt EPPr EPfP GBin GWyn LRHS MRav NLar NRHS WSpi
'Ivory Hearts'[PBR]	CWGN EBee ELan IKil MCot MPnt NAln NLar NSti SCob SPer
§ 'Katie'	EPPr
'Katy'	see *D.* 'Katie'
'King of Hearts'	Widely available
'Luxuriant' 🏆H5	CBcs CBod CRos CSBt ECtt ELan EMor EPfP EShb GKev LRHS LSRN MCot MGos MHol MRav NRHS SCob SPer SPoG SRms SRot SWvt WCAu WFar WMoo WWtn
macrantha	see *Ichthyoselmis macrantha*
'Pearl Drops'	CRos GKev GLog GMaP GWyn LRHS MCot MHCG MMrt NBid NLar NRHS SRms WMoo
'Red Fountain'[PBR]	ECtt MPnt NLar NSti SMad WHil
'Rekka'[PBR]	GEdr
scandens	see *Dactylicapnos scandens*
'Silver Beads'	ELon
spectabilis	see *Lamprocapnos spectabilis*
'Spring Morning'	CElw CSam ECtt EMor EPPr GLet LEdu NGdn WSpi
§ 'Stuart Boothman' 🏆H5	CMac CWCL ECtt EPfP GLet GMaP ILea LEdu LRHS MCot MHol MRav NBro NGdn NLar SPoG SRms SWvt WCAu WFar WKif WMoo
thalictrifolia	see *D. scandens*
ventii	see *Dactylicapnos ventii*

Dichelachne (*Poaceae*)

crinita	SMea

Dichelostemma (*Asparagaceae*)

congestum	CAvo CBor GKev SDeJ WCot
§ ***ida-maia***	CAby CAvo CBor CGrW CWCL EPot GKev SDeJ
- 'Pink Diamond'	CBor EBee GKev SDeJ
volubile	GKev
- 'Pink Giant'	SDeJ

Dichondra (*Convolvulaceae*)

argentea 'Silver Falls'	CPla EShb NPri SCoo SPer SPoG
§ ***micrantha***	EShb
repens misapplied	see *D. micrantha*

Dichopogon (*Asparagaceae*)

strictus	SBrt WSFF

Dichroa ✿ (*Hydrangeaceae*)

from Guizhou, China	WPGP
cyanea NJM 13.104	EBee WPGP
febrifuga B&SWJ 9734	WCru
- B&SWJ 9753	WCru
- HWJK 2430	WSHC
- NJM 10.042	WPGP
- PAB 8639	LEdu
hirsuta new	EBee
- B&SWJ 8207 from Vietnam	WCru
- NJM 10.051 new	WPGP
aff. ***hirsuta*** B&SWJ 8371 from Laos	WCru
- NJM 10.051	WPGP
aff. ***yunnanensis*** B&SWJ 9734	WCru

Dichroa × *Hydrangea* see × *Didrangea*

Dichromena see *Rhynchospora*

Dichrostachys (*Mimosaceae*)

cinerea	SPlb

Dicksonia ✿ (*Dicksoniaceae*)

antarctica 🏆H3	Widely available
fibrosa 🏆H3	CDTJ CKel
sellowiana	CDTJ CKel
squarrosa 🏆H3	CBdn CCCN CDTJ CKel
youngiae	CDTJ CKel

Dicliptera (*Acanthaceae*)

§ ***sericea***	CCCN CHll ECtt EShb MSCN SBch SEND SRkn
suberecta	see *D. sericea*

Dictamnus (*Rutaceae*)

albus	CBcs CHll CRos CSpe CWCL EBee ECha ELan EMor EPfP EWTr LRHS LSun MCot MNrw MRav NRHS SMHy SPer SPoG SWvt WCAu WSpi
- var. ***albus*** 🏆H6	SWvt

§ – var. ***purpureus*** ♀H6	CPla CRos CSpe ECha ELan EMor EPfP ILea LRHS LSun MBel MNrw MRav NEgg NGBl NRHS SPer SPoG SRms SWvt WCAu WKif WSpi
* – var. ***roseus***	IMou
* – ***turkestanicus***	GCal
caucasicus	SMHy WSHC
fraxinella	see *D. albus* var. *purpureus*

× *Didrangea* (*Hydrangeaceae*)

B&SWJ 6605 from Thailand	WCru
versicolor	CAbb CBcs CBod CExl CHll CKel CMCN CRos EBee EMdy EPfP ESwi LRHS MGil SBrt SCob SPoG SWvt WPGP
– B&SWJ 6565	WCru
ytiensis B&SWJ 11790	WCru

Didymochlaena (*Dryopteridaceae*)

lunulata	see *D. truncatula*
§ ***truncatula***	EShb XBlo

Dierama ✿ (*Iridaceae*)

sp.	NHic
CD&R 192	CElw
adelphicum	LLHF
ambiguum	CElw EBee XLum
argyreum	CBcs CBod CBor CCCN CElw CMac CTsd CWCL EBee EMor GBin GEdr GKev GPSL ITim MMuc NLar SPad SPoG SRot WGob WHil XLum
atrum	EBee WHil
'Autumn Dazzler'	CPla
'Ballyrogan Red'	IBlr
Barr hybrids	CBro MMuc
'Black Knight'	CExl
'Blackberry Bells'	CBor CPla CRos CWCL CWGN ELon EMor GBin GPSL GWyn LRHS MAvo MBel MHol NLar NRHS NWad SPer SPoG WSpi
BLUE BELLE ('Rowblu'PBR)	CBod CBor CWCL EBee ECtt GBin IBal LRHS
'Blush'	IBlr
'Candy Stripe'	EBee IBal
'Carmine'	CWCL
'Cinnamon Fairy'	EBee EPfP IBal LRHS NRHS
cooperi	CBor CElw CPou EBee EPfP NBir
'Coral Belle'	EBee IBal LRHS
'Coral Bells'	CKno GCal IBal MNrw
'Cosmos'	CBcs CExl CPla CWCL EUJe LRHS MMrt NWad WFar
'Delicacy'	IBlr
'Desire'	IBlr
§ ***dracomontanum***	Widely available
– 'Hannahbelle' new	IKil
dracomontanum* × *pulcherrimum	SMad
ensifolium	see *D. pendulum*
erectum	CBcs CBod CBor CCCN CMac CTsd CWCL EBee EMor GPSL NLar SRot WGob
formosum	EBee
galpinii	CBod CCCN CPla CWCL EBee LLHF MMuc
grandiflorum	CPou IBlr WSHC
'Guinevere'	CBor CDor CExl CRos CTca CWCL CWGN EBee ECtt ELon GMaP GWyn IBal LEdu LRHS MAvo MRav NBir NChi NGdn NQui SCob SPoG SVen WFar WGwG WHoo WSHC XEll
igneum	Widely available
– CD&R 278	CExl CPou
insigne	CCCN CRos CWCL EBee EMor GAbr LRHS MMrt NLar NRHS NWad WCot WHil
jucundum	CBod CWCL EBee EMor LRHS WCot
'Kilmurry White'	IBal IKil
'Lancelot'	CBcs CElw CExl CRos EBee ECtt IBal IBlr LRHS NBir SWvt WCot WFar WKif WSHC
latifolium	IBlr WGob
'Mandarin'	IBlr MAvo
'Milkmaid'	CExl IBlr
'Miranda'	CBcs CBod CWCL EBee ECtt EMor IBal LRHS LSRN MAvo NLar
mossii	CBcs CBod CBor CCBP CCCN CExl CRos CWCL EMor LRHS MSCN NLar NQui NWad SPlb SPoG SRot SVen WGob WHil XLum
'Painted Lady'	CRos EBee EPfP IBal LRHS NRHS SLon
'Pale Pink'	CWCL
pallidum	CExl
'Pamina'	CExl CPrp IBlr
pauciflorum	CCCN CExl CPrp CRos CWCL EBee EMor GBin IKil LRHS NBir NLar NSla SPer SRot WCot WGob WSHC
§ ***pendulum***	CBro CRos IBlr LRHS MRav SWvt WArt WCot WFar WGob
'Pink Rocket'	CBod CBor CPla CWCL EMor GEdr MHer MHol NCou NHol SPad
Plant World hybrids	ELon WFar
PLANT WORLD JEWELS	CBct CWCL NWad WFar
'Pretty Flamingo'	CExl CPrp IBlr
'Puck'	EBee GCal IBlr MRav
pulcherrimum	Widely available
– var. ***album***	CCCN CWCL GAbr IBlr MHer MNrw WHil
– 'Blackbird'	CBcs CBod CCCN CExl CKel CPla CWCL ELan EMor EUJe GAbr GBin GEdr LRHS LSRN MAvo MHer MMuc MSCN NHol NLar SChF SPer SPoG SWvt WFar WGob WHoo WPGP
– dark cerise-flowered	WHil
– 'Falcon'	IBlr
– 'Flamingo'	IBlr
– 'Flaring Tips'	LRHS
– 'Merlin'	CDor CElw CExl CWCL EBee ECtt ELon GEdr IBal IBlr LRHS NBir SCob SVen SWvt WFar WGwG
– pale-flowered	ECha
– 'Porty'	CTca
– purple-flowered	CWCL
– Slieve Donard hybrids	CWCL EMor WFar WHil WHrl
pumilum misapplied	see *D. dracomontanum*
'Queen of the Night'	IBlr
reynoldsii	CBor CCCN CExl CPla CTsd CWCL EMor GAbr GBin GEdr MBel MMuc NWad SPlb SPoG SRkn SVen WFar WKif WSpi
robustum	CAbb CExl CPou CWCL EMor EWes LRHS WFar WPGP
'Sarastro'	CExl
sertum	EBee
'Snowgoose'	CPla
'Spring Dancer'	CPla CWCL EBee EHoe MHer NHol SPlb
'Tiny Bells'	EBee EDAr GCal GKev IBal MMuc SMHy WSHC

'Titania' IBal IBlr
trichorhizum CCCN CElw CExl CRos CWCL EMor EWTr GKev LPla LRHS NAln NWad WHil
'Tubular Bells' IBlr
tyrium LLHF WHil
'Violet Ice' IBlr
white-flowered MBel
Wildside cross CTca
Wildside hybrids WSHC

Diervilla ✿ (*Caprifoliaceae*)

middendorffiana see *Weigela middendorffiana*
rivularis HONEYBEE ('Diwibru01') LCro LOPS NEoE SGol SPoG WHil
- 'Troja Black' EPPr EPfP MBlu NLar SGol
§ ***sessilifolia*** CBcs CMac EBee EPPr MBlu MRav SLon WCot WFar
- 'Butterfly' CMac EPPr LCro LOPS NLar SCob WFar
- COOL SPLASH ('Lpdc Podaras'[PBR]) (v) CBod CKel CMac EBee ELan LRHS NEoE SPoG SWvt
× ***splendens*** CExl CKel CRos EBee EHoe ELan EPPr EPfP IDee LRHS MBNS MBlu MGil MSwo NLar SPer SPoG SWvt

Dietes (*Iridaceae*)

sp. XBlo
bicolor CAbb CAby CBod CExl CPbh CPrp CTca EBee ESwi LEdu SChr SPoG WSHC
grandiflora CAbb CAby CBod CExl CHll CKel CPbh CSpe ESwi SVen WCot
§ ***iridioides*** CPrp CSpe EBee ESwi WCot WGob XLum
robinsoniana WCot

Digitalis ✿ (*Plantaginaceae*)

NJM 13.013 **new** WPGP
'Albino' CRos EPfP LRHS NRHS
ambigua see *D. grandiflora*
apricot hybrids see *D. purpurea* 'Sutton's Apricot'
canariensis CAbb CBcs CCCN CDTJ CPla CRHN CRos CSpe CTsd EUJe GCal LRHS MGil MMrt SEND SEle SPad SPlb SVen WCFE
ciliata EPPr GKev NSti
davisiana CExl GKev GLog LLHF MNHC
'Elsie Kelsey' ECtt SWvt
eriostachya see *D. lutea*
ferruginea ♀H6 CDor CRos CSpe ECha ECtt ELan EPPr EPfP EWTr GKev GQue LEdu LRHS MRav NBir NDai NDov NGdn NRHS SCob SPer SRms SVen WBrk WCAu WKif WMoo WWFP
- 'Gelber Herold' CBod CDor EMor GBin GJos GMaP LRHS MWat WFar WSpi
- 'Gigantea' ECtt ELan EMor EPfP GAbr LEdu MBNS SCob SHar SPlb WPGP WWtn
fontanesii NWad
'Foxtrot' EPfP
'Glory of Roundway' CBod CDor EBee ECtt LCro LOPS MHol MNrw MPie NCou SPer STPC WCAu WCot
§ GOLDCREST ('Waldigone'[PBR]) CRos LRHS NRHS SPoG
§ ***grandiflora*** ♀H6 Widely available
- 'Carillon' CBod EBee ELan EMor EPfP GJos NBir SCob SRot WHoo
- 'Cream Bell' EPfP LRHS MHol
heywoodii see *D. purpurea* subsp. *heywoodii*
Illumination Series see *D.* × *valinii* Illumination Series
isabelliana CCCN CHll GCal
'John Innes Tetra' EPPr MNrw SPtp WHoo
kishinskyi see *D. parviflora* Jacq.
laevigata CBod EAJP EBee LEdu NBro SEND WArt WMoo
- subsp. ***laevigata*** SPtp
- white-flowered WCot
lamarckii misapplied see *D. lanata*
§ ***lanata*** CRos EBou ECtt ELan EPfP GKev LRHS MBNS MNHC NAln NGdn NRHS NWad SPlb SPtp SRms WGwG
- 'Café Crème' CDor CWld EMor WTor
§ ***lutea*** Widely available
× ***mertonensis*** ♀H5 Widely available
- 'Summer King' CChe CDor ECtt ELan GJos IKil LSRN LSun MHol MWat NPri WFar
minor CPla
'Mont Rosa' **new** WRHF
obscura CCCN EAJP IMou SBrt SPlb SVen WHer WHrl
* - 'Dusky Maid' WFar WHlf
- 'Sunset' GJos
orientalis see *D. grandiflora*
§ ***parviflora*** Jacq. CRos CSam ECha ECtt ELan EPPr EPfP EWTr LCro LRHS MBNS MMuc NBro NChi SEND WArt WWtn
- 'Milk Chocolate' CAbb CDor CSpe ECtt ELan EMor EPfP GKev GMaP LRHS LSRN MHer NBir NEgg NHpl NLar NWad SCob SPtp
'Pink Chapel' ECtt
purpurea CHab EBou ELan ENfk EPfP GPoy GQue LCro LOPS LRHS LSun MHer MMuc MNHC NAln NMir NPri SCob SPlb SPoG WBrk WMoo WOut WSFF
- 'Alba' see *D. purpurea* f. *albiflora*
§ - f. ***albiflora*** Widely available
- - 'Anne Redetzky'[PBR] CSpe LRHS
- 'Apricot Delight' EBee
- 'Bare Necessities' CNat
- 'Berggold' **new** WRHF
- Camelot Series SHar SVic
- - 'Camelot Cream' CRos ELan EPfP LRHS SCob SWvt
- - 'Camelot Lavender' CRos ELan EPfP LRHS SWvt
- - 'Camelot Rose' CRos ELan EPfP LRHS SCob SWvt
- - 'Camelot White' ELan EPfP SCob
- 'Cream Carousel' (Carousel Series) **new** CRos EBee LRHS NRHS
- (Dalmatian Series) 'Dalmatian Crème' EPfP LRHS MAsh NRHS
- - 'Dalmatian Peach' CBod ELan EPfP MAsh MHer
- - 'Dalmatian Purple' CBod ELan EPfP LCro LOPS MAsh MHol
- - 'Dalmatian Rose' CBod ELan EPfP LCro LOPS LRHS MAsh MHol NRHS
- - 'Dalmatian White' CBod ELan EPfP LCro LOPS LRHS
- Excelsior Group CBcs CDor CMac CRos CSBt CTri ECtt EHrv EPfP GJos GMaP LCro LOPS LRHS MJak NHol NMir NRHS SCob SPer SPoG SRms SVic SWvt XLum
- - (Suttons; Unwins) ♀H7 ECtt MRav
- - white-flowered CTri
- Foxy Group CRos EPfP LRHS MJak MNHC NHic NRHS SPoG

	- - 'Foxy Apricot'	SWvt
	- Giant Spotted Group	CRos ECtt EPfP LRHS NRHS SPoG
	- (Gloxinioides Group) 'The Shirley' ♀H7	WMoo
§	- subsp. ***heywoodii***	WMoo
	- - 'Silver Fox'	CBod CRos MHol NDai NRHS WHil
	- 'Lavender Carousel' (Carousel Series) **new**	CRos LRHS NRHS
	- 'Orchid Carousel' (Carousel Series) **new**	CRos LRHS NRHS
	- 'Pam's Choice'	CChe CDor CExl CRos CSpe ECtt ELan EPPr EPfP LCro LOPS LRHS LSRN MWat NEgg NHol NLar NPri NRHS SCob SPer WBor WMoo
	- 'Pam's Split'	MHol SCob
	- 'Primrose Carousel' (Carousel Series)	NEgg NLar SCob
	- 'Purple Carousel' (Carousel Series) **new**	CRos LRHS NRHS
	- 'Serendipity'	CRos EPfP LRHS NRHS
	- 'Snow Thimble'	CDor CRos ELan EPfP LRHS LSun MHol NHic NLar NRHS STPC
§	- 'Sutton's Apricot' ♀H7	CBcs CDor CRos CSBt ECha ECtt EHrv ELan EPfP GMaP GQue LCro LOPS LRHS LSun MBel MRav NBir NGdn NLar NPri NRHS SCob SPer SPoG SWvt WCot WMoo XLum
	- 'White Carousel' (Carousel Series)	CRos LRHS NRHS
	'Red Skin'	NLar NWad
	sceptrum	CCCN CExl MGil SPlb SVen
	'Spice Island'	CBod CDor CRos EBee ECtt EShb LCro LEdu LOPS LRHS MHol MNrw NLar SCob SPad SPer STPC WCot WRHF WSpi
*	***stewartii***	EMor EWes GAbr MMrt NWad WMoo
	thapsi	ELan EPPr EPfP
	- 'Spanish Peaks'	CAbb WArt
	- white-flowered **new**	EPPr
	trojana	CFis ECtt GKev SCob WWtn
	- 'Helen of Troy'	SPtp WArt WHer WSpi
	× ***valinii*** 'Berry Canary' **new**	SPad SPoG
	- FOXLIGHT PLUM GOLD ('Takfoplgo') **new**	LCro LOPS
§	- Illumination Series	CRos LRHS NRHS SCob
§	- - 'Harkstead Apricot'	EBee EPfP ILea MJak NAst NDov NHpl SEle
	- - 'Harkstead Flame'PBR	CRos LRHS MCot MJak NHpl NRHS SPoG
	- - ILLUMINATION APRICOT	see *D.* × *valinii* (Illumination Series) 'Harkstead Apricot'
	- - ILLUMINATION CHERRY BRANDY	see *D.* × *valinii* (Illumination Series) ILLUMINATION RASPBERRY
	- - ILLUMINATION DARK PINK	CBod
	- - ILLUMINATION FLAME	see *D.* × *valinii* (Illumination Series) 'Harkstead Flame'
	- - ILLUMINATION PINK ('Tmdgfp001'PBR)	CAbb CDor EBee EPfP LBuc LCro LOPS MCot MHol MJak MNrw MSCN NHpl NLar SCob SPoG WCAu WCot
	- - ILLUMINATION RASPBERRY ('Tmdg1204'PBR)	CBod CRos EBee EPfP LBuc LRHS MHol MNHC NAst NDov NHpl NLar NRHS SCob
	viridiflora	CExl CSam CSpe ECtt GQue
	'Walberton's Goldcrest'	see *D.* GOLDCREST

dill see *Anethum graveolens*

Dionaea ✿ (*Droseraceae*)

muscipula	CHew EECP LCro LOPS SHmp SPlb WSSs WTyc
- 'Akai Ryu' ♀H3	SHmp WSSs
- 'All Green'	EECP
- 'B52'	EECP WSSs
- 'Big Mouth'	EECP
- 'Bimbo' **new**	EECP
- 'Bohemian Garnet'	EECP WSSs
- 'Coquillage' **new**	EECP
- 'Darwin'	WSSs
- (Dentate Traps Group) 'Dentate Traps'	WSSs
- 'Green Sawtooth' **new**	EECP
- 'Harmony' **new**	EECP
- 'Louchapates' **new**	EECP
- 'Mk1979'	WSSs
- 'Red Shark Teeth ' **new**	EECP
- 'Royal Red'	CHew WSSs
- 'Sawtooth'	EECP WSSs
- shark-toothed	EECP
- 'South West Giant' ♀H3	WSSs
- 'Spider'	EECP
- 'Tiger Fangs'	WSSs
- 'Trichterfulle' **new**	EECP

Dionysia (*Primulaceae*)

'Annielle'	EPot WAbe
aretioides ♀H4	EPot WAbe
- 'Alan Furness'	EPot
- 'Bevere'	EPot WAbe
bryoides	WAbe
'Charlson Emma'	EPot WAbe
'Charlson Jake'	WAbe
'Charlson Petite'	WAbe
'Charlson Pip'	WAbe
'Corona'	WAbe
curviflora	WAbe
'Eric Watson'	WAbe
'Ewesley Kappa'	WAbe
'Ewesley Theta'	WAbe
'Geist'	WAbe
janthina	WAbe
'Judith Bramley'	WAbe
'Lycaena'	WAbe
'Mike Bramley'	WAbe
'Monika'	WAbe
'Pascal'	WAbe
sarvestanica	WAbe
tapetodes	EPot WAbe
- 'Brimstone'	WAbe
- 'Peter Edwards'	WAbe
'Tess'	EPot WAbe
'Zdeněk Zvolánek'	WAbe

Dioon (*Zamiaceae*)

argenteum	CBrP
califanoi	CBrP
caputoi	CBrP
edule ♀H1b	CBrP SPlb
- var. ***angustifolium***	CBrP
merolae	CBrP
rzedowskii	CBrP
spinulosum	CBrP

Dioscorea (*Dioscoreaceae*)

araucana	CPla

deltoidea	CExl
japonica	CAgr LEdu
polystachya	CAgr CRHN LEdu
quinqueloba	WCru
villosa	LEdu

Diosma (*Rutaceae*)

ericoides L.	SWvt
hirsuta 'Silver Flame'	CBod
'Pink Fountain'	see *Coleonema pulchellum* 'Pink Fountain'
'Sunset Gold'	see *Coleonema* 'Sunset Gold'

Diosphaera (*Campanulaceae*)

asperuloides	see *Trachelium asperuloides*

Diospyros (*Ebenaceae*)

austroafricana	SPlb
glabra	SVen
* ***hyrcanum***	NLar
kaki (F)	CBcs CMCN ECrN IDee NLar SAko WCot
- 'Fuyu' (F)	CAgr
- 'Kostata' (F)	CAgr
- 'Mazelii' (F)	CAgr WPGP
- 'Rojo Brillante' (F)	SVic
lotus	CAgr CBcs CMCN EBee GBin LEdu NLar SPlb WMat
- FMWJ 13164	WCru
- PAB 10032	LEdu WPGP
- (f)	IDee LMaj
- 'Albert' (m)	CAgr
- 'Browny' (f/F)	CAgr
lycioides	CPbh SPlb
'Mount Goverla' (F)	CAgr
'Nikita's Gift' (F)	CAgr
'Nikita's Russian' (F)	CAgr
'Nikshoo' (F)	CAgr
ramulosa	SPlb
rhombifolia	NLar
'Russian Beauty' (F)	CAgr
'Russian Red' (F)	CAgr
virginiana (F)	CBcs CMCN NLar SPlb
- 'Morris Burton' (F)	CAgr
- 'Nc-10' (F)	CAgr

Diostea (*Verbenaceae*)

juncea	MGil

Dipelta (*Caprifoliaceae*)

floribunda ♀H5	CBcs CExl CJun CMCN CRos CTho ELan EPfP IArd IDee LRHS MBlu NLar SWvt WPGP
ventricosa	CBcs CExl CJun CRos ELan EPfP IArd LRHS MBlu NLar SBrt SPoG WPGP
yunnanensis	CAby CBcs CCCN CDul CExl CJun CKel CRos CTho EBee ELan EPfP IArd IMou LRHS MBNS NLar SPoG SWvt WPGP WPav

Diphylleia (*Berberidaceae*)

cymosa	CAby ECha GCal GEdr GKev LEdu MNrw MRav SPhx WCot WCru
grayi	GEdr LEdu WCru
sinensis	CExl WCru

Diplacus see *Mimulus*

Dipladenia see *Mandevilla*

Diplarrena (*Iridaceae*)

§ ***latifolia***	CNor GCal IBlr LRHS NCGa
moraea	CAby CElw CJun CMac CSpe CWCL EBee GAbr GCal IBlr IKil LEdu MBel WSHC
- ***minor***	IBlr
- 'Slieve Donard'	IBlr
- West Coast form	see *D. latifolia*

Diplopanax (*Cornaceae*)

stachyanthus B&SWJ 11803	WCru

Diplotaxis (*Brassicaceae*)

muralis	CLau EMor
tenuifolia	CAgr CLau ENfk EWhm MNHC SRms

Dipsacus (*Caprifoliaceae*)

asper PAB 8884	LEdu
§ ***fullonum***	CBod CHab EBou ENfk EPfP LOPS MHer MNHC NGrd NMir NPri SEND SRms WHer WSFF
inermis	CSam ECha NBid
japonicus HWJ 695	SPhx WCru
laciniatus	EBee
pilosus	CBgR NDov
pinnatifidus PAB 2845 new	LEdu
sativus	CWld NHic
strigosus	SPhx
sylvestris	see *D. fullonum*

Dipteracanthus see *Ruellia*

Dipteronia (*Sapindaceae*)

sinensis	CBcs CMCN MBlu

Disa (*Orchidaceae*)

aurata	NDav
Bride's Dream gx	NDav
Child Safety Transvaal gx	NDav
- 'Sonia'	NDav
Colette Cywes gx 'Blush'	NDav
Constantia gx	NDav
Diores gx	NDav
- 'Inca City'	NDav
- 'Inca Gold'	NDav
- 'Inca Princess'	NDav
- 'Inca Warrior'	NDav
Diorosa gx	NDav
Foam gx	NDav
- 'Zoe'	NDav
Glasgow Orchid Conference gx	NDav
Ivan Watson gx	NDav
Kalahari Sands gx	NDav
- 'Tina'	NDav
Kewbett gx	NDav
- 'Pink Gem'	NDav
Kewdior gx	NDav
Kewensis gx 'Alice'	NDav
- 'Ann'	NDav
- 'May'	NDav
- 'Milkmaid'	NDav
- 'Ruth'	NDav
Reheat gx	NDav
Riette gx	NDav
Robert Parkinson gx	NDav
Sealord gx	NDav
Tracey Parkinson gx	NDav

tripetaloides	NDav
Unidiorosa gx 'Tracey'	NDav
uniflora	NDav SPlb
- carmine-flowered	NDav
- pink-flowered	NDav
- red-flowered	NDav
Unifoam gx	NDav
- 'Firebird'	NDav
Unilangley gx	NDav
Watsonii gx 'Bramley'	NDav
- 'Candy'	NDav
- 'Don'	NDav
- 'Sandra'	NDav

Disanthus (*Hamamelidaceae*)

cercidifolius ♀H5	CBcs CDul CMCN CMac CRos EPfP GBin GKin IArd IMou LRHS MBlu MPkF NLar SPoG WHor WMat WPGP
- 'Ena-nishiki' (v)	MBlu NLar WPGP

Discaria (*Rhamnaceae*)

chacaye	WPav

Dischidia (*Apocynaceae*)

ruscifolia new	EShb

Diselma (*Cupressaceae*)

archeri	CAco
- 'Read Dwarf'	CKen

Disepalum (*Annonaceae*)

petelotii B&SWJ 11690	WCru
- FMWJ 13375	WCru

Disporopsis (*Asparagaceae*)

sp.	WBor
B&SWJ 229 from Taiwan	WCru
B&SWJ 1864 from Taiwan	WCru
aspersa	CAvo CBro EPPr EWld GKev ITim LEdu MAvo MNrw NBir WCru WPGP
- tall	CBct CExl WCru
bodinieri FMWJ 13457 new	WCru
- KWJ 12277	WCru
fuscopicta	CAby CBct EHrv EPPr LEdu MPie WCru
longifolia	IMou
- B&SWJ 5284	WCru
luzoniensis	IMou
- B&SWJ 3891	CBct CExl EPPr ESwi GEdr LEdu WCru
'Min Shan'	CExl ELon
* ***nova***	EPPr MAvo
§ ***pernyi***	Widely available
- B&SWJ 1864	EPPr GEdr
- 'Bill Baker'	CBct EBee EPPr LEdu MAvo WSHC
aff. ***pernyi***	WHil
'Shina-no-tsuki'	see *Disporum bodinieri* 'Shina-no-tsuki'
taiwanensis	EBee IMou LEdu
- B&SWJ 3388	CBct GEdr WCru
undulata	CBct CSpe EMor EPPr ILea IMou LEdu MAvo NBid SHar WCru WPGP

Disporum (*Colchicaceae*)

austrosinense	IMou
bodinieri	CBct CExl EMor EPfP
- DJHC 765	WCru
- KWJ 12277	WCru
§ - 'Shina-no-tsuki' (v)	IPot
cantoniense	CBct IMou LEdu WCru WFar
- B&L 12512	CExl
- B&SWJ 1424	WCru
- B&SWJ 9715	WCru
- DJHC 98485	LEdu WPGP
- PAB 8339	LEdu
I - 'Aureovariegata'	CBct EPfP LEdu WCot
- 'Blueberry Bere'	LEdu
- var. ***cantoniense*** f. ***brunneum*** B&SWJ 5290	WCru
- 'Leigong'	WPGP
- var. ***multiflorum*** B&SWJ 11252	WCru
- - B&SWJ 11291	WCru
- var. ***sikkimense*** B&SWJ 2337	WCru
- - B&SWJ 2358	LEdu WCru
- - PAB 13.1711	LEdu
- var. ***y-tiense*** HWJ 1045	WCru
hookeri	see *Prosartes hookeri*
kawakamii B&SWJ 350	WCru
- RWJ 10103	CBct WCru
lanuginosum	see *Prosartes lanuginosa*
leschenaultianum B&SWJ 9484	WCru
- B&SWJ 9505	WCru
leucanthum	EBee ECha WCru
- B&SWJ 2389	WCru
longistylum	CBcs EBee EHrv LEdu
- B&SWJ 2859	WCru
- BWJ 8128	WCru
- L 1564	CBct ESwi LEdu WCru
- 'Green Giant'	CBct CExl EBee EPfP GEdr IDee ILea LEdu LPla LRHS MAvo MBel MSCN NLar WFar WSHC
- 'Night Heron' ♀H6	CBct CDor CExl CRos IMou LEdu LPla LRHS MAvo NRHS SHar WCot WFar
aff. ***longistylum*** NJM 11.011	WPGP
lutescens	EBee EPot WCru
maculatum	see *Prosartes maculata*
megalanthum	CBct CExl EMor LEdu WCru WPGP
- CD&R 2412B	CExl EBee
menziesii	see *Prosartes smithii*
nantouense	EBee
- B&SWJ 359	LEdu WCru
- B&SWJ 6812	WCru
oreganum	see *Prosartes hookeri* var. *oregana*
sessile	EBee LEdu WCru
- B&SWJ 2824	WCru
I - 'Aureovariegatum' (v)	WCru
- 'Awa-no-tsuki' (v)	GEdr
- 'Ginsekai'	GEdr
- 'Kinga' (v)	LEdu
- f. ***macrophyllum***	IMou
- - B&SWJ 4316	WCru
- 'Snow Stream' (v)	GEdr WFar
- 'Variegatum' (v)	CAby CDor CExl CNor CRos EBee ECha ELan ELon EMor EPPr EPfP GCal IMou LEdu LRHS MNrw NHpl NLar NQui NRHS SMad SPhx WCru WFar WPGP WSHC
- var. ***yakushimense***	LEdu
shimadae B&SWJ 399	WCru
smilacinum	EHrv NLar WCru
- B&SWJ 713	CBct WCru
* - 'Aureovariegatum' (v)	EPot LEdu WCru
- pink-flowered	CBct LEdu WCot WCru WSHC

- 'Roseum' new	GKev IPot
smithii	see *Prosartes smithii*
taiwanense	CAvo
- B&SWJ 1513	WCru
- B&SWJ 2018	WCru
tonkinense B&SWJ 11672	WCru
- B&SWJ 11814	WCru
- HWJ 882	WCru
trabeculatum	CBct CDor WCru
- 'Nakafu'	EBee IMou WCru
trachycarpum	see *Prosartes trachycarpa*
uniflorum	CAby CBct CBod CRos EHrv EMor EPfP EUJe GKev LEdu LRHS MHol MMrt MNrw NBid NRHS SMad WHlf WSHC
- B&SWJ 651	CBct LEdu WCru
- B&SWJ 872	WCru
- B&SWJ 4100	WCru
- MSF 800	LEdu
viridescens	CBct EBee EHrv EMor EPPr IMou LEdu WCru WPnP
- B&SWJ 4598	WCru

Distictis (*Bignoniaceae*)

buccinatoria	CHll

Distyliopsis (*Hamamelidaceae*)

tutcheri	CJun

Distylium (*Hamamelidaceae*)

myricoides	NLar
racemosum	CCCN CMac EBee EPfP MBlu NLar SSta WSHC

Dittrichia (*Asteraceae*)

viscosa	WCot

Diuranthera see *Chlorophytum*

Dizygotheca see *Schefflera*

Dodecatheon (*Primulaceae*)

alpinum	GKev NHar
- subsp. ***alpinum***	EBee
amethystinum	GKev
'Aphrodite' PBR	ECtt MHol NLar WFar
austrofrigidum	GEdr SBrt
clevelandii	GEdr GKev WAbe
- subsp. ***insulare***	LLHF
- subsp. ***patulum***	CRos LRHS NRHS
'Comet' new	CBor
conjugens	GKev LLHF XEll
cusickii	see *D. pulchellum* subsp. *cusickii*
dentatum ♀H5	CPBP EBee GEdr LEdu NHar SBrt WAbe WFar
- subsp. ***dentatum***	GKev
- subsp. ***utahense***	GEdr NHar
frigidum	GEdr GKev WAbe
§ ***jeffreyi***	CBod CRos ECtt EPPr EPfP GAbr GEdr GKev LEdu LRHS MBNS MNrw NAln NLar NRHS NSum WAbe WFar
- subsp. ***pygmaeum***	GKev
- 'Rotlicht'	CRos LRHS NRHS
§ ***meadia*** ♀H5	Widely available
- from Cedar County, USA	WAbe
- f. ***album*** ♀H5	CBro CRos ELan EMor EPot GKev LAma LEdu LRHS NAln NHol NHpl NRHS NSum SPer SWvt WFar WPnP WSpi WTyc
- 'Aphrodite'	EPfP WFar
- 'Goliath'	GAbr GWyn NSum
- membranaceous	WAbe
- 'Queen Victoria'	LEdu NLar WFar
- red shades	NSum
'Meteor' new	CBor
pauciflorum misapplied	see *D. pulchellum*
pauciflorum (Dur.) E. Greene	see *D. meadia*
poeticum	SPlb
§ ***pulchellum*** ♀H5	CRos EBee GEdr GKev LLWG LRHS MNrw NRHS NRya WArt WIce
- ***album***	GKev
§ - subsp. ***cusickii***	LEdu
- subsp. ***pulchellum***	GKev
- - 'Red Wings'	CBor CRos ELan ELon EPot GWyn LLHF LRHS NHpl NLar NRHS SPad WTyc
- ***radicatum***	see *D. pulchellum*
- 'Sooke Variety'	WAbe
radicatum	see *D. pulchellum*
tetrandrum	see *D. jeffreyi*

Dodonaea (*Sapindaceae*)

viscosa	SPlb
- 'Purpurea'	CBcs CBod CCht CExl CTsd EBee EUJe LRHS MGil SPoG SVen
- 'Red Wings' (f)	SRkn

Doellingeria (*Asteraceae*)

scabra	see *Aster scaber*
umbellata	CBre CKno EBee ECha EPPr GQue LEdu MMuc MTis NBir NDov NLar WCot WOld WSpi
- 'Weisser Schirm'	MNrw

Dolichandra (*Bignoniaceae*)

§ ***unguis-cati*** ♀H3	CCCN CRHN EShb

Dombeya (*Malvaceae*)

wallichii	CCCN

Dondia see *Hacquetia*

Doodia ✿ (*Blechnaceae*)

aspera	CAby CLAP NBro
- 'Rough Ruby' new	CBdn EUJe
§ ***caudata***	NBro
media	CAbb CAby CBct CLAP CRos EBee EShb EUJe ISha LEdu LLWG LRHS NBro NRHS SPlb WCot
squarrosa	see *D. caudata*

Doronicum (*Asteraceae*)

austriacum	NBid
caucasicum	see *D. orientale*
§ ***columnae***	CBcs GKev
cordatum	see *D. columnae*
§ × ***excelsum*** 'Harpur Crewe'	EBee LEdu MRav NPer SHar
'Finesse'	CRos EPfP GCal GJos LRHS NRHS SRms
'Little Leo'	CBod ELan EMor EPfP GJos GMaP LSRN NHic NLar NRHS SCob SPoG SRms WFar
§ ***orientale***	EPfP GJos MBel MMuc NPri SEND SPoG
- 'Leonardo'	CRos LRHS NGrd NRHS
- 'Magnificum'	CRos CSBt EBee EMor EPfP GMaP LRHS MBNS NAln NGBl NHic NRHS SPoG SRms WCAu WFar

pardalianches	CFis CMea GAbr GCal GJos WBrk WHal WRHF
- 'Goldstrauss'	EBee
plantagineum	MMuc
- 'Excelsum'	see *D.* × *excelsum* 'Harpur Crewe'

Doryanthes (*Doryanthaceae*)

palmeri	CBrP CTsd

Dorycnium see *Lotus*

Douglasia see *Androsace*

vitaliana	see *Vitaliana primuliflora*

Dovyalis (*Salicaceae*)

caffra (F)	XBlo

Doxantha see *Macfadyena*

Draba (*Brassicaceae*)

acaulis	WAbe
aizoides	CRos EBou GJos LRHS NRHS SPlb SRms
aizoon	see *D. lasiocarpa*
§ ***aspera***	GJos
athoa	ITim
aurea var. ***leiocarpa***	CBor
bertolonii Boiss.	see *D. loeseleurii*
bertolonii Nyman	see *D. aspera*
breweri	GJos
bruniifolia	NSla
subsp. ***heterocoma*** var. ***heterocoma***	
- subsp. ***olympica***	GJos
'Buttermilk'	WAbe
compacta	see *D. lasiocarpa* Compacta Group
* ***condensata***	GJos
cretica	GJos
cusickii	GKev NAln
cuspidata	GJos
dedeana	CPBP EPot GJos WAbe
gilliesii	GJos
'John Saxton'	EPot WAbe
kotschyi	SPlb
§ ***lasiocarpa***	GJos XLum
§ - Compacta Group	SIgm
§ ***loeseleurii***	GJos
longisiliqua ♀H5	EPot LLHF WAbe
mollissima	EPot SPlb WAbe
- 'Göteborg'	EPot
nivalis	GJos SPlb
norvegica	GJos ITim
oligosperma	EDAr GJos
ossetica	WAbe
parnassica	GJos
paysonii	SIgm
polytricha	NSla
rigida var. ***bryoides*** compact	EPot WAbe
* - var. ***imbricata***	GCrg NRHS NSla
rosularis	EDAr EPot GJos WAbe
scardica	see *D. lasiocarpa*
sphaeroides	GJos NSla SPlb
yunnanensis	WAbe

Dracaena ✿ (*Asparagaceae*)

aletriformis new	XBlo
cochinchinensis	SPlb
draco ♀H1c	CCCN CMCN EShb SPlb WCot XBlo
elliptica	EShb
fragrans	EUJe
- (Compacta Group) 'Compacta'	XBlo
- Deremensis Group	XBlo
- - 'J.A.Truffaut'	XBlo
- - 'Lemon Lime' (v) ♀H1b	LCro LOPS
- - 'Souvenir d'August de Schrijver' (v)	XBlo
- 'Janet Craig'	LCro LOPS
indivisa	see *Cordyline indivisa*
'Lemon Lime Tips'	XBlo
marginata (v) ♀H1b	LCro LOPS XBlo
- 'Tricolor' (v) ♀H1b	XBlo

Dracocephalum (*Lamiaceae*)

argunense	CAby GBin SPhx SRms
- 'Blue Carpet'	NLar
- 'Fuji Blue'	CExl EDAr EWes NHic SPoG
- 'Fuji White'	CExl SPhx
botryoides	CPBP EDAr EPot MMuc SPhx
calophyllum	GKev
forrestii	GKev
grandiflorum	CPla SPhx WCot XLum
mairei	see *D. renatii*
moldavica	SPhx
nutans	SPhx
origanoides new	CPBP
peregrinum 'Blue Dragon'	SPhx
prattii	see *Nepeta prattii*
§ ***renatii***	SPhx
rupestre	CSpe NSti SPhx
ruyschiana	CFis ELan MMrt SPhx XLum
sibiricum	see *Nepeta sibirica*
* ***tataricum***	CRos LRHS NRHS
virginicum	see *Physostegia virginiana*

Dracophyllum (*Ericaceae*)

prostratum	EPot

Dracunculus (*Araceae*)

canariensis	CBod WCot
muscivorus	see *Helicodiceros muscivorus*
§ ***vulgaris***	CAby CRos EBee EPfP EPot ESwi GKev LRHS MBNS NRHS SEND SPlb WCot WHil
- white-flowered	WCot

Dregea (*Apocynaceae*)

sinensis	CBcs CCCN CHll CKel CRHN CRos EBee ECre ELan EPfP EShb EWes LRHS MRav SEND SPoG SWvt WHil WPGP WSHC
- 'Brockhill Silver'	CKel EPfP LRHS SPoG SWvt
- 'Variegata' (v)	EShb EWes

Drepanostachyum (*Poaceae*)

falconeri J.J.N. Campbell. ex D. McClintock	see *Himalayacalamus falconeri* 'Damarapa'
hookerianum	see *Himalayacalamus hookerianus*
§ ***khasianum***	CExl

Drimiopsis (*Asparagaceae*)

maculata	EShb GKev

Drimys (*Winteraceae*)

andina	CExl MGil MMuc
aromatica	see *Tasmannia lanceolata*

colorata	see *Pseudowintera colorata*
granadensis	WCru
var. ***grandiflora*** B&SWJ 10777	
winteri ♀H4	Widely available
§ - var. ***chilensis***	CBcs CExl CKel EPfP LRHS WCru WPGP
- Latifolia Group	see *D. winteri* var. *chilensis*
- var. ***winteri***	SRms

Drosanthemum (*Aizoaceae*)

eburneum new	SSim
floribundum	SSim
hispidum	CRos ELan EPot LRHS MAsh NRHS SPlb SPoG SSim

Drosera ✿ (*Droseraceae*)

admirabilis	CHew
aliciae ♀H3	CHew EECP SHmp
ascendens	CHew
binata	CHew EECP SHmp
§ - subsp. ***dichotoma*** ♀H3	CHew SHmp
capensis	CHew LCro LOPS SHmp SPlb
- 'Albino' ♀H3	CHew EECP SHmp
dichotoma	see *D. binata* subsp. *dichotoma*
dichrosepala	EECP
filiformis var. ***filiformis***	CHew EECP SHmp SPlb
madagascariensis	SHmp
nidiformis	CHew
rotundifolia	SHmp
scorpioides	EECP SHmp
slackii ♀H3	CHew
spatulata	SHmp

Dryandra (*Proteaceae*)

formosa	CKel CPbh SPlb
polycephala new	CKel
praemorsa	CKel
quercifolia	SPlb

Dryas (*Rosaceae*)

drummondii	GAbr LLHF
§ ***integrifolia***	WAbe
- 'Greenland Green'	WAbe
octopetala ♀H7	CMea CPla CRos GKev LRHS NChi NRHS SPoG SRms SWvt WAbe
- subsp. ***hookeriana***	LLHF
§ - 'Minor' ♀H7	EPot GCrg SIgm WAbe
× ***suendermannii*** ♀H7	EPot GCrg GMaP NHar NSla SBch WAbe
tenella misapplied	see *D. octopetala* 'Minor'
tenella Pursh	see *D. integrifolia*

Drynaria (*Polypodiaceae*)

baronii	WCot

Dryopteris ✿ (*Dryopteridaceae*)

aemula	CBdn EFer
§ ***affinis*** ♀H5	CBdn CDor CKel CLAP CMac CRos CWCL ECha EMor EPfP ERod GMaP LBuc LRHS MCot MGos MMuc NRHS SCob SPer SPoG SRms WCot WFib WShi WSpi XLum
- 'Angustata Crispa'	EBee SRms
- subsp. ***cambrensis***	ISha
- - 'Insubrica'	EFer
- 'Congesta'	CKel
- 'Congesta Cristata'	CWCL ECtt EFer GMaP SRot
- Crispa Group	CBdn CBod CLAP CRos EAJP EMor EPfP LRHS NRHS SCob
§ - 'Crispa Gracilis' ♀H5	CAby CKel CLAP CRos ELan ERod ISha LRHS NBir NEgg NHol NLar NRHS
* - 'Crispa Gracilis Congesta'	CKel EMor LLWG MRav NGdn NWad WCot WFib
§ - 'Cristata' ♀H5	Widely available
- 'Cristata Angustata' ♀H5	CKel CLAP EFer ELan EMor EPfP LLWG NBid NBro NGdn NHol WFib WMoo
- 'Cristata Beeches' new	EBee
- 'Cristata The King'	see *D. affinis* 'Cristata'
- 'Grandiceps Askew'	WFib
- 'Pinderi'	CAby CBdn CLAP EBee EMor EPfP EUJe GBin ISha LLWG LPla LSun MMuc MPie MPnt NCou NLar NRHS SCob WCot WSpi
- Polydactyla Group	SPlb
- - 'Polydactyla Dadds'	CBdn CLAP EBee EMor LLHF NLar
- - 'Polydactyla Mapplebeck' ♀H5	CLAP NBid WFib
- 'Revolvens'	EFer
atrata misapplied	see *D. cycadina*
atrata (Wall. ex Kunze) Ching	CAby CDTJ CRos CWCL ELan LLWG LRHS NEgg NLar NRHS SPoG XLum
× ***australis***	CBdn CLAP EBee ISha
austriaca	see *D. dilatata*
bissetiana	ISha
buschiana	EBee EMor MRav NLar WCot
carthusiana	CKel EBee EFer NLar WSpi XLum
- 'Cristata'	EFer
celsa	EBee ISha
championii	CCCN CLAP CRos EBee EMor ISha LRHS NBro NLar NRHS SRot
aff. ***chrysocoma***	CBdn
clintoniana	CKel CRos EBee ECtt EFer GBin GQue ITim LLWG LPla LRHS MPie NRHS
× ***complexa***	CLAP ISha
- 'Stablerae' ♀H7	CLAP EFer WFib
- 'Stablerae' crisped ♀H7	WFib
coreanomontana	EMor NLar
crassirhizoma ♀H6	CBod CCCN CKel CLAP CRos EBee ECtt EMor EPfP EUJe GAbr GBin ISha LEdu LPla LRHS LSun MMuc NLar NRHS SMad SPoG WCot WPtf WRHF WSpi
cristata	CLAP CWCL EBee EPfP WMoo XLum
§ ***cycadina*** ♀H4	CBcs CBdn CLAP CRos EBee EFer ELan EMor ERod EShb EUJe GBin ISha LEdu LRHS MGos NBid NBir NRHS SCob SPlb SPtp WCot WFib WMoo
§ ***dilatata*** ♀H6	CLAP CRos ECha EFer ELan EPfP ERod LRHS MMuc MRav NRHS WFib WHal WShi
- 'Crispa Whiteside' ♀H6	CAby CBdn CDor CLAP CRos CWCL EBee EFer ELan EMor EPfP ERod EShb EUJe GBin LRHS MRav NBro NEgg NLar NRHS SPlb SPoG WFib WMoo
- 'Cristata'	LSun
- 'Grandiceps'	CMac EFer WFib
- 'Jimmy Dyce'	CLAP CRos EBee GBin ISha LEdu LRHS NRHS
I - 'Lepidota Crispa'	NRHS
- 'Lepidota Crispa Cristata'	CLAP EBee SRot
- 'Lepidota Cristata' ♀H6	CRos CWCL ELan EMOT EMor ERod GKev NBro WFib WMoo

*	- 'Recurvata'	CLAP NLar
	erythrosora ♀H4	Widely available
	- from Guizhou, China	WPGP
	- 'Brilliance' ♀H5	CAby CBct CBdn CCCN CLAP CRos EBee ECtt EUJe GQue ISha LEdu LLWG LPla LRHS LSun MAvo MHol MPie NCou NRHS WCot WRHF
	- var. ***koidzumiana***	CLAP CRos ISha LEdu LRHS NRHS WCot
	- var. ***prolifica***	CBdn CBod CKel CLAP CRos EBee ELan EMor EPfP EWTr GBin GMaP ISha LEdu LRHS MGos NBir NEgg NLar NRHS SPoG SRot WFar WFib
	- 'Radiance'	ISha
	filix-mas ♀H7	CKel CRos CSBt CTri CWCL ECha ELan EMor EPfP ERod GBin GKev GMaP ILea LCro LEdu LOPS LRHS LSun MCot MMuc NHol NRHS SCob SEND SPer WFib WSFF WShi XLum
	- 'Barnesii'	CKel CLAP CRos CWCL EFer ELan EMOT ERod EUJe ISha LRHS NEgg NLar NRHS SEND SPlb
	- 'Crispa'	CRos EPfP LEdu LRHS MPnt NRHS WFib
	- 'Crispa Congesta'	see *D. affinis* 'Crispa Gracilis'
	- 'Crispa Cristata' ♀H7	CBod CChe CKel CLAP CRos CWCL EBee ECtt EFer ELan EPfP ERod EUJe GBin GMaP GWyn IKil LLWG LRHS NBid NBir NBro NRHS SCob SPoG WFib XLum
	- 'Crispatissima'	EBee
	- 'Cristata' ♀H7	CLAP EBee ECtt EFer ELan EMor LCro LLWG LOPS MJak NBro SEND WMoo
	- Cristata Group	EFer
*	- - 'Cristata Grandiceps'	EFer
	- - 'Cristata Jackson'	SPlb
	- - 'Cristata Martindale'	CLAP EBee NBid WFib
	- - 'Fred Jackson'	WFib
	- 'Depauperata'	CLAP
	- 'Furcans'	CRos EBee ECtt ELan LRHS NRHS WMoo
	- 'Grandiceps Wills' ♀H7	NBid WFib
	- 'Linearis'	CRos EFer ELan ISha LRHS MCot MGos NRHS WFib
	- 'Linearis Polydactyla' ♀H7	Widely available
	- 'Parsley'	CLAP EBee ISha
*	- Polydactyla Group	ECha MRav NEgg SCob
I	- 'Revolvens'	WFib
	formosana	CBdn
	goldieana	CBdn CDTJ CLAP CRos EBee ECha ECtt EFer ELan EMOT EMor GMaP ISha LLWG LRHS NBid NBir NEgg NLar NRHS SRot WFar WFib WMoo WPnP WSpi XLum
	hirtipes misapplied	see *D. cycadina*
	intermedia	EBee ISha
	kuratae new	CBdn NBro WPGP
	labordei	CLAP CRos EBee GBin ISha LRHS NRHS
	lacera	ISha
	lepidopoda	CAby CBcs CBdn CDor CLAP CRos ECtt EMor EUJe GBin LEdu LPla LRHS MPie NBro NRHS SPoG WCot WPtf WRHF WSpi
	ludoviciana	CRos ISha LRHS NLar NRHS WSpi
	marginalis	CDTJ CKel CRos EMOT EMor LRHS NLar NRHS SCob WMoo
	namegatae new	WCot
	oreades	WCot
	pseudofilix-mas	ISha
	pseudomas	see *D. affinis*
	pulcherrima	CLAP CRos LRHS NRHS
	pycnopteroides	CLAP
	× ***remota***	CLAP EBee EFer ISha
	× ***separabilis***	ISha
	sieboldii ♀H6	Widely available
	stewartii	CAby CBdn CLAP EMor LLHF MJak NBro
	subarborea	EBee
	submontana new	CRos LRHS NRHS
	tokyoensis ♀H6	CDTJ CLAP CRos ISha LRHS NLar NRHS WSpi
	uniformis	CLAP EFer
	wallichiana ♀H5	Widely available
	- from Yunnan, China	GCal

Duchesnea (*Rosaceae*)

	chrysantha	see *D. indica*
§	***indica***	GJos MRav SEND WMoo WOut XLum
§	- 'Harlequin' (v)	CExl
	- 'Tutti Frutti' new	NHic
	- 'Variegata'	see *D. indica* 'Harlequin'

Dudleya (*Crassulaceae*)

	calcicola	SPlb
	cymosa	SPlb
	- subsp. ***cymosa***	SIgm
	lanceolata	SIgm SPlb

Dugaldia (*Asteraceae*)

	hoopesii	see *Hymenoxys hoopesii*

Dulichium (*Cyperaceae*)

	arundinaceum	LLWG
	- 'Tigress'	LLWG

Dunalia (*Solanaceae*)

	australis	see *Iochroma australe*

Duranta (*Verbenaceae*)

§	***erecta***	CCCN CHll
§	- 'Geisha Girl'	CCCN EShb
	- 'Sapphire Swirl'	see *D. erecta* 'Geisha Girl'
	- 'Variegata' (v)	CCCN
	- white-flowered	SVen
	plumieri	see *D. erecta*
	repens	see *D. erecta*
	serratifolia	CCCN

Duvernoia see *Justicia*

Dyckia (*Bromeliaceae*)

	brevifolia	WCot
	'Burgundy Ice'	WCot
	'Cherry Coke'	WCot
	floribunda new	EShb
	frigida	WCot WGrn
	goehringii	WCot
	jonesiana	WCot
	leptostachya	SEND SPlb WCot WGrn
	'Morris Hobbs'	WCot
	remotiflora	SChr
	velascana	WCot

Dypsis (*Arecaceae*)

§	***decaryi***	CCCN SPlb XBlo
	lutescens ♀H1a	XBlo

Dysosma see *Podophyllum*

Dystaenia (*Apiaceae*)

	takesimana new	EBee LEdu

E

Ecballium (*Cucurbitaceae*)

	elaterium	CDTJ LEdu WCot WPGP
	- 'Lahij'	WPGP

Eccremocarpus (*Bignoniaceae*)

	ruber	see *E. scaber* 'Ruber'
	scaber	CBcs CKel CWCL ELan EShb GKev NPer SPoG
	- 'Aureus'	GKev
	- cream-flowered	NLar
	- red-flowered	CWCL NLar
§	- 'Ruber'	GKev NAln
	- 'Tangerine'	CSpe
	- Tresco Series	GKev NAln

Echeandia (*Asparagaceae*)

	formosa B&SWJ 9147	WCru

Echeveria ✿ (*Crassulaceae*)

	sp.	LCro LOPS
	affinis	CBod CDTJ MHer SRot
	agavoides ♀H2	CDTJ MRav
	- 'Ebony'	WCot
	- 'Lipstick'	WCot
	- 'Red Edge' new	SSim
	albicans	SPlb
	alpina	see *E. secunda*
	ballsii	WCot
	bicolor B&SWJ 14388	WCru
*	'Black Knight'	EUJe MCot SSim
*	'Black Prince'	CDTJ ELan LCro LOPS NPer SPlb SRot WCot
	'Blue Waves'	WCot
*	***cana***	CBod CDTJ NCft SRot SSim
	cante ♀H2	SPlb
	coccinea	ELan
	'Corymbosa'	WCot
	'Curly Locks'	ECtt WCot WGrn
	cuspidata* × *setosa var. ***ciliata***	SSim
	derenbergii ♀H2	MHCG
	× ***derosa***	CDTJ
	'Duchess of Nuremberg'	CBod EUJe SPlb SRot SSim
	'Easter Bonnet' new	SSim
	elegans ♀H2	CDTJ CKel EPfP EUJe LSun NCft NWad SEND SPlb SSim
	'Ghost Buster'	WPGP
*	× ***gilva*** 'Red'	MHol WCot
	glauca Baker	see *E. secunda* var. *glauca*
	'Imbricata'	CBod
	lilacina ♀H2	NCft SPlb SRot SSim
	'Mahogany'	WCot WGrn
	'Mauna Loa'	WGrn
	maxonii B&SWJ 10396	WCru
	minima ♀H2	SPlb
	montana B&SWJ 10277	WCru
	nodulosa	WCot
	- 'Nicolas Bravo' new	SSim
	peacockii	MHer SPlb
	'Perle von Nürnberg' ♀H2	CAbb CCBP EShb SMad
	prolifica	SPlb
	pulidonis ♀H2	MHer SSim
	pulvinata ♀H2	MHCG
I	- 'Rubra'	SPlb
	purpusorum	SPlb
	quitensis B&SWJ 14393 new	WCru
	rosea ♀H2	MHer SSim WCot
	runyonii 'Topsy Turvy' ♀H2	CDTJ EUJe MHer SRot SSim WCot
§	***secunda***	CAbb EUJe SPlb
§	- var. ***glauca***	CDTJ ELan EShb GAbr NCft SEND WPGP
	- - 'Compton Carousel' ♀H2	SSim WCot
*	- - 'Gigantea'	NPer
	'Set-Oliver' × ***setosa***	WCot
	setosa ♀H2	CDTJ NCft
	- var. ***ciliata***	EShb
	shaviana ♀H2	CBod CDTJ EUJe SPlb SRot SSim WCot
	subsessilis	WCot
	'Violet Queen'	EShb

Echeveria × *Sedum* see × *Sedeveria*

Echinacea (*Asteraceae*)

	sp.	CRos
	'12th of July'	EBee
§	'Adam Saul'	CRos LRHS NRHS
§	'After Midnight'PBR (Big Sky Series)	EBee ECtt
	'Aloha'PBR	EMor LRHS NLar NRHS SPoG WCAu
	'Amazing Dream'PBR	CAbb CWGN EBee ECtt LCro LOPS LRHS NRHS
	angustifolia	EMor ENfk EPfP GPoy LRHS SPhx
§	'Art's Pride'PBR	MJak SCob
	'Big Kahuna'PBR	CAbb CWGN EBee ECtt IPot LRHS SCob SPad
	'Buttercream'	EBee NCGa
	'Butterfly Kisses'PBR (d)	CPla EBee LCro LOPS
	'Caribbean Green'	EBee
	'Cherry Fluff' (Cone-fections Series) (d) new	CWGN
	CHEYENNE SPIRIT (mixed)	CDor EAJP ELan EMor LEdu LPla MHol SPhx WFar WTor
	'Chiquita'PBR (Prairie Pixie Series)	CKno CRos EBee EMor LRHS NRHS SPoG
	'Cinnamon Candy' new	EBee
	'Cinnamon Cupcake'PBR new	EBee SPoG
	'Cleopatra'PBR	CWGN EBee EMor NCGa NLar SPoG WCot
	'Colorburst Orange' (Colorburst Series) (d)	CWGN
	'Coral Reef'PBR	ECtt
	'Coupe Soleil' (d)	EBee
	'Cranberry Cupcake'PBR (d)	EBee ECtt
	CRAZY PINK	see *E.* 'Adam Saul'
	CRAZY WHITE	see *E.* 'Noam Saul'
	'Daydream'PBR	CWGN EBee ECtt WSpi
	DELICIOUS CANDY ('Noortdeli')	CWGN WCot
	(Dixie Series) 'Dixie Belle' new	CAbb
	- 'Dixie Scarlet'PBR new	CAbb
	(Double Scoop Series) DOUBLE SCOOP BUBBLEGUM ('Balscblum'PBR) (d)	EBee MHol

Name	Suppliers
- DOUBLE SCOOP LEMON CREME ('Balsclemc') (d)	MHol
- DOUBLE SCOOP MANDARIN ('Balscandin') (d) **new**	EBee
- DOUBLE SCOOP ORANGEBERRY ('Balscoberr'PBR) (d)	EBee
- DOUBLE SCOOP RASPBERRY ('Balsceras'PBR) (d)	EBee MHol
'Eccentric'PBR (d)	CWGN EWTr LRHS MSCN SMad WTor
'Elegance'PBR (Supreme Series) (d)	EBee
'Emily Saul'	see *E.*'After Midnight'
'Evan Saul'	see *E.*'Sundown'
EVENING GLOW ('Eglow'PBR)	CWGN EBee EUJe WSpi WWtn
'Ferris Wheel' (Carnival Series)	CWCL SCob WSpi
'Flame Thrower'PBR	CWGN ECtt EWTr LCro LOPS SCob
'Fourth of July'PBR **new**	CRos NRHS
'Funky Yellow' **new**	WCot
'Gemini Pink'	CRos LRHS NRHS
'Glowing Dream'	EUJe LPla
'Golden Skipper'	CRos ECtt LRHS MAvo NCGa NRHS
'Green Envy'PBR	CBcs CRos CWGN EBee ECtt ELan ELon EMor EPfP GMaP LCro LOPS LRHS MBNS MBel MNrw NLar NRHS SCob SMad WTor
'Greenline'PBR	EBee ECtt LEdu
'Guava Ice'PBR	CDor CWCL EBee EMor LLHF WSpi
§ 'Harvest Moon'PBR (Big Sky Series)	CRos EBee ECtt EPfP LCro LOPS LRHS NRHS SCob SWvt
'Heavenly Dream'PBR	ECtt
'Honeydew'PBR **new**	EBee NCGa
'Hot Lava'PBR	CWGN EBee ECtt EWTr LCro LRHS NRHS
'Hot Papaya'PBR (d)	CWCL CWGN ECtt ELan EMor EUJe IPot LCro LLHF LOPS NAln SCob SMad SPoG SWvt
'Hot Summer'PBR	CBcs CRos CWCL CWGN EBee LEdu LRHS NRHS SCob SGbt
'Indian Summer'	EBee
'Irresistible'PBR (d)	CRos CWGN EBee LCro LOPS LRHS NRHS
'Julia'PBR	ECtt EMor
'Jupiter' (Big Sky Series)	ECtt SCob
'Katie Saul'	see *E.*'Summer Sky'
'Leilani'PBR	CAbb MMrt WCAu
'Mac 'n' Cheese'PBR	EBee LRHS SCob
'Mama Mia'PBR	CAbb CWGN EBee ECtt LCro LOPS LRHS SGbt
MANGO MEADOWBRITE ('CBG Cone3')	CRos EPfP LRHS NRHS
'Marmalade'PBR	CBcs CDor CWCL CWGN EBee EMor EUJe LLHF SCob SPad SPoG WCAu
'Matthew Saul'	see *E.*'Harvest Moon'
'Maui Sunshine'PBR	CAbb EBee ECtt NHpl NLar
'Meditation'PBR	EBee WCot
'Meteor Red'PBR (Meteor Series)	CPla CRos ECtt LRHS NRHS
(Mooodz Series) MOOODZ AWAKE ('Hilmoooawak') **new**	NRHS
- MOOODZ SHINY ('Hilmoooshin')	LRHS NRHS
'Mozzarella' (d)	EBee GBin
§ 'Noam Saul'	CRos LRHS NRHS
'Now Cheesier'PBR	CRos LCro LOPS LRHS NRHS SMad
ORANGE MEADOWBRITE	see *E.*'Art's Pride'
ORANGE PASSION ('Orpass'PBR)	CWGN EBee ECtt LRHS WCAu
'Orange Skipper' (Butterfly Series)	CRos NLar NRHS
'Pacific Summer'	CWGN EBee WSpi
pallida	CCBP CKno CRos CSam CSpe EAJP EBee ELan EMor EPfP EShb GPoy GQue LRHS MBel MGos NDov NGdn NRHS SPer SPhx SRms SWvt WCAu WSpi XLum
- 'Hula Dancer'	CDor GWyn NGdn SPhx
(Papallo Series) 'Papallo Compact Pink' **new**	NLar
- 'Papallo Compact White' **new**	NLar
paradoxa	CRos EHrv ELan EMor EPfP GPoy LPla LRHS MBel MCot NGdn NRHS NSti SPer SPhx SPlb SWvt XLum
PICCOLINO ('Noortpicco'PBR)	CWGN EBee ECtt LRHS
'Pineapple Sundae'PBR **new**	CWGN EBee
PIXIE MEADOWBRITE ('CBG Cone 2')	CWGN EBee ECtt IKil
'Postman' (Butterfly Series) **new**	SPoG
'Purple Emperor'PBR	ECtt MNHC
§ ***purpurea***	Widely available
- 'Alaska'PBR	NGdn
I - 'Alba'	CRos EPfP LRHS NRHS WCot WFar XLum
- 'Amber Mist'PBR (Mistical Series)	EBee
- 'Augustkönigin'	CKno EBee LRHS NDov WCAu WCot
- 'Avalanche'PBR	CBod CWGN EBee ELon EMor LPla
- 'Baby Swan Pink'	CBod CRos EMor GPSL LRHS NLar NRHS
- 'Baby Swan White'	CBod CRos EBee ELon GPSL LRHS NLar NRHS WFar
- Bradfield hybrids	EHrv
- Bressingham hybrids	CRos LRHS MArl MRav NRHS SPer WGwG
- 'Catharina'PBR	CWGN EBee ECtt
- 'Coconut Lime'PBR	CWGN EPfP LCro LOPS WCAu
- DOPPELGANGER	see *E. purpurea* 'Doubledecker'
§ - 'Doubledecker'	CNor CWCL EBee ELan EPfP GWyn LLHF NGdn SGbt XLum
- ELTON KNIGHT ('Elbrook'PBR) ♈H5	CRos ECtt LCro LOPS LRHS NRHS STPC SWvt WCot
- 'Fancy Frills'	ECtt WCot
- 'Fatal Attraction'PBR	CBcs CPar CRos CWGN CWld ECtt EHrv ELan EMor EPfP EWTr GMaP LEdu LRHS LSRN MBNS MBel MRav NRHS SCob SPad SPer SPoG SWvt WCot
- 'Firebird'PBR	CBcs ECtt LEdu LRHS SCob SGbt SPoG
- 'Fragrant Angel'PBR	ECtt LRHS MBel SWvt
- 'Green Eyes'	EBee ECtt
- 'Green Jewel'PBR	CBcs CDor CPar CRos CWGN EBee ECtt EMor EPfP EUJe LCro LOPS LPla LRHS MBel MCot MNrw NDov NLar NRHS NSti SCob SGbt SPad WCAu WCot
- 'Gum Drop'PBR	EBee LRHS
- 'Happy Star'	CDor CRos EBee LRHS NRHS SPhx WGwG
- 'Hope'PBR	CRos EBee ECtt LPla LRHS MBel NLar NRHS WCAu
- 'Jade'	EBee LSRN MBNS NLar

- 'JS Purple Prairie'	IPot
- 'Kim's Knee High'PBR	CBod CKno CRos ECtt EHrv EMor EPfP GMaP LRHS MBel MTin NGdn NLar NRHS SCob SPer SPoG SWvt
- 'Kim's Mop Head'	CRos ECtt EHrv EPfP EWes LRHS MRav NLar WCot
§ - 'Leuchtstern'	CKno CRos ELan LRHS NBir NGdn NRHS XLum
- 'Lilliput'PBR	ECtt NLar
- 'Little Magnus'PBR	CKno CRos ECtt LRHS NRHS SPoG
- 'Lucky Star'	CRos ELan EPfP LRHS NRHS SPhx
- 'Magnus'	Widely available
- 'Magnus Superior'	CBod CDor CMea CRos EBee GBin LRHS LSun MBel MHer MNrw MPie NDai NRHS SPhx SWvt WGwG
- 'Mars'	SCob
- 'Maxima'	CRos ECtt LRHS
- 'Meringue'PBR	SCob
- 'Merlot'PBR	ECtt LRHS NLar
- 'Milkshake'PBR	CWCL CWGN EBee EMor LLHF LRHS WSpi
- MISTRAL ('Echmis'PBR)	CRos EBee LRHS NRHS
- 'Pica Bella'	CBod CRos CWGN ECtt EPfP LRHS NRHS SPad
- 'Pink Double Delight'PBR	MRav NGdn
- 'Pink Glow'	NDov
- 'Pink Poodle'PBR	EBee
- (PowWow Series) POWWOW WHITE ('Pas709018')	CRos LRHS NRHS SPoG WTor
- - POWWOW WILD BERRY ('Pas702917'PBR)	CRos LRHS NRHS SCob SPoG WFar WTor
- 'Prairie Splendor'	CRos EHoe EMor EPfP LRHS MWat NDov NHic SPhx
- 'Primadonna Deep Rose'	ELan GPSL LEdu NGBl SRot SVic
- 'Primadonna White'	LRHS SRms SRot
- 'Purity'PBR	ECtt LRHS SPoG
- 'Rainbow Marcella'	NCGa NLar
- 'Razzmatazz'PBR (d)	CMac EBee ECtt EHrv ELan EMor MRav NGdn SPer SWvt WCot
- 'Red Knee High'PBR	NLar
- 'Robert Bloom'	NBir SWvt WSpi
- 'Rubinglow'	ECtt LCro LOPS NBir NDov NLar SWvt
- 'Rubinstern'	Widely available
- 'Ruby Giant' 🏆H5	CDor CKno CRos ECtt EHrv ELan EMor GMaP GQue LEdu LRHS LSRN LSun MBel MTis NEgg NLar NRHS SGbt SPer WCot
- 'Sensation Pink'PBR	CPar CRos CWGN EBee EMor IPot LRHS NRHS
- 'Southern Belle'PBR	CDor CNor CWCL CWGN EMor IPot MBNS SMad WSpi
- 'Summer Salsa'PBR	CWCL CWGN EBee EUJe LLHF WCot
- 'The King'	CRos LRHS NGdn NLar NRHS WSpi
- 'Tom Thumb'	EBee
- 'Vintage Wine'PBR	CBcs CBod CKno CRos ECtt EHrv ELan LCro LOPS LRHS NEgg NLar NSti SCob SPer SPoG SWvt WCAu WCot
- 'Virgin'PBR	EBee LCro LOPS MAvo MBel NDov NLar SCob WCAu
- 'White Double Delight'PBR (d)	CWCL
- 'White Lustre'	ECha SRms
- WHITE NATALIE ('Norwhinat'PBR)	EBee
- 'White Swan'	Widely available
'Quills and Thrills'PBR (Prairie Pillars Series)	CWGN ECtt MMrt SCob
'Raspberry Tart'	ECtt
'Raspberry Truffle'PBR	EBee ECtt EWTr
(Secret Series) 'Secret Desire'PBR (d)	EBee NHpl
- 'Secret Joy'PBR (d)	NHpl
- 'Secret Love'PBR (d)	CWGN SCob
- 'Secret Lust'PBR (d)	EBee ECtt
- 'Secret Passion'PBR (d)	CWGN EBee ECtt LRHS NHpl SGbt
- 'Secret Pride' (d)	SCob
- 'Secret Romance'PBR	LRHS NHpl NRHS WCAu
simulata	EAJP EBee EWTr
'Solar Flare'PBR (Big Sky Series)	EBee ECtt
(Sombrero Series) SOMBRERO ADOBE ORANGE ('Balsomador')	CBod
- SOMBRERO BAJA BURGUNDY ('Balsombabur')	MHol
- SOMBRERO BLANCO ('Balsomblanc')	MHol
- SOMBRERO FLAMENCO ORANGE ('Balsomenco'PBR)	LRHS MAsh WFar
- SOMBRERO HOT CORAL ('Balsomcor'PBR)	EBee MAsh WFar
- SOMBRERO LEMON YELLOW ('Balsomemy'PBR)	CBod
- SOMBRERO SALSA RED ('Balsomsed'PBR)	CBcs CBod LRHS MAsh WFar
- SOMBRERO SANDY YELLOW ('Balsomselo'PBR)	EBee MAsh WFar
'Spider'	EBee
'Starlight'	see *E. purpurea* 'Leuchtstern'
'Strawberry Shortcake'	EBee
'Summer Cloud'	CRos CWGN EBee LRHS NRHS SCob SMad WTor
'Summer Cocktail'PBR	ELan LCro LOPS LRHS SCob SPoG WTor
'Summer Passion'	SCob
'Summer Samba' (d)	EBee
§ 'Summer Sky'PBR (Big Sky Series)	CRos ECtt EPfP LRHS NRHS
'Summer Sun'PBR	LRHS SPoG
§ 'Sundown'PBR (Big Sky Series)	CPar CRos EBee ECtt EHrv EMor EPfP EWTr LCro LOPS LRHS NLar NRHS NSti SCob SGbt SWvt WCAu
'Sunrise'PBR (Big Sky Series)	CRos EBee ECtt ELan EMor EPfP GMaP LLHF LRHS NEgg NLar NRHS NSti SCob SGbt SPoG SWvt WCAu WSpi
(SunSeekers Series) SUNSEEKERS MELLOW **new**	WTor
- SUNSEEKERS ORANGE **new**	EBee WTor
- SUNSEEKERS WHITE **new**	EBee
- SUNSEEKERS YELLOW **new**	EBee
'Sunset'PBR (Big Sky Series)	ECtt ELan LLHF LSRN NEgg SWvt WSpi
'Supreme Cantaloupe' (d)	CWGN EBee ECtt NCGa
'Tangerine Dream'PBR	CRos EBee ECtt EMor EPfP LRHS NRHS SCob
tennesseensis 'Rocky Top'	LRHS MBNS MGos
'Tiki Torch'PBR	CBcs CRos ECtt EMor LCro LEdu LOPS LRHS MAvo NRHS SCob SPer SPoG SWvt WCot WTor

	'Tomato Soup'[PBR]	Widely available
	'Twilight'[PBR] (Big Sky Series)	LEdu LRHS
	'White Meditation'[PBR]	CBcs EPfP LRHS NRHS SPoG
	'White Mist'[PBR] (Mistical Series)	EBee
	'White Spider'	SCob
	'Yellow Spider'	EBee SCob

Echinops (*Asteraceae*)

	albus	see *E.* 'Nivalis'
§	***bannaticus***	CBcs CMac CPla NBid SCob WWtn
*	- 'Albus'	WCAu
	- 'Blue Globe'	CRos CWld EBee EHoe ELan EPfP EUJe GBin GCal LRHS LSRN LSun MBel MCot MGos MHol NGdn NHol NRHS SCob SPoG WCAu WFar WHoo
	- 'Blue Glow'	CBod
	- 'Star Frost'	CBod CRos EBee ELan EPfP LRHS NLar NRHS SPhx WFar
	- 'Taplow Blue'	Widely available
	maracandicus	WCot
§	'Nivalis'	CBre CRos LRHS NRHS
*	***perringii***	GCal
	ritro misapplied	see *E. bannaticus*
§	***ritro*** L. ♀H7	Widely available
	- 'Blue Cloud'	EBee
	- subsp. ***ruthenicus*** ♀H7	MRav WCot
	- - 'Platinum Blue'	CMea CRos ECtt ELan ELon EMor LRHS NDov NEgg SPhx SRms
	- 'Veitch's Blue' misapplied	see *E. ritro* L.
	- 'Veitch's Blue'	Widely available
	sphaerocephalus	NBir NDov SPlb
	- 'Arctic Glow'	CRos CWld EBee ECha ECtt EHoe EHrv ELan EMor EPfP GMaP LRHS MCot MMuc MTis NDai NDov NGdn NLar NPri NRHS SCob SPer SPlb SPoG SWvt WFar WWtn
	spinosissimus	EBee GKev
	strigosus	WCot
	tjanschanicus	CPla CRos EBee GPSL LRHS MMuc NLar NRHS SEND

Echium ✿ (*Boraginaceae*)

	aculeatum	MEch
	amoenum	CRos CSpe LRHS MEch NHic NRHS SPhx
	angustifolium Mill.	MEch SPhx
	asperrimum	MEch
	bethencourtianum	MEch SVen
	'Blue Steeple'	CPla CWCL MEch
	boissieri	CCCN MEch
	brevirame	MEch
	callithyrsum	MEch
	candicans ♀H1c	CAbb CBcs CBod CCCN CHll CPbh CPla CSde CTsd ECre ELan EUJe GKev MEch NAln SCob SEND SVen
	- 'Dwarf Blue'	CCCN
	decaisnei	MEch SVen
	subsp. ***decaisnei***	
	fastuosum new	SArc
	gentianoides	MEch SPlb SVen
	giganteum	MEch
	hierrense new	MEch
	italicum	CCCN MEch
	lusitanicum	CCCN
	nervosum	MEch
	onosmifolium	MEch SVen
	pininana ♀H3	CAbb CBcs CBod CPbh CPla CRos CTsd ECre ELan EUJe GBin IKil MEch SArc SChr SCob SEND SMad SPhx SVen
	- 'Snow Tower'	CBod CCCN CDTJ CPla ELan IKil LRHS MEch SVen
	pininana × 'Red Rocket' new	CPla
	pininana × ***wildpretii***	CPla MEch
	'Pink Fountain'	CBod CCCN CDTJ CPla CWCL ELan IKil LRHS MEch
	'Red Rocket'	CBcs CBod CCCN CDTJ
	rosulatum	CCCN
	russicum	CBod CCCN CSpe EAJP ELan EUJe GPSL LRHS MEch MNHC SPad SPhx SPlb XEll
	sabulicola	MEch
	simplex ♀H1c	MEch
	strictum	CCCN MEch
	sventenii	MEch SPlb
	tuberculatum	LRHS MEch SPhx WMoo
	virescens	MEch SVen
	vulcanorum new	MEch
	vulgare	CBod CCCN CHab CSpe CWld ELan ENfk LCro LOPS MEch MHer MNHC NMir SPhx WOut WSFF WTre
	- from Armenia	WCot
	- 'Blue Bedder' ♀H7	CSpe MEch SPhx WSFF
	- 'Pink Bedder'	MEch
	- 'White Bedder'	MEch
	webbii	MEch MMrt SVen
	wildpretii ♀H2	CCCN CDTJ CPla CSpe CTsd MEch SPhx SPlb SVen
	- subsp. ***wildpretii***	MEch

Ectotropis (*Aizoaceae*)

§	***alpina***	CRos EWes GEdr LRHS NRHS
	seanii-hoganii	ECtt EPot EWes GCrg GEdr LLHF NSla WAbe

Edgeworthia (*Thymelaeaceae*)

§	***chrysantha***	CBcs CCCN CExl CKel CRos EBee ELan EPfP LCro LOPS LRHS MGos NLar NRHS SArc SPer SPoG
I	- 'Grandiflora'	CBcs EBee ELon ESwi GBin IDee LRHS MGos MPkF NLar NRHS SMad WPGP
	- 'Nanjing Gold' new	MPkF
§	- 'Red Dragon'	IMou LCro LOPS LRHS MPkF NLar SPer
	- f. ***rubra*** hort.	see *E. chrysantha* 'Red Dragon'
	- 'Winter Liebe'	LRHS NLar
	papyrifera	see *E. chrysantha*

Edraianthus (*Campanulaceae*)

	croaticus	see *E. graminifolius*
	dalmaticus	GKev
	- ***albus***	GKev
	dinaricus	GKev
	glisicii new	GKev
§	***graminifolius***	GEdr GKev
	- from Durmitor, Montenegro new	NSla
	- subsp. ***graminifolius***	GKev LLHF
	niveus	GKev NSla
	owerinianus	LLHF
§	***pumilio*** ♀H5	EPot GEdr GJos GKev NSla SIgm SRms WAbe
	- silver-leaved	EPot GKev
	serbicus	GKev
§	***serpyllifolius***	GKev

	- 'Major'	GKev
	sutjeskae	GKev
	tenuifolius	GKev
	wettsteinii	GKev
	zogovicii	see *E. graminifolius*

Egeria (*Hydrocharitaceae*)

§	***densa***	CBen

Ehretia (*Boraginaceae*)

	anacua	CBcs
	rigida	SPlb

Elaeagnus (*Elaeagnaceae*)

	angustifolia	CAgr CArg CBcs CDul EPfP IDee LMaj MCoo MGos NLar NWea SCob SPer SRms XSen
	- Caspica Group	see *E.* 'Quicksilver'
	argentea Pursh	see *E. commutata*
§	***commutata***	CBcs CMac ECrN EHoe EPfP MBlu MCoo NLar SPer
I	- 'Aurea' **new**	NLar
	- 'Zempin'	EPfP LRHS NLar
	× ***ebbingei***	see *E.* × *submacrophylla*
	macrophylla	CKel EBee EPfP LRHS
	multiflora	MBlu NLar SMad SPer WPGP
	- 'Sweet Scarlet'	CAgr
	parvifolia	CCCN CDul ELan
	pungens 'Argenteovariegata'	see *E. pungens* 'Variegata'
	- 'Aurea'	CKel
	- 'Aureovariegata'	see *E. pungens* 'Maculata'
	- 'Dicksonii' (v)	LRHS NLar SLon SPer SRms WFar
	- 'Forest Gold' (v)	ELan EPfP LRHS
	- 'Frederici' (v)	CBcs CCCN CMac EBee EHoe ELan LRHS MAsh MRav NLar SCob SPer SWvt WAvo
	- 'Hosoba-fukurin' (v)	CKel EBee ELan EMil EPfP NLar SLon
§	- 'Maculata' (v)	Widely available
§	- 'Variegata' (v)	CBcs CKel CMac SPer
§	'Quicksilver'	Widely available
§	× ***submacrophylla*** 🏆H5	Widely available
	- 'Coastal Gold' (v)	CBcs CBod CCoa CDul CSde EBee EPfP LSRN MGos SGol SRms WAvo WFar WRHF
I	- 'Compacta'	CCCN CKel EBee ECrN ELan MGos
	- 'Gilt Edge' (v) 🏆H5	Widely available
	- GOLD SPLASH ('Lannou') (v)	CKel CMac EPfP SGol SWvt
	- 'Limelight' (v)	Widely available
	- 'Moonlight'	EPfP MAsh
	- 'Salcombe Seedling'	CCCN
	- 'Svelte Edge'	NLar
	- 'Viveleg'PBR (v)	CCVT CKel ELan EPfP LMaj LRHS NLar NRHS SCob SEWo
	umbellata	CAco CBcs CDul CExl EBee EPfP EWTr IDee LEdu MBlu NLar SPer WSHC
	- 'Amber' (F)	CAgr
	- 'Big Red' (F)	CAgr CFGn
	- var. ***borealis*** 'Polar Lights'	NLar
	- 'Brilliant Rose' (F)	CAgr
	- 'Garnet' (F)	CAgr
	- 'Hidden Springs' (F)	CAgr
	- 'Jewel' (F)	CAgr
	- 'Late Scarlet' (F)	CAgr CFGn
	- 'Newgate' (F)	CAgr CFGn
	- 'Red Cascade' (F)	CAgr LEdu
	- var. ***rotundifolia*** CWJ 12835	WCru
	- 'Ruby' (F)	CAgr CFGn LEdu
	- 'Sweet 'n'Tart' (F)	CAgr LEdu

Elaeocarpus (*Elaeocarpaceae*)

	sylvestris var. ***ellipticus***	LEdu WPGP

elderberry see *Sambucus nigra*

Elegia (*Restionaceae*)

	capensis	CCCN CDTJ CExl CPbh MPkF SPlb WPGP
	elephantina	CBod CCht CPbh LRHS
	equisetacea	CPbh
	grandis	SPlb
	macrocarpa	CCCN CPbh SPlb
	tectorum 🏆H2	CBod CPbh LRHS NRHS SPlb SPoG
	- dwarf	CPbh
	- 'Fish Hoek'	CPbh

Eleocharis (*Cyperaceae*)

	acicularis	LLWG
	palustris	LLWG
	vivipara	XBlo

Elettaria (*Zingiberaceae*)

	cardamomum	GPoy LEdu SPre WJek

Eleutherococcus ✿ (*Araliaceae*)

	from Manipur, India	WPGP
	divaricatus B&SWJ 5027	WCru
	giraldii BWJ 8091	WCru
	hypoleucus B&SWJ 5532	WCru
	aff. ***leucorrhizus*** PAB 8119	WPGP
	nodiflorus PAB 8119	LEdu
	pictus	see *Kalopanax septemlobus*
	senticosus	GPoy LEdu
	- B&SWJ 4568	WCru
	septemlobus	see *Kalopanax septemlobus*
	sessiliflorus B&SWJ 4528	WCru
	- B&SWJ 8457	WCru
	- B&SWJ 8618	WCru
	sieboldianus	MRav SEND
	- 'Variegatus' (v)	CBod CCCN CRos EHoe ELan ELon EPfP EShb ESwi EUJe LRHS MGil MRav NLar SEND SPoG WCFE WSHC WWFP
	trifoliatus PAB 7113	LEdu
	- RWJ 10108	WCru
	wilsonii B&SWJ 14167 **new**	WCru

Ellisiophyllum (*Plantaginaceae*)

	pinnatum	SBrt
	- B&SWJ 197	LEdu WCru

Elmera (*Saxifragaceae*)

	racemosa	EWes

Elodea (*Hydrocharitaceae*)

	canadensis	LLWG NBir WMAq
	densa	see *Egeria densa*

Elsholtzia (*Lamiaceae*)

	flava PAB 13.012	WPGP
	stauntonii	CBcs CBod EBee ECha ELan GPoy LEdu LRHS MGil MHer MNrw NLar NQui SBrt SPer SPhx SRms SWvt WBor WHer WHil WJek XLum

Elymus (*Poaceae*)

arenarius see *Leymus arenarius*
canadensis EPPr
glaucus misapplied see *E. hispidus*
§ ***hispidus*** ♀H6 CBod EPPr MBlu NDov SPer WCFE WCot
§ ***magellanicus*** Widely available
- 'Blue Sword' CRos ELan LRHS MGos NRHS SPtp SRkn SRms
riparius EPPr
villosus EPPr
- var. ***arkansanus*** EPPr
virginicus EPPr SPhx

Embothrium ✿ (*Proteaceae*)

coccineum CBcs CPla EPfP GBin LRHS MGil NRHS SPlb WAbe WPGP WPav
- Lanceolatum Group CAby CBcs CBod CEnd CTsd EBee EPfP EUJe LRHS MBlu MMuc MPkF SAko SArc SPer SSta SWvt
- - 'Inca Flame' CCCN CJun EPfP LRHS SWvt
- Longifolium Group CCCN EPfP IBlr WPGP

Emilia (*Asteraceae*)

coccinea new CSpe

Emmenopterys (*Rubiaceae*)

henryi CBcs CMCN EPfP IArd IMou MBlu NLar

emperor's mint see *Micromeria*

Empetrum (*Ericaceae*)

nigrum GPoy WThu
rubrum MGil

Empodium (*Hypoxidaceae*)

plicatum CBor GKev

Encephalartos ✿ (*Zamiaceae*)

altensteinii CBrP
ferox CBrP
horridus CBrP
lebomboensis CBrP
lehmannii CBrP
natalensis CBrP
villosus CBrP

endive see AGM Vegetables Section

Endymion see *Hyacinthoides*

Engelmannia (*Asteraceae*)

peristenia WHil

Enkianthus ✿ (*Ericaceae*)

campanulatus ♀H5 Widely available
- var. ***campanulatus*** f. ***albiflorus*** CBcs GKin NLar
I - 'Pagoda' CBcs IArd IDee NLar SAko
- var. ***palibinii*** CBcs CRos EPfP GGGa GKin LRHS MAsh MMrt NLar
- 'Red Bells' CBcs CDul EPfP GKin MAsh NLar SGol SWvt WFar
- 'Red Velvet' CBcs GKin NLar
- 'Ruby Glow' CBcs NLar SAko
- 'Showy Lantern' NLar
- var. ***sikokianus*** NLar
- 'Sinsetu' NLar
- 'Tokyo Masquerade' (v) CRos LRHS SPoG
- 'Venus' CBcs GKin NLar
- 'Victoria' CBcs IArd NLar
- 'Wallaby' CBcs GKev IDee NLar
cernuus f. ***rubens*** ♀H5 CBcs GGGa ITim NLar
chinensis CBcs CRos EPfP GGGa LRHS MAsh SPoG
deflexus CRos GGGa IArd IDee LRHS WPGP
I 'Pagoda Red' LRHS
perulatus ♀H5 CBcs CCCN CDul EBee MGil MGos MMrt NLar SPer
serrulatus GGGa

Ennealophus (*Iridaceae*)

fimbriatus GKev

Ensete (*Musaceae*)

gilletii XBlo
- from Malawi XBlo
- from Mozambique XBlo
glaucum CDTJ
§ ***ventricosum*** ♀H2 CCCN CDTJ CHll SEND XBlo
§ - 'Maurelii' ♀H2 CBod CCCN CCht CDTJ CSBt CTsd ESwi EUJe LCro LOPS SChr SEND SPoG
- 'Rubrum' see *E. ventricosum* 'Maurelii'
- 'Tandarra Red' CAbb

Entelea (*Malvaceae*)

arborescens EShb SPlb

Eomecon (*Papaveraceae*)

chionantha CBor CExl CPla CSam CSpe EBee EWld GAbr GCal GEdr LEdu MAvo MRav NBro NHpl NQui SBrt WCru WMoo WPGP XLum

Epacris (*Ericaceae*)

serpyllifolia WThu

Ephedra (*Ephedraceae*)

sp. MPie SArc
andina IMou
distachya GPoy
equisetina RCB/TQ K-1 WCot
gerardiana CRos LEdu LRHS
- CC 3925 new WCot
- var. ***sikkimensis*** GEdr WOld
§ ***major*** XSen
monosperma GEdr WThu
nebrodensis see *E. major*
nevadensis GPoy
sinica GPoy

Epilobium (*Onagraceae*)

angustifolium see *Chamaenerion angustifolium*
- f. ***leucanthum*** see *Chamaenerion angustifolium* 'Album'
californicum misapplied see *Zauschneria californica*
canum see *Zauschneria cana*
dodonaei see *Chamaenerion dodonaei*
fleischeri see *Chamaenerion fleischeri*
garrettii see *Zauschneria californica* subsp. *garrettii*
glabellum misapplied NRHS NSla WCFE
glabellum G. Forst. CSpe MMuc WKif
hirsutum 'Album' EWTr
microphyllum see *Zauschneria cana*
rosmarinifolium see *Chamaenerion dodonaei*
septentrionale see *Zauschneria septentrionalis*

villosum	see *Zauschneria californica* subsp. *mexicana*
'White Wonder Bells'[PBR]	GWyn

Epimedium ✿ (*Berberidaceae*)

from Jian Xi, China	GEdr
from Yunnan, China	WPGP
acuminatum	CAby CSam CWCL ESMi GEdr LEdu MNrw NLar NSum SCob WMoo WPGP WSHC
- CC 031207	XPou
- L 575	CElw CExl EHrv
- 'Galaxy'	CExl CJun CMil LEdu
- 'Night Mistress'	GPSL IMou WPGP XPou
- 'Quinquin'	IMou
- yellow-flowered	WPGP
- - CC 011415	XPou
'Akakage'	CExl
'Akebono'	CAby CJun CMil CRos EBee ECtt ELon EMor EPfP GBin GEdr IMou ITim LLHF LPla LRHS MAsh MNrw NEgg NGBl NLar NRHS NWad SCob SPad SPoG WCot XEll
ALABASTER ('Conalba')	EBee ELan EMor MAvo MBel MTis NEgg
alpinum	CBod CFis CMac CRos CWCL EBee EPot GBin GKev GLog IFro LEdu LRHS NChi NRHS SHar SPer WMoo XLum
'Amanogawa'	CAby CJun CMil EHrv GEdr LEdu XPou
'Amber Queen'[PBR]	Widely available
'Anju'	GEdr
'Arctic Wings'[PBR]	CBor EBee EPfP GEdr NCGa NGdn SMHy SWvt
'Asiatic Hybrid'	CJun WHal
'Autumn Raspberry'	CJun
baojingense	XPou
'Beni-goromo'	GEdr
'Beni-kujaku'	CAby CJun EBee EMor GEdr GGGa GPSL MHol WFar
'Beni-yushima'	GEdr
'Bieke'	SMHy
'Black Sea'	CElw CJun CMil CWCL EBee EMor EPPr EPot ESMi EWTr GBin GPSL IMou LEdu LRHS MNrw MPnt NLar SCob WBor WHil WHoo XPou
brachyrrhizum	CAby CExl CJun GPSL NLar NSum
- CPC 940447	XPou
brevicornu	GEdr WPGP
- Og 82.010	CAby CExl CJun XPou
- Og 88.010	CJun XPou
'Buckland Buzz' **new**	EBee
'Buckland Spider'	CBor CFis EBee EPPr MNrw WCot WPGP
'Buttered Popcorn' **new**	EBee
campanulatum	CAby
- Og 93.087	CExl CJun EBee
× ***cantabrigiense***	CBro CDor CMac CRos CWCL ECtt EPPr GGGa GKev GMaP GPSL ILea LRHS MRav NEgg NHpl NLar NRHS SRms XLum
chlorandrum	CAby EBee EHrv LEdu WPGP
- Og 94.003	XPou
creeping yellow	EBee EMor MNrw
cremeum	see *E. grandiflorum* subsp. *koreanum*
'Dark Secret'	ESMi
'Darrell's Pink'	EBee
davidii	CBor CMil EBee EMor EPPr ESMi GEdr LEdu MNrw NLar SCob WHal WHoo WPGP WSHC
- CPC 960079	CExl XPou
- EMR 4125	CElw CExl CJun EHrv XPou
- dwarf	CAby CExl
diphyllum	CExl CTsd EBee EHrv EPfP GEdr WHal WPGP XPou
- dwarf white	CSam
- pink-flowered	XPou
dolichostemon	CElw IMou
- Og 81.010	CJun WPGP XPou
'Domino'	GPSL WPGP XPou
ecalcaratum	CAby CMil EBee LEdu WPGP
- Og 93.082	CExl CJun XPou
- spurred	XPou
'Egret'	CAby CMil EBee LEdu SMHy WPGP
elongatum	IMou
- CC 012906	XPou
'Emperor'	see *E.* 'Phoenix'
'Enchantress'	CElw CJun CMil EHrv EMor ESMi EWTr EWld MBel MNrw NLar NSum WHal
epsteinii	CAby CDor CMil EBee EPPr ESMi GEdr LEdu MNrw SBrt WPGP WSHC
- CPC 940347	CElw CExl CJun XPou
fangii	CExl
- CC 022008	XPou
- Og	XPou
fargesii	CAby CExl EBee EHrv GEdr LEdu MNrw NCGa NSum WCAu WPGP
- 'Pink Constellation'	CAby CExl CJun EBee GEdr ITim LEdu MNrw SBch WPGP XPou
'Fire Dragon'[PBR]	CBor EPfP GEdr LLHF MBNS MNrw NCGa SPoG WFar
flavum	EBee WPGP
- Og 92.036	CExl CJun EBee EHrv XPou
'Flowers of Sulphur'[PBR]	EBee EMor EPfP GEdr WFar
franchetii	CAby CElw CExl CTsd ELon GEdr
- 'Brimstone Butterfly'	CAby CBor CExl CFis CJun EPPr ESMi GEdr GPSL LEdu NLar WCot WPGP WSpi XPou
'Fukujuji'	GEdr
'Golden Eagle'	CElw CExl CJun EBee EWes MNrw
§ ***grandiflorum*** ♀H5	CBcs CElw CRos CTri CWCL ELan ELon EMor EPfP EWTr GLog LRHS NBir NHpl NLar SCob SPer WPnP
- 'Akagiza Kura'	XPou
- 'Album'	EPot
- 'Beni-chidori'	CJun GEdr NSum
- 'Bicolor Giant'	XPou
- 'Circe'	XPou
- var. ***coelestre***	XPou
- 'Cranberry Sparkle'	EBee
- 'Crimson Beauty'	CAby CJun ECha NLar WHal WHoo WSHC
- 'Dark Beauty' **new**	WHil
- 'Elfenkönigin'	CRos EBee GPSL LRHS NLar
- 'French Braid'	EBee
- 'Freya'	CExl EBee SMHy WSHC XPou
- 'Freya Mk II'	SMHy
- subsp. ***grandiflorum*** **new**	GGGa
§ - var. ***higoense***	CJun GEdr WHal WPGP
- - 'Bandit'	CWCL GEdr XPou
- - 'Saturn'	CMil EHrv XPou
- 'Jennie Maillard'	ELon ESMi WCot
- 'Koji'	EBee WHil WSHC
§ - subsp. ***koreanum***	ECha ESMi GEdr NSum
- 'Kotobuki'	XPou

- 'Kourin'	GEdr
- 'La Rocaille'	CAby CElw EHrv SMHy XPou
- lilac-flowered	CAby WHal
- 'Lilafee'	Widely available
- 'Mount Kitadake'	WAbe XPou
- 'Mugawa-gen-pan'	XPou
- 'Nanum' ♀H5	CAby CJun EBee EMor EPot ESMi EWTr MNrw NEgg NHar NSum NWad SMHy WAbe WPGP XPou
- pink-flowered	EHrv MCot
- 'Princess Susan'	XPou
- 'Purple Pixie'[PBR]	CBod CWCL ECtt EMor EWTr MHol NEgg NLar WFar WHil
- 'Purple Prince'	CExl CMil EBee EHrv WPGP XPou
- purple-flowered	EHrv
- 'Queen Esta'	CAby CExl CJun CMil EBee ESMi LEdu MNrw MRav NSum WPGP WSHC XPou
- 'Red Beauty'	CBod CMac CNor CRos CSpe CWCL EBee ECtt ELan ELon EMor EPfP EUJe GEdr ILea LEdu LRHS MAsh MCot MNrw NCGa NRHS NSum WFar WHil WPGP WPnP
- 'Rose Queen' ♀H5	CAby CRos CSam CWCL EBee EHrv ELan ELon EMor EPfP ESMi GBin LEdu LRHS MNrw MRav NBir NEgg NSti NSum SCob SWvt WFar WMoo WPGP
- 'Roseum'	CBod CMac CMil GMaP GPSL SWvt
- 'Rubinkrone'	CWCL GEdr GMaP IMou LRHS MNrw
- 'Sirius'	CAby CJun
- 'Tancho'	XPou
- f. ***violaceum***	CElw CJun EBee EHrv NSum WCFE
- 'White Beauty'	WSHC
- 'White Queen' ♀H5	CElw CJun EBee EHrv EPPr EWTr LLHF LRHS MBel SMHy WCot WHal XPou
- 'Wildside Red'	CJun
- 'Yellow Princess'	CAby CElw CJun EBee XPou
- 'Yubae'	GEdr
'Hagoromo'	GEdr
'Hakubai'	GEdr
'Harugasumi'	GEdr
'Heavenly Purple'	CJun
higoense	see *E. grandiflorum* var. *higoense*
'Hina Matsuri'	GEdr
hunanense	XPou
ilicifolium	CAby CJun LEdu WPGP
'Jean O'Neill'	CAby CMil EBee EPPr LEdu WCot WPGP WSHC
'Jenny Pym'	EBee
'Jubilation' **new**	WCot
'Jujisei'	XPou
'Kaguyahime'	CElw CJun CMil EHrv EPPr GPSL LEdu WSHC
'King Prawn'	LEdu SMHy WPGP
'Knight Star'	ESMi
'Kodai Murasaki'	XPou
'Koki'	CBor GEdr
koreanum 'Harold Epstein'	XPou
'Korin'	XPou
'Kotobuki'	GEdr
latisepalum	CMil EBee EHrv ESMi GEdr LEdu MNrw WCot
- Og 91.002	CJun
'Lemon Meringue Pie'	CJun
'Lemon Zest'	EBee XPou
leptorrhizum	CAby CDor CElw CExl CJun CWCL EBee EHrv ELon EPPr ESMi EWld GEdr IMou LEdu MNrw NCGa NLar NSum SBrt WCot WHal
- Og Y44	CExl WSHC XPou
- 'Mariko'	CAby CExl CJun CMil LEdu MNrw XPou
lishihchenii	CAby CExl CJun EBee EHrv GEdr WPGP
- CC 96024	XPou
'Little Shrimp'	CJun CRos CTri EBee ELon GMaP GPSL LLHF LRHS MNrw NLar NRHS WSHC
macranthum	see *E. grandiflorum*
macrosepalum	CElw GEdr XPou
'Mandarin Star'	CWCL EBee EMor GEdr GPSL
'Marchant's Sulphur Queen'	SMHy
'Marchant's Twin Set'	SMHy
membranaceum	CAby CMil EBee ESMi GEdr LEdu LLHF NCGa WHal WPGP XEll XPou
- Og 93.047	CExl CJun EPPr GEdr LEdu
mikinorii	CExl GEdr
- CC 990001	WPGP XPou
'Milky Way'	CAby MNrw
'Mine-no-fubuki'	GEdr
'Miyako'	XPou
'Moonlight'	XPou
'Myojo'	EBee GEdr
myrianthum	CAby CJun EBee GEdr LEdu WPGP XPou
ogisui	CAby CDor CElw CMil ESMi IMou LEdu MRav SMHy WPGP XPou
- Og 91.001	CExl CJun EBee EHrv MNrw
- 'Diane'	XPou
§ × ***omeiense*** 'Akame'	CAby CExl CJun CMil EPPr GEdr MNrw XPou
- 'Emei Shan'	see *E.* × *omeiense* 'Akame'
- 'Myriad Years'	XPou
- 'Pale Fire Sibling'	CJun GEdr
- 'Stormcloud'	CAby CElw CExl CJun CMil EBee EPPr IMou LEdu XPou
parvifolium	XPou
'Pathfinder'	EBee ESMi
pauciflorum	EBee EPPr GEdr LEdu WPGP XPou
- Og 92.123	CExl CJun
× ***perralchicum***	CAby CBro CJun CKel CTri ECha GKev IFro NLar WSHC
- 'Fröhnleiten'	Widely available
- 'Lichtenberg'	EBee EWes
- 'Wisley'	CDor CElw CJun EHrv EWes
perralderianum	CBod CMac CSam CWCL EBee GMaP MBel MCot MNrw SRms WHal WPnP
- 'Weihenstephan'	CRos CWCL LRHS NLar WPnP
aff. ***perralderianum***	MPnt
'Perrine's Pink' (Magique Elfes Series)	WCot
'Persian Carpet' **new**	CMil
§ 'Phoenix'	CAby CExl CMil WCot
'Pink Champagne'	EPfP GEdr LEdu WCot WFar WPGP XPou
'Pink Elf'[PBR]	CMil CWCL CWGN EBee EMor EPfP GBin GEdr LLHF MNrw NCGa NGdn NLar NSti SCob SRms WCAu WFar
pinnatum	EBee GMaP MBel WHal XLum
§ - subsp. ***colchicum*** ♀H7	CJun CWCL ELan EMor EPfP EWTr GLog LEdu LRHS MCot MRav NGdn NLar SCob SPer WCAu WCot WFar WPnP WSpi XEll
- - L 321	WPGP
- - 'Thunderbolt'	EBee

	- ***elegans***	see *E. pinnatum* subsp. *colchicum*
	platypetalum	CAby ESMi IMou SBrt WCot
	- Og 93.085	CExl CJun EBee XPou
	'Prince Shrimp' new	SMHy
	pubescens	CAby EHrv
	- CC 022556 from Shaanxi, China	XPou
	- Og 91.003	CExl CJun EBee WPGP
	pubigerum	CDor CJun CRos CSam CWCL EBee EHrv EMor ESMi GAbr GGGa GLog IFro ILea LEdu LPla LRHS MAsh MMuc NEgg NHpl NLar NSum SCob SEND SWvt WCAu WHal WSpi XEll
	qingchengshanense 03124	XPou
	'Red Maximum'	EBee WPGP XPou
	reticulatum	GEdr
	rhizomatosum	CAby CDor EPPr ESMi GEdr GMaP WPGP WSHC
	- Og 92.114	CJun EHrv WCot WPGP XPou
	'Royal Purple' new	XPou
	× ***rubrum*** 🏆H7	Widely available
	- 'Galadriel'	CBor EMor WHoo
	- 'Sweetheart'	GEdr
	sagittatum 'Warlord'	WPGP XPou
	'Sakura-maru'	CBor GEdr
	'Sasaki'	CBor CWCL EPot GPSL NLar WHil XEll
	sempervirens	CAby CJun WHal
	- 'Creamsickle' (v)	GEdr
	- 'Mars'	XPou
	- 'Okuda's White'	EBee XPou
	- 'Violet Queen'	XPou
	× ***setosum***	CJun EHrv ESMi NLar NSum WHal
	'Shien'	XPou
	'Shiho'	CWCL EBee GEdr GPSL MAvo NLar
	shuichengense CC 030175	XPou
	'Sphinx Twinkler'	see *E.* 'Spine Tingler'
§	'Spine Tingler'	CAby CBcs CMil CSpe CWCL EBee ECtt EPau ESwi EUJe GBin GEdr GPSL LEdu MAvo MBel MNrw MPie NBir NLar SCob SMad SPad SPoG SRms WCAu WCot WHoo WPGP XPou
	'Spinners'	EBee ESMi WCot
	'Starcloud'	EBee
	stellulatum	GEdr
	- long-leaved	XPou
	- 'Wudang Star'	CExl CJun CMil CRos EBee EHrv EPot EWes IMou ITim LEdu LRHS MCot SCob WMoo WSHC XPou
	- 'Yukiko'	XPou
	'Sunshowers'	EBee
	sutchuenense CC 990394	XPou
	'Suzuka'	GEdr LEdu
	'Tama-no-genpei'	CJun GEdr LEdu
	'Tanima-no-yuki'	GEdr
	'The Giant'	WCot WPGP XPou
	'Togen'	WCot XPou
	'Tokiwa-gozen'	GEdr
	'Totnes Turbo'	EBee
	trifoliolatobinatum CC 950046	XPou
	truncatum CC 030557	XPou
	× ***versicolor***	CExl EShb SCob SSut
	- 'Cherry Tart'	EBee ESMi XPou
	- 'Cupreum'	CFis CJun CWCL EMor LEdu LRHS WCAu
§	- 'Discolor'	CAby CElw CFis ECha EHrv EPPr NBir SMHy WCot
	- 'Neosulphureum'	CAby CBro CWCL EBee EHrv EPPr LRHS WFar WPGP WSHC WThu
	- 'Sulphureum' 🏆H7	Widely available
	- 'Versicolor'	see *E.* × *versicolor* 'Discolor'
	× ***warleyense***	Widely available
	- 'Orangekönigin'	Widely available
	'Wildside Ruby'	CMil
	'William Stearn'	CExl CJun EBee GEdr WCot XPou
	'Windfire'	EBee
	wushanense	CAby EBee EHrv EPPr ESMi GEdr LEdu XPou
	- Og 93.019	CExl CJun WPGP XPou
	- 'Caramel'	CAby CExl CJun CMil EBee EHrv GEdr GPSL LEdu NSum WCAu WCot WSHC XPou
	- 'Sandy Claws'	WCot
	- spiny-leaved	EBee WCot WFar
	- - CC 014631	WPGP XPou
	'Yachimata-hime'	GEdr
	'Yokihi'	GEdr XPou
	× ***youngianum***	NEgg
	- 'Be My Valentine'	EBee
	- 'Beni-kujaku'	NEgg WFar XPou
	- 'Capella'	XPou
	- 'Fairy Dust'	EBee
	- 'Grape Fizz'	EBee
	- 'Marchacos Sprite'	EBee
	- 'Merlin'	CDor CElw CJun CMil CWCL EBee EMor EPPr EPfP ESMi GEdr GGGa GPSL MBel NLar NSti NSum WHal WSHC
	- 'Niveum' 🏆H5	Widely available
	- 'Roseum'	Widely available
	- 'Ruby Tuesday'	EBee
	- 'Shikinomai'	CExl CJun
	- 'Tamabotan'	CAby CMil GEdr MNrw MRav XPou
§	- 'Typicum'	CElw WSHC
	- 'Yenomoto'	CJun EHrv
	- 'Youngianum'	see *E.* × *youngianum* 'Typicum'
	zhushanense	CAby EBee ESMi LEdu WCot WPGP
	- CC 02885	XPou
	- CC 022403	XPou

Epipactis (*Orchidaceae*)

	Catalina gx	CJun GEdr MNrw
	gigantea	CJun CPla EBee ECha ELan EPot EWld GBin GEdr GKev LRHS MHer MNrw MRav MWts NDav NLAp NRHS WPGP
	- 'Serpentine Night'	CJun NLAp
	gigantea × ***palustris***	CJun
	gigantea × ***veratrifolia***	see *E.* Lowland Legacy gx
	gigantea 'Serpentine Night' × ***thunbergii*** new	NLAp
	helleborine	WHer
	Lizzy Lou gx	CJun
§	**Lowland Legacy gx**	CJun GEdr
	- 'Edelstein'	MNrw WFar
	- 'Frankfurt'	GEdr
	palustris	ECha EWat GEdr LRHS MNrw NDav NLAp NRHS WHer WPnP
	Passionata gx Light Royals Group	CJun GEdr
	Renate gx	CJun
	royleana	CAby CJun GEdr
	Sabine gx	CAby CJun GEdr
	- 'Frankfurt'	MNrw WFar

Epipremnum (*Araceae*)

	pinnatum 'Marble Queen' (v)	XBlo

Episcia (*Gesneriaceae*)

dianthiflora	WCot WDib
'San Miguel'	WDib

Equisetum ✿ (*Equisetaceae*)

'Bandit' (v)	CNat EBee MAvo SMad WMoo
× ***bowmanii***	CNat
* ***camtschatcense***	CBod EShb EUJe SArc SMad SPlb XLum
fluviatile	CNat
giganteum	LLWG
hyemale	CBen CTsd EHoe EWat GQue LLWG LRHS MAvo MMuc MSCN NBro NPer NSti SCob SPlb WCot WMoo WWtn XLum
§ - var. ***affine***	CNat EBee ELan EUJe LEdu SCob WMAq WPGP
- var. ***robustum***	see *E. hyemale* var. *affine*
ramosissimum var. ***japonicum***	SCob WPGP
robustum	SCob
scirpoides	EFer EHoe LLWG MWts NPer NWad WMAq WMoo XLum
sylvaticum	CNat
telmateia	LEdu SMad
variegatum	EBee EFer

Eragrostis (*Poaceae*)

airoides ambig.	CBod
curvula	CBod CElw CKno CMea CRos CWCL ECha EHoe EPPr IMou LRHS MAvo MBel MRav NBir NGdn NWsh SEND SPhx XLum
- S&SH 10	CElw EPPr SMHy WPGP
- 'Totnes Burgundy'	CAby CExl CKno CRos ECha EMor EPPr EPfP EShb LRHS MAvo NRHS SMea SPhx SRms WPGP
elliottii	CKno CSpe ECha EPPr EShb LRHS MAvo SEND SMea
- 'Wind Dancer'	CSde EBee XSen
spectabilis	CBod CKel CKno CSde CTsd EBee ELan EPfP NGdn NWsh SMea WMoo XLum XSen
trichodes	CBod CKno EHoe LEdu NWsh SEND SMea XSen

Eranthemum (*Acanthaceae*)

pulchellum ♀H1b	ECre

Eranthis (*Ranunculaceae*)

albiflora **new**	GKev
cilicica	see *E. hyemalis* Cilicica Group
§ ***hyemalis*** ♀H6	CArg CBro CMea CRos CSpe CTca ELan ELon EMor EPfP GKev LAma LCro LOPS LRHS MAvo NHpl NPri NRHS SCob SDeJ SPhx SWvt WCot WHoo WShi
§ - Cilicica Group	CRos ELon EPot GEdr GKev GMaP IFro LRHS MJak NLar NRHS SCob SDeJ SPer SPhx WBor WCot WShi
- 'Flore Pleno' (d)	EPot GEdr WCot
- 'Grünling'	CAvo EPot WCot
- 'Grünspecht'	EPot GEdr GKev
- 'Orange Glow'	EPot GEdr
- 'Schwefelglanz'	CAvo CBro EBee EPot GEdr GKev WCot
§ - Tubergenii Group	CBro EPot
- - 'Guinea Gold' ♀H6	CMea
- 'Winterzauber' **new**	EBee
pinnatifida	GEdr GKev
× ***tubergenii***	see *E. hyemalis* Tubergenii Group

Ercilla (*Phytolaccaceae*)

volubilis	CBcs CBod CExl CHll CRHN CWGN EPfP EWld IDee LRHS MGil SEND WCru WSHC

Eremophila (*Scrophulariaceae*)

longifolia	SPlb

Eremostachys (*Lamiaceae*)

laciniata	SPhx

Eremurus (*Asphodelaceae*)

bungei	see *E. stenophyllus* subsp. *stenophyllus*
'Emmy Ro'	LAma LRHS NLar
'Foxtrot'	CMea GKev SDeJ
fuscus	GKev LRHS
'Grace'	LAma
'Helena'	LAma LRHS SPhx
himalaicus	ELan EPot ERCP GBin GKev GMaP ILea LAma LRHS NLar SCob SDeJ SPer SPhx
'Image'	CRos LRHS NRHS
× ***isabellinus*** 'Cleopatra'	CMea CRos EBee EPfP EPot ERCP EWhm GKev GMaP LAma LCro LOPS LRHS MBNS MHer NAln NLar SCob SDeJ SPad SPer SPhx SPoG WCot
- 'Obelisk'	LAma LRHS
- 'Pinokkio'	CRos EPot GKev LAma LCro LOPS LRHS NRHS SDeJ SPer SPhx
- Ruiter hybrids	CBod CRos ELan EPfP GKev GMaP LAma LRHS MGos NLar NRHS SDeJ SPer
- Shelford hybrids	CBcs CRos GKev LAma LRHS NRHS SDeJ SPer
- 'Tropical Dream'	LRHS
'Jeanne-Claire'	LAma LRHS NLar
'Joanna' ♀H6	LAma LRHS NLar SPhx
'Lemon Fizz' **new**	SPhx
'Line Dance'	CRos LAma LRHS NRHS
'Moneymaker'	GKev LAma LRHS
'Oase'	GKev LAma LRHS SDeJ
'Rexona'	GKev LAma MBNS SDeJ
robustus ♀H6	CBcs CRos ELan EPot ERCP GBin GKev LAma LRHS NLar NRHS SDeJ SPer SPhx SPlb WCot
'Romance'	CRos ERCP GKev LAma LRHS MBNS NLar NRHS SCob SDeJ
'Rumba'	LAma
'Samba'	LAma NLar
'Sarah Cato'	EBee GKev SPhx
stenophyllus ♀H6	CBod CRos EPot ERCP GKev LCro LOPS LRHS NLar NRHS SDeJ SPhx SPoG
§ - subsp. ***stenophyllus***	CBcs EPfP GMaP MHer MNrw NAln NPer SPer
'Tap Dance'	CRos GKev LAma LRHS NLar NRHS SPhx
'White Beauty Favourite' PBR	ERCP GKev LCro LOPS MHer SDeJ
'White Sensation'	LRHS
'Yellow Giant'	GKev
zenaidae JCA 0.444.409	WCot

Erepsia (*Aizoaceae*)

lacera	SPlb

Erianthus see *Saccharum*

Erica ✿ (*Ericaceae*)

Name	Suppliers
aestiva	SPlb
alopecurus	SPlb
andevalensis f. ***albiflora***	CFst
arborea	SPlb XSen
- var. ***alpina*** 𝕐H4	CTri EPfP GAbr SCob SPer SWhi
§ - - f. ***aureifolia*** 'Albert's Gold' 𝕐H4	CBcs CFst CRos CSBt CTri ELan EPfP GAbr LRHS MGos MMrt NHol NRHS SCob SCoo SPer SPoG SWhi
- 'Arbora Gold'	see *E. arborea* var. *alpina* f. *aureifolia* 'Albert's Gold'
- 'Arnold's Gold'	see *E. arborea* var. *alpina* f. *aureifolia* 'Albert's Gold'
- 'Estrella Gold' 𝕐H4	CBcs CFst CRos CSBt CTri ELan EPfP LRHS MAsh MMrt NHol NRHS SCob SCoo SPer SPoG SWhi
- 'Golden Joy'	CFst
- 'Spring Smile'	CFst
× ***arendsiana*** 'Charnwood Pink'	CFst
- 'Ronsdorf' **new**	CFst
australis f. ***albiflora*** 'Holehird White' **new**	CFst
- - 'Mr Robert' 𝕐H4	CFst GCal
- 'Holehird'	CFst
- 'Polar Express' **new**	CFst
- 'Riverslea' 𝕐H4	CFst CRos CTri GCal LRHS NRHS SCob SPer SPoG SWhi
- 'Trisha'	CFst
bauera	CPbh
caffra	CPbh SPlb
canaliculata 𝕐H3	CBcs
carnea 'Accent'	CFst
- 'Adrienne Duncan' 𝕐H6	GPer SCoo SRms SWhi
- f. ***alba*** 'Golden Starlet' 𝕐H6	CFst CSBt CTri MAsh MJak NHol NWea SCoo SRms SWhi
- - 'Ice Princess' 𝕐H6	CKel ELan MAsh SCoo SRms SWhi
- - 'Isabell' 𝕐H6	CBcs CFst CKel CSBt MAsh SCoo SRms SWhi
- - MADAME SEEDLING	see *E. carnea* f. *alba* 'Weisse March Seedling'
- - 'Rosalinde Schorn'	SRms
- - 'Schneekuppe'	SWhi
- - 'Schneesturm'	CFst SRms
- - 'Snow Queen'	SRms SWhi
- - 'Springwood White' 𝕐H6	CFst CSBt CTri ELan MAsh MMuc NHol SEND SRms SWhi
§ - - 'Weisse March Seedling'	CFst
- - 'Whitehall'	CFst LCro LOPS MAsh SCoo SRms SWhi
- - 'Winter Snow' 𝕐H6	CFst CKel CSBt ELan SCoo SRms SWhi
- 'Amy Doncaster'	see *E. carnea* 'Treasure Trove'
- 'Ann Sparkes' 𝕐H6	CBcs CFst CSBt CTri ELan GPer MAsh NHol SCoo SRms SWhi
- 'Antje'	SWhi
- 'Atrorubra'	SWhi
- f. ***aureifolia*** 'Aurea'	CFst MAsh SCoo SRms SWhi
- - 'Barry Sellers'	SRms
§ - - 'Bell's Extra Special'	SRms SWhi
- - 'Foxhollow' 𝕐H6	CBcs CFst CTri IArd MAsh MJak NHol SCoo SRms SWhi
- - 'Gelber Findling'	SRms
- - 'Hilletje'	SRms SWhi
- - 'January Sun'	SRms
- - 'Westwood Yellow' 𝕐H6	CSBt MAsh NHol SRms SWhi
- 'Aztec Gold'	CFst SWhi
- 'Beoley Pink'	SRms
- 'Branton Bamford'	CFst SWhi
- 'C.J. Backhouse'	SRms
- 'Challenger' 𝕐H6	CKel ELan GPer MAsh SCoo SRms SWhi
- 'Clare Wilkinson'	SRms
- 'Claribelle'	CFst SWhi
- 'Corinna' PBR	CFst SWhi
- 'December Red'	CFst ELan MAsh MMuc SCoo SEND SRms SWhi
- 'Diana Young'	CFst SCoo SWhi
- 'Dømmesmoen'	CFst SRms
- 'Dorset Sunshine'	CFst SWhi
- 'Early Red'	SRms
- 'Eileen Porter'	CFst MMuc SEND
- 'Eva' 𝕐H6	CBcs CFst SRms SWhi
- 'Foxhollow Fairy'	SRms
- 'Gracilis'	SRms
- 'Heathwood'	MAsh SRms SWhi
- 'James Backhouse'	CFst CTri
- 'Jason Attwater'	SRms
- 'Jennifer Anne'	CFst SRms
- 'John Kampa'	SRms
- 'John Pook'	SCoo SRms SWhi
- 'Kathy'	SWhi
- 'King George'	CFst CTri SRms SWhi
- 'Lena'	see *E.* × *darleyensis* 'Lena'
- 'Lesley Sparkes'	CFst
- 'Lohse's Rubin'	SRms SWhi
- 'Loughrigg' 𝕐H6	CTri MAsh MJak NHol SCoo SRms SWhi
- 'March Seedling' 𝕐H6	CFst MAsh NHol SCoo SRms SWhi
- 'Margaret Benson'	SWhi
- 'Margery Frearson'	SRms
I - 'Martin'	SRms
- 'Memory'	SWhi
- 'Myretoun Ruby' 𝕐H6	CBcs CFst CSBt CTri GPer LCro LOPS MAsh NHol SCoo SRms SWhi
- 'Nadja'	SWhi
- 'Nathalie' 𝕐H6	CFst CSBt MAsh SCoo SRms SWhi
- 'Pink Beauty'	see *E. carnea* 'Pink Pearl'
- 'Pink Cloud'	CFst
- 'Pink Mist'	SRms
§ - 'Pink Pearl'	CFst
- 'Pink Spangles' 𝕐H6	CBcs CFst CSBt CTri MAsh MJak SCoo SRms SWhi
- 'Pirbright Rose'	SRms
- 'Polden Pride'	SRms
- 'Porter's Red'	SWhi
- 'Praecox Rubra'	NHol SCoo SRms SWhi
- 'Queen Mary'	SRms
- 'Queen of Spain'	CFst SRms
- 'R.B. Cooke'	MAsh MJak SCoo SRms SWhi
- 'Robert Jan'	SRms
- 'Rosalie' 𝕐H6	CFst CKel IArd MAsh SCoo SRms SWhi
- 'Rosantha'	CFst SRms
- 'Rosea'	SPlb
- 'Rosy Morn'	SRms
- 'Rotes Juwel'	SRms
- 'Rubens' Palette'	SWhi
- 'Rubinette'	SWhi
- 'Rubinteppich'	SRms
- 'Ruby Glow'	NHol SWhi
- 'Sally' **new**	CFst
- 'Saskia'	CFst SWhi
- 'Scatterley'	SRms
- 'Schatzalp'	SRms
- 'Sherwood Creeping'	SRms
- 'Smart's Heath'	SRms
- 'Springwood Pink'	CSBt CTri GPer MAsh NHol SRms SWhi

- 'Tanja'	CFst SWhi
§ - 'Treasure Trove'	CFst SWhi
- 'Viking'	MAsh
- 'Vivellii' 🏆H6	CFst CTri GPer MAsh MJak NHol SCoo SRms SWhi
- 'Walter Reisert'	SRms
- 'Wentwood Red'	SRms
- WHISKY	see *E. carnea* f. *aureifolia* 'Bell's Extra Special'
- 'Winter Beauty'	MJak NHol SWhi
- 'Winter Rubin'	CFst SRms
- 'Winterfreude'	SWhi
- 'Wintersonne' 🏆H6	CFst CKel MMuc SRms SWhi
cerinthoides 🏆H2	CPbh
ciliaris 'Bretagne'	SWhi
- 'Corfe Castle'	CFst
- 'David McClintock'	CFst SWhi
- 'Globosa'	SWhi
cinerea	SWhi
- f. ***alba*** 'Alba Major'	CFst SWhi
- - 'Alba Minor'	CFst MAsh SWhi
- - 'Celebration'	SWhi
- - 'Domino'	MAsh
- - 'Hookstone White'	CFst
- 'Atrorubens'	CFst MJak
- f. ***aureifolia*** 'Anne Berry'	SWhi
- - 'Apricot Charm'	CSBt
- - 'Fiddler's Gold'	MAsh SWhi
- - 'Golden Drop'	CFst CSBt MAsh
- - 'Golden Sport'	CFst SWhi
- - 'Goldilocks'	CFst
- - 'Summer Gold'	SWhi
- 'Bucklebury Red'	CFst
- 'C.D. Eason' 🏆H7	CFst CSBt CTri GPer MAsh SCoo SWhi
- 'Cevennes'	GPer
- 'Champs Hill'	CFst
- 'Coccinea'	SWhi
- 'Creepy Crawly' **new**	CFst
- 'Discovery'	CFst
- 'Eden Valley'	CFst GPer SCoo
- 'Glencairn'	GPer
- 'Heatherbank'	CFst
- 'John Ardron'	CFst
- 'Joseph Murphy'	CFst
- 'Joyce Burfitt'	CFst
- 'Katinka'	CFst GPer SWhi
- 'Lady Skelton'	CFst
- 'Lilac Time'	CFst GPer
- 'Miss Waters'	CFst
- 'Molly Rose'	SWhi
- 'Mrs E.A. Mitchell'	GPer SPlb SWhi
- 'My Love'	CFst SWhi
- 'Ockham'	CFst
- 'Pallas'	CFst
- 'Pentreath'	GPer SWhi
- 'Pink Ice' 🏆H7	CFst CTri GPer MAsh NHol SWhi
- 'Providence'	CFst
- 'Purple Beauty'	GPer SWhi
- 'Romantic Scotland' **new**	GPer
- 'Rosea'	GPer
- 'Rosita'	CFst
- 'Roter Kobold'	SWhi
- 'Sandford Heritage'	CFst
- 'Sandpit Hill'	CFst SWhi
- 'Sherry'	NHol SWhi
- 'Stephen Davis' 🏆H7	CFst GPer MJak NHol SCoo SWhi
- 'Ted Oliver'	CFst
- 'Velvet Night' 🏆H7	CSBt GPer MAsh NHol SWhi
- 'Vivienne Patricia'	CFst
coccinea	CPbh
cooperi	SPlb
curviflora	SPlb
× ***darleyensis*** 'Alba'	see *E.* × *darleyensis* f. *albiflora* 'Silberschmelze'
- f. ***albiflora*** 'Ada S. Collings'	MAsh SRms
- - 'Bing'	SCoo SWhi
- - 'N.R. Webster'	SRms
§ - - 'Silberschmelze'	CKel CSBt CTri MAsh MMuc SCoo SRms SWhi
- - 'White Glow'	CTri MAsh SRms SWhi
- - 'White Perfection' 🏆H5	CBcs CFst CKel IArd MAsh MJak NHol SCoo SPoG SRms SWhi
- 'Archie Graham'	SRms
- 'Arthur Johnson' 🏆H5	CFst CTri MAsh SRms
§ - f. ***aureifolia*** 'Eva Gold'[PBR]	CFst CKel SWhi
- - 'Jack H. Brummage'	CSBt CTri MAsh SRms SWhi
- - 'Mary Helen'	CKel CSBt MAsh NHol SCoo SRms SWhi
- - 'Moonshine'	CFst SRms SWhi
- - 'Tweety'	CBcs CFst CSBt SRms SWhi
- 'Aurélie Brégeon'	CFst SRms
- 'Bert'	SCoo SWhi
- 'Cherry Stevens'	see *E.* × *darleyensis* 'Furzey'
§ - 'Darley Dale'	CFst CKel CSBt ELan GPer MAsh MJak MMuc SCoo SPoG SRms SWhi
- 'Epe'	CFst SRms SWhi
- 'Eva'	see *E.* × *darleyensis* f. *aureifolia* 'Eva Gold'
§ - 'Furzey' 🏆H5	CKel CSBt GPer LCro LOPS MAsh NHol NWea SCoo SRms SWhi
- 'George Rendall'	CTri MAsh SCoo SRms SWhi
- 'Ghost Hills' 🏆H5	CKel CSBt LCro LOPS MAsh MJak SCoo SPoG SRms SWhi
- 'Golden Perfect'	CFst SWhi
- 'Irish Treasure'	CFst
- 'J.W. Porter' 🏆H5	CKel MAsh MJak MMuc SCoo SRms SWhi
- 'James Smith'	SRms
- 'Jenny Porter' 🏆H5	ELan SCoo SWhi
- 'Katia'[PBR] (Winter Belles Series)	CFst CKel SWhi
- 'Kramer's Rote' 🏆H5	CFst CKel CSBt CTri ELan MJak NHol SCoo SPoG SRms SWhi XLum
§ - 'Lena'	CFst
- 'Lucie'[PBR] (Winter Belles Series)	CFst CKel SWhi
- 'Margaret Porter'	CFst CKel SCoo SWhi
- MOLTEN SILVER	see *E.* × *darleyensis* f. *albiflora* 'Silberschmelze'
- 'Phoebe'[PBR] (Winter Belles Series)	CFst CKel SWhi
- 'Pink Perfection'	see *E.* × *darleyensis* 'Darley Dale'
- 'Rubina'[PBR]	CFst SWhi
- 'Snow Surprise'	SWhi
- 'Spring Surprise'[PBR] 🏆H5	CFst SCoo SWhi
- 'W.G. Pine'	SRms
- 'White Spring Surprise'	SWhi
- 'Winter Surprise'	CFst SWhi
- 'Winter Treasure'	CFst SWhi
discolor	CPbh
erigena f. ***alba*** 'W.T. Rackliff' 🏆H5	CBcs CSBt GPer MAsh NHol SCoo SRms SWhi
- f. ***aureifolia*** 'Golden Lady'	CSBt MAsh NHol SCoo SRms SWhi
- - 'Thing Nee'	CFst SRms SWhi
- 'Brightness'	CSBt NHol SCoo SWhi
- 'Golden Jubilee'	CFst SWhi
- 'Irish Dusk' 🏆H5	CBcs CKel CSBt CTri GPer MAsh MMuc SCoo SRms SWhi

- 'Irish Salmon'	SWhi
- 'Superba'	SRms
formosa	CPbh
glandulosa	CPbh
glauca var. ***glauca***	SPlb
× ***griffithsii*** 'Elegant Spike'	CFst
§ - 'Heaven Scent'	CFst
- 'Jacqueline'	CFst SWhi
- 'Valerie Griffiths'	CFst GPer NHol
'Heaven Scent'	see *E.* × *griffithsii* 'Heaven Scent'
lusitanica ♀H4	CFst
- f. ***aureifolia*** 'George Hunt'	CFst CRos ELan LRHS SPer
- GREAT STAR	see *E. lusitanica* 'La Vasterival'
§ - 'La Vasterival'	CFst
- 'Sheffield Park'	CFst CRos LRHS NRHS SPer SPoG
mackayana f. ***eburnea*** 'Doctor Ronald Gray'	CFst
- - 'Shining Light'	CFst SWhi
- 'Errigal Dusk'	CFst
- 'Galicia'	CFst
- f. ***multiplicata*** 'Plena' (d)	WHer
mammosa ♀H2	CPbh SPlb
- cream-flowered	CPbh
- pink-flowered	CPbh
- red-flowered	CPbh
- white-flowered	CPbh
manipuliflora 'Korçula'	CFst
mediterranea misapplied	see *E. erigena*
multiflora	XSen
× ***oldenburgensis*** 'Ammerland' ♀H5	CFst SCoo SRms
'Pat Turpin'	CFst
patersonia	SPlb
perspicua	CPbh SPlb
platycodon subsp. ***maderincola*** f. ***aureifolia*** 'Levada Gold'	CFst
plukenetii	CPbh
scabriuscula	CPbh
§ ***scoparia*** 'Minima'	CCCN
- 'Pumila'	see *E. scoparia* 'Minima'
sessiliflora	CPbh
spiculifolia 'Balkan Rose'	CFst GCal
straussiana	SPlb
× ***stuartii*** 'Irish Lemon' ♀H5	CFst CSBt GPer MJak NHol SWhi
- 'Irish Orange'	CSBt GPer MJak NHol SWhi
terminalis 'Thelma Woolner'	CFst
tetralix	SWhi
- f. ***alba*** 'Alba Mollis' ♀H6	CFst CSBt GPer MAsh SWhi
- - 'Melbury White'	CFst
- f. ***aureifolia*** 'Ruth's Gold'	NHol
- 'Con Underwood'	CFst CSBt GPer SWhi
- 'Hookstone Pink'	CFst
- 'Ken Underwood'	CFst
- 'Riko'	CFst
- 'Samtpfötchen'	CFst
- 'Silver Bells'	CSBt
- f. ***stellata*** 'Pink Star' ♀H6	CFst NHol SWhi
- 'Tina'	CFst
vagans f. ***alba*** 'Cornish Cream' ♀H5	GPer NHol SWhi
- - 'Diana's Gold'	SRms
- - 'Golden Triumph'	CFst
- - 'Kevernensis Alba' ♀H5	GPer
- - 'Lyonesse' ♀H5	MAsh MMuc NHol SWhi
- f. ***aureifolia*** 'Valerie Proudley' ♀H5	CSBt GPer MAsh NHol
- - 'Yellow John'	CFst CKel CSma SRms SWhi
- 'Birch Glow' ♀H5	CFst CSma
- 'Keira'	CFst CSma SRms
- 'Mrs D.F. Maxwell' ♀H5	CBcs CFst CSBt GPer MMuc NHol SWhi
- 'Mrs Donaldson'	CFst
- 'Saint Keverne'	CFst CSBt IArd MAsh MMuc NHol SWhi
- 'Summertime'	CFst
× ***veitchii*** 'Exeter' ♀H4	CFst CRos CSBt ELan LRHS MAsh NRHS SPer SPoG SWhi
- 'Gold Tips' ♀H4	CFst CSBt
versicolor ♀H2	CPbh SPlb
verticillata	CPbh
× ***watsonii*** 'Cherry Turpin'	CFst
- 'Claire Elise'	CFst
- 'Dorothy Metheny'	CFst
- 'Gwen'	CFst
- 'Mary'	CFst SWhi
- 'Pink Pacific'	CFst SWhi
× ***williamsii*** 'Ken Wilson'	CFst GPer
'Winter Fire'	CPbh
woodii	SPlb

Erigeron (*Asteraceae*)

'Adria'	CRos EBee ECtt EUJe LLHF LRHS MBel MMuc NRHS
annuus	CSpe MMuc MNrw NDov SPhx WBrk WSHC WTre
aurantiacus	CBcs
aureus 'Canary Bird' ♀H4	CPBP ECtt EPot GCrg NRHS NSla WAbe
- 'The Giant'	WAbe
AZURE FAIRY	see *E.* 'Azurfee'
§ 'Azurfee'	CBod ELan EPfP GKev GMaP MBNS MHol NBir NHic NLar SPer SPoG SWvt WArt WFar WMoo
BLACK SEA	see *E.* 'Schwarzes Meer'
'Blue Beauty'	CMac CRos EPfP LRHS NRHS SRms
'Charity'	MHCG MRav
chrysopsidis	GKev
- 'Grand Ridge'	CRos EPot LRHS NRHS WAbe
compositus	GKev SRms
§ - var. ***discoideus***	CMea NSla SPlb WHal WHoo WOld
- 'Rocky'	CBod MMuc NSla
DARKEST OF ALL	see *E.* 'Dunkelste Aller'
'Dignity'	CBod ELan LLHF LRHS MBel MBrN MMuc MPie MRav NHol NRHS SWvt WBrk
'Dimity'	ECha NBir NBre WFar WHal
'Dominator'	CWGN WCot WFar
I 'Dunkelste Aller'	CAby CBcs CBod CRos CSam ELan EPfP GBin GLog GMaP LPot LRHS MBel MRav NLar NRHS NSti SCob SGbt SPoG SRms SWvt WCAu WCot WFar WHoo
* ***ereganus***	NBre
flettii	GKev NAln
'Foersters Liebling' ♀H5	EBee MBel MNrw MTis
'Four Winds'	ECtt ELan EWes GKev LRHS NGdn NHpl WBrk
'Gaiety'	NBre
glaucus	CCCN CSBt GJos GQue LRHS MMuc MRav NGdn NHic SEND SMad WArt WBrk WFar
- 'Albus'	ELon LRHS NLar WArt WBor WFar
- 'Elstead Pink'	CTri ECtt ELan WFar
- large-flowered	ELon LRHS

- 'Roger Raiche' CFis MRav
- 'Rose Purple' CFis
- 'Roseus' CBcs SEND
- 'Sea Breeze' CBod CCCN CKel CRos EBee ECtt ELon EPfP GBin GMaP LCro LOPS LRHS MBel MHol MPnt NLar NRHS SCob SGbt SMad SPoG SRms SWvt WBor WBrk WFar WHoo
- 'Sennen' MHCG WBrk
- 'Viewpoint Blue' ELon LRHS
grandiflorus **new** WFar
§ ***karvinskianus*** ♀H5 Widely available
- 'Kew Profusion' CRos LRHS MHol NRHS WHil
- 'Sea of Blossom' CBod CKel GCal NCou WArt
- 'Stallone' CBod LSun MHol NLar WFar
leiomerus GEdr GKev LLHF
linearis LLHF
'Mrs F.H. Beale' WCot
mucronatus see *E. karvinskianus*
multiradiatus GCal
'Nachthimmel' NBre NGdn
philadelphicus MNrw NBir NBro WArt
PINK JEWEL see *E.* 'Rosa Juwel'
PINK TRIUMPH see *E.*'Rosa Triumph'
'Professor Korodi' (d) EBee
'Profusion' see *E. karvinskianus*
pulchellus WBrk
pumilus WGoo
pyrenaicus Rouy see *Aster pyrenaeus*
'Quakeress' CAby CBod CMea ECtt GMaP GQue IKil MBel MMuc MNrw MRav NGdn SCob SWvt WBrk WFar WGwG
§ 'Rosa Juwel' CBod CRos CSBt ECtt ELan EPfP GMaP LRHS MBNS MHol MRav NBir NRHS SPer SPoG SRms SWvt WCAu WFar WMoo
§ 'Rosa Triumph' EBee
'Rotes Meer' CMac EBee MRav
rotundifolius 'Caerulescens' see *Bellis caerulescens*
salsuginosus misapplied see *Eurybia sibirica*
§ 'Schneewittchen' ♀H5 CBod CRos CSam EBee ELan EPPr LRHS MBNS MBel MPie MRav NGdn NRHS SRms SWvt WGwG
§ 'Schwarzes Meer' EBee ELon WCot
scopulinus ITim WOld
simplex CRos LRHS NRHS
'Sincerity' XLum
'Snow Queen' SWvt
SNOW WHITE see *E.* 'Schneewittchen'
'Sommerneuschnee' EBee MTis NDov SCob SHar WCAu
speciosus 'Grandiflora' CBod WArt
'Strahlenmeer' NBre
'Synehurst' WCot WFar
trifidus see *E. compositus* var. *discoideus*
uniflorus MAsh SRms
'Violetta' **new** SPoG
'Wayne Roderick' CRos ECtt ELan EPfP LRHS NRHS WFar
'White Quakeress' CFis CMea LLHF MHCG MRav WCot WFar

Erinacea (*Papilionaceae*)

§ ***anthyllis*** ♀H5 WAbe WThu XEll
pungens see *E. anthyllis*

Erinus (*Plantaginaceae*)

alpinus ♀H6 ECtt EDAr GAbr GJos GKev MAsh NBir NGrd SRms WFar XLum
- var. ***albus*** GMaP SRms WHoo XLum
- 'Doktor Hähnle' EDAr GJos GMaP SRms WHoo XLum

Eriobotrya (*Rosaceae*)

sp. LPra
'Coppertone' see × *Rhaphiobotrya* 'Coppertone'
japonica (F) ♀H4 CAbb CBcs CCCN CRos CTsd ELan EPfP EUJe LPra LRHS MGos MMuc NLar SArc SCoo SEND SPer SPlb SSta SVic WHer WPGP
- 'Gold Nugget' (F) XBlo
- 'Mrs Cookson' (F) CFGn WMat
- 'Oliver' (F) CFGn WMat
- 'Rose-Anne' SGol WPGP

Eriobotrya × *Rhaphiolepis* see × *Rhaphiobotrya*

Eriocapitella see *Anemone*

Eriocephalus (*Asteraceae*)

africanus CBod SPlb WJek

Eriogonum (*Polygonaceae*)

alleni 'Little Rascal' ELan
grande var. ***rubescens*** EBee
ovalifolium GKev
- Wellington form GKev
umbellatum EPot GKev
- var. ***humistratum*** WAbe
- var. ***porteri*** GKev
- var. ***torreyanum*** CMea

Eriophorum (*Cyperaceae*)

angustifolium CBen CWat EHoe LLWG MWts SPlb WMAq WPnP WWtn XLum
chamissonis MWts
latifolium LLWG MWts XLum
rousseauianum LLWG
vaginatum EHoe EWat LLWG XLum

Eriophyllum (*Asteraceae*)

lanatum EBee ECha ELan EPfP MMuc NBid NGBl SHar

Eriostemon (*Rutaceae*)

myoporoides see *Philotheca myoporoides*

Eritrichium (*Boraginaceae*)

aretioides GKev SPlb
villosum GKev

Erodium (*Geraniaceae*)

absinthoides CRos EPot LRHS NRHS XSen
- var. ***amanum*** see *E. amanum*
§ ***acaule*** EPPr
'Almodovar' WCot WFar
§ ***amanum*** CSpe ECtt EWes GMaP
'Ardwick Redeye' EPot
balearicum see *E.* × *variabile* 'Album'
'Caroline' CMea WHoo
carvifolium GKev
§ ***castellanum*** LLHF NLar
- 'La Féline' GCrg
celtibericum EPot
- 'Peñagolosa' XSen
'Cézembre' WCot
chamaedryoides see *E. reichardii*

	– 'Roseum'	see *E.* × *variabile* 'Roseum'
	cheilanthifolium 'David Crocker'	WAbe
	chrysanthum	CElw CTri EBou ECha ECtt EDAr ELan EPfP EPot MMuc MPnt NChi NLar SEND SRot SWvt WSHC XLum XSen
	– (f)	WFar
	– (m)	NRya
	– 'Arcadia'	CMea SPhx
	– pink-flowered	CSpe ECtt EHrv EPot MMuc SEND SRot
	– 'Special Rose'	CSpe
	'County Park'	ECha SHar SRms WFar XSen
	daucoides misapplied	see *E. castellanum*
	daucoides ambig.	GKev
	'Fran's Delight'	CMea CSpe ECtt SBch WAbe WFar WHoo
	'Freedom'	CBor IPot MHol SCob WFar XEll
	'Fripetta'	WIce
	'Géant de Saint Cyr'	ECtt
	'Gini's Choice'	WCot
	glandulosum ♀H5	CCBP EBee ELan EPfP MAsh MMuc NLar SEND SPtp SRms SRot WFar WSHC XLum XSen
	'Grey Blush'	WKif
	gruinum	SPhx
	guttatum misapplied	see *E.* 'Katherine Joy'
	guttatum (Desf.) Willd.	CWGN EPot GMaP SRms
	hymenodes L'Hér.	see *E. trifolium*
	'Julie Ritchie'	CSpe WHoo
§	'Katherine Joy'	CBor ECtt EPot EWes GCrg MHer NRya SRot WFar
	× ***kolbianum***	WAbe WCot WFar WHoo
	– 'Natasha'	CBor ECtt EPPr EPot EWes MHer MMuc SEND WIce WKif
	'Las Meninas'	ECtt WCot
	× ***lindavicum***	GCrg MHer NChi
	macradenum	see *E. glandulosum*
	manescavii ♀H5	Widely available
	'Marchants Mikado'	WKif
	'Maryla'	CBor CMea WFar WIce
	'Merstham Pink'	SRms XLum
	'Mesquita'	CMea
	'Milly'	CMea
	'Pallidum'	CSam
	pelargoniiflorum	CAby CPla CRos CSpe EBee ELan EMor EPfP LRHS MCot MNHC NRHS SAko SEND SRms SWvt WArt WFar WKif WTor
	'Peter Vernon'	MHer
	petraeum subsp. ***petraeum***	EPot
	'Purple Haze'	ELan EMor SRms SRot WFar
§	***reichardii***	CRos CTri ECtt LRHS MBrN NRHS SPoG SRms WCFE
	– 'Album'	CRos EBou GCrg LRHS MAsh MHol MMuc NHpl NRHS SPoG WFar WHoo
	– 'Bianca'	ELan EMor EPfP
	– 'Jenny'	NHpl
	– 'Rubrum'	MAsh
	'Robertino'	WAbe
	rodiei	EWes
	romanum	see *E. acaule*
§	***rupestre***	SRms SRot WIce
	'Souvenir d'Hélène'	XSen
	'Spanish Eyes'	CDor EBee ECtt GCrg LRHS MHol MPie SRot SWvt WCot WFar WKif WWFP
	'Stephanie'	CBor ECtt ELan EPot EWes MHer MMuc SEND WIce XSen
	supracanum	see *E. rupestre*
	'Tiny Kyni'	WFar XSen
	trichomanifolium L'Hér.	EWes
§	***trifolium***	ELan MHer SBch SPhx WBrk
	× ***variabile***	WFar
§	– 'Album'	CMea CRos EPfP EPot GCrg GKev GMaP LRHS MHer NAln NEgg NGrd NRHS SRms SRot SWvt WAbe WBrk WFar WTor
I	– 'Bishop's Form'	CBod CMea CRos ECtt EPfP EPot GCrg GJos GMaP LRHS MAsh MBel MHol MJak NEgg NQui NRHS NRya SPoG SRms SRot SWvt WAbe WBrk WCFE WFar WGwG WHoo WIce
	– 'Candy'	ECtt MHer NHpl SRot
	– 'Flore Pleno' (d)	CRos CTri ELan EPfP EWes GCrg ITim LRHS MHer NHpl NRHS SPoG SRms SRot WBrk
	– 'Red Rock'	CTri
§	– 'Roseum' ♀H5	CBod EBou ECtt ELan MMuc NCou SEND SIgm SPlb SRms WBrk

Erpetion see *Viola*

Eruca (*Brassicaceae*)

vesicaria	ENfk
– subsp. ***sativa***	CSpe GPoy MHer MNHC SRms SVic

Eryngium (*Apiaceae*)

	from Mexico **new**	SBrt
§	***agavifolium***	Widely available
	– giant	SMad WPGP
	alpinum	CBod CSpe ECha GKev GMaP MGos MSCN NAln NBir SCob SPer SPhx SRms SRot WCAu WFar
	– 'Amethyst'	CRos LRHS LSRN NRHS
	– 'Blue Star'	CAby CExl CSpe EBee ECtt EHrv ELan ELon EMor GPSL NAln NLar WBor WFar WSpi
	– 'Slieve Donard'	see *E.* × *zabelii* 'Donard Variety'
	– 'Superbum'	CRos ECtt GAbr GCal GLog LRHS NRHS SRms
	amethystinum	CBod LRHS WFar
	'Blue Jackpot'	CBod EBee ECtt EPfP EWes MBel MHol MNrw
	'Blue Steel'	EBee LLHF
	bourgatii	Widely available
	– Graham Stuart Thomas's selection	CDor CEnd CExl CRos CSpe ECtt EHrv ELan EPPr EWes GAbr GMaP LRHS MBel MCot MHol NBid NBir NEgg NRHS SPad SRms WCAu WCot WHoo WHrl WKif WSpi
	– 'Oxford Blue' ♀H5	LRHS MHer NLar NSla SPtp SWvt
	– 'Picos Amethyst' ♀H5	CBcs CBct CMac CRos EBee EMor EPfP IPot LCro LOPS LRHS LSRN MBel NRHS SCob SCoo SMad SPtp SRms WSHC
	– 'Picos Blue'PBR	Widely available
	bromeliifolium misapplied	see *E. agavifolium*, *E. eburneum*
	bromeliifolium F. Delaroche	CRos LRHS NRHS
	campestre	SPhx
	'Cobalt Star'	GWyn MAvo MRav SMHy
	creticum	MNrw
	cymosum B&SWJ 10267	WCru
	decaisneanum misapplied	see *E. pandanifolium*
	deppeanum F&M 54	WPGP
	Dove Cottage hybrid	MAvo

ebracteatum	CSpe LEdu
- var. ***poterioides***	ELan EMor IPot LPla LRHS NDov SPhx SPtp
§ ***eburneum***	CBod ECha ELan EPfP EWes GMaP ILea LRHS SIgm SMad
aff. ***eburneum***	CMac
'Electric Haze'	CSam ECtt
§ ***giganteum*** 🏆H6	Widely available
- 'Silver Ghost' 🏆H6	CAby CBod CExl CPla CSam CSpe ECtt GMaP LCro LOPS LRHS MHol MSCN NChi NDov NGdn NLar NSti SPhx SWvt WAvo WCot WFar WSpi
glaciale	GKev
- from Sierra Nevada, Spain	SBrt
gracile B&SWJ 10441	WCru
'Green Jade'	CRos LRHS NRHS
guatemalense B&SWJ 10397	ESwi WCru
heterophyllum new	SPhx
horridum misapplied	see *E. eburneum*
horridum ambig.	EWes MNrw NLar SArc
humboldtii B&SWJ 14342	WCru
aff. ***humboldtii*** B&SWJ 14367	WCru
humile B&SWJ 10464	WCru
- var. ***brevibracteatum*** B&SWJ 14735 new	WCru
'Indigo Star'	MAvo
leavenworthii	CRos LRHS NRHS
- 'Purple Sheen' new	MCot
longifolium B&SWJ 14786 new	WCru
maritimum	CEls CKel CPla CPou CSpe GPoy MNHC SPhx SPlb SRms
Miss Willmott's ghost	see *E. giganteum*
× ***oliverianum*** 🏆H5	CDor CMea CTri CWCL ECtt ELan EPfP GAbr GKev LRHS MCot MRav NBir NLar SPer SPoG SWvt WCot WKif
§ ***pandanifolium*** 🏆H4	CKno ELan EUJe EWes GCal MNrw SArc SEND SMHy SPlb SPoG SWvt
- 'Physic Purple'	CAby CDor CSpe ELan GPSL LRHS MAvo SPtp WCot
paniculatum B&SWJ 14367 new	WCru
- B&SWJ 14826 new	WCru
'Pen Blue'	CAby CDor CMea CSam CSpe CWld EBee ECha ECtt EPfP LRHS MAvo MGos MHol MNrw SAko SCob SPoG WCAu WCot WHoo WTor
planum	Widely available
§ - 'Blauer Zwerg'	GMaP LRHS NLar WFar
- 'Blaukappe'	CExl CMea CRos EAJP EBee ELan ELon EMor EPfP LRHS LSun MMuc NLar NRHS SEND SPhx SRms WFar
- BLUE DWARF	see *E. planum* 'Blauer Zwerg'
- 'Blue Glitter'	CBod CCBP CDor CRos EBee ELon GPSL LRHS MWat NLar SPhx SWvt
- 'Blue Hobbit'	CExl CMea CRos EBee ECtt EHoe ELan ELon EPfP GEdr GKev LBuc LRHS LSun MGos MHer MTin NGdn NLar NQui NWad SCob SMad SPad SRms SWvt WFar
- 'Blue Ribbon'	CSam
- 'Flüela'	EShb EWes GCal IKil LRHS LSRN NEgg NRHS
- 'Jade Frost'PBR (v)	CBcs CBct CBod CDor CExl CNor CRos CWCL CWGN EBee ELan EMor EPfP EWes IKil LLHF LRHS MBNS MHol MNrw MTis NLar NPri NRHS SCob SPad SPoG SRms SWvt WCot
- 'Little Blue Wonder'PBR	NHol
- 'Naughty Jackpot' (v)	NLar
- 'Paradise Jackpot'PBR	SRms
- 'Seven Seas'	LRHS MBNS NEgg NRHS
- 'Silver Salentino'	CBod ELon GPSL
- 'Silver Stone'	SRms
- 'Tetra Petra'	LRHS SRms
- 'Tiny Jackpot'	CWGN GEdr GMaP NLar
- 'White Glitter'	CBod EBee ELan
proteiflorum	CBod LRHS NDov SMad SPlb WFar
serbicum	GCal
serra	CRos EWes LRHS NRHS
tricuspidatum	CRos EBee ECtt LRHS NRHS
× ***tripartitum*** 🏆H5	CBcs CBod CRos CTri EBee ECha ECtt EHrv ELan EMor EPfP EWTr GMaP LRHS LSRN MBel MNrw MRav NBro NEgg NLar NRHS SRkn SWvt WAvo
* ***umbelliferum***	GCal MBNS
variifolium	Widely available
- 'Miss Marble'	EPfP LSun NGrd SRms WFar WSHC
venustum	CRos LRHS NRHS SMad
yuccifolium	CSpe EBee EMor EPfP EWes GCal LEdu LRHS MAvo SPhx SPlb SWvt XLum
- 'Kershaw Blue'	WPGP
× ***zabelii***	CDor ECha EMor
- 'Big Blue' 🏆H5	Widely available
§ - 'Donard Variety'	ECtt GCal ILea LRHS MAvo MCot NCGa NLar
- 'Forncett Ultra'	MNrw
- 'Jos Eijking'PBR	Widely available
- 'Neptune's Gold'PBR	CAby CBcs CBct CPla CWGN EBee ECtt EMor EPfP EUJe GMaP LCro LOPS LRHS MHol MJak NEoE NHpl NLar NPri NSti SCob SHar SMad SPad SPer SPoG
- 'Violetta'	CBod CSpe EBee ELon EMor EPfP LRHS MAvo MCot NCGa NDov NLar NRHS WCAu WFar WTor

Erysimum ✿ (*Brassicaceae*)

'Apricot Delight'	see *E.* 'Apricot Twist'
§ 'Apricot Twist'	CBcs CBod CMea CRos CSpe CWCL CWGN ECtt ELan ELon EPfP GBin GMaP LRHS MCot MHol NLar NRHS SCob SCoo SPer SPoG SRms SWvt WFar WHil WHoo
arenicola var. ***torulosum***	see *E. torulosum*
arkansanum	see *E. helveticum*
'Audrey's Pink'	CCBP WHoo
bicolor from La Gomera	WArt
bonannianum new	WCot
'Bowles's Mauve' 🏆H4	Widely available
'Bowles's Purple'	SRms SWvt
'Bowles's Yellow'	MHCG NWad WCot
'Bredon'	NPer WKif
'Butterscotch'	WHoo
cheiri	MHer NGrd NPri
- 'Baden-Powell' (d)	GCal
- 'Blood Red'	CSpe LCro LOPS
- 'Bloody Warrior' (d)	CElw ECtt
- 'Fire King'	LCro LOPS
- 'Harpur Crewe' (d)	NPer SRms WHer
concinnum	see *E. suffrutescens*
'Constant Cheer'	CCBP CElw CMea CSBt CWCL EAJP ECtt ELan EPfP MCot MMuc NLar

	NPer SCob SEND SRkn SRms SWvt WHoo WKif WSpi
'Cotswold Gem' (v)	ELon GPSL MHer MMuc NPer SEND SIgm SWvt
'Dawn Breaker'	ECtt
'Desert Island'	ECtt MAsh
'Dorothy Elmhirst'	see *E.* 'Mrs L.K. Elmhirst'
'Gogh's Gold' (Artist Series)	WHlf
'Golden Jubilee'	ECtt LRHS SRms WIce
§ ***helveticum***	SRms
'Jacob's Jacket'	ECha MBNS MHer NPer
'John Codrington'	GBin NPer WKif WSpi
'Joseph's Coat'	MHCG
kotschyanum	EBou ELon GCrg NRHS NSla SIgm SRms WHal WIce
'Lemon Light'	WHoo
linifolium	SRms
- LEMON YELLOW ('Balcherlemy') (Cheers Series) **new**	CBod
- MIGHTY MAUVE ('Balchermauv') (Cheers Series) **new**	CBod
§ - 'Variegatum' (v)	CCCN CSBt CWCL EAJP ECtt ELan EPfP EUJe LCro LOPS LRHS MHol NHic NPer NPri SCob SHar SPer SPoG SRot WHer XLum
- 'Variegatum' peach-flowered (v)	NQui
'Moonlight'	GMaP MRav NBir SRms WHoo
§ 'Mrs L.K. Elmhirst'	NPer
mutabile	CTri EPfP WHal
'Orange Flame'	CMea EBou ECha GCrg MHer NPer SEND WHoo
'Orange Zwerg'	MMuc WIce
'Paint Box' (Artist Series)	IKil WHlf
'Parish's'	CCBP CElw CFis CSpe CWld WGoo
'Parkwood Gold'	NHpl
'Pastel Patchwork'	CRos CSpe ECtt EPfP LRHS NRHS WCot WFar
Perry's hybrid	NPer
'Perry's Peculiar'	NPer
'Perry's Surprise'	NPer
'Perry's Variegated' (v)	NPer
'Plant World Lemon'	CDor NLar
§ ***pulchellum***	ECha GKev NAln
pumilum DC.	see *E. helveticum*
'Red Jep'	CRos CSpe ELan EPfP LRHS NRHS WNPC WTor
rupestre	see *E. pulchellum*
'Ruston Royal'	ECha MAvo
RYSI COPPER	CRos LRHS NRHS SPoG
RYSI GOLD ('Innrysigol'^{PBR})	NRHS
scoparium	ECha ELon
'Sissinghurst Variegated'	see *E. linifolium* 'Variegatum'
'Spice Island'	ECtt MAsh SCob
'Sprite'	CMea CTri NPer
'Stars and Stripes' (v)	CBod CRos ECtt LRHS SRkn WCFE
§ ***suffrutescens***	EBee
SUNBURST ('Listrace')	CDor ECtt WCot
'Sweet Sorbet'	MBNS NLar SRkn SWvt
§ ***torulosum***	GKev
WALBERTON'S FRAGRANT STAR ('Walfrastar'^{PBR}) (v)	CRos EPfP LRHS NRHS SPoG SRms
WALBERTON'S FRAGRANT SUNSHINE ('Walfrasun')	CRos LRHS NRHS SCoo SPoG
'Wenlock Beauty'	CFis SRms
'Winter Joy'	CRos ELan EPfP IKil LLHF LRHS MBNS NLar SHar
WINTER ORCHID	CWGN NLar
'Winter Passion'	CRos LRHS MBNS NRHS SPoG
WINTER SORBET ('Inneryws'^{PBR})	ECtt ELan EPfP LRHS

Erythraea see *Centaurium*

Erythrina (*Papilionaceae*)

abyssinica	SPlb
amazonica	SPlb
arborescens	SPlb
× ***bidwillii***	CCCN WPGP
crista-galli 🏆^{H3}	CBcs CCCN CDTJ CHll CKel CRos CSpe EBee ELan EPfP LRHS MGil SPlb WCot WPGP
- 'Compacta'	LRHS
flabelliformis	SPlb
guatemalensis	SPlb
herbacea	SPlb
§ ***humeana***	SPlb
latissima	SPlb
lysistemon	SPlb
princeps	see *E. humeana*
rubrinervia	SPlb
speciosa	SPlb
vespertilio	SPlb

Erythronium ✿ (*Liliaceae*)

albidum	GEdr GKev IBlr LAma MPie
americanum	GKev IBlr LAma MNrw WAbe
'Apple Blossom' 🏆^{H4}	IBlr
'Ballyrogan's Blaze'	IBlr
'Beechpark'	IBlr
'Blush'	IBlr
'Bronze Beauty'	IBlr
'Bryn Meifod'	WAbe
'Californian Star'	IBlr
'Californian Sunshine'	IBlr
californicum	CRos EBee GKev IBlr LRHS MAvo MNrw NRHS
- 'Ballyrogan Bronze Bounty'	IBlr
- 'Brimstone'	IBlr
- 'Brocklamont Inheritance' 🏆^{H5}	IBlr
- 'Bronze Edge'	IBlr
- 'Dark Delight'	IBlr
- Plas Merdyn form	IBlr
- 'Stellar'	IBlr
- 'White Beauty' 🏆^{H5}	Widely available
- 'White Beauty' dark-leaved **new**	MAvo
'Carol Scott'	IBlr
caucasicum	EPot
citrinum	LLHF
'Citronella'	GKev IBlr
cliftonii hort.	see *E. multiscapideum* Cliftonii Group
'Craigton Beauty'	IBlr
'Craigton Cover Girl'	IBlr
'Craigton Cream'	IBlr
'Delicacy'	IBlr
dens-canis	CAvo CBod CBro CTca CTri CWCL ELan EMor EPot ERCP GBin GEdr GKev GMaP IBlr IFro LAma LEdu MBel MNrw NBir NEgg NHol NRya SCob WAbe WBor WPnP WShi
- 'Charmer'	GEdr GKev MNrw
- 'Frans Hals'	EPot GEdr GKev LEdu WAbe
- large-flowered	IBlr

	– 'Lilac Wonder' ♀H5	EBee EPot GEdr GKev GMaP LAma LEdu MCot MNrw NWad SDeJ
*	– 'Moerheimii' (d)	GEdr GKev IBlr
	– var. ***niveum***	EPot GEdr IBlr
	– 'Old Aberdeen' ♀H5	CAvo CRos CWCL EHrv IBlr LLHF LRHS MAvo NRHS WAbe
	– 'Pink Perfection'	EBee GEdr GKev LEdu MNrw SDeJ WAbe
	– 'Purple King'	EBee EPot GEdr GKev GMaP LAma LEdu MNrw NHol NHpl NWad SDeJ WAbe
	– 'Rose Queen'	EHrv EPot GEdr GKev GMaP LAma LEdu MAvo MNrw NWad SDeJ
	– 'Snowflake'	CAvo CRos EPot GEdr GKev LAma LEdu LRHS MNrw NBir NHol NHpl NRHS NWad SDeJ WAbe
	– 'Valerie Wollaston' **new**	MAvo
	– 'White Splendour'	EPot GEdr IBlr LEdu MAvo MNrw
	'Eirene'	IBlr
	elegans	EBee GKev NHpl
	'Flaire'	IBlr
	'Flash'	IBlr
§	***grandiflorum***	CWCL EMor
	– subsp. ***chrysandrum***	see *E. grandiflorum*
	'Harvington Snowgoose'	CBro CRos EHrv IBlr LEdu LLHF LRHS NHar NRHS
	helenae	IBlr MNrw
	hendersonii ♀H5	CRos EHrv IBlr LAma LRHS NRHS SPlb WAbe XEll
	– 'Pacific Skies'	IBlr
	– 'Pacific Sunshine'	IBlr
	'Hidcote Beauty'	CRos LLHF LRHS NRHS
	'Janice' ♀H5	IBlr WAbe
	japonicum	EPot GKev LAma MNrw
	'Jeanette Brickell'	IBlr
	'Jeannine'	GKev IBlr
	'Joanna' ♀H5	GEdr IBlr MAvo MNrw WAbe
	'John Brookes'	IBlr
	'Kinfauns Pink'	CWCL EBee ELon EMor EPot GBin GEdr GKev GMaP IBlr LAma LLHF WCot
	'Kondo'	CBod CRos CTri EPfP GKev GMaP IBlr LAma LRHS NBir NHol NLar NRHS NWad SCob SDeJ
	'Lavender Eye'	IBlr
	'Margaret Mathew'	IBlr WAbe
	'Minnehaha'	IBlr
§	***multiscapideum***	CWCL EMor LLHF MAvo MNrw WSHC
§	– Cliftonii Group ♀H4	MAvo WAbe
	'Oregon Encore'	IBlr
	oregonum	CRos CWCL EHrv EMor GKev IBlr LAma LLHF LRHS MNrw NHpl NRHS
	– subsp. ***leucandrum*** 'The Giant'	IBlr
	oregonum × ***revolutum***	IBlr
	'Pagoda' ♀H5	Widely available
	purdyi	see *E. multiscapideum*
	'Purple Heart'	IBlr
	revolutum	CAvo CBro CRos CWCL EBee ELon EMor GBin GEdr GKev GMaP IBlr LAma LCro LOPS LRHS MNrw NAln NHar NHpl NLar NRHS SChF SRot WCru
	– from God's Valley, Oregon	IBlr MNrw
I	– 'Album' **new**	IBlr
	– 'Ballyrogan White Blusher'	IBlr
	– 'Dark Dapple'	IBlr
	– 'Guincho Splendour'	IBlr
	– 'Inferno'	IBlr
I	– 'Inshriach Form'	IBlr
	– Johnsonii Group	EPot WAbe WCru
	– 'Knightshayes'	CRos EBee IBlr LRHS MAvo NRHS
	– 'Knightshayes Pink'	CAvo EHrv IBlr LAma LLHF NBir WShi
	– 'Pink Beauty'	CPla
	– Plas Merdyn form	IBlr
	– 'Rose Beauty'	GKev
	– 'Wild Salmon'	CRos EBee EHrv LLHF LRHS MAvo NHar NRHS
	'Rippling Waters'	IBlr
	'Rosalind'	IBlr NHar WAbe
	rostratum **new**	GKev
	sibiricum	GKev LAma NHpl
	'Spring Fresh'	IBlr
	'Sundisc' ♀H4	ECha GKev IBlr WAbe
	'Sunshine'	IBlr
	'Susannah'	CRos IBlr LRHS NRHS
	tuolumnense	CWCL EHrv EMor GEdr GKev GMaP IBlr LAma MAvo MCot MNrw NAln NHpl NWad SDeJ WAbe
	– EBA clone 2	IBlr
	– EBA clone 3	IBlr
	– Plas Merdyn form	IBlr
	– 'Spindlestone'	CRos GEdr IBlr LAma LLHF LRHS NHar NRHS WAbe
	umbilicatum	EPot GEdr GKev IBlr NHpl
	'White Star'	IBlr
	'Winifred Loraine'	IBlr

Escallonia (Escalloniaceae)

	sp.	CPer
	'Alice'	SCob SPer
	angustifolia var. ***coquimbensis*** **new**	WPav
	'Apple Blossom' ♀H4	Widely available
§	***bifida*** ♀H3	CDul CRos EBee ELan EPfP LRHS NRHS WPGP
	'C.F. Ball'	CBcs CRos CTri ELan EPfP IArd LRHS MAsh MSwo NEgg NWea SGol SRms
	'Compacta Coccinea'	LRHS
	'Donard Beauty'	SRms
	'Donard Brilliance'	SGol SRms
	'Donard Radiance' ♀H4	CBcs CDul CKel CMac CSBt EMOT EPfP EShb NHic NLar NWad NWea SCob SGol SLim SPer SPoG SRms SWvt WFar
	'Donard Seedling'	CBcs CCVT CDul CKel CRos EBou ECrN ELan EMOT EPfP LRHS MAsh MGos MMuc MSwo NEgg NHic NPer NRHS NWea SCob SGol SLim SPer SRms SWvt WFar
	'Donard Star'	EPfP NLar NWad NWea WCFE
	'Donard White'	CBod EPfP NLar SPoG
	'Edinensis'	EPfP NLar SRms WSpi
	'Everest'	CRos LRHS MMuc SLon
	× ***exoniensis***	SRms
	GOLDEN CARPET ('Alcaura')	CBod CRos GBin LRHS MAsh MJak MTin NEoE NRHS SCob SHar SPoG WFar
	'Hopleys Gold'	see *E. laevis* 'Gold Brian'
	illinita	CDul NLar WPav
	'Iveyi' ♀H4	Widely available
	'Jamie' PBR	LLHF LSRN
§	***laevis***	LRHS
§	– 'Gold Brian' PBR	CDul CMac CRos EHoe EPfP LRHS LSRN MAsh MGos MJak NLar NRHS SCob SGol SPer

- 'Gold Ellen' (v)	CKel CRos CSBt CTri EHoe ELan EMOT EPfP EUJe LRHS LSRN MAsh MGos MRav MSwo NEgg NHol NLar NRHS SCob SCoo SEND SLim SPer SPoG SRms SWvt WBor
- PINK ELLE ('Lades'PBR)	CKel CPer CRos CSBt EBee EPfP LCro LOPS LRHS MAsh MGos NRHS SCob SPoG WFar
'Langleyensis' ♀H4	CMac CTri NWea SCob SGol SRms
× ***mollis***	SPer
montevidensis	see *E. bifida*
myrtilloides B&SWJ 14329	WCru
organensis	see *E. laevis*
'Peach Blossom' ♀H4	CBar CKel CRos EBee ELan EPfP LRHS MAsh MMuc MSwo NEgg NHol NRHS SCob SCoo SEND SGol SLim SPer SRms WFar
'Pride of Donard' ♀H4	CAco CSBt EPfP MGos SCob SRms
pulverulenta	WPav
RED CARPET ('Loncar'PBR)	CBcs GBin LRHS SCob SLon WNPC
'Red Dream'	CRos CSBt EPfP GBin LRHS MAsh MGos MSwo NLar NRHS SCob SCoo SPoG SRms SWvt WAvo WFar
'Red Elf'	CKel CMac CRos EBou ELan EMOT EPfP GKin LRHS MGos NEgg NHic SCob SPer SPlb SRms SWvt WFar
'Red Hedger'	CBod CDul CSBt CTsd ECrN ELan MRav SCob SRms
'Red Knight'	CRos LRHS MAsh NEgg NHic NHol NRHS WNPC
resinosa	CExl CMCN CTsd SPlb SRms SVen WPav
revoluta	CTri MGil WPav
rubra 'Crimson Spire' ♀H4	CBar CBcs CDul CKel CRos CSBt CTri ECrN EMOT EPfP GKin LRHS LSRN MAsh MGos MMuc MRav NBir NEgg SCob SEND SGbt SLim SPer SPlb SRms
- 'Ingramii'	SEND
- var. ***macrantha***	Widely available
- 'Pygmaea'	see *E. rubra* 'Woodside'
§ - 'Woodside'	CMCN LLHF NWad SGol SRms
'Silver Anniversary'	MSwo
'Slieve Donard'	CMac MRav NWea SRms
tucumanensis	SPlb
'Ventnor'	SPlb SVen
virgata	WPav

Eschscholzia (*Papaveraceae*)

californica	MBel
- 'Alba'	CSpe
- var. ***maritima***	CSpe
- subsp. ***mexicana*** 'Sun Shades'	SPhx
- 'Mission Bells'	LCro
- 'Red Chief'	LRHS SPhx

Espeletia (*Asteraceae*)

argentea B&SWJ 14322	WCru
killipii B&SWJ 14319	WCru
aff. ***killipii***	WCru
aff. ***lopezii*** B&SWJ 14374	WCru
aff. ***summapacis***	WCru
uribei B&SWJ 14339	WCru

Esterhuysenia (*Aizoaceae*)

alpina	CPBP SPlb

Eucalyptus ✿ (*Myrtaceae*)

sp.	LPra
aggregata	SArc SKin
alpina	SPlb WPav
amygdalina	SPlb
approximans	SKin
archeri	CDTJ CDul CRos EPfP LRHS MGos MMuc NLar SKin
caesia ♀H2	SPlb
camaldulensis	LMaj SPlb
camphora	CCCN CTsd EMOT SKin
cinerea	CTsd SKin SPlb
citriodora	see *Corymbia citriodora*
coccifera	CBcs CSBt CTsd EUJe MMuc NPer SKin SPlb
cordata	EPfP IDee SKin WPGP
crenulata	SKin
crucis subsp. ***crucis***	SPlb
cypellocarpa	SPlb
dalrympleana ♀H5	CAbb CKel CRos EPfP EUJe LRHS LSRN MGos MMuc NPer SEND SKin SLim SPer SPlb WCot WPGP
debeuzevillei	see *E. pauciflora* subsp. *debeuzevillei*
delegatensis	NPer
divaricata	see *E. gunnii* subsp. *divaricata*
erythrocorys	SPlb
eximia	see *Corymbia eximia*
ficifolia	see *Corymbia ficifolia*
fraxinoides	SPlb
gamophylla	SPlb
glaucescens	CAbb CRos LRHS SArc SEWo SKin SPer
globulus	CWCL LPra SPlb
§ ***gregsoniana***	SKin SPlb
gunnii ♀H5	Widely available
- AZURA ('Cagire'PBR)	CKel IBal LCro LOPS LSRN NLar SCob SEWo SLim SLon WMat
§ - subsp. ***divaricata***	SKin
* - 'Silver Drop'	WFar
johnstonii	IDee SKin SPer
kitsoniana	SKin
kruseana	SPlb
kybeanensis	SKin WCot
leucoxylon subsp. ***megalocarpa***	SPlb
ligustrina	SKin
macrocarpa	SPlb
mitchelliana	EBee SKin
moorei var. ***nana***	CDTJ
neglecta	SKin
nicholii	CAbb CBcs CRos CSpe EPfP EWes LRHS MGos MMuc SCoo SKin SPoG WPGP
niphophila	see *E. pauciflora* subsp. *niphophila*
nitens	CDTJ SKin SPlb
§ ***nitida***	SKin
parviflora	SKin
parvula ♀H5	CCCN CMac EPfP MMuc MRav SEND
pauciflora	CCCN CTsd EMOT SPer
§ - subsp. ***debeuzevillei*** ♀H5	CAbb SArc SKin WPGP
- var. ***nana***	see *E. gregsoniana*
§ - subsp. ***niphophila*** ♀H5	Widely available
perriniana	CAco CBcs CRos ECrN EPfP EUJe LRHS MGos SKin SPer SPlb SPoG SWvt WFar WMat
pulverulenta	CMac SPlb WFar
- 'Baby Blue'	CKel CTsd ELan SKin SPer SWvt WFar
regnans	IDee SKin
rossii	SPlb

	rubida	CCCN GAbr IDee SKin
	sideroxylon	SPlb
	- 'Rosea'	SPlb
	simmondsii	see *E. nitida*
	stellulata	SKin
	stricta	SKin
	subcrenulata	EPfP SKin
	tetraptera	SPlb
	torquata	SPlb
	urnigera	CMCN EBee
	vernicosa	SKin
	viminalis	IDee SKin

Eucharidium see *Clarkia*

Eucharis (*Amaryllidaceae*)

§	***amazonica*** ♀H1b	CCCN LAma SDeJ
	grandiflora misapplied	see *E. amazonica*

Eucomis ✿ (*Asparagaceae*)

	ALOHA	see *E.* 'Leia'
	autumnalis misapplied	see *E. zambesiaca*
§	***autumnalis*** (Mill.) Chitt. ♀H4	CBod CBro EPot ERCP GKev LAma LRHS SDeJ SPer SPlb WCot
	- subsp. ***amaryllidifolia***	CBro
	bicolor ♀H4	Widely available
	- 'Alba'	CBro CExl CTca EPot GKev LAma
	- 'Stars and Stripes'	WCru
§	***comosa***	CAvo CBro CHll CPrp CRos CSam CTca EBee ERCP EShb GKev LAma LRHS NRHS SDeJ WCot
	- 'Cherry Blossom'	LAma
	- 'Cornwood'	CAvo CTca GKev
	- 'Johannesburg'	EBee GKev
	- 'Kilimanjaro'	CTca EBee
	- 'Lotte'	CTca
	- 'Oakhurst'	CAby CBod CChe CPla CRos ECtt ESwi LRHS WCot
	- purple-leaved	CAvo EShb
	- 'Sparkling Burgundy' ♀H4	Widely available
	- 'Sparkling Rosy'	ERCP GKev IPot LAma SCob WFar
	- var. ***striata***	CAby EBee
	'Dark Star'	CAbb CSpe ECtt IPot SPad
	'Freckles'	CAby CPla SPad SPoG SRms
	'Glow Sticks'	CWGN ECtt WHil
	humilis	XEll
	- 'Twinkle Stars'	ERCP GKev LAma SCob SDeJ WFar
	'John Treasure'	SMHy
	'Joy's Purple'	CBro CPar CTca
§	'Leia'[PBR]	CBro CTca ERCP GKev LAma LRHS WHlf
	MAUI ('Gsalkele'[PBR]) (Aloha Lily Series) **new**	WHlf
	montana	CBro CPla CPrp CTca EBee EPot ERCP GKev LAma SDeJ WCot
	NANI ('Gsalipol'[PBR]) (Aloha Lily Series) **new**	WHlf
	pallidiflora ♀H3	CAvo LEdu WPGP
	'Pink Gin'	CAvo GKev IPot LAma
	'Playa Blanca'	CTca EBee EShb GKev LAma
	pole-evansii	CBro CExl CPar CTca ELan EUJe GKev LAma MRav SDeJ WAvo WCru WPtf
	- dark	GKev
	- pink-flowered	CPar
I	- 'Purpurea'	CExl GCal
	punctata	see *E. comosa*
	regia JCA 3.230.709	WCot
	undulata	see *E. autumnalis* (Mill.) Chitt.
	vandermerwei ♀H3	CBro CTca EBee EPot LAma LEdu NWad SDeJ SPlb
	- 'Octopus'	CCCN CExl CPrp CTca ELan EPfP GKev MHer WCot WFar
§	***zambesiaca***	CAvo CBro CPla CTca EBee GCal GKev LAma SMHy
	- JCA 3.230.709	WCot
	- JCA 3.231.010	WCot
	- 'White Dwarf'	CBcs CBod SPer WGwG
	'Zeal Bronze'	CTca GCal WAvo

Eucommia (*Eucommiaceae*)

	ulmoides	CDul CMCN EBtc NLar

Eucryphia ✿ (*Cunoniaceae*)

	cordifolia	CMac IDee MBlu WPav
§	***cordifolia* × *lucida***	CCCN SSta
	glutinosa ♀H4	CCCN CRos EPfP GGGa GKev IDee LRHS MAsh SAko WPav
	- 'Miniature'	CBct EPfP WPGP
	× ***hillieri***	WSpi
	- 'Winton'	CBct EBee WPGP
	× ***intermedia***	CCCN CExl CMac CTsd NLar SRms SSta
	- 'Rostrevor' ♀H4	CBcs CExl CJun CMac CRos CTho ELan EPfP GCal GGGa IArd IMou LRHS LSRN MAsh MBlu NLar SSta WPGP WSHC
	'Leatherwood Cream'	WSpi
	lucida	CBcs CCCN CRos LLHF LRHS MMuc NLar NRHS WSpi
	- 'Ballerina' ♀H4	CBcs CBct CJun CMac CRos CTho EBee ELan ELon EPfP GKin LRHS MAsh MPkF NRHS SAko SChF SCoo SMad SPoG WPGP
I	- 'Chaplin's Variety'	CBct EBee WPGP
	- 'Dumpling'	CExl EBee SChF WPGP
	- 'Gilt Edge' (v)	CBcs CRos LLHF LRHS NRHS SPoG
	- 'Leatherwood Cream' (v)	ELon WHor
	- 'Pink Cloud'	CBcs CDul CEnd CExl CJun CMac CRos CTho ELan EPfP GKin IArd LRHS LSRN MBlu MGil MGos MPkF NLar NRHS SAko SWvt WPGP
	- 'Spring Glow' (v)	CExl CRos GCal LLHF LRHS MAsh NRHS
	milliganii	CHll CMac CRos ELon EPfP LRHS MBlu MRav SAko SPer SRms SSta WPGP WSpi
	moorei	CCCN CExl CMac SAko WPGP
	× ***nymansensis***	CHab SArc SRms WSpi
	- 'George Graham'	GGGa
	- 'Mount Usher'	CRos
	- 'Nymans Silver' (v)	CBcs CDul CJun CKel CLnd CMac CRos CTho ELan GGGa LLHF LRHS MAsh SPer SPoG SSta
	- 'Nymansay' ♀H4	Widely available
	'Penwith' misapplied	see *E. cordifolia* × *lucida*
	'Penwith' ambig.	IArd IDee MGos

Eugenia (*Myrtaceae*)

	uniflora	CCCN

Eumorphia (*Asteraceae*)

	sericea	CFis GBin

Eunomia see *Aethionema*

Euodia (*Rutaceae*)

	daniellii	see *Tetradium daniellii*

Name	Suppliers
hupehensis	see *Tetradium daniellii* Hupehense Group

Euonymus ✿ (*Celastraceae*)

	Name	Suppliers
	sp.	LPra
	B&L 12543	EWes
	CC 4522	CExl
	NJM 09.109	CRHN
	NJM 10.106	WPGP
	from Kachin, Burma **new**	WPGP
	alatus	Widely available
	- B&SWJ 8794	WCru
	- var. ***apterus***	EPfP WGrn
	- 'Blade Runner'	CRos EPfP LRHS MGos NRHS SGol
	- CHICAGO FIRE	see *E. alatus* 'Timber Creek'
	- 'Ciliodentatus'	see *E. alatus* f. *striatus*
	- 'Compactus' ♀H6	Widely available
	- 'Fastigiata'	CJun
§	- 'Fire Ball'	CJun
*	- 'Macrophyllus'	CJun EPfP
	- 'Rudy Haag'	CJun
	- 'Select'	see *E. alatus* 'Fire Ball'
	- 'Silver Cloud'	EPfP NLar
§	- f. ***striatus***	CJun
	- - B&SWJ 11051	WCru
§	- 'Timber Creek'	CJun EPfP IDee MBlu NLar
	americanus	EPfP MBlu NLar
	- var. ***angustifolius*** B&SWJ 12905	WCru
	bungeanus	EPfP
	- B&SWJ 8782 from South Korea	WCru
	- 'Dart's Pride'	CJun EPfP NLar
	- 'Fireflame'	CJun WCot
*	- var. ***mongolicus***	EPfP
	- 'Pendulus'	MBlu
	- var. ***semipersistens***	CJun WCru
§	***carnosus***	CJun CMCN
	- CWJ 12425	WCru
	- 'Red Wine'	CJun EPfP LEdu LRHS MBlu NLar WCot
	chibae B&SWJ 11159	WCru
§	***clivicola***	CJun EBee EPfP WCru
	'Copper Wire'	EHoe
	cornutus	SPtp WPGP
	- var. ***quinquecornutus*** ♀H6	CJun CMCN ELan EPfP IArd MBlu MMrt SBrt SPoG WPGP
	'Den Haag'	CJun EPfP LRHS
	echinatus	IArd IDee
	europaeus	Widely available
	- from Slovakia	WCru
	- f. ***albus***	CTho EPfP LRHS NLar SPoG
	- 'Atropurpureus'	CMCN CTho EPfP NLar
	- 'Atrorubens'	CJun
	- 'Aucubifolius' (v)	CMac
*	- 'Aureus'	CNat
	- 'Brilliant'	CJun EPfP LRHS NLar
	- 'Chrysophyllus'	EPfP MBlu
	- var. ***intermedius***	CJun EPfP MBlu
	- 'Miss Pinkie'	CEnd
	- 'Red Cascade' ♀H6	Widely available
	- 'Scarlet Wonder'	CJun IArd NLar
	- 'Thornhayes'	CTho EPfP
	farreri	see *E. nanus*
	fimbriatus	CJun
	fortunei BLONDY ('Interbolwi'[PBR]) (v)	CBcs CKel CRos CTri ELan EPfP LRHS MAsh MGos MJak MMuc MSwo NEgg NLar NRHS SCob SCoo SEND SGol SLim SPoG SRms
	- 'Canadale Gold' (v)	CMac CRos EPfP LRHS MAsh NHol NRHS SLon WAvo
	- 'Coloratus'	EPfP MBlu MSwo
	- 'Country Gold'	WFar
	- DAN'S DELIGHT ('Dandel'[PBR]) (v)	MGos MThu SGol SPoG
	- 'Dart's Blanket'	EBee ELan EPfP MRav SCob SEND SGol
	- 'Emerald Gaiety' (v) ♀H5	Widely available
	- 'Emerald 'n' Gold' (v) ♀H5	Widely available
	- 'Gold Spot'	see *E. fortunei* 'Sunspot'
	- 'Gold Tip'	see *E. fortunei* 'Golden Prince'
	- GOLDEN HARLEQUIN ('Hoogi'[PBR]) (v)	CBcs CKel EPfP LRHS MAsh MThu NWad SPoG SWvt
§	- 'Golden Prince' (v)	CMac MRav MSwo NLar SRms
	- GOLDY ('Waldbolwi'[PBR])	EPfP NLar SGol SPoG
	- 'Harlequin' (v)	CBcs CKel CMac CRos CSBt ELan EPfP LBuc LRHS LSRN MAsh MBlu MGos MJak MRav NBir NRHS SGol SLim SPer SPoG SRms SWvt WFar
	- 'Heins Silver'[PBR]	EBee LRHS MGos SGol
	- 'Hort's Blaze'	EBee
	- 'Kewensis' ♀H5	CMac ELan EUJe GCal GEdr LRHS SArc SCob SPoG WCFE WCru
	- 'Kewensis Variegatus' (v)	MRav
	- 'Longwood'	LRHS
	- 'Minimus'	CDul CKel CSpe EPPr MSwo SCob SMad WBor WPGP XLum
*	- 'Minimus Variegatus' (v)	EPPr SPlb
	- 'Prince John'	CSBt
	- 'Sheridan Gold'	MRav
	- 'Silver Gem'	see *E. fortunei* 'Variegatus'
	- 'Silver Queen' (v)	Widely available
	- 'Silverstone'[PBR] (v)	CKel EMil EPfP LRHS SGol SPoG
	- 'Sunshine' (v)	CKel CRos ELan EPfP LRHS MAsh SLon SPoG WAvo
§	- 'Sunspot' (v)	CBcs CBod CMac EBee ELan MJak MMuc MSwo SEND SGol SRms
§	- 'Variegatus' (v)	SRms
	- 'Wolong Ghost' ♀H5	CExl CMCN CRos ELan LRHS MBlu MGos MMuc NLar NRHS SGol SWvt WCot
	frigidus KWJ 12275	WCru
	- var. ***elongatus*** GWJ 9378	WCru
	grandiflorus misapplied	see *E. carnosus*
§	***grandiflorus*** Wall.	CJun EPfP IArd NLar SCoo
	- f. ***salicifolius*** misapplied	see *E. grandiflorus* Wall.
	hamiltonianus	CKel CMCN EBtc ECrN EPfP EWTr LRHS MMuc SMad
	- 'Fiesta'	CJun NLar
	- subsp. ***hians***	see *E. hamiltonianus* subsp. *sieboldianus*
	- 'Indian Summer'	CJun CKel CRos CTho EMil EPfP EWTr LRHS MAsh NLar NOra SPoG WMat
	- 'Koi Boy'	CJun EPfP SPoG WMat
	- 'Miss Pinkie'	CJun EPfP NLar
	- 'Pink Delight'	CJun
	- 'Poort Bulten'	CJun
	- 'Popcorn'	CJun EPfP LRHS
	- 'Rainbow'	CJun EPfP MMrt
	- 'Red Chief'	CJun EPfP
	- 'Red Elf'	CJun NLar
	- 'Rising Sun'	CBod CJun EPfP NLar
§	- subsp. ***sieboldianus***	CExl CTho EPfP MRav
	- - B&SWJ 10941	SAko WCru
	- - PAB 5337	LEdu
	- - 'Calocarpus'	CJun EPfP
	- - 'Coral Charm'	CJun EPfP NLar
	- 'Snow' (v)	WCot
	- 'Winter Glory'	CJun LRHS MMrt

§ ***huangii*** CJun SPtp
- B&SWJ 3700 WCru
japonicus CBcs CBod CDul CMac ECrN EPfP LMaj SArc SCob SEND SEWo SPer
- 'Albomarginatus' (v) CBcs CKel CTri EHoe EPfP NPri SEND SRms
§ - 'Aureomarginatus' (v) CCVT GBin NPri
- 'Aureopictus' see *E. japonicus* 'Aureus'
- 'Aureovariegatus' see *E. japonicus* 'Ovatus Aureus'
§ - 'Aureus' (v) CBcs CDul CKel CSBt CTsd EPfP LRHS NPri NRHS SCoo SEND SLon SPer
- 'Benkomasaki' ECrN
- 'Bravo' (v) CBar CCVT CDul CKel CRos ECrN EHoe EPfP LMaj LRHS MAsh MGos NPri NRHS SArc SCob SCoo SEWo SLim SPer SPoG SWvt WCot WFar
- 'Carnival Candle' SEND
- 'Charles'[PBR] SPoG
- 'Chollipo' (v) ♀H5 CKel CRos EBee ELan EPfP LRHS SEND SPoG
- 'Compactus' SCoo
- 'Duc d'Anjou' misapplied see *E. japonicus* 'Viridivariegatus'
- 'Duc d'Anjou' Carrière (v) CKel EBee EHoe ELan EPfP EWes MRav SEND SPoG
- 'Elegantissimus Aureus' see *E. japonicus* 'Aureomarginatus'
- EXSTASE ('Goldbolwi'[PBR]) (v) WCot
- 'Francien' (v) EPfP LRHS NLar NRHS
- 'Gold Queen'[PBR] NLar
- 'Golden Maiden' (v) CKel CRos ELan EPfP LRHS MAsh SLim SLon SPoG SRms SWvt
- GREEN MILLENIUM ('Minmil'[PBR]) LRHS
- 'Green Rocket' CBod CCVT CKel CRos EBee EPfP GBin LRHS MGos MRav NRHS SGol SLim SPoG SSta WCot WFar
- 'Green Spider' SPoG
- 'Green Spire' LRHS NLar
- 'Happiness'[PBR] NEoE
- 'Kathy'[PBR] CKel CRos ELan ELon EPfP LRHS MAsh MJak NHic NLar NRHS SCob SPoG
§ - 'Latifolius Albomarginatus' (v) CKel ELan EPfP MRav MSwo SPer SWvt
- 'Luna' see *E. japonicus* 'Aureus'
- 'Macrophyllus Albus' see *E. japonicus* 'Latifolius Albomarginatus'
- 'Maiden's Gold' CSBt
- 'Marieke' see *E. japonicus* 'Ovatus Aureus'
- 'Microphyllus' CMac MRav NEgg SGol SRms
§ - 'Microphyllus Albovariegatus' (v) CDul CKel CMac CSBt CTri ELan EPfP LRHS MGos SCob SEND SIgm SLim SRms SWvt WAvo WFar
§ - 'Microphyllus Aureovariegatus' (v) CMac CRos CSBt ELan ELon EPfP LRHS MAsh MMuc NLar NRHS
- 'Microphyllus Aureus' see *E. japonicus* 'Microphyllus Pulchellus'
- 'Microphyllus Gold Dust' new CBod
§ - 'Microphyllus Pulchellus' (v) CBcs CKel CMac CRos CSBt EPfP LRHS MGos MMuc SEND SPoG SWvt
- 'Microphyllus Variegatus' see *E. japonicus* 'Microphyllus Albovariegatus'
§ - 'Ovatus Aureus' (v) ♀H5 CBar CDul CExl CKel CMac CRos CSBt CTri ELan ELon EPfP LMaj LRHS MGos MRav NLar NRHS SCob SEND SGol SLim SPer SPlb SPoG SRms SWvt WFar
- PALOMA BLANCA ('Lankveld03'[PBR]) CRos LCro LOPS LRHS NRHS SPoG WFar
- 'Président Gauthier' (v) CAco CKel EBee ELan LRHS SCob SCoo SLim SPer SWvt
- 'Pulchellus Aureovariegatus' see *E. japonicus* 'Microphyllus Aureovariegatus'
- 'Robustus' CBod
- 'Rokujo' GEdr
- 'Silver King' CMac
- 'Silver Krista' (v) NLar
- 'Susan' (v) ♀H5 CMac MAsh
§ - 'Viridivariegatus' (v) LRHS WAvo
kachinensis B&SWJ 11668 WCru
kiautschovicus 'Berry Hill' NLar
- 'Manhattan' NLar
latifolius CJun CMCN CTho EPfP IDee IMou LEdu WCru
§ ***laxiflorus*** GWJ 9351 WCru
- HWJ 890 WCru
lucidus CBcs CExl CHll EBtc
macropterus CJun IArd
- B&SWJ 12591 new WCru
morrisonensis see *E. huangii*
myrianthus CJun ELan EPfP EWes IArd MBlu MPkF NLar
aff. ***myrianthus*** slim-leaved NJM 11.016 WPGP
§ ***nanus*** CTri NLar
- var. ***turkestanicus*** CRos LRHS SBrt SLon SRms
obovatus SBrt
'Ogisu' GKev
oxyphyllus ♀H6 CJun CMCN EPfP LRHS MMuc NLar SPtp WCot WCru
- 'Waasland' CJun
phellomanus ♀H6 CBcs CDul CKel CTho EBee EPfP GKin IDee LRHS MBlu MGil MGos MMuc MPkF MRav MSCN NLar NOra SCoo SPer SPoG SWvt WMat WPGP
- 'Silver Surprise' (v) CJun
PIERROLINO ('Heespierrolino'[PBR]) MRav NLar SCoo
§ ***planipes*** CAby CCVT CDul CExl CMCN CRos CTho CTri EBee ECrN ELan EPfP EWTr GKin LRHS MAsh MBlu MGil MMuc MRav NLar NWea SLim SMad SPer SPoG WCot WHor
- B&SWJ 8660 WCru
- 'Dart's August Flame' CJun
- 'Sancho' ♀H6 CJun EPfP LRHS
porphyreus B&SWJ 13914 WCru
- GWJ 9377 WCru
quelpaertensis CJun
'Rokujō Variegated' (v) WCot
rongchuensis 'Cliuicolus' see *E. clivicola*
rosmarinifolius see *E. nanus*
rubescens see *E. laxiflorus*
sachalinensis misapplied see *E. planipes*
sachalinensis (F. Schmidt) Maxim. WCot
- B&SWJ 10835 WCru
sacrosanctus CJun MBlu
sanguineus NLar
sieboldianus var. ***sanguineus*** B&SWJ 11140 WCru
- - B&SWJ 11386 WCru
spraguei SBrt
- CWJ 12446 WCru
tingens CJun CMCN SPtp WPGP

trapococcus EPfP
vagans Wall. WCot
velutinus SPtp
verrucosus CJun NLar
wilsonii LRHS NLar
yedoensis see *E. hamiltonianus* subsp. *sieboldianus*

Eupatoriadelphus see *Eupatorium*

Eupatorium ✿ (*Asteraceae*)

B&SWJ 9052 from Guatemala WCru
FMWJ 13428 from Northern Vietnam WCru
album misapplied see *Ageratina altissima*
album L. NBid
altissimum SRms
amabile NMWJ 14456 **new** WCru
aromaticum see *Ageratina aromatica*
atrorubens see *Bartlettina sordida*
cannabinum CBod CHab ELan GPoy LLWG MBNS MHer MMuc MNHC MWts NBir NMir NPer SEND SPhx WFar WHer WSFF
§ - f. ***albiflorum*** SPhx
- 'Album' see *E. cannabinum* f. *albiflorum*
- f. ***cannabinum*** 'Flore Pleno' (d) CMac ECtt ELan ELon GBin MBel MHer MRav NBir NGdn NLar WCot WFar WSFF WWtn XLum
- - 'Spraypaint' (v) WSFF
capillifolium ♀H3 CAby EBee ECtt ESwi EWes MBel MNrw MPie SHar SMad SPad
- 'Elegant Plume' EBee IPot MNrw
coelestinum see *Conoclinium coelestinum*
dubium 'Baby Joe'PBR CAby CBod CRos CWGN EBee ECtt ELan IPot LRHS MBNS MNrw NEgg NLar NRHS SHar SPad WNPC WSFF WWtn
- 'Little Joe' EBee LEdu MTis NDov WCAu WSFF
fistulosum EBee
- f. ***albidum*** ECha EWhm MMuc
- - 'Bartered Bride' CKno EBee ECtt EPPr EWes GCal MBel WCot WSFF
- - 'Ivory Towers' CBod CDor CRos EBee GJos LRHS NDai NRHS SPtp WCot WPtf WSFF
- - 'Massive White' ♀H7 ELon GCal MNrw NBir NSti
- 'Berggarten' GCal WSFF
- 'Carin' WSFF
fortunei 'Fine Line' (v) WSFF
- 'Pink Elegance' (v) CAby EBee ECtt EMor EShb LLWG LRHS MNrw MPie NRHS SPoG SRms WWtn
- 'Pink Frost' (v) EWTr MWts NGdn
japonicum GPoy
ligustrinum see *Ageratina ligustrina*
lindleyanum CKno LEdu WSFF
- var. ***trisectifolium*** B&SWJ 12742 WCru
maculatum NGdn NLar WHrl
- Atropurpureum Group Widely available
- - 'Ankum's August' EBee IMou LPla
- - 'Gateway' CBod CKno CRos EBee ECtt ELon EPPr EWTr GCal LEdu LRHS MBel NBid NBre NCGa NLar NRHS SMad SWvt WSFF WWtn
- - 'Glutball' CKno CRos ELon GCal IMou LRHS LSun MNrw NChi NRHS SMad WWtn
- - 'Little Red' WSFF
- - 'Orchard Dene' ♀H7 LEdu MAvo SMHy
- - 'Phantom'PBR CRos EBee ECtt ELon EMor GBin IKil LRHS MHol NCGa NLar NRHS SAko SHar SMad SPoG
- - 'Purple Bush' ♀H7 CDor CKno EBee ECtt ELon GBin GCal GQue ILea LCro LOPS LRHS MTis NDov NEgg NGrd SWvt WSFF
- - 'Red Dwarf' CBod ECtt ELon EMor EShb EWTr GBin GQue IKil LEdu LLWG LRHS MBel MHol MPie NRHS SCob SHar SPoG SWvt WHoo WPGP
- - 'Riesenschirm' ♀H7 Widely available
- 'J.S. Humble' IPot MNrw
- 'Snowball'PBR CBod EPfP MTis
makinoi var. ***oppositifolium*** B&SWJ 8449 WCru
'Mask' IPot MNrw NLar
micranthum see *Ageratina ligustrina*
perfoliatum EMor GPoy NBre NLar WSFF
purpureum CBcs CHby CKno ECtt ELon GBin GMaP GPoy IFro LLWG MHer MNHC MWat NAln NBro NChi NEgg NGdn SCob SPer SPlb SRms WCAu WHer WMoo WOld WSFF WWtn
- 'Album' CTri MBel SWvt
rugosum see *Ageratina altissima*
* 'Snowball' LLWG NDov SCob SPoG
weinmannianum see *Ageratina ligustrina*

Euphorbia ✿ (*Euphorbiaceae*)

'Abbey Dore' ♀H7 MAvo SPhx WCot
amygdaloides ECtt SWvt WOut XSen
- 'Bob's Choice' WSHC
- 'Craigieburn' CRos EWes LRHS MRav NRHS
§ - 'Purpurea' Widely available
§ - var. ***robbiae*** ♀H6 Widely available
- - dwarf EWes
- - 'Redbud' EWes
- 'Rubra' see *E. amygdaloides* 'Purpurea'
- 'Variegata' (v) NHic
baselicis EWes
biglandulosa Desf. see *E. rigida*
BLACKBIRD ('Nothowlee'PBR) CBcs CExl CMac CWCL CWGN ECtt ELan EPfP EUJe EWTr LCro LLHF LOPS LRHS MBel MGos MRav NLar SCob SLim SMad SWvt WSpi XEll XSen
'Blue Dome' CSpe
'Blue Haze' CSpe EUJe MAvo WCot WFar WSHC WSpi
capitulata SBrt
cashmeriana CC&McK 607 EWes
ceratocarpa ♀H4 CBod CSpe ECtt EWes GMaP LRHS SEND SIgm SMad SPhx WAvo WCot WSHC WSpi XSen
characias CBcs CMac CRos ECtt EPfP LRHS MCot MRav NPer NRHS SPer SRms SWvt WBrk WCot XSen
- 'Ascot Moonbeam' SPoG WNPC
- 'Black Pearl' CAbb CBcs CRos ECtt ELan EPfP EUJe GBin LRHS MAvo MBel MPnt NLar NPri NRHS SGbt SLim SPer SPoG SRkn SWvt WFar WSpi XSen
- 'Blue Wonder' CBod CExl CRos CSam ECtt ELan EPfP EWes GMaP LRHS MAvo NEgg NLar NRHS WCot WNPC WRHF XSen
- 'BQ' WCot
- subsp. ***characias*** CBod NLar SEND

- - 'Blue Hills' ♀H4	ECtt
- - 'Burrow Silver' (v)	CDor CRos MRav NEgg SWvt WNPC
- - 'Humpty Dumpty'	CBod CExl CRos EBee ECrN ECtt EHrv ELan EPfP GMaP GWyn LRHS LSRN NGdn NLar NPer NPri NRHS SCob SPer SRms SWvt WFar WHlf
- - 'Joshua'	WCot
- 'Eye-catcher' **new**	WCot
- 'Forescate'	EBee EPfP NRHS
- 'Glacier Blue'PBR (v)	CBct CPla CRos CSpe CWGN EBee ECha ELan EMor EPfP LRHS LSRN MAsh MAvo MBel MHol MSCN NHpl NLar NRHS SCob SHeu SPoG SRms WCot WNPC WRHF
- 'Goldbrook'	CWCL EPfP GBin LRHS MRav NRHS
- 'Kestrel' (v)	WCot
- 'Portuguese Velvet'	CBod CExl CRos ECtt EHrv ELan EPfP GWyn LRHS MBel MCot MRav NLar NRHS SArc SLim WCot XSen
- SILVER SWAN ('Wilcott'PBR) (v)	Widely available
- 'Tasmanian Tiger'PBR (v) ♀H4	CBcs CBct CBod CRos CWGN ECtt EWTr EWes GMaP LRHS LSRN MGos MHol MJak MPnt NHpl NLar NRHS SCob SEle SHeu SPoG SRms SWvt WCot WNPC WSpi
- subsp. ***wulfenii***	Widely available
- - 'Bosahan'	CExl
- - 'Emmer Green' (v)	CExl CRos ECtt EWes GMaP MHol NSti WCot
- - 'Jayne's Golden Giant'	SMad
- - 'Jimmy Platt' ♀H4	SRms WCot
§ - - 'John Tomlinson'	EWes MRav WAvo WSpi
- - Kew form	see *E. characias* subsp. *wulfenii* 'John Tomlinson'
- - 'Lambrook Gold'	MNrw MRav NLar NPer SCob SMad WCot WSpi
- - 'Lambrook Gold' seed-raised	see *E. characias* subsp. *wulfenii* Margery Fish Group
§ - - Margery Fish Group	CWCL EPfP LRHS MCot NBir NRHS SPer
- - 'Perry's Tangerine'	EWes NPer
§ - - 'Purple and Gold'	ECtt EWes MNrw SWvt XSen
- - 'Purpurea'	see *E. characias* subsp. *wulfenii* 'Purple and Gold'
- - 'Shorty'	CRos EBee ECtt EUJe GBin LRHS NLar NRHS SPoG XSen
- - 'Silver Shadow' (v)	EBee MAvo MHol NGBl WCot
- - 'Thelma's Giant'	MAvo
- - 'Westacre Giant'	EWes
clavarioides	WAbe
- var. ***truncata***	WCot
'Copton Ash'	CBcs CSpe EBee ECtt EMor IPot LRHS SPhx WCot XSen
corallioides	ECha GWyn LPla LSun NLar NPer NSti WHer WNPC
§ ***cornigera*** ♀H5	CDor CRos EBee ECha LRHS MMuc NBid NGdn NLar NRHS NSti SEND SPhx WCru WFar
- 'Goldener Turm'	ECtt EPfP GBin LCro LOPS LRHS NRHS SCob SMHy SMad SPer SPhx WCot
corollata	SBrt
cyparissias	CBcs ECha ELan MRav NAln NBir NGdn NLar SRms WBrk WFar WMoo XLum XSen
- 'Betten'	see *E.* × *gayeri* 'Betten'
- 'Clarice Howard'	see *E. cyparissias* 'Fens Ruby'
- clone 2	WCot
§ - 'Fens Ruby'	Widely available
- 'Orange Man'	CBcs CBod CKel CRos ECtt EPfP EWes LRHS NEgg NGdn NLar NRHS SPoG SVen SWvt WAul WBrk WFar
- 'Purpurea'	see *E. cyparissias* 'Fens Ruby'
- 'Red Devil'	CDor
- 'Tall Boy'	EBee EWes
deflexa	EBee EWes MAvo
dendroides	CKel LRHS SPtp
'Despina'PBR	LRHS
§ ***donii***	ECha EWes MAvo WSpi XEll
- HWJK 2405	WCru
- 'Amjillasa'	ECha LPla SMHy
dulcis	CBre IFro NBro
- 'Chameleon'	CDor ECtt EHrv ELan ELon EPfP GCal GWyn IFro MGos MRav NBid NBir NLar NPer SCob SPlb SRot SWvt WArt WBrk WCAu WCot WFar WMoo WSpi
'Efanthia'PBR	CDor CEnd CRos EWes GBin LPla LRHS MAvo NRHS
§ ***epithymoides***	Widely available
- 'Bonfire'PBR	CSpe ECha ECtt EUJe MAvo MBel NGBl SAko SPer SPoG WCot WHil
§ - 'Candy'	CWCL EBee ECha EMor LPla MNrw WFar
- 'First Blush' (v)	ECtt MNrw NLar WCot WFar
- 'Geisha'	EWes
- 'Golden Fusion'	EPfP WFar
§ - 'Lacy' (v)	EWes NBir NGdn WFar
§ - 'Major' ♀H6	CExl EBee WKif
- 'Midas'	MNrw SCob SMHy
- 'Senior'	CRos EPfP LRHS MNrw NLar NRHS
EXCALIBUR ('Froeup'PBR)	CBod CExl CMac CWCL ELan ELon LSRN MBNS MMuc MNrw MRav NBir NLar NRHS NSti SEND SPtp SWvt
fischeriana B&SWJ 8575	WCru
§ × ***gayeri*** 'Betten'	EBee EWes GBin LPla XSen
'Golden Foam'	see *E. stricta*
griffithii	CHll LEdu NBro WFar WMoo WWtn
- 'Dixter'	Widely available
- 'Fern Cottage'	CElw EWes GBin
- 'Fireglow'	Widely available
- 'King's Caple'	EMor EWes LRHS NLar SPoG WCru
- 'Wickstead'	CWCL EMor GBin LRHS NLar
'Helena'PBR (v)	CExl LSRN NLar SWvt
heptagona	SEND
hierosolymitana **new**	SBrt
horrida ♀H2	SPlb
hypericifolia DIAMOND FROST ('Inneuphe'PBR)	CSpe ESwi SRkn WCot
- 'Diamond Star'	WCot
ingens	CAbb
jacquemontii	MRav NLar WCot
'Jade Dragon'	LRHS SWvt
'Jessie'	NLar
jolkinii	CExl
KALIPSO ('Innkalff')	EPfP NLar SRot
'Lambrook Silver'	SRkn
lathyris	CBre NLar NPer SRms SVic
longifolia misapplied	see *E. cornigera*
longifolia D. Don	see *E. donii*
longifolia Lam.	see *E. mellifera*
margalidiana ♀H4	EWes WCot
× ***martini***	Widely available
- 'Aperitif'	SPoG
- 'Ascot Rainbow'PBR (v) ♀H5	Widely available

- 'Baby Charm' CBod CRos EBee ECtt ELon EPfP EUJe GBin LRHS LSRN MBel MGos NLar NRHS WFar WNPC XSen
- 'Helen Robinson' ♀H5 WCot
- 'Kolibri' CRos LRHS MPnt NRHS SWvt
- 'Rudolph'PBR CBod ECtt ELan EUJe NLar SPoG
- TINY TIM ('Waleutiny') CRos EBee ECtt EPfP GBin LRHS LSRN NPri NRHS SWvt
- 'Walberton's Red Flush' CRos LRHS NRHS

mauritanica EShb
§ ***mellifera*** ♀H3 Widely available
milii ♀H1b EBak
myrsinites ♀H5 Widely available
nereidum ♀H5 EWes
nicaeensis EBee GCal LRHS SPhx WCot XSen
oblongata CSpe IFro LRHS NLar SEND WCot
palustris ♀H7 Widely available
- 'Teichlaterne' **new** SAko
- 'Walenburg's Glorie' CWCL EBee ECha ELan ELon EWTr GBin LCro LOPS LRHS MNrw MRav NLar NSti SMad WCot WKif
- 'Woodchippings' WCot
- 'Zauberflöte' ELon SRms

paralias WHer
× ***pasteurii*** CBct CDTJ CKel CSam EPfP EUJe EWes GBin GWyn MNrw NBir SPhx WCot WPGP
- Brown's strain CBod ELan EMor EUJe GAbr LSun MNrw WCot WRHF
- 'John Phillips' ♀H4 CBct CExl CKel EBee EPfP LRHS MAvo SChF WPGP
- 'Phrampton Phatty' ♀H4 LRHS WCot WPGP
- 'Roundway Titan' ♀H6 CKel EMil EPfP LRHS SAko SWvt
- 'Skinny Bere' **new** LEdu

pentagona SVen
pilosa 'Major' see *E. epithymoides* 'Major'
pithyusa CPla ECha ELan SEND SPlb WSHC XSen
polychroma see *E. epithymoides*
- 'Purpurea' see *E. epithymoides* 'Candy'
- 'Variegata' see *E. epithymoides* 'Lacy'

portlandica SVen WHer
REDWING ('Charam'PBR) CBcs CMac CWCL ECtt ELan EMor GWyn IKil LBuc LRHS MAvo MBel MHol MNrw MRav NLar NSti SLim SPer SPoG SWvt WCot
reflexa see *E. seguieriana* subsp. *niciciana*
§ ***rigida*** ♀H6 CBod CBro CSpe ELan EUJe EWes GCal SHar SIgm SPhx WCot WSpi XSen
robbiae see *E. amygdaloides* var. *robbiae*
sarawschanica ECha LPla LRHS SMad SPhx
schillingii ♀H5 Widely available
schoenlandii SPlb
seguieriana ECha EWes SPhx
§ - subsp. ***niciciana*** EWTr IMou LRHS MAvo SCob SPhx WCAu WHoo XSen
serrulata Thuill. see *E. stricta*
sikkimensis ♀H5 CExl CMea CRos ECha ELan EWes GBin GCal GLog GWyn IMou LPla LRHS NEgg NLar NPer NRHS SCob SRms WCru WFar
- 'Crûg Contrast' MAvo WCru

spinosa SPlb XSen
§ ***stricta*** CBgR GWyn NWad WSpi
stygiana CAbb CAby CDTJ CExl CWCL ELon EPfP EUJe EWes GBin LPla LRHS MCot SAko SPlb SPtp WCot WCru WPGP WSHC
- subsp. ***santamariae*** CDTJ WPGP WSHC
- subsp. ***stygiana*** EBee WPGP
- 'Torridge' ♀H4 **new** WCot

tirucalli EShb
valdevillosocarpa GWyn NLar SPhx WFar
'Velvet Ruby' GBin GWyn LSRN SWvt WNPC XSen
villosa Waldst. & Kit. ex Willd. GBin
wallichii misapplied see *E. donii*
wallichii Kohli see *E. cornigera*
wallichii ambig. CBod GBin LOPS MRav SCob
wallichii Hook. f. CExl EPfP MNrw SPhx WCot
'Whistleberry Garnet' ♀H7 CBar CKel CMac EBee ELan EPfP EWTr LLHF LRHS MMuc NSti SCob SPhx SWvt WNPC

Euptelea (*Eupteleaceae*)

franchetii see *E. pleiosperma*
§ ***pleiosperma*** CBcs NLar
polyandra EBee EPfP NLar SBrt WPGP

Eurya (*Pentaphylacaceae*)

japonica 'Moutiers' (v) CBcs
- 'Variegata' misapplied see *Cleyera japonica* 'Fortunei'

Eurybia (*Asteraceae*)

§ ***divaricata*** Widely available
§ - 'Eastern Star' WCot WFar WOld WSpi
- Raiche form see *E. divaricata* 'Eastern Star'
- 'Tradescant' IMou MNrw SMad

§ ***furcata*** XLum
§ × ***herveyi*** Widely available
§ ***macrophylla*** CFis CRos ELan GQue LRHS MMuc NLar NRHS SPhx WArt WFar WOld WWtn
- 'Albus' EPPr WFar WOld
- 'Twilight' see *E.* × *herveyi*

§ ***radula*** CSam EPPr EWes IMou MAvo MNrw NLar NWsh WOld WSHC
- 'August Sky' CBod CKno EBee EMor EPPr ITim LRHS MBel MTis NDai NDov SPhx WCot WFar WHoo WRHF

§ ***schreberi*** CDor ECha EPPr EWes LEdu LPla MAvo MNrw MPie NCGa NWsh WCot WFar WHoo WOld WPGP WWtn
§ ***sibirica*** EBou NLar WOld
§ ***spectabilis*** CRos EBou IMou LRHS NRHS WFar WOld
- 'JS Macho Blue' MNrw

Euryops (*Asteraceae*)

abrotanifolius CCCN SVen
§ ***acraeus*** ♀H4 CSBt ECtt ELan EPot EWes GCrg GEdr WAbe
brachypodus SVen
§ ***chrysanthemoides*** CBcs CCCN CSde EShb SEND SVen
- 'Sonnenschein' SPtp

evansii Schltr. see *E. acraeus*
lateriflorus SPlb
pectinatus ♀H3 CBcs CBod CCCN CDTJ CExl CKel CRos CSde CTri CTsd ELan EPfP EShb IKil LRHS MGil MSCN SEND SPtp SVen SWvt WWFP
tenuissimus SVen
tysonii ELon EWes GCal SPlb SVen
virgineus CCCN CExl SPlb SVen

Euscaphis (*Staphyleaceae*)

japonica SPtp

- B&SWJ 11359 WCru
- B&SWJ 12739 WCru

Eustachys (*Poaceae*)

§ ***distichophylla*** CRos LRHS NRHS NWsh

Eustephia (*Amaryllidaceae*)

coccinea WCot

Eutrema (*Brassicaceae*)

§ ***japonicum*** CExl EMor GPoy LEdu
- 'Monzen' GPoy

Eutrochium see *Eupatorium*

Ewartia (*Asteraceae*)

planchonii NRHS SPlb WAbe

Exbucklandia (*Hamamelidaceae*)

tonkinensis KWJ 12209 WCru

Exochorda (*Rosaceae*)

alberti see *E. korolkowii*
giraldii var. ***wilsonii*** CExl EBee ELan EPfP LRHS MBlu MMuc MRav NLar SWvt WCFE
§ ***korolkowii*** LRHS MAsh
× ***macrantha*** LRHS
- 'Irish Pearl' CExl
§ - 'Niagara'[PBR] CBcs CMac CRos EBee EPfP EShb LCro LOPS LRHS LSRN MAsh MGos MPkF NLar NRHS SCob SGol SPoG
- SNOW DAY SURPRISE see *E.* × *macrantha* 'Niagara'
- 'The Bride' ♀H6 Widely available
MAGICAL SPRINGTIME ('Kolmaspirit') LRHS NLar
racemosa EPfP NLar SPer
serratifolia CBcs CKel EBee ELan EPfP LRHS SPoG
- 'Snow White' CEnd CJun EWes GKin IArd IMou LRHS MAsh MBlu NLar SLon SWvt

F

Fabiana (*Solanaceae*)

foliosa 'Cliftonville Limelight' WAbe
imbricata CPbh CRos LRHS MGil SLon SPlb WPav
- 'Prostrata' CBod CRos CTsd ELan LRHS SVen WPav
- f. ***violacea*** ♀H4 CExl CMac CRos CSBt CSpe CTri ELan EPfP LLHF LRHS MMuc SPad SPer SWvt WAvo WHlf WKif WPav
- - dark-flowered CBcs
nana WAbe

Fagopyrum (*Polygonaceae*)

cymosum see *F. dibotrys*
§ ***dibotrys*** CSpe EBee ECha EWld LEdu MMuc XLum
I - 'Cally Form' ESwi GCal

Fagraea (*Gentianaceae*)

ceilanica FMWJ 13099 WCru

Fagus ✿ (*Fagaceae*)

from Guangxi, China **new** WPGP
from Vietnam **new** WPGP
§ ***crenata*** CMCN CMen MBlu
- 'Mount Fuji' CAco CMen LLHF NEgg SBir
engleriana CExl LRHS SBir
grandifolia subsp. ***mexicana*** SBir WPGP
japonica SBir
- var. ***multinervis*** SBir
longipetiolata CBcs CExl CMCN EBee WPGP
- NJM 11.036 WPGP
lucida CExl CMCN MBlu
orientalis CMCN SBir
- 'Iskander' CDul IArd IDee MBlu SGol SMad
sieboldii see *F. crenata*
sylvatica ♀H6 Widely available
- 'Albovariegata' (v) CLnd
- 'Aniek' SGol
- 'Arcuata' SBir
- 'Asterix' LRHS MBlu
- Atropurpurea Group Widely available
- - 'Purpurea Pendula' CAco CBcs CCVT CDul CEnd CMCN CMac CSBt CTri EBee ELan EPfP GKin MAsh MGos MJak NEgg NWea SCoo SGol SLau SLim SPer SPoG WFar WMat WTSh
- - 'Riversii' ♀H6 CBcs CDul CEnd CLnd CMCN CTho CTri EBee ELan EMOT EPfP GKin LPra MGos NWea SPer WMat
- - 'Swat Magret' EPfP
- 'Aurea Pendula' CEnd CMCN MBlu SBir
- 'Bicolor Sartini' MBlu
- 'Birr Zebra' CEnd
- 'Black Swan' CDul CLnd CMCN EBee ELan LSRN MAsh MBlu MGos NEgg NHol NOra SBir SLon SMad SPer SPoG WMat
- 'Bornyensis' MBlu
- 'Brathay Purple' MBlu
- 'Cochleata' CMCN
- 'Cockleshell' MBlu SBir
- 'Cristata' MBlu
§ - 'Dawyck' ♀H6 CBcs CDul CLnd CMac CTho ECrN ELan EPfP LMaj LPra MGos NEgg NLar NWea SBir SCob SGol SLau SPer
- 'Dawyck Gold' ♀H6 CBcs CDul CEnd CLnd CMCN CMac CSBt CTri EBee ELan EMOT GKin LPra MAsh MBlu MGos NEgg NLar NOra NWea SBir SCob SGol SLau SPer WMat WMou
- 'Dawyck Purple' ♀H6 Widely available
- 'Eugen' SBir
- 'Fastigiata' misapplied see *F. sylvatica* 'Dawyck'
- 'Felderbach' SBir
- 'Franken' (v) CAco CDul EBtc MBlu SBir SMad
- 'Green Obelisk' MBlu
- 'Greenwood' MBlu NEgg
- var. ***heterophylla*** CLnd CTho NWea
- - 'Aspleniifolia' ♀H6 CBcs CDul CEnd CKel CMCN CMac EBee ECrN ELan EMOT EPfP EWTr GKin LMaj LPra MBlu MGos NEgg SBir SCoo SGol SLau SPer SPoG WMat WMou
- - (Atropurpurea Group) 'Ansorgei' CEnd MBlu
- - 'Incisa' MBlu
- - f. ***laciniata*** MBlu
- - 'Mercedes' CAco CDul CMCN LLHF MBlu NEgg SMad
- 'Horizontalis' MBlu

- 'Luteovariegata' (v) EBee
- 'Pendula' ♀H6 CAco CBcs CCVT CDul CEnd CKel CMCN CMac CSBt CTho ECrN ELan LPra MGos MSwo NEgg NOra NWea SGol SLau SPer WMat WMou WTSh
- 'Prince George of Crete' CDul
- 'Purple Fountain' ♀H6 CAco CDul CEnd CKel CMCN EBee ELan MAsh MBlu MGos NLar NOra NWea SBir SLau WMat
- Purple-leaved Group see *F. sylvatica* Atropurpurea Group
§ - 'Purpurea Tricolor' (v) CAco CDul CEnd CMCN CMac EBee MBlu MGos NEgg NOra NWea SBir SCoo WMat WMou
- 'Red Obelisk' see *F. sylvatica* 'Rohan Obelisk'
- 'Rohan Gold' CEnd CMCN SGol
- 'Rohan Minaret' SGol
§ - 'Rohan Obelisk' CAco CDul CEnd CMCN ELan LMaj MBlu NEgg NLar SBir SGol
I - 'Rohan Pyramidalis' CEnd CMCN
- 'Rohan Trompenburg' CMCN MBlu
- 'Rohan Weeping' MBlu SBir
- 'Rohanii' CBcs CDul CEnd CMCN CTri ELan EMOT EPfP GKin MGil MGos NEgg SBir SLau
- 'Rolf Marquardt' (v) **new** SMad
- 'Roseomarginata' see *F. sylvatica* 'Purpurea Tricolor'
- 'Rotundifolia' LMaj MBlu NEgg SGol
- 'Spaethiana' GKin
- 'Striata' CAco NEgg
- f. ***tortuosa*** MBlu MPkF NEgg
- - 'Rot Süntel' CDul NEgg
- 'Tricolor' misapplied (v) see *F. sylvatica* 'Purpurea Tricolor' (v)
- 'Tricolor' ambig. (v) SLau
- 'Tricolor' (v) CBcs CLnd ECrN LLHF NHol SGol
- 'Tur' **new** SMad
- 'Viridivariegata' (v) CMCN
- 'Zlatia' CDul CLnd CMCN ELan MBlu MGil MGos NLar NWea SBir SGol SLau

Fallopia (*Polygonaceae*)

aubertii see *F. baldschuanica*
§ ***baldschuanica*** Widely available
§ ***japonica*** var. ***compacta*** WMoo XLum
- - 'Fuji Snow' see *F. japonica* var. *compacta* 'Milk Boy'
§ - - 'Milk Boy' (v) EShb
- - 'Variegata' misapplied see *F. japonica* var. *compacta* 'Milk Boy'
§ ***multiflora*** CBod LEdu WGwG
- var. ***hypoleuca*** CSde SCoo SPoG
- - B&SWJ 120 WCru

Farfugium (*Asteraceae*)

§ ***japonicum*** B&SWJ 884 WCru
- B&SWJ 14699 **new** WCru
- 'Argenteum' (v) SMad WCot
§ - 'Aureomaculatum' (v) ♀H3 ECtt EUJe
- 'Bumpy Ride' WCot
- 'Crispatum' EUJe LEdu
- double-flowered (d) WCru
- var. ***formosanum*** NMWJ 14574 **new** WCru
- var. ***giganteum*** EUJe
- 'Kaimon Dake' WCot
- 'Kinkan' (v) WCot
- 'Ryuto' WCot
- 'Shishi Botan' **new** EUJe
I - 'Tsuwa-buki' WCot

'Last Dance'PBR EBee ECtt NLar
tussilagineum see *F. japonicum*

Fargesia (*Poaceae*)

from Jiuzhaigou, China CBdn CDTJ ERod EUJe MAvo MMuc MWht NLar WPGP XCre
from Taibashan, China **new** XCre
adpressa MWht
conferta **new** XCre
confusa CDTJ
denudata CBct CBdn CDTJ ENBC ERod ESwi NLar XCre
- L 1575 CExl MWht
- Xian 1 CBdn CDTJ XCre
dracocephala CExl ERod GBin MAvo MBrN MMuc MWht WMoo XCre
- 'White Dragon' CDTJ CExl
ferax XCre
'Green Dragon' **new** XCre
'Jiuzaighou 9' **new** XCre
§ ***murielae*** ♀H5 CAgr CBcs CBdn CKel ELan ENBC EPau EPfP ERod LCro LOPS LRHS MGos MJak MMuc MWht SCob SPlb WFar WMoo XCre
- 'Bimbo' CBdn CBod CSBt EPfP ERod GCal LRHS MAvo MWht NLar SCob SWvt WMoo
- 'Dana Jumbo' CRos LRHS NRHS
- 'Grüne Hecke' ERod MWht
- 'Harewood' GBin MWht SWvt
- 'Joy' CBct CBod CKel GBin NLar WMoo
- 'Jumbo' CBod CKel CRos CSBt ELon EPfP ERod EUJe GBin MAvo MGos MJak MWht NGdn NLar NRHS SPer SRms SWvt
- 'Mae' CDTJ MWht
- 'Panda'PBR CRos LRHS NRHS
- 'Simba' Widely available
- 'Vampire' ERod LRHS
murieliae BLUE DRAGONSCALE see *F. murieliae* BLUE LIZARD
§ - BLUE LIZARD ('Japo 72'PBR) **new** MWht
- RED ZEBRA ('Japo 51'PBR) **new** MWht
- 'Superjumbo'PBR CBdn
§ ***nitida*** CAbb CBcs CDul CEnd CRos CSBt ELan EPfP ERod GBin IFro LRHS MAsh MGos MJak MWht NRHS SCob SPoG SRms SWvt WMoo WPGP
- 'Black Pearl' CBdn ENBC XCre
- 'Chennevières' XCre
- 'Ghanzu II' **new** XCre
- 'Great Wall' CBod CDTJ CSBt ELan EUJe GBin MMuc MWht NLar SCob XCre
- Jiuzhaigou 1 see *F.* RED PANDA
- 'Jiuzhaigou 4' CDTJ CExl WPGP
- 'Jiuzhaigou 8' CDTJ
- 'Jiuzhaigou Genf' CDTJ NLar WPGP
- 'Volcano' **new** CBdn XCre
'Obelisk' **new** CBdn
perlonga Yunnan 6 ERod
§ RED PANDA ('Jiu') ♀H4 CExl LCro LOPS MPkF SPoG SWvt
robusta ♀H5 CAbb CBct CDTJ CRos CSBt ELan ENBC EPfP ERod MAvo MBrN MMuc MWht NGdn SSut
- 'Campbell' CBdn EUJe MJak NLar XCre
- 'Ming Yunnan' LEdu WPGP
- 'P. King' ERod MWht

- 'Pingwu'	CBdn CBod CDTJ CKel ENBC ERod EUJe MGos MJak MWht XCre
- 'Red Sheath'	CDTJ CExl CJun ERod MWht WPGP
- 'Wenchuan' **new**	XCre
- 'Wolong'	CExl ERod GBin MWht WPGP XCre
rufa ♀H4	CAbb CBcs CBdn CBod CExl CRos CSBt ELan ELon ENBC EPfP ERod EShb EUJe GBin LCro LOPS LSRN MBlu MBrN MGos MJak MMuc MWht NAln NLar WFar WPGP XCre
§ ***scabrida*** ♀H4	CBdn CDTJ ENBC ERod MAvo MWht SSut WPGP XCre
- 'Asian Wonder'	CBod CKel ECrN ENBC LRHS NLar
similaris KR 4175	MWht
spathacea misapplied	see *F. murielae*
'Tom 1' **new**	XCre
utilis	ERod MMuc MWht SEND XCre
'Winter Joy' **new**	XCre
yulongshanensis	ERod MWht XCre

Fascicularia (*Bromeliaceae*)

andina	see *F. bicolor*
§ ***bicolor***	Widely available
- subsp. ***bicolor***	CBod CMac SMad
- subsp. ***canaliculata***	IBlr LEdu MNrw SChr SPad WPGP
kirchhoffiana	see *F. bicolor*
litoralis	see *Ochagavia litoralis*
pitcairniifolia misapplied	see *F. bicolor*
pitcairniifolia (Verlot) Mez	see *Ochagavia litoralis*

× *Fatshedera* ✿ (*Araliaceae*)

lizei ♀H3	CBcs CDul CKel CMac CRos CSde CTri EBee ECrN ELon EMOT EPfP EShb EUJe EWTr GBin LRHS MAsh MRav SArc SCob SEND SGol SPer SPlb SPoG SWvt WAvo
§ - 'Annemieke' (v) ♀H3	CBcs CBod CKel CRos ELan ELon EMOT EPfP EUJe LRHS MMuc MRav SCob SEND SEle SPoG WAvo
- compact	CKel EMil EPfP
- 'Lemon and Lime'	see × *F. lizei* 'Annemieke'
- 'Maculata'	see × *F. lizei* 'Annemieke'
- 'Variegata' (v) ♀H3	CRos CSde EBee ELan ELon EMOT EPfP EUJe LRHS SCob SEND SPer SWvt WAvo
- 'Variegata' compact (v)	EMil SPoG

Fatsia ✿ (*Araliaceae*)

§ ***japonica*** ♀H5	Widely available
- 'Annelise' (v)	SEND SMad
- 'Moseri'	CBod CExl ELan ESwi MBNS MHol NGdn SWvt WCot
- 'Spider's Web' (v)	Widely available
- 'Variegata' (v) ♀H5	CAbb CMac CRos ELan EPfP LRHS MAsh MGos MRav SCob SEND SLon SPer SPoG WCot WFar
I 'Megafatsia'	CDTJ
papyrifera	see *Tetrapanax papyrifer*
polycarpa	CBcs CDTJ CExl
- B&SWJ 1776	WCru
- B&SWJ 3467	WCru
- B&SWJ 7144	CExl WCru
- RWJ 10133	WCru
- deeply cut leaf	WCot WPGP
- - BWJ 12499	WCru

Fatsia × *Hedera* see × *Fatshedera*

Faucaria (*Aizoaceae*)

tuberculosa ♀H2 **new**	CBod SSim

Feijoa see *Acca*

Felicia (*Asteraceae*)

aethiopica	CPbh
§ ***amelloides***	CCCN SPlb
- 'Santa Anita'	CTri NWad SVen
§ - variegated (v)	CCCN ECtt NPer
§ ***amoena***	CTri
- 'Variegata' (v)	CCCN CTri
capensis	see *F. amelloides*
coelestis	see *F. amelloides*
echinata	CCCN
FELICITARA BLUE ('Wigetablue'PBR)	SPoG
filifolia blue-flowered	SVen
fruticosa	CHll
natalensis	see *F. rosulata*
pappei	see *F. amoena*
§ ***petiolata***	CFis CTri EBee EWes MMuc MNrw
§ ***rosulata***	CFis CSma GCrg GEdr MAsh MBrN MHol NBro NLar SBrt SRot WIce
tenella	WSpi
uliginosa	EWes SBrt SPlb WIce
wrightii	GEdr

fennel see *Foeniculum vulgare*; also AGM Vegetables Section

fenugreek see *Trigonella foenum-graecum*

Ferraria (*Iridaceae*)

§ ***crispa***	CBor LAma WCot
- var. ***nortieri***	WCot
divaricata	WCot
schaeferi	WCot
undulata	see *F. crispa*
variablis **new**	WCot

Ferula (*Apiaceae*)

assa-foetida	WJek
chiliantha	see *F. communis* subsp. *glauca*
§ ***communis***	CMea CRos CSpe ECha EHoe ELan EPPr EWes GBin LEdu LRHS NDov SEND SPad SPhx SPlb SPoG SPtp
- 'Cretan Giant' **new**	WPGP
- 'Gigantea'	see *F. communis*
§ - subsp. ***glauca***	EBee ECha EWes SMHy SSut WCot
- - B&SWJ 12999	WCru
- - NJM 13.001	WPGP
'Giant Bronze'	see *Foeniculum vulgare* 'Giant Bronze'
linkii **new**	SPhx
szowitsiana	NDov
tingitana B&SWJ 14005	WCru
- 'Cedric Morris'	ECha WCot

Ferulago (*Apiaceae*)

cassia	WCot
stellata	WCot
sylvatica PAB 2875	LEdu WPGP

Festuca (*Poaceae*)

actae	XLum
amethystina	CBod CKno EHoe EShb LCro LOPS LRHS MBel MMuc NGdn SCob SEND SMea SPhx SRot WMoo XLum
- 'Aprilgrün'	XLum
arundinacea	CHab MMuc SEND

	californica	CKno IMou
	curvula subsp. ***crassifolia***	EShb
	durissima	XLum
	'Eisvogel'	EPPr
	elegans	EPPr XLum
	eskia	EHoe IMou XLum
	filiformis	CHab
	gamisansii	XLum
§	***gautieri***	EUJe LRHS NWsh SMea XLum
	- 'Hobbit'	CBod
	- 'Pic Carlit'	NLar XLum
	gigantea	CBod CHab MMuc SEND XLum
	glacialis	XLum
	- 'Czakor'	XLum
	glauca Vill.	CAco CBar CBcs CBod EShb GMaP GWyn MBNS MGos MRav NGdn SLim SPer SPlb SRms XSen
I	- 'Auslese'	CBod CExl EShb NGdn
	- 'Azurit'	EHoe EWes NLar NWad SPoG SRms
§	- 'Blaufuchs'	CRos CSBt ELan EPfP EWes GMaP LRHS MBlu MGos NLar NRHS NWad NWsh SLim SPer SPlb SWvt WFar XLum
§	- 'Blauglut'	CRos EBee LRHS MRav NRHS SRms
	- BLUE FOX	see *F. glauca* 'Blaufuchs'
	- BLUE GLOW	see *F. glauca* 'Blauglut'
	- 'Blue Select' **new**	LSun
	- 'Elijah Blue'	Widely available
	- 'Golden Toupee'	CRos CTsd ECha ELan EPfP LRHS MBlu MGos NBir NEgg NLar NRHS SLim SPer SPlb SWvt XLum
	- 'Harz'	EHoe XLum
	- INTENSE BLUE ('Casblue'[PBR])	CKno CRos EHoe ELan EPfP EWes GBin LCro LOPS LRHS LSRN MAsh MGos MPkF NRHS NWsh SMad SPoG SRms
*	- ***minima***	CCCN NWsh
	- 'Pallens'	see *F. longifolia*
	- SEA URCHIN	see *F. glauca* 'Seeigel'
§	- 'Seeigel'	CRos LRHS NRHS NWad
	- SELECT	see *F. glauca* 'Auslese'
	- 'Seven Seas'	see *F. valesiaca* 'Silbersee'
	- 'Silberreiher'	EPPr
	- 'Solling'	XLum
	- 'Uchte'	ECha EPPr WPtf
	'Hogar'	EPPr
	idahoensis	EShb
	- 'Tomales Bay'	CKno
	liviensis	XSen
§	***longifolia***	EPPr
	mairei	CBod CKno ECha EHoe EPPr IMou LPla NWsh SPhx XLum
	ovina	CHab WSFF
	- var. ***gallica***	NWsh
*	- 'Tetra Gold'	SWvt
	paniculata	CKno EHoe XLum
	- subsp. ***spadicea***	XLum
	pratensis	CHab
	punctoria	MMuc SMea
	rubra	CHab CKno WSFF XLum
	scoparia	see *F. gautieri*
	tatrae	MBel MMuc SEND
	valesiaca	SMea XLum
	- var. ***glaucantha***	NGdn XLum
§	- 'Silbersee'	SRms WFar
	- SILVER SEA	see *F. valesiaca* 'Silbersee'
	violacea	EPPr
	vivipara	EHoe NBid XLum
*	'Willow Green'	SPlb

Fibigia (*Brassicaceae*)

I	***clypeata*** 'Select'	CSpe
	eriocarpa **new**	LRHS

Ficaria (*Ranunculaceae*)

	verna	GKev MMuc
	- Alba Group	CSam LEdu NRya
	- anemone-centred	see *F. verna* 'Collarette'
§	- Aurantiaca Group	CDor ECha GCrg NLar NRya SPhx
	- var. ***aurantiacus***	see *F. verna* Aurantiaca Group
	- 'Bowles's Double'	see *Ficaria verna* 'Double Bronze'
	- 'Brambling'	ECha LEdu NLar
	- 'Brazen Child'	SHar
	- 'Brazen Hussy'	Widely available
	- subsp. ***bulbilifer***	see *F. verna* subsp. *verna*
§	- subsp. ***chrysocephala***	EBee ECha IFro MNrw WCot
	- 'Coffee Cream'	NSum
§	- 'Collarette' (d)	EMor GCrg LEdu MHer NBir NLar NRya NSum WFar
	- 'Coppernob'	CDor CFis WCot
	- 'Cracked Parchment'	CNat
	- 'Cupreus'	see *Ficaria verna* Aurantiaca Group
	- 'Dahlem'	EPPr
§	- 'Double Bronze' (d)	LEdu MHer NBir NLar NRya NSum WFar
§	- 'Double Mud' (d)	EPPr LEdu NLar NRya NSum SHar WFar WHal
	- double, cream-flowered	see *Ficaria verna* 'Double Mud'
	- double, green-eyed (d)	LEdu
	- double, yellow-flowered	see *Ficaria verna* Flore Pleno Group
	- 'Dusky Maiden'	NLar NRya NSum WFar
	- 'E.A. Bowles'	see *F. verna* 'Collarette'
	- 'Edna'	WOut
§	- Flore Pleno Group (d)	CBod CDor CMac CTri ECha ELan EPPr NRya NSum SRms WCot WFar
	- 'Fried Egg'	NSum WFar
	- 'Green Petal'	CAby EPPr MCot NBir NRya WFar WHal WHer
	- 'Green Rim'	CNat
	- 'Hyde Hall'	NLar WCot
	- 'Ken Aslet Double' (d)	EPPr MHer WHal
	- 'Lambrook Variegated' (v)	CFis
	- subsp. ***major***	see *F. verna* subsp. *chrysocephala*
	- 'Martin Gibbs' Progeny'	CNat
	- 'Monksilver'	IFro
	- 'Montacute'	CDor CFis
	- 'Old Master'	WCot
	- 'Orange Sorbet' (d)	LEdu NLar NSum WFar
	- 'Petrol Spillage'	CNat
	- 'Primrose'	NRya
	- 'Randall's White'	CAby CDor NSum SHar WFar
	- 'Richard and Val'	WCot
	- 'Rita Pirouet'	WCot
	- 'Salmon's White'	EPPr NBir NLar NRya NSum SHar WFar WHal
	- 'Silver Collar'	LEdu
	- 'Suffusion'	CNat
	- 'Tortoiseshell'	EPPr
§	- subsp. ***verna***	CTri WHer WOut WSFF WShi
	- - 'Chedglow'	WCot
	- 'Wisley Double'	see *Ficaria verna* 'Double Bronze'

Ficinia (*Cyperaceae*)

§	***nodosa***	SPlb
	truncata	GEdr WCot
	- 'Ice Crystal' (v)	CRos ELan EShb LRHS NRHS SPoG

Ficus (*Moraceae*)

afghanistanica 'Silver Lyre' EBee WPGP
benjamina ♀H1c EUJe
- 'Exotica' EUJe
- 'Midnight Lady'[PBR] EUJe

carica (F) CCCN EUJe LMaj LPra SArc SEWo SLon SPad
- 'Adam' (F) CCCN LEdu NLar SEND SMad
I - 'Bauern Feige' (F) NLar SRms
- 'Beall' (F) CCCN
- 'Bellone' (F) CCCN
- 'Black Ischia' (F) CCCN
- 'Bornholm' (F) CCCN IDee LSRN SPre
- 'Bourjassotte Grise' (F) CAgr SDea XSen
- 'Brogiotto' (F) CCCN
- 'Brogiotto Bianco' (F) EMOT
- 'Brown Turkey' (F) ♀H4 Widely available
- 'Brunswick' (F) CAgr CCCN CDul CHll CRHN CTri ELan ELon EPfP EPom EShb EUJe LRHS NLar NRHS SEND SKee SLim SRms WCot WFar WMat
- 'Califfo Blue' (F) SRms
- 'Castle Kennedy' (F) CCCN
- 'Celeste' (F) CCCN SRms
- 'Col de Dame Blanc' (F) XSen
- 'Colummaro Black Apulia' (F) CCCN
- 'Colummaro White Apulia' (F) CCCN
- 'Dalmatie' (F) CAgr CCCN CFGn ELan EPfP EShb IDee LRHS MGos NPri SEND SRms WMat WPGP XSen
I - 'Digitata' (F) MBlu
- 'Digredo' (F) CCCN
- 'Dorée' (F) EPom XSen
- 'Dorée de Porquerolles' (F) CCCN
- 'Filacciano' (F) CCCN
- 'Flanders' (F) CCCN
- 'Goutte d'Or' (F) CAgr CCCN EPfP EPom SDea
- 'Green Ischia' (F) CCCN
- 'Grise de Marseille' (F) CCCN
- 'Grise de Saint Jean' (F) CCCN XSen
- 'Ice Crystal' (F) ♀H5 CRos ECrN ELan EMOT EPfP EShb EUJe LRHS MBlu SMad SPoG SRms WCot WMat WPGP
- 'Jordan' (F) EMOT LRHS
- 'Kadota' (F) CCCN EMOT
- 'Longue d'Août' (F) XSen
- 'Madeleine des Deux Saisons' (F) EPom SEND SKee XSen
- 'Marseillaise' (F) EPfP SDea
- 'Melanzana' (F) CCCN
- 'Morena' (F) SRms
- 'Moscatel' (F) CCCN
- 'Negrétte de Porquerolles' (F) CCCN
- 'Nero' (F) SGol
- 'Newlyn Harbour' (F) ELon
- 'Noire de Barbentane' (F) **new** XSen
- 'Noire de Caromb' (F) CAgr CCCN EPfP LRHS SKee SRms WMat
- 'Noire de Provence' see *F. carica* 'Reculver'
- 'Osborn's Prolific' (F) EPfP SEND SGol SWvt
- 'Panachée' (F) CCCN EMOT EPom LRHS SRms
- 'Perretta' (F) **new** LRHS
- 'Pied de Boeuf' (F) CCCN
- 'Précoce de Dalmatie' (F) CCCN CKel CTho EShb LEdu NLar SRms
- 'Quinta' (F) CCCN
§ - 'Reculver' (F) SEND
- 'Ronde de Bordeaux' (F) CCCN EPfP SEND XSen
- 'Rouge de Bordeaux' (F) CCCN CTsd EMOT EPom NPri SDea SKee SPlb SRms SSta
- 'Safi' (F) CCCN
- 'Saint Johns' (F) SDea
- 'Sultane' (F) CAgr EPom XSen
- 'Tayip 1' (F) **new** CAgr
- 'Tayip 2' (F) **new** CAgr
- 'Verte d'Argenteuil' (F) CCCN
- 'Violette Dauphine' (F) EPfP EUJe IDee LEdu NLar SEND SKee
- 'Violette de Sollies' (F) SVic XSen
- 'Violette Normande' (F) SEND
- 'White Adriatic' (F) SRms
- 'White Genoa' see *F. carica* 'White Marseilles'
§ - 'White Marseilles' (F) CAgr CCCN CMac CRHN ECrN LRHS SDea SEND SKee SRms WMat WPGP
- 'Zamoreica' (F) SEND
- 'Zidi' (F) CCCN

elastica 'Abidjan' EUJe
- 'Robusta' LCro LOPS
- 'Tineke' (v) **new** LCro LOPS

pubigera CExl
pumila ♀H2 EShb
- 'Nana' NWad
- 'Sonny' (v) NWad
- 'Variegata' (v) ♀H2 EShb

punctata **new** EShb

fig see *Ficus carica*; also AGM Fruit Section

filbert see *Corylus maxima*; also AGM Fruit Section (under hazelnut)

Filipendula (*Rosaceae*)

alnifolia 'Variegata' see *F. ulmaria* 'Variegata'
camtschatica CPla EBee ECha ELan IMou MMuc NBid NLar WPGP WWtn
- B&SWJ 10987 WCru
- RBS 0224 NLar
- 'Rosea' MRav

digitata 'Nana' see *F. multijuga*
hexapetala see *F. vulgaris*
- 'Flore Pleno' see *F. vulgaris* 'Multiplex'

'Kahome' CRos ELon EShb EWhm GLog GMaP IKil LLWG LRHS MHol NBid NBir NGdn NLar NRHS NSti SCob SPer SPhx WMoo WPnP
kiraishiensis EBee
- B&SWJ 1571 WCru

koreana CRos EBee LRHS NRHS
§ ***multijuga*** EBee EWhm GCal NHol NLar NWad WBor WMoo
- B&SWJ 10950 WCru
- 'Hjördis' CBod EBee ELon MBel MHol SPad WHil
- var. ***yezoensis*** B&SWJ 10828 IMou WCru

palmata CRos ECha IBlr LLWG LRHS NBre NRHS WMoo
- 'Digitata Nana' see *F. multijuga*
- 'Elegantissima' see *F. purpurea* 'Elegans'
- 'Göteborg' EBee IMou NLar
- 'Nana' see *F. multijuga*
- 'Rosea' CMac LLWG NBir
- 'Rubra' CRos EBee LRHS MRav NGdn NRHS

purpurea CKno EBee ECha ELon GQue IBlr ILea LCro LLWG MMuc SEND SRms WCru WMoo WTyc

- f. ***albiflora*** — ILea LLWG WMoo
§ - 'Elegans' — CRos EBee ELon ILea IMou LLWG LRHS NBid NHol NRHS NWad SCob SPer SRms WFar WMoo WPnP
- 'Pink Dreamland' — SPhx
* - 'Plena' (d) — NLar
'Queen of the Prairies' — see *F. rubra*
§ ***rubra*** — WSFF
§ - 'Venusta' ♀H5 — Widely available
- 'Venusta Magnifica' — see *F. rubra* 'Venusta'
rufinervis B&SWJ 8469 — WCru
- B&SWJ 8611 — WCru
§ ***ulmaria*** — CBen CCBP CHab CHby CWat CWld EMor ENfk GJos GMaP GPoy LCro LOPS MCot MHer MMuc MNHC MWts NGrd NMir WHer WMoo WOut WPnP WSFF WShi XLum
- 'Aurea' — CBod CDor CMac CRos CTri EBee ECha ECtt EHoe ELan EMor EWhm GMaP LEdu LLWG LRHS MRav NBid NLar NRHS SPer SRms WCot WFar WMoo WSHC
- 'Corinne Tremaine' — WHer
- 'Flore Pleno' (d) — EBee LLWG LRHS MRav NBid SPer WCot WFar WHrl
- 'Rosea' — CRos LEdu LLWG LRHS MHer NRHS
§ - 'Variegata' (v) — CRos CWCL EBee ECtt ELan EWhm GQue LLWG LRHS NBid NGdn NLar NRHS SPer SRms WBor WFar WHer WMoo
§ ***vulgaris*** — CDor CHab CWld EMor GLog LEdu LPot MMuc MNHC NBro NGrd NMir NQui WHer
- 'Flore Pleno' — see *F. vulgaris* 'Multiplex'
- 'Grandiflora' — CBre
§ - 'Multiplex' (d) — CDor CMac CRos CSpe ECha ELan EWTr GMaP LLWG LPot LRHS MHer MMrt MMuc MRav NBid NBir NLar NRHS NRya NSti SRms WFar WMoo XLum
- 'Plena' — see *F. vulgaris* 'Multiplex'
- 'Rosea' — NBre

Firmiana (*Malvaceae*)

simplex — CBcs EShb ESwi EUJe LEdu MBlu SMad SPad WPGP

Fitzroya (*Cupressaceae*)

cupressoides — CAco CBcs CDul IArd IDee SLim WPav WThu
- 'Borde Hill' (f) — WThu

Flueggea (*Phyllanthaceae*)

suffruticosa — SBrt

Foeniculum (*Apiaceae*)

vulgare — CAgr CCBP CHby CLau EBou ECha ELan EMor ENfk EPfP GPoy GQue MGos MHer MJak MNHC NPri SCob SEND SPer SPhx SPlb SPoG SRms SVic SWvt
- 'Bronze' — see *F. vulgare* 'Purpureum'
- var. ***dulce*** — ENfk
§ - 'Giant Bronze' — CBod EMor GWyn LCro LEdu LOPS LRHS SCob SPhx WCot WGrn WSpi XSen
- 'Orion' ♀H2 — EKin
§ - 'Purpureum' — Widely available
- 'Smoky' — ECha MRav
- 'Sweet Florence' — LCro SVic
- 'Zefa Fino' ♀H2 — EKin MCtn NRob

Fontanesia (*Oleaceae*)

fortunei — EBtc

Fontinalis (*Fontinalaceae*)

antipyretica — XBlo

Forsythia (*Oleaceae*)

'Arnold Dwarf' — ECrN NBir SRms
'Beatrix Farrand' ambig. — CTri NWea SEND SRms
'Beatrix Farrand' K. Sax — MMuc NLar
'Fiesta' (v) — ELon EPfP MAsh MRav MSwo NEgg NLar SPer WCot WFar
giraldiana — MSwo SRms
GOLD TIDE — see *F.* MARÉE D'OR
'Golden Nugget' — CMac ELan EPfP LBuc MAsh NLar SLon SPoG WCFE WFar
'Golden Times' (v) — CKel CMac CRos LBuc LPot LRHS LSRN MAsh MSwo NEoE NHol NRHS NWea SPoG SWvt WAvo WCot WFar
'Goldstream' (v) — NWad
× ***intermedia*** — CAco EShb
- 'Arnold Giant' — MBlu
- 'Goldrausch' — CRos ELan LCro LOPS LRHS NHic NLar NRHS SAko
- 'Goldzauber' — NWea
- 'Lynwood Variety' ♀H5 — Widely available
- MINIGOLD ('Flojor') — CKel CMac CSBt ELan MSwo NLar SRms
- 'Nimbus'PBR — EBee LCro LOPS LRHS WFar
- SHOW OFF ('Mindor'PBR) — LBuc LRHS
- 'Spectabilis' — CDul EPfP LBuc NHic NWea SCob SCoo SGol SLim WFar
- 'Spectabilis Variegated' (v) — MBNS NEoE
- 'Spring Glory' — MHer WAvo WSpi
- 'Susan Gruninger' (v) — WCot
- 'Variegata' (v) — SRms
- WEEK END ('Courtalyn'PBR) ♀H5 — CBod CEnd CKel CRos EPfP LBuc LRHS MAsh MJak MMuc NHol NLar NRHS SCob SEND SGol SLon SPlb WFar
'Kanarek' — NLar
× ***mandshurica*** — CBcs IMou SAko
§ MARÉE D'OR ('Courtasol'PBR) ♀H5 — CRos EPfP LRHS MAsh MJak MRav NLar NRHS SLon SPer SPoG WFar
MÊLÉE D'OR ('Courtaneur') — SGol WBor
MELISSA ('Courtadic') — NWea
'Northern Gold' — MBlu
ovata 'Tetragold' — NWea
'Paulina' — GEdr NLar WCot
suspensa — CMac CTri EPfP NWea SPlb SRms WSpi
- f. ***atrocaulis*** — CDul WSpi
- 'Nymans' — EWTr MRav NLar NSti SBrt SEND SPer
§ - 'Taff's Arnold' (v) — CExl WAvo WSpi
- 'Variegata' — see *F. suspensa* 'Taff's Arnold'
'Tremonia' — ECrN
viridissima — NWea
- 'Bronxensis' — EPot GEdr LLHF MAsh NBir SIgm WAbe WCot
- CITRUS SWIZZLE ('Mckcitrine'PBR) — NLar WCot
- var. ***koreana*** 'Kumsom' (v) — CRos EBee IArd LRHS NLar SAko
- 'Weber's Bronx' — NLar NWea

Fortunella see *Citrus*

Fothergilla (*Hamamelidaceae*)

gardenii	CBcs CJun CRos EPfP LRHS MBlu MGil MRav NLar SPer SWvt
- 'Blue Mist'	CCCN CEnd CExl CJun CRos EBee ELan ELon EPfP LRHS MAsh NLar SPer SPoG SSta WFar WHor
- 'Glaucophylla'	NLar
- 'Suzanne'	CJun NLar
- 'Zundert'	NLar
× ***intermedia*** BEAVER CREEK ('Klmtwo')	NLar
- 'Blue Shadow'	CBcs CCCN CJun CRos IDee LRHS LSRN MGos MPkF MRav NLar NRHS SGol
- 'Mount Airy' ♀H5	CJun CMCN CRos EPfP LRHS MPkF NLar SSta
- 'Red Licorice'	CJun EPfP NLar
- 'Sea Spray'	CJun NLar
- 'Windy City'	CJun NLar
major ♀H5	CBcs CDul CJun CRos EBee ELan EPfP LCro LOPS LRHS LSRN MAsh MBlu MGil MGos MJak NEgg NLar SPer SWvt WFar WHor WMat WTSh
- 'Bulkyard'	CJun
- Monticola Group	CDul CEnd CJun CRos CTho EPfP LRHS MAsh MMuc SLim SPer SSta
- - 'Huntsman'	CCCN CJun CTho EPfP SPer SSta WFar WHor

Fouquieria (*Fouquieriaceae*)

columnaris	SPlb
splendens	SPlb

Fragaria ✿ (*Rosaceae*)

from Taiwan	WHer
alpina	see *F. vesca* 'Semperflorens'
- 'Alba'	see *F. vesca* 'Semperflorens Alba'
I × ***ananassa*** 'Alba' **new**	WArt
- 'Albion'PBR (F)	CArg LCro LOPS LRHS LSRN NRHS
- 'Alice'PBR (F) ♀H6	CAgr CMac EPom NAln
§ - 'Anablanca' (F)	LRHS
- 'Aromel' (F)	CTri MMuc
- 'Bolero' (F)	NAln
- 'Buddy'PBR (F)	CArg EPom
- 'Calypso' (F)	NAln SDea
- 'Cambridge Favourite' (F) ♀H6	CAgr CArg CMac CRos CSBt CTri EMil EPfP EPom LBuc LCro LOPS LRHS MGos MJak MMuc NAln NPri NRHS SDea SPlb
- 'Cambridge Vigour' (F)	LRHS NRHS
- 'Charlotte'PBR (F) **new**	LRHS
- 'Christine' (F)	CAgr CArg EPom SDea
- 'Cirano'PBR **new**	NAln
- 'Cupid'PBR (F)	CArg LCro LOPS
- 'Darselect'PBR (F)	EPom
- 'Delia' (F)	CRos LRHS NRHS
- DELIZZ ('Liza') (F) **new**	NRHS
- 'Diamante'PBR (F) **new**	NAln
- 'Elan'PBR (F)	LRHS NRHS
- 'Elegance'PBR (F)	CArg EPom
- 'Elsanta' (F)	CArg CRos CSBt CTri ECrN EMil EPfP EPom IArd LBuc LRHS NAln NEgg NPri NRHS SDea SPer WMat
- 'Everest'PBR (F)	LRHS NRHS
- 'Fenella'PBR (F)	CArg CMac EMil EPom LCro LOPS
- 'Finesse' (F)	CSBt LRHS NRHS
- 'Flamenco'PBR (F)	CArg EPom LEdu SDea
- 'Florence'PBR (F)	CAgr CArg CMac CRos CSBt CTri EPom LBuc LRHS NAln NRHS SDea SPer
- 'Florian' (F)	LEdu
- (Fragoo Series) FRAGOO DEEP ROSE ('Tarpan') (F)	CRos LRHS NRHS
- - FRAGOO PINK ('Pikan') (F)	CRos LRHS NRHS
- - FRAGOO WHITE ('Belton') (F)	CRos LRHS NRHS
- Fraise des Bois	see *F. vesca*
- 'Framberry' (F)	EPom LEdu LRHS
* - 'Fresca' (F)	LRHS NRHS
- 'Gariguette' (F)	EPom LRHS
- 'Gorella' (F)	LRHS
- 'Hapil' (F) ♀H6	CTri EMil EPfP EPom LBuc LEdu LRHS
- 'Honeoye' (F) ♀H6	CAgr CArg CRos CSBt EMil EPfP EPom LBuc LCro LEdu LOPS LRHS MMuc SPer
- 'Korona'PBR (F)	CMac EPom
- 'Leo Alba' (F)	CArg
- 'Loran' (F)	CRos LRHS
- 'Mae'PBR (F)	CArg LEdu NAln
- 'Malling Centenary'PBR (F)	EPom
- 'Malling Opal'PBR (F)	EPom
- 'Malwina'PBR (F)	EPom SVic
- 'Manille' (F)	EPom
- 'Merlan'PBR (F)	LRHS NRHS
- 'Mount Everest' (F)	LCro LRHS
- 'Ostara' (F)	NAln
- 'Pandora' (F)	LEdu
- 'Pegasus'PBR (F) ♀H6	CAgr CRos CSBt EPfP EPom LBuc LRHS NRHS
- pineberry (F)	LEdu
- PINK PANDA ('Frel') (F)	CMac CTri EBee ELan LRHS MBel MRav NEgg NGdn NLar NRHS SPer SPoG WCAu
- pink-flowered (F)	GAbr
- 'Red Dream' (F) **new**	LCro LOPS
- 'Red Glory'PBR (F)	LRHS NRHS
- 'Red Princess'PBR (F)	LRHS NRHS
- RED RUBY	see *F.* × *ananassa* 'Samba'
- 'Redgauntlet' (F)	CRos EPfP LRHS NRHS
- 'Rhapsody' (F) ♀H6	CRos LRHS LSRN NRHS
- 'Roman' (F)	LRHS
- 'Rosie'PBR (F)	SDea
- 'Royal Sovereign' (F)	CMac CTri EPom NBir SDea SVic
§ - 'Samba'PBR (F)	CBod EBee ELan GLog LEdu LRHS MBel MNrw NGdn NLar NRHS
- 'Seascape'PBR (F) **new**	NAln
- 'Selva' (F) **new**	NAln
- 'Senga Sengana' (F)	SVic
- SNOW WHITE ('Hansawhit'PBR) (F)	EPom
- 'Sonata'PBR (F)	ELan EPom LRHS NAln
- 'Sweet Ann'PBR (F) **new**	LRHS
- 'Sweetheart' (F)	EPfP LCro LOPS
- 'Symphony'PBR (F) ♀H6	CAgr CRos CSBt EPom LBuc LRHS LSRN NRHS
- 'Temptation' (F)	CRos LRHS NRHS SVic
§ - 'Variegata' (v)	CMea EHrv MRav NPol SPer SPoG WMoo WOut
- 'Vibrant'PBR (F)	EMil EPom
- 'White Dream' (F)	LCro LOPS
'Bowles's Double'	see *F. vesca* 'Multiplex'
chiloensis (F)	IFro LEdu

	- 'Chaval' (F)	ECha EPPr IMou MRav NChi WMoo
	- 'Variegata' misapplied	see *F.* × *ananassa* 'Variegata'
	indica	see *Duchesnea indica*
	'Lipstick'	EBee NLar WSpi
	moschata	CAgr LCro LOPS
	nubicola	CAgr GPoy
	- 'Mount Omei'	EBee
	'Variegata'	see *F.* × *ananassa* 'Variegata'
§	***vesca*** (F)	CAgr CBcs CWld EBou ELan EMor EPfP GPoy GQue LCro LEdu LOPS LRHS MHer MNHC NMir NPol NPri NRHS SPlb SRms SVic WGwG WOut WSFF WShi
*	- var. ***albescens*** new	CLau
	- 'Alexandria' (F)	CLau ENfk NLar NPol
	- 'Alpina Scarletta' (F)	ENfk
	- 'Ana Blanca'	see *F.* × *ananassa* 'Anablanca'
	- 'Baron Solemacher' (F)	NPol WHer
	- 'Capron Royale' (F)	CAgr
	- 'Flore Pleno'	see *F. vesca* 'Multiplex'
	- 'Fructu Albo' (F)	CAgr CBre WMoo
	- 'Golden Alexandra' (F)	ECha EWes EWhm NPol NWad WHer
	- 'Mara des Bois'PBR (F)	EPom LRHS SPer
	- 'Mignonette'	CLau EWhm NPol
	- 'Monophylla' (F)	NPol WHer
§	- 'Multiplex' (d)	EPPr NPol WBor WHer WOut
§	- 'Muricata'	CBre LEdu
	- 'Patchwork'	CNat NPol
	- 'Pineapple Crush' (F)	NPol WHer
	- 'Plymouth Strawberry'	see *F. vesca* 'Muricata'
	- 'Reine des Vallées' (F)	LRHS
	- 'Rügen' (F)	NPol
	- 'Scarlet Beauty' (F)	EPom NPol
§	- 'Semperflorens' (F)	ECrN
§	- 'Semperflorens Alba' (F)	CAgr NWad
	- 'Variegata' misapplied	see *F.* × *ananassa* 'Variegata'
	- 'Variegata' ambig. (v)	EHoe
	- 'White Soul' (F) new	NPol
	- 'Yellow Wonder' (F) new	NPol
	virginiana	CAgr
	- subsp. ***glauca***	EPPr
	viridis	CAgr

Francoa (*Francoaceae*)

	appendiculata	ILea MGil NBir NWad SHeu WHer WMoo WPav
	Ballyrogan strain	IBlr
	'Confetti'	CExl CMea IKil SHar
*	dwarf purple	CElw
	'Purple Spike'	see *F. sonchifolia* Rogerson's form
	ramosa	CPla CTri GKev IBlr ILea NBro WKif WMoo
*	- 'Alba'	CSpe
	sonchifolia	Widely available
	- 'Alba'	EBee WMoo
	- 'Cally Dwarf Purple'	MHer SHeu
	- 'Culm View Lilac'	CKel
	- 'Molly Anderson'	MAvo
	- 'Petite Bouquet'	CKno EWes GKev LRHS SHar SRms
	- 'Pink Bouquet'	CAbb CKno CMac CWGN EBee LRHS SHar SHeu WFar WHlf WOut
	- 'Pink Giant'	CAby CBod CPla CSpe EPau EWhm GAbr GCal GEdr GKev LPot LRHS MBel MPie NRHS NWad SHeu WMoo
§	- Rogerson's form	CElw CRos CTri CWld EHrv ELon EShb GBin IMou LRHS NBir NChi NRHS SHeu WBrk WFar WMoo

Frangula (*Rhamnaceae*)

§	***alnus***	CArg CCVT CDul CHab CPer CTri EWTr LBuc MBlu MGos NWea SEWo WFar WMou WSFF WTSh
	- 'Aspleniifolia'	CSpe CTho ELan EPfP IDee LRHS MBlu MGil MMuc MPkF MRav NLar WCFE WGrn
	- 'Fine Line'	CRos ELan LRHS NLar NRHS SPoG
	- 'Minaret'	MBlu
	- 'Ron Williams'	MBlu WMat
	californica B&SWJ 14057	WCru

Frankenia (*Frankeniaceae*)

	laevis	SRms XSen
	thymifolia	CTri EBou ECtt MAsh MHer MMuc SIgm SPlb WHoo WOld WRHF XLum

Franklinia (*Theaceae*)

	alatamaha	CBcs EBee IArd IDee LRHS MBlu MGil WPGP

Frasera (*Gentianaceae*)

	speciosa	GKev

Fraxinus ✿ (*Oleaceae*)

	americana	CDul
	- 'Autumn Purple'	CDul CEnd
	angustifolia	LPra
	- 'Raywood'	CCVT CDul CEnd ECrN GBin LPra MGos MMuc MSwo SCob SGol
	chiisanensis B&SWJ 12719	WCru
	chinensis	CDul
	excelsior	CCVT CDul CHab ECrN LPra MGos MMuc NGrd SCob SEWo SGol
	- 'Atlas'	LPra
	- 'Aurea Pendula'	CDul CEnd
	- 'Crispa'	NLar
	- f. ***diversifolia***	CDul
	- 'Jaspidea'	CCVT CDul CEnd ECrN EMOT ERod LPra MGos MMuc MSwo SCob SGol
	- 'Pendula'	CCVT CDul CEnd CTsd ECrN LPra SGol
	- 'R.E. Davey'	CDul
	- 'Westhof's Glorie'	CCVT CDul EMOT LPra
	insularis var. ***henryana***	CDul
	mariesii	see *F. sieboldiana*
	nigra 'Fallgold'	CEnd
	ornus	CCVT CDul ECrN MMuc MSwo SEND WTSh
	- 'Anita' new	LPra
	- 'Arie Peters'	CDul
	pennsylvanica	CDul
	quadrangulata	CDul
§	***sieboldiana***	CDul
	velutina	CDul
	xanthoxyloides	CDul

Freesia (*Iridaceae*)

	alba Foster	see *F. lactea*
	alba (G.L. Mey.) Gumbl.	CPbh
	'Blue Moon'	LCro LOPS
	'Delta River'	EPfP SPoG
	'Fragrant Sunburst'	EPfP SPoG
	'Gold River'	SPoG
	grandiflora	CExl CHll
§	***lactea***	XEll

§ ***laxa*** ♀H3	CExl CPbh CSpe CTri GKev LRHS NHpl SChF
- var. ***alba*** ♀H3	CExl CPbh GKev
- blue-flowered	SBrt
- 'Joan Evans'	LLHF SChF
- red-spotted	CExl
'Red River'	SPoG
viridis	CExl
'White River'	EPfP SPoG

Fremontodendron (*Malvaceae*)

'California Glory' ♀H4	CBcs CDul CMac CRos EPfP EUJe IDee LRHS LSRN MAsh MBlu MGil MGos MPkF NRHS SArc SEle SGbt SGol SMad SPer SPoG SVen SWvt
californicum	CTri EBee ELan NLar SEND SNig SPlb WFar
'Pacific Sunset'	LRHS MGos MRav SGol
'Tequila Sunrise' ♀H4	CWGN LRHS WFar

Freylinia (*Scrophulariaceae*)

cestroides	see *F. lanceolata*
§ ***lanceolata***	CBcs CCCN EBee SPlb SVen
tropica	MGil
visseri	SVen

Fritillaria ✿ (*Liliaceae*)

acmopetala ♀H4	CAby CAvo CWCL ELon EMor EPot ERCP GKev ITim LAma MNrw SDeJ SHar WCot WIce WSHC
- subsp. ***wendelboi***	GKev LAma
affinis	CWCL EMor GKev NHpl
- 'Sunray'	GKev
§ - var. ***tristulis***	ELon EMor
- 'Vancouver Island'	LAma
- yellow-flowered	CWCL
amana	CWCL ELon EMor EPot ERCP GKev LLHF WCot
- 'Cambridge'	WCot
- 'Goksan Gold'	GKev
arabica	see *F. persica*
assyriaca	EPot IFro
aurea	LAma
- 'Golden Flag'	EPot LAma SDeJ
ayakoana	GKev
'Beethoven' (Rascal Series)	GKev LAma WCot
biflora	GKev
- 'Martha Roderick'	SDeJ
§ ***bithynica***	ITim LAma
bucharica	EPot GKev LAma
camschatcensis	CRos CWCL ELon EMor EPfP EPot ERCP GBin GEdr GKev GMaP LAma LRHS NBir NHpl NRHS SDeJ WCot WCru
- 'Alaska'	NHar
- 'Aurea'	NHar
- black-flowered	CAby NHar
- double-flowered (d)	GKev LAma
- f. ***flavescens***	GEdr LAma
- green-flowered	CAby
carduchorum	see *F. minuta*
citrina	see *F. bithynica*
conica	GKev
§ ***crassifolia*** subsp. ***kurdica***	ITim
davisii	EPfP EPot GKev LAma LLHF SDeJ
eduardii	GKev
- 'Castor'	EPot GKev LAma
- 'Pollux'	GKev LAma
elwesii	CAvo EPot ERCP GKev ITim LAma LLHF SDeJ WTor
* ***glauca*** 'Golden Flag'	GKev SDeJ
- 'Goldilocks'	LAma SDeJ
graeca	LAma SDeJ
grandiflora	GKev
hispanica	see *F. lusitanica*
imperialis ♀H7	MWat
- 'April Flame'	LAma
- 'Argenteovariegata' (v)	GKev LAma
- 'Aureomarginata' (v)	GKev LAma
- 'Aurora'	CRos EPot ERCP GKev LAma LRHS MJak NAln NChi NLar NPer NRHS SDeJ SPhx WFar
- 'Bach' (Rascal Series) **new**	GKev LAma
- 'Brahms' (Rascal Series) **new**	GKev LAma
- 'Chopin' (Rascal Series)	CAvo GKev LAma
- 'Early Fantasy'	GKev LAma
- 'Early Magic' **new**	GKev LAma
- 'Early Passion'	GKev LAma
- 'Garland Star'	CRos GKev LAma LRHS LSun NLar NRHS SDeJ SPhx
- 'Grenadier'	LAma
- var. ***inodora***	GKev LAma
- 'Inodora Purpurea'	LAma
- 'Lutea'	CAvo CRos ERCP GKev LAma LRHS NAln NChi NRHS SPoG WFar
- 'Mahler' (Rascal Series)	GKev LAma
- 'Maxima'	see *F. imperialis* 'Rubra Maxima'
- 'Maxima Lutea' ♀H7	CRos CWld ELan EPfP EPot ERCP GKev LRHS MJak NLar NRHS SDeJ SPhx SPoG
- 'Orange Beauty'	CRos GKev LAma LRHS NRHS SDeJ
- 'Orange Brilliant'	LAma
- 'Prolifera'	GKev LAma SDeJ
- 'Rubra'	CBod CRos CWld EPfP ERCP EUJe GKev LAma LRHS MJak NLar NRHS WFar
§ - 'Rubra Maxima'	CRos ELan EPfP EPot ERCP GKev LRHS LSun MJak NChi NRHS SDeJ SPhx
- 'Satie' (Rascal Series) **new**	GKev LAma
- 'Slagzwaard'	GKev LAma
- 'Striped Beauty'	EPot GKev LAma SDeJ
- 'Sulpherino'	GKev LAma
- 'Sunset'	GKev LAma
- 'The Premier'	GKev LAma SDeJ
- 'Vivaldi' (Rascal Series)	GKev LAma
- 'William Rex'	CAvo CRos CWCL EPot ERCP GKev LAma LBuc LRHS NRHS SPhx SPoG
involucrata	WCot
karadaghensis	see *F. crassifolia* subsp. ***kurdica***
koidzumiana **new**	GKev
lanceolata	see *F. affinis* var. ***tristulis***
latakiensis	EPot GKev
§ ***lusitanica***	ITim
meleagris ♀H5	Widely available
- var. ***unicolor*** subvar. ***alba*** ♀H5	CAvo ERCP GKev IFro LCro LOPS NHol SCob SDeJ SPer SPhx WPnP WShi
- - - 'Aphrodite'	EPot NBir WCot
messanensis subsp. ***gracilis***	GKev
michailovskyi	CAvo CRos EPfP EPot ERCP EWhm GKev IFro LAma LRHS MNrw NHpl NRHS SDeJ SRms WFar
- 'Multiflorum'	GKev
§ ***minuta***	EPot ERCP GKev LAma SDeJ
nigra Mill.	see *F. pyrenaica*

	pallidiflora ♀H5	CAvo CWCL ELon EMor EPot ERCP LAma NAln NBir NHpl SDeJ SPhx WCot
	- yellow-flowered	ITim
§	***persica***	CPla CWld ECha EPfP EPot ERCP EWhm GKev LAma LRHS MJak NChi NRHS SCob SPhx WCot
	- 'Adiyaman' ♀H4	ELan SDeJ
	- 'Alba'	GKev SDeJ SPhx
	- 'Bicolor'	GKev
	- 'Green Dreams' **new**	LAma
	- 'Ivory Bells'	EPot ERCP GKev LAma LRHS SDeJ
	- 'Magic Bells' **new**	GKev
	- 'Midnight Bells'	GKev IPot
*	- 'Senkoy'	GKev
	- 'Twin Towers Tribute' **new**	LAma
	pinardii	LAma
	pontica ♀H4	CAvo CWCL EMor EPot ERCP GKev ITim LAma NHpl SDeJ SPhx WCot
	pudica	LAma
	- 'Giant'	SDeJ
§	***pyrenaica*** ♀H5	LAma LLHF
	raddeana	CAvo ELon EMor EPot ERCP GBin GKev LAma SDeJ SPhx WCot
	reuteri	EPot GKev LAma
	rubra major	see *F. imperialis* 'Rubra Maxima'
	sewerzowii	EPot GKev LAma WCot
	- 'Brown Eyes'	GKev
	sibthorpiana	EPot GKev
	stenanthera	EPot GKev LAma
	stribrnyi	EPot
	thunbergii	GKev LAma LLHF WCot
	uva-vulpis	CAby CAvo CRos CTca EAJP ECtt ELon EPfP EPot ERCP EUJe GKev GWyn LAma LRHS MNrw NBir NRHS SDeJ WFar
	verticillata	ECha LAma WCru
	whittallii	EPot LAma
	- 'Green Light'	GKev

Fuchsia ✿ (*Onagraceae*)

	'A.M. Larwick'	EBak SLBF
	'A.W. Taylor'	EBak
	'Abbé Farges' (d)	CLoc CRos EBak EPts LRHS NRHS SVic
	'Abundance'	EHDe
	'Achievement' ♀H4	CLoc LCla MJac SVic
	'Adinda' (T) ♀H1c	EPts LCla MHer
	'Ailsa Garnett' (d)	EBak
	'Alan Titchmarsh' ♀H2	EPts LCla SLBF
	'Alaska' (d)	CLoc SVic
	'Alberttina'	SVic
	'Albertus Schwab'	LCla
	'Alderford'	SLBF
	'Alfonso' (d)	SLBF
	'Alice Ashton' (d)	EBak
	'Alice Doran'	LCla
	'Alice Hoffman' (d) ♀H4	CCCN CKel CLoc CMac CRos CSBt EBak EBee ELan EPfP EPts LRHS MAsh MGos MJac NEgg NHic NLar NRHS SEND SLBF SLim SPer SPet SPoG SVic WFar
	'Alicia Sellars'	SLBF
	'Alison Ewart'	CLoc SPet SVic
	'Alison Patricia' ♀H2	EBak LCla MJac SLBF SVic
	'Alison Ruth Griffin' (d)	MJac
	'Alison Ryle' (d)	EBak
	'Alison Sweetman' ♀H2	MJac
	'Allen Jackson'	LCla SLBF
	alpestris	EBak GCal LCla SVic
	'Alyce Larson' (d)	EBak MJac SVic
	'Alyssa May Garcia' (d)	EPts MJac SLBF
	'Amazing Maisie' (d)	SLBF
	'Ambassador'	SVic
	'Amelia Rose'	SLBF
	'Amelie Aubin'	CLoc EBak SVic
§	***ampliata***	LCla
	'Amy'	MJac
	'Amy Lye'	CLoc EHDe SVic
§	'Andenken an Heinrich Henkel' (T)	CLoc EBak SVic
	'André Le Nostre' (d)	EBak SVic
	'Andreas Schwab'	LCla
	andrei	LCla
	'Andrew Carnegie' (d)	CLoc
	'Andrew Hadfield'	SVic
	'Angela Leslie' (d)	CLoc EBak SVic
	'Angel's Flight' (d)	EBak
	'Angel's Kiss' (E)	SLBF
	'Anita'	CLoc EPts MJac SLBF SVic
	'Ann Allen'	SLBF
	'Ann Howard Tripp'	CLoc EPts MJac SVic
	'Ann Reid'	NWms SLBF
	'Anna of Longleat' (d)	SPet
	'Anna Sunshine' (T)	EPts SLBF
	'Annabel' (d) ♀H4	CCCN CLoc CTri EBak EPts LCla MJac SLBF SPet SVic
	'Anneke de Keijzer'	LCla
	'Annie Earle'	EHDe
	'Annie M.G. Schmidt'	EPts LCla
	'Ant and Dec' (d/v)	MJac
	'Anthea Day' (d)	CLoc
	'Antigone'	SLBF
	'Aphrodite' (d)	CLoc
	'Applause' (d)	CLoc EBak EPts SLBF SPet SVic
	aprica misapplied	see *F.* × *bacillaris*
	aprica Lundell	see *F. microphylla* subsp. *aprica*
	'Apricot Ice'	CLoc SVic
	'Arabella Improved'	EHDe SVic
	arborea	see *F. arborescens*
§	***arborescens***	CBcs CBod CHll CLoc CWCL EBak ECre EUJe EWld IDee LCla MCot MHer SDys SVic
	- B&SWJ 10475	WCru
	'Arcady'	CLoc
	'Ariel' (E)	SVic
	'Arkie'	MJac
	'Army Nurse' (d) ♀H4	CLoc CRos ELan ELon EPfP EPts LRHS MGos NBir NLar NRHS SGol SLBF SPet SVic
	'Ashley'	LCla
	'Ashtede'	SLBF
	'Ashville'	SLBF
	'Atlantic Star'	MJac
	'Atomic Glow' (d)	SVic
	'Aubergine'	see *F.* 'Gerharda's Aubergine'
	'Auenland'	MJac
	'Auntie Jinks' ♀H2	EBak MJac SPet SVic
	'Aurora Superba'	CLoc EBak SLBF
	'Autumnale' ♀H2	CLoc EBak EPts NWad SLBF SPet SPoG SVic
	'Avalanche' ambig. (d)	CLoc EBak SLBF
	'Avocet'	CLoc
	'Avon Celebration' (d/v)	CLoc
	'Avon Gem'	CLoc
	'Avon Glow' (d)	CLoc
	'Avon Gold'	CLoc
	'Awake Sweet Love' (T)	EPts
	ayavacensis	LCla
	'Aylisa Rowan' (E)	SLBF

	'Azure Sky' (d)	MJac
	'Baby Blue Eyes' ♀H4	CLoc CRos ELan ELon LRHS LSRN MAsh NRHS SLBF SVic
	'Baby Bright'	LCla
	'Baby Thumb' (v)	EPts
	'Babyface' Tolley (d)	SVic
§	× ***bacillaris*** (E)	CAbb CChe EUJe EWes GCal LRHS SEle SLBF SPoG WHer XLum
§	- 'Cottinghamii' (E)	EWld ILea WSHC
§	- 'Reflexa' (E)	CCCN
	'Baden Powell' (E)	SVic
	'Bagworthy Water'	CLoc
	'Baker's Tri' (T)	EBak
	'Balkonkönigin'	CLoc
	'Ballerina Girl' (E)	SLBF
	'Ballet Girl' (d) ♀H2	CLoc EBak SLBF
	'Bambini'	EPts SLBF
	'Barbara'	CLoc EBak EPts LCla MJac SPet SVic
	'Barbara Evans'	SLBF
	'Barbara Windsor'	MJac
	'Barry's Queen'	see *F.* 'Golden Border Queen'
	'Bashful' (d)	EPts LCla SPet SVic
	'Beacon'	CLoc CMac CRos EBak EPfP EPts LCla LRHS MJac NRHS SGol SLBF SPet SPoG SVic
	'Beacon Rosa' ♀H4	CLoc CRos EPfP EPts LCla LRHS MJac NRHS SLBF SPet SPoG SVic
	'Bealings' (d)	SVic
	'Beauty of Bath' (d)	CLoc
	'Beauty of Clyffe Hall' Lye	EBak EHDe
	'Beauty of Exeter' (d)	EBak LCla
	'Beauty of Prussia' (d)	CLoc
	'Beauty of Swanley'	EHDe
	'Beauty of Trowbridge'	EHDe LCla
	'Bella Rosella' (California Dreamers Series) (d) ♀H2	CLoc EPts MJac SCoo
	'Belvoir Beauty' (d)	CLoc
	'Ben de Jong'	LCla SLBF
	'Ben Jammin'	CLoc EPfP EPts SVic
	'Ben-Ben'	SLBF
	'Berliner Kind' (d)	EBak
	'Bernice Elizabeth' (d) **new**	NWms SLBF
	'Bernie's Big-un' (d)	MJac SLBF
	'Bernisser Hardy' ♀H4	EPts LCla NQui SLBF SLim XLum
	'Bessie Kimberley' (T)	LCla
	'Betsy Huuskes'	SLBF
	'Beverley'	EBak EPts
	'Bianca' (d)	SVic
	'Bicentennial' (d)	CLoc EBak EPts MJac SLBF SPet SVic
	'Billy Green' (T) ♀H2	CLoc EBak EPts LCla MHer MJac SVic
	'Bishop's Bells' (d)	SVic
	'Bittersweet' (d)	SVic
	'Black Prince'	SVic
	'Blacky' (d)	CCCN EBak EUJe GBin SDys SEND SPet SVic
I	'Blanche Regina' (d)	MJac
	'Bland's New Striped'	EBak EPts NHic SLBF
§	'Blauer Engel' (d)	MJac
	'Blaze Away' (d)	MJac
	'Blowick'	MJac SPet
	BLUE ANGEL	see *F.* 'Blauer Engel'
	'Blue Bush'	EPts MJac SVic XLum
	'Blue Eyes' (d)	SPet
	'Blue Gown' (d)	CLoc EBak SVic
	'Blue Lace' (d)	SVic
	'Blue Mirage' (d)	CLoc SVic
	'Blue Pearl' (d)	EBak
	'Blue Pinwheel'	EBak
	'Blue Tit'	LCla
	'Blue Veil' (d)	CLoc MJac SCoo SVic
	'Blue Waves' (d)	CLoc CSBt EBak SVic
	'Blush o' Dawn' (d)	CLoc EBak SLBF SVic
	'Bobby Shaftoe' (d)	EBak
	'Bobby Wingrove'	EBak
	'Bobby's Girl'	EPts
	'Bobolink' (d)	EBak
	'Bob's Best' (d)	EPts
	boliviana Britton	see *F. sanctae-rosae*
	boliviana ambig.	CBcs GCal IDee MHer
§	***boliviana*** Carrière	CHll CLoc LCla
§	- var. ***alba*** ♀H2	CHll CLoc EBak EPts LCla SVic
	- var. ***boliviana***	CRHN SVic
	- var. ***luxurians*** 'Alba'	see *F. boliviana* Carrière var. *alba*
	- f. ***puberulenta*** Munz	see *F. boliviana* Carrière
	'Bon Accorde'	CLoc EBak EPts SLBF
	'Bon Bon' (d)	SVic
	'Bonita' (d)	SVic
	'Bonnie Lass' (d)	EBak
I	'Boogie Woogie' (d)	LCla MJac NWms SLBF
	'Bora Bora' (d)	SVic
	'Borde Hill' (d)	EPts
	'Border Princess'	EBak
	'Border Queen' ♀H4	CLoc EBak EPts MJac SLBF SVic
	'Border Reiver'	SVic
	'Börnemann's Beste'	see *F.* 'Georg Börnemann'
	'Bouffant'	CLoc SVic
	'Bountiful' Munkner (d)	CLoc
	'Bouquet' (d)	SLBF
	'Bow Bells'	CLoc MJac SPet SVic
	'Boy Marc' (T) ♀H1c	LCla
	'Brandt's 500 Club'	CLoc
	'Breckland'	EBak
	'Breeder's Dream' (d)	EBak
	'Breevis Minimus'	SLBF
	'Brenda White'	CLoc EBak SVic
	'Brian C. Morrison' (T)	LCla
	'Brian G. Soanes'	EBak
	'Brian Kimberley' (T)	LCla
	'Bridesmaid' (d)	EBak SVic
	'Brilliant' ambig.	EHDe
	'Brilliant' Bull, 1865	CLoc EBak LCla
	'British Jubilee' (d)	SVic
	'Brookwood Belle' (d) ♀H3	EPts LCla MJac SLBF
	'Brutus' ♀H4	CLoc CRos EBak EPfP EPts LRHS NRHS SCoo SLBF SPet SVic WFar
	'Bryan Breary' (E)	LCla
	'Buddha' (d)	EBak
	'Bugle Boy'	LCla
	'Bunny' (d)	SVic
	'Buster' (d)	LCla
	'Buttercup'	SVic
	'C.J. Howlett'	EBak
	'Caesar' (d)	EBak
	'Cambridge Louie'	EBak SPet
	campos-portoi	EBee MGil WPGP
	'Candy Bells' (d)	CSBt
	canescens misapplied	see *F. ampliata*
	'Canny Bob'	MJac
	'Cara Mia' (d)	CLoc SPet
	'Caradela' (d)	CLoc MJac
	'Cardinal'	CLoc
	'Cardinal Farges' (d)	CLoc SLBF SVic
	'Careless Whisper'	LCla SLBF
	'Carl Drude' (d)	SVic
	'Carla Johnston' ♀H2	CLoc EPts MJac SVic
	'Carmel Blue'	CCCN CLoc LCla SVic
	'Carnoustie' (d)	EBak
	'Carol Grace' (d)	CLoc

Name	Suppliers
'Caroline'	CLoc EBak EPts SVic
'Caroline's Joy'	MJac SCoo SPet
'Cascade'	CLoc EPts MJac SLBF SPet
'Caspar Hauser' (d)	SVic
'Cecil Glass'	EHDe
'Cecile' (d)	CCCN EPts LCla MJac SLBF SVic
'Celebration' (d)	CLoc
'Celia Smedley' 𝕐H3	CLoc CRos EBak EPts LCla LRHS MJac NRHS SLBF SPet SVic
'Centerpiece' (d)	EBak
'Ceri'	CLoc
'Cerrig'	SVic
'Champagne Celebration'	CLoc
'Champion'	XLum
'Chandleri'	SVic
'Chang' 𝕐H2	CLoc EBak LCla SLBF SVic
'Chantelle Garcia' (d)	EPts LCla MJac SLBF
'Chantry Park' (T)	LCla
'Chapel Rossan' (E)	SLBF
'Charisma'	SVic
'Charles Welch'	EPts
CHARLIE DIMMOCK ('Foncha'PBR) (d)	CLoc
'Charlie Gardiner'	EBak
'Charlie Girl' (d)	SVic
'Charming'	CLoc CRos EHDe EPfP LRHS MAsh MJac NRHS SVic XLum
'Chatt's Delight'	SLBF
'Checkerboard' 𝕐H3	CLoc EBak EPts LCla MHer MJac SLBF SPet SVic
'Chelsea Louise'	EPts
'Cherry Lee'	SLBF
'Chessboard'	CLoc
'Chillerton Beauty' 𝕐H4	CBod CLoc CRos CTri ELan ELon EPts LCla LRHS MJac NHic NLar NRHS SEND SLBF SPer SPet SVic WFar
'Chilli Red'	CRos EPfP EPts LRHS MAsh NRHS
'China Lantern'	CLoc SVic
'Chor Echo'	SLBF
'Chris Bright'	MJac
'Chris Tarrant' (d)	EPts
'Christina Becker'	SVic
'Christmas Gem' (T)	MJac
cinerea	LCla
'Cinnabarina' (E)	CLoc SVic
'Cinvenu'	LCla
'Cinvulca'	LCla
'Citation'	CLoc EBak SVic
'City of Adelaide' (d)	CLoc
'City of Leicester'	SPet
'Clair de Lune'	EBak SLBF SVic
'Claire Simone'	SLBF
'Claudia' (d)	LCla MJac SLBF
'Cliff's Hardy'	LCla SVic
'Cliff's Own'	SVic
'Cliff's Unique' (d)	EPts
'Clifton Beauty' (d)	MJac
'Clifton Charm'	EPts LCla MJac SVic
'Clipper'	EHDe
'Cloth of Gold'	CLoc EBak MJac SLBF SPet SVic
'Cloverdale Jewel' (d)	SPet SVic
'Cloverdale Pearl'	EBak MAsh SPet SPoG SVic
'Coachman' 𝕐H4	CLoc EBak EPts LCla SLBF SVic
coccinea	CTsd
'Codex' (d)	SLBF
× ***colensoi***	LCla
'Collingwood' (d)	CLoc
'Come Dancing' (d)	SPet SVic
I 'Comet' Tiret (d)	CLoc
'Connie' (d)	EBak SVic XLum
'Connor's Cascade'	SLBF
'Conspicua' 𝕐H4	LRHS SLBF SVic
'Constance' (d)	CLoc LCla MJac SLBF SPet SVic
'Constance Comer'	MJac
'Constellation' Schnabel, 1957 (d)	CLoc EBak
'Coquet Bell'	EBak
'Coral Baby' (E)	LCla SLBF
'Coral Rose' (d)	SVic
'Coralle' (T) 𝕐H1c	CCCN CLoc EBak EPts LCla MJac SLBF SVic
'Corallina' 𝕐H4	CLoc SEND SVic
* ***cordata*** B&SWJ 9095	WCru
- B&SWJ 10325	WCru
cordifolia misapplied	see *F. splendens*
'Core'ngrato' (d)	CLoc
'Cornelia Smith' (T)	LCla
'Cornish Blue'	CLoc
'Cornwall Calls' (d)	EBak
'Corsage' (d)	SVic
'Corsair' (d)	EBak SVic
corymbiflora misapplied	see *F. boliviana* Carrière
corymbiflora Ruíz & Pav.	SVic
'Costa Brava'	CLoc
'Cotta Bright Star'	LCla
'Cotta Carousel'	LCla
'Cotta Christmas Tree'	LCla SLBF
'Cotta Vino'	SVic
'Cottinghamii'	see *F. × bacillaris* 'Cottinghamii'
'Cotton Candy' (d)	CLoc SVic
'Countdown Carol' (d)	EPts
'Countess of Aberdeen'	EBak SLBF
'Countess of Maritza' (d)	CLoc
'Court Jester' (d)	CLoc
'Cover Girl' (d)	EPts
'Coxeen'	EBak
'Crackerjack'	CLoc
'Crescendo' (d)	CLoc
'Crinkley Bottom' (d)	EPts MJac SLBF
'Crosby Serendipity'	CLoc
'Crystal Blue'	EBak SVic
'Crystal Stars' (d)	SVic
'Cupid'	EBak
'Curly Q'	EBak SVic
'Curtain Call' (d)	EBak SVic
cylindracea misapplied	see *F. × bacillaris*
'Cymru' (d)	SVic
'Dainty'	EBak
'Dainty Lady' (d)	EBak
'Daisy Bell'	CLoc EBak LCla MJac SPet SVic
'Dana Samantha'	EPts
'Dancing Bloom'	EPts
'Dancing Flame' (d) 𝕐H3	CLoc EBak EPts LCla MJac SLBF SVic
'Daniel Pfaller' (d)	MJac
'Danish Pastry'	SPet
'Danny Boy' (d)	CLoc EBak SVic
'Dark Eyes' (d) 𝕐H4	CCCN CLoc EBak MJac SLBF SPer SPet SVic
'Dark Secret' (d)	EBak
'Daryn John Woods'	LCla
'David' 𝕐H4	CLoc ELon EPfP EPts LCla LSRN MJac SLBF SPoG WAvo
'David Alston' (d)	CLoc
'David Clifford' **new**	EHDe
'David Lockyer' (d)	CLoc SVic
'David Savage' (d)	LCla
'Dawn Fantasia' (v)	CLoc EPts

'Dawn Star' (d)	CLoc SVic
'Dawn Thunder' (d)	SVic
'De Groot's Floriant'	LCla
'Debby' (d)	EBak
'Deben Petite' (E)	LCla
'Deborah Jane'	SLBF
'Deborah Street' (d)	CLoc
'DebRon's Black Cherry'	SLBF
'Dee Copley' (d)	EBak
'Deep Purple' (d)	CLoc EPts MJac SCoo SLBF
'Delia Smith' (d)	EPts
'Delicate Blue'	SLBF
'Delicate Purple'	EPts SLBF
'Delphobe'	EPts
'Delta's Bride'	SLBF
'Delta's Drop'	SVic
'Delta's Groom'	LCla SLBF
'Delta's Ko' (d)	SVic
'Delta's Sara'	CRos ELon EPfP LBuc LCro LOPS LPot LRHS MAsh MJac NHic NRHS SLim SLon SPad SPoG WBor WFar
'Delta's Wonder'	SVic
§ ***denticulata*** ♀H2	CLoc CRos EBak EPts LCla LRHS MHer NRHS SLBF SVic
'Desperate Daniel'	EPts
'Devonshire Dumpling' (d) ♀H2	CCCN CLoc EBak EPts MJac SPet SVic
'Diablo' (d)	EBak
'Diamond Wedding'	SVic
'Diana Wright'	WAvo
§ 'Die Schöne Wilhelmine'	SVic
'Dipton Dainty' (d)	CLoc EBak SVic
'Display' ♀H4	CLoc CRos EBak EPfP EPts LCla LRHS MGos MJac NPer NRHS SGol SLBF SPet SPoG SVic
'Diva'	WCot
'Doc'	EPts SPet SVic
'Docteur Topinard'	CLoc
'Doctor'	see *F.* 'The Doctor'
'Doctor Foster' ♀H4	CLoc CTri EBak SVic
'Doctor Olson' (d)	CLoc
'Doctor Robert'	EPts MJac
'Dodo'	LCla SLBF
§ 'Dollar Prinzessin' (d) ♀H4	CLoc CMac CRos EBak EPfP EPts EShb LCla LRHS MGos MJac NHic NPer NRHS SGol SLBF SLim SPet SPlb SVic WFar
'Dominyana'	EBak LCla
'Dopy' (d)	EPts SPet SVic
'Doray'	EPts SLBF
'Doreen Redfern'	CLoc MJac SPet SVic
'Doris Joan'	SLBF
'Dorothea Flower'	CLoc EBak
'Dorothy'	EPts LCla SLBF
'Dorothy Ann'	LCla SLBF
'Dorothy Day' (d)	CLoc
'Dorothy Hanley' (d)	CCCN CLoc ELon EPts MJac SLBF SPet SVic
'Dorrian Brogdale' (T)	LCla
'Drake 400' (d)	CLoc
'Drame' (d)	EBak SVic
'Duchess of Albany'	CLoc EHDe
'Duchess of Cornwall' (d)	EPts
'Duet' (d)	SVic
'Duke of Wellington' Haag, 1956 (d)	CLoc
'Dulcie Elizabeth' (d)	EBak MJac SPet
'Dunrobin Bedder'	SLBF
'Dusky Beauty'	SVic
'Dusky Rose' (d)	CLoc EBak MJac SVic

'Dutch Mill'	CLoc EBak
'Dying Embers' ♀H4	CLoc MHer SVen
'Dymph Werker van Groenland' (E)	LCla
'Earre Barré'	SLBF
'East Anglian'	CLoc
'Easter Belle'	CRos LRHS NRHS
'Ebb 'n' Flow'	EBak
'Ebbtide' (d)	CLoc
'Ed Largarde' (d)	EBak
'Eden Lady'	CLoc SPet
'Eden Princess'	MJac
'Eden Rock' (d)	CLoc
'Edith' ambig.	EPts
'Edith' Brown (d)	LCla SLBF
'Edith Emery' (d)	SPet
'El Cid'	CLoc EBak SVic
'Elaine Ann'	EPts MJac
'Elaine Taylor' (d)	MJac
'Eleanor Leytham'	EBak SVic
ELECTRIC LIGHTS ('Nufu1'[PBR])	EPts
'Elfin Glade'	CLoc EBak SVic
'Elfriede Ott' (T) ♀H1c	CLoc EBak LCla
'Elizabeth Honnorine'	SVic
'Ellie's Charm'	NWms SLBF
'Elma'	LCla MJac
'Elsa' (d)	SVic
'Elsie Mitchell' (d)	SPet
§ 'Emile de Wildeman' (d)	SPet
'Emily Bright'	EHDe
'Emily Eve' (d)	EPts MJac SLBF
'Emma Payne' **new**	SLBF
'Empress of Prussia' ♀H4	CLoc EBak EPts SLBF SVic
encliandra (E)	NWad
§ 'Enfant Prodigue' (d)	CLoc SLBF SPet SVic XLum
'Eppsii'	SLBF
'Eric's Majestic' (d)	MJac
'Ernest Rankin'	SVic
'Ernie'[PBR]	EPts SLBF
'Ernie Wise' (d)	SCoo
'Eroica'	SVic
'Eruption'	CLoc MJac
'Estelle Marie'	CLoc EBak SPet SVic
'Eternal Flame' (d)	EBak EPts SVic
'Ethel May' (d)	MJac
'Eusebia' (d)	SVic
'Eva Boerg' ♀H4	CCCN CLoc CTri EBak EPts SPet SVic WKif
'Evensong'	CLoc EBak SVic
excorticata	CBcs CExl CTsd SPlb WBor
'Fabian Franck' (T)	LCla
'Falklands' (d)	EPts SLBF
'Falling Stars'	CLoc SVic
'Fancy Pants' (d)	CLoc SVic
'Fanfare'	LCla SVic
'Fascination'	see *F.* 'Emile de Wildeman'
'Felicity Kendal' (d)	SCoo
'Fenman'	SVic
'Festival Lights' (E)	SLBF
'Ffion'	EPts
'Fiery Spider'	EBak SVic
'Finn'	EPts
'Fiona'	CLoc EBak SVic
'Fire Mountain' (d)	CLoc SVic
'Firecracker'	see *F.* 'John Ridding'
'Firefly'	SVic
'Firelite' (d)	EBak
'First Success' (E)	LCla SVic
'Flair' (d)	CLoc

'Flamenco Dancer' (California Dreamers Series) (d)	CLoc
'Flamingo' (d)	SVic
'Flamingo Wings' (d)	EPts
'Flanders Field' **new**	NWms SLBF
'Flash' ♀H4	CLoc CRos CTri ELan EMor EPts LCla LRHS MJac MRav NRHS SLBF SPet SPoG SVic
'Flashlight'	EWld LCla MAsh MJac SCoo
'Flat Jack o' Lancashire' (d)	SLBF
'Fleur de Picardie'	SLBF
'Flirtation Waltz' (d)	CLoc EBak MJac SVic
'Flocon de Neige'	SLBF
'Flogman'	EWld LCla
'Floral City' (d)	CLoc
'Florence Turner'	EBak
'Florentina' (d)	CLoc EBak SVic
'Florrie's Gem' (d)	SLBF
'Flying Cloud' (d)	CLoc EBak SVic
'Flying Scotsman' (d)	CLoc EBak EPts SCoo SVic
'Foolke'	EBak
'Forget-me-not'	CLoc SVic
'Fort Bragg' (d)	EBak
'Four Farthings' (d)	EPts
'Foxgrove Wood' ♀H4	EBak EPts SLBF
'Frank Saunders'	LCla SLBF
'Frank Unsworth' (d)	EPts MJac SPet
'Frankfurt 2006'	MJac
'Frankie's Magnificent Seven' (d)	EPts
'Frans Boers' **new**	SLBF
'Franz von Zon'	LCla
'Frau Hilde Rademacher' (d)	EBak EPts SLBF SVic
'Frauke'	SVic
'Fred's First' (d)	SVic
'Friendly Fire' (d)	CLoc
'Frosted Flame'	CLoc LCla MJac SLBF SPet
'Frozen Tears'	EPts
'Frühling' (d)	EBak
'Fuchsiade '88'	CLoc
'Fuji-san'	ELon EPts
fulgens (T) ♀H2	GCal LCla
* - 'Variegata' (T/v)	CLoc EPts LCla
'Fulpila'	LCla SLBF
'Gala' (d)	EBak
'Galadriel'	SLBF
'Garden News' (d) ♀H4	CBod CLoc CRos ELon EPfP EPts LCla LRHS MAsh MJac NBir NGBl NPer NRHS SGol SLBF SPer SPet SVic WFar
'Garden Week' (d)	SVic
'Gartenmeister Bonstedt' (T) ♀H1c	CLoc EWld LCla SVic
'Gary Rhodes' (d)	EBak SCoo
'Gay Fandango' (d)	CLoc
'Gay Señorita'	EBak
'Gay Spinner' (d)	CLoc
'Gemma Fisher' (d)	EPts
GENE ('Goetzgene'PBR) (Shadowdancer Series)	SCoo
'Général Monk' (d)	EBak EPts SGol SVic
'General Wavell' (d)	SVic
'Genii' ♀H4	Widely available
'Geoffrey Smith' (d)	EPts
§ 'Georg Börnemann' (T) ♀H2	CLoc EBak MJac
'George Barr'	CRos LRHS NRHS
§ 'Gerharda's Aubergine'	CLoc

'Gesneriana'	CLoc EBak
'Giant Pink Enchanted' (d)	CLoc
'Gilda' (d)	MJac SVic
'Gilt Edge' (v)	CLoc
'Gina Bowman' (E)	EPts LCla SLBF
GINGER ('Goetzginger'PBR) (Shadowdancer Series)	SCoo
'Gipsy Princess' (d)	CLoc
'Gladiator' (d)	CMac EBak SVic
'Gladys Lorimer'	CRos EPts LRHS NRHS
glazioviana ♀H2	CSde EPts GCal LCla MHer SLBF SMHy SVen
'Glitters'	EBak
§ 'Globosa'	CAgr
'Glowing Embers'	EBak
'Glowing Lilac' (d)	EPts
'Gold Brocade'	ELan
'Golden Anniversary' (d)	CLoc EBak SVic
'Golden Arrow' (T)	LCla SVic
§ 'Golden Border Queen'	CLoc EBak SPet
'Golden Dawn'	CLoc SPet SVic
'Golden Girl'	SLBF
'Golden Herald'	SLBF
'Golden la Campanella' (d/v)	CLoc
'Golden Marinka' (v) ♀H2	CLoc EBak SPet SVic
'Golden Swingtime' (d)	MJac SPet SVic
'Golden Treasure' (v)	CLoc
'Golden Vergeer' (v)	SLBF
'Goody Goody'	SVic
'Gordon's China Rose'	LCla
'Governor Pat Brown' (d)	EBak
'Grace Darling'	EBak
gracilis	see *F. magellanica* var. *gracilis*
'Graf Witte'	SPet SVic
'Grand Prix' (d)	SVic
'Grandad Fred' (d)	SLBF
'Grandad Hobbs' (d)	LCla
'Grandma Sinton' (d)	CLoc
'Grandpa Jack' (d)	SLBF
'Granny Charlton'	WCFE
'Grayrigg'	ELon EPts EShb LCla LSRN SLBF
'Great Ouse' (d)	EPts
'Great Scott' (d)	CLoc
'Green 'n' Gold'	EBak
'Greenpeace'	SLBF SVic
'Grey Lady' (d)	SVic
'Groene Kan's Glorie'	SVic
'Grumpy'	EPts SPet SVic
'Gruss aus dem Bodethal'	CLoc EBak EPts SLBF
'Gunton Park' (T) **new**	EHDe
'Gustave Doré' (d)	EBak
'Gwen Dodge'	SVic
'H.G. Brown'	EBak SLBF
'Hannah Amelia'	MJac
'Hannah Louise' (d)	EPts
'Hans Callaars'	LCla
'Happiness' (d)	SVic
'Happy'	EPts SPet SVic
'Happy Anniversary'	CLoc SVic
'Happy Fellow'	CLoc EBak
'Happy Wedding Day' (d)	CLoc EPts MJac SCoo SPet SVic
'Hapsburgh'	EBak
'Harbour Lites'	SLBF
'Harlow Car'	EPts
'Harmony' Niederholzer, 1946	EBak
'Harriet Lye'	EHDe
'Harry Gray' (d) ♀H2	CLoc EBak EPts MJac SPet SVic
'Harry Taylor' (d)	EPts
'Harry's Sunshine'	SLBF

	hartwegii	LCla MHer
	'Harvey's Reward'	SLBF
	'Hathersage' (d)	EBak
	hatschbachii ♀H2	CRos CSde EBee EPfP EShb EWes GCal LCla LRHS MCot MHer NRHS SBrt SCob SLon SMHy SPlb SVen WMoo WPGP
	'Haute Cuisine' (d)	CLoc SVic
	'Hawaiian Sunset' (d)	CLoc EPts SLBF
	'Hawkshead' ♀H4	Widely available
	'Hayley Jay' (d)	SLBF
	'Hazel' (d)	SVic
	'Heidi Ann' (d) ♀H4	CLoc CRos EBak EPts LRHS MAsh MRav NHic NRHS SLBF SPet SVic
	'Heidi Blue' (d)	SLBF
§	'Heidi Weiss' (d)	CLoc SPet
	'Heinrich Henkel'	see *F.* 'Andenken an Heinrich Henkel'
	'Helen Clare' (d)	CLoc
	'Helen Storer'	MJac
	'Hemsleyana'	see *F. microphylla* subsp. *hemsleyana*
	'Henning Becker' ♀H3	ELan
	'Henri Poincaré'	EBak
	'Her Majesty's Crown' (T)	SLBF
	'Herald' ♀H4	CRos LRHS MGos SLBF SVic
	'Herbé de Jacques'	see *F.* 'Mr West'
	'HeRi Trevally'	SLBF
	'Heritage' (d)	CLoc EBak
	'Herman de Graaff' (d)	SLBF
	'Hermiena'	CLoc EPts SLBF SVic
	'Herps Pierement'	SLBF
	'Herps Serang'	SLBF
	'Hessett Festival' (d)	EBak
	'Hi Di'	NWms SLBF
	hidalgensis	see *F. microphylla* subsp. *hidalgensis*
	'Hidcote Beauty' ♀H2	CLoc LCla SLBF SPet SVic
	'Highland Pipes'	LCla SVic
	'Hindu Belle'	EBak
	'Hinnerike' (E)	LCla SVic
	'Hiroshige' (T)	LCla
	'Hobson's Choice' (d)	SLBF
	'Holly's Beauty' (d)	CLoc EPts
	'Hot Coals'	EPts MJac SVic
	'Howlett's Hardy' ♀H4	CLoc EBak SVic
	'Hula Girl' (d)	EBak MJac
	'Huntsman' (d)	CCCN
	'I Love You'	SLBF
	'Ian Storey'	CRos EPfP LRHS NRHS
	'Iceberg'	EBak SVic
	'Icecap'	SVic
	'Iced Champagne'	CLoc EBak MJac
	'Ichiban' (d)	CLoc
	'Icicles Chandelier' **new**	SLBF
	'Ida' (d)	EBak
	'Igloo Maid' (d)	CLoc EBak SVic
	'Imogen Faye' (d)	LCla SLBF
	'Impudence'	CLoc EBak
	'Impulse' (d)	CLoc
	'Independence' (d)	SVic
	'Indian Maid' (d)	EBak
	'Insulinde' (T)	EPts LCla MHer MJac SLBF
	'Irene L. Peartree' (d)	LCla
	'Irene Sinton' (d)	MJac
	'Iris Amer' (d)	CLoc
	'Isle of Purbeck'	SVic
	'Isn't She Lovely' **new**	NWms SLBF
	'Italiano' (d)	MJac SVic
	'Jack Shahan' ♀H2	CCCN CLoc EBak EPts LCla MJac
	'Jackpot' (d)	EBak
	'James Lye' (d)	EBak EHDe
	'James Travis' (E)	LCla
	'Jan Bremer'	SVic
	'Jane Lye'	EHDe
	'Janice Perry's Gold' (v)	MJac
	'Janie' (d)	CRos EPfP LBuc LRHS MAsh NRHS SVic
	'Jap Vantveer' (T)	LCla
	'Jasper's Formidable' (T)	SLBF
	'Jasper's Lightning' (T)	SLBF
	'Jean Frisby'	CLoc
	'Jean Shelton'	LCla
	'Jean Taylor'	EPts
	'Jean Webb' (v)	WCot
	'Jennifer'	MJac
	'Jennifer Ann'	NRHS SLBF
	'Jenny May'	CLoc EPts LCla
	'Jess'	LCla SLBF
	'Jessimae'	SPet
	'Jester' Holmes (d)	CLoc
	'Jet'	MJac
	'Jezebel' (d)	SVic
	'Jiddles' (E)	LCla
	'Jill Holloway' (T)	SLBF
	'Jim Coleman'	SVic
	'Jim Dodge' (d)	EPts
	'Joan Cooper'	CLoc SLBF SVic
	'Joan Goy'	SVic
	'Joan Knight'	CLoc
	'Joan Margaret' (d)	MJac
	'Joan Morris'	SLBF
	'Joanna Lumley' (d)	EPts
	'Jo-Anne Fisher' (d)	EPts
	'Joanne Jackson'	MJac
	'Joan's Delight'	SVic
	'Joe Kusber' (d)	EBak
	'John Bartlett'	CLoc
	'John Galea'	SLBF
	'John Grooms' (d)	CLoc SVic
	'John Hitchcock' (d)	SLBF
	'John Lockyer'	CLoc
	'John Maynard Scales' (T) ♀H2	LCla MJac
	'John Nicholass'	SLBF
§	'John Ridding' PBR (T/v) ♀H1c	CLoc SPoG
	'John Wright'	LCla
	'Johnny Boy'	SLBF
	'Jon Oram'	CLoc
	'Jose's Joan' (d)	SVic
I	'Joy'	NWms SLBF
	'Joy Patmore'	CLoc SLBF SPet
	'Joyce Sinton'	CLoc
	'Jules Daloges' (d)	EBak
	'Julie Marie' (d)	MJac
	'June Marie Shaw'	MJac
	'Jungle'	LCla SLBF
	'Kaley Jackson'	MJac
	'Karen Isles' (E)	LCla SLBF
	'Karen Louise' (d)	CLoc
	'Kate Taylor' (d)	SLBF
	'Kath van Hanegem'	CLoc SLBF
	'Kathryn Maidment'	SVic
	'Katie Rogers'	EPts
	'Katinka' (E)	LCla
	'Katjan'	GBin LCla SLBF
	'Katrina Thompsen'	CLoc EPts SLBF
	'Ken Tudor'	MJac
	'Kenny Walkling' ♀H2	MJac SLBF

	Name	Suppliers
	'Ken's Pixie'	MJac
	'Kernan Robson' (d)	EBak
	'Keystone'	EBak
	'King's Ransom' (d)	CLoc EBak SPet SVic
	'Kit Oxtoby' (d)	MJac
	'Kiwi' (d)	EBak
	'Klu'	NWms
	'Knockout' (d)	SVic
	'Kobold'	SLBF
	'Kolding Perle'	SLBF
	'Kuniko Atarashi' (d)	EPts
	'Kwintet'	EBak MJac SPet
	'La Bianca'	EBak
	'La Campanella' (d) ♀H2	CCCN CLoc EBak EPts MJac SVic
	'La France' (d)	EBak
	'La Porte' (d)	CLoc
	'La Rosita' (d)	EBak
I	'La Traviata' Blackwell (d)	EBak
	'Lace Petticoats' (d)	EBak SVic
	'Lady Beth' (d)	SVic
	'Lady Boothby' ♀H4	Widely available
	'Lady Framlingham' (d)	EPts
	'Lady in Black' (d)	CBcs MCot SPoG
	'Lady in Grey' (d)	SVic
	'Lady Isobel Barnett'	CLoc EBak MJac SLBF SVic
	'Lady Kathleen Spence'	SPet SVic
	'Lady Patricia Mountbatten'	SVic
	'Lady Ramsey'	EBak
	'Lady Rebecca' (d)	CLoc
	'Lady Thumb' (d) ♀H3	CKel CLoc CMac CRos CSBt EBak EBee EPfP EPts LCro LOPS LRHS MAsh MGos MJac MSwo NEgg NLar NRHS SCoo SGol SLBF SLim SPer SPet SPlb SPoG SVic WFar
	'Laing's Hybrid'	EBak
	'Lakeland Princess'	EBak
	'Lambada'	CLoc
	'Lancashire Lad' (d)	MJac
	'Lancelot'	EBak
	'Lapshead White'	CExl
	'Lassie' (d)	CLoc EBak
	'Last Chance' (E)	SLBF
	'Laura' ambig.	SVic
I	'Laura' (Dutch)	CLoc EPts LCla SLBF
	'Laura Cross' (E)	SLBF
	'Lavender Kate' (d)	EBak
	'Lechlade Apache'	LCla
	'Lechlade Bullet'	LCla
	'Lechlade Chinaman'	SVic
	'Lechlade Gordon'	CRos
	'Lechlade Gorgon'	LCla LRHS NRHS SLBF
	'Lechlade Magician'	EPts LCla SEND SLBF SPet
	'Lechlade Martianess'	SVic
	'Lechlade Potentate'	LCla
	'Lechlade Tinkerbell' (E)	LCla
	'Lechlade Violet' (T)	LCla SVic
	lehmanii	LCla
	'Len Bielby' (T)	LCla
	'Lena' (d) ♀H2	CLoc CMac CTri EBak EPts MJac SLBF SPer SPlb SVic
	'Lena Dalton' (d)	CLoc EBak SVic
	'Leonora'	CLoc SLBF SPet SVic
	'Lesley' (T)	LCla
	'Lesley's Wonder'	MJac
	'Leslie Bowman' ♀H2	LCla SLBF
	'Lett's Delight' (d)	EPts
	'Letty Lye'	EBak EHDe
	'Leverhulme'	see *F.* 'Leverkusen'
§	'Leverkusen' (T)	CLoc EBak LCla MJac
	'Liebriez' (d) ♀H4	EBak SVic

	Name	Suppliers
	'Lilac Lustre' (d)	CLoc SPet SVic
	'Lilac Mist'	SLBF
	'Lilac Queen' (d)	EBak
	'Lillian Annetts' (d) ♀H2	MJac SLBF
	'Lillibet' (d)	CLoc
	'Lime Lite' (d)	MJac
	'Linda Goulding'	EBak SVic
	'Linda Grace'	MJac
	'Linda Hinchliffe'	EPts MJac
	'Lindisfarne' (d)	CLoc EBak MJac
	'Lindsey Victoria' (d)	SVic
	'Lisa' (d)	EPts
	'Little Beauty'	SVic
	'Little Boy Blue'	EPts
	'Little Brook Gem'	SLBF
	'Little Catbells' (E)	SLBF
	'Little Cracker'	SPoG
	'Little Gene'	EBak
	'Little Jessica' (E)	LCla MJac NWad SLBF
	'Little Jewel'	SPet
	'Little Nan'	SLBF
	'Little Tony'	SLBF
	'Loeky'	CLoc SVic
	'Logan Garden'	see *F. magellanica* 'Logan Woods'
	'Lolita' (d)	EBak
	'London 2000'	EPts LCla MJac SLBF
	'London in Bloom'	LCla SLBF
	'Lonely Ballerina' (d)	CLoc
	'Long Distance' (T)	LCla
	'Long Wings'	LCla SVic
	'Lord Byron'	CLoc
	'Lord Jim'	LCla
	'Lord Lonsdale'	EPts LCla SVic
	'Lord Roberts'	CLoc SLBF
	'Lorna Swinbank'	SVic
	'Lorraine's Delight' (d)	SVic
	'Lottie Hobby' (E) ♀H3	CLoc CMac CMea EPts EShb ITim LCla NWad SVic WCot
	'Louise Emershaw' (d)	EBak MJac SVic
	'Louise Nicholls'	MJac
	'Loulabel'	SVic
	'Loveliness'	CLoc EHDe SVic
	'Lovely Linda'	SLBF
	'Love's Reward' ♀H2	CLoc MJac SLBF SVic
I	'Loxensis'	SVic
	loxensis misapplied	see *F.* 'Loxensis', *F.* 'Speciosa'
	'Loxhore Lullaby' (E)	LCla
	'Loxhore Minuet' (T)	LCla
	'Lucy Locket'	MJac
	'Lustre'	SVic
I	'Lycioides'	LCla
	lycioides misapplied	see *F.* 'Lycioides'
	'Lye's Elegance'	EHDe
	'Lye's Excelsior'	EHDe
	'Lye's Favourite'	EHDe
	'Lye's Own'	EHDe SLBF SPet
	'Lye's Perfection'	EHDe
	'Lye's Unique' ♀H3	CLoc EBak EHDe EPts LCla MJac SLBF SPet SVic
	'Lyndon'	MJac
	'Lynette' (d)	CLoc
	'Lynne Patricia' (d)	EPts SLBF
	'Machu Picchu'	CLoc EPts LCla SVic
	macrophylla	WMoo
	'Madame Butterfly' (d)	CLoc
	'Madame Cornélissen' (d) ♀H4	CKel CLoc CMac CRos CSBt CTri EBak ELan EMor EPfP EPts LRHS MAsh MRav NHic NLar NRHS SCob SCoo SEND SLBF SLim SPer SPet SVic WFar XLum

	Name	Suppliers
	magellanica ♀H4	CBcs CRos CTsd LRHS MGil MMuc NPer NRHS NWea SPer SVic WFar WGwG WMoo WSpi
	- 'Alba'	see *F. magellanica* var. *molinae* 'Alba'
	- 'Alba Variegata' (v)	WFar
	- 'Floriade' **new**	CCoa
	- 'Folius Aureus'	WFar
§	- var. ***gracilis*** ♀H4	CAgr CLoc CRos CSde CTri EPfP EUJe LRHS NBro NRHS SVic WMoo
	- - 'Aurea' ♀H4	CBcs CKel CMac CRos CSde CTsd ELan ELon EPfP LCla LRHS MHer MRav NRHS SCoo SLBF SPer SPet SRms SVic WMoo XLum
	- - 'Purple Mountain'	CBod
	- - 'Variegata' (v) ♀H4	CRos CTsd EBak EPfP LRHS MGos MRav NRHS SPer SPet SVic
§	- - 'Versicolor' (v) ♀H4	Widely available
	- 'Lady Bacon'	CBcs CRos ELon EPts EShb EWes GCal LRHS MCot MMuc NRHS NSti SDys SEND SLBF SMHy SPoG WPGP WSHC
§	- 'Logan Woods'	ELon EPfP GKin SLBF WPGP
	- var. ***magellanica***	SCob
	- var. ***molinae***	CDul CLoc CRos CTri EBak EBee ECrN ELan EPfP EShb GBin GWyn LCla LCro LOPS LRHS MBlu MNrw MSwo NBid NPer NSti SCob SPer SPlb WArt WFar WMoo
§	- - 'Alba' ♀H4	CBod CCoa EPts EUJe NAln NLar SGol SHar SPet WFar WGwG WSpi
I	- - 'Alba Aureovariegata' (v)	CBcs CMac SPer SVic WFar XLum
	- - 'Golden Sharpitor' (v)	CCCN WFar
	- - 'Mr Knight's Blush'	WSpi
§	- - 'Sharpitor' (v) ♀H4	CCoa CKel CSde CTsd EBak EBee ELan ELon EPfP LRHS NChi NPer SGol SPer SPoG SVic WFar WKif WMoo WSHC
	- 'Mountain Gold'	CBod
	- var. ***myrtifolia***	CTsd
	- 'Pumila'	CAby CMea EWes GCal MAsh MHer SMHy SRot SVic WAbe WFar WHal WPGP
	- 'Red Mountain'	EWes
§	- 'Thompsonii' ♀H4	SMHy
	- 'Variegata Aurea' (v)	SGol WFar
	'Magic Flute'	CLoc MJac SVic
	'Major Heaphy'	EBak
	'Mama Bleuss' (d)	EBak
	'Mandi Oxtoby' (T)	LCla
	'Mantilla' (T)	CLoc LCla MJac SVic
	'Maori Maid'	MJac
	'Marble Crepe' (T)	SLBF
	'Marbled Sky'	SVic
	'Marcia'[PBR] (Shadowdancer Series)	CLoc
	'Marcus Graham' (d)	CLoc EBak SCoo SVic
	'Margaret' (d) ♀H4	CDul CLoc CTri EBak EPts SEND SLBF SPet SVic WFar
	'Margaret Bird'	LCla
	'Margaret Brown' ♀H4	CLoc CRos CTri LCla LRHS NRHS SLBF SPet SVic
	'Margaret My Own'	EPts
	'Margaret Pilkington'	SVic
	'Margaret Roe'	EBak MJac SPet
	'Margaret Susan'	EBak
	'Margaret Viscountess Thurso'	SLBF
	'Margarite Dawson' (d)	SVic
	'Maria Landy'	MJac SLBF
	'Maria Mathilde' (d)	SLBF
	'Maria Shaw'	EPts
	'Marin Glow' ♀H3	CLoc EBak SVic
	'Marinka' ♀H2	CLoc EBak EPts LCla MJac SPet SVic
	'Marlies de Keijzer' (E)	EPts LCla NWad SLBF SVen
	'Martha Adcock'	SLBF
	'Martin's Inspiration'	LCla
	'Martin's Yellow Surprise' (T)	LCla SLBF SVic
	'Marty' (d)	EBak
	'Mary' (T) ♀H1c	CLoc EPts LCla SLBF SVic WCot
	'Mary Lockyer' (d)	CLoc EBak
	'Mary Poppins'	SVic
	'Mary Thorne'	EBak
	'Mauve Beauty' (d)	SLBF
	'Mauve Wisp' (d)	SVic
	'Mavis Enderby'	MJac SLBF
	'Max Cobi' **new**	LCla NWms SLBF
I	'Maxima'	EPts LCla SLBF
	'Maxine's Smile'	SLBF
	'Meditation' (d)	CLoc
	'Melanie'	SVic
	'Melody'	SPet SVic
	'Melody Ann' (d)	EBak
	'Melting Moments' (d)	SCoo
	'Mendocino Rose'	SVic
	'Mercurius' ♀H4	XLum
	'Merlin'	LCla
	'Merry Mary' (d)	EBak
	'Mersty' (d)	SLBF
I	'Mexicali Rose' Machado	CLoc
	'Michael' (d/v)	EPts
	'Michael Wallis' (T)	SLBF
	'Michelle Wallace'	SVic
	michoacanensis misapplied	see *F. microphylla* subsp. *aprica*
	michoacanensis Sessé & Moç. (E) B&SWJ 9148	WCru
	'Micky Goult' ♀H2	CLoc EPts MJac SLBF SVic
	'Microchip' (E)	LCla
	microphylla (E)	CAby CBcs CBod CElw CExl CLoc CRos CTsd EBak EBee ELon GBin GCal IDee LRHS MGil NRHS SIgm SMHy SVic WAbe
	- B&SWJ 10331	WCru
§	- subsp. ***aprica*** (E)	LCla
	- - B&SWJ 9101	WCru
	- - 'Dolly's Dress' (E)	WCru
§	- subsp. ***hemsleyana*** (E)	CExl SVic
	- - B&SWJ 10478	WCru
	- - 'Silver Lining' (E)	CMil EShb SCob WCot WCru WFar WNPC
§	- subsp. ***hidalgensis*** (E)	CBcs
§	- subsp. ***minimiflora*** (E)	SVic
	- 'Variegata' (E/v)	EWes
	'Midwinter'	SVic
§	'Mieke Meursing' ♀H2	CLoc EBak MJac SPet SVic
	'Miep Aalhuizen'	LCla
	'Millennium'	CLoc EBak EPts MJac SCoo SVic
	'Millfield Alpha'	EPts
	'Millfield Bravo'	EPts
	'Millfield Charlie'	EPts
	'Millfield Delta'	EPts
	'Millfield Echo'	EPts
	'Ming'	CLoc
	'Miniature Jewels' (E)	SLBF
	minimiflora misapplied	see *F.* × ***bacillaris***

minimiflora Hemsl.	see *F. microphylla* subsp. *minimiflora*
'Minipani'	SLBF
'Minirose'	EPts SLBF
'Minnesota' (d)	EBak
'Miramere'	EPts
'Mischief'	SVic
'Miss California' (d)	CLoc EBak
'Miss Lye'	EHDe
'Miss Muffett' (d)	EPts
'Miss Vallejo' (d)	EBak
'Mission Bells'	CLoc EBak EPts SPet SVic
'Misty Blue' (d)	SVic
'Misty Haze' (d)	SVic
'Misty Mease' **new**	MJac
'Molesworth' (d)	MJac
'Money Spinner'	CLoc
'Monsieur Thibaut' ♀H4	SPer
'Mood Indigo' (d)	SVic
'Moonbeam' (d)	CLoc
'Moonglow'	MJac
'Moonlight Sonata'	CLoc SPet
'Moonraker' (d)	SVic
'More Applause' (d)	CLoc
'Morning Light' (d)	CLoc SVic
'Morrells' (d)	EBak
'Moth Blue' (d)	EBak
'Mountain Mist' (d)	SVic
'Mr A. Huggett'	CLoc EPts SLBF
'Mr W. Rundle'	EBak SVic
§ 'Mr West' (v)	ELon MCot SPet WFar
'Mrs B.' (E) **new**	MJac
'Mrs Churchill'	CLoc
'Mrs Grant'	EHDe
'Mrs Hobhouse' (d)	EHDe
'Mrs J Bright'	EHDe
'Mrs Lee Belton' (E)	LCla SLBF
'Mrs Lovell Swisher' ♀H4	EBak LCla SVic
'Mrs Marshall'	SLBF
'Mrs Popple' ♀H4	Widely available
'Mrs W. Castle'	SVic
'Mrs W.P. Wood' ♀H4	CLoc CRos ELon LRHS MSCN SVic
'Mrs W. Rundle'	CLoc SLBF
'Muriel' (d)	CLoc
'My Dad' **new**	NWms SLBF
'My Fair Lady' (d)	EBak
'My Grandchildren'	SLBF
'My Little Cracker'	MJac
'My Mum'	LCla SLBF
'My Pat'	SLBF
'Nancy Lou' (d)	CLoc MJac SLBF SPet SVic
'Natasha Sinton' (d)	CCCN MJac SPet
'Nathan Rhys'	EPts
'Neapolitan' (d)	SLBF
'Neck'	LCla
'Nell Gwyn'	CLoc SVic
'Nellie Nuttall' ♀H2	CLoc EBak EPts SPet SVic
'Neopolitan' (E)	CLoc EPts LCla SVic
'Nephele'	EPts
'Nettala'	SVic
'Nice 'n' Easy' (d)	MJac
'Nicki Fenwick-Raven' (E)	LCla
'Nicki's Findling'	EPts LCla MJac
'Nicola'	EBak
'Nicola Jane' (d)	EBak EPts LCla MJac SLBF SPet SVic
'Nicolette'	MJac
§ ***nigricans*** B&SWJ 10664	WCru
'Niula'	LCla
'Nonchalance' (T)	LCla
'Norman Welton'	MJac SLBF
'Normandy Bell'	EBak SVic
'Northern Jewel'	EPts SLBF
'Northilda'	SVic
'Northumbrian Pipes'	LCla
'Northway'	CLoc MJac SPet SVic
'Norvell Gillespie' (d)	EBak
'Nuance'	LCla
'O Sole Mio'	SVic
'Obcylin' (E)	EPts LCla
'Ocean Beach'	EPts
'Oetnang' (d)	CTri SCoo
'Oh Carol' (E)	LCla
'Old Somerset' (v)	CCCN SVic
'Olga Storey'	CRos LRHS NRHS
'Olive Smith'	EPts LCla MJac
'Olympic Sunset'	SVic
'Oosje' (E)	LCla SVic
'Opalescent' (d)	CLoc SVic
'Orange Crush'	CLoc EBak SPet
'Orange Crystal'	MJac SLBF SVic
'Orange Drops'	CLoc EBak EPts SVic
'Orange Flare'	CLoc EBak SLBF SVic
'Orange King' (d)	CLoc
'Orange Mirage'	CLoc SPet SVic
'Orange Star' (E)	LCla SLBF
'Orangeblossom'	SLBF
'Orient Express' (T) ♀H1c	CLoc MJac SVic
'Ornamental Pearl' (v)	CLoc SLBF
'Other Fellow'	EBak EPts LCla MJac SLBF SPet SVic
'Oulton Empress' (E)	LCla SLBF
'Oulton Fairy' (E)	SLBF
'Oulton Red Imp' (E)	LCla SLBF
'Oulton Travellers Rest' (E)	SLBF
'Our Carol'	SLBF
'Our Hilary'	SLBF
'Our Nan' (d)	MJac
'Our Pamela'	MJac
'Our Spencer'	SLBF
'Our Ted' (T)	EBak EPts
'Overbecks'	see *F. magellanica* var. *molinae* 'Sharpitor'
'P.E. King' (d)	SLBF
'Pacific Queen' (d)	EBak
'Pacquesa' (d)	EBak SPet SVic
'Padre Pio' (d)	EBak MJac
'Pam and Ted Love' **new**	NWms SLBF
'Pam Plack'	LCla SLBF
'Pamela Knights' (d)	EBak
'Pam's People'	LCla
'Panache' (d)	LCla
paniculata (T) ♀H2	CCCN CRHN EBak ELan EPts LCla MCot MHer SLBF WCot WCru
'Panique'	LCla
'Panylla Prince'	LCla
'Papa Bleuss' (d)	EBak
'Papoose' (d)	EBak SLBF SVic
'Party Frock'	CLoc EBak SPet
parviflora misapplied	see *F.* × *bacillaris*
'Pat Meara'	CLoc EBak
'Pathétique' (d)	CLoc
'Patience' (d)	EBak SLBF
'Patio Princess' (d)	CLoc EPts
'Paul Cambon' (d)	EBak
'Paula Jane' (d) ♀H2	MJac SLBF SVic
'Pauline Rawlins' (d)	CLoc
'Peachy' (California Dreamers Series) (d)	CLoc SCoo SLBF
'Peachy Keen' (d)	EBak

'Peacock' (d)	CLoc
'Pee Wee Rose'	EBak SVic
'Peggy Burford' (T)	LCla
PEGGY ('Goetzpeg'[PBR]) (Shadowdancer Series)	SCoo
'Peggy King'	EBak SPet
'Peloria' (d)	CLoc EBak
'Peper Harow'	EBak
'Pepi' (d)	EBak
'Peppermint Candy' (d)	MJac
'Peppermint Stick' (d)	CLoc EBak SPet SVic
'Perky Pink' (d)	EBak EPts
'Perry Park'	MJac SVic
'Perry's Jumbo'	NPer
perscandens	CBcs CExl LCla
'Peter Meredith'	MJac
petiolaris	LCla
- B&SWJ 10675	WCru
'Phaidra' (T)	LCla
'Pharaoh'	CLoc
'Phénoménal' (d)	EBak
'Phryne' (d)	SVic
'Phyll Hendy' **new**	NWms SLBF
'Phyllis' (d) ♀H4	CLoc CRos EBak EPts LCla LRHS MJac NRHS SEND SLBF SPet SVic
'Piet van der Sande'	LCla SLBF
'Pinch Me' (d)	EBak SPet SVic
'Pink Aurora'	CLoc
'Pink Ballet Girl' (d)	CLoc SVic
'Pink Bon Accord'	CLoc SVic
'Pink Cloud'	CLoc EBak
'Pink Cornet'	LCla
'Pink Darling'	CLoc EBak
'Pink Dessert'	EBak
'Pink Fairy' (d)	SPet
'Pink Fandango' (d)	CLoc
'Pink Fantasia' ♀H2	CLoc EBak EPts LCla MJac SLBF SVic
'Pink Galore' (d) ♀H2	CLoc MJac SLBF SPet
'Pink Goon' (d)	SLBF SVic
'Pink Haze'	SVic
'Pink la Campanella'	EBak
'Pink Lace' (d)	SPet
'Pink Marshmallow' (d) ♀H4	CLoc EBak MJac SLBF SPet SVic
'Pink Profusion'	EBak
'Pink Quartet' (d)	CLoc EBak WCot
'Pink Rain'	MJac
'Pink Slippers'	CLoc
'Pink Spangles'	see *F.* 'Mieke Meursing'
'Pink Temptation'	CLoc SVic
'Pinwheel' (d)	CLoc EBak
'Piper's Vale' (T)	MJac
'Pixie'	CLoc EBak MJac SEND SLBF SPet SVic
'Playboy' (d)	SVic
'Playford'	EBak
'Plenty'	EBak SVic
'Pop Whitlock' (v)	SPet SVic
'Popsie Girl' (v)	SLBF
'Port Arthur' (d)	EBak
'Postiljon'	EBak
'Powder Puff' Hodges (d)	CLoc SVic
'Prelude' Blackwell	CLoc
'President'	EBak
'President Barrie Nash'	CLoc
'President George Bartlett' (d) ♀H2	CLoc EPts MJac SLBF
'President Jim Muil'	SLBF
'President Joan Morris' (d)	SLBF
'President John Porter'	MJac SLBF
'President Leo Boullemier'	MJac SPet SVic
'President Margaret Slater'	CLoc SPet SVic
'President Moir' (d)	SLBF
'President Peter Holloway'	EPts LCla MJac NWms SLBF
'President Stanley Wilson' (d)	EBak EPts
'President Wilf Sharp' (d)	SVic
'Preston'	CMac
'Preston Guild' ♀H3	CLoc EBak NPer SDys SPet SRms SVic
'Pride of the West'	EHDe
'Prince of Orange'	CLoc SVic
'Princess Dollar'	see *F.* 'Dollar Prinzessin'
'Princessita'	EBak SPet
procumbens	CAby CBcs CCCN CExl CLoc EBak EHDe ELon EPfP EPts EUJe IDee LCla MCot MHer SBrt SLBF WAbe
- 'Argentea'	see *F. procumbens* 'Wirral'
- grey-leaved	SBrt
- 'Variegata'	see *F. procumbens* 'Wirral'
§ - 'Wirral' (v)	CLoc CTsd EHDe EShb ITim
'Prodigy'	see *F.* 'Enfant Prodigue'
'Profusion' ambig.	SVic
'Prosperity' (d) ♀H3	CKel CLoc CRos EBak EPts LCla LRHS MAsh MJac NRHS SEND SLBF SPet SPoG SVic
'Pumila'	CExl CMac ELan EPfP LRHS SPet SVic WSHC
'Purperklokje'	EBak SVic
'Purple Emperor' (d)	CLoc
'Purple Heart' (d)	CLoc EBak
'Purple Lace'	SVic
'Purple Rain'	EPts
'Pussy Cat' (T)	CLoc EBak SVic
'Putney Pride'	EPts
'Put's Folly' ♀H2	EBak MJac SPet
putumayensis	EBak
'Quasar' (d)	CCCN CLoc EPts MJac SLBF SVic
'Queen Mary'	CLoc EBak
'Queen of Bath' (d)	SVic
'Queen of Hearts' Kennett (d)	SVic
'Queen of Mercia'	MJac
'Queen's Park' (d)	EBak
'Query'	SVic
'R.A.F.' (d)	CLoc EBak EPts SPet SVic
'Radings Gerda' (E)	LCla SLBF
'Radings Mia' (T)	SLBF
'Rambling Rose' (d)	CLoc
'Raspberry' (d)	CLoc EBak SVic
'Reading Ruby'	EPts LCla MJac NWms SLBF
'Reading Show' (d)	EPts SLBF
'Rebeka Sinton' (v)	CLoc EBak
'Red Jacket' (d)	EBak
'Red Rum' (d)	SPet
'Red Shadows' (d)	CLoc EBak
'Red Spider'	CCCN CLoc EBak SCoo SPet SVic
'Red Wing'	CLoc
'Reflexa'	see *F.* × *bacillaris* 'Reflexa'
'Reg Gubler'	SLBF
'Regal'	CLoc
regia subsp. ***regia***	LCla XLum
- subsp. ***reitzii***	CDul LCla XLum
- subsp. ***serrae***	WPGP
'Remember Carole Anne' (d)	SLBF
'Remembering Claire'	EPts
'Remembrance' (d)	EPts LCla SLBF
'Remus' (d)	SVic

Name	Suppliers
'Rene Schwab'	LCla
'Requiem'	CLoc
'Rhapsody' ambig.	SVic
'Riccartonii' ♀H6	Widely available
'Richard John' (v)	SVic
'Ridestar' (d)	CLoc
'Rigoletto'	SVic
'Rijs 2001' (E)	SLBF
'Ringwood Gold'	SVic
'Ringwood Market' (d)	EPts MJac SCoo SPet SVic
'Rivendell'	EPts
'Robert Lutters'	SVic
'Rocket Fire' (California Dreamers Series) (d)	SVic
'Roger de Cooker' (T)	CLoc EPts LCla MJac SVic
'Rohees New Millennium' (d)	SLBF
'Rolla' (d)	EBak
'Rolt's Ruby' (d)	SVic
'Roman City' (d)	CLoc SVic
'Romany Rose'	CLoc
'Ronald L. Lockerbie' (d)	CLoc SVic
'Roos Breytenbach' (T)	CCCN LCla MJac
'Rosamunda' (d)	CLoc
'Rose Aylett' (d)	EBak
'Rose Bradwardine' (d)	EBak
'Rose Churchill' (d)	MJac
'Rose Fantasia' ♀H2	CLoc EPts MJac SLBF
'Rose of Castile'	CLoc EBak EPts LCla MJac SLBF SVic
'Rose of Castile Improved' ♀H4	LCla MJac SLBF SPet
'Rose of Denmark'	CCCN CLoc EBak MJac SCoo SLBF SPet
'Rose Winston' (d)	SCoo
rosea misapplied	see *F.* 'Globosa'
'Rosecroft Beauty' (d/v)	EBak SVic
'Rosemarie Higham' (v)	MJac SCoo
'Rosemary Day'	CLoc
'Rosy Frills' (d)	MJac SVic
'Rosy Morn' (d)	CLoc
'Rough Silk'	CLoc EBak
'Royal Academy' (d)	EPts
'Royal Mosaic' (California Dreamers Series) (d)	MJac
'Royal Purple' (d)	EBak
'Royal Velvet' (d) ♀H2	CCCN CLoc CRos EBak EPts LRHS SLBF SPet SVic
'Rubra Grandiflora'	LCla
'Ruby Tuesday' **new**	MJac
'Ruby Wedding' (d)	SLBF
'Rufus' ♀H4	CDul CLoc CMac EBak ELan EPts LCla MJac MRav SLBF SPet SVic
'Ruth'	SVic
'Ruth King' (d)	EBak
'Ryan'	SLBF
'S'Wonderful' (d)	CLoc EBak
'Sailor'	EPts SVic
'Salmon Cascade'	EPts LCla MJac SLBF
'Salmon Glow'	SVic
'Sam Sheppard'	SLBF
'Samantha's Smile' (d) **new**	NWms SLBF
'San Mateo' (d)	EBak
§ ***sanctae-rosae***	LCla
'Sandboy'	EBak
'Santa Cruz' (d)	CMac SLBF SVic
'Santa Lucia' (d)	CLoc
'Santa Monica' (d)	EBak
'Sapphire' (d)	EBak
'Sappho Phaoon' (T)	EPts
'Sara Helen' (d)	CLoc EBak
'Sarah Brightman' (d)	CLoc
'Sarah Eliza' (d)	SCoo
'Sarah Jane' (d)	EBak SVic
'Satellite'	CLoc EBak SPet SVic
'Saturnus' ♀H4	EBak SEND SPet SPoG
'Saxondale Sue'	SVic
scabriuscula	LCla
'Scarcity'	EBak EHDe SVic
'Scarlet Jester'	EPts SLBF
'Schneeball' (d)	EBak SVic
'Schneewitcher'	EPts
'Schöne Wilhelmine'	see *F.* 'Die Schöne Wilhelmine'
'Sealand Prince'	LCla SVic
'Seattle Blue' (T/d)	SLBF
'Sebastopol' (d)	CLoc
serratifolia Ruíz & Pav.	see *F. denticulata*
'Seventh Heaven' (d)	CLoc MJac SCoo
'Shanley'	SVic
'Sharpitor'	see *F. magellanica* var. *molinae* 'Sharpitor'
'Shatzy B'	EPts SLBF
'Sheila Crooks' (d)	EBak
'Shelford'	CLoc EBak EPts MJac SLBF SVic
'Shell Pink'	SVic
'She's a Beauty'	MJac
'Shirley Halladay' (d)	LCla
'Shirley' PBR (Shadowdancer Series)	SCoo
'Shirley Teece'	EPts
'Showfire'	EBak
'Shrimp Cocktail'	CLoc SGol WFar
'Shuna Lindsay'	LCla
'Shy Lady' (d)	SPet
'Siberoet' (E)	LCla SLBF
'Sid Garcia' **new**	NWms SLBF
'Sierra Blue' (d)	CLoc EBak
'Silver Anniversary' (d)	SVic
'Silver Dollar'	SVic
'Silver Surfer'	LCla MJac SLBF
'Silverdale'	EPts
'Simon J. Rowell'	LCla
simplicicaulis	EBak LCla
'Sincerity' (d)	CLoc SVic
'Siobhan Evans' (d)	SLBF
'Sir Alfred Ramsey'	EBak
'Sir David Jason'	MJac
'Sir Matt Busby' (d)	EPts MJac
'Sister Ann Haley'	EPts
'Sister Sister' (d)	SLBF
'Skater's Waltz' (d)	CLoc
'Sleepy'	EPts SPet SVic
'Sleigh Bells'	CLoc EBak SVic
'Smokey Mountain' (d)	SVic
'Sneezy'	EPts SVic
'Snow Burner' (California Dreamers Series) (d)	CLoc
'Snow White' (d)	SVic
'Snowbird' (d)	SLBF
§ 'Snowcap' (d) ♀H4	CCCN CChe CLoc CRos EBak ELon EPfP EPts GKin LCla LRHS MGos MJac NHic NPer NRHS SCoo SGol SLBF SLim SPet SPoG SVic WFar
'Snowdrift' Colville (d)	CLoc
'Snowdrift' Kennett (d)	EBak
'Snowfire' (d)	CLoc SVic
'Snowflake' (E)	EPts WBor
'Son of Thumb' ♀H4	CLoc CRos EPts LRHS MJac NRHS SCob SGol SLBF SLim SPer SPet SVic
'Sonata' (d)	CLoc SVic

	Name	Suppliers
	'Sophie Louise'	EPts SLBF
	'Sophisticated Lady' (d)	EBak EPts SVic
	'South Gate' (d)	CLoc EBak EPts SPet SVic
	'Space Shuttle'	CLoc LCla
	'Sparky' (T)	CLoc EPts LCla
	'Speciana'	EPts
§	'Speciosa'	EBak LCla
	'Spion Kop' (d)	CCCN SPet
§	***splendens*** ♀H2	CCCN CLoc EBak LCla MCot NPer SLBF
	- B&SWJ 10469	WCru
	'Sporting Chance'	NWms
	'Spring Bells' (d)	CRos LRHS NRHS
	'Squadron Leader' (d)	EBak EPts
	'Squirtie'	SLBF
	'Stanley Cash' (d)	CLoc SPet SVic
	'Star Wars'	CLoc EPts MJac
	'Steeley' (d)	SVic
	'Stella Ann' (T)	EPts LCla
	'Stoke Poges Jewel' **new**	NWms SLBF
	'Straat Cumberland'	LCla
	'Straat Futami' (E)	EPts LCla
	'Straat Kobe' (T)	LCla
	'Straat La Plata'	LCla
	'Straat of Plenty'	LCla
	'Strawberry Delight' (d)	CLoc MJac SPet SVic
	'Strawberry Split' **new**	CKel
	'Strawberry Sundae' (d)	CLoc EBak
	'Strike the Viol' (T)	SLBF
	'String of Pearls'	CLoc MJac SLBF SPet SVic
	'Stuart Lockyer' (d)	CLoc
	'Sue'	SLBF
	'Suffolk Splendour' (d)	EPts
	'Sunny Jim'	SVic
	'Sunray' (v)	CBcs CKel CLoc CMac CRos EBak EPfP LBuc LRHS MAsh MGos NEgg NRHS SCoo SLBF SLim SPoG SVen WCot
	'Sunset'	CLoc
	'Supersport' (d)	SVic
	'Superstar'	SVic
	'Susan Ford' (d)	SPet
	'Susan Green'	EBak MJac
	'Susan McMaster'	CLoc
	'Susan Olcese' (d)	EBak
	'Susan Travis'	CLoc EBak SVic
	'Swanley Beauty'	EHDe
	'Swanley Gem' ♀H2	CLoc EBak SLBF SPet SVic
	'Swanley Pendula'	CLoc
	'Swanley Yellow'	EBak SVic
	'Sweet Hollie'	SLBF
	'Sweet Sarah' (E)	EPts
I	'Sweetheart' van Wieringen	EBak
	'Swingtime' (d) ♀H2	CCCN CLoc EBak EPts LCla MJac SLBF SPet SVic
	sylvatica misapplied	see *F. nigricans*
	'Sylvia Barker' ♀H2	LCla SLBF
	'Sylvia's Choice'	EBak
	'Symphony'	CLoc
	'Syreme' (d)	SLBF
	'T.I.S. Herentals'	SLBF
	'T.S.J.' (E)	LCla
	'Taco'	LCla
	'Taddle'	SLBF
	'Taffeta Bow' (d)	CLoc SLBF SVic
	'Tamworth'	CLoc EBak MJac SVic
	'Tangerine'	CLoc SVic
	'Tanya Bridger' (d)	EBak
	'Tarra Valley'	LCla SVic
	'Task Force'	SVic

	Name	Suppliers
	'Tausendschön' (d)	CLoc
	'Temptation' Peterson	CLoc EBak
	'Tennessee Waltz' (d) ♀H2	CLoc EBak EPts SLBF SPer SPet SVic
	'Tess'	EPts SLBF
	tetradactyla misapplied	see *F.* × *bacillaris*
	'Texas Longhorn' (d)	CLoc EBak SVic
	'Thalia' (T) ♀H1c	CCCN CKel CLoc EBak EPts EUJe LCla LSRN MCot MHer MJac NEgg SLBF SPlb SPoG SVic
	'Thamar'	CLoc EPts SVic
	'That's It' (d)	SVic
	'The Aristocrat' (d)	CLoc EBak
§	'The Doctor'	CLoc EBak
	'The Jester' (d)	EBak
	'The Tarns'	EBak SVic
	'Thomas' (d)	EPts
	'Thompsonii'	see *F. magellanica* 'Thompsonii'
	'Thornley's Hardy'	SVic
	'Three Cheers'	CLoc
	'Three Counties'	EBak
	'Thumbelina'	CRos LRHS NRHS
	'Thunderbird' (d)	CLoc
	thymifolia (E)	CKel CRos LRHS MHer SBch SDys SEND SMHy WKif
	- subsp. ***thymifolia*** (E)	SEle
	'Tiara' (d)	EBak
	'Tillingbourne' (d)	SLBF
	'Time After Time'	CLoc SLBF
	'Timlin Brened' (T)	EBak
	'Timothy Titus' (T) ♀H1c	LCla
	'Ting-a-ling'	CLoc EBak SPet SVic
	'Tinker Bell' Hodges	EBak SVic
	'Tip Toes'	SLBF
	'Tjinegara'	LCla
	'Toby Bridger' (d)	CLoc EBak
	'Toby Foreman'	SLBF
	'Toby S' (d)	SLBF
	'Tolling Bell'	EBak SPet
	'Tom Goedeman'	LCla
	'Tom Knights'	EBak SPet
	'Tom Thumb' ♀H4	Widely available
	'Tom West' misapplied	see *F.* 'Mr West'
	'Tom West' Meillez (v) ♀H2	CChe CKel CLoc CRos CSBt EBak EBee EPts LRHS MAsh MHer MJac MRav MSCN NRHS SGol SLBF SLim WAvo WFar
	'Ton Ten Hove'	LCla
	'Tony Talbot'	MJac
	'Tony's Treat' (d)	EPts
	'Toos'	SVic
	'Torch' (d)	CLoc EBak SVic
	'Torchlight'	EPts LCla
	'Torvill and Dean' (d)	CLoc EPts MJac SLBF SPet
	'Tracid' (d)	SVic
	'Trail Blazer' (d)	CLoc MJac
	'Trailing Queen'	MJac
	'Trase' (d)	EBak SVic
	'Traudchen Bonstedt' (T) ♀H1c	CLoc LCla SVic
	'Traviata'	see *F.* 'La Traviata' Blackwell
	'Treasure' (d)	EBak
	'Tricolor'	see *F. magellanica* var. *gracilis* 'Versicolor'
	'Trientje'	LCla SLBF
	triphylla (T)	EBak MHer
	'Trish's Triumph'	EPts
	'Tristesse' (d)	CLoc EBak
	'Tropicana' (d)	CLoc SVic
	'Troubador' Waltz (d)	CLoc
	'Trudi Davro'	MJac SCoo

'Trudy'	EPts SVic
'Truly Treena' (d)	SLBF
'Trumpeter' Fry	SVic
'Trumpeter' Reiter (T)	CLoc EPts LCla MJac
'Tubular Bells' (T)	LCla
'Tuonela' (d)	CLoc
'Tutti-frutti' (d)	CLoc
'Twinkling Stars'	MJac SVic
'U.F.O.'	SVic
'Ullswater' (d)	EBak
'Uncle Charley' (d)	EBak SVic
'Uncle Jinks'	SPet
'Uncle Steve' (d)	SVic
'University of Liverpool'	CLoc MJac
'Upward Look'	EBak
'Vale of Belvoir'	SVic
'Valerie Ann' (d)	EBak SPet SVic
'Valerie Bradley'	EPts
'Vanessa Jackson'	CLoc MJac SVic
'Vanessa Wright'	CRos LRHS NRHS
'Vanity Fair' (d)	EBak
'Variegated Procumbens'	see *F. procumbens* 'Wirral'
'Veenlust'	EBak MJac
'Velvet Crush'	EPts
'Vendeta'	LCla
'Venus Victrix'	EBak
venusta	EBak LCla
'Vera Garcia'	EPts LCla MJac SLBF
'Versicolor'	see *F. magellanica* var. *gracilis* 'Versicolor'
'Vintage Dovercourt'	LCla
'Violet Bassett-Burr' (d)	CLoc EBak
'Violet Gem' (d)	CLoc
'Violet Rosette' (d)	SVic
VIOLETTA ('Goetzviol') (Shadowdancer Series)	SCoo
'Viva Ireland'	EBak
'Vivien Colville'	CLoc SVic
'Voodoo' (d)	CCCN CLoc EBak EPts LCla SCoo SPet SVic
'Wagtails White Pixie'	EBak
'Waldis Spezi'	LCla
'Walton Jewel'	EBak
'Walz Bella'	LCla
'Walz Estafette' (d)	SVic
'Walz Fluit'	MJac
'Walz Freule'	MJac
'Walz Jubelteen' ♀H2	CLoc ELan ELon EPts LCla MJac SAdn SEle SLBF SVen SVic
'Walz Lucifer'	LCla SLBF
'Walz Mandoline' (d)	SVic
'Walz Panfluit'	LCla
'Walz Polka'	LCla
'Walz Triangel' (d)	SVic
'Wapenveld 150'	LCla
'Wapenveld's Bloei'	EPts LCla SLBF
'War Paint' (d)	CLoc
'Warton Crag'	SVic
'Water Color'	SLBF
'Water Nymph'	CLoc MHer SLBF SVic
'Wattenpost'	SLBF
'Waveney Gem'	CLoc EBak LCla MJac SLBF
'Waveney Queen'	SVic
'Waveney Sunrise'	MJac SVic
'Waveney Waltz'	EBak
'Wedding Bells' ambig.	SVic
'Welsh Dragon' (d)	CLoc EBak
'Wendy' Catt	see *F.* 'Snowcap'
'Wendy Bendy'	EPts MJac
'Wendy Jane Webster'	EPts
'Wendy's Beauty' (d)	CLoc EBak EPts MJac
'Wentworth'	SVic
'Westham'	LCla
'Westminster Chimes' (d)	CLoc SPet
'Wharfedale' ♀H4	CRos ELon EPts LRHS MJac NRHS SLBF SVic
'What's-it' (E)	SLBF
'Whirlaway' (d)	CLoc SVic
'White Academy'	EPts
'White Ann'	see *F.* 'Heidi Weiss'
'White Bride' (d)	SVic
'White Clove'	SVic
'White Galore' (d)	SVic
'White Joy'	EBak
'White King' (d)	CLoc EBak SVic
'White Pixie' ♀H4	EPts MJac SLBF SPet SVic
'White Queen' ambig.	EHDe
'White Spider'	CLoc EBak SVic
'Whiteknights Blush'	CExl CKel EBee EWes GCal LRHS
'Whiteknights Cheeky' (T)	EBak EPts SVic
'Whiteknights Pearl' ♀H4	CTsd ECha EPts LCla MMuc SDys SEND SGol SLBF SVic
'Whitton Starburst'	LCla
'Whoopee' (d)	EPts MJac SLBF
'Wicked Queen' (d)	SVic
'Widnes Wonder'	MJac SLBF
'Wigan Peer' (d)	EPts MJac
'Wight Magic' (d)	MJac
'Wild and Beautiful' (d)	SVic
'Wilhelmina Schwab'	LCla
'Willow Tinsdale'	SGol
'Wilma van Druten'	LCla
'Wilson's Colours'	EPts LCla
'Wilson's Joy'	MJac
'Wilson's Pearls' (d)	SLBF SPet
'Wilson's Sugar Pink'	EPts LCla MJac
'Win and Walt'	NWms SLBF
'Windhapper'	LCla SLBF
'Wine and Roses' (d)	EBak
'Wingrove's Mammoth' (d)	SVic
'Winifred Glass'	EHDe
'Winston Churchill' (d) ♀H2	CLoc EBak EPts MJac SCoo SPet SVic
'Winter's Tale'	NWms SLBF
'Witchipoo'	SLBF
'Woodside' (d)	SVic
'Wyre Light' (E)	SLBF
'Yattendon Lady'	SLBF
'Yvonne Schwab'	LCla
'Zeebrook'	SVic
'Ziegfield Girl' (d)	SVic
'Zifi'	SLBF
'Zolly'	NWms
'Zulu King'	SVic

Fumaria (*Papaveraceae*)

capreolata	WSFF
lutea	see *Corydalis lutea*

Furcraea (*Asparagaceae*)

bedinghausii	see *F. parmentieri*
§ ***foetida***	CCCN CPla EUJe WCot
§ - var. ***mediopicta*** (v)	CPla
- 'Variegata'	see *F. foetida* var. *mediopicta*
gigantea	see *F. foetida*
longaeva misapplied	see *F. parmentieri*
macdougalii	SPlb
§ ***parmentieri***	CBcs CCCN CCht CDTJ CExl CHll CSBt CTsd EShb GBin LEdu LRHS SPlb SVen

G

Gahnia (*Cyperaceae*)

sieberiana	SPlb

Gaillardia (*Asteraceae*)

'African Sunset'	WFar
aristata 'Maxima Aurea'	EPfP NBre SPhx
'Arizona Sun'	CRos EAJP LRHS MNHC SCob SVic
'Bijou'	EBou SWvt
'Celebration'	CRos LRHS NRHS SPoG
'Dwarf Goblin'	NGBl
'Fanfare'[PBR]	CRos CWGN ELon LRHS NRHS SCoo SPer
GOBLIN	see *G.* × *grandiflora* 'Kobold'
× ***grandiflora*** 'Amber Wheels'	EPfP
- 'Arizona Apricot'	LRHS WFar
- 'Arizona Red Shades'	EAJP LRHS WFar
- 'Burgunder'	CSBt CSpe CWld EAJP ELan EPfP LRHS NGBl NRHS SCob SPer SPhx SPoG SWvt
- 'Dazzler' ♀H5	CRos CSBt EBee ELan EPfP LRHS NRHS SPer SPoG
- 'Fanfare Blaze'	CRos LRHS NRHS WFar
- 'Frenzy'[PBR] (Commotion Series)	SPad
- (Gallo Series) GALLO DARK BICOLOR ('Kiegaldab'[PBR])	CBod
- - GALLO PEACH ('Kiegalpea'[PBR])	NRHS
§ - 'Kobold'	CBcs CMac CRos CSBt CTsd EBee ELan ELon EPfP GMaP LRHS NLar NRHS SPer SPlb SPoG SWvt
- (Mesa Series) 'Mesa Red' **new**	CBod
- - 'Mesa Yellow'	CBod
- Monarch Group	WFar
- 'Red Sun'[PBR]	CWGN NLar
- (Sunburst Series) SUNBURST BURGUNDY PICOTEE ('Granretip')	LRHS
- - SUNBURST BURGUNDY	WFar
- (Sunset Dwarf Series) 'Sunset Cutie'	LRHS NRHS SCob SPoG
- - 'Sunset Flash' **new**	SPoG
- - 'Sunset Snappy'	SPad SPoG
- - 'Sunset Sunrise' **new**	SPoG
- 'Tokajer'	CRos EBee ELan EPfP LRHS NBre NRHS SPhx
'Naomi Sunshine'	SHar
§ 'Oranges and Lemons'[PBR]	SCob SHar
SAINT CLEMENTS	see *G.* 'Oranges and Lemons'
'Solar Flare'	SCob

Galactites (*Asteraceae*)

tomentosa	CPla EHoe EWTr
- white-flowered	CPla

Galanthus ✿ (*Amaryllidaceae*)

'Ailwyn' ♀H5	CAvo EHrv GEdr
'Alan's Treat'	GEdr
'Alison Hilary'	CAvo EHrv GEdr LEdu
× ***allenii***	CBro EHrv GKev
alpinus var. ***bortkewitschianus***	CAvo GKev
'Anglesey Not Galatea'	EHrv
'Anne of Geierstein'	MHCG WCot
'Ann's Millennium Giant'	CBro GEdr
'Armine'	CElw GKev WCot
'Art Nouveau'	CElw EHrv
'Atkinsii' ♀H5	CAvo CBro CElw CMea CRos EHrv EMor EPot GAbr GEdr GKev LAma LRHS MAsh MRav NBir NRHS WCot WFar WHoo WShi XEll
'Autumn Beauty'	CRos LRHS NRHS
'Babraham Scented'	GEdr
'Backhouse Spectacles'	GEdr
'Ballerina' (d)	CAvo GEdr WCot
'Barbara's Double' (d)	CAvo EWes GEdr MAsh
'Barbara's Hybrid'	EHrv
'Beethoven' **new**	LAma
'Benhall Beauty'	CElw EHrv EWes GAbr GEdr MAsh
'Bertram Anderson' ♀H5	CAvo EHrv GEdr MAsh WCot
'Bess'	CElw EHrv GEdr
'Big Eyes'	CAvo
'Bill Bishop'	CBro CElw ECha EHrv GEdr MAsh WCot
'Bitton' ambig.	GEdr NPol
'Blewbury'	ECha EHrv ITim LEdu
'Brenda Troyle'	CBro CElw CRos ECha EMor GAbr GEdr GKev LRHS MAsh MHom NPol NRHS WCot WFar
'Brigadier Mathias'	EHrv
'Bungee' **new**	GEdr
'By Gate' **new**	GEdr
'Byfield Special'	CAvo EHrv
byzantinus	see *G. plicatus* subsp. *byzantinus*
cabardensis	see *G. transcaucasicus*
'Caryl Baron'	CAvo
'Castlegar'	CAvo
caucasicus misapplied	see *G. elwesii* var. *monostictus*
caucasicus ambig.	NPol
- 'Comet'	see *G. elwesii* 'Comet'
- var. ***hiemalis*** Stern	see *G. elwesii* Hiemalis Group
- 'John Tomlinson'	see *G. elwesii* 'John Tomlinson'
'Charlotte'	LRHS
'Chequers'	CElw GEdr MAsh
'Cicely Hall'	GEdr MAsh
'Cliff Curtis' **new**	GEdr
corcyrensis spring-flowering	see *G. reginae-olgae* subsp. *vernalis*
- winter-flowering	see *G. reginae-olgae* subsp. *reginae-olgae* Winter-flowering Group
'Cordelia' (d)	CElw GAbr GEdr
'Cowhouse Green'	EHrv GEdr MAsh
'Curly'	CAvo EHrv EWes GEdr MAsh
'Daglingworth'	GEdr
'David Baker'	CAvo GEdr
'Desdemona' (d)	CBro EHrv EPot GAbr GEdr GMaP LLHF WCot WFar
'Devon Marble'	CAvo
'Ding Dong'	EHrv GEdr MAsh MHCG
'Dionysus' (d)	CBro CExl EHrv ELon EMor EPot EWes GEdr GKev LLHF MAsh MHom NBir NWad SDeJ WBrk WFar WShi XEll
'Dodo Norton'	CAvo GEdr
'Dragonfly' **new**	CAvo
'Eliot Hodgkin'	GEdr
§ ***elwesii*** ♀H5	CRos CTri CWld ELan EMor EPfP EPot ERCP GWyn LAma LCro LRHS NAln NBir NPol NRHS SCob SDeJ SEND SPer SRms WCot WFar WHoo WShi
- 'Abington Green'	CAvo ELon
- 'Beany' **new**	CAvo

	- 'Beluga' **new**	GKev LAma
	- 'Bo Bette'	GEdr
	- 'Byrkley' **new**	CAvo
	- 'Cedric's Prolific'	ECha EHrv EMor GEdr WFar
§	- 'Comet' 🏆H5	CElw EHrv GEdr MAsh MAvo MNrw WFar
	- 'Daphne's Scissors'	CElw EHrv GEdr
	- 'David Shackleton'	CAvo CElw EHrv GEdr MAsh
	- 'Deer Slot'	MAsh
	- 'Early Twin'	WCot
	- 'Echoes'	WCot
	- (Edward Whittall Group) 'Two Eyes'	EHrv GEdr
	- 'Elmley Lovett'	CElw
	- var. ***elwesii***	EHrv
	- - 'Big Boy'	GEdr
	- - 'Fenstead End'	CAvo GEdr
	- - 'Fred's Giant'	GMaP
	- - 'Kite'	EHrv ELon GEdr MAsh
	- - 'Magnus'	NBir
	- - 'Maidwell L'	CBro EHrv EPot
	- - 'Paradise Giant'	GEdr
	- - 'Sibbertoft Magnet'	GEdr
	- 'X Files'	EHrv
*	- 'Flore Pleno' (d)	NPol
	- 'Godfrey Owen'	CAvo CElw GEdr MAsh
	- 'Green Brush'	CAvo CBro EWes GKev LAma LRHS
	- 'Grumpy'	EHrv GEdr
§	- Hiemalis Group	CBro EHrv GKev MHom WCot XEll
	- - from Broadleigh Gardens	EHrv
	- - 'Barnes' 🏆H5	ECha EHrv WCot
	- - 'Donald Sims'	EHrv
	- - 'Highdown'	GKev
	- - 'Rainbow Farm Early'	EHrv
	- 'J. Haydn'	LAma
	- 'Jessica'	CAvo
§	- 'John Tomlinson'	GEdr
	- 'Jonathan'	CAvo MAsh
	- 'Jubilee Green' **new**	MAsh
	- 'Kyre Park'	GEdr MAsh
	- late-flowering	GEdr
	- 'Long 'drop'	GEdr MAsh
	- 'Mandarin'	CAvo CElw EWes
	- 'Marielle'	EPPr
	- 'Marjorie Brown'	CAvo CElw CFis ECha EHrv EPot GEdr
	- 'Marlie Raphael' **new**	CAvo
	- var. ***maximus***	see *G. elwesii* 'Yvonne Hay'
	- 'Milkwood'	see *G. elwesii* 'Mrs Macnamara'
	- 'Miss Mowcher'	WCot
§	- var. ***monostictus*** 🏆H5	CAvo CBro CRos ECha EHrv GKev LLHF LRHS MAsh NRHS WBrk WFar WShi
	- - 'B. Britten'	LAma LRHS
	- - 'G. Handel'	LAma LLHF LRHS
	- - 'Grayswood'	GEdr
	- - 'H. Purcell'	EMor GEdr LAma LLHF LRHS
	- - 'Jimmy Platt'	CAvo
	- - 'Lord Monostictus'	CAvo
	- - 'Miller's Late'	CAvo EHrv
	- - 'Mozart'	LAma LRHS
	- - 'Rogers Rough'	SDys
	- - 'Warwickshire Gemini'	MHCG
	- 'Mr Omer'	WCot
	- 'Mr Peggotty'	WCot
§	- 'Mrs Macnamara'	CAvo ECha EHrv ELon GEdr WFar
	- November-flowering	WCot
	- 'Penelope Ann'	ECha EHrv GEdr
	- 'Peter Gatehouse'	EHrv ELon
§	- 'Ransom's Dwarf'	GEdr
	- 'Remember, Remember'	GEdr MAsh
*	- 'Robustus Praecox'	GKev
	- 'Selborne Green Tips'	EHrv
	- 'Sickle'	EHrv
	- 'Sir Edward Elgar'	GKev LAma LLHF LRHS
	- 'Three Leaves'	CElw
	- 'Washfield Colesbourne'	see *G.* 'Washfield Colesbourne'
	- 'Yashmak'	MAsh
§	- 'Yvonne Hay'	EHrv GEdr
	- 'Zwanenburg'	EHrv MAsh
	aff. ***elwesii*** var. ***monostictus***	WFar
	'Epiphany'	EHrv
	'Ermine House' (d)	EHrv GEdr
	'Ermine Lace' **new**	CAvo
	'Erway'	MHom
	'Falkland House'	CElw GEdr
	'Fanny'	CAvo
	'Faringdon Double' (d)	EHrv MAsh
	'Fieldgate Forte'	CAvo
	'Fieldgate Prelude'	EHrv GEdr
	'Fieldgate Superb'	CAvo EHrv MAsh
	'Flevo Cool'	CAvo
	'Fly Fishing'	CAvo
	'Forge Double' (d)	CAvo GEdr
	fosteri	EHrv GEdr GKev
	'Framlingham Double' (d)	EHrv
	'Gabriel'	CAvo GEdr
	'Galadriel'	CAvo GEdr
	'Galatea'	CBro EHrv EMor EPot EWes GAbr ITim MAsh MHom NRya SDys WFar
	'George Elwes'	GEdr
	'Gill Gregory'	GEdr
	'Ginns'	EHrv MAsh
	'Gloria'	CAvo
	(Gold Group) 'Ronald Mackenzie'	GEdr
§	***gracilis***	CBre CExl GEdr GKev NPol WCot
	- 'Corkscrew'	MAsh
	- 'Highdown'	CElw EHrv GKev MHom
	- Kew	CElw
	- 'Vic Horton'	CElw EHrv GEdr WThu
	graecus misapplied	see *G. gracilis*
	graecus Orph. ex Boiss.	see *G. elwesii*
	'Grayling'	see *G. plicatus* 'Percy Picton'
	'Green Comet'	CAvo
	'Green Man'	EHrv GEdr WFar
	'Green Necklace'	EWes GEdr
	'Greenfields'	CAvo GEdr
	green-tipped double (d)	GEdr
	'Headbourne'	ECha
	'Heffalump' (d)	EHrv ELon GEdr MAsh
	'Hercule'	CAvo
	'Hill Poë' (d)	CBro CElw EHrv EPot GEdr ITim LLHF MAsh MHom
	'Hippolyta' (d)	CBro CElw ECha EHrv EMor EPot GEdr GKev LAma LEdu LRHS MAsh MAvo MHom NPol WCot
	'Hobson's Choice'	EHrv GEdr
	'Homersfield'	EHrv ELon
	'Honeysuckle Cottage'	CAvo
	× ***hybridus*** 'Merlin' 🏆H5	CAvo CBro CElw EHrv GEdr MAsh WCot WFar WHoo
	- 'Robin Hood'	EHrv GEdr GKev
	'Icicle'	CElw GEdr
§	***ikariae*** Bak.	EPfP GEdr
	- subsp. ***ikariae*** Butt's form	NPol
	- Latifolius Group	see *G. platyphyllus*
	- subsp. ***snogerupii***	see *G. ikariae* Bak.
	'Imbolc'	EHrv GEdr

(Imperial Group) 'Shepton Merlin'	CElw
'Ivy Cottage Corporal'	EHrv GEdr
'Ivy Cottage Green Tip'	EHrv
'Jacquenetta' (d)	CBro CElw EHrv EWes GEdr ITim LAma LRHS MAsh MHom
'Jade'	CAvo
'James Backhouse'	ECha EHrv EMor WShi
'John Gray'	CBro EHrv EWes GEdr GQue MAsh
'John Nash' **new**	MAsh
'Kersen'	CAvo
'Ketton'	CBro CElw EHrv GEdr LLHF NRya
'Kildare'	CAvo GEdr LEdu
'Kingston Double' (d)	EHrv
'Kinn McIntosh'	WCot
'Lady Beatrix Stanley' (d) ♀H5	CAvo CBro CElw CRos ECha EHrv EPot GEdr GKev LRHS MAsh MHom NRHS NWad WCot WFar
lagodechianus	CBro GEdr GKev
'Lapwing'	EHrv GEdr MAsh
latifolius Rupr.	see *G. platyphyllus*
'Lavinia' (d)	CElw EHrv EWes GEdr MAsh MHom WFar
'Lerinda'	EHrv
'Limetree'	CElw EHrv EWes GEdr ITim MAvo MHom NPol WFar
'Little Ben'	CAvo CElw EHrv GEdr GMaP MAsh
'Little Dorrit'	GEdr MAsh
'Little John'	EHrv GEdr WBrk
'Little Magnet'	CAvo
'Lord Lieutenant'	GEdr MAsh
'Louise Ann Bromley'	CAvo
lutescens	see *G. nivalis* Sandersii Group
'Lyn'	CBro EHrv EMor GEdr NBir
'Magnet' ♀H5	CAvo CBro CElw CMea CRos EHrv ELon EMor EPfP EPot GAbr GEdr GKev LAma LEdu LRHS MAsh MHom NBir NPol NRHS WBrk WCot WFar WHoo WShi XEll
aff. 'Magnet'	GMaP WFar
'Maidwell'	GEdr
'Melanie Broughton'	CAvo GEdr
'Midwinter'	CAvo
'Mighty Atom'	CBro MAsh WBrk
'Mill House'	EHrv
'Moccas'	CElw MHom
'Modern Art'	CAvo GEdr MAsh MHCG
'Moortown' **new**	CAvo
'Mr Thompson'	EHrv
'Mrs Backhouse No 12'	EHrv
'Mrs Thompson'	CElw ECha EHrv GEdr GKev MAsh MNrw
'Mrs Wrightson's Double' (d)	CElw GEdr
'Natalie Garton'	CAvo EHrv GEdr
'Neill Fraser'	EHrv GEdr MHom
'Nerissa' (d)	GEdr
nivalis ♀H5	Widely available
- 'Anglesey Abbey'	CElw EHrv EWes GEdr MHom
- 'April Fool'	MHom
- 'Ballynahinch'	GEdr ITim
- 'Bitton'	EHrv GEdr
- 'Blonde Inge'	GEdr MAsh
- 'Chedworth'	CAvo CElw GEdr WBrk
- 'Chilton Foliat' **new**	CAvo
- 'Cornwood'	GEdr
- dwarf	ITim
- 'Elfin'	CAvo CElw EHrv EWes GEdr WCot
- 'Fluff'	EHrv
- 'Gloucester Old Spot'	GEdr
- 'Green Diamond' **new**	CElw
- subsp. ***imperati***	CExl WBrk
- 'Lutescens'	see *G. nivalis* Sandersii Group
- 'Margery Fish'	CAvo
- 'Maximus'	WShi
- 'Melvillei'	CAvo MAsh
- f. ***pleniflorus*** (d)	GKev NPri SPoG
- - 'Bagpuize Virginia' (d)	GEdr
- - 'Blewbury Tart' (d)	CAvo CBro CElw EHrv ELon EWes GEdr MAsh WBrk WCot WFar
- - 'Flore Pleno' (d) ♀H5	CArg CBro CExl CRos EMor EPfP EPot ERCP GWyn LAma LCro LOPS LRHS MMuc NHpl NRya SCob SDeJ SEND SPer SRms WBrk WCot WHoo WShi
- - 'Lady Elphinstone' (d)	CBro EHrv ELon GEdr LLHF LRHS MAsh MHom NPol NRya WCot
- - 'Octopussy' (d)	GEdr
- - 'Pusey Green Tips' (d)	CBro CElw EPot NPol WCot
- - Scharlockii Group double (d)	GKev
- - 'Walrus' (d)	EHrv ELon GEdr
§ - - 'Wonston Double' (d)	EHrv
- Poculiformis Group	CElw EHrv MAsh
- - 'Angelique'	CAvo MAsh
- - 'Henry's White Lady'	GEdr
- - 'Moreton Mill' **new**	CAvo
- cf. Poculiformis Group	CElw
- 'Puck'	CAvo
- 'Rosemary Mitchell'	MAvo
§ - Sandersii Group	GEdr GMaP WFar
- - 'Norfolk Blonde'	GEdr
§ - Scharlockii Group	CElw ELon MAsh MHom WBrk
- 'Tiny'	GEdr MHom WFar
- 'Tiny Tim'	GEdr ITim WFar
- 'Tippy Green'	GKev
- 'Viridapice' ♀H5	CAvo CBro CElw CExl CWld ECha EMor EPot ERCP GKev GMaP LAma LRHS NBir NPol NWad SDeJ WCot WFar WHoo WShi
- 'Warei'	EHrv
- 'White Cloud'	GKev
- 'White Dream'	CElw GEdr
'Nothing Special'	MAsh
'One Drop or Two'	CAvo
'Ophelia' (d)	CBro EHrv GEdr MAsh MHom NPol WBrk WFar WHoo
'Peardrop'	EHrv GEdr MAsh
'Peg Sharples'	CAvo EHrv GEdr MHom
peshmenii	LEdu
'Philippe André Meyer'	CAvo
§ ***platyphyllus***	CExl
plicatus ♀H5	CAvo CBro CElw CRos EHrv EMor GKev LRHS MCot MHom NPol NRHS WBrk WCot WHoo WShi
- from Coton Manor	EHrv MCot
- 'Amy Doncaster' **new**	MAsh
- 'Augustus' ♀H5	CBro CElw EHrv ELon EPot EWes GEdr MAsh MHom WCot WHoo
- 'Babraham Dwarf'	EHrv
- 'Baxendale's Late'	CAvo GEdr GKev MAsh
- 'Beth Chatto'	EHrv
- 'Bill Clark'	MAsh
- 'Bolu Shades'	GKev
- 'Bowles's Large'	EHrv
§ - subsp. ***byzantinus***	CBro EHrv MAsh MHCG MHom WThu
- - 'Fox Farm'	EHrv
- - 'Ron Ginns'	CAvo
- 'Colossus'	CBro EHrv EWes GKev MAsh WCot

	- 'Diggory'	EHrv GEdr MAsh MHCG
	- 'Duckie'	GEdr MAsh WFar
	- 'E.A. Bowles'	CAvo GEdr
	- 'Edinburgh Ketton'	EHrv
	- 'Florence Baker'	EHrv GEdr
	- 'Gerard Parker'	EHrv GEdr MAsh
I	- 'Grave Concern' **new**	CAvo
	- 'Green Hayes'	EHrv
	- 'Green Teeth'	GEdr MAsh
	- 'Henham No 1'	EHrv
	- 'John Long'	GEdr MAsh
	- 'Madelaine'	CAvo MAsh
§	- 'Percy Picton'	EWes GEdr
	- 'Sally Pasmore'	CAvo
	- 'Sophie North'	CElw EPot GEdr NRya
	- 'The Pearl'	EHrv GEdr MAsh
	- 'Three Ships'	EHrv GEdr MHom NHar
	- 'Trimmer' **new**	CAvo
	- 'Trym'	CAvo CElw GEdr NPol WFar
	- 'Trymlet' **new**	CAvo MAsh
	- 'Wandlebury Ring'	EHrv
	- 'Warham'	CBro CElw EPot GAbr GKev ITim MHom WCot
	- 'Warham Rectory'	EHrv
	- 'Wendy's Gold'	CBro EHrv EPot EWes GEdr GKev LRHS MAsh NRHS WFar
	- 'Woodtown'	IMou
	'Polar Bear'	CAvo GKev LAma
	'Porlock No 2'	EHrv
	'Prestwood White' **new**	MAsh
	'Pride o' the Mill'	CAvo GEdr
	'Primrose Warburg'	CElw EHrv EWes GEdr MAsh WFar
	'Ransom's Dwarf'	see *G. elwesii* 'Ransom's Dwarf'
	reginae-olgae	EHrv GKev MHom
	- from Spetchley **new**	MAsh
	- 'B. Tickner'	EHrv
	- subsp. ***reginae-olgae*** 'Cambridge'	EHrv MHom
	- - 'Tilebarn Jamie'	MHom WCot
§	- - Winter-flowering Group	CBro
§	- subsp. ***vernalis***	LEdu WCot
	- - 'Miss Adventure'	EHrv
	'Reverend Hailstone'	CAvo EHrv GEdr
	'Richard Ayres' (d)	CRos EHrv ELon GEdr LRHS NRHS
	rizehensis	CAvo CBro EHrv GKev MHom
	- Baytop 34474	EHrv GEdr MAsh
	'Rodmarton'	EHrv GEdr MAsh
	'Ruth Birchall'	EHrv
	'S. Arnott' ♀H5	CAvo CBro CElw CExl CMea CRos EBee ECha EHrv EPot ERCP GAbr GKev GMaP LAma LCro LOPS LRHS MAvo NBir NPol NRHS NRya SDeJ WBrk WCot WFar WHoo
	'Saint Anne's'	CElw GEdr MAsh MHom
	'Scharlockii'	see *G. nivalis* Scharlockii Group
	'Seagull'	CElw EHrv GEdr
	'Sentinel'	CAvo CElw EHrv GEdr
	'Silverwells'	EHrv GEdr
	'Sir Herbert Maxwell'	GEdr
	'Snow Fox' **new**	LAma
	'South Hayes'	GEdr
	'Spindlestone Surprise'	EHrv GEdr
	'Sprite'	CAvo
	'St Pancras'	CAvo EHrv
	'Starling'	CAvo
§	'Straffan' ♀H5	CAvo CBro CElw EHrv EMor EPot GEdr LAma MAsh MHom NPol WBrk WCot WFar
	'Sutton Court' **new**	CAvo
	'Sutton Courtenay'	GEdr
	'The Apothecary'	EHrv
	'The Linns'	GEdr
	'The O'Mahoney'	see *G.* 'Straffan'
	'The Wizard'	CAvo
	'Titania' (d)	CElw EHrv ELon GEdr MHom WHoo WShi
§	***transcaucasicus***	GEdr
	'Trotter's Merlin'	CElw
	'Trumps'	CAvo EHrv GEdr MAsh
	'Trympostor'	EHrv GEdr
	'Tryzm'	CAvo
	'Tubby Merlin'	CElw EHrv
	'Uncle Dick'	CAvo
	'Under Cherry Plum' **new**	CAvo
	× ***valentinei*** 'Compton Court'	CBro GEdr ITim
	'Vertigo'	CAvo
§	'Washfield Colesbourne'	CElw ECha EHrv
	'Washfield Warham'	CElw ECha EHrv MAsh
	'Wasp'	CRos GEdr MAsh WCot
	'Welsh Whiskers' **new**	CAvo
	'Welshway'	CAvo GEdr
	'White Admiral'	CAvo
	'White Dreams'	GEdr
	'White Swan' Ballard (d)	CElw EWes GEdr ITim
	'William Thomson'	EWes MAsh
	'Winifrede Mathias'	CElw EHrv MAsh
	'Wisley Magnet'	EHrv
	'Wonston Double'	see *G. nivalis* f. *pleniflorus* 'Wonston Double'
	woronowii ♀H5	CArg CBro CElw CTca CTri EHrv EPfP EPot LAma LCro LEdu LRHS MHom NBir SCob SDeJ SPer WBrk WCot WFar WShi
	- 'Elizabeth Harrison' **new**	MAsh

Galatella (*Asteraceae*)

§	***linosyris***	EBee EWes MAvo NLar SPer SPhx WFar WHer WOld XLum
	- 'Goldilocks'	see *G. linosyris*
§	***sedifolia***	CBod ECtt ELon EPPr GAbr LEdu LRHS MAvo MWat NBid NEgg NRHS NSti SEND SPoG WCot WOld
	- subsp. ***dracunculoides*** RCB AM 5	WCot
§	- 'Jean Polignier'	LPla
	- 'Nana'	CExl EBee GCal MRav NBir NLar NWsh SPer WCot WFar WOld XLum
	- 'Rosea'	IMou

Galax (*Diapensiaceae*)

	aphylla	see *G. urceolata*
§	***urceolata***	EBee GKev IBlr MNrw NHar WSHC

Galega (*Papilionaceae*)

	bicolor	NBir SRms
	'Duchess of Bedford'	ELon WCot
	× ***hartlandii***	CExl
	- 'Alba' ♀H7	ELon EWes GBin IBlr LRHS MArl MCot MRav SHar WCAu WCot WHoo WSHC WWtn XEll
	- 'Lady Wilson' ♀H7	CWld ECtt ELon EMor EPPr EWes GBin MArl MAvo MMrt MNrw SRms WCot WFar WHrl WKif
	'Her Majesty'	see *G.* 'His Majesty'
§	'His Majesty'	EBee ELon EPPr LEdu MAvo MCot MRav WCot
	officinalis	Widely available
	- 'Alba'	CBod ECtt ELan EMor EPfP GMaP LEdu MAvo MBel MBrN MHer

	MMuc SEND SPer SRms WCAu WHrl WKif WMoo WSpi WTre
- COCONUT ICE ('Kelgal') (v)	SPoG
orientalis	EBee ECtt EWes LEdu MArl MAvo MCot MRav SBrt WMoo WPGP WSHC
- PAB 6771	WPGP

Galeobdolon see *Lamium*

Galeopsis (*Lamiaceae*)

tetrahit	WSFF

Galium (*Rubiaceae*)

boreale	IMou
cruciata	see *Cruciata laevipes*
mollugo	CHab CWld NHic
§ ***odoratum***	Widely available
verum	CHab CWld EBee EBou EMor ENfk GJos GPoy MHer MMuc MNHC NGrd NMir SEND SRms WFar

Galtonia (*Asparagaceae*)

candicans ♀H4	Widely available
princeps	CRos CSam ECha GBin IMou LRHS NRHS WPGP
regalis	CExl CTca WPGP
viridiflora	CAby CAvo CBro CTca EBee ECha ELan EPot ERCP EShb GBin GCal GKev MNrw NWad SDeJ WHil XLum

Galvezia (*Plantaginaceae*)

speciosa	CCCN CHll CSpe LRHS

Gamblea (*Araliaceae*)

innovans	WCru
pseudoevodiifolia B&SWJ 11707	WCru

Garcinia (*Clusiaceae*)

mangostana	CCCN

Gardenia (*Rubiaceae*)

augusta	see *G. jasminoides*
florida L.	see *G. jasminoides*
grandiflora	see *G. jasminoides*
§ ***jasminoides*** ♀H1c	CBcs CCCN CKel EBak
- 'Crown Jewel'PBR (d)	CBcs CKel CPla CRos EPfP LCro LOPS LRHS MAsh MPkF NRHS SEle SPoG WCot
- 'Kleim's Hardy'	Widely available

garlic see *Allium sativum*; also AGM Vegetables Section

garlic, elephant see *Allium ampeloprasum* 'Elephant'

Garrya ✿ (*Garryaceae*)

elliptica	CBcs CDul CKel CMac CRos EBee EPfP LRHS LSRN MAsh MGos NPri NRHS SCob
- (f)	MJak MSwo SWvt WSpi
- (m)	CAby CTri NLar SGol SLim WSpi
- 'James Roof' (m) ♀H4	CBcs CBod CDul CKel CMac CRos CSBt EBee ELan EPfP LCro LMil LOPS LRHS LSRN MAsh MGil MGos NEgg NRHS SCob SGbt SGol SLim SPer SPoG SRms SWvt WFar
flavescens	SIgm
× ***issaquahensis***	CRos ELan EPfP IArd IMou LRHS
'Glasnevin Wine' (m) ♀H4	MAsh MGos NRHS SCob SCoo SPoG WSpi
- 'Pat Ballard' (m)	NLar WSpi
× ***thuretii***	CBcs EBee EUJe MJak MMuc NLar SGol WFar

Gasteria ✿ (*Asphodelaceae*)

batesiana ♀H2	SEND
bicolor	SPlb
var. ***liliputana*** ♀H1c	
carinata var. ***verrucosa***	EShb SEND SPlb SSim
'Little Warty' ♀H2 **new**	SSim
nitida var. ***nitida***	WCot
variegated (v)	
'Smokey'	EShb

× *Gaulnettya* see *Gaultheria*

Gaultheria ✿ (*Ericaceae*)

NJM 10.032	WPGP
antarctica	WThu
cuneata	CRos GEdr LRHS MAsh NRHS WThu
aff. ***dumicola*** NJM 10.032	WPGP
forrestii	CExl
- BWJ 7809	WCru
furiens	see *G. insana*
§ ***insana***	WPav
itoana	GEdr
'John Saxton'	WAbe
miqueliana	GEdr NLar WThu
mucronata	EPfP GKev LRHS MAsh MJak NWea WFar
- (m)	CMac CSBt CTri ELan EPfP MGos MMuc NEgg NWad SPer SRms WFar WPav
- 'Alba' (f)	MJak WPav
- 'Bell's Seedling' (f/m) ♀H6	CBcs CDul CRos CTri ELan EPfP LRHS MAsh MMuc NBir NEgg NLar SCob SGbt SPer SPoG
- 'Cherry Ripe' (f)	MMuc WPav
- 'Crimsonia' (f) ♀H6	CBcs CMac EPfP SRms
- 'Indian Lake'	NWad
- 'Lilacina' (f)	CMac MAsh
- 'Lilian' (f)	CSBt EPfP NWad
- MOTHER OF PEARL	see *G. mucronata* 'Parelmoer'
- 'Mulberry Wine' (f) ♀H6	CBcs CSBt ELan MMuc NEgg NHol SPer
§ - 'Parelmoer' (f)	CSBt SPer
- 'Pink Pearl' (f) ♀H6	SRms
- pink-berried (f)	GAbr
- 'Rosea' (f)	MJak WPav
§ - 'Signaal' (f)	CBcs CRos ELan EPfP LRHS MAsh NEgg NLar NWad SCob SPer
- SIGNAL	see *G. mucronata* 'Signaal'
§ - 'Sneeuwwitje' (f)	CBcs CDul CSBt ELan EPfP LRHS MAsh MMuc SPer
- SNOW WHITE	see *G. mucronata* 'Sneeuwwitje'
- 'Thymifolia' (m)	EPfP
- 'Wintertime' (f) ♀H6	CMac SRms
§ ***myrsinoides***	GKev WThu
'Pearls'	EPot NWad WThu
procumbens ♀H5	CAgr CBcs CDul CMac CRos ELan EPfP GBin GKev LRHS MAsh MBlu MGos MJak NAln NEgg NHic NLar NRHS NWea SCob SLim SPer SPlb SPoG SRms SWvt WFar
- 'Very Berry'	CBod EShb NWad

prostrata	see *G. myrsinoides*
schultesii	WThu
shallon	CAgr CDul CSBt EPfP MCoo MJak NLar SPer SRms SWvt WFar
sinensis lilac-berried	GEdr
tetramera	CExl
thymifolia	NWad
trichophylla	NHar
× ***wisleyensis***	CRos LRHS NRHS SLon SRms
- 'Pink Pixie'	CRos LRHS MAsh NLar NRHS
- 'Ruby'	CMac
- 'Wisley Pearl'	SCoo WFar
yunnanensis	CExl

Gaura (*Onagraceae*)

§ GAUDI PINK ('Florgaucompi'PBR)	CRos EPfP LRHS NRHS
'Ice Cool Rosy'	EBee EWTr SHar
lindheimeri ♀H4	CAby CBar CCBP CMea CRos CSBt CSpe EBee ECha ELan EPfP LCro LOPS LRHS MCot MGos MHer NRHS SPer SPoG SWvt WArt WCAu WCFE WHoo WOut XLum XSen
- 'Bargau' (Pink Panache) (v)	SEle
- Belleza Series	CKel CRos CWCL EPau EPfP LRHS NRHS
- - BELLEZA DARK PINK ('Kleau04263')	LRHS NRHS
- - BELLEZA WHITE ('Kleau04264')	LRHS NRHS
- 'Blaze'PBR	CRos LRHS NRHS
- CHERRY BRANDY ('Gauchebra'PBR)	CBod CRos EBee ECtt ELan EPfP GWyn IPot SWvt
- 'Chiffon'	SHar
- compact red	XSen
- 'Corrie's Gold' (v)	CAby CRos EAJP EBee ECha ECtt EHoe ELan EPfP LRHS MHer NRHS
- 'Crimson Butterflies'PBR	CWGN ECtt ELan EPfP
- 'Ellura White'	NRHS
- FREEFOLK ROSY ('Harrfolk') (v)	CDor CRos EBee LCro LOPS LRHS NRHS SCob SHar
- 'Gambit Rose'	EAJP
- GAUDI RED ('Florgaured')	CRos EPfP LRHS NRHS
- GAUDI ROSE ('Florgaucomro'PBR)	CRos LRHS NRHS SCob
- (Geyser Series) GEYSER PINK ('Gaudros'PBR)	EBee EPfP
- - GEYSER WHITE ('Gaudwwhi'PBR)	EBee EPfP
- 'Jo Adela' (v)	ECha EPfP
- KARALEE PETITE ('Gauka')	CWCL EPfP SEle
- KARALEE PETITE IMPROVED	see *G. lindheimeri* LILLIPOP PINK
- KARALEE WHITE ('Nugauwhite'PBR)	CRos CWCL ELan EPfP LRHS NLar NRHS SCoo SPer SPoG
§ - LILLIPOP PINK ('Redgapi'PBR)	CAby CKel CWCL EPfP LRHS MBrN NLar NRHS SCob SPoG
- 'Little Janie'	CBod MHol
- 'My Melody'PBR (v)	CWCL
- 'Occitania' (v)	XLum
- PAPILLON ('Nugaupapil'PBR)	CRos CWCL LRHS NRHS SPer SPoG
- 'Passionate Blush'PBR	CBcs CChe CRos ECtt EPfP LRHS MGos NRHS SLon SPoG SRms
- 'Passionate Pink'	LRHS NRHS
- 'Passionate Rainbow'PBR (v)	CKel CRos CWCL EPfP LRHS NRHS SRms
- 'Pink Dwarf'	EBee EBou EPfP SAdn
- PINK FOUNTAIN ('Walgaupf')	CRos LRHS NRHS
- 'Pink Gin'	SPoG
- ROSYJANE ('Harrosy'PBR)	CAby CBod CChe CMea CRos CWCL EBee ECtt ELan EPfP LCro LOPS LRHS LSRN MBel MNrw MRav NRHS SCob SHar SLon SMad SPer SPoG SRms SWvt XSen
- RUBY RUBY ('Harruby'PBR)	SHar
- 'Siskiyou Pink'	CBar CBcs CBod CRos CSBt CSpe CWCL EAJP EBee ECha ECtt EHoe ELan EPfP LCro LOPS LRHS MBel NRHS SAdn SCob SMad SPer SWvt WCFE WGwG XLum XSen
- SNOW FOUNTAIN ('Walsnofou')	CRos LRHS NRHS
- 'Sparkle White'	CBod EAJP EBee LCro LOPS LRHS WFar
- 'Summer Breeze'	CDor CRos EAJP LRHS LSun NGBl NRHS SPhx
- 'Summer Emotions'	LCro LOPS
- 'The Bride'	CBcs CBod CTri CWCL EBee ECtt EHrv ELan EPfP LRHS LSRN MBel MNHC MRav MWat NHic NRHS SAdn SGbt SWvt WGwG WJam
- 'Tutti Frutti'	SCob
- 'Val's Pink'	WAvo
- 'Vanilla'	CKno
I - 'Variegata' (v)	CWCL SRms
- 'Whirling Butterflies'	CKno CSpe ECtt ELan EPfP LCro LOPS LRHS NRHS SCob SMad SPer SPoG SWvt WCAu
- 'Whiskers Deep Rose'	LCro LOPS MHol WFar
- 'White Dove'	CRos EWTr LRHS NRHS
- 'White Heron'	MNrw
'Rosy Shimmer's'	EBee SHar
sinuata	CAby CFis SHar
STRATOSPHERE PINK PICOTEE	see *G.* GAUDI PINK

Gaylussacia (*Ericaceae*)

baccata (F)	CMac

Gazania (*Asteraceae*)

'Aztec' ♀H2	CCCN
'Bicton Orange'	CCCN CSam ECtt SCoo SVen
'Big Kiss White Flame' (Kiss Series)	LBuc
'Big Kiss Yellow Flame' (Kiss Series)	LBuc
'Blackberry Ripple'	CCCN SCoo
'Blackcurrant Ice'	MCot
'Christopher'	SCoo
'Christopher Lloyd'	CCCN ECtt
'Cornish Pixie'	CCCN
'Cream Beauty'	MCot
krebsiana	CCCN
'Lemon Beauty'	ECtt
'Magic'	CCCN SCoo
'Melbourne Sunshine' **new**	CBor
NAHUI ('Suga119') (Sunbathers Series)	CCCN
'Orange Beauty'	ELan
rigens 'Variegata' (v) ♀H2	CCCN ELan
RUMI ('Suga116') (Sunbathers Series)	CCCN
Sunbathers Series	CPla

SUNSET JANE LEMON SPOT ('Sugajale') (Sunbathers Series)	CCCN CRos LRHS NRHS
SUNSET JANE ('Sugaja'PBR) (Sunbathers Series)	CCCN
'Talent'	SEND
TIGER EYE ('Gazte') (v)	CCCN
TOPTOKAI ('Suga407') (Sunbathers Series)	CCCN CRos LRHS NRHS
TOTONACA ('Suga212') (Sunbathers Series)	CCCN CPla CRos LRHS NRHS

Geissorhiza (*Iridaceae*)

aspera	CPbh
corrugata	GKev
tulbaghensis	CPbh

Gelidocalamus (*Poaceae*)

fangianus	see *Ampelocalamus mocrophyllum*

Gelsemium (*Gelsemiaceae*)

rankinii	LRHS
sempervirens ♀H3	CAby CBcs CCCN CHll CRHN EBee EShb LRHS LSRN MGil SBrt SLim SPoG WCot

Genista (*Papilionaceae*)

	aetnensis ♀H5	ELan EPfP LRHS SArc SBrt SEND SMad SPer SRms WPGP WSpi
§	***canariensis*** ♀H3	CExl CSBt SNig
	cinerea	WCFE XSen
	decumbens	see *Cytisus decumbens*
	'Emerald Spreader'	see *G. pilosa* 'Yellow Spreader'
	fragrans	see *G. canariensis*
	hispanica	CBcs CDul CSBt ELan EPfP LPot MAsh MMuc SCob SPer SRms SWvt WCFE
	lydia ♀H5	Widely available
	monosperma	see *Retama monosperma*
	pilosa	EPot MAsh
	- 'Goldilocks'	LRHS MMuc
	- 'Lemon Spreader'	see *G. pilosa* 'Yellow Spreader'
	- var. ***minor***	NLar WAbe
	- 'Procumbens' ♀H5	CMea GEdr SRot
	- 'Vancouver Gold'	CMac ELan EPfP MRav SPer SRms
§	- 'Yellow Spreader'	MAsh MSwo
§	'Porlock' ♀H3	CBcs CDul CExl CKel CMac CRos CSBt CTri EPfP LRHS MAsh MMuc MRav NRHS SEND WHor
	sagittalis	CKel LRHS MMuc SBrt SPer WWFP
§	× ***spachiana*** ♀H1c	CEnd CTri SPoG
	tinctoria	CHab GPoy MMuc WHer WSFF XSen
§	- 'Flore Pleno' (d) ♀H6	GEdr
	- 'Humifusa'	EPot GCrg GEdr
	- 'Moesiaca'	WAbe
	- 'Plena'	see *G. tinctoria* 'Flore Pleno'
	- 'Royal Gold' ♀H6	MRav NWad SPer SPlb
	umbellata	XSen

Gentiana ✿ (*Gentianaceae*)

§	***acaulis*** ♀H5	CRos EPot GKev GMaP LRHS MAsh NGdn NHar NLar NRHS NSla SIgm SPlb SRms WAbe
	- f. ***alba***	EPot LLHF WThu
	- - 'Snowstorm'	GKev
	- 'Arctic Fanfare' **new**	GEdr
	- B.A. selection **new**	EPot
	- 'Belvedere'	EPot
	- 'Coelestina'	WThu
	- 'Holzmannii'	WAbe
	- 'Krumrey'	EPot GEdr GKev
	- 'Luna'PBR	NLar WIce
I	- 'Maxima Enzian'	EPot GEdr
	- 'Rannoch'	EPot GEdr NLar
	- 'Stumpy'	GCrg GEdr
	- 'Trotter's Variety'	WAbe
	- 'Undulatifolia'	EPot
	- 'Velkokvensis'	EPot
	'Alex Duguid'	CRos GCrg GEdr LRHS NHar
	'Amethyst'	CRos EPot GEdr LRHS WAbe
	angulosa misapplied	see *G. verna* 'Angulosa' hort.
	angulosa M. Bieb.	see *G. verna* subsp. *pontica*
	angustifolia	WAbe XEll
	- Frei hybrid	NSla
	'Ann's Special'	GEdr
	asclepiadea ♀H5	CRos CSpe ELan EMor GAbr GEdr GKev GMaP ITim LEdu LRHS MBel MNrw NBid NBir NLar NRHS SIgm SPer SRms WBor WCAu WCFE WHoo WKif WSHC
	- 'Alba'	CRos EBee EMor GCal GEdr GKev GMaP LEdu LRHS NBid NRHS SPer SRms WCFE
	- dark blue-flowered	GCal WPGP
	- 'Knightshayes'	EBee GKev LEdu
I	- 'Nana'	GKev
	- 'Phyllis'	GKev WHoo
	- 'Pink Swallow'	GEdr WArt
	- 'Rosea'	GEdr GKev MNrw
	- 'White Swallow'	GEdr
	- 'Whitethroat'	GKev
	'Balmoral'PBR	GMaP NHar
	'Barbara Lyle'	WAbe
	bavarica var. ***subacaulis***	SPlb
	× ***bernardii***	see *G.* × *stevenagensis* 'Bernardii'
	'Berrybank Dome'	CRos GMaP LRHS
	'Berrybank Sky'	CRos EPot GAbr GEdr GMaP LRHS NHar SPer
	'Berrybank Snowflakes'	GMaP
	'Berrybank Star'	CRos GEdr LRHS
	bisetaea	SRms
	'Blauer Diamant'	GEdr
	'Blauer Kobold'	GEdr
	'Blauer Zwerg'	GEdr
	'Blue Flame'	GEdr
	'Blue Heaven'	GEdr
	'Blue Magic'PBR	LRHS NLar
	'Blue Sea'	CRos LRHS
	'Blue Silk' ♀H5	CRos CSma EPfP EPot GCrg GEdr GKev LRHS NHar NRHS SPoG WAbe
	brachyphylla	WAbe
	'Braemar'PBR	GMaP NHar
*	***burrowthii***	GEdr
	cachemirica	ITim SIgm
	'Cairngorm'	CRos GEdr LRHS
	'Carmen'	GEdr
	× ***caroli***	WAbe
	clusii	EPot
	'Compact Gem'	EPot GEdr NHar WAbe
§	***cruciata***	ELan GEdr NLar
§	***dahurica***	EBou GEdr GLog MMuc NGdn NLar
	'Dark Hedgehog'	GEdr
	David Sturrock's dark seedling **new**	NHar
	decumbens	GKev
	depressa	EPot GEdr WAbe
	'Devonhall'	GEdr NWad
	'Diana'PBR	LRHS NLar

	dinarica 'Colonel Stitt'	GCrg GEdr WThu
	- 'Frocheneite'	EPot
	'Dumpy'	EPot GEdr
	'Elehn'	GEdr
	'Elizabeth'	GEdr
	'Ettrick'	GEdr
	'Eugen's Allerbester' (d)	CRos CSma EPot GEdr GKev GMaP LRHS NHar NHol NLar NWad SPer WAbe
	farreri	WAbe
	- Silken Star Group	WAbe
	'Faszination'	GEdr
	fetissowii	see *G. macrophylla* var. *fetissowii*
	'Gellerhard'	GEdr
	georgei	EPot
	'Gewahn'	GEdr
I	'Glamis Strain'	CRos GEdr LRHS NHar SPer
	'Glen Moy'	GEdr
	'Glendevon'	GEdr
§	***gracilipes***	GEdr GKev SPlb SRms
	- 'Yuatensis'	see *G. macrophylla* var. *fetissowii*
	grossheimii	GKev
	'Hamburg' **new**	GEdr
	handeliana subsp. ***erectosepala*** **new**	GKev
	'Henry'	GEdr
	Inshriach hybrids	CRos LRHS
	'Inverleith'	CRos GEdr LRHS NHol SPlb
	'Iona'PBR	NHar
	'Joan Ward'	CRos LRHS SPer
	'John Aitken'	GEdr
	'Juwel'	GEdr
	'Kobold'	GEdr
	kochiana	see *G. acaulis*
	kurroo var. ***brevidens***	see *G. dahurica*
	lagodechiana	see *G. septemfida* var. *lagodechiana*
	ligustica	EPot GKev
	'Little Diamond'PBR	LRHS NLar
	'Lucerna'	CRos GCrg GEdr GKev LRHS NAln
	lutea	EMor GAbr GCal GKev GPoy IMou SMad SRms WCAu
	× ***macaulayi***	CPla
	- 'Blue Bonnets'	GEdr
	- 'Elata'	NWad
	- 'Kidbrooke Seedling'	CRos GEdr GMaP LRHS WAbe
	- 'Kingfisher'	CPla CRos GEdr LRHS NBir WAbe
§	- 'Praecox'	EBou
§	***macrophylla*** var. ***fetissowii***	LLHF
	makinoi 'Marsha'PBR	CHll GEdr LRHS NLar SPoG
	- 'White Magic'PBR	GEdr
	'Margaret'	GEdr
	'Maryfield'	GEdr
	'Melanie'	GEdr
	microdonta	EPot LLHF
	'Multiflora'	CRos LRHS
	'Mystic'PBR	NLar
§	***nubigena***	EPot
	'Oban'PBR	GMaP NHar
	occidentalis	EPot
	ornata	CRos LRHS WAbe
	paradoxa ♀H5	GKev LLHF NRHS NSla SBrt SIgm
	phlogifolia	see *G. cruciata*
	pneumonanthe	LRHS NLar SPlb
	przewalskii	see *G. nubigena*
	pumila subsp. ***delphinensis***	WAbe
	purdomii	see *G. gracilipes*
	robusta CC 7494	GKev
	'Sapphire Blue'	GEdr
	saxosa	GCrg GKev GWyn ITim LRHS NBir NHpl NRHS NSla WAbe
	scabra	CRos LRHS
	- 'Little Pinkie'PBR **new**	GEdr
	'Selektra'	GEdr
	septemfida ♀H5	CRos EBou EPot GKev LRHS MAsh MJak NBir NHpl NRHS NSla SPlb SRms WHoo WIce WKif
	- 'Alba'	GKev LLHF
	- var. ***kolakovskyi***	LLHF
§	- var. ***lagodechiana*** ♀H5	LLHF LRHS SRms XLum
	'Serenity'	CRos CSma GEdr LRHS NWad WAbe
	'Shot Silk' ♀H5	CRos EPfP EPot EWes GAbr GCrg GEdr GMaP LRHS MGos NHol NHpl SPoG WAbe WIce
	'Silken Giant'	GEdr WAbe
	'Silken Glow'	WAbe
	'Silken Night'	GEdr WAbe
	'Silken Seas'	CSma GCrg GEdr NWad WAbe
	'Silken Skies' ♀H5	EPot GEdr WAbe
	'Silken Surprise'	WAbe
	sino-ornata ♀H5	CPla CSma EBou EPfP GAbr GKev GMaP LSRN MAsh NHpl NRHS SRms WAbe WIce
	- SDR 5127	MGos
	- 'Alba'	CPla
	- 'Angel's Wings'	CRos GEdr LRHS
	- 'Bellatrix'	GEdr
	- 'Blautopf'	GEdr
	- 'Brin Form'	SRms
	- 'Downfield'	CRos GKev LRHS
	- 'Edith Sarah'	GEdr
	- 'Gorau Glas'	WAbe
	- 'Mary Lyle'	GEdr
	- 'Oha'	GEdr
	- 'Praecox'	see *G.* × *macaulayi* 'Praecox'
	- 'Purity'	CRos GEdr LRHS WAbe
	- 'Starlight'	GEdr NHar
	- 'Weisser Traum'	CRos GEdr LRHS NHar NHol NLar
	- 'White Wings'	GEdr
	'Sir Rupert'	GEdr
	'Sternschuppe'	GKev
	× ***stevenagensis***	CRos LRHS
§	- 'Bernardii'	GEdr
	- dark-flowered	WAbe
	straminea	GKev
	'Strathmore' ♀H5	CRos CSma EWes GAbr GEdr GKev GMaP LRHS NBir SPer SPlb WAbe WIce
	'Surprise'	GEdr
	syringea	WAbe
	szechenyii subsp. ***stolonifera*** **new**	EPot
	ternifolia 'Cangshan'	EPot GEdr
	- 'Dali'	GEdr
	'The Caley'	CRos GEdr GMaP LRHS
	tibetica	EMor GCal GPoy WCAu XLum
	- PAB 2357	LEdu WPGP
	Tough's form	GEdr
	triflora subsp. ***japonica***	NLar
	veitchiorum	EPot LLHF WAbe
	verna	CMea CRos CSma EDAr EPfP EPot EWes GKev LCro LOPS LRHS LSRN NHpl NRHS NSla SIgm SPlb SPoG WAbe WHoo XEll
	- 'Alba'	GEdr NSla WAbe
§	- 'Angulosa' ♀H5	MAsh
	- subsp. ***balcanica***	CPBP
§	- subsp. ***pontica***	WIce

'Violette'	CRos GEdr LRHS NWad
waltonii	EWes
wutaiensis	see *G. macrophylla* var. *fetissowii*
zekuensis	WCot

Geranium ✿ (*Geraniaceae*)

aconitifolium misapplied	see *G. palmatum*
aconitifolium L'Hér.	see *G. rivulare*
'Adam Moreland'	WOut
'Alan Mayes'	CBod CMac ECtt EPPr GBin GKin LRHS NGdn NRHS WCra WFar WPnP WPtf
'Alan's Blue'	EBee
albanum	CElw EPPr GLog GPSL GWyn MMuc WMoo
albiflorum	EBee
anemonifolium	see *G. palmatum*
'Ann Folkard' ♀H7	Widely available
'Ann Folkard' × ***psilostemon***	GWyn LSRN
'Anne Thomson' ♀H7	Widely available
'Ant Chilly' **new**	EBee
× ***antipodeum*** 'Chocolate Candy'PBR	LBuc NRHS SPoG
- 'Pink Spice'PBR	CRos CWGN GKin LBuc LRHS NRHS SPoG SRms
- 'Purple Passion'PBR	LBuc LRHS NRHS SPoG
- 'Sea Spray'	NBro
- 'Stanhoe'	MHCG
- (*G. sessiliflorum* subsp. *novae-zelandiae* 'Nigricans' × *G. traversii* var. *elegans*)	SRms
argenteum	NSla XEll
aristatum	EBee EMor EPPr EWes GCal MNrw MRav NBir SGbt SPhx WCru WMoo
armenum	see *G. psilostemon*
asphodeloides	CElw CRos IFro LRHS MBNS MNrw NBid NBir NRHS SGbt WBrk WFar WMoo
- subsp. ***asphodeloides*** white-flowered	CElw WMoo
- subsp. ***sintenisii***	EPPr
- 'Starlight'	GCal NBid
atlanticum Hook. f.	see *G. malviflorum*
'Azure Rush'	CBod CDor CRos CWGN EBee ECtt EPfP EWTr ILea IPot LRHS MHol NDov NRHS NSti SPoG SRms WCAu WCra WFar WPnP
'Azurro'	EBee LRHS
'Baby Blue'	see *G. himalayense* 'Baby Blue'
'Bertie Crûg'	CBod ECtt EHrv ELon EMor GWyn LLHF LLWG NBir NCou NLar SRms SRot SWvt
biuncinatum	IFro
'Blue Boy'	NLar
'Blue Cloud' ♀H7	Widely available
'Blue Pearl'	EPPr MAvo NBir NSti
§ BLUE SUNRISE ('Blogold'PBR) ♀H7	Widely available
'Blue Thunder'	EPPr
'Blushing Turtle'PBR	CBod EBee ELan EMor EPPr EPfP LBuc MAvo MHol NDov NLar NSti SPoG WCAu WCra WNPC
'Bob's Blunder'	CRos ECtt LLWG LRHS MBNS MBel MHol MNrw MSCN SAko SPoG SRms SWvt WCot WCra WFar WHoo
bohemicum	WHer
- 'Orchid Blue'	SWvt
'Brookside' ♀H7	Widely available

'Buckland Beauty'	CExl EBee EWes SBch
'Buxton's Blue'	see *G. wallichianum* 'Buxton's Variety'
caeruleatum	EBee GCal NLar
canariense	see *G. reuteri*
candicans misapplied	see *G. lambertii*
§ × ***cantabrigiense***	CMac CRos EBee EBou ECtt LRHS MHer MNrw NAln NBir NBro NLar NPer NRHS NSti SRms WBor WCru WMoo
- 'Andrew Clarke'	WBrk
- 'Berggarten'	EBee EPPr NLar SAko WBrk WCra WJam WPtf
- 'Biokovo'	Widely available
- 'Cambridge'	CBod CRos EBee ECha ECtt EHrv ELan EPPr EPfP GAbr GKin LRHS MCot MRav MSwo NRHS SCob SPer SPoG SRms SWvt WBrk WCra WFar WFib WMoo WPnP
- CRYSTAL ROSE ('Abpp')	CRos EBee EPPr LRHS NRHS NSti WCAu WCot
- 'Hanne'	CDor EBee ECtt EPPr EWes WCra
- 'Harz'	CDor EPPr SAko WBrk WCra
- 'Hilary Rendall'	EBee ECtt EPPr
- 'Karmina'	CBod CDor CRos EBee EPPr EPfP GBin LRHS NLar NRHS WCra WFar WHoo WMoo WPnP WSpi XEll XLum
- 'Rosalina'	EPPr WBrk
- 'Show Time'	EPPr
- 'St Ola'	CCBP CDor CRos EBee ECtt EPPr EPfP GMaP ILea LRHS MAsh MNrw MRav NBro NChi NEgg NGdn NRHS NSti SAko SCob WCot WCra WCru WFib WHoo WMoo WPnP WSpi WWtn
- 'Vorjura'	EBee EPPr SAko SMHy WBrk
- 'Westray'PBR	CBod CDor CMac EBee ECtt EPPr GJos GLog MBel MHol MMuc NGdn NLar NRya NSti SCob SEND SRms SWvt WCra WFib WIce WPnP
'Chantilly'	CBod CRos EBee ECtt EPPr EWTr LRHS MAvo NBir NChi NLar NRHS WCru WFib WGwG WPtf
'Chipchase Castle'	NChi
christensenianum B&SWJ 8022	WCru
cinereum	NSla
- 'Apple Blossom'	see *G.* × *lindavicum* 'Apple Blossom'
- 'Elizabeth'	ECtt LSRN
- 'Sateene'PBR	CAby CBor CSma ECtt GMaP MSCN SRms WCra
(Cinereum Group) 'Alice'PBR	CAby CBor CSma EBee LSRN MBNS NLar SRms SRot WFar
- 'Ballerina' ♀H5	Widely available
- 'Carol'	CAby CBor CRos CSma CWGN ECtt EWes GKin LRHS LSRN MBNS MRav MSCN NLar NRHS SWvt WCra WFar WIce
I - 'Heather'	CBor CSma
- 'Janette'	CBor NRHS
- JOLLY JEWEL CORAL ('Noortjjcor') **new**	WCot
- JOLLY JEWEL HOT PINK ('Noortjjhpi') **new**	NCGa
- JOLLY JEWEL LILAC ('Noortlil') **new**	WCot
- JOLLY JEWEL NIGHT ('Noortnight')	IPot MPnt NCGa NSti SHeu WCot WHlf

	- JOLLY JEWEL PINK ('Noortjjhpi') **new**	NCGa
	- JOLLY JEWEL PURPLE ('Noortpur')	IPot SHeu WCot WHil WHlf
	- JOLLY JEWEL RASPBERRY ('Noortjjrab') **new**	IPot NCGa WCot
	- JOLLY JEWEL RED ('Noortimpred')	MAvo MPnt SHeu WCot WHil
	- JOLLY JEWEL SALMON ('Noortsal')	CKno IPot LLWG MBNS MHol MSCN NSti SHeu WCot WHlf
	- JOLLY JEWEL SILVER ('Noortjjsil') **new**	WCot
	- JOLLY JEWEL VIOLET ('Noortvio') **new**	WCot
	- 'Lambrook Helen'	CAby CBor CExl CFis
	- 'Laurence Flatman'	CAby CExl CKno CRos CSpe ECtt ELan EPfP GCrg GMaP LRHS MAvo MCot MPnt NBid NChi NEgg NQui NRHS NSla SPoG SRms SRot WCra WHoo
	- 'Lizabeth'[PBR]	CBor ECtt NLar WCot
	- 'Melody'[PBR]	CAby CBor CSma WCra
	- 'Pandora' **new**	CBor
	- 'Penny Lane'[PBR]	CBor MHol
	- 'Purple Pillow'	CBcs CBor CWGN ECtt ELan EPPr LSRN MHer MHol MRav NChi SAko SCob SPer SRms SRot SWvt WFar WIce
	- RENÉ MACÉ ('Progera')	SRkn
	- ROTHBURY GEM ('Gerfos'[PBR]) 🏆H5	ECtt MAsh MRav SWvt
	- 'Signal'	CBor ECtt EPPr EPot MPnt WCra
	- 'Sophie'[PBR]	CBor CSma LRHS LSRN NRHS
§	- 'Thumbling Hearts'	CBor CWGN EBee ECtt LCro LLWG LPla MHol NCGa NSti SAko SCob WCot
	- THUMPING HEART	see *G.* 'Thumbling Hearts'
	'Claridge Druce'	see *G.* × *oxonianum* 'Claridge Druce'
§	***clarkei*** 'Kashmir White'	Widely available
	- 'Mount Stewart'	CExl EBee EPfP GCal WCru WPGP
	- (Purple-flowered Group) 'Kashmir Purple'	Widely available
	- Raina 82.83	MNrw
	clarum B&SWJ 10246	MAvo WCru
	collinum	EPPr NBir WCru
	'Color Carousel'	EBee GBin
	'Coombland White'	CExl CRos EBee ECtt GCal LRHS MAvo MBel MHol NLar NRHS SPoG WCot WCra WFar WSpi
	'Copper Tiger' **new**	LEdu
	'Coquet Island'	EPPr
	'Criss Canning'	EPPr
	'Curly Girly' **new**	EBee
	'Cyril's Fancy'	EPPr
	dalmaticum 🏆H5	CRos EBee ECha ECtt ELan EPPr EPfP EPot GBin GJos GLog GMaP GWyn LRHS MHer MMuc NGrd NLar NRHS NRya SEND SRms WAbe WCFE WCru WFar WGwG WPnP WSpi
	- 'Album'	CBod CRos EBee ECtt EPfP EPot LRHS MRav NRHS NRya SRms WAbe WCra
	- 'Bressingham Pink'	ECtt EPPr
	- 'Bridal Bouquet'	CPBP ECtt EPot GCrg LLHF NSla
	- 'Stade's Hellrosa'	EPPr
	dalmaticum × ***macrorrhizum***	see *G.* × *cantabrigiense*
	'Danny Boy' 🏆H7	EBee
	'Deep Purple'	EBee
	delavayi misapplied	see *G. sinense*
	'Deux Fleurs'	GBin MAvo MNrw
	'Devon Pride'	CElw EBee EPPr
	'Dilys' 🏆H7	CFis EBee ELan EPPr LPla MAvo MNrw MTis NBir NChi NDov NGdn NGrd NLar WCra WCru WFar WHal WMoo WPnP WSpi
	'Distant Hills'	EBee EPPr
	'Diva'	EBee ELan EPPr LLHF
	donianum	NSla
	'Double Jewel'	see *G. pratense* 'Double Jewel'
	DRAGON HEART ('Bremdra'[PBR])	EBee ECtt ELan EPfP IPot LCro LOPS LPla LRHS LSRN MNrw MPnt NCGa NDov NLar NRHS NSti SCob STPC WCAu WCra WFar WPnP WSpi
	drakensbergense	WFar
	DREAMLAND ('Bremdream'[PBR])	CBod CDor CPou CWGN EBee ECtt EMor GMaP ILea LCro LOPS LPla LRHS LSun MAvo MBNS MHol NCGa NLar SAko SMad WCot WCra
	'Dusky Crûg'	CSam ECtt EHoe EHrv ELan ELon EMor EPPr EPfP EWTr MBel MHol MJak MPie NEgg NHpl NLar NSti SPoG SWvt WCot WCra WFar WSpi
	'Dusky Rose'	CAby CDor CKel ECtt EMor GKev GWyn LBuc NCGa NLar SHar SRot WFar
	'Dylis' **new**	WCAu
	'Elizabeth Ross'	MAvo
	'Elke'	Widely available
	'Elworthy Eyecatcher'	CDor CElw MAvo MNrw WPGP
	'Elworthy Tiger'	CElw EBee WCra
	endressii 🏆H7	CBod CBre CKel CWCL ECha EMor EPfP GMaP LPot MBNS MCot MHer MMuc NAln NBro NPer NPol SCob SEND SPlb SRms SWvt WCra WFar WMoo XLum
	- 'Album'	see *G.* 'Mary Mottram'
	- 'Prestbury White'	see *G.* × *oxonianum* 'Prestbury Blush'
I	- 'Rose'	MAvo
	- 'Wargrave Pink'	see *G.* × *oxonianum* 'Wargrave Pink'
	erianthum	GLog GMaP IMou NLar WCru WMoo
	- 'Axeltree'	WCot
	- 'Blues in the Night'	EBee
	- 'Cally Pearl'	EBee GCal
	- 'Calm Sea'	WCru WMoo
	- 'Neptune'	EBee WCru
	- 'Pale Blue Yonder'	EBee EWes
	eriostemon Fischer	see *G. platyanthum*
	'Eureka Blue'	CPou CRos ECtt LPla LRHS LSun MAvo MHol MTis NLar NRHS NSti SPoG WCot WCra WPnP
	'Eva'	WPnP
	'Expression'	see *G.* 'Tanya Rendall'
	'Extravaganza'	EWes
	'Farncombe Cerise Star'	CElw MAvo
§	***farreri***	CExl CPBP CRos EPot LLHF LRHS NBir NRHS NSla
	'Fay Anna'	CBct CBod EMor EPPr GBin MPnt SCob SPoG WCra WFar
	'Finnish Pink' **new**	NGrd
	'Foundling'	CBct CPla
	fremontii	EWld

gracile	CFis CRos EBee EPfP GMaP LRHS MNrw NBir NRHS WBrk WCru WMoo
- 'Blanche'	CRos EPPr LRHS MNrw NRHS
- 'Blush'	CElw EPPr EWes
- 'Golden Gracile'	see *G.* 'Mrs Judith Bradshaw'
grandiflorum	see *G. himalayense*
'Grasmere'	ECtt
'Gwen Thompson'	WOut
gymnocaulon	CMac EBee EMor NLar WCru
gymnocaulon* × *platypetalum	EBee
'Harmony'	EBee EPPr
harveyi	EWes SPhx WKif
§ ***hayatanum***	CRos LRHS NRHS
- B&SWJ 164	NLar WCru WMoo WPnP
'Hilary'	WWtn
§ ***himalayense***	CBcs CPla CRos ECha ELan EPfP LRHS MBNS MMuc MRav NBir NBro NGrd NRHS SEND SPlb SRms SRot WCra WFar WMoo XLum
- CC 1957 from Tibetan border	CExl EPPr
- ***alpinum***	see *G. himalayense* 'Gravetye'
§ - 'Baby Blue'	CBod CElw CRos EBee ECtt ELon EPPr GBin GCal LRHS MAvo MNrw NGdn NLar NRHS NSti WBrk WCAu WCra WCru WFib WMoo WPnP WPtf
- 'Birch Double'	see *G. himalayense* 'Plenum'
- 'Derrick Cook'	CElw EBee ECha ECtt EPPr EPfP EWTr GCal MAvo MNrw MTis NCGa NGrd NLar NSti SAko WBrk WCAu WCra WHal WHil WHoo WJam WPnP
- 'Devil's Blue'	EPPr WCAu WPtf
§ - 'Gravetye'	Widely available
- 'Irish Blue'	CDor CElw CRos EBee EPPr GCal GMaP LRHS NLar NPol NRHS NSti WCra WFib WMoo WPnP WPtf
- ***meeboldii***	see *G. himalayense*
- 'Pale Irish Blue'	EBee EPPr GCal
§ - 'Plenum' (d)	Widely available
'Hola Guapa'	GBin
ibericum misapplied	see *G.* × *magnificum*
ibericum ambig.	SRms
ibericum Cav.	CRos CTri LRHS NBre NRHS
§ - 'Ushguli Grijs'	EPPr IMou NLar WCot
- 'Black and Blue'	EBee
- 'Blue Springs'	ECtt SAll
- subsp. ***ibericum***	CMac WCra
- subsp. ***jubatum***	EPPr MNrw SGbt SRms
- - 'White Zigana'	CAby ECtt LPot LSRN MAvo NLar NSti SRms WCAu WGwG WWtn
- subsp. ***jubatum* × *renardii***	SWvt
- var. ***platypetalum*** misapplied	see *G.* × *magnificum*
- var. ***platypetalum*** Boiss.	see *G. platypetalum* Fisch. & C.A. Mey.
ibericum* × *libani	EBee
incanum	CAby CCht CMea EBee ELon EWes GCal NBir NHpl SVen WCFE WSpi
- var. ***incanum***	SBch
'Ivan' ♀H7	CBod CElw CRos EBee ECha ECtt EPPr LRHS MTis NChi NLar NRHS WCot WCra WCru WFib WMoo
'J.S. Matu Vu' new	NDov SPoG
'Jean Armour'	CBod ECtt LRHS MAvo NRHS SPoG WCra WFar WGwG
× ***johnsonii***	WFib
- 'Johnson's Blue'	Widely available
'Jolly Bee'	see *G.* ROZANNE
'Joy'	CBod CDor CRos EBee ECtt EPPr GWyn LRHS MAvo MBel MCot MRav NBir NEgg NLar NRHS NSti NWad SBch SRms WCot WCra WFib WGwG WMoo WPnP
§ 'Kanahitobanawa'	EBee
'Karen Wouters'	EPPr
'Kashmir Blue'	CExl CRos EBee ECtt ELan EPfP EWTr GMaP LRHS NLar NRHS SWvt WCAu WCra WFar WKif
'Kashmir Green'	ECtt WMoo
'Kashmir Pink'	CElw CExl CMac CRos ECha ECtt ELan EPfP EWes GBin GKev GMaP LRHS MGos MMuc MNrw NBid NBir NChi NLar NRHS NSti SPer WCra WFar WPnP WSpi
§ 'Khan'	CElw EPPr EWes LRHS MAvo NEoE SDys SMHy WCru
'Kirsty'	EBee EWes NChi
kishtvariense	GCal IMou MAvo MRav NSti WCru
koraiense	CFis WMoo
- B&SWJ 797	WCru
- B&SWJ 878	CExl EBee WCru
koreanum misapplied	see *G. hayatanum*
koreanum ambig.	GCal LRHS NLar NRHS WMoo
- B&SWJ 602	CExl WCru WHoo
krameri	IMou NLar
- B&SWJ 1142	CExl WCru
'Lakwijk Star'	CBod ECtt EMor ILea LRHS NLar SPoG SRms WCra
§ ***lambertii***	NBir
- 'Swansdown'	GCal
'Larch Cottage Velvet'	MAvo
libani	CDor ELon EPPr MCot NBid NSti WBrk WCot WSHC
- RCB RL B-2	WCot
- 'Kew Gardens'	EPPr
'Light Dilys'	EBee EPPr LCro LOPS NDov
'Lilac Ice'	CBod CNor CWGN EBee ECtt EPfP GMaP LCro LOPS LPla LRHS MNrw NDov NLar NRHS NSti SCob WCra
§ × ***lindavicum*** 'Apple Blossom'	CRos EBee EPot LRHS MAsh NSla WFar
linearilobum subsp. ***transversale***	SRot
- - 'Foundling's Friend' new	LCro LOPS MAvo
I - - 'Laciniatum'	WCot
§ 'Little David'	EPPr NLar WCra
'Little Devil'	see *G.* 'Little David'
'Little Gem'	CMea CRos EBee LRHS MAvo NDov NRHS SBch WFar WHoo
lucidum	WOut WPtf WSFF
'Luscious Linda'	WSHC
§ ***macrorrhizum***	CBod CSBt ECrN GBin GJos GKev GKin GWyn IFro LCro LEdu LOPS LSun MCot MRav MSCN MWat NAln NBro SRms WCAu WFar WHil XLum
- 'Album'	CBre CElw CRos CSpe ECha EHrv EPPr EWTr GMaP LRHS MBel MSwo NBid NBro NChi NRHS SAko WBrk WCAu WCot WCra WCru WFar WFib WJam WMoo
- 'Bevan's Variety'	Widely available
- 'Bulgaria'	EPPr WBrk
- 'Cham Ce'	ECtt EPPr

	Name	Suppliers
	- 'Czakor'	CDor CMac CRos EBee ECtt ELan ELon EPPr EPfP LRHS MCot MRav NEgg NGdn NLar NRHS SAko SRms SWvt WBrk WCot WCra WCru WFar WHoo WMoo XLum
I	- 'De Bilt'	EPPr EWes WBrk
	- 'Freundorf'	EBee EPPr EWes GBin GCal GQue SAko
	- 'Galgenveld'	EBee WCra
	- 'Glacier'	EPPr EWes
	- 'Ingwersen's Variety' ♀H7	Widely available
	- 'Lohfelden'	EPPr EWes GCal NAln WBrk WCru
	- 'Mount Olympus'	see *G. macrorrhizum* 'White-Ness'
	- 'Mytikas'	EPPr WBrk
	- 'Olympos'	EBee EPPr NLar
	- 'Pastis' **new**	SPoG
	- 'Pindus'	CBod CRos CWCL EBee EPPr EWes GAbr LRHS NLar NRHS NSti SPtp WCru WFar WPnP
	- 'Prionia'	EPPr GCal SAko WBrk
	- 'Purpurrot'	WBrk
	- 'Ridsko'	EPPr GCal WBrk WCru
	- ***roseum***	see *G. macrorrhizum*
	- 'Rotblut'	EPPr WBrk
	- 'Sandwijck'	EBee EPPr MAvo
	- 'Snow Sprite'	CMea EPPr GJos LLHF MHer NEoE NLar WBrk WHrl WPnP WWFP XLum
	- 'Spessart'	CBar CBod CCBP CRos EBee ECtt ELan ELon EPPr EPfP GBin GMaP GQue LRHS MMuc NLar NRHS SCob SEND SGbt SPer SPhx SPoG SWvt WCra WFar WFib WRHF XLum
	- 'Variegatum' (v)	CFis CRos EBee EHrv ELan GMaP LPot NBir SRms WCot WFar
	- 'Velebit'	EPPr WBrk WCru XLum
§	- 'White-Ness' ♀H7	Widely available
	macrostylum	CDor WCot
	- 'Leonidas'	EPPr
	- 'Talish'	EPPr
	- 'Uln Oag Triag'	EPPr
	maculatum	CFis CRos LRHS MAvo MCot MMrt MNrw MRav NLar NRHS NSti WCru WHal
	- from Kath Dryden	EPPr
	- f. ***albiflorum***	CBod CElw CRos EBee ELan ELon EMor EPPr EWTr GBin LRHS MBel MNrw MTis NChi NLar NRHS NSti SSut WBrk WCra WCru WFar WMoo WPnP
	- 'Beth Chatto'	Widely available
	- 'Elizabeth Ann'[PBR] ♀H7	CSam CWGN EBee ECtt EHrv EPPr GBin LRHS MBel MHol MNrw MSCN MTis NCGa NGdn NLar NSti NWad WCot WCra WFar WFib WHil WMoo WPnP
	- 'Espresso'	Widely available
	- 'Putnam County'	EBee EPPr
	- 'Shameface'	CRos EBee EPPr LRHS NRHS WMoo
	- 'Silver Buttons'	EBee
	- 'Smoky Mountain'	EPPr
	- 'Spring Purple'	CElw EBee EPPr MAvo NLar WFar
	- 'Sweetwater'	EPPr
	- 'Vickie Lynn'	EBee EMor EPPr EWTr NDov WCAu WCra
	maderense ♀H3	CAbb CBcs CBod CCht CPbh CPla CRos CSpe ECre ELan EUJe EWes GKev LRHS NAln NBir NPer NRHS NSti SArc SPhx SVen SWvt WFar
	- 'Guernsey White'	CCCN CPla CRos CSpe WOut
§	× ***magnificum*** ♀H7	Widely available
I	- 'Anemoniflorum' **new**	WCra
	- 'Blue Blood'	CBod CRos EBee ECtt EPPr EPfP GAbr GCal LRHS MBNS MHol NGdn NRHS NSti SRms SWvt WCot WCra WFar WRHF
	- 'Ernst Pagels'	EMor GBin MHol WOut
	- 'Hylander'	EPPr
	- 'Peter Yeo'	EPPr
	- 'Rosemoor'	CBod CElw CRos CWCL ECtt EHrv ELan EPPr EPfP EWTr GCal IKil LCro LOPS LRHS NEoE NRHS SPer SPtp WFar WFib WHoo WPtf WSpi XLum
	- 'Vital'	XLum
	magniflorum	EBee EWes GKev NBid NGdn
	'Maître Hugo'	EBee
§	***malviflorum***	CDor CFis CPla ECha ELan EPPr NSti SBrt WCot WCru WHoo
	- from Spain	EWes
	- pink-flowered	EPPr WSHC
§	'Mary Mottram'	CElw
	'Mavis Simpson' ♀H6	Widely available
	maximowiczii	WPtf
	'Maxwelton'	EBee
	'Melinda'[PBR]	CDor EBee ECtt IKil MMuc NMir NSti WCot WCra WFib WRHF
	'Memories'[PBR]	CBor CSma ECtt LSRN MBNS SRms
	'Menna Bach'	MAvo WFar
	'Meryl Anne'	WPtf
	microphyllum	see *G. potentilloides*
	'Midnight Star'	EBee EPPr EWes
	molle	WSFF
	× ***monacense***	CCBP CRos EBee ELan IMou LEdu LRHS MBNS NRHS WCru WGwG WMoo WPnP WWtn
	- var. ***anglicum***	CDor CRos ECtt EPPr LRHS NLar NRHS WMoo
	- 'Anne Stevens'	EBee
	- 'Claudine Dupont'	CDor CElw EPPr IFro NWad WCot WFib
	- dark-flowered	WMoo
	- 'Emma White'	EBee EPPr NChi NGrd
	- 'Jackie'	EBee EPPr
	- var. ***monacense*** 'Breckland Fever'	EBee EPPr
§	- - 'Muldoon'	NBir WMoo WPnP
	- 'Spotted in the Pass'	EBee
	'Mourning Widow'	see *G. phaeum* 'Lady in Mourning'
	'Mrs Jean Moss'	EBee EPPr EWes MAvo
§	'Mrs Judith Bradshaw'	EMor EPPr
	napuligerum misapplied	see *G. farreri*
	'Natalie'	CRos EBee EPPr LRHS LSRN MAvo NChi NRHS SWvt WJam
	nepalense	SRms
	'Nicola'	CElw CRos EPPr EPfP IFro LRHS MAvo NLar NRHS
	'Nimbus' ♀H7	Widely available
	nodosum	Widely available
	- 'Blueberry Ice'	CDor CElw MAvo
	- 'Clos de Coudray'	CSpe EBee EPPr EWTr ILea MAvo MBel NLar NSti SBch SHar WCAu WCra WFar WHil WPnP
	- 'Dark Heart'	MAvo MCot
	- dark-flowered	see *G. nodosum* 'Swish Purple'
	- 'Darkleaf'	EBee
	- 'Hexham Big Eye'	CDor CElw EBee EMor EWes MAvo WFar
	- 'Hexham Face Paint'	EBee

	– 'Hexham Feathers'	CDor CElw
	– 'Hexham Freckles'	EBee EPPr
	– 'Hexham Lace'	CDor CElw EPPr
	– 'Hexham Whitethroat'	EBee
	– 'Julie's Velvet'	CElw LEdu WHoo WPGP
	– pale-flowered	see *G. nodosum* 'Svelte Lilac'
	– 'Pascal'	EMor EPPr
	– 'Saucy Charlie'	SBch
	– 'Silverwood'	CDor CElw CSpe EBee ECtt EMor EPPr GBin GCal LPla LRHS LSun MBel NRHS NSti SAko SBch SPhx SPoG WCAu WCot WCra WFar WHoo WPnP WWFP
	– 'Simon'	WCra
§	– 'Svelte Lilac'	CBod CRos ECtt EMor EPPr LPla LRHS NBro NHol NRHS SPhx SPoG WBrk WCru WFar WFib WMoo WPnP
§	– 'Swish Purple'	CRos ELon EPPr LRHS MAvo NLar NRHS WCru WMoo
	– 'Tony's Talisman'	EBee EPPr MAvo
	– 'Whiteleaf'	CElw CFis CMac CMea CRos EPPr GBin GCal LRHS NChi NRHS WCru WFar WHal WMoo WPnP
	– 'Wreighburn House White'	EBee EPPr MAvo
	'Nora Bremner'	EBee
	'Nunwood Purple'	EBee EPPr EWes MAvo
	ocellatum	IFro
	'Old Rose'	CRos LRHS NRHS WCru
	oreganum	EBee
§	***orientalitibeticum***	CExl CRos CSpe ECtt EPPr GAbr GKev IFro LRHS MCot MHer MMuc NBid NLar NRHS NRya SEND SMad WCot WMoo
	'Orion' ♀[H7]	Widely available
	'Orkney Blue'	CElw EPPr NChi WCru
	ORKNEY CHERRY ('Bremerry'[PBR])	CMac EBee ECtt EMor GBin LCro LLHF LOPS LRHS MBel SCob SHeu SRkn SRms WCra
	'Orkney Dawn'	MAvo WPnP
	'Orkney Flame'	EBee EPPr
	'Orkney Pink'	EBou ECtt EPPr EPfP LRHS WCra
	'Out of the Blue'	WOut
	× ***oxonianum***	NAln WMoo
	– 'A.T. Johnson' ♀[H7]	Widely available
	– 'Ankum's White'	EBee EPPr EWes
	– 'Beholder's Eye' ♀[H7]	CBod EPPr GWyn MMuc NLar WPnP
	– 'Breckland Sunset'	EBee EPPr NLar
	– 'Bregover Pearl'	CBre WMoo
	– 'Bressingham's Delight'	CRos LRHS NRHS
I	– 'Cally Seedling'	EWes GCal
	– 'Cam Beauty'	WHoo
	– 'Chocolate Strawberry'	EBee EMor EPPr EWes
§	– 'Claridge Druce'	CBod CKel CMac CRos CTri ECha ELan EPPr EPfP EShb GKin GMaP LRHS MRav MSwo NAln NBir NGdn NGrd NLar NRHS SCob SPer SRms WAvo WCra WFar WMoo WWtn XLum
	– 'Coronet'	GCal
	– 'Cream Chocolate'	EBee EMor EPPr
	– 'David Rowlinson'	CDor EBee EPPr
	– 'Dawn Time'	CDor
	– 'Ella'	CWGN
	– 'Elworthy Misty'	CElw CFis EPPr
	– 'Frank Lawley'	NBid NChi WMoo
§	– 'Fran's Star' (d)	WCru
	– 'Frilly Gilly'	EBee
	– 'Hexham Pink'	EBee EPPr EWes
	– 'Hexham White' **new**	EBee EPPr
	– 'Hollywood'	ELan EPPr IFro NLar NPer SAko SRms WCra WMoo
	– 'Iced Green Tea'	EBee
	– 'Irene Hatwell' **new**	EPPr
	– 'Julie Brennan'	CRos EBee LRHS NRHS
	– 'Kate Moss'	EPPr EWes NSti
	– 'Katherine Adele'	CMea CSpe ECha ECtt EMor EPPr EPfP EShb EWes GCal LRHS MAsh MAvo MMuc NLar SEND SRms WCra WFar WFib WHil
§	– 'Kingston'	EPPr
	– 'Königshof'	EPPr EWes
	– 'Kurt's Variegated'	see *G.* × *oxonianum* 'Spring Fling'
	– 'Lace Time'	CAby CBod CBre CCBP CRos ECtt EPPr EPfP GKin LRHS LSRN NEgg NRHS SPer SPoG SRms WCAu WCra WJam WMoo WTyc
	– 'Lady Moore'	EBee EMor EPfP WMoo
	– 'Lambrook Gillian'	CFis EPPr WBrk
	– 'Lasting Impression'	EPPr
	– 'Laura Skelton'	CElw EBee
	– 'Little John'	EPPr EWes
	– 'Maid Marion'	EWes
	– 'Maurice Moka'	EBee ECtt NLar
	– 'Miriam Rundle'	WCru WMoo
	– 'Moorland Jenny'	WMoo
	– 'Moorland Star'	WMoo
	– 'Mrs Molly Kisby'	EBee
	– 'Music from Big Pink'	EBee EPPr EWes
	– 'Pat Smallacombe'	EPPr WMoo
	– 'Patricia Josephine'	NAln WCAu
	– 'Phantom'	EBee EPPr
	– 'Phoebe Noble'	CBre CRos EBee EPPr LRHS MNrw NLar NRHS WCra WFib WMoo
	– 'Phoebe's Blush'	EPPr
§	– 'Prestbury Blush'	CElw
	– 'Prestbury White'	see *G.* × *oxonianum* 'Prestbury Blush'
	– 'Raspberry Ice'	EBee EWes
	– 'Rebecca Moss'	CBod CRos ECha ECtt ELan EPPr GAbr LRHS LSRN NChi NRHS NSti SAko WCru WFib WOut
	– 'Red Sceptre'	EBee
	– 'Rose Clair'	CRos ELan LRHS NAln NBir NLar NRHS WCra WCru WMoo
	– 'Rosenlicht'	CBod EPPr GKin LRHS MAsh MRav NRHS WCra WCru WMoo WPtf XLum
	– 'Rothbury Sarah'	EBee EPPr
	– 'Sandy'	EBee EPPr
	– 'Something Special'	EBee EPPr
§	– 'Spring Fling' (v)	CDor ECtt EWes NWad WFar
	– 'Stillingfleet Keira'	EBee EPPr NSti
	– 'Summer Surprise'	EBee EPPr EWes WCru
	– 'Susan'	EPPr EWes
	– 'Susie White'	EPPr WCru
	– 'Tess'	ECtt MHol WHoo
§	– f. ***thurstonianum***	CAby CBod CBre CMac EBee ECtt EPPr EPfP GAbr GBin IFro LRHS MNrw MRav NBid NBir NBro NLar NRHS SCob SPoG SRms WBrk WCot WCru WFar WMoo WSpi XLum
	– – 'Armitageae'	EBee
	– – 'Breckland Brownie'	EBee EPPr EWes MAvo
	– – 'Crûg Star'	WCru
	– – 'David McClintock'	EBee EPPr WMoo
	– – 'Robin's Ginger Nut'	EBee EWes

	- - 'Sherwood'	CSde EPPr GBee GCal LPot NBro NSti WCra WFar WMoo
	- - 'Southcombe Double' (d)	CBod ECtt ELan EPPr MHol SRms WCra WFar WMoo
§	- - 'Southcombe Star'	EBee EPPr GAbr NBro NGdn WCru WMoo
	- - 'Sue Cox' (d)	EPPr NLar
	- - 'White Stripes'	EBee EMor EPPr
	- 'Trevor's White'	CDor CRos EBee EPPr LRHS NRHS WCru
	- 'Tyne Salmon'	EBee
	- 'Wageningen' ♀H7	CBre CRos EBee EPPr GCal LRHS NGdn NRHS SEND WCot WCru WGwG WHoo WMoo
	- 'Walter's Gift'	CBod CRos ECtt EMor EPPr EPfP EShb GBin LRHS MAvo MRav NBir NBro NChi NLar NPer NRHS SAko WCra WCru WFar WHoo WMoo WPnP WWtn
§	- 'Wargrave Pink'	Widely available
	- 'Waystrode'	EBee
	- 'Westacre White'	ECha EPPr EWes
	- 'Whiter Shade of Pale'	EBee EPPr
	- 'Winscombe'	EPfP GCal WMoo
	× ***oxonianum***	EMor
	× ***sessiliflorum*** subsp. ***novae-zelandiae*** 'Nigricans'	
§	***palmatum*** ♀H4	Widely available
	palustre	EBee EMor EPPr GLog MMuc MNrw NLar WCot WCra WMoo
	- 'Money Peniche'	XEll
	'Pastel Clouds'	GWyn WFar
	PATRICIA ('Brempat') ♀H7	Widely available
	peloponnesiacum	CElw EPPr EWes MNrw NLar NWad WMoo
	'Perfect Storm'	ECtt LLHF
	phaeum	Widely available
	- 'Acorn Bank'	EBee
	- 'Advendo'	EBee EPPr WCra
	- 'Album'	Widely available
	- 'Alec's Pink'	EBee EPPr SHar WCAu WCra WPnP
	- 'All Saints'	EBee LEdu
	- 'Angelina'	EBee EMor EPPr
	- 'Ann Logan'	EBee
	- 'Aureum'	see *G. phaeum* 'Golden Spring'
	- 'Basket of Lavender'	EBee
	- 'Blauwvoet'	EPPr NChi
	- 'Blue Shadow'	CElw EBee EPPr LEdu
	- 'Brown Sugar'	EBee
	- 'Calligrapher'	EPPr NChi WMoo
	- 'Chocolate Biscuit'	EBee EPPr
	- 'Chocolate Chip'	EPPr
	- 'Conny Broe' (v)	CDor EShb WSHC
	- 'Dark Angel'	EBee
	- 'Dark Dream'	EBee NGrd
	- 'David Bromley'	WCru
	- 'David Martin'	EBee EMor EPPr
	- 'Enid'	EPPr
	- 'Garage Door'	EBee
	- 'George Stone'	EPPr NGrd
	- 'Golden Samobor'	CElw EPPr
§	- 'Golden Spring'	EBee EMor EPPr NEoE WFar
	- 'Green Ghost'	EBee EPPr
	- 'Hector's Lavender'	EBee WOut
	- var. ***hungaricum***	EBee EPPr
	- 'James Haunch'	EPPr
	- 'Jenson's Purple' **new**	EBee
	- 'Judith's Blue'	EBee
	- 'Klepper'	EBee EPPr GBin NAln
§	- 'Lady in Mourning'	CExl EBee EPPr GCal IKil NChi SRms WCra WCru WMoo
	- 'Lavender Pinwheel'	CBod CDor EBee SPer WCot WCra
*	- 'Lilacina'	ECha
	- 'Lily Lovell'	Widely available
	- 'Lisa' (v)	CDor CElw CFis ECha EPPr MAvo MNrw SMHy WCot WFar
	- 'Little Boy'	EPPr
	- var. ***lividum***	CBre GMaP MRav SRms WFar XLum
	- - 'Joan Baker'	CDor CFis CSam EBee MNrw NChi NGdn NSti SDys WCru WFib WMoo WOut
	- - 'Majus'	CRos EBee ECtt ELan EMor EPPr EPfP LRHS NRHS WFar WMoo
	- 'Lustige Witwe' (v)	WCot
	- 'Marchant's Ghost'	IFro SMHy
	- 'Margaret Wilson' (v)	CWGN ECtt EShb EWes GAbr GCal LEdu MAvo NBir NEgg NGdn NLar NSti WCot WFar WHil WPnP WSHC
	- 'Mierhausen'	CElw EBee EPPr
	- 'Misty Samobor'	ECha
	- 'Mojito' (v)	WCot
	- 'Moorland Dylan'	WMoo WOut
	- 'Mottisfont Rose'	CDor CElw SBch
	- 'Mourning Widow'	see *G. phaeum* 'Lady in Mourning'
	- 'Mrs Charles Perrin'	CFis CRos
	- 'Night Time'	EBee EPPr
	- 'Nightshade'	EBee EPPr
	- 'Our Pat' ♀H7	EBee EPPr NChi NGrd WCot
	- var. ***phaeum***	CKel
	- - 'Langthorns Blue'	CRos CWCL EBee ELan EPPr EPfP LEdu LRHS MNrw NRHS SWvt WPGP
	- - 'Samobor'	Widely available
	- 'Phantom of the Opera' (v)	CElw EBee EMor EPPr
	- 'Pink Palava'	LEdu
I	- 'Ploeger de Bilt'	EBee
	- 'Purple Moon'	EBee EPPr
	- 'Rachel's Rhapsody'	EBee EPPr
	- 'Raven'	CBod CDor EBee ECtt EMor EPPr IKil LRHS NChi NGrd NLar SCob SPer WCAu WCra WFar
	- 'Ray of Light'	EPPr
	- 'Rise Top Lilac'	EBee WPGP
	- 'Robin's Angel Eyes'	EBee
	- 'Rose Air'	EPPr NAln WMoo
	- 'Rose Madder'	CCBP CDor CElw CMea GCal LEdu MNrw NChi NLar SPhx WCru WGwG WMoo
	- 'Rothbury Ruby'	EBee EPPr
	- 'Saturn'	EPPr
	- 'Séricourt'	MAvo WCot WFib
	- 'Shadowlight'	CBod EBee ECtt EPPr NLar
	- 'Slatina'	EPPr
	- 'Springtime' PBR	CDor EBee IKil MBNS NGdn NLar WCra WFib
	- 'Stillingfleet Ghost'	EBee EPPr LEdu MNrw NChi NSti NHol WCot WHil
	- 'Taff's Jester' (v)	NHol WCot WHil
	- 'Trevor's Recall'	EBee
	- 'Tyne Mist'	EBee EPPr
§	- 'Variegatum' (v)	CBre CMac EBee EHoe ELan EPPr GMaP IFro NBir NBro WHer WMoo
	- 'Vintage Dave'	WOut
	- 'Walküre'	EPPr EWes NGrd NLar WCra
	'Philippe Vapelle'	Widely available
	'Pink Delight'	CElw MAvo SBch
	'Pink Penny'	CBod CDor CWCL ECtt EMor EPPr EPfP GBin IKil MNrw NLar NSti

SPoG SRms WCAu WCra WFar WMoo
§ ***platyanthum*** EPPr MNrw WCru
- 'Ankum' **new** EBee
- var. ***reinii*** GCal WCru
- 'Russian Giant' EPPr
platypetalum misapplied see *G.* × *magnificum*
platypetalum Franch. see *G. sinense*
§ ***platypetalum*** Fisch. & C.A. Mey. CRos EBee EPPr LRHS NBir NRHS WCru XLum
- 'Georgia Blue' WCru
- 'Dark Side of the Moon' EBee EPPr
- 'Genyell' EBee EPPr NChi
- 'Turco' CBod EBee EPPr NLar WCAu WCra
§ ***pogonanthum*** GLog NBir
polyanthes EWes NChi
§ ***potentilloides*** GCal NBir WMoo
pratense CBre CCBP CHab CMac CWld EBee ELan EPPr GJos GMaP MHer MNHC NAln NMir SCob SPer SPlb SPoG SRms WCot WCra WFar WMoo WSFF XLum
- 'Akaton' NLar
- 'Algera Double' CBod ECtt EMor EUJe LLHF MHol WCAu WCot
- 'Bittersweet' EPPr
- 'Black 'n' White' **new** SHeu
- 'Blue Lagoon' EPPr
* - 'Blue Skies' WFar
- 'Blue Sky Thinking' EBee
- 'Carrie's White' EBee
- 'Catforth Cadenza' (v) MAvo
- 'Cloud Nine' (d) **new** WPnP WTyc
- 'Cluden Sapphire' EBee EPPr NEoE NHol WCAu WCra WCru
- 'Delft Blue' CBod WWtn
- 'Delft Blue Butterfly' **new** WCra
§ - 'Double Jewel' (d) CWGN EBee EPfP MAsh MAvo MBNS MHol NBir NLar WFar
- 'Else Lacey' (d) CElw EBee MHol WCot
- 'Flore Pleno' see *G. pratense* 'Plenum Violaceum'
- 'Hexham Spook' EBee
I - 'Himalayanum' NLar
- 'Hocus Pocus' CRos CWGN ECtt ELan LRHS MAvo MBNS MHol MNrw NBro NLar NRHS NSti SCob WCra WFar
- 'Hoo House' WHoo
- 'Ilja' EBee EPPr MNrw
- 'Janet's Special' WHoo
- 'Marshmallow' CBod EBee ECtt EMor MAvo MHol NCGa NSti SPoG WCAu WCot
- 'Milou' WCra
- 'Mrs Kendall Clark' ♀H7 Widely available
- 'Okey Dokey' EBee
- 'Pink Splash' WMoo
- 'Plenum Caeruleum' (d) ECtt EPPr MRav NBid NEgg NLar WSHC
§ - 'Plenum Violaceum' (d) ♀H7 Widely available
- 'Pope's Purple' see *G. pratense* (Victor Reiter Group) BLACK BEAUTY
- var. ***pratense*** f. ***albiflorum*** CRos CSam EPPr EWTr GMaP IFro LRHS MNrw NBid NRHS SCob SGbt SPer WFar WMoo WSpi
- - - 'Galactic' ECtt LRHS LSun MHol NBir NEgg NLar SEND SPoG WCot WCru WFib WMoo WPnP
- - - 'Laura'PBR (d) CExl EBee EPPr EPfP EWes LSRN MHol NGdn NLar NSti SCob WCra WFar WPnP
- - - 'Plenum Album' (d) CBod CWCL EBee ECtt ELan EMor EPPr EWes GBin GWyn LLHF LRHS MBel MNrw MRav NEgg NGdn NLar SGbt SRms SWvt WCot WFar WGwG WSpi
- - - 'Silver Queen' CAby CBod CRos EBee ECtt LRHS NBir NRHS SPoG WAvo WGwG WMoo WPnP
- 'Purple Ghost' CAbb ECtt EMor LRHS NEoE NRHS SPoG WCra WFar
- 'Rectum Album' see *G. clarkei* 'Kashmir White'
- 'Robin's Grey Beard' EBee EPPr
§ - 'Rose Queen' NBir SGbt WCru
- 'Roseum' see *G. pratense* 'Rose Queen'
- 'Southease Celestial' SMHy WGoo
- 'Splish-splash' see *G. pratense* 'Striatum'
- 'Stanton Mill' NBid
- var. ***stewartianum*** MRav
- - 'Elizabeth Yeo' CRos ECtt EPPr LRHS NRHS WCru
- - 'Raina' EPPr
§ - 'Striatum' Widely available
- variegated, white-flowered (v) WCot
§ - (Victor Reiter Group) BLACK BEAUTY ('Nodbeauty'PBR) CAby CExl CRos CWCL CWGN EBee ECtt EMor EPfP EUJe EWes LBuc LRHS MGos MHol MPnt NHpl NLar NRHS SPoG SRkn SRot WFar WHoo WSpi
- - 'Kaya' CBod MHol WCra
- - 'Midnight Blues' CWGN SCob
- - 'Midnight Clouds' CWGN EBee ECtt EPfP LBuc NSti SCob WFar
- - MIDNIGHT GHOST ('Midnightlyona') CBod MAsh MMrt NCGa
- - 'Midnight Reiter' CExl CWGN ELan EPfP GCal GWyn LRHS MBel MHol NBro NChi NGdn NGrd NHpl NLar NQui SCob SDys SWvt WCra WFar WHlf WIce
- - 'New Dimension' WFib
- - 'Purple Heron' LSRN NRHS
- - 'Purple-haze' GPSL GWyn WFar WMoo WSHC
§ - - 'Victor Reiter' CSpe EPPr LEdu NBir NChi NGdn NHpl SRot WCot WCra
- 'Wisley Blue' EPPr WHal
- 'Yorkshire Queen' NGdn NSti WCru
'Prelude' CBre CDor CElw EBee ELon EPPr NBir NEoE NLar SHar WCAu WFib
'Prima Donna' WCAu
procurrens CBre CTri GAbr GCal WBrk WCru WMoo WPtf
§ ***psilostemon*** ♀H7 Widely available
- 'Bressingham Flair' CDor CRos CTri ECtt LRHS MRav NBid NChi NLar NRHS SRms WCra WCru WFar WMoo
- 'Catherine Deneuve'PBR CBod CWGN EBee EPfP EWes ILea NSti SCob WCAu WCra
- 'Coton Goliath' EBee EPPr EWes MAvo
- 'Jason Bloom' CRos EPPr LRHS NRHS
- 'Madelon' NLar
- 'Moorland Jack' WMoo
- 'Mount Venus' **new** IMou
- 'Rosefinch' **new** EBee
pulchrum CDor EWes GWyn
punctatum hort. see *G.* × *monacense* var. *monacense* 'Muldoon'
- 'Variegatum' see *G. phaeum* 'Variegatum'
'Purple Rain' EBee EPPr
pylzowianum NBid NRya WMoo

pyrenaicum	GAbr NSti
- f. ***albiflorum***	GAbr IFro MNrw NBir SPhx WBrk WCot WFar
- 'Bill Wallis'	Widely available
- 'Isparta'	EPPr IFro LRHS MNrw SHar SPhx WBrk WGoo
- 'Summer Sky'	SWvt
- 'Summer Snow'	GPSL GWyn
'Rainbow'PBR	MBNS WCra
Rambling Robin Group	CSpe ECre EWes
* - 'Silver Shadow'	SPhx
rectum	EPPr NBre NLar WCru
- 'Album'	see *G. clarkei* 'Kashmir White'
'Red Admiral'	CBod CMea CSam ECtt EHoe EMor EPPr EPfP GCal LRHS MAvo MHol MNrw NCGa NDov NLar NQui NRHS NSti SPoG SWvt WCot WCra WFar WGwG WHoo WPnP WPtf WWtn
'Red Propellers'	CElw
reflexum	CRos LRHS NRHS WCru
- 'Katara Pass'	NChi
refractoides	WCot
refractum	CExl
regelii	GWyn WCru WMoo
renardii ♀H6	Widely available
- 'Beldo'	MAvo
- blue-flowered	see *G. renardii* 'Whiteknights'
- 'Rothbury Hills'	EPPr
- 'Tcschelda'	ECha ECtt EPPr NBir NLar SRms WCra WFar WMoo
§ - 'Whiteknights'	NBir
- 'Zetterlund'	CBod CRos EBee ELan EPPr EPfP EWTr LRHS NEgg NQui NRHS WFar WMoo
§ ***reuteri***	CTsd SChr WCru
'Richard Nutt'	EBee
richardsonii	CBod CFis EBee EPPr GCal LEdu LRHS MCot MNrw NBir NRHS NWad SPoG WCru WGwG
- pink-flowered	MAvo
- white-flowered	NChi
× ***riversleaianum*** 'Russell Prichard' ♀H4	Widely available
§ ***rivulare***	GLog NLar
robertianum	ENfk EPPr SRms WSFF
§ - 'Album'	EPPr SHar SPhx SRms WHer
- f. ***bernettii***	see *G. robertianum* 'Album'
- 'Celtic White'	CBre EPPr GCal IFro MMuc SEND
robustum	NBir NSti SPlb WGoo WKif
'Rosetta'PBR	CBod MSCN WCra
'Rosie Crûg'	SWvt
rosthornii	WCru
'Rothbury Red'	EBee NChi WCra
§ ROZANNE ('Gerwat'PBR) ♀H7	Widely available
rubescens	see *G. yeoi*
rubifolium	NWad WCru
SABANI BLUE ('Bremigo'PBR)	CMac CSpe CWGN EBee ECtt EPPr EWes LCro LOPS MHol NLar NSti SMHy SPer WCot WCra WSHC
'Salome'	CBcs CBod CDor EBee ECtt EHrv ELan GAbr GLog GWyn ILea MBel MCot NBir NLar NSti SCob SRms SRot SWvt WCot WCra WGwG WKif WMoo
'Sandrine'PBR	CBcs CRos CSam CSpe CWCL CWGN EBee IMou LLHF LRHS MHol MNrw NSti SCob SPoG SRms WCot WCra WPnP
sanguineum	Widely available
- ALAN BLOOM ('Bloger'PBR)	CRos EBee EPPr LRHS NRHS WCra WFib
- 'Album' ♀H5	Widely available
- 'Alpenglow'	EBee EPPr WBrk
- 'Ankum's Pride' ♀H7	CDor CRos CWld EAJP EPPr EPfP LRHS MTis NChi NGdn NLar NRHS NSti SBch WBrk WCra WCru WFib WMoo WPnP
- 'Apfelblüte'	ELon EMor EPPr GBin MTis NLar WCAu WCra
- 'Aviemore' ♀H7	CElw CFis EPPr GBin GCal GQue
- 'Barnsley'	EPPr NBro NEoE
- 'Belle of Herterton'	CElw EPPr MAvo NBid NChi NEoE WBrk WCru
- 'Bloody Graham'	CRos EPPr LRHS MAvo NRHS SPhx WBrk WMoo
- 'Canon Miles'	CElw ECtt EPPr NGrd NLar SRms
- 'Catforth Carnival'	EPPr
- 'Cedric Morris'	CElw ECha ELon EPPr MAvo NBid WBrk WCra WCru WPnP
- 'Compactum'	EPPr WCra WMoo XLum
- dark purple	SSut
- dwarf	WAbe
- 'Elsbeth'	CElw CRos EBee ECha ECtt ELan ELon EPPr EPfP EWes GBin GCal LRHS NGdn NLar NRHS NSti SPoG WBrk WCru WFar WFib WHal WMoo WPnP XLum
- 'Feu d'Automne'	EBee ELon EPPr NLar WBrk WCra
- 'Fran's Star'	see *G.* × *oxonianum* 'Fran's Star'
- 'Glenluce'	CDor CElw ECtt ELon EMor EPPr EPfP EShb GCal LRHS MRav MTis NChi NDov NGrd NLar NRHS NWad SPoG SRms WBrk WCra WFar WHal WPnP
- 'Hampshire Purple'	see *G. sanguineum* 'New Hampshire Purple'
- 'Hannelore'	EBee
- 'Holden'	CElw ELon EPPr WBrk
- 'Inverness'	EBee EPPr WCra XLum
- 'Joanna'	CFis ELon EPPr MAvo WBrk
- 'John Elsley'	EBee ECtt EHoe EPPr LRHS NBro NGdn NRHS NSti WCra WPnP
- 'John Innes'	EPPr
- 'Jubilee Pink'	GCal WCru
- 'Kristin Jacob'	EPPr
- var. ***lancastrense***	see *G. sanguineum* var. *striatum*
- 'Leeds Variety'	see *G. sanguineum* 'Rod Leeds'
§ - 'Little Bead' ♀H5	EPPr GCrg NHpl NWad SBch WBrk XLum
- 'Max Frei'	Widely available
- 'Nanum'	see *G. sanguineum* 'Little Bead'
§ - 'New Hampshire Purple'	EBee ECtt ELon EPPr EWTr LRHS MAvo NBro NDov NGrd NLar SRms WBrk WCra WFib
- 'Nyewood'	EBee ECtt EPPr LRHS NRHS SEND WBrk WCra WCru WFib
- 'Pink Pouffe'	CRos CWGN EBee ECtt ELon LRHS NCGa NRHS SCob SHeu WCra
- 'Pink Summer'	EBee EWTr WCra
I - 'Plenum' (d)	EPPr
- 'Prado'	XLum
- var. ***prostratum*** (Cav.) Pers.	see *G. sanguineum* var. *striatum*
- 'Purple Flame'	see *G. sanguineum* 'New Hampshire Purple'
- 'Red Robin' **new**	EBee
§ - 'Rod Leeds'	EBee
§ - 'Shepherd's Delight'	ECtt EPPr

	- 'Shepherd's Warning' misapplied	see *G. sanguineum* 'Shepherd's Delight'
	- 'Shepherd's Warning' ♀H7	CMea CTri ECtt GCal MMuc MRav NBir NLar SEND WCru WFib WHoo WIce
	- 'Shooting Star'	EPPr
	- 'South Nutfield'	CElw NChi
§	- var. ***striatum*** ♀H5	Widely available
	- - deep pink-flowered	CSBt MSwo SWvt
	- - 'Mottisfont'	SBch
	- - 'Reginald Farrer'	WCru
	- - 'Splendens' ♀H7	CRos EPPr GCal LRHS NBid NChi NRHS SAko WCru
	- 'Vision Light Pink'	CBod EPPr WFar
	- 'Vision Violet'	CBod CSpe EBee EBou EMor MAvo NGrd SRms SWvt WBrk WCra WFar WPnP
	- 'Westacre Poppet'	EWes
	'Sanne'	EPPr EWes LRHS MHol SCob STPC WArt WCot WCra WFar WFib WPGP
	saxatile	EPPr
	- 'Snowstar' **new**	EBee
	'Scapa Flow'	EPPr GCal WSHC
	schlechteri	EWes MMuc SEND WBrk
	'Sea Pink'	EBou
	'Sea Spray'	CTri
	sessiliflorum	GBin
	- subsp. ***novae-zelandiae*** 'Mandy'	GBin
I	- - 'Nigricans'	ECha GAbr LPot SCob WFar
§	- - 'Porters Pass'	EWes NHpl SPlb WFar
	- - red-leaved	see *G. sessiliflorum* subsp. *novae-zelandiae* 'Porters Pass'
	shikokianum	GLog GWyn NLar WPnP
	- var. ***kaimontanum***	WCru
	- var. ***quelpaertense***	CFis EBee MAvo
	- - 'Crûg's Cloak'	WCru
	'Shocking Blue'	NLar NSti WFib
	'Shouting Star'	see *G.* 'Kanahitobanawa'
	'Simonside'	EBee EPPr
§	***sinense***	CExl CRos GCal LRHS MCot NRHS XLum
	'Sirak' ♀H7	Widely available
	soboliferum	CBod CFis NBir NDov NLar SPer WCru WMoo WSHC
	- Cally strain	EBee EPPr GCal LPla WHoo
	- var. ***kiusianum***	CElw
	- 'Rothbury Star'	EBee
	- 'Starman'	EBee ECtt MAsh NLar SCob WCra WMoo WSHC
	'Solitaire'	EBee MAvo WCot
	'Southcombe Star'	see *G.* × *oxonianum* f. *thurstonianum* 'Southcombe Star'
	'Spinners'	CElw CMac CRos EBee ECtt EPPr GCal GMaP LRHS LSRN MAvo MRav NBid NBir NGdn NLar NRHS NSti SPer WCra WCru WFar WFib WMoo WPnP
	stapfianum var. ***roseum***	see *G. orientalitibeticum*
	'Stephanie'	CCBP CElw EPPr EWes LPla LRHS LSRN MAvo MBNS MNrw MRav NChi NGdn NLar NRHS NSti WBor WCAu WPnP WSHC
	'Storm Chaser'	EBee EMor IPot LRHS SCob
	'Strawberry Frost'	LLHF
	subcaulescens ♀H4	CAby CMea CRos CWCL EBee ELan EPPr EPfP LRHS LSRN MCot MRav NBid NEgg NRHS NRya SCob SPer SPhx SRms SWvt WAbe WCFE WFar WIce
	- 'Giuseppii' ♀H5	CExl CRos ECtt ELon EPPr EPfP EPot GAbr GCrg LRHS MRav NBir NRHS SRot SWvt WCra WSpi
	- 'Splendens' ♀H5	CRos CSpe CTri ECtt GCrg LRHS MHer NEgg NRHS NSla SRms WCra WFar
	'Sue Crûg'	CRos EBee ECtt ELan LPla LRHS NChi NEgg NRHS WCru WMoo
	'Sue's Sister'	WCru
	'Summer Cloud'	EPPr WOut
	SUMMER SKIES ('Gernic'PBR) (d)	Widely available
	suzukii B&SWJ 016	CExl
	- NMWJ 14518 **new**	WCru
	'Sweet Heidy'PBR	CBod CDor EBee ECtt EPfP EWTr LLHF LPla MAsh MHol MNrw MSwo NLar NSti SCob WBor WCra WFar WPnP
	sylvaticum	NBid NGdn NMir WArt WFar WMoo WShi
	- f. ***albiflorum***	CBre NSti WCru
	- - 'Cyril's Superb White'	EBee EPPr
	- 'Album' ♀H7	Widely available
	- 'Amanda'	EBee EPPr
	- 'Amy Doncaster'	CAby CDor CElw CExl CRos EBee ECtt ELan EPPr LRHS MRav NBir NEgg NLar NRHS NSti SPer WBor WCot WCra WCru WFar WFib WHoo WMoo WPnP
	- 'Angulatum'	CElw EPPr WMoo
	- 'Birch Lilac'	CElw EBee EPPr GCal LRHS NLar WCra WFib WMoo
	- 'Bridget Lion' **new**	WCra
	- 'Coquetdale Lilac'	CDor EBee EPPr
	- 'Greek Fire'	EBee EPPr MAvo
	- 'Ice Blue'	EPPr NChi
	- 'Immaculée'	EPPr MRav
	- 'Jonah P'	EBee
	- 'Kanzlersgrund'	CElw EPPr
	- 'Lilac Time'	EPPr
	- 'Master Charles Wilson' **new**	EBee
	- 'Master Niall Lawson'	EBee WFar
	- 'Mayflower' ♀H7	Widely available
	- 'Miss Connie Wilson'	EBee EPPr
	- f. ***roseum***	NLar
	- - 'Baker's Pink'	EPPr MNrw MRav NBir WCAu WCru WFar WMoo
	- 'Silva'	MRav WCru
	- subsp. ***sylvaticum*** var. ***wanneri***	WCru
§	'Tanya Rendall'PBR	ECtt EHrv ELan IPot MHer NLar SPer SRms WCot WCra WFar WFib WPnP
	'Terre Franche'	EPPr MAvo NLar SPhx WCra
§	***thunbergii***	EWes WFar WMoo XLum
	- 'Jester's Jacket' (v)	CPla MNrw WFar WMoo WOut
	- pink-flowered	EPPr
	- white-flowered	EPPr
	thurstonianum	see *G.* × *oxonianum* f. *thurstonianum*
	'Tinpenny Mauve'	MAvo
	'Tiny Monster'	Widely available
	transbaicalicum	EPPr XLum
	traversii var. ***elegans***	CRos LRHS NRHS
	tuberosum	CDor CElw ECha GEdr GKev IMou MRav NBir NGdn NQui SPhx WFar
	- subsp. ***linearifolium***	EPPr
	- 'Richard Hobbs'	EPPr
	- 'Rosie's Mauve'	EPPr MAvo

'Ushguli Grijs'	see *G. ibericum* Cav. 'Ushguli Grijs'
'Vectis'	CElw
'Verguld Saffier'	see *G.* BLUE SUNRISE
versicolor	CCBP CMea EBee EPPr EPfP GAbr GCal GPSL MHer NLar SRms WCAu WCra WFar WMoo WPnP XEll
- 'Kingston'	see *G.* × *oxonianum* 'Kingston'
§ - 'Snow White'	EPPr SEND WCru WFib WMoo
- 'White Lady'	see *G. versicolor* 'Snow White'
'Victor Reiter'	see *G. pratense* (Victor Reiter Group) 'Victor Reiter'
violareum	see *Pelargonium* 'Splendide'
viscosissimum	WFib
wallichianum	CFis CPou EBee IFro NBir NChi NSti WMoo
§ - 'Buxton's Variety'	Widely available
- 'Chris'	EWes
- 'Crystal Lake'^PBR	CWGN EBee ECtt EPfP IMou MBNS MHol MNrw NBir NDov NGdn NLar NSti SCob WCAu WCra WFar WPnP
- HAVANA BLUES ('Noorthava'^PBR)	CBod CDor EBee ECha ECtt EPPr EPfP GBin IPot LCro LOPS LRHS MHol MMrt NLar NRHS NSti SCob WCot WCra WFar WHoo
- pale-blue-flowered	CElw
- 'Pink Buxton'	EWes NLar
- pink-flowered	GCal WCru
- 'Rise and Shine'^PBR	CBod CWGN EBee ECtt ELan EPPr EWTr GAbr LCro LOPS MHol MSCN NSti SHar WCAu WCot WCra
- 'Rosetta'	IMou NCGa
- 'Syabru'	MNrw WArt WMoo
- 'Sylvia's Surprise'^PBR	CRos EBee ECtt IMou LRHS LSRN NLar NRHS SCob WCAu WCra
'Wednesday's Child'	WFar
'White Doves'	NDov
wilfordii misapplied	see *G. thunbergii*
Wisley hybrid	see *G.* 'Khan'
wlassovianum	Widely available
- 'Blue Star'	MRav NEoE WCra WFar
§ ***yeoi***	CSpe NBir NSti WCru WOut
yesoense	IFro NSti
- var. ***nipponicum***	WCru
yoshinoi misapplied	see *G. thunbergii*
yunnanense misapplied	see *G. pogonanthum*

Gerbera (*Asteraceae*)

(Garvinea Series) 'Fleurie'^PBR	MBNS
- GARVINEA CATHERINE ('Garcatherine')	MBNS
- GARVINEA LISA ('Garlisa'^PBR)	MHol
- GARVINEA ORANGINA ('Orangina'^PBR)	MBNS
- GARVINEA PAM	see *G.* 'Pam'
- GARVINEA RACHEL ('Garrachel'^PBR)	MHol MNrw
- GARVINEA LETIZIA ('Gartizia') **new**	SPad
- GARVINEA SYLVANA ('Garsylvana'^PBR)	MHol
(Garvinea Sweet Series) GARVINEA SWEET CAROLINE ('Garsweetcaro') **new**	WHlf
- GARVINEA SWEET DREAMS ('Gardreams'^PBR)	SPad
- GARVINEA SWEET GLOW ('Garglow'^PBR)	LRHS MBNS NRHS SPad WHlf
- GARVINEA SWEET MEMORIES ('Garsweetmemo') **new**	WHlf
gossypina	CPla
§ 'Pam'^PBR	MBNS

Gesneria (*Gesneriaceae*)

cardinalis	see *Sinningia cardinalis*

Geum ✿ (*Rosaceae*)

'Abendsonne'	CElw MAvo MNrw MRav NEoE
'Alabama Slammer' (Cocktails Series)	CRos CWCL CWld EBee ECtt ELan EMor EWTr GBin IKil ILea LRHS MAvo MPnt MSCN MTis NDov NEgg NEoE NLar NRHS SBri SCob SHeu SPad SRms WCAu WFar
alpinum	see *G. montanum*
'Apricot Beauty'	CWCL
'Apricot Crush'	MNrw
'Apricot Delight'	LLHF NEoE NWad
'Bachelfe'	SBri
'Baked Beans'	NEoE
'Banana Daiquiri' (Cocktails Series)	CRos CWCL EBee ECtt ELan EMor EPfP IKil LRHS MTis NRHS SCob SHeu WFar
'Beech House Apricot'	CDor CRos CWCL ECtt EWes ILea LRHS MAvo MNrw MRav NEoE NHol NLar NRHS NWad WGrn WMoo XEll
'Beech's Double'	EWes
'Bell Bank'	Widely available
'Birkhead's Creamy Lemon'	EBee MHCG NBir
'Blazing Sunset' (d)	CMac CMea CRos CSpe CWCL EBee ECtt ELan ELon EMor EPfP GWyn ITim LRHS MBNS MBel MHer MHol MNrw MRav NBir NDov NGBl NGdn NRHS SGbt SPoG SRkn SRms
'Blood Orange'	ECtt LRHS MAvo NEoE NRHS
'Borisii'	Widely available
'Bremner's Nectarine'	CElw EPPr MNrw NChi NEoE SHar
'Broomrigg Beauty'	NEoE
'Brown Sugar'	NEoE
bulgaricum	EBee MRav NBir NEoE NLar NRya WFar XLum
calthifolium	EPPr
'Can-can' (d)	CDor CElw MAvo WHoo
'Cantamos'	NEoE
capense	NBre NLar SPlb
'Centurion'	NEoE
chiloense 'Red Dragon'	CElw EMor GPSL LLHF SWvt WHrl
'Chipchase'	CElw MAvo NChi NWad WHoo
coccineum ambig.	GKev
coccineum Sibth. & Sm.	GLog WHoo
- 'Ann'	ECtt
- 'Cooky'	CRos GPSL LRHS MMuc NEoE NGrd NLar NRHS SRms SWvt WFar
- 'Eos'	CBcs CSpe CWCL EBee ECtt ELon EMor EWes GBin LEdu LRHS MHol MNrw MPnt MRav MSCN NEoE NGdn NLar SCob SHeu SPoG SRms WGwG WHrl WMoo
- 'Koi'	CKel CWld EBee ELon EWTr GBin GEdr GPSL GWyn ILea ITim LEdu LSun MHol MSCN NEoE NGrd SPad WFar WMoo
- 'Queen of Orange'	NEoE NGrd SRms SRot WFar
- 'Tango'	CBod
- 'Werner Arends'	ECtt ELon GAbr GCal LRHS MAvo MNrw MRav WCot WFar WMoo

'Copper Pennies'	CElw NEoE
'Coppertone'	CElw CWCL ELan LPla LPot MRav NBir NBro NChi SCob XEll
'Cosmopolitan' (Cocktails Series)	CRos CWCL EBee ELan EMor EWTr GBin IKil ILea LCro LOPS LRHS MAvo MHol MPnt MSCN MTis NDov NEoE NLar NRHS SCob SHeu SPad WFar WPnP
'Cotton Candy'	NEoE SBri
'Country Rock Star'	NEoE WFar
'Cream Crackers'	NEoE WBrk
'Cumbrian Candy'	NEoE
'Cumbrian Cheddar'	NEoE
'Cumbrian Cherrypie'	NEoE WFar
'Cumbrian Cream'	NEoE
'Custard Pie'	NEoE
'Custard Tart'	NEoE
'Dark and Stormy' **new**	MAvo
'Dawn'	NEoE SBri SMHy
'Deano's Delight'	NEoE
'Diamond White'	EWhm
'Diana'	MNrw NLar
'Dingle Apricot'	ECtt GAbr GCal MNrw MRav NBir
'Dolly North' (d)	CElw CWCL EBee EPPr EWhm GWyn MCot MHol MRav NBro NGdn SHar WCAu WHal WJam XEll
'Double Sunrise' (d)	WFar
'East of Eden'	NEoE
'Eden Rising'	NEoE
'Eden Valley Angel'	NChi NEoE WWtn
'Eden Valley Elf'	NEoE
'El Wano'	NEoE
'Elworthy Amber'	CElw
'Emmylou'	NEoE
'Emory Quinn'	CFis ECtt EWes LRHS NEoE
'Fancy Frills'	CElw ECtt MAvo WHoo
'Farmer John Cross'	CAby CElw EBee ECtt ELon EPPr EShb GBin MTis NLar WFar WHal WJam WMoo WOut WWtn
'Feuermeer'	CElw NEoE NLar
'Fire Opal' (d) $\mathbb{Y}^{H7}$	CElw CWCL EAJP GWyn MAvo MNrw NBir NEoE WMoo
'Fire Storm' PBR	CBre CWGN EBee ECtt GAbr IKil LRHS LSun MBel MNrw MPnt MSCN MTis NEgg NGBl NLar SPad SPoG SRms WCot WFar WGrn
'Fireball'	CWCL ECtt EShb GBin LRHS MArl MAsh NLar NRHS
'Firefinch'	NEoE
'Flame'	NEoE NLar
'Flames of Passion' PBR	Widely available
'Flower of Darkness'	NEoE
'Georgenberg'	CBod CRos ECtt EHrv EPfP GMaP LRHS MBel MCot MNrw MRav NBir NGdn NHol NLar NRHS NWad SPer SRms SWvt WCAu WFar WMoo
'Gimlet' (Cocktails Series)	CWGN ECtt ELon EMor EShb GBin NCGa NLar SCob WTyc XEll
'Golden Joy'	CDor CElw LLHF MAvo NEoE WHoo
'Goldfinch' **new**	WFar
'Hannay's'	EBee MHCG NEoE SHar SPtp WOut
'Harvest Moon'	NEoE
'Hearts in Amber'	NEoE WFar
'Herterton Lemon'	CElw WCot
'Herterton Primrose'	CCBP CElw CWCL ECtt EPPr GCal LLHF LLWG NBid NSti WBor WFar WHal WHoo
'Hilltop Beacon' (d)	CDor CElw EBee LLHF LPla MHCG NEoE NLar SBch WFar WGoo WHoo
'Honeydew'	NEoE
* ***hybridum luteum***	NSti
× ***intermedium***	CBre EPPr GPSL MAvo NEoE NGdn NLar WMoo
- 'Diane'	NChi
- 'Hofrennydd'	NWad
'Jolly Roger'	EBee NEoE NWad
'Karlskaer'	CBod CElw CRos CWCL ECtt EWTr EWes GBin GQue LPla LRHS MBel MNrw NGdn NLar NRHS SPtp WFar WGwG WMoo WWtn
'Lady Stratheden' (d) $\mathbb{Y}^{H7}$	Widely available
'Lemon Delight'	CDor CElw MAvo
'Lemon Drops'	Widely available
'Limoncello'	SHeu
'Lionel Cox'	CWCL EHrv ELan GAbr GCal GMaP MBNS MCot MRav NBir NBro NChi NGdn NLar SRms WFar
'Lipstick Sunset'	NEoE
'Lisanne'	CElw CSam CWCL EBee GKev IPot MAvo MNrw MTis NAln NDov SHar SMHy SPtp WCAu
'Little Lottie'	NEoE
'Little Twister'	NEoE
macrophyllum	EBee
'Maddy Prior'	NEoE
magellanicum	CSpe EWes LEdu NBre NLar
- PAB 237	LEdu
'Magic Toybox'	NEoE
'Mai Tai' PBR (Cocktails Series)	Widely available
'Mandarin' (d)	GCal SHar
'Mango'	NDov
'Mango Lassi'	CElw ECtt GBin MSCN MTis NCGa NEoE SHar WCAu WHoo
'Marmalade'	CRos ECtt EWhm GAbr LLWG LPla LRHS MNrw MRav NEoE NLar NRHS SHar SMHy SSut WFar WHrl WKif WMoo WOut
'McClure's Magic'	NEoE
§ ***montanum*** $\mathbb{Y}^{H6}$	CRos EBee EBou GLog LRHS MMuc NBir NRHS NRya NSla SRms XLum
'Moonlight Serenade'	CBod CWCL EBee ECtt EMor GCal LLHF LRHS NEoE NRHS SBri WPtf
'Moorland Sorbet'	NEoE SBri WFar WMoo
'Mrs J. Bradshaw' (d) $\mathbb{Y}^{H7}$	Widely available
'Mrs W. Moore'	CBre CElw CKel CWCL EBee ECtt EShb GAbr IPot MNrw MRav NBir NCGa NChi NEoE NLar NQui SCob WMoo
'Nordek'	CElw ECha ECtt GAbr GCal GQue LRHS MNrw MRav NEgg NGdn NRHS
'Onslow Cream'	LPla
'Peachy Proud'	NEoE
'Pear Drops'	NEoE
'Pineapple Crush'	MAvo
'Pink Frills'	CElw CWCL ECtt EHrv EPPr EWTr EWes EWhm GAbr GBin GQue LEdu LLWG MAvo MPnt MRav NLar SGbt SMHy SPtp
'Pink Petticoats'	MAvo MHol MSCN
'Poco'	CWCL EBee ECtt EPfP EWes EWhm GBin GCal LLHF LRHS MAvo MNrw NEoE NRHS
'Prairie Dancer'	NEoE
'Present'	ECtt NBre NChi NEoE
'Primrose'	EWhm GAbr NEoE NGdn NLar
'Primrose Cottage'	EBee LRHS
'Prince of Orange' (d)	CElw CRos GAbr LRHS MNrw MRav NBre NRHS SWvt WFar WHrl

Godetia see *Clarkia*

Goeppertia (*Marantaceae*)

- § ***argyrophylla*** 'Exotica' — XBlo
- § ***crocata*** 'Tassmania' **new** — LCro LOPS
- ***louisae*** 'Maui Queen' — XBlo
- § ***majestica*** ♀H1a — XBlo
- § ***makoyana*** ♀H1a — XBlo
- § ***picturata*** 'Argentea' ♀H1a — XBlo
- § ***roseopicta*** ♀H1a — XBlo
- - 'Rosastar' — XBlo
- § ***rufibarba*** ♀H1a — XBlo
- ***veitchiana*** 'Medaillon' — LCro LOPS XBlo
- § ***zebrina*** ♀H1a — XBlo
- 'Zoizia' — XBlo

goji berry see *Lycium barbarum*, *L. chinense*

Gomphocarpus ✿ (*Apocynaceae*)

- § ***fruticosus*** — SVen
- § ***physocarpus*** — CBod

Gompholobium (*Papilionaceae*)

- ***scabrum*** — SPlb

Gomphostigma (*Scrophulariaceae*)

- ***virgatum*** — CBod CCCN CExl CFis CSpe EPPr EPfP LLWG MCot MHol MMuc MPie SMad SPhx SPlb WCFE WCot WFar WRHF WTor
- - 'White Candy' — GBin LRHS MGil MPkF SVen

Gomphrena (*Amaranthaceae*)

- ***globosa*** — CCCN

Goniolimon (*Plumbaginaceae*)

- ***collinum*** 'Sea Spray' — EDAr
- ***incanum*** 'Blue Diamond' — GJos NHpl WCot
- § ***tataricum*** — GJos MMuc
- § - var. ***angustifolium*** — SEND SRms

Goodia (*Papilionaceae*)

- ***lotifolia*** — CCCN

gooseberry see *Ribes uva-crispa*; also AGM Fruit Section

Gordonia (*Theaceae*)

- ***axillaris*** — see *Polyspora axillaris*

Gorgonidium (*Araceae*)

- ***intermedium*** — WCot

granadilla see *Passiflora quadrangularis*

granadilla, purple see *Passiflora edulis*

granadilla, sweet see *Passiflora ligularis*

grape see *Vitis*; also AGM Fruit Section

grapefruit see *Citrus* × *aurantium* Grapefruit Group

Graptopetalum (*Crassulaceae*)

- ***filiferum*** — SPlb
- § ***paraguayense*** — SVen

Graptopetalum × *Sedum* see × *Graptosedum*

× *Graptosedum* (*Crassulaceae*)

- 'Darley Sunshine' — NWad
- 'Vera Higgins' **new** — SSim

× *Graptoveria* (*Crassulaceae*)

- 'Ghostly' — WCot

Gratiola (*Plantaginaceae*)

- ***officinalis*** — CBod CRos LLWG LRHS MHer NRHS

Greenovia (*Crassulaceae*)

- § ***aurea*** — NMen SPlb
- ***diplocycla*** 'Gigantea' — SPlb

Grevillea (*Proteaceae*)

- * ***alba*** — SEle
- ***banksii*** 'Canberra Hybrid' — see *G.* 'Canberra Gem'
- - var. ***forsteri*** — SPlb
- 'Bronze Rambler' — CCCN
- § 'Canberra Gem' ♀H4 — Widely available
- 'Clearview David' — CCCN CKel EUJe LRHS LSRN MMuc SLim SVen
- ***crithmifolia*** — SPlb
- 'Desert Flame' — see *G. rosmarinifolia* 'Desert Flame'
- 'Ivanhoe' — CCCN
- ***johnsonii*** — LRHS WHlf
- ***juniperina*** — CBcs CCCN CExl CMac EPfP SEle SLim SVen
- - f. ***sulphurea*** — CCCN CExl EBee ELon EUJe MGil MMuc SEle SPer SPlb WSHC
- ***lanigera*** 'Mount Tamboritha' — CBcs CCCN CExl CMac CSde EBee EPfP EUJe LRHS SEle SLim SPoG SVen WCot WFar
- - prostrate — WAbe WGrn
- ***lavandulacea*** 'Black Range' **new** — WCot
- - 'Penola' — CCCN
- ***leucopteris*** — SPlb
- 'Moonlight' — WHlf
- 'Murray Valley Queen' — WCot WPGP
- 'Olympic Flame' — CBcs CCCN CCht CExl CRos CSBt CTsd EBee ELon EPfP EUJe LRHS MGos MMuc SEle SPoG SVen WBor WGrn
- ***paniculata*** — SPlb
- 'Pink Lady' — CBcs CCCN CKel ELon EPfP LRHS WFar
- 'Poorinda Constance' — WCot
- 'Poorinda Queen' — CCCN
- ***robusta*** ♀H2 — SPlb
- 'Robyn Gordon' — CBcs CCCN
- 'Rondeau' — CCCN
- ***rosmarinifolia*** ♀H4 — CBcs CCCN CExl CMac CSBt CTri CTsd ELan GKin SArc SEle SIgm SLim SLon SPer SPlb SSta WFar
- § - 'Desert Flame' — CBcs CExl
- - 'Jenkinsii' — CCCN CExl CKel CMac CSBt ELan EUJe SEle SLim
- § × ***semperflorens*** — CCCN CRos CSde EBee LRHS SPlb
- 'Spider Man' — CCCN
- ***tolminsis*** — see *G.* × *semperflorens*
- ***victoriae*** — CBcs CCCN CCht CJun CKel CTsd EBee EPfP EUJe LRHS SAko SChF SEle WCot WGrn WHlf WPGP
- - subsp. ***victoriae*** — CExl
- - yellow-flowered — LRHS
- ***williamsonii*** — CBcs CTsd LRHS

Grewia (*Malvaceae*)
occidentalis LRHS

Greyia (*Melianthaceae*)
sutherlandii SPlb

Griffinia (*Amaryllidaceae*)
rochae new GKev

Grindelia (*Asteraceae*)
§ **camporum** SPlb
chiloensis CAbb SMad
integrifolia XLum
robusta see *G. camporum*

Griselinia ✿ (*Griseliniaceae*)
littoralis ♀H5 Widely available
- 'Bantry Bay' (v) CCCN CSde EBee ELan LRHS MAsh SPer SPoG SWvt WFar
- 'Brodick Gold' CExl ELon GKin
- 'Dixon's Cream' (v) CBcs CCCN CDul CKel CMac CRos CSBt EBee EPfP LRHS MRav SGol SLon SRms SVen
- 'Green Favor' EBee
- GREEN HORIZON ('Whenuapai'PBR) CBod CKel ELan IBal LRHS SLim SPer SPoG
- 'Green Jewel' (v) CBod CCCN NLar
- 'Variegata' (v) ♀H4 Widely available
ruscifolia LEdu
scandens CCCN EUJe SEND WCot

guava, common see *Psidium guajava*

guava, purple or strawberry see *Psidium littorale* var. *longipes*

Gueldenstaedtia (*Papilionaceae*)
himalaica CPBP

Guichenotia (*Sterculiaceae*)
macrantha SPlb

Gunnera ✿ (*Gunneraceae*)
chilensis see *G. tinctoria*
cordifolia LLWG
densiflora GEdr
hamiltonii ECha GAbr NBir SRms XLum
killipiana B&SWJ 9009 WCru
magellanica Widely available
- SDR 7035 GKev
- (f) SRms
- 'Osorno' EBee
manicata Widely available
perpensa CBcs CBen CCCN EBee IMou LLWG WFar
prorepens CBod CExl CMac CPla EBee ECha ELan GAbr ILea NWad SRms WFar
scabra see *G. tinctoria*
§ **tinctoria** CBod CCCN CExl CFGn CMac CRos ECha EPfP LRHS MMuc NLar NRHS SEND SRms SWvt WBor WFar

Gymnadenia (*Orchidaceae*)
conopsea NLAp

Gymnocarpium ✿ (*Woodsiaceae*)
dryopteris ♀H5 CKel CLAP EFer EShb GKev GMaP GWyn ISha WAbe WFib WShi
- PAB 1757 LEdu
- PAB 8351 LEdu
- 'Plumosum' ♀H7 CBdn CBod CKel CLAP CRos CWCL EMor ERod EUJe LEdu LRHS NLar NRHS WFar WFib WHal WMoo
oyamense ♀H5 EShb SPlb
robertianum EFer EWld

Gymnocladus (*Caesalpiniaceae*)
chinensis WPGP
dioica CBcs CDul CLnd CMCN EBtc ELan EPfP EUJe LEdu LPra MBlu SMad SPer WHor WPGP WTSh

Gymnospermium (*Berberidaceae*)
§ **albertii** GKev

Gynandriris see *Moraea*

Gynerium (*Poaceae*)
argenteum see *Cortaderia selloana*

Gynostemma (*Cucurbitaceae*)
pentaphyllum CAgr EBee LEdu SRms
- B&SWJ 570 WCru

Gynura (*Asteraceae*)
§ **aurantiaca** 'Purple Passion' ♀H1c EShb
sarmentosa misapplied see *G. aurantiaca* 'Purple Passion'

Gypsophila (*Caryophyllaceae*)
aretioides CRos EPot GKev LRHS NRHS NSla WAbe
§ - 'Caucasica' CPBP LLHF
- 'Compacta' see *G. aretioides* 'Caucasica'
cerastioides CMea CRos CTri EBou ECtt EDAr EMor EPfP EPot GAbr GCrg GWyn LRHS MHer MHol NGdn NHpl NLar NRHS NSla SPlb SRms SWvt WAbe WHoo WIce XLum
- 'Rosy Stripe' GKev
- silver variegated (v) EMor MHol
dubia see *G. repens* 'Dubia'
elegans SVic
fastigiata 'Silverstar' CRos LRHS NRHS
(Festival Series) 'Festival' SGbt
- 'Festival Pink Lady' new CBod
gracilescens see *G. tenuifolia*
'Jolien' (v) WIce
muralis 'Garden Bride' SWvt
- 'Gypsy Deep Rose' CRos ELan EPfP LRHS NRHS WHil
- 'Gypsy Pink' (d) EPfP SWvt
nana 'Compacta' CPBP
NEW LOVE ('Dangypfirm') new WTyc
pacifica WOut
paniculata CBod MHol MRav SRms XLum
- 'Bristol Fairy' (d) CRos CSBt ECha ELan EPfP EWTr GMaP LRHS MBel MJak NLar SCob SHar SPoG SWvt WFar XLum
- 'Compacta Plena' (d) ECtt EPfP GMaP MRav NDov NGdn SRms
- double white-flowered (d) XLum
- 'Flamingo' (d) CBcs CRos ECha LRHS NLar NRHS SPer SWvt XLum
- 'Pacific Pink' EBee
- 'Perfect Alba' LRHS
- 'Perfekta' CBcs SPer

- 'Pink Star' (d)	ECtt
§ - 'Schneeflocke' (d)	LBuc MBel MHol SRms
- SNOWFLAKE	see *G. paniculata* 'Schneeflocke'
- SUMMER SPARKLES ('Esm Chispa'PBR)	CRos LRHS NRHS
- WHITE FIRE ('Dangypwhifa')	EBee
'Pink Festival' (Festival Series) (d)	CDor CRos ECtt EPfP LRHS NRHS SPoG
repens ♀H5	ECtt GBin GJos MAsh SCob SIgm SPlb SWvt WFar XLum XSen
- dark pink-flowered	CPBP
- 'Dorothy Teacher'	CMea CSma ECtt GCrg MAsh WFar
§ - 'Dubia'	EBou ECha ECtt EPot MAsh MHer NLar SRms WIce
- 'Filou Rose'	EBou EDAr
- 'Fratensis'	ECtt LLHF WIce
- PINK BEAUTY	see *G. repens* 'Rosa Schönheit'
§ - 'Rosa Schönheit'	CMea ECha ECtt EPot NDov SPer XLum
- 'Rosea'	CTri EBee EBou ECtt EDAr ELan EPfP GJos GMaP ITim MHol MMuc NGdn NHpl NSla SCob SEND SPoG SRms SWvt WFar WHoo WIce XLum
- 'Silver Carpet' (v)	EBee ELan
- white-flowered	CMea NGdn SWvt
§ 'Rosenschleier' (d) ♀H6	CBod CDor CMea EBee ECha ECtt ELan EPfP LOPS MBel MRav NDov NGdn SIgm SPer SRms SRot SWvt WCAu WHoo WSHC XLum
I 'Rosenschleier Variegata' (v)	EBee ELan EPfP
'Rosy Veil'	see *G.* 'Rosenschleier'
§ ***tenuifolia***	CPBP EPot GMaP ITim NHpl
VEIL OF ROSES	see *G.* 'Rosenschleier'
'White Festival'PBR (Festival Series) (d)	CRos EPfP LRHS NRHS SHar SPoG WTor

H

Haberlea (*Gesneriaceae*)

ferdinandi-coburgii	GEdr
- 'Connie Davidson'	EBee GEdr GKev
rhodopensis ♀H5	ELan EPPr GEdr IMou NHpl NRHS NSla SRms WAbe WCot WKif WThu XLum
- 'Virginalis'	CElw GEdr NSla WAbe WThu

Hablitzia (*Amaranthaceae*)

tamnoides	CAgr MCoo

Habranthus (*Amaryllidaceae*)

andersonii	see *H. tubispathus*
brachyandrus	SRms
gracilifolius	WAbe
martinezii ♀H2	CPBP
§ ***robustus*** ♀H2	CAby CCCN CExl EPot EShb GKev LAma WWFP
§ ***tubispathus*** ♀H2	CPla GKev SBrt WHil

Hacquetia (*Apiaceae*)

epipactis ♀H7	CDor CElw CRos ECha EHrv EMor EPfP EPot GAbr GEdr GKev GMaP LRHS MAvo MBel MCot MMuc NBir NBro NChi NRHS NRya NSum SIgm WCot WHoo WKif WSHC
- 'Harry Foley' (v)	NWad
§ - 'Thor' (v)	ECha EHrv EWes GBin GEdr LLHF MNrw NBir SIgm WAbe
- 'Variegata'	see *H. epipactis* 'Thor'

Haemanthus (*Amaryllidaceae*)

albiflos ♀H2	CPrp ELan EShb GKev LAma NSti SRms
amarylloides	WCot
barkerae	WCot
carneus	WCot
coccineus ♀H2	WCot
humilis	WCot
- subsp. ***hirsutus***	WCot
kalbreyeri	see *Scadoxus multiflorus* subsp. *multiflorus*
katherinae	see *Scadoxus multiflorus* subsp. *katherinae*
natalensis	see *Scadoxus puniceus*
nortieri	WCot
pauculifolius	GKev
pubescens	WCot
sanguineus	WCot

Hagenia (*Rosaceae*)

abyssinica	WPGP

Hakea (*Proteaceae*)

baxteri	SPlb
§ ***drupacea***	CPbh
laurina	CPbh SPlb
§ ***lissosperma***	CBcs EBee EPfP SPlb WPGP
nodosa	CCCN
oleifolia	CPbh
platysperma	SPlb
§ ***salicifolia***	CBcs CCCN SPlb
saligna	see *H. salicifolia*
sericea misapplied	see *H. lissosperma*
- pink-flowered	SPlb
suaveolens	see *H. drupacea*
victoriae	SPlb

Hakonechloa ✿ (*Poaceae*)

macra ♀H7	Widely available
§ - 'Alboaurea' (v) ♀H7	CBcs CExl CKno CRos CTsd ELan EPfP LCro LOPS LRHS LSRN MGos MMuc NRHS SRms WOld
- 'Albovariegata' (v)	CAbb CKno EBee EMor EUJe GCal LCro LEdu LOPS LRHS MAvo SCob WAvo
§ - 'All Gold'	CAby CExl CKno EBee ECha ECtt ELan EMor EPPr EShb EUJe EWes ITim LCro LEdu LRHS MGos MJak SCob SMad SPad SPoG WCot WPGP
- 'Aureola' ♀H7	Widely available
- 'Beni-kaze'	CKno EBee ECtt ELan IMou LPla MAvo MNrw NDov SCob
- 'Fubuki' (v)	EBee
- 'Greenhills' **new**	LPla
- 'Mediovariegata' (v)	EBee ECha
- 'Naomi' (v)	EBee ELan EMor SCob
- 'Nicolas'	CExl EBee ECtt ELan EMor EPfP EWes LCro LEdu LLHF LOPS LPla LSRN MBel NSti SCob
- 'Ogon'	see *H. macra* 'All Gold'
- 'Samurai' (v)	CKno
- 'Stripe It Rich' (v)	CKno EBee ECtt ELan EWes LPla
- 'Sunny Delight' (v) **new**	EBee
- 'Variegata'	see *H. macra* 'Alboaurea'

Halenia (*Gentianaceae*)

	Name	Suppliers
	elliptica	GKev

Halesia (*Styracaceae*)

	Name	Suppliers
§	***carolina***	Widely available
	- Monticola Group	CAco CBcs CCVT CMCN ELan EPfP LSRN MMuc NLar SWvt
I	- - 'Variegata' (v)	EPfP MBlu NLar SSta
	- 'Uconn Wedding Bells'	CJun MBlu WTSh
	- Vestita Group ♀H5	CJun CTho EPfP EUJe EWTr MAsh MBlu MGil MGos MMrt MRav NLar SPer SSta
	- - 'Rosea'	CJun EPfP MBlu NLar
	diptera	CBcs MBlu
	- Magniflora Group	CJun EPfP MBlu SAko SSta
	macgregorii	CMCN MBlu
	tetraptera	see *H. carolina*

× *Halimiocistus* (*Cistaceae*)

	Name	Suppliers
	algarvensis	see *Halimium ocymoides*
§	'Ingwersenii' ♀H4	ELan EWes SPer SRms XLum
	revolii misapplied	see × *H. sahucii*
§	***sahucii*** ♀H4	CBcs CBod CRos CSBt CTri ECha ELan EPfP LRHS MAsh MBNS MRav MSwo NPri SCob SIgm SPer SPoG SRms SWvt XLum
	- ICE DANCER ('Ebhals'PBR) (v)	EBee MAsh SCob SPer SWvt WFar
	'Susan'	see *Halimium* 'Susan'
§	***wintonensis*** ♀H4	CBcs CBod CRos ELan EPfP LRHS MAsh MGil MMuc SCob SLon SPer SRms
§	- 'Merrist Wood Cream' ♀H4	CBcs CBod CMac CRos CSBt EBee ELan EPfP EWTr LRHS LSRN MAsh MGil MRav MSwo NBir SEle SLim SPer SPoG SRkn SWvt WFar WGrn

Halimione (*Amaranthaceae*)

	Name	Suppliers
§	***portulacoides***	CEls

Halimium (*Cistaceae*)

	Name	Suppliers
§	***atriplicifolium***	CAby
§	***calycinum***	CBcs CBod CKel CRos ELan EPfP LRHS MAsh MMuc NRHS SCoo SLim SPer SPoG SWvt WCFE
	commutatum	see *H. calycinum*
	halimifolium misapplied	see *H.* × *pauanum*
§	***lasianthum***	CMac CRos CSBt LRHS MRav SLim
	- 'Concolor' ♀H4	CRos LRHS MAsh MSwo SWvt
	- subsp. ***formosum*** 'Sandling' ♀H4	CRos ELan EPfP LRHS MAsh MMuc SLon SPoG SRms
	libanotis misapplied	see *H. calycinum*
§	***ocymoides***	MGil MSwo WFar WKif
§	× ***pauanum***	CRos LRHS MMuc NRHS
§	'Susan' ♀H4	CRos EBee ELan EPfP LRHS MMrt NRHS SCoo SLim SPer WAbe
§	***umbellatum***	EPfP
	wintonense	see × *Halimiocistus wintonensis*

Halimodendron (*Papilionaceae*)

	Name	Suppliers
	halodendron	CBcs CDul MBlu SPer

Halleria (*Stilbaceae*)

	Name	Suppliers
	lucida	CBcs CCCN EBee SEle SPlb SVen

Haloragis (*Haloragaceae*)

	Name	Suppliers
	erecta	SPlb SVen XLum
	- 'Rubra'	WCot
	- 'Wellington Bronze'	CBod CExl CPla CSpe EBee EHoe ELan EUJe EWld LEdu WHer WMoo XLum

Hamamelis ✿ (*Hamamelidaceae*)

	Name	Suppliers
	'Amethyst'	CJun MBlu SGol
	'Brevipetala'	CEnd CJun LMaj
	'Danny'	CJun
	'Dishi'	CJun
	'Fire Blaze'	CJun MBlu NLar
	× ***intermedia***	CDul
	- 'Advent' ♀H5	CJun NLar
	- 'Amanda'	NLar
	- 'Andre'	WPGP
	- 'Andrea'	NLar
	- 'Angelly' ♀H5	CEnd CJun MBlu NLar
	- 'Anne' ♀H5	NLar
	- 'Aphrodite' ♀H5	CBcs CDul CJun CRos EPfP LRHS MBlu MGos MRav NLar NRHS SCob SPer
	- 'Arnold Promise' ♀H5	Widely available
	- 'Aurora' ♀H5	CJun EPfP MBlu NLar WPGP
	- 'Barmstedt Gold' ♀H5	CJun CRos EPfP IArd LRHS LSRN MGos MRav NLar NRHS SAko SCob SPer SPoG SRms
	- 'Bernstein'	CJun
	- 'Carmine Red'	CJun CMac
	- 'Copper Beauty'	see *H.* × *intermedia* 'Jelena'
	- 'Cyrille'	MMuc
	- 'Diane'	Widely available
§	- 'Feuerzauber'	CEnd CSBt CTri EBee LBuc LMaj NLar SCob SPer SWvt WFar
	- FIRE CRACKER	see *H.* × *intermedia* 'Feuerzauber'
	- 'Frederic'	CJun EPfP
	- 'Gingerbread' ♀H5	CJun EPfP
	- 'Glowing Embers'	CJun
	- 'Harlow Carr'	NLar
	- 'Harry'	CJun LSRN MAsh NLar
	- 'Heinrich Bruns'	CJun
§	- 'Jelena' ♀H5	Widely available
	- 'John'	LSRN
	- 'Limelight'	CJun MBlu MMuc
	- 'Livia'	CJun CRos EPfP LRHS NLar NRHS SCoo
	- MAGIC FIRE	see *H.* × *intermedia* 'Feuerzauber'
	- 'Moonlight'	CJun
	- 'Nina'	EBee EPfP
	- 'Old Copper'	NLar
	- 'Orange Beauty'	CBcs CDul CLnd CRos LRHS MBlu MGos NRHS SAko SCoo SGol SPer WPGP
	- 'Orange Peel'	CDul CJun EBee EPfP NLar
	- 'Ostergold'	CJun NLar
	- 'Pallida' ♀H5	Widely available
	- 'Primavera'	CBcs CJun CKel CLnd
	- 'Ripe Corn'	CJun
	- 'Robert'	CJun CRos LRHS LSRN NRHS
	- 'Rubin' ♀H5	CBcs CJun CRos LRHS MGos NLar NRHS SCoo SPer
	- 'Rubinstar'	CJun
	- 'Ruby Glow'	CBcs CRos LRHS LSRN MAsh MGil MGos NEgg NLar NRHS NWea SCoo SPer SPoG SWvt
	- 'Savill Starlight'	CJun
	- 'Spanish Spider'	CJun MBlu MMuc NLar
	- 'Strawberries and Cream'	CJun
	- 'Sunburst'	CJun CRos LRHS MBlu MGos NLar SGol
	- 'Twilight'	CJun NLar

- 'Vesna' ♀H5	CJun CMac EPfP MAsh MBlu NLar SCoo
- 'Westerstede'	CJun LRHS LSRN MGos MMuc NHol NLar NWea SCob SCoo SEWo SGol SLim WFar WHor
- 'Wiero'	CJun NLar
- 'Zitronenjette'	CJun
japonica	LPra
- 'Pendula'	CJun MBlu
- 'Zuccariniana'	NLar
mollis	Widely available
- 'Boskoop'	MMuc NLar
- 'Coombe Wood'	CJun LRHS
- 'Imperialis'	CJun MAsh
- 'Iwado'	CJun
- 'Jermyns Gold'	CJun CRos EPfP LRHS MAsh NRHS
- 'Kort's Yellow'	CJun
- var. ***pallida***	SEWo SWvt
- 'Wisley Supreme' ♀H5	CJun ELan EPfP MGos SGol
'Rochester'	CJun NLar
vernalis purple-flowered	MBlu
- 'Quasimodo'	MBlu NLar
- 'Sandra'	CBcs CMCN EPfP MAsh MBlu MGos MRav NLar SLon
virginiana	CAgr CMCN GPoy GQue IDee MMuc NWea
- 'Green Thumb' (v)	NLar
- 'Mohonk Red'	CJun
'Yamina'	NLar SGol

Hamelia (*Rubiaceae*)

patens	CCCN

Hanabusaya (*Campanulaceae*)

§ ***asiatica***	SBrt WFar

Haplocarpha (*Asteraceae*)

rueppellii	NHpl SRms

Haplopappus (*Asteraceae*)

coronopifolius	see *H. glutinosus*
§ ***glutinosus***	ECha ECtt EDAr EPot MMuc SPlb SRms
prunelloides var. ***mustersii*** F&W 9384	WCot

Hardenbergia (*Papilionaceae*)

comptoniana ♀H3	CExl
violacea ♀H3	CBod CCCN CHll CRHN CSpe ELan MHer MMuc SEND SLim SPer WCot
- f. ***alba***	CHll SEND
- - 'White Wanderer'	CCCN
- 'Happy Wanderer'	CCCN
- f. ***rosea***	CCCN

Harpephyllum (*Anacardiaceae*)

caffrum (F)	XBlo

Hasteola (*Asteraceae*)

§ ***suaveolens***	LEdu

Hastingsia (*Asparagaceae*)

alba	WSHC

Haworthia ✿ (*Asphodelaceae*)

attenuata	EShb
'Black Prince'	EShb SBch
coarctata ♀H2	SEND
fasciata	SEND
- 'Concolor'	SSim
glabrata var. ***concolor***	EShb
limifolia	EShb
- SPIDER WHITE ('Lock01'PBR)	EShb LCro LOPS
margaritifera	SSim
pumila ♀H2	SEND
tesselata	see *H. venosa* subsp. *tesselata*
§ ***venosa*** subsp. ***tesselata*** ♀H2	SEND

hazelnut see *Corylus*; also AGM Fruit Section

Hebe ✿ (*Plantaginaceae*)

albicans ♀H4	CBcs CRos ELan EPfP GKin LCro LOPS LRHS LSRN MAsh MGos MJak MRav NHic NRHS NWea SCob SCoo SLim SPer SRms SWvt WCFE WOld WSpi XLum
- 'Cobb'	NHic
- prostrate	see *H. albicans* 'Snow Cover'
* - 'Snow Carpet'	CCCN LRHS
§ - 'Snow Cover'	EWes
- 'Snow Drift'	see *H. albicans* 'Snow Cover'
§ 'Alicia Amherst'	CRos LRHS
'Amanda Cook' (v)	NPer
§ 'Amy'	ELon LRHS NHic NPer SPer SWvt WCot
§ × ***andersonii*** 'Andersonii Variegata' (v)	LRHS SRms
- 'Argenteovariegata'	see *H.* × *andersonii* 'Andersonii Variegata'
'Andressa Paula'	CCCN LRHS
anomala misapplied	see *H.* 'Imposter'
§ ***armstrongii***	MMuc NHic SCob
'Autumn Glory'	CRos ELan EPfP LCro LOPS LPot LRHS LSRN MAsh MGos MRav MSwo NBir NHic NRHS NWea SCob SPer SPlb SPoG SVen SWvt XLum
'Autumn Joy'	SWvt
azurea	see *H. venustula*
'Azurens'	see *H.* 'Maori Gem'
'Baby Blush'PBR	NHic
'Baby Boo' (v)	CKel LRHS SCob SLon
'Baby Marie'	CRos CSBt ELan EPfP GKin LBuc LRHS LSRN MSwo NHic NPer NRHS SCob SCoo SPoG SRms SRot SWvt WFar
'Beverley Hills'PBR	CRos CSBt LRHS SCob
'Bicolor Wand'	CCCN CTsd LRHS
bishopiana	EPfP SCob
'Black Beauty'	CRos EPfP LBuc LRHS MJak NHic NRHS SCob
'Black Panther'	ELon
'Blue Clouds' ♀H4	CRos EPfP LLHF LRHS MSwo NRHS NWad SCob SPer WCFE
BLUE ELEGANCE ('Lowgeko'PBR) (Garden Beauty Series)	LRHS
§ 'Blue Gem'	CCoa CKel CMac NHic SCob
BLUE ICE ('Lowapb') (Garden Beauty Series)	LRHS
'Blue Shamrock'	SWvt
BLUE STAR ('Vergeer 1'PBR)	CKel CRos EPfP LBuc LRHS MAsh NRHS SLon SPoG SRms
'Boscawenii'	WHer
'Bouquet'PBR	CKel LLHF
§ 'Bowles's Hybrid'	CCCN LRHS MRav MSwo NHic SCob SEND SRms

	Name	Suppliers
	brachysiphon	CTri NHic SCob SEND SPer SRms SVen
	brevifolia	LRHS
	BRONZE GLOW ('Lowglo') (Garden Beauty Series)	LBuc LRHS
	'Bronzy Baby'[PBR] (v)	NHic SPoG
	buchananii	NPer
§	- 'Fenwickii'	WHoo
	- 'Minor' ambig.	EPot GQue
	- 'Minor' Hort. NZ	GBin GCrg
	'Bullfinch'	LRHS
	'Burgundy Blush' **new**	LBuc SPoG
	'Burning Heart' (v) **new**	LBuc
	buxifolia	see *H. odora*
§	'Caledonia' ♀H4	CBcs CCCN CRos ELan EPfP LCro LOPS LRHS LSRN MAsh MGos NHic NPer NRHS SCob SCoo SLim SPoG SRms SWvt XLum
	'Cara' **new**	NHic
	'Carl Teschner'	see *H.* 'Youngii'
	'Carnea Variegata' (v)	CRos LRHS NHic NRHS SPer SRms
	carnosula	SPer
	catarractae	see *Parahebe catarractae*
	'Celine'	CRos EPfP LRHS NRHS
	'Champagne'	CCCN CRos ELan EPfP LCro LOPS LRHS LSRN MBlu MJak NHic NLar NRHS NWad SCob SCoo SLim SRms XLum
	'Champagne Ice' **new**	LBuc
	CHAMPION ('Champseiont'[PBR])	EBee MSwo NHic NLar SCob SCoo
	'Charming White'	CChe CRos LRHS LSRN NHic SCob
	cheesemanii	WAbe
	'Christabel'	LRHS
	'Claret Crush'[PBR]	SPoG
	'Clear Skies'[PBR]	LLHF SRms
	'Conwy Knight'	SRms
	corstorphinensis	EBtc
	'County Park'	EWes GAbr
	'Cranleighensis'	CTsd LRHS
	cupressoides	GCal NHic
	- 'Boughton Dome'	ELan GEdr MHer NHic WAbe WCFE WHoo WOld
	- 'Golden Dome'	NHic
	'Dark Angel' **new**	LBuc
	darwiniana misapplied	see *H. glaucophylla*
	decumbens	EWes GBin
	'Denise'	LRHS
	'Diamond'	LRHS LSRN SLon SRms
	dieffenbachii	SVen
	diosmifolia	CRos LRHS MAsh NHic NRHS
	- 'Celina' **new**	CKel
	- 'Wairua Beauty'	LRHS
	'Dorothy Peach'	see *H.* 'Watson's Pink'
	'E.B. Anderson'	see *H.* 'Caledonia'
	'Edington'	SPer WCFE
	'Ellie'	LRHS
	elliptica 'Variegata'	see *H.* 'Silver Queen'
	'Emerald Dome'	see *H.* 'Emerald Gem'
§	'Emerald Gem' ♀H4	CBod CKel CRos CTri ELan EPfP EUJe GWyn LRHS LSRN MAsh MGos MHer MJak MMuc MSwo NHic NRHS SArc SCob SPer SPlb SPoG
	'Emerald Green'	see *H.* 'Emerald Gem'
§	'Eveline'	CRos CSBt CTri LRHS NBir WKif
	'Evelyn'	SPer
	'Eversley Seedling'	see *H.* 'Bowles's Hybrid'
	'Eyecatcher'[PBR] (v)	CKel MAsh MJak NEoE
	'Fairfieldii'	WAbe WAvo
	'First Light'[PBR]	CKel CRos LRHS NRHS SCob SRms
	'Fragrant Jewel'	LRHS SEND
	× ***franciscana*** 'Blue Gem' ambig.	CDul CRos CTsd ELan LRHS MAsh MMuc MRav NBir NPer NRHS SCob SEND SPer SPlb SPoG SRms WSpi XLum
	- 'Foreness Pink'	SEND
	- 'Lavender Queen'	LRHS
	- lime variegated (v)	SEND
	- 'Purple Tips' misapplied	see *H. speciosa* 'Variegata'
	- 'Variegata'	see *H.* 'Silver Queen'
I	- 'White Gem'	CKel SRms
	'Frozen Flame' (v)	ELan LBuc LRHS MAsh NRHS SPoG
	(Garden Beauty Series) GARDEN BEAUTY BLUE ('Cliv'[PBR])	CSBt LBuc LCro LOPS LRHS MAsh SRms WSpi
	- GARDEN BEAUTY PINK ('Lowink')	SRms
	- GARDEN BEAUTY PURPLE ('Nold'[PBR])	CRos CSBt LBuc LCro LOPS LRHS MAsh MJak MTin NRHS
	- GARDEN BEAUTY WHITE ('Lowhi')	LRHS
	(Garden Elegance Series) 'Garden Elegance Blush'	LRHS
	- 'Garden Elegance Rose'	LRHS
	'Gauntlettii'	see *H.* 'Eveline'
	'Gibby'	LRHS
§	***glaucophylla***	XLum
I	- 'Variegata' (v)	CRos LRHS NRHS SCoo SPer WKif
	'Gold Beauty' (v)	SRms
	'Gold Pixie'	LBuc
	GOLDEN ANNIVERSARY ('Lowag')	LRHS
	'Golden Nugget'	LRHS
	'Goldrush'[PBR] (v)	SPoG
	gracillima	SCob SEle
	'Gran's Favourite'	LSRN
	'Great Orme' ♀H4	CRos ELan EPfP GBin GLog LRHS LSRN MAsh MGos MJak MRav MSwo NHic NPer NRHS SCob SEND SPer SPlb SPoG SRms SWvt WCFE WOut WSFF
	'Green Globe'	see *H.* 'Emerald Gem'
	'Greensleeves'	CRos LRHS
	'Grethe'	CRos LRHS NRHS SEND
	'Hadspen Pink'	LRHS
	'Hagley Park'	CRos LRHS
	'Hanne'	CRos NRHS
§	'Hartii'	CRos LRHS MRav SCob
	'Headfortii'	EBtc
	'Heartbreaker'[PBR] (v)	CRos ELan EPfP LBuc LCro LOPS LRHS MAsh MGos MJak NPri NRHS SCob SCoo SLim SPoG SWvt
	'High Voltage'[PBR]	MJak NEoE WTyc
	'Highdownensis'	LRHS
	'Highland Jubilee'	MAsh
	'Hinderwell'	NPer
	hulkeana	LLHF MHer SCob WAbe WKif
§	'Imposter'	SRms
	'Inspiration'	CRos LRHS NHic NWad SCob
	'James Stirling'	see *H. ochracea* 'James Stirling'
	'Jane Holden'	LRHS
	'Jewel of the Nile'[PBR] (v)	SPoG
	'John Collier'	GAbr SEND
§	'Johny Day'	LRHS SCob
	'Judy'	LRHS
	'Karna'	LPot
	'Karo Golden Esk'	EPfP
	'Kirkii'	ELan EPfP MSwo NHic SCob XLum
	'Knightshayes'	see *H.* 'Caledonia'

'La Favorite' CTsd
'Lady Ann'PBR (v) CKel CRos CSBt EPfP LBuc LRHS MAsh MJak NHic NRHS SPoG
'Lady Ardilaun' see *H.*'Amy'
laevis see *H. venustula*
laingii GCrg
latifolia see *H.* 'Blue Gem'
'Lavender Spray' see *H.* 'Hartii'
leiophylla SVen
LEOPARD ('Lowand') (Garden Beauty Series) LRHS NPri
'Lilac Fantasy' LRHS
'Lilac Wand' CTsd
'Linda' SEND
'Lindsayi' LRHS
'Lisa' CRos NRHS
'Liz' LBuc LRHS SPoG
lyallii see *Parahebe lyallii*
lycopodioides 'Aurea' see *H. armstrongii*
'Lynash' LRHS
mackenii see *H.* 'Emerald Gem'
macrantha ♀H4 CBod CRos GBin GWyn LRHS SRms
macrocarpa var. ***latisepala*** LBuc
'Magic Summer'PBR LBuc LRHS MAsh NRHS SPoG
§ 'Maori Gem' MRav NHic
'Margery Fish' see *H.* 'Primley Gem'
'Margret' ♀H4 CRos CSBt EBee ECrN EPfP LPot LRHS LSRN MAsh MGos MJak MRav NRHS SCob SCoo SLim SPer SPoG SRms
'Marie Antoinette' CRos LRHS
'Marilyn Monroe'PBR LRHS WTyc
'Marjorie' CDul CKel CMac CRos ELan EPfP GBin LRHS LSRN MJak MSwo NHic NLar NPer NRHS NWea SCob SPer SPoG SRms SWvt WFar
matthewsii 'Turkish Delight'PBR MJak NEoE
MATTY BROWN ('Tull 303') **new** SPad
'Mauve Queen' LRHS
'McKean' see *H.*'Emerald Gem'
MIDNIGHT SKY ('Lowten'PBR) (Garden Beauty Series) LBuc LCro LOPS LRHS NPri SCoo SPoG
'Midsummer Beauty' ♀H4 CRos EPfP LRHS LSRN MGos MJak MRav NBir NHic NRHS SCob SEND SLim SPer SPlb SPoG SRms SWvt WOut WSFF XLum
'Milmont Emerald' see *H.* 'Emerald Gem'
§ 'Mohawk'PBR CRos LRHS MAsh NRHS SPoG WSpi
§ 'Mrs Winder' ♀H4 CCCN CMac CRos ELan EPfP GWyn LRHS LSRN MAsh MCot MGos MJak MRav MSwo NHic NLar NPer NRHS SCob SCoo SGbt SGol SLim SPer SPoG SWvt
'Nantyderry' LRHS MGil WOut
§ 'Neil's Choice' ♀H4 CRos ELon LRHS
'New Zealand' GWyn XLum
'Nicola's Blush' ♀H4 CMac CRos EBee ELon EPfP EShb GBin GWyn LRHS LSRN MCot MRav NBir NHic NLar NRHS SCob SEND SGol SPer SPoG SRms SWvt WKif
ochracea CKel CRos EPfP LRHS NRHS
§ - 'James Stirling' ♀H4 CBcs CDul CMac CRos CSBt ELan LRHS LSRN MAsh MGos MMuc MSwo NHic NLar NWad SCob SCoo SPer SPlb SPoG SWvt WSpi
'Oddity' LRHS
§ ***odora*** CBod CCoa CSde ELan LRHS SArc SCob SEND WSpi XLum
I - 'Nana' MMuc
- 'New Zealand Gold' CBod CRos EPfP LRHS MAsh MMuc NHic NRHS NWad
- var. ***patens*** NWea
- 'Summer Frost' CSde LRHS
'Oratia Beauty' ♀H4 CRos LRHS LSRN MMuc MRav NHic SCob SEND
'Orphan Annie' (v) LSRN NLar
'Pacific Paradise'PBR SPoG
parviflora misapplied see *H.*'Bowles's Hybrid'
parviflora (Vahl) Cockayne & Allan var. ***angustifolia*** see *H. stenophylla*
- 'Holdsworth' CBod LRHS
'Pascal' ♀H4 CBod CRos ELan EPfP LCro LOPS LRHS LSRN MAsh MGos NRHS SCoo SLim SLon SPer SPoG SRms SWvt WFar
'Pastel Blue' NHic
'Patti Dossett' see *H. speciosa* 'Patti Dossett'
pauciramosa GCal SRms
'Pearl of Paradise'PBR CRos LBuc NRHS NWad SPoG
perfoliata see *Parahebe perfoliata*
'Perry's Rubyleaf' NPer
'Petra's Pink' CCCN CRos LRHS
'Pewter Dome' ♀H4 EPfP LRHS MGos MRav SCob SRms SWvt XLum
pimeleoides SCob
- 'Glauca' NPer
- 'Quicksilver' ♀H4 CRos CSBt CTri ELan EPfP LRHS LSRN MGil MGos MMuc MRav NBir NHic NPer NRHS SCob SCoo SLim SPer SRms WAvo WSpi XLum
pinguifolia NLar SPlb
- 'Pagei' ♀H5 Widely available
- 'Sutherlandii' CBcs CDul CKel CRos EUJe LRHS LSRN MAsh MGos MJak NHic NRHS NWea SCob SCoo SWvt WFar XLum
PINK CANDY ('Tulpink') **new** WTyc
'Pink Elephant' (v) ♀H4 LBuc LRHS MAsh NHic SPoG
'Pink Fantasy' LRHS NHic NWad SCob
'Pink Goddess' CRos LRHS NRHS SEND
'Pink Lady'PBR ELan SPoG
'Pink Paradise'PBR CRos ELan EPfP LRHS MJak NHic NRHS NWad SPoG SRms WRHF
'Pink Payne' see *H.* 'Eveline'
'Pink Pixie' LBuc LRHS MAsh NRHS SCoo SPoG SRms
'Pink Wand' CTsd
'Pinocchio' (v) NHic
poppelwellii NLar
'Porlock Purple' see *Parahebe catarractae* 'Delight'
§ 'Primley Gem' CRos LRHS
I 'Prostrata' CSBt
'Purple Emperor' see *H.* 'Neil's Choice'
'Purple King' **new** NHic
'Purple Paradise'PBR NHic SPoG
'Purple Picture' ELon
'Purple Pixie' see *H.* 'Mohawk'
'Purple Princess' CRos LRHS MJak NRHS
'Purple Queen' CRos EShb LRHS MCot MJak NHic NRHS SCob
PURPLE SHAMROCK ('Neprock'PBR) (v) CRos EPfP LRHS MAsh NEgg NLar NRHS SCoo SLim SPer SPoG SRms SWvt
'Purple Tips' misapplied see *H. speciosa* 'Variegata'
'Rachel' LRHS LSRN
§ ***rakaiensis*** ♀H4 Widely available

	Name	Suppliers
	- 'Golden Dome'	see *H. rakaiensis*
	ramosissima	GAbr GBin
	raoulii	SRms WAbe
	RASPBERRY RIPPLE ('Tullyraspb'PBR)	NEoE
	'Raven'	LRHS
	recurva	CSam CTri EMOT LPot LRHS MCot SCob SRms
	- 'Boughton Silver' ♀H5	CRos LRHS LSRN MMuc
	'Red Edge' ♀H4	Widely available
	'Red Moon'	SCob
	'Red Rum'	LBuc LRHS
	'Red Ruth'	see *H.* 'Eveline'
	'Rhubarb and Custard'	LBuc LRHS MAsh MMrt NRHS SCob SPoG WCot
	rigidula	LRHS MMuc SEND
	'Rosie'PBR	LBuc LRHS LSRN NRHS SCoo SPer SWvt
	'Royal Blue'	LRHS
	'Royal Purple'	see *H.* 'Alicia Amherst'
	salicifolia	CCCN CMac CRos CTca ELan EPfP IDee LRHS MMuc MRav NAst NRHS NWad SCob SEND SPlb SRms WFar WSpi XLum
	- pale blue-flowered	SEND
	'Sandra Joy'	LRHS LSRN
	'Santa Monica'	MJak
	'Sapphire' ♀H4	CRos EPfP LRHS MAsh MJak NHic NRHS SCob SCoo SRms SWvt
	'Sarana'	LRHS LSRN
	'Shiraz'	CRos LRHS
	'Silver Dollar' (v)	CCCN CKel GBin LRHS MJak NEgg NRHS NWad SPer SPoG SRms
§	'Silver Queen' (v) ♀H3	CBcs CDul CKel CRos CSBt ELan LCro LOPS LRHS MMuc NLar NPer NRHS SCob SEND SPer SPoG SRms WOut
	'Simon Délaux'	LRHS SEND SPer WOut
	'Sparkling Sapphires'	LBuc LRHS SPoG
	speciosa	NHic
	- 'Johny Day'	see *H.* 'Johny Day'
	- 'La Séduisante'	CTri LRHS SEND WSpi
§	- 'Patti Dossett'	LRHS
	- 'Red Hugh'	SEND
§	- 'Variegata' (v)	CRos LRHS NHic NPer NRHS
	'Spender's Seedling' misapplied	see *H. stenophylla*
	'Spender's Seedling' ambig.	MCot MMuc SCob
	'Spender's Seedling' Hort.	LRHS MRav NHic SEND SPoG SRms
	'Spring Glory'	CRos EPfP LRHS NRHS
§	***stenophylla***	EShb EUJe LRHS LSRN NLar SArc SPer SPlb
	stricta	LRHS SEND
	- var. ***egmontiana***	LRHS
	subalpina	CSBt
	'Summer Blue'	CRos LRHS MBlu
	'Sunset Boulevard'PBR	LLHF MJak
	'Super Red'	CSBt
	'Sweet Kim' (v)	CRos LBuc LRHS NRHS SPoG
	topiaria ♀H4	CAgr CBod CMac CRos CSBt CSam EBou EPfP LRHS MBrN MMuc MRav MSwo NBir NLar NWad SCob SCoo SEND SGbt SPer SPoG WRHF WSpi XLum
	- 'Doctor Favier'	LRHS SRms
	townsonii	LRHS SCob
	'Tricolor'	see *H. speciosa* 'Variegata'
	'Trixie'	WSpi
	'Twisty'	LRHS
	'Valentino'PBR	SCoo
	'Veitchii'	see *H.* 'Alicia Amherst'
§	***venustula***	LRHS MMuc
	vernicosa ♀H4	CRos EPfP LRHS MGos MHer NWad SCob SCoo SEle SPer SPlb SPoG SRot SVen SWvt WSpi
	'Violet Wand'	LRHS
	'Vogue'	LRHS
	'Waikiki'	see *H.* 'Mrs Winder'
§	'Warley'	CRos LRHS NRHS WSpi
	'Warley Pink'	CRos LRHS
	'Warleyensis'	see *H.* 'Warley'
§	'Watson's Pink'	SPer WKif
	'White Gem' (*brachysiphon* hybrid) ♀H4	GWyn LRHS NHic NPer SEND SPer
	'White Heather'	CRos EPfP LRHS NRHS SCob
	'White Paradise'PBR	SPoG
	'Wild Romance'	LBuc LRHS MAsh NRHS SPoG
	'Willcoxii'	see *H. buchananii* 'Fenwickii'
	'Wingletye' ♀H4	CCCN CRos LRHS XLum
	'Winter Glow'	CCCN LRHS
	'Wiri Blush'	LRHS SWvt
	'Wiri Charm'	CBcs CMac CRos CSBt EBee EPfP LRHS MSwo NHic NLar NRHS SCob SEND SPer
	'Wiri Cloud' ♀H4	CBcs CMac CRos EPfP LRHS MMuc MSCN MSwo NHic NRHS SCob SEND SEle SRms
	'Wiri Dawn' ♀H4	CRos ELan EPfP LBuc LRHS NHic NRHS SRms SWvt XLum
	'Wiri Desire'	CCCN CRos LRHS
	'Wiri Gem'	SCob
	'Wiri Image'	CBcs CRos CSBt LRHS MRav NRHS SEND
	'Wiri Joy'	CRos EPfP LRHS NRHS
	'Wiri Mist'	CBcs CRos ELan EPfP LRHS NRHS SCob XLum
	'Wiri Prince'	CRos LRHS
	'Wiri Splash'	CRos LRHS NRHS SGol
	'Wiri Vision'	CRos CSBt LRHS SEND
	'Wiri Vogue'	LRHS
§	'Youngii' ♀H4	CBcs CRos CSBt CTri ELan EPfP GBin LCro LOPS LRHS MHer MJak MMuc MRav NBir NHic NRHS SEND SPer SPlb SPoG SRms SWvt WCFE WHoo WSpi

Hebenstretia (*Scrophulariaceae*)

	Name	Suppliers
	dura	WAbe

Hechtia (*Bromeliaceae*)

	Name	Suppliers
	sp.	WCot

Hedeoma (*Lamiaceae*)

	Name	Suppliers
	ciliolata	WAbe

Hedera ✿ (*Araliaceae*)

	Name	Suppliers
§	***algeriensis***	SArc WFib
	- 'Bellecour'	WFib XLum
§	- 'Gloire de Marengo' (v) ♀H5	Widely available
	- 'Marginomaculata' (v)	CRos EPfP EShb LRHS MAsh SMad SPoG WFib
	- 'Montgomery'	CRos LRHS LSRN NRHS
	- 'Ravensholst' ♀H4	CMac EShb MRav SCob SGol WFib
§	***azorica***	EShb WFib
	- 'Pico'	EShb WFib
	canariensis misapplied	see *H. algeriensis*
	- 'Variegata'	see *H. algeriensis* 'Gloire de Marengo'
	canariensis Willd.	SEND
	- var. ***azorica***	see *H. azorica*

	Name	Suppliers
	chinensis	see *H. nepalensis*
	- typica	see *H. nepalensis*
§	***colchica***	CDul NWea SPer WCFE WFib
	- 'Batumi'	MBNS WFib
	- 'Dendroides'	NWea
	- 'Dentata' ♀H5	MRav SGol WFar WFib
	- 'Dentata Aurea'	see *H. colchica* 'Dentata Variegata'
§	- 'Dentata Variegata' (v) ♀H5	Widely available
	- 'My Heart'	see *H. colchica*
	- 'Paddy's Pride'	see *H. colchica* 'Sulphur Heart'
§	- 'Sulphur Heart' (v) ♀H5	Widely available
	- 'Variegata'	see *H. colchica* 'Dentata Variegata'
	cristata	see *H. helix* 'Parsley Crested'
	helix	CCVT CKel CMac CTri LCro LOPS NWea SCob WSFF XLum
	- 'Adam' (v)	LSRN WFib
	- 'Amber Waves'	WFib
	- 'Anita'	WFib
§	- 'Anna Marie' (v)	WFib
	- 'Arborescens'	EShb WGrn WSFF
	- 'Arborescens Variegata' (v)	EShb
	- 'Ardingly' (v)	WFib
	- 'Atropurpurea'	ELan GBin MMuc SEND WFib
	- (Aureovariegata Group) 'Chrysophylla' (v)	MSwo
	- 'Baltica'	WFib
	- 'Bettina' (v) **new**	WCot
	- 'Bill Archer'	WFib
	- 'Bird's Foot'	see *H. helix* 'Pedata'
	- 'Boskoop'	WFib
	- 'Bredon'	MRav
	- 'Brimstone' (v)	WFib
§	- 'Brokamp'	WFib
	- 'Buttercup' ♀H5	CBcs CDul CMac CRos CTri ELan EPfP GQue LRHS LSRN MAsh MGos MMuc NBid NLar SEND SPer SPoG SRms SWvt WCFE WFib
	- 'Caecilia' (v) ♀H5	EPfP MSwo SWvt WFib
	- 'Caenwoodiana'	see *H. helix* 'Pedata'
	- 'Caenwoodiana Aurea'	WFib
§	- 'Calico' (v)	WFib
	- 'Calypso'	WFib
	- 'Cathedral Wall'	WFib
	- 'Cavendishii'	see *H. helix* Cavendishii Group
§	- Cavendishii Group (v)	SRms WFib
§	- 'Ceridwen' (v) ♀H5	SPlb WFib
	- 'Cheeky'	WFib
	- 'Cheltenham Blizzard' (v)	CNat
	- 'Chester' (v)	CKel WFib
	- 'Chicago'	WFib
	- 'Chicago Variegated' (v)	WFib
§	- 'Classy Lassie' (v)	WFib
	- 'Clotted Cream' (v)	CRos ELon LRHS MAsh WFib
	- 'Cockle Shell'	WFib
	- 'Colin'	GBin
§	- 'Congesta' ♀H5	CMac NBir SRms WFib
	- 'Conglomerata'	ELan NBir SRms WFib
	- 'Courage'	WFib
	- 'Crenata'	WFib
	- 'Crispa'	MRav
	- 'Cristata'	see *H. helix* 'Parsley Crested'
	- 'Curleylocks'	see *H. helix* 'Manda's Crested'
	- 'Curley-Q'	see *H. helix* 'Dragon Claw'
	- 'Curvaceous' (v)	WFib
	- 'Cyprus'	see *H. pastuchovii* subsp. *cypria*
	- 'Dealbata'	see *H. hibernica* 'Dealbata'
	- 'Deltoidea'	see *H. hibernica* 'Deltoidea'
	- 'Diny'	SMad
	- 'Discolor'	see *H. helix* 'Minor Marmorata'
§	- 'Donerailensis'	MBlu NSla WFib
§	- 'Dragon Claw'	WFib
	- 'Duckfoot' ♀H5	EShb GBin WCot WFib
	- 'Dyinnii'	GEdr NLar WCot
	- 'Eileen' (v)	WFib
	- (Elegantissima Group)	CMac CTri EPfP LRHS SPoG WCFE
	'Tricolor' (v)	WFib
	- 'Elfenbein' (v)	WCot WFib
	- 'Erecta'	CDul CRos EPPr GAbr GCal IDee LRHS MBlu NHol NWad SPer SPlb WCFE WFib XLum
	- 'Eva' (v)	WFib
	- 'Fantasia' (v)	WFib
	- 'Feenfinger'	WFib
	- 'Filigran'	WFib
	- 'Flashback' (v)	WFib
	- 'Flavescens'	WFib
	- 'Fluffy Ruffles'	GKev WFib
	- 'Francis'	WFib
	- 'Frosty' (v)	WFib
	- 'Garland'	WFib
	- 'Gavotte'	WFib
	- 'Gilded Hawke'	WFib
	- 'Glache' (v)	MRav WFib
	- 'Glacier' (v) ♀H5	Widely available
	- 'Glymii'	ELan GBin GCal WFib
	- 'Gold Harald'	see *H. helix* 'Goldchild'
	- 'Gold Ripple'	see *H. helix* 'Golden Starlight'
§	- 'Goldchild' (v) ♀H5	CBcs CKel CMac CRos EBee ELon EMOT EPfP EShb EUJe LCro LOPS LRHS MAsh MGos MMuc MRav MSwo NBir NHol NRHS SCob SLim SPer SPoG SWvt WFib
	- 'Golden Ann'	see *H. helix* 'Ceridwen'
	- 'Golden Arrow'	see *H. helix* 'Goldfinger'
§	- 'Golden Curl' (v)	CMac CRos EPfP LRHS WFib
	- 'Golden Ester'	see *H. helix* 'Ceridwen'
	- 'Golden Girl' (v)	WFib
§	- 'Golden Ingot' (v) ♀H5	CRos ELan LRHS WFib
	- 'Golden Jytte'	see *H. helix* 'Classy Lassie'
	- 'Golden Kolibri'	see *H. helix* 'Midas Touch'
§	- 'Golden Starlight' (v)	EShb NLar SEND WFib
	- 'Goldfinch'	WFib
§	- 'Goldfinger'	CRos LRHS MAsh WFib
	- 'Goldheart'	see *H. helix* 'Oro di Bogliasco'
	- 'Goldstern' (v)	MRav WFib
	- 'Gracilis'	see *H. hibernica* 'Gracilis'
	- 'Green Finger'	see *H. helix* 'Très Coupé'
	- 'Green Man'	WFib
	- 'Green Ripple'	CBcs CRos CTri ELan EPfP LRHS MBlu MGos MJak MMuc MSwo MWht NRHS SCob SEND SLim SNig SPer SPlb SRms SWvt WFib
	- 'Halebob'	WFib
	- 'Hamilton'	see *H. hibernica* 'Hamilton'
	- 'Harald' (v)	CTri WFib
	- 'Hazel' (v)	WFib
	- 'Heise' (v)	WFib
	- 'Heise Denmark' (v)	WFib
	- 'Helvig'	see *H. helix* 'White Knight'
	- 'Henriette'	WFib
	- 'Hispanica'	see *H. iberica*
	- 'Hite's Miniature'	see *H. helix* 'Merion Beauty'
	- 'Hullavington'	CNat
	- 'Humpty Dumpty'	CExl
	- 'Ice Cream' (v)	LRHS WCot
	- 'Imp'	see *H. helix* 'Brokamp'
	- 'Ingrid' (v)	SRms
	- 'Ivalace'	EPPr EShb MSwo SRms WFib XLum
	- 'Jake'	WFib
	- 'Jara' arboreal	WCot

	- 'Jasper'	WFib
	- 'Jersey Doris' (v)	WFib
	- 'Jerusalem'	see *H. helix* 'Calico'
	- 'Jubilee' (v)	WFar WFib
	- 'Kaleidoscope' (v)	WFib
	- 'Kevin'	WFib
	- 'Kolibri' (v)	NBir SRms WFib
	- 'Königer's Auslese'	WFib
	- 'Lalla Rookh'	MRav WFib WRHF
	- 'Leo Swicegood'	WFib
	- 'Lightfinger'	ELon WFib
	- 'Little Diamond' (v)	CMac CTri ELan SLon SRms SWvt WFib
	- 'Little Luzii'	WFib
	- 'Luzii' (v)	WFib
	- 'Maculata'	see *H. helix* 'Minor Marmorata'
§	- 'Manda's Crested' ♀[H5]	ELan NLar WFib
	- 'Maple Leaf' ♀[H5]	EShb WFib
I	- 'Marmorata' Fibrex	WFib
	- 'Mathilde' (v)	CKel CRos NRHS WFib
	- 'Melanie'	ECha WCot WFib
	- 'Meon'	WFib
§	- 'Merion Beauty'	EUJe WFib
§	- 'Midas Touch' (v) ♀[H5]	SNig WFib
	- 'Minikin' (v)	WCot
	- 'Minima' Hibberd	see *H. helix* 'Donerailensis'
	- 'Minima' M.Young	see *H. helix* 'Congesta'
§	- 'Minor Marmorata' (v)	XLum
	- 'Minty' (v)	WFib
	- 'Misty' (v)	WFib
	- 'Needlepoint'	XLum
	- 'Niagara Falls'	CRos LRHS
	- 'Nigra Aurea' (v)	WFib
	- 'Obovata'	WFib
	- 'Oro di Bogliasco' (v)	CArg CDul CKel CMac CRos CTri EBee EMOT EPfP LRHS MMuc MRav MSwo NLar NRHS NWad NWea SCob SEND SEWo SLim SPer SPlb SRms SWvt WFar WFib
	- 'Ovata'	WFib
§	- 'Parsley Crested' ♀[H5]	ELan SGol WFib
	- 'Patent Leather'	WFib
	- 'Pedata'	CDul MSwo SRms WFib
	- 'Perkeo'	EUJe WFib
	- 'Peter' (v)	WFib
	- 'Pink 'n' Curly'	WCot WFib
	- 'Pink 'n' Very Curly'	WCot
§	- 'Pittsburgh'	WFib
	- 'Plume d'Or'	WFib
	- f. ***poetarum***	GCal MBlu WCot WFib
	- - 'Poetica Arborea'	EShb
	- 'Raleigh Delight' (v)	WCot
	- 'Ray's Supreme'	see *H. helix* 'Pittsburgh'
	- subsp. ***rhizomatifera***	see *H. helix* 'Rhizomatifera'
§	- 'Rhizomatifera'	WFib
	- 'Richard John'	see *H. helix* 'Golden Curl'
	- 'Ritterkreuz'	WFib
	- 'Romanze' (v)	WCot WFib
	- 'Russelliana'	WFib
	- 'Sagittifolia' Hibberd	CTri EPfP
*	- 'Sagittifolia' ambig.	LRHS MAsh MBlu SPoG
	- 'Sagittifolia Variegata' (v)	WFib
	- 'Saint Agnes'	see *H. helix* 'Golden Ingot'
	- 'Sally'	WFib
	- 'Salt and Pepper'	see *H. helix* 'Minor Marmorata'
	- 'Schäfer Three' (v)	WFib
	- 'Seabreeze'	WFib
	- 'Shamrock' ♀[H5]	WFib
	- 'Shannon'	WFib
	- 'Silver Ferney' (v)	WFib
	- 'Silver King' (v)	WFib
§	- 'Snow Cap' (v)	WFib
	- 'Spetchley'	see *H. hibernica* 'Spetchley'
	- 'Splashes' (v)	WFib
	- 'Sunrise'	WFib
	- 'Suzanne'	see *H. nepalensis* 'Suzanne'
	- 'Tanja'	WFib
	- 'Teardrop'	WFib
	- 'Telecurl'	WFib
	- 'Temptation' (v)	WFib
	- 'Teneriffe' (v)	WFib
	- 'Topazolite' (v)	WFib
§	- 'Très Coupé'	MMuc SArc SEND
	- 'Trinity'	WFib
	- 'Tripod'	WFib
	- 'Triton'	WFib
	- 'Troll'	WFib
	- 'Ursula' (v)	WFib
	- 'Very Merry'	WFib
	- 'Vitifolium'	see *H. hibernica* 'Vitifolia'
§	- 'White Knight' (v) ♀[H5]	WFib
	- 'White Mein Herz'	see *H. helix* 'Snow Cap'
	- 'White Ripple' (v)	WFib
	- 'White Wonder'	LCro LOPS SPoG
	- 'Williamsiana' (v)	WFib
*	- 'Winter Purple Vein'	CNat
	- 'Woerneri'	see *H.* × *soroksarensis* 'Woerneri'
	- 'Yellow Ripple'	see *H. helix* 'Golden Starlight'
	- 'Zebra' (v)	WFib
	hibernica	CCVT CDul CKel CSBt EPfP EWTr LBuc LRHS MJak MRav MSwo NWea SCob SEWo SGol SPer SWvt WFib
	- 'Angularis Aurea' ♀[H5]	WFib
	- 'Anna Marie'	see *H. helix* 'Anna Marie'
	- 'Betty Allen'	WFib
§	- 'Crûg Gold'	WCru
§	- 'Dealbata' (v)	CMac SRms WFib
§	- 'Deltoidea' ♀[H5]	MWht WCFE WFib
	- 'Digitata Crûg Gold'	see *H. hibernica* 'Crûg Gold'
	- 'Ebony'	see *H. hibernica* (Hibernica Group) 'Ebony'
	- 'Glengariff'	WFib
§	- 'Gracilis'	WFib
§	- 'Hamilton'	WFib
§	- (Hibernica Group) 'Ebony'	WFib
§	- - 'Rona' (v)	WFib
	- - 'Sulphurea' (v)	WFib
	- - 'Variegata' (v)	WFib
	- 'Lobata Major'	SRms
	- 'Palmata'	WFib
	- 'Rona'	see *H. hibernica* (Hibernica Group) 'Rona'
§	- 'Spetchley' ♀[H5]	CMac GEdr GKev MRav NLar NPer NWad WCot WFib WGrn
§	- 'Vitifolia'	WFib
§	***iberica***	WFib
	maderensis	WFib
	maroccana 'Morocco'	WFib
	- 'Spanish Canary'	WFib
§	***nepalensis***	WFib
	- KWJ 12345	WCru
	- 'Marbled Dragon'	WFib
§	- 'Suzanne'	WFib
	pastuchovii	EShb WFib
	- from Troödos, Cyprus	see *H. pastuchovii* subsp. *cypria*
	- 'Ann Ala' ♀[H5]	EUJe MBlu WAvo WCot WFib
§	- subsp. ***cypria***	WFib
	- 'Lagocetti'	see *H. pastuchovii* 'Lagodekhi'
§	- 'Lagodekhi'	WFib
§	***rhombea***	WCot WFib

- 'Japonica'	see *H. rhombea*
- 'Variegata' (v)	WFib
* × ***soroksarensis*** 'Woerneri'	NLar WFib

Hedychium ✿ (*Zingiberaceae*)

'Anne Bishop'	SEND
aurantiacum	CBcs CBct CCCN CDTJ CTsd GKev LAma LEdu XLum
aureum new	LEdu WPGP
brevicaule B&SWJ 7171	WCru
'C.P. Raffill'	see *H.* × *moorei* 'Raffillii'
chrysoleucum	CCCN
* 'Clarkei'	CCCN CTsd
coccineum	CDTJ CTsd GKev IKil MNrw
- B&SWJ 5238	WCru
- from Mizoram, India new	WPGP
- var. ***angustifolium***	WPGP
- 'Disney'	CDTJ
- 'Hungphung Stripe'	LEdu WPGP
- 'Khangkhui Tall Boy'	LEdu WPGP
- 'Khonoma Silver'	LEdu WPGP
I - 'Mishmi Form'	GCal
- 'Shillong Ghost'	LEdu WPGP
coronarium ♀H1c	CAbb CAvo CBct CCCN CDTJ CExl CTsd EUJe GKev IKil NRHS SPer XBlo XLum
- B&SWJ 3745	WCru
- 'Gold Spot'	CCCN CTsd EUJe GKev
- var. ***urophyllum***	see *H. flavum* Roxb.
densiflorum	CAbb CCCN CDTJ CExl CTsd ECha EUJe GKev IBlr LCro LEdu LOPS SRms WCot WCru WPGP XLum
- EN 562	CExl
- LS&H 17393	CExl
- 'Assam Orange'	CAvo CCCN CExl CPla CSam CTsd EUJe GCal IBlr IDee IPot LEdu MNrw SChr SEND SPlb WCru WPGP
- pale-flowered	GCal
- 'Sorung'	CDTJ CExl LEdu SChr WPGP
- 'Stephen'	CAvo CBct CCCN CDTJ CExl EBee EUJe IPot LEdu LRHS MNrw SChr SPlb WPGP
'Devon Cream'	CCCN CDTJ CExl LRHS SChr
'Doctor Moy' (v)	CDTJ EUJe
'Elizabeth'	EUJe IPot
ellipticum	CAbb CCCN CDTJ CTsd EUJe GKev LAma MPie XLum
- B&SWJ 8354	WCru
- PAB 7867	LEdu WPGP
'Filigree'	CExl
§ ***flavescens***	CBct CCCN CDTJ CTsd EBee EUJe GKev LAma LCro LOPS
flavum misapplied	see *H. flavescens*
§ ***flavum*** Roxb.	CAbb CBcs IBlr XLum
- HWJ 604	WCru
forrestii misapplied	see *H.* 'Helen Dillon'
forrestii Diels	IDee SPlb
- KWJ 12314	WCru
gardnerianum ♀H2	CAbb CAby CDTJ CExl CTsd EBee EUJe GKev IKil LAma LCro LEdu LOPS LRHS MNrw MSCN SArc SChr SDeJ SPer SPlb WCru XLum
- B&SWJ 12533	WCru
'Gold Flame'	EBee
gracile	WCru
greenii	CBcs CBct CCCN CDTJ CTsd EUJe EWld GKev IDee LEdu MNrw MPie SPlb WBor WCru XLum
- 'Mhui Fang'	WPGP
griffithianum	CCCN CDTJ CTsd IKil XLum
- white-flowered	CCCN
§ 'Helen Dillon'	CCCN CDTJ CExl IBlr SArc WCru WPGP
'Keneggy'	SVen
'Luna Moth'	WPGP
luteum	CTsd
maximum	CDTJ SChr WPGP
- B&SWJ 8261A	WCru
- HWJ 810	WCru
§ × ***moorei*** 'Raffillii'	WCru
'Samsheri'	CCCN SChr
spicatum	CAbb CCCN CDTJ CExl CTsd EUJe GCal GKev GPoy IBlr LEdu MNrw MRav SMHy WPGP
- B&SWJ 7231	WCru
- CC 1705	CExl
- P.Bon. 57188	CExl WPGP
- PAB 13.0718	LEdu
- from Ciaojiang	SBrt
- from Salween Valley, China	CExl
- var. ***acuminatum***	CAby
- 'Himalayan Lipstick'	GKev
- 'Huani'	LEdu
- 'Liberty'	WCru
- 'Shirui Steps'	LEdu
- 'Singalila'	LEdu WCru
- 'Troglodyte' new	LEdu WPGP
'St Martin's'	CCCN
stenopetalum B&SWJ 7155	WCru
'Tahitian Flame' (v)	EUJe
'Tai Pink Princess' (Tai Series)	CTsd
'Tara' ♀H4	CAvo CBct CCht CDTJ CExl CSam EUJe IBlr LEdu LRHS MNrw SArc SMHy SPlb WCru WPGP
tengchongense 'Trum Trom'	WCru
thyrsiforme	CDTJ CTsd EUJe GKev WCru XLum
villosum	CDTJ GCal
- var. ***tenuiflorum***	WPGP
- - KWJ 12305	WCru
wardii	CDTJ CExl CTsd EUJe LRHS WCru WPGP
yunnanense	LEdu SBrt SPlb WPGP
- B&SWJ 9717	WCru
- BWJ 7900	WCru
- L 633	CExl IBlr
- from Cally Gardens	GCal

Hedysarum (*Papilionaceae*)

coronarium	CAby CBod CSpe CWld ELan EPPr SPhx SPoG WKif WOut
hedysaroides	SBrt
multijugum	MBlu WSHC
tauricum	NHic

Heimia (*Lythraceae*)

salicifolia	ECre IMou MGil SBrt WPGP

Helenium ✿ (*Asteraceae*)

'Adios'	WFar
'Amber'	EBee ECtt ILea MAvo MTis WFar
autumnale	CExl CSBt CTri LSRN MMuc MNHC NChi SWvt WFar WPtf XLum
- 'All Gold'	SWvt
- 'Bandera'	ECtt NRHS
- 'Fuego'PBR (Mariachi Series)	CMac CRos CWGN EBee ECtt EMor LCro LOPS LRHS MAvo MNrw MSCN NPri NRHS SRms WNPC

§	- Helena Series	SWvt WFar
§	- - 'Helena Gold'	CBod EPfP NBre
	- - 'Helena Rote Töne'	CBod CChe CRos EBee EPfP LRHS LSun MHol NRHS WHoo
	- - 'Helena Yellow'	CRos LRHS NRHS
	- 'Ranchera'PBR (Mariachi Series) new	NRHS
	- 'Salsa'PBR (Mariachi Series)	CKno CMac CRos EBee ELan EUJe ILea LCro LOPS LRHS MAvo NRHS SPad SRms WNPC WWtn
	- 'Short and Sassy'PBR	CKno EMor NPri NRHS SPoG WNPC
	- 'Siesta'PBR (Mariachi Series)	CRos EBee LRHS MAvo NPri NRHS SRms
	- 'Sombrero'PBR (Mariachi Series)	CBod ECtt EMor LCro LOPS LRHS NEoE NPri NRHS SPoG WNPC WWtn
	'Baronin Linden'	MAvo
	'Baudirektor Linne' ♀H7	CRos ILea LEdu LRHS MTis NRHS SHar
	'Betty'	CBod ECtt
	'Biedermeier'	CWCL ECtt MNrw SAko
	bigelovii	XLum
	'Blütentisch' misapplied	see *H.* 'Riverton Beauty'
	'Blütentisch' Foerster ♀H7	CMea CRos GMaP LRHS MTis NLar NRHS
	'Bressingham Gold'	CRos LRHS MHCG MNrw NRHS WAvo WHrl
	'Bruno'	CRos LRHS MArl NRHS SHar
	'Butterpat' ♀H7	CDor CRos ECtt EHrv GMaP LRHS MArl MNrw MRav NRHS WMoo
	'Can Can'	CRos ECtt ELon EMor EPfP LRHS MAsh MAvo MNrw MTis NGdn NRHS SPer SRms WCAu WFar WGoo WMoo
	'Carmen' (UFO Series)	CBod
	'Chelsey'	CCBP ECtt ELan EMor EPfP GQue LCro LOPS LPla LRHS LSRN MNrw MPie MRav MTis NLar NSti SPoG SRms
	'Chipperfield Orange'	CSam ECtt GMaP MArl NGdn WOld
	'Coppelia'	CRos ECtt LRHS MHol MTis NBir NGdn NRHS WFar
	COPPER SPRAY	see *H.* 'Kupfersprudel'
	DARK BEAUTY	see *H.* 'Dunkle Pracht'
	'Dauerbrenner'	MAvo MTis SHar
	'Die Blonde'	SMHy
	'Double Trouble'PBR	CRos EBee ECtt EMor GBin IKil LLHF LRHS MBNS MHol MSCN NGdn NHpl NRHS SGbt SPer SRms WCot WFar
§	'Dunkle Pracht' ♀H7	CRos EBee ECtt EHrv ILea LSRN NLar WFar WOld
	'El Dorado'	CRos EBee ECtt ELon EMor LEdu LRHS MAvo MBel MTis NRHS NSti SRms WCot WFar
	'Fata Morgana'	CBod ECtt EMor LLHF MAvo MTis NBre SCob
	'Festival'	ECtt
	'Feuersiegel' ♀H7	CRos ECtt EHrv LRHS MAvo NRHS SAko WOld
	'Fiesta'	ECtt MTis WFar
	'Flamenco'	WFar
	'Flammendes Käthchen'	CRos EBee ECtt EHoe LRHS NRHS SAko SHar
	'Flammenrad'	CAby CSam EBee SAko
	'Flammenspiel'	CRos ECtt LRHS MNrw NRHS
	flexuosum	SPhx
	'Gartensonne' ♀H7	CSam LPla
	'Gay-go-round'	CSam
	'Gelbe Waltraut'	MAvo
	'Gold Doubloons'	EBee
	GOLD FOX	see *H.* 'Goldfuchs'
	'Gold Intoxication'	see *H.* 'Goldrausch'
	GOLDEN YOUTH	see *H.* 'Goldene Jugend'
§	'Goldene Jugend'	ECtt ELon WCot
§	'Goldfuchs'	WCot
	'Goldkogel'	EBee
§	'Goldlackzwerg'	CRos GBin LRHS NRHS
§	'Goldrausch'	CAby EBee ECtt EPfP GBin MNrw MTis NGdn SAko WCAu WFar WMoo WOld
	'Hartmut Rieger'	CSam
	'Helena' misapplied	see *H. autumnale* 'Helena Gold'
	hoopesii	see *Hymenoxys hoopesii*
	'Hot Lava'	EBee ECtt MBel MNrw MTis SCob
	'Hot Luv'	WCot
	'Indianersommer'	CDor CWCL ECtt EHrv GMaP GWyn ILea LRHS MNrw NLar SSut WCFE WGoo WSpi
	'Jam Tarts'	WCot
	'Julisamt'	LEdu MAvo
	'July Sun'	NBir
	'Kanaria'	CAby CBod CDor CRos EBee ECtt EMor EPfP GBin GWyn ILea LPot LRHS MAvo MBel MRav MTis NAln NEgg NLar NRHS
	'Karneol' ♀H7	CRos EBee LRHS NRHS
	'Kleine Aprikose'	MTis
	'Kleiner Fuchs'	EHrv
	'Kokarde'	MAvo
	'Königstiger' ♀H7	CRos ECtt GBee GBin ILea LRHS MHCG MNrw NRHS SAko WFar
	'Kugelsonne'	CSam EHrv GBin ILea NBre SAko WCAu
§	'Kupfersprudel'	MAvo MTis SAko
	'Kupferzwerg'	CWCL EAJP ELan IPot NBre SAko
	'Lambada'	EBee SMHy
	'Lemon Queen'	WSpi
	'Little Orange' new	WGoo
	'Loysder Wieck'	CKno EBee ECtt MAvo MTis NGdn WCAu
	'Luc' ♀H7	ELon MAvo MTis WCot
§	'Mahagoni'	LEdu
	MAHOGANY	see *H.* 'Mahagoni'
	'Mahogany'	see *H.* 'Goldlackzwerg'
	MARDI GRAS ('Helbro')	CBod CKel CRos EBee ECtt EMor LRHS MAsh MBel MTis NRHS SPoG SRms WCAu WMoo WNPC
	'Margot'	CAby MTis NBre
	'Marion Nickig'	MAvo WFar
	'Meranti'	CMea MAsh MAvo NDov WCot
	'Moerheim Beauty' ♀H7	Widely available
	'Moth'	MTis NEgg
	'Oldenburg'	WCot
	'Pat's Promise'	CMea
	PIPSQUEAK ('Blopip')	EMor LRHS NBre SRms
	'Poncho' new	MMrt
	'Potter's Wheel'	CBod EBee ECtt SHar SRms WWtn
	puberulum	CRos EPfP LRHS NBir NGrd NRHS
	'Pumilum Magnificum'	EHrv ELan EPfP GQue LEdu NRHS SMad SPer WFar XLum
	'Ragamuffin'	CSam ECtt GQue MAvo MTis WCot
	'Rauchtopas'	CAby EBee GWyn ILea IPot LCro LEdu LOPS LPla MAvo MBel MTis SAko WGoo WPGP
	RED AND GOLD	see *H.* 'Rotgold' Foerster
	'Red Army'	CRos ECtt ELan ELon EMor LEdu LRHS MAvo NGdn NLar NRHS SRkn SRms SWvt WWtn

'Red Glory' MTis
'Red Jewel' CRos EBee ECtt ELan ELon LLHF LRHS MAvo MBel MHol MMuc MNrw MPie NCGa NDai NGdn NLar NRHS SAko SCob WCAu WCFE WCot WHoo WMoo WPGP
'Ring of Fire' ♀H7 SMHy
§ 'Riverton Beauty' CSam ECtt MNrw NChi WCot WHoo WWtn
'Riverton Gem' ECtt GBee GQue MHCG
'Rotgold' misapplied see *H. autumnale* Helena Series
§ 'Rotgold' Foerster EBee ECtt NAln SRms WMoo
'Rouge Foncé' WCot WFar
'Rubinzwerg' ♀H7 Widely available
'Ruby Charm' ECtt EPfP MHol WCot WFar
§ 'Ruby Thuesday' Widely available
'Ruby Tuesday' see *H.* 'Ruby Thuesday'
'Sahin's Early Flowerer' ♀H7 Widely available
'Septemberfuchs' LEdu MCot MTis SAko SPhx
'Sonnenwunder' CSam NBre
'Sophie zur Linden' ECtt MTis WCot
'The Bishop' CBod CKel CRos EBee ECtt EMor EPfP LCro LOPS LRHS MRav NHol NRHS SCob SGbt SPer SWvt WFar WMoo
'Tie Dye' CBod EBee ECtt EPfP MAvo MHol NGdn SPoG WFar
'Tijuana Brass' ECtt NLar
'Tip Top' LRHS
'Vicky' MAvo MHCG SHar
'Vivace' LEdu WCot
'Wagon Wheel' ECtt WCot WFar
'Waltraut' ♀H7 Widely available
'Wesergold' ♀H7 CRos EBee ELon EMor LLHF LPla LRHS MAvo NDov NLar NRHS NSti SPoG
'Wonnadonga' EBee GBin MTis
'Wyndley' CAby CBcs CDor CMea CRos ECtt EHoe EHrv ELan EMor EPfP EShb GMaP LPot LRHS MBel MHer MRav MTis NBir NGdn NLar NRHS SCob SPer SRms WCAu WFar WHoo
'Zimbelstern' ECtt EWTr MAvo MCot MPie MTis NLar WCot WFar WPGP
'Zonnedam' ECtt

Heliamphora (*Sarraceniaceae*)

nutans SHmp

Helianthella (*Asteraceae*)

§ ***quinquenervis*** CBod CRos EBee GCal LLHF LRHS NLar NRHS

Helianthemum (*Cistaceae*)

'Alice Howorth' ECtt WIce
'Amabile Plenum' (d) EWTr GAbr GBin GCal GCrg
'Amy Baring' ♀H5 CRos CTri ECtt GCrg LRHS NRHS NWad SRms WHoo
'Annabel' (d) CRos ECtt GAbr GBin LRHS NRHS WFar
apenninum EPPr LLHF NHic SRms WArt
'Apricot' CTri ECtt
'Apricot Blush' WAbe
'Baby Buttercup' CMea GCrg
'Beech Park Red' CSma CTri ECtt EPot GCrg WAbe WFar WHoo WIce WKif
'Ben Afflick' CRos ECtt LRHS NRHS SIgm SRms
'Ben Alder' ECtt GAbr
'Ben Dearg' CMea ECtt SRms
'Ben Fhada' CAvo CBcs CBod CKel CMea CRos CTri EAJP ECtt ELan EPfP GAbr GCrg GJos GMaP LRHS MAsh NEgg NHic NRHS NSla SEND SPoG SRms SRot WAbe WFar WHoo XLum XSen
'Ben Heckla' CRos ECtt GAbr GCrg LRHS NRHS SRms XLum
'Ben Hope' CRos CTri ECtt ELan EPfP EWTr LRHS MJak NRHS SRms XLum
§ 'Ben Ledi' CBcs ECtt ELan ELon GAbr GCrg GJos GMaP MAsh NHol SEND SGbt SPoG SRms SRot WAbe WIce
'Ben More' CAvo CBcs CKel CRos ECtt ELan EPfP GAbr GCrg GJos GMaP LRHS MAsh MRav MSwo NBir NRHS SEND SIgm SPoG SRms SRot WFar WHoo WIce
'Ben Nevis' CTri ECtt SRms
'Ben Vane' CRos ECtt LRHS NRHS SRms
'Boughton Double Primrose' (d) ECtt WAbe WFar WHoo
'Broughty Beacon' ECtt
'Broughty Sunset' ECtt GAbr
'Bunbury' ECtt ELon EPfP GCrg GJos NBir SPoG SRms WFar
I 'Butter and Eggs' SRms
canum subsp. ***balcanicum*** WAbe
'Captivation' ECtt GCrg NHol
'Cerise Queen' (d) CTri ECha ECtt EPfP GKev MHol MSwo SEND SPer SRms XSen
chamaecistus see *H. nummularium*
'Cheviot' ECtt NBir WHoo XLum
'Chocolate Blotch' CRos ECtt LRHS NRHS NWad SEND SRms XSen
'Coachman's Salmon Coral' **new** GCrg
'Cornish Cream' ECtt NHol SRms
croceum LLHF
cupreum ECtt GKev
'David' NHol
'David Ritchie' WHoo
'Diana' CMea ECtt WIce
'Elfenbeinglanz' GCrg
'Etna' GCrg
'Everton Ruby' see *H.* 'Ben Ledi'
'Fairy' ELan
§ 'Fire Dragon' ♀H4 CMea CRos ECtt ELan EPfP GAbr GCrg GMaP LRHS NBir NRHS SGbt SIgm SRms WAbe WRHF XLum XSen
'Fireball' see *H.* 'Mrs C.W. Earle'
'Georgeham' CAvo CMea CSam CSma EBou ECtt ELon GAbr GCrg NBir NHol SPhx SRms WHoo XLum
§ 'Golden Queen' EBou ECtt EPfP GAbr MAsh MHol MSwo SRms
'Hampstead Orange' CTri
'Hartswood Ruby' CRos GMaP LLHF LRHS MBNS NRHS SAko SRms
'Henfield Brilliant' ♀H4 CExl CRos CSam CSpe ECha ECtt ELan ELon EPfP GAbr GCrg LRHS MHol MRav NBir NHic NHol NRHS NSla SIgm SMad SPoG SRms WCot WHil WHoo XLum
'Highdown' SRms
'Highdown Apricot' CRos ECtt ELon GCrg LLHF LRHS NRHS SPoG SRms WRHF
'Honeymoon' ECtt GCrg NWad

	Name	Suppliers
	'Jubilee' (d) ♀H4	CTri ECtt ELan ELon GJos MAsh MBNS NBir NChi NHol SPoG SRms WKif
	'Karen's Silver'	GCrg WAbe
	'Kathleen Druce' (d)	ECtt NWad
	'Kathleen Mary'	CMea WIce
	'Lawrenson's Pink'	CRos CSma ECtt EWTr GAbr GCrg GJos LRHS MHol NRHS SAko SRms WCAu
	'Lemon Queen'	ECtt GCrg
	'Lucy Elizabeth'	ECtt
	lunulatum	CMea CRos LLHF LRHS NRHS NWad SIgm SRms WAbe
	'Mead Sunset'	CMea ECtt
§	'Mrs C.W. Earle' (d) ♀H4	CRos CTri ECtt ELan EPfP GKev LRHS MBNS NRHS NSla SRms
	'Mrs Clay'	see *H.* 'Fire Dragon'
	'Mrs Croft'	SRms
	'Mrs Hays'	ECtt
	'Mrs Lake'	GAbr
	'Mrs Mold' **new**	GCrg
	'Mrs Moules'	SRms
	mutabile	SPlb SVic
	'New Moon'	CSma
§	***nummularium***	ENfk GPoy MHer MNHC NMir SRms WAbe WIce WSFF
	- subsp. ***grandiflorum***	LLHF
	oelandicum	NSla NWad SRms WAbe
	- subsp. ***alpestre***	EBou
	- subsp. ***italicum***	ITim
	- subsp. ***piloselloides***	GCrg WAbe
	'Old Gold'	ECtt SRms WAbe
	'Orange Phoenix' (d)	ECtt GCrg MBNS NWad
	'Ovum Supreme'	ECtt NHol
	'Peach'	CTri
	'Pershore Orange'	GCrg
	'Pink Angel' (d)	CSma ECtt GCrg MBNS SRms WAbe WFar
	'Pink Glow'	GAbr
	'Praecox'	CMea CTri ECtt SRms WHoo
	'Prima Donna'	ELan EPfP
	'Prostrate Orange'	SRms
	'Raspberry Ripple'	CRos CSma EBou ECtt ELan ELon EPfP EPot GCrg LRHS NRHS SPoG SRms XSen
	'Razzle Dazzle' (v)	CBod EBou ECtt SRms WHil
	'Red Dragon'	EPot GCrg WAbe
	'Red Orient'	see *H.* 'Supreme'
	'Regenbogen' (d)	ECtt GAbr GCal SEND
§	'Rhodanthe Carneum' ♀H4	CMea CRos EAJP EBou ECha ECtt ELan EPfP GCrg GJos GKev GMaP LRHS MMrt MRav MSwo NBir NRHS SEND SPer SPhx SPoG SRms SRot WAbe WKif
§	'Rosakönigin'	EBou ECtt NHol SEND WAbe
	'Rose of Leeswood' (d)	CBod ECtt GJos NEgg SPoG SRms WHoo WKif XLum
	ROSE QUEEN	see *H.* 'Rosakönigin'
	'Roxburgh Gold'	GCrg SRms
	'Ruth'	SEND
	'Saint John's College Yellow'	CRos CSam LRHS NRHS SRms
	'Salmon Queen'	CRos ECtt GAbr LRHS NRHS SEND SRms
	'Shot Silk'	CAvo CSma ECtt EWes SRms
	'Snow Carpet'	CMea
	'Snow Queen'	see *H.* 'The Bride'
	'Sterntaler'	GAbr SAko SRms WFar
	'Strawberry Fields'	ECtt NSla
	'Sudbury Gem'	CRos CTri ECha ECtt GAbr LRHS NRHS SRms
	'Sulphur Moon'	CRos LRHS NRHS SRms
	'Sulphureum Plenum' (d)	ECtt
	'Sunbeam'	EBou ECtt SRms
§	'Supreme'	ECtt ELan EPfP EWes LPla MHol SAko SRms XSen
	'Tangerine'	ECtt
§	'The Bride' ♀H4	Widely available
	'Tigrinum Plenum' (d)	EWes
	'Tomato Red'	ECtt NSla
	umbellatum	see *Halimium umbellatum*
	'Voltaire'	ECtt GCrg NWad
	'Welsh Flame'	ECtt NHol WAbe
	'Whenday'	CMea
	'Wisley Pink'	see *H.* 'Rhodanthe Carneum'
	'Wisley Primrose' ♀H4	Widely available
	'Wisley Rose'	CRos LRHS NRHS
	'Wisley White'	CTri ECha ECtt ELan SHar
	'Wisley Yellow'	ECtt
	'Yellow Queen'	see *H.* 'Golden Queen'

Helianthus (*Asteraceae*)

	Name	Suppliers
	'Anne'	ELon NDov
	atrorubens	MRav NBro
	'Bitter Chocolate'	LEdu MAvo WCot WPGP
	'Capenoch Star' ♀H7	CElw CRos ECtt GMaP LEdu LRHS MArl MRav MTis NBro NLar NRHS SWvt WCAu
	'Capenoch Supreme'	CRos ECtt LRHS NRHS
	'Carine'	ELon LEdu MNrw MTis NLar WCot WFar WOld
	debilis 'Vanilla Ice'	LCro LOPS
*	***decapetalus*** 'Kastle Kobena'	CDor
	- MORNING SUN	see *H.* 'Morgensonne'
	'Dorian Roxburgh'	ECha ECtt MAvo WCot
	× ***doronicoides***	GWyn
	'Double Whammy' (d)	ECtt
	'Flying Saucers' **new**	CKno
	giganteus	CMea SHar
	- 'Sheila's Sunshine'	CElw CRos EBee EPPr EWes GBin ILea LRHS MNrw NDov NRHS SAko SHar SMHy SPhx WFar WOld
	grosseserratus	MPie
	'Gullick's Variety' ♀H7	CBre ECtt EMor NBro NChi NLar SPhx SWvt WFar WOld WWFP XLum
	'Happy Days' ♀H5	CRos CSam ECtt EPfP EWes GBin MBel MHol MTis NCGa NGBl NSti SRms WCot WFar WHoo WOld
	'Hazel's Gold'	CRos LRHS NRHS
	× ***kellermanii***	EBee MAvo SPhx
§	× ***laetiflorus***	GPSL MMuc NLar
	- 'Daniel Dewar'	MMuc
	- var. ***rigidus***	see *H. pauciflorus*
§	'Lemon Queen' ♀H4	Widely available
	'Limelight'	see *H.* 'Lemon Queen'
	'Loddon Gold' ♀H7	CRos ECtt ELan EMor EPfP EShb LRHS MArl MBel MRav MTis NBir NRHS SMad SWvt WBor WCot WFar
§	***maximiliani***	CBod ELan ELon EPPr MMuc SMad SPhx SPtp
	microcephalus	CSam EBee ELon IMou MMuc NDov WPtf
	- 'JS Straffe Prairie Gast'	MNrw
	'Miss Mellish' ♀H7	EBee ECtt GCal LEdu WBor WBrk WCot WFar WHoo
	mollis	CBod CSam MMuc SBrt SPhx WFar
	'Monarch' ♀H5	CMea CSam EBee ECtt EWhm GBee MBel MMuc MRav NLar SMad WCot WFar WHal WOld

§ 'Morgensonne' MTis WBor WCot
× ***multiflorus*** 'Meteor' CRos LRHS NBre NRHS
'O Sole Mio' WCot WFar
occidentalis EPPr
orgyalis see *H. salicifolius*
§ ***pauciflorus*** EBee
quinquenervis see *Helianthella quinquenervis*
'Razzmatazz' SAko
rigidus misapplied see *H.* × *laetiflorus*
rigidus (Cass.) Desf. see *H. pauciflorus*
§ ***salicifolius*** CAby EBee ECtt ELan ELon EPPr GBin LEdu LRHS LSun MBel MCot MHol MMuc MPie MSCN NRHS SAko SEND SMad SPoG SWvt WAul WCot WMoo WPGP XLum
- 'Low Down'PBR SWvt
- 'Table Mountain'PBR LRHS MBel SWvt
- very fine-leaved WCot
scaberrimus see *H.* × *laetiflorus*
'Soleil d'Or' CMea ECtt SRms WFar WHal
strumosus WCot
'Triomphe de Gand' LEdu MTis NDov WFar
tuberosus EBee GPoy
- 'Bleu Patate' LEdu
- 'Drago' LEdu
- 'Dwarf' LEdu
- 'Fuseau' LCro LOPS SVic
- 'Garnet' LEdu
- 'Sakahlinski' LEdu
- 'Sugarball' LEdu

Helichrysum (*Asteraceae*)

adenocarpum SPlb
alveolatum see *H. splendidum*
amorginum 'Pink Bud' MMuc
- RUBY CLUSTER ('Blorub'PBR) CBor CRos LBuc LPla LRHS NRHS
angustifolium from Crete see *H. microphyllum* (Willd.) Cambess.
§ ***arwae*** WAbe
bellidioides see *Anaphalioides bellidioides*
bracteatum see *Xerochrysum bracteatum*
- 'King Fireball' **new** CSpe
'Coco' see *Xerochrysum bracteatum* 'Coco'
coralloides see *Ozothamnus coralloides*
'County Park Silver' see *Ozothamnus* 'County Park Silver'
'Dargan Hill Monarch' see *Xerochrysum bracteatum* 'Dargan Hill Monarch'
'Elmstead' see *H. stoechas* 'White Barn'
frigidum EPot WAbe
hookeri see *Ozothamnus hookeri*
'Icicles' GBin
italicum CBod CCBP CKel EBou ECha ENfk GBin GMaP GPoy GQue GWyn MHer MMuc MNHC SArc SEND SPoG SRms SVen SVic WHer XLum XSen
- 'Dartington' CBod EBou ENfk GBin SRms
- 'Korma'PBR CBod CKel CRos EHoe ELan EPfP EWhm GBin LRHS MAsh NHic NRHS SLon SRms
- subsp. ***microphyllum*** see *H. microphyllum* (Willd.) Cambess.
- 'Nanum' see *H. microphyllum* (Willd.) Cambess.
§ - subsp. ***serotinum*** CBcs CRos EHoe EPfP GPoy LRHS MRav SLim SPer SRms SWvt WRHF
lanatum see *H. thianschanicum*
ledifolium see *Ozothamnus ledifolius*
marginatum misapplied see *H. milfordiae*
microphyllum ambig. MMuc SPer SRms
§ ***microphyllum*** (Willd.) Cambess. ENfk MNHC SEND
§ ***milfordiae*** ♀H4 ITim NRHS SPlb SRms WAbe
orientale EPot XSen
pagophilum WAbe
petiolare ♀H3 CSam EBak ECtt MCot SPer SPoG
- 'Aureum' see *H. petiolare* 'Limelight'
- 'Goring Silver' ♀H3 SPoG
§ - 'Limelight' ♀H3 CSam ECtt MCot NPri SPer SPoG
- 'Variegatum' (v) ♀H3 ECtt MCot SPoG
rosmarinifolium see *Ozothamnus rosmarinifolius*
§ 'Schwefellicht' EBee ECha EPfP MRav SPer WSHC
selago see *Ozothamnus selago*
serotinum see *H. italicum* subsp. *serotinum*
sessilioides EPot WAbe
§ ***splendidum*** ♀H4 LRHS NBro SLon XSen
stoechas XSen
§ - 'White Barn' MAvo WCot WRHF XLum
SULPHUR LIGHT see *H.* 'Schwefellicht'
§ ***thianschanicum*** SRms XLum
- GOLDEN BABY see *H. thianschanicum* 'Goldkind'
§ - 'Goldkind' NBir XLum
- 'White Wonder' CRos LRHS NRHS SArc
trilineatum misapplied see *H. splendidum*
tumidum see *Ozothamnus selago* var. *tumidus*
woodii see *H. arwae*

Helicodiceros (*Araceae*)

§ ***muscivorus*** CAvo WCot

Heliconia ✿ (*Heliconiaceae*)

caribaea 'Burgundy' see *H. caribaea* 'Purpurea'
§ - 'Purpurea' XBlo
'Golden Torch' XBlo
indica 'Spectabilis' XBlo
latispatha 'Orange Gyro' XBlo
* - 'Red Gyro' XBlo
metallica XBlo
psittacorum CCCN
rostrata CCCN XBlo
schiedeana CHll

Helictotrichon (*Poaceae*)

pratense CHab EHoe
§ ***sempervirens*** ♀H5 Widely available
I - 'Pendulum' CBod EUJe GBin XSen
- 'Saphirsprudel' CRos EBee EPfP LRHS MJak NRHS NSti WCot WPGP XSen

Heliophila (*Brassicaceae*)

coronopifolia CSpe

Heliopsis (*Asteraceae*)

GOLDEN PLUME see *H. helianthoides* var. *scabra* 'Goldgefieder'
helianthoides CPla CRos EBee LRHS NBre WFar
- 'Limelight' see *Helianthus* 'Lemon Queen'
- LORAINE SUNSHINE ('Helhan'PBR) (v) CWGN ECtt EMor MHol MSCN NWsh SPoG WCot WFar WRHF
- var. ***scabra*** NHol SRot
- - 'Asahi' CBod ECtt GMaP WHil
- - BALLERINA see *H. helianthoides* var. *scabra* 'Spitzentänzerin'
- - 'Benzinggold' ♀H5 CRos LRHS MRav NRHS
- - 'Bressingham Doubloon' (d) ECtt

	- - 'Burning Hearts' new	EAJP
	- - GOLDEN PLUME	see *H. helianthoides* var. *scabra* 'Goldgefieder'
§	- - 'Goldgefieder' ♀H5	EBee NBre WFar
	- - 'Hohlspiegel'	CRos GBin LRHS NRHS
	- - 'Light of Loddon' ♀H5	CRos LRHS NRHS
	- - 'Mars'	EBee WFar
	- - 'Patula'	EBee ECtt
	- - 'Prairie Sunset'PBR	CBod EBee ECtt SAko
§	- - 'Sommersonne'	CRos ECtt ELan EMor EPfP LRHS NGBl NPer NRHS SCob SPer SRms
§	- - 'Spitzentänzerin' ♀H5	EBee ECtt
	- - 'Summer Nights'	EBee ELan EPfP LCro LOPS MBel MNrw NSti SPhx WFar
	- - SUMMER SUN	see *H. helianthoides* var. *scabra* 'Sommersonne'
	- - 'Sunburst' (v)	CRos LRHS NRHS
	- - 'Venus'	CBod CRos EBee ECtt LRHS MAsh MBel NRHS SRms
	- 'Summer Pink' (v)	CWGN EBee MHer MHol SPoG WCot WFar WRHF
	- 'Sunstruck'	ECtt
	- 'Tuscan Sun'PBR	EBee ECtt NCou SCob

Heliotropium ✿ (*Boraginaceae*)

§	***amplexicaule***	SDys
	anchusifolium	see *H. amplexicaule*
§	***arborescens***	ENfk EPfP EShb MCot MHom
	- 'Chatsworth' ♀H1c	CAby CCCN ECre ECtt MHom
	- 'Dame Alice de Hales'	ECtt MHom
	- dark-flowered	CSam
	- 'Gatton Park'	ECtt MHom
	- 'Lord Roberts'	ECtt MHom
	- 'Mary Fox'	ECtt MHom
	- 'Mrs J.W. Lowther'	ECtt
	- pale lilac-flowered	CSam
	- 'President Garfield'	ECtt MHom
	- 'Princess Marina' ♀H1c	NLar
	- 'Reva'	ECtt MHom
	- 'The Speaker'	ECtt MHom
	- 'White Lady'	CCCN CSpe ECtt MHom
	- 'White Queen'	ECtt MHom
	- 'Woodcote'	ECtt
	'Butterfly Kisses'	SPoG
	'Midnight Sky' new	WHlf
	peruvianum	see *H. arborescens*

Helipterum see *Syncarpha*

anthemoides	see *Rhodanthe anthemoides*

Helleborus ✿ (*Ranunculaceae*)

	abruzzicus	MAsh
	- WM 0227	MPhe
	abschasicus	see *H. orientalis* Lam. subsp. *abchasicus*
*	***acutifolius*** new	NHic
	'Angel Glow'	LRHS NRHS SCob WHil
§	***argutifolius*** ♀H5	Widely available
	- 'Red Riding Hood'	LRHS
	- 'Silver Lace'	ELan ELon EPfP GKev LRHS LSRN MHol NAln NBir NLar NWad SPoG WMoo
	- variegated (v)	GKev
	atrorubens misapplied	see *H. orientalis* Lam. subsp. *abchasicus* Early Purple Group
	atrorubens ambig.	EHrv EWTr MAsh SCob
	atrorubens Waldst. & Kit.	MRav XEll
	- WM 9028 from Slovenia	MPhe
	- WM 9805 from Croatia	MPhe
	- spotted	MPhe
	× ***ballardiae***	EPfP GKev
	- 'Candy Love'PBR	CRos EPfP LRHS MHol NLar NRHS SCob
	- 'December Dawn' new	CKel
	- HGC CAMELOT ('Coseh 940'PBR)	CRos ECtt EPfP LRHS NLar NRHS
	- HGC CHAMPION ('Coseh 730'PBR)	CRos LRHS NRHS
	- HGC JOKER ('Coseh 740'PBR)	LRHS SPoG
	- HGC MAESTRO ('Coseh 890'PBR)	CRos LRHS NRHS
	- HGC MERLIN ('Coseh 810'PBR)	LRHS NLar SPoG
	- HGC SNOW DANCE ('Coseh 800'PBR)	CRos LRHS NRHS SPoG
	bocconei WM 1332 from Sicily	MPhe
	- WM 1334 from Calabria, Italy	MPhe
	- WM 9719 from Italy	MPhe
	- WM 9905 from Sicily	MPhe
	colchicus	see *H. orientalis* Lam. subsp. *abchasicus*
	corsicus	see *H. argutifolius*
	croaticus	MAsh
	- WM 9810	MPhe
	'Dark as Night' new	CBor
	'Dorothy's Dawn' (Frost Kiss Series) new	SPoG
	dumetorum	GCal MAsh
	- WM 1306 from Hungary	MPhe
	- WM 1309 from Slovenia	MPhe
	- WM 9209	MPhe
	- WM 9627 from Croatia	MPhe
§	× ***ericsmithii***	CExl ELon EPfP LLHF LRHS LSRN MAsh NBir NLar SCob WHoo WPGP WSpi
	- 'Bob's Best'	CExl ECtt EPfP ESwi MBNS MHol SRms SWvt
	- HGC MARLON CREAM ('Coseh 980'PBR)	LRHS NRHS
	- HGC MONTE CRISTO ('Coseh 860'PBR)	CRos LRHS NRHS
	- HGC SHOOTING STAR ('Coseh 790'PBR)	CRos ECre LRHS NLar NRHS
	- 'HGC Silvermoon'PBR	LRHS NLar
	- 'Molly's White'	CRos NPri NRHS
	- 'Pirouette'PBR	ECre EPfP LCro LOPS LRHS MAsh NRHS SCob
	- 'Ruby Glow'	ECre EPfP LRHS NRHS SCob
	- 'Snow Love'PBR	CRos EPfP LBuc LRHS NLar NRHS SCob
	- 'Winter Moonbeam'PBR	CBcs CEnd CRos ECtt EHrv EPfP IKil LBuc LRHS LSRN MAsh MHol MJak NRHS SCob SLon SPoG SRms WCot WHil
	- 'Winter Sunshine'PBR	CRos EHrv EPfP LBuc LRHS NRHS SCob SPoG SRms
	foetidus ♀H7	Widely available
	- 'Chedglow'	CNat
	- 'Chedglow Variegated' (v)	CNat
	- 'Gold Bullion'	CAby GEdr MAsh SPoG
	- 'Green Giant'	SEND
	- 'Harvington Pewter'	CRos LRHS NRHS
	- 'Ruth'	MAsh SCob
	- 'Sienna'	SCob
	- 'Vogezen'	SCob

- Wester Flisk Group	CAby CBod CExl ECtt EPfP EUJe GBin GWyn LEdu MAsh NHol NPer SCob SEND SPoG SPtp WPGP WSpi
- Wilgenbroek selection	SCob
- 'Yellow Wilgenbroek'	SCob
Gold Collection	see *Helleborus* with names starting HGC
'Harvington Black'	CRos LRHS NRHS
'Harvington Blush Picotee'	LRHS NRHS SRms
'Harvington Chocolate'	LRHS NRHS
'Harvington Petticoat'	LRHS NRHS
'Harvington Rebekah'[PBR]	CRos LRHS NRHS
HGC CINNAMON SNOW ('Coseh 700'[PBR])	ECre ESwi LRHS NLar NRHS
HGC MADAME LEMONNIER ('Lem 100'[PBR])	CRos LRHS NPri NRHS
HGC PINK FROST ('Coseh 710'[PBR])	CRos ECtt EPfP LRHS NLar NPri NRHS SPoG
Hillier hybrids anemone-centred, spotted pink	CRos LRHS NRHS
Hillier hybrids anemone-centred, yellow	CBod CRos EMor LRHS NRHS
× ***hybridus***	CBod CBro CKel CMac CMea CRos CSam ECha ELan EPfP GKev GMaP ITim LRHS MBel MCot MGos MJak MRav NBid NRHS SCob SPer SRms WAvo WBrk WCAu WCot WJam WMoo
- 'Amber Queen' (Queen Series)	EMor
- anemone-centred	CBod EMor LEdu MNrw WFar
- 'Apple Blossom'	WFar
- 'Apricot Blush' (Winter Jewels Series)	CWGN
- apricot-flowered	WFar
- 'Ashwood Blushing Bride'	MAsh
- 'Ashwood Elegance Pearl'	MAsh
- 'Ashwood Fascination'	MAsh
- Ashwood Garden hybrids	ELan EMor EPfP MAsh MRav SRms
- - anemone-centred	MAsh
- - double-flowered (d)	MAsh
- 'Ashwood Lunar Neon'	MAsh
- 'Ashwood Neon Star'	MAsh
- Ballard's Group	CRos LRHS NRHS WFar
- Barnhaven hybrids, anemone-centred	XBar
- - apricot	XBar
- - dark purple	XBar
- - picotee	XBar
- - pink	XBar
- - red and green	XBar
- - slate	XBar
- - spotted	XBar
- - white	XBar
- - yellow	XBar
- 'Black Beauty'	WSpi
- black-flowered	GMaP WFar
- 'Blue Lady' (Lady Series)	CBar CBcs GAbr LRHS MBNS NCou NGdn SPer
- 'Blue Metallic Lady' (Lady Series)	CBod CExl CKel CTsd EPfP GAbr LRHS MBNS MHol NEgg NGdn NRHS SPer WSpi WTor
- Bradfield hybrids	EHrv MCot
- - anemone-centred	EHrv MCot
- - double-flowered (d)	EHrv MCot
- - picotee	EHrv MCot
- Bradfield Star Group	EHrv
- 'Burgundy'	CBod
- 'Cherry Blossom' (Winter Jewels Series)	CWGN
- 'Cherry Frost'	MAsh
- 'Cinderella'[PBR] (d)	LRHS SPoG
- 'Circe' **new**	EBee
- 'Clare's Purple'	CBod EWTr
- 'Cosmos'	MBNS
- cream-flowered	IFro WFar
- dark picotee	WFar
- dark purple-flowered	WFar
- dark red-flowered	WFar
- dark-flowered	WFar
- deep red-flowered	MHol WFar
- double (d)	MNrw WFar
- - black-flowered (d)	CExl LEdu WFar
- - dark purple-flowered (d)	WFar
- - green-flowered (d)	CBod WFar
- - picotee (d)	CBod GEdr WFar
- - pink-flowered (d)	CBod EMor WFar
- - purple-flowered (d)	CBod EMor GEdr MWat WFar
- - red-flowered (d)	CExl WFar
- - white-flowered (d)	CBod CExl GEdr WFar
- - - picotee (d)	CBod LRHS NRHS
- - yellow-flowered (d)	CBod CExl CWCL IFro WFar
- - - cream-speckled (d)	CRos LRHS NRHS
- 'Double Ellen Picotee' (d)	CWGN
- 'Double Ellen Pink' (d)	LCro LOPS
- 'Double Ellen Purple' (d)	LCro LOPS
- 'Double Ellen Red' (d)	LCro LOPS NDai
- 'Double Ellen White' (d)	CWGN EPfP LCro LOPS
- 'Double Ellen White Spotted' (d) **new**	LCro LOPS
- 'Double Ellen Yellow' (d)	EWTr
- Double Ladies, mixed (d)	GAbr WCot
- Elizabeth Town anemone-centred	IFro
- - double-flowered (d)	IFro
- - picotee-centred	IFro
- - single red-flowered **new**	IFro
- 'Enchantment'	MAsh
- Farmyard anemone-centred	WFar
- - apricot	WFar
- - black	WFar
- - cream	WFar
- - - spotted	WFar
- - dark pink	WFar
- - double apricot (d)	WFar
- - - black (d)	WFar
- - - cream (d)	WFar
- - - - spotted (d)	WFar
- - - pink (d)	WFar
- - - - spotted (d)	WFar
- - - primrose (d)	WFar
- - - - spotted (d)	WFar
- - - red (d)	WFar
- - - slate-grey (d)	CWld WFar
- - - white (d)	WFar
- - - - spotted (d)	WFar
- - green	WFar
- - - spotted	WFar
- - picotee	WFar
- - pink	WFar
- - - spotted	WFar
- - plum	WFar
- - primrose	WFar
- - - dark-eyed	WFar
- - - spotted	WFar
- - red	WFar
- - slate spotted	WFar
- - slate-grey	WFar
- - white	WFar
- - - dark-eyed	WFar

- - - splash	WFar
- - - spotted	WFar
- 'Farmyard Appleblossom'	WFar
- 'Farmyard Woodland'	WFar
- 'Golden Lotus' (d)	CWGN
- 'Green Ripple'	WFar
- green-flowered	WFar
- Harvington apricot	CRos LCro LOPS LRHS NBir NLar NRHS SLon
- - double apricot (d)	CRos LRHS NRHS SHeu
- - - blush (d)	CRos LRHS NRHS
- - - chocolate (d)	CRos LCro LOPS LRHS NRHS SHeu
- - - cream speckled (d)	CRos LRHS NRHS SPoG
- - - dark purple (d)	CRos LRHS NRHS
- - - lime-green (d)	CRos LCro LOPS LRHS NRHS SHeu
- - - pink (d)	CRos LCro LOPS LRHS NRHS SHeu SLon SPoG
- - - - speckled (d)	CRos GAbr LCro LOPS LRHS NRHS SHeu
- - - purple (d)	CRos GAbr LRHS NBir NLar NRHS SHeu SPoG
- - - - cascade (d)	CRos LRHS NRHS SHeu
- - - red (d)	CRos LCro LOPS LRHS NBir NLar NRHS SLon
- - - speckled (d)	CRos SPoG
- - - white (d)	CRos LCro LOPS LRHS NBir NLar NRHS SHeu SLon SPoG
- - - yellow (d)	CRos LRHS NBir NLar NRHS SHeu SLon
- - - - speckled (d)	CRos LRHS NRHS SHeu
- - dusky	CRos LRHS NRHS
- - lime	CRos LCro LOPS LRHS NRHS
- - picotee	CRos LRHS NBir NLar NRHS SHeu SLon SPoG
- - pink	CRos LRHS NLar NRHS SHeu SLon
- - - speckled	LCro LOPS NLar SHeu SLon SPoG
- - red	CRos LCro LOPS LRHS NLar NRHS SLon SPoG
- - speckled	CRos LRHS NRHS SHeu SLon
- - white	CRos LCro LOPS LRHS NLar NRHS SLon SPoG
- - - speckled	LCro LOPS SHeu SLon
- - yellow	CRos LRHS NLar NRHS SHeu SLon SPoG
- - - speckled	CRos LCro LOPS LRHS NLar NRHS SHeu SLon SPoG
- 'Harvington Shades of the Night'	CRos LCro LOPS LRHS NLar NRHS SHeu SLon SPoG
- 'Harvington Smokey Blues'	LCro SHeu SLon
- 'Harvington Smokey Double' (d)	SHeu
- Hillier hybrids slate	CRos LRHS NRHS
- - spotted, double yellow (d)	CRos EPfP LRHS NRHS
- - - - pink (d)	CRos EPfP LRHS NRHS
- - - pink	CRos LRHS NRHS
- - - white	CRos LRHS NRHS
- - - yellow	CRos LRHS NRHS
- - white	CRos LRHS NRHS
- - yellow, magenta eye	CRos LRHS NRHS
- - burgundy	CRos LEdu LRHS NRHS
- 'John Hopkins'	CRos LRHS NRHS
- Kaye's garden hybrids	NAln
- 'Kingston Cardinal'	LRHS MAsh
- Lady Series	CKel EPau NSum
- large, pink-flowered	IFro
- maroon-flowered	WFar
- mauve freckled, double (d)	IFro WFar
- 'Mrs Betty Ranicar' (d)	CBro EPfP ILea SCob SRms
- nearly black-flowered	WFar
- 'Onyx Odyssey'	CWGN
- pale pink-flowered	WFar
§ - Party Dress Group (d)	ELon GBin LSRN NLar SCob WFar
- 'Phoebe'	NPri
- Picotee Group	NLar NPri WFar WHoo
- pink freckled, double (d)	IFro WFar
- 'Pink Lady' (Lady Series)	CBar CBcs CBod CSBt EPau EPfP GKev GQue LRHS MWat NCou NEgg NGdn NRHS SPer
- pink-flowered	MBNS SDeJ WHoo
- pink-red-flowered	WFar
- plum-flowered	MMuc SEND
- 'Pluto'	WFar
- 'Pretty Ellen Pink'	GBin LCro LOPS
- 'Pretty Ellen Red'	LCro LOPS
- 'Pretty Ellen White'	LCro LOPS
- 'Primrose Picotee'	WFar
- primrose-flowered	ELan MCot
- 'Purity'	MAsh
- purple-flowered	WFar
- Queen Series, dark red-flowered	GBin
- - double white-flowered (d)	GBin
- - - yellow-flowered (d)	GBin
- - picotee	GBin
- - pink-flowered	GBin
- - white-flowered	GBin
- - yellow-flowered	GBin
- - 'Queen of the Night'	CExl EPfP WSpi
- red and purple	CBod
- 'Red Lady' (Lady Series)	CBcs CBod CExl CRos EPfP EUJe GAbr GKev LRHS LSRN MBNS NEgg NHol NRHS SPer
- 'Red Star'	CBod
- red-flowered	CBod LEdu WFar WHoo
- slaty blue-flowered	CBod LEdu SEND
- 'Smokey Blue'	CRos ELan LRHS NRHS
- smokey purple-flowered	LSRN SGbt
- 'Speckled Draco'	CExl
§ - spotted	EPfP NEgg WCot WFar WHoo
- - cream	NBir WFar
- - double, pink (d)	GEdr MWat WFar
- - - white (d)	EWTr WFar
- - - yellow (d)	CWld EWTr MWat WCot WFar
- - green	WFar
- - ivory	WFar
- - light purple	WFar
- - pink	CRos IFro LEdu LRHS MBNS NBir NRHS SEND WFar WHoo
- - primrose	ELan SGbt WFar
- - white	IFro MMuc MWat NBir SEND WBor WFar
- - yellow	WFar
- 'Stained Glass'	MAsh
- 'Tricastin'	WPnP
- 'Tutu'^{PBR}	CRos EHrv EPfP LBuc LRHS NRHS SCob SPoG SRms WHil
- Washfield double-flowered (d)	CBod CKel CWld EMor EPau EPfP LEdu MBel SPer SRkn WBor WHil
- 'White Lady' (Lady Series)	CBcs CBod CExl CKel GAbr MBNS NCou NEgg SPer
- 'White Lady Spotted' (Lady Series)	CBod ELon EPfP LRHS MHol NEgg NHol NRHS SPer WTor
- white-flowered	GMaP MWat WCFE WFar WHoo
- white-veined	WFar
- Wilgenbroek hybrids anemone-centred, red	SCob SMad

- - anemone-centred, white freckled	SCob
- - apricot	SCob
- - aubergine with white edge	SCob
- - black	SCob
- - dark	SCob
- - double picotee (d)	SCob
- - - red (d)	SCob
- - - slaty blue (d)	SCob
- - - white (d)	SCob
- - - white-spotted (d)	SCob
- - green	SCob
- - picotee	SCob
- - red	SCob
- - slaty blue	SCob
- - spotted, apricot	SCob
- - - aubergine	SCob
- - - pink	SCob
- - - red	SCob
- - - yellow	SCob
- - white	SCob
- - - with pink edge	SCob
- yellow-flowered	GMaP MCot SEND WFar WHoo
- yellow-freckled, double (d)	IFro
- 'Yellow Lady' (Lady Series)	CBar CBcs CBod CRos CTsd GAbr GKev LRHS MBNS MBel NDai NEgg NRHS SPer WTor
- Zodiac Group	MBNS
§ 'Ivory Prince'PBR	CRos EPfP LBuc LRHS MAsh NRHS SPoG WHlf
liguricus	GKev MAsh
- WM 0230	MPhe
lividus	CBar CRos CSpe EPfP EWes GKev LRHS MBel NAln NBir NRHS SDeJ SRms WCAu
- subsp. ***corsicus***	see *H. argutifolius*
- 'Green Marble'	ELan
- 'Pink Marble'	ELan
- 'Purple Ear'	LRHS
- 'Purple Marble'	EPfP
- 'Purple Rose'	SRms
- 'Rose Green' **new**	CSpe
- 'Silver and Rose' **new**	CSpe
- 'Silver Edge'	EPfP
- 'White Marble'	LRHS MAsh NAln
- white-flowered	GKev
lividus × niger	GKev NAln
'Lucy Black'	LRHS NRHS
'Marshmallow'	WCot
'Moonshine'PBR	CMil MHol NHol NLar NWad SLon WMoo
multifidus	NBir
- WM 1316	MPhe
- subsp. ***hercegovinus***	SCob XEll
- - WM 0020	MPhe
- - WM 0622	MPhe
- subsp. ***istriacus***	CBro MAsh WCot
- - WM 9322	MPhe
- - WM 9324	MPhe
- subsp. ***multifidus***	MAsh
- - WM 9529	MPhe
- - WM 9833 from Croatia	MPhe
niger	Widely available
- Ashwood strain	MAsh
- Blackthorn Group	GKev NLar
- 'Christmas Carol'	CRos EPfP LRHS NRHS
- 'Double Fashion'PBR (d)	SCob
- double-flowered (d)	CDor
- Harvington hybrids	CRos LRHS MAsh NRHS
- - double-flowered (d)	LCro LOPS SPoG
- 'HGC Jacob'PBR	LBuc LRHS LSRN NRHS SRms
- HGC JOEL ('Coseh 210'PBR)	CRos ECtt LRHS NLar NRHS
- HGC JONAS ('Coseh 220'PBR)	CRos ECtt LRHS NRHS
- 'HGC Josef Lemper'PBR	LRHS LSRN NLar SRms
- 'HGC Joshua'PBR	CRos LRHS NRHS
- HGC SNOW FRILLS ('Coseh 230'PBR)	ECtt LRHS NLar NRHS
- HGC WINTERGOLD ('Coseh 2010'PBR)	CRos ECtt LRHS NRHS
- 'Ivory Prince'	see *H.* 'Ivory Prince'
- marbled leaves	SCob
- 'Mini Blanc'	CRos NPri NRHS
- 'Mont Blanc' **new**	WCot
- pink-flowered	MAsh
- 'Potter's Wheel'	CRos EPfP LRHS NBir NRHS SCob
- 'Praecox'	ELon EWes
- Sunset Group	SCob
- 'Wilgenbroek Select'	EPfP SCob
× ***nigercors***	ECtt SCob
- 'Emma'PBR	CEnd CRos ECtt EPfP IKil LRHS MHol NPri NRHS SCob SPoG WCot
- 'HGC Green Corsican'	LRHS NRHS
- HGC ICE BREAKER FANCY ('Hlr 820')	CRos EPfP LRHS NRHS
- HGC ICE BREAKER MAX ('Coseh 750'PBR)	CRos EPfP LRHS MAsh NRHS
- HGC ICE BREAKER PICO ('Coseh 840')	ECre EPfP
- HGC ICE BREAKER PRELUDE ('Coseh 830'PBR) **new**	LRHS NRHS
- 'Morning's Pride'PBR	CRos LRHS NRHS
- 'Pink Beauty'	NLar SCob
× ***nigristern***	see *H.* × ***ericsmithii***
odorus	CBro EBee GCal MAsh MPhe SCob XEll XLum
- WM 0312 from Bosnia	MPhe
- WM 9415	MPhe
- WM 9728 from Hungary	MPhe
- subsp. ***cyclophyllus***	MAsh MPhe SCob
orientalis misapplied	see *H.* × *hybridus*
orientalis ambig.	CBar CKel CTsd CWCL GKev NAln NPri SCob WHil WPtf XSen
orientalis Lam.	CBcs CRos EWes LRHS MPhe MSwo NRHS XLum
§ - subsp. ***abchasicus*** (A. Braun) B. Mathew	CBro GKev MAsh WSpi
§ - - Early Purple Group	CTri GCal MRav NAln SRms
- subsp. ***guttatus*** misapplied	see *H.* × *hybridus* spotted
- subsp. ***guttatus*** (A. Braun & Sauer) B. Mathew	SRkn
- ***olympicus***	see *H. orientalis* Lam. subsp. *orientalis*
§ - subsp. ***orientalis***	GKev
'Painted Bunting' **new**	NPri
'Pink Beauty'PBR	CEnd EPfP NLar SLon SPoG WCot
purpurascens	CBro GKev GMaP LCro LOPS MAsh MRav NAln NBir XEll
- WM 0815 from Romania	MPhe
- WM 9211 from Hungary	MPhe
- WM 9412	MPhe
(Rodney Davey Marbled Group) 'Anna's Red'	CRos EBee ECtt EPfP GBin LCro LOPS LRHS MAsh MHol NRHS SPoG WCot

- 'Penny's Pink'	CBcs CMil CRos ECtt EPfP GBin LRHS LSRN LSun MAsh MHol MJak MNrw NRHS SCob SPoG WCot
× ***sahinii*** 'Winterbells'PBR	CRos EBee LCro LOPS LRHS NRHS SPoG SRms
'Sally's Shell' (Frost Kiss Series) new	SPoG
'Silver Dollar'	EBee EPfP GKev LCro LOPS LRHS LSRN NAln SPoG SRms
'Snow White'	LBuc
(Spring Promise Series) SP CONNY ('Hlr 160'PBR)	CRos EPfP LRHS NRHS
- SP RACHEL	NPri
× ***sternii***	CBcs CBod CRos CTri ELan EMor EPfP GKev GMaP LCro LRHS MBel MNrw NAln NEgg NHic NLar NRHS SCob SPoG WBrk WMoo
- Aberconwy strain	MAsh
- 'Ashwood Silver'	MAsh
- Ashwood strain	MAsh NLar
- Blackthorn Group	CRos EHrv ELon EPfP EUJe LRHS NRHS SWvt
- 'Boughton Beauty'	CMea EHrv ELan SCob WSpi
- 'Tom'	SCob
- 'Wilgenbroek'	SCob
thibetanus	CBro CExl EHrv EWes LAma LLHF MAsh
torquatus	CBro MAsh MPhe NAln XEll
- WM 0609 from Montenegro	MPhe
- WM 0617 from Serbia	MPhe
- WM 9106 from Montenegro	MPhe
- WM 9820 from Bosnia	MPhe
- 'Dido' (d)	CExl WFar
- double-flowered, WM 0621 from Montenegro (d)	MPhe
- Party Dress Group	see *H.* × *hybridus* Party Dress Group
'Verboom Beauty'	CRos LRHS NRHS
viridis	CRos GCal LEdu LRHS MAsh NAln SCob SRms XEll XLum
- WM 0444 from Italy	MPhe
- WM 1303 from Slovenia	MPhe
- WM 9723 from Italy	MPhe
- subsp. ***occidentalis***	CBro MAsh
- - WM 1340 from Germany	MPhe
- - WM 1344 from Spain	MPhe
- - WM 9501 from Wales	MPhe
WALBERTON'S ROSEMARY ('Walhero'PBR) ♀H7	CRos EPfP LRHS MAsh NRHS SHar SPoG WSpi
'White Beauty'PBR	EPfP NLar NRHS SCob SPoG WCot WHil

Helminthotheca (*Asteraceae*)

§ ***echioides***	WHer

Helonias (*Melanthiaceae*)

bullata	GKev

Heloniopsis (*Melanthiaceae*)

acutifolia B&SWJ 218	WCru
- B&SWJ 6817	WCru
- B&SWJ 6836	WCru
japonica	see *H. orientalis*
§ ***kawanoi***	GKev IMou WCot WCru
koreana B&SWJ 4173	WCru
leucantha B&SWJ 11148	WCru
§ ***orientalis***	GCal GKev LLHF WCru
- B&SWJ 6278	WCru
- B&SWJ 6327	WCru
- B&SWJ 6380 from Japan	WCru
- from Korea	EPfP SChF
- var. ***breviscapa***	EPfP GEdr LEdu SChF SMad WCru
- - B&SWJ 5635	WCru
- - B&SWJ 5873	WCru
- - B&SWJ 5938	WCru
- - 'A-so'	LEdu WCru
- 'Dark Single'	GEdr
- var. ***flavida*** B&SWJ 11400	WCru
- - 'Snow White'	GEdr
- variegated (v)	WCru
- var. ***yakusimensis***	see *H. kawanoi*
tubiflora B&SWJ 822	WCot WCru
- 'Temple Blue'	EBee WCru
umbellata	EBee EPfP WMoo WSHC
- B&SWJ 1839	WCru
- B&SWJ 3732	CBct WCru
- B&SWJ 6836	WCru
- B&SWJ 6846	WCru
- B&SWJ 7117	WCru

Helwingia (*Helwingiaceae*)

chinensis	CBcs CBod CCCN CDul CTsd EBtc ESwi EUJe EWTr EWld GBin LEdu MGil MPie NLar SBrt SEND SMad SPoG WBor WPGP
- broad-leaved	EBee NLar WPGP
- narrow-leaved	ESwi
himalaica	CExl ESwi SBrt
japonica	EWld NLar
- broad-leaved	WPGP

Helxine see *Soleirolia*

Hemerocallis ✿ (*Hemerocallidaceae*)

'A Bodacious Pattern'	EStr
'A Groovy Kind of Love'	EStr
'A Lady Named Hank'	EStr
'Aabachee'	CBgR EStr
'Aaron Brown' new	EStr
'Absolute Ripper' new	EStr
'Absolute Treasure'	EStr
'Absolute Zero'	SDay
'Adah'	SDay
'Addie Branch Smith'	SDay
'Adoration'	SPer
'Aerial Display'	EStr
'African Chant'	ELan
'Ageless Beauty'	ELon EStr
'Agnes Elpers'	WAul
'Ahoy Matey'	EStr
'Ahoya'	CBgR
'Airs and Graces'	SDay
'Alabama Jubilee'	WNHG
'Alabama Slammer'	EStr
'Alan'	CRos LRHS MRav NRHS
'Alaqua'	MBNS
'Alec Allen'	SDay
'Aleta Everett Adams' new	EStr
'Alexander the Great'	WHrl
'Alien DNA'	EStr
'Alien Fingerprint' new	EStr
'Aliens in the Garden'	EStr
'All American Baby'	EStr
'All American Chief' ♀H6	EStr
'All American Plum'	CWCL WAul WHrl
'All American Tiger'	SDay
'All American Windmill'	CBgR EStr
'All Fired Up'	EStr SDay
'All the Magic'	SDay
'Allegheny Skyline' new	EStr

'Allegiance'	WNHG
'Alli Sheldon'	ECha
'Alluring Peach'	EStr
'Almond Puff'	SDay
'Alpine Mist'	SDay
'Alternate Universe'	EStr
altissima	EStr MNrw SPhx XLum XSen
'Always Afternoon' ♀H6	CBgR EPfP EStr MNrw SDay WCAu WHrl XSen
'Amadeus'	EStr SCob
'Amazon Amethyst'	WCAu
'Ambassador'	CBgR
'Amber Classic'	ELon
'American Revolution'	CBgR CBod EHrv ELon EStr GBin LSun MBNS MHol NAln NChi SDys SPoG WAul WCot WHrl WMoo WPnP WSpi XLum XSen
'Amerstone Amethyst Jewel'	EStr
'Amy Michelle' (d)	EStr
'Amy's Rainbow'	EStr
'Angel Artistry'	SDay
'Angel in Oz' **new**	EStr
'Angel Rodgers'	EStr
'Angelus Runaway'	EStr
'Angelwalker' **new**	EStr
'Anna Rubinina' **new**	EStr
'Anna Warner'	ELon MMuc SEND
'Annabelle's Ghost'	CBgR
'Annie Welch'	CRos ELon LRHS NBre NRHS
'Antique Lavender'	WCAu
'Antique Rose'	EStr
'Anzac'	CBro CTsd ECha ECtt EHrv EStr NGdn SWvt WMoo
'Apollo'	XSen
'Apollodorus'	WNHG
'Apple Court Chablis'	EStr
'Apple Court Damson'	EStr
'Apple Court Ruby'	ELon
'Apple Swirl'	EStr
'Applique'	EStr
'Après Moi'	NLar
'Apricot Beauty' (d)	WSpi
'Apricot Velvet'	CBgR
'April Fools'	EStr
'Aquarelle'	EStr
'Arabian Magic'	EStr
'Arctic Snow' ♀H6	CBgR CBod CBro CMac CRos ECrc ECtt ELon EMor EStr GKev LRHS MNrw NRHS SCob SDay WAul
'Armed and Dangerous'	EStr
'Arpeggio'	EStr SDay
'Art Gallery Curly-Q'	EStr
'Art Gallery Quilling'	EStr
'Arthur Moore'	SDay
'Artificial Evolution'	EStr
'Asheville Pink Lady'	EStr
'Asheville White Winged Dove' **new**	EStr
'Ashton's Giggles' **new**	EStr
'Asian Artistry'	WNHG
'Asterisk' ♀H6	EStr SDay
'Astolat'	EBee
'Aten'	CBgR CRos SDay
'Atlanta Bouquet'	SDay
'Atlanta Cover Girl'	SDay
'Atlanta Fringe Benefit'	SDay
'Atlanta Full House'	SDay
'Atlas'	WGwG
'Augenstern'	EStr
'August Frost' ♀H6	EStr SDay
'August Morn'	CBgR
'Autumn Minaret'	EStr
'Autumn Red'	CBcs CBgR EStr GKin MMuc MNrw NBir SEND WCot
'Autumn Wood'	SDay
I 'Avant Garde' Moldovan **new**	EStr
'Avant Garde' Russell	EStr WCAu
'Avon Crystal Rose'	WNHG
'Awakening Dream'	SDay
'Awash With Color'	EStr SDay
'Awesome Blossom'	EStr MBNS MNrw
'Aztec Beauty' **new**	EStr
'Aztec Furnace'	EStr SDay
'Aztec Gold'	EStr
'Baby Betsy'	EStr
'Baby Blues'	SDay
'Baby Darling'	SDay
'Baby Red Eyes'	EStr WFar
'Bad Medicine' **new**	EStr
'Baja'	WFar
'Bakabana'	CRos LRHS NRHS
'Bald Eagle'	EStr MNrw
'Bali Hai'	EStr SRms WHrl WSpi
'Bali Watercolor'	EStr
'Bama Bound'	EStr
'Bamboo Blackie'	CBgR XSen
'Banana Cream Beauty'	SDeJ WSpi
'Banana Man'	EStr
'Banbury Cinnamon'	MBNS
'Bandit Man'	EStr SDay
'Barbara Alsop'	EStr
'Barbara Mitchell'	EStr EWTr SDeJ WCAu WNHG XSen
'Barbary Corsair'	EStr SDay
'Baroni'	ECha
'Bas Relief'	EStr
'Batgirl'	EStr
'Battle Hymn'	WCAu
'Bayou Bride'	SDay
'Be Bop a Lula' **new**	EStr
'Bea'	EStr
'Beautiful Design'	EStr
'Beautiful Edgings'	EStr
'Beauty to Behold' ♀H6	SDay
'Becky Lynn'	ECtt EStr
'Bed of Nails'	EStr
'Bed of Roses'	EStr
'Bedarra Island'	SDay
'Before You Accuse Me'	EStr
'Beijing'	SDay
'Bela Lugosi'	CBgR CBod CMac CRos ECrc ELon EPfP EStr GQue ILea LCro LOPS LRHS LSRN LSun MBNS MNrw NBro NChi NEgg NQui NRHS SCob SDay SPer WHrl WNHG
'Believe It'	WNHG
'Bella Isabella'	EStr
'Belly Button Slipknots'	EStr
'Beloved Deceiver'	SDay
'Ben Adams'	SDay
'Ben Bachman'	EStr
'Benchmark'	SDay
'Bengal Fire'	WNHG
'Berlin Oxblood'	WAul
'Berlin Red'	CAby CBod CWCL ECha ELon GBee MNrw SDay WFar
'Berlin Tallboy'	SDay WAul
'Berlin Yellow'	EStr
'Berliner Premiere'	EStr
'Bernard Thompson'	SDay
'Berry Blitz'	EStr

'Berry Patch'	EStr
'Berrylicious'	CBod EStr
'Bertie Ferris'	EStr NLar SDay
'Beside Still Waters' **new**	EStr
'Bess Ross'	XSen
'Best Seller'	CBod WCAu
'Bette Davis Eyes'	CBgR CWat EStr SDay
'Betts Allen'	EStr
'Betty Jenkins'	EStr
'Bettylen'	EStr
'Beyond Riches'	EStr
'Beyond Thunder Dome' **new**	EStr
'Bi-colored Blues'	EStr
'Big Apple'	EStr SDay
'Big Beautiful Babe'	EStr
'Big Bird'	EStr SDay
'Big Blue'	EStr SDay
'Big City Eye'	MBNS
'Big Honking Bahama Richie'	EStr
'Big Ogeeche'	EStr
'Big Smile'	MBNS MNrw SDeJ
'Big Snowbird'	SDay
'Big Time Happy'	LRHS SCob SPoG STPC
'Big World'	CBgR
'Birthday Honours' **new**	SDay
'Bitsy'	ELon SCob WRHF
'Black Adder'	SDay
'Black Ambrosia'	EStr SDay
'Black Arrowhead'	EStr LLWG WCAu
'Black Emanuelle'	CExl EMor LSun MNrw NLar
'Black Eye'	SDay WNHG
'Black Eyed Stella'	WSpi
'Black Eyed Susan'	CBod ECtt EStr
'Black Friday'	EStr
'Black Ice'	SDay
'Black Knight'	NLar SRms
'Black Magic'	CBod CBro CTri ECtt ELan EPfP EUJe GBin GKin GMaP LRHS LSRN MHer MRav NBir NEgg NGdn NRHS SPer WHrl WMoo WNHG
'Black Prince'	CBgR EShb MBNS NBre WAul
'Black Stockings'	EBee ELon EStr EWes MNrw SCob SDeJ
'Blackberries and Cream'	EStr
'Blackberry Candy'	CRos CSam ECtt EStr GKin LRHS MNrw NHol NRHS NWad
'Blackberry Sherbert'	WFar
'Blackberry Sundae'	EStr
'Blacky'	EStr
'Blessed Again'	SDay
'Blessing'	EStr
'Blessing in Disguise' **new**	EStr
'Blizzard Bay'	EStr SDay WFar
'Blizzard Blast'	EStr
'Blonde is Beautiful'	SDay
'Blood Spot'	SDay
'Blue Balloon' **new**	EStr
'Blue Deva' **new**	EStr
'Blue Sheen'	CBgR CMac CRos ECtt EStr GMaP MBNS WFar WMoo WRHF WSpi
'Blue Stardust'	EStr
'Blueberry Breakfast'	EStr WNHG
'Blueberry Candy'	ECtt EStr ILea
'Blueberry Cream'	CWCL ELon MMrt MNrw
'Blueberry Frost'	CBgR
'Blueberry Sundae'	CWat
'Bluethroat'	EStr
'Blufftop Volunteer'	EStr
'Blushing Belle'	NBro NEgg
'Bob Faulkner' **new**	EStr
'Bobby's Lavender Eyes'	EStr
'Bobo Anne'	EStr
'Bohemian Rhapsody'	EStr
'Bold Courtier'	CBgR
'Bonanza'	CBcs CBgR CBro CRos CTri ECha ECtt EMor EPfP EStr EUJe LEdu LPot LRHS MJak MRav NBir NBro NGdn NLar NRHS SCob SEND SPer SRot SWvt WCAu WCot WFar WMoo
'Bone China'	WNHG
'Boney Maroney'	CBgR
'Bonfire Heart' **new**	EStr
'Bonibrae Blue-eyed Baby'	EStr
'Bonnie Boy'	XLum XSen
'Booger'	SDay
'Booroobin Magic'	EStr
'Border Baby'	ECtt
'Border Lord'	EStr
'Border Music'	EStr
'Borgia Queen'	EStr
'Boss Hogg'	EStr
'Both Sides Now'	ECtt
'Boulderbrook Serenity'	SDay
'Bourbon Kings'	EMor SDeJ WHrl WWtn
'Bowl of Cream'	EStr
'Bowl of Roses'	EStr
'Brass Buckles'	see *H.* 'Puddin'
'Brazilian Orange'	XSen
'Breath of Blue Air'	EStr
'Breathless Beauty' **new**	WNHG
'Breathless Charm'	EStr
'Brenda Newbold'	EStr SDay
'Bridget'	ELan
'Bright and Morning Star' **new**	EStr
'Bright Island'	XSen
'Bright Side'	CBgR
'Bright Spangles'	SDay WAul
'Brilliant Circle'	ECtt
'Broadway Last Mohican' **new**	EStr
'Broadway Valentine'	XSen
'Brocaded Gown'	ELan SDay
'Brooklyn Twist'	EStr
'Brookwood Lee Causey' **new**	EStr
'Brown Witch'	ELon
'Browns Ferry Royalty'	EStr
'Bruce'	EStr
'Brutus'	WHrl
'Bubbling Brown Sugar'	EStr SDay
'Bubbly'	SDay
'Bucksport' **new**	EStr
'Bud Producer'	CBgR
'Buddy's Wild and Wonderful'	EStr
'Buenos Aires'	XSen
'Buffys Doll'	SDay
'Bumble Bee'	CAby ECtt EStr NBre SDay
'Burgundy Love'	EStr LLWG
'Burlesque'	SDay WCot
'Burning Daylight' ♀H6	CAby CBgR CRos EBee ECtt EPfP GAbr LRHS MNrw MRav NEgg NRHS SCob SPer SRms WAul WCAu WCot WFar WPtf
'Burning Inheritance'	SDay
'Burnished Ruffles'	EStr

'Butterfly Charm'	SDay
'Butterpat'	SDay
'Butterscotch'	WFar
'Butterscotch Ruffles'	SDay
'Buzz Bomb'	CRos ECrc ECtt ELon EMor EStr GKin LRHS LSRN MCot NEgg NGdn NRHS SPer WFar
'By Myself'	XSen
'Byzantine Emperor'	CRos LRHS NRHS
'Caballero'	EStr
'Cabbage Flower'	SDay XSen
'Cabriolet'	XSen
'Cajun Gambler'	EStr
'Calgary Stampede'	EStr
'Calico Jack'	EStr SPad
'Calico Spider'	EStr XSen
'Caliph's Robes'	SDay
'Call Girl'	SDay
'Calligraphy'	EStr
'Camden Ballerina'	SDay
'Camden Gold Dollar'	SDay
'Camelot Green'	WNHG
'Cameroons'	EStr
'Campfire Embers'	EStr
'Canadian Border Patrol'	EStr MNrw NLar SPer WHrl
'Canary Chaos'	EStr
'Canary Glow'	CTri WFar
'Canary Wings'	CBgR
'Candide'	SDay
'Candor'	SDay
'Candy Gram'	EStr
'Can't Fault Ya'	EStr
'Cantique'	SDay
'Cape Breton'	EBee EStr
'Cara Mia'	CBgR CRos EStr LRHS MBNS NBir NRHS WFar
'Caramba'	CBgR
'Caramel Taffy'	WHrl
'Caribbean Frank League'	SDay
'Caribbean Purple Spires'	EStr
'Carlotta'	SDay
'Carmen Marie'	XSen
'Carmine Monarch'	EStr
'Carnal Emporium' **new**	EStr
'Carolicolossal'	ELon SDay
'Carolina Cool Down'	EStr
'Carolina Cranberry'	ELan
'Carolina Dynamite'	EStr
'Carolina Lemon Squeezer'	EStr
'Caroline Taylor'	WHrl
'Carrick Wildon'	EBee WFar
'Carrot'	SDay
'Cartwheels'	CRos ECha EHrv EShb EStr GBee GKin GMaP LRHS MRav NBro NRHS SPer SRms SSut WCAu WFar WMoo
'Casino Gold'	SDay
'Castile'	SDay
'Cat Dancer' ♀H6	EStr
'Catawampus'	EStr
'Catherine Neal'	EStr SDay
'Catherine Woodbery'	Widely available
'Cathy's Sunset'	CSam ECtt EWhm GKin LRHS LSRN MBNS NBro NGdn NRHS NWad
'Cause for Pause'	EStr
'Caviar'	SDay
'Cedar Waxwing'	MNrw
'Celebration of Angels'	EStr
'Cerulean Warbler'	EStr
'Chamonix'	XSen
'Chance Encounter'	EStr LRHS NHol NRHS
'Changing Latitudes'	WHrl
'Chantilly'	EStr
'Charles Johnston'	CBgR EPfP EStr SDay
'Charlie Pierce Memorial'	EStr
'Checkerboard Curls'	EStr
'Cheerful Note'	WNHG
'Cheese and Wine'	EStr MHol
'Cherokee Star'	EStr
'Cherry Cheeks'	CRos ECtt ELan ELon EStr LRHS MHol MNrw MRav NRHS WCAu WCot WFar WMoo WWtn
'Cherry Eyed Pumpkin' ♀H6	EStr SDay WCAu
'Cherry Grove Beach'	EStr
'Cherry Lace'	XSen
'Cherry Peacock'	EStr
'Cherry Tiger'	EStr
'Cherry Valentine'	ELon GWyn SPad
'Cherrystone'	EStr
'Chesapeake Crablegs'	EStr
'Chesières Lunar Moth'	CBgR ELon
'Chestnut Mountain'	SDay
'Chevron Spider'	EStr
'Chicago Apache'	EBee ELon EPfP EStr LLWG MBNS MBel NBir SDay SPer WSpi
'Chicago Aztec'	ELon
'Chicago Blackout'	ECtt WAul WCot
'Chicago Cardinal'	EStr
'Chicago Cherry'	WNHG
'Chicago Fire'	CBod EBee EPfP MNHC SDay
'Chicago Firecracker'	XLum XSen
'Chicago Heirloom'	WCAu
'Chicago Jewel'	ELon NSti
'Chicago Knobby'	EBee EStr MNrw SDay
'Chicago Knockout'	CRos ELan EPfP LRHS NRHS WAul
'Chicago Peach'	NBir WCAu
'Chicago Petticoats'	WFar
'Chicago Picotee Memories'	EBee
'Chicago Picotee Promise'	WNHG
'Chicago Picotee Queen'	WNHG
'Chicago Queen'	SDay WNHG
'Chicago Rainbow'	CBgR
'Chicago Royal Blue'	CTri
'Chicago Royal Crown'	CAby ECtt EMor LRHS NRHS
'Chicago Royal Robe'	CWCL ELon MBNS NBid SDay SPer SRms WCot WWtn
'Chicago Silver'	SDay WAul
'Chicago Star'	WNHG
'Chicago Sugarplum'	SDay
'Chicago Sunrise'	CBgR CBod CRos ELon GMaP LRHS MRav NAln NGdn NRHS SDay SWvt WAvo WCot
'Chick Flick'	EStr
'Chick Magnet'	EStr
'Chicken Coop Madonna'	EStr
'Chief Sequoia'	EStr
'Child of Fortune'	SDay
'Children's Festival'	CMac CRos ECtt EStr GMaP LPot LRHS MBNS MRav NLar SWvt WFar WMoo
'China Bride'	EStr SCob
'China Lake'	SDay
'Chinese Autumn'	EStr
'Chinese Cloisonne'	EStr
'Chinese Imp'	NLar SDay
'Chinese New Year'	EStr
'Chinese Temple Flower'	SDay
'Chocolate Candy'	CWGN EStr
'Chocolate Splash'	SDay
'Chokecherry Mountain'	CBod EStr MSCN

'Chorus Line'	SDay WNHG
'Christina's Pink Parasol'	EStr
'Christine Lynn'	WNHG
'Christmas Is'	CBgR CMac CPar CWGN EBee ECtt ELon EStr GBin GKin LPot LRHS NHol NRHS WAul WCot WHrl XSen
'Christmas Ornament'	EStr
'Christmas Wishes'	EStr
'Ciarra Vonnie'	SDay
'Cimarron Knight'	CBgR
'Cindy's Eye'	EStr WCot
'Cinnamon Stick'	EStr
'Cinnamon Sunrise'	EStr
citrina ♀H6	CBgR CExl CMac CRos EBee EStr GKev IMou LRHS MBel MCot WCAu WCot WHoo WHrl XLum XSen
citrina × (× ***ochroleuca***)	WCot
'Civil Law'	SDay
'Civil Rights'	SDay
'Classic Caper'	WNHG
'Classic Edge'	SDay
'Claudine'	ELon
'Clearly a Thrill'	EStr
'Cleo'	WHrl
'Clothed in Glory'	EStr MBNS WCot
'Clownfish' **new**	EStr
'Cocktail Party'	EStr
'Colonel Jim Scheurich' **new**	EStr
'Colonel Joe'	WNHG
'Colonel Mustard'	EStr
'Comanche Eyes'	SDay
'Coming Up Roses'	CAby CBod CPar CWld ELon
'Condilla' (d) ♀H6	EStr SDay
'Conspicua'	CBgR SMHy
'Contessa'	CBro CRos LRHS NRHS
'Conway Red Light'	EStr
'Cool It'	LPot MPie NLar SCob SDeJ WHrl
'Cool Jazz'	EStr SDay
'Cooler Than Me'	EStr
'Copper Dawn'	EStr NChi
'Copper Windmill'	CBgR ELon EStr SDay WNHG
'Copperhead'	EStr
'Coral Majority'	EStr
'Coral Mist'	ECrc NBre
'Coral Sparkler'	WNHG
'Corky'	CAby CBro CRos ECha ELan EMor EPfP GBin GCal GMaP GWyn LRHS LSRN MBel MNrw NEgg NGdn NLar NRHS SCob SPer SPhx SSut WAul WCAu WFar WSpi XLum XSen
'Cornwall'	EStr
'Cosmic Blast'	EStr
'Cosmic Hummingbird'	ECtt EStr LRHS NRHS
'Cosmopolitan'	ILea
'Country Club'	EBee GMaP
'Country Melody'	SDay
'Court Magician'	EStr SDay
'Court Troubadour'	ELon
'Cowboy Scarf' **new**	EStr
'Coyote Moon'	EStr SDay
'Crackling Fire' **new**	EStr
'Cranberry Baby'	ECtt EStr WHoo WNHG
'Cranberry Coulis'	CWat
'Crawleycrow'	XSen
'Crayola Violet' **new**	EStr
'Crazy Awesome' **new**	EStr
'Crazy Larry'	EStr
'Crazy Mr Jim'	EStr
'Crazy Pierre'	WHrl XSen
'Cream Drop'	ECtt EMor EPPr GMaP GQue LPot LRHS MCot MRav NBro NGdn NLar NRHS NSti SCob SPer WAul WCot WFar WHrl WMoo
'Crimson Icon'	SDay
'Crimson Pirate'	CBgR CBod CBre CMac CRos ECrc ELon EPfP EStr GBin GKev GLog GQue ILea LPot LRHS LSRN NBir NEoE NQui NRHS SCob SPer SPlb WCAu WFar WHrl WMoo WWtn XLum
'Crimson Wind'	EStr
'Cripple Creek'	EStr
'Croesus'	SRms
'Crystal Cupid'	XSen
'Crystal Pinot'	ELon EStr
'Cumulus Sunset'	EStr
'Cupid's Gold'	SDay
'Curls'	CBgR MBNS SDay
'Curly Cinnamon Windmill' ♀H6	EStr SDay
'Curt's Gift' **new**	EStr
'Custard Candy' ♀H6	CBod CRos CWCL CWGN ECtt EPfP EStr GKin LRHS MBNS MBel NAst NHol NRHS WCAu WNHG
'Cute As Can Be'	EStr
'Cyber Zone' **new**	EStr
'Cyclone Twister'	EStr
'Cynthia Lucius'	EStr
'Cynthia Mary'	ECtt GKin
'Cypriana'	XSen
'Czarina'	EStr
'Daddeeo Segrest'	EStr
'Daddy's Catfish Stew'	EStr
'Dad's Best White'	EStr
'Daily Dollar'	MBNS NGdn
'Dallas Spider Time'	SDay
'Dallas Star'	EStr SDay WHrl
'Dan Mahony'	EStr
'Dan Tau'	SDay
'Dance Ballerina Dance'	EBee SDay
'Dance with Somebody'	EStr
'Dances with Giraffes' **new**	EStr
'Dancing Crab'	CBgR
'Dancing Dreams'	EStr
'Dancing Elf'	EStr
'Dancing in the Rain'	EStr
'Dancing on Ice'	EStr
'Dancing Shiva'	SDay
'Dancing Summerbird'	ELon EStr SDay
'Dancing with Linda' **new**	EStr
'Daring Deception'	CRos ECtt ELon EPfP LRHS MNrw NRHS SCob SDeJ
'Daring Dilemma'	EStr
'Daring Reflection'	SDay
'Darius'	WNHG
'Dark Angel'	NRHS
'Dark Magician'	EStr
'Dark Monkey'	EStr
'Darker Shade'	EStr
'Darrell'	SDay
'David Holman'	WNHG
'David Kirchhoff'	EStr SDay
'Davidson Update'	WNHG
'Daylight'	WNHG
'De Colores'	EStr
'Debussy'	EStr
'Decatur Ballerina'	WNHG
'Decatur Captivation'	WNHG
'Decatur Dictator'	WNHG

'Decatur Imp' SDay WHrl
'Decatur Jewel' WNHG
'Decatur Piecrust' EStr
'Decatur Rhythm' WNHG
'Decatur Supreme' WNHG
'Decatur Treasure Chest' WNHG
'Decidedly Happy' EStr
'Delicate Design' SDay
'Deloris Gould' SDay
'Demetrius' CWat EStr
'Desdemona' EStr XLum
'Desert Dreams' WCot
'Desert Icicle' EStr
'Designer Gown' EStr SDay
'Designer Jeans' EStr SDay
'Designer Rhythm' EStr
'Desirable Duchess' EStr
'Destination Y' XSen
'Destined to See' CBcs CBro ECtt EHrv ELon EStr EWhm LPot MHol MNrw NBir NBro NEgg SPad SPer WAvo WCot WHrl
'Devon Cream' SPer
'Devon Rugby' **new** SDay
'Devonshire' SDay
'Diamond Dust' CKel ECtt LSRN NLar SPer WSpi
'Diana Grenfell' CBgR
'Dick Kitchingman' CBgR
'Dipped in Ink' EStr
'Discarded Beauty' EStr
'Distant Galaxy' EStr WCAu
'Diva Bride' EStr
'Diva's Choice' EStr MHol SCob
'Divertissment' CBgR ELon SDay WHrl
'Dizzy Miss Lizzy' EStr
'Doc Holliday' EStr
'Doctor Doom' **new** EStr
'Doctor Freckles Mr Hyde' EStr
'Doctor McGregor's Garden' **new** EStr
'Doctor Strangelove' **new** EStr
'Dominic' CBgR MBNS SDay WCot WMoo
'Don Stevens' WHrl
'Don's Wild Heather' EStr
'Don't Leave Empty-handed' EStr
'Dorethe Louise' CBgR SDay
'Dorothy McDade' MNrw
'Dot Paul' ELan
'Double Action' (d) SDay
'Double Charm' (d) XSen
'Double Cream' (d) WCot
'Double Cutie' (d) CRos EStr LRHS NLar NRHS SDay SRms
'Double Delicious' (d) WCot
'Double Doubloon' (d) XLum
'Double Dream' (d) CWld EStr WHrl
'Double Firecracker' (d) EBee MBNS NBro NLar XSen
'Double Gardenia' (d) EStr WNHG
'Double Glitter' (d) XSen
'Double Honey' (d) EStr
'Double Oh Seven' (d) ELon
'Double Pink Treasure' (d) SDay
'Double Pompon' (d) EStr
'Double Pop Art' (d) XSen
'Double Red Royal' (d) EPfP EStr XSen
'Double River Wye' (d) CBgR CRos ECtt EMor EShb EStr GBee LRHS MBNS MHer MNrw NGdn NRHS WAul WBrk WCot WFar WHoo WHrl
'Dowager Queen' WNHG
'Dragon Fire Breath' EStr
'Dragon King' SDay
'Dragon Lore' EPfP EStr
'Dragon Seeker' EStr
'Dragon's Eye' CRos LRHS NRHS SDay WNHG
'Dragon's Orb' SDay
'Dream Baby' NBre
'Dresden Doll' SPer
'Driving Me Wild' SDay
'Drooling Lizard' **new** EStr
'Drop Cloth' EStr
'Duke of Earl' CBgR
dumortieri CAgr CBro EBee ECha EHrv ELan EWhm MCot MMuc MRav NBid NBir NSti SCob SEND SPer WCot WWtn XSen
– B&SWJ 1283 WCru
'Dumpy' EStr
'Dune Buggy' XSen
'Dune Needlepoint' EStr WHrl
'Duplex' (d) XSen
'Dutch Art' SDay
'Dutch Artist' (d) EStr
'Dutch Beauty' WFar
'Dutch Gold' MHCG MNrw
'Earl of Warwick' CBgR
'Earlianna' EStr
'Earnest Yearwood' SDay
'Easy Ned' ELon
'Easy Street' SDay
'Eat Our Wake Pintaheads' EStr
'Echo Echo' **new** EStr
'Ed Kirchhoff' XLum
'Ed Murray' EStr SDay WAul WCAu
'Edgar Brown' MBNS SDay WCot
'Edge Ahead' CMac ECtt GKin LRHS NHol NRHS SDay WCAu WHrl
'Edge of Darkness' CKel CWGN EPfP MBNS NSti SDay WFar
'Edith Vaughan' EStr
'Edna Spalding' CRos LRHS NRHS SDay
'Eenie Allegro' CBro ECtt SPer
'Eenie Fanfare' EStr NBir
'Eenie Weenie' CBro ECtt ELon EStr GKev NBro SRms WWtn
'Eenie Weenie Non-stop' ECha EPPr
'Eggplant Escapade' ♀H6 CBgR EStr SDay WHrl
'Egyptian Ibis' WNHG
'Egyptian Queen' CBgR
'Eight Miles High' EStr
'Eighteen Karat' EStr
'El Desperado' CBgR CRos CSam ECtt ELon EStr GQue ILea LRHS MBNS MHol MNrw NEgg NRHS WAvo WCAu WCot
'El Glorioso' CWat EStr
'Elaine Farrant' SDay
'Elaine Strutt' MNrw SDay SWvt WCot WSpi
'Elegant Candy' ♀H6 CBgR CMac EPfP EStr WCAu
'Eleonor' EBee WFar
'Elfin Illusion' EStr
'Elizabeth Salter' CWCL EStr NLar
'Eloquent Silence' SDay
'Elsie Stelter' **new** EStr
'Elva White Grow' SDay
'Elven Elegance' **new** EStr
'Emerald Dew' SDay
'Emerald Empress' **new** EStr
'Emerald Eye' SDay
'Emerald Starburst' EStr

'Emperor's Choice'	SDay
'Emperor's Dragon'	EStr SDay
'Enchanted Forest'	EStr WCAu
'Enchanter's Spell'	SDay
'Enchanting Blessing'	EStr SDay
'English Skies' **new**	EStr
'Entrapment'	ECtt EStr SDeJ WFar
'Entwined in the Vine'	EStr
'Envoyé Spécial'	XSen
'Erica Nichole Gonzales'	SDay
'Erin Prairie'	EStr
esculenta	SMad
'Eternity Road'	EStr
'Etruscan Tomb'	EStr
'Evelyn Claar'	CMac
'Evelyn Lela Stout'	SDay
'Evening Enchantment'	EStr SDay
'Ever So Ruffled'	EStr SDay
'Excellent'	EStr
'Exotic Love'	SDay
'Exotic Spider'	EStr
'Exotic Star'	EStr
'Exotic Treasure'	EStr
'Exploded Pumpkin'	EBee EStr
'Exploding Galaxy'	EStr
'Explosion in the Paint Factory'	EStr
'Eye of the Hurricane'	EStr
'Eye on a String' **new**	EStr
'Eye on America'	EBee ELon
'Eyes are Mosaics'	EStr
'Ezekiel'	XSen
'Fabergé'	SDay
'Fairest Love'	EBee MBNS MNrw
'Fairest of Them'	CBgR
'Fairy Charm'	SDay
'Fairy Summerbird'	SDay
'Fairy Tale Pink'	EStr SDay
'Fall Farewell'	WNHG
'Fall Guy'	SDay
'Fama'	EStr
'Fandango'	SPer
'Farmer's Daughter'	CBgR
'Father James Foster'	EStr
'Fellow'	EStr
'Femme Osage'	EStr SDay
'Feria'	XSen
'Fiestaville'	EStr
'Final Touch'	CBgR CBod EBee EStr LLWG MSwo NBro
'Finders Keepers'	EBee EStr
'Fire and Fog'	EStr
'Fire Bird Suite'	EStr
'Fire Dance'	ELon
'Fire from Heaven'	WHrl
'Fire Tree'	CBgR ELon EStr
'Firelight' **new**	EStr
'Firestorm'	EStr
'First Formal'	SPer
'First Knight'	EStr SDay
'Flaming Firebird'	EStr
'Flaming Sword'	WBrk WRHF
'Flamingo Parade'	EStr
flava	see *H. lilioasphodelus*
'Fleeting Fancy'	SDay
'Flip Fiasco'	EStr
'Florentine Silk'	EStr
'Florida Sunshine' (d)	XSen
'Florissant Miss'	EStr
'Flower Basket' (d)	EStr
'Flower Pavilion'	SDay
'Floyd Cove'	SDay
'Fly Catcher'	CBgR SDay
'Fooled Me' ♀H6	CKel CRos EBee ECtt EPfP EStr LRHS NRHS SDay
'Forbidden Desires'	EStr
'Forest Phantom'	EStr
'Forever Red'	EStr
'Forgotten Dreams'	EBee
forrestii	CExl GKev
'Forsooth'	CBgR
'Forsyth Ace of Hearts'	CBgR
'Forsyth Evening Glow'	EStr
'Forsyth White Buds'	EStr
'Fortress of Solitude' **new**	EStr
'Forty Second Street'	EStr MBNS
'Fragrant Bouquet'	EStr
'Fragrant Pastel Cheers'	SDay
'Fragrant Returns'	ECtt LEdu SPoG
'Fragrant Treasure'	CWld
'Frank Gladney'	XSen
'Frankly Scarlet'	EStr
'Frans Hals'	Widely available
'Fred Ham'	XSen
'Free Wheelin''	EPfP EStr SCob
'French Connection'	SDay
'French Lingerie'	EStr
'French Pavilion'	SDay
'French Porcelain'	SDay
'Fresh Air'	MNrw
'Fried Green Tomatoes'	EStr
'Friends with Benefits'	EStr
'Frilly Bliss'	EStr
'Fritz Schroer'	CBgR
'Frosted Encore'	SDay
'Frosted Vintage Ruffles'	EBee EStr EWes MNrw WCAu
'Frozen Jade'	CRos EBee LRHS NRHS SDay
'Full Grown'	EStr
'Fully Blessed' **new**	EStr
fulva	CTri ELan GPSL LPot MMuc NBir SCob SEND SRms WBrk WHrl XSen
- B&SWJ 8647	WCru
- 'Flore Pleno' (d)	CAvo CMac CTri CWld ECtt ELan GBin LPot MHer MJak MRav NBir NBro NGdn NSti SMad SPer SRms WBrk WCAu WMoo XSen
- 'Green Kwanso' (d)	CBgR CExl CRos ECha ITim LRHS NRHS WFar WPnP WWtn
- var. ***kwanso***	WWtn
- - B&SWJ 6328	WCru
- 'Kwanso' ambig. (d)	CRos LRHS NRHS
- var. ***littorea***	CMac XLum XSen
- var. ***rosea***	LPla WCot XSen
§ - 'Variegated Kwanso' (d/v)	CBro ELon MRav NBir SCob SMad WBor WCot WFar WHer WHoo WHrl
- yellow-variegated (v)	WCot
'Fun Fling'	EStr
'Funicular'	EStr
'Gadsden Light'	EStr SDay
'Gala Greetings'	XSen
'Galaxy Ranger'	EStr
'Gale Storm'	EStr WNHG
'Galena Holiday' **new**	EWes
'Galileo'	EStr
'Garden Crawler'	CBgR
'Garden Portrait'	SDay
'Garrett Allen'	EStr
'Gary Colby'	EStr
'Gay Octopus'	CBgR EStr WHrl

'Gay Rapture'	SPer
'Gemini'	SDay
'Gender Equality' **new**	EStr
'Geneva Firetruck'	EStr
'Gentle Country Breeze'	SDay
'Gentle Rose'	EStr SDay
'Gentle Shepherd'	Widely available
'George Cunningham'	CRos ECtt EHrv ELan LPot LRHS MRav NBir NRHS SDay WFar
'George David'	WHrl
'Georgette Belden'	CRos ECtt GKin LRHS NHol NRHS
'Georgia Cream' (d)	NLar
'Gerda Brooker'	EStr
'Get All Excited'	ELon
'Giant Moon'	CBgR CRos ECtt ELan EStr LRHS NRHS SRms WHal
'Giddy Go Round'	SDay
'Ginger Twist'	EStr
'Girouette'	XSen
'Glacier Bay'	CBgR
'Glazed Heather Plum'	EStr
'Gleber's Top Cream'	EStr
'Gleeman Song'	CBgR
'Glendevon'	EStr
'Glittering Treasure'	XLum
'Glow Appeal' **new**	EStr
'Glowing Heart'	SDay
'Go Seminoles'	EStr
'God's Handicraft'	EStr
'Going Bananas'[PBR]	WCot
'Gold Elephant'	SDay
'Gold Imperial'	NBre
'Golden Bell'	NGdn
'Golden Chimes'	Widely available
'Golden Compass'	EStr
'Golden Firefly'	SDay
'Golden Ginkgo'	LPot SDay WAvo WNHG
'Golden Prize'	NGdn SDay WAvo WCot XSen
'Golden Scroll'	SDay
GOLDEN ZEBRA ('Malja'[PBR]) (v)	CRos CWGN ELan EPfP LRHS MAvo MRav NLar NRHS SRms
'Golliwog'	CBgR EStr
'Gorgeous Smile'	EStr
'Got Milk'	EStr
'Gothic Butterfly'	EStr
'Gothic Window'	SDay
'Graal'	XSen
'Grace and Favour'	SDay
'Graceful Eye'	SDay
'Graceland'	SDay WHrl
'Grand Masterpiece'	EStr NGdn SDay WFar
'Grand Palais'	SDay
'Granite City Towhead'	ELon
'Granny's Smokehouse' **new**	EStr
'Grape Arbor'	WNHG
'Grape Harvest'	WNHG
'Grape Magic'	WCot
'Grape Velvet'	CSpe EStr ILea MHer NSti SRms WCAu WNHG WWtn
'Grapes of Wrath'	EStr
'Great Auntie Picklebottom' **new**	EStr
'Green Arrow' **new**	EStr
'Green Dolphin Street'	SDay
'Green Dragon'	SDay
'Green Eyes Wink'	MHol
'Green Flutter'	CBgR EBee EStr GCal GQue LSRN NBir NGdn NSti SPhx WAvo WSpi
'Green Fringe'	SDay
'Green Goddess'	XLum
'Green Icon' **new**	EStr
'Green Lines'	EStr
'Green Mystique'	EBee EStr SDay
'Green Nautilus'	EStr
'Green Puff'	NBir
'Green Spider'	CBgR SDay
'Green Widow'	SDay
'Greenland'	CRos EBee ECtt EStr LRHS NRHS
'Greywoods Cowgirl Casanova'	EStr
'Greywoods Fashionista' **new**	EStr
'Greywoods Fingers Malone' **new**	EStr
'Greywoods Katz Kando' **new**	EStr
'Greywoods Nautical Nellie'	EStr
'Groove-billed Ani' **new**	EStr
'Groovy Green'	SDay
'Grumbly'	ELan WPnP
'Gryphon Prague Gothic'	EStr
'Guardian Angel'	WCFE
'Gwen Leman'	EStr
'Gypsy Sweetheart'	WNHG
'Hail Mary'	SDay
'Halloween Green' **new**	EStr
'Hamlet'	SDay WNHG
'Happy Apache'	EStr
'Happy Medium'	EStr
'Happy Returns'	CBgR CRos CSBt CTri ECha ELan EPfP EStr GBin LPot LRHS LSRN MBel NGdn NHol NRHS SRms WCAu XLum
'Harbor Blue'	SDay
'Harrods'	EStr
'Harry Barras'	XLum
'Harvest Hue'	SDay
'Having Fun'	EStr
'Hawaiian Nights'	WNHG
'Hawk'	ELon SDay
'Hawkwoman' **new**	EStr
'Hazel'	EStr
'Hazmatter's Ball' **new**	EStr
'Heady Wine'	EStr SDay
'Heart Wishes'	EStr
'Heartless' **new**	EStr
'Heart's Glee'	XSen
'Heavenly Angel Ice'	ELon EPfP EStr
'Heavenly Beginnings'	EStr
'Heavenly Black Bird' **new**	EStr
'Heavenly Curls'	EStr SDay
'Heavenly Fire and Ice' **new**	EStr
'Heavenly Flight of Angels'	EStr
'Heavenly Pink Butterfly'	EStr
'Heavenly Pink Fang'	EStr
'Heavenly Thunderbird'	EStr
'Heavenly United We Stand'	EStr
'Heavenly Way Big' **new**	EStr
'Heidi Eidelweiss'	CExl
'Heirloom Lace'	SDay WCAu
'Helen Sever'	EStr
'Helen Shooter'	EStr
'Helena Seabird'	EStr
'Helix'	EStr SDay
'Helle Berlinerin'	SDay
'Hello Screamer'	EStr
'Helter Skelter'	SDay
'Heman'	EStr
'Henry D. Allnutt'	EStr

'Her Majesty's Wizard'	CBgR ELan ELon
'Here Lies Butch'	EStr
'Hermitage Newton'	SDay
'Hexagon'	EStr
'High Profile'	EStr
'High Tor'	ELon EStr SDay WHrl
'High Water Mark' **new**	EStr
'Highland Lord' (d)	EStr WCAu XSen
'Hold Your Horses'	SDay
'Holiday Delight'	EStr
'Holiday Mood'	ELan
'Holly Dancer' ♀H6	EStr
'Homeward Bound'	SDay
'Honeysuckle Rose'	EStr
'Honor Flight'	EStr
'Hooked on Romance'	EStr
'Hope Diamond'	SDay
'Hoping for Hugs'	EStr
'Hornby Castle'	CBro CRos LRHS NRHS
'Hot Chocolate'PBR	EBee
'Hot Pink Fury'	EStr
'Hot Tamales and Red Hots'	EStr
'Hot Town'	ELan
'Hot Wheels'	CBgR
'Hot Wire'	SDay WNHG
'Houdini'	WCAu
'House Music'	XSen
'House of Orange'	EStr
'Humdinger'	EStr SDay WCot
'Hummingbird'	EStr
'Humungousaur' **new**	EStr
'Hunker Down'	EStr
'Huntress' **new**	EStr
'Hybridizer's Truffle'	EStr
'Hymn'	SDay
'Hyperion'	CBgR CFGn CMac CTri ECha ECtt ELon EShb EStr GKin LEdu MHol MMuc MRav NBid NGdn SDay SEND SPer SWvt WCot WWtn
'I Love to Tell the Story' **new**	EStr
'Ice Carnival'	EStr MBNS NGdn NLar SCob SWvt WSpi
'Ice Castles'	CTri SDay
'Icecap'	CBgR WMoo
'Icy Lemon'	EStr SDay
'Ida Duke Miles'	SDay
'Ida Mae Norris' **new**	EStr
'Ida's Magic'	EStr
'Iditarod'	EStr
'Ikebana Star'	EStr
'Iktomi'	EStr
'Illini Jackpot'	SDay
'I'm a King Bee' **new**	EStr
'Impromptu'	SDay
'In Depth' (d)	MBNS NBro NLar WCot WHrl
'In Her Shoes'	EStr
'In Search of Angels'	EStr
'In Strawberry Time'	WNHG
'Inca Puzzle'	SDay
'Inchon'	EStr
'Increased Complexity'	EStr
'Indian Paintbrush'	ELon NBir WNHG
'Indigo Moon'	XSen
'Indy Heart Stopper'	EStr
'Inner View'	ECtt EStr SDay
'Innocent Blush'	EStr
'Inspired Word'	SDay
'Instant Zéro'	XSen
'Iridescent Jewel'	SDay
'Irish Elf'	EBee ELon GBin SDay SHar
'Irish Veil'	EStr
'Iron Gate Glacier'	EBee EPPr EStr MBNS SDay XLum
'Irresistible You' **new**	EStr
'Isaac'	EStr
'Isabelle Rose'	SDay
'Isle of Dreams'	SDay
'Islesworth' **new**	SDay
'Isolde'	CBgR EStr
'It's Soul Time'	EStr
'Itsy Bitsy Spider'	CBgR
'Itza Mirage'	EStr
'Ivelyn Brown'	EStr SDay
'Ivory Cloud' (d)	EStr
'Ivory Coast'	SDay
'J.T. Davis'	EStr
'James Marsh'	CBgR MNrw NSti WCAu WCot WFar WNHG
'Jane's Prism'	EStr
'Janice Brown'	CWCL ECtt EMor EStr GBee LRHS NHol NLar NRHS SDay WHrl
'Janie Wilson'	WNHG
'Jan's Twister'	EStr MNrw SDay WHrl
'Jason Salter'	EStr SDay WAul
'Jay Turman'	SDay
'Jealous Sky' **new**	EStr
'Jean'	SDay
'Jean Swann'	EStr
'Jedi Dot Pierce'	EStr SDay
'Jellyfish Jealousy' ♀H6	EStr SDay
'Jenny Wren'	EPPr NBro WAul
'Jerry Hyatt' **new**	EStr
'Jersey Breeze'	EStr
'Jerusalem'	SDay
'Jeu de Piste'	XSen
'Jeune Tom'	CBgR
'Jewel Case'	WNHG
'Jim McKinney'	EStr
'Joan Derifield'	EStr
'Joan Senior'	CAby CBgR ECha ECtt ELan EMor EPfP EShb GBin GKin LRHS LSRN MNrw MRav NGdn NHol NRHS NSti SCob SDay SPer SRms WAul WBor WCAu WCFE WCot WPnP WSpi WWtn
'Job Creator'	EStr
'Jockey Club' (d)	ECtt WHrl
'Jogolor'	EStr
'John R. Pike' **new**	EStr
'Johnny Come Lately'	EStr
'Jordan'	LSRN SWvt
'Jordan's Jazz'	EStr
'Josephine Marina'	EStr
'Journey's End'	SDay
'Jovial'	EStr SDay
'Joyful Participation'	EStr
'Juanita's Picotee Delight' **new**	SDay
'Judge Roy Bean'	EStr SDay
'Judy Davidson' **new**	WNHG
'Judy Farquhar' **new**	EStr
'June Melody'	WNHG
'June Rose'	EStr
'Jungle Beauty'	CBgR SDay
'Just My Size'	EStr
'Just Whistle'	EStr
'Justin Brent'	XSen
'Justin George'	SDay
'Justin June'	WHrl
'Kaleidoscopic Intrigue'	EStr

'Kansas Kitten'	EStr
'Karen's Curls' ♀H6	SDay
'Kasia'	WHrl
'Kate Carpenter'	EStr SDay
'Kathleen Salter'	EStr SDay
'Katie Elizabeth Miller'	SDay
'Katisue Herrington' **new**	EStr
'Kazuq'	SDay
'Kecia'	SDay
'Kempion'	CBgR
'Kermit's Scream' **new**	EStr
'Key to my Heart'	CBgR
'Key West Sunset' **new**	EStr
'Kharma Police'	EStr
'Kickin' Chicken' **new**	EStr
'Killer' ♀H6	EStr
'Killer Purple'	EStr
'Kimberly Sue'	EStr
'King George'	EStr
'King Kahuna' (d)	EStr
'King of Anything'	EStr
'King's Gold'	EStr
'King's Throne'	WNHG
'Kirsten My Love'	EStr
'Kiss the Sky'	EStr
'Kissed by Moonlight' **new**	EStr
'Knights in White Satin'	EStr
'Kokomo Queen' **new**	EStr
'Kwanso Flore Pleno'	see *H. fulva* 'Green Kwanso'
'Kwanso Flore Pleno Variegata'	see *H. fulva* 'Variegated Kwanso'
'La Fenice'	EStr
'La Peche'	SDay
'Lacy Doily'	EStr LLHF WCAu
'Lacy Marionette'	ELon SDay
'Lady Betty Fretz'	EBee EStr
'Lady Fingers'	CBgR
'Lady Inara'	EStr
'Lady Liz'	SDay WNHG
'Lady Mischief'	EStr SDay
'Lady Neva' ♀H6	CBgR ELon
'Lady Tiger'	WNHG
'Ladybug Hawk' **new**	EStr
'Ladybug's Two Moons' (d)	EStr
'Ladykin'	ELon
'Lambada'	EStr
'Lamplighter's Circle'	EStr
'Land of Cotton'	XSen
'Land of Enchantment'	EStr
'Land's End'	EStr
'Lark Song'	CRos LRHS NRHS WFar WHrl
'Larry's Candy Stripe Swizzle'	EStr
'Last Song'	EStr
'Late Report' **new**	EStr
'Late Summer Rose'	WNHG
'Laughing Giraffe'	EStr WCot
'Laughton Tower'	SMHy
'Lauradell'	SDay
'Lauren Leah'	SDay
'Lava Burst' **new**	EStr
'Lava Stream' **new**	EStr
'Lavender Blue Baby'	EPfP EStr
'Lavender Bonanza'	SDay
'Lavender Deal'	MNrw WNHG
'Lavender Handlebars'	SDay
'Lavender Memories'	EStr SDay
'Lavender Showstopper'	WCAu
'Lavender Spider'	CBgR
'Lavender Stardust' **new**	SDay
'Lavender Tonic'	WNHG
'Lavender Tutu'	ECtt EStr
'Layers of Gold' (d)	XSen
'Lazy Hazy Days'	EStr
'Leading Edge' **new**	SDay
'Ledgewood's Frequent Flyer' **new**	EStr
'Ledgewood's Irish Spirit'	EStr
'Ledgewood's Sunday Dessert'	EStr
'Leila Mantle'	CBgR
'Lemon Bells'	CWat ECha EPfP EStr GKev GKin GMaP LEdu LRHS NBro NRHS SHar WCAu WSpi
'Lemon Custard'	EStr
'Lemon Dessert'	ELon
'Lemon Madeline'	EStr
'Lemon Mint'	ELon
'Lemonora'	SDay
'Lenox'	SDay
'Leonard Bernstein'	EStr SDay
'Leprechaun's Curls' **new**	EStr
'Let Loose'	EStr
'Let Love Rejoice'	EStr
'Lies and Lipstick'	EStr
'Life is a Highway' **new**	EStr
'Life Unlimited' **new**	EStr
'Light the Way'	GBin LLWG MHol MSCN SPoG WCot
'Light Years Away'	ELon MBNS MNrw
'Like a Gee Six' **new**	EStr
'Lilac Lady'	EStr
'Lilac Wine'	SCob
§ ***lilioasphodelus***	Widely available
'Lillian's Good Intentions' **new**	EStr
'Lilly Dache'	EStr
'Lilting Lady'	EStr
'Lilting Lavender'	ELon WCAu
'Lily Munster'	EStr
'Lime Frost' ♀H6	CBgR EStr
'Lime Painted Lady'	CBgR
'Limetree'	CBgR EStr
'Linda'	MRav
'Linda Sierra' **new**	EStr
'Linda the Green Eyed Lady'	EStr
'Lip Smack' **new**	EStr
'Litchfield Plantation'	EStr
'Little Anna Rosa'	EStr
'Little Audrey'	EStr
'Little Bee'	NBre
'Little Big Man'	SDay
'Little Bugger'	MBNS
'Little Bumble Bee'	MBNS WWtn
'Little Business'	SDay
'Little Cadet'	XLum
'Little Cranberry Cove'	GBin
'Little Dart'	ECha
'Little Deeke'	SDay WHrl
'Little Fantastic'	ELon SDay WWtn
'Little Fat Cat'	EStr
'Little Fellow'	EStr MBNS
'Little Girl'	ELon
'Little Grapette'	ELon EPfP EStr GQue LLWG NLar NSti WAul
'Little Greenie'	SDay
'Little Gypsy Vagabond'	CBgR CWat EStr
'Little Heavenly Angel'	EStr
'Little Isaac'	EStr
'Little Kiki'	SDay

'Little Lassie' CBgR
'Little Maggie' SDay
'Little Men' WCAu
'Little Miss Lucy' EStr
'Little Miss Manners' EStr NLar
'Little Missy' CBgR WHoo WNHG
'Little Monica' SDay
'Little Music Maker' (d) EStr
'Little Paul' EStr
'Little Red Hen' CSam GKin LRHS NBir NBro NEgg NGdn NRHS SDay WFar
'Little Show Stopper' NBro NLar
'Little Showoff' SDay
'Little Swain' SDay
'Little Sweet Talk' ELon
'Little Swirling Shadows' **new** EStr
'Little Tawny' ELon
'Little Toddler' SDay
'Little Velma' **new** EStr
'Little Violet Lace' SDay
'Little Wart' CBgR SDay WHrl
'Little William' **new** EStr
'Little Wine Cup' CMac CRos CSam ECrc ECtt ELon EStr GKin GMaP LPot LRHS MRav NBir NEgg NGdn NRHS SRms WAul WMoo
'Little Women' SDay WHrl
'Little Zinger' SDay
'Littlest Angel' SDay
'Living in Amsterdam' EBee EStr
'Lobo Lucy' ELon EStr
'Loch Ness Monster' EStr
'Lochinvar' CSam MRav
'Loco Bo' EStr
'Lois Burns' SDay
'Lonely Heart' EStr
'Long John Silver' ELon EStr
'Long Stocking' EStr WCot
'Long Tall Sally' EStr
'Longfields Dress Pink' **new** EStr
'Longfields × Factor' EStr
'Longfields Glory' CRos LRHS MBNS NBre NRHS
'Longfields Maxim' (d) EStr MHol SDeJ
'Longfields Pearl' EStr
'Longfields Pride' EStr MBNS SRms WBor
'Longfields Purple Eye' NLar
'Longfields Think Pink' EStr
'Longfields Twins' MBNS WCot WFar
'Longfields Whoopy' CWld ELon EPfP EStr MNrw SCob
longituba AIK 284 WCot
- B&SWJ 4576 WCru
'Look at Me' ELan
'Look Lucky' EStr
'Lost in the Toy Store' EStr
'Lost in the Translation' **new** EStr
'Loth Lorien' CRos EBee LRHS NRHS
'Lots of Hoopla' EStr
'Lotta Dotta' **new** EStr
'Lotus Land' SDay
'Louis McHargue' SDay
'Lourice Abdallah' EStr
'Love Those Eyes' EStr
'Lovely Margie' **new** EStr
'Lovely Rita' EStr
'Loverboy' EStr
'Loving Memories' SDay
'Lowcountry Gem' EStr
'Lucille Lennington' WNHG
'Lullaby Baby' ELan GCal NLar WNHG
'Lunar Sea' EStr
'Lupita Vindaz' EStr
'Luscious Honeydew' WNHG
'Lusty Lealand' MBNS SDay
'Luxury Lace' CAgr EBee ECtt ELan EStr GBin GKin LSRN NBir NGdn NHol NWad SPer WFar WHrl WMoo WWtn XLum XSen
'Lydia Bechtold' EStr SDay
'Lynn Hall' NLar WSpi
'Mabel Fuller' CBgR MRav SPer WHrl
'Mabel Nolen' EStr
'Mable Lewis Nelson' EStr
'Macbeth' EStr MBNS MNrw
'Mad Max' EStr SDay
'Madeline Nettles Eyes' EBee ELon EStr
'Madmoiselle Constanza' **new** SDay
'Maggie Fynboe' CBgR
'Magic Amethyst' CBgR
'Magic Carpet Ride' EStr
'Magic Dancer' EStr
'Magic Lace' EStr
'Magic Masquerade' SDay
'Magic of Oz' EStr
'Magical Messenger' EStr
'Magnificent Rainbow' CBcs
'Mahogany Magic' ♀H6 ELon EStr
'Majestic Dark Eyes' EStr
'Malachite Prism' EStr
'Malaysian Monarch' EStr SDay WNHG
'Malaysian Spice' WNHG
'Maleny Canary' **new** EStr
'Maleny Chantilly Lace' EStr
'Maleny Debutante' EStr
'Maleny Kiwi Dazzler' EStr
'Mallard' CAby CBgR ECtt EHrv EStr LLWG MRav NBir WCot
'Malmaison Plum' EStr SDay
'Mama Sophia' EStr
'Mama's Pajamas' EStr
'Mambo Maid' XSen
'Man on Fire' WNHG
'Manchurian Apricot' SDay
'Marble Faun' SDay
'Margaret Perry' MNrw NLar
'Margaret Seawright' EStr
'Margo Reed Indeed' EStr
'Marietta Charmer' SDay
'Marietta Delight' EStr
'Marilyn Lee Bock' EStr
'Marilyn Morss Johnson' **new** EStr
'Marion Vaughn' ECtt EHrv ELan EMor EPfP GKin GMaP LLWG MBel MRav NSti SPer SWvt WCAu WCot WFar WHoo WPtf WSHC
'Mariska' EStr SDay WNHG
'Marked by Lydia' ELon
'Marshall McLuhan' **new** EStr
'Martina Verhaert' CWGN EBee EStr
'Mary Alice Stokes' EStr
'Mary Ethel Anderson' EStr
'Mary Todd' EBee MBNS XSen
'Mary's Baby' **new** EStr
'Mary's Gold' ♀H6 SDay
'Masada' WNHG
'Mask of Zorro' **new** EStr
'Mata Hari' SDay
'Matchless Fire' **new** EStr
'Maude's Valentine' SDay

'Mauna Loa'	CSBt ELon EStr GQue LPot MNrw NLar SDeJ SWvt WAul WCot
'May May'	CBgR
'Mayan Poppy'	EStr
'Meadow Mist'	CBgR ELon
'Meadow Sprite'	WCot
'Meadowsweet'	EStr
'Mean Mister Mustard'	EStr
'Medieval Guild'	EStr
'Mema's Dingaling'	EStr
'MeMe's Guilty Pleasure'	EStr
'MeMe's Lovin' the Limelight'	EStr
'MeMe's Tuitti Fruitti'	EStr
'Merry Jo's Delight' **new**	EStr
'Merry Moppet'	EStr
'Merry Witch'	EStr
'Metaphor'	ECtt SDay XSen
'Michael Poliga'	EStr
'Michael's Sword'	EStr
'Michele Coe'	ECtt GKin NBro NEgg NGdn SDay WCAu WHrl WMoo
'Mico'	ELon
middendorffii	CMac EStr GKev GMaP NSti WHrl WSpi WThu
'Middle of Nowhere' **new**	EStr
'Midnight Confession' **new**	EStr
'Midnight Magic'	SDay
'Midnight Rambler'	SDay
'Midnight Rendezvous'	EStr
'Mikado'	CBgR CMac
'Mike Reed'	EStr
'Milady Greensleeves'	EStr SDay WHrl
'Milanese Mango'	EStr
'Mildred Mitchell'	CBgR ELon EStr NLar
'Military School'	EStr
'Mimosa Umbrella'	EStr
'Ming Porcelain'	SDay WCAu WNHG
'Mini Pearl'	CRos ECtt ELon EStr EWTr LRHS NRHS SPer
'Mini Stella'	CBro ECtt SHar WFar
'Minnie Wildfire'	EStr
minor	CBro CRos EBee EPPr LRHS NRHS SPhx SRms XSen
– B&SWJ 8841	WCru
'Miracle Maid'	WNHG
'Miss Atomic Bomb' **new**	EStr
'Miss Jessie'	EStr
'Miss North Carolina' **new**	EStr
'Miss Piggy' **new**	EStr
'Missenden'	CBgR MNrw
'Missouri Beauty'	SWvt
'Mister Lucky'	EStr
'Mojave Sunset'	EStr
'Moment of Truth'	NBre
'Monica Marie'	EStr SDay
'Mont Royal Demitasse'	ELon
'Moon Snow'	SDay
'Moon Witch'	EStr
'Moonlight Masquerade'	CBgR ECtt ELon MMuc NLar SDay SRms
'Moonlight Orchid'	WHrl
'Moonlit Caress'	CBgR EBee ECtt NBro
'Moonlit Crystal'	EStr
'Moonlit Masquerade' ♀H6	CWGN EStr MBNS MNrw SDay SEND SHar WHrl
'Moonlit Pirouette'	SDay
'Moonlit Summerbird'	EStr SDay
'Moontraveller'	WCot
'Morgen le Fay'	EStr
'Mormon Spider'	EStr
'Morning Face'	EStr
'Morning Sun'	MBNS WCot
'Morocco Red'	CBro ELan MHCG
'Morpho Butterfly' **new**	EStr
'Moses' Fire'	ECtt EStr MHol NLar WFar
'Mossy Glade'	CBgR
'Mount Joy'	EStr
'Mountain Laurel'	CRos ECtt EStr GKin LRHS MRav NEgg NRHS WFar WGwG
'Moussaka'	CWGN EStr WCAu WFar
'Move Over Moon'	EStr SDay
'Mrs Hugh Johnson'	CChe EShb LPot WHrl
* 'Mrs Lester'	SDay
'Muddy Creek Magic' **new**	EStr
'Muffet's Little Friend'	WHrl
multiflora	XSen
'Multiple Multiplications' **new**	EStr
'Muriel Rhem'	EStr
'Murphy's Law'	EStr
'Muscle Man'	EStr XSen
'My Belle'	SDay
'My Darling Clementine'	EStr SDay WNHG
'My Heart Belongs to Daddy'	EStr
'My Melinda'	SDay
'My Place or Yours' **new**	EStr
'My Reggae Tiger' **new**	EStr
'Mynelle's Starfish'	WHrl
'Mystical Rainbow'	SDay
'Nabis'	SDay
'Nacogdoches Lady'	SWvt
* 'Nana Wallich'	EStr
'Nanuq'	ELon SDay
'Naomi Ruth'	EStr GKev MBNS
'Nashville'	CBro ELan WHrl
'Nashville Lights'	CBgR EStr
'National Memento'	EStr
'Native Reflection'	EStr
'Naughty Red'	EStr
'Navajo Jewel'	EStr
'Navajo Pony'	EStr
'Navajo Princess'	EBee MNrw
'Neal Berrey'	EStr SDay
'Nefertiti'	CBgR ELon NBir WAul WCAu
'Neon Flamingo' **new**	EStr
'Neon Sunshine'	EStr
'Neon Yellow'	EStr
'Neutron Star' **new**	EStr
'Never Ending Fantasy'	EStr
'Never Get Away'	EStr
'New Wine' **new**	WNHG
'New York Follies'	EStr
'Neyron Rose'	GKin LRHS NEgg NGdn NRHS WMoo WWtn XLum
'Nick's Faith'	WHrl
'Night Beacon'	CBgR ECtt ELon EStr GKin LLWG MNrw MPie NLar SCob SDay SDeJ WCAu WHrl
'Night Embers'	ECtt ELon IPot NLar WCAu
'Night Raider'	CBgR EStr SDay WNHG
'Night Whispers'	SPer
'Nile Crane'	CBgR ELon EStr MNrw SDay SPer WAul
'Nile Plum'	EStr SDay
'Nina Winegar'	EStr
'Ninja Storm' **new**	EStr
'Nob Hill'	ELon EStr WHrl XLum
'Nona's Garnet Spider'	ELon

'Nordic Night'	CBgR EWes SDay
'North Wind Drifter'	EStr
'Norton Beauté'	WCot
'Norton Eyed Seedling'	WNHG
'Norton Orange'	EStr
'Not Forgotten'	WNHG
'Nothing is Easy'	EStr
'Notify Ground Crew' **new**	EStr
'Nova'	ELon SDay
'Nowhere to Hide'	EStr
'Nuit Parisienne'	EStr
'Nuka'	XLum
'Nutmeg Elf'	CBgR SDay
'Oakes Love'	MNrw
'Ocean Rain'	EStr SDay WNHG
'Ocean Spirit'	EStr
'Octopus Hugs'	EStr
'Oke-She-Moke-She-Pop'	EStr
'Old San Juan'	EStr
'Old Tangiers' ♀H6	EStr SDay WNHG
'Olive Bailey Langdon'	EStr SDay WCot
'Olive's Odd One'	EStr
'Oloroso'	CBgR
'Olympic Gold'	EStr XSen
'Olympic Showcase'	EStr
'Omomuki'	SDay
'On and On'	EStr GBin GQue
'On Pointe'	EStr
'On Silken Thread'	SDay
'One Above You' **new**	EStr
'One Fire'	XSen
'Oodles'	WHrl
'Open Hearth'	EStr WHrl
'Open my Eyes'	EStr
'Orange Dream'	SDay
'Orange Empire'	SDay
'Orange Exotica'	CBgR
'Orange Nassau'	WCAu WFar
'Orange Prelude'	XSen
'Orangeman' misapplied	MBNS NGdn
'Orchid Beauty'	WMoo
'Orchid Candy'	EStr MBNS NBir
'Orchid Corsage'	ELon EStr
'Oriental Impressions' **new**	EStr
'Oriental Ruby'	SDay
'Orphée'	XSen
'Osterized'	EStr
'Ostrich Plume'	EStr SDay
'Ouachita Beauty'	CBgR ELon
'Our Kirsten'	EStr SDay
'Out of Balance' **new**	EStr
'Outrageous'	CBgR EStr SDay WNHG
'Outrageous Ramona'	WNHG
'Oy Vey'	EStr
'Paige's Pinata'	EStr
'Painted Lady'	WNHG
'Painted Pink'	SDay
'Palace Pagoda'	WNHG
'Pandora's Box'	CExl CRos CTri CWat ECtt EHrv ELan EStr LLWG LRHS MMuc MNrw NBir NGdn NLar SDeJ SWvt WBor WMoo
'Papa Goose'	EStr
'Paper Butterfly'	EStr SDay
'Papilion'	EStr
'Papoose'	XLum
'Paprika Flame'	EStr MHol
'Parade of Peacocks'	CBgR
'Paradise Bar and Grill'	EStr
'Paradise Lost'	EStr
'Pardon Me'	CBro CRos CWld ECtt ELan ELon EStr GKin GMaP LRHS NGdn NRHS SDeJ SWvt WAul WBor WCAu WFar
'Parfait'	CBgR EStr WHrl
'Parrot Tattoo'	EStr
'Parson's Robe'	SDay
'Part-time Princess'	EStr
'Party Pants' **new**	EStr
'Party Queen'	SDay
'Passive Aggressive' **new**	EStr
'Pastel Ballerina'	SDay
'Pat Mercer'	SDay XSen
'Patchwork Puzzle'	EStr
'Patricia Fay'	XSen
'Patrick Starfish' **new**	EStr
'Patriotic Flavor'	EStr
'Patti Neyland'	EStr
'Paula Nettles'	EStr
'Paw Print' **new**	EStr
'Pawn of Prophecy'	EStr
'Peach Jubilee'	EStr
'Peach Magnolia' (d)	EStr
'Peach Whisper'	EStr SDay
'Peacock Maiden'	EStr WHrl XSen
'Pear Ornament'	SDay
'Pearl Anniversary'	EStr
'Pearl Jam'	SDay
'Pearl Lewis'	EStr SDay
'Peggy Jeffcoat'	EStr
'Penelope Vestey'	CBgR EStr NBir
'Pennypurrs' **new**	EStr
'Penny's Worth'	CRos LEdu LRHS MBNS WAul WCot WFar XLum
'Peppermint Ice'	EStr
'Persian Melon Plus'	WCAu
'Persian Ruby'	EStr SDay
'Petite Ballerina'	SDay
'Phyllis Cantini'	SDay
'Piano Man'	EStr MBNS WAul WNHG
'Piccadilly Princess'	EStr
'Pickin' and Grinnin''	EStr
'Piece of the Action'	EStr
'Pigment of Imagination'	EStr
'Pinhill Navajo Beauty'	EStr
'Pink Ambrosia'	ECtt EStr
'Pink Charm'	CMac CRos ECha ECtt EPPr GKin GMaP LRHS NBro NRHS
'Pink Circle'	SDay
'Pink Cotton Candy'	SDay
'Pink Damask' ♀H6	Widely available
'Pink Dazzler'	WNHG
'Pink Delight'	MPie
'Pink Dream'	CBgR NBir NBre
'Pink Flirt'	SDay
'Pink Lady'	MNrw MRav SRms
'Pink Monday'	SDay WNHG
'Pink Puff'	NBir NBre NLar
'Pink Spider'	SDay
'Pink Stripes'	EStr
'Pink Sundae'	WHrl
'Pink Super Spider'	SDay
'Pink Thunderbird' **new**	EStr
'Pink Whip Tips'	EStr
'Pink Windmill'	ELon
'Pinocchio'	SMHy
'Piquante'	SCob
'Pirate Treasure'	EStr MBNS
'Pirate's Patch'	SDay WCot
'Pixie Parasol'	WNHG WSpi
'Pixie Princess'	EStr

'Pleated Petticoats' EStr
'Plum Beautiful' EStr
'Plum Beauty' NLar
'Poinsettia' EStr
'Point of View' EStr
'Pojo' EStr
'Polka Dot Bikini' EStr
'Pony' ELon
'Porcelain Pleasure' SDay
'Possum in a Sack' CBgR
'Post Time' EStr
'Prague Spring' EStr WCAu WHrl WNHG
'Prairie Belle' GKev NLar
'Prairie Blue Eyes' EStr ILea SDay SPlb WCot WHrl
'Prairie Charmer' MMuc SEND WHrl
'Prankster' EStr
'Precious d'Oro' GQue
'President Hadley' **new** SDay
'Pretty Face Nice Legs' EStr
'Pretty Miss' ECtt EMor EStr LRHS NRHS WGwG
'Preview Party' WNHG
'Primal Scream' ♀H6 CAby EStr GAbr LSun MHol MJak SDay SPoG WCot
'Primrose Mascotte' NBir
'Prince of Midnight' SDay
'Prince of Purple' ELon
'Prince Poppycock' EStr
'Prince Redbird' SDay
'Princess Charming' EStr
'Princeton Eye Glow' SDay
'Princeton Silky' ELon
'Printmaker' **new** EStr
'Prize Picotee Deluxe' SDay
'Prize Picotee Elite' SDay
'Protocol' SDay
'Proud Mary' SDay
'Ptarmigan' CBgR EStr
'Pterodactyl Eye' EStr SDay
§ 'Puddin' SDay
'Pueblo Dancer' EStr
'Pug Yarborough' EStr SDay
'Pullin' Strings' EStr
'Pumpkin Kid' SDay
'Pumpkin Prince' EStr
'Punxsutawney Phil' EStr
'Puppet Show' SDay
'Purple Avenger' SDay
'Purple Bicolor' WHrl
'Purple Flame' CBod EStr
'Purple Rain' CWat MBNS MPie SDay SWvt
'Purple Waters' EStr MJak WPnP
'Purpleicious' EStr NLar
'Pursuit of Excellence' SDay
'Putting on the Ritz' EStr
'Pygmy Plum' SDay XSen
'Pyrotechnics' EStr
'Quality of Mercy' SDay
'Quartzitic Scintillation' EStr
'Queen Charlotte' EStr
'Queen Empress' WNHG
'Queen Lily' WNHG
'Queen of Green' EStr
'Queen of May' MNrw WCot
'Quick Results' SDay
'Quietly Awesome' SDay
'Quilt Patch' EStr
'Quinn Buck' SDay
'Ra Hansen' EStr
'Rachael My Love' (d) XSen
'Radiant Greetings' XSen
'Radiant Moonbeam' ♀H6 CBgR EStr
'Raging Bull' **new** EStr
'Raging Tiger' SDay WHrl
'Rain Dance' EStr
'Rainbow Candy' CWGN LLHF
'Rainbow Gold' XSen
'Rainbow Maker' EStr
'Rajah' CBgR CMac EStr NBro SCob SPer WHrl
'Raspberry Candy' CBro EStr MNrw SRms WHrl
'Raspberry Star' EStr
'Raspberry Wine' ECha
'Raspberry Winter' EStr
'Razzle' EStr
'Reach for the Heavens' **new** EStr
'Real Life Drama' EStr
'Real Wind' EStr
'Red Admiral' CRos LRHS NRHS
'Red Bull' **new** EStr
'Red Grace' EStr
'Red Pennant' SDay
'Red Precious' ♀H6 MNrw NAln SMHy WCot
'Red Rain' EStr WHrl XSen
'Red Ribbons' ELon SDay
'Red Rum' CBgR CBod EMor EUJe MSwo NBro NRHS WMoo
'Red Suspenders' ECtt EStr MBNS
'Red Tallboy' EStr
'Red Thrill' WHrl
'Red Twister' ELon EStr
'Red Volunteer' EStr SDay
'Redheaded Hussy' EStr
'Regal Giant' EStr
'Regency Dandy' SDay XSen
'Regency Heights' EStr
'Regency Masquerade' SDay
'Renee' MNrw
'Respighi' EStr
'Return Trip' ELon
'Rhubarb Wine' EStr
'Rhythm of Love' EStr
'Ribbonette' EBee EStr
'Rich Girls' **new** EStr
'Ricky Rose' SDay XSen
'Riley Barron' SDay
'Rise of the Phoenix' EStr
'Rocket Booster' EStr
'Rocket City' ELan EStr WNHG
'Roger Grounds' CBgR
'Rolling Raven' EStr
'Roman Toga' CBgR SDay
'Romanian Rendevous' EStr
* 'Romantic Rose' MBNS NLar WHrl
'Romeo is Bleeding' EStr
'Ron Azzanni' EStr
'Root Beer' GQue WCAu WHrl
'Rorschach Test' **new** EStr
'Rose' SDay
'Rose Emily' CBgR EStr SDay
'Rose F. Kennedy' EStr
'Rose Tattoo' EStr
'Roses in Snow' SDay
'Roswitha' EStr
'Rosy Polyphemus' EStr
'Rosy Returns' EPfP LRHS NLar
'Roy Likes Em Hot' EStr
'Royal Braid' NLar SPer WCot
'Royal Celebration' WCot
'Royal Eventide' XSen
'Royal Heritage' CRos EStr LRHS NRHS SDay

'Royal Parade' SDay
'Royal Robe' CTri
'Royal Saracen' SDay
'Royal Thornbird' CBgR
'Ruby Corsage' EStr
'Ruby Sentinel' SDay
'Ruby Spider' ♀H6 ELon EStr
'Ruby Storm' EStr
'Ruffled Apricot' LPot WNHG
'Ruffled Carousel' WNHG
'Ruffled Dude' EStr
'Ruffled Ivory' SDay
'Ruffled Lemon Lace' EStr
'Ruffled Magic' SDay
'Ruffled Perfection' EStr
'Rumble Seat Romance' WNHG
'Running for the Border' EStr
'Russian Easter' EStr
'Russian Ragtime' EStr
'Russian Rhapsody' ♀H6 SDay
'Ruth Love' **new** WNHG
'Ruth Oliver' EStr
'Sabie' EStr
'Sabine Baur' EStr MNrw WFar
'Sabra Salina' EStr SDay
'Sacred Drummer' SDay
'Saffron Glow' SDay
'Sahara Sand Storm' EStr
'Sahara Song' EStr
'Sallie Brown' EStr SDay
'Salmon Sheen' SPer
'Sammy' EStr SDay WHrl
'Sammy Russell' Widely available
'Sandra Elizabeth' SDay
'Sandy Beckman' EStr
'Santa's Little Helper' EStr
'Saratoga Belle' EStr
'Sariah' SDay
'Satin Glass' CRos LRHS NRHS
'Satin Glow' ECha
'Say Yes' **new** EStr
'Scarlet Flame' ECha WMoo
'Scarlet Orbit' CKel
'Scarlet Prince' WNHG
'Scarlet Ribbons' EStr
'Schnickel Fritz' EBee NAln
'School Girl' CRos LRHS NRHS
'Scorchio' EStr
'Scorpio' CBgR SDay WHrl
'Screaming Demon' EStr WCot
'Sea Swept Dreams' SDay
'Seal of Approval' EBee EStr
'Seal the Deal' EStr
'Sebastian' SDay
'Seductive Fairy Tale' EStr
'Seeing Stars' **new** SDay
'Selma Longlegs' ♀H6 EStr SDay
'Seminole Blood' SDay
'Seminole Wind' SDay
'Semiramide' CBgR WNHG
'Serena Lady' SDay
'Serena Sunburst' ♀H6 CRos EStr LRHS NRHS
'Serene Madonna' ELan ILea
'Serenity Morgan' CBgR
'Serge Rigaud' WHrl
'Shadow Cabinet' **new** EStr
'Shadowed Pink' WNHG
'Shady Lady' SDay
'Shaggy Pumpkin' **new** EStr
'Shaman' Gates SDay
'Shards of Kryptonite' **new** EStr
'Shark Attack' EStr
'She Devil' EStr
'Shelly Victoria' SDay
'Sherry Lane Carr' EStr SDay
'Sherwood Gladiator' WNHG
'She's So Outrageous' **new** EStr
'Shimek September Morning' EStr
'Shinto Etching' EStr
'Shinto Shrine' WNHG
'Shotgun' EStr
'Shreddy' **new** EStr
'Shuffle the Deck' EStr
'Sigudilla' WNHG
'Silent Sentry' EStr
'Silken Fairy' CBgR
'Silken Touch' CBgR EStr SDay
'Siloam Amazing Grace' SDay
'Siloam Angel Blush' SDay
'Siloam Baby Talk' ELon EStr NBir SDay WAul WMoo WPnP
'Siloam Bo Peep' SDay
'Siloam Button Box' WHrl
'Siloam Bye Lo' SDay
'Siloam Cinderella' SDay
'Siloam David Kirchhoff' EBee XSen
'Siloam Doodlebug' CBgR
'Siloam Double Classic' (d) EStr SDay
'Siloam Dream Baby' ELon
'Siloam Ethel Smith' SDay
'Siloam Fairy Ruffles' **new** WNHG
'Siloam Fairy Tale' SDay
'Siloam Flower Girl' SDay
'Siloam French Doll' MBNS NLar
'Siloam French Marble' SDay
'Siloam Frosted Mint' SDay
'Siloam Gold Coin' SDay
'Siloam Grace Stamile' MBNS
'Siloam Helpmate' WNHG
'Siloam John Yonski' SDay
'Siloam June Bug' CBgR ELan WCot
'Siloam Justine Lee' MBNS
'Siloam Little Girl' ECtt EStr
'Siloam Mama' SDay
'Siloam Merle Kent' SDay WAul
'Siloam New Toy' EStr
'Siloam Nugget' EStr
'Siloam Paul Watts' EStr
'Siloam Peewee' ELon
'Siloam Pink Glow' SDay
'Siloam Pocket Size' SDay
'Siloam Red Toy' CRos LRHS NRHS SMHy
'Siloam Ribbon Candy' SDay WNHG
'Siloam Ruffled Infant' SDay
'Siloam Show Girl' CWGN GKin
'Siloam Space Age' WNHG
'Siloam Spizz' SDay
'Siloam Sugar Time' ELon
'Siloam Tee Tiny' WAul
'Siloam Tiny Mite' SDay
'Siloam Tom Thumb' CBgR MBNS
'Siloam Ury Winniford' CBro CMac NLar WHoo
'Siloam Virginia Henson' WWtn
'Silver Ice' SDay
'Silver Lance' EStr SDay
'Silver Sides' **new** EStr
'Silver Veil' SDay
'Simmons Overture' ECtt EStr MNrw
'Sinbad Sailor' NLar

'Sings the Blues'	SDay
'Sink Into Your Eyes'	EStr WHrl
'Sir Blackstem'	GCal
'Sir Galahad' **new**	EStr
'Sir Modred' ♀H6	EStr SDay WNHG
'Sissy Pants' **new**	EStr
'Sister Grace'	SDay
'Sitting on a Rainbow'	EStr
'Sixth Sense'	MBNS
'Skylight' **new**	EStr
'Slapstick'	EStr SDay
'Sleepy'	ECha
'Sleepy Hollow'	EStr
'Slender Lady'	ELon XSen
'Slipping Into the Abyss'	EStr
'Smith Brothers'	ELon
'Smoke on the Water' **new**	EStr
'Smoke Scream'	EStr
'Smoky Mountain Autumn'	WHrl
'Smooch Hollow'	CBgR EStr
'Smuggler's Gold'	ECtt EStr SDay
'Smurfette' **new**	EStr
'Snaggle Tooth'	EStr
'Snowy Apparition'	CRos EBee ECrc ECtt EMor EStr EWTr GBin GKin LRHS NAln NRHS NWad SWvt WCAu
'Snowy Eyes'	GKin WHrl
'So Excited'	SDay
'So Lovely'	XLum
'Soft Cashmere'	XLum
'Solid Geometry'	EStr
'Solid Scarlet'	EStr
'Solomon's Robes'	SDay
'Sombrero Way'	CRos LRHS NRHS SDay
'Someone Special'	EStr SDay
'Somerset Fandango'	CBgR
'Song Sparrow'	CBro
'Soraya Seline'	CBgR
'Sound of Color'	EStr
'South Carolina Peach'	EStr
'South Seas'	EStr
'Southern Cotton'	EStr
'Sovereign Queen'	WNHG
'Spacecoast Dream Catcher'	EStr
'Spacecoast Freaky Tiki'	EStr
'Spacecoast Irish Illumination' **new**	EStr
'Spacecoast Scrambled'	NLar
'Spacecoast Starburst'	EStr WCot
'Spacecoast Sweet Eye' **new**	EStr
'Spanish Fandango'	EStr
'Sparkling Dawn'	EStr
'Sparkling Orange'	SDay
'Spartan Warrior' **new**	EStr
'Spider Breeder'	CBgR ELon EStr
'Spider Man' ♀H6	ELon EStr SDay WCAu XSen
'Spider Miracle'	SDay
'Spider Red'	CWGN EWTr
'Spider Web'	EStr
'Spin Master'	EStr
'Spindazzle'	CBgR SDay
'Spinne in Lachs'	EStr
'Spinneret'	EStr
'Spiral Nebula'	EStr
'Spirit Folk'	EStr
'Splatter'	EStr
'Splittin' Hairs'	EStr
'Spooner'	CBgR
'Spoons for Escargot'	EStr
'Spotted Fever'	EStr
'Spring Willow Song'	EStr SDay
'Springfield Clan'	EStr
'Springmaid Beach'	EStr
'Spunky Monkey'	EStr
'Stack the Deck' **new**	EStr
'Stafford' ♀H6	Widely available
'Staghorn Sumac'	GKin LEdu NHol WCAu
'Star of Kryptonite' **new**	EStr
'Star Poly'	EStr
'Stargate Portal' **new**	EStr
'Starling'	EWes NChi WSpi WWtn
'Starman's Quest'	EStr
'Starstruck'	WNHG
'Startle'	ELon EStr MNrw WCot WHrl
'Steely Blue Eyes'	EStr
'Stella de Oro'	Widely available
'Stella in Purple'	EPfP
'Stewart Mandel' **new**	EStr
'Stoke Poges'	CBgR CBro EBee ELon EPPr EPfP EShb EStr GBin LPot MMuc SPer WHrl
'Stop the Insanity'	EStr
'Stoplight'	CBgR ELon EStr LRHS SMHy WHrl
'Storm Damage' **new**	EStr
'Storm of the Century'	CBod EStr
'Strasbourg'	CMac
'Strawberry Candy' ♀H6	CBgR CMac CRos CSBt ECtt ELon EPfP EStr ILea LLWG LRHS MPie NGdn NLar NRHS SCob SDay SPer WAul WCAu WHrl WMoo WNHG WSpi
I 'Streaker' B. Brown (v)	XSen
'Strider Spider'	EStr
'Strikingly Dramatic'	EStr
'String Bikini'	EStr
'Strutter's Ball'	EStr MJak NGdn SPer WAul WAvo WCAu WHrl
'Stupidville USA'	EStr
'Stu's Old Pink Spider'	CBgR
'Suburban Golden Eagle'	EStr
'Sue Strickfaden'	EStr
'Sugar Cookie'	SDay
'Summer Dragon'	EStr MBNS
'Summer Interlude'	WMoo
'Summer Star'	EStr
'Summer Wine'	CBgR CRos CSBt EBee ECtt ELon EPfP EWTr GMaP LRHS MBel MCot NBir NChi NHol NLar NRHS NSti SCob SPer SSut SWvt WBor WCAu WCot WHoo WHrl WSpi XLum
'Sun Scream' **new**	EStr
'Sunday Gloves'	MBNS WNHG
'Sunday Morning'	SDay
'Sungold Candy'	EStr
'Sunset Lagoon'	EStr
'Sunshine on My Shoulders' **new**	EStr
'Superlative'	EStr
'Supermodel' **new**	EStr
'Svengali'	SDay
'Swan Dance'	EStr SDay
'Sweet Country Luvin''	EStr
'Sweet Goldoni' **new**	EStr
'Sweet Home Louisiana'	EStr
'Sweet Hot Chocolate'	LRHS MNrw
'Sweet Pea'	EStr
'Sweet Sugar Candy'	ECtt SDeJ
'Swirling Spider'	CBgR
'Symphony of Praise' **new**	EStr
'Tachibana' **new**	SDay

'Taj Mahal'	ELon GQue SDay
'Tang'	MBNS
'Tangerine Twist'	EStr
'Tani'	SDay
'Taos'	EStr
'Tar and Feather'	EStr
'Tarantula'	ELon
'Taruga'	SDay
'Tasmania'	SPer
'Tattooed Lady' **new**	SDay
'Tchao Pantin'	XSen
'Techny Peach Lace'	EStr
'Techny Spider'	EStr
'Teenie Girl'	EStr
'Tejas'	CElw ELon SPer
'Témoin'	XSen
'Tequila and Lime'	EStr
'Tet Set'	WNHG
'Tetraploid Siloam Red Toy'	SDay
'Tetraploid Stella de Oro'	SDay
'Tetrina's Daughter'	CBgR EPfP LRHS
'Texas Blue Eyes' **new**	EStr
'Thank Your Lucky Stars'	EStr
'The Bird is the Word'	EStr
'The Blessing of Freedom' **new**	EStr
'The Color of Wonderful' **new**	EStr
'The Ghosts of Boyfriends Past'	EStr
'The New Normal'	EStr
'The Ultimate Sacrifice' **new**	EStr
'Thelma Douglas'	EStr
'Thelma Perry'	LEdu
'Thermal Overload'	EStr
'Thin Man'	EStr
'This World Aflame' **new**	EStr
'Thomas Tew'	EStr
'Thorhalla' **new**	EStr
'Thousand Voices'	EStr
'Three Times a Lady'	EStr
'Thumbelina'	ECha WMoo XLum
§ ***thunbergii***	ECha GCal XLum
- 'Ovation'	MBNS
'Thunder and Lightning'	EStr
'Thundering Ovation'	CWGN
'Thy True Love'	SDay
'Tiger Blood'	EStr
'Tigereye Spider'	EStr
'Tigerling'	EStr
'Tigger'	EStr SDeJ SPad WCAu
'Tiki God' **new**	EStr
'Till I Turn Purple'	EStr
'Timbercreek Ace' **new**	EStr
'Time Lord'	SDay XSen
'Time of Angels'	EStr
'Time Together'	EStr
'Time Window'	EStr
'Tiny Temptress'	SDay
'Tip of the Iceberg'	EStr
'Tis Midnight'	WNHG
'Tixie'	EStr
'Tom Barnes'	EStr
'Tom Collins'	SDay
'Tom Wise'	EStr
'Tone Poem'	WNHG
'Tonia Gay'	SDay
'Tooth'	EStr
'Toothpick'	WHrl
'Tootsie'	SDay
'Topguns Aztec Vision'	EStr
'Topguns Bandit's Bandana'	EStr
'Topguns Cactus Jack'	EStr
'Torpoint'	CBgR MRav NEgg
'Touch of Magic'	EStr
'Towhead'	MRav SDay WCot
'Toyland'	NBir NGdn NLar
'Trahlyta'	CBgR EStr SDay WHrl
'Tramps Like Us'	EStr
'Trance'	EStr
'Treasure Map' **new**	EStr
'Treasure That I Seek'	EStr
'Triade' **new**	EStr
'Tribute to Joe'	EStr
'Trickster'	EStr
'Tripped Out' **new**	EStr
'Trog'	EStr
'Trond'	SDay
'Tropical Fusion' **new**	EStr
'Tropical Hot Flash'	EStr
'Tropical Passion'	EStr
'True Gertrude Demarest'	WHrl
'Trump Card'	EStr
'Tune the Harp'	EStr
'Tupac Amaru'	EStr
'Turkish Tapestry'	CBgR
'Turkish Turban'	SDay
'Turn the Other Cheek'	EStr
'Turtle Island'	EStr
'Tuscawilla Blackout'	XSen
'Tuscawilla Princess'	EStr
'Tuscawilla Tigress'	EStr GKin MNrw SDay WAul WHrl
'Tutankhamun'	EStr SDay
'Tuxedo Junction' ♀H6	EStr
'Tuxedo Whiskers'	EStr
'Twenty Third Psalm'	WHal
'Twilight Swan'	WNHG
'Twist of Lemon'	SDay
'Two Part Harmony'	WHrl
'Ultra Persuasion'	SDay
'Umbrella Parade'	EStr
'Uncle Lurch' **new**	EStr
'Undefinable' **new**	EStr
'Unlock Your Dreams'	EStr
'Up the Wazoo'	EStr
'Upper Class Peach'	EStr SDay
'Uptown Girl'	EStr
'Valiant'	MBNS WHrl
'Valley Sprite'	EStr
'Vanilla Fluff'	EStr
'Vanishing Mist' **new**	EStr
'Varsity'	CExl CRos LRHS NBir NRHS SPer
'Vectis Jean Merritt'	EStr
'Vectis Jean Peirce'	EStr
'Vegas Show Girl' **new**	EStr
'Veins of Truth'	CBgR EStr WCAu
'Velvet Eyes'	EStr
'Velvet Shadows'	CBgR SDay
'Velvet Web'	EStr
'Vendetta'	WNHG
'Venusian Mirage'	EStr
'Vera Biaglow'	EStr SDay
'Vernal Tutone' **new**	WNHG
'Very Berry Ice'	EStr
vespertina	see *H. thunbergii*
'Vesuvian'	SDay
'Veuve Joyeuse'	XSen
'Vi Simmons'	EStr
'Vicountess Byng'	WWtn
'Victoria Aden'	CBro

'Victoria Elizabeth Barnes' WNHG
'Victorian Violet' SDay
'Video' SDay
'Vie en Rose' EStr
'Viewpoint' SDay
'Villa Vanilla' **new** WFar
'Vino di Notte' EStr
'Vintage Bordeaux' ELan SDay
'Vintage Burgundy' CBgR WNHG
'Vintage Passion' EStr
'Vintage Wine' WNHG
'Violent Thunder' EStr
'Violet Cuckoo' EStr
'Violet Hour' EStr SDay
'Violet Patch' **new** SDay
'Viracocha' WNHG
'Virgin's Blush' SPer
'Vohann' SDay
'Volcano Queen' EPfP EStr WFar
'Voodoo Dancer' EStr SCob
'Waiting in the Wings' SDay
'Walking on Sunshine' EStr WCot
'Walnut Hill' EStr
'Walt Disney' GKin
'Walter Kennedy' **new** EStr
'Wanda Evans' EStr
'War Paint' EStr SDay
'Warp Drive' SDay
'Watch Tower' CBgR
'Watchyl Dancing Spider' EStr
'Water Witch' CWat SDay
'Watermelon Man' CBgR
'Waxen Splendor' EStr
'Wayne Johnson' WNHG
'Wayside Green Imp' MNrw
'Web Browser' EStr
'Web Crawler' **new** EStr
'Webster's Aggie' EStr
'Webster's Pastel Beauty' **new** EStr
'Webster's Pinched Peach' **new** EStr
'Webster's Pink Wonder' EStr
'Wee Willie Winkie' WNHG
'Welchkins' SDay WAul
'Wesley Lee Kirby' EStr
'What a Day for a Daydream' EStr
'When I Dream' EStr
'When You Get to Asheville' EStr
'Whichford' CAby CBgR CBro CMea CRos CSam ECha ECtt ELan EPfP GCal GKin LRHS NRHS SPhx WGwG WHrl
'Whip City Fancy Free' EStr
'Whirling Fury' ELon
'White Coral' LRHS LSRN NBro NRHS
'White Edged Madonna' WHrl
'White Ensign' SDay
'White Eyes Pink Dragon' **new** EStr
'White Magician' EStr
'White Pansy' SDay
'White Temptation' EPfP LRHS SDay WAul WHoo WNHG XSen
'White Zone' SDay
'Whoopie' SPad
'Wideyed' XLum
'Wiggle Butt' EStr
'Wigglesworth' EStr
'Wild and Wonderful' LLWG LSun SDay WFar
'Wild at Heart' **new** EStr
'Wild Horses' EWes LRHS MNrw NLar SCob SMad WHrl
'Wild Mustang' EStr
'Wild Planet' **new** EStr
'Wild Wookie' SDay
'William Milo Spalding' EStr
'Wilson Spider' EStr
'Wind Frills' XSen
'Wind Song' ELon SDay
'Wind Storm' EStr
'Windmill Yellow' SDay
'Window Dressing' SDay
'Wineberry Candy' EStr MBNS NLar
'Winged Migration' EStr
'Winnie' EStr
'Winnie the Pooh' SDay
'Winsome Lady' ECha ECtt GKin WHrl
'Winter Wolf' EStr
'Winyah Eye' EStr
'Wired' EStr
'Wisest of Wizards' WHrl
'Wishful Dreaming' EStr
'Wishing Well' WCot
'Wispy Rays' **new** EStr
'Witch Hazel' WCAu WWtn
'Witch Hollow' **new** EStr
'Witch Stitchery' EStr SDay
'Witches Brew' CBgR
'Without Warning' CBgR
'Womanizer' EStr
'Wonder of it All' EStr
'Woodside Ruby' WNHG
'Wounded Heart' SDay
'Wyatt's Cameo' SDay
'Wyoming Wildfire' CBgR
'Xia Xiang' SDay
'Xochimilco' WNHG
'Ya Ya Girl' EStr
'Yabba Dabba Doo' EStr
'Yankee Pinstripes' EStr
'Yazoo Wild Violet' EStr
'Yellow Angel' ELon WCot
'Yellow Lollipop' SDay
'Yellow Rain' WCot
'Yellow Ribbon' EStr
'Yellow Submarine' EPfP
'Yes Man' EStr
'Yesterday Memories' SDay
'Yesterday, Today and Tomorrow' SDay
yezoensis EBtc
'Yum Yum Plum' EStr SDay
'Yuma' WNHG
'Zachary S. Hickey' **new** EStr
'Zagora' EStr WCAu
'Zampa' CBgR EStr SDay
'Zappa' **new** SDay
'Zara' EStr SPer
'Zenobia' EStr
'Zero Dark Thirty' **new** EStr
'Zip Boom Bah' EStr
'Zuni Mountains' WNHG

Hemiboea (*Gesneriaceae*)

subcapitata **new** SBrt

Hemipilia (*Orchidaceae*)

graminifolia GKev LAma

Hepatica ✿ (*Ranunculaceae*)

acutiloba	CWCL GEdr GKev MBel NBir WPnP XEll
- blue-flowered	MAsh
- white-flowered	MAsh
acutiloba × nobilis	SPer
americana	GKev MAsh NBir
- 'Ashwood Marble'	MAsh
- 'Rosea' **new**	CSpe
angulosa	see *H. transsilvanica*
(Forest Series) 'Forest Blue'	EHrv
- 'Forest Pink'	CWCL EHrv ELan GBin GKev XEll
- 'Forest Purple'	ELan GKev LCro XEll
- 'Forest Red'	EHrv ELan GBin GKev LCro WPnP XEll
- 'Forest White'	CWCL EHrv ELan GBin GKev LCro WPnP XEll
henryi	GEdr MAsh
insularis	MAsh
maxima	GEdr LLHF MAsh
× ***media*** 'Ballardii'	GEdr LLHF MAsh
- 'Harvington Beauty'	GEdr IBlr MAsh NBir WSHC
- 'Kim' **new**	GEdr
- 'Millstream Merlin'	GEdr
- 'Silberprinzessin' **new**	GEdr
- 'Violett Prinz'	MAsh
§ ***nobilis*** ♀H6	Widely available
- 'Bibo'	EWld
- blue-flowered	MAsh NSla WAbe
- 'Brockman' (d) **new**	GEdr
- 'Cobalt'	GEdr NSla
- compact evergreen	MAsh
- 'Cremar'	GEdr MAsh
- dark blue-flowered	ITim
- dwarf white-flowered	NSla
- 'Elkofener Heidi'	GEdr
- 'Gold Band' (v)	GEdr
- var. ***japonica***	EWes GEdr MAsh NBir NSla
- - 'Aikawa' (5/d)	GEdr
- - 'Akane' (1)	GEdr
- - 'Akanezora' (6/d)	GEdr
- - 'Akebono' (9/d)	GEdr
- - 'Anjyu' (9/d)	GEdr
- - 'Aozora' (1)	GEdr
- - 'Asahi' (7/d)	GEdr
- - 'Asahizuru' (6/d)	GEdr
- - 'Benifusya' (1)	GEdr
- - 'Benihagure' (9/d)	GEdr
- - 'Benikanzan' (1)	GEdr
- - 'Benikujyaku' (7/d)	GEdr
- - 'Benioiran' (3)	GEdr
- - 'Beniokesa' (9/d)	GEdr
- - 'Benishinjyu' (6/d)	GEdr
- - 'Benisuzume' (1)	GEdr
- - 'Benitaiko' (9/d)	GEdr
- - 'Bojyou' (5A/d)	GEdr
- - 'Daishihou' (9/d)	GEdr
- - 'Dewa' (9/d)	GEdr
- - 'Ebisu-no-hana' (5A/d)	GEdr
- - 'Echigobijin' (1)	GEdr
- - 'Fukujyu' (9/d)	GEdr
- - 'Gosho-zakura' (5A/d)	GEdr
- - 'Gyousei' (1)	GEdr
- - 'Hakurin' (6/d)	GEdr
- - 'Hakusetsu' (9/d)	GEdr
- - 'Hanagoromo' (9/d)	GEdr
- - 'Haruka' (2)	GEdr
- - 'Harukaze' (5A/d)	GEdr
- - 'Harumo-no-Gatari' (8/d)	GEdr
- - 'Haruno-awajuki' (9/d)	GEdr
- - 'Hatsune' (5/d)	GEdr
- - 'Hidamari' (5/d)	GEdr
- - 'Hohobeni' (9/d)	GEdr
- - 'Hokutosei' (7/d)	GEdr
- - 'Hoshizora' (2)	GEdr
- - 'Hosyun' (1)	GEdr
- - 'Isaribi' (1)	GEdr
- - 'Junissen' (6/d)	GEdr
- - 'Kagura' (5A/d)	GEdr
- - 'Kasumino' (1)	GEdr
- - 'Kiko' (9/d)	GEdr
- - 'Kimon' (9/d)	GEdr
- - 'Koshi-no-maboroshi' (7/d)	GEdr
- - 'Kotobuki-hime' (5/d)	GEdr
- - 'Kouen' (6/d)	GEdr
- - 'Kougyoku' (9/d)	GEdr
- - 'Kuetsu' (9/d)	GEdr
- - 'Kurotaiyou' (d) **new**	GEdr
- - 'Kuukai' (8/d)	GEdr
- - f. ***magna***	MAsh
- - 'Manazuru' (9/d)	GEdr
- - 'Minamo' (5/d)	GEdr
- - 'Miwaku' (1)	GEdr
- - 'Miyoshino' (1)	GEdr
- - 'Miyuki' (9/d)	GEdr
- - 'Murasaki-sakama' (9/d)	GEdr
- - 'Murasaki-shikibu' (9/d)	GEdr
- - 'Nanakubo' (1)	GEdr
- - 'Notaniyama' **new**	GEdr
- - 'Noumurasaki' (1)	GEdr
- - 'Oboryo' (1)	GEdr
- - 'Odoriko' (9/d)	GEdr
- - 'Okesabayashi'	GEdr
- - 'Okina' (9/d)	GEdr
- - 'Ō-murasaki' (1)	GEdr
- - 'Orihime' (9/d)	GEdr
- - 'Reeka' (1)	GEdr
- - 'Ryokurei' (5A/d)	GEdr
- - 'Ryokusetsu' (9/d)	GEdr
- - 'Ryokuun' (9/d)	GEdr
- - 'Sadobeni' (1)	GEdr
- - 'Saichou' (7/d)	GEdr
- - Sandan Group (7/d)	GEdr
- - 'Satsuma' (5A/d)	GEdr
- - 'Sawanemidori' (6/d)	GEdr
- - 'Sayaka' (1)	GEdr
- - 'Seikai' (5A/d)	GEdr
- - 'Seizan' (9/d)	GEdr
- - 'Senhime' (9/d)	GEdr
- - 'Sen-nin' (6/d)	GEdr
- - 'Sennin-buraku' (8/d)	GEdr
- - 'Setsudu' (7/d)	GEdr
- - 'Shihou' (9/d)	GEdr
- - 'Shikouden' (9/d)	GEdr
- - 'Shikouryuu' (9/d)	GEdr
- - 'Shio' (9/d)	GEdr
- - 'Shirayuki' (9/d)	GEdr
- - 'Shirin' (9/d)	GEdr
- - 'Shiun' (9/d)	GEdr
- - 'Shoujyouno-homare' (9/d)	GEdr
- - 'Sougetsu' (6/d)	GEdr
- - 'Souhou' (1)	GEdr
- - 'Soushyunka' (9/d)	GEdr
- - 'Subaru' (9/d)	GEdr
- - 'Suien' (9/d)	GEdr
- - 'Syouchikubai' (7/d)	GEdr
- - 'Syunryuu' (9/d)	GEdr

- - 'Taeka' (9/d)	GEdr
- - 'Takase' (9/d) **new**	GEdr
- - 'Takumi' (9/d)	GEdr
- - 'Tamahime' (8/d)	GEdr
- - 'Tamakujyaku' (6/d)	GEdr
- - 'Tamamushi' (9/d)	GEdr
- - 'Tamasaburou' (1)	GEdr
- - 'Tenjinbai' (1)	GEdr
- - 'Tenjin-ume' (1)	GEdr
- - 'Tennyonomai' (6A/d)	GEdr
- - 'Toki' (9/d)	GEdr
- - 'Touen' (9/d)	GEdr
- - 'Touhou' (9/d)	GEdr
- - 'Touryoku' (9/d)	GEdr
- - 'Toyama-chiyo-iwai' (7/d)	GEdr
- - 'Umezono' (1)	GEdr
- - 'Unabara' (9/d)	GEdr
- - 'Usugesyou' (9/d)	GEdr
- - 'Utyuu' (1)	GEdr
- - 'Wakakusa' (9/d)	GEdr
- - 'Wakana' (1)	GEdr
- - 'Yaegoromo' (6/d)	GEdr
- - 'Yahiko' (5/d)	GEdr
- - 'Yahikomurasaki' (1)	GEdr
- - 'Yamahibiki' (9/d)	GEdr
- - 'Yukishino' (2)	GEdr
- - 'Yumes' (7/d)	GEdr
- - 'Yuunagi' (9/d)	GEdr
- - 'Yuunami' (1)	GEdr
- - 'Yuuzen' (5/d)	GEdr
- - 'Yuzuru' (9/d)	GEdr
- large, pale blue-flowered	NSla
- 'Lilac Picotee'	NSla
- patterned leaf	NSla
- pink-flowered	MAsh
- var. ***pubescens***	MAsh NSla
* - var. ***pyrenaica***	LEdu MAsh NSla WAbe WThu
* - - 'Apple Blossom'	NBir
* - - white-flowered	CSpe NBir
- 'Pyrenean Marbles'	NBir
- var. ***rubra***	NSla
- 'Rubra Plena' (d)	CElw GEdr MAsh NSla WPnP
- 'Stained Glass'	EWld
- violet-flowered	MAsh
- 'White Sands'	ELan GBin GEdr
- white-flowered	EHrv GAbr GEdr MAsh XEll
'Noubeni'	GEdr
× ***schlyteri*** Ashwood hybrids	MAsh
- 'The Bride'	GEdr MAsh
§ ***transsilvanica*** ♀H5	CBro EHrv MAsh MCot WCot WThu
- 'Ada Scott'	GEdr MAsh
- 'Blue Eyes'	GEdr GKev
- 'Blue Jewel'	CWCL EBee ELan EPot GBin GEdr MCot MHol WPnP
- blue-flowered	IBlr MAsh
- 'Buis'	ECha GEdr ILea MAsh NLar
- 'Connie Greenfield'	NSla
- 'Eisvogel'	GEdr
- 'Elison Spence' (d)	GEdr IBlr LLHF MAvo MCot
- 'Lilacina'	GEdr MAsh
- 'Loddon Blue'	GEdr IBlr MAsh
- pink-flowered	MAsh
- 'Sieben Bergen'	IBlr
- 'Supernova'	MAsh
- white-flowered	GEdr MAsh
triloba	see *H. nobilis*
yamatutai	GEdr
aff. ***yamatutai***	MAsh

Heptacodium (*Caprifoliaceae*)

jasminoides	see *H. miconioides*
§ ***miconioides*** ♀H7	Widely available
- TIANSHAN ('Minhep')	MPkF SGol WCot

Heptapleurum see *Schefflera*

Heptaptera (*Apiaceae*)

triquetra W&B BGA-2	CSpe

Heracleum (*Apiaceae*)

dulce	EBee
sphondylium	WSFF
stevenii	MHol WCot

Hereroa (*Aizoaceae*)

glenensis	CRos CSma EBou EDAr LRHS NRHS SPlb

Hermannia (*Malvaceae*)

erodioides	CPBP
flammea	SPlb
stricta	CPBP WAbe

Hermodactylus see *Iris*

Herniaria (*Caryophyllaceae*)

glabra	GPoy

Hertia (*Asteraceae*)

§ ***cheirifolia***	CCCN CMea CSde EWes EWld NBir SEND SIgm XLum

Hesperaloe (*Asparagaceae*)

campanulata	WCot
engelmannii	WCot
funifera white-flowered	WCot
'New Blue'	WCot
parviflora	CAco LEdu SChr SIgm SPlb XSen
- creamy yellow-flowered	WCot
- 'Rubra'	MPkF

Hesperantha ✿ (*Iridaceae*)

§ ***baurii***	CPbh GBin LLHF NHpl WThu
coccinea	CBcs CMac CPla CPrp CTri CTsd EBee EHoe EPfP GKev IBlr MWts NChi NEgg NGdn NHol NLar SCob SDeJ SRot WCot WFar WMAq XLum
- f. ***alba***	CBro CExl CMea CPrp CRos CTri CTsd CWCL EBee ECha ELan EPfP GKev ITim LRHS MRav NBir NGdn NLar NRHS SCob SDeJ SPer SPlb SRms SWvt WFar WMoo WSHC
- 'Anne'	NLar WFar
- 'Autumn's Dawn'	WFar
- 'Ballyrogan Giant'	CPrp ECtt IBlr WFar WHer WSHC
- 'Big Moma'	CPrp NAln WFar
- 'Cardinal'	NHol WFar WMoo
- 'Caroline'	CPrp WFar
- 'Cindy Towe'	CAbb CKno EMor LLHF SPoG WFar
- 'Countesse de Vere'	EBee NAln
- 'Elburton Glow'	NAln WFar
- 'Eric's Early'	CPrp WFar
- 'Fenland Daybreak'	Widely available
- 'Gigantea'	see *H. coccinea* 'Major'
- 'Good White'	CWCL NBir SMHy WFar
- 'Grandiflora'	see *H. coccinea* 'Major'
- 'Hilary Gould'	CMea CPrp ECtt WAvo WHal
- 'Ice Maiden'	CAbb EMor GWyn NSti SPoG

- 'Jack Frost' EBee WFar WMoo
- 'Jennifer' ♀H4 CBro CDor CElw CMac CPrp CRos CTri EBee ECha ECtt ELon EPfP GAbr LPot LRHS MCot MMuc MRav NLar NRHS NWad SRms SWvt WAvo WFar WMoo WPnP
- 'Maiden's Blush' CRos ECtt EHrv ELan LEdu LRHS MCot NLar SRms WFar

§ - 'Major' ♀H4 Widely available
- 'Marchants Seedling' **new** SMHy
- 'Marietta' NWad WFar
- 'Mollie Gould' CAvo CPrp ECtt EHrv ELon EPfP LRHS MAvo MHer MNrw MPie NHol NRHS NWad SCoo SRms WAvo WFar WMoo
- 'Mrs Hegarty' CBod CMac CPrp CSam ECtt ELan EMor EPfP GAbr GMaP GWyn MGos MHer MRav MWts NBid NBir NHol NLar SDeJ SPer SPlb SPoG SRms SWvt WFar
- 'November Cheer' CMac ECtt IBlr NBir NLar
- 'Oregon Sunset' CAby CBcs CBod CPla CPrp ECtt ELon EMor LLHF WFar WHil
- 'Pallida' CPrp CSam ECtt EHrv MRav NBir WFar
- 'Pink Marg' CPrp ITim WFar
- 'Pink Princess' see *H. coccinea* 'Wilfred H. Bryant'
- pink-flowered MBel
- 'Professor Barnard' CCCN CSpe EBee ECtt ELon EPfP GWyn MBNS MNrw NBir NLar SRot WFar WRHF
- 'Red Arrow' EWes
- 'Red Dragon' ECtt NHol WHoo

I - 'Rosea' GKev SDeJ WFar
- 'Ruth' WFar
- 'Salmon Charm' CRos ECtt LRHS NRHS WFar WMoo
- 'Salmon's Leap' WFar
- 'Salome' CPrp ECtt WFar
- 'Scarlet Queen' WFar
- 'Silver Pink' IBlr
- 'Snow Drift' WFar
- 'Snow Maiden' CElw CWCL EBee EWTr LRHS WFar
- 'Strawberry' CPrp WFar

§ - 'Sunrise' ♀H4 CBcs CBro CExl CPrp CRos CSBt CSam CWCL EBee ECha EHoe ELan EPfP GKev IBlr LRHS MCot MHer MRav NBir NGdn NRHS NWad SPer SWvt WFar WHoo WKif WMoo
- 'Sunset' see *H. coccinea* 'Sunrise'
- 'Tambara' CPou CPrp CSam ECtt EHrv WFar XLum
- 'Vibrant Scarlet' WFar
- 'Viscountess Byng' CPrp CTri CWCL EBee MNrw NBir

* - 'White Admiral' **new** WFar

§ - 'Wilfred H. Bryant' ♀H4 Widely available
- 'Zeal Salmon' CBro CElw CPou CRos ECha ECtt GAbr NAln NBir WFar

cucullata CPbh
huttonii GEdr ITim LLHF NBir WFar
mossii see *H. baurii*
pauciflora CPbh
vaginata CPbh

Hesperis (*Brassicaceae*)

lutea see *Sisymbrium luteum*
matronalis Widely available
- ***alba*** see *H. matronalis* var. *albiflora*

§ - var. ***albiflora*** CCBP CLau CSpe CWld ELan EPfP EWTr GMaP LCro LOPS LRHS MNHC NAln NGdn SPer SPhx WBrk WCFE WHil WMoo
- - 'Alba Plena' (d) CRos EBee GWyn LRHS LSun MSCN NBir WCAu WCot
- 'Cally Dwarf' (d) GCal

I - 'Variegata' (v) CPla

nivea LEdu
steveniana SPhx

Hesperochiron (*Boraginaceae*)

californicus SBrt

× *Hesperotropsis* see × *Cuprocyparis*

Hesperozygis (*Lamiaceae*)

'Midnight Mojito' (Supermint Series) **new** WHlf

Heteromeles (*Rosaceae*)

arbutifolia see *H. salicifolia*

§ ***salicifolia*** LEdu

Heteromorpha (*Apiaceae*)

arborescens CExl SPlb SVen

Heteropolygonatum (*Asparagaceae*)

'Mikinori Ogisu' EBee
roseolum CAby EWld
urceolatum WCru

Heterotheca (*Asteraceae*)

subaxillaris WCot

Heuchera ✿ (*Saxifragaceae*)

'Alan Davidson' MPnt
'Alison' MPnt
'Amber Waves'PBR CExl CRos ELan LRHS MJak MPnt NBir SCob SWvt

§ ***americana*** MRav NBir SHeu SWvt WGwG
- var. ***americana*** MPnt
- Dale's strain GPSL MPnt NLar SHeu SPlb SWvt WRHF
- 'Harry Hay' EPPr EWld LEdu LPla MPnt SHeu SMHy WPGP WSHC
- 'Marvellous Marble' MPnt NHic SHeu WOut
- 'Ring of Fire' MPnt SHeu SRms SWvt

'Amethyst Myst' CRos EMor EPfP EUJe GKev LRHS LSRN MCot MPnt NAln NRHS SCob SHeu SPer WAvo
'Apple Crisp'PBR MPnt MTin SCob SHeu SWvt WNPC
'Apple Souffle' MPnt SHeu
'Apricot' CWGN MPnt WNPC
'Autumn Glow' (Seasonal Selection Series) CRos LRHS MPnt NRHS SHeu WNPC
'Autumn Haze'PBR MPnt SHeu
'Autumn Leaves'PBR CRos ELan EUJe LCro LOPS LRHS MBel MJak MPnt NRHS SHeu SPoG SWvt
'Baby's Breath' MPnt
'Bardot' MPnt
'Beaujolais'PBR CRos LRHS MBNS MNrw MPnt NBir NRHS SHeu WCot WNPC
'Beauty Colour' CRos ECha ELan EPfP GMaP LRHS LSRN MJak MRav NGdn NRHS SHeu SWvt WJam
'Belle Notte' MPnt SHeu WNPC
'Berry Marmalade'PBR EBee EPfP MAsh MPnt NWad SCob SHeu SPer SWvt WNPC
'Berry Smoothie'PBR CPla CRos CWGN EBee EHoe ELan EPfP EUJe IPot LLHF LRHS LSRN

	MBNS MGos MJak MPnt NHol NLar NPer NRHS NSti SCob SHeu SPer SPoG SWvt
(Big Top Series) 'Big Top Bronze'	EBee SHeu
- 'Big Top Burgundy'	SHeu
- 'Big Top Gold'	CWGN MNrw SHeu
'Bilberry' (Indian Summer Series) **new**	MPnt
'Binoche'[PBR]	CRos EBee LRHS MPnt NRHS SCob SHeu WCot WNPC
'Birkin'	MPnt
'Black Cherry' (Heucheraholics Series) **new**	SHeu
'Black Sea'	MPnt WBrk WCot WNPC
'Black Taffeta'[PBR]	CWGN EBee EPfP LBuc MPnt SHeu SPad WNPC
'Blackberry Crisp'[PBR]	EBee MPnt SHeu WNPC
'Blackberry Jam'	CKel CRos ECha ELan ELon LPot LRHS MPnt NBir NHol NRHS SHeu SWvt WFar
'Blackbird'	MPnt SHeu SWvt WFar WSpi
'Blackout'	MNrw MPnt NLar SHeu
'Blondie in Lime' (Little Cutie Series)	CRos MPnt NLar NRHS SHeu
'Blondie'[PBR] (Little Cutie Series)	CBod CRos CWGN EBee LRHS MPnt NLar NRHS SCob SHeu SPad SPoG WBrk WCot WHlf WNPC
'Blood Red'	MPnt SHeu
'Blood Vein'	MPnt SHeu
'Blushing Down'	MPnt
'Bouquet'	MPnt SHeu
'Boysenberry' (Indian Summer Series)	EBee MPnt SHeu
bracteata	MPnt XLum
'Bressingham Glow'	MPnt SHeu
Bressingham hybrids	NBir SRms SVic
'Bressingham Spire'	MPnt
'Bright and Breezy' (Seasonal Selection Series)	CRos LRHS MPnt NRHS SCob SHeu WNPC
'Bronze Beauty'	MPnt SHeu WBrk WCot
'Brown Sugar'	MPnt SHeu
'Brownfinch'	CElw MAvo MPnt SBrt SHeu WCot
'Brownies'	MPnt SHeu WHrl WPtf WWtn
'Burgundy Frost'	MPnt SHeu WBrk
'Café Olé'	MPnt NLar SCob SHeu WHer
'Cajun Fire'[PBR]	CWGN ELan MPnt SCob SHeu WNPC
'Can-can' ♀H6	CBod CPla CRos CTri ELan ELon EPfP GKev LRHS MNrw MPnt NBir NLar NRHS SCob SHeu SRot SWvt WCAu WSpi
'Canyon Duet'	MPnt SHeu
'Cappuccino'	CRos EBee ELan EPfP LRHS MPnt MRav NAln NRHS SCob SHeu SWvt
'Caramel'[PBR]	CBod CMac CRos CWGN EBee ELan GMaP LCro LLHF LOPS LRHS MAsh MNrw NRHS NSti SCob SGbt SHeu SPer SPoG SWvt WAul WBrk WCot WPnP
'Carmen'	MPnt SHeu
(Carnival Series) CARNIVAL COCOMINT ('Balcarcint'[PBR])	SHeu
- CARNIVAL COFFEE BEAN ('Balcarcean'[PBR]) **new**	CRos LRHS NRHS
- CARNIVAL LIMEADE ('Balcarmade'[PBR])	ELan SHeu
- CARNIVAL PEACH PARFAIT ('Balcarpait')	CRos LRHS NRHS SHeu
- CARNIVAL PLUM CRAZY ('Balcarulm'[PBR])	SHeu
- CARNIVAL ROSE GRANITA	SHeu
- CARNIVAL WATERMELON ('Balcarmelo') **new**	MHol
'Cascade Dawn'	EBee MPnt NBir SWvt
'Cassis'	CWGN LSun MPnt SCob SHeu WCot
'Cézanne' (Master Painters Series)	MPnt SHeu
'Champagne'	MPnt SHeu
'Champagne Bubbles'	CWGN MPnt SHeu
CHARLES BLOOM ('Chablo')	CRos LRHS MPnt NRHS SHeu
'Chatterbox'	MPnt SHeu
'Checkers'	see *H.* 'Quilter's Joy'
'Cherries Jubilee'[PBR]	EPfP GMaP MPnt SHeu SLim
'Cherry Cola'[PBR]	CBcs CBod CPla CRos EBee ELan EPfP LRHS MAsh MAvo MCot MJak MPnt NLar NPri NRHS SCob SHeu SPad SPoG SRkn WCot WFar WNPC WTor
'Chiqui'	MPnt SHeu
chlorantha	MPnt
- 'Burnt Sienna'	GCal
'Chocolate Ruffles'[PBR]	CBcs CNor CRos ECha EHoe EHrv ELan ELon EPfP EShb GMaP LRHS LSRN MCot MGos MRav NBir NRHS SCob SLim SPer SPoG SRms SWvt WFar WHoo WSpi
'Chocolate Veil'	MPnt
'Christa'	MPnt SHeu
'Cinnabar Silver'[PBR]	MPnt NBir SCob
'Circus'[PBR]	CWGN MPnt SCob SHeu WNPC
'Citronelle'	CRos CWGN EPfP LRHS MPnt NRHS SCob SHeu SWvt WCot WPnP
'City Lights'	SHeu
'Coco'[PBR] (Little Cutie Series)	CRos EBee EPfP LRHS MPnt NRHS SHeu WNPC
'Color Dream'[PBR]	MPnt SHeu
coral bells	see *H. sanguinea*
'Coral Bouquet'	MPnt SHeu
'Coral Cloud'	MPnt SHeu
'Coralberry' (Indian Summer Series) **new**	MPnt SHeu
'Corallion'	MPnt
'Cranberry' (Indian Summer Series) **new**	SHeu
CRÈME BRÛLÉE ('Tnheu041') (Dolce Series)	CBcs CExl CRos EHoe ELan EPau EPfP LLHF LRHS MGos NBir NLar NRHS SCob SHeu SLim SPoG SRot SWvt
'Crème Caramel'	CExl MPnt
'Creole Nights'[PBR]	MPnt SHeu
'Crimson Curls'	CRos ELan EPfP LBuc LRHS MPnt NAln NRHS SCob SHeu SRms SWvt WNPC
'Crispy Curly'	MPnt SHeu
cylindrica	EPfP GKev GWyn LRHS MPnt NChi SHeu
- var. ***alpina***	GKev LLHF
- 'Cream'	MPnt
- 'Francis'	MPnt
- 'Greenfinch'	ELan EWTr GLog GMaP GWyn LRHS MPnt MRav NBir SHar SHeu SWvt XLum
- 'Hyperion'	CRos LRHS MPnt NRHS SHeu

'Da Vinci' (Master Painters Series)	MPnt SHeu
'Damask'	CRos LRHS MPnt NRHS SHeu
'Dark Beauty'[PBR]	CRos EMor LRHS NRHS NSti SCob SHeu SPer WNPC
'Dark Secret'[PBR]	EBee MPnt SHeu
'Dark Storm' (Seasonal Selection Series)	CRos EPfP LRHS MPnt NRHS SCob SHeu WNPC
'David'	MPnt SHeu WBrk
'Delta Dawn'[PBR]	CPla CWGN EBee LRHS MHol MPnt SCob SHeu SPoG SWvt WNPC
'Dennis Davidson'	see *H.* 'Huntsman'
'Dew Drops' (v) **new**	SHeu
'Earth Angel'	MPnt SHeu
EBONY AND IVORY ('E and I'[PBR])	CRos EBee EShb GMaP LRHS LSRN MPnt NAln NBir NRHS NWad SCob SRms SRot SWvt WSpi
'Eden's Aurora'	MPnt
'Eden's Mystery'	NLar
'Electra'[PBR]	CMea EBee MBNS MPnt NLar SCob SHeu SWvt
'Electric Lime'	EHoe ELan MPnt NLar SHeu SPoG WNPC
'Elworthy Rusty'	CElw
'Emperor's Cloak'	GLog LEdu SHeu SWvt WHrl WMoo
'Encore'[PBR]	MPnt SHeu
'Fairy Dance'	MPnt
'Fantasia'	SHeu
'Fire Alarm'[PBR]	CRos CWGN EBee ELan LBuc LRHS MPnt NRHS SHeu WNPC
'Fire Chief'[PBR]	CBod CKel CRos CWGN EBee ELan EPfP EUJe LRHS MAvo MPnt NAln NBir NHol NLar NRHS SCob SHeu SPer SPoG SRkn SRot SWvt
'Firebird'	CRos LRHS MPnt NRHS
FIREFLY	see *H.* 'Leuchtkäfer'
'Fireworks'[PBR] ♀H6	MBNS MJak MPnt MRav NLar SHeu SRot
'Fleur' (Fox Series) **new**	MPnt
'Florist's Choice'	SHeu
'Forever Purple'	CBod CRos CWGN EBee EPfP LBuc LRHS MPnt NLar NRHS SHeu SPoG WNPC WTor
'French Quarter'	MPnt SHeu
'Frost' (Little Cutie Series)	MPnt SHeu WNPC
'Frosted Violet'	see *H.* 'Frosted Violet Dream'
§ 'Frosted Violet Dream'[PBR]	EMor LSRN MPnt SCob SHeu SWvt WNPC
'Galaxy'[PBR]	CWGN MPnt SHeu
'Gauguin' (Master Painters Series)	MPnt SCob SHeu
'Georgia Peach'[PBR]	CPla CWGN EBee ELan EPfP MNrw MPnt NBir NLar SHeu SWvt WFar WNPC
'Georgia Plum'	CRos CWGN EBee ELan LRHS MPnt NRHS SHeu WNPC
'Ginger Ale'[PBR]	CRos CWGN EBee ECha ELan ELon EPfP EWes LRHS MBNS MJak MPnt NBir NHol NLar NRHS NSti NWad SCob SHeu SPer SPoG SWvt
'Ginger Peach'[PBR]	ELan EPfP MPnt SCob SHeu WNPC WTor
'Ginger Snap'[PBR] (Little Cutie Series)	MPnt SHeu WNPC
glabra	MPnt SHeu
glauca	see *H. americana*
'Glitter'[PBR]	EBee EPfP MPnt SHeu SPoG WNPC
'Gloire d'Orléans'	MPnt XLum
'Gloriana'	CRos LRHS NRHS
'Gojiberry' (Indian Summer Series)	EBee SHeu
'Gotham'[PBR]	EBee MPnt SCob SHeu WNPC
'Grape Soda'[PBR] (Soda Series)	CWGN MHol MPnt SHeu WNPC
'Green Curl' **new**	WNPC
'Green Goddess' (Heucheraholics Series) **new**	SHeu
'Green Ivory'	MPnt SHeu XLum
'Green Sashay'	MPnt SHeu
'Green Spice'	CBod CRos EBee ELan EPfP LRHS MJak MPnt NAln NBir NHol NRHS SCob SHeu SPer SPoG SWvt
grossulariifolia	GMaP
'Guacamole'	MPnt SHeu
'Guardian Angel'	MPnt SHeu
'Gypsy Dancer'[PBR] (Dancer Series)	MPnt SHeu
'Hailstorm' (v)	MPnt
hallii	MPnt SPlb
HARVEST BURGUNDY ('Balheubur')	CRos LRHS MPnt NRHS SHeu
HARVEST SILVER ('Balheusil')	CRos EPfP LRHS MPnt NRHS SHeu
'Havana'[PBR]	CRos LRHS MPnt NRHS SHeu
'Helen Dillon' (v)	GMaP MPnt NBir SHeu SWvt
'Hercules'[PBR]	LRHS MPnt SCob SHeu
hispida	MPnt
'Hocus Pocus'	SHeu
'Hollywood'[PBR]	CKel EBee EPfP MGos MPnt NBir NHol NLar SCob SHeu SPoG SRot
'Hot Stuff'	SHeu
§ 'Huntsman'	CRos LRHS MPnt MRav NRHS SHeu
'Iron Maiden'	SHeu
'Isabella' (Fox Series) **new**	MPnt
'Jade Gloss'[PBR]	CRos EPfP LRHS MPnt NRHS SHeu SWvt WNPC
'June Bride'	MPnt
'Kadastra'	MPnt SHeu
'Kassandra'[PBR]	CRos EBee LRHS MPnt NRHS SCob SHeu SWvt
KEY LIME PIE ('Tnheu042'[PBR]) (Dolce Series)	CExl CRos CWGN EPfP LRHS MGos NBir NHol NRHS SCob SHeu SRms SWvt WFar
'King Kong'	MPnt
Kira Series	MPnt
- 'Kira Purple Rain Forest'	SHeu
'Lady in Red'	NBre
'Lady Marmalade'	NPri
'Lady Romney'	GCal XLum
'Lemon Chiffon'[PBR]	CRos LRHS MPnt NRHS SHeu
§ 'Leuchtkäfer'	EPfP EWTr GMaP GWyn LPot MHer MMuc MPnt MRav NBir NMir SHeu SPlb SRms WJam XLum
LICORICE ('Tnheu044'[PBR]) (Dolce Series)	CRos GBin LRHS MBNS MGos MPnt NBir NLar NRHS SHeu SLim SPoG SRot SWvt WFar
'Lily the Pink' **new**	SHeu
'Lime Marmalade'	CBcs CBod CKel CMea CRos CWGN EBee ELan ELon EPfP LRHS MAsh MBNS MGos MJak MPnt NHol NLar NPri NRHS NSti SCob SHeu SPer SPoG WFar
'Lime Rickey'[PBR]	CWGN EPfP LRHS MGos NBir NGBl SCob SHeu SWvt WCot
'Lime Ruffles'[PBR]	MPnt SHeu WNPC
'Lipstick'[PBR]	CWGN EBee LRHS MPnt SHeu SWvt WNPC
'Little Tinker'	MPnt SHeu
'Lune Rousse'	MPnt SHeu

'Madison Bride' (Fox Series) **new**	MPnt
'Magic Flute' **new**	SHeu
'Magic Wand' ♀H6	SHeu
'Magma' **new**	SHeu
'Magnum'	CWGN MPnt SHeu WCot
'Mahogany'[PBR]	EPfP MJak MPnt NBir NPri SCob SHeu SLim SWvt WHoo
'Malachite'	CRos EPfP LRHS MPnt NRHS SHeu
'Mango'	MPnt SHeu
'Marmalade'[PBR]	Widely available
'Maroon Blush'[PBR]	SHeu
'Mars'	CRos EPfP LRHS MPnt NRHS SHeu
'Mary Rose'	MPnt SHeu
maxima	MPnt SHeu
'Mega Caramel'	MPnt SHeu
'Mega Citronelle'	MPnt
'Melting Fire'	CChe GPSL LRHS MPnt SHeu
'Mercury'	SHeu
'Metallic Shimmer' (Fox Series)	MPnt WNPC
'Metallica'	SHeu WMoo
micans	see *H. rubescens*
micrantha	GCal MPnt SHeu SRms
- var. ***diversifolia*** misapplied	see *H. villosa*
- 'Martha's Compact'	MPnt
§ - 'Ruffles'	ECha MPnt SHeu
'Midas Touch'	CWGN MPnt NLar SHeu
'Midnight Bayou'	CKel CPla EBee ELan EPfP MPnt NLar NPer SHeu SWvt WNPC
'Midnight Rose'	Widely available
'Midnight Rose Select'	MPnt NWad SHeu
'Midnight Ruffles'[PBR]	MPnt SHeu WFar WNPC
'Milan'[PBR]	CRos ELan LRHS MPnt NRHS SCob SHeu WNPC
'Mini Caramel'	MPnt
'Mini Mouse'	MPnt SHeu
'Mint Frost'[PBR]	CRos ELan LRHS MPnt NBir SHeu SWvt
'Mint Julep'[PBR]	MPnt SHeu
'Miracle'[PBR]	EPfP MPnt SHeu WNPC
'Mocha'[PBR]	MNrw MPnt SHeu SWvt
'Molly Bush' ♀H6	MPnt SHeu
'Morello'	MPnt SCob SHeu WNPC
'Morning Mist' **new**	WNPC
'Mother of Pearl'	MPnt SHeu
'Muscat'	MPnt SHeu
'Mysteria'[PBR]	MPnt SHeu
'Mystic Angel'	MPnt SHeu
'Neptune'	MBel MPnt SHeu
(Northern Exposure Series) Northern Exposure Amber ('Tnheunea') **new**	SHeu
- Northern Exposure Lime ('Tnhheunel') **new**	MPnt SHeu
- Northern Exposure Red ('Tnhheuner') **new**	SHeu
'Oakington Jewel'	MPnt
'Obsidian'[PBR]	Widely available
'Orange Dream'	MPnt SHeu
'Orphée'	MPnt NChi
'Paprika'[PBR]	CMea CRos CWGN EBee EUJe IKil LRHS LSun MBNS MPnt NRHS SHeu WCot WFar WNPC
'Paris'[PBR]	CRos EBee EPfP LRHS LSRN MAsh MBel MGos MPnt NAln NHol NRHS SCob SHeu SPer SPoG WNPC
parishii NNS 93384	MPnt
parvifolia var. ***nivalis***	MPnt
- var. ***utahensis***	MPnt
'Pauline' (Fox Series)	CRos LBuc LRHS MPnt NRHS SHeu WNPC
'Peach Crisp'[PBR]	CWGN EBee MPnt SCob SHeu SRkn WNPC
'Peach Flambé'[PBR]	CBcs CBod CRos CWGN ELan EPfP LRHS MBNS MCot MGos MJak MPnt NBir NDov NEgg NLar NPri NRHS SCob SHeu SLim SPoG SWvt WHer
'Peach Melba'	MPnt SHeu
'Peach Pie'	MPnt
'Peachy Keen'	SHeu
'Pear Crisp'[PBR]	MPnt SCob SHeu WNPC
'Penelope'	EBee MPnt SHeu WNPC
'Peppermint' (Little Cutie Series)	CBod LSun MPnt SHeu WCot WNPC
'Peppermint Spice'[PBR] (21st Century Collection Series)	MPnt SHeu
'Persian Carpet'	CRos LRHS MPnt NBir NRHS SHeu SWvt
(Petite Series) 'Petite Marbled Burgundy'	MPnt SHeu SWvt
- 'Petite Pearl Fairy'	EHoe MPnt SHeu SWvt
- 'Petite Pink Bouquet'	MPnt SHeu
'Pewter Moon'	CRos ELan GMaP MPnt NBir SHeu WFar
'Pewter Veil'	MPnt SHeu
'Phoebe's Blush' (Fox Series)	MPnt WNPC
'Picasso' (Master Painters Series)	MPnt SHeu WNPC
'Pilley Pink'	SHeu
'Pilley Pumpkin'	SHeu
pilosissima	XLum
'Pink Panther' (Heucheraholics Series) **new**	SHeu
'Pink Pearls'	CBod CRos EPfP LRHS MPnt NRHS SCob SHeu WCot WNPC
'Pinot Bianco'	MPnt SHeu
'Pinot Gris'[PBR]	CWGN MPnt SHeu WCot WNPC
'Pinot Noir'	MPnt SHeu WNPC
'Pistache'	LBuc MPnt SHeu WCot WNPC
§ 'Pluie de Feu'	CRos LRHS MPnt MRav SHeu XLum
'Plum Power' **new**	SHeu
'Plum Pudding'[PBR]	Widely available
'Plum Royale'[PBR]	ELan EPfP GKev LRHS MGos MPnt NAln NWad SHeu SWvt
'Pretty Perinne'[PBR]	MPnt SHeu
'Pretty Polly'	CRos LRHS MPnt NRHS SHeu
'Prince'	CRos ELan LRHS MBNS MPnt NRHS SHeu SWvt
'Prince of Orange'	SHeu
'Prince of Silver'	CRos LRHS MPnt NRHS SHeu
pringlei	see *H. rubescens*
pubescens	MPnt SHeu XLum
- 'Alba'	MPnt
pulchella	EBou EDAr GCal GKev GLog LLHF MHer MPnt NLar SHeu SPlb SRms
'Purple Crinkle' **new**	WNPC
'Purple Petticoats' ♀H6	CBcs CBod ELan LPot LRHS MGos MPnt NLar SHeu SLim SPoG SRot
'Quick Silver'	CRos LRHS MPnt NBir NRHS SWvt
§ 'Quilter's Joy'	MPnt
'Rachel'	CRos EBee ELan EPfP GMaP LRHS LSRN MPnt MRav NBir NDov NGdn NRHS SHeu SWvt WGwG XLum
Rain of Fire	see *H.* 'Pluie de Feu'

'Raspberry' (Fox Series)	MPnt
'Raspberry Ice'PBR	MPnt SHeu
'Raspberry Regal' 🏆H6	MPnt MRav NBir SHeu SWvt WCot WSHC
'Rave On'PBR	CWGN EBee ELan MPnt NAln NEgg NHol NLar NWad SCob SHeu SPer SRot SWvt
'Red Dress'	MPnt SHeu
'Red Lightning'	MPnt SHeu
'Red Pearls'	MPnt SHeu
'Red Sea'	LRHS LSun MPnt NRHS SHeu WBrk WCot WNPC
'Red Spangles'	CRos LRHS MPnt NBir NRHS SHeu
'Regina' 🏆H6	CRos EPfP MPnt NRHS SCob SHeu SWvt
'Renoir' (Master Painters Series)	MPnt SHeu
'Rhapsody'	CRos LRHS NRHS
richardsonii	MPnt SHeu XLum
'Rickard'	MPnt
'Rio'PBR	CWGN LBuc MPnt SCob SHeu WHlf WNPC
'Robert'	MPnt
'Root Beer'PBR	CRos EPfP LRHS MPnt NRHS SHeu WNPC
ROSEMARY BLOOM ('Heuros'PBR)	CRos LRHS NRHS SHeu
§ ***rubescens***	GKev NAln NBro WThu
- var. ***versicolor***	GKev
'Ruffles'	see *H. micrantha* 'Ruffles'
'Sanbrot'	MPnt
§ ***sanguinea***	CMac LPot MMrt MPnt MRav NBir
- 'Alba'	LPot MPnt SMHy
- 'Bressingham Blaze' **new**	NHic
- 'Coral Petite'	CRos EDAr LRHS NRHS SHeu
- 'Frosty'	CRos LRHS NRHS
- 'Geisha's Fan'	MPnt SHeu SWvt
- 'Monet' (v)	MPnt SHeu
- var. ***pulchra***	SIgm
- 'Ruby Bells'	CRos CSBt LRHS LSRN MPnt NLar NRHS SHeu SRms
- 'Sioux Falls'	GPSL SHeu
- 'Snow Storm' (v)	ELan MPnt SHeu SRms
- 'Splendens'	MPnt XLum
- 'Taff's Joy' (v)	MPnt
- 'White Cloud' (v)	CBod EPfP EWTr MPnt MWat NBre SHeu SRms XLum
'Sashay' 🏆H6	GBin MPnt SHeu WNPC
'Saturn'	MPnt SHeu SWvt
'Schneewittchen'	MPnt MRav NSti SCob SHeu
'Scintillation' 🏆H6	MPnt
'September Morn' (Seasonal Selection Series)	CRos EPfP LRHS MPnt NRHS SHeu WNPC
'Shanghai'PBR	CRos CWGN EBee EPfP LRHS LSRN MAsh MPnt NRHS SHeu SWvt WFar WNPC
'Shenandoah Mountain'	MPnt
'Shere Variety'	CRos LRHS MPnt NRHS
'Silver Celebration' (Fox Series)	MPnt WNPC
'Silver Dollar'	CWGN EBee MPnt SHeu WCot
'Silver Gilt' **new**	SHeu
'Silver Heart'	CRos EBee LRHS MPnt NRHS
'Silver Indiana'	MPnt SHeu
'Silver Light'PBR	MPnt SHeu
'Silver Lode'PBR	MPnt SHeu
'Silver Scrolls'PBR	CMac CRos EHoe EPfP GMaP LRHS LSRN LSun MAvo MBNS MBel MGos MJak MPnt MRav NBir NEgg NRHS NSti SCob SLim SPoG SRkn SWvt WBrk WCot
'Silver Shadows'	MPnt SHeu
'Silver Streak'	see × *Heucherella* 'Silver Streak'
'Sioux Falls'	MPnt
'Slater's Pink' (Fox Series)	MPnt WNPC
'Snow Angel'	CWGN MPnt NGBl SHeu SPoG WCot WNPC
'Snowfire' (v)	MPnt SHeu
'Southern Comfort'PBR	CRos CWGN EBee LRHS MBNS MPnt NHol NLar NPer NRHS SHeu SLim SPoG SWvt
'Sparkler'	MPnt
'Sparkling Burgundy'	ELan MPnt SHeu SWvt
'Spellbound'PBR	CWGN EBee EPfP MPnt SCob SHeu SPoG SRkn WNPC WPnP
'Starry Night'	MPnt
'Steel City'	MPnt SHeu
'Stormy Seas'	CRos EBee ELan EPfP LRHS MPnt MRav NBir NRHS SCob SHeu SWvt WCAu
'Strawberries and Cream' (v)	EHrv MPnt SHeu
'Strawberry Candy'PBR	CWGN MPnt NBir NLar NWad SHeu SLim WNPC WWtn
'Strawberry Swirl'	CBod CElw ELan EPfP EWTr GMaP MPnt MRav NBir NDov SCob SHeu SWvt WCAu WNPC
'Sugar Berry'PBR (Little Cutie Series)	CRos LBuc LRHS MPnt NRHS SCob SHeu WCot WNPC
SUGAR FROSTING ('Pwheu0104'PBR)	CBod CRos EHoe ELan EPau GKev LRHS LSRN MCot MGos MPnt NCou NHol NPri NRHS SHeu SRot SWvt
'Sugar Plum'PBR	CRos CWGN EBee ELan EPfP LBuc LRHS LSRN MBNS MPnt NPri NRHS SCob SHeu SRot WHoo WNPC
'Sunrise' (Seasonal Selection Series)	MPnt SCob SHeu WNPC
'Sweet Berry'	MPnt
'Sweet Tart'PBR (Little Cutie Series)	CBod CRos LRHS MPnt NLar NRHS SHeu SPer SPoG WCot WNPC
'Swirling Fantasy'PBR	MPnt SHeu WFar
'Tangerine Wave' (Fox Series)	MPnt SHeu WNPC
'Tara'	MPnt SHeu
'Thomas' (Fox Series)	GBin MPnt SHeu WNPC
'Tiramisu'PBR	CRos CWGN LRHS MBNS MJak MPnt NBir NRHS SHeu SWvt
'Tokyo' (City Series) **new**	MPnt SHeu SPoG
'Topaz Jazz' **new**	SHeu
'Tresahor White'	MPnt
'Van Gogh' (Master Painters Series)	MPnt SCob SHeu
'Vanilla Spice'	MPnt SHeu
'Veil of Passion'	NBre
'Velvet Night'	EPfP MPnt NBir SHeu SPlb
'Venus'	CRos CWGN LRHS MBel MHol MMuc MPnt NRHS NSti SHeu WBrk WCFE WCot WHoo WRHF
'Vesuvius'	MPnt SHeu
'Vienna'PBR (City Series)	MPnt SHeu WNPC
§ ***villosa***	CSam GKev LEdu MPnt MRav WPGP XLum
- 'Autumn Bride'	MPnt SHeu SMHy
- BRESSINGHAM BRONZE ('Absi'PBR)	CRos LRHS MPnt NRHS SHeu
- 'Chantilly'	MPnt NAln SHeu
- var. ***macrorhiza***	EShb MPnt NBre XLum
- 'Palace Purple'	Widely available
- 'Palace Purple Select'	CMac CTri LSun MCot MJak NHic SLim SWvt WCAu WSpi

'Virginale' MPnt
'Walnut' (Fox Series) EUJe MPnt SHeu WNPC
'White Marble' MPnt SHeu
'White Spires' CRos LRHS MPnt NRHS SHeu
'White Swirls' MPnt
'William How' MPnt SHeu
'Winter Joy' (Seasonal Selection Series) CRos LRHS MPnt NRHS SCob SHeu WNPC
'Winter Red' CRos LRHS MPnt NRHS SHeu
'XXL' MPnt SCob SHeu
'Zabeliana' MPnt SHeu
'Zipper'[PBR] CWGN LBuc MJak MPnt SHeu WNPC

Heuchera × *Tiarella* see × *Heucherella*

× *Heucherella* ✿ (*Saxifragaceae*)

'Alabama Sunrise'[PBR] CBod CRos ELan EPfP EWhm IKil LRHS MHol MPnt NLar NPer NRHS SCob SHeu SPad SRot SWvt WFar
alba 'Bridget Bloom' CRos ELan EPfP EWTr GMaP LPot LRHS MPnt MRav NRHS SHeu SPer SRms WCAu WFar XLum
§ – 'Rosalie' CRos LRHS MPnt MRav SHeu SPlb WSHC
'Art Deco' MPnt SHeu
'Art Nouveau' EBee MPnt SHeu WNPC
'Autumn Cascade' (Cascade Series) MPnt SHeu
'Berry Fizz' LBuc MPnt SHeu SWvt
'Birthday Cake' MPnt SHeu
'Blue Ridge' MPnt WTor
'Brass Lantern'[PBR] CBod CRos CSpe CWGN EMor EPfP LRHS MAsh MBel MJak MPnt NHol NLar NPri NRHS SCob SHeu SPer SRms SRot SWvt WNPC
'Burnished Bronze'[PBR] CRos EPfP GBin LRHS MPnt NLar NRHS NWad SCob SHeu SRot SWvt
'Buttered Rum'[PBR] EBee MPnt SHeu WNPC
'Chocolate Lace'[PBR] MPnt SHeu
'Cinnamon Bear' MPnt SHeu
'Citrus Shock' EMor MPnt SHeu
'Copper Cascade'[PBR] (Cascade Series) EMor EUJe MPnt SHeu WNPC
'Cracked Ice'[PBR] CBod MHol MPnt SHeu
'Dayglow Pink'[PBR] CDor GMaP LSRN MPnt NLar SCob SHeu
'Fan Dancer' MPnt SHeu
'Fire Frost'[PBR] MPnt SHeu
'Glacier Falls'[PBR] (Falls Series) EMor SHeu WNPC
'Gold Cascade'[PBR] (Cascade Series) EMor MPnt WNPC
GOLD STRIKE ('Hertn041'[PBR]) EMor MBNS MPnt SHeu
'Golden Zebra'[PBR] CRos CWGN EBee ELan EUJe LRHS MBNS MJak MPnt NLar NRHS SHeu SWvt
'Great Smokies' MPnt SHeu
'Gunsmoke'[PBR] MAvo MBel MPnt NWad SCob SHeu SWvt WFar WNPC
HAPPY HOUR LIME ('Tnherhhl') **new** SHeu WNPC
'Heart of Darkness'[PBR] MPnt SHeu
'Honey Rose'[PBR] EBee MPnt SHeu WNPC
'Hot Spot' MPnt SHeu
'Infinity' SHeu
'Kimono'[PBR] ♀H6 CBod CMac CRos EHoe ELan EMor EPfP EShb GKev GMaP GWyn LRHS LSRN MBel MJak MPnt NAln NLar NRHS NWad SCob SHeu WJam
'Mojito' MPnt SHeu WNPC
'Ninja' see *Tiarella* 'Ninja'
'Party Time'[PBR] SHeu
PINK WHISPERS ('Hertn042'[PBR]) MPnt SHeu
'Plum Cascade' **new** EUJe MPnt SHeu WNPC
'Quicksilver' CBcs EPfP GMaP MPnt SHeu SWvt
'Redstone Falls'[PBR] (Falls Series) CWGN EBee MJak MNrw MPnt NLar NSti NWad SHeu SPoG SWvt WCot WHlf WNPC
'Ring of Fire' SWvt
§ 'Silver Streak' CRos LRHS MPnt NRHS SHeu SWvt
'Solar Eclipse' CBcs CKel CRos EBee EMor EShb LCro LOPS LRHS MAsh MAvo MJak MPnt NLar NRHS NSti NWad SCob SHeu SPad SPer SPoG SWvt WFar WNPC
'Solar Power'[PBR] CRos CWGN EBee EMor EPfP LRHS MPnt NLar NRHS NWad SCob SHeu SWvt WFar WNPC
'Stoplight'[PBR] CWGN ECha EMor EPau EPfP GMaP MGos MJak MPnt MRav NBir NEgg NHol NSti SCob SHeu SPer SRkn SRot SWvt WFar
'Summer Snowflake' **new** SHeu
'Sunrise Falls'[PBR] (Falls Series) CBod CWGN EBee MJak MNrw MPnt NWad SHeu SWvt WFar WNPC
'Sunspot'[PBR] (v) EMor NBro SHeu SRms WHer
'Sweet Tea'[PBR] Widely available
'Tapestry'[PBR] CDor CKel CRos ELan EMor EPfP EUJe GMaP LRHS MAvo MBNS MPnt NHol NRHS NSti NWad SCob SHeu SPer SPoG SRkn SRms SRot SWvt WFar
tiarelloides ♀H6 SRms
'Twilight'[PBR] MJak MPnt SHeu WNPC
§ 'Viking Ship' MPnt NBir SHeu
'Yellowstone Falls'[PBR] CWGN EMor MJak MPnt NCou NWad SCob SHeu SWvt WAvo WHlf WNPC

Hexastylis see *Asarum*

Hibanobambusa (*Poaceae*)

tranquillans ERod MMuc MWht SEND
– 'Shiroshima' (v) CAbb CBdn CBod CDTJ CRos ENBC EPfP ERod EUJe MBrN MMuc MWht SEND XCre

Hibbertia (*Dilleniaceae*)

aspera CAbb CBcs CCCN CKel CTsd LRHS WCFE WCot WFar WKif WSHC
§ ***cuneiformis*** CCCN
pedunculata WAbe
procumbens GEdr ITim WAbe
§ ***scandens*** ♀H1c CBcs CCCN CHll CRHN
'Spring Sunshine' CBod SEle
tetrandra see *H. cuneiformis*
volubilis see *H. scandens*

Hibiscus (*Malvaceae*)

aculeatus SBrt
coccineus SBrt SPlb
– white-flowered SBrt
'Cranberry Crush'[PBR] CWGN ELan MNrw
'Eruption' ELon
'Fireball'[PBR] SPoG

FULL BLAST	see *H.* 'Resi'
hamabo	CCCN
huegelii	see *Alyogyne huegelii*
'Jazzberry Jam'[PBR]	ELan MNrw SPoG
'Kopper King'[PBR]	MBNS MNrw SPoG
militaris	SBrt
moscheutos	EBee SBrt SVic XLum
- CAROUSEL JOLLY HEART ('Tahi56') **new**	LCro LOPS
- CAROUSEL PINK CANDY ('Tahi12')	CWGN SPad
- 'Old Yella'[PBR]	ELan SPoG
- 'Royal Gems'[PBR]	ELan
'Newbiscus Pink'	CCCN
'Newbiscus Red'	CCCN
'Newbiscus White'	CCCN
paramutabilis	EWes
§ 'Resi'[PBR]	NPri WMat
rosa-sinensis	EBak SPre
- 'Apple Blossom'	WFib
- 'Arcadian Spring'	WFib
§ - 'Bari' (Sunny Cities Series)	CCCN
- 'Blues Man'	WFib
§ - 'Bordeaux' (Sunny Cities Series)	CCCN
- 'Byron Metts'	WFib
- 'Cajun Cocktail'	see *H. rosa-sinensis* 'Jambalaya'
- 'Candy Floss' (d)	WFib
- 'Carmen Keene'	WFib
- 'China Town'	WFib
- 'Cloud Nine'[PBR]	WFib
- 'Cockatoo'	WFib
- 'Cooperi' (v) ♀H1b	WFib
- 'Courier Mail'	WFib
- 'Dorothy Brady'	WFib
- 'Enid Lewis' (d)	WFib
- 'Fifth Dimension'	WFib
- 'Gabriel'	WFib
- 'Georgia Peach'	WFib
- 'Gwen Mary'	WFib
- 'Helene'	LSRN
- 'Holly's Pride'	WFib
- 'Hot Bikini'	WFib
§ - 'Jambalaya'	WFib
- 'Jayella'	WFib
- 'June's Joy'	WFib
- 'Key West Thunderhead' (d)	WFib
- 'Lemon Chiffon'	WFib
- 'Linda Pear' (d)	WFib
- 'Madame Dupont'	WFib
- 'Me Oh My Oh'	WFib
- 'Mrs Andreasen' (d)	WFib
- 'Rhinestone'	WFib
- 'Roman Candle'	WFib
- 'Rose Flake'	WFib
- 'Rum Runner'	WFib
- 'Soft Shoulders'	WFib
- 'Spanish Lady'	WFib
- 'Sprinkle Rain'	WFib
- (Sunny Cities Series) SUNNY BARY	see *H. rosa-sinensis* 'Bari'
- - SUNNY BORDEAUX	see *H. rosa-sinensis* 'Bordeaux'
- - SUNNY CANCUN ('Hican'[PBR])	CCCN
- - SUNNY TORINO ('Hirio'[PBR])	CCCN
- 'Susan Schlueter'	WFib
- 'Tahitian Christmas'	WFib
- 'Tahitian Desert Sands'	WFib
- 'Tarantella'	WFib
- 'The Path'	WFib
- 'Vermillion Queen'	WFib
- 'Weekend'	WFib
- 'White Swan'	WFib
ROSE MOON ('Walhirosmo')	CRos LBuc LRHS NRHS SPoG
schizopetalus ♀H1b	WFib
sinosyriacus 'Lilac Queen'	CExl CKel CRos EPfP LRHS WPGP
- 'Ruby Glow'	CExl CKel EPfP LRHS LSRN WPGP
'Sunny Premiere'	CCCN
'Swazi Princess' **new**	XBlo
syriacus	CCCN LMaj
§ - 'America Irene Scott'[PBR]	SPoG
- 'Aphrodite'	CRos LRHS MAsh NRHS SSta
- 'Ardens' (d)	CEnd CKel EBee SPer SPoG WFar
§ - AZURRI BLUE SATIN ('Dvpazurri'[PBR]) **new**	SSta
- 'Azzurri'	see *H. syriacus* AZURRI BLUE SATIN
- BLUE BIRD	see *H. syriacus* 'Oiseau Bleu'
- BLUE CHIFFON ('Notwood3'[PBR]) (d) ♀H5	CKel CRos CSBt ELan LCro LOPS LRHS NRHS SPoG
- 'Bredon Springs'	SSta
- CHINA CHIFFON ('Bricutts') (d)	CRos LRHS MMuc SEND SGol SPoG
- 'Coelestis'	SPer
- 'Diana' ♀H5	CDul CKel CRos ELon EPfP EUJe EWTr LRHS LSRN MAsh NRHS SCoo SLon SPer SSta
- 'Dorothy Crane'	CRos EMil LRHS SSta
- 'Duc de Brabant' (d)	CCCN CKel CSBt MBlu SPer
- 'Elegantissimus'	see *H. syriacus* 'Lady Stanley'
- 'Gandini van Aart'	LCro LOPS LRHS SGol SMad
- 'Hamabo' ♀H5	CBod CDul CKel CRos CSBt CTri EBee ELan ELon EPfP LRHS LSRN MAsh MGos MMuc NLar NPri NRHS SCoo SEND SGol SLim SPer SPoG SWvt WFar
- 'Helene'	CRos LRHS LSRN MBlu NRHS SSta
- 'Honghwarang' **new**	SSta
- 'Jeanne d'Arc' (d)	SGol
§ - 'Lady Stanley' (d)	CCCN CKel CMac CRos CSBt LRHS NRHS SCoo SPer
- LAVENDER CHIFFON ('Notwoodone'[PBR]) (d) ♀H5	CRos CSBt ELan ELon EPfP EWes LCro LOPS LRHS LSRN MGos MMuc NRHS SCoo SEND SGol SPer SPoG
- MAGENTA CHIFFON ('Rwoods5') **new**	CRos LCro LOPS NRHS SPoG
- 'Marina'	CBod CCCN CKel CRos ELon EPfP LRHS MBlu MRav NRHS SGol WFar
- 'Mathilde' **new**	SSta
- 'Mauve Queen'	SSta
- 'Meehanii' misapplied	see *H. syriacus* 'Purpureus Variegatus'
- 'Meehanii' (v) ♀H5	CEnd CKel CRos EBee EPfP LRHS SCoo SPer SPoG SSta
- 'Melrose' **new**	SSta
- 'Monstrosus'	EBee MGos NLar
§ - 'Oiseau Bleu' ♀H5	Widely available
- PINK CHIFFON ('Jwnwood4'[PBR]) (d)	CRos ELan LCro LOPS LRHS NRHS
- PINK GIANT ('Flogi')	CDul CMac CRos EPfP LRHS SPer SSta
- PINKY SPOT ('Minspot'[PBR]) **new**	LRHS MMrt
- PURPLE PILLAR ('Gandini Santiago'[PBR])	LCro LOPS SGol
- PURPLE RUFFLES ('Sanchoyo') (d)	EPfP SPoG

§ – 'Purpureus Variegatus' (v)	CMac CRos LRHS
– 'Red Heart' ♀H5	CAco CBod CDul CEnd CKel CMac CRos CSBt CTri ELan EPfP LRHS MAsh MGos MMuc NRHS SEND SLim SPer SPoG SRms SSta SWvt WCFE XSen
– ROSALBANE ('Minrosa')	SGol
– RUSSIAN VIOLET ('Floru')	CEnd CKel CRos EPfP LRHS
– 'Shintaeyang'	CRos LRHS NRHS
– 'Snowdrift' **new**	SSta
I – 'Speciosus' (d)	CKel SPoG WFar
– SUGAR TIP	see *H. syriacus* 'America Irene Scott'
– 'Totus Albus'	SSta
– ULTRAMARINE ('Minultra'PBR)	EPfP LRHS NPri
– 'Variegatus'	see *H. syriacus* 'Purpureus Variegatus'
– WHITE CHIFFON ('Notwoodtwo'PBR) (d) ♀H5	CRos CSBt ELan EPfP EWes LCro LOPS LRHS LSRN MAsh MGos MRav NRHS SCoo SPer SPoG
– 'William R. Smith' ♀H5	CRos LRHS MSwo SPer SSta
– 'Woodbridge' ♀H5	Widely available
trionum	CSpe EBtc LRHS WKif
– 'Sunny Day'	ELan

hickory, shagbark see *Carya ovata*

Hieracium (*Asteraceae*)

aurantiacum	see *Pilosella aurantiaca*
brunneocroceum	see *Pilosella aurantiaca* subsp. *carpathicola*
laevigatum subsp. ***nivale***	MMuc
§ ***lanatum***	NBir NWad
maculatum Sm.	see *H. spilophaeum*
pilosella	see *Pilosella officinarum*
scullyi	EPPr WFar
§ ***spilophaeum***	MMuc NBid NPer NSti WOut
– 'Blue Leaf'	WCot
– 'Leopard'	GJos GPSL NDov
umbellatum	WOut
villosum	GJos WArt WHer
welwitschii	see *H. lanatum*

Hierochloe (*Poaceae*)

odorata	CBod EPPr GPoy LEdu MBNS XLum

Himalayacalamus (*Poaceae*)

asper	CDTJ ERod XCre
§ ***falconeri*** 'Damarapa'	EPfP
§ ***hookerianus***	CExl EPfP IMou XCre
– 'Himalaya Blue'	CDTJ

Himantoglossum (*Orchidaceae*)

hircinum	NLAp
robertianum **new**	GKev

× *Hippeasprekelia* (*Amaryllidaceae*)

'Durga Pradhan'	WCot
'Red Beauty'	WCot
'Red Star'	CCCN

Hippeastrum ✿ (*Amaryllidaceae*)

× ***acramannii*** ♀H2	CAvo GCal WCot
'Alasca'PBR	GKev
'Amputo'	LAma
'Apple Blossom' ♀H2	LAma LCro LOPS SDeJ
'Baby Star' ♀H2	SDeJ
'Balentino'PBR	GKev
'Black Pearl'	LCro LOPS
'Bogota'	LCro LOPS
'Bolero'	LAma
'Christmas Gift'	LAma LCro LOPS
'Clown' ♀H2	LAma SDeJ
Colibri Group **new**	GKev
– 'Rapido'	LCro LOPS
– 'Veneto'	GKev SDeJ
(Diamond Group) 'Bianca'	LAma
– 'Charisma' ♀H2	LAma SDeJ
– 'Fairytale' ♀H2	LCro LOPS SDeJ
– 'Green Magic' ♀H2	LAma
– 'Lemon Lime'	LAma
– 'Picotee' ♀H2	LAma LCro LOPS SDeJ
(Double Diamond Group) 'Alfresco'PBR (d)	LAma SDeJ
(Double Galaxy Group) 'Blossom Peacock' (d)	LAma
– 'Dancing Queen' (d)	LAma
– 'Double Dragon'PBR (d)	LAma
– 'Lady Jane' (d)	LAma SDeJ
'Double Record' (d)	SDeJ
'Fantasy'	LAma
'Ferrari'	LAma
'Flaming Peacock'	LAma
(Galaxy Group) 'Benfica'	LCro LOPS
– 'Flamenco Queen' ♀H2	LAma
– 'Hercules'	SDeJ
– 'Lagoon'PBR ♀H2	LCro LOPS
– 'Limona'PBR	LCro LOPS
– 'Park Red' **new**	GKev
– 'Red Lion' ♀H2	LAma
– 'Rilona'	LAma SDeJ
– 'Susan'	SDeJ
'Grand Diva'	LAma
'Grandeur'	LAma
'Inca'	LAma
'Jewel' (d)	LAma
× ***johnsonii*** ♀H2	CExl WCot
'Liberty'	SDeJ
'Marilyn'PBR (d)	LAma
'Minerva'	SDeJ
'Misty'	LAma
'Mont Blanc'	SDeJ
'Mrs Garfield'	GKev
'Naughty Lady'	LAma
papilio	LAma LCro LOPS MMrt SDeJ
'Pink Floyd'	LAma
puniceum	GKev
'Red Fire' **new**	GKev
'Red Peacock' (d)	LAma SDeJ
'Rosario'	LAma
'Royal Velvet' ♀H2	LAma
'San Antonio Rose'	WCot
'Santiago'	LAma
'Snow Queen'	LCro LOPS
'Sonatini Valentino'	WCot
(Spider Group) 'Emerald'	LAma WCot
– 'Evergreen' ♀H2	LCro LOPS
– 'Lima'	LAma
– 'Sumatra'PBR	LCro LOPS
striatum	WCot
'Swan Lake'PBR	GKev SDeJ
'Sweet Surrender'	LAma
'Toughie'	EBee
vittatum	GKev LAma
'White Dazzler'	LAma

Hippeastrum × *Sprekelia* see × *Hippeasprekelia*

Hippocrepis (*Papilionaceae*)

§ ***comosa*** EDAr WAbe
§ ***emerus*** CBcs CCCN CExl CMac ELan EPfP IMou MAsh MGil MGos MMuc SEND SVen WSpi

Hippophae (*Elaeagnaceae*)

sp. SArc
rhamnoides Widely available
- (m) EPom
- 'Askola' (f/F) CAgr
- 'Dorana' (f/F) CAgr
- 'Frugna' (f/F) CAgr NLar
- 'Hergo' (f/F) CAgr MCoo NLar
- 'Hikul' (m) CAgr CDul NLar WHor
- 'Juliet' (f/F) CAgr
- 'Leikora' (f/F) ♀H7 CAgr CDul ELan EPfP MBlu MCoo NLar SPer
- ORANGE ENERGY ('Habego'PBR) (f/F) CAgr MCoo
- 'Pollmix' (m) ♀H7 CAgr ELan EPfP MBlu MCoo NLar SPer
- 'Pollmix 3' (m) MCoo
- 'Sirola' (f/F) CAgr MCoo
salicifolia CAgr
- GWJ 9221 WCru
- 'Streetwise' new CRos
sinensis LS&E 15724 WPGP
tibetana new CMCN

Hippuris (*Plantaginaceae*)

vulgaris CBen CWat EWat LLWG NPer WMAq XLum

Hirpicium (*Asteraceae*)

armerioides SPlb

Hoheria ✿ (*Malvaceae*)

'Ace of Spades' CAbb CBod CKel CRos ELan ELon EPfP LRHS MGil NLar SEND SMad SPer SWvt
§ ***angustifolia*** EBee EPfP IDee SVen WPGP
angustifolia* × *sexstylosa WPGP
'Borde Hill' CAbb CBcs CDul CJun CKel CMac CRos CTho EBee ELan ELon EPfP GCal LRHS MAsh MGil SEND SPer SWvt WCFE WPGP WSpi
glabrata CMac EPfP GBin IDee NBir
'Glory of Amlwch' ♀H4 CAbb CAby CBcs CDul CJun CTho ELan EPfP GGGa LRHS LSRN SChF SPer SPoG SWvt WKif WPGP WSpi
'Hill House' CHll
§ ***lyallii*** ♀H4 CCCN CExl CTho LRHS LSRN SVen
microphylla see *H. angustifolia*
populnea CBcs CCCN CTsd
- 'Holbrook' CSam
- 'Sunshine' (v) EBee SPoG
sexstylosa CAbb CBcs CTho CTri EPfP LRHS LSRN MGos NEgg SPer SPlb SVen SWvt WFar WSpi
- 'Crataegifolia' EBee MGil NLar
- 'Pendula' CMac
- 'Stardust' ♀H4 Widely available
'Snow White' CKel EUJe LRHS SPoG WMat

Holboellia (*Lardizabalaceae*)

angustifolia NLar WCot WCru
- subsp. ***angustifolia*** LRHS WCru
- - H&M 1504 new WPGP
- subsp. ***linearifolia*** BWJ 8004 WCru
- subsp. ***obtusa*** DJHC 506 WCru
brachyandra HWJ 1023 WCru
aff. ***chapaensis*** B&SWJ 7250 WCru
coriacea CBcs CCCN CHll CKel CRHN CRos CTsd EBee ELan EPfP IDee IMou LEdu LRHS MGil MRav NLar NQui SEND SMad SPer WCFE WCru
- B&SWJ 2818 WCru
latifolia CBcs CCCN CHll CKel CMac CRHN CRos CTri EBee ELan EPfP EUJe LEdu LRHS MGil NLar SAdn SArc SEle SPer SPoG SWvt WBor WCFE WCru WPGP WSHC
- DJHC 98442 WCru
- HWJCM 008 WCru
- HWJK 2014 WCru
- subsp. ***chartacea*** dark-flowered HWJK 2213D WCru
- - pale-flowered HWJK 2213C WCru
- lanceolate-leaved WPGP
- - HWJK 2419 WCru

Holcus (*Poaceae*)

lanatus WSFF
mollis 'Albovariegatus' (v) CWCL ECha EHoe EMOT EPPr GMaP GWyn NBid NBro NPer NSti SPlb SRms XLum
- 'White Fog' (v) CBod CRos EBee EPPr MMuc NWad

Holmskioldia (*Lamiaceae*)

* ***lutea*** CCCN
sanguinea CCCN

Holodiscus (*Rosaceae*)

discolor CBcs CBod CDul CKel CRos CWld EBee ELan EPfP EWes GCal LEdu LRHS MBlu MGil MMuc MRav NLar NQui NRHS SLon SPer SPlb WBor
- var. ***ariifolius*** WSHC

Homalocladium (*Polygonaceae*)

§ ***platycladum*** EShb EUJe

Homeria (*Iridaceae*)

breyniana var. ***aurantiaca*** see *Moraea collina*

Homoglossum see *Gladiolus*

Hordeum (*Poaceae*)

jubatum CDor CKno CSpe CWCL EAJP EHoe EUJe EWes GBee LEdu MAsh NGdn NGrd SPhx
- 'Early Pink' NDov
secalinum CHab

Horminum (*Lamiaceae*)

pyrenaicum IMou MMuc SEND SIgm SRms WPtf
I - f. ***alboviolaceum*** EWhm GCal SBrt
- dark-flowered GCal SBrt WSHC

Hornungia (*Brassicaceae*)

alpina GCrg GEdr NSla XLum

horseradish see *Armoracia rusticana*

Hosta ✿ (*Asparagaceae*)

AGSJ 302	WCot
'A Many-Splendored Thing'	EMic IBal
'Abana' (v)	IBal
'Abba Dabba Do' (v)	CDor ECtt ELon EMic IBal NEgg NSue
'Abba Showtime'	IBal
'Abby' (v)	CBdn EHoe EMic IBal NSue WFar
'Abiqua Ariel'	EMic
'Abiqua Blue Crinkles'	IBal NBir
'Abiqua Blue Edger'	IBal
'Abiqua Blue Madonna'	IBal
'Abiqua Delight' (v)	EMic
'Abiqua Drinking Gourd' ♀[H7]	CBdn CBod CDor ECtt ELon EMic GMaP IBal NEgg NLar NSue
'Abiqua Elephant Ears'	IBal
'Abiqua Ground Cover'	IBal
'Abiqua Moonbeam' (v)	EMic IBal NGdn
'Abiqua Recluse'	EMic IBal
'Abiqua Trumpet'	CBdn EMic IBal LRHS NGdn NLar NNor
'Abraham Lincoln'	IBal
'Academy Flora'	IBal
'Academy Mavrodaphne'	EMic
'Ada Reed'	IBal
'Adorable'	CBdn IBal NSue
aequinoctiiantha	EMic IBal
'Afterglow' (v) **new**	IBal
'Aksarben'	EMic
'Alabama Gold'	EMic
'Alakazaam' (v)	EMic IBal NSue WFar
'Alan Titchmarsh'	IBal
albomarginata	see *H.* 'Paxton's Original' (*sieboldii*)
§ 'Albomarginata' (*fortunei*) (v)	CBcs CMac NBir NGdn SWvt WFar WMoo
'Alex Summers'	EMic IBal WFar
'All That Jazz' (v)	EMic IBal
'Allan P. McConnell' (v)	EMic IBal LRHS LSta MNrw NSue WFar WHal
'Allegan Emperor' (v)	IBal
'Allegan Fog' (v) ♀[H7]	EMic EShb GEdr IBal LRHS LSta NHpl NSue
'Alligator Alley' (v)	EMic IBal
'Alligator Shoes' (v) ♀[H7]	EMic IBal
'Alpine Aire'	EMic IBal
'Alpine Dream'	IBal
'Alternative'	IBal
'Alvatine Taylor' (v)	EMic IBal NGdn
'Amalia' (v)	IBal NSue
'Amanuma'	EMic IBal NSue
'Amazing Grace' (v)	EMic IBal
'Amber Tiara'	EMic IBal
'American Dream' (v)	EMic IBal LRHS
'American Gothic' (v)	IBal
'American Halo'	CBdn EMic IBal NEgg NLar NSti
'American Icon'	EMic IBal
'American Sweetheart'[PBR]	EMic IBal
'Americana' (v)	IBal
'Amethyst Gem'	IBal NSue
'Amos'	IBal
'Amy Elizabeth' (v)	EMic IBal
'Andorian'	IBal NSue
'Andrew'	EMic
'Angel Feathers' (v)	IBal
'Angelique' (v) **new**	IBal
'Anglo Saxon' (v)	IBal
'Ani Machi' (v) ♀[H7]	NSue
'Ann Kulpa' (v)	EMic IBal NGdn
'Annabel Lee'	IBal
'Anne' (v)	IBal LSRN NSue
'Ansly' (v)	IBal
'Antioch' (*fortunei*) (v)	EMic EUJe GLog IBal MRav NLar
'Aoki' (*fortunei*)	EMic IBal
'Aphrodite' (*plantaginea*) (d)	EMic EPfP EWTr
'Apollo'	NNor
'Apple Candy' (v)	CBdn IBal NSue
'Apple Green'	EMic GKev IBal NAln
'Apple Pie'	IBal
'Appletini'	NSue
'Aqua Velva'	IBal
'Arc de Triomphe'	ECtt EMic IBal NLar
'Arch Duke'	IBal
'Arctic Blast'	EMic IBal
'Arctic Circle' (v)	EMic
'Argentea Variegata' (*undulata*)	see *H. undulata* var. *undulata*
'Aristocrat' (Tardiana Group) (v)	CBdn EMic EMor IBal NEgg NGdn WFar
'Asian Pearl' (v)	IBal
'Aspen Gold' (*tokudama* hybrid)	EMic
'Astral Bliss'	IBal
'Atlantis'[PBR] (v) ♀[H7]	EBee EMic EMor IBal NGdn NSue
'Atom Smasher'	NSue
'Atomic Elvis'	IBal NSue
'August Beauty'	EMic IBal
'August Moon'	Widely available
'Aureafolia'	see *H.* 'Starker Yellow Leaf'
'Aureoalba' (*fortunei*)	see *H.* 'Spinners'
'Aureomaculata' (*fortunei*)	see *H. fortunei* var. *albopicta*
'Aureomarginata' ambig. (v)	CRos LRHS NRHS SCoo
'Aureomarginata' (*montana*) (v) ♀[H7]	CMac EHoe ELan EMic GCal GMaP IBal MMuc NEgg NGdn NLar NSue WFar
§ 'Aureomarginata' (*ventricosa*) (v) ♀[H7]	EMic IBal NGdn WFar
'Aureostriata' (*tardiva*)	see *H.* 'Inaho'
'Austin Dickinson' (v)	ECtt EMic IBal LRHS LSta NEgg
'Autumn Frost' (v)	EMic IBal NSue
'Avocado'	CBdn ELon EMic IBal NLar NSue WFar
'Awakening Angel'	EMic
'Azure Snow'	IBal
'Azuretini'	IBal
'Babbling Brook'	IBal NSue
'Baby Blue' (Tardiana Group)	EMic
'Baby Blue Eyes'	EMic IBal NSue
'Baby Booties' (v)	IBal NSue
'Baby Bunting' ♀[H7]	EMic IBal NBro NLar NNor NSue
'Baby Doll' (v)	IBal
'Baby Kim'	EMic
'Backyard Monster' (v)	IBal
'Bailey's Cream' (v)	IBal
'Baja White'	IBal
'Bali-Hai'	IBal
'Ballerina'	IBal LRHS NSue
'Bam Bam Blue'	IBal
'Banana Muffins'	IBal
'Band of Gold'	EMic IBal
'Banyai's Dancing Girl'	EMic IBal
'Barbara Ann' (v) ♀[H7]	CBdn EBee EMic IBal ITim NGdn
'Barbara May'	IBal
'Barney Fife'	IBal
'Battle Star' (v)	EMic IBal NSue
'Beach Boy' (v)	CBdn IBal MNrw NLar NSue
'Bea's Colossus'	IBal
'Beauty Little Blue'	IBal NSue
'Beauty Substance'	EMic IBal NNor NSue

	'Beckoning'	EMic IBal NSue
	'Bedazzled' (v)	IBal
	'Bedford Blue'	EMic IBal
	'Bedford Rise and Shine' (v)	ESwi IBal LRHS LSta
	'Bedford Wakey-Wakey'	IBal
	'Behemoth'	IBal NSue
	'Bell Bottom Blues'	IBal
	bella	see *H. crassifolia*
	'Bells of Edinburgh'	IBal
	'Ben Vernooij' (v)	CBdn EMic IBal
	'Bennie McRae'	IBal
	'Best of Twenty'	IBal NSue
	'Betcher's Blue'	EMic IBal
	'Betsy King'	CMac MRav NLar
	'Bette Davis Eyes'	IBal
	'Betty'	IBal NSue
	'Biddy's Blue'	IBal
	'Big Boy' (*montana*)	EWTr IBal LRHS NSue
	'Big Daddy' (*sieboldiana* hybrid) (v) ♀H7	Widely available
	'Big John' (*sieboldiana*)	IBal
	'Big Mama'	EMic IBal MBNS MNrw NGdn NSue
	'Big Top'	IBal
	'Bigfoot'	IBal
	'Biggie'	IBal
	'Bill Brinka' (v)	EMic IBal
	'Bill Dress's Blue'	EMic NSue
	'Birchwood Blue Beauty'	IBal
	'Birchwood Gem'	IBal
§	'Birchwood Parky's Gold'	EBee ECtt EMic EPfP GMaP IBal MBNS NGdn NHol NLar NNor SCob
	'Birchwood Ruffled Queen'	EMic
	'Bitsy Gold'	EMic
	'Bix Blues'	IBal
	'Bizarre'	EMic
	'Black Beauty'	IBal
	'Black Hills'	EMic IBal
	'Blackfoot'	EMic IBal
	'Blackjack' (*sieboldiana*)	IBal WFar
	'Blarney Stone'	IBal
	'Blaue Venus'	IBal
	'Blaugold'	CBdn
	'Blaze of Glory'	IBal
	'Blazing Saddles' (v)	EMic IBal
	'Blonde Elf'	EHoe EMic IBal MPnt NEgg NGdn NHol NNor
	'Blue Angel' misapplied	see *H. sieboldiana* var. *elegans*
	'Blue Angel' (*sieboldiana*) ♀H7	Widely available
	'Blue Arrow' ♀H7	IBal LRHS MHol NNor NSue
	'Blue Baron'	EMic IBal
	'Blue Belle' (Tardiana Group)	EMic IBal NEoE NGdn
	'Blue Blush' (Tardiana Group)	EMic IBal NGdn
	'Blue Boy'	EMic EWes NNor
	'Blue Cadet'	CMac CRos EBee EHoe EMic EShb GBin GQue LRHS NBir NGdn NLar NRHS NSue NWad WFar
	'Blue Canoe'	IBal
	'Blue Cascade'	EMic IBal NSue
	'Blue Chip'	EMic
	'Blue Circle'[PBR]	EMic IBal
	'Blue Clown'	IBal
	'Blue Cup' (*sieboldiana*)	EMic MRav SRms
	'Blue Danube' (Tardiana Group)	EMic IBal NEgg
	'Blue Diamond' (Tardiana Group)	EMic LRHS NNor NSue WFar
	'Blue Dimples' (Tardiana Group)	ECtt EMic IBal
	'Blue Dolphin'	IBal
	'Blue Edger'	IBal NBir
	'Blue Eyes'	EMic
	'Blue Flame'	ECtt EMic IBal
	'Blue Frost'	IBal
	'Blue Haired Lady'	IBal
	'Blue Hawaii'	CBdn EMic IBal NSue
	'Blue Heart' (*sieboldiana*)	ECha EMic IBal
	'Blue Ice' (Tardiana Group)	EMic NSue
	'Blue Impression'	EMic
	'Blue Ivory' (v)	EBee ECtt ELon EMor NSue SPad
	'Blue Jay' (Tardiana Group)	EMic
	'Blue Lady'	EMic IBal
	'Blue Mammoth' (*sieboldiana*)	CBdn EMic EUJe IBal NEgg NLar NSue
	'Blue Maui'	IBal
	'Blue Monday'	EMic
	'Blue Moon' (Tardiana Group)	EMic GKev IBal NGdn NLar NNor
	'Blue Mountains'	IBal LBuc
	'Blue Mouse Ears' ♀H7	Widely available
	'Blue River' (v)	EMic IBal
	'Blue Seer' (*sieboldiana*)	EMic
	'Blue Shadows' (*tokudama*) (v)	EMic ESwi NLar WFar
	'Blue Skies' (Tardiana Group)	IBal
	'Blue Splendor' (Tardiana Group)	IBal
	'Blue Umbrellas' (*sieboldiana* hybrid)	ECtt ELan EMic EPfP GMaP IBal LRHS NGdn NLar NNor
	'Blue Vision'	IBal
	'Blue Wedgwood' (Tardiana Group)	ELan EMic GQue IBal LRHS MHol MWat NGdn
	'Blue Wonder'	IBal
	'Blue Wu'	IBal
	'Blueberry à la Mode'	IBal
	'Blueberry Cobbler'	IBal
	'Blueberry Muffin'	CBdn EMic NSue
	'Blueberry Tart'	IBal
	'Bluetooth'	IBal
	'Bob Deane' (v)	EMic IBal
	'Bob Olson' (v)	ESwi IBal WFar
	'Bobbie Sue' (v)	IBal
	'Bobcat'	IBal
	'Bogie and Bacall' (v)	IBal
	'Bold Edger' (v)	CBdn EMic IBal
	'Bold Intrigue' (v)	IBal
	'Bold Ribbons' (v)	EMic
	'Bolt out of the Blue'	EMic
	'Bonanza'	EMic
	'Boracay'	IBal
	'Border Bandit' (v)	EMic IBal LRHS NRHS
	'Border Favorite'	EMic
§	'Borwick Beauty' (*sieboldiana*) (v)	ELon EMic IBal NGdn SPer
	'Bottom Line' (v)	IBal
	'Bountiful'	EMic IBal NSue
	'Boyz Toy'	EMic IBal NSue
	'Brandywine'	IBal
	'Brave Amherst' (v)	IBal
	'Brenda's Beauty' (v)	EMic IBal
	'Bressingham Blue'	CAby CRos ECtt ELon GQue IBal LRHS MRav NLar NNor SPer SWvt WFar WMoo
	'Bridal Falls'[PBR] (v)	CBdn IBal NSue
	'Bridal Veil'	EMic IBal

	'Bridegroom'	EMic ESwi IBal
	'Bridgeville'	IBal
	'Brigadier'	IBal
	'Brigham Blue'	IBal
	'Bright Glow' (Tardiana Group)	EMic IBal
	'Bright Lights' (*tokudama*) (v)	EMic NGdn WFar
	'Bright Star' (v)	IBal
	'Brim Cup' (v)	CAby CDor ECtt ELon EPfP EShb GAbr MBNS MNrw NBro NGdn NNor
	'Broadband' (v)	IBal
	'Broadway' (v)	EMic IBal
	'Bronx Bomber' (v)	IBal NSue
	'Brooke'	EMic IBal
	'Brother Ronald' (Tardiana Group)	EMic IBal LRHS NEgg
	'Brother Stefan'	CBdn EMic IBal
	'Brutus'	IBal
	'Buckshaw Blue'	EMic IBal NBir NEoE NGdn WHrl
	'Bulletproof'	IBal
	'Bunchoko'	IBal NNor
	'Burke's Dwarf'	IBal
	'Cadillac' (v)	EMic
	'Cally Atom'	GCal IBal
	'Cally Colossus'	GCal IBal
I	'Cally Strain' (*nigrescens*)	MHer
	'Cally White' (*nigrescens*)	GCal IBal
	'Calypso' (v)	EMic IBal LRHS MNrw NGdn NRHS WFar
	'Camelot' (Tardiana Group)	IBal LRHS NGdn NSue
	'Cameo'	NSue
	'Camouflage'	EMic IBal
	'Canadian Blue'	ECtt EMic IBal LLWG LPot MSCN NLar NSue WFar
	'Candle Wax'	IBal
	'Candy Dish'	CBdn IBal NSue
	'Candy Hearts'	CSam EMic GEdr IBal NNor
	capitata	NNor
	- B&SWJ 588	WCru
	'Captain Kirk' (v) ♀H7	CBdn CRos EMic ESwi IBal LRHS NGdn NRHS NSue WFar
	'Captain's Adventure' (v)	EMic IBal NSue WFar
	caput-avis	see *H. kikutii* var. *caput-avis*
	'Carder Blue'	EMic IBal
	'Carnival' (v)	ELan EMic IBal LPot LRHS NEgg NGdn NHpl SPoG
	'Carol' (*fortunei*) (v)	IBal NEgg NGdn NLar NNor NSue
	'Carolina Blue'	CBdn IBal
	'Carousel' (v)	EMic IBal
	'Carrie' (*sieboldii*) (v)	EMic
	'Cascades' (v)	EMic IBal NGdn
	'Cathedral Windows' (v) ♀H7	CLAP EMic IBal NSue
	'Catherine'	CKel ELon EMic IBal NDai NLar NSue WFar
	'Cat's Eyes' (*venusta*) (v)	NNor
	'Cavalcade' (v)	EMic
	'Celebration' (v)	ELan EMic IBal
	'Celestial'	IBal
	'Celtic Dancer'	EMic IBal
	'Celtic Uplands'	EMic IBal
	'Center of Attention'	EMic IBal NGdn
	'Centerfold'	NSue
	'Cha Cha Cha'	IBal
	'Chabo-unazuki' (*kikutii* var. *caput-avis*)	EMic
	'Chain Lightning' (v)	EMic IBal LSun NSue
	'Challenger'	EMic
	'Chameleon' (v)	EMic
	'Champagne Toast' (v)	IBal NSue
	'Change of Tradition' (*lancifolia*) (v)	EMic
	'Chantilly Lace' (v)	EMic IBal
	'Chariots of Fire' (v)	IBal
	'Chartreuse Waves'	IBal
	'Chartreuse Wiggles' (*sieboldii*)	EMic
	'Cheatin' Heart'	EMic IBal NSue WFar
	'Chelsea Babe' (*fortunei*) (v)	IBal
	'Cherish' ♀H7	NGdn NHpl WFar
	'Cherokee' (v)	IBal
	'Cherry Berry' (v)	CKel CLAP CWGN ECtt EMic EMor EShb GEdr IBal LRHS MBNS MHol MNrw NBro NEgg NEoE NGdn NLar NRHS NSue NWad SCob SHar SPoG WFar WWtn
	'Cherry Tart'	IBal NSue
	'Cherub' (v)	EMic IBal LRHS
	'Chesapeake Bay'	EMic IBal NSue
	'Chesterland Gold'	IBal
	'Chief Sitting Bull'	IBal NSue
	'Childhood Sweetheart' (v)	IBal NSue
	'China Girl'	EMic IBal
	'Chinese Sunrise' (v) ♀H7	CWCL EMic GBin GWyn IBal NNor SRms
	'Chionea' (v)	EThi IBal
	'Chiquita'	IBal
	'Chi-town Classic' (v)	IBal
	'Chodai Ginba'	IBal
§	'Chōkō-nishiki' (*montana*) (v)	CRos EMic IBal LRHS NGdn NNor NRHS
	'Choo Choo Train'	EMic
	'Chopsticks'	EMic
	'Christmas Candy'PBR	CKel ECtt EMic IBal NSue
	'Christmas Charm' (v)	IBal
	'Christmas Cookies'	IBal
	'Christmas Pageant' (v)	EMic IBal
	'Christmas Tree' (v) ♀H7	CRos ECtt EMic EMor ESwi IBal LRHS NEgg NGdn NLar NRHS NSue WMoo
	'Church Mouse'	CBdn IBal NSue
	'Cinderella'	EMic IBal
	'Cinnamon Sticks'	EMic IBal NSue
	'Citation' (v)	IBal
	'City Lights'	CRos ECtt EMic LRHS NEgg NRHS
	'City Slicker' (v)	IBal
	clausa	EMic
	- var. ***normalis***	IBal NBir NGdn NLar
	'Clear Fork River Valley'	EMic IBal
	'Clifford's Forest Fire'	CRos ECtt EMic EUJe IBal LRHS NLar NRHS WFar
	'Clifford's Stingray' (v)	EMic IBal NSue
	'Climax' (v) ♀H7	EMic EPfP IBal
	'Cloudburst'	EMic IBal
	'Clovelly'	IBal
	'Clown's Collar' (v)	EMic IBal
	'Coal Miner'	IBal
	'Coconut Custard'	EMic NSue
	'Cody'	IBal NSue
	'Cold Heart'	EMic IBal
	'Collector's Banner'	IBal
	'Collector's Choice'	IBal NSue
	'Color à la Mode' (v)	IBal
	'Color Festival' (v)	CBod CDor ELon EMic IBal LLWG NLar NSue WFar
	'Color Glory'	see *H.* 'Borwick Beauty'
	'Colored Hulk' (v)	IBal
	'Colossal'	EMic IBal

'Columbus Circle' (v) EMic IBal
'Con Te Partiro' (v) CBdn NSue WFar
'Confused Angel' (v) IBal
'Cookie Crumbs' (v) EMic IBal
'Cool as a Cucumber' (v) IBal NSue
'Coquette' (v) EMic GAbr IBal
'Corkscrew' EMic NSue
'Corn Belt' (v) EMic IBal
'Corn Muffins' EMic
'Corona' (v) EMic
'Corryvreckan' IBal
'Cotillion' (v) CBdn EMic GEdr IBal NSue
'Count Your Blessings' (v) EMic IBal
'Country Mouse' (v) EMic GEdr IBal NHpl NSue SPoG WFar WTor
'County Park' EMic IBal NSue
'Cowrie' (v) IBal
'Cracker Crumbs' (v) ♀H7 EHoe EMic GEdr IBal ITim LRHS MNrw NHpl NNor NSla NSue WCot WFar
'Craig's Temptation' IBal LRHS NRHS NSue
'Cranberry Wine' IBal
§ ***crassifolia*** EMic IBal LRHS XLum
'Cream Cheese' (v) IBal
'Cream Delight' (*undulata*) see *H. undulata* var. ***undulata***
'Crepe Soul' (v) IBal
'Crepe Suzette' (v) EMic IBal NNor
'Crested Reef' EMic
'Crested Surf' (v) EMic IBal
'Crinoline Petticoats' IBal
§ ***crispula*** (v) CRos EMic IBal LRHS MCot MRav NChi NRHS
'Crocodile Socks' (v) IBal
'Crown Prince' (v) IBal NGdn
'Crown Royalty' EMic IBal
§ 'Crowned Imperial' (*fortunei*) (v) EMic IBal
'Crumples' (*sieboldiana*) IBal
'Crusader' (v) ♀H7 CBdn ELon EMic IBal LRHS WFar
'Crystal Dixie' EMic IBal NSue WFar
'Cumulonimbus' IBal
'Cup of Grace' **new** IBal
'Curlew' (Tardiana Group) EMic IBal
'Curls' EMic IBal
'Curly Fries' CBdn EMic IBal NSue
'Curtain Call' IBal
'Cutting Edge' EMic IBal NSue
'Cuyahoga' (v) IBal
'Dab a Green' IBal
'Dance with Me' (v) EMic IBal
'Dancing in the Rain' (v) CWGN NBro WFar
'Dancing Mouse' (v) CBdn IBal NSue WFar
'Dancing Queen' EMic IBal NSue
'Dark Shadows' EMic IBal NGdn NSti WFar
'Dark Star' (v) EMic IBal NGdn
'Dark Victory' EMic
'Dartmoor Forest' IBal
'Dawn' EMic IBal NSue NWad
'Dawn's Early Light' EMic IBal
'Dax' IBal
'Daybreak' ♀H7 EMic IBal NBro
'Day's End' (v) EMic IBal
'Deane's Dream' EMic IBal
'Decorata' EMic
decorata var. ***normalis*** EMic
'Deep Blue Sea' ♀H7 EMic IBal NSue
'Deep Pockets' IBal
'Dee's Golden Jewel' EMic
'Déjà Blu' (v) EMic IBal NSue
'Deliverance' EMic IBal NSue
'Delta Dawn' (v) EMic IBal NGdn
'Delta Desire' IBal
'Desert Mouse'PBR (v) GEdr IBal NSue
'Designer Genes' EMic IBal WFar
'Devil's Advocate' IBal
'Devon Blue' (Tardiana Group) EMic IBal LRHS LSta NNor
'Devon Desire' (*montana*) IBal NLar
'Devon Discovery' IBal
'Devon Giant' EMic NNor
'Devon Gold' EMic GAbr IBal
'Devon Green' ♀H7 Widely available
'Devon Mist' IBal NNor
'Devon Tor' IBal
'Dew Drop' (v) EMic
'Dewed Steel' IBal
'Diamond Tiara' (v) EMic IBal LRHS NBir NGdn NSue WWtn
'Diamonds are Forever' (v) IBal
'Diana Remembered' EMic EMor IBal NGdn NSue WFar
'Dick Ward' EMic IBal
'Dilithium Crystal' IBal NSue WFar
'Dillie Perkeo' IBal
'Dilys' EMic MNrw
'Dimple' EMic
'Dinky Donna' (v) EMic IBal NHpl NSue
'Dinner Jacket' (v) CRos EMor IBal LRHS NRHS
'Dino' (v) IBal
'Dixie Chick' (v) EMic IBal LRHS NHpl NNor NSue
'Dixie Chickadee' (v) NSue
'Dixie Cups' **new** CBdn
'Dixieland Heat' IBal
'Doctor Fu Manchu' IBal
'Domaine de Courson' EMic IBal NSue WFar
'Don Stevens' (v) IBal LRHS
'Dorothy' EMic
'Dorset Blue' (Tardiana Group) EMic IBal LRHS
'Dorset Charm' (Tardiana Group) EMic
'Dorset Flair' (Tardiana Group) EMic IBal
'Doubled Up' CBdn IBal
'Doubloons' EMic
'Dragon Tails' ♀H7 EMic GEdr IBal LRHS NHpl NRHS NSue WFar
'Dragon Warrior' (v) IBal
'Drake's Tail' IBal NLar
'Dream Queen' (v) CBdn CKel ECtt EMic EMor EUJe EWTr IBal IPot LRHS NLar
'Dream Weaver' (v) ♀H7 ELon EMic EUJe IBal IPot LRHS MNrw NBro NEgg NGdn NSue SPoG WFar
'Dress Blues' CMac EMic IBal
'Drummer Boy' EMic IBal
'Duchess' (*nakaiana*) (v) EMic
'Duke of Cornwall' (v) IBal
'DuPage Delight' (*sieboldiana*) (v) EMic IBal NGdn NLar
'Dust Devil' (*fortunei*) (v) IBal
'Dusty Waters' IBal
'Dutch Flame' (v) **new** CBdn NSue
'Eagle's Nest' (v) IBal
'Early Times' IBal
'Earth Angel'PBR (v) ♀H7 CBdn CKel EMic IBal NGdn NSue
'Ebony Towers' EMic IBal
'Edge of Night' EMic IBal
'Edwin Bibby' EMic
'El Capitan' (v) CRos EMic IBal LRHS NRHS

'El Niño'PBR (Tardiana Group) (v) ♀H7	CBdn CDor CWGN EMic EPfP IBal LRHS MNrw NBro NGdn NLar NSue SPoG WFar
§ 'Elata'	EMic
'Elatior' (*nigrescens*)	IBal LRHS
'Elbridge Gerry' (v)	IBal
'Eldorado'	see *H.* 'Frances Williams'
'Eleanor Lachman' (v)	EMic IBal NSue
'Eleanor Roosevelt'	IBal
'Electrocution' (v)	CBdn IBal NSue
'Elegans'	see *H. sieboldiana* var. *elegans*
'Elephant Burgers'	EMic
'Elisabeth'	EMic IBal LSRN
'Elizabeth Campbell' (*fortunei*) (v)	EMic
'Elkheart Lake'	EMic IBal
'Ellen'	EMic
'Ellerbroek' (*fortunei*) (v)	EMic
'Elsley Runner'	IBal NSue
'Elvis Lives'	EMic IBal LRHS NEgg NEoE NGdn NLar NNor NSue
'Embroidery' (v)	EMic
'Emerald Carpet'	IBal NSue
'Emerald Charger' (v)	IBal
'Emerald Crown'	EMic IBal
'Emerald Emperor'	IBal
'Emerald Necklace' (v)	EMic IBal
'Emerald Paisley'	IBal
'Emerald Ruff Cut'	EMic IBal
'Emerald Tiara' (v)	CRos EMic IBal LRHS NLar NSue WFar
'Emeralds and Rubies'	EMic IBal NSue
'Emily Dickinson' (v)	ECtt EMic IBal LRHS NNor
'Empress Wu'PBR	Widely available
'Encore'	IBal
'English Sunrise' (Tardiana Group)	IBal
'Enterprise' (v)	EBee EMic IBal NGdn NSue
'Eola Sapphire'	EMic IBal
'Eos'	IBal NLar
'Eric Smith' (Tardiana Group)	EMic IBal WFar
'Eric Smith Gold'	GKev
'Eric's Gold'	IBal
'Erie Magic' (v)	EMic IBal
'Eskimo Pie' (v)	GEdr WFar
'Essence of Summer'	EMic IBal
'Eternal Flame'	NSue
'Everlasting Love' (v)	IBal
'Excitation'	EMic IBal
'Exotic Presentation' (v)	EMic IBal
'Extasy' (v)	EMic IBal NGdn NSue WFar
'Eye Candy' (v)	IBal
'Eye Catcher'	EMic
'Eye Declare' (v)	IBal
'Fair Maiden' (v)	NHpl
'Faith'	EMic
'Faithful Heart' (v)	EMic IBal NSue
'Fall Dazzler' (v)	IBal
'Fall Emerald'	EMic
'Fan Dance' (v)	IBal
'Fantabulous' (v)	IBal
'Fantasy Island' (v)	CBdn EMic IBal NSue WFar
'Fat Boy'	IBal
'Fatal Attraction'	IBal
'Feather Boa'	EMic IBal LRHS NSue WFar
'Feng Shui'	IBal
'Fenman's Fascination'	EMic IBal
'Fiesta' (v)	IBal
'Final Summation' (v)	EMic IBal NSue
'Final Victory' (v)	IBal
'Finlandia'	IBal
'Fire and Ice' (v) ♀H7	Widely available
'Fire Island' ♀H7	CBdn ECtt ELan ELon EMic EMor EPfP GBin GEdr IBal LRHS MNrw NLar NSue WCot
'Fire Opal' (v)	IBal
'Firefly' (v)	IBal
'Fireplace' (v)	IBal
'Fireworks' (v) ♀H7	CBdn ECtt EMic EMor EPfP GBin GEdr LBuc LSun MBNS MHol MNrw NBro NCou NGdn SMad WCot
'Firn Line' (v)	CBdn IBal
'First Frost' (v) ♀H7	CBdn CRos ECtt ELon EMic EMor EPfP IBal LRHS MNrw NGdn NLar NRHS NSue SPoG
'First Love' (*montana*)	CBdn EMic IBal
'First Mate' (v)	EMic IBal NSue
'Five O'Clock Shadow' (v)	IBal
'Five O'Clock Somewhere' (v)	IBal
'Flapjack' (v)	IBal
'Fleet Week'	EMic IBal
'Flemish Angel' (v)	IBal NSue
'Flemish Design' **new**	IBal
'Flemish Gold'	IBal
'Flemish Master' (v)	IBal
'Flemish Sky'	EMic IBal NGdn NLar
'Flemish Steel'	IBal
'Floradora'	EMic IBal NSue
'Floratini'	NSue
'Flower Power'	CBdn NNor
'Fluted Fountain'	EMic
'Fog Light'	IBal
'Fool's Gold' (*fortunei*)	EMic IBal
'Forbidden Fruit'PBR (v)	CBdn CBod ELan EMor IBal NSue
'Forest Shadows'	IBal
'Formal Attire' (*sieboldiana* hybrid) (v) ♀H7	EMic IBal LRHS
'Forncett Frances' (v)	IBal
'Fortis'	see *H. undulata* var. *erromena*
fortunei	EMic GKev GWyn NNor WFar
§ - var. ***albopicta*** (v)	CBcs CRos CSam ECha EHoe ELan EMic EPfP EUJe GMaP GWyn LCro LPot LRHS MJak MRav NEgg NLar NNor NRHS SPer SRms WBrk WFar WHoo WMoo
- - f. ***aurea***	CMac ECha EHoe EMic MMuc NEgg NLar SRms WFar WHal
- - - dwarf	EMic
- - f. ***viridis***	NNor
§ - var. ***aureomarginata*** (v) ♀H7	CKel CRos CSam CTri ECha EHoe ELan ELon EMic EPfP EShb GMaP IBal LRHS MMuc NGdn NLar NNor NRHS SEND SPer SPlb WFar
- var. ***gigantea***	see *H. montana*
- var. ***hyacinthina***	CKel EMic EPfP IBal LRHS MRav NGdn NLar XLum
- - variegated	see *H.* 'Crowned Imperial'
- var. ***stenantha***	EMic
'Fountain'	CBdn
'Fountain of Youth' (*kikutii*)	IBal
'Fourteen Carats'	EMic IBal
'Fourth of July'	NSue
'Foxfire Palm Sunday' (v)	IBal
'Fragrant Blue'	ELan ELon EMic IBal LBuc LRHS NBro NGdn NHpl SPoG XLum
'Fragrant Blue Ribbons' (v)	EMic IBal

'Fragrant Bouquet' (v) ♀H7	CRos ECtt ELan EMic IBal LRHS LSRN NEgg NGdn NHol NLar NSue WFar
'Fragrant Dream'	CBdn EMic GBin IBal LRHS NLar NRHS NSue
'Fragrant Fire'	CBdn EMic IBal
'Fragrant Gold'	EMic
'Fragrant King'	IBal
'Fragrant Queen'PBR (v)	IBal NSue
'Fragrant Star'	EMic IBal
'Fragrant Surprise' (v)	NSue
'Fran Godfrey'	EMic IBal
'Francee' (*fortunei*) (v) ♀H7	Widely available
§ 'Frances Williams' (*sieboldiana*) (v) ♀H7	Widely available
'Frances Williams Improved' (*sieboldiana*) (v)	EPfP
'Francheska' (v)	EMic IBal
'Frank Lloyd Wright'	IBal
'Free Jazz' (v)	IBal
'Fresh' (v)	EMic IBal NSue
'Fried Bananas'	CBod EMic IBal ITim WWtn
'Fried Green Tomatoes'	EMic IBal NLar NNor
'Friends' (v)	EMic NSue
'Fringe Benefit' (v)	EMic
'Frisian Pride'	EMic IBal NSue
'Frisian Waving Steel'	EMic IBal
'Frosted Dimples'	EMic IBal
'Frosted Frolic' (v)	EMic IBal WFar
'Frosted Jade' (v) ♀H7	EMic EPfP IBal LRHS MMuc NEgg NLar
'Frosted June'	EMic IBal
'Frosted Lollipop' (v) **new**	IBal
'Frosted Mini Hearts'	IBal
'Frosted Mouse Ears'PBR	CBdn IBal NHpl NSue
'Frozen Margarita'	EMic IBal NLar
'Fruit Punch'	EMic IBal
'Fujibotan' (v)	EMic IBal
'Fukurin-Fu' (*venusta*) (v)	GEdr
'Fulda'	EMic IBal
'Full Moon'	EMic
'Funky Monkey'	EMic IBal
'Funny Frolic' (v)	IBal
'Funny Mouse' (v)	CBdn EMic IBal NHpl NSue WFar
'Futura' (v)	IBal
'Gaiety' (v)	ECtt EMic IBal LRHS NRHS
'Gaijin' (v)	EMic IBal NSue
'Garden Party' (v)	IBal
'Garnet Prince'	IBal
'Gay Blade' (v)	IBal
'Gay Feather' (v)	EMic
'Gay Search' (v)	IBal
'Geisha' (v)	EMic IBal LRHS NEoE NGdn NNor NSue
'Geisha Satin Ripples'	IBal
'Gemstone'	NSue
'Gene's Joy'	EMic
'Gentle Giant'	IBal
'Gentle Spirit' (v)	IBal
'George M. Dallas' (v)	IBal
'George Smith' (*sieboldiana*)	CBdn EMic IBal
'Georgia Sweetheart' (v)	IBal
'Ghost Spirit' (v)	EBee IBal NSue WFar
'Ghostmaster' (v)	IBal WFar
'Giantland Mouse Cheese'	IBal NSue
'Giantland Sunny Mouse Ears'	CBdn IBal NSue
'Gig Harbor'	IBal
'Gigantea' (*sieboldiana*)	see *H.* 'Elata'
'Gilded Teacup' (v) **new**	NSue

'Gilt by Association'	EMic IBal
'Gilt Edge' (*sieboldiana*) (v)	EMic
'Gin and Tonic' (v)	EMic NSue
'Gingee'	EMic IBal
'Ginko Craig' (v) ♀H7	CMac CRos ECha EHoe ELan EMic EPfP GKev GMaP IBal LRHS MRav NBir NEgg NGdn NLar NNor NRHS NSti SPer SPoG WFar
'Ginrei'	IBal
'Ginsu Knife' (v)	EMic IBal
'Glacial Towers' (v)	IBal
'Glad Rags' (v)	IBal
'Glad Tidings'	IBal
'Glamour'	EMic IBal NSue
'Glass Hearts'	EMic IBal
glauca	see *H. sieboldiana* var. *elegans*
'Glitter'	EMic IBal
'Glockenspiel'	EMic IBal
I 'Gloriosa' (*fortunei*) (v)	IBal LRHS NSue
'Glory'	CBdn IBal
'Glory Hallelujah'	CBdn EMic IBal
'Goddess of Athena' (*decorata*) (v)	IBal
'Gold Drop' (*venusta* hybrid)	EMic IBal NHol NSue
'Gold Edger'	CDor CMac CRos EHoe ELan EMic EPfP EShb GKev GMaP IBal LRHS MRav NBir NGdn NLar NNor NRHS NSti WFar
'Gold Edger Surprise' (v)	EMic
'Gold Flush' (*ventricosa*)	EMic
§ 'Gold Haze' (*fortunei*)	EMic IBal NBir
'Gold Leaf' (*fortunei*)	IBal
'Gold Pressed Latinum'	IBal
'Gold Regal'	EMic IBal LRHS NRHS WFar
'Gold Rush'	EMic
'Gold Standard' (*fortunei*) (v) ♀H7	Widely available
'Goldbrook' (v)	EMic IBal
'Goldbrook Galleon'	IBal
'Goldbrook Gaynor'	IBal
'Goldbrook Genie'	CBdn IBal
'Goldbrook Girl'	IBal
'Goldbrook Glamour' (v)	IBal
'Goldbrook Gleam' (v)	IBal
'Goldbrook Glimmer' (Tardiana Group) (v)	IBal LRHS LSta
'Goldbrook Glory'	EMic IBal
'Goldbrook Gold'	IBal
'Goldbrook Good Gracious' (v)	IBal
'Goldbrook Grace'	IBal
'Goldbrook Gratis' (v)	IBal
'Goldbrook Grayling'	EMic IBal LRHS NRHS
'Goldbrook Grebe'	IBal LSta
'Goldbrook Greengage' (v)	IBal
'Goldbrook Greenheart'	IBal
'Golden Age'	see *H.* 'Gold Haze'
'Golden Fountain'	EMic
'Golden Gate'	IBal
'Golden Goal'	IBal
'Golden Guernsey' (v)	EMic
'Golden Isle'	EMic IBal
'Golden Meadows'PBR (*sieboldiana*)	CDor ECtt EMic IBal NGdn NSue WFar
'Golden Medallion' (*tokudama*)	CRos ECtt EMic LRHS NEgg NGdn NRHS WFar
'Golden Nakaiana'	see *H.* 'Birchwood Parky's Gold'
'Golden' (*nakaiana*)	see *H.* 'Birchwood Parky's Gold'
'Golden Needles' (v)	NSue
'Golden Oriole'	EMic LRHS NNor

'Golden Prayers' (*tokudama*)	ECtt EHoe ELan MRav NBir NBro NEgg NGdn NLar WFar WHal WSHC
'Golden Regal' **new**	WFar
'Golden Scepter'	EMic IBal LRHS NNor SRms WFar
'Golden Sculpture' (*sieboldiana*)	EMic
'Golden Spades'	EMic NSue
'Golden Spider'	EMic
'Golden Sunburst' (*sieboldiana*)	ECtt NEgg NGdn NLar XLum
'Golden Sweetie'	EMic
'Golden Tiara' (v) ♀H7	Widely available
'Golden Tusk'	IBal
'Golden Waffles'	ECtt EMic NEgg
'Goldsmith'	EMic
'Gone Fishin'' (v)	IBal
'Gone with the Wind' (v)	IBal
'Goober'	IBal
'Good as Gold'	CBdn EMic
'Goodness Gracious' (v)	EMic IBal NSue
'Gorgeous George'	IBal
'Gosan' (*tardiva*)	EMic
'Gosan Gold Midget'	EMic
'Gosan Leather Strap'	ESwi IBal
'Gosan Mina'	EMic
'Gosan Shining'	EMic
gracillima	IBal NRya NWad
'Grand Canyon'	EMic
'Grand Finale'	IBal
'Grand Marquee' (v)	EMic IBal NGdn NLar WFar
'Grand Master'	IBal
'Grand Prize' (v)	EMic IBal NSue
'Grand Rapids'	IBal
'Grand Slam'	IBal
'Grand Tiara' (v)	EMic IBal LRHS NGdn NRHS NSue
'Grand Total'	IBal
'Grant Park'	EMic IBal
'Grape Fizz'	IBal
'Gray Cole' (*sieboldiana*)	EMic IBal ITim
'Great Arrival'	EMic IBal
'Great Escape'[PBR] (v)	CBdn EMic IBal
'Great Expectations' (*sieboldiana*) (v)	CDor CKel CMac CNor CRos ELan EMic EPfP LPot LRHS LSRN MBNS MHer MNHC MNrw NBro NGdn NHpl NLar NNor NRHS SPoG WFar
'Great Lakes Gold'	IBal
'Green Acres' (*montana*)	EMic IBal LEdu WFar
'Green Angel' (*sieboldiana*)	IBal
'Green Cheese'	EMic IBal
'Green Dwarf'	WFar
'Green Eyes' (*sieboldii*) (v)	EMic IBal NSue WFar
'Green Fountain' (*kikutii*)	EMic IBal
'Green Gold' (*fortunei*) (v)	EMic
'Green Lama'	EMic IBal
'Green Mouse Ears'	CBdn CKel EMic IBal NHpl NSue WFar
'Green Piecrust'	EMic NNor
'Green Platter'	EMic
'Green Sheen'	EMic
'Green Velveteen'	IBal
'Green with Envy' (v) ♀H7	EMic IBal LLHF NNor NSue NWad
'Greenie Weenie Bikini'	NSue
'Greensleeves' (v)	IBal
'Grey Ghost'	EMic
'Grey Glacier' (v) **new**	IBal
'Grey Goose' (Tardiana Group)	EMic
'Groo Bloo'	IBal

'Ground Master' (v)	CMac CRos ECtt ELan EPfP GMaP LRHS MRav NBro NGdn NLar NNor NRHS NSti WFar WMoo
'Ground Sulphur'	EMic NSue
'Grover Cleveland'	IBal
'Grünherz'	IBal
'Grunspecht' (Tardiana Group)	IBal
'Guacamole' (v) ♀H7	CAby CBcs CBdn CDor CRos ECha ECtt EHoe ELon EMic EMor EPfP EWTr GBin IBal LRHS NAst NGdn NLar NNor NRHS SCob SPoG WFar
'Guardian Angel' (*sieboldiana*) ♀H7	CBdn EMic IBal NSue
'Gum Drop'	EMic NNor
'Gun Metal Blue'	IBal
'Gunther's Prize' (v)	IBal
'Gunther's Rim' (v)	IBal
'Gypsy Rose' ♀H7	CBdn CKel EMic EShb IBal IPot LRHS NGdn NLar NSue WFar
'Hacksaw'	EMic IBal NSue
'Hadspen Blue' (Tardiana Group) ♀H7	CAby CRos CSBt CWCL EBee ELan EMic EPfP GMaP IBal LRHS MBrN MGos MRav NBir NBro NEgg NGdn NHol NLar NNor NRHS NSti SPer SPoG WSpi
'Hadspen Hawk' (Tardiana Group)	IBal
'Hadspen Heron' (Tardiana Group)	EMic IBal NWad XLum
'Hadspen Honey'	CRos LRHS NRHS
'Hadspen Nymphaea'	IBal
'Hadspen Rainbow'	EMic IBal
'Hadspen Samphire'	EMic IBal NBir NBro
'Hadspen White' (*fortunei*)	EMic IBal NLar
'Haku-chu-han' (*sieboldii*) (v)	EMic NHpl
'Hakujima' (*sieboldii*)	IBal NSue
'Hakumuo' (v)	IBal
§ 'Halcyon' (Tardiana Group) ♀H7	Widely available
'Halcyon Gold'	LSun
'Half and Half'	CBdn EMic IBal NSue
'Hampshire County' (v)	EMic IBal
'Hands Up'[PBR] (v)	CBdn EMic IBal NSue
'Hanky Panky' (v)	CBdn IBal NGdn NSti NSue WFar
'Hannibal Hamlin' (v)	IBal
'Happily Ever After' (v)	IBal
'Happiness' (Tardiana Group)	EHoe EMic IBal MRav
'Happy Camper' (v)	IBal
'Happy Dayz' (v)	IBal
'Happy Hearts'	EMic
'Happy Valley' (v)	IBal NSue
'Harmony' (Tardiana Group)	EMic
'Harpoon' (v)	EMic
'Harriette Ward'	IBal
'Harry van de Laar'	CBdn EMic IBal
'Harry van Trier'	EMic GBin GWyn
'Hart's Tongue'	IBal
'Harvest Delight'	EMic
'Harvest Glow'	IBal
'Hawkeye' (v)	IBal
'Hazel'	EMic IBal
'Heart and Soul' (v)	EMic IBal NSue
'Heart Broken'	IBal
'Heart of Chan'	IBal
'Heart Throb'	EMic
'Heartbeat' (v)	NSue
'Heartleaf'	EMic

Name	Suppliers
'Heart's Content' (v)	IBal
'Heartsong' (v)	CBdn EMic IBal LRHS
'Heat Wave'PBR (v)	EMic IBal
'Heavenly Beginnings' (v)	IBal
'Heavenly Tiara' (v)	NSue
'Heavy Duty'	IBal
'Heideturm'	IBal
'Helen Doriot' (*sieboldiana*)	EMic IBal
'Helen Field Fischer' (*fortunei*)	IBal NLar
helonioides* f. *albopicta misapplied	see *H. rohdeifolia*
'Herifu' (v)	EMic
'Hertha' (v)	EMic
'Hida-no-hana' (*montana*) (v)	IBal
'Hidden Cove' (v)	IBal NSue
'Hidden Treasure' (v)	IBal
'Hideout' (v)	IBal NSue
'High Kicker'	IBal
'High Society' (v)	EPfP IBal MNrw NHpl NNor NSue
'High Tide'	IBal
'Hi-ho Silver' (v)	EMic IBal NSue
'Hilda Wassman' (v)	IBal
'Hillbilly Blues' (v)	NSue
'Hippodrome' (v)	EMic IBal
'Hirao Elite'	EMic IBal
'Hirao Majesty'	IBal
'Hirao Supreme'	EMic IBal
'His Honor' (v)	EMic IBal
'Hoarfrost'	EMic
'Hollywood Lights' (v)	EMic EPfP IBal NGdn NSue
'Holstein'	see *H.* 'Halcyon'
'Holy Molé' (v)	EMic IBal
'Holy Mouse Ears'PBR	CBdn IBal NSue
'Honey Moon'	EMic IBal NNor
'Honeybells'	CBcs CMac CRos EBee ECha ELan EMic EPfP GBin IBal LEdu LRHS MCot MRav NBid NGdn NNor NRHS NSti SPer WCAu WFar XLum
'Honeysong' (v)	EMic IBal NNor
'Hoosier Dome'	EMic
'Hoosier Harmony' (v)	EMic
'Hope' (v)	NLar
'Hot Air Balloon'	IBal
'Hotcakes'	IBal
'Hotspur' (v)	EMic
'Hudson Bay' (v)	EMic IBal
'Humpback Whale'	IBal
'Hush Puppie'	EMic IBal MNrw NHpl NSue WFar
'Hyacintha Variegata' (*fortunei*) (v)	CMac NNor
'Hydon Gleam'	EMic IBal NSue
'Hydon Sunset'	CNor CRos EBee ECtt EMic GEdr IBal LRHS MNrw NBir NLar NNor NRHS NRya NSti NSue WHal
hypoleuca	EMic IBal
'Hyuga-urajiro' (v)	EMic IBal NSue WFar
'Ice Cream' (*cathayana*) (v)	IBal LRHS NGdn NRHS
'Ice Cube' (v)	CBdn IBal NSue
'Ice Prancer'	EMic IBal
'Iced Lemon' (v)	EMic GEdr IBal NHpl NNor NSue WFar
'Illicit Affair'	EMic IBal NHpl NSue
'Imp' (v)	EMic IBal
§ 'Inaho'	LRHS NSue
'Inca Gold'	IBal NSue
'Incoming'	IBal
'Independence' (v)	EBee EMic IBal LRHS NBro NSue SPoG WFar
'Independence Day' (v)	EMic
'Inniswood' (v)	CDor CWCL ECtt EMic IBal MBNS NBro NGdn NLar NSti WFar
'Invincible'	CDor ECtt EMic EMor IBal NBid NEgg NGdn NLar NNor WFar
'Invincible Spirit'	IBal
'Iona' (*fortunei*)	EMic IBal NNor
'Irische See' (Tardiana Group)	IBal
'Irish Eyes' (v)	EMic IBal
'Irish Luck'	EMic IBal NSue
'Iron Gate Delight' (v)	NNor
'Iron Gate Special' (v)	EMic
'Iron Gate Supreme' (v)	EMic
'Iron Sky'	IBal
'Island Charm' (v) ♀H7	CRos EBee GBin IBal LRHS NHpl NLar NRHS NSue SCob WFar
'Itty Gold'	IBal
'Ivory Coast' (v)	CRos ECtt EMic EMor IBal LRHS MHol NRHS
'Ivory Necklace' (v)	EMic IBal
'Ivory Queen' (v)	EMic IBal NSue
'Iwa Yara Moto'	IBal
'Jack of Diamonds'	IBal
'Jade Cascade'	EMic GBin IBal NBir NEgg NLar WFar WHal
'Jade Scepter' (*nakaiana*)	EMic
'Janet Day' (v)	EMic
'Janet' (*fortunei*) (v)	EMic NGdn NNor
'Janet's Green Sox'	EMic
'Jason and Katie' (v)	EMic IBal
'Jaws'	CBdn EMic IBal NSue
'Jaz'	IBal
'Jennifer' (v)	IBal
'Jerry Landwehr'	EMic IBal
'Jewel of the Nile' (v)	EMic IBal
'Jimmy Crack Corn'	EMic IBal NEgg NGdn
'Jingle Bells'	IBal
'John Wargo'	IBal
'Johnny Angel'	EMic
'Joker' (*fortunei*) (v)	NNor
'Jolly Green Giant' (*sieboldiana* hybrid)	EMic
'Joseph'	EMic IBal
'Josephine' (v)	NNor
'Journeyman'	EMic IBal
'Journey's End' (v)	CBdn EMic IBal
'Joyce Trott' (v)	EMic
'Joyful' (v)	IBal
'Jubilee' (v)	EMic IBal
'Judy Rocco'	IBal
'Juha' (v)	EMic
'Jules'	IBal
'Julia' (v)	EMic IBal NSue
'Julie Morss'	EMic GMaP IBal NEgg
'June'PBR (Tardiana Group) (v) ♀H7	Widely available
'June Fever'PBR (Tardiana Group)	ELon EMic ESwi GBin IBal NBro NGdn NLar NSue SPoG WFar
'June Spirit' (v)	IBal NSue
'Jurassic Park'	EMic EUJe IBal LLWG LRHS MNrw NLar
'Just So' (v)	EMic IBal
'Justine'PBR	CBdn EMic IBal NSue
'Kabitan'	see *H. sieboldii* var. *sieboldii* f. *kabitan*
'Kabuki'	IBal
'Kalamazoo' (v)	EMic IBal
'Kaleidochrome' (v)	IBal
'Karin'	EMic IBal

	'Katherine Lewis' (Tardiana Group) (v)	EMic IBal LRHS LSRN NHol
	'Kath's Gold'	EMic
	'Katie Q' (v)	EMic IBal
	'Katsuragawa-beni' (v)	EMic IBal
	'Kayak' **new**	IBal
	'Kelly'	EMic
	'Kelsey'	EMic IBal
	'Kenzie' (v)	EMic IBal
	'Key Lime Pie'	EMic IBal
	'Key West'	EMic
	'Kifukurin' (*kikutii*)	see *H.* 'Kifukurin-hyuga'
§	'Kifukurin-hyuga' (v)	IBal
	'Kifukurin-kiyosumi'	IBal
	'Kifukurin-ko-mame' (*gracillima*) (v)	EMic NSue
	'Kifukurin-otome' (*venusta*) (v)	EMic NSue
	'Kifukurin-ubatake' (*pulchella*) (v)	EMic IBal
	kikutii	CBdn EMic IBal IMou LRHS
§	- var. ***caput-avis***	EMic
§	- var. ***yakusimensis***	EMic GEdr IBal SMad
	'Ki-nakafu-otome' (*venusta*)	EMic IBal
	'Kinbotan' (*venusta*) (v)	EMic GEdr
	'Kinbuchi Tachi' (*rectifolia*) (v)	IBal
	'King James'	IBal
	'King of Spades'	IBal
	'King Tut'	EMic
	'Kingfisher' (Tardiana Group)	LRHS
	'Kingsize'	IBal SArc
§	'Kirishima'	EMic NHpl NSue NWad
	'Kisuji'	see *H.* 'Mediopicta'
	'Kitty Cat'	EMic IBal WFar
	'Kiwi Black Magic'	IBal
	'Kiwi Blue Baby'	EMic IBal
	'Kiwi Blue Ruffles'	IBal
	'Kiwi Blue Sky'	IBal
	'Kiwi Canoe'	IBal
	'Kiwi Cream Edge' (v)	EMic
	'Kiwi Forest'	IBal
	'Kiwi Full Monty' (v)	CBdn CDor EMic IBal NSue WFar
	'Kiwi Hippo'	IBal
	'Kiwi Jordan'	IBal
	'Kiwi Kaniere Gold'	IBal
	'Kiwi Minnie Gold'	IBal ITim
	'Kiwi Parasol'	IBal
	'Kiwi Skyscraper'	IBal
	'Kiwi Spearmint'	WFar
	'Kiwi Sunshine'	IBal
	kiyosumiensis	IBal
	'Klopping Variegated' (v)	EMic
	'Knight's Journey'	IBal
	'Knockout' (v)	MBNS MRav NBro NEgg NGdn NLar NNor
	'Komodo Dragon'	EMic IBal
	'Konkubine'	EMic
	'Korean Snow'	IBal
	'Koriyama' (*sieboldiana*) (v)	EMic
	'Krossa Cream Edge' (*sieboldii*) (v)	IBal
	'Krossa Regal' ♀H7	Widely available
	'La Donna'	IBal
	'Lacy Belle' (v)	CDor CRos CSBt EBee EMic EPfP IBal LRHS NBro NEoE NGdn NRHS NSue
	'Lady Godiva'	IBal
	'Lady Guineverre'	EMic IBal
	'Lady Helen'	EMic
	'Lady in Red'	IBal
	'Lady Isobel Barnett' (v) ♀H7	IBal
	laevigata	IBal
	'Lake Superior'	IBal
	'Lake Tekapo' (v)	IBal
	'Lakeside Accolade'	IBal
	'Lakeside Alex Andra' (v)	IBal
	'Lakeside April Snow' (v)	EMic IBal NGdn
	'Lakeside Baby Face' (v)	EMic IBal NHpl NSue WFar
	'Lakeside Banana Bay' (v)	IBal NGdn
	'Lakeside Beach Bum'	IBal
	'Lakeside Beach Captain' (v)	EMic
	'Lakeside Black Satin'	EMic WFar
	'Lakeside Blue Cherub'	EMic IBal
	'Lakeside Breaking News' (v)	EMic IBal
	'Lakeside Butter Ball'	IBal
	'Lakeside Cha Cha' (v)	CBdn EMic IBal WFar
	'Lakeside Cindy Cee' (v)	IBal
	'Lakeside Circle O' (v)	IBal
	'Lakeside Coal Miner'	EMic NGdn NLar
	'Lakeside Color Blue'	IBal
	'Lakeside Contender'	IBal
	'Lakeside Cupcake' (v)	EMic IBal NGdn NSue
	'Lakeside Cupid's Cup' (v)	IBal
	'Lakeside Dimpled Darling' (v)	NSue
	'Lakeside Dividing Line' (v)	IBal
	'Lakeside Doodad' (v)	IBal NSue
	'Lakeside Down Sized' (v)	CBdn EMic IBal MNrw NSue WFar
	'Lakeside Dragonfly' (v)	ECtt ELon EMic EPfP EShb IBal MNrw NGdn NLar NSue WFar
	'Lakeside Elfin Fire'	EMic GEdr NSue
	'Lakeside Fancy Pants' (v)	CBdn IBal
	'Lakeside Feather Light' (v)	IBal
	'Lakeside Foaming Sea'	IBal
	'Lakeside Full Tide'	IBal
	'Lakeside Hazy Morn' (v)	IBal
	'Lakeside Hoola Hoop' (v)	IBal
	'Lakeside Iron Man'	IBal
	'Lakeside Jazzy Jane' (v)	IBal
	'Lakeside Kaleidoscope'	EMic IBal NGdn
	'Lakeside Keepsake' (v)	IBal
	'Lakeside Khum Kaw'	IBal
	'Lakeside Legal Tender'	IBal
	'Lakeside Lime Time'	IBal
	'Lakeside Little Gem'	IBal NSue
	'Lakeside Little Tuft' (v)	CBdn EMic IBal NLar NSue
	'Lakeside Lollipop'	EMic IBal
	'Lakeside Looking Glass'	EMic
	'Lakeside Love Affaire'	EMic IBal NSue WFar
	'Lakeside Maestro'	IBal NLar
	'Lakeside Maverick'	IBal
	'Lakeside Meadow Ice' (v)	IBal
	'Lakeside Meter Maid' (v)	IBal NSue
	'Lakeside Midnight Miss'	IBal
	'Lakeside Miss Muffett' (v)	EMic NSue
	'Lakeside Missy Little' (v)	IBal
	'Lakeside Neat Petite'	IBal NSue
	'Lakeside Ninita' (v)	EMic IBal LRHS NRHS NSue
	'Lakeside Old Smokey'	IBal
	'Lakeside Paisley Print' (v)	CBdn ECtt EMic IBal MHol MNrw NSue SPad WFar
	'Lakeside Party Dress'	GEdr
	'Lakeside Pebbles'	IBal
	'Lakeside Premier'	EMic IBal
	'Lakeside Prissy Miss' (v)	NSue
	'Lakeside Prophecy'	IBal

'Lakeside Prophecy Fulfilled' (v)	IBal
'Lakeside Rhapsody' (v)	EMic IBal
'Lakeside Ring Master' (v)	IBal
'Lakeside Ripples'	IBal
'Lakeside Rocky Top' (v)	IBal WFar
'Lakeside Roy El' (v)	IBal
'Lakeside Sapphire Pleats'	EMic
'Lakeside Sassy Sally'	IBal
'Lakeside Scamp' (v)	CBdn EMic EMor GEdr NSue
'Lakeside Shadows' (v)	IBal
'Lakeside Shoremaster' (v)	CBdn IBal
'Lakeside Slick Chick' (v)	IBal
'Lakeside Small Fry' (v)	NSue
'Lakeside Sophistication' (v)	IBal
'Lakeside Sparkle Plenty' (v)	IBal
'Lakeside Spellbinder' (v)	CLAP IBal LRHS
'Lakeside Spruce Goose' (v)	EMic IBal
'Lakeside Storm Watch'	EMic IBal NSue
'Lakeside Swan Pon' (v)	IBal
'Lakeside Symphony' (v)	EMic
'Lakeside Tee Ki' (v)	IBal
'Lakeside Whizzit' (v)	IBal NSue
'Lakeside Zesty Zeno' (v)	IBal
'Lakeside Zinger' (v)	EMic IBal NSue
lancifolia	CMac EBee ELan EMic GMaP IBal MRav NGdn NSti SPer SRms WKif WSHC WThu
'Last Dance' (v)	IBal
'Laura Lanier'	EMic IBal
'Laura Z'	IBal
'Lavender Doll'	IBal
'Leading Lady' ♀H7	IBal
'Leather Sheen'	EHoe EMic
'Leatherneck'	IBal
'Lederhosen'	EMic
'Lemon Delight'	EMic ESwi IBal LRHS NNor NRHS NSue WFar
'Lemon Frost'	EMic IBal
'Lemon Lime'	EMic EWld IBal LRHS MNrw NEgg NEoE NNor NRHS NSue WCot
'Lemon Meringue'	EMic
'Lemonade'	GBin IBal
'Leola Fraim' (v)	EMic IBal LRHS
'Let Me Entertain You'	EMic
'Leviathan'	EMic
'Lewis and Clark'	IBal
'Libby'	EMic IBal NSue
'Liberty'[PBR] (v) ♀H7	CBdn CBod CDor CWGN EMic EMor EPfP IBal NBro NGdn NLar NNor NSue SAko SPer
'Light of Zetar'	IBal
'Li'l Abner' (v)	IBal
* ***lilacina***	WFar
'Lily Blue Eyes'	EMic
'Lime Fizz'	EMic IBal NHpl NSue WFar
'Lime Shag' (*sieboldii* f. *spathulata*)	IBal NSue WFar
'Limey Lisa'	EMic IBal NSue
'Linda Sue' (v)	EMic IBal
'Lionheart' (v)	EMic IBal NSue
'Little Aurora' (*tokudama* hybrid)	EMic IBal NSue WFar
'Little Bit'	IBal NSue
'Little Black Scape'	EMic IBal LSRN NEgg NGdn NLar NWad
'Little Blue' (*ventricosa*)	EMic
'Little Bo Beep' (v)	IBal WFar
'Little Boy'	IBal
'Little Caesar' (v)	EMic IBal LRHS NGdn NSue WFar
'Little Devil'	EMic NSue
'Little Doll' (v)	IBal
'Little Jay' (v)	NSue
'Little Maddie'	EMic NSue
'Little Miss Magic'	IBal NSue
'Little Miss Muffett'	NSue
'Little Miss Sunshine'	IBal NSue
'Little Prayer'	WFar
'Little Red Joy'	EMic IBal NSue
'Little Red Rooster'	EMic GEdr IBal NGdn NHpl NLar NNor NSue WFar
'Little Star Struck'	NSue
'Little Stiffy'	EMic IBal
'Little Sunspot' (v)	EMic NSue
'Little Treasure' (v)	EMic IBal NSue WFar
'Little White Lines' (v)	EBee EHoe EMic GKev IBal LRHS NRHS NSue
'Little Willie' (v)	NSue
'Little Wonder' (v) ♀H7	EMic LSta NSue
'Living Water'	EMic
'Lizard Lick'	EMic IBal NSue
'Lollapalooza' (v)	CBdn IBal
'London Fog' (v)	GEdr IBal
'Long Fellow' (v)	IBal
longipes B&SWJ 10806	WCru
longissima var. ***brevifolia***	NSue
'Lost World'	EMic IBal
'Lothar the Giant'	IBal
'Love Pat' ♀H7	CBdn ECtt EMic EPfP IBal LSRN MRav NGdn NLar NNor NSue
'Love Song'	IBal
'Loyalist'[PBR] (v)	EMic IBal LRHS NGdn NLar SPoG WFar
'Lucky Mouse'[PBR] (v)	CBdn EMic IBal NSue
'Lucy Vitols' (v)	EMic ESwi IBal
'Lullabye'	EMic
'Luna Moth'	CBdn CBod IBal
'Lunar Eclipse' (v)	EMic NEgg
'Machete'	IBal
'Mack the Knife'	EMic IBal NLar WFar
'Maekawa'	EMic IBal
'Magic Fire'[PBR] (v)	ECtt EMic EPfP IBal NLar NSue
'Magic Island'	IBal NSue
'Magica'	IBal
'Majesty'	EMic IBal MNrw NGdn
'Major Tom'	IBal
'Majordomo'	EMic
'Malabar' (v)	EMic IBal
'Mama Mia' (v)	CRos EMic EMor EPfP IBal LRHS MBNS NBro NGdn NHol NRHS NWad WFar
'Mango Salsa'	IBal
'Mango Tango' (v)	EMic IBal
'Manhattan'	EMic
'Maple Leaf' (*sieboldiana*) (v)	EMic
'Maraschino Cherry'	EMic IBal LPla NEgg NGdn
'Mardi Gras' (v)	EMic IBal
'Marge' (*sieboldiana* hybrid)	EMic
'Margie's Angel' (v)	NSue
'Margin of Error' (v)	IBal
'Marginata Alba' misapplied	see *H.* 'Albomarginata' (*fortunei*), *H. crispula*
'Marginata Alba' ambig. (v)	NNor
'Marilyn'	EMic IBal NSue
'Marilyn Monroe'	EMic IBal NSue
'Marmalade on Toast'	EMic
'Marquis' (*nakaiana* hybrid)	IBal
'Marrakech'	EMic IBal LRHS NSue
'Mary Joe'	EMic

	Name	Suppliers
	'Mary Marie Ann' (*fortunei*) (v)	EMic IBal
	'Masquerade' (v)	EMic LLHF NSue SMHy WFar WHal WThu
	'Maui Buttercups'	EMic NSue
	'May'	EMic IBal
	'Maya' (*fortunei*) (v)	EMic IBal
	'Medieval Age' (v)	IBal
§	'Mediopicta' (*sieboldii*)	EMic IBal
	'Mediovariegata' (*undulata*)	see *H. undulata* var. *undulata*
	'Medusa' (v)	NGdn NSue
	'Memories of Dorothy'	EMic IBal
	'Mesa Fringe' (*montana*)	EMic NLar
	'Mid Afternoon'	IBal
	'Midas Touch'	NEgg NLar NNor
	'Middle Ridge'	EMic
	'Midnight at the Oasis' (v)	EMic IBal NSue
	'Midnight Ride'	IBal
	'Midwest Magic' (v)	EMic IBal NLar
	'Mighty Mite'	IBal
	'Mikawa-no-yuki'	IBal
	'Mike Shadrack' (v)	EMic IBal
	'Miki'	IBal
	'Mildred Seaver' (v)	CBdn EMic IBal LRHS
	'Millennium'	CBdn ECtt EMic IBal
	'Mini Skirt'	IBal NSue
I	'Minima Aurea'	IBal
	'Minnesota Wild' (v)	IBal
	'Minnie Bell' (v)	IBal
	'Minnie Klopping'	EMic
	minor misapplied f. ***alba***	see *H. sieboldii* var. *alba*
§	***minor*** Maekawa	GEdr ITim NWad WFar XLum
	- - B&SWJ 1209 from Korea	WCru
	- - B&SWJ 8775 from Korea	WCru
	- - B&SWJ 11103 from Japan	WCru
	- from Japan	EMic
	- from Korea	IBal
	'Minor' (*ventricosa*)	see *H. minor* Maekawa
	'Mint Julep' (v)	IBal
	'Minuet' (v)	IBal
	'Minuteman' (*fortunei*) (v) ♀H7	CBcs CDor CRos ECtt ELon EMic EPfP IBal LRHS MBNS MMuc NGdn NHpl NLar NNor NRHS SEND WFar
	'Minutini'	NSue
	'Miracle Lemony'	CBdn IBal NSue
	'Miss Linda Smith'	EMic IBal
	'Miss Ruby'	EMic IBal
	'Miss Saigon' (v)	IBal
	'Miss Susie'	IBal
	'Miss Tokyo' (v)	EMic IBal
	'Mississippi Delta'	EMic
	'Mister Watson'	EMic IBal
	'Misty Waters' (*sieboldiana*)	EMic
	'Misweave' (v) **new**	IBal
	'Moerheim' (*fortunei*) (v)	EMic IBal LRHS WFar WHal
	'Mohegan'	EMic
	'Mohrchen'	EMic
	'Moi Marleen'	EMic
	'Mojito' **new**	EMic
	'Monster Ears'	EUJe IBal NSue
	montana	EMic WFar
	- B&SWJ 4796	WCru
	- B&SWJ 5585	LEdu WCru
	- f. ***macrophylla***	IBal NSue
	aff. ***montana***	WFar
	'Moody Blues' (Tardiana Group)	CBdn EMic
	'Moon Dance' (v)	IBal
	'Moon Lily'	EMic
	'Moon River' (v)	EMic IBal
	'Moon Split' (v)	EMic EPfP IBal NGdn
	'Moon Waves'	IBal
	'Moonbeam'	EMic EShb
	'Moongate Flying Saucer'	EMic
	'Moonlight' (*fortunei*) (v)	EMic GMaP IBal LRHS NEgg NNor
	'Moonlight Sonata'	EMic IBal
	'Moonstruck'^{PBR} (v)	ECtt EMic IBal NSue
	'Morning Light'	ECtt EMic EMor EPfP GBin IBal LLWG MBNS NBro NGdn NLar SRkn WFar
	'Morning Star' (v)	EMic IBal NSue WFar
	'Moscow Blue'	EMic
	'Moulin Rouge'	IBal NSue
	'Mount Everest'	EMic IBal
	'Mount Fuji' (*montana*)	IBal
	'Mount Kirishima' (*sieboldii*)	see *H.* 'Kirishima'
	'Mount Tom' (v)	EMic IBal
	'Mountain Snow' (*montana*) (v)	CRos EMic LRHS NRHS
	'Mourning Dove' (v)	EMic IBal
	'Mr Big'	IBal NGdn WCot
	'Mr Blue'	IBal NSue
	'Mrs Minky'	CRos EMic LRHS NRHS
	'Muffie' (v)	EMic
	'Munchkin' (*sieboldii*)	LLHF WFar
	'My Claire' (v)	IBal
	'My Cup of Tea'	IBal
	'My Precious' (v)	IBal NSue
	'Mystic Mouse'	IBal
	'Mystic Star'	IBal NSue
	nakaiana	EBee EMic GWyn
	'Nakaimo'	IBal NLar
	'Nana' (*ventricosa*)	see *H. minor* Maekawa
	'Nancy'	EMic
§	'Nancy Lindsay' (*fortunei*)	CBdn CDor EMic IBal NGdn NLar
	'Nancy Minks'	EMic IBal
	'Neat and Tidy'	IBal
	'Neat Splash' (v)	CWCL NBir
	'Neelix'	IBal
	'Nemesis' (v)	IBal
	'Neptune'	EMic IBal
	'Nesmith's Giant'	EMic
	'Niagara Falls' ♀H7	CBdn EMic IBal NEgg NGdn NSue
	'Nicola'	CBdn EMic IBal NSue
	'Night before Christmas' (v) ♀H7	EMic EWTr IBal LRHS MBNS MNrw NBro NEgg NGdn NHol NLar NNor WHoo
	'Night Life'	EMic IBal
	nigrescens	EMic IBal LRHS NChi NEgg
	'Niko' (v)	IBal
	'Nippers'	EMic IBal NSue
	'Nokogiriyama'	EMic
	'None Lovelier' (v)	EMic IBal
	'North Hills' (*fortunei*) (v)	EMic IBal NBir NGdn SWvt WFar
	'Northern Exposure' (*sieboldiana*) (v)	EMic IBal NGdn NLar SPoG WFar
	'Northern Halo' (*sieboldiana*) (v)	CDor EMic
	'Norwalk Chartreuse'	IBal
	'Nutty Professor' (v)	IBal
	'Oberon'	NSue
	'Obscura Marginata' (*fortunei*)	see *H. fortunei* var. *aureomarginata*
	'Ocean Isle' (v)	IBal
	'October Sky'	EMic IBal
	'Oder'	EMic IBal
	'Ogon Tachi' (*rectifolia*) (v)	EMic IBal
	'Ogon-chirifu-hime'	EMic IBal
	'Ogon-hime-tokudama'	IBal
	'Ogon-koba'	IBal

Name	Suppliers
'Oh Cindy' (v)	EMic IBal
'O'Harra'	EMic NSue
'Old Faithful'	EMic IBal LRHS
'Old Glory'[PBR] (v)	ECtt EMic IBal
'Olga's Shiny Leaf'	EMic
'Olive Bailey Langdon' (*sieboldiana*) (v)	CDor EMic IBal
'Olive Branch' (v)	EMic IBal
'Olympic Edger'	EMic IBal
'Olympic Glacier' (v)	EMic IBal
'Olympic Gold Medal'	EMic IBal
'Olympic Silver Medal'	EMic IBal
'Olympic Sunrise' (v)	EMic IBal
'Olympic Twilight'	EMic IBal
'On Stage'	see *H.* 'Chōkō-nishiki'
'On the Border' (v)	IBal
'On the Move'	EMic
'One Iota' (v)	IBal
'One Man's Treasure' ♀H7	EMic IBal MBel NEgg NGdn
'Ooh La La' (v)	IBal NSue
'Ophir'	EMic
opipara	NEgg
'Ops' (v)	EMic IBal NSue
'Orange Crush' (v)	IBal
'Orange Marmalade' (v) ♀H7	CAbb CBcs CBdn CBod CRos CWGN ECtt ELan EMic EMor EPfP IBal LCro LOPS LRHS LSun MBNS MNrw MPnt NAst NGdn NLar NRHS NSue SCob SPoG WFar
'Orange Star'[PBR] (v)	CBdn EMic IBal NSue
'Oriana' (*fortunei*)	EMic
'Orion's Belt' (v)	IBal
'Over the Waves'	IBal NSue
'Oxheart'	EMic IBal
'Oze' (v)	EMic
pachyscapa	EMic
'Pacific Blue Edger'	EMic NNor WAul WFar
'Painted Lady' (*sieboldii*) (v)	GKev NAln
'Pamela Lee' (v)	IBal NGdn
'Pandora's Box' (v)	EMic GEdr NHar NHpl NSue WCot WFar WTor
'Panni Splash' (v) **new**	NSue
'Papa' (v)	IBal
'Paradigm' (v)	CRos EMic IBal LRHS LSta NGdn NLar
'Paradise Backstage' (v)	EMic IBal
'Paradise Beach'	EMic IBal WFar
'Paradise Blue Sky'	IBal
'Paradise Expectations' (*sieboldiana*) (v)	EMic IBal
'Paradise Glory'	EMic IBal
'Paradise Gold Line' (*ventricosa*) (v)	IBal
'Paradise Island'[PBR] (*sieboldiana*) (v)	CBdn ECtt EMic EPfP IBal NGdn NSue WFar
'Paradise Joyce'[PBR]	EMic EMor IBal LRHS NEgg NNor NSue
'Paradise Ocean'	EMic IBal
'Paradise on Fire' (v)	EMic IBal NSue
'Paradise Parade' (v)	EMic IBal
'Paradise Passion' (v)	IBal
'Paradise Power'[PBR]	EMic
'Paradise Puppet' (*venusta*) ♀H7	EBee EMic GKev IBal NNor NSue NWad
'Paradise Red Delight' (*pycnophylla*)	EMic IBal
'Paradise Sandstorm'	IBal
'Paradise Standard' (d)	EMic IBal
'Paradise Sunset'	CBdn EMic IBal NHpl NSue WFar
'Paradise Sunshine'	EMic IBal

Name	Suppliers
'Paradise Surprise' (v)	IBal
'Paradise Tritone' (v)	EMic IBal
'Parhelion'	EMic
'Parky's Prize' (v)	IBal
'Party Popper' (v)	CBdn
'Pastures Green'	IBal
'Pastures New'	EMic NEgg
'Pathfinder' (v)	EMic IBal WFar
'Patricia'	EMic
'Patrician' (v)	EMic IBal
'Patriot' (v) ♀H7	Widely available
'Patriot's Fire' (v)	CRos IBal LRHS NRHS
'Patriot's Green Pride'	IBal
'Paul Revere' (v)	CBdn
'Paul's Glory' (v) ♀H7	CBdn CDor CRos EMic EPfP GLog GMaP IBal LRHS NBir NGdn NNor NSue SPoG WFar
§ 'Paxton's Original' (*sieboldii*) (v)	CKel
'Peace' (v)	EMic IBal LRHS
'Peacock Strut'	IBal
'Peanut'	IBal NSue
'Pearl Lake'	EMic IBal NBir NEgg NGdn NHol NLar NNor
'Peedee Absinth'	EMic
'Peedee Elfin Bells' (*ventricosa*)	IBal
'Pelham Blue Tump'	EMic
'Peppermint Ice' (v)	EMic IBal NGdn
'Percy'	EMic
'Permanent Wave'	IBal
'Perry's True Blue'	EMic IBal
'Peter Pan'	EMic IBal NEgg
'Pete's Dark Satellite'	EMic IBal
'Pewterware'	EMic IBal
'Phantom'	IBal
'Philadelphia'	EMic IBal
'Phoenix'	EMic IBal NLar
'Photo Finish' (v)	EMic IBal
'Phyllis Campbell' (*fortunei*)	see *H.* 'Sharmon'
'Picta' (*fortunei*)	see *H. fortunei* var. *albopicta*
'Piecrust Power'	IBal
'Piedmont Gold'	CRos EHoe EMic GBin IBal LRHS NRHS
'Pilgrim' (v)	CDor CRos EMic GEdr IBal LRHS MMuc NBro NEgg NGdn NHpl NRHS SEND WFar
'Pineapple Poll'	EMic NNor WFar WHoo
'Pineapple Upside Down Cake' (v)	EMic IBal NBro NLar
'Pinky'	IBal
'Pin-up' (v)	IBal NSue
'Pistache' (v)	EMic IBal NSue
'Pixie Vamp' (v)	EMic IBal
'Pizzazz' (v)	EMic IBal LRHS NGdn NHol NLar WFar
plantaginea	EMic LEdu LRHS WFar WSpi WWtn
– var. ***grandiflora***	see *H. plantaginea* var. *japonica*
§ – var. ***japonica*** ♀H7	CAby EBee ECha EHrv LRHS MNrw MRav SMHy SMad SPhx WCFE WFar WSpi
'Platinum Tiara' (v)	EMic IBal NBir NSue
'Playmate' (v)	IBal
'Plug Nickel'	EMic IBal NSue
'Pocketful of Sunshine' (v)	IBal NSue
'Poker'	IBal
'Polar Moon' (v)	IBal
'Pole Cat' (v)	IBal
'Pooh Bear' (v)	EMic NSue
'Popcorn'	IBal NSue

Name	Suppliers
'Popo' ♀[H7]	EMic IBal NHpl NSue
'Porter' (*venusta*)	EMic IBal
'Pot of Gold'	EMic
'Potomac Pride'	CRos EMic LRHS NEgg NRHS
'Powder Blue' (v)	IBal
'Powder Keg' (v)	IBal
'Prairie Moon'	NSue
'Prairie Sky'	ECtt EMic EMor IBal NGdn NLar WFar
'Prairie Sunset' (v)	NSue
'Praying Hands' (v) ♀[H7]	CBdn CDor EBee ECha ECtt ELan EMic EMor EPfP GBin GEdr GKev GWyn IBal LEdu LRHS MBNS MBel NDai NEgg NGdn NHpl NLar NSti NSue SCob SRms WFar
'Precious Metal'	IBal
'Prestige and Promise' (v)	IBal
'Pretty Flamingo'	EMic
'Prima Donna'	EMic
'Prince of Wales'	CRos EMic IBal LPla LRHS NNor NRHS SPoG
'Private Dancer'	IBal
'Prom Queen' (v)	EMic IBal
'Proud Dragon' (v) **new**	CBdn IBal
'Proud Sentry'	EMic IBal
'Punk Rock'	IBal
'Punky' (v)	EMic IBal
'Purple Boots'	EMic IBal
'Purple Dwarf'	EHoe EMic IBal MBNS NLar NSue WCru WHal
'Purple Glory'	EMic
'Purple Haze'	EMic IBal NGdn WFar
'Purple Heart'	CAby CBcs ECtt EMor EWTr IBal LCro LOPS LPla LRHS NEoE NHpl NSti NSue NWad SCob WNPC
'Purple Passion'	EMic IBal LSta NSue
'Purple Profusion'	EMic IBal
'Purple Python'	IBal
'Quarter Note' (v)	IBal
'Queen Josephine' (v)	CBdn CRos ECtt EMic EMor EPfP IBal LRHS MBNS NEgg NGdn NHpl WFar
'Queen of the Seas'	CBdn EMic ESwi IBal NSue
'Quill'	EMic NSue
'Quilting Bee'	EMic IBal NSue
'Radiant Edger' (v)	EMic IBal LRHS NHol NRHS NSue
'Rain Dancer'	EMic IBal
'Rain Forest'	EMic IBal
'Rainbow's End' (v)	CBdn EBee ECtt EMic EPfP IBal NLar NSue
'Rainforest Sunrise' (v)	CBod ELon EMic IBal NGdn NSue WFar
'Randy Rachel' (v)	LRHS
'Rare Breed' (v)	EMic IBal
'Rascal' (v)	EMic IBal
'Raspberries and Cream' (v)	IBal
'Raspberry Sorbet'	EMic IBal LRHS LSta NRHS NSue
'Raspberry Sundae' (v)	CBdn CKel CMil CWGN ECtt EMic EMor IBal MHol NGdn NHpl NSue NWad SCob SPoG WNPC
'Rebel Heart' (v)	IBal
rectifolia	NNor
'Red Alert' (v) **new**	IBal
'Red Cadet'	EMic ESwi IBal NSue WFar
'Red Dog'	EMic NSue
'Red Dragon'	EMic IBal
'Red Hot Flash' (v)	EMic IBal
'Red Hot Poker'	IBal
'Red Neck Heaven' (*kikutii* var. *caput-avis*)	IBal
'Red October'	CRos ECtt EMic EPfP EUJe GAbr GQue IBal LEdu LRHS MBNS MHol MPie NEgg NGdn NHpl NLar NRHS WCAu WCot WFar
'Red Salamander'	CBdn EMic ESwi IBal
'Red Sox'	IBal
'Red Stepper'	EMic IBal WFar
'Red Stilts'	IBal
'Red Tubes' (*venusta*)	IBal
'Regal Rhubarb'	EMic IBal
'Regal Splendor' (v) ♀[H7]	CBdn CDor CRos ECtt ELan ELon EMic IBal LCro LOPS LRHS NBro NGdn NNor NRHS NSue SPoG WFar WHoo
'Regal Supreme' (v)	CBdn IBal NSue
'Regal Tot'	NSue
'Reginald Kaye'	EMic
'Rembrandt Blue'	EMic IBal
'Remember Me'[PBR] ♀[H7]	ELan EMic IBal LSRN MBNS MPnt NEgg NHol NNor NSue WFar
'Reptilian'	EMic IBal
'Resonance' (v)	IBal NGdn NLar
'Restless Sea'	EMic NGdn NSue
'Reverend Mac'	IBal
'Reversed' (*sieboldiana*) (v)	EMic EMor IBal LRHS NBro NGdn NNor WFar WHal
'Revolution'[PBR] (v) ♀[H7]	EMic GKev IBal LSRN NBro NEgg NGdn NLar NSue WFar
'Rhapsody' (*fortunei*) (v)	EMic IBal
'Rhein' (*tardiana*)	EMic IBal
'Rhinestone Cowboy' (v)	IBal
'Rhino Hide' (v)	CBdn EMic IBal NSue
'Rhythm and Blues'	CBdn IBal NSue
'Rich Uncle'	IBal
'Richland Gold' (*fortunei*)	EMic
'Rim Rock'	EMic IBal
'Ringtail'	EMic IBal NSue
'Ripple Effect' (v)	CBdn IBal NSue
'Rippled Honey'	EMic IBal NEoE
'Rippling Waves'	EMic
'Riptide'	EMic NGdn
'Risa'	IBal
'Risky Business'[PBR] (v)	CWGN EMic IBal NLar NSue
'Robert Frost' (v)	EMic IBal
'Robin Hood'	EMic IBal NSue
'Robin of Loxley'	EMic IBal
'Robusta' (*fortunei*)	see *H. sieboldiana* var. *elegans*
'Robyn's Choice' (v)	IBal
'Rock and Roll'	EMic IBal
'Rock Island Line' (v)	EMic IBal NSue NWad WFar
'Rock Princess'	IBal LLHF
'Rocket's Red Glare'	IBal
§ ***rohdeifolia*** (v) B&SWJ 10862	WCru
– f. ***albopicta***	ELan
'Roller Coaster Ride'	IBal NSue
'Ron Damant'	IBal
'Rootin'-Tootin'' (v)	IBal
'Roseann Walter' (v)	EMic IBal
'Rosedale Knox'	IBal
'Rosedale Lost Dutchman'	IBal
'Rosedale Melody of Summer' (v)	IBal
'Rosedale Misty Magic' (v)	IBal
'Rosedale Richie Valens'	IBal
'Rosemoor'	IBal LRHS NRHS NSue
'Roxsanne'	EMic
'Roy Klehm' (v)	EMic IBal
'Royal Charm'	IBal
'Royal Charmer' (v)	CBdn IBal

Name	Suppliers
'Royal Flush' (v)	IBal
'Royal Golden Jubilee'	EMic IBal
§ 'Royal Standard' 🏆H7	Widely available
'Royal Tapestry' (v)	IBal
'Royal Tiara' (*nakaiana*) (v)	IBal
'Royalty'	IBal NSue
'Rubies and Ruffles' (v)	IBal
'Ruffled Mouse Ears'	IBal NSue
'Rufus Rider'	IBal
rupifraga	IBal
'Rusty Bee'	IBal
'Ryan's Big One'	EUJe IBal
§ 'Sagae' (v) 🏆H7	CRos EMic EUJe EWhm IBal LRHS MNrw NGdn NNor NRHS WAul WFar WHoo
'Saint Elmo's Fire' (v)	EMic IBal LRHS
'Saint Fiacre'	EMic
'Saint John'	IBal
'Saint Paul'	EMic IBal MNrw NSue
'Saishu-jima' (*sieboldii* f. *spathulata*)	EMic GEdr ITim WCru
'Saishu-yahato-sito' (v)	IBal NSue
'Salute' (Tardiana Group)	EMic
'Samurai' (*sieboldiana*) (v)	EMic MRav NBir NBro NEgg NGdn NLar NNor NSue
'Sarah Kennedy' (v)	IBal
'Sara's Sensation' (v)	IBal NSue
'Satisfaction' (v) 🏆H7	EMic IBal
'Sazanami' (*crispula*)	see *H. crispula*
'Scallion Pancakes'	EMic
'Scarlet Ribbons' (v)	EMic IBal
'Schwan'	GBin
'Sea Current'	IBal
'Sea Dream' (v)	EMic LRHS NEgg NGdn NNor
'Sea Fire'	IBal
'Sea Gulf Stream'	EMic
'Sea Lotus Leaf'	EMic NLar NNor
'Sea Monster'	IBal
'Sea Nymph'	EMic
'Sea Thunder' (v)	EMic EMor IBal LRHS
'Sea Yellow Sunrise'	EMic IBal
'Searing Flame' (v)	IBal
'Second Wind' (*fortunei*) (v)	EMic
'Secret Ambition' PBR (v)	EMic IBal
'Secret Love'	EMic IBal
'Secret Treasure' PBR (v)	IBal
'Seducer' (v)	EMic IBal
'See Saw' (*undulata*)	EMic IBal
'Semperaurea' (*sieboldiana*)	IBal
'September Sun' (v)	EMic IBal LRHS NNor
'Serena' (Tardiana Group)	IBal
'Serendipity'	EMic IBal
'Shade Beauty' (v)	EMic IBal
'Shade Fanfare' (v)	CDor CRos ECtt EHoe ELan ELon EMic EPfP GQue IBal LRHS MBNS MRav NBir NGdn NLar NRHS NSti SPer WFar
'Shade Finale' (v)	IBal
'Shade Master'	EMic
'Shade Parade' (v)	EMic IBal
'Shady Affair'	EMic
§ 'Sharmon' (*fortunei*) (v)	ELon EMic MBNS NEgg NLar
'Sharp Dressed Man'	IBal
'Shazaam'	IBal
'Sheila West'	EMic
'Shelleys' (v)	IBal
'Sherborne Profusion' (Tardiana Group)	EMic IBal
'Sherborne Songbird' (Tardiana Group)	IBal
'Sherborne Swallow' (Tardiana Group)	EMic IBal
'Sherborne Swan' (Tardiana Group)	IBal
'Sherborne Swift' (Tardiana Group)	CBdn EMic ESwi IBal LRHS MWat NRHS
'Shere Khan' (v)	EMic IBal
'Shimmy Shake'	EMic
'Shining Tot' 🏆H7	IBal LLHF NSue
'Shiny Penny' (v)	EMic IBal NSue
'Shiny Sonata'	IBal
'Shirley Levy'	IBal
'Showboat' (v)	EMic LRHS
sieboldiana	CAgr CMac CSBt ECha ELan EMic GMaP MRav MSwo NChi SPlb SRms WMoo XLum
§ - var. ***elegans*** 🏆H7	Widely available
- var. ***mira***	EMic
- var. ***sieboldiana***	NGdn
sieboldiana × venusta	NGdn
sieboldii	GBin MRav
§ - var. ***alba***	IBal
§ - var. ***sieboldii*** f. ***kabitan*** (v)	EMic IBal NGdn NSue
- - f. ***shiro-kabitan*** (v)	EMic LRHS
- f. ***spathulata***	EMic
'Silberpfeil'	EMic NSue
'Silk Road' (v)	IBal
'Silver Bay' 🏆H7	EMic
'Silver Crown'	see *H.* 'Albomarginata'
'Silver Halo' (v)	EMic
'Silver Lance' (v)	EMic IBal
'Silver Lode' (v)	IBal
'Silver Mine'	NSue
'Silver Moon'	EMic IBal
'Silver Serenity'	IBal
'Silver Shadow' (v)	EMic GBin IBal NBir NGdn NLar NNor NWad
'Silver Spray' (v)	IBal
'Silver Star' (v)	IBal
'Silver Threads and Gold Needles' (v)	IBal NHpl NSue
'Silverado' (v)	IBal
'Silvery Slugproof' (Tardiana Group)	IBal LRHS
'Simply Sharon' (v)	IBal
'Singin' the Blues'	IBal
'Singing in the Rain' (v)	IBal NSue
'Sitting Pretty' (v)	IBal
'Sizzle'	EMic IBal NSue
'Sky Dancer'	ECtt EMic IBal NSue
'Sleeping Beauty'	CWGN ECtt EMic IBal NGdn NSue
'Sleeping Star' PBR (v)	IBal NSue
'Slick Willie'	EMic
'Slim and Trim'	EMic IBal NHpl NSue
'Small Parts'	EMic IBal NSue
'Small Sum'	IBal
'Smash Hit' (v)	IBal
'Smiley Face'	NSue
'Smiling Mouse' (v)	IBal NSue
'Smoke Signals'	IBal
'Snake Eyes' (v)	CBdn ELon EMic IBal NSue SCob
'Snow Boy' (v)	EMic IBal NSue
'Snow Cap' (v)	CDor ECtt EMic EMor IBal NEoE NGdn NLar NNor SPoG WFar
'Snow Crust' (v)	EMic
'Snow Flakes' (*sieboldii*)	CMac NBro NEoE NGdn NLar
'Snow Mouse' (v)	EMic IBal NHpl NSue WFar
'Snowden' 🏆H7	ECha EMic EWTr GMaP IBal LRHS NBir NGdn NNor NRHS SPhx WCru

'Snowy Lake' (v)	IBal
'So Sweet' (v)	CRos EBee ECtt EHoe ELan ELon EMic EMor EPfP GBin GEdr GLog LRHS LSun MSwo NBro NGdn NHol NNor NRHS WAvo WFar
'Something Blue'	EMic IBal
'Something Else'	EMic
'Southern Gold'	EMic
'Space Odyssey'	IBal NSue
'Sparkler' (v)	IBal
'Sparkling Burgundy'	EMic LRHS
'Sparky' (v)	IBal
'Spartacus' (v)	EMic IBal NSue
'Spartan Arrow'	NSue
'Spartan Glory' (v)	IBal
'Special Blend' (v)	IBal
'Special Gift'	EMic IBal
'Spellbound' (v)	IBal
'Spilt Milk' (*tokudama*) (v) ♀H7	EMic IBal WHoo
'Spinach Souffle' (v)	IBal
§ 'Spinners' (*fortunei*) (v)	ECha EMic IBal NNor
'Split Decision'	EMic
'Spock's Ears'	IBal
'Spring Break' (v)	EMic
'Spring Fling'	EMic IBal
'Spring Love'	IBal
'Spring Morning' **new**	CBdn
'Spritzer' (v)	EMic MNrw NSue
'Squash Casserole'	IBal NSue
'Stained Glass' (v) ♀H7	CAby CBcs CDor ECtt ELon EMic EMor EPfP GBin IBal LRHS NEgg NGdn NNor NSue WFar
'Stand by Me' (v)	EMic IBal NSue
'Stand Corrected' (v)	IBal
'Star Kissed'	IBal
'Star Light Star Bright'	EMic IBal
'Star Wars' **new**	NSue
'Starburst' stable (v)	IBal
'Stardust'	IBal
'Stargate'	IBal
§ 'Starker Yellow Leaf'	EMic
'Starship' (v)	EMic IBal
'Steffi' (v)	IBal
'Step Sister'	EMic IBal
'Stepping Out' (v)	EMic IBal
'Stetson' (v)	EMic IBal
'Stiletto' (v)	EHoe EHrv ELon EMic GBin GEdr GKev IBal LRHS MBNS MNrw NAln NBro NEoE NGdn NHpl NLar NNor NSue SPoG SWvt WFar WSHC
'Stimulation'	IBal
'Sting' (v)	CBdn
'Stirfry'	EMic SCob
'Stone's Valentine'	EMic
'Strawberry Surprise' (v)	EMic IBal
'Strawberry Yoghurt'	CBdn NSue
'Striker' (v)	IBal NSue
'Striptease' (*fortunei*) (v) ♀H7	CMac EMic EPfP GLog IBal LRHS MBNS MNrw NEgg NGdn NHol NLar NSue WFar
'Stuck in Time'	IBal
'Sugar and Cream' (v)	CBdn EMic IBal LRHS MWat NGdn NNor
'Sugar and Spice' (v)	CBod ELon EMic EPfP IBal
'Sugar Daddy'	EMic IBal
'Sultana' (v)	EMic IBal
'Sum and Substance' ♀H7	Widely available
'Sum and Subtle' (v)	EMic IBal
'Sum Cup-o-Joe' (v)	EMic
'Sum it Up' (v)	EMic
'Sum of All' (v)	EMic EUJe NSue
'Summer Breeze' (v)	EMic IBal NGdn NSue
'Summer Dress'	NSue
'Summer Fragrance'	EBee ECtt EMic GBin IBal LRHS
'Summer Gold'	EMic
'Summer Lovin'' (v)	IBal
'Summer Music' (v) ♀H7	CWCL EMic IBal
'Summer Serenade' (v)	EMic NGdn NSue
'Summer Squall'	IBal
'Sumsational'	IBal
'Sun Catcher'	EMic
'Sun Mouse' **new**	NSue
'Sun Power'	CRos EBee ELon EMic LRHS MBNS NBro NLar NRHS
'Sun Worshipper'	IBal
'Sundance' (v)	IBal
'Sunlight Child'	EMic IBal NSue
'Sunny Smiles' (v)	EMic
'Sunset Grooves' (v)	CBdn IBal
'Sunshine Glory'	EMic IBal
'Super Bowl'	IBal
'Super Nova' (v)	EMic IBal
'Super Sagae'	CDor EMic EUJe IBal WFar
'Surfer Girl'	NSue
'Surprised by Joy' (v)	CBdn EMic IBal NHpl NNor NSue
'Susy'	IBal
'Sutter's Mill'	IBal
'Suzuki Thumbnail'	EMic
'Swamp Thing' (v)	IBal
'Sweet Bo Beep'	EMic IBal LRHS
'Sweet Bouquet'	EMic
'Sweet Home Chicago' (v)	EMic IBal LRHS NRHS
'Sweet Innocence' (v)	EMic IBal
'Sweet Marjorie'	IBal
'Sweet Sunshine'	EMic
'Sweet Susan'	CRos EMic LRHS LSRN MBNS NRHS SPer SWvt
'Sweet Tater Pie'	EMic IBal
'Sweetheart'	EMic
'Sweetie' (v)	EMic IBal LRHS
'Sweetness'	IBal
'Swirling Hearts'	IBal NSue
'Swizzle Sticks'	EMic
'T. Rex'	CDor ELon EMic EMor EUJe IBal NSue WFar
'Tall Boy'	GBin IBal NBir NNor
'Tamborine' (v)	CBdn EMic EMor IBal LRHS
'Tango'	EMic IBal
'Tappen Zee' (v)	EMic IBal
Tardiana Group	GWyn NGdn
tardiflora	CExl IBal LRHS
tardiva	EMic NLar
'Tattle Tails'	CBdn EMic IBal NHpl NSue
'Tattoo'PBR (v)	CWGN EMic LSRN MBNS NLar
'T Dawg' (v)	CBdn
'Tea at Bettys' ♀H7	CBdn EMic IBal NSue
'Teacher's Pride'	NSue
'Tears of Joy'	NSue WFar
'Teaspoon'	EMic IBal NHpl NNor NSue
'Teatime' (v)	CBdn EMic IBal NSue
'Teeny-weeny Bikini' (v)	NSue WFar
'Templar Gold'	IBal
'Temple Bells'	IBal
'Temptation'	EMic IBal NSue
'Tequila Sunrise'	IBal
'Terpsichore'	EMic
'Terracotta'	MCri
'Terry Wogan'	IBal NNor
'Tet-a-Poo'	IBal

'The King' (v)	IBal NSue
'The Leading Edge' (v)	IBal
'The Queen' (v)	IBal
'The Razor's Edge'	IBal WFar
'The Right One' (v)	IBal
'The Shining'	IBal
'The Twister'	EMic
'Theo's Blue'	EMic IBal
'Theo's Red'	IBal
'Thomas Hogg'	see *H. undulata* var. *albomarginata*
'Thumb Nail'	EMic IBal NNor NSue NWad SMHy
'Thumbelina'	EMic IBal LRHS NGdn NRHS NSue
'Thunderbolt'PBR (*sieboldiana*)	EMic EUJe IBal MBNS NGdn NLar WFar
tibae	IBal
'Tick Tock' (v)	CBdn ECtt EMic IBal NSue
'Tickle Me Pink'	EMic IBal NSue WFar
'Tidewater'	IBal
'Tilt-a-Whirl'	IBal
'Time Tunnel' (*sieboldiana*) (v)	EMic IBal
'Timeless Beauty' (v)	IBal NSue WFar
'Tiny Tears'	GAbr NSue
'Titanic'PBR	EMic IBal NSue
'Titanium'	IBal NSue
'Toasted Waffles'	WFar
tokudama	CRos EMic IBal LRHS NBir NGdn NNor NRHS WFar XLum
§ - f. ***aureo-nebulosa*** (v)	EMic IBal NGdn SRms
- f. ***flavocircinalis*** (v) ♀H7	ELon EMic EPfP GMaP IBal NBro WFar WHoo
'Tokyo Smog' (v)	NSue
'Toledo'	IBal
'Tom Schmid' (v)	CBdn EMic IBal MWat NSue
'Tom Thumb'	EMic IBal NSue
'Tongue Twister'	IBal
'Tootie Mae' **new**	CBdn
'Topaz'	IBal
'Topscore'	NNor
'Torchlight' (v) ♀H7	IBal LRHS NSue
tortifrons	EMic IBal
'Tortilla Chip'	EMic IBal WFar
'Tot Tot'	EMic IBal NSue
'Totally Twisted'	EMic IBal NSue
'Touch of Class'PBR (v) ♀H7	CBdn CDor EBee ECtt EMic EMor IBal NGdn NHol NNor NSue WFar WTyc
'Touchstone' (v)	CRos SWvt
'Toy Soldier'	EMic IBal NGdn NLar NSue
'Trail's End'	EMic
'Tranquility' (v)	EMic
'Tremors'	EMic IBal
'Trixi' (v)	IBal
'Tropical Dancer'	IBal
'Tropical Storm' (v)	IBal NSue
'True Blue'	ECtt EMic
'Tsugaru Komachi'	EMic
'Tsugaru Komachi Kifukurin' (v)	IBal
'Turnabout' (v)	IBal
'Turning Point'	IBal LRHS
'Twiggie'	EMic
'Twilight' (*fortunei*) (v)	CAby ECtt EMic EMor EShb IBal LRHS MBNS MHol NEgg NGdn NLar NRHS NSue SWvt WFar
'Twilight Time'	IBal LRHS
'Twinkle Toes'	EMic IBal NSue
'Twist of Lemon'	NEgg
'Twist of Lime' (v)	EMic GKev IBal LRHS NAln NGdn NNor NRHS NSue WCot
'Twitter'	IBal
'UFO'	EMic IBal NSue WFar
'Ultramarine'	IBal
'Ultraviolet Light'	IBal
'Ulysses S. Grant'	IBal
'Unchained Melody'	IBal
undulata (v)	NNor WFar
§ - var. ***albomarginata*** (v)	CMac CRos CSam EMic EPfP GMaP LRHS LSRN MRav NBid NBir NGdn NLar NRHS SCob SPer SRms SWvt WFar XLum
§ - var. ***erromena***	CRos EMic GMaP LRHS NNor NRHS XLum
§ - var. ***undulata*** (v) ♀H7	CRos GMaP IBal LRHS MCot MRav NEgg NGdn NLar NNor NRHS SCob
- var. ***univittata*** (v)	ECha EHrv EMic GKev NAln NBir NEoE NRHS SRms WFar WMoo
'Unforgettable'	EMic IBal
'Upper Crust' (v)	IBal
'Uprising' (v)	IBal
'Urajiro' (*hypoleuca*)	IBal
'Urajiro-hachijo' (*longipes* var. *latifolia*)	IBal
'Valentine Lace'	EMic IBal NAln
'Valley's Blue Curaçao'	IBal
'Valley's Cathedral'	IBal
'Valley's Chute the Chute'	EMic IBal
'Valley's Glacier' (v)	EMic IBal WFar
'Valley's Paparazzi' (v)	IBal
'Valley's Vanilla Sticks'	EMic IBal
'Van Wade' (v)	CBdn EMic IBal
'Vanilla Cream' (*cathayana*)	EMic IBal LRHS NRHS NSue WFar
'Variegata' (*gracillima*)	see *H.* 'Vera Verde'
'Variegata' (*tokudama*)	see *H. tokudama* f. *aureo-nebulosa*
'Variegata' (*undulata*)	see *H. undulata* var. *undulata*
'Variegata' (*ventricosa*)	see *H.* 'Aureomarginata' (*ventricosa*)
'Variegated' (*fluctuans*)	see *H.* 'Sagae'
'Velvet Moon' (v)	EMic IBal
ventricosa ♀H7	CBdn CMac EMic IBal WFar XLum
- BWJ 8160 from Sichuan	WCru
- var. ***aureomaculata***	EMic NBir NNor WFar
'Venus' (d)	CAby ECtt EMic ITim LEdu MHol NGdn NSue WCot WFar
'Venus Star'	EMic
venusta ♀H7	CRos EBee EMic EWld GCal GEdr IBal LRHS MRav NBid NBir NNor NRHS NRya SRot WFar
- B&SWJ 4389	WCru
- dwarf	IBal
- ***yakusimensis***	see *H. kikutii* var. *yakusimensis*
§ 'Vera Verde' (v)	NBir NSue
'Verdi Valentine'	EMic IBal
'Verkade's One'	IBal
'Vermont Frost' (v)	IBal NSue
'Verna Jean' (v)	EMic IBal LRHS NRHS NSue
'Veronica Lake' (v)	ECtt EMic IBal LRHS NNor NRHS NSue WHal
'Victor'	IBal
'Victory' ♀H7	CRos IBal LRHS NRHS NSue
'Viking Ship'	IBal
'Vilmoriniana'	EMic
'Vim and Vigor'	EMic IBal
'Vina'	IBal
'Virginia Reel' (v)	IBal NSue
'Viridis Marginata'	see *H. sieboldii* var. *sieboldii* f. *kabitan*
'Volcano Island'PBR (v)	CBdn IBal NSue
'Vulcan' (v)	EMic IBal

'Wagtail' (Tardiana Group)	EMic IBal
'Wahoo' (*tokudama*) (v)	IBal
'War Paint' ♀H7	CBdn EMic IBal ITim NSue WFar
'Warwick Comet' (v)	EMic IBal
'Warwick Curtsey' (v)	EMic IBal
'Warwick Edge' (v)	EMic IBal NEgg
'Warwick Essence'	EMic IBal
'Warwick Sheen'	IBal
'Watermark' (v)	EMic
'Waukon Glass'	CBdn EMic IBal
'Waukon Thin Ice'	EMic IBal
'Waukon Water'	EMic IBal
'Waving Winds' (v)	IBal
'Waving Wuffles'	EMic
'Wayne' (v)	EMic
'Wayside Blue'	EMic
'Wayside Perfection'	see *H.* 'Royal Standard'
'Weihenstephan' (*sieboldii*)	EMic IBal
'Well Shaked' (v)	IBal
'Weser'	IBal
'Wheaton Blue'	EMic LRHS
'Wheaton Thunder' (v)	EMic
'Wheee!'	ESwi IBal NSue
'Whirligig' (v)	EMic
'Whirling Dervish' (v)	IBal
'Whirlwind' (*fortunei*) (v) ♀H7	EBee ELan EMic EPfP IBal LRHS MNrw MRav NBro NEgg NGdn NLar NNor NSue SPoG SPtp WAul WCAu WFar WHoo
'Whirlwind Tour' (v)	IBal
'Whiskey Sour'	IBal
'White Bikini' (v)	CBdn IBal NSue
'White Ceiling'	IBal
'White Christmas' (*fortunei*) (v)	NGdn
'White Christmas' (*undulata*) (v)	EMic
'White Dove' (v)	EMic IBal NSue
'White Edger'	EMic
'White Elephant' (v)	IBal
'White Fairy' (*plantaginea*) (d)	EMic
'White Feather' (*undulata*)	CRos CWGN EBee ELan EPfP LRHS MNrw NBir NEoE NGdn NLar NNor NRHS SMad SPoG WFar
'White Gold'	EMic
'White Jewel' (v)	IBal
'White Knight'	IBal
'White On' (*montana*)	EMic
'White Triumphator' (*rectifolia*)	IBal
'White Trumpets'	EMic
'Wide Brim' (v) ♀H7	Widely available
'William Lachman' (v)	IBal NLar
'Wily Willy'	IBal
'Wind River Gold'	EMic
'Windsor Gold'	see *H.* 'Nancy Lindsay'
'Winfield Blue'	EMic IBal NBir
'Winfield Gold'	EMic
'Winfield Mist' (v)	IBal
'Winsome' (v)	EMor IBal LRHS NSue
'Winter Lightning' (v)	NNor
'Winter Snow' (v)	CBdn CDor EMic EUJe IBal LRHS NSue WFar
'Winter Warrior' (v)	EMic IBal
'Wogon' (*sieboldii*)	EMic GKev GMaP ITim NAln
'Wogon's Boy'	EMic LRHS WAvo
'Wolverine' (v) ♀H7	CBod CRos EBee ECtt EHoe EMic GBin LRHS MBNS NGdn NRHS NSue SPad SWvt WFar
'Woodland Elf' (v)	IBal NSue
'Woolly Mammoth' (v)	IBal
'Woop Woop' (v)	EMic IBal NSue
'World Cup'	IBal
'Worldly Treasure'	IBal
'Wrinkles and Crinkles'	EMic
'Wylde Green Cream'	IBal NGdn
'Xanadu' (v)	IBal
'X-ray' (v)	NSue
'Yakushima-mizu' (*gracillima*)	EMic IBal NSue
'Yankee Blue'	IBal
'Yellow Boa'	EMic IBal NSue
'Yellow Edge' (*fortunei*)	see *H. fortunei* var. *aureomarginata*
'Yellow Edge' (*sieboldiana*)	see *H.* 'Frances Williams'
'Yellow Polka Dot Bikini' (v)	CBdn EMic IBal NSue
'Yellow River' (v)	CBdn CRos EBee EMic IBal LRHS NGdn NNor NRHS NSue WFar
'Yellow Splash' (v)	CBdn EMic LRHS NNor
'Yellow Splash Rim' (v)	EMic
'Yesterday's Memories' (v)	EMic IBal
'Yin' (v)	EMic IBal
yingeri	WPGP WSHC
- B&SWJ 546	LEdu WCru
'Yucca Ducka Do' (v)	EMic IBal
'Zager Blue'	EMic
'Zager Green'	EMic
'Zager White Edge' (*fortunei*) (v)	CBdn EMic IBal
'Zebra Stripes' (v)	IBal
'Zion's Hope'	EMic
'Zitronenfalter'	IBal
'Zodiac' (*fortunei*) (v)	IBal
'Zorro'	IBal
'Zounds'	CBdn CRos EBee ECtt EMic EPfP EShb IBal LRHS MRav NGdn NLar NRHS NSue SRms WFar

Hottonia (*Primulaceae*)

palustris	LCro LLWG LOPS NPer

Houstonia (*Rubiaceae*)

caerulea misapplied	see *H. michauxii*
caerulea L.	EBou SPlb SRot
- var. ***alba***	EWes SPlb SRot
- 'Millard's Variety'	WIce
§ ***michauxii*** 'Fred Mullard'	EWes GCrg

Houttuynia (*Saururaceae*)

cordata	CAgr CKel CMac GKev GPoy LEdu LLWG LPot NAln NSti WFar WWtn XLum
§ - 'Boo-Boo' (v)	CMac
§ - 'Chameleon' (v)	Widely available
- 'Fantasy' (v)	LLWG
- 'Flame' (v)	CKel CMac CPla LLWG MHol WFar
- 'Flore Pleno' (d)	CBen CMac CPla CWat ECha EPfP EWld LCro LLWG LOPS MRav MSCN NBir NPer SPer SPlb SRms XLum
- 'Joker's Gold'	CMac ECtt ELan EMor EPPr EPfP WFar
- 'Pied Piper' (v)	ELan NBir SPtp
- 'Terry Clarke'	see *H. cordata* 'Boo-Boo'
- 'Tricolor'	see *H. cordata* 'Chameleon'
- Variegata Group (v)	LLWG LPot NBro

Hovea (*Papilionaceae*)

celsii	see *H. elliptica*

§ ***elliptica*** SPlb
montana SPlb

Hovenia (*Rhamnaceae*)

dulcis CAgr CBcs EPfP LEdu MBlu NLar SEND
- B&SWJ 11024 WCru
- NJM 11.003 WPGP

Howea (*Arecaceae*)

§ ***belmoreana*** ♀H1b XBlo
§ ***forsteriana*** ♀H1a CCCN LCro LOPS SPlb XBlo

Hoya (*Apocynaceae*)

§ ***australis*** EShb
bella see *H. lanceolata* subsp. *bella*
carnosa ♀H2 EBak EOHP WWFP
- 'Compacta Regalis' (v) NPer
- 'Krinkle 8' NPer
- 'Tricolor' (v) CCCN NPer
- 'Variegata' (v) EShb
* ***compacta*** 'Tricolor' NPer
darwinii misapplied see *H. australis*
gracilis CCCN EShb
lacunosa CCCN
§ ***lanceolata*** CCCN EShb
subsp. ***bella*** ♀H1c
linearis EShb

Hugueninia (*Brassicaceae*)

tanacetifolia SBrt
subsp. ***suffruticosa***

Humata (*Davalliaceae*)

tyermannii CCCN CMen EShb ISha LEdu SBrt SPlb WCot WFib
- 'Bunny' CCCN LCro LOPS
- 'Selcka' CMen

Humea see *Calomeria*

elegans see *Calomeria amaranthoides*

Humulus ✿ (*Cannabaceae*)

japonicus 'Variegatus' (v) SGol
lupulus CBcs EPfP GPoy IKil NLar NMir SCob SRms WHer WSpi
- 'Aureus' ♀H6 Widely available
- 'Aureus' (f) CRHN ELon GCal GKev SPoG WCot
* - ***compactus*** GPoy
- 'Fuggle' CAgr GPoy SDea
- 'Golden Tassels' (f) CBod CKel CRos ECrN ELon LRHS MGos MJak MMuc MNHC NLar SEND SGol SNig SPer SPoG WBor WFar
- (Goldings Group) 'Cobbs' SDea
- - 'Mathons' SDea
- 'Hallertauer' SDea
- 'Northern Brewer' EBee IPot
- 'Prima Donna' CAgr CMac LEdu MCoo MMuc NLar SPer SPoG SWvt
- 'Taff's Variegated' (v) EWes
- 'Wye Challenger' CAgr GPoy MHer
- 'Wye Northdown' CAgr SDea

Hunnemannia (*Papaveraceae*)

fumariifolia CSpe SBrt

Hutchinsia see *Hornungia*

rotundifolia see *Thlaspi cepaeifolium* subsp. *rotundifolium*

Hyacinthella (*Asparagaceae*)

glabrescens WCot
leucophaea GKev

Hyacinthoides (*Asparagaceae*)

aristidis WCot
'Bakkum Blue' GKev LAma WHil
ciliolata CBro GKev SBch WAbe WCot
§ ***hispanica*** NBir SEND WCot
- 'Alba' CRos LRHS NRHS
- subsp. ***algeriensis*** WCot
- 'Dainty Maid' GKev WCot
- 'Excelsior' GKev
- 'Miss World' GKev WCot
- 'Queen of the Pinks' GKev WCot
- 'Rose' SEND
- 'Rose Queen' GKev
- 'White City' GKev WCot
§ ***italica*** ♀H6 GKev WCot WShi
lingulata LLHF WCot
mauritanica GKev
§ ***non-scripta*** Widely available
- 'Alba' CAvo GKev LAma LRHS MMuc NBir SEND SRms WHil
- 'Bracteata' CNat WCot
- 'Chedglow Weeping' **new** CNat
- cleistogamous CNat
- double-flowered, blue (d) **new** WCot
- - pink (d) **new** WCot
- - white (d) **new** WCot
- long-bracteate, white-flowered WCot
- 'Rosea' GKev ILea
- 'Wavertree' GKev
reverchonii WCot
- from Spain WCot

Hyacinthus ✿ (*Asparagaceae*)

amethystinus see *Brimeura amethystina*
azureus see *Muscari azureum*
comosus 'Plumosus' see *Muscari comosum* 'Plumosum'
orientalis 'Aiolos' GKev SDeJ
- var. ***albulus*** 'Roman Blue' **new** CAvo
- - 'Roman White' **new** CAvo
- 'Anastasia' CAvo
- 'Anna Liza' SDeJ
- 'Anna Marie' ♀H4 GKev LAma SDeJ
- 'Apricot Passion' ERCP GKev SDeJ
- 'Blue Eyes' ERCP SDeJ
- 'Blue Festival' ♀H4 GKev SDeJ
- 'Blue Giant' LAma SDeJ
- 'Blue Jacket' ♀H4 GKev LAma SCob SDeJ
- 'Blue Magic' SDeJ
- 'Blue Pearl' PBR GKev LCro LOPS SDeJ
- 'Blue Star' LAma SDeJ
- 'Blue Tango' GKev
- 'Carnegie' CArg CAvo ERCP GKev LAma LCro LOPS SDeJ
- 'Chestnut Flower' (d) SDeJ
- 'China Pink' CRos GKev LRHS NRHS SDeJ
- 'City of Haarlem' ♀H4 CArg CRos GKev LAma LRHS NRHS SDeJ
- 'Crystal Palace' (d) LAma SDeJ
- 'Dark Dimension' LAma
- 'Delft Blue' ♀H4 CArg CAvo CRos EPfP GKev LAma LCro LOPS LRHS NRHS SCob SDeJ SPer WShi

	Name	Suppliers
	- 'Eros' **new**	SDeJ
	- 'Fondant'	CArg CRos LRHS NRHS SDeJ SPer
	- 'General Köhler' (d)	LAma SDeJ
	- 'Gipsy Princess'	LAma
	- 'Gipsy Queen' ♀H4	CAvo GKev LAma SCob SDeJ WCot
	- 'Gypsy Princess'	MJak
	- 'Hollyhock' (d) ♀H4	LAma SCob SDeJ
	- 'Ibis'	SCob
	- 'Jan Bos' ♀H4	CArg CRos GKev LAma LCro LOPS LRHS MJak NRHS SCob SDeJ
	- 'Lady Derby'	SDeJ
	- 'L'Innocence' ♀H4	SCob
	- 'Madame Sophie' (d)	SDeJ
	- 'Miss Saigon' ♀H4	CAvo ERCP SDeJ
	- multi-flowered	ERCP SDeJ
	- 'Odysseus'	LAma SDeJ
	- 'Ostara' ♀H4	LAma
	- 'Paul Hermann' ♀H4	GKev SDeJ
	- 'Peter Stuyvesant'	ERCP LAma LCro LOPS SDeJ
	- 'Pink Festival' ♀H4	GKev SDeJ
	- 'Pink Pearl'	CAvo CRos EPfP GKev LAma LCro LOPS LRHS MJak NRHS SDeJ
	- 'Pink Royal' (d)	LAma
	- 'Purple Sensation'PBR	GKev SDeJ
	- 'Purple Star'	LCro LOPS
	- 'Red Magic'	SDeJ
	- 'Rosette' (d)	LAma SDeJ
	- 'Royal Navy' (d) ♀H4	ERCP MJak SDeJ SPer
	- 'Sky Jacket'	GKev LCro LOPS SCob
	- 'Snow Crystal' (d)	ERCP
	- 'Splendid Cornelia'	ERCP GKev MJak SDeJ
	- 'White Festival' ♀H4	GKev SDeJ
	- 'White Pearl'	CAvo CRos EPfP GKev LAma LCro LOPS LRHS MJak NRHS SCob SDeJ SPer
	- 'Woodstock'	CAvo EPfP ERCP GKev LAma LCro LOPS SCob SDeJ WCot
	- 'Yellowstone'	SDeJ

Hydrangea ✿ (*Hydrangeaceae*)

	Name	Suppliers
	angustipetala	see *H. scandens* subsp. *chinensis* f. *angustipetala*
	anomala subsp. ***anomala*** BWJ 8052 from China	WCru
	- - HWJK 2065 from Nepal	WCru
§	- - 'Winter Glow'	EBee ESwi MRav SGol WCru WFar
	- subsp. ***glabra*** B&SWJ 6804	WCru
	- - 'Crûg Coral'	SPoG WCru
§	- subsp. ***petiolaris*** ♀H5	Widely available
	- - B&SWJ 5996 from Yakushima	WCru
	- - B&SWJ 6337	WCru
§	- - var. ***cordifolia***	CBcs NBro NLar
	- - - B&SWJ 6081	WCru
	- - - B&SWJ 11487	WCru
§	- - - 'Brookside Littleleaf'	IDee NBro NLar WFar
	- - dwarf	see *H. anomala* subsp. *petiolaris* var. *cordifolia*
	- - 'Early Light' (v)	SGbt
	- - var. ***megaphylla*** B&SWJ 4400	WCru
	- - - B&SWJ 8497	WCru
*	- - var. ***minor*** B&SWJ 5991	GEdr WCru
	- - 'Mirranda' (v)	CBcs ELan EPfP GCal MGos MNHC MSCN NBro NLar SGol SPer SPoG SRms SWvt WBor
§	- - var. ***ovalifolia***	CRHN ESwi LRHS
	- - - B&SWJ 8799	WCru
	- - - B&SWJ 8846	WCru
	- - 'Silver Lining'PBR	CBcs CRos CWGN EBee EMil EPfP LCro LOPS LRHS NRHS SMad SPoG
	- - 'Summer Snow' (v)	CRos LLHF LRHS NRHS SPoG
	- - var. ***tiliifolia***	see *H. anomala* subsp. *petiolaris* var. *ovalifolia*
	- - 'Yakushima'	WCru
	- subsp. ***quelpartensis***	see *H. anomala* subsp. *petiolaris* var. *ovalifolia*
	- 'Winter Surprise'	see *H. anomala* subsp. *anomala* 'Winter Glow'
§	***arborescens***	CExl MRav WPGP
	- 'Annabelle' ♀H6	Widely available
	- 'Bounty'	MAsh SGol
§	- subsp. ***discolor***	GBin LEdu
	- - 'Sterilis'	GGGa SHyH WPGP
	- 'Eco Pink Puff'	WPGP
	- 'Emerald Lace'	MBlu SGol
	- 'Grandiflora'	CBcs NBro NEgg WPGP
	- 'Hayes Starburst'PBR	CKel CMil CRos CWGN EBee EPfP LEdu LLHF LRHS MAsh MMrt MPkF SGol SHyH SMad SPoG SWvt WPGP
	- 'Hills of Snow'	NLar
	- INCREDIBALL ('Abetwo'PBR)	CBcs CKel CRos ELan EPfP GBin LCro LRHS LSRN MAsh MBlu NLar NRHS SGol SLon SPoG
	- INCREDIBALL BLUSH ('Ncha4') **new**	LCro LOPS LRHS
§	- INVINCIBELLE SPIRIT ('Ncha1'PBR)	CAby CBcs CKel CRos ECre ELan ELon EPfP LCro LLHF LOPS LRHS LSRN MAsh MBlu MPkF MThu NLar NRHS SCob SGol SHyH SLon SMad SPer SPoG SWvt WSpi
	- 'Invincible Spirit'	see *H. arborescens* INVINCIBELLE SPIRIT
	- LIME RICKEY ('Smnhalr')	LCro LOPS LRHS SGol
	- 'Magical Pinkerbell' **new**	LRHS
	- 'Picadilly'	NLar
	- 'Pink Annabelle'	see *H. arborescens* INVINCIBELLE SPIRIT
	- 'Pink Pincushion'	NBro NLar WFar
	- 'Puffed Green'	NLar
	- subsp. ***radiata***	CRos LRHS MRav SGol WFar WPGP
	- - 'Samantha'	EBee EPfP LLHF LRHS SCob SPoG WPGP
	- RUBY ANNABELLE ('Ncha3') **new**	LCro LOPS
	- 'Ryan Gainey'	LEdu WSpi
	- 'Sheep Cloud'	MBlu
	- 'Vasterival'	NLar
	- 'Visitation'	CSpe
	- WHITE DOME ('Dardom'PBR)	NBro
	aspera	CMac SHyH SLon SSta WCru WKif WPGP
	- HWJCM 452	WCru
	- from Gongshan, China	CExl CMil WPGP
	- 'Anthony Bullivant' ♀H5	CKel EPfP IArd IDee LRHS MAsh NLar SAko SGol SHyH SWvt WKif
	- 'Bellevue'	IArd WPGP
	- 'Cardinal'	SGol
	- 'Dark Chocolate'	CRos
	- Farrell form	WPGP
	- HOT CHOCOLATE ('Hpopr012')	CAby CMil ELan EUJe MBlu MGos MJak SCob SGol SHyH SPoG
	- Kawakamii Group	CExl CSpe ESwi LRHS NLar SGol SHyH SWvt WCru WPGP
	- - B&SWJ 3456	WCru
	- - B&SWJ 3527	WCru
	- - B&SWJ 6702	WCru
	- - B&SWJ 6714	WCru

- - B&SWJ 6827	WCru
- - B&SWJ 6996	WCru
- - B&SWJ 7101	WCru
- - 'August Abundance'	WCru
- - 'Formosa'	WCru
- - 'Maurice Mason'	CExl
- - 'September Splendour'	WCru
- Kawakamii Group × ***involucrata***	EPfP WPGP WSpi
- 'Koki'	WPGP
- 'Macrophylla' ♀H5	EPfP GCal GKin MGil MGos MRav NLar SHyH SPer SWvt WCru WPGP WSpi
- 'Mauvette'	CMil CRos EPfP GKin LRHS MBlu NBro NLar SCob SGol SHyH SPer WCru
- 'Peter Chappell' ♀H5	CExl CKel CMac CMil LRHS NLar SHyH WPGP
§ - subsp. ***robusta***	CExl LRHS WPGP WSpi
- - B&SWJ 13999	WCru
- - GWJ 9430	WCru
- - KR 10735 **new**	WPGP
- - WWJ 11888	WCru
- 'Rocklon'	ESwi NLar SGol
- 'Rosthornii'	see *H. aspera* subsp. *robusta*
- 'Sam MacDonald'	CExl CMil CRos EPfP LRHS NLar WPGP WSpi
- 'Sapa'	EPfP WPGP
§ - subsp. ***sargentiana***	Widely available
- - 'La Fosse'	WPGP
- - large-leaved	CExl WCru
- 'Spinners'	NLar
- subsp. ***strigosa***	CDul CExl CKel CRos CSde EPfP LRHS SMad SWvt WCru WPGP
- - B&SWJ 8201	WCru
- - KWJ 12151 from northern Vietnam	WCru
- - from Gongshan, China	CExl
- - 'Gongshan'	WPGP
- 'Taiwan Pink'	IArd NLar SGol
- 'The Ditch'	ESwi NLar
§ - Villosa Group	Widely available
- - 'Trelissick'	WPGP
- - 'Velvet and Lace' ♀H5	EPfP LRHS MGos NLar
asterolasia B&SWJ 10481	WCru
§ 'Blue Deckle' (L)	CAbb CMac MAsh MGos MRav NBro NLar SDys SGol SHyH WBor
cinerea	see *H. arborescens* subsp. *discolor*
davidii B&SWJ 8307	WCru
- B&SWJ 11692	WCru
- B&SWJ 11717	WCru
- f. ***purpurascens*** KWJ 12233B	WCru
'Dharuma'	CRos GKin LRHS SAko SGol
EARLY SENSATION ('Bulk' PBR)	CBcs CKel CRos ECrN EPfP EShb GBin GKin LRHS MSwo NRHS SGol SHyH SPoG WFar WGrn WMoo
'Garden House Glory'	CExl CMil SAko WPGP
glabrifolia	see *H. scandens* subsp. *chinensis*
glandulosa B&SWJ 4031	WCru
'Glyn Church'	EPfP SAko SChF WPGP
aff. ***gracilis*** B&SWJ 3942	WCru
heteromalla	CMCN LEdu NBro WPGP
- B&SWJ 2142 from India	WCru
- B&SWJ 2602 from Sikkim	WCru
- BWJ 7657from China	WCru
- GWJ 9337 from Sikkim	WCru
- HWJ 526 from Vietnam	WCru
- HWJ 938 from Vietnam	WCru
- HWJCM 180	WCru
- HWJK 2127 from Nepal	WCru
- KR 9913 from India	WPGP
- Bretschneideri Group	CKel EBee EPfP GKin SHyH WCru
- 'Fan Si Pan'	WCru
- 'Long White'	NLar
- 'Morrey's Form'	NLar WCru
- 'Nepal Beauty'	EBee EPfP ESwi MMrt NLar SGol WPGP
- 'Snow in June' **new**	GGGa
- 'Snowcap'	EPfP IArd LRHS NLar SBrt SHyH
§ - f. ***xanthoneura*** NJM 11.009	WPGP
- - 'Wilsonii'	WCru WKif
- 'Yalung Ridge'	WCru
aff. ***heteromalla***	SGol WSpi
'Hidcote Pink'	see *H. macrophylla* 'Juno'
hirta	MBlu
- B&SWJ 5000	WCru
- B&SWJ 11022	WCru
indochinensis	CExl ESwi
- B&SWJ 8307	WCru
- WWJ 11609	WCru
integerrima	see *H. serratifolia*
integrifolia B&SWJ 022	WCru
- B&SWJ 6967	NLar WCru
involucrata	CKel LLHF LRHS MMrt SBrt SGol SHyH WSpi
- B&SWJ 4790	WCru
- B&SWJ 11578	WCru
- dwarf	CExl WCru
- 'Hortensis' (d)	CDul CMil MRav NLar SMad WCru WKif WPGP WSpi
- var. ***idzuensis***	WCru
- 'Mihara-kokonoe'	SGol WPGP
- 'Multiplex'	ESwi MBlu WCru
- 'Oshima'	WPGP
- 'Plena' (d)	CKel LRHS MRav NLar SHyH WPGP WSpi
- 'Plenissima' (d)	WCru
- 'Sterilis'	CKel CMil WCru
- 'Tokada Yama'	CMil IArd IDee NLar
- 'Viridescens' ♀H4	CBcs LRHS NLar SHyH WCru WPGP
- 'Yohraku-tama' ♀H4	NLar SGol WPGP
- 'Yokudanka' (d)	CMil IArd IDee NLar WPGP
- 'Yoraku' (d)	WCru
kawagoeana var. ***grosseserrata*** B&SWJ 11500	WCru
- - B&SWJ 11511	WCru
lobbii	see *H. scandens* subsp. *chinensis*
longifolia CWJ 12413	WCru
longipes	CExl WCru
- var. ***fulvescens*** B&SWJ 8188	WCru
- var. ***longipes***	CExl
luteovenosa	WCru
- B&SWJ 5647	WCru
- B&SWJ 5929	WCru
- B&SWJ 6220	WCru
- B&SWJ 6317	WCru
macrophylla 'AB Green Shadow' PBR (H)	MMrt SCob SGol
- 'Adria' (H)	NLar SGol
- 'Aduarda'	see *H. macrophylla* 'Mousmée'
- 'All Summer Beauty' (H)	CBod ELan ELon EUJe GBin GGGa MAsh SHyH
- ALPEN GLOW	see *H. macrophylla* 'Alpenglühen'
§ - 'Alpenglühen' (H)	CBcs CExl CSBt LRHS MJak SHyH SLim

	Name	Suppliers
	- 'Altona' (H) ♀^{H5}	CBcs CBod CCVT CRos EPfP IArd LCro LOPS LRHS MAsh MGos MRav NBir NLar SHyH SPer SRms
	- 'Amethyst' (H/d)	LRHS
	- 'Ami Pasquier' (H)	CBcs CKel CMac CRos CSBt CSde CTri ELan EPfP LRHS LSRN MRav MSwo NEgg SAko SCob SCoo SHyH SLim SNig SPoG SRms SWvt
	- 'Amor' (H)	SCob SGol
*	- 'Aureomarginata' (v)	WCot
	- 'Ave Maria' (H)	GGGa MAsh
§	- 'Ayesha' (H)	Widely available
	- 'Bachstelze' (Teller Series) (L)	MAsh WPGP
	- 'Baroque Angel'^{PBR} (H) **new**	SGol
	- 'Bavaria'^{PBR} (H)	GKin SGol WFar
	- 'Beauté Vendômoise' (L)	CMil LRHS NLar SHyH
	- 'Bela'^{PBR} (H)	LRHS MAsh SCob
	- 'Benelux' (H)	CBcs
	- 'Bergfink' (Teller Series) (L)	NLar
	- BERLIN ('Rabe'^{PBR}) (City-line Series) (H)	MAsh SGol
	- 'Bichon' (H)	SGol
	- 'Bicolor'	see *H. macrophylla* 'Harlequin'
	- Black Steel Series (H)	LRHS NRHS
	- - 'Black Steel Zambia' (H)	ELan LCro LOPS SGol WCot
	- - 'Black Steel Zebra' (H)	ELan LBuc SGol
	- 'Black Trombone' (H) **new**	SGol
	- BLACKBERRY PIE ('Makz') (Flair and Flavour Series) (L) **new**	CRos SPoG
§	- 'Blanc Bleu' (L)	EPfP LRHS LSRN SLim WFar
§	- 'Blauer Prinz' (H)	CBod SHyH SRms
	- 'Blauer Zwerg' (H)	MNHC
§	- 'Bläuling' (Teller Series) (L) ♀^{H5}	CBod GKin LRHS LSRN MAsh SCob SGol SLim
§	- 'Blaumeise' (Teller Series) (L) ♀^{H5}	CCht CDul CKel CSBt EBee ELon EShb GGGa LRHS MAsh MGil MGos MRav NLar NRHS SCob SCoo SGol SHyH SLim SLon SPoG SWvt WFar WPGP
	- 'Blue Bonnet' (H)	CDul EPfP LRHS LSRN MRav SHyH SPer
	- BLUE BUTTERFLY	see *H. macrophylla* 'Bläuling'
	- BLUE PRINCE	see *H. macrophylla* 'Blauer Prinz'
	- BLUE SKY	see *H. macrophylla* 'Blaumeise'
	- BLUE TIT	see *H. macrophylla* 'Blaumeise'
	- 'Blue Wave'	see *H. macrophylla* 'Mariesii Perfecta'
	- BLUEBIRD	see *H. macrophylla* 'Bläuling'
	- 'Bluebird' misapplied	see *H. serrata* 'Bluebird'
§	- 'Blushing Bride' (H)	LCro LOPS
	- 'Bodensee' (H)	CCVT CMac MAsh MJak SCob WFar WSpi
	- 'Bottstein' (H)	CCVT
	- 'Bouquet Rose' (H)	ECtt MJak MMuc NLar SEND SHyH
	- 'Brestenburg' (H)	MAsh
	- 'Brügg' (H)	CKel LRHS MAsh SAko SGol SHyH SLim SPer
	- CAIPIRINHA ('H212907') (H) **new**	SGol
	- 'Cameroun' (H)	MAsh SGol
	- 'Camilla'^{PBR} (H)	SGol WFar
	- 'Camino' (L)	EPfP SGol
	- CARDINAL	see *H. macrophylla* 'Kardinal' (Teller Series)
§	- 'Cardinal Red' (H)	CRos ECre LRHS NRHS WFar WMoo
	- 'Cendrillon' (H)	LLHF
	- CHIQUE ('Hbachi'^{PBR}) (H)	LRHS NRHS
	- 'Choco Chic' (L)	MAsh SGol
	- CLARISSA ('Hba 208901'^{PBR}) (H)	LRHS
	- 'Cocktail' (H)	SGol
	- 'Coco' (Beautensia Series) (H)	LRHS NRHS
	- 'Coco Blanc' (H/d)	SCob SGol
	- COLOR FANTASY (H)	MBrN
	- 'Cordata'	see *H. arborescens*
	- 'Cotton Candy Two' (L)	CRos EPfP LRHS MMrt NRHS
	- 'Dark Angel' (L)	ELan LCro LOPS LRHS NRHS SGol
	- 'Dark Angel Purple' (L)	LOPS
	- 'Dart's Romance' (L)	SHyH
	- DEEP PURPLE DANCE ('Schrolla02'^{PBR}) (Music Collection) (H) **new**	MGos
	- 'Deutschland' (H)	CTri
	- 'Doctor Jean Varnier' (L)	CDul EMil EPfP SHyH
	- DOLCE FARFALLE ('Dolfarf') (H)	WCot
	- DOLCE GIPSY ('Dolgip'^{PBR}) (L)	EPfP LRHS MGos
	- DOLCE KISS ('Dolkis'^{PBR}) (L)	EPfP LRHS MGos SGol
	- 'Domotoi'	see *H. macrophylla* 'Setsuka-yae'
	- 'Doppio Bianco'	see *H. macrophylla* 'Wedding Gown'
	- 'Doris' (H)	SCob SGol SHyH
	- DRAGONFLY	see *H. macrophylla* 'Libelle'
	- EARLY BLUE ('Hba 202911'^{PBR}) (H)	CRos LRHS MAsh NRHS SCob SGol SPoG
§	- 'Early Sensation' (Forever & Ever Series) (H)	CMac GKin LLHF MHol
§	- 'Eisvogel' (L)	SHyH
	- 'Eldorado' (H)	MGil SHyH WSpi
	- 'Elégance' (L)	MAsh SGol
	- ENDLESS SUMMER ('Bailmer') (H)	ELan
	- ENDLESS SUMMER BLUSHING BRIDE	see *H. macrophylla* 'Blushing Bride'
§	- 'Enziandom' (H)	CBcs CExl CSBt MAsh SGol
	- ETERNITY ('Youmetwo'^{PBR}) (H/d)	MAsh WCot
	- 'Etoile Violette' (L)	LRHS SGol
	- 'Europa' (H) ♀^{H5}	CBcs CExl NLar SHyH
	- EXPRESSION ('Youmesix') (H/d)	SGol
	- 'Fanfare'^{PBR} (H)	SGol
§	- 'Fasan' (Teller Series) (L)	MAsh NBro SGol WFar
	- FIRELIGHT	see *H. macrophylla* 'Leuchtfeuer'
	- FIREWORKS	see *H. macrophylla* 'Hanabi'
	- FIREWORKS BLUE	see *H. macrophylla* 'Jōgasaki'
	- FIREWORKS PINK	see *H. macrophylla* 'Jōgasaki'
	- FIREWORKS WHITE	see *H. macrophylla* 'Hanabi'
	- (Forever & Ever Series) FOREVER & EVER PEPPERMINT ('Rie 13'^{PBR})	CSBt SGol
	- - FOREVER & EVER TOGETHER ('Rie 05') (H/d)	CRos CSBt LRHS SGol SPoG
	- FOREVER AND EVER	see *H. macrophylla* 'Early Sensation'
	- 'Forever Pink' (H)	GGGa MAsh NLar SGol
	- FOREVER ('Youmeone'^{PBR}) (H/d)	CSBt
§	- 'Frau Fujiyo' (Lady Series) (H)	CExl
§	- 'Frau Katsuko' (Lady Series) (H)	SPer

§ - 'Frau Mariko' (Lady Series) (H)	MRav SGol
§ - 'Frau Taiko' (Lady Series) (H)	SPer
- 'French Cancan' (Rendez-vous Series) (L)	SGol
- 'Frillibet' (H)	MRav NLar
- FRISBEE ('H211903'[PBR]) (L) **new**	ELan SGol
- 'Ganku Bo Chokens' (H)	WCot
- 'Gartenbaudirektor Kühnert' (H)	SHyH
§ - 'Générale Vicomtesse de Vibraye' (H) ♀H5	CBcs CBod CChe CDul CEnd CKel CRos CSde CTri EBee ELan ELon EPfP GBin LRHS MAsh MGil NRHS SCob SHyH SLim SNig SPer SPoG WBor
- GENTIAN DOME	see *H. macrophylla* 'Enziandom'
- 'Geoffrey Chadbund'	see *H. macrophylla* 'Möwe'
- 'Gerda Steiniger' (H)	SHyH
- 'Gertrud Glahn' (H)	SHyH
- 'Gimpel' (Teller Series) (L)	MAsh
§ - GLAM ROCK ('Horwack'[PBR]) (H)	CBcs LCro LOPS MCot SGol
- 'Glowing Embers' (H)	IArd
- GOLDRUSH ('Nehyosh') (L/v)	CDul NHol SRms WCot
- 'Goliath' (H)	ELon
- 'Gräfin Cosel' (H)	SGol
§ - 'Grant's Choice' (L)	NBro
- GREAT STAR	see *H. macrophylla* 'Blanc Bleu'
- 'Grünes Gewölbe' (H)	SGol
- 'Hamburg' (H)	CBcs CTri ECtt EPfP LRHS SCob SHyH SLim WFar WMoo
§ - 'Hanabi' (L/d) ♀H5	CBcs MBlu MGil NLar SGol SHyH WSpi
§ - 'Harlequin' (H)	CMac WCot
- 'Hatfield Rose' (H)	SHyH
- 'Hatsu-shime' (L)	CMil NLar
- 'Heinrich Seidel' (H)	CBcs CTri SHyH WMoo
- 'Hercule Poirot' (H)	SGol
- 'Hobella'[PBR] (Hovaria Series) (L)	CBcs SGol WCot WFar
- 'Hobergine'[PBR] (Hovaria Series) (H)	SGol
- 'Holehird Purple' (H)	MAsh
- 'Holibel'[PBR] (Hovaria Series) (H) **new**	SGol
- 'Homigo'[PBR] (Hovaria Series) (H)	SGol
- 'Hopaline'[PBR] (Hovaria Series) (H)	WPGP
- 'Hopcorn'[PBR] (H)	SGol
- HOT RED ('Hba 206901'[PBR]) (H)	CRos LRHS NRHS
- 'Hot Red Violet' (H)	LCro LOPS MJak SPoG
- 'Inspire'[PBR] (H) **new**	SGol
- 'Izu-no-hana' (L/d)	CAbb CBcs CKel CMil EPfP GBin MBlu MGil NLar SGol SHyH SPoG WBor WSpi
- 'James Grant'	see *H. macrophylla* 'Grant's Choice'
- JIP BLUE ('H213910') (H) **new**	SGol
- 'Jofloma' (H)	NLar
§ - 'Jōgasaki' (L/d)	CBcs CExl CRos CSde LRHS MAsh MBlu NLar SDys SHyH WPGP
- 'Jomari' (Fireworks Series) (L/d) **new**	SGol
- 'Joseph Banks' (H)	CBcs CTri EWld SHyH
§ - 'Juno' (L)	SGol SHyH
- 'Kardinal'	see *H. macrophylla* 'Cardinal Red' (H)
§ - 'Kardinal' (Teller Series) (L) ♀H5	MAsh SCob SGol SHyH SPoG
- 'Kardinal Violet' (L)	LCro LOPS
- 'King George' (H)	CBar CBcs CBod CDul CKel CRos CSBt EBee ECtt ELon EPfP EUJe LRHS MGil MGos MMuc NEgg NHol NRHS SAdn SAko SCob SGol SHyH SLim SPer SPoG SWvt WFar WMoo
- KINGFISHER	see *H. macrophylla* 'Eisvogel'
§ - 'Klaveren' (L) ♀H5	CMil MAsh NBro SHyH
- 'Kluis Superba' (H)	CTri SHyH
- 'Koria'[PBR] (L)	LRHS NRHS SGol SPoG
§ - 'Kumico' (H)	SGol
- 'L.A. Dreamin' (H)	SGol
- 'La France' (H)	CBod CRos CTri LRHS MGil MNHC SCob SHyH SLim SPoG
- 'La Marne' (H) **new**	LRHS
- 'La Vie en Rose' (H)	SGol
- 'Lady Fujiyo'	see *H. macrophylla* 'Frau Fujiyo'
- 'Lady in Red' (L)	CMil CRos EPfP LRHS NRHS SPoG
- LADY KATSUKO	see *H. macrophylla* 'Frau Katsuko'
- 'Lady Mariko'	see *H. macrophylla* 'Frau Mariko'
- 'Lady Oshie' (Teller Series) (L)	SGol
- 'Lady Taiko Blue'	see *H. macrophylla* 'Frau Taiko'
- 'Lady Taiko Pink'	see *H. macrophylla* 'Frau Taiko'
- 'Lanarth White' (L) ♀H5	Widely available
- 'Lemon Wave' (L/v)	NLar
§ - 'Leuchtfeuer' (H)	CRos ELon LRHS MGil SGol SHyH WMoo
§ - 'Libelle' (Teller Series) (L) ♀H5	CBcs CKel CMac CRos ELan ELon EPfP EShb LPot LRHS MGos MMuc MRav NBir NLar NRHS SCob SEND SGol SHyH SLim SPer SPoG
- 'Lilacina'	see *H. macrophylla* 'Mariesii Lilacina'
- LITTLE LIME	see *H. paniculata* 'Jane'
- 'Love You Kiss'[PBR] (Hovaria Series) (L) ♀H5	CBcs CRos ELon LRHS NLar NRHS SCoo SGol SPoG WCot
- LOVE ('Youme H1917'[PBR]) (H/d)	LOPS SGol SPer SPoG
§ - 'Maculata' (L/v)	WGwG
- 'Madame A. Riverain' (H)	EPfP NLar SHyH
- 'Madame Emile Mouillère' (H) ♀H5	Widely available
- 'Madame Plumecocq' (H)	LRHS
- (Magical Series) MAGICAL AMETHYST ('Hokomathyst'[PBR]) (H)	CBcs SGol
- - MAGICAL CLEOPATRA ('Hortmaclepa') (H) **new**	SGol
- - MAGICAL CORAL ('Hokomac'[PBR]) (H)	CBcs SGol
- - MAGICAL CRYSTAL ('Ankong'[PBR]) (H) **new**	SGol
- - MAGICAL GREENFIRE ('Qufu') (H)	SGol
- - MAGICAL HARMONY ('Hortmahar'[PBR]) (H)	NLar
- - MAGICAL JADE ('Hortmaja'[PBR]) (H)	EPfP MBlu WCot
- - MAGICAL NOBLESSE ('Hokomano'[PBR]) (H)	CBcs SGol
- - MAGICAL OCEAN ('Hortmoc'[PBR]) (H)	NLar

Name	Suppliers
- - MAGICAL REVOLUTION ('Hokomarevo') (H)	CBcs SGol
- - MAGICAL RUBY RED ('Kolmaru'[PBR]) (H) **new**	SGol
- - MAGICAL RUBY TUESDAY (H) **new**	SGol
- - MAGICAL WINGS ('Hortmawin'[PBR]) (H) **new**	MBlu
- 'Maréchal Foch' (H)	CTri NLar
- 'Mariesii' (L)	CRos CTri ELan GBin LRHS MGil MSwo NLar SHyH SPer
§ - 'Mariesii Grandiflora' (L)	CMac CRos EPfP LRHS MMuc NAln NBro SGol SHyH SPer SRms WMoo
§ - 'Mariesii Lilacina' (L) ♀[H5]	MMuc SEND SHyH SPer WMoo WSpi
§ - 'Mariesii Perfecta' (L)	Widely available
- 'Masja' (H)	CBar CBcs CCVT ELon GKin IArd MAsh MGos MMuc MRav MSwo NBro NLar SAko SCob SGol SHyH SLim WBor WMoo
- 'Mathilde Gütges' (H)	CCVT
- 'Max Löbner' (H)	SHyH
- 'Merveille' (H)	NBro
- 'Merveille Sanguine' (H)	Widely available
- 'Messalina' (L)	SCob SHyH
- 'Mini Penny'[PBR] (H)	SGol
- MINTY ICE ('Es11'[PBR]) (Flair and Flavour Series) (H)	SGol
- 'Mirai'[PBR] (H)	CBcs EPfP ESwi LRHS NRHS WCot WPGP
- 'Miss Belgium' (H)	CMac CTri GKin
§ - 'Mousmée' (L)	SHyH
- 'Mousseline' (H)	LRHS MAsh
§ - 'Möwe' (Teller Series) (L) ♀[H5]	CBcs CEnd CExl CMil ECtt ELon EPfP GBin MAsh MGil MMuc SCob SCoo SEND SGol SHyH SLim SPer SRms SSta WSpi
- MRS KUMICO	see *H. macrophylla* 'Kumico'
- 'Mrs W.J. Hepburn' (H)	CSBt SPer
§ - 'Nachtigall' (Teller Series) (L) ♀[H5]	EPfP MAsh SHyH WPGP
- 'Nadeshiko-gaku' (L)	SHyH
- 'Nanping'[PBR] (Sturdy Series) (L)	SPoG
- 'Niedersachsen' (H)	CTri MRav SHyH
- NIGHTINGALE	see *H. macrophylla* 'Nachtigall'
- 'Nigra' (H)	CAby CBcs CBod CExl CMac CRos CTsd ELan ELon EPfP EWTr GBin LRHS MGil MGos MMuc MNHC MRav NBro NLar NRHS SAdn SEND SHyH SLim SPer WGrn WGwG
- 'Nikko Blue' (H)	CBcs EBee EUJe GKin MJak NLar SHyH
- NIZZA ('Ranice'[PBR]) (City-line Series) (H)	SCob
- var. ***normalis*** (L)	CExl
§ - 'Nymphe' (H)	SCob SHyH
- 'Oregon Pride' (H)	GGGa MAsh WFar WMoo
- 'Otaksa' (H)	CMil NLar
- 'Papagei' (Teller Series) (L)	SPer
- PASSION ('Youmefour') (L)	WCot
- 'Pax'	see *H. macrophylla* 'Nymphe'
- 'Pfau' (Teller Series) (L) ♀[H5]	CBod CMil ELon GBin MAsh MGil SHyH WSpi
- PHEASANT	see *H. macrophylla* 'Fasan'
- 'Pia' (H)	CExl CMac CMil CRos EShb GBin LRHS MRav SCob SMad SPer SRms WSpi
- PIGEON	see *H. macrophylla* 'Taube'
- 'Pink Lollipop' (Flair and Flavour Series) (H)	SGol
- 'Pirate's Gold' (v)	EHoe WFar
- 'Prinses Beatrix' (H)	SHyH
- 'Quadricolor' (L/v) ♀[H5]	CExl CHll CMac CMil CTsd EHoe GCal MGos MHol MRav SAdn SHyH SPlb SRms WCot
- 'Queen Elizabeth' (H)	GKin
- 'R.F. Felton' (H)	CBcs SHyH
- 'Radiant' (H)	SRms
- 'Rathen' (H) **new**	SGol
- 'Red Angel' (H)	LRHS NRHS SGol
- 'Red Baron'	see *H. macrophylla* 'Schöne Bautznerin'
- 'Red Beauty'[PBR] (H)	CRos LRHS NRHS SGol
- 'Red Red' (H)	MAsh
- REDBREAST	see *H. macrophylla* 'Rotkehlchen'
- 'Regula' (H)	SHyH
- 'Renate Steiniger' (H)	CBod EBee MRav SCob SGol SHyH SLim WMoo WSpi
- ROMANCE ('Youmenine'[PBR]) (H/d)	CRos LRHS MAsh NRHS SCob SGol SPoG WCot
- 'Rosita' (H)	MAsh NBir SCob SGol
- 'Rotdrossel' (Teller Series) (L)	GBin
§ - 'Rotkehlchen' (Teller Series) (L)	CKel NLar SGol SHyH SLim SPlb SWvt
- 'Rotschwanz' (Teller Series) (L) ♀[H5]	CMil GBin LRHS MAsh NLar SHyH WBor WPGP
- 'Rouge Baiser' (H)	SGol
- 'Royal Red' (H)	LRHS SGol
- 'Sabrina' (H)	CBcs CBod CChe CRos CTsd LLHF LRHS MAsh NRHS SCob SGol SHyH SRkn WMoo
- 'Saint Claire' (H)	CBcs
- 'Salsa' (H)	CRos LLHF LRHS MAsh MMrt NRHS SGol SHyH
- 'Sandra' (Dutch Ladies Series) (L)	CBcs
- 'Saskia' (Dutch Ladies Series) (H)	SGol
- SCHLOSS WACKERBARTH	see *H. macrophylla* GLAM ROCK
- 'Schneeball' (H)	CCVT MAsh NRHS SCob SGol
§ - 'Schöne Bautznerin' (H)	CCVT LRHS SAdn SCob SHyH SLim WMoo WSpi
- 'Sea Foam' (L)	NLar
- 'Selina' (Dutch Ladies Series) (L)	CBcs CRos EPfP LLHF LRHS LSRN NRHS SCoo SGol
- 'Selma'[PBR] (Dutch Ladies Series) (L)	CBcs EPfP SGol SHyH
§ - 'Setsuka-yae' (L/d)	CMil SGol
- 'Shakira' (H)	LLHF SGol
- 'Shamrock' (L)	SHyH
- 'Sheila' (Dutch Ladies Series) (L)	CBcs EShb LCro LOPS LSRN
- 'Shin-ozaki' (H)	NLar
- 'Shooting Star'[PBR] (L)	LRHS
- 'Sibilla' (H)	MJak SGol SHyH SPlb WFar
- 'Sindarella' (H)	GBin
- SISTER THERESE	see *H. macrophylla* 'Soeur Thérèse'
- 'Sita' (L)	LLHF SHyH
§ - 'Soeur Thérèse' (H)	CBar CBcs CSBt EPfP MAsh MMuc NLar SGol SWvt WGwG
- 'Spike'[PBR] (H)	LRHS NRHS

- STAR GAZER ('Kompeito'PBR) (Double Delight Series) (L/d) **new** — SGol
- STRAWBERRIES 'N' CREAM ('Mak2') (L) **new** — SPoG
- subsp. ***stylosa*** — WCru WPGP
- - MF 942115 — WPGP
- * - 'Sunset' (L) — CBcs
- 'Superba' (H) — SCob
- 'Sweet Fantasy' (Hovaria Series) (H) — ELan EPfP SGol
- § - 'Taube' (Teller Series) (L) — CBcs CDul CExl CKel ELan MAsh SGol SHyH SLim SWvt
- 'Teller Pink' — see *H. macrophylla* 'Taube'
- 'Teller Red' — see *H. macrophylla* 'Rotkehlchen'
- Teller variegated — see *H. macrophylla* 'Tricolor'
- Teller Weiss — see *H. macrophylla* 'Libelle'
- TIFFANY ('H211902'PBR) (Flair and Flavours Series) (L) **new** — SGol
- 'Tivoli'PBR (H) — CRos LRHS NRHS SCob WFar
- 'Tivoli Pink' (H) **new** — LCro LOPS
- 'Tokyo Delight' (L) ♀H5 — CExl CMac LRHS MAsh SDys SHyH
- 'Tovelit' (H) — SGol
- § - 'Tricolor' (L/v) — CBcs CTri CTsd ELan EShb LRHS MGos NLar SHyH SLon SPer WAvo WFar
- 'Variegata' — see *H. macrophylla* 'Maculata'
- 'Veitchii' (L) ♀H5 — CBcs CDul CExl CMil CRos CSBt ECre EPfP LRHS MGos MRav MSwo SHyH SPer
- 'Vicomte de Vibraye' — see *H. macrophylla* 'Générale Vicomtesse de Vibraye'
- 'Warabe' — see *H. serrata* 'Warabe'
- § - 'Wedding Gown'PBR (L/d) — LCro LOPS SGol
- 'Weisse Königin' (H) — SHyH
- 'Westfalen' (H) ♀H5 — CMac IArd
- 'White King'PBR (H) **new** — SGol
- 'White Spirit' (L) **new** — SGol
- 'White Wave' — see *H. macrophylla* 'Mariesii Grandiflora'
- 'Wudu'PBR (H) — SGol
- 'Xian'PBR (Sturdy Series) (H) — SGol
- 'Yola' (H) — NBro WFar
- YOU & ME TOGETHER ('Youmefive'PBR) (H/d) — MAsh
- 'Zebra'PBR (H) — ELan LCro LOPS MHol SCob WCot
- 'Zhuni Hito' (L) — NLar
- 'Zorro'PBR (L) ♀H5 — CBcs CBod CKel CRos CSpe CWGN ELan EMOT EPfP ESwi GGGa LRHS MAsh MGos NRHS SCob SCoo SHyH SLim SLon SPer SPoG WBrk WCot WMoo
- 'Zurichsee' — SHyH

aff. ***mangshanensis*** BWJ 8120 — WCru

MISS SAORI ('H20-2') (H/d) — CBcs CRos CWGN EMil LCro LOPS LRHS NRHS SPoG

paniculata — CMCN NAln
- B&SWJ 3556 from Taiwan — WCru WFar
- B&SWJ 5413 from Japan — WCru
- B&SWJ 8894 from Japan — WCru
- 'Ammarin' — MAsh NLar
- ANGEL'S BLUSH — see *H. paniculata* 'Ruby'
- BABY LACE ('Piihp-1') — SGol
- 'Big Ben' ♀H5 — CRos EPfP GGGa LRHS NRHS
- BOBO ('Ilvobo'PBR) — CKel CRos EPfP LRHS MGos MPkF NRHS SCob SGol
- 'Bombshell'PBR — CKel EBee EMil LCro LOPS NLar NRHS SCob SGol SHyH
- 'Brussels Lace' — CAbb CDul EPfP GBin GWyn LSRN MRav NLar NRHS SCob SGol SHyH SLon SSta
- 'Burgundy Lace' — MBlu NLar
- CANDLELIGHT ('Hpopr013'PBR) — MMrt SGol
- 'Chantilly Lace' — GBin SCob
- CONFETTI ('Vlasveld 02'PBR) — LCro LOPS SGol
- DART'S LITTLE DOT ('Darlido'PBR) — GBin LSRN NLar WFar WPGP
- DIAMANT ROUGE ('Rendia'PBR) — ELan LCro LOPS LRHS MPkF NRHS SGol
- DIAMANTINO ('Ren101'PBR) — SGol
- 'Dolly' — CRos EPfP LRHS LSRN SHyH SPoG
- 'Everest' — CBod CRos EPfP EWTr LEdu LRHS MMrt NLar NRHS SHyH SPoG
- 'Floribunda' — CRos ELan EPfP LRHS NRHS WFar
- FRAISE MELBA ('Renba') — SGol
- 'Grandiflora' — Widely available
- 'Great Escape' — NLar
- GREAT STAR — see *H. paniculata* 'Le Vasterival'
- 'Greenspire' — CRos EPfP LRHS MBlu MRav NRHS SHyH WFar
- 'Harry's Souvenir' — NLar
- § - 'Jane'PBR — CKel CWGN EMOT EMil LOPS LRHS MAsh MMrt NLar NRHS SGol SPoG
- 'Kyushu' — Widely available
- 'Last Post' — NRHS
- § - 'Le Vasterival'PBR — MAsh WSpi
- 'Levana'PBR — CMil SGol SHyH WFar
- 'Limelight'PBR ♀H5 — Widely available
- LITTLE QUICK FIRE ('Smhplqf') **new** — SGol
- (Magical Series) MAGICAL CANDLE ('Bokraflame'PBR) — ELan EPfP NRHS SGol WCot
- - MAGICAL FIRE ('Bokraplume'PBR) — LRHS NLar NRHS SCob SGol
- - MAGICAL FLAME ('Bokratorch'PBR) — ELan EPau
- - MAGICAL HIMALAYA ('Kolmahima') — MGos SGol
- - MAGICAL MONT BLANC ('Kolmamon') — EBee
- - MAGICAL MOONLIGHT ('Kolmagimo'PBR) — ECrN SGol
- - MAGICAL STARLIGHT — see *H. paniculata* PERLE D'AUTOMNE
- - MAGICAL SUMMER ('Bokrathirteen') **new** — SGol
- - MAGICAL VESUVIO ('Kolmavesu') — EBee MGos SGol
- 'Mathilde' — NLar
- MEGA MINDY ('Ilvomindy'PBR) — CBcs SCob SGol
- 'Mega Pearl' — LSRN NLar
- 'Melody' — NLar
- 'Mount Aso' — NBro SGol
- 'October Bride' — CEnd NLar WPGP
- 'Papillon' — WPGP
- 'Pee Wee' — LLHF NLar
- § - PERLE D'AUTOMNE ('Degustar') — SGol
- 'Phantom' ♀H5 — Widely available
- 'Pink Beauty'PBR (H) — LSRN

	- PINK DIAMOND ('Interhydia') ♀H5	Widely available
	- 'Pink Lady'	NBro SCob SGol SHyH
	- PINKY-WINKY ('Dvppinky'PBR) ♀H5	CDul CKel CRos CWGN ECrN EPfP ESwi GKin IArd LBuc LCro LLHF LOPS LRHS MBlu MGos MPkF NLar NRHS SCob SCoo SGol SHyH SLim SPoG SSta WFar
	- POLAR BEAR ('Wrhpbb2')	EBee SCob SGol SHyH
	- 'Praecox'	MRav WCru
	- PRIM'WHITE ('Dolprim')	LRHS
	- 'Rosy Morn'	CRos LRHS
§	- 'Ruby'	CBcs LSRN NLar SGol
	- 'Savill Lace'	LSvl
	- 'Silver Dollar' ♀H5	CKel CRos EPfP IArd LCro LOPS LRHS LSRN MAsh NHic NRHS SCob SGol SHyH SNig SWvt WFar WSpi
	- 'Sparkling' **new**	SGol
	- 'Starlight Fantasy'	see *H. paniculata* PERLE D'AUTOMNE
	- SUNDAE FRAISE ('Rensun'PBR)	CBod CChe CRos CTsd CWGN EBee EPfP EShb GGGa LPot LRHS MAsh MGos MPkF NRHS SGol WGrn
	- 'Tardiva'	CBcs CTho EBee EPfP GKin LCro LOPS MGos MRav NBro SCob SGol SHyH SPer SRms SWvt WFar WPGP
	- 'Tender Rose'	NLar
	- 'Unique'	CBcs CDul CKel CRos CTho ELan EPfP LRHS LSRN MAsh MRav MSwo NAln NBro NLar NRHS SCob SCoo SGol SHyH SPer SSta WAvo WCru WFar WKif WPGP
	- VANILLE FRAISE ('Renhy'PBR)	Widely available
	- 'White Goliath'	NLar
	- 'White Lace'	NLar
	- 'White Lady'	CBcs LRHS NRHS SGol
	- 'White Moth'	GGGa LLHF LRHS NAln NBro NLar SAdn SHyH
	- 'Wim's Red'PBR	CBcs ELan EPfP EShb ESwi LCro LOPS MMrt MThu NLar SCob SGol SSta WSpi
	- 'Yuan-Yang'	WCru
	peruviana var. ***oerstedii*** B&SWJ 10750	WCru
	peruviana* × *seemannii	CEnd GKin IArd MJak SSta
	petiolaris	see *H. anomala* subsp. *petiolaris*
	'Preziosa' ♀H4	Widely available
	quercifolia	Widely available
	- 'Alice'	CJun CKel CMac EBee ELan EPfP ESwi LRHS LSRN MAsh NLar SCob SGol SHyH WPGP
	- 'Alison'	SGol
I	- 'Amethyst' Dirr	CJun NLar SGol
	- 'Applause'	CRos EBee ELan EPfP LRHS NLar SGol
	- 'Back Porch'	NLar SGol
	- 'Burgundy'	CBcs CJun CMil EBee EPfP ESwi IArd LRHS MBlu NLar SGol WPGP WSpi
	- 'Flore Pleno'	see *H. quercifolia* SNOWFLAKE
	- 'Harmony'	CJun CKel CMil CRos EBee ELan EPfP ESwi LRHS MGos NLar NRHS SHyH SSta WPGP
	- ICE CRYSTAL ('Hqopr010'PBR)	CKel CMil EBee ELan EPfP LRHS MJak MMrt NLar SCob SGol SHyH SMad WAvo WPGP WSpi
	- 'Lady Anne'	WPGP
	- 'Little Honey'PBR	SGol
	- LITTLE HONEY ('Brihon')	LRHS MAsh SGol WPGP
	- 'Munchkin'	LRHS SGol
	- 'Pee Wee'	CBcs CJun CKel CRos EBee ELan EPfP LRHS MAsh MPkF SAko SGol SHyH SLon SPoG SSta SWvt WPGP
	- 'Queen of Hearts' **new**	ESwi
	- 'Ruby Slippers'	ESwi LRHS MThu SGol
	- 'Sike's Dwarf'	CJun CSpe ELan MPkF MRav NLar SCob SGol WCFE
	- 'Snow Giant'	CJun
	- SNOW QUEEN ('Flemygea') ♀H5	CBcs CKel CMCN CRos ELan ELon EPfP EThi EWTr LCro LOPS LRHS LSRN MAsh MGos MPkF MRav MSwo NLar SCob SGol SHyH SLim SPer SPoG SWvt WFar WPGP WSpi
	- 'Snowdrift'	CJun
§	- SNOWFLAKE ('Brido') (d) ♀H5	CBcs CEnd CKel CMac CMil CRos CSde CWGN ELan EPfP LCro LOPS LRHS MAsh MGos MPkF MRav NAln NLar NRHS SGol SHyH SIgm SLon SPer SPoG WCFE WPGP WSpi
	- 'Tennessee Clone'	CJun CKel EBee LRHS NAln NLar
	'Renatea'	CSBt
	sargentiana	see *H. aspera* subsp. *sargentiana*
	scandens	NBro
	- B&SWJ 5448	WCru
	- B&SWJ 5481	WCru
	- B&SWJ 5496	WCru
	- B&SWJ 5523	WCru
	- B&SWJ 5602	WCru
	- B&SWJ 5725	WCru
	- B&SWJ 5893	WCru
	- B&SWJ 6159	WCru
	- B&SWJ 6317	WCru
§	- subsp. ***chinensis***	CExl
	- - B&SWJ 1488	WCru
	- - B&SWJ 3214	WCru
	- - B&SWJ 3410 from Taiwan	WCru
	- - B&SWJ 3420	WCru
	- - B&SWJ 3423 from Taiwan	WCru
	- - B&SWJ 3487 from Taiwan	WCru
	- - B&SWJ 3869	WCru
	- - BWJ 8000 from Sichuan	WCru
	- - BWJ 8035	WCru
§	- - f. ***angustipetala***	WPGP
	- - - B&SWJ 3454	WCru
	- - - B&SWJ 3553	WCru
	- - - B&SWJ 3667	WCru
	- - - B&SWJ 3733	WCru
	- - - B&SWJ 3814	WCru
	- - - B&SWJ 6038 from Yakushima	WCru
	- - - B&SWJ 6041 from Yakushima	WCru
	- - - B&SWJ 6056 from Yakushima	WCru
	- - - B&SWJ 6787	WCru
	- - - B&SWJ 6802	WCru
	- - - B&SWJ 7121	WCru
	- - - B&SWJ 7128	WCru
§	- - - 'Golden Crane'	SCob WCru WPGP
	- - - 'Monlongshou'	see *H. scandens* subsp. *chinensis* f. *angustipetala* 'Golden Crane'
	- - 'Big White'	EBee WPGP
	- - f. ***formosana***	CMil SBrt
	- - - B&SWJ 1488	WCru
	- - - B&SWJ 7058	NLar
	- - - B&SWJ 7097	NLar WCru
	- - f. ***macrosepala*** B&SWJ 3423	ESwi WCru

	- - - B&SWJ 3476	WCru
	- - - CWJ 12441	WCru
	- - f. ***obovatifolia*** B&SWJ 3487b	WCru
	- - - B&SWJ 3683	WCru
	- - - B&SWJ 3869 from the Philippines	WCru
	- - - B&SWJ 7121	WCru
	- subsp. ***liukiuensis***	WCru
	- - B&SWJ 11471	WCru
	- - B&SWJ 6022	WCru
	- 'Splash' (v)	CMil
	seemannii	Widely available
	- 'Roger Grounds' (v)	WCot
	aff. ***seemannii***	CBod GKin WSpi
	SEMIOLA ('Inovalaur'PBR)	CRos EBee EPfP LRHS NRHS SGol SLim
	serrata	CExl CTri WKif
	- B&SWJ 6184	WCru
	- B&SWJ 6241	WCru
	- PAB 4757	LEdu
	- 'Acuminata'	see *H. serrata* 'Bluebird'
	- 'Aigaku' (L)	CExl CMil
	- 'Aka-tsanayama' **new**	LRHS
	- 'Akabe-yama'	NBro NLar
	- 'Akishino-temari'	EBee WPGP
	- Amacha Group	SGol
	- - 'Amagi-amacha' (L)	CMil NBro NLar
	- - 'Ō-amacha' (L)	CMil WPGP
	- 'Amagyana' (L)	CExl
	- subsp. ***angustata***	WCru
	- 'Ao-yama'	WPGP
	- AVELROZ ('Dolmyf'PBR)	EPfP SGol
	- 'Belladonna'	LRHS NBro
	- 'Belle Deckle'	see *H.* 'Blue Deckle'
	- 'Beni-gaku' (L)	CExl CRos ECre LRHS MAsh NBro NLar NRHS SCob SGol SHyH
	- 'Beni-temari'	LRHS NBro
	- 'Beni-yama' (L) ♀H5	CMil
	- 'Blue Billow' (L)	NBro NLar
	- BLUEBERRY CHEESECAKE	see *H. serrata* TUFF STUFF
§	- 'Bluebird' (L) ♀H5	Widely available
I	- 'Boothii' (L) **new**	CMac
	- 'Cap Sizun'	SChF SGol WPGP
	- 'Chiba Cherry-lips'	ESwi WCru
	- 'Chiri-san Sue' (d)	WCru
	- COTTON CANDY	see *H. serrata* TUFF STUFF
	- 'Crûg Bicolor' (L)	WCru
	- 'Crûg Caerulean'	WCru
	- 'Crûg Cobalt' (L)	ESwi GGGa WCru
	- 'Crûg Sō Cool' (L)	WCru
	- 'Diadem' (L) ♀H5	CAbb CExl CMil ELon EPfP LRHS NBro SHyH
	- 'Forget Me Not'	LRHS NBro
	- 'Fuji Snowstorm' (v)	CMil
	- 'Fuji Waterfall'	see *H. serrata* 'Fuji-no-taki'
	- 'Fuji-no-shirayuki' (L/d)	LRHS
§	- 'Fuji-no-taki' (L/d) ♀H5	CMil WPGP
	- 'Gaka'	LRHS
	- 'Golden Showers' (L)	NBro
	- 'Golden Sunlight'PBR (L)	SGol SWvt
	- 'Graciosa' (L)	LLHF
	- 'Grayswood' (L) ♀H5	CBcs CBod CDul CExl CKel CMac CRos CSBt ELan EPfP LRHS MAsh MGil MRav NBro NRHS SCob SGol SHyH SLim SPer WKif WPGP
	- 'Hakucho' (L/d)	CMil NBro WPGP
	- 'Hallasan' misapplied	see *H. serrata* 'Maiko', 'Spreading Beauty'
	- 'Hallasan' R. & J. de Belder (L)	CMil WPGP
	- 'Hime-benigaku' (L)	CMil MAsh WFar
	- 'Impératrice Eugénie' (L)	LRHS NLar
	- 'Intermedia' (L)	CExl NBro
	- 'Kiyosumi' (L) ♀H5	CBcs CEnd CExl CKel CMil ECre ELon EPfP LRHS NBir NLar SBrt SHyH WBor WCot WCru WPGP
	- 'Klaveren'	see *H. macrophylla* 'Klaveren'
	- 'Koreana' (L)	SAko SGol
	- 'Kurenai' (L)	CMil NBro NLar WPGP
	- 'Kurohime' (L)	EBee NBro WPGP
	- 'Macrosepala' (L)	WPGP
§	- 'Maiko' (L)	IArd
	- 'Midori' (L)	CExl
	- 'Mikamba'	see *H. serrata* 'Mikanba-gaku'
§	- 'Mikanba-gaku' (L)	SGol
	- 'Mikata Yae'	CMil WPGP
	- 'Miranda' (L) ♀H5	CExl CMil CRos EPfP LRHS MAsh NBro NLar SDys SGol SHyH WFar
	- 'Miyama-yae-murasaki' (L/d) ♀H5	CExl CMil SGol SRms WPGP
	- 'Momo-beni-yama'	CMil NBro
	- 'Mont Aso'	CMil IArd NLar
	- 'Niji' (L)	WPGP
	- 'Odoriko-amacha'	CMil EBee LRHS SChF WPGP
	- 'Otsu-hime'	NLar
	- 'Panachée' (L/v)	SHyH
	- 'Pretty Maiden'	see *H. serrata* 'Shichidanka'
§	- 'Prolifera' (L/d)	CMil LLHF
	- 'Pulchella'	see *H. serrata* 'Prolifera'
	- 'Ramis Pictis' (L)	CBcs NBro NLar SHyH
	- 'Rosalba' (L) ♀H5	CExl ECre NBro
	- 'Santiago'PBR (L)	EPfP SGol WCot WPGP
	- 'Sekka'	WPGP
§	- 'Shichidanka' (L/d)	EPfP LLHF LRHS NBro SHyH
	- 'Shichidanka-nishiki' (L/d/v)	CExl ECre
	- 'Shinonome' (L/d)	CExl CMil
	- 'Shirahuzi' (L/d)	SGol
	- 'Shirofuji' (L/d) ♀H5	CMil LLHF MAsh
	- 'Shiro-gaku' (L)	CMil MAsh NBro NLar
	- 'Shiro-maiko'	WPGP
	- 'Shirotae' (L/d)	CExl LRHS SGol
	- 'Shōjō' ♀H5	CMil EBee NBro SGol SHyH WPGP
*	- subsp. ***sinensis***	GKev
§	- 'Spreading Beauty' (L)	WPGP
	- 'Suzukayama-yama'	CMil SChF WPGP
*	- var. ***thunbergii*** 'Plena' (L/d)	WCru
	- 'Tiara' (L) ♀H5	CAbb CExl CKel CMil CRos EBee EPfP GGGa LRHS LSRN MAsh NBir NBro NLar NRHS SDys SGol SHyH SLim SPoG WPGP
§	- TUFF STUFF ('Mak 20'PBR) (L)	CRos EPfP LRHS NRHS SCob SGol SPoG
	- 'Veerle' (L)	NBro NLar SGol
§	- 'Warabe'	SGol
	- 'Yae-no-amacha' (L/d)	CBcs CExl CMil NBro NLar
	- subsp. ***yezoensis***	CMil NLar SGol
	- - 'Hime-gaku'	CMil
§	***serratifolia***	CBcs CExl IArd IDee SSta WPGP
	- HCM 98056	WCru
	sikokiana B&SWJ 5035	WCru
	- B&SWJ 5855	WCru
	- B&SWJ 11174	WCru
	- B&SWJ 11381	WCru
	'Silver Slipper'	see *H. macrophylla* 'Ayesha'
	steyermarkii B&SWJ 10501	WCru

tiliifolia	see *H. anomala* subsp. *petiolaris* var. *ovalifolia*
villosa	see *H. aspera* Villosa Group
xanthoneura	see *H. heteromalla* f. *xanthoneura*
aff. ***zhewanensis*** MF 93117	WCru

Hydrastis (*Ranunculaceae*)

canadensis	EMor GPoy LEdu

Hydrocharis (*Hydrocharitaceae*)

morsus-ranae	CBen CHab CWat EWat LLWG MWts NPer WPnP

Hydrocleys (*Alismataceae*)

nymphoides	XBlo

Hydrocotyle (*Araliaceae*)

asiatica	see *Centella asiatica*
sibthorpioides 'Crystal Confetti' (v)	LLWG
vulgaris	CWat EWat

Hydrophyllum (*Boraginaceae*)

canadense	IMou
virginianum	LEdu WHal

Hylomecon (*Papaveraceae*)

hylomeconoides	EWld WCru
§ ***japonica***	CAby CRos EBee ELan EPot EWld GEdr GKev GLog IMou LEdu LRHS MAvo NBir NHar NHpl NQui NRHS NRya WCot WCru WPGP WThu

Hylotelephium (*Crassulaceae*)

§ 'Abbey Dore'	CBod CRos ECtt ELan ELon EPfP LRHS MTis NBir NCGa SPhx WCAu
AMBER ('Florseamb')	WCot
§ ***anacampseros***	GQue MHer MMuc NWad SEND XLum
'Aquarel'	GBin GWyn
'Autumn Charm'	see *H.* (Herbstfreude Group) 'Lajos'
AUTUMN JOY	see *H.* (Herbstfreude Group) 'Herbstfreude'
'Beach Party' (Party Hardy Series)	EBee
§ 'Bertram Anderson' ♀H7	Widely available
'Birthday Party' (Birthday Party Series)	SPoG
'Blade Runner'	LRHS
'Blue Pearl'PBR (SunSparkler Series)	CAbb CSpe EBee LCro LOPS LRHS MPnt SPoG WHil
§ 'Carl' ♀H7	Widely available
§ ***cauticola*** ♀H5	EPot GCal MAsh MMuc MRav NWad SRms SRot WAbe WIce XLum
- 'Coca-Cola'	CBod CMac CWGN EBou ECtt EHoe EMor GBin GWyn LRHS MAsh MAvo MCot MRav NBir NDov NHpl NRHS NWad SPhx SPoG SSim SWvt WFar WHoo
- 'Lidakense' ♀H5	CMea CSpe CTri ECha ECtt EPot GBin GCrg MAsh MHer NHol NLar NRHS NWad SPlb SRot XLum XSen
- 'Robustum'	see *H.* 'Ruby Glow'
'Cherry Tart'PBR (SunSparkler Series)	ECtt
'Chocolate Cherry' **new**	SHeu
'Chocolate Drop'PBR	CWGN ECtt NLar SDys SHeu SRms WHlf
'Chocolate Sauce'	MAvo
'Class Act'PBR	CRos ECtt LRHS MNrw NLar NRHS SPoG SRms
'Cloud Walker'PBR	ECtt MNrw SPoG WFar
'Crazy Ruffles'	ECtt WCot
cyaneum 'Sakhalin'	CRos LRHS NRHS
'Dark Jack'	ECtt EPfP EUJe GQue MTis NGdn WCot
'Dazzleberry'PBR (SunSparkler Series)	EPfP LCro LOPS
'Diamond Edge' (v)	ECtt IKil
§ ***erythrostictum***	GBin XLum
- B&SWJ 11384 **new**	WCru
- 'Frosty Morn' (v)	Widely available
§ - 'Mediovariegatum' (v)	CDor CRos ELan LPot LRHS MHer MNrw NLar SWvt WFar WMoo XLum
§ ***ewersii***	ECtt GCrg MAsh MMuc NBro NLar SPhx SPlb WTor
- CC 5288	GKev
- var. ***homophyllum*** 'Rosenteppich'	CRos EPPr EPfP GWyn LBuc LRHS NRHS SPoG SRms SWvt WAvo WMoo
'Firecracker'PBR (SunSparkler Series)	LOPS WNPC
'Frosted Fire'	MAsh NSti SRms WFar
'Green Expectations'	GBin MRav NBre
§ Herbstfreude Group	CRos EHrv LPot LRHS MJak NRHS NWsh
- 'Autumn Fire'	EBee MAsh
- 'Beka' (v)	MAvo
- 'Elsie's Gold' (v)	CRos EBee ECtt EPfP LRHS MAvo MNrw SRms
§ - 'Herbstfreude' ♀H7	Widely available
- 'Jaws'PBR	CKno EBee ECtt IKil NLar WCot WFar XLum
§ - 'Lajos' (v)	MAsh NEoE WCot WFar
- 'Mini Joy'	CRos ELon LRHS MHol MNrw NRHS
'Ice Ruffles' (v)	SPoG WFar
'José Aubergine'PBR	CBod CKno CRos EBee ECtt EPfP IPot LRHS MAsh MAvo MBel MRav MTis NDov NHol NLar NRHS NSti SCob SHeu SPoG SRms WCAu WPGP
§ 'Joyce Henderson'	CDor CElw CRos ELan EPfP LRHS MCot MRav MTis NChi NLar NRHS SPer SRms WAvo WBrk WCot WMoo WOld XSen
'Lac d'Oô' **new**	GBin
'Lime Zinger'PBR (SunSparkler Series)	ECtt LCro LOPS WNPC
I 'Marchants Best Red' ♀H7	LRHS MNrw MRav SPhx WCot
§ 'Matrona' ♀H7	Widely available
§ 'Mr Goodbud'PBR ♀H7	CAby CBct CBod ECtt LRHS LSun MAsh MAvo MHol MNrw NBir NEgg NRHS SAko SHeu SPoG SRms WCAu WCot WSpi WTor
§ 'Munstead Red'	CBod CDor CRos EBee ECha ECtt EPfP GBin LRHS MAvo MNrw MRav MTis NLar NRHS SPer SPhx SRms WCAu WFar WKif WMoo
'Pinky'	EBee
§ ***pluricaule***	CRos EBou ECtt EHoe EPot GCrg LRHS NBro NHol NRHS NWad SIgm SPlb SRms WHoo
'Pool Party'PBR (Party Hardy Series)	CRos EPfP LRHS NLar NRHS SRms
§ ***populifolium***	ECha GCal IMou MHer MMuc NLar XLum
§ 'Red Cauli' ♀H7	Widely available

	'Red Rum'	GBin GWyn
	'Red Setter'	SAko SPhx WPGP
§	'Ruby Glow' ♀H5	Widely available
	'Ruby Port'	CSpe
§	***sieboldii***	EUJe GPSL
	- 'Dragon'	MHCG
	- 'Mediovariegatum' (v) ♀H4	EHoe MHer MRav SPlb XLum
§	***spectabile*** ♀H6	CBod CTri ELan EPfP GJos LRHS MCot MHer MRav NGdn NRHS SCob SPlb SRms WBor WBrk WFar WSFF
	- BLACK BEAUTY ('Florseblab')	ECtt MNrw NLar
	- Brilliant Group	CBar MJak SRms WCAu
	- - 'Brilliant' ♀H7	CBcs CBod CRos CSBt CTri CTsd ECha ECtt ELan EPfP LCro LOPS LRHS MAvo MGos MRav NAln NGdn NLar NWsh SCob SPer SPoG SWvt WFar WMoo WSpi
	- - 'Carmen'	NBir XLum
	- - 'Hot Stuff'	CAby CRos ECtt ELan EPfP LRHS LSRN NCou NRHS SPoG SRms SRot WCot
	- - 'Lisa'	GBin GWyn NLar
	- - 'Meteor'	MRav NLar
	- - 'Neon'	CRos EPfP LRHS MAsh MAvo NRHS
	- - 'Pink Fairy'	MNrw
	- - 'Rosenteller'	CKno GBin NBre
§	- - 'Septemberglut'	CRos LRHS NBre NRHS WSpi XLum
	- - 'Steven Ward'	CKno EWes
	- 'Crystal Pink'PBR	MNrw NLar
	- 'Humile'	XLum
	- 'Iceberg'	CBod CRos EBee ECha ECtt EHrv EPfP EWTr GBin LPot LRHS MCot MGos MRav NAst NCGa NGdn NLar NRHS SCob SPer SPhx SWvt WFar WMoo WSFF WSpi XLum XSen
	- 'Nordlicht'	GWyn
	- 'Pink Chablis' (v)	WCot
	- SEPTEMBER GLOW	see *H. spectabile* (Brilliant Group) 'Septemberglut'
	- 'Stardust'	CRos CTri EBee EPfP GBin GKev GMaP LCro LRHS MRav MTis NAln NRHS SGol SPer SRms WBrk WFar XLum
	- 'Variegatum'	see *H. erythrostictum* 'Mediovariegatum' (v)
	- WALBERTON'S PIZAZZ	CRos EPfP LRHS NRHS SPoG
§	'Stewed Rhubarb Mountain'	CBod CKno CRos EBee ECha ECtt ELan EPfP LRHS MBNS MRav NLar NRHS SGbt WCAu WMoo
	'Sunset Cloud'	ECtt EWes GCal LPla LPot MRav
§	***tatarinowii***	WCot
§	***telephium***	IFro NBir SRms WSFF XLum
§	- Atropurpureum Group	MRav NLar SWvt
	- - 'African Pearl'	GWyn WCFE
	- - 'Arthur Branch'	CRos GWyn LRHS NRHS
	- - 'Bon Bon'	CBod EPfP MBNS MTis NLar SPoG
	- - 'Bressingham Purple'	CRos EBee LRHS NRHS
	- - 'Chocolate'	ECtt GPSL NLar
	- - 'Dark Knight'	CRos EPfP LRHS NRHS
	- - 'El Cid'	EWes
	- - 'Karfunkelstein' ♀H7	CKno CRos EBee ECha ECtt GBin GLog LCro LOPS LPot LRHS MHol MTis MWat NBir NDov NRHS SPhx WCot XLum
	- - 'Leonore Zuuntz'	NBre
	- - 'Lynda et Rodney'	EWes
	- - 'Lynda Windsor'	ECtt EPfP NLar SWvt
	- - 'Möhrchen'	GMaP MRav NGdn NLar SPhx WMoo
	- - 'Picolette'	CRos EBee ECtt EPfP LRHS MNrw NCGa NGdn NRHS SPoG SRms WCot WMoo
	- - 'Postman's Pride'PBR	CWGN ECtt EPfP GBin GWyn NGdn
§	- - 'Purple Emperor' ♀H7	Widely available
	- - 'Purple Moon'	SPhx
	- - 'Ringmore Ruby'	EBee MNrw SPhx WCot WPGP
	- - 'Xenox'PBR ♀H7	CBct CBod CRos CWGN EBee ECtt EHoe EPfP GBin IPot LRHS MAsh MAvo MBNS MCot MNrw NLar NRHS SCob SPoG SRms WAvo WCAu
	- 'Cherry Truffle'PBR **new**	SHeu
	- 'Coral Reef'PBR	CSpe
	- Emperor's Waves Group	CPla ELan MNHC NGdn NWad WRHF
§	- subsp. ***fabaria***	ECtt MRav NWsh WCot
	- - var. ***borderei***	CElw LPla SBch SPhx
	- 'Jennifer'	CAby EBee ECtt GQue MBel MHol MPie WCAu WCot WHoo
	- subsp. ***maximum*** 'Atropurpureum'	see *H. telephium* Atropurpureum Group
	- - 'Gooseberry Fool'	CMea EBee ECtt ELan EPfP GMaP LRHS NAst NEoE SPhx SRms
	- 'Moonlight Serenade'PBR	CRos EBee ECtt EPfP LRHS NRHS SRms
	- 'Orange Xenox'PBR	EPfP LPla
	- 'Rainbow Xenox'PBR	SCob
	- 'Raspberry Truffle'	LRHS SDys SHeu
§	- subsp. ***ruprechtii***	CDor CRos ECha ECtt EHoe EPPr EPfP GMaP LRHS MCot MRav NLar NRHS NSti SPer SPhx WMoo WWtn
	- - 'Citrus Twist'	CRos EBee ECtt LRHS MRav NRHS
	- - 'Hab Gray'	CAby CSpe EBee ECtt EWes EWld LRHS NLar SAko SBch SRms
	- - 'Pink Dome'	ECha
	- 'Strawberries and Cream'	CMac CRos EBee ECha ECtt ELan ELon EPfP EShb EWTr GMaP LCro LRHS MBNS MBel MMuc MRav NEoE NGdn NLar NRHS SGbt SPer WMoo
	- 'Sunkissed'PBR	ECtt LPla NLar
	- 'Touchdown Flame'PBR **new**	SHeu
	- 'Twinkling Star'PBR	ECtt MNrw NLar
	- YELLOW MATRONA ('Eline'PBR)	LCro LOPS MAsh WHlf
	- 'Yellow Xenox'PBR	CRos EBee ECtt LRHS NLar NRHS SCob
	'Thundercloud'PBR	CBod EPfP GJos LBuc MTin SCob SRms WMoo
	'Thunderhead'	SHeu
	'Touchdown Teak'PBR	CKno EBee LEdu MAsh NRHS SHeu WTor
§	***ussuriense***	EPfP GBin GCal GPSL NBir SIgm
	- 'Chuwangsan'	EWld WCru
	'Veluwse Wakel'	ECtt GBin GWyn
§	'Vera Jameson' ♀H5	CRos ECha ECtt EHoe ELan EPfP EShb GKev LRHS LSRN MBel MCot MRav MWat NAln NBir NHol NRHS NSti NWsh SIgm SPer SRms SWvt WHoo WKif WMoo WSpi
§	***viviparum***	NLar
	- B&SWJ 8662	WCru
	WALBERTON'S PINK WHISPER	CRos EPfP LRHS NRHS SPoG

'Washfield Purple' see *H. telephium* (Atropurpureum Group) 'Purple Emperor'

Hymenanthera see *Melicytus*

Hymenocallis (*Amaryllidaceae*)

× ***festalis*** see *Ismene* × *deflexa*
- 'Zwanenburg' see *Ismene* × *deflexa* 'Zwanenburg'
harrisiana CCCN GKev SDeJ
longipetala see *Ismene longipetala*
'Sulphur Queen' see *Ismene* 'Sulphur Queen'

Hymenolepis (*Asteraceae*)

parviflora see *Athanasia parviflora*

Hymenosporum (*Pittosporaceae*)

flavum EShb

Hymenoxys (*Asteraceae*)

grandiflora see *Tetraneuris grandiflora*
§ ***hoopesii*** CBod CMac CRos EMor GMaP GWyn LPot LRHS MPie NAln NBir NGrd NLar NRHS SCob SPer SRms WFar XLum

Hyoscyamus (*Solanaceae*)

niger GPoy WSFF

Hypericum ✿ (*Hypericaceae*)

CC 4131 CExl
CC 4544 CExl
aegypticum CPBP CTri MHer SIgm SPlb WAbe WThu
androsaemum ECha ELan MHer MMuc MSwo NPer SEND WFar WMoo WOut
§ - 'Albury Purple' ELan EShb NLar WMoo XLum
- 'Autumn Blaze' CBcs
- 'Excellent Flair' NLar
§ - f. ***variegatum*** 'Mrs Gladis Brabazon' (v) CMac EShb NBir WCot
'Archibald' EWes NWad
athoum WIce WThu
aviculariifolium var. ***uniflorum*** GJos
balearicum MMuc SBrt WAbe XSen
bellum GCal SPtp
buckleyi WAbe
calycinum CBod CDul CMac CTri ELan EPfP LBuc MGos MRav NWea SCob SEND SGol SPer SRms SWvt WFar WMoo XLum
- 'Brigadoon' ♀H5 MAsh SGol
- CARNIVAL ('Crowthyp') (v) NEoE SPad WMoo
cerastioides CSma CTri EDAr EWes GJos MMuc NGdn NHic SIgm SRms WAbe
coris EWes SRms
cuneatum see *H. pallens*
× ***cyathiflorum*** 'Gold Cup' CMac LRHS MAsh
× ***dummeri*** 'Peter Dummer' NLar WSpi
'Eastleigh Gold' CMac
elodes CWat LLWG
'Fancy Pants' LEdu WPGP
forrestii ♀H5 MMuc SEND
fragile misapplied see *H. olympicum* f. *minus*
frondosum 'Sunburst' CKel
GOLDEN BEACON ('Wilhyp'PBR) ♀H5 CBod CEnd CRos CSpe EMOT ESwi LRHS MAsh MHer MMuc MNrw NBir NEgg NRHS NWad SEND WCot
grandiflorum see *H. kouytchense*
grandifolium EDAr GCal
henryi L 753 SRms
- subsp. ***hancockii*** NJM 10.092 WPGP
'Hidcote' see *H.* × *hidcoteense* 'Hidcote'
§ × ***hidcoteense*** 'Hidcote' ♀H5 Widely available
- 'Hidcote Variegated' (v) MAsh SLim SRms
hirsutum CHab NMir
imbricatum SIgm
× ***inodorum*** 'Albury Purple' see *H. androsaemum* 'Albury Purple'
- 'Autumn Surprise'PBR ELon NEgg NEoE NWad
- 'Dream' NLar
- 'Elstead' ECtt EPfP MRav NLar NWad NWea WSpi
- MAGICAL CHERRY ('Kolmcherrip'PBR) ELan EPfP SCob
- MAGICAL GRACE ('Kolmagrace'PBR) **new** MMrt
- MAGICAL LIGHTNING ('Kolmligh'PBR) **new** MMrt NEoE
- MAGICAL LIMELIGHT ('Kolmalimeli'PBR) ELan
- MAGICAL PUMPKIN ('Kolmapuki'PBR) NEoE SCob
- MAGICAL SUNSHINE ('Kolmasun'PBR) NEoE SCob SPer
- MAGICAL UNIVERSE ('Kolmuni'PBR) NEoE SCob
- MAGICAL WHITE ('Kolmawhi'PBR) ELan EPfP MMrt NEoE SCob SPoG
- MAGICAL WHITE FALL ('Kolmwhifa'PBR) SCob
- 'Rheingold' MAsh NLar
- 'Ysella' MRav
kalmianum SBrt
- SUNNY BOULEVARD ('Deppe'PBR) **new** LCro LOPS
kamtschaticum XLum
kazdaghense EWes
§ ***kouytchense*** ♀H5 CDul CRos EPfP EWes GBin LRHS MAsh MMuc MRav SEND SPoG SWvt WCFE WKif WSpi
lancasteri CRos EPfP ESwi LRHS MAsh SPoG SPtp
leschenaultii misapplied see *H.* 'Rowallane'
'Little Misstery' CKel CRos EBee EMOT EMil EPfP LBuc LRHS MAsh NEoE NRHS SPoG
maclarenii EWes
MAGICAL BEAUTY ('Kolmbeau'PBR) CBod ELon EPfP MMrt NEoE NLar SCob SPer SPoG
MAGICAL DREAM ('Kolmdream'PBR) SCob
MAGICAL FALL ('Kolmfa'PBR) SCob
MAGICAL FLAME ('Kolmagif') SCob
MAGICAL PINK ('Kolmpin') SCob
MAGICAL RED ('Kolmred') EPfP MJak NEoE NLar SCob SPoG
MAGICAL RED STAR ('Kolmarest'PBR) SCob
MAGICAL SWEETHEART ('Kolmsweet') SCob
MIRACLE ATTRACTION ('Alldiablo'PBR) CRos LRHS NLar SRms
MIRACLE BLIZZ ('Allblizz') CRos LRHS NRHS
MIRACLE BLOSSOM ('Allblossom'PBR) CRos LRHS NRHS

MIRACLE FANTASY ('Hymirfan')	NLar
MIRACLE SUMMER ('Hymirsum')	EPfP NEoE NLar
MIRACLE WONDER ('Hymirwon')	CRos LRHS NLar
× ***moserianum*** ♀H5	CDul CMac CRos EMOT EPfP EWes LRHS MJak NPer SCob SLon SPer SRms WFar
- 'Daybreak'	CRos LRHS MAsh NEoE SGol SPoG WRHF
§ - 'Tricolor' (v)	Widely available
- 'Variegatum'	see *H.* × *moserianum* 'Tricolor'
'Mr Bojangles'	EMOT
'Mrs Brabazon'	see *H. androsaemum* f. *variegatum* 'Mrs Gladis Brabazon'
oblongifolium	CExl
olympicum ♀H4	CRos CTri ECha ELan GJos LRHS MAsh NEoE NRHS SCob SEND SPer SRms SWvt WIce XLum XSen
- 'Grandiflorum'	see *H. olympicum* f. *uniflorum*
§ - f. ***minus***	CSma CTri ECtt MAsh NGdn NHpl SPlb SRms WHrl
§ - - 'Sulphureum'	CBod CChe CRos ELon EWTr EWes GMaP LRHS NBir NRHS SHar SPer SRms SWvt WCFE
- - 'Variegatum' (v)	EWes NBir SWvt
§ - f. ***uniflorum***	EBou MMuc NBro
- - 'Citrinum' ♀H5	CMea CSpe ECha ECtt EPfP MHol MMuc MRav NLar SEND SIgm SPad WAbe WCot WHoo WHrl WKif WSHC XSen
orientale	EWes GLog
§ ***pallens***	WAbe
patulum **new**	SPtp
- var. ***henryi*** Rehder & hort.	see *H. pseudohenryi*
perforatum	CBod CCBP CHab CHby ENfk EPfP GJos GPoy IRos MHer MNHC NGrd NLar NMir SEND SRms WHer WMoo WSFF
- 'Topaz'	GJos
polyphyllum misapplied	see *H. olympicum* f. *minus*
- 'Citrinum'	see *H. olympicum* f. *minus* 'Sulphureum'
- 'Grandiflorum'	see *H. olympicum* f. *uniflorum*
prolificum	MMrt WCFE
§ ***pseudohenryi***	MMrt SPtp
quadrangulum L.	see *H. tetrapterum*
reptans misapplied	see *H. olympicum* f. *minus*
reptans Hook.f. & Thomson ex Dyer	EWes GCrg NWad SBrt
revolutum PAB 3861	LEdu WPGP
§ 'Rowallane' ♀H4	CDul CTri GCal LRHS NLar SPoG SWvt
subsessile	CExl
'Sungold'	see *H. kouytchense*
'Sweet Lion'	CMac
§ ***tetrapterum***	CBod MMuc
trichocaulon	EWes ITim
uralum	CPla SPtp
- HWJ 520	WCru
- NJM 10.097	WPGP

Hypocalyptus (*Papilionaceae*)

sophoroides	SPlb

Hypochaeris (*Asteraceae*)

radicata	CHab NMir

Hypocyrta see *Nematanthus*

Hypoestes (*Acanthaceae*)

aristata	CExl EShb SVen

Hypolepis (*Dennstaedtiaceae*)

millefolium	CRos EBee LEdu LRHS

Hypoxis (*Hypoxidaceae*)

hirsuta	CCCN GKev
hygrometrica	WThu
longifolia **new**	MAsh
parvula	CAby XLum
§ - var. ***albiflora*** 'Hebron Farm Biscuit'	CCCN EWes GEdr NWad SRot WAbe WFar

Hypoxis × *Rhodohypoxis* see × *Rhodoxis*

H. parvula × ***R. baurii***	see × *Rhodoxis hybrida*

Hypsela (*Campanulaceae*)

longiflora	see *H. reniformis*
§ ***reniformis***	EBou GCrg ITim LLWG MAsh MSCN NHpl

Hyssopus ✿ (*Lamiaceae*)

from Georgia	EWes
officinalis	CBod CCBP CHby CLau CMea EBou ECha ELan ENfk EPfP GMaP GPoy MHer MJak MNHC MRav NBir NGrd NPri SEND SPer SPlb SPoG SRms SVic WSHC XLum
- f. ***albus***	ECha ENfk EPfP GPoy MHer MNHC SPlb SRms WArt WHer XLum XSen
- subsp. ***aristatus***	CBod CLau EBou ELon ENfk EPfP GPoy IMou MHer MNHC SPoG WHoo XLum XSen
- 'Blaue Wolke'	NHic
- 'Caeruleus'	WArt
- subsp. ***officinalis***	XSen
- 'Roseus'	CBod EBou ECha ENfk EPfP GPoy MHer MHol MNHC SPer SPoG WArt WHer XLum XSen
- f. ***ruber***	CLau
- white-flowered	CBod

Hystrix (*Poaceae*)

patula	CBod EHoe EMor EPPr EShb MNrw SPlb XLum

I

Iberis (*Brassicaceae*)

ABSOLUTELY AMETHYST ('Ib2401')	ELan GBin MCot SPoG WFar WIce
candolleana	see *I. violacea* Candolleana Group
commutata	see *I. sempervirens*
gibraltarica	SRms
- 'Betty Swainson' ♀H4	CSpe ELan NWad SPhx
- 'Lavish'	CBod MHol
jordanii	see *I. violacea*
'Masterpiece'[PBR]	CRos ECtt ELan LRHS NPer NRHS SPoG WFar
'Pink Ice'	CRos LRHS MCot NRHS WFar WIce WTor
pruitii	see *I. violacea*
saxatilis	CRos ITim LRHS NRHS SIgm WThu
semperflorens	WAvo WBrk WCFE

§ ***sempervirens***	CMea CTri EBou ELan EPfP MAsh MCot MMuc NBro SEND SHar SIgm SRms WCFE XSen
- 'Appen-Etz'	CRos EPfP GMaP LRHS NRHS NWad SRms
- 'Elfenreigen'	GCal
- 'Fischbeck'	CRos SRms SRot
- 'Golden Candy'	CSma CTri ECtt EHoe NHpl SPoG SRms WIce XSen
- 'Little Gem'	see *I. sempervirens* 'Weisser Zwerg'
- 'Pygmaea'	WHil
- SCHNEEFLOCKE	see *I. sempervirens* 'Snowflake'
- 'Snow Cushion'	EPfP LSun WRHF
§ - 'Snowflake' ♀H5	CBod CCBP EBou EPfP EPot GKev GMaP MCot SPer SPoG SRms SRot SWvt WBrk WIce XLum
§ - 'Weisser Zwerg'	CMea EBou ECha ECtt ELan GCrg GMaP MRav SIgm SRms WHoo WThu
'Snowball'	MHol SRms
umbellata	ECrN
§ ***violacea***	NSla SPlb WAbe
§ - Candolleana Group	GEdr

Ichthyoselmis (*Papaveraceae*)

§ ***macrantha***	EPot IMou WCru WSHC

Idesia (*Salicaceae*)

polycarpa	CBcs CMCN EBee EPfP SChF WPGP
- CWJ 12837	WCru

Ilex ✿ (*Aquifoliaceae*)

sp.	LPra
× ***altaclerensis*** (Hort. ex Loud.) Dallim. 'Balearica' (f)	CJun
§ - 'Belgica Aurea' (f/v) ♀H6	CBcs CJun CTho EPfP MSwo NEgg NHol NLar WAvo
- 'Camelliifolia' (f) ♀H6	CBcs CJun CTho MBlu NEgg SGol SPer WSpi
- 'Camelliifolia Variegata' (f/v)	CMac
- 'Golden King' (f/v) ♀H6	Widely available
- 'Hendersonii' (f)	NEgg
- 'Hodginsii' (m)	CTri
- 'Howick' (f/v)	CJun
- 'Lawsoniana' (f/v) ♀H6	CBod CCVT CJun CKel CMac CRos CSBt CTri EHoe EPfP EShb LRHS MAsh MBlu MJak MMuc NEgg NHol NRHS NWea SCob SEND SGol SLim SLon SPer SPoG SRms WAvo WFar
- 'Purple Shaft' (f)	CJun CMCN MRav
- 'Ripley Gold' (f/v)	CJun CMac CRos LRHS MAsh MRav NWea WAvo
- 'Silver Sentinel'	see *I.* × *altaclerensis* 'Belgica Aurea'
- 'W.J. Bean' (f)	CJun
- 'Wilsonii' (f)	NEgg NLar
aquifolium ♀H6	Widely available
- 'Alaska' (f)	CCCN CCVT CDul CJun CKel CMCN CRos EPfP LBuc LMaj LRHS MAsh MJak NLar NOra NRHS NWea SGol SWvt WAvo WFar WMat
- 'Amber' (f) ♀H6	CJun CTho NLar NWea
- 'Ammerland' (f) **new**	CJun
- 'Angustifolia' (f)	CJun CRos WCFE
- 'Angustifolia' (m or f)	EPfP LRHS SPoG
§ - 'Argentea Marginata' (f/v) ♀H6	Widely available
§ - 'Argentea Marginata Pendula' (f/v)	CMac CRos CTri ELan EPfP LRHS MAsh SRms WCot WFar
- 'Argentea Pendula'	see *I. aquifolium* 'Argentea Marginata Pendula'
- 'Argentea Variegata'	see *I. aquifolium* 'Argentea Marginata'
- 'Atlas' (m)	CBcs LBuc SWvt
- 'Aurea Marginata' (f/v)	CMac EPfP LMaj MGos NOra NWea SCob SEWo WAvo WCFE WFar WMat
- 'Aurea Regina'	see *I. aquifolium* 'Golden Queen'
- 'Aureomaculata'	NEgg
- 'Aurifodina' (f)	CJun NEgg WAvo
- 'Bacciflava' (f)	CBcs CDul CJun CMac CTho CTri ELan ELon EPfP IArd MBlu MGos MJak MRav NEgg NLar NWea SPer SRms SWvt WCFE WFar
- 'Crassifolia' (f)	EBee
- 'Elegantissima' (m/v)	CJun
- 'Fastigiata Sartori'	NLar
- 'Ferox' (m)	CJun CRos ELan EPfP LRHS NEgg
- 'Ferox Argentea' (m/v) ♀H6	Widely available
- 'Ferox Aurea' (m/v)	CJun ELon MAsh NEgg
§ - 'Flavescens' (f)	MBlu NEgg
- 'Frogmore Silver' (m/v)	CJun
- 'Glanzzwerg'	SAko
- 'Gold Flash' (f/v)	CJun LRHS NLar
- 'Golden Milkboy' (m/v)	CJun CMac MAsh SGol WAvo WCot
§ - 'Golden Queen' (m/v) ♀H6	NBir SRms
- 'Golden Tears' (f/v)	CJun
- 'Golden van Tol' (f/v)	CBcs CJun CLnd CSBt CTri EBee ELan ELon EPfP EShb LRHS MAsh MBlu MGos MJak MSwo NEgg NLar SCoo SGol SRms WFar
- 'Green Minaret'	SAko
- 'Handsworth New Silver' (f/v) ♀H6	Widely available
- 'Harpune' (f)	CJun IArd SAko
- 'Hastata' (m)	IArd IDee
- HECKENZWERG ('Hachzwerg'PBR)	SAko
- 'Ingramii' (m/v)	CJun LRHS
- 'J.C. van Tol' (f) ♀H6	Widely available
- 'Latispina' (f)	CJun
- 'Lichtenthalii' (f)	CJun IArd NEgg
- 'Madame Briot' (f/v) ♀H6	CDul CJun CKel CMac CRos CTri EBee EHoe ELan EMOT EPfP LBuc LRHS MAsh MRav MSwo NEgg NHol NPri NRHS NWea SEND SGol SPer SPoG SRms SWvt WFar
- 'Monstrosa' (m)	CJun
- moonlight holly	see *I. aquifolium* 'Flavescens'
- 'Myrtifolia' (f)	CKel NEgg SWvt WPav
- 'Myrtifolia' (m)	CJun CMac ELan EPfP NLar SMad WPav
- 'Myrtifolia Aurea' (m/v)	NWea SWvt
- 'Myrtifolia Aurea Maculata' (m/v)	CBod CJun CRos CTri ELan LRHS MAsh MRav NEgg SPoG SWvt WCot
- 'Northern Lights' (v)	EPfP MSwo
- 'Pendula' (f)	MRav
- 'Pyramidalis' (f) ♀H6	CBcs CDul CJun CKel CMac CRos CTri ELan LPra LRHS MAsh MGos MJak NLar NWea SCob SGol SPer SRms WFar
- 'Pyramidalis Aureomarginata' (f/v)	NLar
- 'Pyramidalis Fructu Luteo' (f) ♀H6	MAsh NWea
- 'Recurva' (m)	CJun CMac
- 'Rubricaulis Aurea' (f/v)	CJun NEgg NLar
- 'Scotica' (f)	CJun NWea
- SIBERIA ('Limsi'PBR) (f)	LPra

	Name	Suppliers
	- 'Silver King'	see *I. aquifolium* 'Silver Queen'
	- 'Silver Lining' (f/v)	CJun
	- 'Silver Milkboy' (f/v)	EPfP MBlu WFar
	- 'Silver Milkmaid' (f/v)	CJun CRos LRHS MAsh MJak MMuc NEgg NRHS SLim SWvt
§	- 'Silver Queen' (m/v) $\mathbb{Y}^{H6}$	CBar CBcs CCVT CDul CEnd CRos ECrN EPfP LRHS MAsh MGos MJak MRav MSwo NBir NEgg NHol NLar NOra NPri NWea SAko SLim SLon SPer SPoG SWvt WMat
	- 'Silver Sentinel'	see *I.* × *altaclerensis* 'Belgica Aurea'
	- 'Silver van Tol' (f/v)	CBod CJun CKel CLnd EBee ELan EPfP EShb MAsh NEgg NLar NPer WFar
	- 'Somerset Cream' (f/v)	CJun CTri
*	- 'Variegata' (v)	SArc
	- 'Victoria' (m)	CJun
	- 'White Cream' (m/v)	SAko
	- 'Zig Zag' (f)	CJun
	× ***aquipernyi*** DRAGON LADY ('Meschick') (f) $\mathbb{Y}^{H6}$	CBod CJun CTho IArd LMaj LRHS NEgg NLar
	- 'San Jose' (f)	CJun
	× ***attenuata***	WFar
	- 'Sunny Foster' (f/v)	CBcs CMCN LRHS SAko WFar
	× ***beanii***	CJun
§	***bioritsensis***	CMCN
	'Brilliant' (f)	NEgg
	cassine L.	CMCN
	chapaensis HWJ 946	WCru
	'Clusterberry' (f)	CJun NEgg
	colchica	CMCN
	cornuta	EPfP ESwi
	- B&SWJ 8756	WCru
	- 'Anicet Delcambre' (f)	CJun
	- 'Burfordii' (f)	NLar
§	- 'Dazzler' (f)	CJun
	- 'Ira S. Nelson' (f)	CJun IArd SAko
	- 'Mercury' (f)	CJun
	- 'O. Spring' (f/v)	CJun CMac WSpi
	crenata	CAco CKel CMCN CTri EPfP MGos NHol NWea SArc SCob SPer STrG WFar
*	- 'Akagi'	WFar
	- 'Aureovariegata'	see *I. crenata* 'Variegata'
	- 'Carolina Upright' (m)	EBee SEWo
	- 'Convexa' (f) $\mathbb{Y}^{H6}$	CDul CJun CRos CTho EPfP LRHS MAsh MRav NEgg NRHS NWea SCob SPer WMoo
	- 'Convexed Gold' (f/v)	EPfP NLar NWad SPoG WFar
	- DARK GREEN ('Icoprins11'^{PBR})	CKel CLnd ELan EPfP LBuc LCro LOPS LRHS LSRN NWea SMad SPer SVic
	- 'Dwarf Pagoda' (f)	SAko
	- Fastigiata Group	CRos LRHS NRHS SCob WFar
	- - 'Fastigiata' (f) $\mathbb{Y}^{H6}$	CAco CRos EPfP LRHS LSRN MAsh MGos NLar SPer SPoG
	- - 'Sky Pencil' (f)	CMCN
*	- 'Glory Gem' (f)	CBcs LSRN
	- 'Glorie Gem' (m) **new**	SEWo
	- 'Golden Gem' (f/v) $\mathbb{Y}^{H6}$	CBor CJun CMac CRos CSBt CTri EBee ELan EPfP LRHS MAsh MGos MSwo NLar NRHS NWad NWea SAko SGol SPer SPoG SWvt WFar WThu
	- 'Green Hedger' $\mathbb{Y}^{H6}$	CLnd CPer EPfP MGos
	- 'Green Lustre' (f)	LSRN
	- 'Hetzii' (f)	CBod WMoo
	- 'Luteovariegata'	see *I. crenata* 'Variegata'
	- 'Mariesii' (f)	CMac EBee MBlu
I	- 'Pyramidalis' (f)	CMac MRav NWea
§	- 'Shiro-fukurin' (f/v)	CJun CMCN CRos ELan EPfP LRHS NRHS SLon SPoG
	- 'Snowflake'	see *I. crenata* 'Shiro-fukurin'
	- 'Stokes' (m)	CBod MSwo NLar NWad WMoo
§	- 'Variegata' (v)	CMCN CMac CRos EPfP LRHS NLar NRHS
	cyrtura (f)	WPGP
	- (m)	WPGP
	'Dazzler'	see *I. cornuta* 'Dazzler'
	dimorphophylla 'Somerset Pixie' (f)	CJun
	dipyrena	SAko
	'Doctor Kassab' (f)	CMCN
	'Elegance' (f)	MBlu WFar
	excelsa	CMCN
	aff. ***gagnepainiana*** FMWJ 13168	WCru
	glabra	CJun
	- f. ***leucocarpa*** 'Snow White' (f)	CJun
	'Good Taste' (f)	CJun WFar
	'Hohman' (f)	CJun
	'Indian Chief' (f)	CJun WAvo
	× ***koehneana***	CCVT MMuc SEND
	- 'Chestnut Leaf' (f) $\mathbb{Y}^{H5}$	CBcs CBod CCVT CDul CJun CLnd CMCN CTho ELan EWTr LPra LRHS MRav NEgg NLar SSta WFar WGrn
	laevigata	CMCN
	latifolia	CJun NLar
	'Leonardo'	EBee
*	'Little Diamond'	LSRN
	'Mary Nell' (f)	CJun IArd
	× ***meserveae***	LPra
§	- 'Anny's Dwarf' (m) **new**	LRHS
	- BLUE ANGEL ('Conang') (f)	CBod CCCN CDul CKel CMac CRos CSBt CTho EBee ELan EPfP EUJe LRHS MRav NEgg NLar NRHS NWea SPer SPoG SRms WAvo WFar
	- BLUE MAID ('Mesid') (f)	CCCN LOPS LRHS MGos NEgg NLar NRHS
	- BLUE PRINCE ('Conablu') (m) $\mathbb{Y}^{H6}$	CBcs CCCN CDul CKel CMCN CMac CRos ELan LBuc LPra LRHS MBlu MJak MMuc NEgg NHol NLar NWea SCob SLim SPer WFar
	- BLUE PRINCESS ('Conapri') (f) $\mathbb{Y}^{H6}$	CBcs CCVT CKel CMCN CMac CPer CTho ELan EPfP LBuc LPra MBlu MGos MJak MRav NEgg NLar NWea SCob SCoo SLim SPer WFar
	- CASTLE SPIRE ('Hachfee'^{PBR})	CLnd ECrN SLim WFar
	- CASTLE WALL ('Hecken Star'^{PBR})	ECrN LRHS NLar SEWo SLim WFar
	- GENTLE	see *I.* × *meserveae* 'Anny's Dwarf'
	- 'Goliath' (f)	WFar
	- 'Heckenpracht'^{PBR}	WFar
	- LITTLE RASCAL ('Mondo') (m)	CRos EPfP LRHS MGos
	- 'Little Sensation'	LRHS MBlu SPoG
	myrtifolia	MAsh MRav NHol
	'Nellie R. Stevens' (f)	CAco CCVT CJun CKel CTho EBee ECrN ELan EPfP LMaj LPra NLar NPri SCob SEWo WAvo WMat
	opaca	CMCN
	pedunculosa	NLar
	perado	NEgg
	- subsp. ***azorica***	WPGP
	- - B&SWJ 12526	WCru
	- subsp. ***platyphylla***	CMCN EBee MBlu SArc
	pernyi	CJun CMCN CMac EBtc MAsh

- var. ***veitchii***	see *I. bioritsensis*
rotunda	LEdu
rugosa	CMCN
'September Gem' (f)	CJun CMCN NEgg
serrata	CMac CMen
- 'Koshobai' (f)	CMen
- 'Leucocarpa' (f)	CMac
spinigera	CBcs
sugerokii	WCru
var. ***longipedunculata*** B&SWJ 10856	
'Tanager' (f)	CJun
triflora var. ***kanehirae***	CDul NLar
verticillata	CMCN EBee LRHS NWea WFar
- (f)	CBcs EBtc ELon EPfP MMrt NLar
- (m)	EBtc ELon EPfP MMrt NLar
- f. ***chrysocarpa*** (f)	NLar
- 'Maryland Beauty' (f)	CJun NLar
- 'Southern Gentleman' (m)	CJun MBlu NLar
- 'Winter Gold' (f)	CJun MBlu
- 'Winter Red' (f)	CJun CMCN MBlu
vomitoria	CMCN EBtc
× ***wandoensis***	WFar
'Washington' (f)	IArd WFar
'William Cowgill' (f)	CJun
yunnanensis	EBee IArd IDee

Iliamna see *Sphaeralcea*

Tillandsia (*Bromeliaceae*)

baileyi × ***ionantha***	NCft

Illicium (*Schisandraceae*)

anisatum	CBcs CCCN CExl EPfP LEdu NLar SSta WPGP WSHC
- B&SWJ 8411	WCru
floridanum	CBcs CCCN SBrt SSta
- 'Halley's Comet'	CExl NLar
aff. ***griffithii*** WWJ 11911	WCru
- WWJ 11971	WCru
- WWJ 11974	WCru
henryi	CExl EBee EPfP LRHS NLar WPGP
aff. ***henryi***	CBcs
lanceolatum	CExl
- KWJ 12245	WCru
macranthum B&SWJ 11809	WCru
majus WWJ 11919	WCru
aff. ***majus***	WCru
- WWJ 12017	WCru
merrillianum HWJ 1015	WCru
mexicanum	CExl
oligandrum	CExl WPGP
philippinense CWJ 12466	WCru
simonsii	CExl MBlu WPGP
- BWJ 8024	WCru
tashiroi CWJ 12468 **new**	WCru
'Woodland Ruby'	NLar WPGP

Ilysanthes see *Lindernia*

Impatiens (*Balsaminaceae*)

CC 4980	CExl
P1961	GCal
from China, Darrell Probst collection **new**	WFar
apiculata	WFar
arguta	CExl CHll CSam CSpe EBee EShb EWld GCal SBrt WBor WFar WPGP WSHC
- 'Alba'	CExl CSpe MPie WFar
- big blue-flowered **new**	ESwi
- big form **new**	CSpe WFar
auricoma × ***bicaudata***	MPie WDib
bicaudata	CSpe SPlb
congolensis	CCCN
aff. ***corchorifolia*** B&SWJ 13927	WCru
ernstii	CExl
flanaganae	CSpe ESwi SBrt WFar WPGP
forrestii	WFar
gomphophylla	CDTJ WFar
insignis	EBee EWld GCal WFar
keilii	WDib
kilimanjari	CSpe MPie WCot
subsp. ***kilimanjari***	
kilimanjari × ***pseudoviola***	CSpe MPie WDib WFar
langbianensis HWJ 1054	WCru
'Little Brother Montgomery'	CHll
macrophylla B&SWJ 10157	WCru
mengtszeana PB 02-519 **new**	WFar
namchabarwensis	CCCN
niamniamensis ♈H1b	CHll EBak EShb WDib
- 'Congo Cockatoo'	CDTJ NPer SRms
- 'Golden Cockatoo' (v)	CDTJ CHll EBak EShb
noli-tangere	WSFF
omeiana	CCCN CPla CSpe EBee EPPr ESwi EWld GCal GEdr GWyn ILea LEdu MNrw MSCN NLar SPtp WCru WFar WPGP WPtf
- DJHC 98492	WCru WFar
- 'High Voltage' **new**	WFar
- 'Ice Storm'	CDTJ EBee ESwi EWld GCal GEdr LEdu NLar WCot WCru WFar WPGP
- 'Pink Nerves'	EBee ESwi LEdu MPie WFar
- 'Red Leaf'	ESwi GCal
- 'Sango'	CPla CSpe EWld LEdu WFar
- variegated (v)	GEdr
oxyanthera 'Milo'	SBrt WFar
parasitica	WDib
platypetala B&SWJ 9722	WCru
pritzelii 'Sichuan Gold'	CDTJ EBee GCal MPie WFar
puberula	WFar
- HWJK 2063	EBee ESwi EWld SBrt WCru WPGP
qingchengshanica 'Emei Dawn'	CExl EBee ESwi GCal WCru WFar WPGP
repens ♈H1b	MPie WDib
rothii	GCal WCot WPGP
rupestris **new**	CDTJ
scabrida	CSpe
§ 'Secret Love'	CCCN
sodenii ♈H1c	CDTJ EShb ESwi GCal WDib
- 'Madonna'	CSpe
stenantha	EBee ESwi GEdr SBrt WFar
tinctoria	CAby CDTJ CExl CHll CSpe EBee ESwi EWld GCal SBrt
- from Cherangani, Kenya	EBee GCal
tuberosa	WDib
uniflora	SBrt WBor
VELVETEA	see *I.* 'Secret Love'
walleriana DeZire Series	NPri

Imperata (*Poaceae*)

cylindrica	CMen XLum
- 'Red Baron'	see *I. cylindrica* 'Rubra'
§ - 'Rubra'	Widely available

Incarvillea (*Bignoniaceae*)

arguta	GKev XLum
- from Tajikistan **new**	WPGP
brevipes	see *I. mairei*
compacta	GKev LLHF
- BWJ 7620	WCru
- var. ***qinghaiensis*** **new**	EPot
delavayi	CAby CBcs CBod CRos CTsd ECha EDAr ELan EPfP GKev LCro LOPS LRHS MGos MSCN NAln NBir NRHS SDeJ SPad SRms SVen SWvt WFar XLum
- 'Alba'	see *I. delavayi* 'Snowtop'
- 'Bees' Pink'	CPla CRos EPfP LPla LRHS
§ - 'Snowtop'	CAby CBod CRos EBee EDAr ELan EPfP EWld GBin LRHS MHol NBir NRHS SDeJ SWvt WBor WCot WFar
cf. ***delavayi***	MHol
grandiflora	GKev
himalayensis 'Frank Ludlow'	GKev
lutea	GKev
§ ***mairei***	CRos GKev GWyn LRHS NAln NRHS SRms
- var. ***mairei*** f. ***multifoliata***	see *I. zhongdianensis*
- white-flowered	GKev
olgae	ELan GKev
sinensis var. ***przewalskii***	GKev
'Snowdrop'	EMor
younghusbandii	EPot GKev
§ ***zhongdianensis***	CFis EBee EDAr EPot GEdr GKev LLHF SBrt
- BWJ 7692	WCru
- BWJ 7978	WCru
- white-flowered	GKev

Indigofera (*Papilionaceae*)

§ ***amblyantha***	CBcs CCCN CExl CRos EPfP LRHS MAsh MBlu NLar NRHS SEND SPlb WCFE WSHC WSpi
aff. ***amblyantha***	MMrt
balfouriana Craib BWJ 7851	WCru
cassioides	WCru
§ 'Claret Cascade' 🏆H5	WSHC
dielsiana	CCCN CRos ELan EPfP LRHS WSpi
'Dosua'	MMuc SEND
frutescens	CPbh
gerardiana	see *I. heterantha*
hancockii	CExl EPfP SChF WPGP WSHC
hebepetala	EPfP SBrt WPGP WSHC
§ ***heterantha*** 🏆H5	Widely available
heterophylla	CCCN
himachalensis	EBee
- H&M 1818	WPGP
himalayensis	CExl EBee MGil
- Yu 10941	CExl WPGP
- 'Silk Road'	CCCN CDul CKel CRos EBee ELan EPfP GKev LRHS MBlu MGos MSCN NLar NRHS SPoG SPtp WSpi
§ ***howellii***	CExl SChF WCru WPGP
§ - 'Reginald Cory' 🏆H5	EPfP
kirilowii	CRos ELan EPfP LRHS MBlu NLar WHlf WPGP WSHC WSpi
- var. ***alba***	CKel EPfP LRHS WSHC
§ ***pendula***	CCCN CExl CMac CRos CSde CSpe CWGN EBee ELan EPfP GKev LRHS MGil SPoG WCFE WKif WPGP WSHC WSpi
- B&SWJ 7741	WCru
potaninii misapplied	see *I. howellii*, *I. howellii* 'Reginald Cory', *I. amblyantha*, *I.* 'Claret Cascade', *I. pendula*
potaninii ambig.	CBcs CExl CMac MMrt WHer
pseudotinctoria	CCCN SRms
aff. ***pseudotinctoria***	CCCN
splendens	CSpe
subverticillata	LRHS WSHC
szechuensis	LRHS SMad WSpi
tinctoria	CCCN

Indocalamus (*Poaceae*)

latifolius	ERod MMuc MWht
- 'Hopei'	XCre
longiauritus	XCre
solidus	see *Bonia solida*
§ ***tessellatus*** 🏆H5	CAbb CBcs CBod ELon ENBC ERod MWht NGdn SMad WMoo XCre
- f. ***hamadae***	ERod MWht XCre

Indosasa (*Poaceae*)

gigantea	ERod

Inula (*Asteraceae*)

acaulis	WCot
barbata	GCal
conyzae	GJos
dysenterica	see *Pulicaria dysenterica*
ensifolia	CBcs ELan EMor EPfP EUJe LRHS MBel WHlf WHoo XLum
- 'Compacta'	GCal
- 'Gold Star'	EBee MBNS MRav NBid NBir WAvo WFar
glandulosa	see *I. orientalis*
helenium	CBod CCBP CHab CHby EBou EMor ENfk GPoy LCro LEdu LOPS MHer MNHC NBid NBir NDai NGrd NLar SRms WGwG WHer WMoo
hirta	XLum
hookeri	CChe CMea CSam ECha ELan EShb GBin GCal GMaP GWyn IFro ILea LEdu LLWG MBel MHol MMuc NBid NChi NDov NPer NSti SEND WBrk WCAu WOld WWtn
- GWJ 9033	WCru
macrocephala misapplied	see *I. royleana*
magnifica	Widely available
- 'Sonnenstrahl' 🏆H7	EPPr LEdu NLar SPhx
oculus-christi	EBee EWes WCot WMoo
§ ***orientalis***	CRos EBee EPfP LRHS NGBl NLar NRHS SPad SPer SRms XLum
racemosa	CRos EBee EPPr EWes GBin GCal GQue LRHS MNrw NRHS SPlb SRms WBor
- 'Sonnenspeer'	NBid NLar WPtf
§ ***royleana***	GCal MNrw MRav WArt

Inulanthera (*Asteraceae*)

calva	WCot

Iochroma (*Solanaceae*)

§ ***australe*** 🏆H3	CBcs CCCN CExl CHll CSpe EBee ELan EMdy LSRN MGil SEND SPlb SPoG SPtp SVen WCot WPGP
§ - 'Andean Snow'	CCCN CHll CSpe EShb MGil WHil WPGP
§ - 'Bill Evans'	EShb
- blue-flowered	see *I. australe* 'Bill Evans'

- white-flowered	see *I. australe* 'Andean Snow'
cyaneum	CCCN CHII ECre SPlb SVen
- purple-flowered	CCCN CHII
gesnerioides 'Coccineum'	CCCN CHII
§ ***grandiflorum***	CCCN CHII SEND
warscewiczii	see *I. grandiflorum*

Ipheion (*Alliaceae*)

'Alberto Castillo' ♀H4	Widely available
'Alice'	WCot
'Diana'	WCot
'Jessie'	CAby CBro CMea CPrp CRos EBee ECha EPot EWes GKev LAma LLHF LRHS NHpl NRHS SCob SDeJ WBrk WHoo WRHF WTor
'Judy'	WCot
'Rolf Fiedler' ♀H4	CAvo CBro CPrp CRos CTri EBee ELan EPfP EPot ERCP EWes GKev LAma LRHS NRHS NRya SCob SDeJ SRms WAul WFar WHil
sellowianum	CAby WCot
'Tessa'PBR	CRos EBee EWes GKev LLHF LRHS NHpl NRHS
§ ***uniflorum***	CBro CFis CTri ECha GKev ITim LAma SEND SRms WBrk WCot XLum
- f. ***album***	CBro CPrp CRos EBee ECha EWes LEdu LRHS NRHS SCob WCot WHil
- 'Charlotte Bishop'	CAvo CBro CPrp CRos EBee ECha ELon EPot ERCP EWes GKev LAma LLHF LRHS MNrw NBir NHpl NRHS NRya SCob SDeJ SRms WArt WAul WBrk WCot WHil WHoo
- 'Froyle Mill' ♀H5	CAvo CBro CPrp CRos ELon EPot ERCP EWes GKev LRHS MNrw NHpl NRHS SCob SDeJ SRms WCot WHoo WWFP
- subsp. ***tandiliense***	EBee EPPr
- f. ***violaceum***	SCob
- 'Wisley Blue' ♀H5	CBro CExl CPrp CRos CTri EAJP ECha ELan ELon EPfP EPot ERCP EShb GKev LAma LRHS MRav NRHS NRya SCob SDeJ SPoG SRms WCot WHoo
- 'Wisley Star'	GKev

Ipomoea (*Convolvulaceae*)

acuminata	see *I. indica*
alba	CBre CCCN EShb
batatas	CCCN
- 'Bonita' **new**	LRHS
- (Bright Ideas Series) BRIGHT IDEAS BLACK	EShb
- - BRIGHT IDEAS LIME ('Fripalligr')	EShb
-(Sweet Caroline Series) 'Sweet Caroline Light Green'PBR	EUJe
- - 'Sweet Caroline Purple'PBR	EUJe
- - 'Sweet Caroline Sweetheart Light Green'PBR	ESwi
- - 'Sweet Caroline Sweetheart Purple'PBR	ESwi
cairica	WCot
carnea	CCCN
coccinea var. ***hederifolia***	see *I. hederifolia*
§ ***hederifolia***	CCCN
× ***imperialis*** 'Sunrise Serenade'	CCCN
§ ***indica*** ♀H1c	CCCN CHII CRHN ECre EShb SPer
learii	see *I. indica*
§ ***lobata*** ♀H1c	CSpe
mauritiana	CCCN
'Milky Way'	CCCN
muellerii	CCCN
× ***multifida***	CSpe
purpurea 'Grandpa Otts'	LCro LOPS
- 'Kniola's Black Night'	CSpe
quamoclit	CSpe
tricolor 'Heavenly Blue' ♀H1c	LCro LOPS
versicolor	see *I. lobata*

Iresine (*Amaranthaceae*)

BLAZIN' LIME	see *I.* 'Lime'
BLAZIN' ROSE	see *I.* 'Rose'
§ 'Lime'	EUJe
§ 'Rose'	EUJe

Iris ✿ (*Iridaceae*)

AGSJ	EPPr
KR 3739	GEdr
'Abbey Chant' (IB)	WCAu XSen
'Abbondanza' (TB)	WCAu
'About Town' (TB)	WCAu
'Action Front' (TB)	CBod CKel CRos CWld EIri EPfP ESgI EShb LRHS MGos NRHS SDeJ WCAu WGwG
'Actress' (TB)	CKel CRos EPfP LRHS LSRN MGos NRHS WGwG
'Adobe Rose' (TB)	SIri XSen
'Adventuress' (TB)	XSen
'Afternoon in Rio' (TB)	WCAu
'Agatha Christie' (IB)	WCAu
'Aggressively Forward' (TB)	WCAu
'Aglow Again' (MTB)	SDys
'Agnes James' (CH)	CBro MAvo
'Ahwahnee Princess' (SDB)	ELon
'Aichi-no-kagayaki' (SpH)	WCot XLum
'Alabaster Unicorn' (TB)	ESgI
albicans ♀H5	CBro EPot GKev LEdu
- 'Blue Pygmy'	CKel
'Alcazar' (TB)	LSRN
'Alene's Other Love' (SDB)	WCAu
'Alexia' (TB)	CKel
'Alibi' (La) **new**	CRos
'Alice Harding' (TB)	ESgI
'Alida' (Reticulata)	EPfP EPot ERCP GKev LAma LCro LLHF LOPS LRHS NBir NRHS SDeJ WBrk XEll
'Alizes' (TB) ♀H7	CKel ESgI LRHS WViv XSen
'Allegiance' (TB)	WCAu
'Ally Oops' (SpH)	WCAu
'Amadora' (TB)	CKel EIri
'Amber Queen' (DB)	CKel ECtt ELan LRHS NBir NRHS SDeJ SPer
'Ambroisie' (TB) ♀H7	ESgI
'American Patriot' (IB)	CKel WCAu
'Amethyst Flame' (TB)	SRms WCAu
'Amherst Blue' (IB)	EIri
'Amherst Caper' (SDB)	EIri
'Amherst Glacier' (IB)	WCAu
'Amphora' (SDB)	CBro
'Ancient Echoes' (TB)	ESgI
'Andalou' (TB) ♀H7	CWCL WViv XSen
'Angel Unawares' (TB)	WCAu
'Angel's Touch' (TB)	ESgI

anglica	see *I. latifolia*
'Ann Chowning' (La)	LCro WPnP
'Ann Dasch' (Sib)	WAul
'Annabel Jane' (TB)	CKel ELon WCAu
'Anne Elizabeth' (SDB)	CBro
'Annemarie Troeger' (Sib) 🏆H7	ELon
'Annick' (Sib)	CRos EBee LRHS MMrt NRHS XSen
'Annikins' (IB)	CKel
'Antarctique' (IB)	ESgI
'Aphrodisiac' (TB)	XSen
aphylla	GBin SBrt WAbe
- 'Slick'	SDys
'Apollo' (Dut)	CAvo
'Appointer' (SpH)	NChi WWtn
'Apricorange' (TB)	CKel SRms WCot
'Apricot Blaze' (TB)	ESgI
'Apricot Drops' (MTB) 🏆H7	ESgI WCAu
'Apricot Frosty' (BB)	WCAu XSen
'Apricot Silk' (IB)	CCCN CKel NQui WCot
'Apricot Topping' (BB)	WCAu
'Aquamarine' (IB)	MHol
'Arab Chief' (TB)	CKel
'Archie Owen' (Spuria)	WCAu
'Arctic Age' (TB)	WCAu
'Arctic Fancy' (IB)	CKel
'Arctic Fox' (TB)	WCAu
'Arctic Sunrise' (TB)	CKel ESgI
'Arctic Wind' (IB)	WCAu
arenaria	see *I. humilis*
'Argus Pheasant' (TB)	ESgI
'Around Midnight' (TB)	CRos LRHS NRHS
'Arpège' (TB)	CKel GWyn XSen
'Arrows' (La) new	LLWG
'Art Deco' (TB)	SIri XSen
'As de Coeur' (TB)	XSen
'Ascension Crown' (TB)	ESgI
'Ask Alma' (IB)	SIri XSen
'Astrid Cayeux' (TB)	ESgI
'Astro Flash' (TB)	ESgI
'Atlantic Crossing' (Sib)	SIri WAul
'Attention Please' (TB)	CKel
attica	CBro CPBP GEdr GKev LLHF WThu
- blue-flowered	GKev
- lemon-flowered	EPPr GKev WAbe WThu
'Attitude' (IB)	WCAu
§ ***aucheri*** 🏆H4	EPot GKev LLHF XSen
- indigo-flowered	GKev
- 'Snow White'	GKev
'Aunt Josephine' (TB)	ESgI
'Aurélie' (TB)	WViv
'Austrian Sky' (SDB)	CAby CKel CMac ECtt ELon EPfP LRHS NRHS SDeJ WAul WCot
'Autumn Circus' (TB)	WCAu
'Autumn Echo' (TB)	ESgI XSen
'Autumn Encore' (TB)	CKel SRms
'Autumn Leaves' (TB)	WCAu
'Autumn Princess' (Dut)	CAvo GKev SDeJ
'Autumn Riesling' (TB)	WCAu
'Autumn Tryst' (TB)	ESgI WCAu
'Avalon Sunset' (TB)	EIri
'Awesome Blossom' (TB)	ESgI
'Az Ap' (IB)	ELon WCAu
babadagica	WAbe
'Babbling Brook' (TB)	CKel GWyn XSen
'Baby Bengal' (BB)	XSen
'Baby Blessed' (SDB)	CBro WCAu
'Baby Sister' (Sib)	CRos ELon GBin LRHS LSRN NBro NRHS WFar
'Bach Toccata' (MTB)	SDys
'Back in Black' (TB)	CKel
'Badlands' (TB)	WCAu
'Baie Rose' (IB)	SIri
'Bal Masqué' (TB)	ESgI WViv XSen
'Ballerina Pink' (BB)	WCAu
'Ballistic' (SDB)	WCAu
'Ballyhoo' (TB)	WCAu XSen
'Baltic Star' (TB)	WCAu
'Banbury Beauty' (CH) 🏆H4	MAvo NLar
'Banbury Gem' (CH)	MAvo NLar
'Banbury Melody' (CH)	MAvo
'Banbury Ruffles' (SDB)	ESgI LRHS NLar WCAu
'Bandera Waltz' (TB)	WCAu
'Bang' (TB)	CKel
'Bangles' (MTB) 🏆H7	SDys WCAu
'Banish Misfortune' (Sib)	WAul
'Bar de Nuit' (TB)	ESgI
'Barbara May' (TB)	WCAu
'Barbara My Love' (TB)	WCAu
barbatula BWJ 7663	WCru
'Barcoo' (La) new	LLWG
barnumiae	GKev
subsp. ***barnumiae*** new	
'Batik' (BB)	SIri WCot XSen
'Bayberry Candle' (TB)	CKel WCAu
'Be My Baby' (BB)	WCAu
BEAUTY SUPER MIX (Dut)	GKev
'Bedtime Story' (IB)	XSen
'Before the Storm' (TB)	CKel ELan ELon ESgI LRHS WCAu XSen
'Being Busy' (SDB)	ESgI
'Bel Azur' (IB)	ESgI LRHS
'Belgian Princess' (TB)	WCAu
'Belise' (Spuria) 🏆H7	WCot
'Belle de Nuit' (TB)	WViv
'Ben a Factor' (MTB)	ESgI
'Benbow' (TB)	WMil
'Benton Ankarat' (TB)	NRHS
'Benton Apollo' (TB)	ECha EMal LRHS NRHS
'Benton Argent' (TB)	ECha NRHS
'Benton Arundel' (TB)	EMal LRHS NRHS
'Benton Bluejohn' (TB)	EMal LRHS NRHS
'Benton Caramel' (TB)	ECha EMal LRHS NRHS
'Benton Cordelia' (TB)	EMal LRHS NRHS
'Benton Daphne' (TB)	EMal LRHS NRHS
'Benton Dierdre' (TB)	CKel ECha ECtt ELan ELon EMal LRHS NRHS SRms
'Benton Duff' (TB)	ECha NRHS
'Benton Evora' (TB)	ECha EMal LRHS NRHS
'Benton Farewell' (TB)	ECha LRHS NRHS
'Benton Judith' (TB)	ECha NRHS
'Benton Lorna' (TB)	ECha EMal LRHS NRHS
'Benton Menace' (TB)	ECha EMal LRHS NRHS
'Benton Nigel' (TB)	ECha ECtt ELan EMal LRHS NRHS WCAu WGwG
'Benton Nutkin' (TB)	EMal LRHS NRHS
'Benton Olive' (TB)	ECha EMal LRHS NRHS
'Benton Opal' (TB)	ECha EMal LRHS NRHS
'Benton Pearl' (TB)	ECha EMal LRHS NRHS
'Benton Primrose' (TB)	ECha EMal LRHS NRHS
'Benton Sheila' (TB)	ECha ELan ELon
'Benton Susan' (TB)	ECha ECtt EMal LRHS NRHS WGwG
'Berkeley Gold' (TB)	CKel CRos CSBt ECtt ELan EWes LRHS NRHS SCob SDeJ SPer WGwG
'Berlin Bluebird' (Sib)	SMHy
'Berlin Ruffles' (Sib) 🏆H7	CKel EWes WAul
'Berlin Sky' (Sib)	ESgI EWes
'Berlin Tiger' (SpH) 🏆H7	CKel EPPr EWTr LLWG MWts NLar SCob SMHy WMoo

'Bermuda Triangle' (BB)	SDys
'Best Bet' (TB)	CBod ESgI WCAu
'Bethany Claire' (TB)	ESgI WCAu
'Betty Cooper' (Spuria)	WCAu
'Betty Simon' (TB)	CWCL XSen
'Beverly Sills' (TB)	CKel CRos EIri EPfP LCro LRHS MHer MRav NRHS SCob SDeJ WCAu XSen
'Bewilderbeast' (TB)	XSen
'Bianco' (TB)	GWyn WCAu WHil
'Bibury' (SDB) ♀H7	WCAu
bicapitata	CPBP
'Bickley Cape' (Sib)	GBin
'Big Blue' (Sib)	WFar
'Big Heart' (Sib)	EIri
'Big Squeeze' (TB)	SIri WCAu
biglumis	see *I. lactea*
biliottii	CBro
'Bishop's Robe' (TB)	CKel ESgI LRHS
'Black as Night' (TB)	XSen
'Black Aura'	NWad
'Black Cherry Delight' (SDB)	ESgI
'Black Dragon' (TB)	CCCN CKel GWyn XSen
'Black Flag' (TB)	XSen
'Black Gamecock' (La)	CWCL ECtt EWTr IPot LCro LLWG LOPS MNrw MSCN MWts NLar WCAu WFar WMAq WPnP WWtn
'Black is Back'	WCAu
'Black Knight' (TB)	LRHS MJak MRav NLar NQui WKif WSpi
'Black Night' (IB)	NEgg
'Black Prince' (IB)	SCob
'Black Suited' (TB)	SIri
'Black Swan' (TB)	CAby CBor CKel CMac ECha ECtt ELan EPfP ESgI EShb EUJe EWTr GCal LCro LOPS LRHS LSRN NQui NRHS SCob SPer SPoG SRms WCot XSen
'Black Tie Affair' (TB)	CKel ELan EPfP ESgI LRHS MAsh NRHS WCAu XSen
'Black Watch' (IB)	CKel GWyn
'Blackbeard' (BB) ♀H7	WCAu
'Blackberry Tease' (TB)	WCAu
'Blackberry Towers' (TB)	ESgI
'Blackcurrant' (IB)	WCAu
'Blackout' (TB)	ESgI
'Blast' (IB)	CKel
'Blatant' (TB)	ESgI WCAu XSen
'Blaue Milchstrasse' (Sib)	GBin GWyn MMrt
'Blaues Schweben' (Sib)	GBin
'Blazing Light' (TB)	XSen
'Blenheim Royal' (TB)	ESgI WCAu XSen
'Blitzen' (IB)	WCAu
bloudowii	WAbe
'Blue Admiral' (TB)	GBin
'Blue Bird' (Sib)	ECtt LLWG SPoG WFar WGob
'Blue Burgee' (Sib)	ECha
I 'Blue Butterfly' (Sib)	EBee EPfP NGdn
'Blue Denim' (SDB)	CMea CRos ECtt ELon EPfP GMaP MHol MRav NBir NLar WCot
'Blue Duchess' (TB)	WArt
'Blue Eyed Blond' (IB)	CKel
'Blue Eyed Brunette' (TB)	WCAu
'Blue Giant' ambig. (Dut)	LLWG
'Blue Hendred' (SDB)	NBir WCAu
'Blue Hill' (Reticulata)	GKev LAma
'Blue Hour' (TB)	WCAu
'Blue King' (Sib)	CDor ELan EPfP GMaP ILea LRHS MRav NBro NGdn SCob SPer WMoo
'Blue Meadow Fly' (Sino-Sib)	LLHF
'Blue Mere' (Sib)	MCot
'Blue Moon' (Sib)	ELon IMou MJak WFar
'Blue Mountain Mist' (La) **new**	LLWG
'Blue Mystery' (J)	LLHF
'Blue Note Blues' (TB)	WCAu
'Blue Note' (Reticulata)	CRos EPfP EPot ERCP GKev IPot LAma LLHF LRHS NRHS
'Blue Pigmy' (SDB)	CBod CWat ECtt EPfP LRHS MRav MTin NLar NRHS SDeJ SPer
'Blue Reverie' (Sib)	ELon ESgI
'Blue Rhythm' (TB)	CKel CRos ELan ELon EPfP EUJe GBin GMaP GPSL LCro LRHS MRav NAln NRHS SCoo SDeJ SPer WCAu
'Blue Sapphire' (Dut)	MHol
'Blue Sapphire' (TB)	CKel ESgI WCAu
'Blue Sceptre' (Sib)	IBlr
'Blue Shimmer' (TB)	CBod CMac CRos EBee ECha ELan EPfP ESgI EShb LRHS LSRN MWat NRHS SDeJ SPer SRms WCAu WGwG
'Blue Splash' (IB)	WCAu
'Blue Staccato' (TB)	WCAu XSen
'Blue Suede Shoes' (TB)	ESgI LSRN XSen
'Blue Trill' (TB)	WCAu
'Bluebeard's Ghost' (SDB) ♀H7	WCAu
'Bluebird Wine' (TB)	CKel MNHC
'Blushing Pink' (TB)	CKel
'Bockingford' (MTB)	SIri
'Bold Encounter' (TB)	WCAu
'Bold Pretender' (La)	ECtt ELon EPfP LLWG MBNS NLar WHil
'Bold Print' (IB)	CAby CKel CRos ELon IPot LRHS LSRN MGos MHer MWat NRHS SPoG WCAu
'Bollinger'	see *I.* 'Hornpipe'
'Boo' (SDB)	CPBP WCAu XSen
'Border Happy' (TB)	WCAu
'Border Town' (Spuria)	WCAu
'Bottled Sunshine' (IB)	LRHS
'Bound for Glory' (La)	LLWG
'Bournemouth Ball Gown' (Sib)	WAul
'Bournemouth Beauty' (Sib) ♀H7	WAul
'Bouzy Bouzy' (TB)	ESgI XSen
'Bracknell' (Sib)	WAul
bracteata	EBee SPhx
'Braithwaite' (TB)	CAby CKel CRos CWGN ELan EPfP ESgI EShb LRHS NRHS SDeJ SPer SRms WCAu WGwG WTor
'Brannigan' (SDB)	NBir NRHS NSti
'Brasilia' (TB)	NBir
'Brassie' (SDB)	CBro MBNS XSen
'Breakers' (TB) ♀H7	CKel WCAu
'Breezy Blue' (SDB)	WCAu
'Brenchley' (IB)	SIri
'Bridal Icing' (TB)	WCAu
'Bride's Halo' (TB)	LSRN WCAu XSen
'Bright Button' (SDB)	CKel ESgI
'Bright Vision' (SDB)	ESgI
'Bright White' (MDB)	CBro CKel
'Bright Yellow' (DB)	MRav
'Brighteyes' (IB)	SRms
'Brindisi' (TB)	XSen
'Brise de Mer' (TB)	XSen
'Bristo Magic' (TB)	XSen
'Bristol Gem' (TB)	XSen

'Broad Shoulders' (TB) WCAu
'Broadleigh Angela' (CH) CBro
'Broadleigh Carolyn' (CH) ♀H5 CElw WSHC
'Broadleigh Lavinia' (CH) CBro
'Broadleigh Nancy' (CH) CBro
'Broadleigh Peacock' (CH) CElw NLar WSHC
'Broadleigh Penny' (CH) NLar
'Broadleigh Rose' (CH) CBro CElw MAvo MBrN WSHC
'Broadway Baby' (IB) ESgI
'Broadway Star' (TB) CKel
'Bronzaire' (IB) CKel EIri WCAu WGwG
'Bronze Beauty' (Dut) ERCP GKev
'Bronze Beauty' (TB) SDeJ
'Bronze Beauty' van Tubergen (*boogiana* hybrid) NBir SDeJ
'Brother Carl' (TB) XSen
'Brown Chocolate' (TB) WCAu
'Bruce' (TB) WCAu
'Brummit's Mauve' (TB) WCAu
'Bruno' (TB) LSRN NLar WMil
'Brussels' (TB) ESgI
bucharica misapplied see *I. orchioides* Carrière
bucharica ambig. CAvo GKev LSun MNrw NHpl SDeJ XSen
§ ***bucharica*** Foster ♀H5 CBro EPot LAma
* - 'Baldschuan Yellow' (J) GKev
* - 'Top Gold' (J) GKev
'Buckwheat' (TB) CKel SIri
'Buisson de Roses' (TB) XSen
bulleyana CBro GKev SRms WArt
- BWJ 7912 WCru
- black-flowered CExl GKev
- - SDR 1792 EBee
'Bumblebee Deelite' (MTB) ♀H7 CBor CKel WCAu
'Bundle of Joy' (Sib) ECtt WGob
'Bundle of Love' (BB) WCAu
'Burgermeister' (TB) XSen
'Burgundy Party' (TB) XSen
'Burka' (TB) ESgI
'Burmese Dawn' (TB) CKel
'Burnt Toffee' (TB) ESgI SIri XSen
'Burst' (TB) CKel WCAu
'Butter and Sugar' (Sib) ♀H7 Widely available
'Buttermere' (TB) SRms
'Butterpat' (IB) ESgI
'Butterscotch Carpet' (SDB) WCAu
'Butterscotch Kiss' (TB) CKel CMac CRos ELan ELon EPfP GMaP LRHS MGos MRav NBir NLar NRHS SDeJ SPer WHoo
'Buzzword' (SDB) WCAu
'Bye Bye Blues' (TB) ESgI XSen
'Cabaret Royale' (TB) ESgI XSen
'Cable Car' (TB) CKel CWCL ESgI
'Caesar' (Sib) SDys SRms
'Caesar's Brother' (Sib) CKel CRos ELan GWyn LCro LOPS LRHS MGos NHol NLar NRHS SHar SPer WBrk WFar WHoo WWtn
'Cajun Rhythm' (TB) CKel XSen
'Caldron' (TB) **new** CKel
'Calgary' (TB) WCAu
'Caliente' (TB) MRav WCAu XSen
'California Style' (IB) XSen
§ Californian hybrids CElw CKel CMac CPBP NBir WCot
'Calm Stream' (TB) WCAu
'Calypso Mood' (TB) XSen
'Cambridge' (Sib) ♀H7 CKel CRos EHoe EIri EPfP IMou LRHS NRHS WAul WFar
'Camelot Rose' (TB) WCAu XSen
'Cameo Blush' (BB) XSen
'Cameo Wine' (TB) ESgI MNrw XSen
'Cameroun' (TB) ESgI
canadensis see *I. hookeri*
'Canadian Streaker' (TB/v) WCot
'Canary Bird' (TB) ESgI
'Candy Rock' (IB) WCAu
'Cannington Ochre' (SDB) CBro
'Canonbury Belle' (Sib) WAul
'Can't Touch This' (TB) WCAu
'Cantab' (Reticulata) CRos EPot ERCP GKev LAma LRHS NBir NRHS SCob SDeJ
'Captain Indigo' (IB) ESgI WCAu
'Captive Sun' (SDB) CKel CWld EPfP LRHS MAsh NRHS SIri WTor
'Caramel' (TB) XSen
'Cardinal' (TB) WMil
'Care to Dance' (TB) WCAu
'Careless Sally' (Sib) WAul WCAu
'Carfax' (TB) WMil
'Caribbean Dream' (TB) CKel XSen
'Carnaby' (TB) CBod CKel ELon EPfP ESgI EShb LRHS MRav MSCN NRHS SDeJ WCAu WGwG XSen
'Carnival Time' (TB) CKel CMac CRos CWGN ECtt EPfP LRHS MCot NRHS SPer XSen
'Carolina' (Reticulata) CRos LAma LLHF LRHS NRHS
'Carolina Gold' (TB) CKel XSen
* 'Caronte' (IB) ESgI
'Carriage Trade' (TB) LRHS
'Carriwitched' (IB) CKel
'Cartouche' (BB) **new** SIri
'Casbah' (TB) XSen
'Cascade Rhythm' (TB) WCAu
'Cascade Springs' (TB) XSen
'Cascade Sprite' (SDB) SRms
'Catalyst' (TB) XSen
'Cat's Eye' (SDB) ESgI SIri WCAu
'Catwalk Idol' (La) LLWG
caucasica CMac
'Cayenne Capers' (TB) ESgI
* 'Cedric Morris' EWes
'Cee Cee' XSen
'Celebration Song' (TB) ESgI SIri WCAu XSen
'Celestial Glory' (TB) XSen
'Cerdagne' (TB) XSen
'Chalkhill' (SDB) WCAu
chamaeiris see *I. lutescens* subsp. *lutescens*
'Champagne Elegance' (TB) CKel EIri EPfP NBir XSen
'Champagne Encore' (IB) ELon
'Champagne Frost' (TB) XSen
'Champagne Waltz' (TB) SIri XSen
'Chance Beauty' (SpH) ♀H7 WCAu
'Change of Pace' (TB) ESgI WCAu XSen
'Chanted' (SDB) WCAu XSen
'Chantilly' (TB) CKel CRos ELan EUJe LRHS MRav MSCN NBir NGdn NLar NRHS SPer
'Chapeau' (TB) ESgI WCAu
'Charlotte's Tutu' (La) LLWG
'Charmaine' (TB) XSen
'Chartreuse Bounty' (Sib) ECtt ELan EMor EWTr EWes GAbr GMaP MHol NLar NSti WFar
'Chasing Rainbows' (TB) SDys WCAu
'Cheap Frills' (TB) WCAu
'Cher' (TB) LSRN
'Cherished' (TB) CKel
'Cherished One' (La) LLWG
'Cherry Blossom Song' (TB) SIri
'Cherry Garden' (SDB) CBod CBro CKel CPBP CRos CWat CWld ECtt EHrv ELan ELon EPfP

		EShb EWes GMaP LRHS MBNS MRav MTin NBir NGdn NLar NRHS SDeJ WAul WCot
	'Cherry Twist' (La)	LLWG
	'Cherub's Smile' (TB)	XSen
	'Chicken Little' (MDB)	CBro
	'Chief Moses' (TB)	WCAu
I	'Chieftain' (SDB)	MRav
	'Childhood Sweetheart' (La)	LLWG
	'Chilled Wine' (Sib)	ELan ELon LRHS
	'China Dragon' (TB)	XSen
	'Chinese Coral' (TB)	XSen
	'Chinese Treasure' (TB)	XSen
	'Chinook Winds' (TB)	WCAu
	'Chivalry' (TB)	ESgI
	'Christine Mullins' (Sib)	WBor
	'Christmas Angel' (TB)	WCAu
	Chrysofor Group	CAby
	chrysographes ♀H6	CBcs CBod CBro CDor CKel CRos CSpe CTsd CWCL EHoe EPfP EWhm GJos GKev LCro LOPS LRHS MBel MHer MRav NRHS NSti SCob SPoG WFar XSen
	- BWJ 7930	WCru
I	- 'Black Beauty'	EPfP
	- 'Black Gold'	MHol NLar
I	- 'Black Knight'	CExl CRos EPfP GBin GCal LRHS MCot NAln NChi NLar NRHS SMad
I	- 'Black Velvet'	GEdr WSpi
	- black-flowered	Widely available
	- 'Bob's Fancy'	SDeJ
	- dark-flowered	GKev NAln WFar
	- hybrid	WFar
	- 'Inshriach'	IMou
	- 'Kew Black'	CExl GKev LEdu NBir WHil
	- 'Kilmurry Black'	IKil
	- 'Mandarin Purple'	GCal GQue SPer
	- yellow-flowered	WFar
	chrysographes* × *forrestii	NBir
	'Château d'Auvers-sur-Oise' (TB)	SIri WViv
	'Chubby Cheeks' (SDB)	CKel WCAu
	'Ciel et Mer' (TB)	WViv
	'Cimarron Rose' (SDB)	ESgI
	'Cimarron Strip' (TB)	CKel EPfP WCot XSen
	'Cinque Terre' (TB)	WCAu
	'Circle of Light' (TB)	WCAu
	'Circus Stripes' (TB)	XSen
	'Cirrus Veil' (SDB)	WCAu
	'Citoyen' (TB)	XSen
	'Citronnade' (TB)	ESgI
	'City of Paradise' (TB)	ESgI
	'Claire' (Reticulata) **new**	NBir
	'Clairette' (Reticulata)	CRos EPot GKev LAma LRHS NRHS SCob SDeJ
	'Clara Garland' (IB)	WCAu
	'Clarence' (TB)	CKel ESgI WCAu XSen
	clarkei B&SWJ 2122	WCru
	- CC 2751	CExl
	- SDR 3819	GKev
	'Class Ring' (TB)	WCAu
	'Classic Look' (TB)	ESgI SIri
	'Classic Navy' (BB)	ESgI
	'Clee Hills' (Sib)	WAul
	'Cleedownton' (Sib)	WAul
	'Clematis' (TB)	WMil
	'Cleo' (TB)	NSti
	'Cleo Murrell' (TB)	ESgI
	'Cleve Dodge' (Sib)	ESgI XLum
	'Cliffs of Dover' (TB)	CKel EIri ESgI GCal MCot SCob SRms
	'Cloudcap' (TB)	SRms
	'Clownerie' (TB)	WViv
	'Clyde Redmond' (La) ♀H5	WMAq
	'Coal Face' (TB)	WCAu
	'Coal Seams' (TB)	WCAu
	'Coalignition' (TB)	WCAu
	'Codicil' (TB)	EIri XSen
	colchica	LEdu
	'Colette Thurillet' (TB)	CKel WViv XSen
	'Colin's Pale Blue' (Sib)	NCGa SMHy
	'Collingwood Ingram'	WThu
	'Color Glory' (TB)	SIri
	'Color Me Blue' (TB)	WCAu
	'Color Splash' (TB)	XSen
	'Color Strokes' (TB)	WCAu
	'Colorific' (La)	WGob
	'Colortart' (TB)	XSen
	'Coming Up Roses' (TB)	XSen
	'Con Fuoco' (TB)	XSen
	'Concertina' (IB)	WCAu
	'Concoction' (IB) **new**	GKev
	'Concord Crush' (Sib)	MHol WGob WPnP WTor WWtn
	confusa ♀H4	CHll SArc SMad XSen
§	- 'Martyn Rix'	CAbb CAby CBct CMac CPou CRos ELon EPfP GCal IDee LRHS MPie SBrt SEND SRms WGwG WWFP
	'Conjuration' (TB)	CKel SIri WCAu
	'Connection' (TB)	WCAu
	'Constant Wattez' (IB)	CKel ESgI NLar
	'Constantine Bay' (TB)	ESgI
	'Consummation' (MTB)	CRos
	'Contrast in Styles' (Sib)	ECtt MNrw MSCN NQui WFar WGob WWtn
	'Copatonic' (TB)	ESgI WCAu
	'Copper Capers' (TB)	ESgI
	'Copper Classic' (TB)	ELon ESgI LSRN WCAu
	'Coquet Waters' (Sib)	NBid WAul
	'Coral Point' (TB)	WCAu
	'Coral Splendor' (TB)	WCAu
	'Coral Sunset' (TB)	XSen
	'Cordoba' (TB)	WCAu XSen
	'Coronation Anthem' (Sib)	WAul
	'Côte d'Or' (TB)	XSen
	'Country Kisses' (TB)	WCAu
	'County Town Red' (TB)	SIri
	'Cozy Calico' (TB)	WCAu
	'Cracklin' Burgundy' (TB)	XSen
	'Crackling Caldera' (TB)	MMrt WCot
	'Cranapple' (BB) ♀H7	ESgI WCAu
	'Cranberry Ice' (TB)	ELon XSen
	'Cranberry Sauce' (TB)	SIri WCAu
	'Cranbrook' (IB) ♀H7	SIri
	'Crathie' (TB)	ECha EMal LRHS NRHS
	'Cream Beauty' (Dut)	GKev LCro LOPS SDeJ
	'Cream Pixie' (SDB)	WCAu
	'Creative Artistry' (La)	LLWG
	cretensis	see *I. unguicularis* subsp. *cretensis*
	'Crinoline' (TB)	CKel XSen
	'Crispette' (TB)	WCAu
	cristata	EPot GEdr GKev NHpl SMad
	- 'Abbey's Violet'	EBee
	- 'Alba'	CPBP GEdr WAbe WThu
	crocea ♀H6	EBee GBin GKev WCAu
	'Croftway Lemon' (TB)	ELon
	'Cross Current' (TB)	WCAu
	'Crowned Heads' (TB)	WCAu XSen
	'Crushed Ice' (La)	LLWG
	'Crystal Glitters' (TB)	ESgI

'Cumulus' (TB)	SIri
cuniculiformis	WCot
'Cup Race' (TB)	WCAu XSen
'Curlew' (IB)	WCAu
'Cutie' (IB)	ESgI WCAu
'Cyanea' (DB)	GKev
'Cyclamint' (La)	LLWG
cycloglossa	GKev
'Daedalus' (Rc)	GKev
'Daemon Imp' (MTB)	WCAu
'Dahdah' (TB)	WCAu
'Dainty Lace' (La)	LLWG
'Dale Dennis' (DB)	XSen
'Dame de Coeur' (TB)	SIri
'Dance Ballerina Dance' (Sib)	CBod CWCL EBee EPfP GWyn MRav NCGa NLar WFar WGob
'Dance for Joy' (TB)	XSen
'Dance On' (Reticulata)	LAma
'Dance the Night Away' (TB)	WCAu
'Dancer's Veil' (TB)	CKel CMac CRos EBee ECtt ELon ESgI LRHS MRav NRHS SPer WArt WCAu
'Dancing Lilacs' (MTB)	ESgI
'Dancing Nanou' (Sib)	ECtt
danfordiae	CRos EPfP EPot GKev LAma LCro LOPS LRHS MJak NHpl NRHS SCob SDeJ
danfordiae × histroides* var. *sophensis **new**	GKev
'Daphne' (TB) **new**	WMil
'Dardanus' (Rc)	EPot ERCP GKev SDeJ WCot
'Dark Circle' (Sib)	EBee WFar
'Dark Crystal' (SDB)	ESgI
'Dark Desire' (Sib)	MRav
'Dark Drama' (TB)	WCAu
'Dark Spark' (SDB)	WCAu
'Dark Vader' (SDB)	ESgI
'Darkness' (IB)	SIri
'Darkside' (TB)	XSen
'Daughter of Stars' (TB)	ELon
'Dauntless' (TB)	ESgI
'Dawn of Fall' (TB)	ESgI
'Dawn Waltz' (Sib)	LLWG WCAu WFar WGob
'Dawning' (TB) ♀H7	ESgI
'Dazzling' (IB)	WCAu
'Dazzling Gold' (TB)	CKel ESgI XSen
'Dear Currier' (Sib)	WAul
'Dear Delight' (Sib)	CBod ELon ILea LLHF MNrw NLar WFar
'Decadence' (TB)	WCAu
§ ***decora***	LLHF SBrt WAbe
'Deep Black' (TB)	CKel CRos CSpe CWGN EBee EHrv ELan EPfP ESgI EUJe GMaP LRHS LSRN MBNS MCot MRav MWat NLar NRHS NWad SDeJ SPer SPoG WGwG
'Deep Pacific' (TB)	WCAu
'Deep Sea Quest' (La)	LLWG
'Deepening Shadows' (CH)	MAvo
'Deft Touch' (TB)	XSen
delavayi ♀H6	EWes GMaP
- SDR 50	CExl GKev
- 'Didcot'	CRos LRHS NRHS
'Delirium' (IB)	WCAu
'Delta Blues' (TB)	SIri
'Delta Butterfly' (La)	WMAq
'Demon' (SDB)	XSen
'Demure Illini' (Sib)	MNrw
'Denys Humphry' (TB)	WCAu
'Derwentwater' (TB)	SRms WCAu
'Desert Echo' (TB)	CKel XSen
'Desert Jewel' (La)	LLWG
'Desi Brouwer' (IB)	SIri
'Devil May Care' (IB)	ESgI
'Devonshire Cream' (TB)	WCAu
'Devoted' (SDB)	WCAu
'Dewful' (Sib)	WFar
'Diabolique' (TB) ♀H7	XSen
'Diamond Ring' (TB)	SDys
dichotoma	SBrt
'Disco Jewel' (MTB)	ESgI
'Discovered Treasure' (TB)	WCAu
'Discovery'[PBR] (Dut)	SDeJ
'Disguise' (TB)	WCAu
'Distant Chimes' (TB)	CKel
'Distant Music' (La)	LLWG
'Ditzy' (SDB)	SIri
'Diversion' (TB)	ESgI
'Dividing Line' (MTB)	WCAu
'Dixie Darling' (TB)	ESgI XSen
'Dixie Pixie' (SDB)	WCAu
'Dolce' (SpH)	WCAu
'Dolly Madison' (TB)	ESgI
§ ***domestica***	CBro CHll CPla ELan EUJe GKev LRHS SPlb SRms WSHC
- 'Crûg Colossal'	WCru
- 'Freckle Face'	CWCL MHol
'Dominion' (TB)	WMil
'Dotted Swiss' (TB)	XSen
'Double Byte' (SDB)	XSen
'Double Espoir' (TB)	XSen
'Double Lament' (SDB)	CBro
'Double Standards' (Sib)	NLar WFar WGob
'Double Vision' (TB)	XSen
'Douce Reverie' (TB)	WViv
douglasiana	GCal GKev
'Dover Beach' (TB)	SIri
'Dover Castle' (BB) ♀H7	SIri
'Downtown Brown' (TB)	WCAu
'Draco' (TB)	ESgI XSen
'Drama Queen' (TB)	WCAu
'Dream Indigo' (IB)	WCAu XSen
'Dreaming Green' (Sib)	EBee
'Dreaming Orange' (Sib)	ECtt
'Dreaming Spires' (Sib)	GBin
'Dreaming Yellow' (Sib)	CAby CAvo CBar CBre CKel CRos CSam CWld ECha EPfP EShb EWhm GBin GKin LRHS MRav NGdn NRHS SPer WAul WCAu WGob WGwG WMoo WWtn
'Dresden Candleglow' (IB)	WCAu
'Drive Me Wild' (TB)	WCAu
'Dualtone' (TB)	CKel
'Dude Ranch' (TB)	WCAu
'Duke of Bedford' (TB)	WMil
'Dunkler Wein' (Sib)	EWes
'Dunlin' (MDB)	CBro NBir
'Dural White Butterfly' (La)	EPfP
'Dusky Challenger' (TB)	CKel EBee ESgI LCro LOPS SRms WCAu XSen
'Dusky Evening' (TB)	XSen
'Dutch Chocolate' (TB)	CKel EWes LCro LOPS XSen
DYNAMIC DUET (mixed) (Dut)	GKev
'Dynamite' (TB)	XSen
'Dyonisos' (TB)	SIri
'Eagle's Flight' (TB)	XSen
'Earl of Essex' (TB)	WCAu XSen
'Early Frost' (IB)	CKel
'Early Light' (TB) ♀H7	ESgI WCAu

	Name	Suppliers
	'Easter' (SDB)	SIri
	'Eastertime' (TB)	ESgI
	'Eastman Winds' (La)	LLWG
	'Easy' (MTB)	EIri
	'Echo de France' (TB)	CKel ESgI SRms XSen
	'Edge of Winter' (TB)	CKel XSen
	'Edith Wolford' (TB)	CCCN CKel CWld GWyn MMrt SCob XSen
	'Edna Grace' (La)	LLWG
	'Ed's Blue' (DB)	ELan
	'Edward' (Reticulata)	EPot GKev LAma SDeJ
	'Edward of Windsor' (TB)	ELan GMaP LRHS NLar SCob
	'Ego' (Sib)	ECha ELon EPfP MAvo WFar WMoo
	'Eileen Louise' (TB) ♀H7	WCAu
	'Eleanor's Pride' (TB)	ESgI SRms WCAu
	elegantissima	see *I. iberica* subsp. *elegantissima*
	'Elizabeth of England' (TB)	GKev
	'Elizabeth Poldark' (TB)	ESgI XSen
	'Ellesmere' (Sib)	WAul
	'Elsa Sass' (TB)	ESgI
	'Elsie Petty' (IB)	SIri
	'Elvinhall'	CBro
	'Emperor' (Sib)	CWat NSti
	'Encre Bleue' (IB)	ESgI
	'Endless Love' (TB)	EIri
	'English Charm' (TB)	ESgI XSen
	'English Cottage' (TB)	CKel CRos CTsd ELon EWTr GCal LSRN MHer NLar SRms WCAu XSen
	'Ennerdale' (TB)	SRms
	'Enriched' (MTB) ♀H7	WCAu
§	***ensata***	CBcs CBro CRos CTri ELan EPfP GKev LRHS LSun MJak MMuc MNrw NAln NLar NRHS SPlb SRms WBor WPnP WWtn
	- 'Activity'	SHar WFar
	- 'Agrippine'	XSen
	- 'Alba'	ECha MMuc
I	- 'Amethyst'	XSen
	- 'Angel Mountain'	IPot MBNS WFar WGob
	- 'Angelic Choir'	LLWG
	- 'Aquamarin'	XSen
	- 'Asian Warrior'	WFar
	- 'August Emperor'	MBel
	- 'Azuma-kagami'	MNrw
	- 'Azure'	WFar WMoo
I	- 'Blue King'	NHol
	- 'Blue Spritz'	LLWG
	- 'Carnival Prince'	WFar WMoo
	- 'Cascade Crest'	WFar
	- 'Celestial Emperor'	LLWG
	- 'Center of Interest'	NBir
*	- 'Charm'	CRos LRHS NRHS
	- 'Christina's Gown'	WFar WGob
	- 'Crepe Paper'	WFar
	- 'Cry of Rejoice'	EBee ECtt WCAu
	- 'Crystal Halo' ♀H7	EBee EWTr WWtn
I	- 'Darling'	EPfP EWTr WFar WMoo
	- 'Diamant'	XSen
	- 'Dirigo Editor' **new**	LLWG
	- 'Dramatic Moment'	WFar WSpi
I	- 'Dresden China'	WFar
	- 'Eden's Blush'	EBee
	- 'Eden's Charm'	CRos
	- 'Eden's Delight'	CRos
	- 'Eden's Paintbrush'	EShb SPer
	- 'Electric Rays'	LLWG WFar
I	- 'Emotion'	CMac CRos WFar
I	- 'Fortune'	CBod EBee EHrv GBin IKil WWtn
	- 'Freckled Geisha'	CMac EBee ECtt ELon EPfP IPot NBir NQui SRms WFar
	- 'Frilled Enchantment' ♀H7	IPot WFar
	- 'Galatea Marx'	CBod CExl LEdu WFar
	- 'Gipsy'	CKel CMac EBee LRHS
	- 'Gold Bound'	ECtt WGob
	- 'Good Omen'	WGob
	- 'Gracieuse'	CRos CTsd LRHS NLar
	- 'Greywoods Catrina'	LLWG WFar WGob
	- 'Gusto'	CMac EBee ELon EPfP MNrw SRms WFar
	- 'Harlequinesque'	ECtt IPot WFar WGob
	- 'Harpswell Chantey'	IPot
	- 'Hercule'	CExl NBir WFar
	- Higo white	SPer
	- 'Hoshi-akari'	WFar
	- 'Ike-no-sazanami' **new**	LLWG
	- 'Imperial Velvet'	WFar
	- 'Indigo Delight'	LLWG
*	- 'Innocence'	EHrv NLar SRms WFar WMoo
	- 'Iso-no-nami'	WFar
	- 'Jocasta'	EPfP WFar
	- 'Jodlesong'	WFar
	- 'Kalamazoo'	WFar
	- 'Katy Mendez' ♀H7	IPot
	- 'Kogesho'	NLar
	- 'Koh Dom'	SPer
	- 'Kongo-san'	NLar WFar
	- 'Kuma-funjin'	CExl EBee
	- 'Kumo-no-obi'	CExl GBin LRHS MCot NHol NRHS WFar
	- 'Lady in Waiting'	ECtt EPfP WGob WWtn
	- 'Laughing Lion'	ECtt IKil WCAu WFar WMoo
	- 'Light at Dawn'	MBel WMoo
	- 'Lilac Blotch'	SPer
	- 'Loyalty'	CExl CRos LRHS SHar WFar
	- 'Momogasumi'	ECtt LLWG MNrw NQui WHil
	- 'Momozomo'	LLHF
§	- 'Moonlight Waves'	CExl CMac CRos EBee ELan EPfP GBin GKin GMaP IPot LLWG LRHS MCot MHer MRav NGdn NHol NRHS SRms WFar WGob WSpi
	- 'Oase'	ECtt
	- 'Ocean Mist'	ECtt IKil
	- 'Oku-banri'	CExl EBee WFar
	- 'Oriental Eyes'	NGdn
	- pale mauve-flowered	NBir
	- 'Pin Stripe'	WMoo
	- 'Pink Frost'	EBee EPfP MHer WFar
	- 'Pleasant Earlybird'	WFar
	- 'Pleasant Journey'	ECtt EHrv
	- 'Prairie Frost'	NLar
	- 'Pure Emotion' **new**	LLWG
	- 'Purple Parasol'	LLWG
	- purple-flowered	SPer
	- 'Queen's Tiara'	ECtt ELon EWTr IPot WBor WGob WTyc
	- 'Rakka-no-utage'	NLar
	- 'Rivulets of Wine'	LLWG
§	- 'Rose Queen' ♀H7	CExl CMac CRos CSam ECha ELan EPfP GBin GKin GMaP LRHS MCot MRav NBir NGdn NHol NRHS SPer SRms WFar WMoo XLum
	- 'Rowden King'	NChi
	- 'Rowden Mikado'	MAvo NChi
I	- 'Royal Banner'	ECtt LRHS WFar
	- 'Royal Crown'	XLum
I	- 'Ruby King'	LEdu LRHS
	- 'Ruffled Dimity'	IPot
I	- 'Sensation'	CWCL ECtt GBin IKil NLar SRms WWtn
	- 'Snowy Hills'	XLum

	- 'Sorcerer's Triumph'	WFar
	- 'Splish Splash' **new**	GKev LAma
	- var. ***spontanea*** B&SWJ 1103	WCru
	- - B&SWJ 8699	WCru
	- 'Stippled Ripples'	IPot
	- 'Sugar Dome' **new**	LLWG
	- 'Sunrise Ridge' **new**	LLWG
	- 'Taketori-hime' (v)	XLum
	- 'Tessa Dark Eyes' **new**	LLWG
	- 'Topas'	EBee WFar XSen
	- 'Tropical Storm' **new**	EWTr
	- 'Umi-kaze'	NLar
	- 'Variegata' (v) ♀H7	CMac CRos CSpe EBee ECha EIri ELon EPfP GBin GMaP LEdu LLWG LRHS MHer MHol MMuc NLar NRHS NSti SEND SPoG SRms WFar WMoo WPnP WWtn
	- 'Velvety Queen'	ECtt
	- 'Wave Action'	EWTr IPot
I	- 'White Ladies'	CSBt LRHS WSpi
	- 'Wine Ruffles'	LSRN
	- 'Yako-no-tama'	WFar WMoo
	- 'Yedo-yeman'	IMou WFar
	'Epicenter' (TB)	XSen
	'Eramosa Miss' (BB)	WCAu
	'Eramosa Skies' (SDB)	WCAu
	'Erect' (IB)	CKel
	'Eric the Red' (Sib)	ELon
	'Erste Sahne' (Sib)	GBin
	'Eternal Bliss' (TB)	SIri
	'Evadne' (TB)	WMil
	'Evening Drama' (TB)	WCAu
	'Evening Gown' (TB)	XSen
	'Ever After' (TB)	LCro XSen
	'Ever Again' (Sib)	ELon
	'Everything Plus' (TB)	ESgI XSen
	'Ewen' (Sib)	CPou GKin GLog GMaP ILea LEdu NGdn WAul WCot
	'Exotic Isle' (TB)	EPPr ESgI XSen
	'Exotic Star' (TB)	CKel
	'Experiment' (SDB)	EIri
	'Expose' (TB)	WCAu
	'Extra' (BB)	CPBP LLHF
	'Extra Dazzle' (La)	LLWG
	'Eye Catcher' (Reticulata)	CMea EPot ERCP GKev LAma
	'Eye Magic' (IB)	CKel XSen
	'Eye of Tiger'	see *I.* 'Tigereye'
	'Eye Shadow' (SDB)	WCAu
	'Eyebright' (SDB) ♀H7	CBro WCAu
	'Fabiola' (Reticulata)	CRos EPot ERCP LAma LLHF LRHS NRHS SDeJ
	'Fabuleux' (TB)	SIri
	'Face of an Angel' (TB)	WCAu
	'Faenelia Hicks' (La)	WMAq
	'Fall Fiesta' (TB)	XSen
	'Fanciful Whimsy' (IB)	WCAu
	'Fancy Brass' (TB)	SIri
	'Fanfaron' (TB)	ESgI XSen
	'Farleigh Damson' (SDB)	SIri
	'Fashion Holiday' (IB)	SIri
	'Fashion Lady' (MDB)	CBro
	'Fathom' (IB)	WCAu
	'Faubourg-St John' (La) **new**	LLWG
	'Feather and Fan' (La)	LLWG
	'Feminine Charm' (TB)	MRav
	'Festive Skirt' (TB)	CKel WCAu
	'Feu du Ciel' (TB) ♀H7	CKel ESgI XSen
	'Few Are Chosen' (La)	LLWG
	'Fiddlin' Around' (TB)	WCAu
	'Fiesta Time' (TB)	CWCL XSen
	'Film Festival' (TB)	ESgI
	'Finalist' (TB)	XSen
	'Finola' (Reticulata)	ERCP GKev LAma
	'Firebreather' (TB)	EPfP MHol
	'Firebug' (IB)	ESgI XSen
	'Firecracker' (TB)	MRav WCAu
	'First Interstate' (TB)	ESgI XSen
	'First Movement' (TB)	ESgI
	'First Romance' (SDB)	LSRN
	'First Violet' (TB)	ESgI
	'Five Star Admiral' (TB)	XSen
	'Flaming Dragon' (TB)	XSen
	'Flaming Victory' (TB)	XSen
	flavescens	WCAu XSen
	'Flavours' (BB)	WCAu
	'Fleece of White' (BB)	WCAu
	'Flibbertigibbet' (SDB)	SIri
	'Flight of Butterflies' (Sib) ♀H7	Widely available
	'Flirting Again' (SDB) ♀H7	SIri
	'Floorshow' (TB)	XSen
§	'Florentina' (IB/TB) ♀H6	CBro CHby CKel GCal GPoy LRHS MRav NBid NBir SAko SEND WCAu XSen
	'Florentine Silk' (TB)	WCAu
	'Flumadiddle' (IB)	CBro
	'Flûte Enchantée' (TB)	XSen
	'Focus' (TB)	XSen
	foetidissima ♀H6	Widely available
	- 'Aurea'	WCot
	- ***chinensis***	see *I. foetidissima* var. *citrina*
§	- var. ***citrina***	CBre EWld GAbr LEdu NLar SChr WGwG
	- 'Fructu Albo'	WCot
	- var. ***lutescens***	NSti
	- 'Variegata' (v) ♀H5	CBct NBir NPer WAvo WOut WTor
	'Fogbound' (TB)	WCAu
	'Foggy Dew' (TB)	CRos EPfP LRHS NRHS SDeJ
	'Fondation Van Gogh' (TB)	XSen
	'Foolish Fancy' (TB)	SIri
	'Footloose' (TB)	SIri XSen
	'Fordwich' (SDB)	SIri
	'Forecasting Rain' (SDB)	SIri
	'Foreign Legion' (TB)	WCAu
	'Foreigner' (TB)	WCAu
	'Forest Light' (SDB)	CBro ESgI
	'Forever Blue' (SDB)	WCAu
	'Forever Gold' (TB)	XSen
*	'Forever Trevor' (CH)	MAvo
	'Forge Fire' (TB)	ESgI
	formosana B&SWJ 3076	WCru
	'Forrest Hills' (TB)	EPfP LRHS NRHS
	forrestii ♀H6	CAby CBro CExl CMac EPfP GAbr GCal GKev GLog LRHS NAln NBir SPtp SRot
	'Fort Apache' (TB)	EWes
	'Fortunata' (TB)	XSen
	'Fortunate Son' (TB)	CWld WCAu
	'Fortune Teller' (TB)	CKel
	'Fourfold Blue' (SpH)	GBin
	'Fourfold Lavender' (Sib)	EWes NLar WCAu
	'Fourfold White' (Sib)	ESgI
	'Framboise' (TB)	XSen
	'Francina' (TB)	WMil
	'Frank Elder' (Reticulata)	CRos EPot ERCP GKev LAma LLHF LRHS NRHS SDeJ WAbe
	'Frappe' (TB)	CKel
	'French Can Can' (TB)	CKel GWyn SIri
	'French Rose' (TB)	WCAu

'Fresno Calypso' (TB)	CKel ESgI WCAu XSen
'Friends' Song' (La) **new**	LLWG
'Frimousee' (TB)	WViv
'Fringe of Gold' (TB)	CBod
'Frison-roche' (TB)	CWCL WViv
'Frisounette' (TB)	ESgI
'Fritillary Flight' (IB) ♀H7	CKel
'From this Moment' (La)	LLWG
'Frontier Marshall' (TB)	XSen
'Frost and Flame' (TB)	CAby CKel CRos CWld EBee ECtt ELan GBin LCro LRHS MAsh MRav NBir NLar NRHS SDeJ SPoG WGwG
'Frosted Angel' (SDB)	CBro
'Frosted Velvet' (MTB)	WCAu
'Frosty Jewels' (TB)	XSen
'Fruit Cocktail' (IB)	XSen
fulva ♀H5	CKel EBee EWat EWhm GCal MMrt NBir NSti SBrt WCAu WCot
× ***fulvala*** ♀H5	EWes NBir NSti
- 'Violacea'	CRos LRHS NRHS
'Furnaceman' (SDB)	CBro
'Futuriste' (TB)	SIri WViv
'Gai Luron' (TB)	CKel
§ ***galatica***	GKev
'Gallant Moment' (TB)	SIri XSen
'Galway' (IB)	SIri XSen
'Game Plan' (TB)	WCAu
'Gandalf the Grey' (TB)	ESgI
'Garnet Storm Dancer' (La)	LLWG
'Gay Parasol' (TB)	CKel
'Gelbe Mantel' (Sino-Sib)	NBir NSti
'Gemstone Walls' (TB)	ESgI
'George' (Reticulata) ♀H7	CAby CAvo CRos CWCL EMor EPfP EPot ERCP GKev LAma LRHS NRHS SDeJ WBor WBrk WHoo XEll
'Gerald Darby'	see *I.* × *robusta* 'Gerald Darby'
§ ***germanica***	MMuc SEND WCot WGwG
- var. ***florentina***	see *I.* 'Florentina'
§ - 'Nepalensis'	WCAu
- 'The King'	see *I. germanica* 'Nepalensis'
'Ghost Train' (TB)	CKel SIri
'Gingerbread Castle' (TB)	WCAu
'Gingerbread Man' (SDB)	CBro CMea EHrv ESgI EWld GEdr MBrN WCAu
'Girly Girl' (TB)	WCAu
'Glacier Gold' (TB)	XSen
'Glad Rags' (TB)	XSen
'Gladiator's Gift' (La)	LLWG
'Gladys Austin' (TB)	XSen
'Glas-y-Dorlan' (Sib)	GCal
'Glenthorn' (TB)	SIri
'Glowing Embers' (TB)	ESgI
'Gnu' (TB)	XSen
'Go Between' (TB)	WCAu
'Godfrey Owen' (TB)	WCAu
'Going Home' (TB) ♀H7	SIri
'Going My Way' (TB)	CKel ESgI SIri WCAu XSen
'Gold Burst' (TB)	XSen
'Gold Country' (TB)	XSen
'Gold Galore' (TB)	SIri
'Gold of Autumn' (TB)	CKel WArt
'Golden Alps' (TB)	SRms WCAu
'Golden Beauty' (SpH)	GKev SDeJ
'Golden Child' (SDB)	XSen
'Golden Edge' (Sib)	CBod ELon GBin GQue LCro LLWG LOPS NLar WCAu WFar WGob
'Golden Encore' (TB)	CKel WCAu
'Golden Fireworks' (La)	LLWG
'Golden Muffin' (IB)	CKel
'Golden Panther' (TB)	WCAu
'Golden Violet' (SDB)	ESgI
'Golden Zebra' (TB) **new**	MHol MSCN
'Good Looking' (TB)	ESgI WCAu
'Good Show' (TB)	ESgI WCAu XSen
'Good Vibrations' (TB)	XSen
'Goodbye Heart' (TB)	LSRN
'Gordon' (Reticulata)	CAvo CRos EPfP EPot ERCP GKev IPot LAma LRHS NRHS SCob
gormanii	see *I. tenax*
'Gossip' (SDB)	CBro
'Got the Melody' (TB)	WCAu
'Goudhurst' (SDB)	SIri
'Gracchus' (TB)	WCAu
'Grace Sturtevant' (TB)	WMil
gracilipes	GEdr SBrt
- 'Alba'	GEdr
gracilipes × ***lacustris***	GEdr
graeberiana	EPot GKev SDeJ
graminea ♀H6	CAvo CBro CFis CMac EHrv EIri ELan GKev IFro NBir NChi NSti WCot XEll
- var. ***pseudocyperus***	GBin GCal SDys
graminifolia	see *I. kerneriana*
'Granada Gold' (TB)	SRms XSen
'Grand Amiral' (TB)	WViv
'Grand Waltz' (TB)	XSen
'Grandis' (Sib)	GBin
'Granny Jean' (Sib)	CKel
'Grapelet' (MDB)	CPBP
'Great Gatsby' (TB)	CKel
'Great Lakes' (TB)	ESgI
'Grecian Skies' (TB)	ESgI
'Green Eyed Lady' (TB)	ESgI
'Green Ice' (TB)	LRHS MRav
'Green Prophecy' (TB)	CKel
'Green Spot' (SDB) ♀H7	CBod CBro CKel CRos ECha ECtt EHrv LRHS MRav NBir NLar NRHS SDeJ SPer WAul WCAu
'Grenade' (TB)	SIri WViv
grey-flowered (Sib)	ELon
'Gringo' (TB)	WCAu
'Grooving' (BB)	ESgI
'Grosser Wein' (Sib)	GBin
'Guatemala' (TB)	WCAu
'Gull's Wing' (Sib)	EPfP EWTr LCro LLWG LOPS LRHS MHol NLar NSti SPoG WGob WPnP WTyc
'Gurkha's Dance' (SDB)	SIri
'Gypsy Beauty' (Dut)	CAvo ELan GKev LCro LOPS MNrw SDeJ WRHF
'Gypsy Jewels' (TB)	CKel XSen
'Gypsy Romance' (TB) ♀H7	EIri SIri WCAu
'Gypsy Tart' (SDB)	SIri
'Habit' (TB)	WCAu
'Hail Mary' (La) **new**	LLWG
'Hakuna Matata' (AB)	SDys
halophila	see *I. spuria* subsp. *halophila*
'Happenstance' (TB)	WCAu
'Happy Mood' (IB)	EIri WCAu
'Harbor Blue' (TB)	CKel CTsd WCAu
'Harlow Gold' (IB)	ESgI
'Harmony' ambig.	SCob SPer
'Harmony' (IB)	CRos
'Harmony' (Reticulata)	CAby CAvo EPfP EPot GKev LAma LCro LOPS LRHS MJak NRHS SCob SDeJ WArt WBrk
'Harpswell Happiness' (Sib) ♀H7	CKel EBee ELon EPfP GBin ILea WAul WGob WMoo
'Harpswell Haze' (Sib)	ECha

	'Harpswell Velvet' (Sib)	GBin
	'Harriette Halloway' (TB)	CRos CWGN EPfP EShb LRHS LSRN NLar NRHS WCot
	'Harvest King' (TB)	XSen
	'Harvest of Memories' (TB)	CKel ESgI GWyn SPoG
	'Haut les Voiles' (TB)	WViv
	'Haute Couture' (TB)	XSen
	'Haviland' (TB)	XSen
	'Headcorn' (MTB) 🏆H7	SIri
	'Headline Banner' (BB)	WCAu
	'Headway' (Spuria)	WCAu
	'Heart's Radiance' (MTB)	SDys
	'Heather Carpet' (SDB)	WCAu
	'Heather Stream' (La)	ELon
	'Heavenly Blue' (Sib)	SPer
	'Heavenly Days' (TB)	WCAu
	'Helen Astor' (Sib)	CDor MRav
	'Helen Collingwood' (TB)	ESgI
	'Helen Proctor' (IB)	ESgI WCot XSen
	'Helen Traubel' (TB)	WCAu
	'Helena Terry' (TB)	ESgI
	'Helene C.' (TB)	WViv XSen
	'Hellcat' (IB)	WCAu
	'Hello Darkness' (TB) 🏆H7	ESgI WCAu WCot XSen
	'Hell's Fire' (TB)	ELan ELon WCAu
	'Hemstitched' (TB)	MHol
	'Her Royal Highness' (TB)	LCro LOPS
	'Here Be Dragons' (Sib)	WCAu
	'Here Comes The Sun' (TB)	WCAu
	'Hester Prynne' (TB) **new**	WMil
	'Heure Bleue' (TB)	WViv
	'Hey True Blue' (TB)	WCAu
	'High Blue Sky' (TB)	WCAu
	'High Command' (TB)	CKel WCAu
	'High Peak' (TB)	WCAu
	'Highland Mist' (La)	LLWG
	'Hildegarde' (Dut)	SDeJ
	'Hindenburg' (TB)	CKel
	'His Royal Highness' (TB)	WCAu
	'Hissy-Fit' (IB)	CKel
	histrio	EPot
	- subsp. ***aintabensis***	GKev
	histrioides 'Halkis'	CRos EPot ERCP GKev LAma LRHS NRHS SDeJ
	- 'Lady Beatrix Stanley'	CAvo CRos EPot ERCP GKev LAma LLHF LRHS MNrw NRHS SDeJ WBrk WHoo
	- 'Major'	LAma
	- var. ***sophenensis***	EPot GKev LAma
	'Hoar Edge' (Sib)	NChi WAul
	'Hocus Pocus' (SDB)	CKel CWGN EPfP LRHS NRHS WAul
	'Hohe Warte' (Sib) 🏆H7	GBin WAul WCAu
	'Holden Clough' (SpH) 🏆H7	CExl CPla EBee ELan EPPr EPfP GBin GMaP LEdu MMuc MNrw MRav NBir NChi NGdn NSti NWad WBrk WFar WSHC
	'Holden's Child' (SpH)	LLWG WCAu
	'Holidaze' (IB) 🏆H7	CKel EIri
	'Holy Night' (TB)	CKel SRms
	'Honey Glazed' (IB)	ELon WCAu
	'Honey Stars' (La)	LLWG
	'Honeylove' (SDB)	SDys
	'Honeyplic' (IB) 🏆H7	SIri
	'Honington' (SDB)	WCAu
	'Honky Tonk Blues' (TB)	ESgI LSRN
	hoogiana 🏆H5	GKev
I	- 'Amphion'	GKev
I	- 'Antiope'	GKev
	- 'Purpurea'	GKev
§	***hookeri***	CFis CRos CSma GEdr GKev GMaP MHol NHpl NSla SPtp WAbe WIce WThu
	'Hopelessly Devoted' (La)	LLWG
§	'Hornpipe' (TB)	WCAu
	'Hortensia Rose' (TB)	SIri WViv
	'Hot and Spicy' (La)	LLWG
	'Hot Spiced Wine' (TB)	SIri
	'Hot to Trot' (TB)	ESgI
	'Hottentot' (SDB)	WCAu
	'Howler' (TB)	WCAu
	'Hubbard' (Sib)	LCro LLWG LOPS MBel MNrw SPoG WFar WGob
	'Huckleberry Fudge' (TB)	XSen
	'Hugh Miller' (TB)	WCAu
§	***humilis***	GCrg
	hyrcana	GKev WCot
	'I Feel Good' (TB) 🏆H7	WCAu
	'I Pink I Can' (TB)	WCAu
	'I Repeat' (TB)	XSen
	'I Seek You' (TB)	ESgI
§	***iberica*** subsp. ***elegantissima***	GKev
	'Ice and Indigo' (SDB)	WCAu
	'Ice Dancer' (TB) 🏆H7	CKel
	'Ice Etching' (SDB)	WCAu
	'Ice Wings' (BB)	WCAu
	'Ida' (Reticulata)	LAma
	'Ila Crawford' (Spuria) 🏆H7	XSen
	'Illini Charm' (Sib)	WFar WMoo
	illyrica	see *I. pallida*
	'I'm Back' (TB)	WCAu
	imbricata	GKev
	'Immortality' (TB)	CBod CKel CRos CWGN EPfP GKev GWyn LRHS SCob WCAu WTor XSen
	'Imperative' (IB)	SIri WCAu
	'Imperial Opal' (Sib)	ECtt NGdn WFar WGob
I	'Imperial Velvet' (Sib)	ELon WFar
	'Imprimis' (TB)	XSen
	'In a Flash' (IB)	WCAu
	'In Love' (TB)	XSen
	'In Town' (TB)	XSen
*	'Incoscente' (TB)	ESgI
	'Indeed' (IB)	ESgI
	'Indian Chief' (TB)	CCCN CRos CWCL EPfP ESgI MCot MHer MRav WCAu
	'Indian Idyll' (IB)	CKel
	'Indiana Sunset' (TB)	CKel
	'Indigo Princess' (TB)	XSen
	'Infanta' (SDB)	WCAu
	'Ink Patterns' (TB)	WCAu
	'Inn-Keeper' (La) **new**	LLWG
	'Innocent Pink' (TB)	ESgI
	innominata	CPla CRos GKev LRHS NBir NBro NRHS NSla SRms WAbe
	- yellow-flowered	NRya
	'Inside Job' (TB)	WCAu
	'Inspired' (TB)	WCAu
	'Intermediary' (IB)	WCAu
	'Interpol' (TB)	ESgI XSen
	'Intrepid' (TB)	WViv
	'Invicta Celebration' (BB) **new**	SIri
	'Invicta Daybreak' (IB)	SIri
	'Invicta Gold' (SDB)	SIri
	'Invicta Reprieve' (IB)	SIri
	'Invicta Sapphire' (TB) **new**	SIri
	'Irene' (TB)	WCAu
	'Iriade' (TB)	WCAu

'Irisades' (TB) SIri WViv
'Irish Chant' (SDB) WCAu
'Irish Gold' (TB) WCAu
'Irish Harp' (SDB) ESgI
'Irish Squire' (TB) WCAu
'Isabelle' (Sib) LSRN XSen
'Island Sunset' (TB) SIri
'Isobel Rose' (TB) SIri
'Italian Ice' (TB) EIri
'Italian Velvet' (TB) WCAu
'It's Amazing' (IB) WCAu
'I've Got Rhythm' (TB) CKel
'J.S. Dijt' (Reticulata) CAvo CRos EPot ERCP GKev LAma LCro LOPS LRHS MGos NRHS SDeJ
'Jack Attack' (La) WMoo WWtn
'Jac-y-do' (Sib) EWes
'Jamie Roo' (TB) SIri
'Jane Phillips' (TB) ♀H7 Widely available
'Janet Lane' (BB) CKel
japonica ♀H4 CExl NLar NPer SPlb WCot WFar XLum XSen
– B&SWJ 8921 WCru
– 'Bourne Graceful' CExl
– 'Ledger' CAby CExl CHll CMac ECha EHrv MRav SEND SMad WWFP
– 'Monty' WWFP
– 'Rudolph Spring' EBee GCal WSHC
§ – 'Variegata' (v) ♀H4 CAby CBcs CBct CBro ECha ELan ESwi NPer NSti SArc WAvo WBrk WFar WOut WWFP XSen
'Jasper Gem' (MDB) EPot
'Java Bleue' (TB) SIri
'Jazz Festival' (TB) SIri WCAu XSen
'Jazz Hot' (La) LLWG
'Jazzed Up' (TB) XSen
'Jean Cayeux' (TB) ESgI
'Jean Guymer' (TB) ESgI
'Jeanne Price' (TB) ESgI LSRN
'Jesse's Song' (TB) ESgI WCAu XSen
'Jewel Baby' (SDB) CBro
'Jeweler's Art' (SDB) ESgI
'Jiansada' (SDB) CBro
'Jigsaw' (TB) XSen
'Jitterbug' (TB) EHrv WCAu
'Jive' (SDB) WCAu
'Joanna' (TB) LSRN NLar
'John' (IB) CKel LSRN
'Joie de Vivre' (La) **new** LLWG
'Joyce' (Reticulata) CRos EPfP EPot GKev LAma LRHS NRHS SDeJ
'Joyful Skies' (TB) WCAu
'Jubilant Spirit' (Spuria) EWes
'Jubilee Gem' (TB) CKel
'Juliet' (TB) ESgI
'Jump Start' (IB) WCAu
'June Prom' (IB) CKel LRHS NRHS
'June Rose' (IB) CKel
'Jungle Fires' (TB) WCAu
'Jungle Shadows' (BB) ESgI MRav NBir WCAu
'Jurassic Park' (TB) CKel WCAu XSen
'Just Imagine' (La) LLWG
'Just Jennifer' (BB) WCAu
'Kabluey' (Sib) EBee ECtt MWts WFar WGob
'Kaboom' (Sib) MHol WFar
kaempferi see *I. ensata*
'Kahuna' (IB) WCAu
'Karen' (TB) LSRN
'Kasim' (J) GKev
'Katharine Hodgkin' (Reticulata) ♀H7 CAby CAvo CRos CTca EBee ECha EMor EPfP EPot ERCP GAbr GKev LAma LCro LOPS LRHS MNrw MRav NBir NHpl NLar NRHS SCob SDeJ WBrk WCot WFar WHoo
'Katherine's Gold' (Reticulata) **new** ERCP
'Kathleen Mary' (Sib) CKel
'Katie-Koo' (IB) ♀H7 CKel
'Katy Petts' (SDB) ESgI
'Keeping up Appearances' (TB) WCAu
kemaonensis PAB 8473 LEdu
'Kent Arrival' (Sib) SIri
'Kent Compote' (IB) SIri
'Kent Pride' (TB) CAby CBod CKel CRos ECha ECtt EPfP ESgI EUJe GBin LCro LOPS LRHS MCot MRav MSCN NRHS SCob SPer SPoG SRms WCAu
'Kent Skylark' (IB) **new** SIri
'Kentish Icon' (SDB) SIri
'Kentish Lad' (IB) SIri
'Kentucky Derby' (TB) XSen
§ ***kerneriana*** ♀H5 CBro EHoe GKev NBir
'Kęstutis Genys' (Sib) WAul
'Kildonan' (TB) WCAu
'Kimzey' (TB) **new** CKel
'Kingfisher' (Sib) WAul
'Kirkstone' (TB) WCAu
kirkwoodii GKev
'Kiss of Summer' (TB) ♀H7 ESgI SDys
'Kiss the Girl' (Sib) WCAu
'Kissing Circle' (TB) ESgI
'Kita-no-seiza' (Sib) EWTr LLWG NGdn WFar
'Kiwi Slices' (SDB) CWat
'Knick Knack' (MDB) CBro CKel CPBP CRos ELan ELon EPfP GMaP LRHS MRav MTin NRHS SDeJ SPoG
korolkowii GKev
'Kuh-e-Abr' (Reticulata) GKev LAma
'La Meije' (TB) SIri WViv
'La Senda' (Spuria) WCot
'Lace Legacy' (TB) LSRN
'Laced Cotton' (TB) WCAu XSen
§ ***lactea*** SBrt SMHy XEll XSen
– CC 7174 GKev
lacustris CPBP WAbe WCot XSen
– 'Captain Collingwood' WAbe
'Lacy Snowflake' (TB) LRHS
'Lad' (SDB) WCAu
'Lady Belle' (MTB) ESgI
'Lady Byng' (TB) WMil
'Lady Essex' (TB) WCAu
'Lady Friend' (TB) WCAu XSen
'Lady in Red' (SDB) ESgI WCAu
'Lady Mohr' (AB) WCAu
'Lady of the Night' (BB) WCAu
'Lady Vanessa' (Sib) CPou EBee ELon MRav NSti WGob
laevigata CRos CWat EPfP EWat ITim MRav NBro NPer SRms WCAu WFar WMAq WMoo WShi
– var. ***alba*** LLWG SRms WMoo
– 'Atropurpurea' LLWG
– blue-flowered LLWG
– 'Colchesterensis' CWat EWat NGdn NPer WMAq WMoo
I – 'Dorothy' NGdn
– 'Dorothy Robinson' EPfP MRav
I – 'Elegante' EWat
* – 'Elgar' WMAq
– 'Liam Johns' LLWG
– 'Monstrosa' EWat

	- 'Richard Greaney'	EWat LLWG
	- 'Rose Queen'	see *I. ensata* 'Rose Queen'
	- 'Rowden Starlight'	LLWG
	- 'Royal Cartwheel'	LLWG
I	- 'Snowdrift'	CWat EWat LLWG MJak NBir NGdn NLar NPer WCAu WFar WMAq WMoo
	- 'Variegata' (v) ♀H7	CBen CWat ECha EHoe ELan ELon EPfP EWat LLWG MWts NBro NGdn NPer WMAq WMoo WPnP WWtn
	- 'Violet Garth'	EWat
	- 'Weymouth'	see *I. laevigata* 'Weymouth Blue'
§	- 'Weymouth Blue'	EWat LLWG
	- 'Weymouth Purity'	EWat
	laevigata* × *versicolor Tamberg hybrid	LLWG
§	'Lake Niklas' (Sib)	ELon MHol NCGa
	'Lambourn Hills' (TB)	WCAu
	'Langport Chapter' (IB)	CKel ESgI
	'Langport Chief' (IB)	CKel
	'Langport Claret' (IB)	CKel ESgI
	'Langport Curlew' (IB)	CKel ESgI
	'Langport Duchess' (IB)	ESgI
	'Langport Fairy' (IB)	CKel
	'Langport Flame' (IB)	CKel ESgI WArt
	'Langport Hope' (IB)	CKel
	'Langport Jane' (IB)	CKel
	'Langport Lady' (IB)	CKel
	'Langport Lord' (IB)	ESgI
	'Langport Minstrel' (IB)	CKel ESgI
	'Langport Pearl' (IB)	CKel
	'Langport Phoenix' (IB)	WArt
	'Langport Pinnacle' (IB)	CKel
	'Langport Smoke' (IB)	CKel
	'Langport Star' (IB)	CKel ESgI
	'Langport Storm' (IB)	CKel ELon EPfP LRHS MRav NRHS SDeJ WHoo
	'Langport Sun' (IB)	ESgI
	'Langport Sylvia' (IB)	CKel
	'Langport Violet' (IB)	CKel ESgI
	'Langport Vista' (IB)	CKel
	'Langport Wren' (IB) ♀H7	CAby CBro CKel CRos ELon EPfP ESgI EShb GCal LRHS MBel NBir NGdn NRHS WAul WPtf
	'Langthorns Pink' (Sib)	ELan MRav WAul WCAu
	'Lark Rise' (TB) ♀H7	CKel
	'Larue Boswell' (TB)	EPfP
§	***latifolia***	GKev WShi
	- alba	WCot
	- 'Duchess of York'	EBee
	- 'Isabella'	GKev SDeJ
	- 'King of the Blues'	CAvo EBee GKev SDeJ
	- 'Mansfield'	MNrw
	- 'Montblanc'	CAvo GKev SDeJ
	- 'Queen of the Blues'	SDeJ
	- wild-collected	GCal
	'Latin Lark' (TB)	ESgI
	'Latino' (IB)	WCAu
	'Laura Louise' (La)	LLWG WGob
	'Laurenbuhl' (Sib)	CExl
	'Lavanesque' (TB)	WCAu
	'Lavender Bounty' (Sib)	GBin
	'Lavender Light' (Sib)	WAul
	lazica ♀H5	CBct CBod CBro CMac CSpe EIri EPPr EPfP EPot GKev IBlr LRHS MMrt MRav NAln NBir NCGa NChi NSti SBrt SEND SPer SPlb SRms WAul WGwG WHil
	- 'Joy Bishop'	CJun
*	- 'Richard Nutt'	CJun ELon WCot WSHC
	- 'Turkish Blue'	IBlr
	'Legato' (TB)	ESgI
	'Lemon Brocade' (TB)	WCAu
	'Lemon Flare' (SDB)	MRav SRms
	'Lemon Ice' (TB)	CKel ECha GBin LRHS NRHS SDeJ SPer
	'Lemon on Ice' (SDB)	WCAu
	'Lemon Pop' (IB)	WCAu
	'Lemon Puff' (MDB)	CBro LLHF WCAu
	'Lemon Veil' (Sib)	MNrw WGob
	'Lena' (SDB)	CBro
	'Lenora Pearl' (BB)	XSen
	'Lent A. Williamson' (TB)	GMaP
	'Leo Hewitt' (Sib)	ELon
	leptophylla	GKev
	'Let's Elope' (IB)	ESgI WCAu
	'Licorice Stick' (TB)	XSen
	'Light Beam' (TB)	XSen
	'Light Cavalry' (IB)	ESgI
	'Light Laughter' (IB)	WCAu
	'Lilli-white' (SDB)	CKel CRos CWat EHrv ELon EPfP LRHS MRav NRHS SPoG
	'Lilting' (TB)	XSen
	'Limbo' (SpH)	LLWG
	'Lime Fizz' (TB)	XSen
	'Limeheart' (Sib)	CPou LLHF
	'Limelight' (TB)	SRms
	'Linda's Child' (TB)	WCAu
	lineata	GKev
	'Lingering Love' (TB)	WCAu
	'Lion King' (Dut) ♀H7	GAbr LCro LOPS MMrt MNrw
	'Little Black Belt' (SDB)	LRHS
	'Little Blackfoot' (SDB)	WCAu WCot
	'Little Blue-eyes' (SDB)	ESgI WCAu
	'Little Bluets' (SDB)	ESgI
	'Little Dream' (SDB)	WCAu
	'Little Episode' (SDB)	CBro ELon
	'Little Firecracker' (SDB)	WCAu
	'Little Nutkin' (La)	LLWG
	'Little Rosy Wings' (SDB)	CBro CPBP
	'Little Shadow' (IB)	MRav SRms
	'Little Sheba' (AB)	WCAu
	'Little Showoff' (SDB)	ESgI
	'Little Tilgates' (CH)	WCot WSHC
	'Little Twinkle Star' (Sib)	WFar
	'Living Waters' (TB)	ESgI
	'Local Color' (TB)	ESgI SIri XSen
	'Local Hero' (IB)	WCAu
	'Lodore' (TB)	SRms
	'Logo' (IB)	WCAu
	'Lollipop' (SDB)	ESgI
	longipetala	EPPr NBir
	'Looking Forward' (TB)	ESgI
	'Loop the Loop' (TB)	CKel CMac CTsd SPoG
	'Loose Valley' (MTB) ♀H7	SIri
	'Lord Warden' (TB)	CKel CRos ECtt EPfP LRHS NRHS WGwG
	'Lorilee' (TB)	ESgI WCAu
	'Lost in Love' (TB)	WCAu
	'Lottie Lou' (TB)	SIri
	'Lotus Land' (TB)	WCAu
	'Louisa's Song' (TB)	WCAu
	Louisiana hybrids	ELan
	'Louvois' (TB)	CKel ESgI NLar
	'Love the Sun' (TB)	ESgI XSen
	'Lovely Again' (TB)	CKel GKev MRav WCAu
	'Lovely Leilani' (TB)	ESgI
	'Lovely Señorita' (TB)	WCAu

	Name	Suppliers
	'Love's Tune' (IB)	CKel CRos LRHS NRHS WTor
	'Low Ho Silver' (IB)	WCAu
	'Loyalist' (TB)	CPar SIri
	'Luli-Ann' (SDB)	CKel
	'Lullaby of Spring' (TB)	CKel
	'Lullingstone Castle' (Kent Castles Series) (IB)	SIri
	'Lumarco' (TB)	WViv
	'Lumière d'Automne' (TB)	XSen
	'Lure of Gold' (IB)	WCAu
	'Lurline' (TB)	WMil
	lutescens ♀H7	EPot GKev WAbe
§	- subsp. ***lutescens***	XSen
	- subsp. ***subbiflora***	EPot
	'Ma Mie' (IB)	WViv
	'Mabel Coday' (Sib)	EBee
	'Mad Magenta' (Sib)	GBin
	'Madeira Belle' (TB)	CKel EPfP ESgI LRHS NRHS WAul WCAu WGwG
	'Magharee' (TB)	ESgI
	'Magic Man' (TB)	XSen
	'Magic Masquerade' (TB)	WCAu
	'Magical Encounter' (TB)	SIri
	magnifica ♀H5	GKev
	- 'Agalik'	GKev
	- 'Alba'	GKev
*	'Mahogany Mix' (Dut)	GKev
	'Maid of Orange' (BB)	CKel WCAu
	'Maisie Lowe' (TB)	ESgI
	'Majestic' (TB)	WMil
	'Majestic Overtures' (Sib)	LLWG
	'Majestic Ruler' (TB)	WCAu
	'Making Eyes' (SDB)	ELon WCAu
	'Mambo Italiano' (TB)	WCAu
	'Man About Town' (TB)	WCAu
	'Mandarin Purple' (Sino-Sib)	NEgg
	'Mango Entree' (TB)	WCAu
	'Mango Smoothy' (BB)	ESgI
	'Man's Best Friend' (IB)	SIri
	'Marden Beech' (IB)	SIri
	'Marden Meadow' (MTB)	SIri
	'Margot Holmes' (Cal-Sib)	WFar
	'Margrave' (TB)	XSen
	'Marguérite' (Reticulata/v)	WCAu
	'Marilyn Holmes' (Sib)	GLog GQue WCot
	'Mariposa Autumn' (TB)	SIri
	'Marjaneh' (J)	GKev
	'Marjorie' (TB)	SRms
	'Marmalade Skies' (BB)	WCAu
	'Mars Landing' (Reticulata) **new**	EPot GKev LAma
	'Marsh Marigold' (TB)	WMil
	'Martyn Rix'	see *I. confusa* 'Martyn Rix'
	'Mary Frances' (TB)	CKel WCAu XSen
	'Mary McIlroy' (SDB) ♀H7	CBro
	'Marybill' (TB)	SIri
	'Master Touch' (TB)	CKel ELon XSen
	'Material Girl' (TB)	WCAu
	'Matinata' (TB)	CKel XSen
	'Maui Moonlight' (IB) ♀H7	CKel ESgI NLar WCAu
	'May Melody' (TB)	WCAu
	'Maya Mint' (MDB)	LLHF
	'Meadow Court' (SDB)	CBro CKel WCAu
	'Medici Prince' (TB)	WCAu
	'Medway Valley' (MTB) ♀H7	SIri WCAu
	'Megglethorp' (IB)	WCAu
	'Meg's Mantle' (TB)	CKel
	mellita	see *I. suaveolens*
	'Melon Honey' (SDB)	CKel ELon WCAu
	'Melted Butter' (TB)	WCAu
§	'Melton Red Flare' (Sib)	CRos CWld EMor GBin LRHS MBNS NRHS WAvo
	'Memphis Memory' (Sib)	EBee ELan ELon MHol NLar SPer WFar WGob
	'Men in Black' (TB)	WCAu
	'Mer du Sud' (TB) ♀H7	EIri ESgI LCro LRHS WViv XSen
*	'Merebrook Blue Lagoon' (La)	WMAq
	'Merebrook Jemma J' (La)	WMAq
	'Merebrook Purpla' (La)	WMAq
	'Merebrook Rum 'n' Raisin' (La)	WMAq
*	'Merebrook Rusty Red' (La)	WMAq
*	'Merebrook Snowflake' (La)	WMAq
	'Merebrook Sunnyside Up' (La)	WMAq
	'Merebrook Symphony' (La)	WMAq
	'Mescal' (TB)	WCAu
	mesopotamica	see *I. germanica*
	'Metaphor' (TB)	WCAu
	'Mezza Cartuccia' (IB)	ESgI
	'Miami Beach' (TB)	WCAu
	'Midas Mite' (MDB)	LLHF
	'Midhurst White' (TB)	SIri
I	'Midnight Blue' (MDB)	CBro
	'Midnight Caller' (TB)	ESgI XSen
	'Midnight Treat' (TB)	WCAu
	'Midsummer Night's Dream' (IB)	ESgI
	'Mighty Mouse' (MDB)	ELon
	milesii ♀H3	CExl GBin GKev NBir SBrt WSHC
	'Millennium Sunrise' (TB)	WCAu
	'Mini-Agnes' (SDB)	CBro
	'Minidragon' (SDB)	SIri
	'Minisa' (TB)	ESgI
	'Miss Nellie' (BB)	CKel
	'Mission Ridge' (TB)	MHol
	missouriensis	CMac EPPr
	'Mist on the Mountain' (TB)	CKel
	'Mister Roberts' (SDB)	ESgI
	'Mistress of Camelot' (TB)	SDys
	'Mme Chéreau' (TB)	WCAu
	'Monsieur-Monsieur' (TB)	ESgI
	Monspur Group	WCot
	'Moon Silk' (Sib)	CBro ECtt ELon EWes LLHF SCob WCot WFar WGob
	'Moonlight Waves'	see *I. ensata* 'Moonlight Waves'
	'Moonlit Water' (TB)	WCAu
	'Morning Show' (IB)	CKel
	'Morwell' (TB)	WMil
	'Morwenna' (TB) ♀H7	ESgI
	'Mother Earth' (TB)	ESgI
	'Mount Everest'PBR (TB) **new**	SDeJ
	'Mountain Lake' (Sib)	EPfP EShb GBin LRHS NRHS WFar WGob WSpi
	'Mrs Nate Rudolph' (SDB)	WCAu
	'Mrs Rowe' (Sib)	CPou EIri ELon MRav WAul WFar
	'Mrs Tait' (Spuria)	NChi
	'Mrs Valerie West' (TB)	WMil
	'Mrs Wright's Pink'	WCAu
	'Muggles' (SDB)	SIri
	'Murder Mystery' (TB)	WCAu
	'Murmuring Morn' (TB)	WCAu
	'Music' (SDB)	SIri
	'Must Unite' (TB)	WCAu
	'My First Kiss' (Sib)	WAul
	'My Kayla' (SDB)	ESgI
	'My Love' (Sib)	IMou WAul
	'My Seedling' (MDB)	CBro

	'Myra' (SDB)	XSen
	'Mysterieux' (TB)	SIri
	'Mystic' (TB)	WMil
	'Mystic Beauty' (Dut)	SDeJ
	'Mystic Dragon' (TB)	SDys
	'Mythology' (TB) **new**	SIri
	'Nada' (SpH)	WCot
	'Naivasha' (TB)	CKel
	'Nancy Hardy' (MDB)	CBro
	'Naples' (TB)	SIri
	'Natascha' (Reticulata)	EPot GKev LAma SCob SDeJ
	'Natasha' (MTB) **new**	EMor
	'Natchez Trace' (TB)	CKel LRHS XSen
	'Navajo Jewel' (TB)	ESgI WCAu XSen
	'Navy Brass' (Sib)	WAul
	'Needlecraft' (TB)	XSen
	'Needlepoint' (TB)	ESgI
	'Negro Modelo' (SDB)	WCAu
	'Neige de Mai' (TB)	ESgI
*	'Nel Jupe' (TB)	LRHS NLar
	nepalensis	see *I. decora*
	'Neutron Dance' (TB)	WCAu
	'New Argument' (J)	LLHF
	'New Centurion' (TB)	XSen
	'New Face' (TB)	WCAu
	'New Idea' (MTB)	CBro ESgI WCAu
	'New Leaf' (TB)	WCAu
	'New Snow' (TB)	WCAu
	'Nibelungen' (TB)	CBro WCAu XSen
	'Night Edition' (TB)	CKel ESgI XSen
	'Night Game' (TB)	XSen
	'Night Owl' (TB)	CKel ELon ESgI MHer
	'Night Ruler' (TB)	WCAu
	'Nights of Gladness' (TB)	ESgI
	'Nine Lives' (SDB)	WCAu
	'No Down Payment' (TB)	WCAu
	'Noctambule' (TB) ♀H7	SIri WViv
	'Noon Siesta' (TB)	ESgI
	× ***norrisii***	CRos LRHS NRHS
	'North Downs' (BB)	SIri
	'North Star' (TB) **new**	GKev
	'Northern Jewel' (IB)	SIri
	'Northumberland Piper' (TB)	SIri
	'Nottingham Lace' (Sib)	LLHF
	'Nouveau Riche' (TB)	WCAu
	'Now and Forever' (La)	LLWG
	'Obligato' (IB)	CKel
	'Obsidian' (TB)	WCAu
	'Ochre Doll' (SDB)	CBro CKel
	ochroleuca	see *I. orientalis* Mill.
	'O'Cool' (IB)	CKel
	'October' (TB)	ESgI
	'October Sun' (TB) **new**	CKel
	'Oh Happy Day' (La)	LLWG
	'Oh Jamaica' (TB)	WCAu XSen
	'Oh So Cool' (MTB)	ESgI
	'Oklahoma Bandit' (IB)	CKel
	'Oklahoma Centennial' (TB)	WCAu
	'Oktoberfest' (TB)	XSen
	'Ola Kalá' (TB)	CBod CKel CRos GMaP LRHS MGos NLar NRHS SPer XSen
	'Old Black Magic' (TB)	ESgI XSen
	'Old Flame' (TB)	XSen
	'Olympiad' (TB)	ESgI XSen
	'Olympic Challenge' (TB)	ESgI MRav
	'Olympic Torch' (TB)	WCAu
	'Ominous Stranger' (TB)	ESgI MMrt WCAu
	'Once Again' (TB)	XSen
	'One Desire' (TB)	XSen
	'Open Sky' (SDB)	LRHS XSen
	'Opposing Forces' (TB)	WCAu
	'Orageux' (IB)	SIri
	'Orange Caper' (SDB)	CKel CMac CRos ECtt ESgI LRHS MRav MTin NRHS WCot
	'Orange Glow' (TB) **new**	GKev
	'Orange Harvest' (TB)	ESgI XSen
	'Orange Order' (TB)	WCAu
	'Orange Thunder' (TB)	CKel
	'Orchidarium' (TB)	CKel
	orchioides misapplied	see *I. bucharica* Foster
§	***orchioides*** Carrière	ELan
	'Oregon Skies' (TB)	ESgI
	'Oriental Beauty' (Dut)	GKev LCro LOPS NAln
	'Oriental Beauty' (TB)	SDeJ
	orientalis ambig.	CAvo EWes MNrw
§	***orientalis*** Mill. ♀H6	GBin GCal GKev MMuc SEND WCot WCru XSen
	'Orinoco Flow' (BB) ♀H7	CKel ESgI WCAu
	'Orloff' (TB)	ESgI
	'Orville Fay' (Sib)	GWyn WCot
	'Osborne's Grey' (Sib)	WAul
	'Ottawa' (Sib)	CPou CRos CWat LRHS MMuc NRHS WFar
	'Oulo' (TB)	XSen
	'Our House' (TB)	ESgI
	'Our Marcus' (TB)	SIri
	'Our Sassy' (La) **new**	LLWG
	'Out of the Dark' (TB)	WCAu
	'Out Yonder' (TB)	WCAu
	'Outset' (Sib)	ELon
	'Over Easy' (SDB)	CKel
	'Overjoyed' (TB)	WCAu XSen
	'O'What' (SDB)	ESgI
	'Owyhee Desert' (TB)	WCAu
	'Ozark Maid' (MTB)	SDys
	Pacific Coast hybrids	see *I.* Californian hybrids
	'Pacific Mist' (TB)	WCAu
	'Pacific Panorama' (TB)	XSen
	'Pagan Dance' (TB)	WCAu
	'Pagan Pink' (TB)	XSen
	'Pagan Princess' (TB)	WCAu
I	'Pageant' (Sib)	WCot
	'Pageant' (TB)	WFar
	'Paint It Black' (TB)	XSen
	'Painted Lady' (Reticulata) **new**	ERCP
	'Pale Shades' (IB)	CBro CKel
§	***pallida***	CBro CMac CPla EHrv ESgI GMaP MRav SCob SEND SRms WCAu XSen
§	- 'Argentea Variegata' (TB/v)	Widely available
	- 'Aurea'	see *I. pallida* 'Variegata' Hort.
	- 'Aurea Variegata'	see *I. pallida* 'Variegata' Hort.
	- subsp. ***cengialtii***	XSen
	- var. ***dalmatica***	see *I. pallida* subsp. *pallida*
§	- subsp. ***pallida***	CExl CKel CRos ECha ELan EPfP GCal LRHS NRHS SPer
	- 'Variegata' misapplied	see *I. pallida* 'Argentea Variegata'
§	- 'Variegata' Hort. (v) ♀H7	CBcs CBro CKel CMac CRos CWat ECha ELan EPfP ESgI LRHS MAsh MHol MRav NRHS SPer SPlb SPoG SRms SRot SWvt WBrk XSen
	'Palm Springs' (IB)	CRos EPot GKev LRHS SDeJ
	'Palm Springs' (Reticulata)	LAma NRHS SDeJ
	'Palomino' (TB)	WCAu
	'Pamplemousse' (IB)	SIri
	'Pansy Purple' (Sib)	LRHS MNrw WHil
	'Panther' (SDB)	WCAu

Name	Suppliers
'Papillon' (Sib)	CRos CTri ECtt ELan ELon EWes GWyn LRHS MBel NBir NGdn NRHS NSti SCob SDeJ SPer WAul WFar WWtn
'Paprika Fono's' (TB)	WCAu
'Paradise' (TB)	CKel
paradoxa	GKev
'Paris Lights' (TB)	XSen
'Parisian Dawn' (TB)	WCAu
'Parisien' (TB)	EIri
'Parting Glances' (IB) **new**	WCAu
'Party Dress' (TB)	CKel CMac CRos EBee ELan EShb LRHS MRav NBir NLar NRHS NWad SPoG SRms WGwG
'Party's Over' (TB)	WCAu
'Passionate Embrace' (TB)	WCAu
'Pastel Accent' (La)	LLWG
'Patina' (TB)	EIri LRHS WCAu
'Patricia Elizabeth Linnegar' (TB)	WCAu
'Patterdale' (TB)	NBir
'Paul Black' (TB) ♀H7	WCAu
'Pauline' (Reticulata)	CAvo CRos EPfP EPot ERCP GKev LAma LRHS NRHS SCob
'Pauline' (TB)	WRHF
'Pause' (SDB)	WCAu
'Peaceful Waters' (TB)	XSen
'Peach Eyes' (SDB)	CBro CKel
'Peach Picotee' (TB)	ESgI XSen
'Peaches in Wine' (La)	LLWG
'Peachy Face' (IB)	XSen
'Pearl Queen' (Sib)	MCot
'Pearls of Autumn' (TB)	WCAu
'Pearly Dawn' (TB)	ECtt
* 'Pêche Melba' (TB)	XSen
'Peebee and Jay' (MTB)	WCAu
'Pelion Hills'	LRHS
'Penny a Pinch' (TB)	CKel
'Percheron' (Sib)	ESgI MNrw
'Perfect Interlude' (TB)	EIri XSen
'Perfect Vision' (Sib) ♀H7	MHCG
'Performer' (MTB)	EIri
'Perry's Blue' (Sib)	CBcs CKel CMac CRos CSBt EBee EHrv EPfP EWTr GKin GMaP IKil LCro LOPS LRHS LSun MGos MHol MRav NBir NGdn NPer NRHS SPer SRms WFar WWtn
I 'Perry's Favourite' (Sib)	WAul
'Perry's Pigmy' (Sib)	ELon
'Persian Berry' (TB)	WCAu XSen
'Persimmon' misapplied	see *I.* 'Tycoon'
'Persimmon' ambig. (Sib)	CAby CKel CRos ECtt EShb GKin GQue LRHS NRHS WFar WGwG WMoo
'Peter Hewitt' (Sib) ♀H7	MAvo WAul WCAu
'Petit Tigre' (IB)	SIri
'Petite Monet' (MTB)	ESgI
'Petite Polka' (SDB)	NLar
'Phyllis Bliss' (TB) **new**	WMil
'Pigeon' (SDB)	XSen
'Pinewood Amethyst' (CH)	MAvo
'Pinewood Charmer' (CH)	CElw
'Pink Attraction' (TB)	ESgI XSen
'Pink Bubbles' (BB)	WCAu XSen
'Pink Charm' (TB)	CKel CRos EPfP LRHS NRHS SDeJ SPlb SPoG
'Pink Confetti' (TB)	XSen
'Pink Empress' (IB) **new**	CKel
'Pink Haze' (Sib)	CDor CKel ESgI
'Pink Horizon' (TB)	XSen
'Pink Kitten' (IB)	WCAu WGwG XSen
'Pink Lavender' (TB)	ELon SRms
'Pink Parfait' (Sib)	MBNS MHol NGdn WFar WGob WTor WWtn
'Pink Pele' (IB)	ESgI
'Pink Quartz' (TB)	ESgI
'Pink Swan' (TB)	XSen
'Pink Taffeta' (TB)	XSen
'Pinnacle' (TB)	CKel GCal
'Pioneer' (TB)	WMil
'Pipes of Pan' (TB)	ESgI MRav WCAu
'Pirate Prince' (Sib)	NPer
'Pirate's Quest' (TB)	ESgI XSen
'Piroska' (TB)	ESgI XSen
* 'Piu Blue' (TB)	ESgI
'Pixie' (DB)	GKev NAln NRHS
'Pixie' (Reticulata) ♀H7	CAvo ELan EPot ERCP LAma LRHS SDeJ WHoo XEll
'Pleasures of May' (Sib)	EBee ELon WGob
'Pledge Allegiance' (TB)	ESgI WCAu
'Plickadee' (SDB)	CBro
'Plissée' (Sib) ♀H7	GBin GWyn
'Plum Lucky' (SDB)	SIri
'Plum Wine' (SDB)	CKel
'Poem of Ecstasy' (TB)	WCAu
'Poesie' (TB)	WViv
'Pogo' (SDB)	CBod CKel CMac CRos ECtt EShb GMaP LRHS MRav MTin NBir NRHS SDeJ SRms
'Polar Ice' (TB) **new**	ERCP
'Polvere di Stelle' (TB)	ESgI
pontica **new**	GKev
'Post Master' (La) **new**	LLWG
'Pounsley Purple' (Sib)	CPou
'Power Point' (TB)	WCAu
'Prairie Thunder' (AB)	WCAu
'Presence' (TB)	SIri
'Pretender' (TB)	WCAu
PRETTY IN BLUE (mixed) (Dut)	GKev SDeJ
'Pretty Please' (TB)	ESgI
'Primrose Cream' (Sib)	WCot
'Primrose Drift' (TB)	ESgI
'Prince Indigo' (TB)	MRav
'Prince of Burgundy' (IB)	WCAu
'Prince of Tuscany' (DB) **new**	CBor
'Princess Beatrice' (TB)	WCAu
'Princess Bride' (BB) ♀H7	WCAu
'Princess Osra' (TB)	WMil
'Princesse Caroline de Monaco' (TB)	CKel ESgI WViv
prismatica	GKev
'Private Eye' (TB)	WCAu
'Professor Blaauw' (Dut) ♀H5	CAvo CWCL
'Prosper Laugier' (IB)	MNHC WCAu
'Protocol' (IB)	CKel
'Proud Tradition' (TB)	SIri WCAu XSen
'Provençal' (TB)	CKel ELon ESgI WCAu XSen
'Prussian Blue' (Sib) ♀H7	GBin SMHy
pseudacorus	Widely available
- B&SWJ 5018 from Japan	WCru
- 'Alba'	NGdn SRms
- var. ***bastardii***	CBen CWat ECha ELon EPfP LCro LLWG LOPS NPer SLon SPer WBrk WFar WMoo WPnP WWtn XLum
- 'Clotted Cream'	GLog
- 'Come in Spinner'	LLWG
- cream-flowered	NBir

	- 'Crème de la Crème'	CKel ELon EPfP EWTr LLWG NLar NSti NWad WFar
	- 'Dragonfly Dance'	LLWG
	- 'Flore Pleno' (d)	CBen LLWG NLar NPer SRms WBrk WCot WFar WPnP WWtn
I	- 'Golden Fleece'	SPer
	- 'Golden Queen'	EWat LLWG
	- 'Ivory'	LLWG
	- 'Kelis Choice'	LLWG
	- 'Krill'	EBee EPPr LLWG
	- 'Mandchurica'	XBlo
	- 'Mini Mart'	LLWG
	- 'Roy Davidson' ♀H7	CBre CBro GCal LLWG MWts NLar WCot WFar WWtn
	- 'Spartacus'	EBee
	- 'Sulphur Queen'	GBin LLWG NLar WCot
	- 'Sun Cascade'	GBin
	- 'Tiger Brother'	CBro LLWG WBrk
	- 'Turnipseed'	WCot
	- 'Variegata' (v) ♀H7	Widely available
	'Puddy Tat' (SDB)	WCAu
	'Pulse Rate' (SDB)	CBro
	pumila	CPla CRos EPot ITim LRHS MCot NRHS NSla
	- f. ***atroviolacea***	CKel WAbe
*	- 'Gelber Mantel'	NBir WFar
	- 'Violacea' (DB)	SRms
	- yellow-flowered	WAbe
	'Pumpin' Iron' (SDB) ♀H7	CKel ESgI
	'Pure As Gold' (TB)	CWCL ESgI WCot XSen
	'Purple Gem' (Reticulata)	CAby CRos EPfP LAma LRHS NRHS
	'Purple Hill' (Reticulata)	LAma
	PURPLE LAVENDER MIX (Dut)	GKev
	'Purple Mere' (Sib)	MHCG
	'Purple Sensation' (Dut)	SDeJ
	'Purple Study' (MTB)	WCAu
	purpurea	see *I. galatica*
	'Pussycat Pink' (SDB)	ESgI WCAu
	'Quaker Lady' (TB)	ESgI WCAu
	'Quark' (SDB)	CBro CKel
	'Quechee' (TB)	CKel CWCL CWld EPPr EPfP ESgI GMaP LBuc LRHS MCot MRav NLar NRHS NWad SCob SDeJ SPer WGwG
	'Queen in Calico' (TB)	ESgI WCAu
	'Queen Jeanne' (La)	LLWG
	'Queen of Angels' (TB)	WCAu
	'Queen of Hearts' (TB)	XSen
	'Queen's Circle' (TB) ♀H7	WCAu
	'Rabbit's Foot' (SDB)	SIri
	'Radiant Apogee' (TB)	EIri
	'Radiant Burst' (IB)	SIri
	'Rain Dance' (SDB) ♀H7	ESgI
	'Rainbow Candy' (TB)	WCAu
	'Rainbow Etude' (TB)	WCAu
	RAINBOW GRAND MIXTURE	SDeJ
	'Rainbow High' (TB)	WCAu
	'Rainbow Rim' (SDB)	ESgI WCAu
	'Rainbow Tour' (TB)	WCAu
	'Rajah' (TB)	CAby CBod CKel CRos EHrv ELan EUJe GMaP LRHS LSRN MHer MNrw MRav NRHS SDeJ SPoG WAul
	'Rameses' (TB)	ESgI
	ramsayi	GCal
	'Rancho Rose' (TB)	XSen
	'Rare Edition' (IB)	CKel NBir WArt XSen
	'Rare Quality' (TB)	XSen
	'Rare Treat' (TB)	XSen
	'Rarer than Rubies' (TB)	WCAu
	'Raspberry Acres' (IB)	MRav WCAu
	'Raspberry Blush' (IB) ♀H7	CBod CKel CRos EIri EPfP GBin LRHS MRav NRHS SDeJ WAul WGwG WHoo WTor XSen
	'Raspberry Tiger' (SDB)	WCAu
	'Razoo' (SDB)	CKel CPBP
	'Re La Blanche' (TB)	SIri
	'Real Coquette' (SDB)	SIri
	'Rebecca Perret' (TB)	WCAu
	'Recurring Delight' (TB)	WCAu
	'Red Ember' (Dut)	CAvo ERCP GKev LCro LOPS MMrt MNrw WRHF
	'Red Flare' (TB)	WFar
	'Red Flash' (TB)	ESgI
	'Red Heart' (SDB)	ELon ESgI MRav XSen
	'Red Orchid' (IB)	ELan ESgI LRHS SRms WCAu
	'Red Revival' (TB)	MRav WCAu
	'Red Rufus' (TB)	CKel
	'Red Rum' (TB)	EWes
	'Red Zinger' (IB)	CMac ESgI LRHS
	'Redelta' (TB)	XSen
	'Reflets Safran' (TB)	SIri XSen
	'Regal' (Reticulata)	LAma
	'Regal Surprise' (SpH) ♀H7	EWat LLWG WWtn
	'Regality' (Sib)	EBee MHer MMuc
	'Regards' (SDB)	CBro XSen
	'Regency Buck' (Sib)	WFar
§	***reichenbachii***	GKev LLHF WAbe
	'Rendez-Vous' (Dut)	SDeJ
	'Repartee' (TB)	XSen
	reticulata	ELan EUJe GKev SDeJ SPer
	- var. ***bakeriana***	LAma LLHF XEll
	'Rhapsody' (Reticulata)	CRos EPot ERCP GKev LAma LLHF LRHS NRHS SDeJ
	'Rheingauperle' (TB)	ESgI
	'Rhett' (La)	EBee
	'Rigamarole' (Sib)	MWts SCob WFar WGob
	'Rikugi-sakura' (Sib)	ELon LLHF NLar WCot WGob
	'Rimfire' (TB)	ELan
	'Ringo' (TB)	LSRN MRav WCAu
	'Rio Rojo' (TB)	WCAu
	'Rip City' (TB)	ESgI
	'Rising Moon' (TB)	SIri
	'Rive Gauche' (TB)	ESgI
	'River Avon' (TB)	WCAu
	'Riverbuds' (SDB)	SIri WCAu
	'Roanoke's Choice' (Sib)	CBro CElw ELon EWes MNrw NCGa WFar
	'Roaring Jelly' (Sib)	EWes NLar WCAu WCot WGob
	'Rob Cornell' (TB)	ESgI
	'Robe d'Été' (TB)	WViv
§	× ***robusta*** 'Dark Aura' ♀H7	LLWG LRHS MAvo MWts SIri WCAu WCot
§	- 'Gerald Darby'	CBod CRos CSpe CWat CWld EBee EHrv ELan EPPr EPfP EWhm LRHS MCot MHer MHol MNrw NCGa NGdn NLar NRHS NSti SCob WBrk WCAu WFar WMoo WOut WPnP WSpi
	- 'Mountain Brook'	LLWG
*	- 'Purple Fan'	LLWG
	'Robusto' (TB)	CKel
	'Rochester Castle' (Kent Castles Series) (IB)	SIri
§	'Rocket' (TB)	GMaP LBuc LRHS MRav NBir NRHS SDeJ SPer
	'Romantic Evening' (TB)	EIri WCAu XSen
	'Romney Marsh' (IB)	SIri
	'Romola' (TB)	WMil

	Name	Suppliers
	'Roryu' (SpH)	LLWG
	'Rosalie Figge' (TB)	CMac ESgI MHol WCAu WCot
	'Rosé' (TB)	LSRN
	'Rose Queen'	see *I. ensata* 'Rose Queen'
	'Rose Violet' (TB)	WCAu
	'Rosebud Melody' (Sib)	GBin GWyn
	'Roseplic' (TB)	LRHS
	'Rosette Wine' (TB)	ESgI
	'Rosselline' (Sib)	MAvo WAul
	'Rosy Bows' (Sib)	EBee WCAu WFar
	'Rosy Veil' (TB)	ESgI
	'Rosy Wings' (TB)	ESgI
	'Roucoulade' (TB)	SIri
	'Rouge Gorge' (TB)	SIri WViv
	'Roussette' (IB)	SIri
	'Rowden Aurelius' (Sib)	WAul
I	'Royal Blue' (Sib)	EBee ECha
	'Royal Crusader' (TB)	WCAu XSen
	'Roy's Repeater' (SpH)	WCAu
	'Rubacuori' (TB)	ESgI
	'Ruby' (Reticulata)	LAma
	'Ruby Chimes' (IB)	ESgI WCAu
	'Ruby Contrast' (TB)	WCAu
	'Ruby Eruption' (SDB)	EIri WCAu
	'Ruby Morn' (TB)	WCAu
	rudskyi	see *I. variegata*
	'Ruffled Velvet' (Sib) ♀H7	CBcs CDor CElw CKel ECtt ELan EPfP GBin GLog GMaP ILea IMou LRHS MAvo MCot MHol MRav NChi NLar SCob SPer WAul WCAu WFar WWtn
	'Ruffles and Flourishes' (Sib)	LLWG WCAu
	'Ruffles Plus' (Sib)	WGob
	'Russet Crown' (TB)	CKel
	'Rustle of Spring' (TB)	WCAu
	'Rustler' (TB)	WCAu
	'Rusty Beauty' (Dut)	SDeJ
	'Ruth Margaret' (TB)	CKel
	'Ruth Rowlands' (TB)	ESgI
	ruthenica	WHil
	- var. ***nana***	CExl GEdr GKev
	'Sable' (TB)	CBod CKel CRos EHrv ELan EPfP ESgI GMaP LRHS MRav NLar NRHS SCob SDeJ SPer WAul WCAu WGwG
	'Sable Night' (TB)	CKel ESgI
	'Safari Sunset' (TB)	WCAu
	'Sailor' (IB)	WCAu
	'Sailor's Dream' (MTB)	WCAu
	'Saint Crispin' (TB)	CRos EPfP GMaP LRHS MRav NRHS SPer SPoG WGwG
	'Salamander Crossing' (Sib) ♀H7	WAul WCAu
	'Sally Jane' (TB)	WCAu
	'Salonique' (TB)	NLar WCAu
	'Saltwood' (SDB)	CBro
	'Saltwood Castle' (Kent Castles Series) (IB)	SIri
	'Salzburg Echo' (TB)	WCAu
	'Sam Carne' (TB)	WCAu
	× ***sambucina***	XSen
	'San Diego' (TB)	ESgI
	'San Francisco' (TB)	ESgI
	'Sandling Sunset' (TB)	SIri
	'Sandy Caper' (IB)	WCAu
§	***sanguinea*** 'Snow Queen'	CAvo CBcs CKel CRos EHoe ELan EPfP GBin GKev GWyn IKil IMou LRHS MMuc NBid NLar NQui NRHS NSti SCob SPer WAul WCAu WCot WFar WMoo WWtn
	'Sapphire Beauty' (Dut)	GKev SDeJ
	'Sapphire Gem' (SDB)	CKel ESgI LSRN WCAu
	'Sapphire Hills' (TB)	LRHS WCAu XSen
	'Sasha Borisovich' (TB)	ESgI
	'Savoir Faire' (Sib)	ECha
	'Scandinavian Girl'	WCAu
	'Scent Sational' (Reticulata)	CMea EPot GKev LAma
	'Scented Wonder' (TB)	WCAu
	schachtii	EPot
	- purple-flowered	WAbe
	'Scramble' (Sib)	NEgg WCAu WCot WFar
	'Scribe' (MDB)	CBro NBir
	'Sea Breeze' (Reticulata)	EPot ERCP GKev LAma
	'Sea Fret' (SDB)	CBro
	'Sea Green' (Reticulata)	LAma
	'Sea of Joy' (TB)	CKel XSen
	'Sea Power' (TB)	SIri
	'Sea Shadows' (Sib)	ESgI NBir WCAu
	'Seafire' (SDB)	WCAu
	'Seakist' (TB)	WCAu
	'Season Ticket' (IB)	XSen
	'Seastone' (SDB)	WCAu
	'Second Look' (TB)	GKev XSen
	'Second Wind' (TB)	WCAu
	'Secret Melody' (TB)	XSen
	'Self Evident' (MDB)	LLHF
	'Semiramis' (TB)	CKel
	'Semola' (SDB)	ESgI
	'Senlac' (TB)	ELan NLar WMil
	'Señor Frog' (SDB)	ESgI
	serbica	see *I. reichenbachii*
	'Serene Moment' (TB)	SIri
	'Serenity Prayer' (SDB)	WCAu
	setosa ♀H7	CFis CMac CRos CTri CWCL EAJP GBin GKev LRHS MNrw NCGa NHpl NRHS WOld
	- ***alba***	NLar
	- var. ***arctica***	GKev LEdu
I	- 'Baby Blue'	CRos EPfP LRHS MBNS MJak NRHS
	- subsp. ***canadensis***	see *I. hookeri*
	- var. ***nana***	see *I. hookeri*
	'Shaker's Prayer' (Sib) ♀H7	GBin MNrw WGob
	'Shakespeare's Sonnet' (SDB)	ESgI
	'Shampoo' (IB)	WCAu
	'Share the Spirit' (TB)	WCAu
	'Sharp Dressed Man' (TB)	WCAu
	'Sharrie Carrie' (TB)	SIri
	'Sheila Ann Germaney' (Reticulata)	CRos EPot ERCP GKev LAma LLHF LRHS NRHS WRHF
	'Shelford Giant' (Spuria) ♀H7	NEgg
	'Sherbet Lemon' (IB) ♀H7	WCAu
	'Shifnal'	WCAu
	'Shirley Chandler' (IB) ♀H7	SIri
	'Shirley Pope' (Sib) ♀H7	EWTr EWes GBin GWyn LRHS NSti WFar WMoo WPnP WSpi
	'Shirley's Choice' (Sib)	SIri
	'Short Distance' (IB)	SIri
	'Showdown' (Sib)	CRos ECtt GMaP LRHS NRHS
	'Shrawley' (Sib)	WAul
	shrevei	see *I. virginica* var. *shrevei*
	'Shurton Demon' (TB)	CKel
	'Shurton Inn' (TB)	CKel SRms WCAu
	'Shurton Princess' (TB) ♀H7	CKel
	sibirica	CAvo CTri CTsd GAbr GBin GKev MCot MMuc NChi SCob SPlb SRot WArt WBrk WCFE WFar WGwG WHer WMoo WShi
	- PAB 6119	LEdu
	- 'Niklas Sea'	see *I.* 'Lake Niklas'
	- 'Redflare'	see *I.* 'Melton Red Flare'

	– 'Snow Queen'	see *I. sanguinea* 'Snow Queen'
	'Sibirica Alba'	ECha EPfP SRms WBrk WFar
	sichuanensis	CExl SPlb
	'Side Effect'	WCAu
	'Sidney Linnegar' (TB)	WCAu
	'Sierra Blue' (TB)	ESgI
	'Sierra Grande' (TB)	SIri XSen
	'Sierra Nevada' (Spuria)	XSen
	'Sign of Leo' (TB)	CKel XSen
	'Silkirim' (TB)	CKel
	'Silver Edge' (Sib) ♀H7	Widely available
	'Silver Peak' (TB) **new**	CKel
	'Silverado' (TB)	CKel ESgI GBin LRHS WCAu
	'Silvery Beauty' (Dut) ♀H7	CAvo ELan GKev LCro LOPS NBir SDeJ
	'Silvery Princess' (Dut)	SDeJ
	sindjarensis	see *I. aucheri*
	'Sinfonietta' (La)	LLWG WCot
	'Sing to Me' (TB)	WCAu
	'Sinister Desire' (IB)	SIri
	sintenisii ♀H6	CBro CPBP GKev LLHF SBrt WAbe WArt XSen
	'Sir Michael' (TB)	ESgI
	'Siva Siva' (TB)	CKel MRav
	'Sixtine C' (TB)	SIri
	'Skating Party' (TB)	CKel ESgI XSen
	'Skiers' Delight' (TB)	LRHS
	'Sky Beauty' (Dut)	SDeJ
	'Sky Hooks' (TB)	XSen
	'Sky Tracery' (MTB)	SDys
	'Sky Wings' (Sib)	CSam ECha MArl WMoo
	'Skydancer' (SDB)	WCAu
	'Skyfire' (TB)	CKel ESgI
	'Skylark's Song' (TB)	EIri
	'Small Sky' (SDB)	CBro
	'Smart' (SDB)	WCAu
	'Smart Aleck' (TB)	ESgI
	'Smart Girl' (TB)	EIri
	'Smart Move' (TB)	ESgI
	'Smiling Faces' (TB)	WCAu
	'Smitten Kitten' (IB)	LSRN WCAu
	'Smokey Salmon' (TB)	CKel
	'Smooth' (SDB)	SDys
	'Snow Season' (SDB)	ESgI
	'Snow Tracery' (TB)	LRHS NRHS
	'Snow Troll' (SDB)	WCAu
	'Snowcrest' (Sib)	CBre GBin LRHS MRav NCGa NRHS WAul WHoo WWtn
	'Snowmound' (TB)	CCCN CKel ESgI WCAu
	'Snowy Owl' (TB)	CKel WCAu
	'Snugglebug' (SDB)	WCAu
	'Social Event' (TB)	ESgI XSen
	'Soft Blue' (Sib) ♀H7	ELon WAul WCAu
	'Solid Mahogany' (TB)	MRav
	'Solo Flight' (TB)	SDys
	'Somerset Blue' (TB)	CKel
	'Somerton Dance' (SDB)	CKel
	'Song of Norway' (TB)	EIri XSen
	'Sonoran Sands' (IB)	SDys
	'Sopra il Vulcano' (BB)	ESgI
	'Sorbonne' (TB)	WCAu
	'Sordid Lives' (TB)	WCAu
	'Sostenique' (TB)	ESgI
	'Southcombe White' (Sib)	SMHy
	'Souvenir de Madame Gaudichau' (TB)	ESgI
	'Sparkling Rose' (Sib)	Widely available
	'Sparkling Waters' (TB)	ESgI
I	'Speckles' (Sib)	EPPr
	'Spellbreaker' (TB)	ELon SIri
	'Spice Lord' (TB)	WCAu
	'Spiced Custard' (TB)	EIri ESgI WCAu
	'Spiced Lemon' (TB)	WCAu
	'Spicy Cajun' (La)	WHil
	'Spinning Wheel' (TB)	SIri
	'Spirit of Memphis' (TB)	XSen
	'Splashacata' (TB)	WCAu XSen
	'Spot of Tea' (MDB)	LLHF
	'Spot On' (Reticulata)	EPot GKev LAma LLHF
	'Spreckles' (TB)	CKel ESgI
	'Spree' (SDB)	WCAu
	sprengeri	GKev
	'Spring Blush' (MTB) ♀H7	SIri
	'Spring Festival' (TB)	WCAu
	'Spring Kiss' (TB)	SIri
	'Spring Madness' (TB)	WCAu
	'Spring Time' (Reticulata)	LAma SDeJ
	spuria	CMac CPou
§	– subsp. ***halophila***	GKev
	– subsp. ***notha*** CC 725	WCot
	– subsp. ***ochroleuca***	see *I. orientalis* Mill.
	'Spy' (BB)	WCAu
	'Square Dance Skirt' (TB)	SDys
	'St Louis Blues' (TB)	ESgI XSen
	'Stairway to Heaven' (TB)	ESgI WCAu
	'Stapleford' (SDB)	CBro
	'Staplehurst' (MTB) ♀H7	SIri
	'Star Cluster' (Sib)	WFar
	'Star in the Night' (TB)	WCAu
	'Star Shine' (TB)	WCAu
	'Stardate' (SDB)	CKel
	'Starheart' (IB)	WCAu
	'Starship' (TB)	XSen
	'Starwoman' (IB) ♀H7	SDys
	'Staten Island' (TB)	ESgI SRms WCAu
	'Stella Polaris' (TB)	ELon
	'Stellar Lights' (TB)	EIri WCAu
	'Stephen Wilcox' (Sib)	WAul
	'Stepping Out' (TB) ♀H7	CBod CKel CMac CPar CRos EPfP ESgI GBin LRHS NRHS SCob SDeJ WCAu WTor
	'Steve' (Sib)	CPar EWes
	'Stilo Libero'	WCAu
	'Stingray' (TB)	ESgI
	'Stitch in Time' (TB)	EIri WCAu
	'Stockholm' (SDB)	CKel
	stolonifera	GKev
	– 'Augustus' (Rc)	GKev
	– 'Caligula' (Rc) **new**	GKev
	– 'Morning Coffee' (Rc)	GKev
	– 'Zwanenburg Beauty' (Rc)	GKev
	'Stop the Music' (TB)	XSen
	'Storm' (Reticulata)	LAma
	'Storm Center' (TB)	CKel
	'Stormy Circle' (SDB)	WCAu
	'Storrington' (TB)	ECha ECtt EMal LRHS NRHS
	'Strange Brew' (TB)	WCAu
	'Strathmore' (TB)	ECha EMal LRHS NRHS
	'Strawberry Fair' (Sib) ♀H7	WCAu
	'Strictly Jazz' (TB)	WCAu
	'Strike it Rich' (TB)	ESgI
	'Strozzapreti' (TB)	ESgI
	'Strut' (TB)	WCAu
	'Strut your Stuff' (TB)	WCAu
	'Study In Black' (TB)	XSen
	stylosa	see *I. unguicularis*
§	***suaveolens***	CPBP CPou GEdr NHpl NWad
	– var. ***flavescens***	see *I. suaveolens* yellow-flowered
§	– purple-flowered	GCrg GEdr GKev WAbe
	– 'Rubromarginata'	CPBP

	- var. ***violacea***	see *I. suaveolens* purple-flowered
§	- yellow-flowered	GKev WAbe
	'Succès Fou' (TB)	SIri WViv
	'Sugar' (IB)	NSti WCAu
	'Sugar Blues' (TB)	WCAu
	'Sugar Magnolia' (TB)	SIri
	'Sugarmouse' (BB) **new**	SIri
	'Sultan's Palace' (TB)	CKel EBee ESgI LCro LRHS NLar WSpi XSen
	'Sultry Mood' (TB)	CKel
	'Summer Holidays' (TB)	XSen
	'Summer Revels' (Sib)	EWes MAvo
	'Summer Sky' (Sib)	CBre LEdu MHCG MSCN WArt WAul WCot
	'Sunadokei' (SpH) **new**	LLWG
	'Sunblaze' (TB)	WCAu
	'Sunday Brunch' (TB)	MNHC
	'Sunlit Shores' (La)	LLWG
	'Sunny Dawn' (IB)	CKel
	'Sunny Disposition' (TB)	XSen
	'Sunnyside Delight' (TB)	WCAu
	'Sunnyside Up' (TB)	GKev
	'Sunset Sky' (TB)	CKel
	'Sunshine' (Reticulata)	EPot LAma SDeJ
	'Sunshine' (TB) **new**	GKev
	'Superstition' (TB) ♀H7	CBod CKel CWld EIri ELan ESgI EWes LCro LOPS LRHS MRav SCob WCAu XSen
	'Supreme Sultan' (TB)	CKel CWCL ESgI SCob WCAu XSen
I	'Surprise' (Dut)	MNrw
	'Susan Bliss' (TB)	CKel ELan EPfP ESgI WCAu WMil
	'Sutton Valence' (Sib)	SIri
	'Swain' (TB)	ESgI
	'Swan Ballet' (TB)	ESgI
	'Swank' (Sib)	WAul
	'Swans in Flight' (Sib)	WCAu
	'Swazi Princess' (TB)	ELon SRms
	'Sweet Kate' (SDB)	WCAu
	'Sweet Lavender' (TB)	WMil
	'Sweet Lena' (TB)	ESgI
	'Sweet Musette' (TB)	SRms WCAu
	'Sweeter than Wine' (TB)	MRav
	'Swingtown' (TB)	WCAu
	'Swirling Waters' (La)	LLWG
	'Swiss Majesty' (TB)	WCAu
	'Swizzle' (IB)	XSen
	'Sybil' (TB)	GBin
	'Sylvan' (TB)	XSen
	'Sylvia Murray' (TB)	WCAu
	'Symphony' (Dut)	NBir SDeJ
	'Syncopation' (TB)	ELon ESgI WCAu XSen
	'Tact' (IB)	SIri
	'Take Me Away' (TB)	SDys
	'Tall Chief' (TB)	CKel WCAu
	'Tamberg' (Sib)	CKel
	'Tan Tingo' (IB)	XSen
	'Tangerine Sky' (TB)	LRHS
	'Tantara' (SDB)	XSen
	'Tantrum' (IB)	WCAu XSen
	'Tanz Nochmal' (Sib)	GBin
	'Tanzanian Tangerine' (TB)	WCAu
	taochia	CPBP
	'Tarn Hows' (TB)	ESgI SRms
	'Taubenblau' (Sib)	SAko
	'Teal Velvet' (Sib)	CKel ECha ELon EPfP EWes GLog LRHS MCot SCob WFar WGob
	'Tealwood' (Sib)	GBin
	'Teapot Tempest' (BB)	WCAu
	'Teasaucer Hill' (MTB) ♀H7	SIri
	tectorum	GKev LRHS SChr WCot XLum XSen
	- BWJ 8191	WCru
	- 'Alba'	GKev WThu XSen
	- 'Cruella'	EPfP GWyn MSCN
	- 'Variegata' misapplied	see *I. japonica* 'Variegata'
	- 'Variegata' (v)	ECrN SRms
	'Tell Fibs' (SDB)	CBro
	'Teller of Tales' (La)	LLWG
	'Temper Tantrum' (Sib)	LRHS WCAu
	'Temple Gold' (TB)	CKel NPer
	'Temple Meads' (IB)	ESgI WCAu
	'Templecloud' (IB) ♀H7	CKel
	'Tempting Fate' (TB)	SIri WCAu
§	***tenax***	CRos EBee LRHS NRHS
	'Tenebrae' (TB)	WMil
	'Tennison Ridge' (TB)	WCAu
	'Tenterden' (BB) **new**	SIri
	'Teverlae' (Sib)	CRos EBee LRHS NRHS
	'Thaïs' (TB)	ESgI
	'The Citadel' (TB)	ELon
	'The Rocket'	see *I.* 'Rocket'
	'Thelma Perry' (Sib)	EPfP
	'Theseus' (AB)	GKev
	'Third Charm' (SDB)	CBro
	'Third World' (SDB)	CBro
	'This and That' (IB)	WCAu
	'Thornbird' (TB) ♀H7	EIri ESgI SRms WCAu
	'Three Quarters' (Sib)	ELon NChi
	'Thriller' (TB)	ESgI WCAu XSen
	'Thunder Echo' (TB)	SIri
	'Thundering Ovation' (TB)	WCAu
	TIGER MIXED (Dut)	GKev
§	'Tigereye' (Dut)	ERCP GBin GKev LCro LOPS MNrw SDeJ
	tigridia	CExl
	'Time to Shine' (SDB)	WCAu
	'Time Zone' (TB)	WCAu
	tingitana	GKev
	'Tinkerbell' (SDB)	CPBP CWld EBee GMaP LRHS NBir NRHS SDeJ WTor
	'Titan's Glory' (TB) ♀H7	CKel CMac ESgI LEdu LRHS MRav SRms WCot WHoo
	'Tollong'	IKil ILea IMou
	'Tom Tit' (TB)	WCAu WMil
	'Tomato Bisque' (La) **new**	LLWG
	'Top Flight' (TB)	CKel ELan LRHS NRHS SRms
	'Top Gun' (TB)	ESgI
	'Topaz Jewel' (TB)	MHol
	'Topolino' (TB)	CKel
	'Torero' (TB)	SIri
	'Total Eclipse' (TB)	SRms
	'Totally Cool' (SDB)	LSRN
	'Touch of Mahogany' (TB)	WCAu
	'Town Flirt' (TB)	WCAu
	'Trajectory' (SDB)	WCAu
	'Trapel' (TB)	ESgI
	'Trencavel' (TB)	ESgI
	'Trenwith' (TB)	ESgI
	'Trim the Velvet' (Sib)	WAul
	'Triple Whammy' (TB)	ESgI XSen
	'Tristan'	CKel
	'Tristram' (TB)	WMil
	'Tropic Night' (Sib)	CKel CRos CSam CTri EBee ECtt EHrv EIri ELan EPfP GBin GKin LCro LOPS LRHS MBel MCot MRav MSCN MWts NRHS NRya NSti SSut WAul WAvo WBrk WFar WGob
	tuberosa	CAby CAvo CBro CFis CTri CWCL ECha ELan ERCP LAma LPot MHer MPie SDeJ WShi
	- MS 76	WCot

	- MS 964	WCot
	- PB	WCot
	'Tulip Festival' (TB)	CKel CRos
	'Tumble Bug' (Sib)	LLWG WGob
	'Tumultueux' (TB)	WViv
	'Tut's Gold' (TB)	ESgI
	'Tuxedo' (TB)	XSen
	'Twist of Twilight' (La)	LLWG
	'Two Sided Coin' (TB)	WCAu
§	'Tycoon' (Sib)	CRos EShb GBin LRHS NChi NRHS SPer
	typhifolia	GKev
	'Tyrian Dream' (IB)	WCAu
	'Ultimate' (SDB)	WCAu
	'Uncle Charlie' (TB)	WCAu
	'Undercurrent' (TB)	WCAu
	'Unfinished Business' (TB)	WCAu
§	***unguicularis***	Widely available
	- from Karpathos, Greece	GKev
	- 'Abington Purple'	CJun EIri
	- 'Alba'	CAvo CExl XEll XSen
	- subsp. ***angustifolia***	WSHC
§	- subsp. ***cretensis***	GKev
	- - white-flowered	WSHC
	- 'Diana Clare'	CJun
	- 'Marondera'	CAvo CJun
	- 'Mary Barnard' ♀H5	CAvo CBro CJun CPou CRos EHrv LRHS MHer NBir NRHS WHoo
	- 'Peloponnese Snow'	GEdr SBrt
§	- 'Walter Butt'	CAvo CJun EBee NBir XEll
	'Vague à l'Ame' (TB)	ESgI
	'Valda' (Sib)	EBee ELon
	'Valerie Joyce' (TB)	WCAu
	'Vamp' (IB)	CKel GBin XSen
	'Vanilla Mist' (La)	LLWG
	'Vanilla Skies' (TB)	WCAu
	'Vanity' (TB)	XSen
	'Vanity's Child' (TB)	WCAu XSen
§	***variegata*** ♀H7	CMea EBee GBin GKev XSen
	- from Podyjí, Moravia	SBrt
	'Velvet King' (TB)	ESgI
	'Velvet Purple'	XBlo
	'Velvet Smile' (Reticulata)	LAma
	'Venita Faye' (TB)	WCAu
	'Verity Blamey' (TB)	CKel
	versicolor	CBen CSpe CWat GBin GKev GMaP GPoy MMuc MNHC MWts SEND SPlb SRms WArt WCAu WFar WMAq WMoo WPnP WShi
	- 'Algonquin'	LLWG
	- 'Bellerive Harmony' **new**	LLWG
	- 'Between the Lines'	LLWG
	- 'Candystriper'	LLWG
	- 'China West Lake'	LLWG
	- 'Claret Cup'	CPou ILea SHar
	- 'Kermesina'	CWat ECha ELan LLWG MMuc MWts NPer NSti SRms WFar WMAq WMoo WPnP
	- 'Mint Fresh'	LLWG
	- 'Mysterious Monique'	CWat LLWG MWts
	- purple-flowered	EWat
	- 'Rosea'	EWat
	- 'Rowden Allegro'	LLWG
	- 'Rowden Aria'	LLWG
	- 'Rowden Cadenza'	EWat LLWG
	- 'Rowden Calypso'	LLWG
	- 'Rowden Cantata'	LLWG
	- 'Rowden Concerto'	LLWG
	- 'Rowden Electro'	LLWG
	- 'Rowden Lyric'	LLWG
	- 'Rowden Melody'	LLWG
	- 'Rowden Pastorale'	LLWG
	- 'Rowden Sonata'	LLWG
	- 'Rowden Waltz'	LLWG
	'Vi Luihn' (Sib)	ECha ELon SAko WMoo
	'Vibrations' (TB)	ESgI WCAu
	'Victoria Falls' (TB)	CKel ESgI MHol
	'Victorian Secret' (Sib)	EBee ELon WCAu
	'Viel Schnee' (Sib)	ELon
	'Vin Nouveau' (TB)	XSen
	'Vinho Verde' (IB)	CKel
	'Vino Rosso' (SDB)	ESgI
	'Violet Beauty' (Reticulata)	CRos GKev LAma LRHS NRHS
	'Violet Classic' (TB)	WCAu
	'Violet Harmony' (TB)	ESgI
	'Violet Icing' (TB)	CKel
	'Violet Rings' (TB)	WCAu
	'Violet Turner' (TB)	MHol
	virginica	LLWG
	- 'De Luxe'	see *I.* × *robusta* 'Dark Aura'
	- 'Lavender Lustre'	LLWG
	- 'Orchid Purple'	LLWG
	- 'Pale Lavender'	LLWG
	- 'Pink Perfection'	LLWG
§	- var. ***shrevei***	LLWG
	- 'Slightly Daft'	LLWG
	'Vitafire' (TB)	ESgI
	'Vitality' (IB)	ELon ESgI
	'Voilà' (IB)	CMea ESgI
	'Volts' (SDB)	XSen
	'Volute' (TB)	ESgI
	'Voyage' (SDB)	XSen
	'Wabash' (TB)	CKel WCAu XSen
	'Waihi Wedding' (La)	LLWG
	'Walmer Castle' (Kent Castles Series) (IB)	SIri
	'Walter Butt'	see *I. unguicularis* 'Walter Butt'
	'War Chief' (TB)	EPfP ESgI MRav WCAu
	'War Sails' (TB)	SIri WCAu
	warleyensis	EPot GKev
	wattii	CExl GCal IKil WGwG
	- KWJ 12172	WCru
	'Wealden Butterfly' (Sib) ♀H7	SIri WAul
	'Wealden Carousel' (Sib)	SIri WAul
	'Wealden Mystery' (Sib)	SIri WAul
	'Wealden Skies' (Sib)	SIri WAul
	'Wealden Spires' (Sib)	WAul
	'Wealden Summer' (Sib)	WAul
	'Wearing Rubies' (TB)	ESgI WCAu
	'Webelos' (SDB)	MRav NRHS
	'Wedding Candles' (TB)	CKel
	'Wedding Vow' (TB)	CKel EIri
*	'Wedgwood Blue' (Sino-Sib)	GBin
	'Weisse Etagen' (Sib)	ELon
	'Welch's Reward' (MTB)	ESgI
	'Welcome Discovery' (TB)	WCAu
	'Welcome Return' (Sib)	LLWG LRHS MMuc WGob WMoo
	'Welfenfürstin' (Sib)	GBin SAko
	'Welfenprinz' (Sib) ♀H7	SMHy WAul
	'Wench' (TB)	WCAu
	'Westar' (SDB)	CKel
	'Westwell' (SDB)	WCAu
	'Westwood' (IB) **new**	SIri
	'What Again' (SDB)	XSen
	'What's New' (TB)	WCAu
	'Whee' (SDB)	WCAu
	'Whispering Spirits' (TB)	WCAu
	'White Caucasus' (Reticulata)	EPot ERCP GKev LAma LLHF XEll

	'White City' (TB)	CKel CRos EPfP ESgI GMaP LRHS MRav MWat NPer NRHS SCob SDeJ SPer SRms WCAu
	'White Gem' (SDB)	ESgI
	'White Knight' (TB)	EBee EPfP WSpi
I	'White Queen' (Sib)	ESgI
	'White Reprise' (TB)	ESgI XSen
	'White Swirl' (Sib)	CAby CBar CBro CKel CRos CTri EBee ECha ECtt EHrv ELon EPfP EUJe GBin GLog GWyn LCro LRHS MRav NBro NLar NRHS NSti SCob SPer SRms WCAu WFar WGob WPnP
	'White Triangles' (Sib)	ELon
	'White Umbrella' (La)	ECtt LLWG
	'White van Vliet' (Dut)	SDeJ
	'White Wine' (MTB)	WCAu
	'White-Wave' (TB)	XBlo
	'Widow's Veil' (SDB)	ESgI
	'Wild Jasmine' (TB)	WCAu
	'Wild Wings' (TB)	LRHS MCot SGbt WCAu
	wilsonii ♀H7	CExl GKev NRya WGob
	'Windjammer Seas' (TB)	SDys
	'Wine Wings' (Sib) **new**	WGob
	'Winemaster' (TB)	SIri
	'Winesap' (TB)	ESgI
	winogradowii ♀H7	CBro CRos EPot ERCP GKev LAma LLHF LRHS NRHS WAbe XEll
	- white-flowered	GKev
	'Winter Olympics' (TB)	CBod CKel CRos ELan EPfP LRHS MRav NRHS SPer WGwG
	'Wintry Sky' (TB)	WCAu
	'Wise' (SDB)	WCAu
	'Wish Upon a Star' (SDB)	WCAu
	'Wishful Thinking' (TB)	SIri
	'Wisteria Sachet' (IB)	WCAu
	'Witch's Wand' (TB)	ESgI
	'Wizard's Return' (SDB)	SIri
	'Wonders Never Cease' (TB)	WCAu
	'Wondrous' (TB)	ESgI
	'Word of Warning' (La)	LLWG
	'Wrangler' (IB)	SIri
	xiphioides	see *I. latifolia*
	xiphium var. ***lusitanica***	GKev
	'Yaquina Blue' (TB)	WCAu
	'Yarai' (SpH)	LLWG
	'Yasha' (SpH)	LLWG
	'Yellow Flirt' (MTB)	WCAu
	'Yellowtail' (Sib) **new**	MSCN
	'Yeoman' (TB)	WMil
	'Yes' (TB)	ESgI
	'Yippy Skippy' (SDB)	WCAu
	'Yukiyanagi' (SpH) **new**	LLWG
	'Zakopane' (Sib)	EWes WAul
	'Zantha' (TB)	XSen
	'Zero' (SDB)	CKel SIri
	'Zinger' (BB)	WSpi
	'Zweites Hundert' (Sib)	WFar WKif

Isatis (*Brassicaceae*)

	glauca	GJos
	tinctoria	CBod CHab CHby ENfk GJos GPoy MHer MNHC SRms WTre
	- subsp. ***athoa*** **new**	WCot

Ismene (*Amaryllidaceae*)

	'Advance'	LAma
§	× ***deflexa*** ♀H1c	CCCN EShb GKev LAma LCro LOPS SDeJ WCot
§	- 'Zwanenburg'	CGrW GKev
§	***longipetala***	GKev
§	'Sulphur Queen' ♀H1c	CBor CGrW GKev SDeJ

Isodon (*Lamiaceae*)

	calycinus	SPlb
	effusus	WPGP
	excisus	EBee EWld WPGP
	longitubus	EWld GEdr LEdu SBrt
	- B&SWJ 11027	WCru
	rubescens	IMou SMad WCot

Isolepis (*Cyperaceae*)

§	***cernua***	CBen CWat LCro LLWG LOPS LRHS MWts SCoo WArt WCot WMAq
	nodosa (Rottb.) R. Br.	see *Ficinia nodosa*

Isoloma see *Kohleria*

Isomeris see *Cleome*

Isoplexis see *Digitalis*

Isopogon (*Proteaceae*)

	anemonifolius	CCCN CKel SPlb
	anethifolius	SPlb
	formosus	MPkF

Isopyrum (*Ranunculaceae*)

	biternatum	LEdu
	hallii	EBee
	nipponicum	WPGP
	thalictroides	EBee EPot GEdr IMou LEdu LLHF NRya SDys WCot

Isotoma (*Campanulaceae*)

	sp.	SWvt
§	***axillaris***	CSpe NPer SCoo SPer
	- 'Fairy Carpet'	CBod NCou NHpl SRms
	fluviatilis	NLar

Itea (*Iteaceae*)

	chinensis	CExl
	ilicifolia ♀H5	Widely available
*	- 'Rubrifolia'	ELan SLon
	virginica	CBcs CMCN ELon LRHS MMrt MRav SLon
§	- 'Henry's Garnet' ♀H5	CDul CEnd CKel CMCN CMac CRos CSBt EBee ECrN EPfP EUJe GBin LEdu LRHS MGil MGos NLar NRHS SCob SEle SGol SPad SPer SPoG SRms SWvt WPGP
	- LITTLE HENRY ('Sprich'PBR)	CKel CMac CSBt EBee EPfP LSRN NLar SCob
	- 'Long Spire'	NLar
	- 'Merlot'	CBod MBlu NLar SGol
	- 'Sarah Eve'	CMCN NLar
	- 'Saturnalia'	NLar
	- Swarthmore form	see *I. virginica* 'Henry's Garnet'
	yunnanensis	CBcs CExl MBlu NLar WSHC

Itoa (*Salicaceae*)

	orientalis var. ***glabrescens***	CMCN

Ixeris (*Asteraceae*)

	stolonifera	XLum

Ixia (*Iridaceae*)

	'Blue Bird'	CWld GKev LAma SDeJ
	'Castor'	CWld

'Giant'	GKev SDeJ WHil
'Hogarth'	CWld GKev LAma WHil
'Jesse'	SDeJ WHil
latifolia	CPbh
'Mabel'	CAvo CWCL GKev WCot WHil
maculata	WHil
'Marquette'	GKev WHil
paniculata 'Eos'	GKev
polystachya	CPbh
'Rose Emperor'	GKev LAma SDeJ WHil
scillaris	CPbh
'Spotlight'	CAvo GKev WHil
thomasiae	WCot WHil
'Venus'	CTca CWCL CWld ERCP GKev LAma SDeJ WHil
viridiflora	WHil
'Yellow Emperor'	CTca GKev SDeJ WHil

Ixiolirion (*Ixioliriaceae*)

pallasii	see *I. tataricum*
§ ***tataricum***	EBee GKev LAma SDeJ

J

Jaborosa (*Solanaceae*)

integrifolia	CExl EBee LEdu SVen XLum

Jacaranda (*Bignoniaceae*)

acutifolia misapplied	see *J. mimosifolia*
§ ***mimosifolia*** ♀H1c	CBcs CCCN CPla SPlb

Jacobaea (*Asteraceae*)

§ ***maritima***	SEND
- 'Ramparts'	ECre
- 'Silver Dust' ♀H4	EPfP

Jacobinia see *Justicia*

Jamesbrittenia (*Scrophulariaceae*)

§ ***microphylla***	CPBP

Jamesia (*Hydrangeaceae*)

americana	CBcs CMCN LLHF NLar SBrt WCru WSHC

Jasione (*Campanulaceae*)

§ ***heldreichii***	NBir SRms
jankae	see *J. heldreichii*
§ ***laevis***	EPfP GAbr SRms WMoo
§ - 'Blaulicht'	CRos ECha EPfP LRHS MSCN NAln NEgg NRHS SPlb WMoo
- BLUE LIGHT	see *J. laevis* 'Blaulicht'
montana	MNHC SRms WRHF
perennis	see *J. laevis*

Jasminum ✿ (*Oleaceae*)

CC 4728	CExl
CW&T 6374	CMCN
affine	see *J. officinale* f. *affine*
angulare ♀H2	CExl CHll CRHN EShb WFib
azoricum ♀H2	CBcs CCCN CHll CRHN CTsd CWCL EPfP EShb SEND SPre WFib
beesianum	Widely available
bignoniaceum	WSHC
blinii	see *J. polyanthum*
dispermum	CRHN NLar
farreri	see *J. humile* f. *farreri*
§ ***floridum***	EWes
fruticans	CMac EBee ELon LRHS SBrt SEND WCru WGob
- RCB UA 22	WCot
giraldii misapplied	see *J. humile* f. *farreri*
giraldii Diels	see *J. floridum*
grandiflorum misapplied	see *J. officinale* f. *affine*
grandiflorum L. 'De Grasse' ♀H2	CRHN EShb WFib
humile	CExl MGil NLar SEND SPtp WKif
§ - f. ***farreri*** Farrer 867	WPGP
- var. ***glabrum***	see *J. humile* f. *wallichianum*
- 'Pershore Purple' **new**	WAvo
§ - 'Revolutum' ♀H5	CAby CBcs CDul CHll CKel CMac CRHN CRos CSBt CWCL EBee ELan EPfP EShb GCal LRHS MGos MRav NLar SEND SGbt SLon SPer SPoG SRms SWvt WSHC
§ - f. ***wallichianum*** B&SWJ 2559	WCru
- - PAB 2534	LEdu
- - PAB 9962	LEdu
humile × ***parkeri***	SEle
§ ***mesnyi*** ♀H3	CBcs CCCN CExl CHll CKel CMac CRHN CSde CTri EBak EMOT EPfP EShb LRHS SBch SEND SGol SPer SVen WSHC
multiflorum	CCCN
multipartitum	CHll EShb
- bushy	CSpe
§ ***nudiflorum*** ♀H5	Widely available
- 'Argenteum'	see *J. nudiflorum* 'Mystique'
- 'Aureum'	CKel CMac CRos ELan LRHS MAsh MBNS MRav NLar SPer SPoG SRms
§ - 'Mystique' (v)	CRos ELan LRHS MRav NRHS SLon
odoratissimum	WFib
officinale	Widely available
- CC 1709	WMoo
§ - f. ***affine***	CBcs CCCN CKel CRHN CRos CTri CWCL ELan EPfP LRHS MAsh MRav NRHS SCoo SLim SRms
§ - 'Argenteovariegatum' (v) ♀H5	CKel CMac CRos CWGN EHoe ELan EMOT EPfP LRHS LSRN MAsh MGos MHer MMuc MRav SEND SMad SPer SPoG SWvt WCFE WSHC
- 'Aureovariegatum'	see *J. officinale* 'Aureum'
§ - 'Aureum' (v)	CBcs CKel CMac CRos CTsd CWCL ELan EPfP LRHS MAsh MHer MJak NBir NPri SCoo SLim SLon SPer SRms
- 'Clotted Cream'	see *J. officinale* 'Devon Cream'
- 'Crûg's Collection'	WCru
§ - 'Devon Cream' PBR	Widely available
- FIONA SUNRISE ('Frojas' PBR) ♀H5	Widely available
- 'Grandiflorum'	see *J. officinale* f. *affine*
- 'Inverleith' ♀H5	CCCN CKel CRos CWCL EBee ECtt ELan EPfP LRHS MAsh MBNS MGos MRav NRHS SCoo SLim SNig SPad SPer SPoG WGrn WSHC
- SUNBEAM ('Lobeam')	CKel CRos EBee LRHS NRHS SNig
- 'Variegatum'	see *J. officinale* 'Argenteovariegatum'
parkeri	CBcs CCCN CMac CRos CTri EBee ELon EPot GEdr GMaP LRHS MBNS MGil NLar SEle WThu XEll
- 'Bychan'	WAbe
§ ***polyanthum*** ♀H2	CBcs CExl CKel CRHN CSBt CSde CTri EBak ELan EPfP EShb LCro LOPS SEND SLim SPer SPre SRms

	– dark red-leaved	CCCN CExl CKel EBee EPfP
	primulinum	see *J. mesnyi*
	reevesii hort.	see *J. humile* 'Revolutum'
	sambac ♀H2	CBcs CCCN CHll CRHN ELan SPre WFib
	– 'Grand Duke of Tuscany' (d)	CCCN SPre
	– 'Maid of Orleans' (d)	CCCN EShb SPre
	sieboldianum	see *J. nudiflorum*
§	***simplicifolium*** subsp. ***suavissimum***	CHll CRHN
	stenalobium	WCot WFib
	× ***stephanense***	Widely available
	suavissimum	see *J. simplicifolium* subsp. *suavissimum*

Jatropha (*Euphorbiaceae*)

cinerea	SPlb
integerrima	CCCN
multifida	SPlb

Jeffersonia (*Berberidaceae*)

diphylla	CRos EBee EPPr EPot GKev LAma LEdu LRHS MBel MNrw NBir NChi NRHS WCru WPGP WPnP WThu
dubia	CAby CRos EPot EWes EWld GKev LEdu LLHF LRHS MNrw NBir NRHS SBrt WAbe WCot WPGP WThu XEll
– 'Alba'	SIgm
– 'Sunago-fu' (v)	GEdr

jostaberry see *Ribes* × *nidigrolaria*

Jovellana (*Calceolariaceae*)

punctata	CBcs CCCN CExl CTsd EBee GCal IArd IBlr IMou SPlb
– var. ***coerulea***	IBlr
sinclairii	CExl CHll
violacea ♀H3	CAbb CBcs CCCN CExl CKel CMac CPla CRos CTsd EBee EPfP GCal IBlr IDee IMou LRHS MGil SEle SVen WPGP WPav

Jovibarba ✿ (*Crassulaceae*)

§	***allionii***	CBod CMea CTri EBou EDAr EPot MHer MSCN NHpl NMen SRms SSim WFar WHal WHoo
	– 'Oki'	CRos LRHS NMen NRHS SRms
	allionii × ***hirta***	SDys SPlb
§	***arenaria***	GAbr NMen XLum
*	***echiniformis***	XLum
	'Emerald Spring'	GFgr
§	***heuffelii***	CRos LRHS NHpl NMen NRHS WFar XLum
	– 'Aiolos'	NHol
	– 'Almkroon'	NHol NWad
	– 'Anabokonak'	NMen
	– 'Angel Wings'	NMen SRms WHoo
	– 'Aquarius'	NMen
	– 'Be Mine'	NMen
	– 'Beacon Hill'	NMen
	– 'Belcore'	NMen XLum
	– 'Benjamin'	NMen
	– 'Big Red'	NHol NWad
	– 'Blaze'	NMen
	– 'Bolero'	NMen
	– 'Bora'	NWad
	– 'Brandaris'	SDys
	– 'Brocade'	MSCN NHol NWad
	– 'Bronze Ingot'	NMen
§	– 'Cherry Glow'	NMen
	– 'Chocoleto'	NMen
I	– 'Compacta'	NMen
	– 'Copper King'	NMen
	– 'Crater' **new**	NMen
	– 'Elmo's Fire'	NMen
	– 'Emerald and Ruby' **new**	WFar
	– 'Eos Moment'	NMen
	– 'Fan Joy'	NMen
	– 'Gento'	NMen
	– 'Geronimo'	NHol NMen
	– 'Giuseppi Spiny'	NMen SPlb
	– var. ***glabra***	WHoo
	– – from Anaba Kanak, Bulgaria	NHol
	– – from Haila, Montenegro/ Kosovo	NMen
	– – from Jakupica, Macedonia	NMen
	– – from Kapaenianum	NMen
	– – from Ljuboten, Balkans	NMen
	– – from Ošljak, Albania	NMen
	– – from Treska Gorge, Macedonia	NMen SRms
	– 'Gladiator'	NMen
	– 'Gold Rand'	NHol
	– 'Golden Touch' **new**	WFar
	– 'Grand Slam'	NMen
	– 'Green Land'	NMen
	– 'Greenstone'	NHol NMen
	– 'Harmony'	NHol
	– 'Henry Correvon'	NMen
	– var. ***heuffelii***	NMen
	– 'Idylle'	NMen
	– 'Ikaros'	NHol
	– 'Inferno'	NMen
§	– 'Inge'	NMen
	– 'Ithaca'	NHol NWad
	– 'Iuno'	NHol
	– 'Jade'	NMen
I	– 'Jovi King'	NMen
	– 'King Sunny'	NMen
	– var. ***kopaonikensis***	NMen
	– 'Lucky Bell'	NMen
	– 'Mary Ann'	NMen
	– 'Miller's Violet'	NMen
	– 'Mink'	NMen
	– 'Minuta'	NMen
	– 'Mystique'	CMea NMen WHoo
	– 'Nannette'	NMen
	– 'Orion'	NMen XLum
	– var. ***patens***	NMen
	– 'Pink Skies'	NMen
	– 'Pink Star'	NMen
	– 'Prisma'	NMen
	– 'Purple Haze'	XLum
	– 'Purple Heide'	NMen
	– 'Serenade'	NMen SRms
	– 'Silex'	NMen
	– 'Springael's Choice'	NMen
	– 'Sun and Silver Edge' **new**	WFar
	– 'Sundancer'	NMen
	– 'Sungold'	NHol NWad
	– 'Sylvan Memory'	NMen
	– 'Tan'	NMen
	– 'Tancredi'	NMen
	– 'Torrid Zone'	MBrN NMen
	– 'Tuxedo'	NHpl NMen
	– 'Violet'	NMen SDys
	– 'Xanthoheuff'	NMen
	– 'Yodelheuff'	NMen

§ ***hirta***	EDAr GAbr GKev NAln NMen WFar XLum
- from Wintergraben, Austria	SPlb SRms
- 'Belansky Tatra'	NMen SRms
- subsp. ***glabrescens*** from High Tatra, Slovakia/Poland	XLum
- - from Smeryouka, southern Carpathians	NMen
- var. ***neilreichii***	CRos LRHS NRHS SRms
- 'Purpurea'	XLum
preissiana	NMen
§ ***sobolifera***	EDAr EPot GKev NMen SPlb WHal XLum
- 'Green Globe'	CRos LRHS NMen NRHS SDys
- 'Miss Lorraine'	XLum

Jubaea (*Arecaceae*)

§ ***chilensis*** ♀H2	CPHo EUJe SArc SPlb WHor
spectabilis	see *J. chilensis*

Juglans ✿ (*Juglandaceae*)

§ ***ailanthifolia***	CBcs CMCN IDee
- B&SWJ 11026	WCru
- var. ***cordiformis*** 'Brock' (F)	CAgr
- - 'Campbell Cw3' (F)	CAgr
- - 'Fodermaier' seedling (F)	CAgr
- - 'Imshu' (F)	CAgr
- - 'Rhodes' (F)	CAgr
- - 'Simcoe' (F)	CAgr
ailanthifolia × ***cinerea***	see *J.* × *bixbyi*
§ × ***bixbyi***	CAgr
cinerea (F)	LMaj
- 'Beckwith' (F)	CAgr
- 'Booth' (F)	CAgr
- 'Booth' seedling (F)	CAgr
- 'Chamberlin' (F) **new**	CAgr
- 'Craxezy' (F)	CAgr
- 'Kenworthy' seedling (F)	CAgr
- 'Myjoy' (F)	CAgr
mandshurica (F)	CBcs
- B&SWJ 12550 from Korea	WCru
- BWJ 8097 from China	WCru
- RWJ 9905 from Taiwan	WCru
microcarpa	CMCN
microcarpa × ***nigra***	EMOT
nigra (F) ♀H6	CAco CBcs CCVT CDul CFGn CHab CLnd CMCN CMac CPer CSBt CTho EBee ECrN ELan EPfP LPra MAsh MGos MMuc NOra NWea SDea SEND SGol SPer WMat WTSh
- 'Bicentennial' (F)	CAgr
- 'Emma Kay' (F)	CAgr
- 'Laciniata'	EPfP MBlu
- 'Potsdam' (F)	CAgr
- 'Thomas' (F)	CAgr
- 'Weschke' (F)	CAgr
regia (F)	Widely available
- 'Axel' (F)	CAgr WMat
- 'Broadview' (F)	CAgr CArg CDul CEnd CFGn CTho ELan EMOT EPom LBuc LRHS MBlu MGos NOra SCoo SDea SEWo SKee SPoG SSFT SVic WMat
- 'Buccaneer' (F)	CAgr CArg CDul CFGn CTho ELan EMOT EPom NOra SDea SKee WMat
- 'Chandler' (F)	CAgr
- 'Corne du Périgord' (F)	CAgr
- 'Excelsior of Taynton' (F)	WMat
- 'Ferjean' (F)	CAgr
- 'Fernette'[PBR] (F)	CAgr NOra WMat
- 'Fernor' (F)	CAgr WMat
- 'Franquette' (F) ♀H6	CAgr EMOT NOra WMat
- 'Hansen' (F)	CAgr
- 'Hartley' (F)	CAgr
- 'Laciniata' ♀H6	CDul CMCN
- 'Lara' (F) ♀H6	NOra WMat
- 'Mayette' (F)	CAgr ECrN
- 'Meylannaise' (F)	CAgr
- 'Mini Multiflora 14' (F) **new**	CAgr
- number 16 (F)	WMat
- 'Parisienne' (F)	CAgr SGol
- 'Plovdivski' (F)	EMOT WMat
- 'Proslavski' (F)	CDul WMat
- 'Purpurea'	CMCN MBlu
- 'Rita' (F)	EMOT LBuc
- 'Ronde de Montignac' (F)	CAgr
- 'Sychrov' (F)	EMOT WMat
sieboldiana	see *J. ailanthifolia*
sigillata	LEdu

jujube see *Ziziphus jujuba*

Juncus (*Juncaceae*)

articulatus	LLWG XLum
bulbosus	CNat
§ ***decipiens*** 'Curly-wurly'	CRos EPfP LRHS NRHS NWad WBrk
- 'Spiralis'	see *J. decipiens* 'Curly-wurly'
effusus	CBen CWat LRHS NPer WMAq XLum
- 'Carman's Japanese'	NSti
- 'Gold Strike' (v)	LLWG
§ - f. ***spiralis***	CBen CRos CSpe CWat EHoe EPfP GQue LRHS MAsh MJak NBir NRHS SPlb SVic WMAq XLum
ensifolius	CWat EHoe EWat EWes LLWG MMrt MWts NPer NSti WMAq
inflexus	CBen CWat LLWG XLum
- 'Afro'	NBro NWsh SPlb
pallidus	EPPr GCal
patens 'Carman's Gray'	CKno CRos CWCL GCal GQue LRHS MMuc NRHS NWad
- 'Elk Blue'	CKno
subnodulosus	LLWG
'Swarm of Hedgehogs'	NWsh

Junellia (*Verbenaceae*)

azorelloides	WAbe
congesta	WAbe
§ ***micrantha***	WAbe
odonnellii	WAbe
§ ***succulentifolia***	WAbe
thymifolia	CPBP WAbe

Juniperus ✿ (*Cupressaceae*)

sp.	LPra
chinensis	CMen
- 'Aurea' ♀H6	CBcs SEND
§ - 'Blaauw' ♀H6	CMac CMen LRHS SGol SLim
- 'Blue Alps' ♀H6	CAco EMOT LRHS MGos MMuc NEgg SCob SCoo SEND SGol SLim
- 'Bokor' **new**	CAco
- 'Echiniformis'	CKen
- 'Expansa Aureospicata' (v)	CMac EMOT EPfP SEND SPoG SRms
§ - 'Expansa Variegata' (v)	EMOT SLim
- 'Itoigawa'	CMen
- 'Kaizuka Variegata'	see *J. chinensis* 'Variegated Kaizuka'
- 'Kuriwao Gold'	see *J.* × *pfitzeriana* 'Kuriwao Gold'

§	- 'Parsonsii'	WCFE
	- 'Plumosa Aurea' ♀H6	CAco LRHS
	- 'Plumosa Aureovariegata' (v)	CKen
	- 'Pyramidalis' ♀H6	EMOT EPfP MAsh SCoo
	- 'San José'	CMen
§	- var. ***sargentii***	CMen
	- 'Shimpaku'	CKen CMen
	- 'Stricta'	CAco CSBt LRHS SGol SLim
	- 'Sulphur Spray'	see *J.* × *pfitzeriana* 'Sulphur Spray'
§	- 'Variegated Kaizuka' (v)	EMOT SCoo SLim
	- 'Wilson's Weeping'	NLar
	communis	CAco CDul CFGn CHab CPer GPoy NWea WTSh
	- (f)	NWea
	- 'Arnold'	NLar
	- 'Arnold Sentinel'	CKen
	- 'Barton'	NLar NWad
	- 'Barton Gem'	NWad
	- 'Brien'	CKen
	- 'Brynhyfryd Gold'	CKen SLim
	- 'Compressa' ♀H7	CBcs CBod CKen CMac CSBt CTri EMOT EPfP EUJe GEdr LBee LRHS MAsh MGos MJak NEgg NHol NWea SLim SPer SPoG WIce
	- 'Corielagan'	CKen
	- 'Cracovia'	CKen
	- var. ***depressa***	GPoy SEND SGol
	- 'Depressa Aurea'	CKen CSBt EMOT LBee
	- 'Depressed Star'	EMOT SPoG
	- 'Effusa'	CKen
	- 'Gold Cone'	CKen ELan EMOT EPfP EUJe LBee MAsh MGos SLim SPoG
	- 'Goldschatz'	CKen EPfP LRHS SLim SPoG
	- 'Green Carpet' ♀H7	CAco CDul CKen ELan EMOT EPfP GKin LBuc LRHS MAsh MGos NLar SCoo SLim SPoG WCFE
	- 'Greenmantle'	LRHS
	- 'Haverbeck'	CKen
	- 'Hibernica' ♀H7	CDul CSBt ELan EMOT EPfP EWTr LRHS MGos MJak NWea SLim SPer SPoG
	- 'Hibernica Aurea'	CMac
	- 'Hornibrookii'	NWea SRms
I	- 'Horstmann's Pendula'	NLar
	- 'Kenwith Castle'	CKen
	- 'Pyramidalis'	SPlb
	- 'Repanda' ♀H7	CAco CBcs CKel CMac CSBt EMOT EPfP LRHS MGos NLar NWea SCoo SGol SLim SPer SPoG WFar
	- 'Sentinel'	LRHS WCFE
	- 'Sieben Steinhauser'	CKen
	- 'Silver Mist'	CKen
	- Suecica Group	NWea
	- 'Zeal'	CKen
	conferta	see *J. rigida* subsp. *conferta*
	- 'Blue Lagoon'	CAco
	- var. ***maritima***	see *J. taxifolia*
	davurica 'Expansa'	see *J. chinensis* 'Parsonsii'
	- 'Expansa Albopicta'	see *J. chinensis* 'Expansa Variegata'
	- 'Expansa Variegata'	see *J. chinensis* 'Expansa Variegata'
	× ***gracilis*** 'Blaauw'	see *J. chinensis* 'Blaauw'
	'Grey Owl' ♀H7	CAco CKel ELan EMOT LRHS MMuc NWea SEND SGol SLim SRms
	horizontalis	NWea
I	- 'Andorra Variegata' (v)	EMOT SCoo
	- 'Bar Harbor'	CMac NWea
§	- 'Blue Chip'	CAco CKen ELan EPfP LBee MGos MJak NBir NWea SCoo SPoG
	- 'Blue Moon'	see *J. horizontalis* 'Blue Chip'
	- 'Blue Rug'	see *J. horizontalis* 'Wiltonii'
	- 'Emerald Spreader'	EMOT
	- 'Glacier'	LRHS
	- 'Glauca'	NWea
	- 'Golden Carpet' ♀H7	ELan LBuc LCro LOPS LRHS NLar
	- 'Grey Pearl'	CKen
	- 'Hughes'	CAco LBee MRav NWea
	- ICEE BLUE ('Monber') ♀H7	CKen ELan EPfP LRHS MAsh NLar SPoG
	- 'Jade River'	CAco
	- 'Limeglow' ♀H7	CAco ELan EMOT EPfP EUJe MGos NLar SCoo SPoG
	- 'Mother Lode'	CKen
	- 'Neumann'	CKen
	- 'Pancake'	NLar
	- 'Plumosa'	CAco
	- 'Prince of Wales'	MAsh NWea
	- 'Turquoise Spreader'	CSBt SGol
	- 'Villa Marie'	CKen SPoG
§	- 'Wiltonii'	CDul NWea
	- 'Yukon Belle'	CKen
	× ***media***	see *J.* × *pfitzeriana*
	oxycedrus	XSen
§	× ***pfitzeriana***	CDul CMac NWea SCob SGol WFar
	- 'Arctic'	NLar
	- 'Blaauw'	see *J. chinensis* 'Blaauw'
	- 'Blue and Gold' (v)	CKel CKen SPoG
	- 'Blue Cloud'	see *J. virginiana* 'Blue Cloud'
§	- 'Carbery Gold' ♀H6	CBcs CMac CSBt EPfP GKin LRHS MAsh MGos SCoo SLim SPoG
	- 'Gold Coast'	CKen CSBt LBee MGos SGol
	- GOLD SOVEREIGN ('Blound')	LBee
	- 'Gold Star'	LRHS
	- 'King of Spring'	SLim
§	- 'Kuriwao Gold'	EMOT GKin SEND SGol
	- 'Mint Julep'	CAco CKel CSBt EPfP LRHS SCob SCoo SGol SLim
	- 'Old Gold' ♀H6	CBod CKel EMOT EPfP GKin LBee LCro LOPS LRHS MGos MJak MMuc NEgg NWea SCoo SEND SGol SPer SPlb WCFE WFar
	- 'Old Gold Carbery'	see *J.* × *pfitzeriana* 'Carbery Gold'
	- 'Pfitzeriana'	see *J.* × *pfitzeriana* 'Wilhelm Pfitzer'
	- 'Pfitzeriana Aurea'	CKel CMac EMOT LRHS NWea SCob SGol
	- 'Pfitzeriana Glauca'	CAco CKel
§	- 'Sulphur Spray' ♀H6	CDul LRHS MMuc SEND SLim
§	- 'Wilhelm Pfitzer'	NWea
	phoenicea	XSen
	- subsp. ***turbinata*** new	XSen
§	***pingii*** 'Glassell'	NLar
	- 'Hulsdonk Yellow'PBR	LRHS SLim SPoG
§	- var. ***wilsonii***	CKen
	procumbens 'Kishiogima'	LRHS
	- 'Nana' ♀H7	CKen CMac CSBt EPfP LBee LRHS MAsh MGos MJak NEgg NHol NLar SCoo SLim SPoG
	recurva	IDee
	- 'Castlewellan'	MGil NLar WFar WHor
	- var. ***coxii***	CMac NHol NLar NWea SRms WCFE
§	- 'Densa'	CKen
	- 'Nana'	see *J. recurva* 'Densa'
	rigida	CMen
§	- subsp. ***conferta***	CMac EMOT SEND SGol
	- - 'All Gold' ♀H6	LRHS SLim SPoG
*	- - 'Blue Ice'	CKen
	- - 'Blue Pacific'	CKen EMOT LRHS SGol SPoG

- - 'Blue Tosho' CDul NLar
- - 'Silver Mist' CKen

sabina NWea
- 'Knap Hill' see *J.* × *pfitzeriana* 'Wilhelm Pfitzer'
- 'Skandia' CKen
- 'Tamariscifolia' CBcs CKel GKin LBee LRHS MGos MJak NWea SEND SGol SLim SPer SPoG WCFE

sargentii see *J. chinensis* var. *sargentii*

scopulorum 'Blue Arrow' ♀H6 Widely available
- 'Blue Banff' CKen
- 'O'Connor' **new** CAco
- 'Skyrocket' CBcs CCVT CDul CKel CMac CNWT CSBt ECrN EMOT EPfP LMaj LPra MGos MJak MRav NWea SCob SGol SRms WCFE
- 'Springbank' WCFE
- 'Wichita Blue' CCVT EPfP

squamata 'Blue Carpet' ♀H7 CAco CBcs CDul CKen CMac CSBt EPfP LBuc LRHS MAsh MGos MJak NEgg NHol NLar NWea SCob SEND SGol SLim SPer SPoG WCFE WFar
- 'Blue Star' ♀H7 CBod CKel CKen CMac CSBt ELan EMOT EPfP LBee LCro LOPS LRHS MAsh MGos MJak NEgg NHol NLar NWea SGol SLim SPer SPoG WCFE WFar
- 'Blue Star Variegated' see *J. squamata* 'Golden Flame'
- 'Blue Swede' see *J. squamata* 'Hunnetorp'
- 'Chinese Silver' CAco
- 'Dream Joy' CKel CKen NLar NWad
- 'Filborna' LBee NLar
- 'Floreant' SLim SPoG
- 'Glassell' see *J. pingii* 'Glassell'

§ - 'Golden Flame' (v) CKen
- 'Holger' ♀H7 CAco CKel CMac EPfP LBee LRHS MAsh MGos MJak NHol NLar SCoo SLim SPoG WFar

§ - 'Hunnetorp' LRHS WFar
- 'Meyeri' NWea SGol
- 'Tropical Blue' SPoG
- 'Wilsonii' see *J. pingii* var. *wilsonii*

§ **taxifolia** CSBt

thurifera **new** XSen

virginiana CAco LPra NWea

§ - 'Blue Cloud' SLim
- 'Frosty Morn' CKen
- 'Golden Spring' CKen
- 'Pendula' CAco
- SILVER SPREADER ('Mona') CKen
- 'Sulphur Spray' see *J.* × *pfitzeriana* 'Sulphur Spray'

Jussiaea see *Ludwigia*

Justicia (*Acanthaceae*)

americana LLWG SBrt

aurea EShb

§ **brandegeeana** ♀H1b CCCN EShb
- 'Lutea' see *J. brandegeeana* 'Yellow Queen'
- variegated (v) EShb

§ - 'Yellow Queen' EShb
- yellow-flowered EShb

§ **carnea** CHII EShb WFar
- 'Alba' CCCN
- dark-leaved CHII EShb
- 'Radiant' SMad

guttata see *J. brandegeeana*

'Penrhosiensis' EShb

pohliana see *J. carnea*

rizzinii ♀H1b CBcs CCCN CHII EUJe SEle SRot

spicigera CCCN EShb

suberecta see *Dicliptera sericea*

K

Kadsura (*Schisandraceae*)

coccinea B&SWJ 11793 WCru
- FMWJ 13489 WCru

heteroclita FMWJ 13385 WCru
- WWJ 11947 WCru

japonica CBcs
- B&SWJ 1027 WCru
- B&SWJ 4463 from Korea WCru
- B&SWJ 11109 from Japan WCru
- B&SWJ 14672 **new** WCru
- from Japan WSHC
- 'Fukurin' (v) NLar
- 'Variegata' (v) CCCN CKel CRos EBee EPfP LRHS WSHC
- white fruit NLar

aff. **japonica** NMWJ 14550 **new** WCru

Kaempferia ✿ (*Zingiberaceae*)

rotunda CCCN LAma

Kageneckia (*Rosaceae*)

oblonga SPlb

Kalanchoe (*Crassulaceae*)

beharensis ♀H1b CCCN CDTJ ELan EShb WCot
- 'Fang' ♀H1b CDTJ ELan EShb WCot
- 'Rusty' CDTJ CSpe

daigremontiana EShb

§ **delagoensis** CCCN EShb

fedtschenkoi 'Variegata' (v) WCot

hildebrandtii EShb

humilis EShb WCot

laciniata EShb

laetivirens SSim

manginii ♀H1b EShb

'Oak Leaf' EShb

orgyalis EShb WCot

pinnata EShb

'Piton Pink' **new** LCro LOPS

'Prebella' **new** EShb

pubescens EShb

pumila ♀H1b EShb SAll SBch

serrata EShb

sexangularis EShb

* **synsepala laciniata** **new** EShb

'Tessa' ♀H1b WCot

thyrsiflora EShb
- 'Bronze Sculpture' CAbb CBct EUJe SSim

tomentosa ♀H1b EShb SAll WCot

tubiflora see *K. delagoensis*

kale, curly see AGM Vegetables Section (under borecole)

Kalimeris (*Asteraceae*)

altaica EMor EPPr

§ **incisa** CMea MMuc

- 'Alba' CKno ECha ELon NLar WCAu WFar
- 'Blue Star' CAby CKno ECha ECtt ELon GMaP GQue IKil MNrw NLar SCob WCAu WFar WPtf WSHC
- 'Charlotte' EWes GBee LPla MNrw NBre NDov SAko SPoG WFar WGoo
- 'Edo Murasaki' **new** SBrt
- 'Madiva' CAby CSam EBee ELon GBee IMou LPla NDov SAko WGoo
- 'Nana Blue' EBee NDov SPoG

integrifolia MMuc
- 'Daisy Mae' **new** NDov

'Mon Jardin' EBee WCot

§ ***mongolica*** CMac ECha MMuc SAko WFar WGoo WSHC
- 'Antonia' EBee IMou NDov WCot

§ ***pinnatifida*** CRos LRHS NRHS
- 'Hortensis' EBee MNrw

§ ***yomena*** 'Shogun' (v) CBod CKel CMac ECha ECtt EHoe EMor EPfP LEdu LRHS MNrw MPie NBir NRHS NSti SPer SPoG SRms WFar WPtf XLum
- 'Variegata' see *K. yomena* 'Shogun'

Kalmia ✿ (*Ericaceae*)

angustifolia ♀H5 GKev MGil WSpi
- var. ***angustifolia*** f. ***candida*** LRHS
- f. ***rubra*** ♀H6 CCCN CDul CRos EBee ELan EPfP LRHS MAsh NLar SPer WFar WSpi

I - 'Rubra Nana' CMac

§ ***buxifolia*** ♀H4 NLar WThu
- 'Maryfield' WAbe

latifolia CBcs EPfP LRHS NWea SPer SWvt
- 'Alpine Pink' WSpi
- 'Bandeau' GGGa
- 'Bay State' LRHS NLar
- 'Bridesmaid' NLar
- 'Bullseye' SAko SPoG
- 'Carousel' CBcs CCCN NLar
- 'Clementine Churchill' CMac
- 'Eskimo' GGGa
- 'Freckles' ♀H6 CMac SPoG
- 'Galaxy' GGGa LRHS NLar SAko
- 'Ginkona' GGGa LRHS SAko
- 'Kaleidoscope' GGGa LSRN NLar
- 'Little Linda' ♀H6 NLar
- 'Minuet' CBcs CCCN CRos GGGa LRHS MAsh MGil NLar SPoG SWvt
- 'Mitternacht' GGGa
- 'Moyland' GGGa LSRN
- f. ***myrtifolia*** CRos LRHS
- - 'Elf' CRos LRHS NLar
- 'Nani' GGGa
- 'Nipmuck' CMac
- 'Olympic Fire' ♀H6 CBcs CRos ELan GGGa LRHS MGil NLar SAko SWvt WSpi WTSh
- 'Olympic Wedding' SPoG
- 'Ostbo Red' CBcs CMac CRos LRHS LSRN MGil MMuc SAko SPoG SWvt
- 'Peppermint' GGGa LRHS NLar
- 'Pink Charm' ♀H6 CMac SAko
- 'Pinwheel' LRHS MGil MJak NLar SAko SPoG
- 'Quinnipiac' MJak
- 'Snowdrift' LRHS NLar

§ ***microphylla*** WAbe

polifolia CBcs CCCN LCro LOPS LRHS MGil NLar SPer WThu
- 'Alba' see *K. polifolia* f. *leucantha*
- 'Glauca' see *K. microphylla*

§ - f. ***leucantha*** LRHS WAbe
- 'Newfoundland' **new** CBcs

§ ***procumbens*** WAbe

Kalmiopsis (*Ericaceae*)

leachiana 'Glendoick' LRHS

Kalmiopsis × *Phyllodoce* see × *Phylliopsis*

Kalmiopsis × *Rhodothamnus* see × *Kalmiothamnus*

× *Kalmiothamnus* (*Ericaceae*)

'Haytor' ITim

'Sindelberg' ITim

Kalopanax ✿ (*Araliaceae*)

pictus see *K. septemlobus*

§ ***septemlobus*** CBcs EPfP MMuc NLar SEND SPtp
- var. ***magnificus*** B&SWJ 10900 WCru
- f. ***maximowiczii*** CDul EPfP MBlu NLar

Keckiella (*Plantaginaceae*)

corymbosa B&SWJ 14096 WCru

Keiskea (*Lamiaceae*)

japonica GEdr
- pink-flowered SBrt

Kelseya (*Rosaceae*)

uniflora WAbe

Kennedia (*Papilionaceae*)

coccinea CCCN WHil

macrophylla CRHN

nigricans CCCN WHil

rubicunda CCCN CRHN WHil

Kentia (*Arecaceae*)

belmoreana see *Howea belmoreana*

forsteriana see *Howea forsteriana*

Kentranthus see *Centranthus*

Kerria (*Rosaceae*)

japonica misapplied single see *K. japonica* 'Simplex'

japonica (L.) DC. CBod CTho
- (d) see *K. japonica* 'Pleniflora'
- 'Albescens' NLar WCot
- 'Buttercup' NLar
- 'Golden Guinea' ♀H5 CExl CMac CRos ELan EPfP IFro LRHS MAsh MGos MRav NRHS SCob SCoo SPer SPoG SRms SWvt WFar
- 'Honshu' IArd

§ - 'Picta' (v) CMac CTho EBee ELan MGos MRav MSwo SCob SGol SLim SLon SRms WAvo WFar

§ - 'Pleniflora' (d) ♀H5 Widely available

§ - 'Simplex' CExl CMac EShb SRms
- 'Variegata' see *K. japonica* 'Picta'

Keteleeria (*Pinaceae*)

evelyniana CAco

Khadia (*Aizoaceae*)

acutipetala CCCN

Kiggelaria (*Flacourtiaceae*)

africana	SVen

Kirengeshoma (*Hydrangeaceae*)

palmata	Widely available
- 'Black Style'	EBee
- dwarf	WCot
- Koreana Group ♀H7	Widely available

Kitagawia (*Apiaceae*)

§ ***litoralis***	EBee

Kitaibela (*Malvaceae*)

vitifolia	CExl CSpe EPPr NBid NSti SEND SPlb WAvo WFar WHer WOut

Kitchingia see *Kalanchoe*

kiwi fruit see *Actinidia deliciosa*

Klasea (*Asteraceae*)

§ ***bulgarica***	MAvo NDov SPhx WGoo
§ ***coronata*** subsp. ***insularis*** B&SWJ 8698	WCru
§ ***lycopifolia***	WCot
§ ***radiata*** subsp. ***gmelinii***	EBee EMor EPPr LRHS NRHS

Kleinia (*Asteraceae*)

articulata	see *Curio articulata*
§ ***grantii***	CSpe SBch WCot
neriifolia	EShb WCot
repens	see *Curio repens*

Knautia (*Caprifoliaceae*)

§ ***arvensis***	CBod CCBP CElw CHab CWld EBee EPfP GCal LCro LOPS MHer MNHC NLar NMir SPer SPhx SRms WArt WCAu WHer WMoo WOut WSFF
- white-flowered	SPhx
dipsacifolia	LPla SHar
'Jardin d'en Face'	LRHS
§ ***macedonica***	Widely available
- 'Crimson Cushion'	CSpe ECtt
- dark-flowered	IFro
- 'Mars Midget'	CBod CExl CHll CRos CSpe EBee ELan ELon EMor EPfP GCal GMaP LRHS MBel MGos NLar NRHS SCob SPhx SPoG SWvt WFar WHil WHoo WSHC
- Melton pastels	CBod CChe CDor CExl CRos EBee ELan EPPr EPfP GJos GMaP LRHS MGos NLar NPer NRHS SPhx SPoG SRkn SRms SRot SWvt WCAu WFar
- pink-flowered	SRms
- 'Red Baron'	CChe
- 'Red Knight'	CDor CRos EBee EPfP GWyn LRHS MBNS NLar NRHS
- short	ECtt
- tall, pale-flowered	SPhx
- 'Thunder and Lightning'PBR (v)	CBct CBod CDor CRos CWGN EBee ECtt EMor EPfP EWes IKil ILea LBuc LRHS MAsh MHol MNrw MRav NLar NRHS SPer SPoG SRms WCAu WCot WKif
sarajevensis	MAvo

Knightia (*Proteaceae*)

excelsa	CBcs

Kniphofia ✿ (*Asphodelaceae*)

'Ada'	ELon
albescens	SPlb
'Alcazar'	CBcs CBod ECtt ELon EMor EPfP EUJe EWhm LCro LOPS MAvo MHer SCob SPer SWvt WCAu WCFE WFar WSpi
'Ample Dwarf'	ECtt WCot
'Amsterdam'	MWat
angustifolia	SPlb
'Apricot'	CRos LRHS NRHS WCot
'Apricot Souffle'	WCot
'Atlanta'	CRos LRHS NRHS
'Barton Fever' ♀H6	WCot
baurii	CExl SPlb
'Bees' Jubilee'	MAvo NChi
'Bees' Lemon'	Widely available
§ 'Bees' Sunset' ♀H5	CAvo CRos CSam EBee ECha ECtt EPfP EUJe LRHS MAvo MMuc NLar NRHS SEND SPoG SWvt WAul WSHC
'Bees' Yellow'	SBch WAvo
'Blacksmith's Delight' **new**	MAvo
'Border Ballet'	CRos LBuc LRHS NBir NGdn NLar NRHS XLum
brachystachya	SPlb
'Bressingham Comet'	CRos EBee ECtt GKev LRHS NBir NRHS SRms
BRESSINGHAM SUNBEAM ('Bresun')	CRos EBee ECtt LRHS NBir NRHS
'Bressingham Yellow'	ECtt EUJe
'Brimstone' Bloom ♀H5	CDor CPrp CRos ECtt EMor EPfP LEdu LRHS MMuc NBir NRHS SEND SPtp SWvt WFar WGwG
bruceae	SPlb SVen
'Buttercup' ♀H5	CAvo LSRN
'Butterfly'	EBee
'C.M. Prichard' misapplied	see *K. rooperi*
'C.M. Prichard' Prichard	WCot
'Candlelight'	EBee ECtt WSHC
'Candy Apple'	EBee
caulescens	Widely available
- LEG 053	GKev
- 'Coral Breakers'	CExl CPrp ECtt ELon GMaP LRHS MAvo MHol NEgg NRHS SEND WCot
- early-flowering	WSpi
- 'John May'	CAby CBod CTsd EBee ECtt ESwi LEdu MAvo MHer SCob SWvt WCot
- short	ECha
- 'Tiny Girl'	ECtt
'Champagne'	WCot
'Chichi'	MAvo WCot
'Christmas Cheer'	EBee
citrina	CSpe GKev GLog MBrN NGBl WCot XLum
'Cobra'	CDor CRos EBee ECtt GMaP LRHS NRHS WAul WCot
'Coral Flame' ♀H5	CRos LRHS NRHS
'Coral Sceptre'	WCot
'Creamsicle'PBR (Popsicle Series)	ECtt SCob WCot
'Dingaan'	EBee ECtt MNrw MTis NBir NLar WCot
'Dorset Sentry'	CAby CBod EBee ECtt ELon EMor EPfP LRHS MBel MGos MNrw NBir NEgg NLar WCot WFar

'Drummore Apricot'	CPrp CRos ECha ECtt ELan EPfP LRHS LSRN MPie NBir NEgg NRHS NWsh SPtp WCot WFar WGwG
'Early Buttercup'	WFar
'Early Orange'	CSBt
'Early Red'	CSBt
'Early Yellow'	CSBt
'Elvira'PBR	CRos ECtt EMor EUJe LRHS MBNS NRHS SAko SPoG WCot
EMBER GLOW ('Tneg'PBR) (Glow Series)	CAbb EBee ECtt LCro LOPS
ensifolia	ECtt NGdn SVen XLum
'Ernest Mitchell'	WCot
Express hybrids	XLum
'Feuerkerze'	SAko
'Fiery Fred' ♀H6	CPrp CRos EBee ECtt ELon EPfP EUJe EWhm GBee LRHS MAvo MMuc NRHS NWsh WAul WCot WHoo WSpi
FIRE GLOW ('Tnfg'PBR) (Glow Series)	NLar
'First Sunrise'PBR	ECtt LRHS MJak
'Flamenco'	CRos ELon LRHS NGdn NRHS SCob SRms WFar
'Flaming Torch'	ECtt
'Florence Bedecked'	WCot
fluviatilis	GKev
foliosa Hochst.	LEdu
'Frances Victoria'	WCot
galpinii misapplied	see *K. triangularis* subsp. *triangularis*
galpinii ambig.	CRos LRHS NRHS SPer SRms XLum
galpinii Baker ♀H4	EMor MMuc
'Gelbe Flamme' **new**	SAko
'Gilt Bronze'	WCot
'Gladness'	MAvo NBir WCot
'Goldelse'	CRos EBee LRHS NBir NRHS
'Goldfinch'	CSam
gracilis	LEdu
'Grandiflora'	CMac
'Green and Cream'	MHCG
'Green Jade'	CAby CBcs CExl CRos EBee ECha ECtt ELan EMor EUJe EWTr LRHS MBel MCot MNrw MRav NBir NGBl NLar NRHS SEND SGbt SPer SRms WCAu WCot WFar
'Green Jewel'	LRHS
'H.E. Beale'	WCot
'Hen and Chickens'	ECtt MAvo WCot WFar
hirsuta	CRos LRHS NRHS SRms WSHC
- 'Fire Dance'	CRos CSde LRHS LSun NHic NRHS WFar
'Ice Queen'	CAvo CBcs CDor EBee ECha ECtt ELon EPPr GKev MAvo MHer MNrw MRav MTis NChi NLar SEND SRms SWvt WCAu WCot WFar WJam
ichopensis	LEdu SVen WPGP
'Incandesce' ♀H5	CBod EBee EMor EWhm MBNS MNrw NCou SPoG WCot
'Innocence' ♀H4	CRos EBee EPfP LRHS NRHS
'Jane Henry'	LEdu
'Jenny Bloom'	CPrp CRos ECtt ELan ELon EPfP EUJe GCal GMaP LEdu LRHS MRav NLar NRHS NSti SEND SPtp SRms WAul WCot WFar
'Jess's Delight'	MAvo WCot
'John Benary'	CMac CPrp CRos ECtt EPPr GLog GMaP IKil LLWG LRHS MBel NBir NEgg NLar NRHS SEND SPtp SRms WCot WGwG WKif
'Jonathan' ♀H5	WCot
laxiflora	WPGP
'Lemon Popsicle'PBR (Popsicle Series)	CAbb CBct CKel CRos CWCL CWGN ELan EMor LRHS NAst NPri NRHS SCob SRms WFar
'Light of the World'	see *K. triangularis* subsp. *triangularis* 'Light of the World'
'Limelight'	CPar EBee ECtt EUJe
linearifolia	CExl EBee SPlb WCot XLum
'Little Elf'	CDor XLum
'Little Maid'	CBcs CBod CRos CSBt CWCL ECha ECtt EHrv ELan EMor EPfP EPot EShb GMaP GWyn LRHS MHer MRav MTis NBir NLar NRHS SCob SPer SRms SWvt WCAu WCot WFar
'Lord Roberts'	MAvo MRav WCot
'Luna'	WCot
macowanii	see *K. triangularis* subsp. *triangularis*
'Mango Popsicle'PBR (Popsicle Series)	CAbb CKel CMac CRos EBee ECtt ELan EMor EUJe EWTr LRHS MAvo MBel MNrw MPnt NAst NLar NPri NRHS NSti SCob SMad SPoG SRms WCot WFar WHoo WWFP
'Mermaiden'	CRos ECtt MMuc MNrw SEND WCot
'Minister Verschuur'	CRos EBee ECtt LRHS NRHS
'Modesta'	WSHC
'Molten Lava'	EBee
'Moonstone' ♀H5	CSam EBee ECtt ELon EMor EUJe GBin LLHF LSun MNrw MTis NLar NSti SEND SPoG WCot WRHF WSpi
'Mount Etna'	WAvo
multiflora 'November Glory'	WCot WFar
'Nancy's Red'	Widely available
nelsonii Mast.	see *K. triangularis* subsp. *triangularis*
'New Sensation'	WCot
'No Rhyme Nor Reason'	WCot
§ 'Nobilis' ♀H5	CAby CExl CRos ECha ECtt ELan ELon EMor EUJe GAbr GMaP LRHS LSRN MBel MHol MMuc MNrw NGdn SArc SEND SPer SRms SWvt WCAu WCot
northiae ♀H4	CCht CExl CPla CTsd EBee ELan ELon EPfP EUJe EWes GCal MAvo MNrw NLar SArc SEND SMad SPad SPlb SWvt WCot WCru WPGP WSpi XLum
'Old Court Seedling'	EBee WCot WFar
'Orange Fackel' **new**	SAko
'Orange Vanilla Popsicle'PBR (Popsicle Series)	CAbb CBct CKel CRos CSBt ECtt EMor EWTr LRHS MAvo MPnt MThu NAst NLar NPri NRHS SCob SPad SPoG WFar WTyc
§ 'Painted Lady'	CDor CSam CSde CTri EBee ECtt GMaP MAvo MHol MNrw NLar SEND SWvt WCot
'Papaya Popsicle'PBR (Popsicle Series)	CBct CKel CRos CWGN EBee ECtt ELan ELon EMor EUJe LRHS MAvo MNrw MThu NLar NRHS SCob SPoG SRms WFar WSpi
parviflora	XLum
pauciflora	CPbh WCot
'Penny Rockets' ♀H6	CRos EPPr LRHS NRHS
'Percy's Pride'	Widely available

'Pfitzeri' SRms
'Pineapple Popsicle'PBR (Popsicle Series) CAbb CRos CWGN ECtt EMor MPnt NAst NEoE NLar SCob SRms
'Primrose Upward' ♀H6 WCot
I 'Primulina' Bloom CRos EBee LRHS NRHS
'Prince Igor' misapplied see *K.* 'Nobilis'
'Prince Igor' Prichard ECtt NBir
'Red Rocket'PBR EBee EWTr LRHS MNrw WCot
'Redhot Popsicle'PBR (Popsicle Series) CBod CKel CWGN EMor EPot LRHS MAvo MHol MNrw MPnt SPoG WCot
'Rich Echoes' ♀H5 CAby CAvo CBod CWGN EBee ECtt ELon EMor ESwi EWhm GBin LEdu LLHF MHol MNrw MTis NLar WCot
ritualis CExl
§ ***rooperi*** ♀H5 Widely available
'Royal Castle' CExl CRos GMaP LRHS MJak NBir NGdn NRHS SCob SEND SRms WFar XLum
'Royal Standard' ♀H5 CBcs CBod CRos EBee ECtt ELan ELon EMor EPfP EUJe GMaP LCro LOPS LRHS NLar NRHS SCob SPer SPoG SPtp SWvt WCAu WFar WGwG WSpi
rufa Baker LEdu MAvo WPGP
'Safranvogel' ♀H5 EBee ECtt WCot
'Samuel's Sensation' misapplied see *K.* 'Painted Lady'
'Samuel's Sensation' Samuel ♀H5 CRos EBee ECtt EPPr LRHS NLar NRHS SWvt WCot
sarmentosa CExl SPlb SVen WCot
'Saturn' MAvo
'Scorched Corn' EMor MAvo
'Sherbet Lemon' MNrw WCot
'Shining Sceptre' misapplied see *K.* 'Bees' Sunset'
'Slush Puppy' ECtt
'Springtime' WCot
'Star of Baden-Baden' MAvo MMuc NBir SEND SMad WCot
Stark's early perpetual-flowering hybrids XLum
'Strawberries and Cream' CKel CPrp CTsd EBee ECha ECtt ELon EWld NLar SGbt SWvt
stricta XLum
'Sunningdale Yellow' ♀H5 ECha ECtt EHrv EUJe GMaP MAvo SMHy SRms WHoo WSpi
'Sweet Corn' **new** EMor
'Tawny King' ♀H5 Widely available
'Tetbury Torch'PBR CBod CExl CRos CWGN EBee ECtt EMor LRHS MAvo MCot NRHS SEND SPtp SWvt WAul WCAu
thomsonii CExl NGdn
- 'Kichocheo' EBee GCal LEdu MAvo WCot
- var. ***snowdenii*** misapplied see *K. thomsonii* var. *thomsonii*
- var. ***snowdenii*** ambig. CExl WPGP XLum
§ - var. ***thomsonii*** LEdu SMHy WSHC
- - 'Stern's Trip' ♀H4 EBee
'Timothy' ♀H5 Widely available
'Toffee Nosed' ♀H5 CBod CPrp CRos ECtt ELon EMor EPPr EPfP EWhm GBin LRHS MRav NBir NEgg NGdn NLar NRHS SCob SEND SPer SPtp SRkn SSut SWvt WAul WCAu WCot WSHC
'Torchbearer' WCot
triangularis EMor GKev WFar XLum
§ - subsp. ***triangularis*** EPfP SCob SRms SVen XLum
§ - - 'Light of the World' ECtt EWTr GAbr LRHS MHer NBir NLar NRHS SCob SPtp SWvt WCot WFar
'Tuckii' misapplied SRms
typhoides NBir SPlb
tysonii SPlb XLum
uvaria CPrp CRos EBee GKev LCro LOPS LRHS NBir NHic NRHS SCob SRms SVic WCAu WCot XLum XSen
'Vanilla' LRHS MMuc NAln NLar SEND
'Vesta' CRos LRHS NRHS
'Vincent Lepage' NLar
'Wol's Red Seedling' CSam ECtt ELon GBee MCot MNrw SEND WCot WGwG WHoo
'Wrexham Buttercup' ♀H6 CDor CSam EBee ECtt ELan EMor EUJe EWTr EWhm GMaP LSRN MAvo MCot MHol MNrw MTis NAln NLar SCob SEND WCot WFar WHal WSpi
'Yellow Cheer' WCot
'Yellow Hammer' Slieve Donard CSam ECha ELon MMuc SEND

Knowltonia (*Ranunculaceae*)

filia CExl

Koeleria (*Poaceae*)

glauca CBod CRos ECha EHoe EPfP EShb GMaP LRHS MBNS MJak NGdn NRHS NWsh SCob SPlb SWvt WFar XSen
pyramidata SMea
vallesiana EHoe SMea

Koelreuteria (*Sapindaceae*)

bipinnata IDee LRHS
elegans subsp. ***formosana*** CMCN
paniculata CAco CCVT CDul CLnd CMCN CMac CTri ECrN ELan EMOT EPfP LEdu LMaj LPra MGos MMuc NWea SEND SGol SPer SPlb WFar WHor WTSh
- 'Beachmaster' NLar
- 'Coral Sun'PBR ♀H5 CExl ELan EPfP EUJe LRHS MBlu MGos NOra WCot WMat
- 'Fastigiata' CDul EBee EPfP MBlu SCoo WHor
- 'Rosseels' EMOT NLar
- 'September' EPfP MBlu

Kohleria (*Gesneriaceae*)

'Ampallang' WDib
'An's Nagging Macaws' WDib
'Brazil Gem' WDib
'Bristol's Evil Storm' WDib
'Cybele' WDib
'Dark Velvet' WDib
eriantha ♀H1c CTsd WDib
'Flashdance' WDib
'Hcy's Jardin de Monet' WDib
'Heartland's Blackberry Butterfly' WDib
hirsuta WDib
'Jester' ♀H1b WDib
'Lilla Gubben' WDib
'Manchu' WDib
'Marquis de Sade' WDib
'Queen Victoria' WDib
I ***sciadotydaea*** WDib
'Silver Feather' WDib
§ 'Sunrise' WDib
'Sunshine' see *K.* 'Sunrise'
'Texas Rainbow' WDib
warszewiczii ♀H1b WDib

'Yf's Emma' WDib
'Yf's Josse' WDib

kohlrabi see AGM Vegetables Section

Kolkwitzia (*Caprifoliaceae*)

amabilis CExl CSBt CTri ELan EPfP GBin NEgg NWea SCob SGol SPlb SRms WCFE WMoo WSHC
- DREAM CATCHER ('Maradco') CMac EPfP MAsh MRav NEoE NLar SCob SGol WSpi
- 'Pink Cloud' ♀H5 Widely available

Kosteletzkya (*Malvaceae*)

virginica MHol WArt

kumquat see *Citrus japonica*

Kunzea (*Myrtaceae*)

ambigua EBee IDee SPlb
- pink-flowered SEle
'Badja Carpet' SEle
baxteri CPbh CTsd
ericifolia SPlb
§ **ericoides** CTsd GPoy
parvifolia SPlb
pauciflora SPlb

L

Lablab (*Papilionaceae*)

purpureus 'Ruby Moon' CSpe

+ *Laburnocytisus* (*Papilionaceae*)

'Adamii' CDul CMac EBee ELan EPfP ESwi LSRN MGil MGos NLar SMad SPer

Laburnum ✿ (*Papilionaceae*)

alpinum NWea SPlb
- 'Pendulum' CAco CCVT ELan EMOT LCro LSRN MAsh MGos MRav SGol SPer SPoG
§ **anagyroides** CAco CDul LPra MMuc NWea SEND SRms WMou
- 'Erect' SPoG WMat
'Famous Walk' see *L.* × *watereri* 'Vossii'
vulgare see *L. anagyroides*
× **watereri** LPra
§ - 'Vossii' ♀H6 Widely available
* - 'Vossii Pendulum' CCVT

Lachenalia ✿ (*Asparagaceae*)

§ **aloides** CGrW CPbh SDeJ
- var. **aurea** see *L. flava*
- var. **luteola** see *L. flava*
- var. **quadricolor** see *L. quadricolor*
- var. **vanzyliae** see *L. vanzyliae*
bifolia see *L. bulbifera*
§ **bulbifera** ♀H2 GKev WCot
- 'George' ♀H2 WCot
contaminata ♀H2 CGrW CPbh
ensifolia LLHF WCot
§ - subsp. **maughanii** new GKev
§ **flava** ♀H2 CAby CPbh SBch WCot
kliprandensis GKev
latimerae WCot
liliiflora CGrW GKev
longituba ♀H2 CPBP GKev
maughanii see *L. ensifolia* subsp. *maughanii*
'Namakwa' (African Beauty Series) ♀H1c GKev
'Nelsonii' SBch WCot
obscura WCot
orthopetala WCot
I 'Pearsonii' SPlb
pendula see *L. bulbifera*
pustulata blue-flowered CGrW
pygmaea CPBP
§ **quadricolor** ♀H2 CGrW CTsd WCot
'Romaud' (African Beauty Series) GKev SDeJ
'Romelia' (African Beauty Series) WCot
'Ronina' (African Beauty Series) GKev
'Rosabeth' (African Beauty Series) GKev WCot
rubida WCot
'Rupert' (African Beauty Series) ♀H2 GKev SDeJ WCot
tricolor see *L. aloides*
unicolor WCot
§ **vanzyliae** ♀H2 WCot
zeyheri WCot

Lactuca (*Asteraceae*)

alpina see *Cicerbita alpina*
perennis EPPr WHer

Lagarostrobos ✿ (*Podocarpaceae*)

§ **franklinii** CBcs IDee WPGP
- 'Fota' (f) WThu
- 'Picton Castle' (m) WThu

Lagenaria (*Cucurbitaceae*)

siceraria 'Speckled Swan' SVic

Lagerstroemia (*Lythraceae*)

indica ♀H3 CBod CCCN EPfP IDee MGil SEND SEle SPlb SVen WFar
- B&SWJ 12660 WCru
- BERRY DAZZLE ('Gamad VI') new LCro LOPS
- 'Cedar Lane Red' see *L. indica* 'Cedar Red'
§ - 'Cedar Red' new WPGP
- 'Red Imperator' CBcs
- RHAPSODY IN PINK ('Whit VIII') CBcs LRHS
- 'Rosea' CBcs CKel LRHS SEND
- 'Superviolacea' EUJe
- (With Love Series) WITH LOVE BABE ('Milaperl') new SPoG
- - WITH LOVE CHERIE ('Cov') new CWGN SPoG
- - WITH LOVE VIRGIN ('Milabla') new LCro LOPS
STRAWBERRY DAZZLE ('Piilag-II') LRHS
subcostata CWJ 12352 WCru
'Tuscarora' WPGP
'Tuskegee' WPGP
'Virgin' new CWGN

Lagotis (*Plantaginaceae*)

glauca GEdr
takedana GEdr

Lagunaria (*Malvaceae*)

patersonii	CHll LRHS WPGP

Lagurus (*Poaceae*)

ovatus	SAdn

Lamiastrum see *Lamium*

Lamium (*Lamiaceae*)

album	CHab NMir
- 'Friday' (v)	NBir
armenum	WAbe
- subsp. ***sintenisii***	WAbe
flexuosum	EPPr
§ ***galeobdolon***	CTri CWld EShb MHer NAln SPhx SRms WHer WWtn XSen
§ - 'Florentinum' (v)	CMac ECha GQue MMuc MRav SPer WCAu WFar
- 'Hermann's Pride'	CRos EHoe ELan ELon EPfP GMaP LRHS NBir NMir NRHS SPer SPoG SRms SWvt WAul WHoo WMoo XLum
- 'Kirkcudbright Dwarf'	EPPr EWes GBin NBre XLum
§ - 'Silberteppich'	ECha MRav XLum
- 'Silver Angel'	XLum
- SILVER CARPET	see *L. galeobdolon* 'Silberteppich'
- 'Variegatum'	see *L. galeobdolon* 'Florentinum'
garganicum subsp. ***garganicum***	EWes WHoo
- subsp. ***pictum***	see *L. garganicum* subsp. *striatum*
- subsp. ***reniforme***	see *L. garganicum* subsp. *striatum*
§ - subsp. ***striatum***	CDor WAbe
LAMI DARK PURPLE (Lami Series)	CRos LRHS NRHS
luteum	see *L. galeobdolon*
maculatum	GWyn MMuc SRms WCot WWtn
- 'Album'	EPfP SPer SRms WWtn
- 'Anne Greenaway' (v)	EWes LPot SCob WMoo
§ - 'Aureum'	ECtt SWvt WFar XLum
- 'Beacon Silver'	CMac CRos EBee ECha ECtt EHrv ELan EMor EPfP EShb GWyn LCro LOPS LPot LRHS MGos MJak MMuc NBir NRHS SCob SPer SPlb SPoG SRms SWvt WFar WJam XLum
- 'Brightstone Pearl'	ELon EWes EWld SHar
- 'Cannon's Gold'	ECtt SWvt WMoo
- 'Chequers' ambig.	EBee
- 'Chequers Board'	GAbr
- 'Dingle Candy'	MHCG
- 'Elisabeth de Haas' (v)	NBre
- 'Forncett Lustre'	EWes
- 'Ghost'	CKel ECtt ELon EPPr LBuc LRHS NLar SRms
- 'Gold Leaf'	see *L. maculatum* 'Aureum'
- GOLDEN ANNIVERSARY ('Dellam'PBR) (v)	CBod CKel CRos ELan LRHS LSRN NBro NHic NRHS SWvt
- 'Golden Nuggets'	see *L. maculatum* 'Aureum'
- 'Golden Wedding'	SRms
- LAMI MEGA PURPLE (Lami Series)	EBee
- 'Margery Fish'	SRms
- 'Orchid Frost'	EBee ELon GQue
- PINK CHABLIS ('Checkin'PBR)	CBod ELon MHol MRav NCou NLar SPer
- 'Pink Nancy'	SWvt
- 'Pink Pearls'	CSBt NLar SHar WMoo
- 'Pink Pewter'	CRos EBee ECha ECtt ELan EMor EPfP EShb GMaP GWyn LRHS NRHS SCob SPlb SPoG SRms WWtn
- 'Purple Dragon'	IPot SPoG
- 'Red Nancy'	CRos ELan EMor EPfP LRHS NLar NRHS SWvt XLum
§ - 'Roseum'	EBee ELan GWyn MCot MRav SPer WMoo XLum
- 'Shell Pink'	see *L. maculatum* 'Roseum'
- 'Silver Shield'	EWes
- 'Sterling Silver'	CSam
- 'White Nancy'	CRos CSBt EBee ECha ECtt EHoe EHrv ELan ELon EMor EPfP GMaP GWyn LPot LRHS LSRN MCot MRav NBir NGrd NRHS SCob SPer SPoG SRms SWvt WCAu WJam
- 'Wootton Pink'	MHCG NBir SWvt
'Marshmallow'	ELon
orvala	Widely available
- 'Album'	CDor CExl CRos EBee EHrv ELan EMor EPPr GBin IPot LEdu LPla LRHS MBel NAln NBir NCGa NLar SEND SHar WCAu WHer
- 'Silva'	CExl CRos EPPr EPfP IPot LEdu LRHS WCot
purpureum	GJos
sandrasicum	CPBP WAbe
'Wisley White'	NBir

Lamium × *Stachys* (*Lamiaceae*)

LILAC FALLS	see *Stachys* LILAC FALLS

Lampranthus (*Aizoaceae*)

aberdeenensis	see *Delosperma aberdeenense*
apricot-flowered	CRos LRHS NRHS
aurantiacus	CBcs
blandus	CBcs CCCN
'Blousey Pink'	SVen
§ ***brownii***	CBcs CCCN CRos ELan EPfP LRHS NRHS SPlb
coccineus	CPla
deltoides	see *Oscularia deltoides*
edulis	see *Carpobrotus edulis*
'Exposure'	CCCN SSim
glaucus	SEND
multiradiatus	SEND
oscularis	see *Oscularia deltoides*
'Pink'	CPla ELan SPlb SSim
purple-flowered	CBod SPlb
roseus	CCCN CRos CSma LRHS NRHS
'Salmon Pink'	SPlb
'Shanklin'	SPlb SVen
spectabilis	CBcs CCCN CTri GLet
- orange-flowered	CBod SSim WFar
- purple-flowered	CPla SPlb SSim
- 'Tresco Apricot'	CCCN
- 'Tresco Brilliant'	CBod CCCN CKel ELon SSim
- 'Tresco Fire'	CAbb CCCN CExl CSma ELon SPlb SRms SVen
- 'Tresco Orange'	CCCN CPla
- 'Tresco Peach'	CCCN
- 'Tresco Purple'	ELan
- 'Tresco Red'	CCCN CPla ELon EUJe SEND SSim
- white-flowered	GKev SPlb SVen WFar
- yellow-flowered	CPla EUJe SSim SVen WFar
stipulaceus	SPlb
'Tresco Pearl'	CPla

Lamprocapnos (*Papaveraceae*)

§ ***spectabilis*** ♀H6	Widely available
- 'Alba' ♀H7	Widely available
- 'Gold Heart'PBR	CAby CBcs CBod CRos CWCL CWGN EBee ECha ECtt ELon

EMor EPfP GLet LRHS MAsh MGos MHol MRav MSCN NBid NHpl NLar NRHS NSti SCob SPoG WCot WFar WHil WSpi
- 'Love Hearts' MHol
- 'Valentine' ♀H6 Widely available

Lamprothyrsus (*Poaceae*)

hieronymi CBod CSde
- RCB RA K2-2 CAby CKno EBee ELon MAvo MHol WCot WPGP

Lancea (*Phrymaceae*)

tibetica CPBP GEdr

Lantana ✿ (*Verbenaceae*)

'Calippo Tutti Frutti' CPla EUJe
camara ELan EShb SEle
- (Lucky Series) LUCKY PEACH ('Balucpea') SPoG
- - LUCKY PURE GOLD ('Balucpure'[PBR]) SPoG
- - LUCKY RED FLAME ('Balandimfla') SPoG
- - LUCKY SUNRISE ROSE ('Balandrise'[PBR]) SPoG
- - LUCKY WHITE ('Balucwite'[PBR]) SPoG
- 'Mine d'Or' EUJe
- orange-flowered CCCN
- pink-flowered CCCN ELan
- red-flowered CCCN
- white-flowered CCCN
'Chapel Hill Gold'[PBR] EMdy
'Dallas Red' CRos EMdy LRHS NRHS
'Miss Huff' EMdy
§ ***montevidensis*** CSam EShb
* - ***alba*** EShb
sellowiana see *L. montevidensis*
'Sunny Side Up'[PBR] EMdy

Lapageria ✿ (*Philesiaceae*)

rosea ♀H3 CCCN CExl CRHN CTsd SAdn SChF SWvt WPGP WPav
- var. ***albiflora*** ♀H3 CRHN SChF
- - 'Hugletts Blush' SChF
- 'Beatrix Anderson' CRHN
- 'Flesh Pink' CExl CRHN
- 'Pink Panther' CRHN WPav
- 'Tierra del Fuego' CRHN

Lapeirousia (*Iridaceae*)

cruenta see *Freesia laxa*
laxa see *Freesia laxa*

Lapsana (*Asteraceae*)

communis 'Inky' CNat

Lardizabala (*Lardizabalaceae*)

biternata see *L. funaria*
§ ***funaria*** WCru WPav

Larix ✿ (*Pinaceae*)

decidua CAco CCVT CDul CMen CPer ECrN ELan EMOT EPfP EWTr LPra MGos MMuc NEgg NWea SEND SPlb WTSh
- 'Corley' CKen
- 'Krejci' NLar
- 'Little Bogle' CKen LRHS MAsh MBlu NEgg SLim SMad
- 'Lucek' NLar SLim
- 'Oberförster Karsten' CKen
- 'Pendula' CMen
- 'Puli' ♀H7 LRHS MAsh MBlu NHol NLar NOra SPer SPoG WMat
- 'Raohuil' NLar
- 'Roman' NLar
× ***eurolepis*** see *L. × marschlinsii*
gmelinii var. ***gmelinii*** CMen
- 'Tharandt' CKen
§ ***kaempferi*** CAco CCVT CDul CMen CPer ELan EPfP LBuc LMaj LPra LRHS NEgg NWea SCoo SEWo WTSh
- 'Bambino' CKen SLim
- 'Bingman' CKen
- 'Blue Ball' CKen NLar
- 'Blue Dwarf' ♀H7 LRHS SLim
- 'Blue Rabbit' CKen NEgg
- 'Cruwys Morchard' CKen
- 'Diana' CAco CEnd CKen CMen LRHS MAsh NEgg NHol SLim
- 'Elizabeth Rehder' CKen
- 'Grant Haddow' CKen
- 'Grey Pearl' CKen LRHS MAsh SLim
- 'Hobbit' CKen NEgg
- 'Jakobsen' LRHS NLar
- 'Jakobsen's Pyramid' CMen MAsh WMat
- 'Little Blue Star' CAco
- 'Lobby Dosser' CMen NEgg
I - 'Nana' CKen CMen NEgg NHol
I - 'Nana Prostrata' CKen
- 'Pendula' CEnd EPfP LPra SPoG
- 'Stiff Weeper' ♀H7 LRHS NEgg NLar
- 'Varley' CKen
- 'Wehlen' CKen
- 'Wolterdingen' CKen LRHS NLar
laricina 'Arethusa Bog' CKen
- 'Bear Swamp' CKen
- 'Bingman' CKen
- 'Blue Sparkler' NLar
- 'Hartwig Pine' CKen
- 'Iron Red' NLar
- 'Michigan Tower' NLar
- 'Newport Beauty' CKen
- 'Stubby' CKen NLar
leptolepis see *L. kaempferi*
§ × ***marschlinsii*** CCVT MMuc NWea
- 'Domino' CKen CMen
- 'Gail' CKen
- 'Julie' CKen

Laser (*Apiaceae*)

trilobum GEdr SPhx
- PAB 3382 LEdu WPGP

Laserpitium (*Apiaceae*)

gallicum SPhx
halleri SPhx
latifolium EBee SPhx
§ ***siler*** CSpe IMou IPot MNrw NDov SPhx SPlb WSHC WSpi

Lasiagrostis see *Stipa*

Lasiospermum (*Asteraceae*)

bipinnatum SPlb

Lathraea (*Orobanchaceae*)

clandestina CAvo

Lathyrus ✿ (*Papilionaceae*)

§	***articulatus***	CSpe
§	***aureus***	CBor CDor CSpe EBee EPPr EWld GCal MCot MHer MNrw NBid NBir SBrt SPhx WAul WCAu WFar WHal
	- 'Cally Variegated' (v)	GCal
	chilensis	GWyn WPav WSHC
	cirrhosus	WSHC
	clymenum articulatus	see *L. articulatus*
	cyaneus misapplied	see *L. vernus*
	davidii	EPPr LEdu SBrt WBor WCot WPav
	fremontii hort.	see *L. laxiflorus*
	gmelinii	SBrt
	grandiflorus ♀H6	CCBP CMea EBee NChi NHpl SMHy WCot
	inermis	see *L. laxiflorus*
	japonicus	CEls EBee
	- subsp. ***maritimus***	GJos SPhx WCot
	laevigatus	SBrt
	latifolius ♀H7	CAgr CRHN CSde EPPr EPfP GQue MHol NPer SRms SVic WBrk WCot WFar WHer XLum
§	- 'Albus' ♀H7	CFlo CTri SHar SRms WFar WKif XLum
	- pale pink-flowered	MBel
	- PINK PEARL	see *L. latifolius* 'Rosa Perle'
	- 'Red Pearl'	CBcs CFlo CKel CRos CWGN EBee ELan EPfP GAbr LBuc LRHS LSRN NLar NRHS SEND SPer SPlb SPoG SRms SWvt WFar
§	- 'Rosa Perle' ♀H7	CBcs CBod CFlo CKel CRos CTri EBee ECha ELan LCro LOPS LRHS LSRN MHer MRav NBir NLar NPer NRHS SPer SPoG SWvt WBor WFar WMoo XLum
	- 'Rose Queen'	GJos
	- WEISSE PERLE	see *L. latifolius* 'White Pearl'
	- 'White Pearl' misapplied	see *L. latifolius* 'Albus'
§	- 'White Pearl' ♀H7	CBcs CBod CKel CRos CWGN EBee ECha ELan EPfP EWTr GAbr LBuc LCro LOPS LRHS LSRN MBel MHer MRav NBir NLar NPer NRHS SPer SPoG SRms SWvt WBor WFar XLum
§	***laxiflorus***	CBor MCot WMoo WOut WSHC
	linifolius	EBee NLar SBrt
	montanus	GPoy
	nervosus	MCot SRms
	niger	CFis CSpe EBee EWld LEdu MCot MHer MMrt SHar
	nissolia	WSFF
	odoratus	SVic
	- 'Anniversary'	MCot
	- 'Beaujolais'	LCro LOPS
	- 'Beth Chatto'	MCot
	- 'Betty Maiden'	MCot
	- 'Blue Medley'	MCot
	- 'Blue Velvet'	CSpe
	- 'Bobby's Girl' ♀H2	LCro LOPS
	- 'Burnished Bronze'	MCot
	- 'Cathy' ♀H2	EPfP
	- 'Charlie's Angel' ♀H2	LCro LOPS MCot
	- 'Cupani'	LCro LOPS MNHC
	- 'Daphne'	LCro LOPS
	- 'Dark Passion'	MCot
	- 'Dawn'	MCot
	- 'Ethel Grace'	MCot
	- 'Evening Glow' ♀H2	MCot
	- 'Flora Norton'	CSpe
	- 'George Priestley'	MCot
I	- 'Gwendoline' ♀H2	LCro LOPS
	- 'High Scent' ♀H2	LCro LOPS
	- 'Honey Pink'	MCot
	- 'Honeymoon'	MCot
	- 'Jilly' ♀H2	MCot
	- 'Karen Louise'	LCro LOPS
	- 'Linda C'	LCro LOPS
	- MAMMOTH MIXED	CWCL
	- 'Marion'	MCot
	- 'Marti Caine'	MCot
	- 'Matucana' ♀H2	CSpe ELan LCro LOPS SPhx
	- 'Midnight'	LCro LOPS
	- 'Milly'	MCot
	- 'Misty Mountain'	MCot
	- 'Mollie Rilstone'	LCro LOPS MCot
	- 'Mrs Bernard Jones' ♀H2	LCro LOPS MCot
	- 'Mrs Collier'	CSpe
	- 'Oxford Blue'	LCro LOPS
	- 'Painted Lady'	LCro LOPS
	- 'Pluto'	LCro LOPS
	- 'Promise'	MCot
	- 'Restormel'	LCro LOPS MCot
	- 'Richard and Judy'	MCot
	- 'Royal Wedding'	LCro LOPS
	- SPENCER MIXED	LOPS
	- 'Tara'	LCro LOPS
	- 'Wedding Day' ♀H2	MCot
	- 'White Frills'	LCro LOPS
	palustris	EBee LLWG MMuc SPlb
	pratensis	CHab EBee NMir WSFF
	pubescens	EBee
	roseus	EBee GCal WSHC
	rotundifolius ♀H6	GAbr GLog SMHy SPhx WSHC
	- 'Tillyperone' ♀H7	EBee SPhx WSHC
	sativus	CSpe MCot
	subandinus	SPlb
	sylvestris	EBee WBrk
	tingitanus	CSpe
	transsylvanicus	GBin SBrt SPhx
	tuberosus	EBee LEdu WCot WSHC
	'Tubro'	EBee
	venetus	EBee EWes MAvo MNrw SPhx WSHC
§	***vernus*** ♀H6	Widely available
	- 'Albiflorus'	MNrw XEll
	- 'Alboroseus' ♀H5	CDor ELan EMor EPPr EPfP EWTr GCal IFro ILea MAvo MNrw NBir NChi NLar SPhx SPoG SWvt WCAu WCot WFar WHoo WOut
	- var. ***albus***	CMea MNrw NChi SRms WCot
	- ***aurantiacus***	see *L. aureus*
	- 'Caeruleus'	WHoo
*	- 'Cyaneus'	CDor WCot
	- 'Dama Emily'	SHar
	- 'Dama Violetta'	SHar
I	- 'Filifolius'	CSpe
	- 'Flaccidus'	CAby MAvo MNrw WCot
*	- 'Gracilis'	EBee LEdu NLar SHar WPGP
	- 'Little Elf'	SHar
	- 'Madelaine'	WCot
I	- 'Pendulus'	SHar
	- purple-flowered	CRos LRHS MMuc NRHS SEND
	- 'Rainbow'	CRos EPfP LRHS MPie NRHS
	- 'Rosenelfe'	CRos GJos LEdu MAvo MHer SPhx WCot WHal WHil
	- f. ***roseus***	CRos ECha LRHS MMuc MRav NBir NRHS SEND SRms WBrk WCot
	- 'Spring Melody'	EBee EHrv MRav SHar WCot
	- 'Subtle Hints'	NCGa SHar WCot
	- 'Winter Blush'	SHar

Latua (*Solanaceae*)

pubiflora	WPav

Laurelia (*Atherospermataceae*)

§ ***sempervirens***	WPGP
serrata	see *L. sempervirens*

Laureliopsis (*Atherospermataceae*)

philippiana	CBcs CMCN EBee IDee NLar WPGP

Laurentia see *Isotoma*

Laurus (*Lauraceae*)

§ ***azorica***	CBcs
canariensis	see *L. azorica*
nobilis ♀H4	Widely available
- f. ***angustifolia*** ♀H4	CJun CMac CTsd LRHS MBlu MHer MMuc MRav NLar SArc SCob SEND SPoG WAvo
- 'Aurea' ♀H4	CBcs CKel CMac ELan ELon EPfP MHer MMuc NLar SCob SEND SLon SPer SPoG SWvt WMoo
- clipped pyramid	LSRN
- 'Crispa'	MRav
- variegated (v)	CMac SRms
rotundifolia	CAco

Lavandula ✿ (*Lamiaceae*)

'After Midnight'	see *L.* 'Avonview'
'Alba'	see *L. angustifolia* 'Alba', *L.* × *intermedia* 'Alba'
'Alba' ambig.	SPer
§ ***angustifolia***	CCVT CKel CRos EBee ENfk EPfP GPoy GWyn LCro LOPS LRHS LSRN MGos MHer MHol NAln NGdn NLar NPer NPri NRHS SCob SDow SLim SPlb SPoG XLum XSen
- 'Alba' misapplied	see *L. angustifolia* 'Blue Mountain White'
§ - 'Alba'	ELan EPfP GPoy MHer MRav MSwo SCob SLon SPlb SVen SVic WAvo WGwG WJek WSpi XSen
- 'Alba Nana'	see *L. angustifolia* 'Nana Alba'
- 'Arctic Snow'	CBcs CRos ENor EPfP LCro LOPS LRHS MAsh MHer MSwo NGdn NRHS SDow SFai SGol SPoG SRms WLav WSpi XSen
- AROMATICO BLUE ('Lablusa'PBR)	CRos LRHS NRHS
- AROMATICO FORTE BLUE ('Laa20001')	CRos LRHS NRHS SPoG
- AROMATICO SILVER ('Lasila')	CRos LRHS NRHS
- 'Ashdown Forest'	EBee ELan ENfk EWhm MNHC SAdn SCob SDow SFai SPer SRms WLav WSpi XSen
- 'Babelle'	XSen
- 'Backhouse Purple'	SDow
- 'Beechwood Blue' ♀H5	SCob SDow WLav
- 'Betty's Blue'	SDow
- BLUE CUSHION ('Lavandula Schola'PBR)	ELan LCro LOPS LSRN MAsh NAst SFai SPoG SRms WLav
- BLUE ICE ('Dow3'PBR)	ENor SAko SDow SFai SGol WLav XSen
- 'Blue Lance'	MHol
§ - 'Blue Mountain White'	SDow WLav XSen
- 'Blue Rider'	LRHS NRHS WLav
- 'Blue River'	CBod
- BLUE SCENT ('Syngablusc')	LRHS
§ - 'Bowles's Early'	WGwG
- 'Bowles's Grey'	see *L. angustifolia* 'Bowles's Early'
- 'Bowles's Variety'	see *L. angustifolia* 'Bowles's Early'
- 'Cedar Blue'	ELan EWhm MHer MHol SDow SRms WGwG WLav
- 'Coconut Ice'	ELan EMOT WLav WSpi XSen
- 'Compacta'	SDow WLav
- 'Crystal Lights'	EMOT
- 'Dursley White'	WLav
- 'Dwarf Blue'	CBod CRos LSRN MHed SRms WFar XSen
- 'Elizabeth'	ENor LSRN SCob SDow SFai SPoG WLav XSen
- (Ellagance Series) 'Ellagance Ice'	SRms
- - 'Ellagance Purple'	CRos LRHS NRHS SRms
- - 'Ellagance Sky'	CBod MHol NRHS SRms
- 'Essence Purple'	CBod
- 'Felice'PBR	LRHS
- 'Folgate' ♀H5	CBod ECtt EWhm MHer MNHC NAln NGdn SDow SRms WAvo WHoo WLav WSpi
- GARDEN BEAUTY ('Lowmar'PBR) (v)	MAsh XSen
- GRANNY'S BOUQUET ('Lavang38')	EMOT GWyn WSpi XSen
- 'Havana'	EBee LRHS MAsh MHol SPoG XSen
§ - 'Hidcote' ♀H5	Widely available
- 'Hidcote Pink'	EWhm MHer MNHC MRav NAln NGdn SCob SDow SPer SRms XSen
- 'Hidcote Superior'	NGdn
- 'Imperial Gem' ♀H5	Widely available
- 'Jean Davis'	see *L. angustifolia* 'Rosea'
- 'Lady'	NPer WSpi
- 'Lady Ann'	SDow WLav
- 'Lavenite Petite'PBR	CRos ENor LRHS LSRN SFai WLav WSpi XSen
- LITTLE LADY ('Batlad') ♀H5	CMea ECtt ENor LCro LOPS LRHS LSRN MAsh MHed MNHC MSwo NAln NLar NRHS SAko SFai SGol SPoG SRms SWvt WHoo WLav WSpi XSen
- LITTLE LOTTIE ('Clarmo') ♀H5	EWhm LSRN MHer SDow WLav XSen
- 'Loddon Blue'	CRos ENor EPfP EWhm LRHS MAsh NRHS SDow SFai SRms WLav WSpi XSen
§ - 'Loddon Pink'	CRos ELan ENor EPfP EWhm GMaP LRHS MAsh MMuc MRav NGdn NRHS SEND SFai SRms WAvo WLav XSen
- 'Lullaby Blue'	SDow
- 'Maillette'	NGdn SDow SRms WLav
- 'Melissa'	MHol XSen
- MELISSA LILAC ('Dow4'PBR)	CBcs CRos CSBt ENfk ENor LCro LOPS LRHS LSRN MAsh MGos MHer MNHC NRHS SDow SFai SRkn SRms WLav XSen
- 'Middachten'	XSen
- 'Miss Dawnderry'	SDow
- 'Miss Donnington'	see *L. angustifolia* 'Bowles's Early'
- 'Miss Katherine'PBR ♀H5	CRos ECtt ELan ENor EPfP LRHS MAsh MHed SDow SPoG WLav XSen
- MISS MUFFET ('Scholmis') ♀H5	SDow SRms WLav XSen
- 'Munstead'	Widely available
§ - 'Nana Alba' ♀H5	CMea CRos ELan ENfk EPfP EWhm GMaP GPoy LRHS MAsh MHer

	NAln SDow SPer SRms SWvt WSpi XSen
- 'Nana Atropurpurea'	SDow XSen
- 'Nikita'	XSen
- 'No 9'	SDow
- 'Pacific Blue'	XSen
- 'Peter Pan'	ECtt ELan MAsh MHer MNHC SDow WLav XSen
- PLATINUM BLONDE ('Momparler'PBR)	CNor CRos ENor LRHS MAsh NRHS SFai SPoG XSen
- 'Princess Blue'	CRos ENor LRHS WLav
- 'Purity'	SDow
- 'Purple Treasure' **new**	SDow
§ - 'Rosea'	Widely available
- 'Royal Blue'	LRHS
- 'Royal Purple'	EWes NGdn SDow SWvt WLav XSen
- 'Royal Velvet'	SDow
- 'Saint Jean'	SDow
- 'Siesta'	XSen
- 'Silver Blue'	XSen
- 'Silver Mist'	CBod CMea SRms WHer XSen
- 'Sophie'	XSen
- 'Thumbelina Leigh'PBR	ENor MAsh SFai SRms WSpi XSen
- 'Twickel Purple'	CBar CBcs CRos EBee ELan EPfP LRHS LSRN MAsh MHed MHol MNHC NRHS SCob SDow SFai SPer SRms SWvt WLav WSpi XSen
- 'Walberton's Silver Edge'	see *L.* × *intermedia* WALBERTON'S SILVER EDGE
aristibracteata	MHer WLav
§ 'Avonview'	MHer WLav
'Ballerina' ♀H4	EAJP SDow
§ 'Bee Brilliant'PBR	ENfk EWhm WLav
§ 'Bee Cool'PBR	WLav
§ 'Bee Happy'	ENfk EWhm NBir WLav XSen
§ 'Bee Pretty'	ENfk EWhm
'Blue Star'	EPfP EWhm MNHC
'Bouquet of Roses'	CRos LRHS NRHS
buchii var. ***buchii***	SDow SVen WLav
'Bulls Cross'	WLav
canariensis	MHer SDow SVen WLav
× ***chaytoriae*** 'Bridehead Blue'	SDow
- 'Gorgeous'	SDow
- 'Helen'	SDow
- 'Joan Head'	XSen
- 'Molton Silver'	XSen
- 'Richard Gray' ♀H4	CKel LRHS LSRN MHed MHer MNHC NLar SDow SIgm SRms WAvo WLav XSen
§ - 'Sawyers' ♀H4	CBod CRos EBou EPfP EShb GMaP LRHS LSRN MAsh MCot MHed MHer MNHC MRav NBir NEgg NPer NRHS SCob SDow SEND SGol SPer SPhx SPoG SRms WGwG XSen
- 'Silver Sands'	EBee ELan EPfP MCot SFai SPoG XSen
× ***christiana***	CRos ENor LRHS SDow SFai SVen WLav
'Cornard Blue'	see *L.* × *chaytoriae* 'Sawyers'
dentata	ENfk SEND SRms WJek XSen
§ - var. ***candicans***	MHer SDow SRms WLav
- var. ***dentata*** 'Dusky Maiden'	SDow WLav
- - 'Ploughman's Blue'	SVen WGwG
- - f. ***rosea***	SDow
- - 'Royal Crown' ♀H3	WLav
- silver-leaved	see *L. dentata* var. *candicans*
'Devonshire Compact'	CSBt MHol SRms
'Fathead'	CBcs CBod CChe CRos ECtt ELan EMOT EPfP LRHS LSRN MAsh MGos MHer MNHC NBir NGdn NLar SCob SCoo SDow SFai SGol SPoG WAvo WLav
'Flaming Purple'	SDow
× ***ginginsii*** 'Goodwin Creek Grey' ♀H4	MHer SDow SGol SRms WGwG WLav
'Hazel'	CRos EPfP LRHS NRHS
'Helmsdale'PBR	CEnd CRos CSBt ELan ENor EPfP GMaP IKil LCro LRHS LSRN MAsh MRav NGdn NLar SCob SCoo SFai SGol SLim SPer
heterophylla misapplied	see *L.* × *heterophylla* Viv. Gaston Allard Group
§ × ***heterophylla*** Viv. Gaston Allard Group	WLav
- - 'African Pride'	SVen
- - 'Meerlo' **new**	SFai
'Hidcote Blue'	see *L. angustifolia* 'Hidcote'
× ***intermedia*** 'Abrialii'	SDow
§ - 'Alba' ♀H5	CMea MHed MHer MNHC SCob SEND SPer SVen XSen
- 'Anniversary Bouquet'	SDow
- 'Arabian Night'	see *L.* × *intermedia* 'Impress Purple', 'Sussex'
- 'Arabian Night' ambig.	SRms
§ - Dutch Group	CBod CRos CSBt ENfk EPfP LRHS MAsh MNHC MRav MSwo SArc SCoo SDow SFai SLim SPer SRms SVic XSen
- 'Edelweiss'	CBod CRos CSBt EAJP ENfk EPfP EWhm LRHS MAsh MNHC MRav NAln NAst NEgg NGdn NLar NRHS SCob SDow SFai SGol SPer SPoG SRms SWvt WGwG WLav WSpi XSen
§ - 'Enigma'	CBar
- 'Fragrant Memories'	NAln SDow SRms WLav XSen
- 'Fred Boutin'	WSpi
- GOLDBURG ('Burgoldeen') (v)	SGol
- 'Grappenhall' misapplied	see *L.* × *intermedia* 'Enigma', 'Pale Pretender'
- 'Grappenhall' ambig.	EWhm NAln WSpi XSen
- 'Grey Hedge'	SRms WLav
- 'Gros Bleu'	SDow SFai WLav XSen
- 'Grosso'	Widely available
- (Heavenly Series) 'Heavenly Angel'	ENor SAko SDow SFai XSen
- - 'Heavenly Night'	LSRN SDow XSen
- - 'Heavenly Scent'	ENor SDow SFai XSen
- 'Hidcote Giant' ♀H5	CRos EPfP GCal LRHS NPer NRHS SDow WKif WLav WSpi XSen
§ - 'Impress Purple'	SDow WAvo WLav XSen
- 'Lullingstone Castle'	ENfk EWhm SDow SRms WAvo WLav
- 'Old English' misapplied	see *L.* × *intermedia* 'Seal'
- 'Old English'	CBod CLau ENfk SDow SRms
- Old English Group	MMuc MNHC SEND WHoo WLav XSen
- 'Olympia'	SAko SDow SPoG XSen
§ - 'Pale Pretender'	CSBt GQue MHer MSwo SPer SRms
- PHENOMENAL ('Niko'PBR)	ENor LSRN SFai XSen
- 'Provence'	SDow SFai SRms XSen
§ - 'Seal'	ENfk GMaP MNHC SCob SDow SRms XSen
§ - 'Sussex' ♀H5	CBod CFis CRos EPfP LRHS NRHS SDow WLav
- 'Twickel Purple'	ELan EWes NLar SGol

Name	Suppliers
§ - WALBERTON'S SILVER EDGE ('Walvera') (v)	CRos EMOT EPfP LBuc LRHS MGos NRHS SCoo SDow SFai SRms XSen
'Jamboree'	WLav
'Jean Davis'	see *L. angustifolia* 'Rosea'
lanata 🏆H3	ECha SRms WLav XSen
§ ***latifolia***	XSen
I 'Lavender Lace'	LSRN
'Loddon Pink'	see *L. angustifolia* 'Loddon Pink'
'Madrid Blue'	see *L.* 'Bee Happy'
'Madrid Pink'	see *L.* 'Bee Pretty'
'Madrid Purple'	see *L.* 'Bee Brilliant'
'Madrid White'	see *L.* 'Bee Cool'
minutolii	SDow
multifida	MHer WLav
officinalis	see *L. angustifolia*
PASSIONNÉ ('Lavsts 08'PBR) 🏆H4	EMOT WLav
pedunculata	EBee ENor XSen
- subsp. ***lusitanica***	CRos EPfP LRHS NRHS SPoG
- - LUSI PINK ('Wijs02'PBR)	ENfk SFai
- - 'Lusi Purple'	CRos LRHS NRHS SFai SPoG
§ - subsp. ***pedunculata***	CAby CBar CBod CKel CRos ECha ELan EPau EPfP LCro LOPS LRHS LSRN MAsh MGos MJak MNHC MSwo NAln NGdn NRHS SCob SDow SFai SGol SPer SRms WAvo WSpi
- - 'James Compton' 🏆H3	CRos ECha LRHS MAsh NGdn
- subsp. ***sampaiana*** 'Purple Emperor'	CRos EPfP LRHS NRHS WLav
pinnata	ENfk ENor MHol SDow
'Pretty Polly' 🏆H4	CBcs CRos ELan EPfP LRHS MAsh SDow SFai SRkn WLav
'Pukehou'	CRos EPfP LRHS NRHS SCoo WLav
'Purple Ribbon'	LRHS
'Regal Splendour'PBR	CRos CSBt ELan EMOT ENor EPfP LRHS LSRN MAsh MGos MHer MNHC NPri NRHS SCob SCoo SDow SFai SGol SLim SPoG SRms WLav
ROCKY ROAD ('Fair09'PBR)	ENor SFai WLav
'Rosea'	see *L. angustifolia* 'Rosea'
rotundifolia	SDow
'Silver Edge'	see *L.* × *intermedia* WALBERTON'S SILVER EDGE
'Silver Line' **new**	CRos LRHS NRHS
SILVER SANDS ('Fair 14'PBR)	ENfk
'Somerset Mist'	WLav
spica nom. rejic.	see *L. angustifolia*, *L. latifolia*
- 'Hidcote Purple'	see *L. angustifolia* 'Hidcote'
stoechas	CBcs CBod CDul CRos CSBt ECha ELan EPfP GMaP GPoy LRHS LSRN MJak MNHC MSwo NRHS SCob SDow SIgm SPer SPlb SWvt WArt
- var. ***albiflora***	see *L. stoechas* subsp. *stoechas* f. *leucantha*
- 'Anouk'PBR	EBee ELan EPfP LRHS SPoG
- 'Antibes' (Provençal Series)	SRms
- 'Arles' (Provençal Series)	CPla
- 'Bandera'	CBod
- (Bella Series) BELLA LAVENDER ('Bellav')	CRos LRHS NRHS
- - BELLA ROSE ('Belros')	CRos LRHS NRHS
- 'Blueberry Ruffles'PBR (Ruffles Series)	ELan
- 'Boysenberry Ruffles'PBR (Ruffles Series)	ELan ENfk XSen
- 'Dark Royalty'PBR	ELan
- JAVELIN BLUE ('Jin Bulle') (Javelin Series)	CRos LRHS NRHS
- 'Lace'	LSRN WLav
- LITTLE BEE DEEP PURPLE ('Florvendula Deep Purple') (Little Bee Series)	CRos LRHS NRHS
- 'Mulberry Ruffles'PBR (Ruffles Series)	ELan
- 'Night of Passion'	SDow
- 'Papillon'	see *L. pedunculata* subsp. *pedunculata*
- subsp. ***pedunculata***	see *L. pedunculata* subsp. *pedunculata*
- 'Pink Angels'	ELan
- 'Purley'	SRms
- Ruffles Series	ENfk
- 'Silver Anouk'PBR	CBod EPfP LRHS
- 'Spring-break Princess'	CRos LRHS NRHS
§ - subsp. ***stoechas***	EPfP MSwo SCob SDow
f. ***leucantha***	
- - - 'Snowman'	CBcs CRos CSBt EPfP LRHS MAsh MHer NRHS SCob SCoo SFai SPoG SWvt
- - LILAC WINGS ('Prolil'PBR)	CRos ENor EPfP LRHS NLar NRHS SCoo SDow SFai WLav
- - 'Provençal'	CRos LRHS NRHS SCob SCoo
- - 'Purple Wings'	CRos ELan EPfP LRHS MAsh MGos SLim
- - f. ***rosea***	ENor
- - - 'Kew Red'	CBcs CTri ENfk LRHS MGos MHer SDow SFai SRms SWvt WLav
- 'Sugarberry Ruffles'PBR (Ruffles Series)	ENfk
- 'Victory'	CRos LRHS NRHS SPoG
- 'With Love'PBR	SDow
TIARA ('Fair 10'PBR)	CAby CRos CSBt ENfk ENor LRHS LSRN MGos NEoE NLar NRHS SCoo SFai SPad SPoG SRms WLav
'Van Gogh'	SDow
vera misapplied	see *L.* × *intermedia* Dutch Group
vera DC.	see *L. angustifolia*
viridis	CRos ELan EPfP LRHS MHer NPer NRHS SDow SRms WJek WLav
'Whero Iti'	SDow
'Willow Vale' 🏆H3	CRos ENor EPfP EWhm LRHS MAsh MHer NRHS SDow SWvt WAvo WJek

Lavatera (*Malvaceae*)

Name	Suppliers
arborea	CPla SChr SEND WHer
- 'Rosea'	see *L.* × *clementii* 'Rosea'
- 'Variegata' (v)	CPla ELan MAvo NPer SEND WCot
bicolor	see *L. maritima*
cachemiriana	NAln NPer
CHAMALLOW ('Inovera'PBR)	CRos LRHS LSRN
× ***clementii*** 'Barnsley'	Widely available
- 'Barnsley Baby'	CBod CRos EBee ELan LBuc LRHS MAsh NGdn NLar NPer NPri SChF SEle SPer SPoG SRkn SWvt WFar WNPC
- 'Blushing Bride'	CBod CRos EPfP LRHS LSRN MGos NLar SWvt
- 'Bredon Springs' 🏆H5	CBod CDul CRos CSBt EBee ECha ELon EPfP LRHS LSRN MAsh MGos MMuc MSwo NGdn NRHS SEND SGol SLim SPer SWvt WAvo XLum
- 'Burgundy Wine' 🏆H5	CBcs CKel CMac CRos EBee ELan EPfP LRHS MAsh MGos MJak MSwo NBir NEgg NLar NPer NPri NRHS SGbt SGol SLim SLon SPer SPoG SWvt WAvo WFar
- 'Candy Floss' 🏆H5	LRHS NBir NLar NPer SGol

- 'Eye Catcher'	LRHS MSwo NLar SPer
- 'Kew Rose'	CBod MMuc MSwo NLar NPer SEND SLim SRms XLum
- 'Lavender Lady'	NPer SEND
- 'Lisanne'	CRos LRHS MMuc MSwo SGol
- 'Mary Hope' ♀H5	CKel CRos EBee EPfP EWld LRHS MAsh NRHS SEle SWvt
- MEMORIES ('Stelav')	CRos LRHS LSRN
- 'Pavlova'	CExl
§ - 'Pink Frills'	SWvt WCot WFar
- RED RUM ('Rigrum'PBR) ♀H5	CBod CMac CRos CSBt EBee EPfP LBuc LLHF LRHS LSRN MAsh MGos MHol NEgg NLar NPri NRHS SCob SEND SLim SPoG SWvt WFar
§ - 'Rosea' ♀H5	CBcs CDul CKel CMac CRos EBee ECrN EPfP LCro LOPS LRHS LSRN MAsh MGos MNHC NBir NEgg NHol NPri NRHS SCob SGbt SGol SLon SPer SPoG SWvt
- RUBY STAR ('Jostar')	CRos EBee LRHS MTin NRHS SCob
- 'Songbird'	NRHS SCob
§ - 'Wembdon Variegated' (v)	NPer
'Frederique'	CMac CRos LBuc LRHS NLar SWvt WKif
'Grey Beauty'	LRHS
'Magenta Magic'PBR	NLar SPoG
§ ***maritima*** ♀H3	CBod CExl CMac CRos CSde ELan EPfP LRHS SEND SEle SRkn SRms SWvt WCFE WCot WFar WKif WOut
- 'Princesse de Lignes'	XLum
olbia	SPlb SRms WFar
- 'Lilac Lady'	ECha ECrN ELan EWTr MGos MMuc NLar SGol WFar WKif
'Peppermint Ice'	see *L. thuringiaca* 'Ice Cool'
'Pink Frills'	see *L.* × *clementii* 'Pink Frills'
'Rosea'	see *L.* × *clementii* 'Rosea'
tauricensis	MAvo
thuringiaca	GCal LPla
- 'First Light'	SPhx
§ - 'Ice Cool'	NLar SCob SWvt WKif
'Variegata'	see *L.* × *clementii* 'Wembdon Variegated'
'White Angel'PBR	NLar
'White Satin'PBR	NHol

Lawsonia (*Lythraceae*)

inermis	WSFF

Ledebouria (*Asparagaceae*)

adlamii	see *L. cooperi*
concolor misapplied	see *L. socialis*
§ ***cooperi***	CBor EAJP EShb LEdu LRHS MPie NRHS SBrt WBor WHil WPGP XLum
§ ***socialis***	EShb EUJe LEdu MCot MPie WCot
- green-leaved **new**	EShb
violacea	see *L. socialis*

Ledum see *Rhododendron*

leek see AGM Vegetables Section

Leiophyllum see *Kalmia*

Lembotropis see *Cytisus*

Lemna (*Araceae*)

gibba	NPer
minor	CWat NPer
polyrrhiza	see *Spirodela polyrrhiza*
trisulca	CWat EWat NPer

lemon see *Citrus* × *limon*

lemon balm see *Melissa officinalis*

lemon grass see *Cymbopogon citratus*

lemon, rough see *Citrus* × *taitensis*

lemon verbena see *Aloysia citrodora*

lemonquat see *Citrus* × *limon* × *C.* × *taitensis*

Leonotis (*Lamiaceae*)

leonitis	see *L. ocymifolia*
leonurus	CBcs CCCN CDTJ CHll CSam ECre EMdy EShb EWes LRHS SMad SPlb XLum
- var. ***albiflora***	CCCN EShb
nepetifolia	CHll
- var. ***nepetifolia*** 'Staircase'	CCCN
§ ***ocymifolia***	CCCN CExl
- var. ***raineriana***	CHll

Leontice (*Berberidaceae*)

albertii	see *Gymnospermium albertii*

Leontochir (*Alstroemeriaceae*)

ovallei	CCCN

Leontodon (*Asteraceae*)

hispidus	CHab NMir
§ ***rigens***	CSpe ELan GEdr MHer MMuc NBid NBir WFar WMoo
- B&SWJ 12527	WCru WSHC
- 'Girandole'	see *L. rigens*

Leontopodium (*Asteraceae*)

alpinum	see *L. nivale* subsp. *alpinum*
- subsp. ***nivale***	see *L. nivale* subsp. *nivale*
calocephalum **new**	GKev
coreanum	GKev NAln
haastioides	WAbe
jacotianum	GKev
nanum	GKev NAln SPlb
§ ***nivale*** subsp. ***alpinum***	CPla CTri EBou ELan EPfP GKev MAsh NHpl SPlb SPoG SRms XLum
- - 'Everest'	EDAr
- - 'Matterhorn'	GEdr GMaP NLar
- - 'Mignon'	EBou EPfP EWes GMaP WAbe
§ - subsp. ***nivale***	GKev
§ ***ochroleucum*** var. ***campestre***	NLar XLum
palibinianum	see *L. ochroleucum* var. *campestre*
pusillum	WAbe
souliei	NSla SRot XLum
stracheyi	GKev

Leonurus (*Lamiaceae*)

cardiaca	CBod GPoy MHer MNHC NGrd SRms
- 'Grobbebol'	EPPr WCot WHer
sibiricus L.	GCal
turkestanicus	EBee

Leopoldia (*Asparagaceae*)

sp.	CPla
caucasica	GKev

comosa see *Muscari comosum*
tenuiflora see *Muscari tenuiflorum*
weissii GKev

Lepechinia (*Lamiaceae*)

bella CSpe SDys
chamaedryoides CExl
hastata CSpe LRHS SIgm SPlb WOut
salviae WFar WHer

Lepidium (*Brassicaceae*)

campestre CHab
latifolium ENfk LEdu

Lepidozamia (*Zamiaceae*)

peroffskyana CBrP

Leptinella (*Asteraceae*)

atrata subsp. ***luteola*** ELan
'County Park' EDAr
dendyi ECtt ELan EWes GEdr MHer NSla WIce
dioica GBin
- 'Minima' **new** WFar
hispida see *Cotula hispida* (DC.) Harv.
§ ***minor*** WMoo
§ ***pectinata*** ITim
§ ***potentillina*** CTri ECha EHoe GQue MBNS NLar SRms WMoo XLum
§ ***pyrethrifolia*** EDAr
reptans see *L. scariosa*
§ ***scariosa*** GAbr
§ ***squalida*** ECha GBin MBel NSti WMoo
§ - 'Platt's Black' CBcs EBee ECha ECtt EDAr EHoe EWes GAbr GBin GCrg GKev GWyn MBel MHer NHpl NLar SPtp SWvt WFar WGwG WMoo XLum

Leptodermis (*Rubiaceae*)

oblonga 'Summer Stars' LRHS

Leptopus (*Euphorbiaceae*)

§ ***chinensis*** EWTr WCot

Leptospermum ✿ (*Myrtaceae*)

citratum see *L. petersonii*
'Copper Sheen' CBcs
'County Park Blush' ELon
cunninghamii see *L. myrtifolium*
'Electric Red' (Galaxy Series) CAbb CBod CKel LRHS SEle
ericoides see *Kunzea ericoides*
flavescens misapplied see *L. glaucescens*
flavescens Sm. see *L. polygalifolium*
§ ***glaucescens*** SPlb
§ ***grandiflorum*** CBcs ELan EPfP SVen
grandifolium LRHS
'Havering Hardy' SEle
humifusum see *L. rupestre*
juniperinum SPlb
'Karo Pearl Star' MPkF
laevigatum SVen
§ ***lanigerum*** CExl CTri CTsd EPfP SPlb SPtp SVen
- 'Cunninghamii' see *L. myrtifolium*
liversidgei SPlb
§ ***myrtifolium*** CMac CTsd EWes
nitidum SPlb
obovatum CTsd
§ ***petersonii*** MHer
phylicoides see *Kunzea ericoides*
'Pink Cascade' CBcs CMac CTri SEle
§ ***polygalifolium*** CKel SPlb
prostratum see *L. rupestre*
pubescens see *L. lanigerum*
'Red Cascade' SWvt
rodwayanum see *L. grandiflorum*
rotundifolium CBcs CCht SPlb
- from Jervis Bay EBee
§ ***rupestre*** CTri SPlb SVen WKif WSHC
scoparium CTsd GPoy SPlb SVen WJek
- 'Adrianne' CRos EPfP LRHS MRav NRHS
- 'Appleblossom' ♀H3 CBcs CEnd CKel EPfP SAko SEle SGol
- 'Blossom' (d) CBcs CMac
- 'Burgundy Queen' (d) CBcs CCCN CMac CSBt
- 'Chapmanii' CCCN WPGP
- 'Coral Candy' CBcs CCCN CCht CEnd WFar
- 'Crimson Glory' (d) CSBt
- 'Elizabeth Jane' MMuc WFar
- 'Gaiety Girl' (d) CKel CSBt
- 'Jubilee' (d) CBcs CCCN CKel CMac
- 'Leonard Wilson' (d) CTri
- 'Martini' CAbb CBcs CBod CCCN CKel CMac CRos CSBt EPfP LRHS MMuc NRHS SGol SPoG WHlf
- (Nanum Group) 'Kea' CBcs MHer MRav
- - 'Kiwi' ♀H3 CAbb CBcs CCCN CRos CSBt EBee ELan EPfP EUJe LRHS MAsh MMuc SEle SLim SLon SPoG WFar
- - 'Nanum' CCCN
- - 'Pipit' ITim
- - 'Tui' CMac CSBt MPkF
- 'Nichollsii' ♀H3 CBcs SVen
- 'Nichollsii Nanum' ♀H4 WAbe WThu
- 'Pink Damask' SWvt
- var. ***prostratum*** misapplied see *L. rupestre*
- 'Red Damask' (d) ♀H3 CAbb CBcs CBod CCCN CDul CExl CKel CMac CRos CTri EBee EHoe ELan EPfP LRHS LSRN MAsh MMuc MRav NRHS SAko SEle SGol SLim SPlb SPoG SVen SWvt WFar
- 'Red Ensign' SPoG
- 'Red Falls' CExl
- 'Ruby Glow' (d) LSRN
* 'Ruby Wedding' CRos ELan EPfP LRHS LSRN MAsh SLon SPoG
- 'Snow Flurry' CBcs CKel CRos EPfP LRHS NRHS SGol SVen WFar
- 'Sunraysia' CTsd
- 'Winter Cheer' (d) CBcs CRos EPfP LRHS NRHS SGol
- 'Wiri Donna' CSde
- 'Wiri Joan' (d) CBcs
- 'Wiri Kerry' (d) MPkF
- 'Wiri Linda' CBcs CMac
'Silver Sheen' ♀H3 CAbb CBcs CCCN CCht CEnd CKel CRos CSde ELan EPfP LRHS MAsh NLar SPer SPoG SVen WPGP

Lespedeza (*Papilionaceae*)

bicolor CAgr CCCN LRHS MMuc WCFE WFar WSHC
- 'Yakushima' NLar
buergeri CRos LRHS MMrt NLar SHar WSHC
capitata EBee
japonica SPlb
thunbergii ♀H5 CBcs CHll CRos CSde EBee ELan EPfP LRHS MAsh MBlu MGil NRHS

	SLon SMad SPer SPoG SSta WCFE WHlf WPGP WSHC
- subsp. ***formosa***	EBee MGil
- 'Gibraltar'	EBee WPGP
- 'Summer Beauty'	CBcs
- subsp. ***thunbergii*** 'Albiflora'	ELan LRHS WPGP
- - 'Edo-shibori'	EBee ELan NLar SPer WPGP
- - 'White Fountain'	CRos EPfP LRHS MAsh NRHS SPoG WSHC
tiliifolia	see *Desmodium elegans*

Lesquerella (*Brassicaceae*)

arctica	WCFE
- var. ***purshii***	GKev

lettuce see AGM Vegetables Section

Leucadendron (*Proteaceae*)

'Amy' **new**	CKel
argenteum	CBcs CCCN CKel CPbh SPlb
'Burgundy Sunset' **new**	CKel MPkF
'Burgundy Sweet'	CBcs
conicum	CPbh
'Cream Delight'	CCCN CKel
daphnoides	SPlb
'Deacon Red'	MPkF
'Disco Date' **new**	CKel
discolor	SPlb
eucalyptifolium	CPbh SPlb
galpinii	CPbh
gandogeri	CPbh
gandogeri × ***spissifolium*** **new**	CKel
'Gem' **new**	CKel
'Highlights'	CCCN CKel
'Inca Gold' ♀H1c	CBcs CKel CPbh
'Jack Harre'	LRHS MPkF
'Jester' (v) **new**	CKel
'Jubilee Crown' **new**	MPkF
laureolum	CCCN CKel CPbh
modestum 'Strawberry Fair'	CCCN CKel
'Pisa'	MPkF
'Red Dwarf'	CPbh
'Safari Magic'	CCCN CKel
'Safari Sunset' ♀H3	CBcs CCCN CKel CPbh IDee MPkF
'Safari Sunshine'	CPbh
salicifolium	SPlb
salignum	CCCN CPbh
- 'Fireglow'	LRHS MPkF
- 'Winter Red' **new**	CKel
'Senorita' **new**	CKel
sessile	CPbh
'Sixteen Candles' **new**	CKel
strobilinum	CPbh
'Summer Sun' **new**	CKel
'Sundance'	MPkF
tinctum	CPbh

Leucaena (*Mimosaceae*)

leucocephala	SPlb

Leucanthemella (*Asteraceae*)

§ ***serotina*** ♀H7	Widely available
- 'Herbststern'	IMou NLar

Leucanthemopsis (*Asteraceae*)

§ ***alpina***	NSla
hosmariensis	see *Rhodanthemum hosmariense*

Leucanthemum ✿ (*Asteraceae*)

'Angel'	ELon NCou NLar WArt
atlanticum	see *Rhodanthemum atlanticum*
catananche	see *Rhodanthemum catananche*
'Hazel's Dream' **new**	IKil
hosmariense	see *Rhodanthemum hosmariense*
mawii	see *Rhodanthemum gayanum*
maximum misapplied	see *L.* × *superbum*
§ ***maximum*** (Ramond) DC.	NBro NPer
- ***uliginosum***	see *Leucanthemella serotina*
nipponicum	see *Nipponanthemum nipponicum*
'Osiris Neige'	ECtt ILea XLum
'Real Charmer'	CRos LRHS MAsh MHol NEoE NRHS SEle SRms WAvo
'Sante'	CRos EBee ELan EMor LCro LOPS LRHS MHol NRHS
'Sunshine Peach'	CRos EBee LPot LRHS NRHS SRot
§ × ***superbum***	CMac MMuc SEND WBrk
- 'Aglaia' (d)	Widely available
- 'Alaska'	CAni CBod CExl CRos CTsd EBee ELan GBin LRHS LSun MCot NLar NRHS SCob SPer SWvt WRHF XLum
- 'Amelia'	CRos EBee LRHS NBre NRHS
- 'Andernach'	CAni
- 'Anita Allen' (d)	CAni ECtt WCot
- 'Anna Camilla'	CAni
- 'Antwerp Star'	NBre NLar WBrk
- 'Banana Cream'	CBcs CRos CWGN EBee ECtt ELon EUJe IPot LCro LEdu LRHS MAsh MHol MSCN NLar NRHS SCob SEle SPoG STPC WFar WHoo WTor
- 'Banwell'	CAni
- 'Barbara Bush' (v/d)	SWvt
§ - 'Beauté Nivelloise'	CAni CElw CRos EBee ECtt EPfP GWyn IPot LRHS MBel MMrt NAln NBir NRHS SMad SRms WFar WSpi
- 'Becky'	CElw CMac CRos EBee ECha ELan ELon EWTr EWes GBin GWyn IPot LLHF LRHS LSRN NEoE NLar NRHS WCAu WJam WSpi
- 'Bishopstone'	CAni CSam EBee ECtt ELan LEdu LLHF NCGa
- 'Bridal Bouquet'PBR	CBod CRos ECtt LRHS NRHS
- 'Brightside'	CRos ELan ELon EMor LRHS NRHS WFar WMoo
- BROADWAY LIGHTS ('Leumayel'PBR)	CRos EBee EMor EPfP EWes GBin LPot LRHS MAsh MRav NAln NBir NRHS SCob SRms WAvo WCAu WFar WGrn WHil WSpi WTor
- 'Christine Hagemann'	CAni CElw EBee ECtt EWTr EWes ILea IPot MAvo MNrw MRav NCGa SHar WBrk WCFE
- 'Cobham Gold' (d)	NBre
- 'Colwall'	CAni
- 'Crazy Daisy'	CAni CChe CRos CTri EAJP ECtt EMor GWyn LRHS NRHS SRot SWvt WFar
- 'Devon Mist'	CAni
- 'Droitwich Beauty'	CAni ECtt LLHF WAvo WHil WHoo
- 'Duchess of Abercorn'	CAni CSam
- 'Dwarf Snow Lady'	NBre NLar
- 'Easton Lady'	CAni
- 'Eclipse'	CAni
- 'Edgebrook Giant'	CAni WBrk WHil
- 'Edward VII'	CAni
- 'Eisstern'	EBee LEdu MAvo NCGa SHar

	- 'Elworthy Sparkler'	CElw MAvo WBrk
	- 'Engelina'PBR	EBee NBir NLar WCAu
	- 'Esther Read' (d)	CRos EBee ECtt ELan EPau EPfP GBin LRHS LSRN NBro NChi NEgg NLar NRHS SRms SWvt WBrk WCot WFar
§	- 'Everest'	CAni SRms
	- 'Exhibition'	CRos EBee LRHS NRHS
	- 'Fiona Coghill' (d)	CAni CBod CElw CWGN ECtt EPfP GBin IKil LRHS MBel MNrw MSCN NBir NEgg NGdn NLar NRHS STPC WCot WHoo
	- 'Firnglanz'	CAni GBin
	- 'Flore Pleno' (d)	MMuc SEND SPlb
	- FREAK! ('Leuz0001'PBR)	CBcs CBod CRos EBee EPfP LRHS NRHS
	- 'Goldfinch'PBR	CWCL CWGN EAJP ECtt EMor ILea LLHF LRHS MAsh MBel NAst NHpl NPri SPoG SRms WCot WHil WTor
	- 'Goldrausch'PBR	CRos EBee ECtt EHrv ELan EPfP LEdu LLHF LRHS MBel MRav NBir NEgg NGdn NRHS SCob SGbt SRms SWvt WFar
	- 'Gruppenstolz'	CAni SAko
	- 'H. Seibert'	CAni MArl
	- 'Harry'	CAni
	- 'Highland White Dream'PBR	CRos IKil LRHS NRHS
	- 'Horace Read' (d)	CAni CDor CElw CMea ECtt NBir SWvt
	- 'Ice Star'	CRos EBee LRHS NRHS
	- 'Jennifer Read'	CAni
§	- 'John Murray' (d)	CAni NBir NWsh WFar
	- 'Lacrosse'	CRos EBee EPfP LRHS NLar NRHS SCob WCAu WFar
	- 'Laspider'	CRos EBee GBee LRHS NRHS SRot
	- 'Little Miss Muffet'	CSBt CWGN EBee ECtt LEdu LLHF LRHS MBNS MPie NRHS
	- 'Little Princess'	see *L.* × *superbum* 'Silberprinzesschen'
	- 'Luna'	WHlf
	- 'Majestic'	CAni
	- 'Manhattan'	CAni CDor EBee EWes GBin
	- 'Margaretchen'	CAni
	- 'Marion Bilsland'	CAni NChi WBrk
	- 'Mayfield Giant'	CAni
	- 'Mount Everest'	see *L.* × *superbum* 'Everest'
	- 'Northern Lights'	IKil
	- 'Octopus'	CAni
	- 'Old Court'	see *L.* × *superbum* 'Beauté Nivelloise'
	- 'Paladin'PBR	CBod ECtt GBin
	- 'Phyllis Smith'	CAni CRos EBee ECtt ELan ELon GBin GWyn LSRN MAvo MHer MPie MRav NCGa NGdn SCob SMad WBrk WCAu WCot WMoo
	- 'Polaris'	CRos EBee LRHS NBre NRHS WMoo XLum
	- 'Rags and Tatters'	CAni ECtt EWes
	- 'Real Dream'PBR	CRos EBee ELan EMor LCro LOPS LRHS MTis NEoE NRHS SCob WFar
	- 'Real Galaxy'PBR	CRos ELan LBuc LRHS MTis NEoE NRHS SPoG
	- 'Real Glory'	CRos ECtt ELan ILea LRHS MHol MTis NEoE NHpl NRHS SCob WCAu WFar
	- 'Real Neat'	CAby CRos EBee ECtt ELan EMor LRHS MAsh MHol MTis NEoE NHpl NRHS SCob SHar STPC WAvo
	- 'Schwabengruss'	CAni
	- 'Shaggy'	see *L.* × *superbum* 'Beauté Nivelloise'
	- 'Shapcott Gossamer'	CAby CAni CBod CPou EBee ECtt EMor MTis NGBl SCob SPoG SRms WCot
	- 'Shapcott Ruffles'	CAni CBod EBee ECtt EMor EUJe MTis WCot
	- 'Shapcott Summer Clouds'	CAni CBod CDor CElw CKno EBee ECtt ELon GAbr GMaP MBNS MBel MHol MSCN MTis SPoG WCot
§	- 'Silberprinzesschen'	CAni CRos CSBt EBou ELon EMor EPfP GMaP GWyn LRHS NRHS SPlb SRms WMoo XLum
	- 'Snehurka'	CAni CRos LLHF LRHS NRHS WCot WHoo
	- 'Snow Lady'	EAJP EBee EPfP GWyn LPot LRHS NPer NRHS SRms WFar
	- 'Snow Queen'	GWyn
	- 'Snowbound'	CRos NEoE NRHS
	- 'Snowcap'	CBod CRos ECha EPfP LRHS MBel MRav NRHS SPer SWvt WCAu WGwG
	- 'Snowdrift'	CAni CRos LRHS MWat NBre NLar NRHS WBrk WCot WFar WMoo
§	- 'Sonnenschein'	CAby CBod CDor CRos EBee ECha ECtt ELan EPfP GMaP GQue LRHS LSRN MArl MHol MRav NBir NEgg NGdn NRHS NWsh SPer SRms WCAu
	- 'Starburst' (d)	CRos EBee ELan LRHS NRHS SRms WFar
	- 'Stina'	EBee GBin XLum
	- 'Summer Snowball'	see *L.* × *superbum* 'John Murray'
	- 'Sunny Side Up'PBR	CBod CWCL EBee ECtt EWes LRHS NAln NLar NRHS SCob SRot WAul WFar
	- SUNSHINE	see *L.* × *superbum* 'Sonnenschein'
	- 'T.E. Killin' (d) ♀H4	CBod CRos EBee ECha ECtt ELan EPau EPfP GBin LCro LRHS MRav MWat NRHS SPtp WCAu WFar WHoo
	- 'Victorian Secret'PBR	CBod CRos EBee ECtt GBin LBuc LRHS MBel MNrw NEoE NRHS SCob SMad WCot WHil WHlf WHoo WTor
	- 'White Iceberg' (d)	CAni
	- WHITE MOUNTAIN ('Gfleuwhmtn'PBR)	CRos LRHS NRHS
	- 'Wirral Pride'	CAni CRos CSam EPfP WBrk
	- 'Wirral Supreme' (d) ♀H5	CAni CBcs CRos CSBt CTsd EBee ELan EPfP GMaP ILea IPot LCro LOPS LRHS MNrw MRav NBir NEgg NLar NRHS SCob SPer SRms SWvt WBrk WCAu WFar WJam WMoo WSpi
	'Tizi-n-Test'	see *Rhodanthemum catananche* 'Tizi-n-Test'
§	***vulgare***	CBod CHab CMac CWld EBou ENfk EPfP EShb GAbr GBin GJos GQue LCro LOPS MHer MMuc MNHC NGrd NMir SEND SPhx WCAu WFar WHer WMoo WOut WSFF WShi XLum XSen
	- 'Filigran'	CRos LRHS NHic NRHS WFar
	- 'Lollipop' **new**	GWyn
§	- 'Maikönigin'	CRos GWyn LCro LOPS LRHS NRHS XLum
	- MAY QUEEN	see *L. vulgare* 'Maikönigin'
	- 'Sunny'	CBre
	'White Knight'	CRos LRHS NRHS

Leucocoryne (*Alliaceae*)

'Andes' ♀H3 — CCCN GKev SDeJ
'Dione' — GKev SDeJ
ixioides 'Blue Ocean' — GKev SDeJ
'Spotlight' — GKev
'Sunny Stripe' — GKev
'White Dream' — GKev SDeJ

Leucogenes (*Asteraceae*)

grandiceps — WAbe
leontopodium — EPot ITim NRHS NSla WAbe
tarahaoa — EPot WAbe

Leucogenes × *Raoulia* see × *Leucoraoulia*

Leucojum ✿ (*Amaryllidaceae*)

aestivum — CAby CBcs CDor CTri EAJP EBee GKev LAma LRHS MCot MMuc NBir NChi NEgg NHol NRHS SDeJ SEND SRms WCFE WCot WFar WHil WShi
- 'Gravetye Giant' ♀H7 — Widely available
- var. ***pulchellum*** — CElw
autumnale — see *Acis autumnalis*
longifolium — see *Acis longifolia*
roseum — see *Acis rosea*
tingitanum — see *Acis tingitana*
trichophyllum — see *Acis trichophylla*
valentinum — see *Acis valentina*
vernum ♀H5 — Widely available
- var. ***vagneri*** — ECha SDys WSHC

Leucophysalis (*Solanaceae*)

sinense BWJ 8093 — WCru

Leucophyta (*Asteraceae*)

§ ***brownii*** — CCht

Leucopogon (*Ericaceae*)

§ ***colensoi*** — MGil WThu
ericoides — GKev
§ ***fraseri*** — WThu

× *Leucoraoulia* (*Asteraceae*)

§ ***loganii*** — WAbe

Leucosceptrum (*Lamiaceae*)

canum — CExl SBrt
- GWJ 9424 — WCru
japonicum B&SWJ 10804 — WCru
- B&SWJ 10981 — WCru
stellipilum var. ***formosanum*** — IMou
- - B&SWJ 1926 — WCru
- - RWJ 9907 — SBrt WCru
- var. ***tosaense*** B&SWJ 8892 — WCru

Leucospermum (*Proteaceae*)

(Carnival Series) 'Carnival Copper' — CBcs CCCN CKel
- 'Carnival Orange' **new** — CKel
- 'Carnival Red' — CCCN CKel
- 'Carnival Yellow' **new** — CKel
conocarpodendron 'Mardi Gras Ribbons' — CKel
cordifolium — CCCN CKel CPbh
- 'Vlam' **new** — CKel
- 'White Gold' **new** — CKel
erubescens 'Mardi Gras Tricolor' **new** — CKel
glabrum — SPlb
heterophyllum 'Hullabaloo' **new** — CKel
'High Gold' **new** — CKel
'Rigoletto' **new** — CKel
'Scarlet Ribbon' — CCCN
'So Cheerful' **new** — CKel
'So Exquisite' **new** — CKel
'Soleil' **new** — CKel
'Succession' — CCCN CKel
'Tango' — CKel CPbh
'Vulkano' — CCCN CKel

Leucostegia (*Davalliaceae*)

immersa PAB 7836 — LEdu WPGP

Leucothoe (*Ericaceae*)

axillaris — MAsh
- 'Curly Red'PBR — CBod CKel CMac CRos EBee ELan EPfP LRHS MAsh MGos MJak MPkF NLar NRHS SGol SLim SLon SPoG SWvt WFar
- TWISTING RED ('Opstal20'PBR) — MBlu SLim
CARINELLA ('Zebekot') — CRos LRHS NLar NRHS SPoG
davisiae — NLar
§ ***fontanesiana*** — CMac GKev
- 'Makijaz'PBR (v) — EPfP NLar SPoG
- 'Rainbow' (v) — CBcs CBod CDul CKel CMac CRos EBee EPfP LRHS MGos NLar SGbt SGol SLim SPer SPoG SRms SSta SWvt WFar WMoo
- 'Rollissonii' ♀H6 — MRav SRms
- WHITEWATER ('Howw'PBR) (v) — CMac CSBt MPkF NLar
keiskei BURNING LOVE ('Opstal50'PBR) — NLar
- HALLOWEEN ('Opstal16'PBR) — EBee
- 'Royal Ruby' — MAsh MGos MJak MPkF NEgg NLar SGbt SGol SPoG WFar WMoo
'Little Flames'PBR — SPad
LOVITA ('Zebonard') — MRav NLar SCoo
RED LIPS ('Lipsbolwi'PBR) — EPfP
SCARLETTA ('Zeblid') ♀H6 — CBcs CBod CDul CKel CMac CRos CSBt CTri EPfP LCro LOPS LRHS MAsh MGos MJak MRav NEgg NHol NLar NRHS NWad SGol SLim SPad SPer SPoG SWvt WFar
walteri — see *L. fontanesiana*

Leuzea (*Asteraceae*)

centaureoides — see *Rhaponticum centaureoides*
rhaponticoides — see *Rhaponticum exaltatum*

Levisticum (*Apiaceae*)

officinale — CAgr CBod CCBP CHby CLau EBou EMor ENfk EPfP EWhm GAbr GPoy LEdu MHer MMuc MNHC NGrd NPri SEND SPlb SRms SVic WHer

Lewisia ✿ (*Portulacaceae*)

sp. — NAln
'Archangel' — EPot NRya
Ashwood Carousel hybrids — CPBP CTri MAsh NHar NRya
Birch strain — CBcs ELan
brachycalyx ♀H4 — EWes GCrg LLHF

Brynhyfryd hybrids pink-flowered	GKev NAln
- white-flowered	GKev
- yellow-flowered	GKev
cantelovii	MAsh
columbiana	MAsh NHpl
- 'Alba'	EPot GKev NRHS NRya NSla
- 'Rosea'	GKev MAsh
- subsp. ***rupicola***	MAsh NSla
- subsp. ***wallowensis***	MAsh NSla
congdonii	MAsh
cotyledon ♀H4	CRos CWCL GKev GMaP ITim LLHF LRHS NHpl NRHS NSla SIgm SSim WIce
- f. ***alba***	CWCL
- - 'Snowstorm'	LLHF
- 'Ashwood Ruby'	MAsh
- Ashwood strain	CRos EPfP EWes LRHS MAsh NHpl SRms WOld
- 'Brannan Bar'	MAsh
- 'Bright Eyes'	GKev
- var. ***cotyledon***	LLHF
- double-flowered (d)	GKev NAln
- ELISE MIXED	MHol
- var. ***heckneri***	MAsh
- var. ***howellii***	LLHF
- hybrid	GKev NRya SPoG
- 'John's Special'	MAsh
- magenta-flowered	CWCL
- orange-flowered	CWCL
§ - 'Regenbogen'	LRHS MHer MHol
- rose-pink-flowered	CWCL
- salmon-flowered	CWCL
- Sunset Group ♀H4	ELon EPfP GCrg NHpl NLar WRHF
- 'White Splendour'	MAsh
'George Henley'	CPBP EPot EWes LLHF MAsh NRya WAbe
glandulosa	NSla
leeana	MAsh
'Little Mango'	EDAr GCrg NHar NRya NSla SSim WRHF
'Little Peach'	CWCL ECtt EDAr EPot GBin MAsh NHpl NRya NSla SSim
'Little Plum'	CMea ECtt EDAr GBin GCrg GEdr ITim LRHS MAsh NHpl NLar NRya NSla SSim WHoo WThu
LITTLE TUTTI FRUTTI MIXED	CSma
longipetala 'Little Raspberry'	EDAr NSla
§ ***nevadensis***	CRos EBou EPot GKev LRHS NRHS NRya SIgm WThu
I - 'Alba'	GKev NHpl
- ***bernardina***	see *L. nevadensis*
- 'Rosea'	NHpl NRya NSla
oppositifolia	LLHF MAsh
- 'Richeyi'	EPot
'Pinkie'	CPBP GCrg MAsh NHpl
pygmaea	CRos EBou EWes GEdr GKev ITim LRHS MAsh MHer NBir NRHS NRya NSla SPlb XLum
- carmine-flowered	GKev
pygmaea* × *rediviva	LLHF
Rainbow mixture	see *L. cotyledon* 'Regenbogen'
'Rawreth'	LLHF
rediviva	EPot GKev LLHF MAsh NHpl
- dark pink-flowered	GKev
- subsp. ***minor***	CPBP
- white-flowered	GKev
serrata	MAsh
'Trevosia'	MAsh
tweedyi ♀H4	CPBP CRos EPot GKev LRHS MAsh NHar NHpl NRHS NRya SPlb WAbe
- 'Alba'	WAbe
- 'Elliott's Variety'	MAsh
- 'Rosea'	CRos EPot LRHS MAsh NHar NRHS WAbe

Leycesteria (*Caprifoliaceae*)

crocothyrsos	CBcs EBee ILea MGil NLar NWad SPoG WFar
formosa	Widely available
- from Longstock	SLon
- 'Gold Leaf'	CBod CMac CPla GAbr MGil MHer SHar SPad WBor WFar WPtf
- GOLDEN LANTERNS ('Notbruce'PBR) ♀H4	CAby CBcs CKel CRos CSBt EBee ELan EPfP LBuc LRHS LSRN MAsh MGos MMrt MMuc MSwo NEgg NLar NRHS SCoo SLim SPer SPoG SRms SWvt WFar WMoo
- 'Golden Pheasant' (v)	EHoe
- 'Jealousy' **new**	EUJe
- 'Lydia'	LRHS
- 'Purple Rain'	CRos EBee EPfP EWes LRHS MAsh MGos NLar NRHS

Leymus (*Poaceae*)

from the Falkland Islands	ELon EPPr
§ ***arenarius***	CAby CBod CElw CKno CSpe ECha EHoe ELan EShb GBin GMaP LRHS MMuc NBid NBro SEND SGbt SGol SPlb SRms WFar WMoo XLum XSen
- 'Blue Dune' **new**	EBee
cinereus	WCot
hispidus	see *Elymus hispidus*

Lhotzkya see *Calytrix*

Liatris (*Asteraceae*)

aspera	SPhx
cylindracea	SPhx
elegans	GKev SPlb
ligulistylis	NDov SPhx
mucronata	NLar
pycnostachya	CSpe NLar SAko SRms
scariosa	SPhx
- 'Alba'	CBcs CBod LSun SAko SPhx
§ ***spicata***	Widely available
- 'Alba'	CBod CMac CSBt EAJP ECha ELan EMor EPfP GBin GKev LSRN MSCN NAln NLar NPri SCob SPer SPlb XLum
- ***callilepis***	see *L. spicata*
- 'Floristan Violett'	CMea CRos CTri EBee EPfP GMaP LRHS MHer MHol MJak MWat NEgg NLar NRHS SCob SCoo SPlb SPoG SWvt WFar WGwG WMoo WWtn XLum
- 'Floristan Weiss'	CExl CRos CTri EPPr EPfP ERCP GMaP LRHS MBel MHer MJak MRav NLar NRHS SDeJ SPoG SRms SWvt WFar WGwG WMoo WWtn
- GOBLIN	see *L. spicata* 'Kobold'
§ - 'Kobold'	CMac CRos EBee EBou ELan EMor EPfP GBin LCro LRHS LSun MBel MRav NBir NEgg NLar NRHS SGbt SPad SRms STPC SWvt WCAu WFar WMoo XLum
squarrosa	SPhx

Libanotis see *Seseli*

montana	see *Seseli libanotis*

Libertia ✿ (*Iridaceae*)

'Amazing Grace'	EBee GCal
breunioides	see *L. cranwelliae*
chilensis [H3]	Widely available
- Elegans Group	CExl EBee WCru
§ - Formosa Group	CBcs CBod CBro CCBP CElw CExl CRos CTri EBee ELan GCal GKev LRHS MMuc NAln NChi NRHS NSti SArc SCob SPer SPtp SRms SWvt WHer
- Procera Group	CAby CSpe EBee EPfP GBin GCal GLog LEdu LRHS SMad SPlb SPtp WPGP WSHC
§ ***cranwelliae***	CExl WPGP
falcata new	IFro
formosa	see *L. chilensis* Formosa Group
grandiflora ambig.	CCht MMrt NRHS WHlf
'Grasshopper'	CAby GBin
ixioides	CBcs ECha ILea LEdu LRHS MMuc SPtp WPGP
- 'Goldfinger' (v)	CBcs CBct CBor CExl CKno CMac CRos CWCL EBee ELan EMor EPfP EShb LEdu LLWG LRHS MHol MJak MPkF NHol NRHS SLon SPoG SWvt WCot WFar WGrn WHer
- 'Highlander'	LRHS MHol
- 'Taupo Blaze'	CBod CBor CMac EBee EPfP LRHS MRav SLon SPoG
- 'Taupo Sunset'[PBR]	CBcs CCCN CExl CRos EPfP LRHS MBNS MPkF SWvt
- 'Tricolor'	CSde ECha GEdr MRav
'Nelson Dwarf'	EBee GCal
paniculata	CExl EBee
peregrinans	CAbb CBod CExl CKno CRos CSpe EBee ECha EHoe ELan GCal GKev IFro ILea LEdu LRHS MMuc MRav NAln NBir NRHS SEND SPer SPtp SRkn SWvt WPGP
- 'Gold Leaf'	CBcs CCCN CTri CTsd EBee ELan EPfP LRHS SMad SWvt WFar
- 'Gold Stripe'	CPla ELan SWvt
pulchella ambig. blue-flowered	GKev
pulchella misapplied	CRos LRHS NRHS
sessiliflora	CExl NBir
- 'Ballyrogan Blue'	EBee GKev
- 'Caerulescens'	CBcs CCCN CCht CExl CMac CPla EPfP LRHS NBir NCGa NGBl SMad SPer SPtp WMoo
'Sunset Strain'	CKel CPla EMor LRHS WFar
tricocca misapplied	see *L. umbellata*
§ ***umbellata*** HCM 98.089	WPGP

Libocedrus (*Cupressaceae*)

chilensis	see *Austrocedrus chilensis*
decurrens	see *Calocedrus decurrens*
plumosa	CBrP

Libonia see *Justicia*

Ligularia (*Asteraceae*)

amplexicaulis	GCal
aff. ***atkinsonii*** WJC 13663	WCru
'BBQ Banana' new	CBod WWtn
'Bottle Rocket'[PBR]	CBor NLar
'Britt Marie Crawford'[PBR] [H6]	Widely available
clivorum	see *L. dentata*
§ ***dentata***	CPla ECtt NBro SRms
- 'Dark Beauty'	MBNS
- 'Desdemona'	Widely available
- 'Enkelrig'	EBee
- 'Franz Feldweber'	EBee
- 'Midnight Lady'	ELan EMor GPSL GWyn MHol NLar
- 'Orange Princess'	NPer
- 'Osiris Café Dark'[PBR]	SCob
- 'Osiris Fantaisie' (v)	CDor CExl EBee ECtt EPfP EWes GWyn ILea LLHF MAvo MBel MHol MNrw NLar NSti SPoG WCot WFar WPnP
- 'Othello'	CBod CRos EBee ECtt EPfP GAbr LRHS NBid NEgg NGdn NLar NRHS NWad SCob SWvt WCAu
- 'Sommergold'	ECha WFar
- 'Twilight'	CBct ECtt MBNS
§ ***fischeri***	ECha
- B&SWJ 2570	WCru
- B&SWJ 4381	WCru
- B&SWJ 4478	WCru
- B&SWJ 5653	WCru
- B&SWJ 8802	WCru
- var. ***megalorhiza*** 'Cheju Charmer'	ELon WCru
'Franz Marc'	GCal
'Garden Confetti'	ECtt
'Gold Torch'	ECtt NLar
§ 'Gregynog Gold' [H6]	CRos ECha ECtt GBee GMaP LRHS MRav NBro NLar NRHS
× ***hessei***	CRos GMaP LRHS MMuc NRHS WWtn
hodgsonii	EPPr MRav
- B&SWJ 10855	WCru
intermedia B&SWJ 606a	WCru WSHC
japonica	CDor CRos ECha LEdu LRHS NLar NRHS WWtn
- B&SWJ 2883	WCru
- 'Rising Sun'	CExl NLar WCot WCru
'Laternchen'[PBR]	ECtt NLar SAko
'Little Rocket'[PBR]	CBct CBod CExl EBee ECtt ELon EPfP MBNS MWts NBro NGdn NLar NRHS SCob SPoG WFar WHil
'Osiris Café Noir'	ECtt EUJe ILea NLar SCob SMad WFar WMoo
'Osiris Pistache' (v)	EBee ECtt
× ***palmatiloba***	see *L.* × *yoshizoeana* 'Palmatiloba'
§ ***przewalskii***	Widely available
- SSSE 176	WCot
- 'Dragon Wings'	EWTr GBin MAsh MHol NEoE NLar SCob
- 'Dragon's Breath'	ECtt EUJe GBin MAsh MHol SCob
'Savill Spire'	LSvl
sibirica	CSam MMuc NLar WArt WMoo
- B&SWJ 4383	WCru
- B&SWJ 5841	WCru
- var. ***speciosa***	see *L. fischeri*
smithii	see *Senecio smithii*
speciosa	see *L. fischeri*
stenocephala	EBee EMor NBro NLar SCob WWtn XLum
'Sungold'	CMac CRos CSam ECtt LRHS NGdn NRHS
tangutica	see *Sinacalia tangutica*
'The Rocket' [H6]	Widely available
tussilaginea	see *Farfugium japonicum*

- 'Aureo-maculata' — see *Farfugium japonicum* 'Aureomaculatum'
veitchiana — CBod CSam GCal WWtn
vorobievii — CElw GCal NLar
'Weihenstephan' — CRos GCal LRHS NRHS
wilsoniana — CRos GAbr LRHS MMuc MRav NRHS SEND WFar WWtn
- B&SWJ 14195 — WCru
§ × ***yoshizoeana*** 'Palmatiloba' — CRos ELan ELon EWes GCal LRHS MRav NRHS SPhx WFar WWtn
'Zepter' ♀H6 — CAby CBct CBod CRos ECtt EPfP EShb GAbr GBee GCal GQue LRHS MMuc NEgg NHol NLar NRHS NWad WCot WWtn

Ligusticum (*Apiaceae*)

hultenii — WCot
lucidum — EPfP LEdu MAvo NSti SPhx SPtp WBor WCot WPGP
- subsp. ***lucidum*** — CSpe
mutellina — LPla
porteri — EBee
§ ***scoticum*** — CPla EBee EMor EWes GBin GLog GPoy LEdu LRHS MAvo MBel MHer SPhx SPtp SRms WFar WJek WOut WPGP WPtf
- variegated (v) — LEdu WCot

Ligustrum ✿ (*Oleaceae*)

B&L 12261 — WPGP
§ ***delavayanum*** — CKel EBtc ELan EShb GKev SGol STrG WCFE WPGP
- B&L 12083 — CExl
ibota — EBtc NLar
- MUSLI ('Muster'PBR) (v) — LRHS SPoG WCot
ionandrum — see *L. delavayanum*
japonicum — CLnd CRos EBar ECrN LMaj LPra LRHS LSRN SEND SGol SPer
- B&SWJ 14604 **new** — WCru
I - 'Aureum' — CKel EMOT
- 'Coriaceum' — see *L. japonicum* 'Rotundifolium'
- GREEN CENTURY ('Melgreen'PBR) — LRHS WMat
- 'Korea Dwarf' — NLar
§ - 'Rotundifolium' — CBcs CDul CExl CHll CKel CRos EBee ELan EPfP LRHS MAsh MRav NLar SPer SPoG WCFE WCot WFar
§ - 'Silver Star' (v) — NLar SGol
§ - 'Texanum' — ECrN EPfP LMaj LRHS NLar SArc WCFE
- 'Texanum Argenteum' — see *L. japonicum* 'Silver Star'
- 'Variegatum' (v) — SGol
lucidum ♀H5 — CCVT CDul CSBt CSde CTri ELan EUJe EWTr GCal IDee LPra MRav NLar NWea SArc SCob SEND SGol SPer SWvt WFar
- Guiz 296 — CExl
- 'Curly Wurly' — CRos LRHS NRHS
- 'Excelsum Superbum' (v) ♀H5 — CCVT CLnd CMac CRos EBar ECrN ELan EPfP LMaj LPra LRHS LSRN MGos SGol SPoG WCot
- 'Golden Wax' — CJun MRav
- 'Tricolor' (v) ♀H5 — CRos ELan EPfP LRHS MAsh MGos SMad SPer SWvt
obtusifolium var. ***regelianum*** — MMuc NLar
ovalifolium — Widely available
§ - 'Argenteum' (v) — CBcs CCVT CDul CMac CTri ECrN EHoe ELan EMOT EShb MMuc MRav NEgg SEND SGol SLim SPer SPoG SWvt WFar
- 'Aureomarginatum' — see *L. ovalifolium* 'Aureum'
§ - 'Aureum' (v) ♀H5 — Widely available
- 'Lemon and Lime' (v) — CBod EBee EHoe ELan LSRN MAsh MThu SCob SCoo SRms SWvt WCot
- 'Variegatum' — see *L. ovalifolium* 'Argenteum'
- 'Vicaryi' — CDul ELan EPfP GBin MGos NEoE NWad SCob SGol SPer WFar
quihoui — CKel CRos CTri EBee ELan EPfP IDee LRHS MBlu NLar SEND SLon SPer SPoG
sempervirens — EPfP
sinense — CMCN MRav
- 'Multiflorum' — WFar
- var. ***myrianthum*** **new** — SPtp
- 'Sunshine' — CRos LRHS NRHS SPoG
- 'Variegatum' (v) — MRav SPer
strongylophyllum — CExl
texanum — see *L. japonicum* 'Texanum'
tschonoskii — MBlu
undulatum 'Lemon Lime and Clippers' — CKel CRos EShb LRHS MBNS NLar NRHS SCob SPoG WMoo
vulgare — CArg CBcs CCVT CDul CHab CKel CMac CPer CTri ECrN ELan EPfP LBuc MMuc MSwo NWea SCob SEND SEWo SWvt WMat WMou WSFF WTSh
- 'Lodense' — EBtc

Lilium ✿ (*Liliaceae*)

'Abbeville's Pride' (Ia/b) — SDeJ
'Acapulco' (VII-/d) — SDeJ
§ 'Acoustic' (Colour Carpet Series) (VIIa/b-c) — CRos LRHS NRHS
'Adonis' (Ic/d) — GEdr
African Queen Group (VI-/a) ♀H6 — ERCP LAma LCro LOPS SCoo SRms
- 'African Queen' (VIb-c/a) — MCri SDeJ
'Altari' (VIIIa-b/b) — SDeJ
amabile var. ***luteum*** (IXc/d) — MCri
'Ambergate' — SDeJ
'Anastasia' (VIIIb-c/b-d) — GKev LAma LCro LOPS SDeJ
'Annemarie's Dream' (Ia/c) — SDeJ
'Apeldoorn' (Ia/b) — MCri
APOLLO (Ia/b) — see *L.* 'Blizzard'
'Apricot Fudge' (VIIIa/b) **new** — GKev
'Arabian Knight' (IIc/d) — GKev LAma SDeJ WFar
'Arena' (VIIa/b) — SCoo
auratum 'Gold Band' — see *L. auratum* var. *platyphyllum*
§ - var. ***platyphyllum*** (IXb/c) — MCri SDeJ
- - B&SWJ 4824 — WCru
- - B&SWJ 5041 — WCru
- var. ***virginale*** (IXb/c) — GKev MCri SDeJ
Backhouse hybrids — see *L.* × *dalhansonii* Backhouse Group
'Baferrari' (VIIa/b) — SDeJ
'Bamako' (VIIa-b/b) — SDeJ
'Barbara North' (Ic/d) — GEdr
'Barbaresco' (VIIa-b/b) — SCoo
'Beijing Moon' (VIb-c/a) — SDeJ
'Belgrado'PBR (VIIa/b-c) — SDeJ
'Belladonna'PBR (VIIIb-a/b) — SDeJ
'Belle Epoque' (VIIb/b-c) — SDeJ
Bellingham Group (IVc/d) — GEdr
'Bergamo' (VIIb/b) — SCoo SDeJ
'Beverly Dreams' (VIIIa/a) — ERCP
'Beverly Hills'PBR (VIIIa-b/b) — SDeJ

	Name	Suppliers
	'Black Beauty' (VIIIb-c/d)	CCBP CTsd GKev LAma LCro LOPS MCri NHpl SDeJ
	'Black Dragon'	see *L. leucanthum* var. *centifolium* 'Black Dragon'
§	'Blizzard' (Ia/b)	NBir SDeJ
	'Boogie Woogie' (VIIIa-b/b)	SDeJ
	'Bracelet' (VIIIa-b/b)	SDeJ
	'Brasil'PBR (Ia/b)	GKev
	BRASILIA ('Zora') (VIIa/b-c)	SDeJ
	BRIGHT PIXIE ('Ceb Bright') (Ia/b)	SDeJ
	'Bright Star' (VIb-c/c)	LAma MCri
	'Broken Heart' (VIIb-a/c)	SDeJ
	brownii (IXb-c/a)	GKev
	bulbiferum var. ***croceum*** (IXa/b)	XEll
	'Butter Pixie'PBR (Ia/b)	NBir SDeJ
§	***canadense*** (IXc/a)	GEdr LAma WCot WCru XEll
	- var. ***flavum***	see *L. canadense*
	'Cancun' (Ia/b-c)	SDeJ
	candidum (IXb/a)	CAvo CBcs CTca CTri ECha EHrv ELan EPot ERCP GKev LAma LSun MWat SDeJ SRms WSpi WWFP
	'Candy Blossom' (Ia/b)	SDeJ
	'Casa Blanca' (VIIb/b-c) ♀H6	CAvo CBro GKev LAma LCro LOPS NAln NBir SCoo SDeJ
	'Cecil' (VIIIa/b)	SDeJ
	cernuum (IXc/d)	LAma SDeJ
*	- 'Album'	SDeJ
	'Chameleon' (II)	CAvo LAma
	'Chill Out' (VIIa/b)	LCro LOPS
§	'Chocolate Canary' (Ic/-)	SDeJ
	Citronella Group (Ic/d)	NHpl SDeJ
	'Claude Shride' (IIc/d)	CAvo CBro GEdr GKev IPot LAma LRHS NHpl SDeJ
	'Cocktail Twins' (Ia/b)	SDeJ
§	'Coldplay' (Colour Carpet Series) (VIIa-b)	CRos LBuc LRHS NRHS
	columbianum (IXc/d) B&SWJ 9564	WCru
	'Con Amore' (VIIb/b)	SCoo
	'Conca d'Or'PBR (VIIIb/b)	SDeJ
	'Connecticut King' (Ia/b)	MCri
	'Creation' (VIa/b)	SDeJ
	'Crimson Pixie' (Ia/b)	CRos LCro LOPS NRHS SDeJ
	× ***dalhansonii*** (IIc/d)	CAby CWld ERCP SDeJ
§	- Backhouse Group (IIc/d)	WFar
	- 'Guinea Gold' (II)	GKev IPot LAma
	- 'Mrs R.O. Backhouse' (IIc/d)	GEdr SDeJ
	- 'Sutton Court' (II)	GEdr
	- Terrace City Group (II)	GKev LAma SDeJ
	'Dark Romance' (Romance Series) (VIIb/b)	CRos LRHS NRHS
	dauricum var. ***alpinum*** (IXa/b)	MCri
	- f. ***rebunense*** (IXa/b) **new**	CBor
	davidii (IXc/d)	CExl LAma MCri NHpl SDeJ WCru
§	- var. ***willmottiae*** (IXc/d)	MCri WCru
	DAZZLER ('Maru') (Colour Carpet Series) (VIIa/b)	LBuc LRHS
	'Debby' (VIIIa-b/b-c)	SDeJ
	'Delicate Joy' (Ia/b)	CRos
	'Dimension' (Ia/b-c)	LAma LCro LOPS
	'Disco' (Ia)	SDeJ
	distichum B&SWJ 794 (IXb-c/d)	WCru
	- B&SWJ 4465	WCru
	'Dizzy' (VIIa-b/b-c)	CBod CTsd SDeJ
	duchartrei (IXc/d)	CAby CExl WCru
	'Electric Yellow'	see *L.* 'Yellow Electric'
	'Elgrado' (Ia/b)	SDeJ
	'Elodie'PBR (Ia/b)	CAvo LAma SDeJ
	'Elusive' (VIIIb/b-d)	GKev SDeJ
	'Enchantment' (Ia/b)	SDeJ
	'Eros' (Ic/d)	GEdr
	'Eurydike' (Ic/d)	GEdr
	'Expression' (VII)	SDeJ
	'Eyeliner'PBR (VIIIa/b)	LAma
	fargesii (IXc/d)	CExl
	'Fata Morgana' (Ia/b) ♀H6	LAma SCoo SDeJ
	'Fire King' (Ib/d)	SCoo SDeJ SRms
	'Fopapo' (Ia-b/c)	SDeJ
	'Forever Marjon' (Ib-a/b-c)	GKev
	'Forever Susan' (Ia/b)	GKev IPot SDeJ
	formosanum (IXb/a)	MCot
	- short, from high altitude RWJ 10005 (IXb/a)	WCru
	- var. ***formosanum*** B&SWJ 1589 (IXb/a)	WCru
	- var. ***pricei*** (IXb/a)	CAby CRos EAJP EBou EDAr ELan GBin GEdr LEdu LRHS MHer MTin NRHS SRms WIce
	- - 'Snow Queen' (Vb/a)	EShb SDeJ
	'Foxtrot' (Ia/b)	SDeJ
	'Friso' (VIIIb/b)	GKev SDeJ
	'Fusion' **new**	NHpl
	'Garden Party' (VIIb/b) ♀H6	GKev SDeJ
	'Gaybird' (IIc/c)	GKev
	'Gironde' (Ia/b)	SDeJ
	GLIMMER	see *L.* 'Acoustic'
	'Gold Band' (VII)	SDeJ
	'Gold Class' (VIIIb-a/b-c)	SDeJ
	'Golden Matrix' (Ia/b) **new**	CBod
	Golden Splendor Group (VIb-c/a) ♀H6	GKev LAma MCri SCoo SDeJ
	'Golden Stone' (VIIIa-b/b)	SDeJ
	'Grand Cru' (Ia/b)	SDeJ
	'Hannah North' (Ic/d)	GEdr
	hansonii (IXb-c/d)	CWCL ECha GBin GKev LAma MCri NHpl SDeJ
	- B&SWJ 4309	WCru
	- B&SWJ 4756 from Aomori, Japan	WCru
	- B&SWJ 8506	WCru
	- B&SWJ 8528	WCru
	'Happy Kiss' (Ia/b-c) **new**	GKev
	'Happy Sunrise' (Ia/b-c) **new**	GKev
	henryi (IXc/d) ♀H6	CAvo EBee GKev LAma MCri SCob SDeJ WCru
	'Hit Parade' (VII)	SDeJ
	'Honeymoon' (VIIIa-b/b)	SDeJ
	'Hotline' (VIIa/b)	LCro LOPS
	humboldtii (IXc/d)	CWCL
	'Ice Pixie' (Ia/b)	SDeJ
	'Inuvik' (Ia/b)	GKev SDeJ
	'Ivory Pixie' (Ia/b)	NRHS SDeJ
	'João Pessoa' (Ia/b-c)	SDeJ
	'Jo's Choice' (VIa-b/a)	SDeJ
	'Josephine' (VIIa/b)	GKev SDeJ
	'Joy'	see *L.* 'Le Rêve'
	'Karen North' (Ic/d)	GEdr
	'King Pete' (Ib/b-c)	SDeJ
	'Kingdom'PBR (VIIIa/b-c)	SDeJ
	'Kushi Maya'PBR (VIIIc/b-c)	GKev IPot SDeJ
	'Lady Alice' (VI-/d)	GKev SDeJ
	'Lake Tulare' (IVc/c-d)	GEdr
§	***lancifolium*** (IXc/d)	EPot GBin XLum
	- B&SWJ 4352	WCru

	- var. ***flaviflorum*** (IXc/d)	MCri SDeJ
	- 'Flore Pleno' (IXc/d)	CRos EPPr GCal GKev GQue LRHS MHer NBir NRHS SDeJ WCot WCru WHil XLum
	- var. ***fortunei*** (IXc/d)	EPPr GCal
	- - B&SWJ 539	WCru
	- pink-flowered	SDeJ
	- 'Splendens' (IXc/d)	CAvo GKev MCri NBid SDeJ WCot
	'Landini'PBR (Ia/b)	CAby SDeJ
	'Lankon' (VIIIc/a)	CAby ERCP
	lankongense (IXc/d)	CBor CWCL EPot GBin GGGa GKev LAma WCru
	- BWJ 7554	WCru
	- BWJ 7691	WCru
	'Late Morning' (VIIIb-c)	SDeJ
	'Latvia' (Ia/b)	MCri SDeJ
	'Lazy Lady'	see *L.* 'Chocolate Canary'
§	'Le Rêve' (VIIa-b/b)	SDeJ
	leichtlinii (IXc/d)	CAvo CCBP EPot GBin IMou LLHF MCri NHpl SDeJ
	- 'Iwashimiza' (IXc/d)	MCri
	'Lemon Pixie' (Ia/b)	NRHS
	'Leslie Woodriff' (VIIIb-c/d)	IPot
	leucanthum	MCri WCru
	var. ***centifolium*** (IXb-c/a)	
	- - BWJ 8130	WCru
§	- - - 'Black Dragon' (IXb-c/a)	MCri
	'Levi'PBR **new**	SDeJ
	lijiangense (IXc/d)	GEdr GKev MCri XEll
I	'Linda' (Ia/b)	SDeJ
	'Little John' (VIIa-b/b)	CBod SDeJ
	'Little Kiss' (Ia/d)	SDeJ
	LOLLYPOP ('Holebibi') (Ia/b)	NRHS SCoo SDeJ
	'Londrina' (Ia/b)	SDeJ
	longiflorum (IXb/a)	CTsd EBee MCri SCoo XLum
	- B&SWJ 11376	WCru
	- 'Foliis Variegatis' (Vb/a/v)	MAvo
	- 'Rose'	SDeJ
	- 'White Heaven'PBR (Vb/a)	LCro LOPS
	longiflorum* × *pardalinum **new**	GKev
	'Lovely Girl' (VII-/b)	SDeJ
	'Luxor' (Ia/b)	CTsd NBir
	'Luzia' (VIIa-b/c)	CRos LRHS NRHS
	mackliniae (IXc/a) ♀H5	CWCL EWes GCal GGGa GKev ITim NBir WHal WPGP
	- PAB 9327	LEdu WPGP
	- PAB 9668	LEdu WPGP
	- from Nagaland, India	GGGa
	- deep pink-flowered	GGGa
	'Magic Star'PBR (VIIa-b/b)	SDeJ
	'Manitoba Morning' (IIc/c)	GKev LAma NHpl SDeJ
	'Mapira' (VIIIb/b)	GKev IPot SDeJ
	'Marco Polo' ambig.	SCoo SDeJ
	'Marie North' (Ic/d)	GEdr
	'Maroon King' (II)	GKev WFar
	martagon (IXc/d) ♀H6	CAvo CBro CWCL ECha EHrv ELan EMor EPot ERCP GKev GPoy ITim LAma LCro LOPS LRHS NAln NBir NChi NGrd NHpl SDeJ SRms WCAu WPnP WShi WSpi
	- var. ***albiflorum*** (IXc/d)	EHrv LAma SDeJ
	- var. ***album*** (IXc/d)	CAvo CBro CSpe ELan EMor EPot GBin GKev LAma LRHS MCot NBir NChi NRHS SDeJ SRms WShi
	- var. ***cattaniae*** (IXc/d)	EPot GEdr MCri
	- 'Fairy Morning' (IIc/c)	GKev WFar
	- var. ***hirsutum*** (IXc/d)	GEdr
	- 'Slate's Morning' (IIc/c)	GKev
	'Mascara' (Ia-b/b)	GKev
	'Matrix' (Ia-b/b)	CBod
	medeoloides (IXc/d) B&SWJ 4184	WCru
	- B&SWJ 4363	WCru
	'Miss Feya' (VIIIb/c)	CAby LAma SDeJ
	'Miss France' (VIIb/b-c)	SDeJ
I	'Miss Lily' (VIIIb/b-c)	SDeJ
	'Miss Lucy'PBR (VIIa-b/b-c)	LAma SDeJ
	MISS RIO	see *L.* 'Rio'
	'Mister Job' (VIIIa/c)	SDeJ
	'Mona Lisa' (VIIb/b-c)	CRos LAma LRHS MCri NGdn NRHS SDeJ
	monadelphum (IXc/d)	LAma SDeJ XEll
	- pale-flowered	GKev
	'Mont Blanc' (Ia/b-c)	SDeJ
	'Monte Negro' (Ia/b)	MCri
	'Montezuma'PBR (VIIa-b/b)	SDeJ
	'Montreux' (Ia/b-c)	SDeJ
	'Mount Cook' (VIIa/b)	GKev SDeJ
	'Muscadet'PBR (VIIa-b/b)	GKev IPot LAma SDeJ
	'Navona' (Ia/b)	GKev SDeJ
	nepalense (IXc/a)	CAby CBcs CBro CExl CWCL EPot ERCP GBin GKev LAma LCro LOPS MCot SDeJ WCot WCru WPnP XLum
	- B&SWJ 2985	WCru
	'Netty's Pride' (Ia/b-c)	CAvo ERCP IPot SDeJ
	'New Wave' (Ia/b)	SDeJ
	'Night Flyer' (Ib-c/b-c)	GKev IPot SDeJ
	'Nove Cento' (Ia/b)	MCri SDeJ
	'Orange County' (Ia/b)	SDeJ
	'Orange Electric' (Ia/b)	SDeJ
	'Orange Marmalade' (IIb/c-d)	GKev LAma NHpl SDeJ
	'Orange Pixie' (Ia/b)	CRos NRHS SCoo
	'Orange Planet' (VIa/a)	SDeJ
	'Orange Twinkle' (Ib-c/b)	SDeJ
	'Orania'PBR (VIIIb/b)	GKev SDeJ
*	Oriental Superb Group	NGdn
	oxypetalum var. ***insigne*** (IXb-c/b)	EPot GBin NHpl
	'Pan' (Ic/d)	GEdr
	pardalinum (IXc/d) ♀H6	CWCL EBee ERCP GKev WCot WCru
	- var. ***giganteum*** (IXc/d)	MCri MNrw
	- subsp. ***pardalinum*** (IXc/d)	SDeJ
§	- subsp. ***vollmeri*** (IXc/d)	WCru
§	- subsp. ***wigginsii*** (IXc/d)	WCru
	× ***parkmanii*** 'Journey's End' (VIIb/c)	LAma
	- 'Rosy Dimple' (VIIa/b)	SDeJ
	'Passion Moon' (VIIb-c/a)	GKev SDeJ
	'Patricia's Pride' (Ia-b/b-c)	SDeJ
	'Peach Butterflies' (Ic/d)	SDeJ
	'Peach Dwarf' (Ia/b-c)	SDeJ
	'Peach Pixie' (Ia/b)	NBir SCoo
	'Pearl Carolina' (Ic/c)	GKev
	'Pearl Jennifer' (Ib-a/c)	GKev SDeJ
	'Pearl Jessica' (Ib-c/b-c)	GKev SDeJ
	'Pearl Justien' (Ia-b/c)	GKev SDeJ
	'Pearl Loraine' (Ib-c/b-c)	GKev SDeJ
	'Pearl Melanie' (Ib/c)	SDeJ
	'Pearl Sonja' (Ib/b)	SDeJ
	'Pearl Stacey' (Ib-c/b-c)	GKev SDeJ
	'Peggy North' (Ic/d)	GEdr
	'Pepard Gold' (IIc/d)	GEdr GKev LAma
	philippinense (IXa-b/a)	GKev LAma WPGP

'Pieton' (Ia/b-c) SDeJ
'Pimento' (VIIa/b) SDeJ
'Pink Flavour' (Ic/c) GKev SDeJ
'Pink Heart' LBuc
'Pink Morning' (IIc/c) GKev IPot NHpl
Pink Perfection Group (VIb/a) ♀H6 ERCP GKev LAma LCro LOPS MCri SCoo SDeJ
'Pink Pixie'[PBR] (Ia/b) NBir NRHS SDeJ
poilanei misapplied see *L. primulinum*
'Polar Star' (VIIa-b/b) SDeJ
pomponium (IXc/d) CBor
§ ***primulinum*** (IXc/a) HWJ 681 WCru
- WWJ 11679 WCru
- var. ***ochraceum*** (IXc/a) WCru
- aff. var. ***ochraceum*** (IXc/a) KWJ 12064 WCru
'Proud Bride' (VIIa/b) CBod SDeJ
'Prunotto'[PBR] (Ia-b/b) **new** SDeJ
§ ***pumilum*** (IXc/d) EPot GKev LAma SDeJ
'Purple Eye' (Ia-b/b) ERCP SDeJ
'Purple Prince' (VIIIa-b/a-b) SDeJ
pyrenaicum (IXc/d) IFro NAln WShi XEll
'Red Carpet' (Ia/b) MCri NBir SDeJ
'Red County' (Ia/c-b) SDeJ
'Red Electric' (Ia/b) SDeJ
'Red Flavour' (Ic/b-c) SDeJ
'Red Hot' (VIIIc-d/b) SDeJ
'Red Life' (Ib-a/c) **new** NHpl
'Red Morning' (VIIIa-b/b) GKev
'Red Twinkle' SDeJ
'Red Velvet' (Ic/d) CAvo GKev SDeJ
regale (IXb/a) ♀H6 CAvo CBro ECha ELan EMor ERCP EShb EWTr GKev LAma LCro LOPS LRHS MCot MCri NAln SCob SDeJ SPer SRms
- 'Album' (IXb/a) CAvo ERCP GKev IMou LAma LCro LOPS LRHS MCri SCob SCoo SDeJ
§ - 'Royal Gold' (IXb/a) MCri
'Reinesse' (Ia/b) CRos NRHS SDeJ
§ 'Rio' (VIIb/b-c) SCoo
RIO NEGRO ('Corvara'[PBR]) (VIIa-b/b-c) SDeJ
'Robert Swanson' (VIIIb-c/b) GKev LAma SDeJ
'Robina' (VIIIa-b/b-c) WCot WWFP
'Rose Arch Fox' (IIc/c-d) GKev LAma
'Rosella's Dream' (Ia/b) SDeJ
ROSELILY CAROLINA ('DL044040') (VIIa-b) **new** MSCN
ROSELILY ELENA ('DL04581') (VIIa-b) **new** MSCN
'Rosemary North' (Ic/d) GEdr
'Rosselini' (VIIIa-b/b) SDeJ
rosthornii (IXc/d) CExl GKev LAma WCru
'Royal Gold' see *L. regale* 'Royal Gold'
rubellum (IXb/a) GEdr
'Russian Morning' (IIc/c) GKev
'Russian Red' (IIc/d) LAma
sachalinense (IXa/b) RBS 0235 EPPr
'Salinas' (VIIa/b) SDeJ
'Salmon Flavour' (Ic/b-c) GKev
'Salmon Tiger' SDeJ
'Salmon Twinkle' (Ib-c/c) SDeJ
sargentiae (IXb-c/a) GCal
'Satisfaction' (VIIIa-b/-) SDeJ
'Scarlet Delight' (VIIb-c/c-d) SDeJ
'Scarlet Morning' (IIc/c) **new** GKev
'Scheherazade' (VIIIc/d) GKev LAma MCri SDeJ
'Serrada'[PBR] (VIIIa-b/b) ILea
'Set Point' (VIIb/b) SDeJ
'Showwinner' (VIIa/b-c) CRos LRHS NRHS
'Sixth Sense' (VII) **new** LCro
'Slate's Select' (II) LAma
'Smoky Mountain' (VIIIc/d) SDeJ
'Souvenir'[PBR] (VIIa-b/b) SDeJ
SPARKLER see L. 'Coldplay'
speciosum B&SWJ 4847 (IXb-c/d) WCru
- B&SWJ 4924 WCru
- var. ***album*** (IXb-c/d) GKev NBir NHpl SDeJ WFar
- var. ***rubrum*** (IXb-c/d) ECha LAma LCro LOPS NBir SDeJ SRms
§ - - 'Uchida' (IXb-c/d) CExl GKev SDeJ
- var. ***speciosum*** (IXb-c/d) **new** CAvo
'Sphinx' (Ia/d) WCot
'Spring Pink' (Ia/-) SDeJ
'Stainless Steel' (Ia/b) SDeJ
'Star Gazer' (VIIa/c) CBod CRos GKev LAma LRHS NRHS SCob SCoo SDeJ
'Starfighter' (VIIa-b/c) SDeJ
'Sunny Morning' (IIc/d) GKev LAma
'Sunset Matrix' (Ia/b) **new** CBod
superbum (IXc/d) GKev LAma WCru WPGP
'Sweet Lord' (Ia/b) SDeJ
'Sweet Surrender' (Ib-c/c-d) SDeJ
'Tailor Made' (Ia/b) SDeJ
taliense (IXc/d) WCru
'Tarragona'[PBR] (VIIIb/b) SDeJ
tenuifolium see *L. pumilum*
Tiger Babies Group (VIIIb-c/c-d) GKev SDeJ
'Tigeredition' (VIIa-b/b-c) LCro LOPS
'Tigerwoods' (VIIa/c) LCro LOPS
tigrinum see *L. lancifolium*
'Tiny Dino'[PBR] (Ia-b/b) MAsh
'Tiny Ghost'[PBR] (Ia-b/b-c) MAsh
'Tiny Invader'[PBR] (Ia-b/b-c) MAsh
'Tiny Nanny'[PBR] (Ia-b/b-c) MAsh
'Tiny Skyline'[PBR] (Ia-b/b) MAsh
'Tom Pouce' (VIIa/b) SDeJ
'Toronto' (Ia-b/b) SDeJ
'Toscane' (Ia/b-c) SDeJ
TRIUMPHATOR ('Zanlophator'[PBR]) (VIIIb/a-b) ILea MCot SDeJ
tsingtauense (IXa/c) GKev LAma SDeJ
- B&SWJ 519 WCru
- B&SWJ 4263 WCru
- B&SWJ 4698 WCru
'Uchida Kanoka' see *L. speciosum* var. *rubrum* 'Uchida'
'Urandi' (VIIIc/b) GKev SDeJ
'Val Di Sole'[PBR] (Ia/b) SDeJ
'Venezuela' (VIIa-b/b-c) SDeJ
'Venture' (Ia/b) NNor
'Visaversa' (VIIIa-b/b) SDeJ
'Vivaldi' (Ia/b) SDeJ
vollmeri see *L. pardalinum* subsp. *vollmeri*
wallichianum (IXb/a) GKev LAma SDeJ XLum
wardii (IXc/d) CExl
'Whistler' (Ia/c) SDeJ
'White Paradise' (V) SCoo
'White Pixels' (Ia/b) SDeJ
'White Planet' (VIa/a) GKev

	'White Present' (Vb/a)	SDeJ
	'White Twinkle' (Ia-b/b)	SDeJ
	wigginsii	see *L. pardalinum* subsp. *wigginsii*
	willmottiae	see *L. davidii* var. *willmottiae*
	'Wine Electric' (Ia/c)	SDeJ
	xanthellum var. ***luteum*** (IXb-c/d)	WCru
	'Yellow Bruse' (Ic/c) **new**	SDeJ
	'Yellow County' (Ia/b-c)	SDeJ
§	'Yellow Electric' (Ia/b-c)	SDeJ
	'Yellow Eye' (Ia/b)	SDeJ
	'Yeti' (Ia/b)	SDeJ

lime see *Citrus × aurantiifolia*

lime, Philippine see *Citrus × microcarpa*

limequat see *Citrus × floridana*

Limnanthes (*Limnanthaceae*)

	douglasii ♀H5	LCro LOPS MNHC NPri
	- subsp. ***rosea***	CSpe

Limonium (*Plumbaginaceae*)

	bellidifolium	CFis CMea EBou EDAr
	cosyrense	CMea MHer
	dumosum	see *Goniolimon tataricum* var. *angustifolium*
	gmelinii	SPlb
*	- subsp. ***hungaricum***	XLum
	latifolium	see *L. platyphyllum*
	minutum	CPla
	perezii	GJos
§	***platyphyllum***	CBod CMea CRos EPfP GMaP LRHS LSun MHer MMuc NRHS SCob SEND SPer SRms SSut WCAu WHoo XSen
	- 'Blue Cloud'	SRms
	- 'Robert Butler'	CBod ECtt GCal MRav
	- 'Violetta'	CBod CTri EBee ECtt ELan EPfP GBin LRHS MBel MPie NRHS SPer SPoG WAul WGwG WHoo
	'Salt Lake'	NRHS
§	***sinuatum***	NPri SVic
	- Fortress Series **new**	CWCL
	tataricum	see *Goniolimon tataricum*
	vulgare	LRHS WHer XSen

Linaria (*Plantaginaceae*)

	aeruginea	CMea CPBP
	- 'Lindeza Violet'	CSpe
	- 'Neon Lights'	CSpe EDAr NGdn SPoG WFar
	- subsp. ***nevadensis*** 'Gemstones'	SBch
	alpina	CSpe GJos NRya NSla SRms
	anticaria 'Antique Silver'	CExl MRav WHil
	cymbalaria	see *Cymbalaria muralis*
§	***dalmatica***	CBod EPPr MMuc MPie NBid NGBl NSti SPhx WCot WFar WMoo WWFP
	dalmatica × purpurea	WCot
	'Dartmoor Sunset'	LLHF
	'Dial Park'	CBod EBee MAvo MHol SPad WCot WRHF
	× ***dominii*** 'Carnforth'	SHar
	- 'Yuppie Surprise'	NBir
	'Florence Lily Sophia Brown'	WCot WFar
	genistifolia	WCot
	- W&B BGB-6	WCot WFar
	- subsp. ***dalmatica***	see *L. dalmatica*
	hepaticifolia	see *Cymbalaria hepaticifolia*
*	***lobata alba***	SPlb
*	'Lucy's Pink' **new**	ECha
	origanifolia	see *Chaenorhinum origanifolium*
	pallida	see *Cymbalaria pallida*
	'Peachy'	CAby CBod CDor CSpe ECha ECtt GBin MHol MSCN MTis SMHy SPad SPoG WCot WFar WHrl WRHF WWFP
	pilosa	see *Cymbalaria pilosa*
	'Pink Kisses'	MHol MSCN SPad SPoG WCot WFar
	purpurea	CBod CDor CTri EHoe ELan EMor EPfP MHer MNHC NBro NPer NPol SEND SPhx SRms WCot WFar WMoo WSFF WTor
	- 'Alba'	see *L. purpurea* 'Springside White'
	- 'Brown's White Strain'	CBre EPPr WCot
	- 'Canon Staid' **new**	CNat
	- 'Canon Went'	CBod CBre CCBP CDor CRos CSpe CTri EBee ELan EPfP GJos LCro LOPS LRHS MNHC NBir NPol NRHS SGbt SPer SPhx SRms SWvt WCAu WCot WFar WHer WKif WMoo
	- 'Freefolk Piccolo'	SHar
	- pink-flowered	CSpe
	- 'Poached Egg'	CMea WGoo
	- 'Radcliffe Innocence'	see *L. purpurea* 'Springside White'
§	- 'Springside White'	CBod CDor CSpe GJos LRHS NBir NGdn SBch SPhx WFar
	- 'Vainglorious'	CNat
	repens	WCot WHer
	× ***sepium***	WCot
	triornithophora	ELan SPlb WKif WMoo WWFP
	- 'Pink Budgies'	LLHF
	- purple-flowered	WMoo
	- 'Rosea'	CSpe
	tristis	SBrt
	vulgaris	CHab CWld EBou EMor EPfP MHer MMuc MNHC NMir SRms WHer WMoo
	- f. ***peloria***	CPBP

Lindelofia (*Boraginaceae*)

	anchusoides misapplied	see *L. longiflora*
	anchusoides (Lindl.) Lehm.	NBid
§	***longiflora***	GCal WSHC
	macrostyla **new**	SBrt

Lindera (*Lauraceae*)

	aggregata	CBcs WPGP
	angustifolia	NLar
	- FMWJ 13156	WCru
	assamica B&SWJ 13984	WCru
	benzoin	CBcs CMCN EPfP LRHS MBlu NLar
	erythrocarpa B&SWJ 6271	WCru
	- B&SWJ 8730	WCru
	metcalfiana var. ***dictyophylla*** KWJ 12312	WCru
	obtusiloba ♀H5	CBcs MBlu NLar WPGP
	- B&SWJ 8723	WCru
	- B&SWJ 11054	WCru
	- B&SWJ 12555 from Korea	WCru
	praecox	NLar
	- B&SWJ 10802	WCru
	- B&SWJ 10953 from north Japan	WCru

– B&SWJ 11125 from south Japan	WCru
reflexa	NLar
sericea B&SWJ 11123	WCru
– B&SWJ 11141	WCru
– var. ***lancea*** B&SWJ 11071	WCru
– – B&SWJ 11118	WCru
tonkinensis FMWJ 13123	WCru
triloba B&SWJ 5570	WCru
– B&SWJ 11121	WCru
– B&SWJ 11466	WCru
umbellata B&SWJ 10881	WCru
– var. ***membranacea*** B&SWJ 6227	WCru
– – B&SWJ 10837	WCru

Lindernia (*Linderniaceae*)

grandiflora	CBod GAbr LLWG WTor

Linnaea (*Caprifoliaceae*)

borealis	CExl EPot NSla WAbe XEll
– subsp. ***americana***	NWad

Linum (*Linaceae*)

	arboreum ♀H4	GKev LLHF NBir
	campanulatum	WThu
	capitatum	NSla
	flavum	GKev XSen
	– 'Compactum'	CMea EBou GAbr GKev LLHF NSla SRms
	'Gemmell's Hybrid' ♀H4	EPot EWes GCrg NBir WAbe WThu
	grandiflorum 'Bright Eyes'	CSpe
	– 'Rubrum'	CSpe
	hypericifolium	SPhx
	– from Lagonaki, Caucasus	SBrt
	kingii var. ***sedoides***	WAbe
	narbonense	LRHS SIgm SPhx
§	***perenne***	CBod EBou ECha ELan ENfk EPfP GKev GMaP MHer MNHC NAln SCob SPer SPoG WSHC
	– 'Album'	EBee ECha ELan EPfP
	– subsp. ***alpinum*** 'Alice Blue'	WAbe
§	– 'Blau Saphir'	MBel NHol
	– BLUE SAPPHIRE	see *L. perenne* 'Blau Saphir'
	– 'Himmelszelt'	LSun
	– 'Nanum Sapphire'	see *L. perenne* 'Blau Saphir'
	rigidum	CPla
	sibiricum	see *L. perenne*
	suffruticosum subsp. ***salsoloides*** 'Nanum'	WThu
	uninerve	WAbe

Lippia (*Verbenaceae*)

sp.	SWvt
canescens	see *Phyla nodiflora* var. *canescens*
chamaedrifolia	see *Glandularia peruviana*
citriodora	see *Aloysia citrodora*
dulcis	ENfk MNHC SRms
nodiflora	see *Phyla nodiflora*
repens	see *Phyla nodiflora*

Liquidambar ✿ (*Hamamelidaceae*)

	acalycina	CBcs CDul CJun EBee ELan EMOT EPfP NLar NOra SBir SCoo SGol SLim SSta WMat WPGP
	– 'Burgundy Flush' ♀H6	CJun NLar SBir SSta
	– 'Spinners'	CRos ELan LMil LRHS SBir WPGP
	formosana	CAco CMCN CMac IArd IMou SBir SGol SSta WPGP
	– 'Afterglow'	CJun NLar
	– 'Ellen'	CJun NLar
	– Monticola Group	CJun SLim SSta
	orientalis	CDul CJun CLnd CMCN EBtc EPfP IDee SBir SSta
	– 'M. Foster'	NLar
	styraciflua	Widely available
	– 'Andrew Hewson'	CJun CLnd CRos EBee EPfP LRHS MAsh MBlu NRHS SBir SSta
	– 'Anja'	CJun MBlu SBir SSta
	– 'Anneke'	CJun SBir SSta
	– 'Aurea'	see *L. styraciflua* 'Variegata' Overeynder
	– 'Aurea Variegata'	see *L. styraciflua* 'Variegata' Overeynder
	– 'Aurora'	CJun SBir
	– 'Burgundy'	CJun CLnd LLHF MBlu SBir SSta
I	– 'Corky'	LRHS SSta
	– 'Emerald Sentinel'	CJun SSta
	– 'Festeri'	CEnd SBir SSta
	– 'Festival'	CJun CLnd MBlu SGol
	– 'Frosty' (v)	CJun SBir SSta
	– 'Globe'	see *L. styraciflua* 'Gum Ball'
	– 'Gold Beacon'	NLar
	– 'Golden Sun'PBR	CKel LSRN NLar
	– 'Golden Treasure' (v)	CDul CJun CLnd CMCN LSRN MAsh MGos SBir SGol SSta
	– 'Goldmember'	CJun SSta
	– 'Granary Sunset'	SBir SSta
§	– 'Gum Ball'	CCVT CEnd CLnd CMCN EBee ELon EPfP EWes LLHF NLar SBir SCob SLim SPoG SSta SWvt
	– HAPPIDAZE ('Hapdell')	CJun SBir
	– 'Jennifer Carol'	NLar SBir SSta
	– 'Kia'	CEnd CJun SBir
	– 'Lane Roberts' ♀H6	CDul CKel CLnd CMCN CMac CSBt CTho EBee ELan EMOT EPfP EWTr IArd LRHS LSRN MAsh MBlu MGos NLar NOra SBir SCob SCoo SPer SPoG SSta SWvt WCFE WMat
	– 'Lynn'	SBir SSta
	– 'Manon' (v)	CJun
	– 'Midwest Sunset'	CJun EBee MBlu NLar SBir
	– 'Moonbeam' (v)	CJun SBir SCob SLim SSta
	– 'Moraine'	CJun
	– 'Naree'	MMrt NLar SSta
	– 'Nina'	SSta
	– 'Nyewood'	SBir
	– 'Oconee'	CEnd LLHF MAsh SSta WCot
	– 'Paarl' (v)	CLnd EMOT SGol
	– 'Palo Alto' ♀H6	CEnd EMOT EPfP MAsh MBlu SBir SCoo SLim SMad SSta WMat WMou WPGP
	– 'Parasol'	CAco CEnd CJun CLnd EBtc SBir SSta
	– 'Pendula'	CJun CLnd MBlu SBir SSta
	– 'Penwood' ♀H6	CJun NLar SBir SSta
	– 'Red Sunset'	SSta
	– 'Rotundiloba'	CJun CMCN EPfP LLHF LRHS MAsh MBlu SSta WPGP
	– 'Savill Torch'	CJun LSvl SBir SSta
	– 'Schock's Gold'	CJun NLar SSta
§	– 'Silver King' (v)	CJun CLnd CMCN CMac EBee LRHS MAsh MGos NLar SCoo SGol SLim SPer SSta
	– 'Simone'	SBir SGol SSta
	– 'Slender Silhouette' ♀H6	Widely available

– 'Stared'	CDul CEnd CJun CLnd EMOT EPfP GQue MBlu MGos NOra SBir SCoo SLim SSta WMat WMou
– 'Thea'	CJun CRos EBee EMOT EPfP LRHS MAsh MBlu NRHS SBir SSta
– 'Variegata' misapplied	see *L. styraciflua* 'Silver King'
§ – 'Variegata' Overeynder (v)	CJun CMac EBee ELan EMOT SBir SLim SSta
– 'White Star' (v)	CJun
– 'Woorby Rose'	CJun NLar SBir
– 'Worplesdon' ♀H6	Widely available

Liriodendron (*Magnoliaceae*)

chinense ♀H6	CBcs CDul CMCN EBee EPfP MBlu SGol WMou WPGP
× ***sinoamericanum*** 'Chapel Hill'	MBlu NLar
– 'Doc Deforce's Delight'	MBlu NLar
tulipifera ♀H6	Widely available
– 'Aureomarginatum' (v) ♀H6	CBcs CCVT CDul CEnd CMCN CTho ECrN ELan EMOT EPfP EWTr LLHF MAsh MBlu MGos MSwo NEgg NLar SCob SGol SMad SPer SPoG SSta WMat
– 'Fastigiatum'	CDul CEnd CLnd CMCN CTho EBee ECrN ELan EMOT EPfP LMaj LPra MAsh MBlu MGos NLar SGol SPer
– 'Glen Gold'	CEnd MBlu NLar
– 'Purgatory'	MBlu
– 'Roodhaan'	MBlu NLar
– 'Rotundiloba'	MBlu
– 'Snow Bird' (v)	SPoG WMat

Liriope ✿ (*Asparagaceae*)

'Big Blue'	see *L. muscari* 'Big Blue'
§ ***exiliflora***	CHll CKel
– 'Ariaka-janshige' (v)	CRos LRHS NRHS
– SILVERY SUNPROOF misapplied	see *L. spicata* 'Gin-ryu', *L. muscari* 'Variegata'
graminifolia misapplied	see *L. muscari*
hyacinthifolia	see *Reineckea carnea*
'Majestic'	CBct MHer WHoo
minor	CMac
§ ***muscari*** ♀H5	Widely available
– 'Alba'	see *L. muscari* 'Monroe White'
– AMETHYST ('Liptp')	CBod EBee NRHS WMoo WNPC
§ – 'Big Blue'	CAbb CBct CBod CChe CExl CKel CMac CRos EBee ECtt ELan ELon EPfP EShb EUJe GBin GQue LRHS LSRN MJak MRav MSwo NLar NRHS SArc SCob SGol SPoG SWvt WMoo
– 'Big Pink'	CBod
– 'Christmas Tree'	WHoo WMoo
– 'Gold-banded' (v)	CBct CKel EBee EPfP EUJe GWyn LRHS SCob WFar
– 'Goldfinger'	CExl EBee SMad
– 'Ingwersen'	CExl CKno CRos EBee ELon EPPr EPfP EWTr NRHS SCob XLum
– ISABELLA ('Lirf')	EBee EPPr
– 'John Burch' (v)	CBct CExl ELon NLar WGob
– 'Lilac Wonder'	EMor EPPr LRHS SCob
– 'Majestic' misapplied	see *L. exiliflora*
– 'Moneymaker'	CKel EPPr EPfP MNrw SCob SPoG XEll
§ – 'Monroe White'	CBct CExl CKel CMac EBee EHrv ELan EPfP EShb LCro LOPS MJak MRav NBid NDai NLar SCob SMad SPer SWvt
– 'Okina' (v)	CAby CBro CPla EBee ELon EUJe MBNS MBel MNrw NGBl NLar NSti SMad SPer SPoG WBrk WCot
– 'Pee Dee Ingot'	SPoG
– 'Purple Passion'	SCob
– 'Royal Purple'	CBct EBee ECtt ELon EPfP LRHS MAsh NLar NRHS SCob SPer WHoo WMoo
– 'Silver Ribbon'	CBro EPfP LSRN MGos
§ – 'Variegata' (v)	CExl CPla CRos EBee EHrv ELan EWes LEdu LRHS MAsh MAvo MJak NBir NRHS SPer SPoG SWvt
– 'Webster Wideleaf'	EBee WCot
platyphylla	see *L. muscari*
spicata	CBod EBee GCal XLum
– 'Alba'	MRav
§ – 'Gin-ryu' (v)	CBct CExl CKel CMac ELan EPfP EShb EWes MRav NSti SCob SGol SPer WBrk WJam XLum
– 'Silver Dragon'	see *L. spicata* 'Gin-ryu'

Litchi (*Sapindaceae*)

chinensis	CCCN

Lithocarpus ✿ (*Fagaceae*)

densiflorus var. ***echinoides***	CMCN
edulis	CExl SArc

Lithodora (*Boraginaceae*)

§ ***diffusa***	SGol SRot
– 'Alba'	CKel CWCL SPer SPoG
– 'Compacta'	CSma SRot WAbe
§ – 'Grace Ward' ♀H5	CBod ECtt ELan EPfP MHol MMuc NRHS NWad WIce
§ – 'Heavenly Blue' ♀H5	Widely available
– 'Pete's Favourite'	NWad
– 'Picos'	NLar NSla SIgm WAbe WThu
– 'Star'PBR	CRos ELan ELon EPfP GKev LRHS MHol NAln NHpl NLar NRHS SCoo SPer SPoG SRot SWvt WFar WIce
– 'White Star'	WIce
× ***intermedia***	see *Moltkia* × *intermedia*
§ ***oleifolia*** ♀H4	CRos LLHF LRHS NBir NRHS
rosmarinifolia	CRos EBee LRHS NRHS WCFE
zahnii	CRos LLHF LRHS NRHS SVen
– 'Azure-ness'	SBch SChF WAbe
– compact	SIgm

Lithophragma (*Saxifragaceae*)

parviflorum	CAby

Lithops ✿ (*Aizoaceae*)

hallii ♀H2 **new**	SSim

Lithospermum (*Boraginaceae*)

diffusum	see *Lithodora diffusa*
doerfleri	see *Moltkia doerfleri*
'Grace Ward'	see *Lithodora diffusa* 'Grace Ward'
'Heavenly Blue'	see *Lithodora diffusa* 'Heavenly Blue'
officinale	GPoy NMir
oleifolium	see *Lithodora oleifolia*
purpureocaeruleum	see *Buglossoides purpurocaerulea*

Lithraea (*Anacardiaceae*)

caustica **new**	WPav

Litsea (*Lauraceae*)

NJM 13.047 **new**	WPGP

glauca see *Neolitsea sericea*
japonica SVen

Littonia (*Colchicaceae*)

modesta see *Gloriosa modesta*

Livistona (*Arecaceae*)

chinensis ♀H2 CPHo XBlo

Llagunoa (*Sapindaceae*)

glandulosa new WPav

Loasa (*Loasaceae*)

acanthifolia GCal
triphylla var. ***volcanica*** EBee EWes WSHC

Lobelia ✿ (*Campanulaceae*)

'Bordervale' WBor
bridgesii CDTJ CExl CRos EBee ECtt EWes EWld GCal LEdu LRHS SPlb WKif WMoo WPav
§ ***cardinalis*** ♀H3 CMac CWld ELon EWld GMaP LCro LOPS NGBl NLar NPer SPlb SRms SWvt WFar WMAq
- 'Bee's Flame' CNor CRos CWGN ECtt IKil LRHS MArl MRav NEgg NGdn NRHS SPtp SRkn WOut WWtn
- 'Black Truffle' EBee ECtt SPad SRms
- 'Chocolate Truffle'PBR MBel
§ - 'Elmfeuer' CWCL ECtt NLar SPlb SPoG SWvt XLum
§ - 'Queen Victoria' ♀H3 Widely available
- 'Russian Princess' misapplied CRos CWld EPfP LLWG LRHS MAsh MHol NCGa NGdn NRHS SPoG SRkn SWvt WFar WOut
chinensis LLWG
'Cinnabar Deep Red' see *L.* × *speciosa* 'Fan Tiefrot'
'Cinnabar Rose' see *L.* × *speciosa* 'Fan Zinnoberrosa'
COMPLIMENT BLUE see *L.* × *speciosa* 'Kompliment Blau'
COMPLIMENT DEEP RED see *L.* × *speciosa* 'Kompliment Tiefrot'
COMPLIMENT PURPLE see *L.* × *speciosa* 'Kompliment Purpur'
COMPLIMENT SCARLET see *L.* × *speciosa* 'Kompliment Scharlach'
'Compton Pink' CBcs CBod EBee ECtt ELan EMor EShb EWes IPot LBuc LRHS NGBl NRHS NSti SCob WFar WOut
davidii PAB 8547 LEdu
Elizabeth Strangman selection NDov
erinus BIG BLUE ('Weslobigblue'PBR) CPla
- 'Crystal Palace' ♀H2 CPla NPri
- (Fountain Series) 'Fountain Blue' NPri
- - 'Fountain White' NPri
- 'Kathleen Mallard' (d) CCCN
- Riviera Series NPri
- 'Sapphire' NPri
- WATERFALL BLUE ICE (Waterfall Series) NPri
excelsa CSpe GCal SBrt SEND WPav
FAN DEEP RED see *L.* × *speciosa* 'Fan Tiefrot'
FAN DEEP ROSE see *L.* × *speciosa* 'Fan Orchidrosa'
FAN SALMON see *L.* × *speciosa* 'Fan Lachs'
'Flamingo' see *L.* × *speciosa* 'Pink Flamingo'
fulgens see *L. cardinalis*
- SAINT ELMO'S FIRE see *L. cardinalis* 'Elmfeuer'
× ***gerardii*** see *L.* × *speciosa*
gibberoa CDTJ
'Gladys Lindley' LRHS
'Grape Knee-Hi' CRos ECtt LLHF LRHS NRHS
'Hadspen Purple' see *L.* × *speciosa* 'Hadspen Purple'
inflata GPoy
laxiflora CFis CHll WFar
- var. ***angustifolia*** CAby CDTJ CPbh CPla CWCL EWld GCal SBrt SMHy SRms WCot
linnaeoides SPlb
§ ***montana*** EWld
- B&SWJ 8220 WCru
pedunculata see *Pratia pedunculata*
polyphylla WPav
'Queen Victoria' see *L. cardinalis* 'Queen Victoria'
sessilifolia CExl LLWG MPie WArt
- B&SWJ 8875 WCru
siphilitica CBcs CExl CMac CRos CSam ELan EMor EPfP GCal ILea LEdu LPot LRHS MAvo MHer MMuc NCGa NEgg NGdn NRHS SPer SPlb SRms SWvt WFar WHlf WHoo WMoo XLum
- f. ***albiflora*** EBee ECtt LEdu
- - 'Alba' CSam EMor EPfP LPot SBch SRms SWvt WFar WHrl WMoo
- blue-flowered CSpe CWld SWvt
- 'Rosea' MNrw
'Sombre Purple' new EBee
§ × ***speciosa*** IKil NDai SVic WMoo XLum
- 'Butterfly Blue' CNor ELan SGbt
- 'Butterfly Rose' SRot
- 'Cherry Ripe' LLHF
- 'Cranberry Crush' CAbb CRos ECtt LRHS NRHS
- CRIMSON PRINCESS ('Gencrim'PBR) (Princess Series) CAbb EUJe MJak SPoG
- 'Dark Crusader' CBod CRos EBee ECtt EPfP LRHS MPie NDov NRHS WOut
- Fan Series MRav NAln
- - 'Fan Blau' ELan EMor EPfP LRHS MCot MHol SCob WFar WMoo
- - 'Fan Burgundy' ELan EMor EPfP LRHS MCot MHer MHol NGdn NLar SCob
§ - - 'Fan Lachs' CBod CWld EMor EPfP LRHS MHer MHol WFar WHlf WMoo WOut WTor
§ - - 'Fan Orchidrosa' ♀H5 EPfP LRHS NRHS SRot
- - 'Fan Scharlach' ♀H5 CWld EPfP LRHS NAst NLar NRHS SPoG SRot SWvt WFar WHlf
§ - - 'Fan Tiefrot' ♀H5 SRms SWvt WMoo
§ - - 'Fan Zinnoberrosa' ♀H5 SRms SRot SWvt WMoo
§ - 'Hadspen Purple'PBR CAby CKel CMac CRos CSpe CWGN CWld EBee ECtt ELon EMor EPfP EWTr ILea IPot LCro LOPS LRHS LSRN MAsh MBel MCot MRav NDov NRHS NSti SHar SPoG SRms SWvt
- 'Kimbridge Beet' CKel CMac EBee LRHS
- Kompliment Series WFar
§ - - 'Kompliment Blau' SWvt WFar
* - - 'Kompliment Pale Pink' WFar
§ - - 'Kompliment Purpur' MMuc SWvt
§ - - 'Kompliment Scharlach' ♀H5 CWat EPfP MNrw NPer NRHS SWvt
§ - - 'Kompliment Tiefrot' EPfP LRHS MMuc MNrw SWvt
- 'Monet Moment' CRos CWCL EBee ECtt EWes IKil ILea LRHS NLar NRHS SWvt
- 'Pauline' ECtt

- 'Pink Elephant' ♀H3	ECtt ELan EMor LLHF NRHS SHar WCFE
§ - 'Pink Flamingo'	CKel ELan LRHS WMoo
- ROSE PRINCESS ('Genross'PBR) (Princess Series)	EMor EWTr IKil LCro LOPS MJak SPoG
- 'Ruby Slippers'	EBee EPfP
- 'Russian Princess' purple-flowered	ECtt EHoe ELan ELon MBel MHer MPie NDov NGBl NHol SCob SPer SPtp WFar WKif WMoo WWtn
- SCARLET PRINCESS ('Genlet'PBR) (Princess Series)	CAbb LCro LOPS
- 'Sparkling Burgundy'	LRHS
- 'Sparkling Ruby'	CBod EBee EMor EPfP EWTr IKil LBuc MCot NRHS SWvt WMoo
- 'Starship Deep Rose'	CRos MHol NRHS
- 'Starship Scarlet'	CRos LRHS MHol NRHS SCob
- 'Tania'	Widely available
§ - 'Vedrariensis'	CMac CRos CSpe ECtt EPfP LRHS MBel MHer MMuc MNrw NAln NGBl NRHS SRms SWvt WCFE WFar WHoo XLum
'Tania's Sister'	EBee MHol WCot WFar
treadwellii	see *Pratia angulata* 'Treadwellii'
tupa	Widely available
- JCA 12527	IBlr
- Archibald's form	CExl WPGP
valida	SWvt
- 'True Blue'	SWvt
vedrariensis	see *L.* × *speciosa* 'Vedrariensis'
wollastonii	SPlb

Lobostemon (*Boraginaceae*)

belliformis	CPbh

Lobularia (*Brassicaceae*)

maritima 'Snow Crystals'	NPri
PRINCESS IN PURPLE **new**	MHol
SNOW PRINCESS ('Inlbusnopr'PBR)	CPla MHol NPri

Loeselia (*Polemoniaceae*)

mexicana	CHll

loganberry see *Rubus* × *loganobaccus*; also AGM Fruit Section

Loiseleuria see *Kalmia*

Lomandra (*Asparagaceae*)

hystrix	SPlb
longifolia	GCal LEdu SPlb
- PLATINUM BEAUTY ('Roma13') (v) **new**	SPoG
- TANIKA ('Lm300'PBR)	GBin

Lomaria see *Blechnum*

Lomatia (*Proteaceae*)

dentata	MGil MRav
ferruginea	CBcs CCCN CDTJ CExl CSde CTsd EBee LRHS MPkF SArc SPoG WCru WPGP
fraseri	CCCN CKel CRos EBee EPfP LRHS NLar SPoG
longifolia	see *L. myricoides*
§ ***myricoides***	CBcs CCCN CExl CKel CRos CTsd EBee EPfP LRHS NLar SLon SPer SPoG
tinctoria	CBcs CExl CPbh EPfP LRHS MPkF

Lomatium (*Apiaceae*)

columbianum	SIgm
grayi	SPhx

Lonicera ✿ (*Caprifoliaceae*)

sp.	CMen
KR 291	ELon
KR 10106	WPGP
KR 10608 **new**	CRHN
§ ***acuminata***	CMCN EBee
- B&SWJ 3480	WCru
- B&SWJ 6743	CRHN WCru
- B&SWJ 6815	WCru
- var. ***acuminata***	WCot
albertii	CDul EPfP MBNS NLar
alseuosmoides	CBcs CDul CRHN EBee LEdu LRHS MMuc NLar SEND SLon SPoG WCru WPGP WSHC
× ***americana*** misapplied	see *L.* × *italica*
§ ***americana*** (Mill.) K. Koch	CBcs CFlo EPfP LEdu MSwo NLar SEND SLim SRms WBor WSHC
§ × ***brownii*** 'Dropmore Scarlet'	Widely available
- 'Fuchsioides' misapplied	see *L.* × *brownii* 'Dropmore Scarlet'
caerulea	CDul CRos EPom EWTr IDee LRHS MRav SCob SDea SRms SVic WBor
- var. ***altaica***	LEdu
- 'Atut'	NLar
- 'Duet'	NLar
- var. ***edulis***	CAgr EPfP LBuc LEdu MCoo MMuc NLar SDea SEle WMat
- var. ***kamtschatica***	EPom IDee LCro LOPS NLar WPGP
- - 'Balalaika' (F)	CAgr MCoo
- - 'Borealis' (F)	CAgr
- - 'Eisbar' (F)	CAgr
- - 'Erin' (F) **new**	LEdu
- - 'Fialka'PBR (F)	NLar
- - 'Honey Bee' (F)	CAgr
- - 'Indigo Gem' (F)	CAgr
- - 'Kalinka' (F)	CAgr
- - 'Larisa' (F)	LEdu WPGP
- - 'Maries' (F)	LEdu WPGP
- - 'Morena'PBR (F)	EPom
- - 'Rebecca' (F)	LEdu WPGP
- - 'Ruth' (F)	LEdu WPGP
- - 'Sinoglaska' (F)	GCal NLar
- - 'Vicky' (F)	LEdu WPGP
- - 'Wojtek' (F)	NLar
- 'Kirke'	NLar
* - var. ***longifolia***	NLar
§ ***caprifolium***	CFlo CRHN CRos ECrN EPfP LRHS NLar WCot
- 'Anna Fletcher'	CRHN WCFE
- 'Cornish Cream'	SGol
- f. ***pauciflora***	see *L.* × *italica*
CAPRILIA EVER ('Inov42'PBR)	CKel MJak
'Celestial'PBR	CRos EPfP LRHS
chaetocarpa	CEnd WSHC
ciliosa	CRHN
'Clavey's Dwarf'	EPPr
crassifolia	GEdr NLar SBrt
- 'Little Honey'	MBNS MMrt MPie MRav NLar SPoG
deflexicalyx	CMCN NLar
demissa	EPfP
'Early Cream'	see *L. caprifolium*
'Elegant'	LBuc SArc SCob

elisae	CBcs CMac CRos CWld EPfP EWTr GBin IMou LLHF LRHS MMuc NLar NRHS SEle SMad SPoG SSta WCot
etrusca	MRav XSen
- 'Donald Waterer'	CFlo CRHN CRos EPfP LRHS LSRN NLar WFar
- 'Michael Rosse'	ELan IArd LRHS MBNS NLar SNig
- 'Superba' ♀H5	CFlo CRHN CRos EBee ELan EPfP LEdu LRHS NLar SEND SLim SNig SPer WSHC
'Fire Cracker'	NLar SLon
flexuosa	see *L. japonica* var. *repens*
fragrantissima	Widely available
giraldii misapplied	see *L. acuminata*
giraldii Rehder	CRHN EBee WSHC
glabrata	NLar SCoo
- B&SWJ 2150	WCru
'Golden Trumpet'	CWGN EPfP LSRN SPer
grata	see *L.* × *americana* (Mill.) K. Koch
× ***heckrottii***	CRHN CSBt NLar
§ - 'American Beauty'	CKel EBee
- 'Gold Flame' misapplied	see *L.* × *heckrottii* 'American Beauty'
- 'Gold Flame' ambig.	CFlo GKin LSRN NLar SCob
- 'Gold Flame' hort. ♀H5	CArg CDul CMac CRos EBee ELan EMOT EPfP LBuc LCro LOPS LRHS MAsh MJak MMuc NRHS SEND SLim SNig SPer SPoG SRms SWvt WFar WMoo WSHC
§ ***henryi***	CArg CBcs CDul CKel CMac CRHN CRos EBee EMOT EPfP GKin LRHS LSRN MAsh MGos MJak MMuc MSwo NRHS SCob SEND SLim SPer SPlb SRms WCFE WFar WSHC
- B&SWJ 8109	WCru
- NJM 11.033 **new**	WPGP
- 'Copper Beauty' PBR	CBcs CEnd CKel CMac CRos EPfP EUJe LBuc LCro LOPS LRHS LSRN MAsh MGos MJak MRav NLar NRHS NWad SCob SEND SGol SLon SPer SPoG SRms WCot WPGP
- var. ***subcoriacea***	see *L. henryi*
hildebrandiana ♀H2	CCCN CExl CRHN
hirsuta	EBee SBrt
hispidula	SBrt
'Honey Baby' PBR	ELon EPfP NHol NWad
implexa	CMCN CRHN
insularis	see *L. morrowii*
involucrata	CExl CHll CMCN EBee MBNS MBlu MMuc SEND WCFE
- var. ***ledebourii***	CBcs CKel CRos ELan EPfP LLHF LRHS MGil NLar
- - 'Vian'	NLar
§ × ***italica***	CRHN CRos CTri EBee LRHS MBNS MSwo NPer SCoo SPer
§ - HARLEQUIN ('Sherlite' PBR) (v)	CKel CMac CRos EPfP LRHS SPlb SRms SWvt
japonica	CMen WFar
§ - 'Aureoreticulata' (v) ♀H5	CDul CMac CRos EHoe ELan EMOT EPfP EShb LRHS MRav NPer SGol SRms WFar
- 'Cream Cascade'	MSwo NLar SCoo SGol
- 'Dart's Acumen'	CRHN
- 'Dart's World'	CArg CKel CRos CSBt EBee LRHS NLar NRHS
- 'Halliana'	Widely available
- 'Hall's Prolific' ♀H5	CDul CKel CRos CSBt EBee ELan EPfP LBuc LCro LOPS LRHS LSRN MAsh MBlu MGos MRav MSwo NRHS SCob SGol SLim SNig SPad SPoG SWvt WFar
§ - 'Horwood Gem' (v)	ECtt NLar SCoo SLim
- 'Maskerade' (v)	LLHF NBro NLar
- 'Mint Crisp' PBR (v)	CDul CKel CMac CPla CRos CSBt CWGN EBee ECrN ECtt ELan EMOT EPfP EShb LRHS LSRN MGos MJak NLar SGol SLon SPad SPer SPoG SRms SWvt
- 'Peter Adams'	see *L. japonica* 'Horwood Gem'
- 'Princess Kate'	ELan NLar SRms
§ - var. ***repens*** ♀H5	CDul CKel CMac CRos CSBt CTri ECrN ECtt ELan EPfP EShb LRHS MRav MSwo NLar NRHS SCoo SGol SLim SLon SNig SPad SPer SPoG SRms WFar
- 'Variegata'	see *L. japonica* 'Aureoreticulata'
korolkowii	EPPr LLHF MBNS MMuc NBir NLar WAvo WCFE WCot WSHC
- 'Blue Velvet'	CAgr MCoo NLar
- 'Mayberry Farm'	MCoo
- var. ***zabelii*** misapplied	see *L. tatarica* 'Zabelii'
lanceolata BWJ 7935	WCru
'Lemon Beauty' (v)	CBcs CBod CKel CMac CRos EBee EHoe EMOT EPfP EShb LRHS LSRN MBNS MGos NBir NLar NWad SCob SGol SPer SPoG SRms SWvt WAvo WFar
maackii	CHll CMCN CRos EPPr EPfP LRHS MRav NLar NRHS WCFE
* ***macgregorii***	CMCN
macrantha B&SWJ 11687	WCru
- WWJ 11606	WCru
'Mandarin' ♀H5	CBcs CRHN LCro LOPS LRHS MBlu MJak NLar SCoo SGol SWvt WSHC
maximowiczii var. ***sachalinensis***	NLar
§ ***morrowii***	SBrt
- 'Ullung do'	CMCN
myrtillus	NLar SBrt
nitida	CAco CArg CBar CBcs CCVT CDul CMac CMen CPer CSBt CTri ECrN ELan EPfP NAln NWea SCob SEND SEWo SGol SPer WMat WTSh XSen
- 'Baggesen's Gold' ♀H5	Widely available
- EDMÉE GOLD ('Briloni')	MAsh WCot
- 'Ernest Wilson'	EPPr
- 'Golden Glow' PBR	NEoE
- 'Lemon Queen'	MMuc MSwo
§ - 'Maigrün'	CBar CBcs CBod CCVT CDul CKel CRos EBee ELan EMOT EPfP EShb LRHS MSwo NEoE NRHS SCob SPer SWvt WFar
- MAYGREEN	see *L. nitida* 'Maigrün'
- 'Red Tips'	CKel EHoe EShb NLar SCob SCoo SRms
- 'Silver Beauty' (v)	CDul CMac ECrN MGos MSwo SCob SPer SPlb SPoG SRms SWvt WFar
- 'Tidy Tips'	MTin NEoE SCob
- 'Twiggy' (v)	CSBt EDAr EHoe EUJe LRHS NHol NLar NWad SPoG WAvo WFar
periclymenum	CCVT CDul CKel CPer CTri CWld GPoy MHer MRav NMir NWea SCob SPlb WSFF XSen
- 'Belgica' misapplied	see *L.* × *italica*
- 'Belgica'	Widely available
- CHIC ET CHOC ('Inov205' PBR)	LRHS SPoG WCot
- 'Florida'	see *L. periclymenum* 'Serotina'

- 'Fragrant Cloud'	LBuc LRHS NRHS
- 'Graham Thomas' ♀H5	Widely available
- 'Harlequin'	see *L.* × *italica* HARLEQUIN
- 'Heaven Scent'	CFlo LBuc LCro LOPS LSRN NLar WFar
- 'Honeybush'	CJun CWGN MAsh MGos NHol NWad SLim WFar
- 'Munster'	WSHC
- 'Purple Queen'	CChe
- 'Red Gables'	CRHN CRos ELon LSRN MBNS NLar SCoo SEND SWvt WCot WKif
- 'Rhubarb and Custard'	LCro LOPS WNPC
- 'Scentsation'PBR	CFlo CKel CMac CRos CSBt CWCL CWGN EBee ELan EPfP EUJe GBin LRHS MAsh MJak NCGa NLar NRHS SCoo SLon SPoG WHlf
- 'Serotina' ♀H5	Widely available
- 'Strawberries and Cream' **new**	LCro LOPS WNPC
- 'Sweet Sue'	CFlo CKel CRHN CRos CSpe CTsd EBee ELan ELon EPfP EWTr LRHS LSRN MAsh MBNS MGos MSwo NEgg NLar NRHS SCoo SNig SPoG SWvt WFar
- 'Winchester'	SRms
pileata	Widely available
- 'Moss Green'	CBod EShb
- 'Silver Lining' (v)	WCFE
pilosa Maxim.	see *L. strophiophora*
pilosa (Kunth) Willd. ex Kunth	CRHN
- F&M 207	WPGP
prolifera	CRHN NLar
× ***purpusii***	CHll CMac CRHN CTri EBee ECrN LMaj MBNS SCob SRms WCFE WFar
- 'Spring Romance'	CMac
- 'Winter Beauty' ♀H6	Widely available
quinquelocularis	CMCN
ramosissima	NLar
reticulata 'Silver'	NLar
saccata	EPfP
sempervirens	CRHN CSBt IDee MBNS MRav WSHC
- 'Cedar Lane'	CRHN CRos LRHS SBrt
- 'Dropmore Scarlet'	see *L.* × *brownii* 'Dropmore Scarlet'
- 'Leo'	CWGN
- f. ***sulphurea***	CMCN WSHC
- - 'John Clayton'	CRos EPfP LRHS
setifera 'Daphnis'	CJun EPfP
similis var. ***delavayi*** ♀H5	CFlo CKel CRHN CRos CWGN ELan EMOT EPfP LRHS MAsh MRav NEgg NLar NRHS SEND SRms SWvt WCot WCru WSHC
'Simonet'	CWCL EBee NLar
'Spring Purple'	NLar
standishii	CTri WFar
- var. ***lancifolia*** 'Budapest'	CRos ELan ELon EPfP IArd IDee LLHF LRHS MAsh MBlu MRav NLar SRms WFar
§ ***strophiophora***	WAvo
subaequalis	CRHN
- Og 93.329	CExl WPGP WSHC
syringantha	CBcs CRHN CTho CWld EBee ECrN ELan EPfP MMuc MNrw MRav NEgg NLar NWad SBrt SEND SEle SPer WCFE WFar WSHC
tangutica	NWad
tatarica	CHll CMCN MRav
- 'Arnold Red'	CBcs ELan EPfP MBlu NLar SEND
- 'Hack's Red'	CAby CMCN EBee EPfP LEdu LRHS NLar SCoo SPer SVen SWvt WBor WGrn
§ - 'Zabelii'	MNrw
× ***tellmanniana*** ♀H5	Widely available
- 'Joan Sayers'	SCoo WCFE
- 'Pharaoh's Trumpet'	SLon
thibetica	MBlu
tomentella B&SWJ 2654	WCru
tragophylla ♀H5	CKel CSBt ELan GCal IMou MBNS MRav NLar SCoo SLim SWvt
- 'Maurice Foster'	CRHN EBee NLar
turczaninowii	LLHF
× ***xylosteoides***	NLar
xylosteum	EBtc EPPr MMuc NLar

Lophomyrtus ✿ (*Myrtaceae*)

§ ***bullata*** ♀H2	CDTJ SPer
- 'Matai Bay'	LRHS
× ***ralphii*** 'Black Pearl'	CKel CMac CRos EShb LRHS SCoo SEle SGbt SLim WFar WGrn
- 'Gloriosa' (v)	CCCN
- 'Kathryn'	CBcs CCoa CKel CSde LRHS NLar
- 'Krinkly'	SVen
- 'Little Star' (v)	CBcs CCht CRos CSde LRHS SEle
- Logan's form (v)	CBcs CKel LRHS MGil NLar NRHS WAvo
- 'Magic Dragon'PBR (v)	CKel CRos ELan LCro LOPS LRHS MPkF NRHS SEle SGbt SPoG WFar
- 'Multicolor' (v)	CBcs CCoa EBee EPfP LRHS MRav SVen
- 'Pixie'	CBcs CCoa CKel CSde LRHS MAsh SEle SLim SPoG SVen
- 'Red Dragon'	CBcs CMac CRos LRHS MAsh MGos NRHS WFar
- 'Wild Cherry'	LRHS

Lophosoria ✿ (*Dicksoniaceae*)

quadripinnata	CBdn CDTJ CKel

Lophospermum (*Plantaginaceae*)

'Cream Delight'	CCCN
§ ***erubescens*** ♀H2	CRHN SBch
- 'Bridal Bouquet'	CPla
LOFOS WINE RED ('Sun-asaro') (Lofos Series)	EShb
§ 'Magic Dragon'	CPla SEND SLim
§ 'Red Dragon'	CCCN SBch
§ ***scandens***	CCCN

loquat see *Eriobotrya japonica*

Loropetalum (*Hamamelidaceae*)

chinense	SEle
§ - 'Chang Nian Hong'	LCro LOPS LRHS WHlf
- EVER RED	see *L. chinense* 'Chang Nian Hong'
- HOT SPICE	SEle
- 'Ming Dynasty'	CKel MAsh SEle SSta WFar
- var. ***rubrum***	CExl
- - BLACK PEARL	see *L. chinense* var. *rubrum* 'Pearl'
- - 'Blush'	CBcs SEle SGol
- - 'Daybreak's Flame'	CBcs MGil SEle SGol SNig
- - 'Fire Dance'	CAby CBcs CBct CBod CCCN CExl CHll CKel CPla CSde CTsd CWld EPfP EShb LCro LOPS LRHS MAsh MGos MMuc NRHS SEle SPad SPoG SRkn SWvt WCot WFar
- - 'Fire Glow'	CRos
§ - - 'Pearl'PBR	WCot
- 'Tang Dynasty'	CBct EBee WFar

Lotus (*Papilionaceae*)

sp.	NHic
berthelotii	CCCN CDTJ ECtt EShb EUJe LPot MCot
- deep red-flowered ♀H1c	SWvt
berthelotii* × *maculatus ♀H1c	CCCN MCot MSCN
corniculatus	CHab CWld EBou GJos LCro LOPS MCoo MHer MMuc MNHC NGrd NMir SEND SRms WSFF
- 'Stephen Jackson' **new**	CNat
creticus	SPhx
hirsutus ♀H4	CBod CExl EBou ECha EHoe ELan EPfP LPot MAsh MCot MRav NSti SEND SLon SPer SPhx SPlb SPoG SWvt WIce WSHC XLum XSen
- 'Brimstone' (v)	MRav SPer SPoG SWvt
- LITTLE BOY BLUE ('Lisbob'PBR)	CRos CSBt EPfP LRHS NRHS
- 'Lois'	LRHS SPoG WAvo WCot
jacobaeus	MCot
maritimus	WWFP XLum
mearnsii	SPlb
pedunculatus	CHab MCoo NMir SPhx WSFF
pentaphyllus	XSen
tetragonolobus	SPhx SVic WSFF

lovage see *Levisticum officinale*

Loxostigma (*Gesneriaceae*)

kurzii GWJ 9342	WCru

Ludwigia (*Onagraceae*)

natans	XBlo
palustris	LLWG

Luetkea (*Rosaceae*)

pectinata	GEdr

Luma ✿ (*Myrtaceae*)

§ ***apiculata*** ♀H4	Widely available
§ - 'Glanleam Gold' (v)	Widely available
- 'Nana'	LEdu WJek
- 'Penlee'	WJek
- 'Rainbow's Gold' (v)	EShb
- 'Saint Hilary' (v)	CBcs EPfP WJek WPav
- 'Variegata' (v)	CTri WFar
§ ***chequen***	CBcs CBod CCoa CSBt CSde EShb LEdu NLar WPGP WPav

Lunaria (*Brassicaceae*)

§ ***annua***	GJos LCro LOPS MNHC WCot WSFF
- var. ***albiflora*** ♀H7	NBir SEND WCot
I - - 'Alba Variegata' (v) ♀H7	CSpe WBrk
- 'Chedglow'	CNat CSpe LEdu LRHS MAvo SBch WCot
- 'Corfu Blue' ♀H6	CSpe EWes MAvo SPtp WCot
- 'Cynthia'	CNat
- 'Munstead Purple' ♀H7	CSpe
- 'Nettleton'	CNat
- purple-leaved	CMea
- 'Rosemary Verey'	WCot
- 'Ruth'	EBee LEdu WCot
- 'The Optimist'	CNat
- 'Variegata' (v)	CSpe GJos NBir WCot
biennis	see *L. annua*
rediviva ♀H7	CRos CSpe ECha EMor EPPr EUJe GAbr GBin GCal GMaP IBlr IFro LEdu LRHS MBel MMuc NBid NChi NPer NRHS NSti SBrt SEND WCAu WCot WFar WPGP
- 'Partway White' (v)	CFis CMil MAvo WCot

Lunathyrium (*Woodsiaceae*)

petersenii	ISha
pycnosorum	ISha

Lupinus ✿ (*Papilionaceae*)

arboreus ♀H4	CBcs CDul CKel CRos CSBt CTri CWCL ELan EPfP LRHS MAsh MCoo MGil MHer MNHC MNrw MRav NAln NBir NLar NRHS SCob SEle SPer SPlb SPoG SRms SVic WFar
- 'Barton-on-Sea'	CWld MGil
- blue and white-flowered	SCob WFar
- 'Blue Boy'	ELan LRHS LSRN SWvt
- blue-flowered	CBod CRos CWCL CWld GPSL LRHS MGil NLar NRHS SCob SPer SPlb SPoG SRms SWvt WFar WOut
- 'Chelsea Blue'	CRos EPfP LRHS NRHS
- cream-flowered	SCob
- prostrate	WAvo
- 'Snow Queen'	CPla CWCL SCob SPer SPoG SWvt
- 'Sulphur Yellow'	SWvt
- white-flowered	CBod CSpe CWld ELan GMaP LEdu MMrt SCob SPlb
- yellow and blue-flowered	NBir SRkn WFar
- yellow-flowered	CBod CWld ELan SCob SWvt
arcticus	EBee
argenteus	GKev
'Beefeater'	CRos CWCL ELan EPfP EWes GBee LBuc LLHF LRHS NPri NRHS SPoG
'Blossom'PBR	CRos CWCL CWGN EWes LLHF LRHS LSRN NPri NRHS SPoG
caespitosus	see *L. lepidus* var. *utahensis*
'Camelot Blue' (Camelot Series)	EPfP
'Cashmere Cream'	CRos CWCL CWGN EBee LRHS NPri NRHS
'Chameleon'	CRos LBuc LRHS NRHS
chamissonis	CCCN CRos CSpe CWCL EBee ELan EWes LRHS NRHS SIgm SPer WKif
'Chandelier' (Band of Nobles Series)	CAby CBcs CBod CRos CSBt CTri ELan ELon EPfP GAbr GMaP ILea LCro LOPS MAsh MCot MJak MSCN MWat NBir NGBl NHol NLar SCob SGbt SPer SPoG SWvt WCAu WFar
'Desert Sun'PBR	CRos CWCL EPfP LRHS NLar NPri NRHS SPoG
'Dwarf Lulu'	see *L.* 'Lulu'
Gallery Series	CBod CSBt SCoo SPlb WFar
- 'Gallery Blue'	CBod CRos EAJP ECtt ELan EPfP EWhm LBuc LCro LOPS LRHS LSRN MHol NLar NPri NRHS SCoo SPer SPoG WFar
- 'Gallery Pink'	CRos EAJP ELan EPfP EWhm LRHS MHol NLar NPri NRHS SCoo SPer SPoG WFar
- 'Gallery Red'	CBod CRos EAJP ECtt ELan EPfP EWhm LCro LOPS LRHS MHol NLar NPri NRHS SCoo SPer SPoG WFar
- 'Gallery Rose'	EWhm LSRN NRHS SPoG WFar
- 'Gallery Pink Bicolor' **new**	CBod
- 'Gallery White'	CBod CRos EAJP ELan EPfP EWhm LRHS MHol NLar NPri NRHS SCoo SPer SPoG WFar

	– 'Gallery Yellow'	CBod CRos EAJP ECtt ELan EPfP EWhm LRHS MHol NLar NPri NRHS SPer SPoG WFar
	'Gladiator'PBR	CRos CWCL ECtt EPfP EWes LLHF LRHS MHol MJak MMrt NLar NRHS SPoG
	'Heathcliffe Blue'	WOut
	'Judy Harper'	ECtt GBee LRHS
	'Jupiter'	LRHS NLar NPri
	'King Canute'	CRos CWCL CWGN EPfP LRHS MMrt NCGa NLar NPri NRHS
	latifolius subsp. ***parishii***	EBee
	lepidus	CPbh
§	– var. ***utahensis***	SPlb
§	'Lulu'	CRos EPfP LRHS NRHS SGbt SPer SPoG SWvt
	'Magic Lantern'	CRos CWCL EPfP LRHS MMrt NRHS SPoG
	'Manhattan Lights'PBR	CBcs CChe CRos CWCL CWGN EPfP EWes ILea LLHF LRHS MHol MJak NAst NLar NPri NRHS SPoG
	'Masterpiece'PBR	CBcs CRos CWCL EPfP EWes GBin ILea LCro LLHF LOPS LRHS LSRN MCot NLar NPri NRHS SPoG WCAu
	Minarette Group	CRos EPfP LRHS MNrw NRHS SRms
	'Morello Cherry'	CWCL
	'My Castle' (Band of Nobles Series)	CBcs CBod CRos CSBt CTri ECtt EHrv ELan EPfP GAbr GMaP LRHS LSRN LSun MAsh MGos MJak MWat NAln NGBl NLar NRHS SGbt SPer SPoG SWvt WFar WMoo
	nanus	LCro LOPS
	'Neptune'	CWCL
	'Noble Maiden' (Band of Nobles Series)	Widely available
	nootkatensis	GLog
	'Pam Ayres'	ECtt GBee GBin LRHS
	perennis	CBod
	'Persian Slipper'PBR	CChe CEnd CRos CWCL CWGN ECtt EPfP EWes LBuc LCro LLHF LOPS LRHS LSRN MCot NLar NPri NRHS SPoG WCAu
	'Polar Princess'	CRos CWCL CWGN ECtt EWes GBee GBin LRHS NCGa NPri NRHS SPoG
	polyphyllus var. ***burkei***	EBee
	'Purple Emperor'	NCGa
	'Purple Swirl'	CRos ECtt EPfP LRHS NPri NRHS
	'Rachel de Thame'	CChe CRos CWCL CWGN EBee EWes LRHS MHol NLar NPri NRHS SPoG
	'Red Rum'PBR	CEnd CRos CWCL CWGN LBuc LRHS LSRN NLar NPri NRHS SPoG
	× ***regalis*** Russell Group	CPla CSBt EPfP MHer SPlb SRms SVic SWvt WFar
	'Rote Flamme'	ELon EWes SCob WOut
	Russell hybrids	see *L.* × *regalis* Russell Group
	'Saffron'PBR	CEnd CRos LBuc LRHS LSRN NPri NRHS
	'Salmon Star'PBR	CRos CWCL CWGN LRHS NLar NRHS
	sericeus	SPhx
	'Silver Fleece'	CCCN CRos CWld LRHS NRHS WFar
	'Tequila Flame'PBR	CRos CWCL LBuc LLHF LRHS NLar NPri NRHS SPoG
	'Terracotta'	CWCL LRHS NPri NRHS SPoG
	texensis	CSpe
	'The Chatelaine' (Band of Nobles Series)	CAby CBcs CBod CRos CSBt ECtt ELan ELon EPfP GMaP ILea LRHS LSRN LSun MAsh MJak NBir NGBl NHol NLar NRHS SCob SPer SPoG SWvt WCAu WFar WMoo
	'The Governor' (Band of Nobles Series)	Widely available
	'The Page' (Band of Nobles Series)	CAby CBcs CBod CRos ELan ELon EPfP GMaP ILea LCro LOPS LRHS LSRN LSun MAsh MNHC MSCN NLar NRHS SCob SPer SPoG SWvt WFar WMoo
	'Thundercloud'	EBee
	'Towering Inferno'	CEnd CRos CWCL ECtt EPfP EWes LBuc LRHS NAst NLar NPri NRHS SPoG
	variicolor	SIgm
	varius subsp. ***orientalis***	SPhx
	Woodfield hybrids	LRHS

Luzula (Juncaceae)

	alpinopilosa	EPPr
	× ***borreri*** 'Botany Bay' (v)	CRos GBin LRHS NRHS
	'Engel'	EPPr EWes
	forsteri	IMou
	luzuloides 'Schneehäschen'	NWsh WSHC
	maxima	see *L. sylvatica*
	nivalis	GAbr
	nivea	Widely available
	pedemontana	EBee SMea
	pilosa	GCal
	– 'Grünfink'	EBee
	– 'Igel'	CBod CKno EBee EShb LEdu NBid SCob
§	***sylvatica***	CRos ELan EPPr GBin GQue LRHS MMuc MRav NBro NLar NMir NPol NRHS SCob SEND SPer WShi XLum
	– 'A. Rutherford'	see *L. sylvatica* 'Taggart's Cream'
	– from Tatra Mountains, Slovakia	EPPr
	– 'Aurea'	CAby CKel CKno CRos ECha ELon EPPr GWyn LRHS MJak MMuc MRav NRHS NSti NWsh SEND WCot WFar WGrn WMoo WPtf
	– 'Aureomarginata'	see *L. sylvatica* 'Marginata'
I	– 'Auslese'	EPPr EPfP WMoo
	– 'Bromel'	EPPr
	– 'Hohe Tatra' ♀H7	CBod CSpe EHoe EPPr EWes GBin GMaP GQue LEdu MBNS NGdn SCob SPer SPoG
§	– 'Marginata' (v) ♀H7	CKno CPla EBee ECha EHoe ELon EMor EPPr EUJe GBin GMaP LRHS MAvo MBNS MMuc MRav NBid NGdn NLar NSti SArc SCob SEND WCot WHoo WMoo
	– 'Mariusz'	EPPr
*	– f. ***nova***	ELon EPPr
	– 'Onderbos'	EBee
	– 'Solar Flair'	EUJe GBin NRHS
	– 'Starmaker'	CBod
§	– 'Taggart's Cream' (v)	CRos EBee EHoe GCal LRHS NHol NRHS NWad WMoo
	– 'Tauernpass'	EPPr GCal LRHS SPhx
	– 'Thierry's Cream' (v)	EBee EMor MAvo MHol SPoG WBrk WCot
	– 'Wäldler'	EBee EPPr
	– 'Wintergold'	EPPr
	ulophylla	GEdr SIgm SPlb WAbe WThu

Luzuriaga (*Luzuriagaceae*)

polyphylla HCM 98202	WCru
radicans	CCCN CRHN CTsd GEdr WCru WPav WSHC
- RH 0602	ESwi WCru

Lychnis (*Caryophyllaceae*)

alpina	CMac EDAr NGdn WFar WIce XLum
- 'Rosea'	MBel NBir
- 'Snow Flurry'	GKev
§ × ***arkwrightii***	ECha LRHS NRHS
- 'Orange Zwerg'	CRos SGbt
- 'Vesuvius'	CBcs CMac EAJP EBee MBel SPer SRms WGwG
chalcedonica 🏆H7	Widely available
- 'Alba Plena' (d) **new**	NAln
- var. ***albiflora***	EMor EPPr EPfP MBel NBro NLar WCAu WHrl WMoo
- 'Carnea'	CRos EPPr LRHS MBNS NGdn NRHS SPhx
- 'Dusky Salmon'	WHrl
- 'Flore Pleno' (d)	EShb GCal WCot
- 'Pinkie'	MMuc NLar NWad
- 'Rauhreif'	NLar SPhx WHer
- 'Rosea'	CBod EMor EPfP NBir WHrl WMoo
* - 'Salmonea'	EMor EPPr GPSL NBir SRms
cognata B&SWJ 4234	WCru
§ ***coronaria*** 🏆H7	Widely available
- MESE 356	MAvo SPhx
- 'Abbotswood Rose'	see *L.* × *walkeri* 'Abbotswood Rose'
- 'Alba' 🏆H7	Widely available
- 'Angel's Blush'	GQue NBir NGrd NLar SRkn
- Atrosanguinea Group	CBod CBre CRos EPfP GMaP IBlr LRHS MBel MHol MRav MWat NEgg NGdn NRHS NSti NWad SPer WTor
- 'Blood Red'	CSpe LEdu LRHS WBrk
- 'Cerise'	CCBP MArl NBir
- dark red-flowered	MAvo
- GARDENERS' WORLD ('Blych') (d)	CBod CRos CSpe EBee ECha ECtt ELan ELon EMor EWes IKil IPot LRHS MAsh MBNS MBel MHol NRHS NSti SPer SRkn WBrk WCot
- Oculata Group	CBod CSpe CTsd EBee ELan EMor EPPr EPfP LEdu LPot SPlb WFar WKif WMoo
coronata	CTsd
§ - var. ***sieboldii***	SBrt SPhx
dioica	see *Silene dioica*
flos-cuculi	Widely available
- var. ***albiflora***	CBre CSam EMor NBro NLar WHer WMoo
- dark pink-flowered **new**	IFro
- JENNY ('Lychjen'PBR) (d)	CDor CRos EBee ECtt ELan EMor EPfP LEdu LRHS LSRN MBNS MBel MHol MNrw MSCN NDov NRHS NSti SCob SRkn WCAu WCot
- 'Little Robin'	EBou LLWG
- 'Nana'	GAbr GJos MHol NGdn NLar SPad WGwG
- 'Petite Jenny' (d)	CRos EBee ECtt EMor GWyn LRHS MBNS NAst NRHS SPoG WCot WTor
- 'White Robin'	Widely available
flos-jovis 🏆H6	CRos ECha EPfP GJos LRHS NBir NRHS SRms WMoo XLum
- 'Hort's Variety'	CRos EBee LRHS NBir NRHS
- 'Minor'	see *L. flos-jovis* 'Nana'
§ - 'Nana'	CPla NHic SBch
- 'Peggy'	CRos EBee EBou EMor LRHS NBre NGdn NHic NLar
× ***haageana***	SRms
'Hill Grounds'	CElw EBee ECha ECtt WCot WGoo WSHC
miqueliana	EBee WMoo
'Molten Lava'	CRos EPfP LRHS NRHS SRms WHlf
§ ***viscaria***	CWld ECha EMor GJos GPSL WMoo
- 'Alba'	ECha NBre XLum
- ***alpina***	see *L. viscaria*
§ - subsp. ***atropurpurea***	EWes GJos LRHS MMuc MPie SHar SPhx SRms WArt WMoo WPtf
- 'Feuer'	EWes NGBl WMoo
- 'Firebird'	EWes
- 'Plena' (d)	IKil IPot NBir SRkn
- 'Schnee'	GJos NGBl NLar
- 'Snowbird'	CTsd
- 'Splendens'	EMor MBel NGrd WFar XLum
- 'Splendens Plena' (d) 🏆H5	CCBP XLum
§ × ***walkeri*** 'Abbotswood Rose' 🏆H7	IBlr MAvo MJak
wilfordii	GKev NWad
§ ***yunnanensis***	NSti SPhx WBrk
- ***alba***	see *L. yunnanensis*

Lycianthes (*Solanaceae*)

§ ***rantonnetii*** 🏆H3	CBcs CCCN CHll ELan EShb SEND SPoG WAvo WKif
- 'Variegata' (v)	CHll WCot

Lycium (*Solanaceae*)

afrum	SVen
barbarum	CAgr CBcs CCCN CDul CLau CSBt ECrN EPom IDee LCro LEdu LOPS MAsh MCoo MGil MJak NLar SCob SDea SEND SPre SVic SWvt
- 'Big Lifeberry'	CAgr LEdu
- 'Number 1 Lifeberry'	CAgr
- 'Sweet Lifeberry'	CAgr LEdu
chinense	NQui

Lycopodium (*Lycopodiaceae*)

clavatum	GPoy

Lycopsis see *Anchusa*

Lycopus (*Lamiaceae*)

europaeus	CHab EBee GPoy MMuc WGwG WSFF

Lycoris (*Amaryllidaceae*)

aurea	GKev LAma SDeJ WHil
radiata	CCCN GKev LAma SDeJ WHil

Lygeum (*Poaceae*)

spartum	XSen

Lygodium (*Lygodiaceae*)

japonicum	WFib

Lygos see *Retama*

Lyonothamnus (*Rosaceae*)

floribundus subsp. ***aspleniifolius***	CCCN CExl EBee SArc WPGP

Lysichiton (*Araceae*)

camtschatcensis 🏆H7	CBen CTsd CWat ECha EPfP EUJe LCro LLWG LOPS LRHS NLar NPer NRHS SWvt WPnP WShi XLum
× ***hortensis***	ECha

Lysiloma (*Mimosaceae*)

watsonii	SPlb

Lysimachia (*Primulaceae*)

albescens	CExl XLum
§ ***atropurpurea***	CBod CRos CSpe EAJP EBee ELan GPSL LRHS NRHS SPer
- 'Beaujolais'	CChe CExl CRos CWld LCro LEdu LOPS LRHS MGos MHol MWat NGBl NRHS SCob SPoG SPtp
- 'Geronimo'	CSpe
barystachys ♀H6	CSam LEdu MArl MBel MRav SHar WCot WOut XLum
- PAB 8755	LEdu
- 'Huntingbrook'	LEdu MAvo WPGP WWtn
CANDELA ('Innlyscand')	CAby CBod CSpe ECtt GWyn LRHS MHer MHol MMuc NCou NGBl NRHS SPoG WCot WMoo WTor WWtn
candida	WCot
christinae new	LEdu
ciliata	CMac CRos ECha GMaP LRHS MNrw NBir NGdn NLar NRHS
§ - 'Firecracker' ♀H7	Widely available
- 'Purpurea'	see *L. ciliata* 'Firecracker'
clethroides ♀H6	Widely available
- 'Geisha' (v)	EBee WCot
- 'Lady Jane'	CPla CRos MAvo MNrw SRms
- 'Leigong Storm'	WPGP
§ ***congestiflora***	NPer
- 'Midnight Sun'PBR	CCCN ECtt
- 'Outback Sunset'PBR (v)	ECtt
- 'Persian Carpet'	WCot
- 'Persian Chocolate'	WCot WFar
ephemerum ♀H6	Widely available
fortunei	WFar XEll XLum
japonica var. ***minutissima***	ITim SRot
lichiangensis	CExl CRos GKev GPSL IMou LRHS NBir NRHS WMoo
lyssii	see *L. congestiflora*
minoricensis	GKev WSpi XLum
nemorum	CWld IMou
- 'Lola Playle'PBR	WCot
- 'Pale Star'	CBre
nummularia	CSBt CWat EPfP GPoy MJak NBir WBrk
- 'Aurea' ♀H5	CMac CSBt EBou ECha ECtt EPfP GAbr GQue LCro LOPS LPot MHer MJak MMuc MRav NBid NBir NBro NLar NMir NPri SEND SPer SPoG SRms SWvt WMoo WWtn XLum
paridiformis	WPGP
var. ***paridiformis*** NJM 11.067	
- var. ***stenophylla***	CExl GBin SPtp
punctata misapplied	see *L. verticillaris*
punctata L.	CBod CSBt EBou ECha EPfP GAbr GMaP MHer MMuc MRav NBro NMir NPer SCob SPer SPlb SRms WBrk WCAu WFar WMAq WMoo
§ - 'Alexander' (v)	Widely available
- 'Gaulthier Brousse'	EBee MHCG WCot
- GOLDEN ALEXANDER ('Walgoldalex'PBR) (v)	CBod CChe CExl CKel CRos LBuc LRHS MBNS NHol NLar NRHS WMoo
- 'Golden Glory' (v)	WCot
- 'Hometown Hero'	EBee NLar
- 'Ivy Maclean' (v)	SWvt
- 'Variegata'	see *L. punctata* 'Alexander'
- ***verticillata***	see *L. verticillaris*
'Purpurea'	see *L. atropurpurea*
sertulata	EBee
SNOW CANDLES ('L9902')	EBee EWes MNrw WFar
terrestris new	EBee
thyrsiflora	CWat EBee LLWG NPer WCot WMAq
§ ***verticillaris***	CTri WCot
vulgaris	CHab EWat LLWG WMoo
- subsp. ***davurica***	WCot
- - B&SWJ 8632	WCru

Lysionotus (*Gesneriaceae*)

gamosepalus B&SWJ 7241	WCru
kwangsiensis HWJ 625	WCru
pauciflorus	IArd
- B&SWJ 303	WCru
- B&SWJ 335	WCru
- HWJ 643 from Vietnam	WCru
- HWJ 811 from Vietnam	WCru
- dwarf B&SWJ 189	WCru
- 'Lady Lavender'	EBee MBNS
serratus HWJK 2426	WCru

Lythrum (*Lythraceae*)

alatum	NDov
anceps	NBre NLar
'Rose Dream'	NWad
salicaria	CBen CHab CWat CWld EBou ENfk GJos LLWG MCot MHer MMuc MNHC MWts NAln NBro SEND SPlb SRms WBrk WHer WMoo WPnP WSFF WShi WWtn XLum
- 'Augenweide'	XLum
- 'Blush' ♀H7	Widely available
§ - 'Feuerkerze' ♀H7	CAby CBod CMea CRos CSam CWld EBee ECtt ELan ELon EPfP EShb GBin LRHS MArl MBel MCot MRav NBir NEgg NHol NRHS NSti SCob SPer WFar WWtn
- FIRECANDLE	see *L. salicaria* 'Feuerkerze'
- 'Happy'	ELon
- 'Lady Sackville'	EBee ECtt ELon EMor GMaP IKil IPot MCot MTis NLar WSHC
- 'Little Robert'	ECtt WFar
- 'Morden Pink'	CTri EBee ELan MMuc NLar NRHS SCob SEND WFar XLum
- 'Red Beauty'	LSun
- 'Robert'	Widely available
- 'Robin'	CRos ECtt EMor LLHF LRHS MAsh MHol NDov NPri NRHS SGbt SRot SWvt
- 'Rose'	NBir SWvt
- 'Stichflamme'	ELon
- 'Swirl'	CMea ECtt ELan ELon EMor EPfP IKil ILea LEdu LLWG MTis NDov NRHS NSti SHar WHoo
- 'The Beacon'	CPla EBee EMor NLar SRms
- 'Zigeunerblut'	ECtt ELon MRav NLar WCAu XLum
virgatum	SMHy SPhx WCFE WMoo WOut WSHC
- 'Dropmore Purple'	Widely available
- 'Helene'	IMou NDov
- pale-flowered	NDov
- 'Rose Queen'	ECtt IPot MRav SMHy
- 'Rosy Gem'	CRos EBee EMor EPfP GJos GMaP LRHS NBro NRHS SCob SRms SWvt WFar

- 'The Rocket' CAby CBod CTri EPfP EShb GCal LRHS MPie MRav NBro NDov NRHS SWvt WFar WPnP

M

Maackia (*Papilionaceae*)

amurensis CBcs CMCN EPfP GBin NLar
hupehensis MBlu

Macadamia (*Proteaceae*)

integrifolia (F) XBlo

mace, English see *Achillea ageratum*

Macfadyena (*Bignoniaceae*)

unguis-cati see *Dolichandra unguis-cati*

Machilus see *Persea*

Mackaya (*Acanthaceae*)

§ ***bella*** ♀H1b CHll EShb

Macleaya (*Papaveraceae*)

cordata misapplied see *M.* × *kewensis*
§ ***cordata*** (Willd.) R. Br. ♀H6 CRos EBee EMor LRHS LSun MHol NBir NRHS SPer SPlb SRms WMoo XLum
- NJM 11.002 WPGP
§ × ***kewensis*** EBee NDai SCob SPoG
- 'Flamingo' ♀H6 CExl EBee EBou ECha ECtt GBin GWyn LRHS MBNS MPie NRHS SWvt WCot WWtn
§ ***microcarpa*** GJos MHol
- 'Kelway's Coral Plume' ♀H6 CBcs CBod CExl CKel CMac CRos EBee ECtt ELan EPfP GAbr GBin GMaP LCro LOPS LRHS LSRN MRav NAln NBid NBro NEgg NLar NRHS SPer SPoG SWvt WBor WWtn
- 'Spetchley Ruby' CExl EBee ECha EUJe GBin LRHS MRav NLar SPhx WCot XLum

Maclura (*Moraceae*)

pomifera CBcs CMCN IDee MBlu SBrt SEND SPlb
- 'Cannonball' SAko
- var. ***inermis*** IArd
- 'Naughty Boy' NLar
- 'Pretty Woman' NLar
tricuspidata B&SWJ 12755 WCru
- 'Parthenos' (F) CAgr
- seedless (F) **new** CAgr

Macrodiervilla see *Weigela*

Macropiper (*Piperaceae*)

§ ***excelsum*** GPoy

Macrothelypteris (*Thelypteridaceae*)

torresiana CBdn WPGP

Macrozamia (*Zamiaceae*)

communis CBrP
dyeri see *M. riedlei*
lucida CBrP
moorei CBrP
§ ***riedlei*** CBrP

Maddenia (*Rosaceae*)

hypoleuca IDee MBlu NLar

Maesa (*Primulaceae*)

japonica CExl
- CWJ 12371 WCru
montana CExl

Magnolia ✿ (*Magnoliaceae*)

acuminata CBcs CDul CMCN LMaj
- 'Blue Opal' CBcs CJun LRHS
* - 'Kinju' CEnd CJun
- 'Koban Dori' CBcs CJun
- 'Moegi Dori' NLar
- 'Patriot' CMCN
- 'Patriot' × (× ***brooklynensis*** 'Yellow Bird') MAsh
- 'Seiju' CJun
- var. ***subcordata*** 'Miss Honeybee' CBcs CJun
- - 'Mister Yellowjacket' CJun
'Advance' CBcs CJun
'Albatross' CBcs CEnd CJun WPGP
'Alex' CJun LRHS
'Alixeed' CJun
'Amber' CJun
'Ambrosia' CJun
'Angelica' CJun
'Anilou' CJun
'Ann' CExl
'Anna' CJun
'Anticipation' CBcs CEnd CJun WPGP
'Apollo' CBcs CJun LSRN WPGP
'Archangel' CJun
ashei see *M. macrophylla* subsp. *ashei*
'Asian Artistry' CJun LRHS
'Athene' ♀H5 CBcs CEnd CJun LMil SAko WPGP
'Atlas' CBcs CEnd CJun WPGP
'Aurora' CBcs CJun
'Avocet' **new** LRHS
'Banana Split' LMil LRHS MAsh
'Betty' CBcs CMac ELon EMOT LRHS LSRN MBlu MGos MMuc NLar SLim SSta
'Big Dude' CBcs CEnd CJun EPfP IDee SCob SLim
'Binette' **new** CJun
biondii CBcs IMou MBlu NLar
'Black Beauty' CBcs CJun LRHS WHor
'Black Swan' WPGP
BLACK TULIP ('Jurmag1'[PBR]) CBcs CDul CRos CTho ELan EPfP GGGa LBuc LCro LMil LOPS LRHS MAsh MGos NLar SCoo SLon SPer SPoG WHor WPGP
'Blackbird' LRHS
'Blushing Belle' CJun SAko
'Brenda' CJun
'Brixton Belle' CBcs WPGP
× ***brooklynensis*** 'Evamaria' CTho
- 'Golden Joy' CJun
- 'Hattie Carthan' CBcs CJun LRHS
- 'Woodsman' CBcs NLar NOra WMat
- 'Yellow Bird' CBcs CDul CEnd CJun CMCN EBee EPfP EWTr IArd LMil LRHS LSRN MAsh MBlu MGos MThu NLar NPri SCob SPoG WMat
BURGUNDY STAR ('Jurmag4') CBcs LCro LOPS SPer
'Butterbowl' CJun

'Butterflies'	CBcs CCCN CDul CJun CRos CTho CTsd ELan EMOT EPfP LRHS LSRN MBlu MGos NLar NOra NRHS SGol SPer SRms SSta WFar WMat WSpi
'Caerhays Belle' ♀H5	CBcs CJun IArd LMil LRHS NLar SAko SPoG WPGP
'Caerhays Surprise' ♀H5	CBcs CEnd CJun WPGP
campbellii	CBcs CMCN EPfP LRHS
- Alba Group	WPGP
- - 'Chyverton'	WPGP
- - 'Ethel Hillier'	CBcs
- - 'Sir Harold Hillier'	CJun WPGP
- - 'Strybing White'	WPGP
- 'Ambrose Congreve'	WPGP
- 'Betty Jessel'	CBcs CJun WPGP
- 'Darjeeling' ♀H4	CBcs CJun LRHS WPGP
- 'Lionel de Rothschild'	WPGP
- subsp. ***mollicomata***	EPfP LRHS
- - 'Lanarth'	CBcs WPGP
- - 'Peter Borlase'	WPGP
- - 'Werrington'	CBcs
- 'Queen Caroline'	LRHS WPGP
- (Raffillii Group) 'Charles Raffill'	CDul EPfP LMil LRHS SPoG WHor
- - 'Kew's Surprise'	CBcs WPGP
- 'Sidbury'	CBcs CTho WHor
campbellii* × *sprengeri	WPGP
'Candy Cane'	CJun
'Carlos'	CBcs CJun
cathcartii	WPGP
- B&SWJ 11802	WCru
- HWJ 874	WCru
cavaleriei var. ***platypetala***	CExl
caveana	LEdu
- NJM 13.037	WPGP
- NJM 13.044	EBee WPGP
'Cecil Nice'	CJun
CHAMELEON	see *M.* 'Chang Hua'
§ 'Chang Hua'	CJun
changhungtana* × *insignis new	WPGP
'Charles Coates'	CJun EPfP NLar WPGP
'Charming Lady'	CJun
chevalieri B&SWJ 11802	WCru
- DJHV 06037	WCru
- HWJ 621	WCru
CHINA TOWN ('Jing Ning')	CJun
'Columnar Pink'	NLar
'Coral Lake'	CJun LMil LRHS
'Cornish Chough'	WPGP
crassifolia hort.	see *M. fansipanensis*
'Crescendo'	CJun
'Crystal Chalice'	CJun
'Cup Cake'	CJun
'Curlew'	WPGP
cylindrica misapplied	see *M.* 'Pegasus'
cylindrica ambig.	CBcs CMCN SPtp
cylindrica E.H.Wilson 'Bjuv'	CJun
'Daphne' ♀H6	CBcs CDul CEnd CJun EPfP GGGa LMil LRHS LSRN MAsh NLar SCob SLim SPoG WPGP
'Darrell Dean'	CJun
'David Clulow' ♀H5	CBcs CJun LMaj SSta WPGP
dawsoniana	CBcs CMCN IDee IMou WSpi
- 'Barbara Cook'	CJun
- 'Chyverton Red'	CBcs WPGP
- 'Ruby Rose' new	CJun
- 'Valley Splendour'	CJun
'Daybreak' ♀H6	CBcs CJun CTho ELan LMil LRHS MBlu MRav NOra SGol SSta WMat WPGP
'Deborah'	CJun
delavayi	CBcs CBrP CDul CMCN CTho EPfP EUJe LRHS SArc SEND WPGP
'Delia Williams'	CBcs WPGP
§ ***denudata*** ♀H6	CBcs CDul CMCN CTho EPfP LMil MBlu SSta
- 'Double Diamond'	CJun
- FESTIROSE ('Minfor')	LRHS
- 'Forrest's Pink'	CBcs LMaj LRHS
- FRAGRANT CLOUD ('Dan Xin')	CJun
- 'Gere'	CBcs CJun
- 'Ghost Ship'	CJun
- YELLOW RIVER ('Fei Huang')	CBcs CEnd CJun LMaj MJak NOra SPoG WHor WMat
doltsopa	CAby CBcs CCCN CExl EPfP IMou LRHS SSta WPGP
- B&SWJ 13996	WCru
- NJM 12.028	WPGP
- NJM 12.047	WPGP
- 'Silver Cloud'	CExl
'Early Rose'	CJun
'Elegance'	CJun
'Elisa Odenwald'	LMil LRHS
'Elizabeth' ♀H6	CBcs CJun CKel CMCN CRos CTho EPfP LMil LRHS LSRN MAsh MBlu MGos NLar NPri NRHS SPer SPoG SRms SWvt WMat
'Emma Cook'	CJun
§ ***ernestii***	CExl WPGP
§ - subsp. ***ernestii***	IArd
'Eskimo'	CJun
'Eternal Flames'	NLar
'F.J. Williams'	CBcs WPGP
'Fairy' new	MThu
FAIRY BLUSH ('Micjur01'PBR)	CBcs LCro LOPS MGos
FAIRY CREAM ('Micjur02')	CBcs CCCN LCro LOPS LRHS
FAIRY MAGNOLIA WHITE ('Micjur05')	CBcs CCCN ELon LCro LOPS SPoG
§ ***fansipanensis*** FMWJ 13054	WCru
- FMWJ 13163	WCru
'Felicity'	CJun
FELIX JURY ('Jurmag2'PBR)	CBcs ELan EPfP LRHS
figo	CBcs CBod CCCN CExl CHll CRos CTsd EBee ELan EPfP EShb LRHS MGil NRHS SSta WPGP
'Fireglow'	CJun
'Flamingo'	CJun
floribunda FMWJ 13384 from Tonkin, Vietnam	WCru
- NJM 09.179	WPGP
- WWJ 11874	WCru
- WWJ 11982 from Tonkin, Vietnam	WCru
- WWJ 11996	WCru
- WWJ 12003	WCru
- WWJ 12011	WCru
- 'Fansipan Furry'	WCru
- 'Furry Uok'	WPGP
fordiana	CExl
§ ***foveolata*** B&SWJ 11749	WCru
- DJHV 06105	WCru
- WWJ 11900	WCru
- WWJ 11929	WCru
- WWJ 11955	WCru
'Frank Gladney'	CJun
'Frank's Masterpiece'	CJun

'Galaxy' ♀H6	CBcs CDul CEnd CJun CMac ELon EPfP IArd IDee LMaj LMil LRHS MAsh MGos MMuc NLar NPri SAko SLim SSta WMat WMou
'Genie'PBR	CBcs CRos LMaj LMil LRHS NLar NRHS SCob WPGP
'George Henry Kern' ♀H6	CBcs CDul CKel CLnd CRos CTho EMOT EPfP LRHS MGos MJak MMuc NEgg NLar NPri NRHS SEND
'Ghislaine' **new**	WPGP
'Gladys Carlson'	CJun
globosa	CExl CRos LEdu LRHS NRHS WPGP
'Gold Crown'	CJun
'Gold Star' ♀H6	CBcs CDul CEnd CJun CRos CTho LMil LRHS MGos NLar NOra NPri NRHS SAko SPoG SSta WMat WPGP
'Golden Endeavour'	CJun
'Golden Gala'	CJun
'Golden Gift'	CJun LMil LRHS MAsh WPGP
'Golden Pond'	CJun LRHS
'Golden Rain'	CJun
'Golden Sun'	CJun IArd
'Goldfinch'	CJun
I × ***gotoburgensis*** Chollipo clone	WPGP
grandiflora	CMCN EBee EMOT EPfP ESwi LCro LEdu LOPS LPra LSRN MGos MMuc MRav NEgg NLar NPri SArc SCob SEND SEWo WTSh
- ALTA ('Tmgh'PBR)	LRHS
- 'Blanchard'	CBcs CJun LRHS NLar
- 'Bracken's Brown Beauty'	CRos LMil LRHS NRHS
- 'Charles Dickens'	SVen
- 'Edith Bogue'	EUJe LRHS NEgg NLar SSta
- 'Exmouth'	CBcs CDul CEnd CMCN CMac CRos CSBt CTho CTri CTsd ELan EMOT EPfP EUJe LMil LRHS LSRN MAsh MBlu MGos NLar NRHS SCob SPer SPoG SRms SSta SWvt
- 'Ferruginea'	CBcs CJun EPfP NLar SGol
- 'Flore Pleno' (d)	SGol
- 'François Treyve'	EMOT EPfP LRHS LSRN
- 'Galissonnière'	CBcs CCVT CRos ECrN EPfP LMaj LPra LRHS MGos NPri SCob SGol SWvt
- 'Goliath'	ELan EMOT EPfP LMaj LRHS NPri SEWo SPer SSta
- 'Harold Poole'	CJun
- 'Kay Parris' ♀H5	CJun CRos EPfP LMil LRHS MAsh NRHS SPoG
- 'Little Gem'	CBcs CBod CCCN CJun CRos ELan ELon EMOT EPfP IDee LRHS LSRN NLar SGol SPer SPoG SSta WFar
- 'Mainstreet'	CJun LRHS
- 'Monlia'	CJun
- 'November Fox'	LRHS
- 'Overton'	CJun
- 'Praecox'	LPra
- 'Russet'	CJun
- 'Saint Mary'	CJun
- 'Samuel Sommer'	CJun SLim
- 'Symmes Select'	CJun
- 'Treyvei'	CJun
- 'Victoria' ♀H5	CJun CRos CTho CTri ELan ELon EPfP LMil LRHS LSRN MAsh MBlu MGos NLar NRHS SPer SSta
'Green Bee'	CBcs CJun
'Hawk'	CBcs EBee WPGP
'Heaven Scent' ♀H5	Widely available
'Helen Fogg'	CJun
heptapeta	see *M. denudata*
'Honey Belle'	CJun
'Honey Flower'	CJun
'Honey Liz'	LRHS
HONEY TULIP ('Jurmag5')	CBcs SPer
§ 'Hong Yun'	CJun
'Hot Flash'	CBcs CJun
'Hot Lips'	CJun
hypoleuca	see *M. obovata* Thunb.
'Ian's Red'	CBcs CJun LMaj LMil LRHS SCob WMat WPGP
§ ***insignis***	CBcs CExl EBee LEdu LRHS WPGP
- B&SWJ 11810	WCru
- NJM 12.040	WPGP
- WWJ 11854	WCru
insignis × ***yuyuanensis***	WPGP
'Iolanthe'	CBcs CEnd CJun CMCN CTho EPfP LRHS MAsh MGos WPGP
'Iufer'	CJun
'J.C. Williams'	CBcs CJun SSta WPGP
'Jane'	CBcs CJun CMac CRos EPfP LMil LRHS MAsh MGos MRav NRHS
'Jersey Belle'	CJun
'Joe McDaniel'	CBcs CJun IArd NLar SAko
'John Bond'	SSta
'John Congreve'	CJun WPGP
'Joli Pompom'	CBcs CJun LRHS NLar SSta
'Judy Zuk'	CBcs CJun LRHS
× ***kewensis*** 'Wada's Memory'	see *M. salicifolia* 'Wada's Memory'
'Kim Kunso' **new**	SSta
kobus	CBcs CCCN CCVT CDul CLnd CMCN CNWT CRos CTho CTsd EPfP EWTr GKin LMaj LPra MBlu NLar NWea SCob SEWo SPer WMou
- B&SWJ 12751	WCru
- 'Esveld Select'	CJun
- 'Janaki Ammal'	CJun SAko
§ - 'Norman Gould'	CJun CMCN EPfP
- 'Octopus'	CJun
- pink-flowered	CBcs CJun
- 'White Elegance'	CJun
- 'Wisley Star'	CJun SSta
kwangtungensis **new**	WPGP
laevifolia	CExl CJun CMCN CTho IArd IDee IMou LRHS MGil SChF WPGP WSHC
- 'Dali Velvet'	CExl
- 'Gail's Favourite'	CRos EPfP LMil LRHS MAsh NRHS
- 'Mini Mouse'	CRos EPfP LMil LRHS MAsh NRHS
'Laura Saylor'	CJun
'Leda'	CBcs CJun SSta WPGP
'Legacy'	CJun WPGP
'Lemon Star'	CBcs LRHS
'Lennarth Jonsson'	CJun
§ ***liliiflora***	LPra
- 'Darkest Purple'	CJun NPri
§ - 'Nigra' ♀H6	Widely available
- 'Raven'	LMil LRHS WPGP
* 'Limelight'	CBcs CJun EPfP NLar NOra WMat WPGP
× ***loebneri***	LPra
- 'Ballerina'	CBcs
- 'Donna' ♀H6	CBcs CJun EPfP LMil LRHS LSRN SSta
- 'Encore'	CJun
- 'Green Mist'	CJun CRos LRHS NRHS
- 'Leonard Messel' ♀H6	Widely available
- 'Lesley Jane'	CJun

	Name	Suppliers
	- 'Mag's Pirouette' ♀H6	CAby CBcs CDul CJun EPfP LLHF LMil LRHS SAko SPoG SSta
	- 'Merrill' ♀H6	CBcs CDul CJun CLnd CMCN CMac CNWT CRos CTho ELan EMOT EPfP LMaj LMil LPra LRHS MAsh MGos MMuc MRav NEgg NLar NRHS SGol SSta
	- 'Neil McEacharn'	CJun
	- 'Pink Cloud'	CJun
	- 'Powder Puff'	CJun
	- 'Raspberry Fun'	CJun IArd
	- 'Snowdrift'	CJun LMaj SLim
	- 'Star Bright'	CJun
	- 'White Stardust'	CJun
	- 'Wildcat' ♀H6	CBcs CJun NLar SLim SSta
	- 'Willow Wood'	CJun
	'Lois' ♀H6	CBcs CEnd CJun CRos EPfP GGGa LMil LRHS LSRN NLar NRHS SSta WPGP
	'Lombardy Rose'	NLar
	lotungensis	WPGP
	'Lotus'	CBcs CJun WPGP
	'Lucy Carlson'	CJun
	'Luscious' **new**	CJun
	macrophylla	CBcs CBrP CMac EPfP IDee LRHS MBlu MPkF NLar WPGP
§	- subsp. ***ashei***	CBcs CMCN WPGP
	- subsp. ***ashei*** × ***macrophylla*** subsp. ***dealbata***	WPGP
	- subsp. ***ashei*** × ***virginiana***	CJun WPGP
	- 'Julian Hill'	CMCN
	macrophylla × ***sieboldii***	CJun
	'Malin'	CJun
	'Manchu Fan'	CBcs CJun EPfP IArd LRHS LSRN SChF WPGP
§	'March Til Frost'	CBcs CJun LMil LRHS NRHS WPGP
	'Margaret Helen'	CBcs CJun WPGP
	'Marj Gossler'	CJun
	'Marjorie Congreve'	WPGP
	'Mark Jury'	CBcs
	martinii	CBcs
	'Mary Nell'	CJun
	'Maryland'	CJun GGGa
	maudiae	CBcs CExl NLar
	'Maxine Merrill'	CBcs CJun
	'May to Frost'	see *M.* 'March Til Frost'
	'Milky Way' ♀H5	CBcs CDul CJun EPfP MGos WPGP
	'Mister Yellowjacket'	CJun
	'Moondance'	CJun
	'Nimbus'	CJun CRos LRHS NRHS WPGP
	nitida	CExl
	obovata Diels	see *M. officinalis*
§	***obovata*** Thunb.	CBcs CDul CJun CMCN CTho EPfP IDee NLar WPGP
	- B&SWJ 10821	WCru
	- B&SWJ 12626	WCru
	- pink-flowered	WPGP
	obovata × ***sargentiana*** var. ***robusta***	WPGP
§	***officinalis***	CBcs NLar
	- var. ***biloba***	CBcs GKev MBlu NLar WPGP
	'Old Port'	CBcs
	'Olivia'	CJun WPGP
	'Paul Cook'	CBcs CEnd
	'Peaches 'n' Cream'	CBcs CJun
	'Peachy'	CBcs CJun LRHS
§	'Pegasus' ♀H6	CBcs CEnd CJun LMil LRHS SSta
	'Peppermint Stick'	CTsd WMat
	'Peter Smithers'	CJun
	'Petit Chicon'	CBcs EBee
	'Phelan Bright'	CBcs CJun SAko WPGP
	'Phillip Tregunna'	CBcs WPGP
	'Phil's Masterpiece'	CJun
	'Pickard's Stardust'	EPfP
	'Pickard's Sundew'	see *M.* × *soulangeana* 'Sundew'
	'Piet van Veen'	CJun
	'Pink Delight'	CJun
	'Pink Goblet'	CRos LRHS NRHS
	'Pink Surprise'	CJun
	'Pinkie'	CJun
	'Porcelain Dove'	CJun LMil LRHS WPGP
	'Premier Cru'	LRHS
	'Princess Margaret'	CBcs CJun LMil
	'Pristine'	EPfP LMil LRHS
	× ***proctoriana***	CBcs CRos EBee LMil LRHS MBlu MMuc NRHS WPGP
	- 'Robert's Dream'	CJun CRos LRHS MAsh NRHS SSta
	- 'Slavin's No 44'	CJun
	'Purple Breeze'	LRHS MBlu NLar SAko
	'Purple Globe'	CEnd CJun
	'Purple Platter'	CBcs
	'Purple Sensation'	CBcs CJun SLim WPGP
	'Purple Star' **new**	WPGP
	quinquepeta	see *M. liliiflora*
	'Raspberry Ice'	CBcs CMac CRos EPfP LRHS MAsh NRHS SRms
	'Raspberry Swirl'	SSta
	'Rebecca's Perfume'	CJun LRHS NLar WMat
	'Red as Red'	CBcs CJun SLim
	'Red Baron'	CJun
	'Red Lion'	CJun LRHS
	'Ricki'	CBcs CJun LSRN MBlu
	'Roseanne'	CJun
	rostrata	CBcs CExl IArd WPGP
	'Rouged Alabaster'	CBcs
	'Royal Crown'	CBcs CDul EPfP IArd LRHS
	'Royal Flush'	NEgg
	'Ruby'	CBcs CJun
	'Ruth'	CBcs
	salicifolia	CBcs CMCN MMuc WSpi
	- var. ***concolor***	CJun
	- 'Garden House Upright'	EBee
	- 'Jermyns'	CJun
	- 'Louisa Fete'	CJun
	- 'Miss Jack'	CMCN
*	- 'Rosea'	CJun
	- upright	WPGP
	- 'Van Veen'	CJun WPGP
§	- 'Wada's Memory' ♀H6	CDul CExl CJun CMCN CRos CTho ELan EPfP LMaj LMil LRHS MAsh MBlu MMuc NPri NRHS SPer SSta WFar WMat
	- 'Windsor Beauty'	CJun LSvl SSta
	sapaensis FMWJ 13315	WCru
	- FMWJ 13330	WCru
	- HWJ 533	WCru
	- NJM 09.168	WPGP
	'Sara Koe'	CJun WMat
	sargentiana	CBcs SSta
	- 'Broadleas'	CJun
	- var. ***robusta***	CBcs CMCN CTsd EPfP MMuc
	- - 'Blood Moon'	CBcs CJun EBee WPGP
	- - 'Multipetal'	WPGP
	'Satisfaction'	CBcs NLar
	'Sayonara' ♀H6	CBcs CJun LMaj LRHS
	'Scented Gem' **new**	SSta
	'Schmetterling'	see *M.* × *soulangeana* 'Pickard's Schmetterling'

	'Sentinel'	WMat
	'Serene'	CBcs CEnd CJun EPfP IArd LMil LRHS
	SHIRAZZ ('Vulden')	CBcs EPfP IArd LMil LRHS NLar SCob SPoG WPGP
	sieboldii	CAco CBcs CJun CLnd CMCN CMac CRos CTho EMOT EPfP EWTr GKin LMil LPra LRHS LSRN MBlu MGos MMuc MPkF MRav NLar NRHS SPad SPer SPoG WHor WMou WPGP WSpi
	- B&SWJ 4127	WCru
	- 'Colossus' ♀H6	CJun EBee IArd MBlu SAko WPGP
	- 'Genesis'	CJun NLar
	- 'Genesis' × ***tripetala***	CJun
	- 'Genesis' × ***virginiana***	CJun
	- 'Michiko Renge' (d)	CJun
	- 'Min Pyong-gal'	CJun
	- 'Pride of Norway'	CJun EBee
	- subsp. ***sieboldii*** B&SWJ 12553 from Korea	WCru
	- subsp. ***sinensis***	CBcs CJun CMCN CTho ELan EPfP WPGP
I	- - 'Grandiflora'	CJun WPGP
	- 'White Flounces' (d)	NLar
	'Sir Harold Hillier'	CBcs WPGP
	'Snow Goose'	CJun
	'Solar Flair'	CBcs CJun IArd NLar
	× ***soulangeana***	Widely available
	- 'Alba Superba'	CBcs EMOT EPfP LCro LOPS LRHS MBlu MMuc MRav NLar SLim SPoG WFar WSpi
	- 'Alexandrina'	CBcs CLnd EPfP MBlu NLar
	- 'André Leroy'	EPfP LRHS
	- 'Beugnon'	IArd
	- 'Brozzonii' ♀H5	CBcs CMac EPfP LMil LRHS SSta
	- 'Cleopatra'PBR	CBcs
	- 'Fukuju'	CJun
	- 'Lennei'	CBcs CMCN CMac CRos CSBt CTho EMOT EPfP IArd LRHS MGos MRav NRHS SPoG SRms WFar
	- 'Lennei Alba'	CMCN ELan IArd MBlu NOra WFar WMat WSpi
	- 'Nigra'	see *M. liliiflora* 'Nigra'
	- 'Pickard's Opal'	CMCN
§	- 'Pickard's Schmetterling' ♀H5	CBcs EPfP LMil MAsh
	- 'Pickard's Snow Queen'	CBcs CJun
	- 'Pickard's Sundew'	see *M.* × *soulangeana* 'Sundew'
	- 'Picture'	CBcs
	- 'Purpliana'	NPri
	- RED LUCKY	see *M.* 'Hong Yun'
	- 'Rubra' misapplied	see *M.* × *soulangeana* 'Rustica Rubra'
§	- 'Rustica Rubra'	CBcs CDul CMCN CRos CTri ELan EPfP LMil LRHS LSRN MAsh NRHS SGol SRms
	- 'San José'	CJun LMil LRHS MAsh WFar
	- 'Speciosa'	SSta
§	- 'Sundew'	CKel EPfP NLar
	- 'Superba'	CMac LRHS
	- 'Verbanica'	EPfP LMil LRHS MAsh
	'Spectrum' ♀H6	CEnd CJun CKel EPfP IArd IDee IMou LMil LRHS MBlu MGos MMuc SSta
	sprengeri	CTsd
	- from Guizhou, China	WPGP
	- var. ***diva***	CBcs CEnd CExl LMil WPGP
	- - 'Burncoose' ♀H6	CBcs
	- - 'Copeland Court' ♀H6	CJun LMil LRHS WPGP

- - 'Dark Diva'	CJun
- - 'Diva'	LRHS WPGP
- - 'Eric Savill' ♀H6	CBcs CJun WPGP
- - 'Lanhydrock'	CBcs CJun WPGP
- - 'Marwood Spring'	CJun LMil WPGP
- - 'Westonbirt'	WPGP
'Spring Rite'	CJun
'Star Wars' ♀H5	CBcs CCVT CEnd CExl CJun CKel CRos CTho ECrN ELan EPfP GGGa LMil LRHS MAsh MGos NLar NOra NRHS SEWo SPoG SSta WMat WPGP
'Stellar Acclaim'	CBcs CJun LMil
stellata	Widely available
- 'Centennial' ♀H6	CJun CTho LMil
- 'Chrysanthemumiflora'	CJun LSvl
- 'Dawn'	CJun
- 'Jane Platt' ♀H6	CBcs CJun CRos ELan EPfP LMil LRHS MGos NRHS SSta WPGP
- f. ***keiskei***	CBcs CEnd CJun MGos NHol
- 'Kikuzaki'	CJun
- 'King Rose'	CBcs CJun CTsd EPfP
- 'Massey'	CJun
- 'Norman Gould'	see *M. kobus* 'Norman Gould'
- 'Rosea'	CBod CJun CLnd CMCN ELan ELon EPfP LMaj LMil MGos MRav MSwo NEgg NLar NPri SCob WFar
- 'Rosea Massey'	CJun
- 'Royal Star' ♀H6	CAby CAco CBcs CCVT CEnd CJun CLnd CMCN CRos CTho CTri ELon EPfP EUJe LMil LRHS MBlu MGos MRav NEgg NLar NRHS SGol SPer SSta WFar WMou
- 'Scented Silver'	CJun CRos LMil LRHS
- 'Shi-banchi Rosea'	CJun
- 'Water Lily'	CBcs CJun CMCN CRos CTho ELan ELon EPfP LMil LRHS LSRN MAsh MBlu MGos NEgg NRHS SPer SPoG SSta WHor WPGP
- 'Wisley Stardust'	LRHS
'Summer Solstice'	CBcs CJun LRHS SSta WPGP
'Sun Ray'	CJun
'Sunburst'	CBcs CJun SRms
'Sundance'	CJun IArd MBlu NLar
'Sunrise'	CBcs CDul LRHS NLar SAko
'Sunsation'	CBcs CJun ELan LRHS SLim
'Sunset Swirl'	CJun
'Sunspire'	CJun NLar
'Suntown'	CJun
'Susan' ♀H6	Widely available
'Susanna van Veen'	CBcs CEnd CJun WPGP
'Swedish Star'	CJun
'Sweet Merlot'	CBcs CJun
'Sweet Valentine'	CBcs CJun WPGP
'Sweetheart' ♀H5	CBcs CJun
'Sybille'	CMCN SLim WPGP
'Theodora'	LRHS SSta
× ***thompsoniana***	CBcs CMCN
- 'Olmenhof'	IArd
'Thousand Butterflies'	CJun
'Tina Durio'	LRHS WMat
'Todd Gresham'	CJun
'Todd's Forty Niner'	CJun
'Tranquility'	CBcs CJun
tripetala	CBcs CExl CMCN CTho ELan EPfP LMaj MBlu NLar SSta
- 'Bloomfield'	CJun
'Ultimate Yellow'	CJun NLar
× ***veitchii***	CBcs
- 'Columbus'	CJun LRHS WPGP
- 'Peter Veitch'	CTho

virginiana CBcs CJun CMCN LMaj
- var. ***australis*** 'Green Shadow' SGol
- - 'Satellite' NLar
§ - 'Jim Wilson' CJun EPfP MBlu
- MOONGLOW see *M. virginiana* 'Jim Wilson'
'Vulcan' CBcs CEnd CJun CMCN ELan EPfP IArd LRHS NLar
× ***watsonii*** see *M.* × *wieseneri*
'Wedding Vows' CJun
'White Mystery' CJun
§ × ***wieseneri*** CBcs CJun CMCN CRos EBee EPfP LRHS MBlu NLar WPGP
- 'Aashild Kalleberg' CBcs CJun WPGP
- 'William Watson' SSta
wilsonii ♀H6 CBcs CCVT CDul CExl CJun CMCN CRos CTho CTri ELan EPfP IArd IDee LRHS MBlu MGos MMuc MNrw NWea SEND SSta WGob WPGP WSHC
- 'Gwen Baker' CEnd CJun
'Yellow Fever' CBcs CJun CTho WPGP
'Yellow Garland' CJun
'Yellow Lantern' ♀H6 CBcs CEnd CJun CRos ELan EPfP GGGa LMaj LMil LRHS LSRN MAsh MBlu NLar NRHS SPoG SSta WPGP
'Yellow Sea' CJun LRHS
Yuchelia No. 1 CBcs WPGP
yunnanensis CCCN MPkF
zenii CBcs CMCN IArd IDee IMou
- 'Pink Parchment' CJun

× *Mahoberberis* (*Berberidaceae*)

aquisargentii CBcs CKel CMac CRos EBee EMil EPfP LRHS MMuc MRav NLar SCob SEND WFar
'Dart's Desire' NLar
miethkeana SRms
§ ***neubertii*** NLar

Mahonia ✿ (*Berberidaceae*)

§ ***aquifolium*** CAco CAgr CBcs CDul CPer ECrN GPoy MGos MMuc MRav NWea SCob SEND SGol SPer SPlb SWvt
- 'Apollo' ♀H5 CBcs CKel CMac CRos CSBt CTho EBee ELan EPfP LCro LOPS LRHS LSRN MAsh MBlu MGos MJak MRav NLar SCob SCoo SPer SPoG SRms SWvt WFar
- 'Atropurpurea' CMac CSBt CTsd ELan EPfP MRav NLar SPer
- 'Fascicularis' see *M.* × *wagneri* 'Pinnacle'
- 'Moseri' NLar SPer
- 'Smaragd' CMac CRos ELan EPfP LRHS LSRN MBlu MGos MRav NLar SCob
- 'Versicolor' MBlu
'Arthur Menzies' CRos LRHS NRHS
§ ***bealei*** CBcs CBod CDul CKel CRos CSBt CTho ELan ELon EPfP LRHS MAsh MGos MRav MSwo NEgg NLar NPer NWea SCob SCoo SGol SLim SWvt
BLACKFOOT ('Bokrafoot'PBR) CRos ELan EPfP LRHS MAsh SLon
bodinieri WPGP
- Og 93.033 WPGP
chochoco CExl
confusa × ***gracilipes*** WSpi
§ ***duclouxiana*** SPtp
- KR 7692 WPGP
eurybracteata CExl CKel LRHS WCru WPGP
- subsp. ***ganpinensis*** SEND WPGP
- - 'Soft Caress' CBcs CKel CMCN CRos CTsd EBee ELan EPfP EUJe LCro LOPS LRHS MGos MJak NLar NRHS SCob SCoo SGol SMad SPad SPoG SWvt
- 'Minganpi'PBR LSRN
- 'Sweet Winter' EBee IDee LRHS MAsh MMrt SPer SWvt
eutriphylla misapplied see *M. trifolia*
fargesii see *M. sheridaniana*
fortunei CBcs
- 'Curlyque' **new** WPGP
- 'Winter Prince' NLar
gracilipes CExl EBee EPfP EWes GCal IDee IMou MBlu NLar SMad WAvo WCru WPGP
gracilis EBee
haematocarpa EBee SIgm WPGP
huiliensis see *M. sheridaniana*
japonica ♀H5 CAco CBar CBcs CMac CRos CTri EBee ECrN ELan EPfP LRHS MAsh MGos MMuc MRav MSwo NHol NLar NRHS SCob SEND SGbt SPer SPoG SRms SSta WCFE
- 'Gold Dust' MBlu NLar
lanceolata WPGP
leschenaultii B&SWJ 9535 WCru
× ***lindsayae*** WPGP
- 'Cantab' ♀H4 EBee EPfP SChF WPGP
lomariifolia see *M. oiwakensis* subsp. *lomariifolia*
longibracteata GKin
mairei see *M. duclouxiana*
× ***media*** 'Buckland' ♀H4 CBcs CDul CMac CRos CTho EPfP NWea SCob SRms
- 'Charity' Widely available
- 'Lionel Fortescue' ♀H4 CBcs CMac CRos CSBt CTho EBee ELan EMOT EPfP GKin LRHS MAsh NEgg NRHS SCob SPer SWvt WHor
- 'Winter Sun' ♀H4 Widely available
moranensis CExl EBee
- T 292 WPGP
napaulensis NLar
- 'Maharajah' IArd IDee IMou NLar
nervosa CBcs CMac EPfP MBlu NLar WCru WPGP
- B&SWJ 9562 WCru
- B&SWJ 13580 WCru
neubertii see × *Mahoberberis neubertii*
nevinii SBrt
nitens EBee WCru WPGP
- 'Cabaret'PBR ♀H4 CBcs CRos EBee EPfP LCro LOPS LRHS LSRN MAsh MBlu MGos NRHS SCob SPoG SSta SWvt WSpi
oiwakensis NLar WPGP
- B&SWJ 371 WCru
- B&SWJ 3660 WCru
- PBR 371 from Hong Kong WCru
§ - subsp. ***lomariifolia*** ♀H4 CExl CRos EPfP EWes LRHS SArc SPtp
pallida CExl SPtp WPGP
'Pan's Peculiar' WPGP
pinnata misapplied see *M.* × *wagneri* 'Pinnacle'
pinnata (Lag.) Fedde 'Ken S. Howard' NLar WPGP
- 'Maurice Foster' NLar
- subsp. ***insularis*** 'Schnilemoon' WPGP
repens GKev NLar WSpi
- 'Rotundifolia' SPlb
× ***savilliana*** EBee NLar WPGP

§ ***sheridaniana*** Og 93033 WPGP
- Og 93056 **new** WPGP
SIOUX ('Bokrasio'PBR) CRos LRHS MAsh NRHS SPoG
§ ***trifolia*** GCal IArd IMou LRHS
- EKB 4618 WPGP
trifoliolata SMad
volcania B&SWJ 10400 **new** WCru
× ***wagneri*** SWvt
- 'Aldenhamensis' NLar
- 'Fireflame' GCal
- 'Hastings' Elegant' NLar
§ - 'Pinnacle' ♀H5 CDul CRos ELan EPfP LRHS MAsh MBlu NLar SPoG SWvt WFar
- 'Sunset' MBlu NLar
- 'Undulata' MBlu NLar SPer
- 'Vicaryi' NLar

Maianthemum (*Asparagaceae*)

amoenum B&SWJ 10390 WCru
atropurpureum WCru
bicolor LEdu
bifolium CAvo CBct GLog GMaP LEdu MAvo MBel MNrw NBro SRms WCru WThu XLum
§ - subsp. ***kamtschaticum*** CAvo EHrv EMor EPPr GKev LEdu MAvo NLar NRya WCot WPGP
- - B&SWJ 4360 WCru
- - CD&R 2300 WCru
- - var. ***pumilum*** EBee GCal LEdu WCru
canadense EAJP EBee EPPr EPot GCal GKev LEdu MNrw NBid WCru
chasmanthum see *M. bifolium* subsp. *kamtschaticum*
comaltepecense B&SWJ 10215 WCru
dilatatum see *M. bifolium* subsp. *kamtschaticum*
flexuosum LEdu
- B&SWJ 9069 WCru
- B&SWJ 9079 WCru
- B&SWJ 9150 WCru
aff. ***flexuosum*** B&SWJ 9026 WCru
- B&SWJ 9055 WCru
formosanum B&SWJ 349 EPPr WCru
forrestii WCru
fuscum GEdr WCot WCru WPnP
- var. ***cordatum*** WCru
- 'Shirui Giant' **new** WPGP
- 'Tangkhul Giant' LEdu
gigas B&SWJ 10470 WCru
henryi EHrv GEdr LEdu WCru WPGP
- B&SWJ 4714 EHrv
- BWJ 7616 WCru
japonicum EHrv LEdu
- B&SWJ 1179 WCru
- B&SWJ 4714 WCru
- B&SWJ 7306 WCru
oleraceum CBct CExl GEdr GKev LEdu WFar WHil WPnP
- B&SWJ 2148 WCru
- purple-flowered GEdr
paniculatum LEdu SHar
- B&SWJ 9137 WCru
- B&SWJ 9140 WCru
- purple-flowered B&SWJ 9139 WCru
pendent, B&SWJ 10305 from Guatemala WCru
purpureum GEdr GKev LEdu
- G-W&P 150 EPPr
racemosum ♀H6 Widely available
- subsp. ***amplexicaule*** GCal ILea
- - 'Emily Moody' CBct CExl EPPr EPfP IPot SChF WCot WPGP
- 'Major' CRos LRHS NRHS
aff. ***salvinii*** CBct
- B&SWJ 9000 WCru
- B&SWJ 9088 WCru
- B&SWJ 10402 WCru
scilloideum B&SWJ 10407 WCru
* - var. ***roseum*** B&SWJ 10335 CBct WCru
stellatum CBct CRos CSam EBee ECha EMor EPPr EPfP GQue ILea IMou LEdu LRHS NChi NLar NRHS WCru WFar WPnP XLum
szechuanicum WCru
tatsienense CBct CExl EHrv GEdr LEdu WCru

Maihuenia (*Cactaceae*)

poeppigii SPlb
- F&W 9670 WCot
- JCA 2.575.600 WCot

Maihueniopsis (*Cactaceae*)

darwinii SPlb

Mallotus (*Euphorbiaceae*)

japonicus B&SWJ 14613 **new** WCru
- B&SWJ 14679 **new** WCru

Malotigena (*Aizoaceae*)

§ ***frantiskae-niederlovae*** CCCN CSma EBou EPot GCrg GEdr GKev NHpl SMad SSim WHal WIce XLum
- 'Album' see *M. frantiskae-niederlovae* 'White Nugget'
- 'Gold Nugget' ♀H3 CRos LRHS NRHS
§ - 'White Nugget' CCCN CRos CSma EPot EWes GEdr LRHS NHpl NRHS SSim WIce

Malus ✿ (*Rosaceae*)

§ 'Adirondack' ♀H6 CLnd CSBt EBee ELan EMOT EPfP EWTr LBuc LCro LOPS LRHS MMuc NLar NOra NPri SCoo SPoG WJas WMat
'Admiration' see *M.* 'Adirondack'
× ***adstringens*** 'Almey' ECrN
- 'Hopa' CAgr CDul CLnd
- 'Simcoe' EBee EMOT
'Aldenhamensis' see *M.* × *purpurea* 'Aldenhamensis'
'Allow Super' (D) WMat
baccata CDul CLnd CMCN CTho SCoo SEND SPlb
- var. ***mandshurica*** CTho
- 'Street Parade' EWTr LMaj
(Ballerina Series) 'Ballerina Bolero' (D) EMOT SDea WMat
- 'Ballerina Polka' (D) EMOT WMat
- 'Ballerina Samba' (D) CArg LCro WMat
'Barbara' WMat
§ ***bhutanica*** CDul CLnd
- 'Mandarin' SCoo
'Bramley 20' (C) CSBt WMat
brevipes CLnd LRHS SCoo
- 'Wedding Bouquet' ♀H6 EBee EMOT EPfP LCro LSRN MAsh NLar NOra SPer WMat
'Butterball' ♀H6 CDul CLnd CNWT CSBt CTho EBee EMOT EPfP EPom LMaj LRHS NOra NWea SCoo SLim SPer SPoG SRms SVic WJas WMat WMou WWct

Name	Suppliers
'Candymint Sargent'	CLnd NOra SLim SPoG
'Captain Tom' (C/D)	WMat
'Cave Hill'	CLnd
'Cheal's Scarlet'	CHab
* 'Cheal's Weeping'	CAco CLnd CMac EMOT EWTr MJak NEgg SRms WMou
COCCINELLA ('Courtarou')	LMaj SGol
'Comtesse de Paris' ♀H6	CDul CLnd EBee EPfP LRHS MAsh MBlu NLar NOra WMat
CORALBURST ('Coralcole')	MAsh NOra SPoG WMat
coronaria	SPtp
- var. ***dasycalyx*** 'Charlottae' (d)	CCVT CDul CLnd EWTr LPra SPer
- 'Elk River'	CLnd NOra SCoo WMat
'Cowichan'	CLnd ECrN SSFr
'Crimson Brilliant'	CLnd
'Crittenden'	EPfP MRav
'Dartmouth'	CDul CHab CLnd CSBt CTri
'Directeur Moerlands'	CArg CCVT CSBt ECrN EMOT EPfP LMaj LRHS NOra SCoo SEND SPer SWvt WMat
domestica 'Acklam Russet' (D)	CHab SBdl SKee
- 'Acme' (D)	ECrN SBdl SDea
- 'Adams's Pearmain' (D)	CArg CHab CLnd CTho CTri ECrN MAsh NOra NWea SBdl SCob SDea SKee WMat WWct
- 'Admiral'PBR (D)	SBdl SKee
- 'Advance' (D)	SBdl SKee
- 'Akane' (D)	SBdl SDea
- 'Akerö' (D)	SKee
- 'Aldenham Blenheim' (D) **new**	SBdl
- 'Alderman' (C)	SBdl
§ - 'Alexander' (C)	SBdl
- 'Alfriston' (C)	CAgr CHab SBdl SKee WMat
§ - 'Alkmene' (D) ♀H6	CAgr ECrN NOra SDea
- 'All Doer' (C/D/Cider)	EMOT
- 'All Red Gravenstein' (D)	SBdl
- 'Allen's Everlasting' (D)	SBdl SDea SKee
- 'Allington Pippin' (D)	CArg CHab CSBt CTri ECrN MGos NOra SBdl SDea SKee WMat
- AMBASSY ('Dalil'PBR) (D)	SSFr
- 'Amber' (D) **new**	SBdl
- 'American Beauty' (D) **new**	CLnd SBdl
- 'American Mother'	see *M. domestica* 'Mother'
- 'Ames' (D) **new**	SBdl
- 'Ananas Reinette' (D)	CHab SKee
- 'Anna Boelens' (D)	SBdl SDea
- 'Annie Elizabeth' (C)	CAgr CArg CDul CHab ECrN EMOT IArd MGos NOra SBdl SDea SKee SSFr SVic WJas WMat WWct
- 'Anniversary' (D)	SDea
- 'Antonovka' (C)	SBdl SKee
- 'Apache' (F)	SSFr
- 'Api' (D)	EMOT LSRN NOra NPri SBdl SCob SKee WMat
- 'Api Noir' (D)	SBdl
- 'Ard Cairn Russet' (D)	ECrN IArd SBdl SDea SKee
- 'Arkansas' (D)	SBdl SKee
- 'Aroma' (D) **new**	SBdl
- 'Aromatic Russet' (D)	SBdl SKee
- 'Arthur Turner' (C) ♀H6	CArg CCVT CHab CLnd CTri ECrN EMOT EPom LBuc MWat NOra SBdl SDea SKee SSFr WJas WMat
- 'Arthur W. Barnes' (C)	SBdl
- 'Ascot' (D) **new**	SBdl
- 'Ashmead's Kernel' (D) ♀H6	Widely available
- 'Ashton Bitter' (Cider)	CHab CTri
- 'Ashton Brown Jersey' (Cider)	CArg
- 'Askham Pippin' (F)	MCoo
- 'Astrachan Large Fruited' (D) **new**	SBdl
- 'Autumn Harvest' (C/D)	SBdl
- 'Autumn Pearmain' (D)	SBdl SDea
- 'Baker's Delicious' (D)	ECrN NOra SBdl SDea SKee SSFr WMat
- 'Baldwin' (D) **new**	SBdl
- 'Ballarat Seedling' (D)	SBdl
- 'Ball's Pippin' (D) **new**	SBdl
- 'Ballyfatten' (C)	IArd SBdl
- 'Ballyvaughan Seedling' (D)	IArd
- 'Balsam'	see *M. domestica* 'Green Balsam'
- 'Banana Pippin' (F)	CEnd
- 'Banns' (D)	ECrN SBdl
- 'Barchard's Seedling' (D) **new**	SBdl
- 'Bardsey' (D)	CAgr CArg CHab EPom NOra SKee WGwG WMat
- 'Barnack Beauty' (D)	CHab LEdu NOra SBdl SKee
- 'Barnack Beauty' sport (D) **new**	SBdl
- 'Barnack Orange' (D)	SBdl SKee
- 'Barnhill Pippin' (D) **new**	SBdl
- 'Baron Ward' (C)	CHab SBdl
- 'Baron Wood' (C)	SBdl
- 'Bascombe's Mystery' (D)	SBdl SKee
- 'Baumann's Reinette' (D)	SBdl
- 'Baxter's Pearmain' (D)	SBdl SDea
- 'Beauty of Bath' (D)	CAgr CArg CCVT CDul CHab CLnd CTho CTri ECrN ELan EMOT EPom LBuc MRav NOra SDea SKee SPer SSFr WJas WMat WWct
- 'Beauty of Bedford' (D)	SBdl
- 'Beauty of Hants' (C/D)	ECrN SBdl
- 'Beauty of Kent' (C)	SBdl SDea SKee
- 'Beauty of Moray' (C)	SBdl
- 'Beauty of Stoke' (C)	SBdl
- 'Bedfordshire Foundling' (C) **new**	SBdl
- 'Bedwyn Beauty' (C)	SBdl
- 'Beeley Pippin' (D)	SBdl SDea SKee
- 'Bell Apple' (Cider/C)	CTho
- 'Belle de Boskoop' (C/D) ♀H6	CAgr CHab ECrN MCoo NOra SBdl SCob SDea SKee
- 'Belle de Pontoise' (D)	SBdl
- 'Belle Flavoise' (F)	SBdl
- 'Belledge Pippin' (C/D)	SBdl
- 'Belle-fille Normande' (C)	SBdl
- 'Belle-fleur de France' (C)	SBdl
- 'Belvoir Seedling' (C/D)	SBdl
- 'Bembridge Beauty' (F)	CHab SDea
- 'Benenden Early' (D)	SBdl SKee
- 'Benoni' (D) **new**	SBdl
- 'Ben's Red' (D)	CAgr CEnd CFGn CTho SBdl SKee WMat
- 'Bess Pool' (D)	CHab SBdl SDea
- 'Betty Geeson' (C) **new**	SBdl
- 'Bewley Down Pippin'	see *M. domestica* 'Crimson King' (Cider/C)
- 'Billy Down Pippin' (F)	CTho
- 'Bismarck' (C)	SBdl
- 'Black Dabinett' (Cider)	CArg CEnd CTho WMat
- 'Blaze' (D)	SBdl
- 'Blenheim Orange' (C/D) ♀H6	Widely available
- 'Blood of the Boyne' (D)	IArd

Cultivar	Suppliers
- 'Bloody Butcher' (C)	SBdl
- 'Bloody Ploughman' (D)	CArg CHab CLnd ECrN NOra SBdl SKee SLon WMat
- 'Blue Moon' (D)	LRHS
- 'Blue Pearmain' (D)	SBdl SDea SKee
- 'Bodil Neergaard' (D) **new**	SBdl
- 'Boiken' (D) **new**	SBdl
- BOLERO	see *M. domestica* 'Tuscan'
- 'Bonum' (D/C)	WMat
- 'Bosbury Pippin' (D) **new**	SBdl
- 'Bossom' (D) **new**	SBdl
- 'Bountiful' (C)	CAgr CArg CDul CLnd CMac CSBt CTri ECrN EMOT EPom LRHS LSRN MAsh MRav NOra SBdl SDea SKee SSFT SSFr WMat WWct
- 'Bow Hill Pippin' (C)	SBdl
- 'Box Apple' (D)	SBdl SKee
- 'Brabant Bellefleur' (C) **new**	SBdl
- 'Braddick's Nonpareil' (D)	SBdl
- 'Bradley's Beauty' (C/D)	NWea
- 'Braeburn' (D)	CAgr CArg CDul CLnd CSBt ECrN EMOT EPom LBuc LEdu LRHS MWat NOra NWea SBdl SCob SDea SEND SEWo SKee SPer SSFr WJas WMat
- 'Braeburn Hillwell' (D)	EPom NOra
- 'Braintree Seedling' (D)	ECrN SBdl
- 'Bramley's Seedling' (C) ♀H6	Widely available
- 'Bramley's Seedling' clone 20 (F)	CFGn CLnd CSBt CTsd LSRN MAsh MNHC MWat NLar NOra NWea SCoo SDea SKee SLim SPoG WWct
- 'Bramshott Rectory' (D/C)	SBdl
- 'Bread Fruit' (C/D)	CEnd CFGn
- 'Breitling' (D)	SBdl
- 'Brenchley Pippin' (D)	SBdl SKee
- 'Bridgwater Pippin' (C)	SKee
- 'Bright Future' (D)	CArg EPom NOra WMat WWct
- 'Brith Mawr' (C)	WGwG
- 'Broad-eyed Pippin' (C)	SBdl
- 'Broadholme Beauty' (C)	CArg EPom MAsh NOra WMat
- 'Brookes's' (D)	SBdl SKee
- 'Brown Crofton' (D)	IArd SBdl
- 'Brownlee's Russet' (D)	CAgr CHab CTho CTri MCoo NEgg NOra SDea SKee SSFr WMat
- 'Brown's Apple' (Cider)	CAgr CArg CHab CTri ECrN NOra WMat
- 'Brown's Seedling' (D)	SBdl
- 'Budimka' (D)	SBdl
- 'Burrowhill Early' (Cider)	WMat
- 'Bushey Grove' (C)	SBdl SDea
- 'Byeloborodovka' (C/D) **new**	SBdl
- 'Byfleet Seedling' (C)	SBdl
- 'Byford Wonder' (C) **new**	SBdl
- 'Calville Blanc d'Hiver' (D)	NOra SKee
- 'Cambusnethan Pippin' (D)	SKee
- 'Camelot' (Cider/C)	EMOT SBdl
§ - 'Captain Broad' (Cider/D)	CEnd CTho
- 'Captain Kidd' (D)	EPom NOra
- 'Carlisle Codlin' (C)	NLar NOra SDea WMat
- 'Caroline' (D)	ECrN
- 'Carswell's Honeydew' (D)	SKee
- 'Carswell's Orange' (D)	SKee
- 'Catherine' (C)	ECrN
- 'Catshead' (C)	CAgr CArg CHab CTri ECrN NOra SDea SKee WMat WWct
- 'Cellini' (C)	NOra SDea SKee
- 'Cevaal' (D)	WWct
- 'Channel Beauty' (D)	WGwG
- 'Charles Ross' (C/D) ♀H6	Widely available
- 'Charlotte' PBR (C)	EMOT SDea
- 'Cheddar Cross' (D)	CAgr CCVT CTri ECrN SKee
- 'Chelmsford Wonder' (C)	ECrN SKee
- 'Chips' (F)	SKee
- 'Chisel Jersey' (Cider)	CAgr CTri NOra SKee
- 'Chivers Delight' (D)	CAgr CArg ECrN EMOT EPom LBuc LRHS MCoo NOra SDea SKee SSFr WJas
- 'Christmas Pearmain' (D)	CAgr CArg CLnd ECrN SDea SKee SSFr WMat
- 'Christmas Pippin' PBR (D) ♀H6	CArg CRos CTri EPom LBuc LCro LRHS MCoo MWat NLar NOra NPri NRHS WMat
- 'Cider Lady's Finger' (Cider)	SKee
- 'Cissy' (D)	WGwG
- 'Claygate Pearmain' (D)	CAgr CHab CTho CTri ECrN MCoo NOra SDea SKee SVic WMat
- 'Clopton Red' (D)	ECrN
- 'Cobra' (F)	CAgr CArg MAsh MCoo NOra NPri SKee SPoG SSFr WJas WMat
- 'Cockle Pippin' (D)	CAgr SDea
- 'Cockpit' (C)	CHab NWea
- 'Coleman's Seedling' (Cider)	CTho
- 'Collogett Pippin' (C/Cider)	CEnd CTho CTsd
- 'Core Blimey' (D)	EPom LRHS
- 'Cornish Aromatic' (D)	CAgr CArg CDul CFGn CTho CTri CTsd NOra SDea SKee WMat
- 'Cornish Gilliflower' (D)	CAgr CEnd CHab CTho ECrN MCoo NOra SDea SKee WMat
- 'Cornish Honeypin' (D)	CEnd SKee SSFr
- 'Cornish Longstem' (D)	CAgr CEnd
- 'Cornish Mother' (D)	CEnd CFGn CTho CTsd
- 'Cornish Pine' (D)	CEnd SDea SKee
- 'Coronation' (D)	CHab SDea
- 'Costard' (C)	CHab SKee
- 'Cottenham Seedling' (C)	SKee
- 'Coul Blush' (D)	SKee WMat
- 'Court of Wick' (D)	CAgr CArg CDul CHab CTho ECrN NOra SVic WMat
- 'Court Pendu Plat' (D)	CAgr CArg CHab GQue LEdu MAsh MWat NOra SDea SKee SSFT WJas WMat WWct
- 'Court Royal' (Cider)	SKee
- 'Cox Cymraeg' (D)	WGwG
- 'Cox's Orange Pippin' (D)	Widely available
- 'Cox's Pomona' (C)	SDea SKee
- 'Cox's Rouge de Flandres' (D)	SKee
- 'Cox's Selfing' (D)	CDul CMac CSBt CTri EPfP LBuc LRHS MAsh MGos MNHC NLar SDea SKee SPer SPoG WJas WMat WWct
- 'Crawley Beauty' (C)	CAgr CArg CHab SDea SSFT WMat
- 'Crawley Reinette' (D)	CHab
- 'Crimson Beauty' (D)	SKee
- 'Crimson Beauty of Bath' (D)	CAgr
- 'Crimson Bramley' (C)	IArd SKee
- 'Crimson Cox' (D)	SDea
§ - 'Crimson King' (Cider/C)	CAgr
- 'Crimson King' (D)	CAgr CHab CTri
- 'Crimson Peasgood' (C)	ECrN
- 'Crimson Victoria' (Cider)	CTho
- CRISPIN	see *M. domestica* 'Mutsu'

	Cultivar	Suppliers
§	- 'Cripps Pink'[PBR] (D) **new**	SSFr
	- 'Croen Mochyn' (D)	WGwG
§	- 'Crowngold' (D)	EPom
	- 'Cutler Grieve' (D)	SDea
	- 'Dabinett' (Cider)	CAgr CArg CHab CLnd CMac CTho CTri EMOT EPom LBuc NOra SDea SKee WMat WWct
	- 'D'Arcy Spice' (D)	CAgr ECrN EPfP GQue MCoo MWat NOra SDea SKee WMat WWct
	- 'Deacon's Blushing Beauty' (C/D)	SDea
	- 'Deacon's Millennium' (D)	SDea
	- 'Decio' (D)	SKee
	- 'Devon Crimson Queen' (D)	CTho
	- 'Devonshire Buckland' (C)	CEnd CTho
	- 'Devonshire Crimson Queen' (D)	SDea
	- 'Devonshire Quarrenden' (D)	CAgr CDul CHab CTho CTsd NOra SDea SKee SVic WMat
	- 'Diamond' (D)	WGwG
	- 'Diamond Jubilee' (D)	SKee
	- 'Discovery' (D) ♀H6	Widely available
	- 'Doctor Harvey' (C)	ECrN SKee
	- 'Doctor Hogg' (C) **new**	CLnd
	- 'Doctor Kidd's Orange Red'	see *M. domestica* 'Kidd's Orange Red'
	- 'Doddin' (D)	WWct
	- 'Domino' (C)	MCoo
	- 'Don's Delight' (C)	CTho WMat
	- 'Downton Pippin' (D)	CHab
	- 'Dredge's Fame' (D)	SKee
	- 'Duchess of Oldenburg' (C)	NOra SKee
	- 'Duchess's Favourite' (D)	SKee
	- 'Duke of Cornwall' (C)	CTho
	- 'Duke of Devonshire' (D)	CSBt CTri NWea SDea
	- 'Dumeller's Seedling'	see *M. domestica* 'Dummellor's Seedling'
§	- 'Dummellor's Seedling' (C) ♀H6	CHab MCoo NOra SDea SKee
	- 'Dunkerton Late Sweet' (Cider)	CArg CCVT CHab EMOT SBdl WMat
	- 'Dunn's Seedling' (D)	SDea
	- 'Early Blenheim' (D/C)	CEnd
	- 'Early Bower' (D)	CEnd
	- 'Early Julyan' (C)	SKee
	- 'Early Victoria'	see *M. domestica* 'Emneth Early'
	- EARLY WINDSOR	see *M. domestica* 'Alkmene'
	- 'Early Worcester'	see *M. domestica* 'Tydeman's Early Worcester'
	- 'Eccleston Pippin' (D)	SKee
	- 'Ecklinville' (C)	SDea
	- 'Eden' (F)	WMat
	- 'Edith Hopwood' (D)	ECrN
	- 'Edward VII' (C) ♀H6	CHab EMOT NOra SDea SKee WMat WWct
	- 'Egremont Russet' (D) ♀H6	Widely available
	- 'Ellis' Bitter' (Cider)	EMOT SKee SVic
	- 'Ellison's Orange' (D) ♀H6	CAgr CArg CDul CHab CLnd CMac CSBt CTri ECrN EMOT EPfP EPom LBuc LRHS MMuc MWat NOra NWea SBdl SCob SDea SEND SKee SLon SPer SSFr SVic WJas WMat WWct
	- 'Elstar' (D) ♀H6	CCVT CLnd ECrN EMOT EPom NOra SBdl SDea SKee
	- 'Elton Beauty' (D)	SDea SKee
§	- 'Emneth Early' (C) ♀H6	CAgr CArg CHab ECrN NOra SDea WJas WMat WWct
	- 'Emperor Alexander'	see *M. domestica* 'Alexander'
	- 'Empire' (D)	NOra SDea SKee
	- 'Encore' (C)	SDea
	- 'English Codlin' (C)	CTho CTri
	- 'Epicure'	see *M. domestica* 'Laxton's Epicure'
	- 'Ernie's Russet' (D)	SDea
	- 'Eros' (D)	ECrN
	- 'Esopus Spitzenburg' (D)	SKee
	- 'Evening Gold' (C)	SDea
	- 'Eve's Delight' (D)	SDea
	- 'Excelsior' (C)	ECrN
	- 'Exeter Cross' (D)	CSBt ECrN SDea
	- 'Fair Maid of Devon' (Cider)	CAgr CArg CDul CEnd CTho WMat
	- 'Fall Pippin' (D)	SKee
	- 'Falstaff'[PBR] (D)	CAgr CDul CTri ECrN EPfP EPom LSRN MGos NOra SBdl SCob SCoo SDea SKee SPer SSFr
	- 'Fameuse' (D)	NOra SKee
	- 'Farmer's Glory' (D)	CAgr CTho WMat
	- 'Fiesta'[PBR] (D) ♀H6	Widely available
	- 'Fillbarrel' (Cider)	CHab
	- 'Fillingham Pippin' (C)	CHab SKee
	- 'Firedance' (D)	LRHS
	- 'Firmgold' (D)	SDea
	- 'First and Last' (D)	NOra WMat
	- 'Flamenco'	see *M. domestica* 'Obelisk'
§	- 'Flower of Kent' (C)	CHab EPom MAsh NOra NWea SDea SKee SSFr WMat
	- 'Flower of the Town' (D)	CHab
	- 'Forge' (D)	CAgr CHab SDea SKee
	- 'Fortune'	see *M. domestica* 'Laxton's Fortune'
	- 'Foster's Seedling' (D)	SKee
	- 'Foxwhelp' (Cider)	CArg CHab SKee
	- 'Francis' (D)	ECrN SKee
	- 'Frederick' (Cider)	CArg WMat
	- 'French Crab' (C)	SDea
	- 'Freyberg' (D)	NOra
	- 'Fuji' (D)	LMaj NOra SDea SKee
	- 'Gala' (D)	CSBt CTri EBee EPom NOra SBdl SCob SCoo SDea SKee SSFr WMat
	- 'Galaxy'[PBR] (D)	NOra
	- 'Galloway Pippin' (C)	NLar NOra SKee WMat
	- 'Garden Fountain' (D)	LRHS
	- 'Garnet' (D)	SKee
	- 'Gascoyne's Scarlet' (C/D)	SDea SKee
	- 'Gavin' (D)	CAgr SDea
	- 'Genesis II' (C/D)	SDea
	- 'Genet Moyle' (C/Cider)	CTri MCoo WMat
	- 'George Carpenter' (D)	CTri SDea
	- 'George Cave' (D)	CDul ECrN EMOT IArd MCoo NOra SBdl SDea SKee SSFr WJas
	- 'George Neal' (C)	CAgr SDea
	- 'Gibbon's Russet' (D)	IArd
	- 'Gladstone' (D)	CAgr NOra SKee WMat WWct
	- 'Glansevin' (D)	WGwG
§	- 'Glass Apple' (C/D)	CEnd CTho
	- 'Glockenapfel' (C)	SKee
	- 'Gloria Mundi' (C)	SDea SKee
	- 'Gloster '69' (D)	CLnd SDea SKee
	- 'Gloucester Cross' (D)	SKee
	- 'Golden Ball' (Cider)	CTho
	- 'Golden Bittersweet' (D)	CAgr CTho WMat
	- 'Golden Delicious' (D)	CArg CCVT CDul CMac EBee ECrN ELan EMOT EPom LBuc LRHS MJak NOra NPri SBdl SCob SDea SEWo SKee SSFr SVic WMat

Cultivar	Suppliers
- 'Golden Glow' (C)	SDea
- 'Golden Harvey' (D)	CAgr SKee
- 'Golden Jubilee' (F)	CEnd
- 'Golden Knob' (D)	CTri SKee
- 'Golden Noble' (C) Y^{H6}	CAgr CTri ECrN EMOT IArd MCoo NOra SDea SKee
- 'Golden Nugget' (D)	CAgr
- 'Golden Pippin' (C)	CAgr NOra SKee WMat
- 'Golden Reinette' (D)	SKee
- 'Golden Russet' (D)	CAgr ECrN NOra SDea SKee
- 'Golden Spire' (C)	CHab MCoo NOra SDea SKee
- 'Grandpa Ailes' (D)	CTho
- 'Grandpa Buxton' (C)	CHab
- 'Granny Smith' (D)	CBcs CDul ECrN EMOT LMaj LSRN NOra SBdl SDea SKee SPer SVic WMat
- 'Gravenstein' (D)	CHab NOra SBdl SDea SKee
§ - 'Green Balsam' (D)	CHab CTri
- 'Green Roland' (C/D)	ECrN
- 'Greenfinch' (D)	LRHS
- 'Greensleeves'[PBR] (D) Y^{H6}	CAgr CArg CDul CMac CTri EBee ECrN ELan EMOT EPfP EPom MAsh MGos MMuc NLar NOra NWea SBdl SCob SDea SEND SKee SLim SPer SSFT SSFr WJas WMat WWct
- 'Greenup's Pippin' (D)	CHab
- 'Grenadier' (C) Y^{H6}	CAgr CArg CHab CLnd CTri ECrN EMOT EPom MGos MJak MMuc NLar NOra SBdl SCob SDea SEND SKee SLon SPer SSFT SSFr WJas WMat
- 'Groninger Kroon' (D) **new**	CLnd
- 'Guillevic' (Cider)	CHab
- 'Gwell Na Mil' (D)	WGwG
- 'Halstow Natural' (Cider)	CAgr
- 'Hambledon Deux Ans' (C)	CLnd SDea
- 'Hambling's Seedling' (C)	SKee
- 'Hangy Down' (Cider)	CArg WMat
- 'Harling Hero' (D)	ECrN
§ - 'Harry Master's Jersey' (Cider)	CAgr CArg CTho CTri EPom NOra SDea SKee WMat WWct
- 'Harvey' (C)	SDea SKee
- 'Hawthornden' (C)	CHab SKee
- 'Herefordshire Beefing' (C)	SKee
- 'Herefordshire Redstreak' (Cider)	CAgr CArg EMOT EPom NOra WMat
- 'Herefordshire Russet'[PBR] (D)	CArg CDul CFGn EMOT EPom LBuc LRHS MAsh MCoo NLar NOra NRHS SKee SPer SSFr WJas WMat WWct
- 'Herring's Pippin' (C/D)	CDul CTri SDea
- 'Hibb's Seedling' (C)	SKee
- 'High View Pippin' (D)	SKee
- 'Hoary Morning' (C)	CTho ECrN SDea SKee
- 'Hocking's Green' (C/D)	CAgr CEnd CTsd
- 'Hollow Core' (C)	CAgr
- 'Holstein' (D)	LMaj NOra SBdl SDea SKee
- 'Honey Pippin' (D)	ECrN
§ - 'Honeygold' (D)	CEnd
- 'Horsham Russet' (D)	SKee
- 'Howgate Wonder' (C) Y^{H6}	CAgr CArg CCVT CDul CHab CLnd CSBt CTri EBee ECrN EMOT EPfP EPom LBuc LRHS MMuc MWat NOra NWea SBdl SDea SKee SPer SSFr SVic WJas WMat WWct

Cultivar	Suppliers
- 'Hubbard's Pearmain' (D)	SKee
- 'Hunter's Majestic' (D/C)	ECrN
- 'Hunthouse Pippin' (C) **new**	SKee
- 'Idared' (D)	ECrN NOra SBdl SDea SKee SSFr SVic WMat
- 'Improved Keswick' (C/D)	CEnd
- 'Improved Lambrook Pippin' (Cider)	CArg CTri
- 'Ingrid Marie' (D)	SDea SKee SSFr
- 'Irish Peach' (D)	CAgr CArg CFGn CHab CTri ECrN IArd MCoo NOra SDea SKee SSFr WMat
- 'Isaac Newton's Tree'	see *M. domestica* 'Flower of Kent'
- 'Isle of Wight Pippin' (D)	CLnd SDea
- 'Isle of Wight Russet' (D)	SDea
- 'Jackson's'	see *M. domestica* 'Crimson King' (Cider/C)
- 'Jacques Lebel' (C)	SKee
- 'James Grieve' (D) Y^{H6}	Widely available
- 'James Lawson' (D)	SKee
- JAZZ ('Scifresh') (D) **new**	SSFr
- 'Jefferies' (D)	SKee
- 'Jersey Beauty' (C/D) **new**	CLnd
- 'Jerseymac' (D)	SDea
- 'Jester' (D)	ECrN SDea SSFr
- 'Joaneting' (D)	CAgr CHab
- 'John Broad'	see *M. domestica* 'Captain Broad'
- 'John Standish' (D)	CAgr CTri SDea SKee
- 'John Toucher's'	see *M. domestica* 'Crimson King' (Cider/C)
- 'Johnny Andrews' (Cider)	CAgr
- 'Johnny Voun' (D)	CEnd
- 'Jonagold' (D) Y^{H6}	CArg CLnd CTri ECrN ELan EMOT EPom IArd NLar NOra SBdl SDea SKee SPer SSFr WWct
- 'Jonagold Crowngold'	see *M. domestica* 'Crowngold'
§ - 'Jonagored'[PBR] (D)	NOra SBdl SDea WMat
- 'Jonathan' (D)	NOra SDea SKee
- 'Jordan's Weeping' (C)	SDea
- 'Josephine' (D)	SDea
- 'Joybells' (D)	SKee
- 'Jubilee'	see *M. domestica* 'Royal Jubilee'
- 'Julie's Late Golden' (F)	CTri
- 'Jumbo' (C/D)	CLnd EMOT MAsh MCoo NOra SKee WJas WMat
- 'Jupiter'[PBR] (D) Y^{H6}	CAgr CArg CDul CSBt CTri ECrN EMOT LSRN MJak MRav NLar NOra NWea SBdl SDea SKee SLon SSFr WJas WMat
- 'Kandil Sinap' (D)	SKee
- 'Kapai Red Jonathan' (D)	SDea
- 'Karmijn de Sonnaville' (D)	NOra SDea SKee
§ - 'Katja' (D)	Widely available
- KATY	see *M. domestica* 'Katja'
- 'Kemp' (D)	SDea
- 'Kenneth' (D)	WGwG
- 'Kent' (D) Y^{H6}	ECrN SDea
- 'Kentish Fillbasket' (C)	SKee
- 'Kerry Pippin' (D)	IArd
- 'Keswick Codlin' (C)	CArg CHab ECrN GQue LRHS MCoo NEgg NLar NOra NWea SDea SKee SSFr WJas WMat
§ - 'Kidd's Orange Red' (D) Y^{H6}	CAgr CArg CDul CMac CRos CTri ECrN EMOT EPfP EPom LBuc LRHS MWat NOra SDea SKee SLon SSFr WMat WWct
- 'King Byerd' (C/D)	CEnd CTho
- 'King George V' (D)	SKee
- 'King Luscious' (D)	SDea

§ - 'King of the Pippins' (D) ♀H6 — CArg CFGn CHab CLnd CTri ECrN EPom LBuc MCoo NOra SDea SKee SVic
- 'King Russet' (D) ♀H6 — SDea
- 'King's Acre Pippin' (D) — NOra SDea WMat
- 'Kingston Bitter' (Cider) — CTho
- 'Kingston Black' (Cider/C) — CAgr CArg CDul CEnd CHab CLnd CMac CTho CTri EMOT EPom MGos NOra SDea SKee WMat
- 'Knobby Russet' (D) — SKee SSFr
- 'Lady Henniker' (C) — CDul CEnd CHab ECrN SDea SKee
- 'Lady Hollendale' (D) — SKee
- 'Lady Lambourne' (C/D) — CHab
- 'Lady of the Wemyss' (C) — SKee
- 'Lady Sudeley' (D) — CEnd CHab SDea SKee
- 'Lady's Finger' (C/D) — CEnd
- 'Lady's Finger of Lancaster' (C/D) — CHab SKee
- 'Lady's Finger of Offaly' (D) — IArd SDea
- 'Lambourne Pippin' (F) — CTho
- 'Lamb's Seedling' (D) — SKee
- 'Landsberger Reinette' (D) — SKee
- 'Lane's Prince Albert' (C) ♀H6 — CAgr CArg CHab CLnd CSBt CTri ECrN EMOT EPfP LRHS MGos MRav MWat NOra NWea SBdl SCoo SDea SSFr SVic WJas WMat
- 'Langley Pippin' (D) — SDea SKee

§ - 'Laxton's Epicure' (D) ♀H6 — CAgr CHab CTri ECrN EMOT SDea SKee

§ - 'Laxton's Fortune' (D) ♀H6 — CArg CDul CHab CMac CSBt CTri ECrN IArd LRHS NOra SBdl SDea SKee SSFr WJas WMat WWct
- 'Laxton's Pearmain' (D) — MCoo
- 'Laxton's Royalty' (D) — SDea

§ - 'Laxton's Superb' (D) — CArg CBcs CCVT CDul CHab CLnd CMac CSBt CTri ECrN EMOT EPom GKin LBuc MCoo NOra NPri NWea SBdl SCob SDea SEWo SKee SPer SSFr SVic WJas WMat WWct
- 'Lemon Pippin' (C) — ECrN ELan NOra SDea SKee
- 'Liberty' (D) — SDea
- 'Limelight' (D) ♀H6 — CArg EBee EMOT MAsh MCoo NLar NOra SCoo SKee SSFT SSFr WMat
- 'Linda' (D) — SKee
- 'Link Wonder' (D) — CEnd
- 'Little Pax' (D) — EPom MCoo NLar NOra
- 'Llwyd Hanner Goch' (D) — WGwG
- 'Lodi' (C) — SDea
- 'London Pearmain' (D) — ECrN
- 'London Pippin' (C) — CAgr
- 'Longkeeper' (D) — CAgr CEnd
- 'Lord Burghley' (D) — SDea
- 'Lord Derby' (C) — CAgr CArg CDul CFGn CHab CLnd CMac CTho ECrN EMOT EPom LRHS MRav NOra SBdl SDea SEND SKee SPer SSFT SVic WMat WWct
- 'Lord Grosvenor' (C) — SKee
- 'Lord Hindlip' (D) — CHab NOra SDea WMat WWct
- 'Lord Lambourne' (D) ♀H6 — CAgr CArg CDul CHab CLnd CMac CRos CSBt CTri ECrN ELan EMOT EPom LSRN MAsh MCoo MGos MWat NLar NOra SBdl SDea SKee SLon SPer SSFr WJas WMat WWct
- 'Lord Nelson' (C) — SKee
- 'Lord of the Isles' (Cider) — CAgr
- 'Lord Rosebery' (D) — SKee
- 'Lord Stradbroke' (C) — ECrN SKee
- 'Lord Suffield' (C) — CTri ECrN SKee
- 'Lough Tree of Wexford' (D) — IArd
- 'Lucombe's Pine' (D) — CAgr CEnd CFGn CTho ECrN SVic
- 'Lucombe's Seedling' (D) — CTho
- 'Lynn's Pippin' (D) — ECrN SKee
- 'Mabbott's Pearmain' (D) — SDea
- 'Machen' (D) — WGwG
- 'Madresfield Court' (D) — SDea WWct
- 'Major' (Cider) — CAgr WMat
- 'Maldon Wonder' (D) — ECrN
- 'Malling Kent' (D) — SDea
- 'Maltster' (D) — MCoo
- 'Manaccan Primrose' (C/D) — CEnd CFGn
- 'Mannington's Pearmain' (D) — WMat
- 'Marged Nicolas' (D) — WGwG
- 'Margil' (D) — SDea
- 'Markham Pippin' (D) — MCoo
- 'Marriage-maker' (D) — SKee
- 'Mary's Apple' (F) — SDea
- 'Maxton' (D) — ECrN
- 'May Queen' (D) — SDea WWct
- 'Maypole'PBR (D) — MJak SDea
- 'McIntosh' (D) — NOra SKee
- 'Médaille d'Or' (Cider) — CArg SKee WMat
- 'Melon' (D) — SDea
- 'Melrose' (D) — ECrN
- 'Mère de Ménage' (C) — SDea SKee
- 'Meridian'PBR (D) — CAgr ECrN MCoo NOra SDea SSFr WMat
- 'Merton Knave' (D) — SDea
- 'Merton Russet' (D) — SCob SDea
- 'Merton Worcester' (D) — ECrN SDea SKee
- 'Michelin' (Cider) — CAgr CArg CTri MGos NOra SDea WMat WWct
- Miel d'Or — see *M. domestica* 'Honeygold'
- 'Miller's Seedling' (D) — NOra SKee
- 'Millicent Barnes' (D) — SDea SKee
- 'Monarch' (C) — CAgr CTri ECrN EPom SDea SKee SSFr
- 'Monmouthshire Green' (D) — WGwG
- 'Montfort' (D) — ECrN
- 'Morgan's Sweet' (C/Cider) — CArg CEnd CHab CTho CTri NOra SDea SKee WMat
- 'Moss Orchard' (D) — LPra
- 'Moss's Seedling' (D) — SDea

§ - 'Mother' (D) ♀H6 — CAgr CEnd CLnd CTri ECrN SDea SKee SSFr

§ - 'Mutsu' (C/D) — CArg CLnd CTri ECrN EMOT MRav NOra SDea SKee SPer SSFr WMat
- 'Mylor Pike' (D) — CEnd
- 'Nancy Jackson' (C) — CHab
- 'Nant Gwrtheyrn' (D) — WGwG
- 'Nettlestone Pippin' (D) — SDea
- 'Newton Wonder' (C) — CAgr CArg CDul CHab CSBt CTho CTri ECrN EMOT EPom LRHS MCoo MGos NOra SBdl SDea SKee SSFr WJas WMat WWct
- 'Newtown Pippin' (D) — SDea
- 'Nine Square' (D) — CTho
- 'Nittany Red' (D) — SDea
- 'Nolan Pippin' (D) — ECrN
- 'Nonpareil' (D) — SKee
- 'Norfolk Beauty' (C) — ECrN SKee
- 'Norfolk Beefing' (C) — CArg CHab ECrN NOra SDea SKee WMat
- 'Norfolk Royal' (D) — CLnd ECrN NOra SDea
- 'Norfolk Royal Russet' (D) — NOra SKee WMat

Name	Suppliers
- 'Norfolk Summer Broadend' (C)	ECrN
§ - 'Northwood' (Cider)	CTho WMat
- 'Nutmeg Pippin' (D)	ECrN SDea
- NUVAR CHEERFULL GOLD (D)	SKee
- NUVAR FRECKLES (D)	SKee
- NUVAR GOLDEN HILLS (D)	SKee
- 'Oaken Pin' (D)	CEnd CTho
§ - 'Obelisk'PBR (D)	CArg EMOT NOra SDea SKee WMat
- 'Old Pearmain' (D)	SDea
- 'Old Somerset Russet' (D)	CTho
- 'Opalescent' (D)	CEnd
- 'Orleans Reinette' (D)	CAgr CArg CLnd CTri ECrN EMOT EPom LBuc MWat NOra SDea SKee SSFr WJas WMat WWct
- 'Oslin' (D)	SKee WMat
- 'Otava'PBR (C/D)	SKee
- 'Paignton Marigold' (Cider)	CTho
- 'Payhembury' (C/Cider)	CAgr
- 'Pear Apple' (D)	CAgr CEnd
- 'Pearl' (D)	NOra SDea SKee WMat
- 'Peasgood's Nonsuch' (C) ♀H6	CAgr CArg CHab ECrN EPom IArd LSRN MAsh NOra SDea SKee SLon WMat
- 'Pendragon' (D)	CEnd CTho
- 'Peter Lock' (C/D)	CAgr CEnd CTho
- 'Peter's Pippin' (D)	SDea
- 'Peter's Seedling' (D)	SDea
- 'Pethyre' (Cider)	CCVT
- 'Pig Aderyn' (C)	CHab WGwG
- 'Pig y Colomen' (C)	WGwG
- 'Pig's Nose Pippin' (D)	CEnd CTsd
- 'Pig's Nose Pippin' Type III (D)	CAgr
- 'Pig's Snout' (Cider/C/D)	CEnd
- 'Pine Apple Russet of Devon' (D)	CEnd
- 'Pine Golden Pippin' (D)	SKee
- 'Pine Apple Russet' (C/D)	CAgr
- PINK LADY	see *M. domestica* 'Cripps Pink'
- 'Pinova'PBR (D)	CAgr EPom SSFr
- 'Pitmaston Pine Apple' (D)	CArg CHab CTho CTri ECrN EMOT MCoo MWat NOra SCob SDea SKee SLon SSFr WMat WWct
- 'Pitmaston Russet Nonpareil' (D)	SKee
- 'Pixie' (D) ♀H6	CSBt EMOT EPom LRHS MWat NOra NPri SCob SDea SKee SLon WWct
- 'Plum Vite' (D)	CAgr CTri
- 'Plympton Pippin' (C)	CEnd CTho CTri
- POLKA ('Trajan'PBR) (D)	NOra SDea SKee
- 'Polly' (C/D)	SKee
- 'Polly Whitehair' (C/D)	SDea
- 'Pomeroy of Somerset' (D)	CHab CTho CTri SKee
- 'Ponsford' (C)	CAgr CTho WMat
- 'Port Wine'	see *M. domestica* 'Harry Master's Jersey'
- 'Porter's Perfection' (Cider)	CTri NOra
- 'Prince Charles' (D)	SKee
- 'Princesse' (F)	CLnd ECrN SDea
- 'Queen' (C)	CAgr ECrN SDea
- 'Queen Caroline' (C)	SKee
- 'Queen Cox' (D)	CLnd CTri ECrN EPom LSRN NOra SBdl SDea SKee SLon SSFr SWvt WMat WTSh
- 'Queens' (D)	CEnd
- 'Rajka'PBR (D)	GQue NOra SKee WWct
- 'Red Alkmene'	see *M. domestica* 'Red Windsor'
- 'Red Belle de Boskoop' (D)	CAgr
- 'Red Bramley' (C)	CDul ECrN
- 'Red Charles Ross' (C/D)	SDea
- 'Red Delicious'	see *M. domestica* 'Starking'
- 'Red Devil' (D)	CAgr CLnd CMac CSBt CTri ECrN EMOT EPom LRHS MRav MWat NLar NOra NPri NRHS NWea SCob SCoo SDea SEWo SKee SLim SLon SSFT SSFr WJas WMat WWct
- 'Red Ellison' (D)	CTri ECrN SDea
- 'Red Falstaff'PBR (D) ♀H6	CAgr CArg CCVT CDul CMac CTri EBee ECrN EMOT EPfP GKin LBuc LRHS LSRN MAsh MCoo NLar NOra NRHS SKee SLim SLon SPer SPoG SSFT WMat WWct
- 'Red Fuji' (D)	SDea
- 'Red Gravenstein' (D)	SBdl
- 'Red James Grieve' (D)	SDea SKee
- 'Red Joaneting' (D)	SKee
- 'Red Jonagold'	see *M. domestica* 'Jonagored'
- 'Red Jonathan' (D)	SDea
- 'Red Miller's seedling' (D)	ECrN SDea
- 'Red Pixie' (D)	CArg GQue MCoo WMat
- 'Red Rattler' (D)	CTri
§ - 'Red Windsor' (D)	CArg CDul CLnd CMac CRos CTri EMOT EPom LBuc LCro LOPS LRHS MAsh NLar NOra SCoo SDea SKee SLim SPoG SSFr WJas WMat
- 'Redcoat Grieve' (D)	SDea
- 'Redsleeves' (D)	CAgr CLnd ECrN EMOT NOra SDea
- 'Reine des Reinettes'	see *M. domestica* 'King of the Pippins'
- 'Reinette Descardre' (D)	SVic
- 'Reinette Rouge Etoilée' (D)	SDea
- 'Resi'PBR (C/D)	WWct
- 'Reverend Greeves' (C)	SDea
- 'Reverend McCormick' (D)	CTho
- 'Reverend W. Wilks' (C)	CAgr CArg CHab CSBt CTri ECrN EMOT EPom NOra SBdl SDea SKee SSFr WJas WMat WWct
- 'Ribston Pippin' (D) ♀H6	CArg CDul CTho CTri ECrN EMOT MCoo MRav MWat NOra NWea SDea SKee SLon SSFr WJas WMat WWct
- 'Rival' (D)	CAgr SDea
- 'Rivers' Nonsuch' (D)	CHab
- 'Rome Beauty' (D)	SDea
- 'Rosemary Russet' (D) ♀H6	CAgr CArg CHab CTho ELan MCoo NOra SDea SKee SLon SSFr WMat WWct
- 'Rosette' (D)	CArg EPom LBuc LRHS MAsh NLar NOra WMat
- 'Ross Nonpareil' (D)	CAgr IArd NOra SDea WMat
- 'Rosy Blenheim' (D)	ECrN
- 'Rough Pippin' (D)	CEnd
- 'Roundway Magnum Bonum' (C/D)	CAgr CTho SDea
- 'Royal Gala' (D)	CMac ECrN EMOT EPom LBuc MRav SCob SDea SLon
§ - 'Royal Jubilee' (C)	SKee
- 'Royal Russet' (C)	CAgr CEnd ECrN SDea SKee
- 'Royal Somerset' (C/Cider)	CTho CTri WMat
- RUBINETTE ('Rafzubin') (D)	ECrN NOra SDea SKee
- RUBINETTE ROSSO ('Rafzubex'PBR) (D)	NOra WMat

- 'Rubinola'^{PBR} (D) SKee WWct
- 'Ruby' Thorrington (D) ECrN
- 'Saint Ailred' (D) SKee
- 'Saint Cecilia' (D) CHab SDea WGwG
- § 'Saint Edmund's Pippin' (D) ♀H6 CHab CTho ECrN ELan EPfP MCoo NOra SDea SKee SSFr
- 'Saint Edmund's Russet' see *M. domestica* 'Saint Edmund's Pippin'
- 'Saint Everard' (D) SKee
- 'Saltcote Pippin' (D) SKee WMat
- 'Sam Young' (D) CAgr SKee
- 'Samba' (C/D) LOPS
- 'Sandlands' (D) SDea
- 'Sandlin Duchess' (D) NOra WMat
- 'Sandringham' (C) ECrN
- 'Sanspareil' (D) CAgr SKee
- 'Santana'^{PBR} (D) ♀H6 NOra WMat
- 'Saturn' (D) CAgr CArg CCVT CTri NOra SDea SKee SSFr WMat WWct
- 'Saw Pits' (D) CAgr CEnd
- 'Scarlet Crofton' (D) IArd
- 'Scarlet Nonpareil' (D) SDea SKee
- 'Scotch Bridget' (C) CArg CHab GQue NBid NOra SKee WMat WWct
- 'Scotch Dumpling' (C) GBin GKin GQue LRHS MCoo NOra SKee WMat
- 'Scrumptious'^{PBR} (D) ♀H6 Widely available
- 'Severn Bank' (C) SKee
- 'Sheep's Nose' (C) CHab IArd SDea SKee
- 'Shenandoah' (C) SKee
- 'Sidney Strake' (C) CAgr CEnd
- 'Sir Isaac Newton's' see *M. domestica* 'Flower of Kent'
- 'Sir John Thornycroft' (D) SDea
- 'Sisson's Worksop Newtown' (D) MCoo
- 'Slack Ma Girdle' (Cider) CArg NOra SKee WMat
- 'Smart's Prince Arthur' (C) CHab SDea
- 'Snell's Glass Apple' see *M. domestica* 'Glass Apple'
- 'Somerset Lasting' (C) CTri
- 'Somerset Redstreak' (Cider) CAgr CArg CHab CTri NOra SBdl WMat
- 'Sops in Wine' (Cider/D) CArg CTsd ECrN NOra SKee SVic WMat
- 'Sour Bay' (Cider) CAgr
- 'Spartan' (D) Widely available
- 'Spencer' (D) CTri ECrN
- 'Spotted Dick' (Cider) CTho
- 'Stamford Pippin' (D) SDea
- 'Stanway Seedling' (C) ECrN
- 'Star of Devon' (D) CEnd SDea SKee
- 'Stark' (D) SDea
- § 'Starking' (D) ECrN LMaj NOra
- 'Stark's Earliest' (D) SVic
- 'Stembridge Cluster' (Cider) CTri
- 'Steyne Seedling' (D) SDea
- 'Stirling Castle' (C) CAgr NOra SKee WMat
- 'Stoke Edith Pippin' (D) SKee
- 'Stoke Red' (Cider) CArg NOra SKee WMat
- 'Strawberry Pippin' (D) CDul
- 'Striped Beefing' (C) ECrN
- 'Sturmer Pippin' (D) CSBt CTri ECrN MWat NOra SDea SKee WWct
- 'Summer Golden Pippin' (D) SKee
- 'Summerred' (D) ECrN SDea
- 'Sunburn' (D) ECrN
- 'Sunnydale' (D/C) SDea
- 'Sunrise'^{PBR} (D) EMOT NOra SCob SKee
- 'Sunset' (D) ♀H6 Widely available
- 'Suntan' (D) ECrN MWat NOra SDea SKee
- 'Superb' see *M. domestica* 'Laxton's Superb'
- 'Sussex Mother' (C/D) CHab SKee
- 'Sweet Alford' (Cider) CArg CTho ECrN WMat WWct
- 'Sweet Bay' (Cider) CAgr
- 'Sweet Caroline' (D) SDea
- 'Sweet Coppin' (Cider) CArg CTri WMat
- 'Sweet Lilibet' see *M. domestica* 'Red Windsor'
- 'Sweet Merlin' (D/Cider) **new** NWea
- 'Sweet Pethyre' (C) EMOT
- 'Sweet Society' (D) EMOT NOra SKee WJas WMat
- 'Tamar Beauty' (D) CEnd
- 'Tan Harvey' (Cider) CEnd
- 'Taunton Cross' (D) CAgr CArg WMat
- 'Taylor's' (Cider) CAgr SDea
- 'Ten Commandments' (Cider/D) SDea SKee WWct
- TENTATION ('Delblush'^{PBR}) (D) SDea
- 'The Rattler' (Cider) CEnd
- 'Thomas Rivers' (C) SDea
- 'Thorle Pippin' (D) SKee
- TICKLED PINK ('Baya Marisa') (C/D) CArg EPom LRHS NLar NOra SPer WMat
- 'Tidicombe Seedling' (D) CTho WMat
- 'Tom Putt' (C) CAgr CArg CCVT CDul CHab CLnd CSBt CTho CTri LBuc NOra SDea SKee WJas WMat WWct
- 'Tommy Knight' (D) CAgr CEnd CFGn
- 'Topaz'^{PBR} (D) ♀H6 SKee
- 'Totnes Apple' (D) CTho
- 'Tower of Glamis' (C) CHab GQue SKee
- 'Tregonna King' (C/D) CTho CTsd
- 'Tremlett's Bitter' (Cider) CAgr CArg CHab CTho NOra SDea SKee SVic WMat
- 'Trwyn Mochyn' (C) WGwG
- § 'Tuscan'^{PBR} (D) EMOT SDea SKee
- 'Twenty Ounce' (C) SKee
- § 'Tydeman's Early Worcester' (D) CAgr CHab CLnd ECrN SBdl SDea SKee SSFr WWct
- 'Tydeman's Late Orange' (D) CArg CHab CTri ECrN MCoo NOra SBdl SDea SKee WMat
- 'Tyler's Kernel' (C) SKee
- 'Upton Pyne' (C/D) CTho SDea
- 'Veitch's Perfection' (C/D) CTho WMat
- 'Venus Pippin' (C/D) CEnd
- 'Vicary's Late Keeper' (C) CTho
- 'Vickey's Delight' (D) SDea
- 'Vileberie' (Cider) CTri
- 'Violette' (C) SKee
- 'Vista-bella' (D) ECrN EMOT SBdl SDea
- 'Wagener' (D) ECrN SDea SKee
- WALTZ ('Telamon'^{PBR}) (D) EMOT SDea
- 'Warner's King' (C) ♀H6 CTri NOra SDea SKee
- 'Wealthy' (D) SDea SKee
- 'Wellington' (C) see *M. domestica* 'Dummellor's Seedling'
- 'Wellington' (Cider) CAgr
- 'Welsh Russet' (D) SDea
- 'Werrington Wonder' (D) CEnd
- 'West View Seedling' (D) ECrN
- 'White Joaneting' (D) SKee
- 'White Melrose' (C) NOra SDea WMat
- 'White Paradise'^{PBR} (C) SKee
- 'White Transparent' (C/D) SDea SKee
- 'White Winter Pearmain' (D) SDea
- 'Whitpot Sweet' (Cider) CEnd

– 'William Crump' (D)	CDul CHab CTho ECrN NOra SDea WMat WWct
– 'Willoughby' (D)	MCoo
– 'Windsor Early' (D) **new**	SSFr
– 'Winesap' (C/D) **new**	SKee
– 'Winston' (D) ♀H6	CAgr CCVT CMac CTri ECrN MCoo SDea SKee SVic WWct
– 'Winter Banana' (D)	CArg CHab ECrN GQue NOra SDea SKee SVic WMat
– 'Winter Gem' (D)	CAgr CArg CCVT CDul CLnd ECrN EPom LBuc NOra SCob SDea SKee SSFr WJas WMat
– 'Winter Peach' (D/C)	CAgr ECrN
– 'Winter Quarrenden' (D)	SDea
– 'Winter Queening' (D/C)	SDea
– 'Winter Red' (F)	CEnd
– 'Woodbine'	see *M. domestica* 'Northwood'
– 'Woodford' (C)	ECrN SKee
– 'Woolbrook Pippin' (D)	CAgr CEnd CTho WMat
– 'Woolbrook Russet' (C)	CEnd ECrN SKee
– 'Worcester Pearmain' (D) ♀H6	Widely available
– 'Wormsley Pippin' (D)	ECrN
– 'Wyken Pippin' (D)	ECrN SDea SKee WWct
– 'Yarlington Mill' (Cider)	CAgr CArg CHab CTri NOra SDea SKee SVic WMat WWct
– 'Yellow Ingestrie' (D)	CArg CHab CLnd MCoo NOra WMat WWct
– 'Yorkshire Aromatic' (C)	SKee
– 'Yorkshire Greening' (C)	CHab NOra SKee
– 'Zabergäu Renette' (D)	NOra SKee
'Donald Wyman'	CLnd EPfP LMaj MAsh NLar NOra SCoo WMat
§ 'Echtermeyer'	CTri SDea
'Elise Rathke'	CLnd
'Evelyn'	CLnd NOra WMat
§ 'Evereste' ♀H6	Widely available
florentina	CTho
– 'Rosemoor'	CLnd
× ***floribunda*** ♀H6	Widely available
fusca	CLnd
'Gardener's Gold'	CEnd CLnd CTho SRms
× ***gloriosa*** 'Oekonomierat Echtermeyer'	see *M.* 'Echtermeyer'
'Golden Gem'	CLnd EMOT GQue MAsh NOra SEWo SKee WMat
'Golden Hornet'	see *M.* × *zumi* 'Golden Hornet'
'Gorgeous'	Widely available
'Harry Baker'	CCVT CDul CEnd CLnd CMac CSBt ECrN EMOT EMil EPfP EPom EWTr LSRN MBlu MRav NOra SCoo SDea SLim SPer SPoG WJas WMat WMou WWct
× ***hartwigii***	CLnd
'Hillieri'	see *M.* × *scheideckeri* 'Hillieri'
'Honeycrisp'PBR	CFGn NOra WMat
hupehensis ♀H6	CAby CDul CEnd CLnd CMCN CSBt CTho CTri EBee EPfP EWTr IMou LRHS MBlu MGos MRav NLar NOra NWea SPer WMat WMou WTSh
'Hyde Hall Spire'	SCoo
'Hyslop' **new**	CLnd
'Indian Magic'	EBee EPfP EWTr LRHS MAsh NLar NOra SPer WHCr WMat
'Indian Summer'	CLnd
JELLY KING ('Mattfru') ♀H6	CLnd EBee ECrN EMOT EPfP EPom LBuc LRHS LSRN MAsh NLar NOra NPri NWea SPer SPoG WHCr WMat
'John Downie' (C)	Widely available
'Kaido'	see *M.* × *micromalus*
kansuensis	CLnd
'Lady Northcliffe'	CDul CLnd
'Laura' ♀H6	CDul CLnd EBee EMOT EPfP EPom EWTr LRHS LSRN MAsh NLar NOra NPri SCoo SKee SLim SLon SPer SPoG WJas WMat WMou
'Louisa'	EBee EPfP NOra NWea SCoo SGol SLim WMat
× ***magdeburgensis***	CCVT CDul CLnd CSBt
'Makamik'	LPra
'Mariri Red' (D)	WMat
'Mary Potter'	CLnd
§ × ***micromalus***	CLnd
× ***moerlandsii***	CLnd
– 'Liset'	CDul CEnd CLnd ECrN EMOT LPra MRav NEgg NOra SCoo WFar
§ – 'Profusion'	CBcs CDul CTri ECrN ELan EMOT EPfP LCro LOPS LPra MGos MJak MRav MSwo NOra NPri NRHS NWea SCob SEND SGol SPer SRms SWvt WJas WMou WSpi
'Mokum'	CLnd LMaj
'Molten Lava'	CLnd MAsh
'Montreal Beauty'	CLnd EPom WJas
niedzwetzkyana	CLnd CTho
NUVAR CARNIVAL	SKee
NUVAR MARBLE	EBee NOra SKee WMat
PERPETU	see *M.* 'Evereste'
'Peter's Red' **new**	CLnd
'Pink Mushroom'	ECrN EMOT
'Pink Perfection'	CEnd EWTr NLar NOra NPri NWea SPoG WMat
'Pond Red'	CLnd
'Prairifire'	CDul CLnd EMOT EWTr LRHS MAsh NOra NPri SCoo SLim SLon SPoG WMat
prattii	CLnd CTho EBee EPfP GLog
– 'Pourpre Noir'	CLnd
'Princeton Cardinal' ♀H6	CLnd CMac EPfP SCoo SLim SPoG WMou
'Professor Sprenger'	see *M.* × *zumi* 'Professor Sprenger'
'Profusion'	see *M.* × *moerlandsii* 'Profusion'
prunifolia	MBlu
– var. ***rinkii***	CLnd
'Purple Prince'	CLnd
§ × ***purpurea*** 'Aldenhamensis'	CLnd SDea
– 'Eleyi'	CLnd CNWT EPfP LPra NWea
– 'Lemoinei'	CDul
– 'Neville Copeman'	CCVT CDul CLnd EMOT EPom SSFr WJas
– 'Pendula'	see *M.* 'Echtermeyer'
'R.J. Fulcher'	CTho
'Ralph Shay'	CLnd
'Red Ace'	CDul
'Red Barron'	CLnd
'Red Glow'	CDul CLnd ECrN WJas
'Red Jade'	see *M.* × *scheideckeri* 'Red Jade'
'Red Jewel' **new**	CLnd
§ 'Red Jonaprince'PBR	WMat
RED OBELISK ('Dvp Obel')	CCVT CLnd LBuc NOra SCoo SPoG WMat
'Red Peacock'	CLnd
'Red Prince'	see *M.* 'Red Jonaprince'
'Roberts Crab'	EBee EWTr
§ × ***robusta***	CLnd EMOT LPra LSRN NWea SLon SRms
– 'Dolgo'	CLnd CSBt EBee EMOT EPom EWTr LCro MBlu NLar NOra SCoo SKee SPoG WMat

	- 'Red Sentinel' ♀H6	Widely available
	- 'Red Siberian'	SDea SPer
	- 'Yellow Siberian'	CLnd
	'Rosehip'	CLnd EBee EMOT LBuc LCro LOPS NLar NOra NPri WMat WMou
	'Royal Beauty'	CDul CLnd EMOT EPfP EUJe EWTr LMaj LRHS MAsh MBlu MGos MJak MSwo NOra NPri SCoo SLon SPer WMat
	'Royalty'	CBcs CDul CLnd CSBt EBee ECrN ELan EMOT LBuc LCro LMaj LOPS LPra LRHS MGos MJak MMuc MRav MSwo NEgg NOra NWea SCob SEND SEWo SGol SPer WJas WMat WMou
	'Rudolph'	CCVT CDul CLnd CNWT EBar ECrN EMOT LBuc LMaj LPra LSRN MAsh MGos NOra NPri SCoo SEWo SLim SPer SPoG WJas WMat WMou
	'Ruth Ann'	CLnd
	sargentii	CDul CLnd CTho EWTr NOra NWea
	- 'Candy Mint'	EBee EWTr MAsh WHCr WMat
	- 'Tina'	LPra MAsh NOra SPoG WMat
	'Satin Cloud'	CLnd
§	× ***scheideckeri*** 'Hillieri'	CDul CLnd LPra MBlu
§	- 'Red Jade'	CDul CLnd CTri ELan EMOT LPra MGos MJak MRav MSwo NWea SPer SRms WJas
	Siberian crab	see *M.* × *robusta*
	sieboldii	see *M. toringo*
	sieversii	CDul CLnd
	sikkimensis B&SWJ 2431	WCru
	'Silver Drift'	CLnd
	'Simon'	WMat
	'Snowcloud'	CDul CLnd ECrN EMOT MAsh SLim
	'Snowdrift'	CLnd
	'Street Parade'	CLnd
	'Striped Beauty'	LPra
	× ***sublobata***	CLnd
	'Suffolk Pink'	ECrN
	SUGAR TYME ('Sutyzam')	CLnd
	'Sun Rival' ♀H6	CCVT CDul CEnd CLnd CMac EBee ELan EMOT EPfP EPom LRHS MAsh MBlu MRav NOra NPri SCoo SEWo SLim SPer SPoG SRms WJas WMat
	sylvestris	CAco CArg CCVT CDul CFGn CHab CLnd CPer ECrN EPfP LBuc LPra MJak MMuc MRav NWea SEND SEWo SPer SPre WMou WTSh
	'Tinsley Quince' (D)	WMat
§	***toringo***	CTho ECrN EPfP LEdu LMaj LPra NOra
I	- var. ***arborescens***	CLnd CTho
	- 'Browers'	CNWT LMaj
	- 'Scarlett' ♀H6	CCVT CDul CLnd EMOT EPfP EWTr IArd LMaj LRHS LSRN NLar NOra NWea SCoo SEWo SLim SPer SPoG WMat WMou
	- 'Wintergold'	MMuc
	- 'Wooster'	CLnd
	toringoides	see *M. bhutanica*
	transitoria ♀H6	CDul CEnd CLnd CMac CTho EBee ECrN ELan EMOT EPfP EWTr GKin MAsh MBlu MRav NLar NOra NWea SCoo SLau SPer WMat WMou WPGP
	- 'Thornhayes Tansy'	CDul CTho NOra SLim SPoG WMat
	trilobata	CDul CTho EBee ELan EPfP LMaj MBlu MGos MMuc SCoo SEND
	- 'Guardsman'	CLnd CMac EMOT EPfP NPri WMat
	tschonoskii	CDul CLnd CMCN CMac CTri ELan EMOT LMaj LPra MBlu MGos MJak MMuc NWea SEND SPer SRms SWvt WJas WMou WTSh
	- 'Belmonte'	MBlu
	'Van Eseltine'	CAgr CDul CMac CSBt ECrN EMOT EPfP MMuc SPer WJas
	'Veitch's Scarlet'	CDul CHab CSBt
	VELVET PILLAR ('Velvetcole')	SPer
	WEEPING CANDIED APPLE ('Weepcanzam')	CLnd
	'White Angel'	CLnd EWTr
	'White Star'	CCVT CDul CLnd CSBt EBee ECrN EMOT EWTr NOra SEWo SLon WMat
	'Winter Gold'	CDul LPra SGol
	'Wisley Crab'	CLnd EMOT SDea SKee SLon SRms
	yunnanensis	EPfP WPav
	- var. ***veitchii***	CLnd CTho
	× ***zumi***	GLog
	- var. ***calocarpa***	CLnd CTho
§	- 'Golden Hornet'	Widely available
§	- 'Professor Sprenger'	CLnd EPfP LMaj LPra NOra SCoo

Malva (*Malvaceae*)

	alcea	CAgr
	- var. ***fastigiata***	CMac CRos EPPr LRHS SPer SRms WOut
	- 'Royal Flush'	NRHS
	bicolor	see *Lavatera maritima*
	moschata	CAgr CBcs CBod EBee ECha ELan ENfk EPfP GPoy GQue LPot MHer MMuc MNHC NLar NMir SPer SPlb SRms WFar WHer WMoo WOut
§	- f. ***alba*** ♀H5	CBcs CBod CRos CSpe ECha ELan ELon EPfP IFro LEdu LPot LRHS MHer MNHC NBir NGBl NLar NRHS SPer SPhx SPoG SRms SWvt WArt WBrk WFar WGwG WHer WKif WMoo
	- 'Appleblossom'	WOut
	- 'Romney Marsh'	see *Althaea officinalis* 'Romney Marsh'
	- 'Rosea'	CRos EPfP LRHS NPer NRHS SPoG SWvt
	- 'Snow White'	see *M. moschata* f. *alba*
	- 'White Perfection'	WFar
	pusilla	CCCN
	sylvestris	CBod SRms WMoo
	- 'Blue Fountain' PBR	EBee LRHS SRms
	- 'Brave Heart'	SWvt WOut
	- MARINA ('Dema' PBR)	NLar
	- var. ***mauritiana***	LCro LOPS NPer WArt WMoo WOut
	- - 'Bibor Fehlő'	CSpe EBee
	- - 'Primley Blue'	CBod EBee ECtt ELan EMor EPfP GMaP ILea LRHS MRav NPer WSpi
	- - 'Zebrina'	EPfP MEch NGBl NPer SAko SWvt WMoo
	- 'Perry's Blue'	NPer

Malvastrum (*Malvaceae*)

× ***hypomadarum***	see *Anisodontea* × *hypomadara* (Sprague) D.M. Bates

Malvaviscus (*Malvaceae*)

arboreus	CHll

mandarin see *Citrus reticulata* Mandarin Group

mandarin, Cleopatra see *Citrus reticulata*

Mandevilla ✿ (*Apocynaceae*)

§	× ***amabilis***	CCCN
	- 'Alice du Pont' ♀H1c	CBcs CCCN ELan EMdy EShb SPre
	× ***amoena***	see *M.* × *amabilis*
	'Audrey'PBR (Vogue Series)	CBcs CWGN SPoG
	boliviensis ♀H1c	CCCN CRHN EMdy
	(Diamantina Series) DIAMANTINA OPALE CITRINE ('Lancalifornia') **new**	EMdy
	- DIAMANTINA OPALE GRENAT ('Lanutah') **new**	EMdy
	'Ginger' (Vogue Series)	CAbb CBcs CWGN SPoG
§	***laxa*** ♀H2	CBcs CCCN CHll CKel CRHN CSam CSpe ECre ELan EMdy EShb LRHS SBrt SVen
	(Rio Series) RIO DEEP RED ('Fisrix Dered'PBR)	CCCN
	- RIO PINK ('Fisrix Pinka'PBR)	CCCN
	- RIO WHITE ('Fisrix Whit'PBR)	EMdy
	'Ruby' (Vogue Series)	CAbb CWGN
	sanderi	CCCN EShb SPre
	- 'Pink of Hint'	EMdy
	- 'Rosea'	CCCN
	splendens ♀H1c	CBcs CCCN CHll EMdy
	suaveolens	see *M. laxa*
	Sundaville Series	CCCN
	- SUNDAVILLE CREAM PINK ('Sunparapibra'PBR)	EMdy
	- SUNDAVILLE DARK RED ('Sunparabeni'PBR)	EMdy
	- SUNDAVILLE GRAND RED ('Sunpara15') **new**	EMdy
	- SUNDAVILLE IMPROVED WHITE 16 ('Sunparamakuho') **new**	EMdy
	- SUNDAVILLE PEARL ('Patmandewi') **new**	EMdy
	- SUNDAVILLE PINK ('Sunmandecripi') **new**	EMdy
	- SUNDAVILLE PRETTY RED ('Sunmanderemi'PBR)	EMdy
	- SUNDAVILLE PRETTY ROSE ('Sunparaprero'PBR)	EMdy
	- SUNDAVILLE RED ('Sunmandecrim'PBR)	EMdy
	- SUNDAVILLE ROSE STAR ('Sunpararosta'PBR) **new**	EMdy

Mandragora (*Solanaceae*)

	autumnalis	GEdr SBrt SPhx WSFF
§	***officinarum***	GCal GEdr GPoy

Manettia (*Rubiaceae*)

	cordifolia **new**	SBrt
	inflata	see *M. luteorubra*
§	***luteorubra***	CCCN

Manfreda see *Agave*

× *Mangave* see *Agave*

mangetout see AGM Vegetables Section (under pea)

Mangifera (*Anacardiaceae*)

	indica (F)	CCCN SPre
	- 'Kent' (F) **new**	SVic

Manglietia see *Magnolia*

	yunnanensis	see *Magnolia insignis*

mango see *Mangifera indica*

Manihot (*Euphorbiaceae*)

	carthaginensis	SPlb

Mantisia (*Zingiberaceae*)

	saltatoria PAB 4208	LEdu WPGP

Maranta (*Marantaceae*)

	leuconeura var. ***erythroneura*** ♀H1b	XBlo
	- var. ***kerchoveana*** ♀H1b	XBlo

Margyricarpus (*Rosaceae*)

§	***pinnatus***	EWld SIgm WPav
	setosus	see *M. pinnatus*

Mariscus see *Cyperus*

marjoram, pot see *Origanum onites*

marjoram, sweet see *Origanum majorana*

marjoram, wild, or oregano see *Origanum vulgare*

marrow see AGM Vegetables Section

Marrubium (*Lamiaceae*)

§	***bourgaei*** var. ***bourgaei*** 'All Hallows Green'	ECha ECtt LRHS NEgg NRHS SRms
	candidissimum	see *M. incanum*
*	***cylleneum*** 'Velvetissimum'	WCot XSen
§	***incanum***	SEND XSen
	libanoticum	NSti
	supinum	EBou ECha LRHS SEND
	vulgare	CBod EBee ENfk GJos GPoy MHer MNHC SRms WJek

Marsdenia (*Apocynaceae*)

	formosana CWJ 12354	WCru
	oreophila	CBcs CKel CRHN GCal LRHS SPoG WPGP
	- Mabiluo form	GCal

Marshallia (*Asteraceae*)

	grandiflora	EBee
	trinerva	ELon

Marsilea (*Marsileaceae*)

	mutica	EWat LLWG
*	***schelpiana***	XBlo

Massonia (*Asparagaceae*)

	depressa ♀H2	SChF WCot
	echinata	GKev SChF WCot
	pustulata ♀H2	EUJe GKev SChF WCot

Mathiasella (*Apiaceae*)

	bupleuroides	WHil
	- 'Green Dream'	CAby CAvo CBcs CBod CBre CSpe EBee ECtt ELan EUJe EWld GBin ILea LCro LEdu LOPS LRHS MBel MHol MNrw NSti SCob SMad SPoG WCAu WCot

Matricaria (*Asteraceae*)

chamomilla	see *M. recutita*
maritima	see *Tripleurospermum maritimum*
parthenium	see *Tanacetum parthenium*
§ ***recutita***	GPoy MNHC
tchihatchewii	XLum XSen

Matteuccia ✿ (*Onocleaceae*)

orientalis ♀H5	CAby CBdn CBod CDTJ CKel CLAP CRos CWCL ECha EFer EMor ERod EUJe GCal GMaP IBal LEdu LLWG LRHS MMuc NBid NLar NRHS SEND WMoo WPnP XLum
pensylvanica	CRos LRHS NRHS
struthiopteris ♀H5	Widely available
* - 'Depauperata'	CLAP
- 'Jumbo'	CBdn CCCN CRos GBin ISha LRHS NRHS
- 'The King'	WCot

Matthiola (*Brassicaceae*)

fruticulosa 'Alba'	CAby EPfP SMad WPGP
- subsp. ***perennis***	NSti WHal
incana	LRHS MArl SVic WKif
- ***alba***	CWld EBee ECha ELan LRHS MHol SEND SPad SPhx WCot WRHF
- 'Low' **new**	WCot
- purple-flowered	CWld SEND
- VINTAGE MIXED	NPri
scapifera	CPBP WAbe
sinuata	CEls
white-flowered perennial	CMea CSpe NPer

Maurandya (*Plantaginaceae*)

antirrhiniflora **new**	CPla
§ ***barclayana***	CSpe IDee
erubescens	see *Lophospermum erubescens*
lophantha	see *Lophospermum scandens*
lophospermum	see *Lophospermum scandens*
'Magic Dragon'	see *Lophospermum* 'Magic Dragon'
'Red Dragon'	see *Lophospermum* 'Red Dragon'
§ ***scandens***	CPla

Maytenus (*Celastraceae*)

boaria	CMCN IArd LEdu MGos SAko SArc SEND
disticha (Hook.f.) Urb.	LEdu
magellanica	WPGP

Mazus (*Phrymaceae*)

reptans	CBod EBou ECtt GEdr NLar NPer NQui XLum
- B&SWJ	CExl
- 'Albus'	CBod ECtt LLWG NLar SPlb
- 'Blue'	LLWG

Mecardonia (*Plantaginaceae*)

'Goldflake'	CCCN

Meconopsis ✿ (*Papaveraceae*)

§ ***baileyi*** ♀H5	CBcs CBod CRos CTri EBee EPfP GGGa GKev ITim LCro LOPS LRHS NAln NBir NChi NEgg NRHS WFar WSFF
* - var. ***alba***	CBod CPla CRos CTsd EBee GCal GGGa GKev IMou LRHS NAln NRHS
- 'Hensol Violet'	CPla CTsd EBee GEdr GGGa GKev NRHS
- violet-flowered	ITim
Ballyrogan form	GEdr GKev
betonicifolia misapplied	see *M. baileyi*
'Cally Purple'	GCal
cambrica	see *Papaver cambricum*
chelidoniifolia	CAby CRos LRHS NBid NRHS WCru
× ***cookei***	EBee GKev NHpl NSum
- 'Old Rose'	GEdr GGGa GMaP
'Edrom'	GEdr
Fertile Blue Group	ITim
- 'Blue Ice'	see *M.* (Fertile Blue Group) 'Lingholm'
- 'Cally Lingholm'	GCal
- 'Harry Bush'	GEdr
- 'Lingholm'	Widely available
- 'Louise'	GEdr GMaP
- 'Mop-head' ♀H5	GEdr GKev GMaP
§ George Sherriff Group	EBee GCal MArl NBir
- 'Ascreavie'	GEdr GKev GMaP
- 'Barney's Blue'	GEdr GKev GMaP
- 'Dalemain' ♀H5	GEdr GMaP
- 'Branklyn' ambig.	CExl GEdr
- 'Huntfield'	GEdr GGGa GKev GMaP
- 'Jimmy Bayne'	GEdr GMaP
- 'Susan's Reward' ♀H5	GEdr GMaP
grandis misapplied	see *M.* George Sherriff Group
grandis ambig.	CRos ITim NEgg
- GS 600	see *M.* George Sherriff Group
- 'Burgundy'	GWyn
(Infertile Blue Group) 'Bobby Masterton' ♀H5	GEdr GKev GMaP
- 'Bryan Conway'	GEdr
- 'Crarae'	GEdr GGGa GKev GMaP
- 'Crewdson Hybrid'	GCal GEdr GKev GMaP
- 'Cruickshank'	GKev
- 'Dawyck'	see *M.* (Infertile Blue Group) 'Slieve Donard'
- 'Maggie Sharp'	GEdr
- 'Mrs Jebb' ♀H5	GEdr GGGa GMaP
- 'P.C.Abildgaard' ♀H5	GEdr GGGa GKev GMaP
§ - 'Slieve Donard' ♀H5	CRos GCal GEdr GGGa GKev GMaP LRHS NRHS
integrifolia	CCCN
'Inverewe' ♀H5	GEdr
'Jim's Ex'	GKev
'Keillour' ♀H5	GEdr
'Keillour Violet'	GKev
'Marit' ♀H5	GEdr GKev GMaP
'Mervyn Kessell'	GEdr GKev
'Mildred'	GEdr
napaulensis misapplied	EBee GAbr GKev ITim
- red-flowered	CPla
napaulensis DC.	NAln
- B&SWJ 13952	WCru
nudicaulis	see *Papaver nudicaule*
paniculata	EBee GGGa
- B&SWJ 13922	WCru
prattii **new**	CPla
'Pride of Angus' **new**	GEdr
pseudointegrifolia	GGGa
punicea	GGGa GKev NHpl
- 'Sichuan Silk'	NHpl
quintuplinervia ♀H5	CPla GEdr GKev NHpl NSla
- Farrer's form	GEdr
- 'Kaye's Compact'	GEdr
racemosa	EWld
× ***sheldonii*** misapplied (fertile)	see *M.* Fertile Blue Group
× ***sheldonii*** misapplied (sterile)	see *M.* Infertile Blue Group

× ***sheldonii*** ambig.	CBcs GAbr LRHS NBir NLar NPer NRHS
'Stewart Annand'	GEdr GKev GMaP
'Strathspey'	GEdr GMaP NHpl
sulphurea new	GGGa
superba	GGGa
villosa	see *Cathcartia villosa*
wallichii Hook.	GGGa
'Willie Duncan'	GEdr GMaP
wilsonii subsp. ***orientalis***	CPla

Medeola (*Asparagaceae*)

virginiana	EBee

Medicago (*Papilionaceae*)

arborea	SEND SPlb
lupulina	CHab
sativa	SVic WHer WSFF
- 'Lucerne' new	CWld

Medinilla (*Melastomataceae*)

magnifica ♀H1a	CCCN

medlar see *Mespilus germanica*; also AGM Fruit Section

Meehania (*Lamiaceae*)

cordata	EBee
urticifolia	GCal GEdr WPnP
- B&SWJ 1210	WCru
- 'Japanblau'	IMou

Megaskepasma (*Acanthaceae*)

erythrochlamys	SVen

Melaleuca (*Myrtaceae*)

acuminata	SPlb
alternifolia	CAby CBcs CCCN CTsd EShb GPoy MHer NWad SPlb SVen
armillaris	CCCN CTsd IDee SEND SPlb
cuticularis	SPlb
decussata	SPlb
§ ***diosmatifolia***	CExl
diosmifolia	CPbh
ericifolia	CTri CTsd SEND SPlb
erubescens	see *M. diosmatifolia*
fulgens	SPlb
gibbosa	CExl CKel SEND SVen
hypericifolia	CExl SPlb SVen
linariifolia	CCCN SPlb
nesophila	SPlb
pungens	SPlb
pustulata	SVen
squamea	SEND SPlb
squarrosa	CExl CHll EBee SPlb SVen
thymifolia	SPlb
trichophylla	SPlb
wilsonii	IDee

Melampodium (*Asteraceae*)

§ ***montanum*** AZTEC GOLD ('Starbini'PBR)	NPri
- 'Sunbini'PBR	CCCN

Melandrium see *Vaccaria*

rubrum	see *Silene dioica*

Melanoselinum (*Apiaceae*)

§ ***decipiens***	CBre CSpe CWld IMou LEdu LRHS MHer MNrw WOut WPGP

Melanoseris (*Asteraceae*)

taliensis BWJ 7891	WCru

Melanthium (*Melanthiaceae*)

virginicum	MNrw

Melia (*Meliaceae*)

§ ***azedarach***	CBcs CCCN SBrt SPlb
- B&SWJ 14625 new	WCru
- var. ***japonica***	see *M. azedarach*

Melianthus (*Melianthaceae*)

comosus	CDTJ CPla ESwi EWes NLar SCoo SPlb WPGP
major ♀H3	Widely available
villosus	EBee EWes SPad SPlb

Melica (*Poaceae*)

altissima 'Alba'	IKil LCro LRHS
- 'Atropurpurea'	CBod CCBP CRos EBou ECha EHoe LRHS MNrw NRHS SEND SPlb SPoG
ciliata	EAJP EHoe ELon EPPr WPtf XLum XSen
- subsp. ***taurica***	SPhx
cupani	EPPr
nutans	CWCL EAJP EHoe EPPr EShb GMaP GQue MAsh NWsh SPhx WCot
persica	EPPr
transsilvanica 'Red Spire'	SGol SMea XLum
uniflora	IMou NWsh
- f. ***albida***	CKno CRos ECha EHoe GCal GQue LRHS MAvo MRav NRHS SPhx WCot WSHC
- 'Variegata' (v)	CBre ECha EHoe EShb GCal LPla MAvo WCot

Melicytus (*Violaceae*)

alpinus	WThu
crassifolius	EBee
obovatus	NLar
ramiflorus	CDul

Melilotus (*Papilionaceae*)

albus	SPhx
officinalis	CHab WHer

Meliosma (*Sabiaceae*)

dilleniifolia WJC 13819 new	WCru
- subsp. ***cuneifolia***	CBcs CExl EBee IArd SBrt WPGP
- subsp. ***tenuis***	CBcs CExl
myriantha var. ***discolor*** MF 97132	WCru
pinnata var. ***oldhamii***	CExl
simplicifolia subsp. ***pungens***	CExl
veitchiorum	CBcs CExl NLar SBrt WPGP

Melissa ✿ (*Lamiaceae*)

officinalis	CBod CCBP CHab CLau EBou EMor ENfk GMaP GPoy GQue LCro LEdu LOPS MHer MJak MMuc MNHC NBir SEND SPhx SPlb SRms SVic WArt WBor XLum
- 'All Gold'	CBre CLau ECha EHoe ENfk GQue NBid SPer SPoG SRms
- subsp. ***altissima***	MNHC

§ - 'Aurea' (v) CBod CExl CLau EBou ELan EMor GPoy MHer MMuc MNHC MRav NBid NBir NBro NGrd SEND SPer SPoG SRms WFar WMoo
* - 'Compacta' GPoy LEdu
- 'Gold Leaf' NHic WPtf
- 'Lemona' CAgr
- 'Lime Balm' LEdu NPol
- 'Variegata' misapplied see *M. officinalis* 'Aurea'

Melittis (*Lamiaceae*)

melissophyllum CAby CMea CRos GAbr IMou LEdu LRHS MHol MNrw MPie MPnt MRav NRHS SHar WCAu WCot WPtf
- subsp. ***albida*** CBct CBod EBee EMor ILea LEdu LRHS SCob SPhx WCAu WCot WTor
- pink-flowered LEdu WCot
- 'Royal Velvet Distinction'PBR CBct CBod CRos EBee ELan EMor EPfP GEdr ILea LRHS MHol MRav MSCN NHpl NRHS SCob SHar SPoG WCot

Melliodendron (*Styracaceae*)

xylocarpum CExl SAko

melon see AGM Vegetables Section

Melothria (*Cucurbitaceae*)

scabra LRHS SVic

Menispermum (*Menispermaceae*)

canadense CTri GPoy
dauricum NLar

Mentha ✿ (*Lamiaceae*)

angustifolia Corb. see *M.* × *villosa*
angustifolia Host see *M. arvensis*
aquatica CBen CBod CHab CWat GPoy MHer MJak MWts NMir NPer NPol SPlb SRms SVic WHer WMAq WMoo WPnP WSFF XLum
§ ***arvensis*** MHer
- 'Banana' CBod EMor ENfk LEdu MHer MNHC SRms SVic WJek
- 'Lemon' EMor LEdu
- var. ***piperascens*** CBod LEdu MHer SRms WJek
§ - - 'Sayakaze' CLau
- 'Thai' ENfk SRms
asiatica MHer
'Berries and Cream' CBod CLau ENfk LEdu MHer MNHC SRms
Bowles's mint see *M.* × *villosa* var. *alopecuroides* Bowles's mint
cervina CBen CWat LEdu LLWG MHer MWts SRms WJek XLum
* - ***alba*** ENfk MHer MWts WJek WMAq
I 'Chocolate Peppermint' CLau ENfk EWhm LEdu NBir NLar
citrata see *M.* × *piperita* f. *citrata*
cordifolia see *M.* × *villosa*
corsica see *M. requienii*
crispa L. (1753) see *M. spicata* var. *crispa*
crispa ambig. × (× ***piperita***) MJak
'Eau de Cologne' see *M.* × *piperita* f. *citrata*
eucalyptus mint MHer
× ***gentilis*** see *M.* × *gracilis*
§ × ***gracilis*** CBod CLau ENfk EWhm GAbr GJos NGrd NLar NPri NSti SRms SVic
- 'Aurea' see *M.* × *gracilis* 'Variegata'
§ - 'Variegata' (v) CCBP ECha EMor GPoy LEdu MCot MHer MNHC NPri SPlb WHer WJek XLum
* 'Hillary's Sweet Lemon' ENfk MHer SRms
'Jessica's Sweet Pear' **new** ENfk
'Julia's Sweet Citrus' MHer
lavender mint CBod CLau GPoy LEdu MHer MNHC SRms
§ ***longifolia*** ENfk LEdu MMuc SEND SPlb SRms
- Buddleia Mint Group CCBP ENfk GAbr LEdu MHer MRav NSti WJek XLum
- - variegated (v) CBod LEdu WJek
- 'Lake Van' LEdu
- subsp. ***schimperi*** LEdu SRms WJek
- silver-leaved GAbr LEdu MHer MNHC SEND SRms SVic WJek
* - 'Variegata' (v) GAbr SRms
Nile Valley mint CLau LEdu SRms
× ***piperata*** f. ***citrata*** 'Kumin' LEdu
× ***piperita*** CHby ECha EHoe EMor GJos GPoy LCro LOPS MHer MNHC NGrd NPol NPri SPlb SVic
- 'Black Mitcham' CLau SPhx WJek
- black peppermint CAgr CBod CHby CLau ENfk EPfP LEdu MMuc MNHC NBir NLar SEND SRms SVic
§ - f. ***citrata*** CBod CHby CLau CTri ECha EMor ENfk GAbr GMaP GPoy GQue LEdu MHer MNHC MRav NBir NLar NPer NPri SPlb SRms SVic WGwG WJek
- - 'Basil' CBod CLau EMor GLog LEdu MHer MNHC MRav SRms SVic WJek
- - 'Bergamot' SRms
- - 'Chocolate' CBod CCBP EMor ENfk EPfP EWhm GJos LEdu LRHS MHer MNHC NGrd NPer NRHS SPlb SRms SVic WFar WGwG WJek XLum
- - 'Grapefruit' CBod EWhm MHer MNHC NWad SRms
- - 'Lime' CLau EMor ENfk EWhm LEdu MHer SPlb SRms SVic WFar WJek
- - 'Orange' CLau EMor ENfk LEdu MHer MMuc MNHC NGrd NPer SRms WJek
- - 'Swiss Ricola' CLau MHer WJek
- 'Crispa' NPol
§ - 'Multimentha' SRms
- 'Strawberry' ENfk SVic
- 'Swiss' CBod ENfk GJos LEdu NGrd NLar SRms WHer
pulegium CBod CHby ENfk EWhm GJos GPoy LEdu LLWG MHer MNHC SPlb SRms SVic WHer WSFF
- 'Cunningham Mint' **new** WJek
- 'Upright' CBod ENfk GPoy MHer SRms WJek
§ ***requienii*** CBod EBou ENfk GAbr GCal GPoy LEdu LLWG MHer MNHC NBir NRya NWad SPlb SRms WArt WGwG WJek WNPC XEll
rotundifolia misapplied see *M. suaveolens*
rotundifolia (L.) Huds. see *M.* × *villosa*
rubra var. ***raripila*** see *M.* × *smithiana*
sachalinensis **new** SVic
'Sayakaze' see *M. arvensis* var. *piperascens* 'Sayakaze'
§ × ***smithiana*** CCBP CLau EMor ENfk GPoy LEdu MHer MNHC MRav NBir NGrd SRms SVic WJek
§ ***spicata*** CAgr CBod CCBP CTri CTsd ENfk GJos GPoy LCro LOPS MCot

		MHer MJak MMuc MNHC NPol NPri SEND SPlb SRms SVic WHer XLum
	- Algerian fruity	LEdu
	- 'Cretan'	LEdu
*	- var. ***crispa***	CCBP ECha EMor ENfk LEdu MHer MMuc MNHC NRya SPlb SRms SVic WGwG WJek
	- - 'Moroccan'	CLau EBou EMor ENfk EWhm GAbr GJos GLog GPoy LEdu MHer MNHC NGrd NLar NPri SRms SVic
	- 'Crispula'	XLum
	- 'Guernsey'	CLau SRms
	- 'Kentucky Colonel'	LEdu
	- 'Mexican'	CLau
	- 'Newbourne'	CLau SRms
	- 'Nile Valley'	LEdu WJek
	- 'Russian'	CAgr LEdu MHer SVic
	- 'Spanish'	CCBP NGrd NLar SRms
	- 'Spanish Furry'	MHer
	- 'Tashkent'	CHby CLau ENfk EWhm LEdu LRHS MHer MNHC NGrd NRHS SRms WFar WGwG WHer WJek
I	'Strawberry Mint'	CLau EWhm LEdu MHer SRms WFar
§	***suaveolens***	CAgr CBod CCBP CHby EBou ENfk GJos GMaP GPoy GQue MHer MNHC NAln NGrd SPlb SRms SVic WSFF
*	- 'Grapefruit'	CAgr CLau EMor LEdu SVic
*	- 'Pineapple'	CBod CLau EBou ENfk EWhm GLog SVic WFar WJek
	- subsp. ***timija***	LEdu MHer SRms WJek
	- 'Variegata' (v)	CCBP CTri ECha EHoe EMor GJos GMaP GPoy GQue LEdu MCot MHer MMuc MNHC MRav NPri NSti SPlb SRms SVic WHer XLum
	'Sweet Pear'	MHer SRms
	sylvestris L.	see *M. longifolia*
I	'Tangerine Mint'	LEdu
	Thüringer minze	see *M.* × *piperita* 'Multimentha'
§	× ***villosa***	MMuc SEND
	- var. ***alopecuroides*** new	EMor
§	- - Bowles's mint	CBre CLau GPoy LEdu MHer MNHC NBir NLar NSti SRms WHer WJek
	- 'Jack Green'	CLau
	viridis	see *M. spicata*

Mentzelia (*Loasaceae*)

	lindleyi new	WHil

Menyanthes (*Menyanthaceae*)

	trifoliata	CBen CWat EWat GPoy LLWG MWts NPer WHal WMAq WSFF WWtn XLum

Menziesia see *Rhododendron*

	alba	see *Daboecia cantabrica* f. *alba*
	ciliicalyx lasiophylla	see *Rhododendron multiflorum* var. *purpureum*
	polifolia	see *Daboecia cantabrica* 'Polifolia'

Mercurialis (*Euphorbiaceae*)

	perennis	GPoy WHer WSFF WShi

Merendera (*Colchicaceae*)

§	***montana***	EPot GKev
	- 'Norman Barratt'	WCot
	pyrenaica	see *M. montana*
	sobolifera	WCot

Merrilliopanax (*Araliaceae*)

	alpinus B&SWJ 13906 new	WCru
	- B&SWJ 13939	WCru

Mertensia (*Boraginaceae*)

	franciscana	GCal
	lanceolata	EBee
§	***maritima***	CRos CSpe CWCL EBee EWes GKev GPoy LEdu LRHS NAln NBir NRHS SMad SPlb SRms WHoo
	- subsp. ***asiatica***	see *M. maritima*
	pterocarpa	see *M. sibirica*
	pulmonarioides	see *M. virginica*
§	***sibirica***	CSpe SBrt SPlb
§	***virginica*** ♀H4	CBod CWCL EBee ECtt EHrv ELan EPfP EPot IFro LAma LCro LEdu LOPS LRHS MBel MHol MNrw MPie NAln NBir NLar NSti SRms WFar
	viridis	SPlb

Merwilla (*Asparagaceae*)

§	***plumbea***	WCot

Merxmuellera (*Poaceae*)

	cincta	see *Capeochloa cincta*

Mesembryanthemum (*Aizoaceae*)

	brownii	see *Lampranthus brownii*
	crystallinum	NPri

Mespilus ✿ (*Rosaceae*)

	'Flanders Giant' (F)	LRHS WMat
	germanica (F)	CDul CHab CLnd CMCN CNWT CTri ECrN EUJe EWTr LMaj LPra MGil NLar SLon WFar
	- var. ***apyrena*** (F)	WMat
	- 'Brabant Giant' (F)	IArd
	- 'Bredase Reus' (F)	ELan SKee
	- 'Dutch' (F)	SDea SKee
	- 'Iranian' (F)	SKee
	- 'Large Russian' (F)	CAgr
	- 'Monstrous' (F)	SDea
	- 'Nottingham' (F) ♀H6	Widely available
	- 'Royal' (F)	CAgr CFGn LRHS MCoo NOra SCoo SKee WMat
	- 'Westerveld' (F)	CLnd CRos EPom SKee

Metapanax ✿ (*Araliaceae*)

	davidii	WPGP
	delavayi	SPtp WPGP

Metaplexis (*Apocynaceae*)

	japonica	SBrt

Metasequoia ✿ (*Cupressaceae*)

	glyptostroboides	Widely available
	- 'Chubby'PBR	EPfP NLar SMad
	- 'Emerald Feathers'	SLim
	- 'Fastigiata'	see *M. glyptostroboides* 'National'
	- GOLD RUSH ('Golden Oji') ♀H7	Widely available
	- 'Golden Dawn'	NLar
	- 'Hamlet's Broom'	SLim
	- 'Little Creamy'	NLar
	- 'Little Giant'	MBlu
	- 'Matthaei Broom'	MBlu SLim SMad
	- 'McCracken's White' (v)	NLar SLim
	- 'Miss Grace'	NLar SLim

§ - 'National' MBlu
- 'Schirrmann's Nordlicht' SLim
- 'Sheridan Spire' CEnd MBlu
- 'Waasland' MBlu
- 'White Spot' (v) MBlu

Metrosideros (*Myrtaceae*)

sp. CPla
carminea CCCN
§ ***excelsa*** CHll ECre ESwi
- 'Parnell' CBcs CCCN
- 'Vibrance' CCCN
kermadecensis 'Twisty' (v) CBcs
- 'Variegata' (v) CBcs
lucida see *M. umbellata*
robusta CBcs CCCN SPlb
- ***aureovariegata*** (v) CCCN EShb
§ 'Springfire' CCCN
× ***subtomentosa*** 'Mistral' IDee MPkF
'Thomasii' see *M.* 'Springfire'
tomentosa see *M. excelsa*
§ ***umbellata*** CBcs CCCN CTsd EBee
- 'Gold Nugget' CBcs CCCN MPkF SSta
- MOONLIGHT ('Lowmoo') CBcs CCCN SEle SLim

Meum (*Apiaceae*)

athamanticum CRos CSpe EBee EMor EPPr GCal GPoy IMou LEdu LRHS MRav SIgm SPhx WJek WSHC

Michauxia (*Campanulaceae*)

campanuloides CSpe GJos
tchihatchewii CDTJ GJos NGBl

Michelia see *Magnolia*

fulgens see *Magnolia foveolata*
sinensis see *Magnolia ernestii* subsp. *ernestii*
wilsonii see *Magnolia ernestii*

Microbiota (*Cupressaceae*)

decussata ♀H7 CBcs CMac CSBt LBee LRHS MGos NHol NWea WFar WPav
- 'Gold Spot' (v) WFar
- 'Jakobsen' CKen
- 'Trompenburg' CKen

Microcachrys ✿ (*Podocarpaceae*)

tetragona IDee WThu

Microglossa (*Asteraceae*)

albescens see *Aster albescens*

Microlepia (*Dennstaedtiaceae*)

strigosa CBdn CCCN CLAP CRos EBee EShb ISha LEdu LRHS NRHS WPGP
- 'MacFaddeniae' CBdn CLAP CRos EBee ISha LEdu LRHS NRHS WPGP

Micromeria (*Lamiaceae*)

sp. SRms SVic
corsica see *Acinos corsicus*
fruticosa WJek
juliana EBee XLum
rupestris see *M. thymifolia*
§ ***thymifolia*** SPlb

Microseris (*Asteraceae*)

ringens hort. see *Leontodon rigens*

Microsorum (*Polypodiaceae*)

§ ***diversifolium*** CKel EShb WCot WPGP
musifolium 'Crocodyllus'PBR EShb

Microtropis (*Celastraceae*)

petelotii HWJ 719 WCru

Milium (*Poaceae*)

effusum 'Aureum' ♀H7 Widely available
- 'Yaffle' (v) CBod CBre CKno EPPr EShb

Millettia (*Papilionaceae*)

japonica 'Hime Fuji' WPGP
murasaki-natsu-fuji see *M. reticulata*
pachycarpa CMen
§ ***reticulata*** CExl

Mimetes (*Proteaceae*)

chrysanthus SPlb
cucullatus CPbh
- 'Crackerjack Red' CCCN CKel

Mimosa (*Mimosaceae*)

pudica ♀H1b CCCN CDTJ EShb ESwi NAln

Mimulus (*Phrymaceae*)

'Andean Nymph' see *M. naiandinus*
§ ***aurantiacus*** ♀H2 CMac CSpe EBak ECtt EShb GCal MGil NPer SPlb SPoG SRms
- 'Primrose' MGil
× ***bartonianus*** see *M.* × *harrisonii*
cardinalis ♀H4 EBee ELan EPfP EWes GKev LLWG NAln NBir WBor WMoo
- gold-flowered EBee
- 'Red Dragon' CBod CFis WHrl
cardinalis × ***lewisii*** EWes
cupreus NAln
- 'Whitecroft Scarlet' ♀H4 GCrg
'Eleanor' ECtt EShb
glutinosus see *M. aurantiacus*
- ***atrosanguineus*** see *M. puniceus*
- ***luteus*** see *M. aurantiacus*
§ ***guttatus*** LCro LOPS NPer WMoo
§ × ***harrisonii*** EWes
'Highland Orange' EPfP GWyn MAsh SPlb SPoG WIce
'Highland Pink' EPfP GWyn MAsh NHpl SPlb SPoG
'Highland Red' ♀H5 EBou EPfP GKev GWyn MAsh NHpl SPlb SPoG WIce
'Highland Yellow' GWyn NHpl SPlb SPoG WIce
hose-in-hose (d) NPer
langsdorffii see *M. guttatus*
lewisii ♀H3 EBee EWes MNrw SRms
'Lothian Fire' CWat
luteus CWat GAbr LLWG NPer WBrk WMAq XLum
- 'Variegatus' ambig. (v) NPer
Magic Series SVic
moschatus EBee
§ ***naiandinus*** ♀H4 EWes GKev SPlb
'Orange Glow' LLWG MJak
§ 'Orkney Gold' (d) ECtt
'Popacatapetl' CSpe
primuloides EWes SPlb
§ ***puniceus*** SChF SRkn
RED EMPEROR see *M.* 'Roter Kaiser'
ringens CBen CWat EBee LLWG NBir NPer SPlb SRms WMAq WMoo

§ 'Roter Kaiser' LCro LOPS
yellow hose-in-hose see *M.* 'Orkney Gold'

Mina see *Ipomoea*

mint, apple see *Mentha suaveolens*

mint, basil see *Mentha* × *gracilis*

mint, Bowles's see *Mentha* × *villosa* var. *alopecuroides*

mint, curly see *Mentha spicata* var. *crispa*

mint, eau-de-Cologne see *Mentha* × *piperita* f. *citrata*

mint, ginger see *Mentha* × *gracilis*

mint, horse or long-leaved see *Mentha longifolia*

mint (pennyroyal) see *Mentha pulegium*

mint (peppermint) see *Mentha* × *piperita*

mint, round-leaved see *Mentha suaveolens*

mint (spearmint) see *Mentha spicata*

Minuartia (*Caryophyllaceae*)

parnassica see *M. stellata*
§ ***stellata*** EPot GKev
verna subsp. ***caespitosa*** CTri
- - 'Aurea' see *Sagina subulata* var. *glabrata* 'Aurea'

Mirabilis (*Nyctaginaceae*)

dichotoma EShb
jalapa CExl EPfP GKev LAma SDeJ SRms WHil
- 'Buttermilk' CCCN
longiflora EShb SBrt WHil
multiflora EBee WHil

Miscanthus (*Poaceae*)

capensis SPlb
chejuensis B&SWJ 8803 WCru
'Dronning Ingrid' CKno EPPr IMou MNrw SMea XLum
'Elfin' CKno
flavidus ESwi SRms XLum
floridulus misapplied see *M.* × *giganteus*
floridulus ambig. MMuc MNrw SCob SPlb XLum
floridulus (Labill.) Warb. ex K. Schum. & Lauterb. WJ 522 WCru
§ × ***giganteus*** CBod CKno EHoe ELon EPPr EUJe GCal MAsh MNrw MWht NWsh SCob SDys SVic WCot WMoo XLum
- 'Aksel Olsen' SAko
- 'Gilt Edge' (v) CKno EPPr NWsh
- 'Gotemba' (v) ELon EPPr EWes
- 'Jubilar' (v) MWht
- 'Meidl' SAko
'Navajo' **new** EUJe NAst
nepalensis CAby CExl CKno CMea CRos CSam CSde CWCL EBee ECha ECre EHoe EMor EUJe EWes GCal LEdu LRHS LSun MAsh MAvo MNrw NDov NRHS SPlb SPtp SRms WPGP
- NJM 09.141 WPGP
- 'Shikola' WCru
oligostachyus IMou SDys
§ - 'Afrika' CMea EBee EPPr GBin IMou MAvo MNrw WPGP
I - 'Nanus Variegatus' (v) CKno EHoe LEdu SAko WCot
'Purpurascens' CBod CKno CRos ECha EHoe EPPr LPot LRHS LSRN MAsh MNrw NRHS SCob SGol SPer WMoo XLum
sacchariflorus misapplied see *M.* × *giganteus*
sacchariflorus ambig. CBcs CKno CRos EBou ECha EHrv ELan EPfP LRHS MBrN NGdn NRHS SPer WMoo
sacchariflorus (Maxim.) Hack. LEdu WSpi
sinensis CRos CTri GAbr LEdu WFar WMoo XSen
- 'Abundance' CKel CKno CRos EPfP LRHS NRHS
- 'Adagio' ♀H6 CBar CBod CKno CRos CSde ECtt EHoe ELon EMor EPPr EShb EWhm GBin ILea LRHS MAsh MNrw NRHS NWad NWsh SCob SMHy SMad SMea SPoG SRms WCot WMoo XLum XSen
- 'Afrika' see *M. oligostachyus* 'Afrika'
- 'Aldebaran' IMou MNrw
- 'Andante' CKno
- 'Arabesque' EPPr XLum
- 'Augustfeder' EPPr MAvo SMea XLum
- 'Autumn Light' EPPr SMea XLum
- 'Barney Campbell' NWsh
- 'Blütenwunder' EPPr NWsh XLum
- 'Bogenlampe' GBin
- 'China' ♀H6 CKno CPar CRos EHoe ELon EPPr EPfP EShb EWes IPot LEdu LRHS MAsh MAvo MNrw NRHS NWsh SDys SRms WMoo
- 'Cindy' CKno
- var. ***condensatus*** LEdu
- - NJM 11.021 WPGP
- - 'Cabaret' (v) CBod CKno CRos EHoe EPPr EPfP EShb EUJe GMaP ILea LEdu LRHS LSRN MNrw NRHS NSti NWsh SMad SPoG WCot WFar WHal WMoo WPGP WSpi XLum XSen
- - 'Central Park' see *M. sinensis* var. *condensatus* 'Cosmo Revert'
§ - - 'Cosmo Revert' EPPr NWsh WPGP
- - 'Cosmopolitan' (v) ♀H6 Widely available
- - 'Emerald Giant' see *M. sinensis* var. *condensatus* 'Cosmo Revert'
- - 'Laigong' LEdu
- 'David' ELon EPPr LEdu MBNS XLum
- 'Dixieland' (v) CKno ELan ELon EMor EPPr EWes IMou LEdu
- 'Dreadlocks' CKno EBee EPPr GBin MAvo MNrw
- 'Dresdner Rotgold' SAko
- EARLY HYBRIDS **new** EBou
- 'Emmanuel Lepage' CKno EPPr LPla MAvo NWsh XLum
- 'Etincelle' CKno EPPr EWes ILea
- 'Federriese' EBee GBin
- 'Ferner Osten' ♀H7 Widely available
- 'Feuergold' SAko
- 'Flamingo' ♀H6 Widely available
- 'Flammenmeer' EPPr SAko
- 'Gearmella' EPPr
- 'Gewitterwolke' ♀H6 EWes NWsh SMHy XLum
- 'Ghana' ♀H6 CSpe EBee ELon EMor EPPr EUJe GBin IMou LEdu LPla MAvo MNrw

SDys SMHy SMad SPoG SRms SSut XLum
- 'Giraffe' CDTJ CKno EWes LEdu XLum
- 'Gnome' CKno EHoe EPPr EShb EUJe IMou LRHS MAsh MTin NRHS SRms
- 'Gold Bar'[PBR] (v) CBod CChe CDul CKel CRos CWGN ECha EHoe ELon EPfP EUJe LRHS LSRN MAsh MBNS NGdn NLar NRHS NWad SEle SGol SPad SPer SPoG WMoo
- 'Gold Breeze'[PBR] CRos LRHS NRHS
- 'Gold und Silber' ♀H6 XLum
- 'Goldfeder' (v) EWes XLum
- 'Goliath' CKno ELan ELon EPPr EUJe GBin GLog LEdu MBNS NAln WFar XLum
- 'Gracillimus' Widely available
- 'Graziella' CBod CEnd CKno CRos CSam EHoe EPPr EPfP GBin GWyn LRHS MAsh NGdn NRHS SPer SRms WFar WMoo XSen
- 'Grosse Fontäne' ♀H6 EHoe ELon EPPr GBin LEdu LRHS LSRN NWsh SMHy WCot WMoo XLum
- 'Gutenberg Gold' XLum
- 'Haiku' CKno EPPr LEdu XLum
- 'Helga Reich' EWes
- 'Hercules' EPPr MAvo XLum
- 'Hermann Müssel' CRos EBee EPPr EWes IMou LEdu LRHS NRHS SMHy SMea XLum
§ - 'Hinjo' (v) CDul ECha EHoe ELon GBin LRHS MAsh NGdn NRHS NWsh WCot
- 'Ibiza' **new** CKno
I - 'Jubilaris' (v) EPPr EUJe
- 'Juli' CRos EPPr LRHS NRHS WSpi
- 'Kaskade' ♀H6 CBod CKno CPar CRos EHoe EPPr EUJe GBin LEdu LRHS MMuc NDov NLar NRHS NWsh SMad WMoo
- 'Kirk Alexander' (v) EPPr
- 'Kleine Fontäne' ♀H6 Widely available
- 'Kleine Silberspinne' ♀H6 Widely available
- 'Korea' EBee EPPr
- 'Krater' CRos EBee EHoe EPPr ILea LRHS MBrN NRHS NWsh SDys SMea XLum
- 'Kupferberg' SMea XLum
- 'Kupferzwerg' EBee EPPr
§ - 'Little Kitten' CKno EPPr EUJe LEdu NDai SMea SRms WMoo XLum
- LITTLE NICKY see *M. sinensis* 'Hinjo'
- 'Little Zebra'[PBR] (v) EBee EPfP EUJe GMaP LSRN MGos MPnt NLar NWsh SCob SEle SMad SRms
- 'Malepartus' Widely available
- 'Memory' EPPr
- 'Morning Light' (v) ♀H6 Widely available
- 'Nippon' CRos EHoe EPPr EPfP GBin LEdu LRHS MAsh NGdn NRHS NWsh SCob SDys SPer WSpi XLum
- 'Nishidake' EPPr XLum
- 'November Sunset' EPPr EWes XLum
- 'Overdam' ECtt NGdn
- 'Poseidon' EPPr MAvo SDys SMad XLum
- 'Positano' XLum
- 'Professor Richard Hansen' CKno EBee EPPr EWes SMHy SMea XLum
- 'Pünktchen' (v) CRos ECha EHoe ELon EPPr GBin LRHS NRHS SCob SMHy SRms WMoo XLum
- 'Purple Fall' CKno CPar CRos CSpe EWes GBin GMaP IPot LRHS MAvo MNrw NRHS STPC
- 'Red Chief' CRos EPPr EPfP EUJe EWes IMou LPla LRHS MAvo NDov NLar NRHS SCob WMoo WTor
- RED CLOUD ('Emphis01') **new** LCro LOPS
- 'Red Meister' CKno CRos EPfP LRHS NRHS
- 'Red Tower' EWes
- 'Red Wine' GBin MNrw
- 'Roland' CKno EPPr SMad XLum
- 'Rosi' GBin MAsh
- 'Roterpfeil' EPPr
- 'Rotfeder' EPPr
- 'Rotfuchs' EBee MAvo XLum
- 'Rotsilber' CBod CKno CRos ECha EHoe EMor EPPr EUJe GMaP IArd LEdu LRHS MAsh MJak MMuc NRHS NWsh SRms WHoo WMoo WPtf XLum
- 'Russia' MAvo NWsh
- 'Samurai' EPPr GMaP MAvo MNrw
- 'Sarabande' ♀H6 EHoe EPPr SMHy SMea WMoo WSpi
- 'Septemberrot' ♀H6 EPPr MMuc SCob SEND
- 'Serim' EPPr
§ - 'Silberfeder' ♀H6 Widely available
- 'Silberpfeil' (v) NWsh
- 'Silberspinne' EBee EPPr GBin ILea NDai SCob SMHy SMea SPlb XLum
- 'Silberturm' EPPr XLum
- SILVER FEATHER see *M. sinensis* 'Silberfeder'
- 'Silver Sceptre' MAvo SMHy
- 'Silver Stripe' EPPr MAvo
- 'Sioux' CRos ECtt EPPr EPfP EShb EUJe GBin GQue LRHS MAsh MBNS NRHS SPer
- 'Sirene' EHoe EPPr MBNS MMuc NBir
- 'Spätgrün' EPPr
- 'Starlight' CKno
- 'Strictus' (v) ♀H6 Widely available
- 'Super Stripe' (v) EPPr IMou
- 'Taiwan' EBee EPPr
- 'Tiger Cub' (v) EPPr EWes
- 'Undine' ♀H6 CKel CMea ECha EHoe EPPr EPfP MBel MBrN MMuc NWsh WMoo XLum
- 'Variegatus' (v) CBod CRos ECha ECtt EHoe ELan ELon EPPr EPfP EUJe GMaP LRHS LSRN LSun MMuc MRav NGdn NRHS NSti SCob SGol SPer SPoG SRms WCot WMoo XLum
- 'Verneigung' GBin
- 'Vorläufer' EPPr GBin
- 'Westacre Wine' EWes
- 'Wetterfahne' EPPr LEdu
§ - 'Yaku-jima' CBod CRos CSam ECha ECtt EPPr LRHS MMuc MWht NRHS SCob SMea
- 'Yakushima Dwarf' Widely available
- 'Zebrinus' (v) ♀H6 Widely available
- 'Zwergelefant' EBee MAvo SMHy XLum

tinctorius 'Nanus Variegatus' misapplied see *M. oligostachyus* 'Nanus Variegatus'

transmorrisonensis CKno CRos EHoe ELan EPPr EUJe LEdu LPla LRHS MAvo NDov NRHS NWsh WCot WPGP

yakushimensis see *M. sinensis* 'Little Kitten', *M. sinensis* 'Yaku-jima'

Mitchella (*Rubiaceae*)

repens	CBcs CBod EBee GEdr IMou LEdu MNrw WCru
undulata B&SWJ 10928	WCru
* - f. ***quelpartensis*** B&SWJ 4402	WCru

Mitella (*Saxifragaceae*)

acerina B&SWJ 11029	EWld WCru
breweri	CMac ECha EWld GCal GLog IMou MAvo MPnt MRav NSti WBor WMoo WPnP
caulescens	ECha NBro
diphylla	MHer
formosana B&SWJ 125	WCru
furusei var. ***subramosa*** B&SWJ 11097	WCru
× ***inami***	IMou
- B&SWJ 11122	WCru
japonica B&SWJ 4971	WCru
kiusiana B&SWJ 5888	WCru
makinoi	EWld MAvo
- B&SWJ 4992	CExl WCru
pauciflora B&SWJ 6361	WCru
stylosa B&SWJ 5669	WCru
yoshinagae B&SWJ 4893	CExl EPPr WCru WMoo

Mitraria (*Gesneriaceae*)

coccinea	CCCN CExl CHll CMac CPbh CTsd GBin GEdr GKev MBlu NLar SLon SPer SPlb WPav
- Clark's form	EUJe LRHS NLar
- 'Lago Puyehue'	CAbb CBcs CCCN CExl CKel CRos EBee EPfP LRHS MAsh MGil SPlb SVen SWvt WPav WSHC WThu
- 'Lake Caburgua'	CAby CCCN CSpe ELon EWld GCal NLar WPav

Modiolastrum (*Malvaceae*)

lateritium	CHll CRHN CRos CSpe CTri EBee ELan EPPr LRHS MAvo NBir SPhx SPoG SRms WAvo WHal WSHC XLum

Moehringia (*Caryophyllaceae*)

muscosa	WCot

Molinia ✿ (*Poaceae*)

altissima	see *M. caerulea* subsp. *arundinacea*
'Autumn Charm'	CKno
caerulea	CKno CPla CRos EPPr LRHS MAsh MBlu NRHS
§ - subsp. ***arundinacea***	CKno CSpe CWCL ECha EPPr SSut WPtf XLum
- - 'Automne Bronze'	EPPr
- - 'Bergfreund'	CKno CSam EBee EHoe EPPr GBin MAvo SMHy
- - 'Black Arrows'	MAvo NDov
- - 'Breeze'	CKno NDov
- - 'Cordoba'	CBod CKno EBee ECha EMor EPPr GBin GQue MAvo NDov SMHy WMoo XLum
- - 'Fontäne'	CSam EHoe EPPr GQue MAsh MAvo SPhx
- - 'Granada'	EPPr
- - 'JS Mostenveld' (v)	EPPr GBin
- - 'JS Witches Broom'	GBin
- - 'JS Yellow Pipe'	GBin
- - 'Karl Foerster'	CBod CKno CRos CWCL EHoe EMor EPPr EPfP EShb EUJe EWhm GBin GMaP GQue IKil LRHS MNrw MTis NBid NLar NRHS NWsh SCob SPer WCAu WCot WMoo XLum XSen
- - 'Les Ponts de Cé'	EBee EPPr
- - 'Liebreiz'	EPPr
- - 'Moorland Mist'	WMoo
- - 'Skyracer'	CBod CKno CRos CSde EBee EHoe ELan ELon EMor EPPr EUJe GBin GCal GLog GMaP GQue LEdu LRHS MAvo MNrw NRHS SMHy SPhx WCot WGrn WMoo
- - 'Staefa'	EPPr
- - 'Sunbeam'	EPPr
- - 'Tears of Joy'	EBee EPPr
- - 'Transparent'	Widely available
- - 'Windsaule'	CKno EPPr IMou MAvo NDov
- - 'Windspiel' ♀H7	CBod CKno CRos CSam CWCL EBee EBou ECha EHoe EMor EPPr EShb GBin GQue IKil LRHS MAvo MNrw NDov NRHS NWsh SPer SPoG WCot WMoo XLum
- - 'Zuneigung'	CKno CRos CSam ECha EPPr LRHS MAvo NRHS
- subsp. ***caerulea***	EPPr
- - 'Carmarthen' (v)	CRos EHoe EPPr LRHS NRHS
- - 'Claerwen' (v)	ECha EPPr MAvo SPhx WMoo
- - 'Coneyhill Gold' (v)	EPPr
- - 'Dark Defender'	EPPr LEdu MAvo NDov SPhx
- - 'Dauerstrahl'	CKno EBee EPPr GCal GQue LEdu MAsh MNrw NBid NDov
- - 'Edith Dudszus'	CBod CKno CMea CRos CSam EBou ECha EHoe ELan ELon EMor EPPr GBin GQue LRHS MBel MBrN NDov NGdn NHol NRHS SCob SPer WGrn WMoo
- - 'Heidebraut'	CBod CMea CRos CSam EBee EHoe EHrv ELon EMor EPPr EPfP GBin GMaP GQue LCro LOPS LRHS MBel MRav NDov NRHS SAko SCob SPhx WCot WMoo
- - 'Heidezwerg'	EBee EMor EPPr GBin
- - 'Igel'	EBee EPPr GBin
- - 'Moorflamme'	CSam MAvo
- - 'Moorhexe' ♀H7	Widely available
- - 'Overdam'	EBee EPPr NDov
- - 'Poul Petersen'	CKno EBee EHoe EMor EPPr GBin MBel NDai NDov SPhx
- - 'Rotschopf'	EBee
- - 'Strahlenquelle'	CBod CSam EPPr EWhm GBin GQue LRHS NDov NHol NRHS NWsh
- - 'Variegata' (v) ♀H7	Widely available
- 'Showers of Gold'	SPhx
- 'Winterfreude'	EPPr
litoralis	see *M. caerulea* subsp. *arundinacea*

Molopospermum (*Apiaceae*)

peloponnesiacum	CAby CSpe EBee EMor EPPr GCal LEdu LRHS MMrt NDov SBrt SMHy SPhx WCot WCru WPGP WSHC

Moltkia (*Boraginaceae*)

§ ***doerfleri***	CPla GCal NBir NChi SBrt WSHC
§ × ***intermedia*** ♀H4	CMea CRos LRHS NRHS SIgm WAbe
petraea	CRos LLHF LRHS NRHS

Moluccella (*Lamiaceae*)

laevis	CSpe LCro LOPS SPhx SVic

Monanthes (*Crassulaceae*)

laxiflora	WCot
pallens	WCot

Monarda ✿ (*Lamiaceae*)

'Adam'	GBee GCal GQue LSRN MRav NGrd NLar WMon WSHC
'Aquarius'	CBod CRos CWCL CWld EAJP EPPr GQue IKil LRHS NLar NRHS WCAu WFar WMon WMoo XLum
austromontana	see *M. citriodora* subsp. *austromontana*
'Baby Spice'	WMon
§ 'Balance'	CRos EBee ECtt LRHS MMrt MRav NGdn NRHS WMon WSHC XLum
'Beauty of Cobham' 🏆H4	Widely available
(Bee-You Series) 'Bee-Free' **new**	SHeu
- 'Bee-Happy' **new**	SHeu
- 'Bee-Lieve' **new**	SHeu
- 'Bee-True' **new**	SHeu
'Bergamo'	LCro LOPS MHol
§ 'Blaustrumpf'	CElw CRos ECtt EPfP EWes LRHS NAln NGrd NLar NRHS SPer WFar WMon WSHC XLum
BLUE STOCKING	see *M.* 'Blaustrumpf'
BOWMAN	see *M.* 'Sagittarius'
bradburyana	CFis EBee LPla LRHS MMuc SAko SBrt SPhx
- Schm. 2004-0076	WMon
- 'Maramek'	IPot
- 'Ozark'	SAko
'Cambridge Scarlet'	Widely available
'Cambridge Star'	MArl
'Camilla'	WGoo WMon
'Capricorn'	WMon XLum
'Cherokee'	WMon
citriodora	GPoy NSti SRms SVic
§ - subsp. ***austromontana***	NBir
- - 'Bees' Favourite'	IKil
'Comanche'	EWes NLar WMon
'Croftway Pink'	CBcs CRos CSBt CWCL ECha ECtt ELan EPfP EUJe GMaP LCro LOPS LRHS MTis NHol NLar NRHS SPer SWvt WAvo WBor WCAu WFar WMon WSHC XLum
I 'Dark Ponticum'	WMon
didyma	CBod CCBP CLau EBou ENfk EPfP MNHC NBro SRms SVic WFar
- 'Alba'	NLar
- BALMY LILAC ('Balbalmac')	CBod CRos LRHS MHol NRHS SPoG
- BALMY PINK ('Balbalmink'[PBR]) **new**	SPoG
- BALMY PURPLE ('Balbalmurp'[PBR])	CRos LRHS MHol NRHS SCob SPoG WFar WHil
- BALMY ROSE ('Balbalmose'[PBR]) **new**	CBod
- 'Coral Reef'	CRos LRHS NRHS WFar WMon
- 'Cranberry Lace'[PBR]	CRos EBee ECtt EPfP LRHS MBel NLar NRHS SPoG WCAu
- 'Pardon My Cerise' **new**	NCGa
- 'Pardon My Pink'	CBod EBee NCGa NLar SPad
- 'Pardon My Purple'	CBod NCGa NLar SPoG WHil
- 'Pink Lace'[PBR]	CRos ECtt EPfP LRHS LSun MHol MNrw NHol NLar NRHS NSti SCob SPoG WCAu WFar WHil WMon WMoo
- 'Sugar Lace'[PBR]	NLar
'Earl Grey'	CBod ECtt MHer SCoo WFar WMon
'Elsie's Lavender'	EBee EPfP LRHS NAln NDov NLar NRHS WFar WMon WSHC
'Elworthy'	CElw WWFP
'Eugens Kirschrot'	WMon
'Eugens Purpursamt'	WMon
§ 'Feuerschopf'	EBee
'Fireball'[PBR]	CBcs CBct CBod CRos CWCL EAJP EBee ECtt EPfP EShb EUJe LCro LLHF LOPS LRHS LSRN MHer MHol MTis NHol NLar NRHS SRkn WBor WCAu WFar WHil WMon
FIRECROWN	see *M.* 'Feuerschopf'
§ 'Fishes'	CElw CExl CMac CRos EBee ECtt EHrv ELan EPPr EWes GQue IKil LEdu LRHS MRav NDov NGdn NLar NRHS SGbt SWvt WFar WMon WMoo WPtf
fistulosa	CBod CFis CHby CMac EBou MMuc MNHC SRms WArt WMoo XLum
- 'Humdinger' **new**	EBee WMon
- var. ***menthifolia*** 'Mohikaner'	EBee NDov SAko WGoo WMon
- 'Wahpe Washtemna'	NDov
'Gardenview Scarlet' 🏆H4	Widely available
GEMINI	see *M.* 'Twins'
'Gewitterwolke'	CSam ECtt MNrw NDov WMon
'Hartswood Wine'	EWes LEdu WFar WMon
'Häuptling'	WMon
'Heidelerche'	EBee WFar WMon
'Huckleberry'	WMon
'Jacob Cline'	CDor CMea CRos EAJP ECtt EPPr EWes GBin GWyn IMou IPot LEdu LPla LRHS MBel MNrw NBre NCGa NLar NRHS SGbt SHar SPhx SRms WBor WCAu WFar WMon WMoo XLum
'Kardinal'	GBin LRHS MTis NDov NLar WMon XLum
'Lederstrumpf'	EBee WMon
LIBRA	see *M.* 'Balance'
'Loddon Crown'	CTsd ECtt LPla MBNS MHer NHol NLar SHar WCAu WFar WMon WSHC
'Mahogany'	CBod CRos CWld EBee ECtt ELan EMor GMaP IKil IPot LRHS MCot MRav NRHS NSti SCob SPer SPhx SPoG WFar WMon XLum
'Marshall's Delight' 🏆H4	CBod CRos CWCL EBee ECtt EPfP EWes GQue LEdu LRHS MNHC MNrw MRav NDov NLar NRHS SWvt WCAu WFar WMon
'Melissa'	CRos EBee EPfP LRHS LSRN MAvo NBre NLar NRHS WMon WSHC
menthifolia	SRms
'Mohawk'	CBod CWld ECtt EHrv EPPr EPfP GQue ILea LRHS MPie MRav NDov NGdn NGrd NRHS WAvo WCAu WMon WPtf XLum
'Neon'	LRHS NDov SPhx WMon
'On Parade'	CElw CSam CWCL CWld ECtt ELon GBee GPSL LEdu LPla LRHS MMrt MTis NDov NGdn NRHS WAul WMon
'Othello'	CRos LRHS NDov NRHS WGoo WMon
'Ou Charm'	EBee EWes NLar WFar WMon

Panorama Series	SPlb
– 'Panorama Red Shades'	EPfP WCFE WFar WMon
'Pawnee'	WGoo WMon
PETITE DELIGHT ('Acpetdel')	NLar WMon XLum
'Petite Wonder'	EBee WFar WMon
'Pink Supreme'[PBR]	CBct CRos ECtt ELan EPfP LRHS MTis NLar NRHS SCoo WFar WHil WMon WMoo WTor
'Pink Tourmaline'	NDov WMon
PISCES	see *M.* 'Fishes'
'Poyntzfield Pink'	GPoy LEdu LPla
PRAIRIE NIGHT	see *M.* 'Prärienacht'
§ 'Prärienacht'	Widely available
punctata	CFis MNHC WArt
– 'Bee Bop'	LCro LOPS WHlf
'Purple Ann'	XLum
'Purple Lace'[PBR]	CRos LRHS NRHS WFar WMon
'Purple Tower'	EWes
'Purpurkrone'	CSam
'Raspberry Wine'	CBod CDor CRos CSam EBee ECtt EMor EPPr EWes LEdu LRHS MTis NRHS WFar WMon WMoo WPGP
'Rebecca'	WMon
'Remie'	WMon
'Ruby Glow'	CRos CSam EHrv GWyn LRHS LSRN NRHS WMon
§ 'Sagittarius'	EBee LRHS MAvo MBNS NGdn NRHS NSti SPoG WFar WMon
'Saxon Purple'	EBee LPla MBel NDov NLar WMon XLum
§ 'Schneewittchen'	CAby CBod CWCL EBee ECha ECtt EHrv ELan EPfP LRHS MRav MTis NAln NHol NLar SCob SCoo SGbt SPer SPoG SRms SWvt WCAu WFar WMon XLum
'Scorpion'	CBod CRos EBee ECtt EHrv ELan EPfP GBin GQue LCro LEdu LOPS LRHS MNHC MRav NBir NDov NEgg NGdn NLar NRHS NSti SPoG SWvt WCAu WHlf WMon XLum
'Shelley'	ECha WMon
'Sioux'	EHrv EWes
'Snow Maiden'	see *M.* 'Schneewittchen'
'Snow Queen'	EBee ECtt EShb LRHS MBel MPie NRHS
SNOW WHITE	see *M.* 'Schneewittchen'
'Squaw' ♀H4	Widely available
'Talud' ♀H4	CSam EBee IPot MNrw NDov WMon
'Tante Polly'	WMon
§ 'Twins'	EAJP GKev LSRN NLar SWvt WFar WMon WMoo WSHC
'Vintage Wine'	CElw CWCL NDov WMon
'Violacea'	NHol WFar WMon
'Violet Queen' ♀H4	CRos CWCL EBee ECtt ELan EWes GQue LEdu LRHS MBel MCot NEoE NRHS SCoo SPhx WCot WFar WMon WPtf
'Violette'	EBee WFar WMon
'Westacre Purple'	EPPr EWes

Monardella (*Lamiaceae*)

macrantha subsp. ***hallii***	CPBP
odoratissima	MHer SPhx

Monstera (*Araceae*)

deliciosa (F) ♀H1b	LCro LOPS XBlo

Montbretia see *Crocosmia*

Montia (*Portulacaceae*)

perfoliata	see *Claytonia perfoliata*
sibirica	see *Claytonia sibirica*

Moraea (*Iridaceae*)

alticola	GCal SPlb
bipartita	WCot
§ ***collina***	CBor GKev
huttonii	CBor CCCN CFis CPbh CSpe CTsd GAbr GKev NWad SBrt SMad WKif WSHC
iridioides	see *Dietes iridioides*
longifolia (Jacq.) Pers.	MHol
mediterranea	GKev
ochroleuca	CBor GKev
polystachya	CGrW
sisyrinchium	GKev SDeJ
spathacea	see *M. spathulata*
§ ***spathulata***	CExl GCal GKev WCot
vegeta	SBrt

Morella (*Myricaceae*)

californica	CAgr
pensylvanica	CAgr CDul NLar

Moricandia (*Brassicaceae*)

moricandioides	WCot

Morina (*Caprifoliaceae*)

* ***afghanica***	NWad WArt
bulleyana	see *M. nepatensis* var. ***delavayi***
longifolia	Widely available
§ ***nepatensis*** var. ***delavayi***	GKev
persica	EWes NWad
polyphylla	GPoy

Morinda (*Rubiaceae*)

umbellata WWJ 11688	WCru

Morisia (*Brassicaceae*)

hypogaea	see *M. monanthos*
§ ***monanthos***	CTsd GCrg GEdr LRHS SRot WIce
– 'Fred Hemingway'	ELan EPot LRHS NSla WAbe

Morus ✿ (*Moraceae*)

sp.	LPra
§ ***alba***	CBcs CCVT CDul CHab CLnd CMCN ECrN ELan EMOT EPfP LBuc LMaj LPra MRav SDea SPre SVic WFar WMou WTSh
– 'Issai' (F)	MGos
– 'Laciniata'	ELan
– 'Macrophylla'	CMCN MBlu
– 'Pakistan' (F)	CAgr SPoG
– 'Paradise' (F)	CAgr WMat
– 'Pendula'	CDul CEnd CMCN CMac ELan LPra MBlu NOra SCoo SDea SPoG SWvt WMat
– 'Platanifolia'	LPra MBlu
– var. ***tatarica***	CAgr LEdu NLar
'Black Tabor' (F)	CAgr
'Capsrum' (F)	CAgr WMat
'Carman' (F)	CAgr WMat
cathayana	WPGP
'Illinois Everbearing' (F)	CAgr WMat
'Italian' (F)	CAgr WMat
'Ivory' (F)	CAgr WMat
kagayamae	see *M. alba*
latifolia 'Spirata'	NLar

	macroura new	WSpi
	nigra (F)	Widely available
§	– 'Chelsea' (F) ♀H6	CDul CEnd CFGn CSBt CTho CTri EPfP EPom EWTr LRHS MGos NOra NWea SCoo SEWo SKee SLim SPer SPoG SSFT WMat
	– 'Izvor' (F)	CAgr
	– 'Jerusalem' (F) ♀H6	NOra WMat
	– 'King James'	see *M. nigra* 'Chelsea'
	– 'Large Black' (F)	EPom
	– 'Repsime' (F)	CAgr
	– 'Sham Dudu' (F)	CAgr
	rubra	EBtc
	– 'Nana'	NLar
	'Wellington' (F)	CCVT CEnd EMOT EUJe LRHS LSRN NOra SSFT WMat

Mosla (*Lamiaceae*)

	dianthera	GCal

Muehlenbeckia ✿ (*Polygonaceae*)

	astonii	EBee WPGP
	axillaris misapplied	see *M. complexa*
§	***axillaris*** (Hook. f.) Endl.	CBcs CTri EBee EShb GBin MGil XLum
§	***complexa***	Widely available
	– 'Nana'	see *M. axillaris* (Hook. f.) Endl.
	– small-leaved	EUJe
	– 'Spotlight'PBR (v)	EShb
	– 'Texture Big Leaf'	WPGP
	– var. ***trilobata***	CBcs EShb ESwi EUJe SSta XLum
	platyclados	see *Homalocladium platycladum*

Muhlenbergia (*Poaceae*)

	capillaris	CBcs EBee MBNS MMrt SMad
	dumosa	CKno WCot WPGP
	emersleyi	EBee
	japonica 'Cream Delight' (v)	EHoe
	lindheimeri	CKno SMea WCot
	mexicana	SRms
	rigens	CKno XLum

Mukdenia (*Saxifragaceae*)

	acanthifolia	GCal LEdu WPGP
	rossii	CAby CPla EHrv ELon GBin GCal LEdu LPla MBel MNrw NBid NLar WMoo WOld WPGP XLum
	– from Japan	GCal
	– from Korea	GCal
	– 'Crimson Fans'	see *M. rossii* 'Karasuba'
	– dwarf	GCal MNrw
§	– 'Karasuba'	Widely available
	– 'Shishiba'	GEdr LEdu

× *Mukgenia* (*Saxifragaceae*)

§	'Flame'	CAby CBct CMil EBee EMor EUJe GEdr IBal MHol MPnt SMad SPad SPoG
	NOVA	see × *M.* 'Flame'

mulberry see *Morus*

Murraya (*Rutaceae*)

	exotica	see *M. paniculata*
	koenigii	see *Bergera koenigii*
§	***paniculata***	EShb

Musa ✿ (*Musaceae*)

	from Yunnan, China	see *M. itinerans* 'Yunnan'
§	***acuminata*** Cavendish Group (AAA Group) (F)	EUJe
	– 'Dwarf Cavendish' (AAA Group) (F) ♀H1b	CAbb CBct CBod CCht ELan EUJe SPlb XBlo
	– 'Williams' (AAA Group) (F)	XBlo
	– 'Zebrina' ♀H1b	CDTJ CRos LRHS XBlo
	basjoo ♀H2	CAbb CBcs CCht CHll CSBt ELan EPfP EUJe LCro LEdu LOPS MGos MMuc SArc SChr SEND SMad SPer SPlb SPoG
I	– 'Rubra'	CCCN
	'Cavendish Super Dwarf'	XBlo
	cavendishii	see *M. acuminata* 'Dwarf Cavendish'
§	***coccinea*** ♀H1b	XBlo
	ensete	see *Ensete ventricosum*
	'Helen'	EUJe
	hookeri	see *M. sikkimensis*
	itinerans var. ***xishuangbannaensis*** 'Mekong Giant'	EUJe
§	– 'Yunnan'	EUJe
	lasiocarpa ♀H2	CDTJ CHll EUJe LCro LOPS MGos MPkF SPlb
	nana misapplied	see *M. acuminata* 'Dwarf Cavendish'
	ornata ♀H1b	CCCN XBlo
	× ***paradisiaca*** 'Ney Poovan' (AB Group) (F)	CCCN
§	***sikkimensis*** ♀H2	CDTJ EUJe SPlb XBlo
	– 'Red Tiger'	CCCN CDTJ MPkF
	uranoscopus misapplied	see *M. coccinea*
	velutina ♀H1b	CCCN EUJe

Muscari ✿ (*Asparagaceae*)

	ambrosiacum	see *M. muscarimi*
	anatolicum	WCot
	armeniacum ♀H6	CArg CRos CTri GKev GWyn LCro LOPS LRHS MJak NAln NRHS SCob SEND SPer SRms WCot WShi
	– PAB 6748	LEdu
	– 'Album'	SCob
	– 'Argaei Album'	GKev
	– 'Artist'	GKev SDeJ
	– 'Atlantic'	CRos GKev LRHS NRHS
	– 'Blue Spike' (d)	GKev LAma NBir NEgg SDeJ WGwG
	– 'Cantab'	SDeJ XLum
	– 'Carola'	GKev
	– 'Christmas Pearl' ♀H4	GKev
	– 'Cupido'	GKev
	– 'Dark Eyes'	EMor GKev SCob SDeJ
	– 'Early Giant'	SDeJ
	– 'Fantasy Creation'	GKev SDeJ
	– 'Gül'	WCot
	– 'Helena'	GKev
	– 'Lady Blu'	LRHS
	– 'Manon'	GKev
	– 'Pauline'	GKev
	– 'Peppermint'	CRos ERCP GKev LAma LRHS NRHS SDeJ SPhx
	– 'Saffier' ♀H5	GKev LAma WCot
	– 'Siberian Tiger'	CRos EPot GKev LAma LRHS MJak NRHS WTor
	– 'Touch of Snow'	GKev LAma LRHS SPhx
	– 'Valerie Finnis'	CAby CAvo EPfP EPot ERCP GKev LRHS NLar SCob SDeJ SMad WBrk WCot
	aucheri ♀H6	NRya
*	– var. ***bicolor***	WCot

	- 'Blue Magic'	CAvo EPot ERCP GKev LAma LRHS SDeJ
	- 'Ocean Magic'	CAvo GKev LAma NHpl NLar
	- 'White Magic'	CAvo EMor ERCP GKev LAma LRHS NHpl SCob SDeJ WBrk WFar
§	***azureum*** ♀H6	CAvo CTca ELan ERCP GKev GMaP LAma LRHS NAln NLar SPer SPhx WCot WFar
	- 'Album'	GKev LAma SPhx WCot
	- 'Bling Bling'	ERCP LAma LRHS SDeJ WCot
	'Baby's Breath'	see *M.* 'Jenny Robinson'
	'Big Smile'	CRos EPfP GKev LRHS NRHS WCot
	'Blue Eyes'	WCot
	botryoides	GKev LAma SCob WCot
	- 'Album'	CAvo CTca CTri EPfP GKev LAma LCro LOPS SCob SDeJ SRms WCot WShi
	bourgaei	GKev WCot
	caucasicum	WCot
	chalusicum	see *M. pseudomuscari*
	coeleste	GKev WCot
	commutatum	GKev
	- white-flowered	GKev
§	***comosum***	CBro ERCP GKev NEgg WCot WFar
	- 'Monstrosum'	see *M. comosum* 'Plumosum'
§	- 'Plumosum'	ELan GKev LAma SCob SDeJ WCot
	discolor	GKev
	inconstrictum	WCot
	'Ivor's Pink'	WCot
§	'Jenny Robinson' ♀H5	EHrv GKev LAma LRHS SDys SMad SPhx WArt WCot
	'Joyce Spirit'	ERCP LAma LRHS
	latifolium ♀H6	CAby CRos CTca ERCP GKev LAma LCro LOPS LRHS NEgg NLar NRHS SCob SDeJ WBor WCot
*	- 'Blue Angels'	NBir
	macbeathianum	WCot
§	***macrocarpum***	CTca ECha LAma
	- 'Golden Fragrance'PBR	CAvo CBro CExl EPot ERCP GKev LAma MNrw SDeJ
	'Memory of Gary Fisher'	WCot
	mirum	WCot
	'Morgenhimmel'	GKev
	moschatum	see *M. muscarimi*
	'Mount Hood'	EMor ERCP GKev SCob SDeJ SPhx
	'Mountain Lady'	GKev
§	***muscarimi***	CAvo CTca GKev LAma SDeJ WCot
	- var. ***flavum***	see *M. macrocarpum*
§	***neglectum***	GKev LAma NLar SEND WCot WShi
	pallens	GKev
	paradoxum	see *Bellevalia paradoxa*
	parviflorum	GKev WCot
	'Pink Sunrise'	EMor EPot ERCP GKev LRHS NHpl SCob SDeJ WCot
	'Pink Surprise'	LAma
§	***pseudomuscari*** ♀H5	GKev WCot
	pulchellum	GKev
	subsp. ***clepsydroides***	
	- subsp. ***pulchellum***	GKev
	racemosum	see *M. neglectum*
	'Rosy Sunrise'	WArt WCot
	'Sky Blue'	WCot
	'Superstar'	GKev
§	***tenuiflorum***	WCot
	aff. ***tenuiflorum*** JCA 0.691.251	WCot
	'Venus'	GKev LAma WCot
	verticillaris	GKev
	'White Beauty'	GKev SPhx WCot
	'Winter Amethyst'	WCot

Muscarimia (*Asparagaceae*)

ambrosiacum	see *Muscari muscarimi*
macrocarpum	see *Muscari macrocarpum*

Musella see *Musa*

Mussaenda (*Rubiaceae*)

'Tropic Snow'	CCCN

Musschia (*Campanulaceae*)

aurea new	WHil

Mutisia (*Asteraceae*)

oligodon	GKev

Myoporum (*Scrophulariaceae*)

	acuminatum	see *M. tenuifolium*
	laetum	CExl IDee SPlb SVen
§	***tenuifolium***	SPlb SVen

Myosotidium (*Boraginaceae*)

§	***hortensia***	CAbb CAby CBcs CBct CBod CExl CPla CRos CSpe CTsd EUJe EWes GBin GCal GKev IBal IKil LRHS NAln NRHS SChF SChr
	- white-flowered	IKil
	nobile	see *M. hortensia*

Myosotis (*Boraginaceae*)

§	***alpestris***	NSla
	australis	WCot
	decumbens	GEdr
	dissitiflora 'Elegantissima' (v)	CNat
	'Malmesbury'	CNat
	MY OH MY ('Myomark'PBR)	CBod
	palustris	see *M. scorpioides*
	pulvinaris	CPBP SPlb
	pygmaea	NAln
	rakiura	EWes
	rupicola	see *M. alpestris*
§	***scorpioides***	CHab CWCL CWat LCro LLWG LOPS MMuc MWts NMir SCoo SPlb SRms WBrk WMAq WMoo WPnP XLum
	- 'Alba'	LLWG MWts
	- 'Ice Pearl'	ECha
	- MAYTIME ('Blaqua') (v)	LLWG NBir
	- 'Mermaid'	CBen CWat ECha EWat LLWG SRms WPtf
	- 'Pinkie'	LLWG
	- 'Snowflakes'	CWat EWat
	sylvatica	LCro LOPS MMuc NMir
	- 'Bluesylva' (Sylva Series) ♀H6	LRHS WHil
	- 'Ultramarine' ♀H6	WMoo
	terglovensis	GEdr

Myrica (*Myricaceae*)

gale	CAgr GPoy NLar WGwG WSpi

Myricaria (*Tamaricaceae*)

germanica	NLar

Myriophyllum (*Haloragaceae*)

propinquum	LLWG
spicatum	EWat MWts WMAq
verticillatum	CWat SCoo

Myrrhidendron (*Apiaceae*)

glaucescens B&SWJ 14252	WCru
pennellii B&SWJ 14240	WCru

Myrrhis (*Apiaceae*)

odorata	CAby CBre CCBP CHby CLau CMac CSpe ECha EMor ENfk EWhm GBin GPoy IFro LCro LOPS LRHS MHer MMuc MNHC SCob SPad SPer SPhx SPtp SRms SWvt WPGP WSFF WWFP
- 'Forncett Chevron'	LEdu SPhx

Myrsine (*Primulaceae*)

africana	EShb MHer
australis	SVen
divaricata	SVen
nummularia	WThu

Myrteola (*Myrtaceae*)

§ ***nummularia***	ITim WPav WThu

Myrtus ✿ (*Myrtaceae*)

apiculata misapplied	see *Luma apiculata*
bullata	see *Lophomyrtus bullata*
chequen	see *Luma chequen*
communis ♀H4	Widely available
- 'Flore Pleno' (d)	MHer
- 'Jekka's All Gold' **new**	WJek
- 'Jenny Reitenbach'	see *M. communis* subsp. *tarentina*
- 'Merion'	WJek
- 'Microphylla'	see *M. communis* subsp. *tarentina*
- 'Nana'	see *M. communis* subsp. *tarentina*
- 'Pyewood Park'	SRms WJek
§ - subsp. ***tarentina*** ♀H4	Widely available
- - 'Compacta'	LRHS SCoo SLon
- - 'Microphylla Variegata' (v)	EShb MNHC SPer SRms WJek
I - - 'Variegata' (v)	CBod EPfP
- 'Tricolor'	see *M. communis* 'Variegata'
§ - 'Variegata' (v)	CBod CMac CRos CSBt CTri CWld EBee ELan ELon ENfk EPfP EShb EUJe LEdu LRHS MGil MHer MSwo NLar NRHS SGbt SGol SLon SPer SPoG WAvo WCFE WFar WJek WSHC
'Glanleam Gold'	see *Luma apiculata* 'Glanleam Gold'
lechleriana	see *Amomyrtus luma*
luma	see *Luma apiculata*
nummularia	see *Myrteola nummularia*
ugni	see *Ugni molinae*

N

Nandina (*Berberidaceae*)

BLUSH PINK ('Aka'PBR)	CMac LRHS LSRN MThu SCob SPoG
domestica	Widely available
- B&SWJ 4923	WCru
- B&SWJ 11113	WCru
- 'Filamentosa'	EPfP LRHS MPkF NLar SCob SGol SMad
- 'Fire Power'	Widely available
- FLIRT ('Murasaki'PBR)	MAsh SCob SGol
- 'Gulf Stream'	CBod CRos ELan LBuc LRHS LSRN MAsh MGos MPkF NLar NRHS SPad
- 'Harbour Dwarf'	CEnd LRHS WFar
- var. ***leucocarpa***	NLar
- MAGICAL LEMON AND LIME ('Lemlin')	LCro LOPS LRHS NRHS SGol
- 'Nana'	see *N. domestica* 'Pygmaea'
- OBSESSED	see *N. domestica* 'Seika'
- PLUM PASSION ('Monum')	CRos EPfP LRHS MAsh MGos NRHS SCob
§ - 'Pygmaea'	CMen SGol
- 'Red Dragon' **new**	MPkF
- 'Richmond' ♀H5	CBcs CDul CKel CRos EBee EPfP LRHS MAsh MGos NLar NPri NRHS SCob SPer SPoG SWvt WCFE WFar
§ - 'Seika'PBR	CMac CRos CWGN EBee ELan EPfP EUJe LCro LOPS LRHS MAsh MGos MPkF MThu NRHS SCob SGol SMad SPoG
- SIENNA SUNRISE ('Monfar')	CBod LRHS SGol
- 'Sunset'PBR	EBee LSRN NLar SCob
- 'Tuscan Flame'	LRHS
- 'Twilight'PBR (v)	CWGN
- 'Wood's Dwarf'	CBcs MPkF NLar WFar

Nannorrhops (*Arecaceae*)

arabica	see *N. ritchieana*
§ ***ritchieana***	SPlb
- blue-leaved	SPlb

Napaea (*Malvaceae*)

dioica	LEdu SPhx WCot

Narcissus ✿ (*Amaryllidaceae*)

'Abba' (4) ♀H6	CFen CQua
'Abbey Road' (5)	CQua
'Aberfoyle' (2) ♀H6	CQua
'Abstract' (11a)	CQua
'Accent' (2)	CQua
'Accomplice' (3)	IEsk
'Achduart' (3)	CQua
'Achentoul' (4)	CQua
'Achnasheen' (3)	CQua
'Acropolis' (4)	CQua GKev SDeJ
'Actaea' (9) ♀H6	CBro CFen CQua GBin GKev LCro LOPS SCob SDeJ
'Acumen' (2)	CQua
'Admiration' (8)	CQua
'Adorable Lass' (6)	CQua
'Ad-Rem' (2)	CFen
'Adversane' (3)	CQua
'Advocat' (3)	CQua
'Aflame' (3)	CFen
'After All' (3)	CFen
'Agnes Mace' (2)	IEsk
'Ahwahnee' (2)	CQua IEsk
'Ainley' (2)	CQua
'Aintree' (3)	CQua
'Aircastle' (3)	CQua
'Airtime' (2)	IEsk
'Albatross' (3)	CQua WShi
'Albus Plenus Odoratus'	see *N. poeticus* 'Plenus' ambig.
'Alex Jones' (2)	CQua
'All Rounder' (3)	IEsk
'Alnwick Magic' (4) **new**	NAln
'Alpine Winter' (1)	IEsk
'Alto' (2)	IEsk
'Altruist' (3)	CQua ERCP SDeJ
'Altun Ha' (2)	CQua IEsk
'Amabilis' (3)	GCro

'Amazing Grace' (2)	CQua IEsk
'Amber Castle' (2)	CQua
'Ambergate' (2)	CQua GKev LAma SDeJ
'Ambergris Caye' (1)	CQua
'American Dream' (1)	CQua
'American Goldfinch' (7)	CQua
'American Heritage' (1)	CQua
'American Robin' (6)	CQua
'Amstel' (4)	CQua
'Andalusia' (6)	CQua
'Andrew's Choice' (7) ♀H6	CQua
'Angel' (3)	CQua
'Angel Face' (3)	CQua IEsk
'Angel's Breath' (5) ♀H6	CQua EPot GKev
Angel's tears	see *N. triandrus* subsp. *triandrus* var. *triandrus*
'Angel's Whisper' (5)	CQua GKev
'Angel's Wings' (2)	CQua
'Angels Wood' (2)	IEsk
'Angkor' (4)	CQua
'An-gof' (7)	CQua
'Animal Crackers' (2)	CQua
'Ann Sonia' (4)	IEsk
'Anna Panna' (3)	IEsk
'Annequin' (3)	CQua
'Anniversary' (2)	MJak
'Apollo Gold' (10)	CQua NHpl
'Apotheose' (4)	CFen MJak SDeJ
'Apricot Whirl' (11a)	CQua GKev LRHS
'April Dawn' (2)	IEsk
'April Love' (1)	CQua
'Ara' (6)	CQua
'Aranjuez' (2)	CFen CQua
'Arctic Gem' (3)	CQua
'Arctic Gold' (1) ♀H6	CQua LAma
'Ard Righ' (1)	GCro
'Areley Kings' (2)	CQua
'Argent' (4)	CQua
'Argosy' (1)	CQua
'Arid Plains' (3)	IEsk
'Ariel'PBR (8)	ELan GKev
'Ark Royal' (1)	CFen
'Arkle' (1) ♀H6	CQua GKev SDeJ
'Arleston' (2)	CQua IEsk
'Armada' (2)	CFen CQua
'Armidale' (3)	CQua IEsk
'Armoury' (4)	CQua
'Arndilly' (2)	CQua
'Arpege' (2)	CQua
'Arthurian' (1)	IEsk
'Articol' (11a)	CQua
'Arwenack' (11a)	CQua
'Ascot' (4)	SDeJ
'Ashland' (2)	IEsk
'Ashmore' (2)	CQua IEsk
'Ashton Wold' (2)	CQua
§ ***assoanus*** (13)	EPot GKev LLHF WCot WShi
'Astropink' (11a)	CQua
§ ***asturiensis*** (13)	GKev LLHF SEND
- giant	see *N. asturiensis* 'Wavertree'
§ - 'Wavertree' (1)	CQua LLHF
'Auchranie' (2)	IEsk
'Audubon' (2)	CQua GKev SDeJ
'Aunt Betty' (1)	CQua
'Auntie Eileen' (2)	CQua
§ ***aureus*** (13)	CQua
'Autumn Habit' (3)	IEsk
'Avalanche' (8) ♀H4	CFen CQua ELan GKev LCro LOPS SDeJ
'Avalanche of Gold' (8)	CQua
'Avalon' (2)	CQua ERCP GKev SDeJ
'Baby Boomer' (7)	ERCP GKev LAma
'Baby Moon' (7)	CAby CFen CQua EPot ERCP GKev LAma SDeJ
'Back Flash' (2)	CQua
'Badanloch' (3)	CQua
'Badbury Rings' (3) ♀H6	CQua IEsk
'Bailey' (2)	IEsk
'Bala' (4)	CQua
'Balalaika' (2)	CQua
'Baldock' (4)	CQua
'Ballydorn' (9)	IEsk
'Ballygarvey' (1)	CQua
'Ballyrobert' (1)	CQua
'Balmacara Beauty' (2) **new**	GCro
'Balvenie' (2)	CQua
'Bandesara' (3)	CQua
'Bandit' (2)	CQua IEsk
'Banker' (2)	CQua IEsk
'Banstead Village' (2)	CQua
'Bantam' (2) ♀H6	CQua SDeJ
'Barbara Hunt' (7)	CQua
'Barbary Gold' (2)	CQua
'Barn Dance' (3)	CQua
'Barnesgold' (1)	IEsk
'Barnham' (1)	CQua
'Barnsdale Wood' (2)	CQua
'Barrett Browning' (3)	GKev SDeJ
'Barrii' (3)	CQua
'Bath's Flame' (3)	CAvo CQua GCro WShi
'Bear's Gold' (4)	CQua
'Beaulieu' (1)	CQua
'Beautiful Dream' (3)	CQua
'Beautiful Eyes' (7)	GKev
'Beauvallon' (4)	SDeJ
'Bebop' (7)	CBro
'Bedruthan' (2)	CQua
'Beersheba' (1)	CQua GKev
'Belcanto' (11a)	CQua SDeJ
'Belisana' (2)	SDeJ
'Bell Rock' (1) ♀H6	CQua
'Bell Song' (7)	CBro CFen CQua SDeJ WShi
'Bella Estrella' (11a)	ERCP GKev
'Bells of Joy' (5)	IEsk
'Belzone' (2)	CQua
'Ben Hee' (2)	CQua IEsk
'Berceuse' (2)	CQua
'Bere Ferrers' (4)	CQua
'Bergerac' (11a)	CQua
'Bernardino' (2)	CQua GCro
'Beryl' (6)	CQua GKev WShi
'Best Friend' (3)	CQua
'Best Seller' (1)	CArg
'Bethal' (3)	CQua
'Bethan-Sîan' (2)	CQua
'Betsy MacDonald' (6)	CQua
'Biffo' (4)	CQua
BIGGAR BOUNTIFUL (2)	GCro
'Bikini Beach' (2)	IEsk
'Bilbo' (6)	CBro CQua
'Billy Graham' (2)	CQua
'Binkie' (2)	CQua SPer
'Birchwood' (3)	CQua
'Birma' (3)	SDeJ
'Birthday Girl' (2)	IEsk
'Bishops Light' (2)	CQua
'Bittern' (12)	CQua GKev SDeJ
'Blackstone' (2)	CQua
'Blair Athol' (2)	CQua
'Blakey' (2)	CQua

	Name	Suppliers
	'Blarney' (3)	CQua
	'Blisland' (9)	CQua
	'Blossom' (4)	CQua
	'Blossom Lady' (4)	CQua
	'Blue Danube' (1)	CQua IEsk
	'Blushing Maiden' (4)	CQua
	'Bob Spotts' (2)	CQua
	'Bobbysoxer' (7)	CBro CQua
	'Bobolink' (2)	CQua
	'Boconnoc' (2)	CQua
	'Bodelva' (2)	CQua
	'Bodwannick' (2)	CQua
	'Bolton' (7)	GCro
	'Bombay' (2)	CFen
	'Bon Viveur' (11a)	IEsk
	'Bonython' (1)	GCro
	'Border Beauty' (2) 🏆H6	CQua
	'Bosbigal' (11a)	CQua
	'Boscastle' (7)	CQua
	'Boscoppa' (11a)	CQua
	'Boslowick' (11a) 🏆H6	CQua
	'Bosmeor' (2)	CQua
	'Bossa Nova' (3)	CQua
	'Bossiney' (11a)	CQua
	'Bosvale' (11a)	CQua
	'Bosvigo' (11a)	CQua
	'Boulder Bay' (2) 🏆H6	IEsk
	'Bouzouki' (2)	IEsk
	'Brackenhurst' (2)	SDeJ
	'Brahms' (2)	CFen
	'Brandaris' (11a)	CQua
	'Bravoure' (1) 🏆H6	CQua GBin SDeJ
	'Breezand Tristar' (11a) 🏆H6	CBro GKev
	'Brentswood' (8)	CQua
	'Brian's Favorite' (2)	CQua
	'Bridal Crown' (4) 🏆H6	CFen EPfP GKev LAma LCro LOPS LRHS NAln SDeJ
	'Brideshead' (2)	CFen
	'Bright Flame' (2)	CQua
	'Bright Spangles' (8)	IEsk
	'Bright Spot' (8)	CQua
	BRIGHTERWELL (2/3)	GCro
	'Brightling' (2)	GCro
	'Brilliancy' (3)	CQua GCro
	'Brindle Pink' (2)	IEsk
	'Broadland' (2)	CQua
	'Broadway Star' (11b)	LAma SDeJ
	'Broadway Village' (2)	CQua
	'Brodick' (3)	CQua
	'Bronzewing' (1)	IEsk
	'Brooke Ager' (2) 🏆H6	IEsk
	'Broomhill' (2) 🏆H6	CQua
	'Broughshane' (1)	CQua GKev
	broussonetii (13)	EPot GKev
	- from Morocco	WPGP
	'Brunswick' (2)	CFen GCro SDeJ
	'Bryanston' (2) 🏆H6	CQua
	'Buckshead' (4)	CQua
	'Budock Water' (2)	CQua
	'Bugle Major' (2)	CQua
	bulbocodium (13) 🏆H4	CBro CRos GKev LCro LOPS LRHS NRHS SRms WCot
§	- subsp. ***bulbocodium*** (13)	CBro
§	- - var. ***citrinus*** (13)	CRos LRHS NRHS
	- - var. ***conspicuus*** (13)	CBro CQua CTca CWld ERCP GKev LAma SDeJ WCot WShi XLum
*	- - var. ***filifolius*** (13)	CBro
§	- - var. ***graellsii*** (13)	NSla
	- - var. ***nivalis*** (13)	EPot GKev
§	- Golden Bells Group (10)	CAby CQua CRos CWCL EPfP EPot GBin GKev LRHS NHol NRHS SCob SDeJ
	- var. ***mesatlanticus***	see *N. romieuxii* subsp. *romieuxii* var. *mesatlanticus*
	- subsp. ***obesus*** (13)	GKev WCot
	- - JW 90-13	GKev
§	- - 'Diamond Ring' (10)	CQua CRos EPot GKev LAma LRHS MNrw NRHS
	- subsp. ***praecox*** (13)	CRos LRHS NRHS
	- - var. ***paucinervis*** (13)	GKev
	- subsp. ***tananicus***	see *N. cantabricus* subsp. *tananicus*
	- subsp. ***vulgaris***	see *N. bulbocodium* subsp. *bulbocodium*
	'Bunclody' (2)	CQua
	'Bunting' (7) 🏆H6	CQua
	'Burning Bush' (3)	IEsk
	'Burning Ring' (3)	IEsk
	'Burravoe' (1)	CQua
	'Burt House' (2)	IEsk
	'Busselton' (3)	IEsk
	'Bute Park' (4)	CQua
	'Butter and Eggs' (4)	GKev
	'Butterscotch' (2)	CQua
	'Cadgwith' (2)	CQua
	'Cairngorm' (2)	SDeJ
	'Cairntoul' (3)	CQua
	'Calamansack' (2)	CQua
	calcicola (13)	GKev
	'Calgary' (4)	CQua GKev WCot
	'California Rose' (4)	CQua
	'Camaraderie' (2)	IEsk
	'Camelot' (2) 🏆H6	CFen CQua MJak SDeJ
	'Cameo Angel' (2)	CQua
	'Cameo Baron' (2)	CQua
	'Cameo Frills' (2)	CQua
	'Cameo Gem' (1)	CQua
	'Cameo King' (2)	CQua
	'Cameo Marie' (3)	CQua
	'Camilla Duchess of Cornwall' (2)	CFen CQua
	'Campernelli' (7)	CQua
	'Campernelli Plenus'	see *N.* 'Double Campernelle'
	'Campion' (9)	CQua
	'Canaliculatus' (8)	CAby CArg CFen CQua CRos CTri ERCP GKev LAma LCro LOPS LRHS MJak NRHS SCob SDeJ SPer
	canaliculatus Gussone	see *N. tazetta* subsp. *lacticolor*
	canariensis (13)	CQua
	'Canary' (7)	CQua
	'Canarybird' (8)	CQua GKev
	'Canasta' (11a)	CQua
	'Candlepower' (1)	CQua
	'Canisp' (2)	CQua
	'Cantabile' (9) 🏆H6	CQua
	cantabricus (13)	CQua
	- subsp. ***cantabricus*** (13)	EPot GKev
§	- subsp. ***tananicus*** (13)	GKev
	'Cantatrice' (1)	CQua
	'Canterbury' (5)	CQua
	'Canticle' (9)	IEsk
	'Capax Plenus'	see *N.* 'Eystettensis'
	'Cape Cornwall' (2)	CQua
	'Cape Helles' (3)	IEsk
	'Cape Point' (2)	CQua IEsk
	'Capisco' (3)	CQua
	'Capree Elizabeth' (2)	GKev
	'Carbineer' (2)	CQua GCro SDeJ
	'Cardiff' (2)	CFen CQua
	'Cargreen' (9)	CQua

'Carib Gipsy' (2) 🏆H6	CQua
'Caribbean Snow' (2)	CQua
'Carlton' (2) 🏆H6	CArg CFen CQua EPfP GKev LAma LCro LOPS SCob SDeJ
'Carn Brea' (3)	CQua
'Carnearny' (3)	CQua
'Carnkeeran' (2)	CQua
'Carnkief' (2)	CQua
'Carnyorth' (11a)	CQua
'Carole Lombard' (3)	CQua
'Carolina Dale' (2)	IEsk
'Carra' (8)	CQua
'Carwinion' (2)	CQua
'Casiah' (2)	CQua
'Cassata' (11a)	GKev LAma NBir SDeJ
'Cassopolis' (2)	CQua
'Castanets' (8)	CQua IEsk
'Casterbridge' (2)	CQua
'Castle Rings' (4)	CQua
'Castlerock' (2)	CFen
'Cataract' (1)	IEsk
'Catistock' (2)	CQua
'Causeway Gem' (6)	IEsk
'Causeway Julie' (3)	IEsk
'Causeway Ringer' (3)	IEsk
'Causeway Sunset' (2)	IEsk
'Causeway Sunshine' (1)	IEsk
'Causeway Torch' (2)	IEsk
'Causeway Winner' (2)	IEsk
'Cavalli King' (4)	CQua
'Caye Chapel' (3)	CQua
'Cazique' (6)	CQua
'Cedar Hills' (3)	CQua
'Cedric Morris' (1)	CQua ECha WSHC
'Celestial Fire' (2)	CQua
'Celtic Gold' (2)	CQua
'Centenary Gold' (2)	CQua
'Centrefold' (3)	CQua
'Cha-cha' (6)	CQua
'Changing Colors' (11a)	GKev SDeJ
'Chanson' (1) 🏆H6	CQua IEsk
'Chanterelle' (11a)	GKev LAma SDeJ
'Charity May' (6)	CQua
'Charleston' (2)	CQua
'Charlie Connor' (1)	CQua
'Chasseur' (2)	IEsk
'Chaste' (1)	CQua IEsk
'Chat' (7)	CQua
'Cheer Leader' (3)	CQua
'Cheerfulness' (4) 🏆H6	CArg CFen CQua ELan GKev LAma LCro LOPS NPer NRHS SDeJ
'Cheesewring' (3)	CQua
'Chelsea Girl' (2)	CQua
'Cheltenham' (2)	CQua
'Chemeketa' (2)	GKev
'Chérie' (7)	CQua
'Cherish' (2)	CQua
'Cherry Glow' (3)	IEsk
'Cherry Ice' (2)	CQua
'Cherrygardens' (2)	CQua IEsk
'Chesapeake Bay' (1)	CQua
'Chesterton' (9) 🏆H6	CQua
'Chickadee' (6)	CQua
'Chicken Hill' (1)	CQua
'Chickerell' (3)	CQua
'Chief Inspector' (1)	CQua IEsk
'Chiffon' (2)	CFen
'Chiloquin' (1)	CQua
'China Doll' (2)	CQua
'China Gold' (10)	CQua
'Chinchilla' (2)	CQua
'Chingah' (1)	IEsk
'Chinita' (8)	CQua
'Chipper' (5)	CQua
'Chit Chat' (7) 🏆H6	CQua LLHF SDeJ SPlb
'Chiva' (7)	LLHF
'Chobe River' (1)	CQua IEsk
'Chortle' (3)	IEsk
'Chromacolor' (2) 🏆H6	GKev
'Churchfield Bells' (5)	CQua
'Churston Ferrers' (4)	CQua
'Chy Noweth' (2)	CQua
'Cinder Hill' (2)	IEsk
'Cisticola' (3)	CQua IEsk
citrinus	see *N. bulbocodium* subsp. *bulbocodium* var. *citrinus*
'Citron' (3)	CQua
'Citronita' (3)	CQua
'Citrus Souffle' (4)	IEsk
'Clare' (7)	CQua
'Classic Gold' (10) 🏆H6	CQua
'Claverley' (2)	CQua
'Clean Sweep' (3)	IEsk
'Cloth of Gold' (8)	CQua
'Cloud Nine' (2)	CBro
'Clouded Yellow' (2)	CQua
'Clouds Hill' (4)	CQua
'Clovelly Ayr' (9)	CQua
'Codlins and Cream'	see *N.* 'Sulphur Phoenix'
'Coker's Frome' (9)	CQua
'Coldbrook' (2)	CQua
'Colin's Joy' (2)	CQua
'Coliseum' (2)	IEsk
'Colleen Bawn' (1)	CQua
'Colley Gate' (3)	CQua
'Colliford' (2)	CQua
'Colorama' (11a)	CQua
'Colorful' (2)	IEsk
'Colville' (9)	CQua
'Comal' (1)	CQua
'Come to Good' (2)	CQua
'Compressus'	see *N.* × *intermedius* 'Compressus'
'Conestoga' (2)	CQua
'Congress' (11a)	CQua
'Conowingo' (11a)	CQua
'Conspicuus' ambig. (3)	GCro LAma WShi
'Constantinople' (4)	GKev
'Content' (1)	CQua
'Contralto' (2)	IEsk
'Cool Autumn' (2)	CQua
'Cool Crystal' (3)	CQua
'Cool Evening' (11a)	CQua
'Cool Shades' (2)	CQua
'Coolmaghery' (2)	IEsk
'Coombe Creek' (6)	CQua
'Copperfield' (2)	CQua
'Coral Ribbon' (2)	GKev
'Corbiere' (1)	CQua
'Corbridge' (2)	CQua
'Corby Candle' (2)	CQua
'Corky's Song' (2)	CQua
'Cornish Chuckles' (12) 🏆H6	CFen CQua
'Cornish Gold' (1)	LCro LOPS
'Cornish King' (1)	GKev
'Cornish Pride' (2)	CFen
'Cornish Sun' (2)	CQua
'Cornish Vanguard' (2) 🏆H6	CFen CQua
'Cornsilk' (11a)	CQua
'Corofin' (3)	CQua

Name	Suppliers
'Corozal' (3)	CQua
'Corroboree' (2)	IEsk
'Cosine' (11a)	IEsk
'Cotinga' (6)	CBro CQua GKev SDeJ
'Countdown' (2)	CQua
'Court Martial' (2)	CFen
'Coverack Glory' (2)	CQua
'Crackington' (4) ♀H6	CQua IEsk
'Cragford' (8)	SDeJ
'Craig Stiel' (2)	CQua
'Creag Dubh' (2)	CQua
'Creed' (6)	CQua
'Crenver' (3)	CQua
'Crevenagh' (2)	IEsk
'Crewenna' (1)	CQua
'Crill' (7)	CQua
'Crimson Chalice' (3)	CQua
'Cristobal' (1)	CQua
'Croesus' (2)	CQua
'Crofty' (6)	CQua
'Croila' (2)	CQua
'Crowndale' (4)	CQua IEsk
'Crugmeer' (11a)	CQua
'Cryptic' (1)	CQua IEsk
'Crystal Star' (2)	CQua
cuatrecasasii var. ***segimonensis*** (13)	GKev
'Cudden Point' (2)	CQua
'Cul Beag' (3)	CQua
'Culmination' (2)	CQua
'Cultured Pearl' (2)	CQua IEsk
'Cum Laude' (11a)	ERCP SDeJ
'Curlew' (7) ♀H6	CQua GKev LCro LOPS SDeJ WShi
'Curly' (2)	GKev SDeJ
'Cuscarne' (8)	CQua
cyclamineus (13) ♀H6	CAvo CBro CExl CRos CWCL EPot LEdu LLHF LRHS NRHS SRms
'Cyclope' (1)	CQua
'Cynosure' (2)	GCro
cypri (13)	CQua
'Cyros' (1)	CQua
'Dailmanach' (2)	CQua IEsk
'Dailmystic' (2)	IEsk
'Dainty Miss' (7)	CQua GKev
'Dalcharn' (2)	LRHS
'Dallas' (3)	CFen CQua
'Dalmeny' (2)	CQua
'Dambuster' (4)	IEsk
'Damson' (2)	CQua GCro
'Dan du Plessis' (8)	CFen CQua
'Dardanelles' (2)	IEsk
'Dateline' (3)	CQua
'David Alexander' (1)	CQua
'David Mills' (2)	CQua
'Dawn Brooker' (2)	CQua
'Dawn Cloud' (2)	CQua
'Dawn Sky' (2)	CQua
'Daydream' (2)	CQua
'Daymark' (8)	CQua
'Daymer Bay' (1)	CFen
'Dayton Lake' (2)	CQua
'De Lacey' (11a)	CQua
'Dean' (2)	CQua
'Debutante' (2)	CQua
'December Bride' (11a)	CQua
'Decision' (2)	IEsk
'Defence Corps' (1)	IEsk
'Del Rey' (1)	CQua
'Dell Chapel' (3)	CQua
'Delnashaugh' (4)	CQua ERCP GKev LAma NHol SDeJ
'Delos' (3)	CQua
'Delta' (11a)	CQua
'Delta Flight' (6)	IEsk
'Demand' (2)	CQua
'Demeanour' (3)	IEsk
'Demmo' (2)	CQua IEsk
'Dena' (3)	IEsk
'Denali' (1)	CQua IEsk
'Derek Tangye' (2)	CQua
'Derringer' (7)	CAvo
'Descant' (1)	IEsk
'Desdemona' (2) ♀H6	CQua GKev SDeJ
'Desert Bells' (7)	CQua
'Desert Orchid' (2)	CQua
'Dewy Dell' (3)	IEsk
'Diamond Ring'	see *N. bulbocodium* subsp. *obesus* 'Diamond Ring'
'Dick Wellband' (2) **new**	GCro
'Dick Wilden' (4)	ELan SDeJ
'Dickcissel' (7) ♀H6	CQua ERCP
'Dignitary' (2)	IEsk
'Dimity' (3)	CQua
'Dimple' (9)	CQua
'Discreet' (2)	IEsk
'Disquiet' (1)	CQua IEsk
'Diversity' (11a)	IEsk
'Doctor Hugh' (3) ♀H6	CQua IEsk
'Doctor Jazz' (2)	CQua
'Doctor Who' (4)	CQua
'Dolcoath' (2)	CQua
'Doombar' (1)	CQua
'Dorchester' (4)	CQua IEsk
'Dorneywood' (1)	IEsk
'Dorothy Yorke' (2)	GCro
§ 'Double Campernelle' (4)	CQua GKev MJak SDeJ WShi
'Double Fashion' (4)	SDeJ
double pheasant eye	see *N. poeticus* 'Plenus' ambig.
double Roman	see *N.* 'Romanus'
'Double White' (4)	CQua
'Doublet' (4)	CQua
'Doubtful' (3)	CQua
'Dove Song' (2)	IEsk
'Dove Wings' (6)	CQua
'Dover Boy' (11a)	CQua
'Dover Cliffs' (2)	CQua
'Downfield' (4)	IEsk
'Downing College' (2)	CQua
'Downlands' (3)	CQua
'Dragon Run' (2)	CQua
'Drama Queen' (11a)	IEsk
'Dream Catcher' (2)	IEsk
DREAM TORTE (1)	GCro
'Dreamlight' (3)	CQua GKev
dubius (13)	EPot GKev
'Duchess of Westminster' (2)	GCro
'Duiker' (6)	IEsk
'Duke of Windsor' (2)	CFen
'Dunkeld' (2)	CQua GCro
'Dunkery' (4)	CQua
'Dunley Hall' (3)	CQua IEsk
'Dunskey' (3)	CQua
'Dunstan's Fire' (1)	IEsk
'Dupli Kate' (4)	IEsk
'Dutch Lemon Drops' (5) ♀H6	CQua EPot
'Dutch Master' (1) ♀H6	CFen CQua GKev LAma LCro LOPS SCob SDeJ
'Early Bride' (2)	CFen CQua
'Early Flame' (2)	CFen
'Early Sensation' (1) **new**	LRHS NRHS

	'Early Splendour' (8)	CQua
	'Earthlight' (3)	CQua
	'Easter Moon' (2)	CQua GKev LCro LOPS
	'Eastern Dawn' (2)	CFen CQua SDeJ
	'Eastern Promise' (2)	CQua
	'Eaton Song' (12) 𝕐H6	CQua GKev
	'Ebony' (1)	CQua
	'Eddy Canzony' (2)	CFen CQua
	'Eden Gold' (2)	CFen
	'Edenderry' (1)	IEsk
	'Edgbaston' (2)	CQua
	'Edge Grove' (2)	CQua
	'Editor' (2)	IEsk
	'Edna Earl' (3)	SDeJ
	'Edward Buxton' (3)	CFen CQua
	'Egard' (11a)	CQua
	'Egmont King' (2)	CQua
	'Eira Hibbert' (3)	CQua
	'Eland' (7)	CQua
	'Elburton' (2)	CQua
	'Elegance' (2)	CQua
	'Elegant Queen' (2)	IEsk
	'Elf' (2)	CQua
	'Elfin Gold' (6)	CQua
	'Elite' (8) **new**	GKev
	'Elizabeth Ann' (6)	CQua
	'Elka' (1) 𝕐H6	CAby CAvo CBro CQua ECha ERCP GKev LLHF NAln WShi
	'Ellen' (2)	CArg
	'Elmbridge' (1)	IEsk
	'Elphin' (4)	CQua
	'Elrond' (2)	CQua
	'Elven Lady' (2)	CQua
	'Elvira' (8)	CQua WShi
	'Emcys' (6)	GKev
	'Emerald City' (3)	IEsk
	'Emerald Pink' (3)	CQua
	'Emily' (2)	CQua
	'Eminent' (3)	CQua
	'Emperor' (1)	CQua
	'Empress' (1)	GCro
	'Empress of Ireland' (1)	CQua IEsk
	'Englander' (6)	EPot
	'English Caye' (1)	CQua IEsk
	'Ensemble' (4)	CQua
	'Epona' (3)	CQua
	'Erin' (3)	CQua
	'Erlicheer' (4)	CQua GKev SDeJ
	'Estrella' (3)	CQua
	'Estremadura' (2)	CQua
	'Ethos' (1)	IEsk
§	***eugeniae*** (13)	GKev WCot
	'Euryalus' (1)	CQua
	'Evangeline' (3)	GCro
	'Eve Robertson' (2)	CQua
	'Evelyn Roberts' (11a)	CQua
	'Evening' (2)	CQua
	'Evesham' (3)	CQua IEsk
	'Exotic Beauty' (4)	CQua
	'Exotic Mystery' (11a)	GKev
	'Extravaganza' (4)	SDeJ
	'Eyeglass' (3)	CQua
	'Eyelet' (3)	CQua
	'Eyrie' (3)	CQua
§	'Eystettensis' (4)	IBlr WFar
	'Fair Prospect' (2)	CQua
	'Fairgreen' (3)	CFen
	'Fairlawns' (3)	CQua
	'Fairmile' (3)	CQua
	'Fairy Chimes' (5)	CQua EPot
	'Fairy Footsteps' (3)	CQua
	'Fairy Island' (3)	CQua
	'Fairy Magic' (2)	IEsk
	'Fairy Tale' (3)	CQua
I	'Faith' (1)	SDeJ
	'Falaise' (4)	CQua
	'Falconet' (8) 𝕐H6	CQua GKev MJak SDeJ
	'Falmouth Bay' (3)	CQua
	'Falstaff' (2)	CQua
	'Far Country' (2)	CQua
I	'Fashion' (11b)	CQua
	'Fashion Model' (2)	IEsk
	'Fastidious' (2)	CQua
	'February Gold' (6) 𝕐H6	CArg CAvo CBro CQua CRos CTri ELan EPfP EPot ERCP GCro GKev LAma LCro LOPS LRHS NBir NRHS SDeJ SRms WShi
	'February Silver' (1)	CBro CQua EPot ERCP GKev LAma SDeJ
	'Feeling Lucky' (2)	CQua
	'Felindre' (9)	EPot
	'Feline Queen' (1)	IEsk
	'Feock' (3)	CQua
	'Ferial Wendy' (2)	CFen
	fernandesii (13)	EPot WCot
	- from Spain	ITim
	- var. ***cordubensis*** (13)	CBro CQua GKev LLHF
	'Ferndown' (3)	CQua
	'Fertile Crescent' (7)	CQua
	'Feu de Joie' (4)	GCro
	'Ffitch's Ffolly' (2)	CQua
	'Fiery Maiden' (2)	CFen CQua
	'Fiery Ring' (3)	IEsk
	'Filoli' (1)	CQua IEsk
	'Filskit' (2)	CQua
	'Finchcocks' (2)	CQua
	'Fine Gold' (1)	CQua
	'Fine Romance' (2)	CQua
	'Fine Trim' (2)	IEsk
	'Finland' (2)	CFen CQua
	FINTRY BEAUTY (2)	GCro
	'Fiona MacKillop' (2)	CQua
	'Fire-Blade' (2)	CQua
	'Firebrand' (3)	CQua WShi
	'Firefighter' (3)	IEsk
	'Firehills' (2)	CQua
	'Firetail' (3)	CQua GCro GKev
	'First Born' (6)	CQua
	'First Hope' (6)	CFen
	'Flambards Village' (4)	CQua
	'Flamingo Fantasy' (2) **new**	MJak
	'Fletching' (1)	CQua IEsk
	'Flirt' (6)	CQua
	'Flomay' (7)	CQua
	'Flower Drift' (4)	SDeJ
	'Flower Record' (2)	LAma
	'Flusher' (2)	CQua
	'Flycatcher' (7)	CQua
	'Flying High' (3)	CQua
	'Foff's Way' (1)	CQua
	'Folkestone Girl' (11a)	CQua
	'Forge Mill' (2)	CQua
	'Forged Gold' (2)	IEsk
	'Fortissimo' (2)	GKev SDeJ
	'Fortune' (2)	CArg CQua LAma MJak SDeJ
	'Fossie' (4)	CQua
	'Foundling' (6)	CQua
	'Fowey' (3)	CFen
	'Foxfire' (2)	CQua
	'Foxhunter' (2)	CQua GKev

'Fragrant Breeze' (2)	CQua SDeJ
'Fragrant Rose' (2)	CQua ERCP GKev
'Frances Delight' (11a)	CQua
'Frank' (9)	IEsk
'Frank Miles' (2)	CQua GCro
'Freedom Rings' (2)	CQua
'Freedom Stars' (11a) ♀H6	IEsk
'Fresco' (11a)	IEsk
'Fresh Lime' (1)	CQua
'Frigid' (3)	CQua
'Front Royal' (2)	CQua
'Frosted Pink' (2)	IEsk
'Frostkist' (6)	CBro CQua
'Frosty Snow' (2)	GKev
'Frozen Jade' (1)	CQua
'Fruit Cup' (7)	GKev LCro SDeJ
'Fuco' (1)	CQua
'Full House' (4)	SDeJ
'Fulwell' (4)	CQua
'Furbelow' (4)	CQua
'Gabriella Rose' (4)	CQua
gaditanus (13)	CBro
gaditanus* × *rupicola subsp. ***watieri*** (13)	GKev
'Gambas' (1)	CQua
'Gamebird' (1)	CQua IEsk
'Ganilly' (2)	CFen
'Garden Opera' (7) ♀H6	CFen
'Garden Treasure' (2)	IEsk
'Gatecrasher' (1)	IEsk
'Gay Kybo' (4) ♀H6	CQua
'Gay Song' (4)	CQua
'Gay Time' (4)	CFen SDeJ
gayi (13)	CQua WShi
'Geevor' (4)	CQua
'Gellymill' (2)	CQua
'Gemini Girl' (2)	CQua
'Gentle Giant' (2)	SDeJ
'Geometrics' (2)	IEsk
'George Leak' (2)	CFen CQua
'Georgia Moon' (2)	CFen
'Georgie May' (2)	CQua
'Geranium' (8) ♀H6	CBro CFen CQua ERCP GKev LAma LCro LOPS LRHS NRHS SDeJ WShi
'Gettysburg' (2)	CQua
'Gigantic Star' (2)	SDeJ
'Gillan' (11a)	CQua
'Gin and Lime' (1)	CQua
'Gipsy Moon' (2)	CQua
'Gipsy Queen' (1)	CBro CQua EPot LLHF WCot WFar WShi
'Gironde' (11)	CQua
'Glacier' (1)	CQua
'Glapthorne' (2)	CQua
'Glasnevin' (2)	CQua IEsk
'Glasney' (3)	CQua
'Glen Cassley' (3)	CQua IEsk
'Glen Clova' (2)	CQua
'Glendermott' (2)	CQua
'Glendurgan' (2)	CQua
'Glenfarclas' (1)	CQua
'Glenside' (2)	CQua
'Glissando' (2)	CQua
'Gloria Townsin' (4)	CQua
'Gloriosus' (8)	CQua
'Glorious' (8)	CQua
'Glory of Lisse' (9)	WShi
'Glover's Reef' (1)	CQua
'Glowing Phoenix' (4)	CQua
'Glowing Red' (4)	CQua
'Goblet' (1)	SDeJ
'Golant' (2)	CQua
'Gold Bond' (2)	CQua
'Gold Cache' (11a)	CQua
'Gold Charm' (2)	CQua
'Gold Convention' (2) ♀H6	CQua IEsk
'Gold Ingot' (2) ♀H6	IEsk
'Gold Medallion' (1)	CQua
'Gold Top' (2)	CQua
'Golden Amber' (2)	CQua
'Golden Anniversary' (2)	CFen CQua
'Golden Aura' (2) ♀H6	CQua
'Golden Bear' (4)	CQua
'Golden Bells'	see *N. bulbocodium* Golden Bells Group
'Golden Cheer' (2)	CFen CQua
'Golden Cycle' (6)	CQua
'Golden Dawn' (8) ♀H4	CFen CQua SDeJ
'Golden Ducat' (4)	CArg CFen CQua LAma MJak NBir SDeJ
'Golden Echo' (7)	SDeJ
'Golden Flute' (2)	IEsk
'Golden Gamble' (11a)	IEsk
'Golden Harvest' (1)	CQua LAma NPer
'Golden Incense' (7)	CQua
'Golden Jewel' (2) ♀H6	CQua
'Golden Joy' (2)	CQua
'Golden Lady' (1)	CQua
'Golden Lion' (1)	CFen
'Golden Marvel' (1)	CQua
'Golden Mary' (3)	GCro
'Golden Orbit' (4)	CQua
'Golden Peak' (1)	IEsk
'Golden Perfection' (7)	CQua
'Golden Phoenix' (4)	CQua WShi
'Golden Rain' (4)	CQua
'Golden Rapture' (1)	CQua
'Golden Sheen' (2)	CQua
'Golden Splash' (11a)	IEsk
'Golden Spur' (1)	CQua GCro LAma
'Golden Torch' (2)	CQua
'Golden Twins' (7)	CQua
'Golden Vale' (1)	CQua
'Goldfinger' (1) ♀H6	CQua IEsk SDeJ
'Goldhanger' (2)	CQua IEsk
'Golitha Falls' (2)	CQua
'Good Fella' (2)	CQua
'Good Intentions' (2)	IEsk
'Good Measure' (2)	CQua
'Good Success' (11a)	CQua
'Goonbell' (2)	CQua
'Goose Green' (3)	GKev
'Gorran' (3)	CQua
'Gossmoor' (4)	CQua
graellsii	see *N. bulbocodium* subsp. *bulbocodium* var. *graellsii*
'Grand Monarque'	see *N. tazetta* subsp. *lacticolor* 'Grand Monarque'
'Grand Opening' (4)	IEsk
'Grand Primo' (8)	LCro LOPS
'Grand Primo Citronière' (8)	CQua
'Grand Prospect' (2)	CQua
'Grand Soleil d'Or' (8)	CQua GKev LAma LCro LOPS SDeJ
'Great Expectations' (2)	CQua
'Greatwood' (1)	CQua
'Greek Surprise' (4)	IEsk
'Green Eyed Lady' (3)	GKev SPhx XEll
'Green Howard' (3)	CQua
'Green Island' (2)	CFen GKev SDeJ
'Green Lawns' (9)	CQua

'Green Lodge' (9)	IEsk
'Green Pearl' (3)	SPhx XEll
'Greenodd' (3)	CQua
'Greenpark' (9)	IEsk
'Grenoble' (2)	CQua
'Gresham' (4)	CQua
'Gribben Head' (4)	CQua
'Guiding Spirit' (4)	CQua
'Gulliver' (3)	CQua GCro
'Gunwalloe' (11a)	CQua
'Guy Wilson' (2)	CQua
'Gwawr' (2)	CQua
'Gwendoline Rae' (3)	CQua
'Gwenllian' (3)	CQua
'Gwennap' (1)	CQua
'Gwinear' (2)	CQua
'Habit' (1)	IEsk
'Hacienda' (1)	CQua
'Half Moon Caye' (2)	CQua
'Halley's Comet' (3)	CQua
'Halloon' (3)	CQua
'Halzephron' (2)	CQua
'Hambledon' (2) ♀H6	CQua
'Hampton Court' (2)	CQua IEsk
'Hannah Jesse' (7)	CQua
'Happy Dreams' (2)	IEsk
'Happy Fellow' (2)	CQua
'Happy Valley' (2)	IEsk
'Harbour View' (2)	IEsk
'Harmony Bells' (5)	CQua
'Harpers Ferry' (1)	CQua
'Harpsicord' (11a) **new**	GKev
HARTLAND'S IRVING (1)	GCro
'Hartlebury' (3)	CQua
'Harvard' (2)	CQua
* 'Hat' (10)	EPot
'Havelock' (2)	GCro
'Hawera' (5) ♀H6	CArg CAvo CBro CFen CQua CTca CTri EPfP EPot ERCP GKev GQue LAma LCro LOPS LRHS SDeJ WShi
'Heamoor' (4) ♀H6	CQua
hedraeanthus (13)	EPot
'Helford Dawn' (2)	CQua
'Helford Sunset' (2)	CQua
'Helios' (2)	CQua
hellenicus	see *N. poeticus* var. *bellenicus*
'Hello Gorgeous' (11a)	IEsk
henriquesii	see *N. jonquilla* var. *henriquesii*
'Henry Irving' (1)	CQua GCro
'Hero' (1)	CQua
'Heslington' (3)	CQua
'Hexameter' (9)	CQua
'Hexworthy' (3)	CQua
'Hibernian' (4)	IEsk
'Hicks Mill' (1)	CQua
'High Life' (2)	CFen
'High Society' (2) ♀H6	CQua LCro LOPS SDeJ
'Highfield Beauty' (8) ♀H6	CQua
'Highgrove' (1)	CQua
'Highlite' (2)	CQua
'Hilda's Pink' (2)	CQua
'Hill Head' (9)	IEsk
'Hillstar' (7) ♀H6	CQua GKev SDeJ
'Hindenburg' (1)	CQua
hispanicus (13)	CQua
- var. ***propinquus*** (13)	GKev
'Hocus Pocus' (3)	IEsk
'Holland's Glory' (4)	GCro
'Holly Berry' (2)	CFen
'Hollywood' (2)	CFen
'Holme Fen' (2)	CQua
'Home Fires' (2)	CFen CQua
'Homestead' (2) ♀H6	IEsk
'Honey Pink' (2)	CQua
'Honeybird' (1)	CQua
'Honeybourne' (2)	CQua IEsk
'Honeyorange' (2)	IEsk
'Hoopoe' (8) ♀H6	CQua
'Hope House' (2)	IEsk
'Horace' (9)	CQua GCro
'Horn of Plenty' (5)	CQua GKev
'Hornpipe' (1)	IEsk
'Hors d'Oeuvre' (1)	CBro
'Hospodar' (2)	CQua
'Hot Affair' (2)	IEsk
'Hot Date' (3)	IEsk
'Hot Gossip' (2)	CFen CQua
'Hot Lava' (2)	IEsk
'Hotspur' (2)	CQua
HOWICK BEAUTY (2)	GCro
HOWICK'S HALF NELSON (2)	GCro
'Hugh Town' (8)	CQua SEND
'Hugus' (7)	CQua
'Hullabaloo' (2)	IEsk
'Hummingbird' (6)	EPot
'Hunting Caye' (2)	CQua
'Huntley Down' (1)	CQua
'Hyperbole' (2)	IEsk
'Ice Dancer' (2)	CQua IEsk
'Ice Diamond' (4)	CQua
'Ice Emerald' (3)	IEsk
'Ice Follies' (2) ♀H6	CArg CFen CQua EPfP GKev LAma LCro LOPS LRHS NBir SCob SDeJ SPhx
'Ice King' (4)	GKev NBir SDeJ
'Ice Wings' (5) ♀H6	CFen CQua EPot GKev SDeJ WShi
'Idless' (1)	CQua
'Idol' (7)	CQua
'Immaculate' (2)	CQua
'Impeccable' (2)	IEsk
'Inara' (4)	CQua
'Inbal'[PBR] (8)	GKev
'Inca' (6)	CQua GKev
'Inchbonnie' (2)	CQua
× ***incomparabilis*** (13)	MMuc SEND
'Independence Day' (4)	CQua
'Indian Maid' (7) ♀H6	CQua IEsk
'Indian Ruler' (2)	CFen
'Indora' (4)	CQua
'Inglescombe' (4)	GCro
'Innisidgen' (8)	CQua
'Innovator' (4)	CQua
'Innuendo' (2)	IEsk
'Insulinde' (4)	CQua
'Interim' (2)	CFen CQua SDeJ
× ***intermedius*** (13)	CBro CQua GKev
§ - 'Compressus' (8)	CBro CQua WShi
'Intrigue' (7) ♀H6	CQua
'Invercassley' (3)	CQua
'Inverpolly' (2)	CQua
'Ipi Tombi' (2)	GKev
'Irene Copeland' (4)	CQua GCro GKev
'Irish Cream' (3)	CQua
'Irish Fire' (2)	CQua
'Irish Light' (2)	CQua
'Irish Linen' (3)	CQua
'Irish Luck' (1)	CArg
'Irish Minstrel' (2) ♀H6	CFen CQua
'Irish Rum' (2)	CQua
'Irish Trip' (7)	IEsk

'Irish Wedding' (2)	CQua
'Isambard' (4)	CQua
'Island Pride' (8)	CQua
italicus (13)	GKev
'Itsy Bitsy Splitsy' (11a)	IEsk
'Itzim' (6) 🏆H6	CBro CQua GKev SDeJ
'Jabberwocky' (11a)	CQua
'Jack Snipe' (6) 🏆H6	CAby CBro CQua EPot ERCP GKev LAma LCro LOPS LRHS NHol SCob SDeJ SEND WCot WShi XEll
'Jack Wood' (11a)	CQua IEsk
'Jacob Maurer' (6)	CQua
'Jamage' (8)	CQua
'Jamaica Inn' (4)	CQua
'Jambo' (2)	CQua
'Jamboree' (2)	CQua
'Jammin' (3)	IEsk
'Janelle' (3)	CQua
'Janet's Gold' (2)	IEsk
'Jantje' (11a)	CQua
'Jauno' (1)	IEsk
'Javelin' (2)	CQua
'Jeanine' (2)	CQua
'Jeanne Bicknell' (4)	CQua
'Jeannie Tangye' (2)	CQua
'Jenny' (6) 🏆H6	CBro CQua EMor EPot ERCP GKev LAma LCro LOPS NBir SDeJ WShi
'Jenny Out' (7) 🏆H6	CFen
'Jersey Lace' (2)	CQua
'Jersey Roundabout' (4)	CQua
'Jersey Star' (4)	CQua
'Jersey Torch' (4)	CQua
'Jetfire' (6) 🏆H6	CArg CQua CRos EPfP EPot ERCP GKev IFro LAma LCro LOPS LRHS NHol NRHS SCob SDeJ WShi
'Jimmy Noone' (1)	CQua
'Jim's Gold' (2)	CQua
'Jodi' (11b)	IEsk
'Jodi's Sister' (11a)	IEsk
'Johanna' (5)	CBro
'John Daniel' (4)	CQua
'John Evelyn' (2)	GCro
'John Lanyon' (3)	CQua
'John's Delight' (3)	CQua
'Joke Fulmer' (2)	CFen
'Jolly Good' (2)	IEsk
jonquilla (13)	CBro CQua EPot GKev LAma WShi
§ - var. ***henriquesii*** (13)	CQua EPot
'Joppa' (7)	CQua
'Joy Bishop'	see *N. romieuxii* 'Joy Bishop'
'Joybell' (6)	CQua
'Juanita' (2)	CFen NPer SDeJ
'Jules Verne' (2)	CQua
'Julia Jane'	see *N. romieuxii* 'Julia Jane'
'Jumblie' (12) 🏆H6	CBro CRos EPot LRHS NRHS SDeJ
'Jumbo Gold' (1)	CTri
juncifolius Req. ex Lag.	see *N. assoanus*
'June Allyson' (2)	CFen
'June Lake' (2)	CQua IEsk
'Kabani' (9)	CQua
'Kaka Point' (2)	IEsk
'Kamms' (1)	CQua
'Kamura' (2)	CQua
'Kantzeewai' (2)	IEsk
'Karamudli' (1)	CQua
'Kate Davies' (2)	CQua
'Katherine Jenkins' (7) 🏆H6	CQua
'Kathy A' (5)	IEsk
'Kathy's Clown' (6)	CQua
'Katie Heath' (5)	ERCP GKev SDeJ
'Katrina Rea' (6)	CQua
'Kaydee' (6) 🏆H6	CQua EMor GKev SDeJ WShi
'Kea' (6)	CQua
'Keats' (4)	CQua
'Kebaya' (2)	CQua
'Kedron' (7)	ERCP GKev SDeJ
'Kelly Bray' (1)	CQua
'Ken Sunshine Johnson' (2)	CQua
'Kernow' (2)	CQua
'Kidling' (7)	CQua
'Killara' (8)	CQua
'Killearnan' (9)	CQua
'Killigrew' (2)	CQua
'Killivose' (3)	CQua
'Kilworth' (2)	CQua
'Kimmeridge' (3)	CQua
'King Alfred' (1)	CArg CQua LCro LOPS SDeJ SPer
'Kingham' (1)	CQua
'Kinglet' (7)	CQua
'King's Grove' (1)	CQua
'Kings Pipe' (2)	CQua
'Kingscourt' (1)	CQua
'Kingsleigh' (1)	IEsk
'Kingsmill Lake' (2)	CQua
'Kiss Me' (1)	GKev
'Kissproof' (2)	SDeJ
'Kit Hill' (7)	CQua
'Kitten' (6)	CQua
'Kiwi Magic' (4)	CQua IEsk
'Kiwi Sunset' (4)	CQua IEsk
'Knight of Saint John' (2)	CFen
'Knightsbridge' (1)	CQua
'Knocklayde' (3)	CQua
'Knowing Look' (3)	IEsk
'Kokopelli' (7) 🏆H6	CBro CQua EPfP GKev SDeJ
'Korora Bay' (1)	IEsk
'La Belle' (7)	LLHF SDeJ
'Ladies' Choice' (7)	IEsk
'Lady Ann' (2)	IEsk
'Lady Be Good' (2)	CQua
'Lady Diana' (2)	CQua IEsk
'Lady Eve' (11a)	IEsk
'Lady Godiva' (3)	GCro
'Lady Hilaria' (2)	CQua
'Lady Margaret Boscawen' (2)	CQua GCro
'Lady Marina Cowdray' (1)	CFen
'Lady Moore' (3)	GCro
'Lady Sainsbury' (2)	CFen
'Lady Serena' (9)	CQua
'Lake Alabaster' (2)	CQua
'Lake District' (2)	IEsk
'Lalique' (3)	CQua
'Lamanva' (2)	CQua
'Lamlash' (2)	IEsk
'Lanarth' (7)	GCro
'Lancaster' (3)	CFen CQua GKev
'Landewednack Lady' (4)	CQua
'Langarth' (11a)	CQua
'Lapwing' (5)	IEsk
'Larkhill' (2)	CQua
'Larkwhistle' (6)	GKev SDeJ
'Las Vegas' (1)	GKev SDeJ
'Latchley Meadows' (2)	CQua
'Latvian Freedom' (2) **new**	GKev
'Laura Webb' (4)	CQua
'Laurelbank' (2)	IEsk
'Lauren' (3)	IEsk
'Laurens Koster' (8)	CQua GKev
'Lava Flow' (3)	IEsk

Name	Suppliers
'Lavender Lass' (6)	CQua
'Lavender Mist' (2)	CQua
'Leading Light' (2)	CQua
'Lee Moor' (1)	CQua
'Leedsii' (3)	CQua
'Lemon Beauty' (11b)	CQua GKev SDeJ
'Lemon Brook' (2)	CQua
'Lemon Cocktail' (1)	IEsk
'Lemon Cycla' (6)	CQua
'Lemon Drizzle' (2)	CQua
'Lemon Drops' (5)	CQua CTca EPot ERCP GKev SDeJ SPhx WShi
'Lemon Haze' (2)	CQua
'Lemon Silk' (6)	CBro CQua ELan
'Lemonade' (3)	CQua
'Lennymore' (2)	CQua IEsk
'Lewis George' (1)	CQua
'Lezant' (3)	CQua
'Liberty Bells' (5)	CQua GQue LAma
'Liebeslied' (3)	CQua
'Lieke' (7)	EPfP EPot ERCP GKev LCro LOPS SDeJ
'Life' (7)	CQua
'Lifeline' (1)	IEsk
'Lighthouse' (3)	CQua
'Lighthouse Reef' (1)	CQua IEsk
'Lilac Charm' (6)	CQua IEsk
'Lilac Mist' (2)	CQua IEsk
'Lilliput' ambig.	CQua
'Lima's Green Goddess' (8)	IEsk
'Lima's Shooting Stars' (12)	IEsk
'Limbo' (2)	CQua GKev
'Limequilla' (7)	CQua IEsk
'Lincolnshire Lady' (3)	CQua
'Lindsay Joy' (2)	CQua
'Little Alice' (4)	IEsk
'Little Beauty' (1)	CQua LAma
'Little Dancer' (1)	CBro CQua
'Little Dianne' (8)	IEsk
'Little Dorr' (4)	IEsk
'Little Flik' (12)	CQua
'Little Jewel' (3)	CQua
'Little Meg' (7)	CQua
'Little Oliver' (7)	SDeJ
'Little Rusky' (7)	CBro CQua
'Little Sentry' (7)	CBro CQua
'Little Soldier' (10)	CQua EPot
'Little Tyke' (2)	CQua
'Little Witch' (6)	CQua GKev LAma SCob SDeJ WShi
'Littlefield' (7)	CQua
'Livelands' (1)	CQua
'Liverpool Festival' (2)	CQua
'Living Colour' (3)	CQua
'Lizard Beacon' (2)	CQua
'Lobularis'	see *N. lobularis* (Haw.) Schult. & Schult. f.
lobularis misapplied	see *N. nanus*
§ ***lobularis*** (Haw.) Schult. & Schult. f. (13)	CAby CAvo CBro CQua CRos CTca CTri CWld EPot ERCP GKev LCro LOPS LRHS NRHS SCob SDeJ SPer
'Loch Alsh' (3)	CQua IEsk
'Loch Assynt' (3)	CQua
'Loch Brora' (2)	CQua
'Loch Coire' (3)	CQua
'Loch Fada' (2)	CQua
'Loch Fyne' (2)	GCro
'Loch Hope' (2)	CQua
'Loch Leven' (2)	CQua
'Loch Loyal' (2)	CQua
'Loch Lundie' (2)	CQua
'Loch Maberry' (2)	CQua
'Loch Naver' (2)	CQua
'Loch Owskeich' (2)	CFen CQua
'Logan Rock' (7)	CQua
'Longitude' (1)	IEsk
'Lordship' (1)	CQua
'Lorikeet' (1)	CQua GKev
'Lostwithiel' (2)	CQua
'Loth Lorien' (3)	SPer
'Lothario' (2)	LAma
'Lough Gowna' (1)	IEsk
'Louise de Coligny' (2)	ERCP
'Loveday' (2)	CFen
'Lowin' (1)	CFen
'Lubaantun' (1)	CQua
'Lucie Nottingham' (4)	CQua
'Lucifer' (2)	CAvo CQua GCro WShi
'Lundy Light' (2)	CQua
'Lutana' (2)	IEsk
'Lyme Bay' (1)	IEsk
'Lynher' (2)	CQua
'Lyrebird' (3)	CQua
'Lyric' (9)	CQua
'Lysander' (2)	CQua
'Madam Speaker' (4)	CQua
'Madame Plemp' (1)	GCro
'Madison' (4)	CQua GKev
MAGGIE MAYBE (2)	GCro
'Magic Moment' (3)	CQua
'Magician' (2)	CQua
'Magna Carta' (2)	CQua
'Magnificence' (1)	CFen CQua GCro
'Maker's Mark' (1)	CQua
'Malpas' (3)	CQua
'Malvern City' (1)	CFen CQua
'Mamma Mia' (4)	IEsk
'Manaccan' (1)	CQua
'Mangaweka' (6)	CQua
'Manly' (4) ♀H6	CQua ELan ERCP GKev SDeJ
'Mantle' (2)	CQua
'Margaret Herbert' (7)	CQua
'Maria Pia' (11a)	IEsk
'Marie Curie Diamond' (7) ♀H6	CFen CQua
'Marieke' (1)	LAma SDeJ
'Marilyn Anne' (2)	CQua
'Marine Corps' (2)	IEsk
'Marjorie Hine' (2)	CQua
'Marjorie Treveal' (4)	CQua
'Marlborough' (2)	CQua
'Marlborough Freya' (2)	CQua
'Marshfire' (2)	CQua
'Martha Washington' (8)	CQua
'Martinette' (8)	CAvo CFen CQua SDeJ
'Martinsville' (8)	CQua
'Mary Bohannon' (2)	GKev SDeJ
'Mary Copeland' (4)	CQua
'Mary Kate' (2)	CQua
'Mary Lou' (6)	IEsk
'Mary Moore' (2)	CQua
'Mary Rosina' (4)	CQua
'Mary Veronica' (3)	CQua
'Marzo' (7)	IEsk
'Masked Light' (2)	CFen
'Matador' (8)	CFen CQua IEsk
'Mawla' (1)	CQua
'Max' (11a)	CQua
'Maximus Superbus' (1)	CQua
'Maya Dynasty' (2)	CQua
'Mayor's Choice' (11a)	CQua

'Maywood' (11a)	CQua
'Mazzard' (4)	CQua
'Media Girl' (2)	IEsk
× ***medioluteus*** (13)	CBro CQua WShi
'Medway Gold' (7)	CQua
'Melancholy' (1)	CQua
'Melbury' (2)	CQua
'Meldrum' (1)	CQua
'Melen' (2)	CFen
'Memento' (1)	CQua
'Menabilly' (4)	CQua
'Mên-an-Tol' (2)	CQua
'Menehay' (11a) ♀H6	CQua
'Mer d'Or' (1)	IEsk
'Merlin' (3) ♀H6	CFen CQua LAma SDeJ
'Merry Bells' (5)	CQua
'Merrymeet' (4)	CQua
'Mersing' (3)	CQua
'Merthan' (9)	CQua
'Midas Touch' (1)	CQua
'Midget'	see *N. nanus* 'Midget'
MIDTOWN AEROLITE (2)	GCro
MIDTOWN ALFIE (1)	GCro
MIDTOWN AMBER (2)	GCro
MIDTOWN BRIGADIER (2)	GCro
MIDTOWN LAURIE (1)	GCro
'Mike Pollock' (8)	CFen CQua
'Milan' (9)	CQua
'Millennium Gold' (1)	CQua
'Millennium Sunrise' (2)	CQua
'Millennium Sunset' (2)	CQua
'Milly's Magic' (2)	CQua
'Minard' (4)	CQua
minimus misapplied	see *N. asturiensis*
'Minnie Hume' (3) **new**	GCro
'Minnow' (8) ♀H6	CArg CAvo CBro CFen CQua CRos EPfP EPot ERCP GKev LAma LCro LOPS LRHS MJak NBir NRHS SCob SDeJ SPer
'Minnowlet' (11a)	CQua
minor (13) ♀H5	CQua ECha EPot GCro GKev WFar WShi
- 'Douglasbank' (1)	ITim LLHF
- 'Little Gem' (1) ♀H6	CBro CQua CTri GKev LAma SDeJ
- var. ***pumilus*** 'Plenus'	see *N.* 'Rip van Winkle'
- Ulster form (13)	IBlr
'Mint Julep' (3) ♀H6	SDeJ
'Mirar' (2)	CQua
MISLEEDING (2)	GCro
'Misquote' (1)	CQua
'Miss Diddles' (7)	CQua
'Miss Klein' (7)	LLHF
'Miss Muffit' (1)	CQua
'Miss Primm' (2)	IEsk
'Mission Bells' (5) ♀H6	CQua
'Mission Impossible' (11a)	CQua
'Mist of Avalon' (4)	CQua
'Misty Glen' (2) ♀H6	CQua EPfP GKev MJak SDeJ SPhx
'Mite' (6) ♀H6	CAvo CBro CQua EPot GKev LAma LLHF NHpl WShi
'Mithrel' (11a)	CQua
'Mitylene' (2)	CQua
'Modern Art' (2)	CQua SDeJ
'Modulation' (2)	SDeJ
'Mondragon' (11a)	CQua GKev
'Mongleath' (2)	CQua
'Monks Wood' (1)	CQua
'Monksilver' (3)	CQua
'Monmouthshire' (2)	CQua
'Montclair' (2)	CQua
'Montego' (3)	CQua
'Monterrico' (4)	CFen
'Montroig' (2)	IEsk
'Moon Dream' (1)	CQua
'Moon Ranger' (3)	CQua
'Moon Shadow' (3)	CQua IEsk
'Moonstruck' (1)	CQua
'Morab' (1)	CQua
'Moralee' (4)	CQua
'More and More' (7) **new**	EPot GKev
'Morval' (2)	CQua
moschatus (13) ♀H6	CAvo CBro CQua EPot GKev WShi
'Mother Duck' (6)	LAma
'Motmot' (8)	CQua
'Mount Fuji' (2)	CQua
'Mount Hood' (1) ♀H6	CArg EPfP GKev LAma NBir SDeJ SPer
'Mountain Poet' (9)	CQua
'Mousehole' (3)	CQua
'Mowser' (7)	CQua
'Mr Sweet' (2)	CQua
'Mrs Langtry' (2)	CAvo CQua GCro WShi
'Mrs R.O. Backhouse' (2)	CQua WShi
'Muiranna' (1)	IEsk
'Mulatto' (1)	GCro
'Mullion' (3)	CQua
'Mulroy Bay' (1)	CQua
'Murlough' (9)	CQua
'Muscadet' (2)	CFen CQua
'Music Maker' (2)	IEsk
'My Story' (4) ♀H6	SDeJ
'My Sunshine' (2)	CQua
'My Sweetheart' (3)	CQua
'My Word' (2)	CFen
'Mystic' ambig. (3)	CQua
'Mzungu' (2)	IEsk
'Namraj' (2)	CQua
'Nancegollan' (7)	CQua GKev
'Nangiles' (4)	CQua
'Nanpee' (7)	CQua
'Nanpusker' (2)	CFen
'Nansidwell' (2)	CQua
'Nanstallon' (1)	CQua
'Nantucket Red' (3)	IEsk
§ ***nanus*** (13)	CQua CWCL EMor
§ - 'Midget' (1)	CBro CQua EPot ERCP GKev LAma NHpl WShi
'Nare Celebration' (2)	CFen
'Narrative' (2)	IEsk
'National Treasure' (2)	IEsk
'Navigator' (2)	IEsk
'Nelly' ambig.	CQua
'Nessa' (7)	CQua
'Nether Barr' (2)	CQua
'New Hope' (3)	CQua
'New Life' (3)	CQua
'New Penny' (3)	CQua IEsk
'New World' (2)	CQua
'New-Baby' (7)	CQua ERCP GKev MMrt SDeJ
'Newcomer' (3)	CQua
'Nickelodeon' (8)	CQua
'Night Music' (4)	CQua
'Nightcap' (1)	CQua
'Niphetos' (2)	GCro
'Niveth' (5)	CAvo CFen CQua GCro
§ ***nobilis*** (13)	CQua EPot GKev
- var. ***leonensis*** (13)	ITim
'Nonchalant' (3)	CQua
'Norma Jean' (2)	CQua
'North Rim' (2)	CQua

Name	Suppliers
'Noss Mayo' (6)	CQua
'Notre Dame' (2) ♀H6	CQua
'Nuage' (2)	CFen
Nylon Group (10)	CBro EPot GKev
'Nynja' (2)	CQua
'Oadby' (1)	CQua
'Obdam' (4)	SDeJ
'Obsession' (2)	CQua
obsoletus (13)	GKev WCot
obvallaris (13) ♀H6	CAvo CBro CFen CQua CTca EPot ERCP GCro GKev LCro SDeJ WHer WShi
'Ocarino' (4)	CFen CQua
'Odd Job' (12)	CQua
× ***odorus*** (13)	CQua WShi
- 'Plenus' (4)	CQua ERCP
'Oh Wow' (3)	IEsk
old pheasant's eye	see *N. poeticus* var. *recurvus*
'Olympic Medal' (1)	IEsk
'Ombersley' (1)	CQua
'Omri' (8)	GKev
'Oops' (2)	IEsk
'Orange Phoenix' (4)	CQua WShi
'Orange Progress' (2)	SDeJ
'Orange Queen' (3)	GKev
'Orange Supreme' (2)	CQua
'Orange Tint' (2)	CQua
'Orange Walk' (3)	CQua
'Orangery' (11a)	GKev LAma SDeJ
'Orbital Pink' (3)	IEsk
'Orchard Place' (3)	CQua
'Oregon Pioneer' (2)	IEsk
'Orkney' (2)	CQua
'Ormeau' (2)	CQua
'Ornatus' (9)	CQua GCro GKev WShi
'Oryx' (7) ♀H6	CQua
'Osmington' (2)	CQua
'Ouma' (1)	CQua
'Ouzel' (6)	CQua
'Owyhee' (2)	CQua
'Oxford Gold' (10) ♀H6	CAvo CQua GKev MNrw
'Oykel' (3)	CQua
pachybolbus (13)	CQua
'Pacific Coast' (8) ♀H6	CQua LCro LLHF LOPS
'Pacific Mist' (11a)	CQua
'Pacific Rim' (2)	CQua IEsk
'Pacific Waves' (3)	CQua
'Painted Desert' (3)	CQua
'Palace Pink' (2)	IEsk
'Pale Sunlight' (2)	CQua
pallidiflorus (13)	ECha
- var. ***pallidiflorus*** (13)	GKev
'Palmares' (11a)	CQua SDeJ
'Pamela Hubble' (2)	CQua
'Pamela Joan' (2)	CQua
'Pampaluna' (11a)	CQua
'Panache' (1)	CQua
panizzianus (13)	CQua
'Panorama Pink' (3)	IEsk
'Pantaloon' (4)	IEsk
'Paper White'	see *N. papyraceus*
'Paper White Grandiflorus' (8)	CQua EPfP NRHS SDeJ SPer
'Papillon Blanc' (11b)	ERCP GKev
'Papua' (4)	CFen CQua
§ ***papyraceus*** (13)	CQua GKev
- 'Ziva' (8)	CAvo GKev LCro LOPS SDeJ
'Paramour' (4)	IEsk
'Parcpat' (7)	CQua
'Parisienne' (11a)	GKev SDeJ
'Park Springs' (3)	CQua
'Parkdene' (2)	CQua
'Partisan' (2)	IEsk
'Passionale' (2) ♀H6	CQua LAma NBir
'Pastiche' (2)	CQua
'Pat Brown' (2)	CQua
'Pat Redman' (3)	CQua
'Patabundy' (2)	CQua
'Pathos' (3)	IEsk
'Patois' (9)	CBro CQua
'Patrick Hacket' (1) ♀H6	CFen CQua
'Pay Day' (1)	CQua
'Peach Prince' (4)	CQua
'Pearl Wedding' (3)	CQua
'Pearlshell' (11a)	CQua
'Peeping Jenny' (6)	GKev SDeJ
'Peeping Tom' (6) ♀H6	CBro CQua ERCP GKev LAma LRHS SDeJ SRms
'Peggy's Gift' (3)	IEsk
'Pelynt' (3)	CQua
'Pemboa' (1)	CQua
'Pencrebar' (4)	CQua EPot GKev LAma NHol SDeJ WShi
'Pend Oreille' (3)	CQua
'Pengarth' (2)	CQua
'Penjerrick' (9)	CQua
'Penkivel' (2) ♀H6	CQua
'Pennance Mill' (2)	CQua
'Pennine Way' (1)	CQua
'Penny Perowne' (7)	CQua
'Pennyfield' (2)	CQua
'Penpol' (7)	CFen CQua
'Penril' (6)	CQua
'Penselwood' (2)	CQua
'Penstraze' (7)	CQua
'Pentewan' (2)	CQua GCro
'Pentille' (1)	CQua
'Pentire' (11a)	CQua
'Penvale' (7)	CQua
'Peppercorn' (6)	CQua
'Percuil' (6)	CQua
'Perdredda' (3)	CQua
'Peridot' (2) **new**	GKev
'Perimeter' (3)	CQua
'Peripheral Pink' (2)	CQua
'Perlax' (11a)	CQua
'Perpetuation' (7)	CQua
'Personable' (2)	CQua
'Petanca' (5)	IEsk
'Peter Chown' (11a)	CQua
'Petit Four' (4)	LAma LRHS SDeJ
'Petrel' (5)	CQua ERCP GKev SDeJ WShi
'Phantom' (11a)	CQua
'Phil's Gift' (1)	CQua
'Phoenician' (2)	CQua IEsk
'Picatou' (3)	IEsk
'Picket Post' (3)	IEsk
'Picoblanco' (2)	CBro CQua
'Pinafore' (2)	WFar
PINEAPPLE PLEMP (1)	GCro
'Pineapple Prince' (2) ♀H6	CQua
'Pink Angel' (7)	CQua
'Pink Champagne' (4)	CQua
'Pink Charm' (2)	CQua GKev NBir SDeJ
'Pink China' (2)	CQua
'Pink Formal' (11a)	CQua
'Pink Glacier' (11a)	CQua
'Pink Holly' (11a)	CQua
'Pink Ice' (2)	CQua
'Pink Pageant' (4)	CQua

Name	Suppliers
'Pink Paradise' (4)	CQua
'Pink Parasol' (1)	SDeJ
'Pink Pride' (2)	CArg
'Pink Silk' (1)	CQua GKev SDeJ
'Pink Smiles' (2)	CFen
'Pink Surprise' (2)	CQua
'Pink Tango' (11a)	CQua
'Pinza' (2) ♀H6	CQua SDeJ
'Pipe Major' (2)	CQua MJak
'Pipers Barn' (7)	CQua
'Piper's Gold' (1)	CQua
'Pipestone' (2)	CQua
'Pipit' (7)	CAvo CBro CFen CQua EPfP EPot ERCP GKev LAma LRHS NBir SDeJ WShi
'Pismo Beach' (2)	CQua
'Pistachio' (1) ♀H6	GKev
'Pitchroy' (2)	CQua
'Pitt's Diamond' (3)	CQua
'Pixie's Sister' (7) ♀H6	CQua LLHF
'Pledge' (1)	CQua
'Plymouth Hoe' (1)	CQua
§ ***poeticus*** var. ***hellenicus*** (13)	CBro CQua GCro IEsk
- old pheasant's eye	see *N. poeticus* var. *recurvus*
- var. ***physaloides*** (13)	CQua GKev
- 'Plenus' misapplied	see *N. poeticus* 'Spalding Double White', *N.* 'Tamar Double White'
§ - 'Plenus' ambig. (4)	CAby CBro CQua ERCP GKev SDeJ WShi
§ - var. ***recurvus*** (13) ♀H6	CAby CAvo CBro CFen CQua CTca ELan ERCP GKev LAma LCro LOPS NBir SCob SDeJ SEND SPer SPhx WShi
§ - 'Spalding Double White' (4)	CQua
- white-flowered (13)	SDeJ
'Poetry in Motion' (9)	IEsk
'Poet's Way' (9)	CQua IEsk
'Pol Crocan' (2)	CQua IEsk
'Pol Dornie' (2)	CQua
'Pol Voulin' (2)	CQua IEsk
'Polar Ice' (3)	CFen CQua GKev LAma SDeJ
'Polbathic' (2)	CQua
'Polgoon' (2)	CFen
'Polgooth' (2)	CQua
'Polindra' (2)	GCro
'Polly's Pearl' (8)	CQua
'Polmenor' (2)	CQua
'Polnesk' (7)	GCro
'Polonaise' (2)	CQua
'Polruan' (7)	CQua
'Poltreen' (4)	CQua
'Polwheveral' (2)	CQua
'Polyphant' (2)	CQua
'Pomona' (3)	GCro
'Pooka' (3)	CQua IEsk
POOLEWE PINTUCK (2)	GCro
'Poppy's Choice' (4)	CQua
'Pops Legacy' (1)	CQua
'Porthchapel' (7)	CQua
'Portloe Bay' (3)	CQua
'Portrait' (2)	CQua
'Portrush' (3)	CQua
'Potential' (1)	CQua
'Powerstock' (2)	IEsk
'Praecox' (9)	CBro
'Prairie Fire' (3)	CQua
'Pratincole' (3)	IEsk
'Preamble' (1)	CQua
I 'Precocious' (2) ♀H6	CQua GKev SDeJ
'Predator' (1)	IEsk
'Premiere' (2)	CQua
'Presidential Pink' (2)	CQua
'Pretty Baby' (3)	CQua
'Pretty in Yellow' (11a) **new**	SDeJ
'Pride of Cornwall' (8)	CQua
'Primegold' (2)	CFen
'Primrose Beauty' (4)	CFen CQua
'Princeps' (1)	CQua GCro
'Princess Alexandra' (6)	CFen
'Princess Diana' (6)	CFen
'Princess Zaide' (3)	GKev
'Printal' (11a)	SDeJ
'Priorsford' (2)	IEsk
'Prism' (2)	CQua
'Problem Child' (2)	IEsk
'Probus' (1)	CQua
'Professor Einstein' (2)	GKev SDeJ
'Prologue' (1)	CQua
'Prom Dance' (11a) ♀H6	GKev
'Prototype' (6)	LAma LRHS
'Proud Fellow' (1)	IEsk
'Proverbial Pink' (2)	IEsk
pseudonarcissus (13)	CArg CHab CQua CWld LCro LOPS MMuc WHer WShi
- JMH 7821	GKev
- subsp. ***eugeniae***	see *N. eugeniae*
- subsp. ***nobilis***	see *N. nobilis*
- var. ***porrigens*** (13)	GCro
- subsp. ***pseudonarcissus*** double-flowered (4)	CQua
'Ptolemy' (1)	CFen
'Pueblo' (7)	CQua GKev LRHS SDeJ
'Pukenui' (4)	CQua
pumilus ambig. (13)	CAvo CQua LLHF SDeJ
'Punchline' (7) ♀H6	CQua
'Punter' (2)	CQua IEsk
'Puppet' (5)	CQua SDeJ
'Purbeck' (3) ♀H6	CQua
'Quail' (7) ♀H6	CFen CQua CTca GKev LAma MJak SDeJ
'Quasar' (2) ♀H6	CQua
Queen Anne's double daffodil	see *N.* 'Eystettensis'
'Queen Fiona' (1)	IEsk
'Queen Juliana' (1)	CQua
'Queen Mum' (1)	CQua
'Queen of Spain' (5)	CQua GKev
'Queen of the North' (3)	GCro
'Queen's Guard' (1)	IEsk
'Queensland' (2)	CFen
'Quetta' (3)	GCro
'Quick Step' (7)	CQua
'Quiet Hero' (3)	IEsk
'Quiet Magic' (2)	IEsk
'Quiet Waters' (1)	IEsk
'Radiant Gem' (8)	CQua
radiiflorus (13)	EPot
- var. ***poetarum*** (13)	CQua
- var. ***radiiflorus*** (13)	GCro
- var. ***stellaris*** (13)	GCro
'Radjel' (4)	CQua
'Rainbow' (2) ♀H6	CQua
'Raj' (2)	CQua
'Rame Head' (1)	CQua
'Rameses' (2)	CQua
'Raoul Wallenberg' (2)	SDeJ
'Rapid Stride' (6)	IEsk
'Rapture' (6) ♀H6	CQua ERCP GKev IEsk SPhx WShi
'Rashee' (1)	CQua

'Raspberry Ring' (2) CQua
'Rathowen Gold' (1) CQua
'Ravenhill' (3) CQua
'Rebekah' (4) CQua
'Recital' (2) CQua
'Red Beacon' (3) **new** GCro
'Red Devon' (2) CArg CFen GKev LCro LOPS LRHS SDeJ
'Red Era' (3) CQua
'Red Mantle' (2) CQua
'Red Marvel' (3) CFen
'Red Reed' (1) IEsk
'Red Rim' (9) GCro
'Red Socks' (6) CQua
'Refrain' (2) CQua
'Regal Bliss' (2) CQua
'Regal Glow' (1) IEsk
'Reggae' (6) ♀H6 CQua LRHS SDeJ
'Rembrandt' (1) CFen CQua
'Rendezvous Caye' (2) CQua
'Renovator' (1) CQua
'Repertoire' (3) IEsk
'Replete' (4) CQua CWld GKev SDeJ
requienii see *N. assoanus*
'Resistasol' (1) IEsk
'Resolute' (2) GCro
'Reverse Image' (11a) CQua
'Rheban Red' (2) IEsk
'Ridgecrest' (3) CQua
rifanus see *N. romieuxii* subsp. *romieuxii* var. *rifanus*
'Rijnveld's Early Sensation' (1) ♀H6 CAvo CBro CFen CQua ECha ERCP GKev LCro LOPS SDeJ
'Rikki' (7) CBro CQua
'Rima' (1) CQua
'Rimmon' (3) CQua
'Rimski' (2) IEsk
'Ring Fence' (3) IEsk
'Ring Flash' (2) IEsk
'Ringing Bells' (5) CQua
'Ringleader' (2) CQua
§ 'Rip van Winkle' (4) CAby CBro CFen CQua CRos CTca EPfP EPot ERCP GKev LAma LRHS MJak NAln NHol NHpl NRHS SCob SDeJ SPer WShi
'Rippling Waters' (5) CQua LAma
'Rising Star' (7) ♀H6 IEsk
'Rival' (6) CQua
'River Queen' (2) CQua IEsk
'Roberta' (1) CFen
'Roberta Watrous' (7) IEsk
'Rockall' (3) CQua
'Rocoza' (2) IEsk
'Roger' (6) CQua
'Rogue' (2) CBro
'Romance' (2) ♀H6 LAma
§ 'Romanus' (4) CQua
romieuxii (13) ♀H4 CRos LRHS NRHS WCot
- JCA 805 EPot
- SF 370 WCot
- subsp. ***albidus*** (13) EPot GKev
- - SF 110 WCot
- - var. ***zaianicus*** SB&L 82 from Morocco WCot
§ - 'Joy Bishop' (10) EPot
§ - 'Julia Jane' (10) CQua ERCP GKev WCot
* - subsp. ***pallidus*** SB&L 237 WCot
§ - subsp. ***romieuxii*** var. ***mesatlanticus*** (13) EPot
§ - - var. ***rifanus*** (13) B 8929 WCot

§ - 'Treble Chance' (10) EPot
'Rongoiti Gem' (4) CQua
'Rosannor Gold' (11a) CQua
'Roscarrick' (6) CQua
'Rose of May' (4) CQua WShi
'Rose of Tralee' (2) CQua
'Rose Royale' (2) CQua
'Rose Villa' (2) CQua
'Rosemary Pearson' (2) CQua
'Rosemerryn' (2) CQua
'Rosemoor Gold' (7) ♀H6 CFen CQua
'Rosemullion' (4) CQua
'Rosevine' (3) CQua
'Roulette' (2) SDeJ
'Round Oak' (1) CQua
'Roxton' (4) IEsk
'Royal Armour' (1) CFen
'Royal Ballet' (2) CQua
'Royal Connection' (8) CQua
'Royal Marine' (2) CQua
'Royal Princess' (3) CQua GKev
'Royal Regiment' (2) CQua
'Rubh Mor' (2) CQua
'Ruby Red' (2) CQua
'Ruby Wedding' (2) IEsk
'Rubythroat' (2) CQua
'Ruddy Duck' (2) IEsk
'Ruddy Rascal' (2) IEsk
'Rugulosus' (7) CQua
'Runkerry' (4) IEsk
rupicola (13) CBro CQua GKev LLHF NSla WCot
§ - subsp. ***watieri*** (13) CBro CQua ERCP GKev NHpl
'Rustom Pasha' (2) CQua
'Rytha' (2) CQua
'Saberwing' (5) CQua
'Sabine Hay' (3) CQua EPot GKev
'Sabrosa' (7) ♀H6 CBro CQua GKev LLHF
'Sacajawea' (2) CFen
'Sacré Coeur' (2) IEsk
'Saffron Strand' (3) IEsk
'Sagana' (9) CQua
'Sailboat' (7) ♀H6 CAvo CBro CQua GKev LCro LOPS SDeJ SPer
'Saint Agnes' (8) CQua
'Saint Budock' (1) CQua
'Saint Day' (5) CQua
'Saint Dilpe' (2) CQua
'Saint Keverne' (2) ♀H6 CFen CQua SDeJ
'Saint Keyne' (8) CQua
'Saint Louie Louie' (6) IEsk
'Saint Olaf' (3) GCro
'Saint Patrick's Day' (2) CFen CQua LAma SDeJ
'Saint Peter' (4) CFen CQua
'Saint Petroc' (9) CQua
'Saint Piran' (7) CQua
'Salakee' (2) CQua
'Salcey Forest' (1) CQua
'Salome' (2) ♀H6 CQua LAma LCro LOPS NBir NPer SCob SDeJ
'Salute' (2) CQua
'Samantha' (4) CQua
'Sandra's Diamond' (3) CQua
'Sandycove' (2) CQua
'Sandymount' (2) CQua
'Santa Claus' (4) CQua
'Sarah Dear' (2) CQua
'Sarah Markillie' (11a) CQua
'Sargeant's Caye' (1) CQua IEsk
'Satchmo' (1) CQua
'Satin Blanc' (7) IEsk

'Satsuma' (1) CQua
'Saturn' (3) CQua
'Savoir Faire' (2) IEsk
'Saxby' (11a) CQua
'Scarlet Chord' (2) CQua
'Scarlet Elegance' (2) CQua
'Scarlet Gem' (8) SDeJ
'Scarlet Tanager' (2) IEsk
'Scarlett O'Hara' (2) CFen
'Scilly White' (8) CFen CQua WShi
'Scorrier' (2) CQua
'Scrumpy' (2) CQua
'Sea Dream' (3) CQua
'Sea Green' (9) CQua
'Sea Legend' (2) CQua
'Sea Moon' (2) IEsk
'Sea Princess' (3) GKev SDeJ
'Seagull' (3) CQua GCro LAma WShi
'Sealing Wax' (2) CFen CQua
'Season's Greetings' (7) IEsk
'Segovia' (3) ♀H6 CAvo CBro CQua EPot ERCP GKev IFro LAma LRHS NRHS SDeJ SPhx
'Sempre Avanti' (2) CArg GKev LAma SDeJ
'Sentinel' (2) **new** GKev SDeJ
'Seraglio' (3) CQua
'Serena Lodge' (4) ♀H6 CQua
'Sextant' (6) CQua
'Sheelagh Rowan' (2) CQua IEsk
'Sheer Joy' (6) CQua
'Shepherd's Hey' (7) CQua SDeJ
'Sherborne' (4) ♀H6 CQua
'Sherpa' (1) CQua IEsk
'Sheskin' (2) IEsk
'Shining Light' (2) CQua
'Shockwave' (2) CQua
'Shrimp Boat' (11a) IEsk
'Sidley' (3) CQua IEsk
'Sidney Torch' (2) CFen
'Signet Ring' (3) IEsk
'Signorina' (2) IEsk
'Silent Valley' (1) IEsk
'Silk Cut' (2) CQua
'Silver Chimes' (8) CAvo CBro CFen CQua GKev LAma LCro LOPS NBir SDeJ
'Silver Convention' (1) CQua
'Silver Crystal' (3) IEsk
'Silver Kiwi' (2) CQua
'Silver Monarch' (2) IEsk
'Silver Moon' (2) CFen
'Silver Plate' (11a) CQua
'Silver Sabre' (2) IEsk
'Silver Smiles' (7) GKev SPhx
'Silver Surf' (2) CQua
'Silversmith' (2) CQua
'Silverthorne' (3) CQua
'Silverwood' (3) CQua
'Sinopel' (3) GKev LAma SDeJ
'Sir Samuel' (2) CQua
'Sir Watkin' (2) CQua GCro
'Sir Winston Churchill' (4) ♀H6 CAvo CQua GKev LAma LCro LOPS LRHS SCob SDeJ SPer
'Sirius' (2) GCro
'Sissy' (6) CQua
'Skerry' (2) CQua
'Skilliwidden' (2) ♀H6 CQua
'Skookum' (3) CQua
'Slieveboy' (1) CQua
'Small Fry' (1) CQua
'Small Talk' (1) ♀H6 CQua LLHF
'Smiling Twin' (11a) SDeJ
'Smokey Bear' (4) CQua
'Smooth Sails' (3) CQua
'Snipe' (6) CAvo CQua GKev WShi
'Snook' (6) CQua
'Snoopie' (6) CQua
'Snow Baby' (1) **new** ERCP
'Snow Frills' (2) CQua
'Snowball' (4) GKev
'Snowcrest' (3) CQua
'Snowshill' (2) CQua
'Snowy Canyon' (4) IEsk
'Soft Focus' (2) IEsk
'Solar Eclipse' (2) IEsk
'Solar Tan' (3) CQua
'Soleil d'Or' (8) CQua
'Solera' (2) IEsk
'Solferique' (2) CQua
'Solveig's Song' (12) EPot
'Sonata' (9) CQua
'Songket' (2) CQua
'Sophia' (2) CQua
'Sophie Girl' (2) GKev
'Soprano' (2) CQua IEsk
'Sorbet' (11b) SDeJ
'Sorcerer' (3) CQua
'South Street' (2) CQua
'Southease' (2) CQua
'Southern Gem' (2) GCro
'Spaniards Inn' (4) CQua
'Sparkling Tarts' (8) CQua
'Sparnon' (11a) CQua
'Spartan Gold' (2) IEsk
'Special Envoy' (2) CQua
'Speenogue' (1) IEsk
'Spellbinder' (1) CQua NAln SDeJ
'Spencer Tracy' (2) CFen CQua
'Spin Doctor' (3) IEsk
'Spirit of Rame' (3) CQua
'Spoirot' (10) ♀H6 CAby CQua ERCP GBin GKev LEdu MNrw NHpl SDeJ
'Sportsman' (2) CQua
'Spring Dawn' (2) LCro LOPS SPer
'Spring Lustre' (3) IEsk
'Spring Morn' (2) CQua
'Spun Honey' (4) CQua
'Stadium' (2) CFen
'Stainless' (2) CAvo GKev SPhx
'Standard Value' (1) CFen
'Stann Creek' (1) CQua
'Stanway' (3) CQua
'Star Glow' (2) CQua
'Star Quality' (3) IEsk
'Starfire' (7) CQua
'State Express' (2) CQua
'Steenbok' (3) IEsk
'Stella' (2) CQua GCro WShi
'Stellar Glow' (3) IEsk
'Stenalees' (6) CQua
'Step Child' (6) CQua
'Step Forward' (7) CQua
'Steren' (7) CQua
'Stilton' (9) CQua
'Stinger' (2) CQua
'Stint' (5) ♀H6 CQua GKev SDeJ
'Stoke Charity' (2) CQua
'Stoke Doyle' (2) CQua
'Stonham Gold' (2) CQua
'Stormy Weather' (1) CQua
'Stratosphere' (7) ♀H6 CQua SDeJ
'Strines' (2) ♀H6 CQua

	Name	Suppliers
	'Suave' (3)	CQua GKev SDeJ
	'Subtle Shades' (2)	IEsk
	'Suda' (2)	GCro
	'Sugar and Spice' (3)	CQua
	'Sugar Cups' (8)	CQua
	'Sugar Loaf' (4)	CQua
	'Sugar Rose' (6)	CQua
	'Sugarbush' (7)	WShi
	'Suisgill' (4)	CQua
	'Sukey' (6)	CQua
§	'Sulphur Phoenix' (4)	CQua GCro WShi
	SULPHUR STAR (2)	GCro
	'Sumo Jewel' (6)	CQua
	'Sun Disc' (7) 🏆H6	CBro CFen CQua CTri GKev LAma LCro LOPS MJak SCob SDeJ WShi
	'Sunday Chimes' (5)	CQua
	'Sundial' (7)	CBro LAma
	'Sunny Girlfriend' (11a)	SDeJ
	'Sunnyside Up' (11a) 🏆H6	SDeJ
	'Sunrise' (3)	CQua
	'Sunstroke' (2)	CQua
	'Suntory' (3)	CQua
	'Surfside' (6) 🏆H6	CQua CWld GKev SDeJ SPhx
	'Surprise Packet' (2)	IEsk
	'Surrey' (2)	CQua
	'Suzie Dee' (6)	IEsk
	'Suzie's Sister' (6)	IEsk
	'Suzy' (7) 🏆H6	CFen SDeJ
	'Swaledale' (2)	CQua
	'Swallow' (6)	CQua SDeJ
	'Swan of Avon' (1)	CQua
	'Swanpool' (3)	CQua
	'Sweet Blanche' (7)	CQua
	'Sweet Lorraine' (2)	CQua
	'Sweet Memory' (2)	CQua
	'Sweet Pomponette' (4)	SDeJ
	'Sweet Sue' (3)	CQua
	'Sweetness' (7) 🏆H6	CAvo CFen CQua GCro GKev LAma LCro LOPS NAln SDeJ WShi
	'Swift Arrow' (6) 🏆H6	CQua
	'Swing Wing' (6)	CQua
	'Swoop' (6)	SDeJ
	'Sydling' (5)	CQua
	'Tahiti' (4) 🏆H6	CFen CQua ELan GKev LAma LCro LOPS SCob SDeJ
	× ***taitii*** (13)	GKev WShi
	'Talgarth' (2)	CQua
	'Talskiddy' (6)	CQua
§	'Tamar Double White' (4)	CBro CQua
	'Tamar Fire' (4) 🏆H6	CQua
	'Tamar Lad' (2)	CQua
	'Tamar Lass' (3)	CQua
	'Tamar Snow' (2)	CQua
	'Tamara' (2)	CArg CFen CQua
	'Tangent' (2)	CQua
	'Tangerine Tango' (4)	IEsk
	'Tao' (3)	CQua
	'Tasgem' (4)	CQua
	'Taslass' (4)	CQua
	tazetta (13)	CQua GKev
	- subsp. ***aureus***	see *N. **aureus***
§	- subsp. ***lacticolor*** (13)	CQua ERCP GKev SDeJ
§	- - 'Grand Monarque' (8)	CQua
	- subsp. ***ochroleucus*** (13)	CQua
*	- var. ***odoratus***	CQua WShi
	- subsp. ***tazetta***	CQua
	'Teal' (1)	CQua
	'Tehidy' (3)	CQua
§	'Telamonius Plenus' (4)	CBro CQua GBin GCro GKev SEND WShi
	'Temba' (1)	IEsk
	'Temple Cloud' (4)	IEsk
	Tequila Sunrise Group (12)	IEsk
	'Terminator' (2)	CQua IEsk
	'Terracotta' (2)	CQua
	'Terwegen' (4)	CFen
	'Tête Bouclé'PBR (4) **new**	LAma
	'Tête Deluxe' (4) **new**	SPer
	'Tête Rosette'	LCro
	'Tête-à-tête' (12) 🏆H6	CArg CAvo CBro CFen CQua CRos CTca CWCL EMor EPfP EPot ERCP GAbr GKev GQue LAma LCro LOPS LRHS NAln NHpl NRHS SCob SDeJ SPer
	'Thalia' (5)	CArg CAvo CBro CQua CTca EPfP ERCP GKev IFro LAma LCro LOPS MJak NBir NHol SCob SDeJ SPer SPhx WShi
	'The Alliance' (6) 🏆H6	CQua
	'The Caley' (2)	CQua
	'The Grange' (1)	CQua
	'The Mount' (2)	IEsk
	'Thistin' (1)	IEsk
	'Thomas Kinkade' (2)	CQua
	'Thoughtful' (5)	CQua
	'Three Oaks' (1)	CQua
	'Tibet' (2)	CFen CQua
	'Tickled Pink' (11a)	IEsk
	'Tideford' (2)	CQua
	'Tidy Tippet' (2)	IEsk
	'Tiercel' (1)	CQua
	'Tiffany Jade' (3)	CQua
	'Tiger Moth' (6)	CQua
	'Timolin' (3)	CQua
	'Tinhay' (7)	CQua
	'Tiritomba' (11a)	CQua
	'Tittle-tattle' (7)	CFen CQua
	'Toby' (2)	SDeJ
	'Toby the First' (6)	GKev
	'Top Hit' (11a)	CQua
	'Topolino' (1) 🏆H6	CAvo CBro CFen CQua CRos EPot ERCP GKev IFro LAma LCro LOPS LRHS NRHS SCob
	'Topsy Turvy' (4)	CQua
	'Toreador' ambig. (3)	CFen
	'Toretta' (3)	IEsk
	'Torianne' (2) 🏆H6	CQua
	TOROSAY ELEGANCE (2)	GCro
	'Torridon' (2)	CQua
	'Toto' (12) 🏆H6	CAvo CBro CQua ERCP GKev LCro LOPS SDeJ
	'Tracey' (6)	CQua GKev IEsk
	'Transmitter' (4)	CQua
	'Treasure Hunt' (2)	IEsk
	'Trebah' (2) 🏆H6	CQua
	'Treble Chance'	see *N. romieuxii* 'Treble Chance'
	'Treble Two' (7)	CQua
	'Trecara' (3)	CQua
	'Tregarrick' (2)	CQua
	'Treglisson' (2)	CFen
	'Trelawney Gold' (2)	CFen CQua
	'Trelissick' (7)	CQua
	'Tremelling' (2)	CFen
	'Tremough Dale' (11a)	CQua
	'Trena' (6) 🏆H6	CQua ERCP SDeJ
	'Trendy Trail' (3)	IEsk
	'Trentagh' (3)	IEsk
	'Trenwith' (1)	CQua
	'Trepolo' (11b)	SDeJ

'Tresamble' (5)	CBro CQua EPfP GCro GKev LAma LCro LOPS NAln NBir SDeJ
'Tresserve' (1)	GCro
'Trevaunance' (6)	CQua
'Treverva' (6)	CQua
'Treviddo' (2)	CQua
'Trevithian' (7)	CQua GCro GKev LAma SDeJ
'Trewarvas' (2)	CQua
triandrus var. ***albus***	see *N. triandrus* subsp. *triandrus* var. *triandrus*
§ - subsp. ***triandrus*** var. ***triandrus*** (13)	GBin
'Tricollet' (11a)	SDeJ
'Trident' (3)	CQua
'Trielfin' (5)	IEsk
'Trigonometry' (11a) ♀H6	CQua IEsk
'Tripartite' (11a) ♀H6	CFen CQua GKev IEsk SDeJ
'Triple Crown' (3) ♀H6	CQua IEsk
'Tristram' (2)	CQua
'Tropic Isle' (4)	CQua
'Trousseau' (1)	CFen CQua
'Tru' (3)	CQua
'Truculent' (3)	CQua
'Trumpet Warrior' (1) ♀H6	CQua IEsk
'Tryst' (2)	CQua
'Tudor Minstrel' (2)	CQua
'Tuesday's Child' (5) ♀H6	CQua
'Turncoat' (6)	CQua
'Tutankhamun' (2)	CQua
'Tweety Bird' (6)	SPer
'Twicer' (2)	CQua IEsk
'Twilight Zone' (2)	IEsk
'Twink' (4)	CQua GCro
'Twinkling Yellow' (7) ♀H6	CBro GKev
'Tyrone Gold' (1) ♀H6	CQua
'Tyrree' (1)	IEsk
'Tywara' (1)	CQua
'Ulster Bank' (3)	CQua
'Ulster Bride' (4)	CQua
'Ultimus' (2)	CQua
'Uncle Duncan' (1)	CQua
'Unique' (4) ♀H6	CQua GKev LAma SDeJ
'Unsurpassable' (1)	CFen CQua GCro LAma
'Upalong' (12)	CQua
'Upshot' (3)	CQua
'Urchin' (2)	IEsk
'Utiku' (6)	CQua
'Val d'Incles' (3)	CQua
'Valdrome' (11a)	CQua
'Valediction' (3)	CQua
'Valinor' (2)	CQua
'Van Sion'	see *N.* 'Telamonius Plenus'
'Vanilla Peach' (11a)	GKev LRHS MJak SDeJ
'Vantage' (2)	CQua
'Vaticaan' (1)	SDeJ
'Velocity' (6)	GKev LAma
'Vendell' (3)	IEsk
'Verdant Sparks' (7)	IEsk
'Verdin' (7)	CQua CWld
'Verger' (3)	LAma SDeJ
'Vernal Prince' (3) ♀H6	CQua
'Verona' (3) ♀H6	CQua
'Vers Libre' (9)	CQua
'Version' (2)	IEsk
'Victoria' (1)	CQua
'Video Kid' (2)	IEsk
'Viking' (1) ♀H6	CQua
'Village Green' (3)	IEsk
'Vineland' (6)	CQua
'Violetta' (2)	CQua

'Virginia Waters' (3)	CQua
'Viva Diva' (3)	IEsk
'Volare' (2)	CQua
'Volcanic Rim' (3)	IEsk
'Vulcan' (2)	CQua
'W.P. Milner' (1)	CAvo CBro CQua EMor EPfP EPot ERCP GKev LAma LCro LOPS SDeJ SEND SPhx WShi
'Walden Pond' (3)	CQua
'Waldorf Astoria' (4)	CQua
'Walton' (7)	CQua
'Waltz' (11a)	CQua
'Warbler' (6) ♀H6	CQua GKev LAma SDeJ
'Warleggan' (2)	CFen
'Warm Day' (2)	IEsk
'Warm Welcome' (2)	IEsk
'Warmington' (3)	CQua
'Warmwell' (3)	IEsk
'Watamu' (3)	IEsk
'Waterperry' (7)	GKev LAma
'Watership Down' (2)	CQua
'Watersmeet' (4)	CQua
watieri	see *N. rupicola* subsp. *watieri*
'Wave' (4)	CQua SDeJ
'Wavertree'	see *N. asturiensis* 'Wavertree'
'Waxwing' (5)	CQua
'Wee Bee' (1)	CQua
'Welcome' (2)	CFen CQua
'Welsh Rugby Union' (1)	CQua
'Welsh Warrior' (1)	CQua
'Wendron' (1)	CFen
'West Post' (3)	IEsk
'Westward' (4)	CQua
'Whang-hi' (6)	CQua
'Wheal Bush' (4)	CQua
'Wheal Coates' (7) ♀H6	CQua
'Wheal Jane' (2)	CQua
'Wheal Kitty' (7)	CQua
'Wheal Rose' (4)	CQua
'Wheatear' (6) ♀H6	CQua IEsk
'Whetstone' (1)	CQua
'Whipcord' (7) ♀H6	CQua IEsk
'Whisky Galore' (2)	CQua
'Whisky Mac' (2)	CQua
'White Empress' (1)	CQua
'White Lady' (3)	CAvo CQua GCro GKev LAma WShi
'White Lion' (4) ♀H6	CFen CQua LAma SDeJ
'White Marvel' (4)	CQua GKev SDeJ
'White Medal' (4)	GKev SDeJ
'White Nile' (2)	CQua GCro
'White Star' (1)	IEsk
'White Tea' (2)	CQua IEsk
'White Tie' (3)	CQua
'Whitewell' (2)	GCro
'Wicklow Hills' (3)	CQua
'Widgeon' (2)	CQua
'Wild Honey' (2)	CQua
'Wild Rover' (1)	IEsk
'Will Scarlett' (2)	CQua
willkommii (13)	CBro CQua EPot GKev
'Wimbledon County Girl' (2) ♀H6	CQua
'Winholm Jenni' (3)	CQua
'Winifred van Graven' (3)	CFen CQua
'Winter Sun' (8) **new**	GKev LRHS
'Winter Waltz' (6)	CQua CWld
'Wisley' (6) ♀H6	ERCP
'Witch Doctor' (3)	CQua
WOODCROFT BEAUTY (2)	GCro
WOODCROFT GOLD (2)	GCro

'Woodland Prince' (3)	CQua
'Woodland Star' (3)	CQua
'Woodley Vale' (2)	CQua
'Woodstar' (5) **new**	EPot
'Woolsthorpe' (2)	CQua
'World Class' (5)	CQua
'Wy' East' (1)	IEsk
'Xit' (3)	CAvo CBro CQua EPot
'Xunantunich' (2)	CQua
'Yellow Cheerfulness' (4) ♀H6	CArg CQua ELan EPfP GKev LAma LCro LOPS NRHS SCob SDeJ SPer
'Yellow River' (1) ♀H6	LAma
'Yellow Triumphator' (1)	CFen
'Yellow Xit' (3)	CQua GKev
'York Minster' (1)	CQua
'Young American' (1)	CQua
'Young Blood' (2)	CQua IEsk
'Your Grace' (2)	CQua
'Yummy Mummy' (2)	IEsk
'Yum-Yum' (3)	IEsk
'Zekiah' (1)	CQua
'Zion Canyon' (2)	CQua
'Zoë's Pink' (3)	CQua
'Zwynner' (2)	IEsk

Nardostachys (*Caprifoliaceae*)

grandiflora	see *N. jatamansi* 'Grandiflora'
§ ***jatamansi*** 'Grandiflora'	GPoy

Nassauvia (*Asteraceae*)

darwinii	WAbe
digitata	SPlb
gaudichaudii	SPlb WAbe
lagascae	WAbe

Nassella (*Poaceae*)

cernua	EPPr
tenuissima	see *Stipa tenuissima*
trichotoma	CAby EHoe LPla WHal
- 'Palomino'	CRos LRHS NRHS

Nasturtium (*Brassicaceae*)

'Banana Split'	CCCN
officinale	EWat MWts SVic WMAq

Natal plum see *Carissa macrocarpa*

nectarine see *Prunus persica* var. *nectarina*

Nectaroscordum (*Alliaceae*)

§ ***siculum***	CArg CAvo CBod CBre CBro CPla CSpe CTri EAJP ELan ERCP GKev LCro LEdu LOPS LRHS MBel MJak NAln NBir NChi NSti SCob SDeJ SPer SPoG WBor
§ - subsp. ***bulgaricum***	CAby CBro CRos CTca CWCL EBee ECha EHrv EPfP EPot EWhm GKev LRHS LSun MNrw NRHS SPhx WBrk WCot WPnP XEll XLum
- subsp. ***bulgaricum*** × ***tripedale***	GKev
tripedale	CAvo CBro EPot ERCP GKev

Neillia (*Rosaceae*)

affinis	CBod CDul CExl CKel CRos EBee EPfP GCal LLHF LRHS MGil NBid NLar SLon SPad SPoG SWvt
longiracemosa	see *N. thibetica*
rubiflora	CPla
sinensis	NLar
§ ***thibetica***	Widely available
thyrsiflora	EBee
- PAB 3267	LEdu
- var. ***tunkinensis*** HWJ 505	WCru

Nelumbo (*Nelumbonaceae*)

lutea	XBlo
nucifera	XBlo
'Pink 'n' Yellow'	EWat

Nematanthus (*Gesneriaceae*)

'Apres'	WDib
'Black Magic'	WDib
'Christmas Holly'	WDib
'Freckles'	WDib
§ ***gregarius*** ♀H1b	WDib
§ - 'Golden West' (v)	WDib
- 'Variegatus'	see *N. gregarius* 'Golden West'
'Lemon and Lime'	WDib
radicans	see *N. gregarius*
'Tropicana' ♀H1b	WDib

Nemesia (*Scrophulariaceae*)

§ AMELIE ('Fleurame'PBR)	EPfP LBuc NPri SPoG WJam
(Aroma Series) AROMA PLUMS & CUSTARD **new**	NPri
- AROMA RHUBARB & CUSTARD **new**	NPri
'Belcombe Blue' **new**	CSpe
BERRIES AND CREAM ('Fleurbac'PBR)	ECtt EPfP LBuc MCot SPoG
BLUE LAGOON ('Pengoon'PBR) (Maritana Series)	MCot SCoo
§ BLUEBIRD ('Hubbird'PBR)	CHll
'Bordeaux' **new**	SPoG
caerulea 'Joan Wilder' (clonal)	WAvo
CANDY GIRL ('Pencand') (Maritana Series)	SCoo
§ ***denticulata*** ♀H3	CRos ELon LRHS MHer NEgg SCoo
- 'Confetti'	see *N. denticulata*
'Easter Bonnet' (French Connection Series)	NPri SPoG
'Fleurie Blue'	EPfP LBuc SPoG
FRAMBOISE ('Fleurfram'PBR)	EPfP LBuc NPri
fruticans Benth.	ELon
HONEY GIRL ('Penhon') (Maritana Series)	SCoo
'Innocence' ♀H3	SCoo
(Karoo Series) KAROO BLUE ('Innkablue'PBR)	SCoo
- KAROO DARK BLUE ('Innemkadab'PBR)	MCot
- KAROO SOFT BLUE ('Innkarsofb'PBR)	MCot
MARITANA SKY LAGOON ('Pensky') (Maritana Series)	SCoo
'Mirabelle'	EPfP LBuc NPri SPoG
MYRTILLE ('Fleurmyr'PBR)	EPfP LBuc SPoG
NESIA BANANA SWIRL (Nesia Series) **new**	NPri
OPAL INNOCENCE	see *N.* AMELIE
RASPBERRIES AND CREAM ('Fleurrac')	EPfP LBuc SPoG
'Sugar Almond'	CMac
'Sundrops'	NPri
(Sunsatia Series) SUNSATIA BANANA ('Intraibana')	SPoG

	- SUNSATIA BLACKBERRY ('Inuppink'PBR)	SCoo
	- SUNSATIA CHERRY ON ICE	CPla NPri SPoG
	- SUNSATIA CRANBERRY ('Intraired'PBR)	SCoo
	- SUNSATIA LEMON ('Intraigold'PBR)	SCoo
	- SUNSATIA PEACH ('Inupcream')	SCoo
	(Sunsatia Plus Series) SUNSATIA PLUS PAPAYA ('Innemnewpa')	NPri
	sylvatica	CSpe
	'Vanilla Lady'	ECtt
	'Wisley Vanilla'	CRos EPfP LBuc LRHS NPri NRHS SPoG

Nemophila (*Boraginaceae*)

	menziesii 'Penny Black'	CSpe SPer

Neodypsis (*Arecaceae*)

	decaryi	see *Dypsis decaryi*

Neohenricia (*Aizoaceae*)

	sibbettii ♀H2 **new**	CPBP

Neolepisorus (*Polypodiaceae*)

	lancifolius	CExl

Neolitsea (*Lauraceae*)

	glauca	see *N. sericea*
	polycarpa B&SWJ 11705	WCru
	- KWJ 12309	WCru
§	***sericea***	CBcs CCCN EBee WPGP
	- B&SWJ 12738	WCru
	- CWJ 12800	WCru
	- yellow-fruited CWJ 12830	WCru

Neomarica (*Iridaceae*)

	caerulea	WCot

Neopanax ✿ (*Araliaceae*)

§	***arboreus***	CDTJ CTsd EBee LEdu
§	***laetus*** ♀H3	WPGP

Neoregelia ✿ (*Bromeliaceae*)

	'Atlantis'	NCft
	carolinae (Meyendorffii Group) 'Meyendorffii'	XBlo
	'Fireball' ♀H1b	NCft
	'Hojo Rojo'	XBlo
	lilliputiana	NCft
	'Luca'	SPlb
	'Marconfos'	XBlo
	'Narciss'	NCft
	pauciflora	NCft
I	***paulinae*** 'Paulinae'	NCft
I	***schultesiana***	NCft
I	- 'Variegata' (v)	NCft

Neoshirakia (*Euphorbiaceae*)

	japonica	MBlu WPGP
	- B&SWJ 8744	WCru

Neottia (*Orchidaceae*)

	ovata	NLAp

Nepenthes ✿ (*Nepenthaceae*)

	sp.	SRms
	alata × ***ventricosa*** ♀H1b	SHmp
	'Bloody Mary'PBR	SHmp
	bongso	SHmp
	burbidgeae × ***robcantleyi***	SHmp
	× ***burkei*** × ***hamata***	SHmp
	× ***burkei*** × ***singalana***	SHmp
	(***copelandii*** × ***truncata***) × ***spathulata***	SHmp
	densiflora	SHmp
	diatas	SHmp
	dubia × ***singalana***	SHmp
	dubia × ***spathulata***	SHmp
	fusca	SHmp
	fusca × ***maxima***	SHmp
	glabrata × ***spathulata***	SHmp
	× ***hookeriana*** ♀H1a	SHmp
	jacquelineae × ***spectabilis***	SHmp
	'Linda'PBR	SHmp
	'Louisa'	SHmp
	macfarlanei	SHmp
	maxima × (× ***mixta***)	SHmp
	maxima × ***talangensis***	SHmp
	mira × ***spathulata***	SHmp
	ovata	SHmp
	ovata × ***ventricosa***	SHmp
	petiolata × ***veitchii***	SHmp
	platychila × ***spathulata***	SHmp
	ramispina	SHmp
	'Rebecca Soper' ♀H1b	SHmp
	robcantleyi	SHmp
	robcantleyi × ***spathulata***	SHmp
	robcantleyi × ***talangensis***	SHmp
	sanguinea	SHmp
	sibuyanensis	SHmp
	singalana	SHmp
	spectabilis	SHmp
	talangensis	SHmp
	talangensis × ***veitchii***	SHmp
	truncata highland form	SHmp
	- 'King of Spades' × ***truncata*** 'Queen of Hearts'	SHmp
	ventricosa	SHmp

Nepeta ✿ (*Lamiaceae*)

	from China	EWes
	'Blue Beauty'	see *N. sibirica* 'Souvenir d'André Chaudron'
	'Blue Dragon'	CBod CKel CMea CNor ECtt GBin GPSL GQue GWyn LRHS MAvo MPie MTis NLar NRHS SPad SPoG SRms WCot WFar WHoo
*	***buddlejifolium***	NLar
*	- 'Gold Splash'	NLar
	camphorata	WSpi
	cataria	CBod CCBP CTsd EBou ENfk GJos GPoy MHer MNHC NBro NGrd SRms SVic WMoo WSpi
§	- 'Citriodora'	CBod ENfk SPhx SRms SVic
	'Chettle Blue'	CDor MAvo
	citriodora Dum.	see *N. cataria* 'Citriodora'
	clarkei	CBod GMaP MRav MTis WArt WMoo WSpi
	curviflora	SPhx
	'Dropmore'	CRos EBee GWyn LRHS MTis NLar NRHS WSpi
	'Early Bird'	IPot WCAu WHil
§	× ***faassenii*** ♀H7	Widely available

- 'Alba' EBee ECtt ELan EPfP EWhm LPot LRHS NLar SRms WArt WSpi
- 'Blauknirps' EBee
- 'Blue Wonder' CBod CRos EBee ELan EPfP LRHS MHol MTis NDov NLar NRHS WCAu WFar WSpi
- 'Crystal Cloud' **new** CRos LRHS NRHS
- 'Gletschereis' EBee WCAu
- 'Kit Cat' CRos EBee ECtt EPfP GBin GWyn LRHS LSRN MAsh MBel MHol MTis NGrd NRHS SWvt WCAu WCFE XSen
- 'Purrsian Blue'PBR CBod MHol MTis NCou SPoG
- 'Senior' XLum

glechoma 'Variegata' see *Glechoma hederacea* 'Variegata'
govaniana Widely available
grandiflora CDor MRav NBre
- 'Blue Danube' EBee GBin GWyn MTis NCGa XLum
- 'Blue Elf' NDov
- 'Bramdean' ♀H6 CCBP CDor CMea CRos CSde EBee ECtt EPfP EWes GBin GWyn LRHS MCot MRav MTis NRHS SPhx SRms WCAu WCot XLum
- 'Dawn to Dusk' Widely available
- 'Pool Bank' CElw EBee ECtt EWes MAvo MTis NAln XLum
- 'Summer Magic'PBR CBod CRos EBee EMor EPfP GBin LRHS MBel NAst NCGa NLar NRHS SCob SHar SPoG SRkn SWvt WCAu WFar WNPC WTor
- 'Wild Cat' EPfP MTis WCAu
- 'Zinser's Giant' EBee SAko

hederacea 'Variegata' see *Glechoma hederacea* 'Variegata'
'Hill Grounds' CKno ECha LSun MAvo MHol WCot
italica LRHS SHar SPhx
'Joanna Reed' GBin NCGa WSpi
JUNIOR WALKER ('Novanepjun'PBR) CRos EBee GMaP IKil LCro LOPS LRHS LSRN MAsh MBel NDov NRHS SCob SWvt
kubanica CRos CSpe EBee IKil IMou LRHS MBel MRav NLar NRHS SPhx SPtp WArt WCAu WCot WSHC
'Lamendi' NDov
latifolia 'Super Cat' EBee ELan EPfP
§ 'Leeds Castle' CBod CSam EBee ECtt LRHS MTis NAln NGdn NRHS NSti SHar SPer SPoG WCAu WHal
'Limelight' MHer NLar
longipes hort. see *N.* 'Leeds Castle'
macrantha see *N. sibirica*
manchuriensis 'Manchu Blue' EBee
'Maurice' WGoo
mussinii misapplied see *N.* × *faassenii*
mussinii Spreng. see *N. racemosa*
nervosa CDor CSpe EAJP ECha ELan EPfP NBro NLar NSti SHar SPer
- 'Blue Carpet' CSpe NEgg
- 'Blue Moon' CRos EBee EPfP EWes LRHS MBNS MHol MMrt MPie NDov NLar NQui NRHS SRms WFar WSpi
- 'Forncett Select' CSam MRav NBre
- 'Pink Cat' CMea CRos EPfP LPot LRHS NLar NRHS WFar
- 'Schneehäschen' SAko WSpi

§ ***nuda*** CBod CFis ECha EWes LPla MAvo MRav SHar SMHy WGoo
- 'Accent' EBee
- subsp. ***albiflora*** ECha
* - 'Grandiflora' NBre WMoo
- 'Lake Sevan' **new** LEdu
- 'Purple Cat' EBee EPfP LLHF NDov
- 'Romany Dusk' ECha LEdu LPla
- 'Snow Cat' SPhx

pannonica see *N. nuda*
parnassica EMor EPPr EWTr GLog GQue MAvo MBel MCot MHol MMuc MTis NAln WArt WMoo WPtf
phyllochlamys CPBP
'Pink Candy' SPhx SRms
'Poseidon' MAvo
§ ***prattii*** NLar SEND
'Purple Haze'PBR CBod EBee ECtt MHol NLar NRHS
§ ***racemosa*** ♀H7 CHby CMac CRos EBou EPfP EWhm GJos GWyn LRHS MCot MNHC SCob WMoo
- RCB AM 3 WCot
- ***alba*** CBod CDor XLum
- 'Amelia' CBod EBee EPfP MAvo MHer WAvo WCAu WGoo WTor
- 'Felix' **new** WFar
- 'Grog' EWTr GBin GWyn LRHS MAvo MTis NAst NCGa NLar SPoG
- 'Little Titch' CBod EBee ECha ECtt EPfP GWyn LRHS LSRN MAsh MCot NGdn NLar SCob WHoo
- 'Senior' CBod MHol
- 'Snowflake' CBcs CMea CRos ECtt ELan EPfP EShb GMaP GQue GWyn LRHS MTis NBir NRHS SCob SPer SPoG SWvt WAvo WCAu WSpi WTor
- 'Superba' NBre XSen
- 'Toria' IMou MAvo MTis NDov
- 'Walker's Low' ♀H7 Widely available

* 'Rae Crug' ECtt EWes
reichenbachiana see *N. racemosa*
§ ***sibirica*** CRos ECha ELan EPfP LRHS MMuc NBid NBro NLar NRHS SRkn WArt WCAu WCot XLum
§ - 'Souvenir d'André Chaudron' ♀H6 CAby CDor CRos CSam CWCL EBee EHrv ELan EPfP GCal GMaP GWyn IPot LRHS MBel MCot MHer MRav MTis NAln NLar NRHS SCob SPer SPoG WCAu WHil WSpi
'Six Hills Giant' Widely available
'Six Hills Gold' CDor EBee LBuc MAsh SCob WCAu WSpi WTor
stewartiana LLHF MRav WMoo
subsessilis CAby CBod CRos ECtt EHrv ELan EMor EPfP GLog GMaP IKil LRHS MBel MCot MRav NBid NBir NGdn NLar NRHS NSti SCob SPhx SPoG SRms WCAu WCru
- 'Blue Dreams' ELon EMor GQue GWyn MHol NLar SCob SHar SPhx SRkn WArt WSpi XLum
- 'Candy Cat' ELan MCot MTis NBre NLar
- 'Cool Cat' EBee ELan EPfP LSRN NBre NLar
- 'Laufen' IPot
- NIMBUS ('Yanim') MHol MPnt
- 'Pink Dreams' CBod EAJP EBee ELan EMor EPfP GBee GWyn LRHS MHer SCob XLum
- pink-flowered ECha EPPr SPhx
- 'Sweet Dreams' EMor EPfP EShb LRHS MRav MTis NLar NRHS NSti XLum
- 'Washfield' MTis NLar SAko

transcaucasica	SPhx
- 'Blue Infinity'	NGrd WMoo
tuberosa	CDor CPla ECha EMor EPPr WCot WMoo XSen
'Veluws Blauwtje'	ECha NLar WSpi
'Veluwse Wakel'	IMou
'Weinheim Big Blue'	MAvo NCGa
'Weinheim Summer Blues' new	ECha
wilsonii	GBin
yunnanensis	EBee EPPr IPot MPie SPhx WPGP

Nephrolepis (*Lomariopsidaceae*)

cordifolia	CBdn
duffii	EShb
exaltata ♀H1b	LCro LOPS
- 'Bostoniensis'	EShb
- 'Smithii'	EShb
- 'Verona'	WCot

Nerine ✿ (*Amaryllidaceae*)

	'Afterglow'	LAma LRHS WCot
	'Alexandra'	WCot
	alta	see *N. undulata* Alta Group
	angustifolia	SPtp WAbe
	'Aurora'	WCot
	'Baghdad'	SChr WCot
	'Belladonna'	WCot
	'Bennett-Poë'	WCot
	'Berlioz'	WCot
	'Blanchefleur'	WCot
	bowdenii ♀H5	Widely available
	- 'Alba' misapplied	see *N. bowdenii* 'Pallida'
	- 'Alba' ambig.	CPrp CTca EBee ELan EPot ERCP SCoo SMHy
	- 'Alba'	CAby CBro CWCL ECha EMor GKev IBal LAma LRHS MNrw NHoy SCob SDeJ WCot WFar
	- 'Albivetta'	EBee ELon GKev IBal LAma MNrw NHoy
	- 'Blanca Perla'	ELan EShb GKev LAma MNrw NHoy
	- 'Castlewellan'	IBlr
	- 'Codora'	see *N.* 'Codora'
	- 'Edelweiss' new	NHoy
	- 'Ella K'	EPfP EPot GKev IBal LAma LCro LOPS MNrw NHoy SPer WFar
	- 'Eric Smith'	WCot
	- 'Gletsjer'	NHoy WCot
	- Irish clone	WCot
	- 'Isabel'	CAby CBro CMac ECha ELan EPot ERCP EWTr EWes GBin GKev IBal LAma NHoy SDeJ WBor WCot WHil WHoo
	- 'Kathleen Pollock'	WCot
	- 'Linda Vista'	WCot
	- 'Lipstick' new	NHoy
	- 'Marjorie'	EMal LRHS NRHS
	- 'Mark Fenwick'	CBro WCot
	- 'Marney Rogerson'	CBro SMHy WCot
§	- 'Mollie Cowie' (v)	GCal IBlr WCot WCru
	- 'Mount Stewart'	IBlr WCot
	- 'Nikita'	ERCP GKev IBal LAma LRHS MNrw NHoy SCob SDeJ WCot
	- 'Ostara'	CBod ELan EPot GKev IBal LAma LCro LOPS LRHS MNrw NHoy WCot WFar
§	- 'Pallida'	LRHS
	- 'Patricia'	EPot GKev IBal LAma LRHS MNrw NHoy
	- 'Pink Surprise'	CAvo WCot
	- 'Pink Waveline'	SMHy
§	- 'Quinton Wells'	CAby CTca WCot
	- 'Richard Blakeway-Phillips'	WCot
	- 'Robert Smith'	WCot
	- 'Rowie'	LRHS
	- 'Sheila Owen'	WCot
	- 'Stam 63'	EPot ERCP GKev IBal LAma LRHS
	- 'Stefanie'	CAby ELan EMor EShb EWTr GKev IBal LAma NHoy SDeJ
	- Ted Allen No 2	WCot
	- 'Variegata'	see *N. bowdenii* 'Mollie Cowie'
	- 'Vesta K'	EPot GKev IBal LAma LRHS NHoy
	- 'Wellsii'	see *N. bowdenii* 'Quinton Wells'
	bowdenii* × *sarniensis	WFar
	'Canasta'	WCot
	'Caryatid'	WCot WFar
	'Catherine'	WCot
	'Catkin'	WCot
	'Clent Charm'	WCot
§	'Codora'	CCCN EPfP SPer WCot WFar
	'Corlette'	WCot
	corusca 'Major'	see *N. sarniensis* var. *corusca*
	'Countess of Mulgrave'	WCot
	'Cranfield'	WCot
	crispa	see *N. undulata* Crispa Group
	'Cynthia Chance'	WCot
	'Diana Oliver'	WCot
	'Doris Vos'	WCot
	Elegance Series	CBro LRHS NHoy WCot
	- 'Elegance Red'	ELan
	'Elspeth'	WCot
	'Exbury Red'	WCot
	'Falaise'	WCot
	filamentosa misapplied	see *N. filifolia* Baker
	filamentosa ambig.	CBro
§	***filifolia*** Baker	CSpe GKev WAbe
	'Firelight'	WCot
	flexuosa	see *N. undulata* Flexuosa Group
	gaberonensis	WAbe
	'Giraffe'	WCot
	'Glacier'	EBee LRHS MNrw
	gracilis	WCot
	'Harlequin'	WCot
	'Helena'	WCot
	'Hera'	CBro ELon
	'Hertha Berg'	WCot
*	***hirsuta***	GKev WCot
	humilis ♀H2	CBro
	- from Bredasdorp, South Africa	WCot
	'Iman'	WCot
	'Isobel'	CSpe LEdu LRHS WFar XEll
	'Janet'	WCot
	'Jenny Wren'	SChr WCot
	'King Leopold'	WCot WFar
	'King of the Belgians'	LAma LRHS
	'Kinn McIntosh'	WCot
	krigei	WCot XEll
	'Kyle'	WCot
	'Lady Cynthia Colville'	WCot
	'Lady Downe'	WCot
	'Lady Eleanor Keane'	WCot
	'Lady Havelock-Allen'	WCot
	'Lady Llewellyn'	WCot
	'Lady St Aldwyn'	WCot
	'Lambourne'	WCot
	laticoma	WCot
	'Lawlord'	WCot

'Leila Hughes' WCot
'Long Island Beauty' WCot
'Lucinda' WCot
'Lyndhurst Salmon' WCot
'Malvern' WCot
'Maria' WCot
masoniorum ♀H2 GKev SBch WAbe
'Meadowbankii' WCot
'Miss E. Cator' WCot
'Miss Florence Brown' WCot
'Miss Frances Clarke' WCot
'Mr John' CBro EBee ELan ERCP GKev LAma LRHS NHoy WCot XEll
'Mrs Cooper' WCot
'Mrs Dent Brocklehurst' WCot
'Natasha' WCot
'Nena' WCot
'November Cheer' LAma
'Oberon' WCot
'Ophelia' WCot
'Owslebury' WCot
'Pamela' LRHS
'Pink Triumph' CBcs CMac CTsd EBee ELan EPot ERCP EShb GKev IBal LAma LRHS NHoy NRHS SDeJ SPer WCot WHoo
'Plymouth' SChr
pudica pink-flowered WCot
'Quivotina' WCot
'Red Pimpernel' LAma NHoy
'Regina' WCot
'Rembrandt' WCot
'Rose Princess' WCot
'Rushmere Star' SChr WCot
'Ruth' WCot WFar
sarniensis CBro ECha EPot GKev LRHS SDeJ WCot WFar
* - 'Alba' NHoy
* - 'Borde Hill White' WCot
§ - var. ***corusca*** LAma
- - 'Major' MPie SChr WCot
- var. ***curvifolia*** CBro
- - f. ***fothergillii*** WCot
- 'Hanley Castle' WCot
- 'Lydia' **new** NHoy
- 'Mother of Pearl' WCot
- 'Mottistone' WCot
- red-flowered **new** NHoy
- rose-pink-flowered **new** NHoy
- 'Salmon Star' LRHS
- var. ***sarniensis*** CBor
'Snowflake' WCot
'Stephanie' CCCN CTca ELon EShb LAma LEdu LRHS MNrw WCot WHoo
'Susan Norris' WCot
'Tweedledee' WCot
undulata CAby CCCN CTca ECha EHrv EPot GCal GKev IBal LAma MPie NHoy SDeJ SPer
§ - Alta Group WCot
§ - Crispa Group CBod EPfP WFar
§ - Flexuosa Group MRav
- - 'Alba' ♀H3 CAby CAvo CBro CRos CTca ECha EWTr GKev MRav WCot
× ***versicolor*** 'Mansellii' CBro
'Vicky' WCot
'Virgo' LAma
'Winter Sun' LRHS SRms
'Zeal Giant' ♀H3 CAvo CBro GCal WCot
'Zeal Grilse' WCot
'Zeal Purple Stripe' WCot
'Zennor' WCot

Nerium (*Apocynaceae*)

§ ***odoratum*** 'Miss Agnes Campbell' SEND
oleander misapplied see *N. oleander* 'Soeur Agnès'
oleander L. CAbb CBcs CHll CTri EBak ELan EShb SEND SPer SPlb SPoG
- from Morocco **new** WPGP
- 'Agnes Campbell' see *N. odoratum* 'Miss Agnes Campbell'
- 'Album' CTri EShb LRHS SEND
- 'Album Maximum' CCCN
- 'Album Plenum' (d) XSen
- 'Alsace' SEND
* - 'Atlas' XSen
* - 'Barcelona' SEND
- 'Cavalaire' (d) XSen
* - 'Claudia' SEND
- 'Commandant Barthélemy' (d) XSen
- double apricot (d) SEND
- 'Flavescens Plenum' (d) EShb XSen
- 'Hardy Red' XSen
- 'Isle of Capri' CCCN
- 'Italia' XSen
- 'Jannoch' XSen
- 'Louis Pouget' (d) XSen
- 'Madame Allen' (d) EShb
- 'Magaly' SEND
- 'Margaritha' SEND XSen
* - 'Maurin des Maures' CCCN
- 'Minouche' SEND
- 'Petite Red' XSen
- 'Professeur Granel' (d) EShb XSen
- 'Provence' (d) XSen
- 'Red Beauty' XSen
- 'Roseum Plenum' (d) SEND
§ - 'Soeur Agnès' CAco XSen
- 'Soleil Levant' ELan XSen
- 'Splendens Giganteum' (d) EShb
- 'Tito Poggi' XSen
- 'Variegatum' (v) ♀H2 CHll ELan EShb
- 'Villa Romaine' XSen
- white-flowered ELan

Neviusia (*Rosaceae*)

alabamensis NLar

Nicandra (*Solanaceae*)

physalodes CHby ELan ENfk NBir SEle WSFF
- 'Splash of Cream' (v) CCCN MNHC
- 'Violacea' CSpe GLog SRms SWvt

Nicotiana ✿ (*Solanaceae*)

alata CSpe GDun WSFF
- 'Grandiflora' CBre LCro LOPS
excelsior GDun
glauca CCCN CDTJ CHll GDun SPlb
glutinosa GDun
'Hopleys' CSpe
knightiana CDTJ CSpe GDun
langsdorffii ♀H2 CSpe GDun SPhx
- 'Hot Chocolate' CSpe
'Lime Green' ♀H2 CSpe LCro LOPS
maritima GDun
mutabilis CBre CCBP CSpe GDun LCro LOPS SDys SPhx
- 'Marshmallow' CBod

'Perfume Deep Purple' (Perfume Series) — CSpe SPhx
quadrivalvis — GDun
rustica — GDun SPhx
× ***sanderae*** Cuba Series — NPri
solanifolia — GDun SPlb
suaveolens — GDun LCro LOPS SPhx
sylvestris ♀H2 — CBod CDTJ CSpe ELan EPfP GDun LCro LOPS MMuc NPri SDys SEND SPhx SPoG SWvt WHil
tabacum — GDun
'Tinkerbell' — CSpe

Nidularium (*Bromeliaceae*)

innocentii — XBlo

Nierembergia (*Solanaceae*)

frutescens — see *N. scoparia*
§ ***repens*** — NLar WCot XLum
rivularis — see *N. repens*
§ ***scoparia*** — CSpe

Nigella (*Ranunculaceae*)

damascena 'Albion Green Pod' — LCro
- 'Miss Jekyll' ♀H7 — LCro LOPS LRHS MNHC SPhx
- 'Miss Jekyll Alba' ♀H7 — CSpe
- 'Oxford Blue' — LCro LOPS
- Persian Jewels Group — SVic
hispanica L. — SPhx
papillosa 'African Bride' — CSpe MNHC SPhx
- 'Delft Blue' — LCro
- 'Midnight' — CSpe SPhx

Nigritella see *Gymnadenia*

Niphidium (*Polypodiaceae*)

crassifolium — EShb WCot

Nipponanthemum (*Asteraceae*)

§ ***nipponicum*** — CBod EBee ELon GBin GCal GWyn IMou LRHS MMuc NLar NSti SAko SPoG SRms WHil XLum
- 'Hama-giku' — NWad

Noccaea see *Thlaspi*

Nolina (*Asparagaceae*)

bigelovii — WCot
lindheimeriana — WCot
microcarpa — XSen
nelsonii — CCht SArc SPlb XSen
parviflora — XSen
texana — WCot

Nomocharis (*Liliaceae*)

aperta — CExl EHrv GCal GGGa GKev LAma NHpl WCru
- ACE 2271 — EHrv
- CLD 229 — EHrv
mairei — see *N. pardanthina*
meleagrina — GEdr NHpl
§ ***pardanthina*** — EBee NHpl
- f. ***punctulata*** — GGGa
saluenensis — GGGa

Nonea (*Boraginaceae*)

lutea — EPPr NSti WHal

Nothochelone see *Penstemon*

Nothofagus ✿ (*Nothofagaceae*)

sp. — LPra
§ ***alpina*** — WPav
antarctica — CBcs CDul CMCN CNWT CTho EBee ELan EPfP EWTr GKin LMaj LPra MBlu MGos MMuc NOra NWea SAko WMat
betuloides — GBin IArd SAko SPlb WPGP
cunninghamii — CBcs CBrP IArd IDee SAko SPlb
dombeyi ♀H5 — CBcs EPfP GBin IArd IDee MBlu SArc WPGP WSpi
fusca — SAko WPGP
menziesii — WPGP
moorei — WPGP
nervosa — see *N. alpina*
nitida — CBcs
obliqua — GAbr SPlb WMou WPav
procera Oerst. — see *N. alpina*

Notholaena see *Cheilanthes*

Notholirion (*Liliaceae*)

bulbuliferum — EBee GBin
campanulatum — EBee
macrophyllum — EBee GBin
thomsonianum — CBor GKev

Nothoscordum (*Alliaceae*)

bivalve — IMou
dialystemon — EPot LLHF NHpl WAbe
montevidense — WCot
neriniflorum — see *Allium neriniflorum*
ostenii — WCot

Nothotsuga (*Pinaceae*)

longibracteata **new** — SPtp

Nuphar (*Nymphaeaceae*)

japonica — LLWG
lutea — CBen CHab LCro LLWG LOPS
- subsp. ***advena*** — LLWG
pumila — LLWG

Nuytsia (*Loranthaceae*)

floribunda — SPlb

Nylandtia (*Polygalaceae*)

spinosa — SPlb

Nymphaea ✿ (*Nymphaeaceae*)

alba (H) — CBen CHab CWat LCro LOPS MWts NBir SVic WCAu WMAq
'Alba Plenissima' (H) — EWat
'Albatros' misapplied — see *N.* 'Hermine'
§ 'Albatros' Latour-Marliac (H) — CWat LLWG NPer WMAq XBlo
'Albatross' — see *N.* 'Albatros' Latour-Marliac, *N.* 'Hermine'
* 'Albida' — LLWG WMAq XBlo
'Almost Black' (H) — CBen EWat LCro LLWG LOPS
'Amabilis' (H) — CBen EWat WMAq
'Andreana' (H) — EWat LLWG
'Angelique' (H) **new** — LLWG
'Anna Epple' (H) — LLWG
'Arc-en-ciel' (H) — CBen EWat LLWG WMAq
'Atropurpurea' (H) — CBen EWat LLWG NPer WMAq
'Attorney Elrod' (H) **new** — LLWG
'Attraction' (H) — CBen EWat LLWG MWts NPer SVic WMAq XBlo XLum
'Augustus McCray' (H) — LLWG

	'Aurora' (H)	LCro LLWG LOPS MWts SVic WMAq
	'Barbara Davies' (H)	EWat LLWG
	'Barbara Dobbins' (H)	CBen EWat LCro LLWG LOPS
	'Bateau' (H)	CBen LLWG
	'Bernice Ikins' (H)	LLWG
	'Betsy Sakata' (H)	EWat LLWG
	'Black Cherry' (H)	LLWG
	'Black Princess' (H)	CBen EWat LLWG
	'Bua Rapee' (H) **new**	LLWG
	'Burgundy Princess' (H)	CWat EWat LLWG NPer
	candida (H)	CBen MWts NPer WMAq
	'Candidissima' (H)	CBen MWts
§	***capensis*** (T/D)	XBlo
	'Carolina Sunset' (H)	EWat LLWG
	'Caroliniana Nivea' (H)	CBen
	'Caroliniana Perfecta' (H)	CBen
	'Celebration' (H)	EWat LLWG
	'Charlene Strawn' (H)	EWat LLWG WMAq
	'Charles de Meurville' (H)	CBen LCro LLWG LOPS NPer SVic WMAq
	'Chompoo Pairat' (H) **new**	LLWG
	'Château le Rouge' (H)	CBen LLWG
	'Chubby' (H)	LLWG
	'Citrus Twist' (H) **new**	LLWG
	'Cliff Tiffany' (H)	CBen
	'Clyde Ikins' (H)	EWat LLWG XBlo
	'Colonel A.J. Welch' (H)	CBen NPer WMAq
	'Colorado' (H)	CBen EWat LLWG NPer
	colorata	see *N. capensis*
	'Colossea' (H)	CBen CWat NPer
	'Comanche' (H)	CBen EWat LLWG NPer WMAq
	'Conqueror' (H)	CBen LLWG NPer SVic
	'Crazy Pom Pom' (H) **new**	LLWG
	'Cynthia Ann' (H)	LLWG
	'Dallas' (H)	LLWG
§	'Darwin' (H)	CBen CWat LLWG MWts NPer SLon WMAq
	'David' (H)	CBen EWat LLWG
	'Debbie June' (H)	LLWG
	'Denver' (H)	EWat LLWG
	'Ellisiana' (H)	LLWG NPer
	'Escarboucle' (H) ♀H5	CBen CWat EWat LLWG NPer SVic WMAq XBlo
§	'Fabiola' (H)	LLWG NPer WMAq
	'Fiesta' (H)	CBen
	'Fire Cracker' (H) **new**	LLWG
	'Fire Crest' (H)	CBen LLWG NPer SVic WMAq
	'Florida Sunset' (H)	EWat
	'Fritz Junge' (H)	CBen
	'Froebelii' (H)	CBen CWat EWat NPer WMAq
	'Fuchsia Pom-pom' (H)	LLWG
	'Fulva' (H)	LLWG
	'Galatée' (H)	CBen
	'Georgia Peach' (H)	LLWG
	'Gladstoniana' (H) ♀H5	CBen MWts NPer WMAq
	'Gloire du Temple-sur-Lot' (H)	CBen EWat LLWG NPer WMAq
	'Gloriosa' (H)	CBen LLWG NPer
	'Gold Medal' (H)	CBen EWat LLWG
	'Gonnère' (H) ♀H5	CBen CWat EWat LLWG MWts NPer SLon WMAq
	'Graziella' (H)	WMAq
	'Gypsy' (H)	EWat LLWG
	'Hal Miller' (H)	LLWG
	'Hassell' (H)	LLWG
	'Hazorea Dagan White' (H)	EWat LLWG
	'Helen Fowler' (H)	WMAq
	'Helen Hariot' (H)	LLWG
	× ***helvola***	see *N.* 'Pygmaea Helvola'
§	'Hermine' (H)	CBen NPer WMAq
	'Hidden Violet' (H)	LLWG
§	'Highlight' (H)	EWat LLWG
	'Hilite'	see *N.* 'Highlight'
	'Hollandia' misapplied	see *N.* 'Darwin'
	'Indiana' (H)	CBen LLWG NPer WMAq
	'Inner Light' (H)	EWat LLWG
	'Irene Heritage' (H)	CBen
	'J.C.N. Forestier' (H)	CBen
	'James Brydon' (H) ♀H5	CBen CWat EWat LLWG MWts NPer SLon SVic WMAq
	'Jean de Lamarsalle' (H)	LLWG
	'Jerusalem Dawn' (H)	LLWG
§	'Joanne Pring' (H)	CBen
	'Joey Tomocik' (H)	CBen CWat EWat LLWG WMAq
	'Lactea' (H)	CBen LLWG
	'Laura Strawn' (H)	EWat
	'Laydekeri Fulgens' (H)	CBen EWat LLWG MWts WMAq
	'Laydekeri Lilacea' (H)	CBen LLWG WMAq
	'Laydekeri Rosea' misapplied	see *N.* 'Laydekeri Rosea Prolifera'
§	'Laydekeri Rosea Prolifera' (H)	CBen EWat
	'Lemon Meringue' (H)	LLWG
	'Lemon Mist' (H)	LLWG
	'Lily Pons' (H)	CBen EWat LLWG
	'Liou' (H)	CBen LLWG
	'Little Champion' (H) **new**	LLWG
	'Little Sue' (H)	EWat LLWG
	'Livingstone' (H)	LLWG
	'Lucida' (H)	CBen LLWG WMAq
	'Lucky Red' (H) **new**	LLWG
	'Madame Bory Latour-Marliac' (H)	CBen
	'Madame Wilfon Gonnère' (H)	CBen CWat EWat LLWG MWts NPer SVic WMAq
	'Manee Siam' (H) **new**	LLWG
	'Mangkala Ubol' (H)	CBen
	'Marliacea Albida' (H)	CBen CWat EWat LCro LLWG LOPS MWts NPer WMAq XBlo XLum
	'Marliacea Carnea' (H)	CBen LCro LOPS MWts NPer WMAq
§	'Marliacea Chromatella' (H) ♀H5	CBen CWat EWat MWts SVic WMAq XBlo XLum
	'Marliacea Rosea' (H)	CBen WMAq XBlo XLum
	'Martha' (H)	EWat
	'Mary' (H)	EWat LLWG
	'Masaniello' (H)	CBen WMAq
	'Maurice Laydeker' (H)	CBen LLWG
	'Maxima'	see *N.* 'Odorata Maxima'
	'Mayla' (H)	CBen EWat LLWG NPer
§	'Météor' (H)	CBen EWat WMAq
	mexicana (H)	LLWG
	'Miss Siam' (H) **new**	LLWG
	'Moon Dance' (H)	LLWG
	'Moorei' (H)	CBen MWts WMAq
	'Mrs Richmond' misapplied	see *N.* 'Fabiola'
	'Mrs Richmond' Latour-Marliac (H)	CBen XBlo
	'Munkala Ubon' (H)	LLWG
	'Murillo' (H)	EWat
	'Neptune' (H)	LLWG
	'Newchapel Beauty'	WMAq
	'Newton' (H)	CBen CWat LLWG WMAq
	'Nigel' (H)	EWat LLWG
	'Norma Gedye' (H)	CBen CWat WMAq
§	***odorata*** (H)	CBen LLWG WMAq
§	- var. ***minor*** (H)	CBen EWat WMAq
	- 'Pumila'	see *N. odorata* var. *minor*
	- subsp. ***tuberosa*** (H)	CBen

	'Odorata Alba'	see *N. odorata*
	'Odorata Juliana' (H)	EWat
§	'Odorata Maxima' (H)	WMAq
	'Odorata Sulphurea' (H)	LLWG MWts
	'Odorata Sulphurea Grandiflora' (H)	LLWG XBlo
	'Odorata William B. Shaw'	see *N.* 'W.B. Shaw'
	'Panama Pacific' (T/D)	XBlo
	'Patio Joe' (H)	EWat LLWG
	'Paul Hariot' (H)	EWat LLWG NPer WMAq
	'Peace Lily' (H)	EWat LLWG
	'Peach Glow' (H)	EWat LLWG
	'Peaches and Cream' (H)	EWat LLWG
	'Perry's Baby Red' (H)	CBen CWat EWat LLWG MWts NPer WMAq
	'Perry's Double White' (H)	EWat LLWG NPer
	'Perry's Double Yellow' (H)	LLWG
	'Perry's Dwarf Red' (H)	LLWG
	'Perry's Fire Opal' (H)	EWat LLWG NPer
	'Perry's Orange Sunset' (H)	LLWG
	'Perry's Pink' (H)	WMAq
	'Perry's Red Bicolor' (H)	LLWG
	'Perry's Red Glow' (H)	LLWG
	'Perry's Red Star' (H)	EWat
	'Perry's White Star' (H)	LLWG
	'Perry's Yellow Sensation'	see *N.* 'Yellow Sensation'
	'Peter Slocum' (H)	CBen EWat
	'Phoebus' (H)	CBen
	'Picciola' (H)	LLWG
	'Pink Beauty' (H)	LLWG
	'Pink Grapefruit' (H)	LLWG XBlo
	'Pink Lemonade' (H) **new**	LLWG
	'Pink Opal' (H)	EWat LLWG
	'Pink Peony' (H)	EWat
	'Pink Pom-pom' (H)	LLWG
	'Pink Pumpkin' (H)	EWat LLWG
	'Pink Ribbon' (H) **new**	LLWG
	'Pink Sensation' (H)	CBen EWat LLWG NPer SLon WMAq
	'Pink Sparkle' (H)	EWat LLWG
	'Pink Starlet' (H)	EWat
	'Pink Sunrise' (H)	EWat LLWG
	'Pink Tulip' (H) **new**	LLWG
	'Pinwaree' (H)	LLWG
	'Pöstlingberg' (H)	LLWG
	'Prakeisap' (H) **new**	LLWG
	'Princess Elizabeth' (H)	LLWG SVic
	'Purple Fantasy' (H)	LLWG
	'Pygmaea Alba'	see *N. tetragona*
§	'Pygmaea Helvola' (H) ♀H5	CBen CWat EWat LCro LLWG LOPS MWts NPer SLon SVic WMAq
	'Pygmaea Rubis' (H)	WMAq
	'Pygmaea Rubra' (H)	CBen CWat EWat LCro LLWG LOPS MWts NPer SVic WMAq
	'Queen of the Whites' (H)	LLWG
	'Radiant Red' (H)	LLWG
	'Ray Davies' (H)	CBen LLWG
	'Razzberry' (H)	LLWG
	'Red Paradise' (H)	LLWG
	'Red Queen' (H) **new**	LLWG
	'Red Spider' (H)	CWat EWat LLWG NPer SVic
	'Reflected Flame' (H)	EWat LLWG
	'Rembrandt' misapplied	see *N.* 'Météor'
	'René Gérard' (H)	CBen LLWG MWts NPer WMAq
	'Rosanna Supreme' (H)	LLWG
	'Rose Arey' (H)	CBen EWat LCro LOPS NPer WMAq
	'Rose Magnolia' (H)	CWat
	'Rosennymphe' (H)	CBen NPer WMAq
	'Rosy Morn' (H)	CBen LLWG
	'Savanlamp' (H) **new**	LLWG
	'Seignoureti' (H)	LLWG
	'Shady Lady' (H)	LLWG
	'Siam Angel' (H) **new**	LLWG
	'Siam Jasmine' (H) **new**	LLWG
	'Siam Purple 1' (H)	LLWG
	'Siam Purple 2' (H)	LLWG
	'Siam Sunset' **new**	LLWG
	'Sioux' (H)	CBen LLWG NPer SVic WMAq XBlo
	'Sirius' (H)	CBen LLWG
	'Snow Princess' (H)	EWat
	'Snowflake' (H)	LLWG
	'Solfatare' (H)	EWat LLWG
	'Splendida' (H)	WMAq
	'Starbright' (H)	EWat LLWG
	'Starburst' (H)	LLWG
	'Steven Strawn' (H)	LLWG
	'Sunny Pink' (H)	CBen EWat LLWG
	'Superba' (H)	CBen
	'Sweet Pea' (H) **new**	LLWG
	'Tan-khwan' (H)	LLWG
§	***tetragona*** (H)	CWat EWat LCro LLWG LOPS NPer WMAq
	– 'Alba'	see *N. tetragona*
	– 'Johann Pring'	see *N.* 'Joanne Pring'
	'Texas Dawn' (H)	CBen CWat LLWG SLon WMAq XBlo
	'Thomas O'Brian' (H)	LLWG
	'Thongsup' (H) **new**	LLWG
	'Tuberosa Flavescens'	see *N.* 'Marliacea Chromatella'
	'Tuberosa Richardsonii' (H)	CBen NPer
	'Venusta' (H)	EWat
	'Vésuve' (H)	LLWG
	'Virginalis' (H)	CBen LLWG NPer WMAq
	'Virginia' (H)	LLWG
§	'W.B. Shaw' (H)	CBen NPer WMAq
	'Walter Pagels' (H)	EWat LLWG MWts WMAq
	'Wanvisa' (H)	CBen LCro LLWG LOPS
	'Weymouth Red' (H)	CBen
	'White Star' (H)	LLWG
	'White Sultan' (H)	CWat LCro LLWG LOPS
	'William Falconer' (H)	CBen LLWG NPer
	'Yellow Princess' (H)	EWat
	'Yellow Queen' (H)	LLWG
§	'Yellow Sensation' (H)	CBen
	'Yellow Watermelon' (H) **new**	LLWG
	'Yul Ling' (H)	EWat LLWG
	'Ziyu' (H)	EWat

Nymphoides (*Menyanthaceae*)

indica	XBlo
peltata	CBen CBod CHab CWat EWat LCro LLWG LOPS NPer SVic WMAq WPnP XLum

Nyssa ✿ (*Nyssaceae*)

sp.	LPra
aquatica	CBcs IDee MBlu SSta
leptophylla	NLar SBir WPGP
shweliensis FMWJ 13122	WCru
sinensis	CBcs CDul CMCN CRos CTho ELan EPfP IDee LRHS MAsh MBlu MPkF NLar SBir SPer WFar
– 'Inferno'	CDul CTho EBee NLar NWea SPoG
– 'Jim Russell' ♀H5	LRHS NLar SBir WPGP
– Nymans form	SBir
sylvatica	Widely available
– 'Autumn Cascades'	CJun CRos EPfP LRHS MAsh MBlu SBir SSta

	- var. ***biflora***	SSta
	- Bulk's form	SSta
	- 'Haymen's Red'	see *N. sylvatica* RED RAGE
	- 'Isabel Grace'	CRos EPfP LRHS MAsh SBir
	- 'Jermyns Flame'	CRos EPfP LRHS MAsh NLar SBir
	- JOLLY ('Yiping') (v)	MPkF
	- 'Lakeside Weeper'	CRos EBee LRHS SBir
	- 'Miss Scarlet' (f)	NLar SBir SSta
	- 'Pendula'	SBir
§	- RED RAGE ('Haymanred')	EPfP LRHS MAsh MPkF NLar SBir
	- 'Red Red Wine'	NLar SBir
	- 'Sheffield Park'	MAsh SBir SLim
	- 'Valley Scorcher'	NLar
	- 'Wildfire'	LRHS MPkF NLar SBir SGol
	- 'Windsor'	CRos EPfP LRHS MAsh NLar SBir
	- 'Wisley Bonfire' (m) ♀H6	CDul CJun CRos ELan EPfP LRHS MAsh NLar NRHS NWea SBir SMad SPoG SSta WPGP

O

Oakesiella see *Uvularia*

Ochagavia (*Bromeliaceae*)

	carnea	WCot
	elegans	WCot
§	***litoralis***	SArc SMad
*	***rosea***	SPlb

Ochna (*Ochnaceae*)

	serrulata	CCCN

Ocimum (*Lamiaceae*)

	'African Blue'	CBod CSpe ENfk EWhm GPoy MHer MHol SPoG SRms
§	× ***africanum***	ENfk MNHC
	- 'Lime'	ENfk MNHC
§	- 'Perpetuo'PBR (v)	ENfk
	- PESTO PERPETUO	see *O.* × *africanum* 'Perpetuo'
	- 'Siam Queen'	MHer SRms
	basilicum	EWhm GPoy LOPS NPri SRms
	- 'Anise'	see *O. basilicum* 'Horapha'
	- 'Ararat'	SRms
	- 'Aristotle'	SRms
I	- 'British Basil'	SRms
	- ***camphorata***	see *O. kilimandscharicum*
	- 'Christmas'	SRms
	- 'Cinnamon'	ENfk MNHC SRms WJek
	- 'Crimson King'PBR	SRms
	- 'Dark Opal'	ENfk SRms
	- 'Genovese'	CLau MHer MNHC
	- 'Glycyrrhiza'	see *O. basilicum* 'Horapha'
	- 'Green Globe'	SRms
	- 'Green Ruffles'	SRms
	- 'Holy'	see *O. tenuiflorum*
§	- 'Horapha'	CLau ENfk MNHC WJek
*	- 'Horapha Nanum'	ENfk SRms
	- 'Lemonade' ♀H1c	SRms
	- 'Magic Mountain'	SPoG
	- 'Magic White'	SPoG
	- 'Medinette' new	CLau
	- 'Mrs Burns' Lemon' ♀H1c	EKin MCtn SRms WJek
	- 'Napoletano'	ENfk LOPS SRms
	- 'Puck'	SRms
	- var. ***purpurascens*** 'Purple Ruffles'	ENfk LCro LOPS LRHS NRHS SRms
	- - 'Red Rubin'	LRHS MHer NRHS SRms WJek
	- var. ***purpurascens*** × ***kilimandscharicum***	CSpe GPoy WJek
	- 'Sweet Genovese'	SVic
	- 'Thai'	see *O. basilicum* 'Horapha'
	× ***citriodorum***	see *O.* × *africanum*
§	***kilimandscharicum***	CLau GPoy
	minimum	ENfk MHer MNHC SRms
	sanctum	see *O. tenuiflorum*
	'Spice'	ENfk
§	***tenuiflorum***	GPoy MNHC SPre WJek

Odontonema (*Acanthaceae*)

	schomburgkianum	CCCN
	tubaeforme	CCCN

Oemleria (*Rosaceae*)

	cerasiformis	CBcs CJun CTri EBtc EPfP LEdu LRHS MGil MMuc WCot WGwG WSHC

Oenanthe (*Apiaceae*)

	fistulosa	LLWG
	javanica	LEdu
	- 'Flamingo' (v)	CBod CWat EBee ELan EWat GCal LEdu LLWG MWts NBro SRms WMAq XLum
	lachenalii	LLWG
	pimpinelloides	CHab LLWG

Oenothera ✿ (*Onagraceae*)

	sp.	MHol
§	***acaulis***	CSpe EBee MNrw WCot
§	- 'Aurea'	XLum
	- 'Lutea'	see *O. acaulis* 'Aurea'
	'Apricot Delight'	SGbt WMoo
§	***biennis***	CFis EBou ELan ENfk GAbr GJos GPoy LCro LOPS MHer MNHC NBro SPhx SRms WBrk WHer WSFF
	'Blood Orange'	CPla GEdr
	caespitosa	NAln
	childsii	see *O. speciosa*
	cinaeus	see *O. fruticosa* subsp. *glauca*
	'Colin Porter'	WMoo
	'Copper Canyon'	EBee
	'Crown Imperial'	CChe CMac MArl NHol SHar SLon
§	***elata*** subsp. ***hookeri***	EWes NBre
	erythrosepala	see *O. glazioviana*
	'Finlay's Fancy'	WCru
§	***fruticosa***	NLar SPlb
	- 'African Sun'PBR	ECtt MMrt SRot
	- 'Camel' (v)	MNrw NEoE XLum
	- FIREWORKS	see *O. fruticosa* 'Fyrverkeri'
§	- 'Fyrverkeri'	CBcs CMea CRos ECtt GMaP GWyn LEdu LRHS MRav NRHS SCob SMad SPer SWvt WArt WCAu XLum
§	- subsp. ***glauca***	CElw CFis ILea MHer SRms
	- - 'Erica Robin' (v)	CChe CDor CRos ECtt EHoe GBin LPla LRHS MNrw MRav NEgg NGdn NRHS SMad SRot SWvt WCot WHoo
	- - 'Longest Day'	MBrN
	- - SOLSTICE	see *O. fruticosa* subsp. *glauca* 'Sonnenwende'
§	- - 'Sonnenwende'	CBre CElw CRos ILea IMou LRHS MMrt NEoE NLar NRHS WMoo XLum
	- HIGHLIGHT	see *O. fruticosa* 'Hoheslicht'
§	- 'Hoheslicht'	EBee NLar
	- 'Lady Brookeborough'	MRav
	- 'Michelle Ploeger'	NBre

	- 'Yellow River'	CElw EBee
	- 'Youngii'	MMuc SEND
	'Give-me-Sunshine'	SLon WMoo
	glabra Miller	see *O. biennis*
§	***glazioviana***	NAln NBir
	hookeri	see *O. elata* subsp. *hookeri*
	kunthiana	EBou ECha NHic WMoo
	- 'Glowing Magenta'	SPoG
	lamarckiana	see *O. glazioviana*
	'Lemon Sunset'	EAJP EHoe WMoo
	linearis	see *O. fruticosa*
§	***macrocarpa*** ♀H5	CBod CHab EBee EBou ECha ELan EPfP EShb LRHS MBel MHer MMuc SEND SPer SPhx SPlb SPoG SRms SRot SVic SWvt WCAu WGwG WHoo WMoo XLum XSen
	- subsp. ***fremontii*** 'Silver Wings'	ELan SPhx
	- subsp. ***incana***	CSpe SPhx WHoo
	- - 'Silver Blade'	LLHF
	missouriensis	see *O. macrocarpa*
	oakesiana	SPhx
	odorata misapplied	see *O. stricta*
	odorata Hook. & Arn.	see *O. biennis*
	odorata Jacquin	XLum
	- cream-flowered	CSpe
	organensis	EBee MNrw
	pallida	CFis
	- 'Innocence'	LCro
§	***perennis***	MPie SRms WThu XLum
	pilosella	IMou
	- 'Mella Yella'	ELan
	- 'Yella Fella'	ELan NWad
	pumila	see *O. perennis*
	rosea	XLum
§	***speciosa***	GCal MMuc SEND SRms XLum
*	- 'Alba'	EBee EWes XSen
	- var. ***childsii***	see *O. speciosa*
	- 'Pink Petticoats'	ECha LSun NHic NPer
	- 'Rosea'	SPlb
	- 'Siskiyou'	CAby CBcs CRos ECtt ELan EPfP ILea LEdu LRHS MHol MNrw NRHS SCob SCoo SMad SPer SPoG WGwG XLum
	- TWILIGHT ('Turner01'PBR) (v)	CAbb EBee ECtt ELan ILea LRHS NEoE NHol NLar SCob SHar
§	***stricta***	CMea GCal MNrw WGwG
	- 'Sulphurea'	CDor CMea EAJP ELan GCal IFro LCro LRHS NPer SPhx
	'Summer Sun'	CBod LRHS NRHS WCAu
	'Sunny Delight'	ECtt MHol
	taraxacifolia	see *O. acaulis*
	tetragona	see *O. fruticosa* subsp. *glauca*
	- var. ***fraseri***	see *O. fruticosa* subsp. *glauca*
	versicolor 'Sunset Boulevard'	CRos CSpe CTsd GCal LRHS MSCN NHic NRHS SPer WMoo XLum

Olea (*Oleaceae*)

	sp.	LPra
	europaea (F)	Widely available
	- 'Arbequina' (F)	EOli
	- 'El Greco' (F)	CBcs
	- 'Fastigiata'	LRHS NPri
	- 'Leccino' (F)	LMaj
	- 'Peace' (F)	CDoy
	- 'Picual' (F)	EOli

Olearia ✿ (*Asteraceae*)

	arborescens 'Moondance' (v)	CBcs CSBt EBee LRHS SCob
	argophylla	CExl
	avicenniifolia	CMac
§	***cheesemanii***	CExl NLar NWad SPer SVen
	- compact	LRHS
	erubescens	LRHS
	erubescens × ***ilicifolia***	SVen
	gunniana	see *O. phlogopappa*
	× ***haastii***	Widely available
§	'Henry Travers'	CCCN CExl EPfP GCal SVen
	ilicifolia	EPfP LRHS
	insignis	see *Pachystegia insignis*
	lacunosa	IDee WHor WPGP
	macrodonta ♀H4	Widely available
	- 'Major'	CCCN EBee NLar SCob
	- 'Minor'	CCCN CKel CMac EBee ELan EPfP GCal SPlb SRms WPGP WSpi
§	× ***matthewsii***	CCoa CKel SPer
	× ***mollis*** misapplied	see *O.* × *matthewsii*
	× ***mollis*** (Kirk) Cockayne	CMac CRos CSde LRHS WKif
	- 'Zennorensis' ♀H4	CBcs CCCN EBee WKif
	myrsinoides	CSde
	nummularifolia	CBcs CCCN CKel CTri CTsd ELan EPfP GBin LRHS NLar SPer SVen SWvt WKif
	× ***oleifolia*** 'Waikariensis'	CCCN CExl CRos LRHS SEND SLon WCFE
	paniculata	CCCN CCoa CRos CSde CTri CTsd EPfP LRHS MMuc SEND SRms SVen
§	***phlogopappa***	CTri SVen
	- 'Comber's Blue'	CBcs CCCN CKel CRos ELan EPfP LRHS MMuc SAko SCob SPer
§	- 'Comber's Pink'	CBcs CCCN CExl CKel CRos ELan EPfP LRHS MAsh MMuc NPer SAko SCob SEle SNig SPer SPoG
	- 'Rosea'	see *O. phlogopappa* 'Comber's Pink'
	ramulosa	CCCN CExl CSde
	- 'Blue Stars'	CMac LRHS SRms
	rani misapplied	see *O. cheesemanii*
	× ***scilloniensis*** misapplied	see *O. stellulata* DC.
	× ***scilloniensis*** ambig.	CBcs CBod CCoa CKel CRos EWld LRHS MAsh MGil SCob SPoG WKif
	× ***scilloniensis*** Dorrien-Smith ♀H4	CCCN MMuc
	- 'Master Michael' ♀H3	CCCN CCht CRos CTri ELon EPfP EWld LRHS NLar SNig SPer SPoG WCFE
	semidentata misapplied	see *O.* 'Henry Travers'
	solandri	CBod CCCN CCoa CMac CSde EPPr IDee LRHS NLar SEND
	- 'Aurea'	CBcs
	'Stardust'	LRHS SPlb SVen
	stellulata misapplied	see *O. phlogopappa*
§	***stellulata*** DC.	CCht CExl CMac CSBt EPfP MAsh SPer
	- 'Michael's Pride'	CExl
	traversii	CBcs CBod CCCN CCoa CRos CSBt CSde CTsd EPfP LRHS SEND WHer
	- 'Compacta'	CCCN
	- dwarf **new**	CBod EBee
	- 'Tweedledee' (v)	SEND
	- 'Tweedledum' (v)	CBod CCCN CCoa CSde WRHF
	- 'Variegata' (v)	CBcs
	virgata	CCCN IDee NLar
	- var. ***laxiflora***	WHer
	- var. ***lineata***	CCht CCoa CSde MMuc NLar SEND WHer
	- - 'Dartonii'	CBcs CBod CRos LRHS NLar SPlb SSta SVen

Oligoneuron see *Solidago*

Oligostachyum (*Poaceae*)

lubricum see *Semiarundinaria lubrica*
§ ***oedogonatum*** MWht

olive see *Olea europaea*

Olsynium (*Iridaceae*)

biflorum GEdr
§ ***douglasii*** ♀H5 CBor CBro EBee ELon EPot GAbr GEdr ITim LLHF NHar NHpl NRHS NRya NSla
- 'Album' CBor EBee ELon EPot EWes LLHF MNrw NHar NRya NSla SBrt WFar
- var. ***inflatum*** EWes
§ ***junceum*** CSpe SPlb WKif
trinerve B&SWJ 10459 WCru

Omphalodes ✿ (*Boraginaceae*)

'Blue Eyes' ELon GEdr MHol WCot
cappadocica ♀H5 CMac EPfP EPot EWld GBin NBro NPer NSla NWad SRms WBrk
- 'Alba' SPoG
- 'Cherry Ingram' ♀H5 Widely available
- 'Lilac Mist' EBee SRms SWvt
- 'Starry Eyes' Widely available
§ ***linifolia*** ♀H3 CSpe ELan GWyn LCro LOPS MCot SPhx
- ***alba*** see *O. linifolia*
luciliae GKev
nitida CSpe EWes EWld GWyn IMou LLHF MMuc MNrw NQui SHar
verna CBod CRos CSpe CTri EBee ECha ELan EPPr EPfP GAbr GEdr GJos GMaP GWyn LRHS MCot MNrw NChi NLar NRHS SCob SPer SPlb SPoG WBor WCAu WFar
- 'Alba' CBre CMac EBee ECha ELan EMor EPPr EPfP GAbr GBin GEdr GMaP MBel MCot MNrw NAln NBid NChi NGdn NLar SCob SPer SRms SWvt WBor WBrk WPnP
- 'Elfenauge' EBee GMaP IMou NBir NLar WCot
I - 'Grandiflora' WCot

Omphalogramma (*Primulaceae*)

delavayi EPot GEdr

Oncostema see *Scilla*

onion see *Allium cepa*; also AGM Vegetables Section

Onixotis (*Colchicaceae*)

stricta see *Wurmbea stricta*

Onobrychis (*Papilionaceae*)

montana SPhx
viciifolia CWld SPhx WArt

Onoclea ✿ (*Onocleaceae*)

sensibilis ♀H6 Widely available
- copper-leaved CJun EBee EPfP EWes WPGP
- 'Rotstiel' EBee

Ononis (*Papilionaceae*)

natrix SPhx
spinosa CDor IMou MHer WSpi

Onopordum (*Asteraceae*)

acanthium CDor CRos ECha ELan ENfk EPfP GAbr GMaP GPoy LRHS LSun MWat NGBl NRHS SHar SPhx WSpi
arabicum see *O. nervosum*
cyprium SPhx
illyricum SPhx
messeniacum WHil
§ ***nervosum*** ♀H7 CSpe SEND
tauricum **new** NAln

Onosma (*Boraginaceae*)

alborosea EBee ECha ECre ELan GCal IMou SEND WKif
echioides GJos
nana EDAr EPot WAbe WOld

Onosmodium (*Boraginaceae*)

molle SBrt

Onychium ✿ (*Pteridaceae*)

contiguum WCot
japonicum CBdn CExl CLAP CRos EBee EFer ISha LEdu LRHS MRav NRHS SPlb WAbe WCot
- 'Dali' CLAP

Ophiopogon ✿ (*Asparagaceae*)

BWJ 8244 from Vietnam WCru
from India GCal
'Black Dragon' see *O. planiscapus* 'Nigrescens'
bodinieri EShb EWes LEdu
- B&L 12505 EBee EPPr
caulescens B&SWJ 8230 WCru
- B&SWJ 11813 WCru
aff. ***caulescens*** B&SWJ 11287 WCru
- HWJ 590 WCru
chingii EBee EPPr EWes GCal IMou LEdu WCot
* - 'Crispum' EBee
clavatus KWJ 12267 WCru
formosanus B&SWJ 3659 WCru
'Gin-ryu' see *Liriope spicata* 'Gin-ryu'
graminifolius see *Liriope muscari*
'Hosoba Kokuryu' CAbb EShb LLHF LRHS NEoE WOut
intermedius EPPr EShb WCot
- GWJ 9387 WCru
§ - 'Argenteomarginatus' (v) EWes
- 'Variegatus' see *O. intermedius* 'Argenteomarginatus'
§ ***jaburan*** CMac EBee EMor LEdu
- 'Variegatus' see *O. jaburan* 'Vittatus'
§ - 'Vittatus' (v) EWes LEdu WCot
japonicus CMac CTsd EBee EShb LEdu LRHS SCob SGol XLum XSen
- B&SWJ 1871 WCru
- 'Compactus' WPGP
- 'Gyoku-Ryu' EBee GCal
- 'Kigimafukiduma' CExl CMac MRav NGdn SGol
- 'Kyoto' EPPr ESwi
- 'Lengteng Giant' LEdu
- 'Minor' CKno EBee ELon EPPr LRHS NLar SCob WPGP XLum
- 'Nanus Variegatus' (v) EBee SMad
- 'Nippon' EHoe EPPr NGdn
- 'Silver Dragon' (v) EPPr WCFE
* - 'Variegatus' (v) CDTJ CMac LEdu SRms
aff. ***latifolius*** KWJ 12031 WCru
malcolmsonii B&SWJ 7271 WCru

parviflorus GWJ 9387 — WCru
– HWJK 2093 — WCru
planiscapus — CCBP CExl CKno CSpe ECha EPPr NBro NWsh SPtp WMoo
* – 'Albovariegatus' (v) — WFar
– 'Black Beard' — CKno EMor EUJe GWyn LRHS MAsh NRHS SHar SPoG WFar
– 'Black Needle' — EBee
– 'Black Smaragd' — EBee
– f. ***leucanthus*** — CDor EPPr WCot
– 'Little Tabby' (v) — CMil EBee EShb ESwi WCot WGrn WHal WHoo WOut WSHC
§ – 'Nigrescens' ♀H5 — Widely available
scaber B&SWJ 1842 — ESwi WCru
– B&SWJ 3655 — WCru
'Spring Gold' — EShb

Ophrys (*Orchidaceae*)

apifera — NLAp
bombyliflora — NLAp
heldreichii — NLAp
holoserica — NLAp
insectifera — NLAp
lutea — NLAp
scolopax — NLAp
subsp. ***heldreichii*** new
speculum — NLAp
tenthredinifera — NLAp

Oplopanax (*Araliaceae*)

horridus B&SWJ 9551 — WCru
japonicus — WCru

Opopanax (*Apiaceae*)

chironium — SBrt SPhx
– PAB 845 — LEdu WPGP
– PAB 872 — WPGP

Opuntia (*Cactaceae*)

angustata — see *O. phaeacantha*
basilaris var. ***cordata*** — SPlb
camanchica — see *O. phaeacantha*
compressa — see *O. humifusa*
elata — SChr
§ ***engelmannii*** — SChr
erinacea var. ***utahensis*** — see *O. polyacantha* var. *erinacea*
§ ***ficus-indica*** — SPlb
fragilis — SPlb XSen
§ ***humifusa*** — CDTJ SChr SPlb XLum XSen
joconostle — see *O. ficus-indica*
lindheimeri — see *O. engelmannii*
linguiformis — see *O. engelmannii*
macrocentra — EUJe
monacantha — SEND
§ ***phaeacantha*** — SChr
– NNS 99-264 — WCot
– var. ***major*** NNS 95-285 — WCot
pollardii — see *O. humifusa*
polyacantha — SChr SPlb
– 'Carmin' — XSen
§ – var. ***erinacea*** — SChr WCot
salmiana — SEND
spinosior — see *Cylindropuntia spinosior*
tardospina — see *O. engelmannii*

orange, sour or Seville see *Citrus* × *aurantium* Sour Orange Group

orange, sweet see *Citrus* × *aurantium* Sweet Orange Group

Orbea (*Apocynaceae*)

§ ***variegata*** ♀H2 — EShb

Orbexilum (*Papilionaceae*)

pedunculatum var. ***psoralioides*** — SBrt

Orchis (*Orchidaceae*)

anthropophora — NLAp
elata — see *Dactylorhiza elata*
foliosa — see *Dactylorhiza foliosa*
fuchsii — see *Dactylorhiza fuchsii*
italica — NLAp
laxiflora — see *Anacamptis laxiflora*
maculata — see *Dactylorhiza maculata*
maderensis — see *Dactylorhiza foliosa*
majalis — see *Dactylorhiza majalis*
§ ***mascula*** — NLAp WHer
militaris — NLAp
morio — see *Anacamptis morio*

oregano see *Origanum vulgare*

Oreocharis (*Gesneriaceae*)

aurea B&SWJ 11718 — WCru

Oreomyrrhis (*Apiaceae*)

argentea — CSpe

Oreopanax ✿ (*Araliaceae*)

dactylifolius — WCot
floribundus — see *O. incisus*
§ ***incisus*** B&SWJ 10669 — WCru
sectifolius — WCru
B&SWJ 14805 new
xalapensis B&SWJ 10444 — WCru

Oreopteris ✿ (*Thelypteridaceae*)

§ ***limbosperma*** — EFer

Oreostemma (*Compositae*)

alpigenum var. ***alpigenum*** — LLHF
– var. ***haydenii*** — LLHF

Origanum ✿ (*Lamiaceae*)

sp. — LCro
from Kalamata, Greece — SEND
acutidens — XSen
amanum ♀H4 — CPBP EWes NBir NRHS NSla WAbe
– var. ***album*** — WAbe
'Amethyst Falls' — CWCL XSen
'Barbara Tingey' — EPot EWes SIgm SRms WAbe WCFE
'Bristol Cross' — ECtt EPPr LEdu MAsh MHer WGoo WTor XSen
'Buckland' — ECtt EPot WSHC
caespitosum — see *O. vulgare* 'Nanum'
§ ***calcaratum*** — LLHF
creticum — see *O. vulgare* subsp. *hirtum*
dictamnus — EPot GPoy LLHF MHer SIgm WAbe WJek WOld XEll
'Dingle Fairy' — EBee ECtt EPot EWTr EWes GJos MCot MHer NBir SBch SRot SWvt WMoo WSpi XSen
'Emma Stanley' — WAbe
'Frank Tingey' — LLHF
'French' — CLau SRms
'Gold Splash' — WMoo

'Golden Narrow' CRos LRHS NRHS
heracleoticum L. see *O. vulgare* subsp. *hirtum*
'Hot and Spicy' CBod EBou ECrN EMor ENfk EWhm SRms WJek XSen
§ × ***hybridinum*** WAbe
'Jekka's Beauty' WJek
'Kent Beauty' ♀H4 Widely available
laevigatum ♀H6 EPot MHer NBro NPer WCot WKif WMoo WSHC XSen
I - 'Aromaticum' IMou
- 'Dingle' **new** NLar
- dwarf SIgm
- 'Herrenhausen' ♀H7 Widely available
- 'Hopleys' ♀H6 CBod CDor CMea CRos CTri CWld EBee ECha EHrv ELan EPfP LEdu LRHS MCot MHer MHol MMuc MRav MWat NBir NLar NRHS SEND SPer SPhx SPoG WSHC XSen
- 'Purple Charm' EDAr SRms
majorana CHab ENfk GQue MHer MJak MNHC SRms SVic WJek
I - 'Aureum' GKev NAln
- Italian **new** WJek
- PAGODA BELLS ('Lizbell'PBR) CBod XSen
- var. ***tenuifolium*** **new** WJek
minutiflorum LLHF
'Norton Gold' CBre ECha ECtt MHer NPer
'Nymphenburg' XSen
onites CBod CHby CLau EBou EMor ENfk GQue MHer MNHC SPlb SRms
- 'Limelight' NWad
'Pilgrim' XSen
pulchellum see *O.* × *hybridinum*
'Rosenkuppel' ♀H7 CAby CBar CBod CDor CMea EBee ECha ECtt ELan EPPr GQue LCro LOPS LRHS MHer NDov NLar SPer SPhx SPlb SRms SWvt WCAu WMoo XSen
'Rotkugel' ELon WCFE XSen
rotundifolium ♀H4 CMea ELan IMou LEdu MHer NBir WThu
- hybrid CMea
scabrum subsp. ***pulchrum*** 'Newleaze' SBch
syriacum WJek
tournefortii see *O. calcaratum*
vulgare CCBP CHab CMea CTsd CWld EBou GJos GMaP GPoy LCro LOPS MHer MMuc MNHC NBro NGrd NMir NPol NPri SEND SPer SPlb SRms SVic WArt WHer WSFF XLum
- 'Acorn Bank' CBod EBou ECtt ENfk EWes LEdu MHer MNHC NLar SPoG SRms WHer WJek
- var. ***album*** WArt
- 'Aureum' ♀H6 Widely available
- 'Aureum Crispum' CBod ECha ENfk GBin GQue GWyn NBid SRms
- 'Compactum' CBod CCBP CLau CMea EBee EBou ECha ECtt EMor ENfk EWhm GCal GPoy LEdu MHer MNHC NBir NPol NRHS NSla SPlb SRms WAbe WJek XLum
- 'Corinne Tremaine' (v) WHer
- 'Country Cream' (v) CCBP CElw CLau EBee ECtt EHoe ENfk EPfP EWes EWhm GJos LRHS MHer MNHC NBir NGdn NPri NRHS SPer SPoG SRms SRot WCFE
- 'Curly Gold' CLau
§ - 'Gold Tip' (v) CBod CMea EBou EMor ENfk EWhm GJos MCot MHer MHol MNHC SPlb SRms WHer
- 'Golden Shine' EHoe EWes EWhm
§ - subsp. ***hirtum*** CHby EMor GPoy SPlb XSen
- - 'Greek' CBod CCBP CLau EBou EMor ENfk EWhm MHer MNHC SRms SVic WJek
§ - 'Nanum' SRms WJek XSen
- 'Pink Mist' MNrw SRms WHoo
- 'Polyphant' (v) NBir SRms XSen
- 'Thumble's Variety' CBod CMea CRos EBee ECha ECtt EHoe EPfP GCal LRHS MAsh MHer MRav NRHS SWvt WCFE WMoo XLum XSen
- 'Tomintoul' GPoy
- 'Variegatum' see *O. vulgare* 'Gold Tip'
- 'White Charm' CBod EBee NWad
'Z'Attar' MNHC

Orixa (*Rutaceae*)

japonica CExl NLar WPGP
- 'Variegata' (v) NLar

Orlaya (*Apiaceae*)

grandiflora ♀H7 CAvo CBre CPla CSpe LCro LEdu LOPS LRHS MAvo MCot SPhx WHal WTor

Ornithogalum (*Asparagaceae*)

arabicum CBro CCCN GKev IMou LAma SDeJ SRms
arcuatum WCot
atticum GKev
baeticum GKev
balansae see *O. oligophyllum*
caudatum see *O. longibracteatum*
cuspidatum GKev
dubium ♀H2 ELan SDeJ
- hybrids GKev
fimbriatum GKev
lanceolatum GKev WCot
§ ***longibracteatum*** CAvo GKev SChr WHer
magnum CAvo CBro CWCL EBee ERCP GBin GKev MCot MNrw SDeJ WCot XEll
montanum GKev
'Mount Fuji' GKev
'Namib Gold' GKev SDeJ
nanum see *O. sigmoideum*
narbonense GKev WCot
nutans ♀H5 CAby CAvo CMea CWCL EAJP EBee EPot GKev LAma LRHS MMuc MNrw NBir NRHS SDeJ SEND SPer WFar WShi
§ ***oligophyllum*** EPot GKev MNrw SDeJ
§ ***orthophyllum*** GKev
ponticum WCot
- 'Sochi' EBee ERCP GKev XEll
pyramidale EBee GKev
- short SMHy
pyrenaicum CAvo CSpe ECha EPPr GKev WCot WShi XEll
reverchonii EBee ERCP GKev WShi
saundersiae EUJe GKev
sibthorpii see *O. sigmoideum*
§ ***sigmoideum*** GKev
sintenisii GKev
tenuifolium see *O. orthophyllum*
thyrsoides ♀H2 CCCN GKev LAma LCro LOPS LRHS SDeJ

umbellatum CAvo CHab CRos CTri EBee GKev GPoy LAma LRHS MCot MMuc MNrw NRHS SDeJ SEND SRms WBrk WShi

Orontium (*Araceae*)

aquaticum CWat EWat LCro LLWG LOPS MWts NPer SEND WMAq

Orostachys (*Crassulaceae*)

boehmeri new WCot
furusei WHal
iwarenge CBod CRos GKev NAln SPlb SSim
§ ***spinosa*** CRos EDAr EWes LRHS NRHS SPlb WAbe

Orthophytum (*Bromeliaceae*)

gurkenii WCot

Orthrosanthus (*Iridaceae*)

chimboracensis JCA 13743 CPou EBee
laxus CAbb CBod CPla CWCL LLHF NBir SMad WMoo
multiflorus CBor CPbh CSde EBee IKil
polystachyus CAby CTsd LPla WSHC

Orychophragmus (*Brassicaceae*)

violaceus CCCN

Oryzopsis (*Poaceae*)

lessoniana see *Anemanthele lessoniana*
miliacea CSpe EHoe EPPr MAvo NSti SEND WCot WPGP WSHC
paradoxa EPPr

Osbeckia (*Melastomataceae*)

stellata NJM 13.058 WPGP

Oscularia (*Aizoaceae*)

§ ***deltoides*** ♀H2 CCCN EShb SAll SVen WFar

Osmanthus (*Oleaceae*)

armatus CBcs CJun CMac EPfP LRHS NLar SEND SGol
× ***burkwoodii*** ♀H5 Widely available
§ ***decorus*** CBcs CHll CMac CTri EBee EPfP MGos MRav NLar NWea SBrt SGol SPer WPav
- 'Angustifolius' NLar
delavayi ♀H5 Widely available
- 'Frank Knight' EPfP LRHS MAsh
- 'George Gardner' CMac SRms
- 'Heaven Scent' new SPoG
- 'Latifolius' CExl CJun CRos LRHS MAsh SLon SWvt
forrestii see *O. yunnanensis*
× ***fortunei*** CBcs CCVT CExl CKel CRos EBee EPfP LMaj LRHS
fragrans CBcs SLon SWvt WPGP
- f. ***aurantiacus*** SCob
§ ***heterophyllus*** CBcs CDul CMac EBee ELan EPfP LMaj MGos MRav NAln NLar SCob SGol SPer SRms SSta WCFE
§ - all gold CKel EBee ELan EMil EPfP LRHS SPer SPoG
- 'Argenteomarginatus' see *O. heterophyllus* 'Variegatus'
§ - 'Aureomarginatus' (v) CBcs CTsd ELon MGil SCob SLon SRms WCFE
- 'Aureus' misapplied see *O. heterophyllus* all gold
- 'Aureus' Rehder see *O. heterophyllus* 'Aureomarginatus'
§ - 'Goshiki' (v) ♀H5 Widely available
- 'Gulftide' CDul CRos EPfP LRHS MAsh MGos MJak NLar NRHS
- 'Kembu' (v) NLar
- 'Myrtifolius' CMac NLar
- 'Ōgon' EPfP NLar
- 'Purple Shaft' ♀H5 CRos ELan EPfP LRHS MAsh NRHS
- 'Purpureus' CBcs CBod CDul CMac CTsd EBee ELon EWTr MGos MRav MSwo NLar SCob SCoo SEND SGol SLon SPer WRHF
- 'Rotundifolius' CMac NLar
- 'Sasaba' NLar
- TRICOLOR see *O. heterophyllus* 'Goshiki'
§ - 'Variegatus' (v) ♀H5 CBcs CDul CKel CMac CRos CSBt ECrN EHoe ELan ELon EPfP LRHS LSRN MAsh MGos MRav MSwo NEgg NLar SEND SGbt SGol SLim SPer SPoG SRms SVen WSHC
ilicifolius see *O. heterophyllus*
serrulatus EPfP LRHS NLar WPGP
suavis NLar
§ ***yunnanensis*** ♀H5 CBcs CMCN EBee EPfP MBlu MRav NLar SArc WPGP WSHC

× *Osmarea* see *Osmanthus*

Osmaronia see *Oemleria*

Osmorhiza (*Apiaceae*)

aristata B&SWJ 1607 WCru

Osmunda ✿ (*Osmundaceae*)

sp. CCCN
asiatica EBee WCru
cinnamomea ♀H6 CBdn CBod CCCN CKel CLAP CRos CWCL EBee EFer EMor EWes ISha LEdu LRHS MMuc NBro NLar NRHS
claytoniana CBdn CLAP CRos EBee EFer IBal ISha LRHS NBro NLar NRHS WCot XLum
japonica CLAP EBee EMor ISha NBro
regalis ♀H6 Widely available
- from southern USA CLAP
- 'Cristata' ♀H6 CRos GCal LRHS NBid NRHS SWvt WFib
- 'Purpurascens' Widely available
- var. ***spectabilis*** CCCN CLAP CRos GBin ISha LRHS NRHS
- 'Undulata' WFib

Osteomeles (*Rosaceae*)

subrotunda WPGP

Osteomeles × *Pyracantha* see × *Pyracomeles*

Osteospermum (*Asteraceae*)

3D Series SPoG
- 3D VIOLET ICE ('Kleoe14223') new NPri
'African Queen' see *O.* 'Nairobi Purple'
BANANA SYMPHONY ('Sekiin47') (Symphony Series) CCCN MBNS
barberae misapplied see *O. jucundum*
barberae (Harv.) Norl. 'Compactum' WFar
'Blue Streak' CCCN CMac

'Buttermilk' ♀H3 CCCN ELan
'Cannington John' CCCN
'Cannington Joyce' CCCN
'Cannington Roy' CBcs CCCN CEnd CMac CRos CSma EBee ECtt ELan ELon EPfP GBee LRHS NRHS WFar
caulescens misapplied see *O.* 'White Pim'
ecklonis CBcs CCCN CDTJ CHll CTri NBro NGdn
- var. ***prostratum*** see *O.* 'White Pim'
Flowerpower Double Series (d) LBuc
- FLOWERPOWER DOUBLE WHITE ('Kleoe10179'PBR) (d) NPri
'Giles Gilbey' (v) CCCN
'Gweek Variegated' (v) CCCN
'Helen Dimond' LRHS NRHS
'Hopleys' ♀H3 SEND
'Iced Gem' LBuc LRHS NRHS
'In the Pink' LCro LOPS
'Irish' ECtt EPot SIgm WIce
§ ***jucundum*** ♀H3 CCht CMea CRos CTri ECha GAbr LCro LOPS LRHS LSRN NBir NPer NRHS SPlb SRms WIce WThu
- 'Blackthorn Seedling' ♀H3 CCCN CMea CWGN ECha SPtp
- var. ***compactum*** CBod CMac CPBP CPrp CRos CTsd ELan ELon EPfP GBee GLog GMaP LRHS LSRN MHol MSCN NPer NPri NRHS SPer SPtp SWvt WHil
- 'Elliott's Form' WHoo
- 'Nanum' EDAr
'Keia' (Springstar Series) CCCN
§ 'Lady Leitrim' ♀H3 CBar CBod CCCN CPla CPrp CRos CSma CWGN ECha ECtt ELan ELon EPfP GLog GMaP LRHS LSRN MCot MHol NPer NPri NRHS SEND SPer SPoG SPtp SWvt WHil
'Lisa Traxler' SVen
MILK SYMPHONY ('Seiremi') (Symphony Series) CCCN
§ 'Nairobi Purple' CBcs CBod CCCN CCht CRos EBee ECtt ELan EShb LRHS MHol NPri NRHS SSut SWvt WFar WHil
NASINGA CREAM ('Aknam'PBR) (Cape Daisy Series) CCCN
ORANGE SYMPHONY ('Seimora'PBR) (Symphony Series) CBcs CCCN MBNS
'Pale Face' see *O.* 'Lady Leitrim'
'Peggyi' see *O.* 'Nairobi Purple'
'Pink Gem' EDAr MHer WFar
'Pink Whirls' ♀H3 CCCN
'Port Wine' see *O.* 'Nairobi Purple'
'Serenity Bronze' WBor
'Silver Sparkler' (v) ♀H3 CCCN CDTJ MHer SVen
'Snow Pixie' CBod CRos CWGN EBee ECtt ELan ELon LRHS NPri SPoG SWvt WHil WIce
SONJA see *O.*'Sunny Sonja'
'Sparkler' CCCN
'Stardust'PBR CRos ECtt LBuc LRHS NPer NRHS SCoo
(Sunny Series) 'Sunny Bronze' CSpe
- 'Sunny Carlos'PBR SPoG
- 'Sunny Cherry' SPoG
- 'Sunny Mary'PBR SPoG
§ - 'Sunny Sonja'PBR SPoG
- 'Sunny Victoria'PBR SPoG
- 'Sunny Xena'PBR SPoG
I 'Superbum' CBod EBee MHol WFar
'Tauranga' see *O.* 'Whirlygig'
'Tresco Peggy' see *O.*'Nairobi Purple'
'Tresco Pink' CCCN
'Tresco Purple' see *O.* 'Nairobi Purple'
'Weetwood' ♀H3 CCCN CEnd CMea CRos ECtt ELan EPPr EPot GLog LRHS MCot MHer NRHS SPoG SWvt WFar
'Westwood White' EDAr
§ 'Whirlygig' ♀H3 CCCN
§ 'White Pim' ♀H3 CDTJ CHll CPrp NPer SEND
'Wine Purple' see *O.* 'Nairobi Purple'
'Wisley Pink' NEgg
'Zaurak' (Springstar Series) CCCN
'Zulu' (Cape Daisy Series) CCCN

Ostrowskia (*Campanulaceae*)

magnifica EPot GKev

Ostrya (*Betulaceae*)

sp. LPra
carpinifolia CBcs CCVT CDul CLnd CMCN ELan EMOT EPfP LMaj LPra MBlu MMuc NLar NOra NWea SEND SGol SWvt WMat WTSh
japonica CDul CMCN
virginiana SBrt

Otatea (*Poaceae*)

aztecorum ERod

Otholobium (*Papilionaceae*)

glandulosum EBee

Othonna (*Asteraceae*)

cheirifolia see *Hertia cheirifolia*
coronopifolia SVen

Othonnopsis see *Hertia*

Ourisia (*Plantaginaceae*)

alpina new GQue
× ***bitternensis*** 'Cliftonville Canary' WAbe
- 'Cliftonville Crimson' WAbe
- 'Cliftonville Damask' WAbe
- 'Cliftonville Ling' WAbe
- 'Cliftonville Old Rose' WAbe
- 'Cliftonville Pink' WAbe
- 'Cliftonville Roset' WAbe
caespitosa GAbr WAbe
- var. ***gracilis*** MHol
coccinea EWes EWld GBin GKev NBir NHpl WHal
'Loch Ewe' CExl EWld GKev NAln
macrophylla NWad
microphylla WAbe
- f. ***alba*** WAbe
- 'Hollowcliffe' WAbe
polyantha 'Cliftonville Scarlet' WAbe
'Snowflake' ♀H4 GAbr IMou NHpl NWad

Ovidia (*Thymelaeaceae*)

andina new MGil

Oxalis (*Oxalidaceae*)

from Mount Stewart WMoo

acetosella GPoy MHer MMuc NQui WHer WShi
- var. ***rosea*** IFro IMou
- var. ***subpurpurascens*** WCot
adenophylla ♀H4 CExl CRos ELan ELon EPfP EPot GBin GKev GMaP LAma LRHS MJak MPie NAln NEgg NHol NHpl NLar NRHS SDeJ SPoG SRms WBrk
adenophylla* × *enneaphylla see *O.* 'Matthew Forrest'
'Anne Christie' CPBP NSla WAbe
arenaria F&W 10584 WCot
§ ***articulata*** ELan MAvo NPer SEND WSHC XLum
- 'Alba' ELan WCot XLum
- f. ***crassipes*** 'Alba' WCot
- 'Festival' GKev
§ - subsp. ***rubra*** GKev SDeJ
bowiei EPot WCot
- 'Amarantha' GKev
* - ***purpurea*** new CBor
brasiliensis CBor GKev
'Dark Eye' EPot
dentata 'Pot of Gold' GKev
deppei see *O. tetraphylla*
§ ***depressa*** EPot EWes GKev LLHF NBir NSla SBch SDeJ
'Double Trouble' (d) CBor GKev
enneaphylla ♀H4 CElw CRos ELon GBin GEdr GMaP LLHF LRHS NRHS NRya
- F&W 2715 CPBP
- 'Alba' CElw CPBP NRya NSla
- subsp. ***ibari*** EPPr GEdr NRHS NRya NSla
- 'Minutifolia' GEdr NRya
* - 'Minutifolia Rosea' CPBP
- 'Rosea' CBor CElw EPot GKev ITim LLHF NAln NLar NRya NSla
- 'Sheffield Swan' CPBP GEdr LLHF NRHS NSla WAbe
- 'Ute' EPot GEdr NRya
'Fanny' GKev
flava white-flowered EPot GKev
floribunda misapplied see *O. articulata*
gracilis EPot GKev
griffithii 'Pink Charm' GEdr
- 'Snowflake' GEdr
'Gwen McBride' CPBP GEdr WAbe
hedysaroides misapplied see *O. spiralis* subsp. *vulcanicola*
hedysaroides Kunth CCCN
'Hemswell Knight' CPBP
hirta SBch
- 'Gothenburg' GKev ITim
imbricata LLHF
inops see *O. depressa*
'Ione Hecker' ♀H4 CBor EPot GCrg GKev ITim NHpl NLar NRya WAbe WOld
'Irish Mist' (v) GKev
* ***karroica*** NHpl WCot
§ ***laciniata*** CPBP EPot
- hybrid GEdr
lactea double-flowered see *O. magellanica* 'Nelson'
lasiandra CCCN GKev
§ ***latifolia*** LLHF
magellanica GAbr IMou SPlb WMoo
- 'Flore Pleno' see *O. magellanica* 'Nelson'
§ - 'Nelson' (d) GBin NBir NPer WMoo WPtf
magnifica GKev
massoniana ♀H2 WAbe WCot
§ 'Matthew Forrest' CPBP WCot
§ ***megalorrhiza*** GKev NWad SChr
melanosticta EPot GEdr GKev SDeJ WCot
§ - 'Ken Aslet' ♀H2 GKev ITim NHpl SDeJ
obtusa EPot GKev MPie
- apricot-flowered SDeJ
oregana CMac ELon EWld GCal SPhx WCot WCru
- 'Bob Haszeldine' GEdr
- 'Klamath Ruby' WSHC
- f. ***smalliana*** EWld GEdr IMou MNrw NLar WCot WCru
- white-flowered new WCot
perdicaria CRos EPot EWes GKev LRHS NRHS WAbe WIce
- 'Citrino' WAbe WCot
'Pink Pillow' new CBod
polyphylla* var. *heptaphylla GEdr
purpurea 'Ken Aslet' see *O. melanosticta* 'Ken Aslet'
regnellii see *O. triangularis* subsp. *papilionacea*
'Ridgeway Jewel' CPBP
'Ridgeway Sapphire' CPBP
rosea misapplied see *O. articulata* subsp. *rubra*
semiloba GCal NCGa
Slack Top hybrids NSla
'Slack's 53' NSla
'Snipe' NSla
§ ***spiralis* subsp. *vulcanicola*** CCCN GCal
- - 'Burgundy' NPri
- - 'Sunset Velvet' WCot
squamata CPla LLHF
squamoso-radicosa see *O. laciniata*
succulenta Barnéoud see *O. megalorrhiza*
succulenta ambig. CHll CSpe GCal
'Sunny' GKev
§ ***tetraphylla*** CExl GKev NPer
- 'Iron Cross' GKev LAma LSun MPie NBir NLar SDeJ SPlb
'Tina' CPBP WAbe
triangularis CCCN CExl MHer NBir NPer WBrk
- 'Birgit' GKev SDeJ
- BURGUNDY WINE ('JR Oxburwi') (Xalis Series) CWGN NPer
- 'Marmer' (v) GKev
- 'Mijke' GKev
§ - subsp. ***papilionacea*** ♀H2 GKev LAma
- - 'Atropurpurea' CSpe SDeJ
- subsp. ***triangularis*** EUJe GKev WWFP
tuberosa EPfP GPoy LEdu SPoG WHer
- 'Amarillo' LEdu
- 'Baumi Golden' LEdu
- 'Polar Bere' LEdu
- scarlet-flowered, white-eye LEdu
'Ute' CPBP NRHS NSla
valdiviensis CPla NWad
versicolor ♀H3 CBor EPot GEdr GKev ITim NBir SDeJ WHil XEll
- 'Golden Cape' CBor GKev
vespertilionis Zucc. see *O. latifolia*
I 'Waverley Hybrid' GCrg GKev LLHF

Oxycoccus see *Vaccinium*

Oxydendrum ✿ (*Ericaceae*)

arboreum CBcs CEnd CMCN CRos EBee EPfP IArd LRHS MAsh MBlu MMuc NLar SPer SPoG SSta WHor

Oxypetalum (*Apocynaceae*)

caeruleum see *Tweedia coerulea*

Oxyria (*Polygonaceae*)

digyna	CAgr

Oxytropis (*Papilionaceae*)

campestris var. ***gracilis***	GKev NAln WSHC
lambertii	CPBP
podocarpa	SPlb
purpurea	SPlb
sajanensis	CPBP
shokanbetsuensis	CPla

Ozothamnus (*Asteraceae*)

§ ***coralloides***	EPot WAbe
§ 'County Park Silver'	EWes GCrg GEdr GKev WAbe
§ ***hookeri***	CBct EBee SVen WCFE WCot WPGP
§ ***ledifolius***	CBcs CBod ELan EPfP LRHS SBrt SPer WSHC
§ ***rosmarinifolius***	CBcs CRos CTsd ELan EPfP LRHS MAsh MSwo SPer SVen
- 'Silver Jubilee'	CBcs CBod CCht CKel CRos CSBt ECre ELan EPfP GCal LRHS MAsh MMuc MRav MSwo NRHS SLon SPer SPlb SRkn
§ ***selago***	ELan
- 'Major'	SPlb
§ - var. ***tumidus***	EBee ITim WThu
'Threave Seedling'	CCht CKel CRos EBee ELan LRHS MAsh SPer

P

Pachyphragma (*Brassicaceae*)

§ ***macrophyllum***	ECha EHrv ELon EWTr EWld GCal IBlr IMou LEdu MBel MMuc MRav NLar NSti WCot WCru WPGP WPnP WSHC

Pachypodium (*Apocynaceae*)

lamerei ♀H1a	EUJe SPlb

Pachysandra (*Buxaceae*)

axillaris	GCal WCot
- BWJ 8032	WCru
- 'Crûg's Cover'	ESwi EWld SMad WCru
- var. ***stylosa***	MRav
procumbens	EHrv GKev IMou MNrw NAln NLar WCot
- 'Angola' (v)	WCot
terminalis	Widely available
- 'Green Carpet'	CBcs CChe CExl CMac CRos CSBt EBee ELan EPfP EUJe GMaP LRHS LSRN MAsh MGos MSwo NEgg NHol NLar NRHS SCob SGol SLim SMad SNig SPer SPoG SWvt XLum
- 'Green Sheen' ♀H5	CBod CRos ECha ELan EPPr EPfP EWTr LRHS NRHS
- 'Silver Edge' (v)	EBee
- 'Variegata' (v) ♀H5	Widely available

Pachystachys (*Acanthaceae*)

lutea ♀H1b	CCCN

Pachystegia (*Asteraceae*)

§ ***insignis***	CAby GKev LRHS

Paederota (*Plantaginaceae*)

§ ***bonarota***	GEdr GKev WAbe
lutea	GEdr WCot

Paeonia ✿ (*Paeoniaceae*)

'Ace of Hearts'	GBin
albiflora	see *P. lactiflora*
'Alexander Woollcott' new	GBin
'America'	CKel GBin NAln
'Anne Rosse' (S) new	SPtp
anomala	EPot GKev ILea MPhe NLar
arietina	see *P. mascula* subsp. *arietina*
'Armani'	EBee ELon EPfP LRHS
'Asahiminato'	CKel
'Athena'	CRos GBin LRHS NRHS
'Aurelia'	GKev
'Avant Garde'	GBin
'Bai Xue Ta' (S)	NTPC
banatica	see *P. officinalis* subsp. *banatica*
§ 'Bartzella' (d) ♀H6	CBod CKel CRos ELan ELon EPfP GBin ILea LCro LOPS LPla LRHS NLar NRHS SPoG WCAu WCot
beresowskii	GKev
'Berry Garcia'	GBin
'Black Pirate' (S) ♀H5	CKel
'Blaze'	CKel CRos EWTr GMaP ILea LRHS NRHS WCAu WCot
'Border Charm'	CKel GBin ILea
'Bridal Icing'	CKel GBin NCGa WCAu
'Bride's Dream'	GBin
broteroi	WThu
'Buckeye Belle' (d)	CKel EBee ELan EPfP EWTr GBin GMaP ILea LCro LOPS LRHS LSRN MBel NCGa NLar SCob SPer SPoG WCAu WCot
'Burma Midnight'	GBin WKif
'Callie's Memory'	CKel ELon GBin ILea WCAu
cambessedesii ♀H3	CBro CRos CSpe EPot GBin GEdr GKev LRHS NBir NRHS NSla WAbe WKif WSHC
cambessedesii × ***mlokosewitschii***	CRos LRHS NRHS
'Cameo Lullaby'	GBin
'Canary Brilliant'PBR	CKel GBin ILea
'Carina'	CKel
'Carol'	ILea LSRN
caucasica	see *P. mascula* subsp. *mascula*
× ***chamaeleon***	GKev LPla
'Chocolate Soldier'	GBin NCGa
'Claire de Lune'	CKel GBin GMaP ILea LRHS MGil NAln NCGa WCAu WCot WKif WTor
'Claudia'	GBin
'Color Magnet'	CKel GBin WCAu
'Command Performance'	GBin NCGa WCAu
'Convoy' (d)	GBin
'Copper Kettle'	CKel GBin ILea
'Cora Louise'	CKel ELan ELon GBin ILea LRHS WCAu WHil
'Coral Charm' ♀H7	CKel EPfP GBin GMaP ILea LCro LOPS LRHS LSRN MHol MMrt NCGa NLar NPri SCob SDeJ WCAu WCot XSen
'Coral Fay'	GBin
'Coral 'n' Gold'	NPri
'Coral Sunset'	CKel EWTr GBin ILea LCro LOPS NCGa NLar NPri SCob SDeJ SPer WCot WHil WTyc
'Coral Supreme'	GBin

	corallina	see *P. mascula* subsp. *mascula*
	coriacea	GBin
	'Court Jester'	CKel ELan GBin ILea
	'Cutie'	GBin
	'Cytherea'	GBin LRHS WCAu
	'Dancing Butterflies'	see *P. lactiflora* 'Zi Yu Nu'
	'Daredevil' (S)	GBin
	daurica misapplied	see *P. mascula* subsp. *triternata*
	- subsp. ***coriifolia*** RCB UA 12	WCot
	'Dawn Glow'	GBin
	decora	see *P. peregrina*
	delavayi (S)	CKel CPla CRos CSpe CTho CTsd ELan EPfP GCal GKev GMaP LCro LRHS MAsh MGos NAln NBir NEgg SPer SPoG SRms WCot
	- BWJ 7775	WCru
	- from China (S)	MPhe
	- var. ***angustiloba*** f. ***alba*** (S)	CExl
§	- - f. ***angustiloba*** (S)	GBin GKev MMuc SCob SEND
§	- - f. ***trollioides*** (S)	CExl SPtp
	- var. ***atropurpurea***	see *P. delavayi* var. *delavayi* f. *delavayi*
	- 'Cally Amber'	GCal
§	- var. ***delavayi*** f. ***delavayi*** (S)	CPla
§	- - f. ***lutea*** (S)	CCVT CJun CKel CRos CTho EPfP GBin GKev GLog GMaP IFro LEdu LRHS MAsh MGos NBir NEgg SCob SLon SPoG SRms WHoo
	- var. ***lutea***	see *P. delavayi* var. *delavayi* f. *lutea*
	- 'Mrs Colville' (S)	GCal
	- Potaninii Group	see *P. delavayi* var. *angustiloba* f. *angustiloba*
	- 'Tapestry' (S)	CSpe
	- Trollioides Group	see *P. delavayi* var. *angustiloba* f. *trollioides*
	delavayi × suffruticosa	LSRN NAln
	'Diana Parks'	GBin ILea NLar
	DRIZZLING RAIN CLOUD	see *P. suffruticosa* 'Shiguregumo'
	'Early Bird'	GBin
	'Early Scout'	ELon GBin LRHS SCob
	'Early Windflower'	CKel GBin ILea WCAu
	'Eden's Perfume'	CBod CKel ELon EPfP IKil LRHS NLar SPer
	'Eliza Lundy' (d)	GBin
	'Ellen Cowley'	GBin NCGa WCAu
	emodi	CKel CPla CSpe GBin GKev ILea LRHS MCot WCAu WCot
	'Etched Salmon'	CKel GBin
	'Fairy Princess'	GBin
	'First Arrival'	CKel GBin ILea MHol WCAu
	'First Dutch Yellow'	see *P.* 'Garden Treasure'
	'Flame'	CRos EPfP EWTr GMaP ILea LRHS MNrw NCGa NRHS NSti SDeJ WCot
	'Fragrant Pink Imp'	GBin
	'Fuso-no-tsukasa' (S) **new**	CKel
§	Gansu Group (S)	CKel MPhe NTPC
	- 'Bai Bi Lan Xia' (S)	MPhe
	- 'Bai Zhang Bing' (S)	NTPC
	- 'Bing Shan Xue Lian' (S)	MPhe
	- 'Bing Xin Zi' (S)	NTPC
	- 'Dan Feng Ling Kong' (S)	NTPC
	- 'Dan Feng Zhan Chi' (S)	NTPC
	- 'Er Long Nao Hai' (S)	MPhe
	- 'Fen Guan Yu Zhu' (S)	NTPC
	- 'Fen He' (S)	MPhe NTPC
	- 'Fen Jin Yu' (S)	NTPC
	- 'Gan Lan Yu' (S)	NTPC
	- 'Guan Yu Zhu' (S)	NTPC
	- 'Han Hai Bing Xin' (S)	MPhe
	- 'Hei Fa Nü Lang' (S)	MPhe
	- 'Hei Feng Die' (S)	MPhe NTPC
	- 'Hei Xuan Feng' (S)	MPhe NTPC
	- 'Hei Yuan Shuai' (S)	MPhe
	- 'Hong Lian' (S)	MPhe
	- 'Hui He' (S)	MPhe
	- 'Jiao Rong' (S)	MPhe
	- 'Ju Hua Fen' (S)	MPhe
	- 'Lan He' (S)	MPhe
	- 'Lan He Qi Ming' (S)	NTPC
	- 'Lan Tian Meng' (S)	MPhe
	- 'Lan Yu San Cai' (S)	NTPC
	- 'Long Yuan Hong' (S)	MPhe
	- 'Mo Hai Yin Bo' (S)	MPhe
	- 'Ren Mian Tao Hua' (S)	NTPC
	- 'Ri Yue Tong Hui' (S)	MPhe
	- 'San Hua Nu' (S)	MPhe
	- 'Shu Sheng Peng Mo' (S)	MPhe
	- 'Tao Hua Nu' (S)	MPhe
	- 'Tie Mian Wu Si' (S)	MPhe
	- 'Tong Xin Tong De' (S)	MPhe
	- 'Xiao Xue' (S)	MPhe
	- 'Xiong Mao' (S)	MPhe
	- 'Xue Hai Bing Xin' (S)	MPhe NTPC
	- 'Xue Hai Dan Xin' (S)	NTPC
	- 'Xue Lian' (S)	NTPC
	- 'Xue Shan Fei Cai' (S)	NTPC
	- 'Xue Yuan Yu Hui' (S)	NTPC
	- 'Ye Guang Bei' (S)	MPhe
	- 'Yi Du Chun Qiu' (S)	NTPC
	- 'Yin Yang Shan' (S)	MPhe
	- 'Yu Ban Xiu Qiu' (S)	MPhe
	- 'Yu Lou Cang Jiao' (S)	MPhe
	- 'Yu Lu Lian Dan' (S)	MPhe
	- 'Yuan Yang Pu' (S)	MPhe
	- 'Zi Ban Bai' (S)	NTPC
	- 'Zi Die Ying Feng' (S)	MPhe NTPC
	- 'Zi Yan' (S)	NTPC
	- 'Zong Ban Bai' (S)	MPhe NTPC
	Gansu Mudan Group	see *P.* Gansu Group
	'Garden Peace'	WCAu
§	'Garden Treasure'	CKel CRos GBin LRHS NRHS SDeJ SPoG WCAu
	'Going Bananas'	CKel
	'Golden Bowl'	CKel GBin
	'Golden Dream'	see *P.* 'Bartzella'
	'Golden Isles'	CKel
	'Golden Thunder'	CKel
	'Happy'	GBin
	'Hei Hua Kui'	see *P. suffruticosa* 'Hei Hua Kui'
	'Henry Bockstoce' (d)	ELon GBin GMaP ILea MGil NCGa NLar WCAu
	'Hillary'	CKel ELan GBin ILea WCAu
	'Ho-gioku'	CKel GBin NCGa
	'Hoki'	CRos LRHS NRHS
	'Hong Bao Shi' (S)	NTPC
	'Honor'	WCAu
	humilis	see *P. officinalis* subsp. *microcarpa*
	'Huo Lian Jin Dan' (S)	NTPC
	'Illini Warrior'	CKel
	'Isani Gidui'	see *P. lactiflora* 'Isami-jishi'
	japonica misapplied	see *P. lactiflora*
	japonica (Makino) Miyabe & Takeda	CAby
	'Jay Cee'	GBin
	'Jean E. Bockstoce'	NAln
	'Jin Ge' (S)	NTPC
	'Joanna Marlene'	GBin WCAu

	'Joseph Rock'	see *P. rockii*
	'Joyce Ellen'	NLar
	'Julia Rose'	CBod CKel CRos GBin ILea LRHS NLar NRHS SMad SPoG WCAu WHil
	'Kasagayama'	CKel
	'Kinkaku'	see *P.* × *lemoinei* 'Souvenir de Maxime Cornu'
	'Kinko'	see *P.* × *lemoinei* 'Alice Harding'
	'Kinshi'	see *P.* × *lemoinei* 'Chromatella'
	'Koikagura'	CKel
	'Kokamon'	CKel
	'La Donna' (d)	GBin
§	***lactiflora***	GCal
	- from East Russia	GCal
	- 'Abalone Pearl'	GBin
	- 'Adolphe Rousseau'	CKel ILea LCro LOPS LRHS WCAu
	- 'Agida'	ECtt GBin LRHS MRav NRHS WGwG
	- 'Albert Crousse'	CBcs CKel GBin MRav NBir
	- 'Albâtre'	CKel
	- 'Alertie'	GBin LRHS
	- 'Alice Harding'	CKel GBin WCAu
	- 'Allan Rogers'	GBin
	- 'Amabilis'	ILea WHil
	- 'Amalia Olson'	GBin
	- 'Amibilis'	ELon
	- 'Angel Cheeks'	CKel GBin IPot LCro LOPS NLar WCAu
	- 'Ann Cousins'	CKel MGil WCAu
	- 'Antwerpen'	LRHS NRHS
	- 'Argentine'	CKel
	- 'Asa Gray'	CKel
	- 'Auguste Dessert'	CKel WCAu
§	- 'Augustin d'Hour'	CKel ILea SHar WGwG
	- 'Aureole'	MRav
	- 'Avalanche'	CKel CRos EPfP GBin ILea LRHS NLar NRHS
	- 'Ballerina'	MRav
	- 'Barbara'	CKel GBin WCAu
	- 'Baroness Schröder'	CKel GBin MGil WCAu
	- 'Barrington Belle'	CKel CRos EPfP LRHS MBel NRHS WFar WHoo
	- 'Bess Bockstoce'	WCAu
	- 'Bessie'	GBin
	- 'Bev'	GBin
	- 'Big Ben'	CKel GBin ILea LRHS NLar
	- 'Black Beauty'	CRos EBee GBin IPot LRHS NRHS SCob SDeJ
	- 'Blush Queen'	CKel CWld GBin WCAu
	- 'Border Gem'	CSam CWld LRHS MRav NRHS WCAu
	- 'Bouchela'	NSti
	- 'Boule de Neige'	CKel GBin ILea
	- 'Bouquet Perfect'	CRos GBin LRHS NRHS
	- 'Bowl of Beauty' ♀H6	Widely available
	- 'Bowl of Cream'	CKel GBin LRHS SWvt WCAu
	- 'Bridal Gown'	GBin WCAu
	- 'Bridal Shower'	GBin
	- 'Bridal Veil'	CKel
	- 'Bunker Hill'	CKel CRos ECtt ELon GBin ILea LRHS NRHS SPer SWvt WGwG
	- 'Butter Bowl'	GBin
	- 'Candidissima'	GBin
	- 'Candy Stripe'	CKel GBin
	- 'Catharina Fontijn'	CKel CRos GBin ILea LRHS NCGa NRHS WCAu
	- 'Celebrity'	CBod CKel SCob
	- 'Charles Burgess'	CKel ELon GBin ILea NCGa SCob WCAu

- 'Charlie's White'	CBod CKel GBin ILea IPot LRHS NCGa NLar SDeJ SPer WCAu
- 'Charm'	WCAu
- 'Cheddar Charm'	GBin
- 'Cheddar Cheese'	CKel NCGa
- 'Cheddar Supreme'	GBin
- 'Cherry Hill'	GBin
- 'Chiffon Parfait'	GBin
- 'Claire Dubois'	CKel CRos EBee LRHS NRHS
- 'Class Act'	GBin
- 'Cora Stubbs'	CKel GBin LRHS SPer
- 'Corinne Wersan'	GBin
- 'Cornelia Shaylor'	CKel WCAu
- 'Couronne d'Or'	GBin ILea
- 'Crimson Glory'	CKel
- 'Cringley White'	SRms
- 'Crinkles Linens'	GBin
- 'Dawn Pink'	CKel EPfP
- 'Daystar'	MRav
- 'Dinner Plate'	CKel GBin MGil SHar WCAu
- 'Do Tell'	CKel EBee ELon EPfP GBin ILea NCGa NLar SPer WCAu
- 'Docteur H. Barnsby'	CKel
- 'Doctor Alexander Fleming'	CBod CKel CRos EBee EPfP GBin ILea LRHS MBNS MGil MHol MNrw MWat NAln NBir NRHS SDeJ SWvt WCAu WFar
- 'Doreen'	CKel CRos EBee GBin LRHS NRHS WCAu
- 'Drumline'	SDeJ
- 'Duchesse de Nemours' ♀H6	Widely available
- 'Duchesse d'Orléans'	GBin
- 'Edulis Superba'	CWld EUJe GBin ILea LEdu LRHS MBNS MRav NPer NRHS WCAu
- 'Elaine'	MRav
- 'Elsa Sass'	CKel GBin ILea WCAu
- 'Embraceable Pink'	GBin
- 'Emma Klehm'	CKel GBin ILea LSRN WCAu
- 'Evelyn Tibbets'	GBin
- 'Fairy's Petticoat'	CKel GBin WCAu
- 'Fancy Nancy'	GBin
- 'Félix Crousse' ♀H6	CBcs CKel CTri ELan GBin GMaP ILea LRHS LSRN MBNS MRav NBir NLar NPri SDeJ SPer WCAu WFar XSen
- 'Felix Supreme'	GBin
- 'Festiva Maxima' ♀H6	CKel CRos CTri EBee ELan EPfP GBin ILea LCro LOPS LRHS MGil NBir NEgg NLar NPri NRHS SPer SPoG SRkn SRms SWvt WCAu WFar WHoo WKif
- 'Festiva Supreme'	CKel GBin
- 'Florence Ellis'	WCAu
- 'Florence Nicholls'	CKel ELan GBin ILea WCAu
- 'Foxtrot'	GBin
- 'Fuchsia Dragonfly'	GBin
- 'Fuji-no-mine'	NCGa
- 'Garden Lace'	SDeJ WCAu
- 'Gardenia'	CKel CRos ELan EWTr GBin LRHS NLar NRHS SDeJ WCot WKif
- 'Gay Paree'	CKel CWCL GBin ILea MGil MRav NCGa NLar SCob WCAu WKif WTor
- 'Général Joffre'	MRav
- 'Général MacMahon'	see *P. lactiflora* 'Augustin d'Hour'
- 'Germaine Bigot'	CKel MRav WCAu
- 'Gertrude Allen'	GBin
- 'Gilbert Barthelot'	WCAu
- 'Gladys McArthur'	GBin
- 'Gleam of Light'	CKel
- 'Globe of Light'	CKel

– 'Go-Daigo'	GBin
– 'Golden Fleece'	NCGa
– 'Goldilocks'	CKel GBin WCAu
– 'Great Sport'	MRav
– 'Green Halo'	CKel GBin WCot
– 'Hakodate'	CKel NCGa
– 'Hansina Brand'	GBin
– 'Hari-ai-nin'	ILea
– 'Helen Hayes'	WCAu
– 'Henri Potin'	CKel NCGa
– 'Hermione'	GBin
– 'Honey Gold'	CKel GBin ILea LRHS SPoG WCAu WSpi
– 'Hot Chocolate'	CKel GBin WCAu
– 'Immaculée'	CKel GBin IKil ILea LCro LOPS LRHS MMrt MRav NCGa SCob SPer SPoG WKif
– 'Inspecteur Lavergne'	CKel CRos EBee ECtt EPfP GBin ILea LRHS NGdn NRHS SGol SPer WCAu WCot
– 'Instituteur Doriat'	CKel LRHS NCGa WCAu
§ – 'Isami-jishi'	CKel
– 'Jacorma'	ILea LRHS NCGa NLar
– 'Jadwigha'	ILea
– 'James Kelway'	CKel
– 'Jan van Leeuwen'	CKel ELon EPfP GBin GMaP LCro LOPS LRHS NCGa WCAu WCot WKif WTor
– 'Jappensha-ikhu'	GBin
– 'Jeanne d'Arc'	CKel
– 'Joker'	GBin WCAu
– 'Judith Eileen'	WCAu
– 'June Rose'	GBin
– 'Kansas'	CKel CRos CWCL EBee ELan EPfP GBin ILea LRHS MHol NAln NBir NCGa NGdn NLar NPri NRHS SCob SPoG WCAu WCot WFar
– 'Karl Rosenfield'	CBcs CBod CKel CRos EBee EPfP GBin ILea LCro LOPS LRHS LSRN LSun MGil MJak MNrw MRav NEgg NLar NPri NRHS SCob SGol SPer SPoG SRms SWvt WFar WHoo XSen
– 'Kelway's Glorious'	CKel EPfP EWTr GBin LRHS MBNS MRav NLar NRHS WCAu WGwG WHoo WKif
– 'Kelway's Majestic'	MRav
– KIEV **new**	NRHS
§ – 'Koningin Wilhelmina'	EPfP MNrw
– 'Krinkled White'	CKel CRos ELon EPfP GBin GKev GMaP ILea LRHS MRav NCGa NLar NPri NRHS SDeJ SPoG WCAu WKif
– 'La Belle Hélène'	CKel
– 'Lady Alexandra Duff' ♀H7	CKel EWTr GBin ILea LRHS MRav NBir NGdn SWvt WCAu WKif
– 'Lady Anna'	CBod ILea
– 'Lady Liberty' **new**	NCGa
– 'Lady Orchid'	EPfP
– 'Lancaster Imp'	GBin
– 'Largo'	WCAu
– 'Laura Dessert' ♀H6	CKel GBin IKil ILea LCro LOPS LRHS WCAu WKif
– 'Le Cygne'	CKel NCGa
– 'L'Éclatante'	LRHS
– 'Lemon Queen'	GKev NCGa
§ – 'L'Étincelante'	GBin
– 'Lilac Times'	CKel
– 'Little Pink Lullaby'	GBin
– LONDON	CRos LRHS NRHS
– 'Longfellow'	CKel
– 'Lord Kitchener'	CKel CSam EPfP GBin LRHS MWat NRHS WGwG
– 'Louis van Houtte'	ILea NEgg
– 'Love's Touch'	GBin
– 'Lowell Thomas'	GBin WCAu
– 'Ma Petite Cherie'	GBin
– 'Madame Calot'	CKel CRos LRHS NCGa NRHS WCAu
– 'Madame Claude Tain'	WCot
– 'Madame Emile Debatène'	CKel EBee MBNS MHol WCAu WFar
– 'Madame Gaudichau'	MAvo WCot
– 'Madelon'	CKel
– MADRID	CRos LRHS NRHS
– 'Maestro'	GBin
– 'Magic Melody'	CKel
– 'Mammoth Rose'	GBin
– 'Mandarin's Coat'	NCGa
– 'Marie Lemoine'	CKel GBin ILea LRHS NCGa WCAu WCot
– 'Mary E. Nicholls' **new**	GBin
– 'Matilda Lewis'	GBin
– 'Mischief'	MRav
– 'Miss America' ♀H7	CKel EPfP GBin NCGa WCAu WKif
– 'Miss Eckhart'	CKel
– 'Mister Ed'	GBin WCAu
– 'Mistral'	CKel
– 'Monsieur Jules Elie' ♀H6	CKel EBee ELan EPfP GBin ILea LCro LOPS LRHS MWat NGdn NLar SPer WCAu
– 'Monsieur Martin Cahuzac'	CKel ILea LRHS
– 'Moon of Nippon'	IKil ILea NCGa WCAu
– 'Moon River'	CBcs CKel EPfP GBin NLar WCAu
– 'Moonstone'	CKel SCob
– 'Morning Kiss'	EPfP NCGa
– 'Mother's Choice'	CKel GBin LCro LOPS LSRN NGdn NLar SHar WCAu WCot
– 'Mr G.F. Hemerik'	CKel GBin NCGa WCAu WCot
– 'Mrs Edward Harding'	CKel
– 'Mrs Franklin D. Roosevelt'	GBin
– 'Mrs Livingston Farrand'	GBin
– 'My Pal Rudy'	GBin
– 'Myrtle Gentry'	CKel GBin NCGa WCAu
– 'Nancy Nora'	ILea SPer
– 'Nellie Shaylor'	CKel GBin ILea NCGa
– 'Neomy Demay'	CKel
– 'Neon'	GBin LRHS
– 'Nice Gal'	GBin WCAu
– 'Nick Shaylor'	GBin
– 'Nippon Beauty'	CKel GBin IKil ILea LRHS NCGa NLar SCob SDeJ WCAu WCot WFar WTor
– 'Noémie Demay'	LRHS
– 'Nymphe'	CKel MRav NCGa NLar SDeJ WCAu
– 'Paul M. Wild'	CKel ELan ILea NLar WCAu
* – 'Pecher'	CRos EPfP LRHS NLar NPer NRHS SDeJ
– 'Peter Brand'	CKel ECtt ELan GBin ILea LSRN NCGa NLar SCob
– 'Petite Elegance'	CKel GBin WCAu
– 'Petite Porcelain'	GBin WCAu
– 'Philippe Rivoire'	CKel GBin ILea
– 'Philomèle'	CKel
– 'Pietertje Vriend Wagenaar'	GBin
– 'Pillow Talk'	CKel EBee ELan GBin ILea NLar SPoG WCAu
– 'Pink Cameo'	WCot WFar
– 'Pink Delight'	GBin NCGa
– 'Pink Giant'	EUJe GBin WCAu
– 'Pink Parfait'	CKel ILea LRHS NAln NCGa NLar SPer

– 'Pink Princess'	GBin NAln
– 'Plink Platters'	GBin
– 'Port Royale'	GBin
– 'President Franklin D. Roosevelt'	ECtt LRHS MPie NRHS
– 'Président Poincaré'	MRav
– 'President Taft'	see *P. lactiflora* 'Reine Hortense'
– 'Primevère'	CBod CKel ECtt EWTr ILea LRHS NBir NCGa NLar SCob SPer WFar
– 'Princess Bride'	GBin
§ – 'Purple Spider'	EBee LRHS MHol NCGa
– 'Queen Wilhelmina'	see *P. lactiflora* 'Koningin Wilhelmina'
– 'Raspberry Sundae'	CKel CRos ELan ELon EPfP EWTr GBin ILea LRHS MRav NAln NLar NRHS SPer SPoG WCAu WCot
– 'Ray Payton'	GBin
– 'Red Queen'	CKel GBin NCGa
– RED SARAH BERNHARDT	EPfP EUJe GBin ILea SDeJ SPer
– 'Red Spider'	see *P. lactiflora* 'Purple Spider'
§ – 'Reine Hortense'	CKel ECtt LRHS MRav
– 'Renato'	CRos LRHS LSun NRHS
– 'Riches and Fame'	LRHS
– 'Rigolote' **new**	NCGa
– ROME	CRos LRHS NRHS
– 'Ruth Clay' **new**	EWTr
– 'Salmon Dream'	CKel GBin
– 'Santa Fe'	CKel CRos EBee EPfP LRHS NLar NRHS
– 'Sarah Bernhardt' ♀H6	Widely available
– 'Sea Shell'	GBin GMaP IKil ILea WCAu
– 'Sebastiaan Maas'	ILea
– 'Serene Pastel'	CKel GBin WCAu
– 'Shawnee Chief'	GBin
– 'Shirley Temple'	CKel CRos EBee ELan EPfP GBin IKil ILea LCro LOPS LRHS MBNS MGos MHol MJak MRav NBir NGdn NPri NRHS SDeJ SPoG WCAu WCot WFar
– 'Silver Flare'	see *P. lactiflora* 'L'Étincelante'
– 'Silver Rose'	GBin
– 'Sir Ernest Shackleton'	MRav
– 'Snow Mountain' **new**	CKel
– 'Soft Salmon Joy'	GBin
– 'Solange'	CKel IKil ILea LRHS NAln NLar
– 'Sorbet'	CKel EBee ELon EPfP IKil ILea IPot LRHS MHol NBir NLar NPer SDeJ SMad WCAu WFar
– 'Surugu'	NAln WCAu
– 'Sweet Sixteen'	GBin
– 'Sword Dance'	CKel CRos ELon EPfP GBin ILea LRHS NCGa NRHS SDeJ WCAu WSpi
– 'Tamate-boko'	NCGa
– 'The Fawn'	CKel GBin ILea WCAu
– 'The Mighty Mo'	GBin NCGa
– 'The Nymph'	LRHS NBir
– 'Tom Eckhardt'	CKel GBin NCGa SPer WCAu
– 'Top Brass'	CKel ECtt GBin ILea MRav NCGa NLar SDeJ WCAu
– 'Twitterpated'	ELon
– 'Unique'	CKel ELan
– 'Victoire de la Marne'	CKel ILea
– 'Violet Dawson'	GBin
– 'Vivid Rose'	GBin
– 'Vogue'	CKel EPfP LRHS MRav NCGa NRHS SWvt WCAu
– 'W.F. Turner'	CKel
– 'Walter Faxon'	GBin
– 'Waltz'	GBin
– 'Westerner'	GBin WCAu
– 'White Cap'	CKel GBin ILea NCGa NLar WCAu
– 'White Sands'	GBin
– WHITE SARAH BERNHARDT	SPer
– 'White Wings'	CBcs CKel CTri ECtt ELan EPfP EWTr GBin GMaP ILea LRHS MBel NAln NCGa NLar NRHS NSti SMad SPer SWvt WCot
– 'Whitleyi Major' ♀H6	WCot
– 'Wilbur Wright'	CKel GBin WCAu
– 'Wine Red'	GBin
– 'Władysława'	CKel GBin LRHS NCGa SPer WCot
§ – 'Zi Yu Nu'	LSRN NRHS
– 'Zuzu'	GBin
× ***lagodechiana***	GKev LEdu
'Late Windflower'	CKel GBin GKev LPla WCAu
'Le Printemps'	CKel GBin
'Leda' (S)	GBin
'Legion of Honour'	GBin
× ***lemoinei*** (S)	WHal
§ – 'Alice Harding' (S)	CKel NTPC
§ – 'Chromatella' (S)	CKel
– 'High Noon' (S) ♀H5	CKel EBee LRHS MPhe NAln
§ – 'Souvenir de Maxime Cornu' (S)	CKel CRos EBee LRHS NRHS
'Lemon Chiffon'	GBin WCAu
'Lemon Dream' [PBR]	CKel ELan ILea MCot WCAu
lobata 'Fire King'	see *P. peregrina*
'Lollipop' (d)	CKel ELan ILea
'Lorelei' (d)	GBin
'Love Affair'	GBin WCAu
ludlowii (S)	Widely available
ludlowii × ***suffruticosa*** 'Hakuojisi'	CRos LRHS NRHS
lutea	see *P. delavayi* var. *delavayi* f. *lutea*
'Mackinac Grand'	GBin
'Magenta Gem'	GBin
'Mahogany' **new**	GBin
'Mai Fleuri'	WCAu
mairei	CExl GGGa
'Many Happy Returns'	CKel GBin ILea
'Martha Bulloch'	CKel
mascula	CBro GEdr GKev GLog IMou LLHF NBir WCot
§ – subsp. ***arietina***	CSpe
– – W&B BG A-4	WCot
– 'Immaculata'	MHol
§ – subsp. ***mascula***	GKev
§ – subsp. ***russoi***	GKev LPla WThu
– – 'Reverchoni'	EPot
§ – subsp. ***triternata***	EPot GKev WCot
'Merry Mayshine'	GBin GKev
'Mikokunohata'	CKel
'Mikuhino-akebono'	CKel SDeJ
mlokosewitschii ♀H6	CBro CExl CMea CPBP CRos CSpe ECha GBin GEdr GKev ILea LEdu LRHS MBel MNrw NBir NEgg NRHS SLon SWvt WAbe WCot WHoo WKif WSpi
– hybrids	GKev
mollis	see *P. officinalis* subsp. *villosa*
'Montezuma'	GBin
'Moonrise'	CKel GBin
'Morning Lilac'	CKel GBin ILea WCAu
'Murad of Hershey Bar' (S)	GBin
'Muramatsu No Yuki'	CKel
'My Love'	GBin WCAu
'New Orange' **new**	GBin
'Norwegian Blush'	CKel GBin ILea WCAu
'Nosegay'	GBin

	'Nova'	CKel GBin
	obovata	CPla GKev LLHF
	- var. ***alba*** ♀H5	CExl CSpe GEdr GKev LLHF WSHC WSpi
	- 'Grandiflora'	WKif
	- var. ***willmottiae***	CExl
	officinalis	GKev MCot WCot
	- from NW Croatia	LEdu
	- WM 9821 from Slovenia	MPhe
	- 'Alba Plena' (d)	CKel CPou CRos EPfP GMaP ILea LRHS MBel MRav NEgg NLar NRHS SPer SWvt WFar
	- 'Anemoniflora Rosea' ♀H7	CRos EPfP LRHS NRHS SPer SWvt WCAu
§	- subsp. ***banatica***	GKev MPhe
	- subsp. ***humilis***	see *P. officinalis* subsp. *microcarpa*
	- 'James Crawford Weguelin'	WCot
§	- subsp. ***microcarpa***	GKev
	- 'Mutabilis Plena' (d)	IBlr
	- 'Rosea Plena' (d) ♀H7	CRos ECtt ELan EPfP GMaP LRHS NEgg SCob SWvt WCot WFar
	- 'Rubra Plena' (d) ♀H7	CKel CPou CRos CTri EBee ECtt ELan EPfP GBin GMaP IKil ILea LCro LOPS LRHS LSun MBel MHol MRav NEgg NGdn NLar SCob SPer SRms SWvt WBor WCAu WCot
§	- subsp. ***villosa***	LRHS SEND
	'Old Faithful'	GBin
	'Old Rose Dandy'	CKel ELan GBin ILea
	'Orange Glory'	CKel
	'Oriental Gold'	CKel WHil
	ostii (S)	CExl CKel
§	- 'Feng Dan Bai' (S)	CKel
	'Oukan' (S)	CKel
	'Paladin'	GBin
	papaveracea	see *P. suffruticosa*
	paradoxa	see *P. officinalis* subsp. *microcarpa*
	'Paris'	CRos LRHS NRHS
	'Pastel Splendor'	CKel CRos ELan GBin ILea LRHS NRHS WCAu
	'Pastelegance' (d)	GBin
	'Paula Fay'	CKel EPfP EWTr GBin GMaP ILea IMou MGil MRav NCGa NLar SDeJ WCAu WCot
§	***peregrina***	CBro CKel GEdr GKev LEdu MPhe SBrt
	- 'Fire King'	CKel ILea
§	- 'Otto Froebel' ♀H7	CKel GBin GEdr NLar WCot WKif
	- 'Rosabella'	CRos LRHS NRHS
	- 'Sunshine'	see *P. peregrina* 'Otto Froebel'
	'Picotee'	GBin
	'Pink Ardour' **new**	GBin
	'Pink Doodle Dandy'	GBin
	'Pink Hawaiian Coral'	CKel GBin ILea NLar WCot WTor
	potaninii	see *P. delavayi* var. *angustiloba* f. *angustiloba*
	'Prairie Charm'	CKel ILea
	'Prairie Moon'	CKel GBin NLar
	'Purple Sensation' **new**	GBin
	'Red Charm'	CKel ELon EPfP GBin IKil ILea LRHS NCGa SPer WCAu WFar WHil WKif WSpi WTor
	'Red Grace' (d)	GBin
	'Red Magic'	EPfP WFar WSpi
	'Red Red Rose'	GBin
	'Renown' (S)	CKel
§	***rockii*** (S)	CKel CSpe GBin MPhe SPtp WSpi
	- from Tianshui, Gansu	MPhe
	- from Wenshian, Gansu	MPhe
	- hybrid	see *P.* Gansu Group

	- subsp. ***taibaishanica*** (S)	GKev
	'Roman Gold'	CKel
	romanica	see *P. peregrina*
	'Roselette'	GBin LRHS WCAu
	russoi	see *P. mascula* subsp. *russoi*
	'Salmon Chiffon'	GBin
	'Sango-kai'	CKel
	'Scarlet Heaven'	CKel ELan GBin ILea
	'Scarlet O'Hara'	GBin SPer WCAu WCot
	'Scrumdidleumptious' (d)	GBin
	'Seeing Blue'	NCGa
	'Sequestered Sunshine'	CKel WCAu
	'Shikounishiki'	CKel
	'Shimano-fuji'	CKel LRHS
	'Shining Light'	SCob
	'Show Girl'	GBin
	'Showanohokori'	CKel
	'Silver Dawn'	GBin
	'Simply Red'	CKel
	sinensis	see *P. lactiflora*
	'Singing in the Rain'	CKel ILea
	× ***smouthii***	CRos GEdr LRHS NRHS
	'Sonoma Kaleidoscope'	CKel ILea
	'Sonoma Sun'	CKel
	'Sonoma Velvet Ruby' **new**	GBin
	'Soshi'	GBin LRHS NLar SHar
	'Spring Carnival' (S)	GBin
	'Starlight'	CKel GBin LCro LOPS LRHS WCot WTor
	sterniana	CExl
§	***suffruticosa*** (S)	GKev MGil MGos
	- 'Akashigata' (S)	CKel
	- 'Alice Palmer' (S)	CKel
	- BEST-SHAPED RED	see *P. suffruticosa* 'Zhuan Yuan Hong'
	- BIRD OF RIMPO	see *P. suffruticosa* 'Rimpo'
	- BLACK DRAGON BROCADE	see *P. suffruticosa* 'Kokuryū-nishiki'
	- BLACK FLOWER CHIEF	see *P. suffruticosa* 'Hei Hua Kui'
	- BROCADE OF THE NANIWA	see *P. suffruticosa* 'Naniwa-nishiki'
	- 'Cardinal Vaughan' (S)	CKel
	- CHARMING AGE	see *P. suffruticosa* 'Howki'
	- 'Dou Lu' (S)	NTPC
	- DOUBLE CHERRY	see *P. suffruticosa* 'Yae-zakura'
	- 'Duchess of Kent' (S)	CKel
	- 'Duchess of Marlborough' (S)	CKel
	- ETERNAL CAMELLIAS	see *P. suffruticosa* 'Yachiyo-tsubaki'
	- 'Feng Dan Bai' (S)	NTPC
	- FLIGHT OF CRANES	see *P. suffruticosa* 'Renkaku'
	- FLORAL RIVALRY	see *P. suffruticosa* 'Hana-kisoi'
	- 'Gekkyu-den' (S)	LRHS
*	- 'Glory of Huish' (S)	CKel
	- 'Godaishu' (S)	CKel
	- 'Guan Shi Mo Yu' (S)	NTPC
	- 'Hai Huang' (S)	NTPC
§	- 'Hakuo-jisi' (S/d)	CKel LRHS
	- 'Hakushin' (S)	LRHS
§	- 'Hana-daijin' (S)	LRHS
§	- 'Hana-kisoi' (S)	CKel CRos EBee LRHS NRHS
	- 'Hei Hai Sa Jin' (S)	NTPC
§	- 'Hei Hua Kui' (S)	NTPC
§	- 'Howki' (S)	LRHS NTPC
	- 'Iso-no-nami' (S)	LRHS
	- JEWEL IN THE LOTUS	see *P. suffruticosa* 'Tama-fuyo'
	- JEWELLED SCREEN	see *P. suffruticosa* 'Tama-sudare'
	- 'Jin Jiang Hong' (S)	NTPC
	- 'Jitsugetsu-nishiki' (S)	CKel
	- 'Joseph Rock'	see *P. rockii*
	- KAMADA BROCADE	see *P. suffruticosa* 'Kamada-nishiki'
§	- 'Kamada-fuji' (S)	CKel LRHS

§ - 'Kamada-nishiki' (S) CKel
§ - 'Kaow' (S) CKel CRos LRHS NRHS
- KING OF FLOWERS see *P. suffruticosa* 'Kaow'
- KING OF WHITE LIONS see *P. suffruticosa* 'Hakuo-jisi'
- 'Kinkaku' see *P.* × *lemoinei* 'Souvenir de Maxime Cornu'
- 'Kinshi' see *P.* × *lemoinei* 'Alice Harding'
- 'Kokucho' (S) CKel
§ - 'Kokuryū-nishiki' (S) CKel
- 'Koshino-yuki' (S) CKel LRHS
- 'Lan Bao Shi' (S) NTPC
- MAGNIFICENT FLOWER see *P. suffruticosa* 'Hana-daijin'
- 'Montrose' (S) CKel
* - 'Mrs Shirley Fry' (S) CKel
- 'Mrs William Kelway' (S) CKel
§ - 'Naniwa-nishiki' (S) CKel
- 'Nigata Akashigata' (S) CKel
- PRIDE OF TAISHO see *P. suffruticosa* 'Taisho-no-hokori'
- 'Reine Elisabeth' (S) CKel
§ - 'Renkaku' (S) CKel LRHS
§ - 'Rimpo' (S) CKel WSpi
- 'Rou Fu Rong' (S) WSpi
- 'Sakurajishi' (S) new CKel
§ - 'Shiguregumo' (S) CKel
- 'Shimadaigin' (S) CKel CRos LRHS NRHS
- 'Shimane-chōjuraku' (S) CKel LRHS
- 'Shimane-hakugan' (S) CKel
- 'Shimane-seidai' (S) CKel
- 'Shimanishiki' (S) CKel
- 'Shin Shima Kagayaki' (S) CKel LRHS
- 'Shin-fusōtsukasa' (S) LRHS
- 'Shintoyen' (S) CKel
- SNOWY PAGODA see *P. suffruticosa* 'Xue Ta'
- 'Sumi-no-ichi' (S) CKel
- 'Superb' (S) CKel
§ - 'Taisho-no-hokori' (S) CKel
§ - 'Taiyo' (S) CKel CRos EBee LRHS NRHS
§ - 'Tama-fuyo' (S) CKel
§ - 'Tama-sudare' (S) CKel
- THE SUN see *P. suffruticosa* 'Taiyo'
- WISTERIA AT KAMADA see *P. suffruticosa* 'Kamada-fuji'
- 'Wu Long Peng Sheng' (S) CKel WSpi
§ - 'Xue Ta' (S) CKel
§ - 'Yachiyo-tsubaki' (S) CKel LRHS
§ - 'Yae-zakura' (S) LRHS
- 'Yatsu-kazishi' (S) new EBee
- 'Yin Hong Qiao Dui' (S) CKel NTPC
- 'Yoshinogawa' (S) LRHS
- 'Zhao Fen' (S) NPer NTPC
* - 'Zhuan Yuan Hong' (S) NAln
'Sunny Girl' WCAu
'Sunshine' see *P. peregrina* 'Otto Froebel'
'Syukiden' CKel
'Taiheko' CKel
'Tama-usagi' new CKel
'Ten' i' CKel
tenuifolia CAby CBro CJun CPla CSpe EPot EWes EWld GBin GCal GEdr GKev ILea LLHF MAvo MBel NSti SMad WCAu WSpi
- subsp. ***biebersteiniana*** GKev
- 'Plena' (d) GBin
- 'Rosea' GBin
tenuifolia* × *veitchii* var. *woodwardii CJun
'Terrific Gal' GBin
veitchii CKel EPot GCal GKev GMaP NBid NLar WCot WPGP WSpi
- pale-flowered GCal
- var. ***woodwardii*** CExl CJun GAbr GKev LLHF LPla NWad WCot WHoo WThu
'Vesuvian' CKel
'Viking Full Moon' CKel ILea
'Walter Mains' WCAu
'Watermelon Wine' CKel GBin ILea WCAu
'White Emperor' CKel ELan GBin ILea
WHITE PHOENIX see *P. ostii* 'Feng Dan Bai'
'White Towers' EPfP NCGa WFar
'Whopper' GBin
'Wine Angel' GBin
wittmanniana GBin GCal GEdr
- PAB 3673 LEdu
- 'Rosea' WCAu
'Yankee Doodle Dandy' (d) GBin
'Yellow Crown' CKel MHol
'Yellow Emperor' CKel
'Yellow Gem' CKel GBin
'Yellow Waterlily' CKel
'Yokohama' GBin

Paesia (*Dennstaedtiaceae*)

scaberula NBir WCot

pak choi see AGM Vegetables Section

Pallenis (*Asteraceae*)

§ ***maritima*** CCCN

Panax (*Araliaceae*)

ginseng GPoy
japonicus WCru
- BWJ 7932 WCru

Pancratium (*Amaryllidaceae*)

illyricum XEll
maritimum CSpe GKev SDeJ WCot

Pandorea (*Bignoniaceae*)

jasminoides ♀H1c CCCN CHll CPla CRHN CTri EBak EShb
- 'Alba' CRHN EShb
§ - 'Charisma' (v) CBcs CCCN CHll CKel ECre EPfP EShb SEND WAvo
- 'Lady Di' CCCN
- 'Rosea' CCCN WAvo
- 'Rosea Superba' ♀H1c CBcs CRHN SEND
- 'Variegata' see *P. jasminoides* 'Charisma'
lindleyana see *Clytostoma calystegioides*
pandorana CHll CRHN MGil SLim WAvo
- 'Golden Showers' CBcs CCCN CRHN MRav

Panicum (*Poaceae*)

amarum EPPr
- var. ***amarulum*** CKno
- 'Dewey Blue' EPPr IPot SMHy
bulbosum EBee EHoe EPPr
clandestinum CRos EHoe EPPr EShb EWes LRHS MMuc NRHS SMea
§ 'Fibre Optics' CSpe
'Frosted Explosion' CSpe LRHS
miliaceum CRos LRHS NRHS
- 'Violaceum' SPhx
virgatum CKno EPPr MAsh XLum
- 'Blue Tower' CKno CRos ELon EPPr LRHS NRHS SMea XLum
- 'Cardinal' CKno EMor EPPr MNrw WFar WHoo
- 'Cheyenne Sky' EBee
- 'Cloud Nine' ♀H5 CKno EPPr LRHS MAvo SMea WHal

– 'Dallas Blues'	CBod CKno EAJP EBee ECha EHoe ELan ELon EMor EPPr EShb EUJe EWes LRHS MAvo NLar NRHS NWsh SCob SMHy SPer SPoG WMoo XLum
– 'Emerald Chief'	LRHS
– 'Farbende Auslese'	EPPr MAvo
– 'Hänse Herms'	CBod CKno CRos EHoe ELon EMor EPPr LRHS NLar NRHS SMea WFar
– 'Heavy Metal'	Widely available
– 'Heiliger Hain'	CRos EPPr LRHS MAvo NRHS WCot WFar
– 'Külsen Moor'	IPot WCot
I – 'Kupferhirse'	EPPr GQue MAvo WFar
– 'Kurt Bluemel'	EBee
– 'Nican'	EBee EPPr MAvo
– 'Northwind'	CKno CRos EBee EHoe ELon EPPr EPfP GBin LRHS MAvo NRHS SCob SMHy SMad SMea SRms WFar
– 'Prairie Fire'	ECtt
– 'Prairie Sky'	CBod CKno CRos EBee EHoe ELon EPPr EUJe EWhm GMaP LEdu LRHS MAsh MAvo MMuc NBro NLar NRHS NWsh SCob SGbt SMHy SMad SMea SRms WMoo
– 'Purple Haze'	CKno CRos LRHS NRHS
– 'Red Cloud'	CKno MAvo SMHy
– 'Rehbraun'	CBod CRos CSde EBee EHoe EMor EPPr EPfP LCro LOPS LRHS LSRN MJak MMrt NRHS SRms WCAu XLum
– 'Rotstrahlbusch'	CKno EBee EHoe EMor EPPr GMaP LSun MAvo SPer SRms WCot WMoo XLum
– 'Rubrum'	EHoe ELan EPPr MAvo SRms WAvo WMoo
– 'Sangria' **new**	CKno CSpe SPad SPoG
– 'Shenandoah' 🏆H5	Widely available
– 'Squaw'	CBod CKno CMac CRos EBou ECtt EHoe EMor EPPr EPfP EShb EUJe EWhm LRHS MAvo MJak MMuc NDov NRHS NWsh SMad SPer SRms WCot WFar WMoo
– 'Straight Cloud'	EPPr WFar
– 'Strictum'	EHoe EPPr EWes GQue SCob SMHy SPer SPhx WMoo
I – 'Strictum Compactum'	CBod
– 'Thundercloud' **new**	CKno
– 'Warrior'	CBod CKno CRos CTri EAJP ECtt EHoe EHrv ELan ELon EMor EPPr EPfP EWhm LRHS MAsh MAvo NLar NRHS SCob SPer WFar
– 'Wood's Variegated' (v)	WCot

Papaver ✿ (*Papaveraceae*)

alboroseum	CRos LRHS NRHS
alpinum	CRos CSpe EBou LRHS MAsh NGdn NRHS
anomalum	SPhx
atlanticum	EBou NBro SPhx SPlb
– 'Flore Pleno' (d)	CSpe GAbr IFro NBro NGdn
bracteatum	see *P. orientale* var. *bracteatum*
burseri	SRot
§ ***cambricum***	CCCN CExl CMac CRos CTri EBee EHrv ELan LEdu MMuc NPri NRHS SPer WBrk WCot WFar WHer
– var. ***aurantiacum***	WCot
– double-flowered, orange (d)	NBir
§ – 'Frances Perry'	CSpe GAbr GCal GKev
– 'Rubrum'	see *P. cambricum* 'Frances Perry'
carmeli	SPhx
'Cease Fire' **new**	WCot
commutatum 🏆H5	CSpe LCro LOPS SPhx
– 'Ladybird' 🏆H5	GAbr SPoG SVic
dubium	CSpe GPoy LRHS SPhx
– subsp. ***lecoqii*** 'Albiflorum'	CSpe LRHS SPhx
glaucum	LRHS SPhx
guerlekense	WCot
W&B BG-K-5 **new**	
'Heartbeat' (Super Poppy Series)	EPfP IPot LRHS MHol NCou SCob WCot WFar
heldreichii	see *P. pilosum* subsp. *spicatum*
lateritium	CPou SRms
'Lauffeuer'	CSam
'Matador'[PBR] 🏆H6	CRos LRHS NNor NRHS WCot
'Medallion' (Super Poppy Series)	LRHS
§ ***miyabeanum***	CRos CSpe ELan LRHS NRHS SRot
– ***tatewakii***	see *P. miyabeanum*
'Moondance'	CRos LRHS NRHS
§ ***nudicaule***	LCro LOPS SVic
– Champagne Bubbles Group	CBod CRos CSBt LRHS NNor NRHS WFar
– – 'Champagne Bubbles Orange'	ELan
– – 'Champagne Bubbles Pink'	ELan
– – 'Champagne Bubbles Scarlet'	ELan
– – 'Champagne Bubbles White'	ELan
– – 'Champagne Bubbles Yellow'	ELan
– var. ***croceum*** 'Flamenco'	NNor
– Garden Gnome Group	see *P. nudicaule* Gartenzwerg Group
§ – Gartenzwerg Group 🏆H7	CRos EPfP LRHS NHic NRHS SPoG SRot SWvt
– 'Kelmscott Giant'	SVic
– orange-flowered	LRHS
– 'Pacino'	CSBt EAJP LRHS
– 'Party Fun' (mixed)	EAJP
– Wonderland Series	NNor
orientale	CBcs CTsd EPfP NAln NHic SRms SVic
– 'Aglaja' 🏆H7	CBcs CDor CKno ECtt LRHS NEgg NGdn SPad SPhx SPoG WCAu WCot WSpi
– 'Allegro'	CBod CRos CSBt EBee EPfP GMaP LRHS LSun MBNS MRav NAln NGdn NRHS SCob SPer SPlb SPoG SVic SWvt WFar
– 'Baby Kiss'[PBR]	ECtt WFar
– 'Beauty Queen'	CDor MRav NGdn
– 'Black and White' 🏆H7	MRav NEgg
– 'Bolero'	CElw CRos ECtt NLar
– 'Bonfire'	SCob
§ – var. ***bracteatum***	NBir
– 'Brilliant'	CBod CRos EPfP EUJe LRHS NGdn NRHS WFar WMoo
– 'Brooklyn' (New York Series)	ECtt LRHS LSRN
– 'Burning Heart'	CRos CWGN ECtt LRHS
– 'Carmen'[PBR]	ECtt
* – 'Carneum'	CRos LRHS NRHS SPoG SRms
– 'Cedar Hill'	MRav
– 'Cedric Morris' 🏆H7	ECha
– 'Central Park' (New York Series)	CRos EPfP LRHS NCGa NPri NRHS SPoG WFar
I – 'Charming' pink-flowered	ECtt SPhx
– 'Charming' red-flowered	LRHS NRHS

- 'Clochard' CElw ECtt IPot
- 'Coral Reef' EPfP WMoo
- 'Curlilocks' CRos LRHS MRav NRHS SRms SWvt WFar
- 'Double Pleasure' (d) ECtt
- double red shades (d) NGdn
- 'Doubloon' (d) WFar
- 'Dwarf Allegro' NPri
- 'Dwarf Allegro Vivace' CRos LRHS NRHS
- 'Effendi' 🏆H7 NAln
- 'Fancy Feathers'[PBR] ECtt
- 'Fiesta' ELon
- 'Flamenco' WFar
* - 'Flore Pleno' (d) NGdn
- 'Forncett Summer' ECtt MHol SPer SPoG WCAu WCot
- 'Frosty' (v) SHar
- 'Fruit Punch' MNHC
- 'Garden Glory' ECtt LSRN
- 'Glowing Embers' ECtt WHlf
- Goliath Group ELan MRav NBro SCob SRms WFar
- - 'Beauty of Livermere' CBod CDor CRos CSam CTri CWCL EAJP ECha ELan EPfP ILea LCro LOPS LRHS LSun MBel NAln NGdn NLar NNor NPri NRHS SGbt SPer SPoG SRms WArt WCAu WFar WMoo
§ - - 'Beauty of Livermere' clonal ECtt WCot
- 'Guardsman' see *P. orientale* (Goliath Group) 'Beauty of Livermere' clonal
- HAREMSTRAUM (mixed) **new** WFar
- 'Harlem' (New York Series) CBcs CElw CRos ELon EPfP IPot LRHS MNrw MSCN NCGa NLar NRHS STPC
- 'Harvest Moon' (d) CBod CRos ECtt LRHS NPer NRHS SPoG WHal
- 'Indian Chief' NPer WFar
- 'Inferno'[PBR] ECtt
- 'John III' 🏆H7 SPhx
- 'John Metcalf' ECtt MRav
- 'Juliane' NAln
- 'Karine' 🏆H7 CRos EPPr LRHS NRHS
- 'King Kong' ECtt LSun NCou WCot WFar
- 'Kleine Tänzerin' CBod SEND WFar
- 'Ladybird' CRos EPfP LRHS NRHS
- 'Lauren's Lilac' LSRN
- 'Little Patty Plum'[PBR] EPfP
- 'Louvre' (Parisienne Series) WFar
- 'Maiden's Blush' ECtt
- 'Mandarin'[PBR] MHol
- 'Manhattan' (New York Series) CElw CRos CSam ECtt EPfP ILea IPot LRHS MNrw NRHS NSti SGbt SPoG WFar
- 'Marcus Perry' CRos LRHS NRHS
- 'Marlene' EBee IPot LRHS WCAu WHlf
- 'May Queen' (d) ECtt EWes IBlr MRav WCot WFar
- 'Miss Piggy'[PBR] ECtt IKil SGbt WCot WFar
- 'Mrs Marrow's Plum' see *P. orientale* 'Patty's Plum'
- 'Mrs Perry' CRos ECtt ELan IFro LRHS NAln NPer NRHS SGbt SPer SRms WBrk WFar
- 'Orange Glow' WMoo
- 'Papillon'[PBR] CBcs LRHS NRHS WCot
- 'Paradiso'[PBR] CSpe
§ - 'Patty's Plum' Widely available
- 'Perry's White' CBcs CRos EBee ECtt EPfP LRHS MRav NChi NRHS SPer SRkn SWvt WCAu WSpi
- 'Petticoat' ECtt
- 'Picotée' CBcs CRos ECtt ELan LRHS MRav NEgg NRHS SRot SWvt WFar WMoo
- 'Pink Ruffles'[PBR] CRos ECtt LRHS NRHS SGbt WFar
- 'Pinnacle' WFar
- 'Pizzicato' CRos EAJP ELan EPfP LRHS NNor NPer NRHS WFar WMoo
- 'Place Pigalle' (Parisienne Series) ECtt
- 'Plum Pudding' CRos LRHS NRHS
- 'Prince of Orange' SWvt
- PRINCESS VICTORIA LOUISE see *P. orientale* 'Prinzessin Victoria Louise'
- 'Prinz Eugen' WFar
§ - 'Prinzessin Victoria Louise' CDor CRos ELan EPfP GMaP LRHS MNHC NCGa NGdn NNor NPri NRHS SPoG SRms WBrk
- 'Queen Alexandra' CBod CDor MBel NPri WArt
- 'Raspberry Brûlée' CRos EBee LRHS NRHS
- 'Raspberry Queen' CDor CRos ECtt EPfP IPot LRHS MRav NCGa NChi NLar NRHS WHal
- 'Rembrandt' MJak WCot
- 'Royal Chocolate Distinction' CBod ECtt ELan EPPr EPfP IPot LRHS LSRN SCob WFar
- 'Royal Wedding' Widely available
- 'Ruffled Patty'[PBR] ECtt ELan EPfP IKil SGbt SPad WCot
- 'Salmon Glow' (d) WFar
- 'Scarlet King' CMac
- scarlet-flowered SEND
- 'Scarlett O'Hara'[PBR] (d) ECtt WFar
- 'Snow Goose' CDor CRos CSam CWGN EBee ECtt EPfP ILea IPot LRHS LSun NCou NLar NRHS SPoG WCAu WCot WKif
- 'Springtime' MRav
- 'Staten Island' (New York Series) MAvo MNrw
- 'Tiffany' ECtt LSRN NEgg
- 'Türkenlouis' CBod CRos ECtt IPot LRHS MRav NPri NRHS SPoG WBrk WFar
- 'Turkish Delight' CRos ILea LRHS MRav NBir NRHS SWvt WCAu
- 'Walking Fire' MNrw
- 'Watermelon' SPoG
- 'White Ruffles'[PBR] CBod IKil MSCN SGbt

pavoninum SPhx
§ ***pilosum*** subsp. ***spicatum*** CSpe ECha NBir SPhx WMoo
pseudocanescens SPhx
radicatum CPla
rhoeas CHab LCro LOPS MNHC NNor NPri SPhx SVic

- Angels' Choir Group (d) NNor
- 'Bridal Silk' LCro
- 'Bridal White' LOPS SPhx
- Mother of Pearl Group CSpe LCro LOPS LRHS SPhx
- Shirley Group NNor

rupifragum ECha MMuc SPhx WCot

- 'Double Tangerine Gem' see *P. rupifragum* 'Flore Pleno'
§ - 'Flore Pleno' (d) CDor CSpe EPPr GBin NChi SVic WBrk WMoo
- 'Orange Bubbles' CBod
- 'Tangerine Dream' GPSL

'Shasta' (Super Poppy Series) LRHS WFar
somniferum CLau ENfk GPoy SVic

- 'Blackcurrant Fizz' (d) LCro LOPS SPhx
- 'Boudoir Babe' (d) CSpe
- 'Double Shiraz' (d) LRHS SPhx
- (Laciniatum Group) 'Crimson Feathers' NNor
- - 'Danebrog' NNor

- 'Lauren's Grape' CSpe LRHS SPhx WArt
- 'Lilac Pompom' (d) LCro LOPS
- (Paeoniiflorum Group) 'Black Beauty' (d) CSpe LRHS SDeJ SPhx SVic
- - 'Black Paeony' (d) LCro LOPS LRHS SPhx
- - 'Schwarzer Drachen' (d) LRHS
- 'Persian White' SPhx
- 'Ragged Red' (d) CSpe
- subsp. ***setigerum*** NNor
- single black-flowered new CSpe
- single white-flowered CSpe
- 'White Cloud' (d) CSpe

thianschanicum SPhx
triniifolium GCal MMuc SPhx WCot

papaya (pawpaw) see *Carica papaya*

Parabenzoin see *Lindera*

Paracaryum (*Boraginaceae*)

racemosum SIgm

Parachampionella see *Strobilanthes*

Paradisea (*Asparagaceae*)

liliastrum misapplied see *P. lusitanica*
liliastrum (L.) Bertol. ♀H5 EBee GCal LRHS NBid NChi WHil WPtf
§ ***lusitanica*** CAvo CNor CSam CSpe CTca EBee ECtt EPot GBin GCal GKev IBlr LEdu MCot MHol SPhx WCot WPGP XEll

Parahebe (*Plantaginaceae*)

'Angela' MSCN
× ***bidwillii*** GCrg GJos MHer SRms SRot
- 'Kea' ECtt SRot
§ ***catarractae*** CExl ELan EPfP ITim LRHS MSCN NBir NRHS SRms WKif
- 'Avalanche'PBR CRos CWGN GMaP LRHS MAsh NRHS SCob SPoG WHlf WNPC
- 'Baby Blue' CRos LRHS NRHS
- blue-flowered SPer
§ - 'Delight' ♀H4 CExl CRos EWes GMaP GQue LRHS MHer NPer NRHS SRot
- subsp. ***diffusa*** NPer SRot
- 'Miss Willmott' ECtt SPer SPlb
- 'Porlock' CBod EAJP EBee EPfP GKev GWyn NAln NSla SPad SRms SRot WHoo WTor
- 'Porlock Purple' see *P. catarractae* 'Delight'
- 'Rosea' MAsh SRms
- white-flowered CSpe GAbr SRms
- 'Whittallii' GBin

densifolia see *Chionohebe densifolia*
§ ***formosa*** SPlb SVen
'Greencourt' see *P. catarractae* 'Delight'
'Jean' GBin GCrg
'Kenty Pink' MMuc
linifolia 'Blue Skies' ECtt EPot GBin
§ ***lyallii*** CPla CTri EBee ELan EPfP GMaP MHer MMuc MRav MSwo NQui SPlb SRms WKif
- 'Julie-Anne' ♀H4 GCal LRHS
- 'Snowcap' EBee LRHS MRav SPlb SRms
'Mervyn' CNor CTri
§ ***perfoliata*** CDor CExl CMea CSde EBee ECha ECre ELan GAbr GCal GMaP LEdu LRHS MAsh MCot MNrw MRav SBrt SEND SPer SRms WWFP XLum
'Snow Clouds' CBar CMea CRos CSpe EAJP EBee ECtt ELan EPfP GBin GKev LRHS MMuc NEoE NHpl NRHS NSla SBch SMHy SPad SRot WFar WHoo WTor WWFP

Parakmeria see *Magnolia*

Paranomus (*Proteaceae*)

reflexus SPlb

Paraquilegia (*Ranunculaceae*)

adoxoides see *Semiaquilegia adoxoides*
§ ***anemonoides*** CExl GKev WAbe
grandiflora see *P. anemonoides*

Parasenecio (*Asteraceae*)

delphiniifolius B&SWJ 5789 WCru
- B&SWJ 10885 WCru
- B&SWJ 11189 WCru WSHC
- B&SWJ 11415 WCru

farfarifolius WCru
- var. ***acerinus*** B&SWJ 11549 WCru
- - B&SWJ 11554 WCru
- var. ***bulbifer*** WCru

hastatus var. ***farfarifolius*** see *P. maximowiczianus*
kiusianus B&SWJ 11460 WCru
§ ***maximowiczianus*** B&SWJ 11468 WCru
mortonii GWJ 9419 WCru
- HWJK 2214 WCru

tebakoensis B&SWJ 11167 WCru
- B&SWJ 11536 WCru

Paraserianthes (*Mimosaceae*)

distachya see *P. lophantha*
§ ***lophantha*** ♀H2 CExl EBak SPlb

Parasyringa see *Ligustrum*

× *Pardancanda* see *Iris*

Pardanthopsis see *Iris*

Parietaria (*Urticaceae*)

judaica GPoy WHer WSFF

Paris ✿ (*Melanthiaceae*)

chinensis WCru
- B&SWJ 265 from Taiwan WCru

fargesii LAma WCru
- var. ***brevipetalata*** WCru
- var. ***petiolata*** WCru

forrestii WCru
incompleta GCal LEdu MAvo WCru
japonica GEdr LAma WCru
lancifolia B&SWJ 3044 from Taiwan WCru
polyphylla CSpe EPot GEdr GKev LAma MNrw NBid NHpl NLar WCru WPnP
- B&SWJ 2125 WCru
- HWJCM 475 WCru
- var. ***polyphylla*** GKev
- var. ***stenophylla*** LAma WCru
- var. ***yunnanensis*** GEdr
* - - ***alba*** GCal MAvo

quadrifolia CSpe EBee EMor EPfP GCal GEdr GKev GPoy LEdu MAvo MNrw

	NLar SPhx WCru WFar WHer WPnP WShi
tetraphylla	WCru
thibetica	EBee GKev NBid WCru
- var. ***apetala***	WCru
- var. ***thibetica***	GEdr
verticillata	LAma WCru
- 'Ryokutei' (d)	WCru

Parnassia (*Celastraceae*)

foliosa	GEdr NHar
gansuensis	NHar
- SDR 5128	EBee GKev
nubicola	GKev NAln
palustris	WHer
- var. ***yakushimensis***	NHar

Parochetus (*Papilionaceae*)

communis ambig.	CExl MSCN NPer SBrt
- subsp. ***africanus*** ♀H2	WHil
* - 'Blue Gem'	CCCN

Parolinia (*Brassicaceae*)

ornata	WCot

Paronychia (*Caryophyllaceae*)

sp.	SIgm
§ ***capitata***	CTri SRms WHoo
kapela	SPlb XSen
§ - subsp. ***serpyllifolia***	XLum
- - 'Binsted Gold' (v)	XLum
nivea	see *P. capitata*
serpyllifolia	see *P. kapela* subsp. *serpyllifolia*

Parrotia ✿ (*Hamamelidaceae*)

persica	Widely available
- PAB 13.046	LEdu
- 'Bella'	CJun EMOT MBlu WMou
- 'Biltmore'	CJun NLar SSta
- 'Burgundy'	CJun EPfP NLar
- 'Cobhay Upright' **new**	CJun
- fastigiate	CJun
- 'Felicie'	CJun EPfP IArd NLar
- 'Het Plantsoen'	NLar
- 'Horizontalis'	CJun
- 'Jodrell Bank'	CJun MBlu NLar SBir
- 'Pendula'	CJun CMCN EPfP MBlu SSta
- 'Persian Carpet'	NLar
- PERSIAN SPIRE ('Jlpn01') **new**	CBcs
- 'Summer Bronze'	CJun CRos LRHS LSRN MAsh SBir
- 'Vanessa' ♀H6	CBcs CCVT CJun CLnd CMCN CRos CTho EPfP EWes IArd LMaj LRHS MAsh MBlu NLar NRHS SBir SGol SSta WMou
subaequalis	CBcs CDul CJun EBee NLar NWea WPGP

Parrotia × *Sycopsis* see × *Sycoparrotia*

Parrotiopsis (*Hamamelidaceae*)

jacquemontiana	CBcs CJun GBin MBlu NLar

parsley see *Petroselinum crispum*; also AGM Vegetables Section

parsnip see AGM Vegetables Section

Parthenium (*Asteraceae*)

integrifolium	CRos EMor GPoy IMou LRHS NRHS SPhx WCot WHlf

Parthenocissus (*Vitaceae*)

§ ***henryana*** ♀H5	Widely available
- 'Malene'	EShb
himalayana 'Purpurea'	see *P. himalayana* var. *rubrifolia*
§ - var. ***rubrifolia***	CBcs CMac ELan EUJe GBin MAsh MRav SLim SLon SPtp WCru
inserta misapplied	see *P. quinquefolia*
inserta ambig.	CMac CTsd NLar
laetevirens	NLar
§ ***quinquefolia***	Widely available
- var. ***engelmannii***	CBcs EBee EMOT EShb LBuc SCob SEND WCFE
- 'Guy's Garnet'	WCru
- RED WALL ('Troki')	CRos LRHS NRHS
- STAR SHOWERS ('Monham') (v)	EBee EPfP NLar
- 'Yellow Wall'PBR	CRos LRHS NRHS
semicordata B&SWJ 6551	WCru
striata	see *Cissus striata*
thomsonii	see *Cayratia thomsonii*
§ ***tricuspidata***	CCVT CDul EPfP MAsh MGos SArc SCob SGol SPer
- 'Beverley Brook'	CRHN ELon LSRN NLar SNig SRms
- 'Crûg Compact'	WCru
- 'Fenway Park'	CFlo CKel EBee ELan LRHS MRav NLar
- 'Green Spring'	CBcs ELan IArd MGos NLar
- 'Lowii'	CMac CRos EPfP LRHS MBlu MRav NLar NRHS SLon SNig SPoG
- 'Purpurea'	CKel
- 'Robusta'	EBee EMOT
§ - 'Veitchii' ♀H5	Widely available

Pasithea (*Hemerocallidaceae*)

caerulea	MHol SMHy WCot WPGP WSHC

Paspalum (*Poaceae*)

glaucifolium	MNrw
quadrifarium RCB RA S-5	WCot

Passiflora ✿ (*Passifloraceae*)

actinia	CCCN CRHN SPlb
'Adularia'	CCCN
alata (F) ♀H1c	CCCN
× ***alatocaerulea***	see *P.* × *belotii*
× ***allardii***	CCCN
ambigua	CCCN
§ 'Amethyst' ♀H3	CBcs CCCN CFlo CKel CRHN CSBt LSRN MAsh MGil SPoG
amethystina misapplied	see *P.* 'Amethyst'
§ ***amethystina*** Mikan	CRos ECre LRHS NRHS
'Anastasia'	CCCN
'Andy'	CCCN
'Anemona'	CCCN
'Angelo Blu'	CCCN
'Annika'	CCCN
antioquiensis misapplied	see *P.* × *exoniensis*
antioquiensis ambig.	CBcs CCCN CTsd
antioquiensis H. Karst. ♀H2	CHll CRHN
'Ariane'	CCCN
× ***atropurpurea***	CCCN MGil
§ ***aurantia***	CCCN
banksii	see *P. aurantia*
§ × ***belotii***	CCCN
- 'Impératrice Eugénie'	see *P.* × *belotii*
- 'Perfume Passion'PBR	CCCN
'Betty Myles Young'	CCCN CKel CRHN ECre
'Blue Bird'	CCCN
'Blue Bouquet'	CCCN

	Plant	Suppliers
	'Blue Crown'	CCCN
	'Blue Moon'	CCCN
	'Blue Stripper'	CCCN
	'Blue Velvet'	CCCN
	bogatensis B&SWJ 14951 **new**	WCru
	'Byron Beauty'	CCCN
	'Byte'	CCCN
§	***caerulea*** 🏆H4	Widely available
	- 'Chinensis'	CCCN
	- 'Clear Sky' PBR	CCCN CFlo CKel ELan EPfP EUJe EWTr NLar SNig SRms
	- 'Constance Eliott' 🏆H4	CAgr CBcs CCCN CFlo CKel CMac CRHN CRos EBee ELan EPfP LCro LOPS LRHS MAsh MGos MHer NLar NRHS SCob SGol SNig SPer SWvt
	- 'Pierre Pomié'	CCCN
I	- 'Rubra'	CCCN CSBt SLim
	- WHITE LIGHTNING ('Yanpas' PBR)	CCCN CFlo CKel CRos ELan EMOT EPfP EUJe LRHS NAln NRHS SLim SPoG SWvt
	× ***caeruleoracemosa***	see *P.* × *violacea*
	× ***caponii***	CCCN
	- 'John Innes'	CCCN
	'Celine'	CCCN
	chinensis	see *P. caerulea*
	citrifolia	CCCN
	citrina	CCCN
*	***classica*** × ***coccinea***	CCCN
	× ***colvillii***	CCCN CHll
	'Coordination'	CCCN
§	***coriacea***	CCCN
	'Crimson Tears'	CCCN
	cuatrecasasii B&SWJ 14834 **new**	WCru
§	'Damsel's Delight'	CCCN CFlo CKel CRos CWGN EBee ECre LRHS NRHS
	'Daylight'	CCCN
	'Debby'	CCCN
	× ***decaisneana*** (F)	CCCN
	'Divertido'	CCCN
	EDEN ('Hil Pas Eden') 🏆H3	CCCN CFlo CKel SRkn
	edulis (F)	CBcs CCCN CPla MGil SPre SVic
	- 'Byte' (F)	CCCN
§	- f. ***edulis*** (F)	CCCN
	- f. ***flavicarpa*** (F)	CCCN
	- 'Norfolk' (F)	CCCN
	- 'Parati' (F)	CCCN
	'Elizabeth' (F)	CCCN
	'Empress Eugenie'	see *P.* × *belotii*
	'Evatoria'	CCCN
§	× ***exoniensis*** 🏆H2	CCCN CHll CRHN CSBt ECre
	'Fairylights'	CCCN
	'Fantasma'	CCCN
	'Fata Confetto'	CCCN
	'Fledermouse'	CCCN
	'Flying V'	CCCN
	foetida	WHil
	'Grand Duchess'	CCCN
	gritensis	CCCN
	'Guglielmo Betto'	CCCN
	'Heidi'	CCCN
	'Hetty Nicolaas'	CCCN
	'Hildegard'	CCCN
	'Hill House'	CHll
	incarnata (F)	CCCN GPoy SPlb
	'Incense' (F) 🏆H2	CCCN SPlb
	'Inspiration'	CCCN
	'Jara'	CCCN
	'Jelly Joker'	CCCN

	Plant	Suppliers
	'Justine Lyons'	CCCN CKel
	karwinskii	CCCN
	× ***kewensis***	CCCN
	'Lady Margaret'	CCCN
	'Lambiekins'	CCCN CFlo CKel
§	***ligularis*** (F)	CCCN
	'Lilac Lady'	see *P.* × *violacea* 'Tresederi'
	'Livie'	CCCN
	lowei	see *P. ligularis*
	lutea	CCCN
	'Luzmarina'	CCCN
	'Manapany'	CCCN
	manicata (F)	CCCN
	- B&SWJ 14284	WCru
	- B&SWJ 14868 **new**	WCru
	'Maria'	CCCN
	'Marijke'	CCCN
	'Mary Jane'	CCCN
I	***matthewsii*** 'Alba'	CRHN
	'Mavis Mastics'	see *P.* × *violacea* 'Tresederi'
	mayana	see *P. caerulea*
	membranacea (F)	CCCN
	'Michael'	CCCN
	'Minai'	CCCN
	'Mini Lamb'	CCCN
	mixta (F)	CCCN
	- B&SWJ 14832 **new**	WCru
	- clone 2	CCCN
	- red-flowered	CCCN
	aff. ***mixta*** B&SWJ 14302 **new**	WCru
	mollissima misapplied	see *P. tarminiana*
	mollissima ambig. (F)	CBcs CCCN SPlb
	mollissima (Kunth) L.H. Bailey (F) 🏆H2	CRHN
	- B&SWJ 14876 **new**	WCru
	'Monika Fischer'	CCCN
	mucronata	CCCN
	murucuja	CCCN
	'New Incense'	CCCN
	'Nightshift'	CCCN
	obtusifolia	see *P. coriacea*
	onychina	see *P. amethystina* Mikan
	'Panda'	CCCN
	'Party Animal'	CCCN CFlo CKel ECre
	'Pink Festival'	CCCN
	'Pink Nightmare'	CCCN
	'Pink Passion' PBR	CCCN
	'Pinky'	CCCN
	× ***piresiae***	CCCN
	'Poppet'	CCCN CKel
	'Precioso'	CCCN
	'Pura Vida'	CCCN
	'Purple Companion'	CCCN
	'Purple Haze'	CCCN CKel CRos CTsd ELan LCro LOPS LRHS NLar NRHS WFar
	'Purple Passion'	see *P. edulis* f. *edulis*
	'Purple Pendulum'	CCCN
	'Purple Rain'	CCCN
	quadrangularis (F) 🏆H1a	CCCN CHll
	quinquangularis	CCCN
	racemosa 🏆H1a	CCCN
	- 'Buzios'	CCCN
	- pink-flowered	CCCN
	'Red Inca'	CCCN
	reitzii	CCCN
	riparia	CCCN
	semiciliosa B&SWJ 14824 **new**	WCru
	sexocellata	see *P. coriacea*
	'Silly Cow'	see *P.* 'Damsel's Delight'

'Silvie'	CCCN
'Simply Red'	CCCN
'Snow Queen'	CWGN WHil
'Star of Bristol' ♀H2	CKel
'Star of Kingston'	CCCN
'Star of Surbiton'	CCCN LRHS
'Sunburst'	CCCN
'Surprise'	CCCN
§ ***tarminiana*** (F)	CCCN CRHN CSBt
- B&SWJ 14960 **new**	WCru
- white-flowered	CCCN
'Temptation'	CCCN
tetrandra	CExl
× ***tresederi***	see *P.* × *violacea* 'Tresederi'
trifasciata	CCCN
tripartita	WCru
B&SWJ 14768 **new**	
- B&SWJ 14807 **new**	WCru
tucumanensis tetraploid	CCCN
tulae	CCCN
venusta	CCCN
§ × ***violacea*** ♀H2	CCCN CRHN
- 'Eynsford Gem'	CCCN
- 'Lilac Lady'	see *P.* × *violacea* 'Tresederi'
- 'Sabin'	CCCN
§ - 'Tresederi'	CCCN
- 'Twin Star'	CCCN
- 'Victoria'	CCCN CSBt NLar
vitifolia (F)	CCCN
- 'Innocentiae'	CCCN
'White Queen'	CCCN
'White Surprise'	CCCN
'White Wedding'	CCCN CKel EWTr
'Wilgen Heintje'	CCCN
'Wilgen K Verhoeff'	CCCN
'Wilgen Marieke'	CCCN
'Winterland'	CCCN

passion fruit see *Passiflora*

passion fruit, banana see *Passiflora mollissima* (Kunth) L.H. Bailey

Pastinaca (*Apiaceae*)

sativa	CHab SVic WCot
- subsp. ***sylvestris*** **new**	NGrd

Patersonia (*Iridaceae*)

occidentalis	LRHS SPlb

Patrinia ✿ (*Caprifoliaceae*)

gibbosa	CSam CSpe EBee ECtt EMor GEdr MMrt MMuc NLar SPhx WFar WMoo WPnP
- B&SWJ 874	WCru
heterophylla	GKev
intermedia	EBee
cf. ***monandra***	EBee
aff. ***punctiflora***	ECha NDov
rupestris B&SWJ 12654	WCru
scabiosifolia	CElw CHll CKno CSpe ECha ECtt EMor EWld LRHS MAvo NBir NLar SPhx WFar WHoo WMoo
- B&SWJ 8740	WCru
- 'Nagoya'	MNrw
triloba	CRos CSpe EMor GCal GEdr LRHS MMrt NLar NRHS WFar WMoo
* - 'Minor'	ECtt
- var. ***palmata***	EBee GKev NAln WMoo
villosa	CExl EBee IMou SPhx

Paulownia (*Paulowniaceae*)

catalpifolia	EBee NLar SAko
elongata	NLar
fargesii misapplied	see *P. tomentosa* 'Lilacina'
fortunei	MBlu SPlb
- FAST BLUE ('Minfast') ♀H5	CExl LSRN SGol
kawakamii	CBct CMCN EBee EPfP SChF WPGP
- RWJ 9909	WCru
'Purple Spendour'	SAko
tomentosa ♀H5	Widely available
- W 769	WPGP
- 'Coreana'	WCru
§ - 'Lilacina'	NChi

Pavonia (*Malvaceae*)

multiflora ambig.	CCCN
strictiflora	CCCN
* ***volubilis***	CCCN

pawpaw (false banana) see *Asimina triloba*

pawpaw (papaya) see *Carica papaya*

pea see AGM Vegetables Section

peach see *Prunus persica*

pear see *Pyrus communis*; also AGM Fruit Section

pear, Asian see *Pyrus pyrifolia*

pecan see *Carya illinoinensis*

Pedicularis (*Orobanchaceae*)

bicornata	CPla

Pelargonium ✿ (*Geraniaceae*)

'A.M. Mayne' (Z/d)	WFib
'Aaron West' (St)	WFib
'Abba' (Z/d)	WFib
'Abbie Hillier' (R)	WFib
'Abel Carrière' (I/d)	WFib
abrotanifolium (Sc)	ENfk MHer SVen WFib WGwG
acetosum	GCal MHer WFib
'Ada Green' (R)	WFib
'Ada Sutterby' (Dw/d)	WFib
'Adam's Quilt' (Z/C)	SAll
'Ade's Elf' (Z/St)	WFib
'Ainsdale Beauty' (Z)	WFib
alchemilloides	WFib
'Alcyone' (Dw/d)	SAll
'Alde' (Min)	SAll
'Aldwyck' (R) ♀H1c	WFib
'Alex Kitson' (Z)	WFib
'Algenon' (Min/d)	WFib
I 'Alice' (Min)	WFib
'Alison March' (Dw/Z/v/d)	WFib
'Allesley Shadow' (Dw/d)	ECtt WFib
alpinum	MHer
'Alta Bell' (R)	ELan
'Always' (Z/d)	SAll
'Amari' (R)	WFib
'Ambrose' (Min/d)	SAll WFib
AMELIT ('Pacameli'PBR) (I/d)	MCot SSea
'American Prince of Orange' (Sc)	SPet
AMETA ('Pacmeta'PBR) (Z)	SSea
'Amethyst' (R)	SAll SCoo WFib
I 'Amy' (Dw)	WFib

Name	Suppliers
(Angeleyes Series) ANGELEYES BICOLOR ('Pacbicolor'[PBR]) (A)	MCot
- ANGELEYES ORANGE ('Paccrio'[PBR]) (A)	WCot
- ANGELEYES RANDY ('Pacra') (A)	SSea
'Angelique' (Dw/d)	SAll WFib
'Ann Hoystead' (R) [H1c]	WFib
'Annabelle Stephenson' (Dw/d)	WFib
'Annsbrook Beauty' (A/C)	SPet WFib
'Annsbrook Jupitor' (Z/St)	WFib
(Antik Series) ANTIK ORANGE ('Tikorg'[PBR]) (Z) [H1c]	SPoG
- ANTIK PINK ('Tikpink'[PBR]) (Z)	SPoG
- ANTIK SCARLET ('Tikscarl'[PBR]) (Z)	SPoG
- ANTIK VIOLET ('Tikvio'[PBR]) (Z)	SPoG
'Antoine Crozy' (Z × I/d)	WFib
'Apache' (Z/d)	WFib
appendiculatum	MHer
'Apple Betty' (Sc)	NWsh WFib
'Apple Blossom Rosebud' (Z/d) [H1c]	ECtt EShb MHer SAll WFib
'Apricot' (Dw/v)	SAll
'Apricot Fool' (U/Sc)	WFib
'Apricot Glace' (U/Sc)	MHer WFib
'April Hamilton' (I)	WFib
'April Showers' (A)	WFib
'Arctic Frost' (I)	WFib
§ 'Arctic Star' (St) [H1c]	CSpe WBrk WFib
'Ardens' [H1c]	CNor CPbh CSpe EBee EUJe MCot MHer SAll SCob SWvt WCAu WCot WFib WWFP
'Ardwick Cinnamon' (Sc)	ENfk MHer NWsh SAll SPet SRms WFib
'Arnside Fringed Aztec' (R)	MHer WFib
'Ashby' (Dec/Sc) [H1c]	CSpe ECtt ENfk MHer SAll SPet WFib
'Ashfield Blaze' (Z/d)	SAll
'Ashfield Jubilee' (Z/C)	SAll WFib
'Ashfield Serenade' (Z) [H1c]	WFib
'Askham Fringed Aztec' (R) [H1c]	WFib
asperum Ehr. ex Willd.	see *P.* 'Graveolens'
'Athabasca' (Min)	SAll
§ 'Atomic Snowflake' (Sc/v)	CSpe ECtt ENfk MNHC NWsh SAll SPet SRms WFib
'Atrium' (U)	MHer NWsh WFib
'Attar of Roses' (Sc) [H1c]	CCht ECtt ENfk MCot MHer MNHC NCou NPri NWsh SAll SBch SPet SPoG SRms WBrk WFib WGwG
'Aurora' (Z/d)	ECtt SAll
australe	MCot MHer NWsh SBch SVen WFib
'Australian Mystery' (R/Dec) [H1c]	CSpe ECtt SPet WFib
'Aztec' (R) [H1c]	SAll WFib
'Baby Bird's Egg' (Min)	WFib
'Baby Brocade' (Min/d)	SAll
'Baby Harry' (Dw/v)	WFib
'Balcon Lilas'	see *P.* 'Roi des Balcons Lilas'
'Balcony Red' (I)	ECtt
'Ballerina' (R)	see *P.* 'Carisbrooke'
I 'Ballerina' (Min)	WFib
'Banstead Village' (Z)	SAll
'Barbara Eldridge' (Z)	WFib
§ 'Barbe Bleu' (I/d) [H1c]	WFib

Name	Suppliers
barklyi	WFib
'Baronne A. de Rothschild' (Z/d)	WFib
'Bath Beauty' (Dw)	CSpe
'Beacon Hill' (Min)	SAll
'Beatrice Cottington' (I/d)	WFib
'Beauty of Calderdale' (Z/C)	WFib
'Beauty of Eastbourne' misapplied	see *P.* 'Lachskönigin', *P.* 'Eastbourne Beauty'
'Belinda Adams' (Min/d) [H1c]	SAll
BELLADONNA ('Fisopa') (I/d)	SCoo
'Bembridge' (Z/St/d)	WFib
'Ben Matt' (R)	WFib
§ 'Bergpalais'[PBR] (Z/d)	SSea
'Berkswell Carnival' (A)	ELan SPet
'Berkswell Jester' (A)	SAll
'Berkswell Lace' (A)	MHer
'Beromünster' (Dec)	ECtt MHer WFib
'Bert Pearce' (R)	WFib
'Beryl Gibbons' (Z/d)	SAll WFib
'Beryl Reid' (R)	WFib
'Betty' (Z/d)	SAll
betulinum	CPbh WFib
'Betwixt' (Z/v)	WFib
'Big Apple' (Sc)	SRms
'Bird Dancer' (Dw/St) [H1c]	CSpe MHer SAll WBrk
(Birdbush Series) 'Birdbush Bobby' (Sc)	SRms
- 'Birdbush Bold and Beautiful' (Sc)	SRms
- 'Birdbush Eleanor' (Z)	WFib
- 'Birdbush Nutty' (Sc)	SRms
'Birthday Girl' (R) [H1c]	ECtt WFib
'Bitter Lemon' (Sc)	ECtt WFib
'Black Butterfly'	see *P.* 'Brown's Butterfly'
'Black Country Bugle' (Z/d)	WFib
'Black Knight' (A)	SPet
'Black Knight' (R)	ECtt MHer
'Black Pearl' (Z/d)	SAll
'Black Prince' (R/Dec)	CSpe WFib
'Black Vesuvius'	see *P.* 'Red Black Vesuvius'
'Blackcurrant Yhu' (Dec)	MPtG
BLANCHE ROCHE ('Guitoblanc') (I/d)	MHer SAll SCoo SSea
§ 'Blandfordianum' (Sc)	MHer NWsh
I 'Blandfordianum Album' (Sc)	WFib
'Blandfordianum Roseum' (Sc)	MHer WFib
'Blazonry' (Z/v)	WFib
(Blizzard Series) BLIZZARD BLUE ('Fisrain'[PBR]) (I)	SCoo
- BLIZZARD RED ('Fizzard') (I)	SCoo
- BLIZZARD WHITE ('Fisbliz'[PBR]) (I)	SCoo
'Blue Beard'	see *P.* 'Barbe Bleu'
'Bob Newing' (Min/St)	WFib
'Bobberstone' (Z/St)	WFib
'Bold Ann' (Dw/Z/d)	WFib
'Bold Appleblossom' (Z)	WFib
'Bold Bridesmaid' (Dw/d)	WFib
'Bold Carousel' (Z/d)	WFib
'Bold Cherie' (Dw/d)	WFib
'Bold Cherub' (Z/d)	WFib
'Bold Cyclamen' (Dw/d)	WFib
'Bold Debonair' (Dw/d)	WFib
'Bold Dove' (Dw)	WFib

'Bold Flame' (Z/d)	WFib
'Bold Gem' (Z/d)	WFib
'Bold Limelight' (Z/d)	WFib
'Bold Minstrel' (Z/d)	WFib
'Bold Moonlight' (Dw)	WFib
'Bold Pixie' (Dw/d)	WFib
'Bold Princess' (Z/d)	WFib
'Bold Special' (Z)	WFib
'Bold Spirit' (Z)	WFib
'Bold Sunset' (Z/d) ♀H1c	WFib
'Bolero' (U) ♀H1c	MPtG SAll WFib
'Bon Bon' (Min/St)	WFib
'Bontrosai'[PBR] (Sc)	MCot
'Bornholm' (d)	SAll
'Bosham' (R)	WFib
'Both's Snowflake' (Sc/v)	WFib
'Bourbon Rose' (Sc) **new**	MHer
bowkeri	WFib
'Brackenwood' (Dw/d) ♀H1c	SAll
'Bramford' (Dw)	SAll
BRAVO ('Fisbravo') (Z/d)	WFib
'Brenda' (Min/d)	WFib
'Brenda Hyatt' (Dw/d)	SAll WFib
'Brian West' (Min/St/C)	WFib
'Brian West Butterfly' (Z/St) ♀H1c	WFib
'Bright Eyes' ambig. (Dw)	WFib
'Brightstone' (Z/d)	ECtt WFib
'Brilliant' (Dec)	ENfk SPet WFib
'Brilliantine' (Sc)	ENfk MHer SRms WFib
'Britannia' (R)	WFib
'Brixworth Charmer' (Z/v)	SAll
'Brixworth Pearl' (Z)	WFib
'Broadway' (Min)	SAll
'Brook's Purple'	see *P.* 'Royal Purple'
'Brookside Flamenco' (Dw/d)	SAll WFib
'Brookside Primrose' (Min/C/d)	WFib
'Brookside Serenade' (Dw)	WFib
§ 'Brown's Butterfly' (R)	ECtt WFib
'Brunswick' (Sc)	MHer WFib
'Bushfire' (R) ♀H1c	WFib
BUTTERFLY ('Fisam'[PBR]) (I)	SCoo
caespitosum	MHer
caffrum	WFib
- 'Diana'	MHer
'Cal'	see *P.* 'Salmon Irene'
'California Brilliant' (U)	MHer
'Calignon' (Z/St)	WFib
'Caligula' (Min/d)	SAll
'Cameo' (Dw/d)	SAll WFib
'Camisole' (Dw/d)	SAll
'Camphor Rose' (Sc) ♀H1c	SRms
'Can-can' (I/d)	WFib
canescens	see *P.* 'Blandfordianum'
'Cape Town' (Dw/Z/v)	WFib
capitatum	ENfk WFib
'Capri' (Sc)	WFib
'Captain Starlight' (A) ♀H1c	EShb MHer SPet WFib
'Carefree' (U) ♀H1c	ECtt WFib
§ 'Carisbrooke' (R) ♀H1c	WFib
'Carmel' (Z)	WFib
carnosum	MHer
'Carol Gibbons' (Z/d) ♀H1c	SAll
'Carole Munroe' (Z/d)	WFib
'Caroline' (Dec)	WFib
'Caroline Schmidt' (Z/d/v)	ECtt MCot SAll WBrk WFib
'Carolyn Hardy' (Z/d)	WFib
CASCADE LILAC	see *P.* 'Roi des Balcons Lilas'
caucalifolium subsp. ***caucalifolium***	MHer
- subsp. ***convolvulifolium***	WFib
'Cedric Morris Corvette' (Z)	WFib
'Celebration' (Z/d)	WFib
'Celestial Rose' (Z/d)	WFib
'Cézanne' (R)	MCot SAll
'Charity' (Sc) ♀H1c	ENfk MCot MHer MNHC NWsh SAll SPet SRms WFib
'Charlotte Bronte' (Dw/v)	WFib
'Charmay Cocky' (Z/d)	WFib
'Charmay Hampshire' (Z/d)	WFib
'Charmay Snowflake' (Sc/v)	SRms
'Charmay Snowflurry' (Sc/v)	WFib
'Chavarri Hermanos' (Z/d)	WFib
'Chelsea Gem' (Z/d/v) ♀H1c	WFib
'Chelsea Morning' (Z/d)	WFib
'Cherry' (Min)	WFib
'Cherry Baby' (Dec) ♀H1c	ECtt WFib
'Cherry Orchard' (R)	WFib
'Chew Magna' (R)	WFib
'Chieko' (Min/d)	WFib
'Chinese Cactus' (Z/St)	WFib
'Chinz' (R)	ECtt
§ 'Chocolate Peppermint' (Sc)	ECtt ELan ENfk MCot MHer NWsh SPet SRms WFib
'Chocolate Tomentosum'	see *P.* 'Chocolate Peppermint'
'Chocolate Twist' (St/C)	SAll
'Choun Cho' (I)	WFib
'Chrissie' (R)	WFib
'Christopher Ley' (Z)	SAll
'Cindy' (Dw/d)	WFib
'Citriodorum' (Sc) ♀H1c	ELan MCot MHer WFib
'Citronella' (Sc)	SRms WFib
'Claret Rock Unique' (U)	WFib
'Clatterbridge' (Dw/d) ♀H1c	SAll
'Clorinda' (U/Sc)	ENfk MCot MHer MNHC NWad SAll SPet SRms WFib
'Clown' (R)	WFib
'Coddenham' (Dw/d)	WFib
'Cola Bottles'	CPla ELan NPer SPet SPoG WFib
§ 'Colonel Baden-Powell' (I/d)	WFib
COLORADO NOVA ('Genu'[PBR]) (Z)	SSea
COLUMBIA (St)	WFib
'Colwell' (Min/d)	WFib
'Concolor Lace'	see *P.* 'Shottesham Pet'
'Contrast' (Z/C/v)	SAll SCoo SPoG WFib
'Cook's Peachblossom' (Z/d)	SAll WFib
'Copthorne' (U/Sc) ♀H1c	MCot MHer NWsh SPet SRms WFib
cordifolium	GCal WFib
- var. ***rubrocinctum***	MHer NWsh
coriandrifolium	see *P. myrrhifolium* var. *coriandrifolium*
'Cornell' (I/d)	WFib
cortusifolium	MHer
'Cotta Lilac Queen' (I/d)	ECtt SAll
'Cottenham Bliss' (A)	WFib
'Cottenham Cynthia Haird' (A)	WFib
'Cottenham Delight' (A)	WFib
'Cottenham Glamour' (A) ♀H1c	MHer
'Cottenham Harmony' (A)	WFib
'Cottenham Jubilee' (A)	MHer
'Cottenham Surprise' (A) ♀H1c	MPtG SPet

'Cottenham Wonder' (A) ♀H1c SPet WFib
'Cottontail' (Min) SAll
cotyledonis WFib
'Countess of Scarborough' see *P.* 'Lady Scarborough'
'Cover Girl' (Z/d) WFib
'Covina' (R) WFib
'Cramdon Red' (Dw) WFib
'Crampel's Master' (Z) SAll WFib
'Creamery' (d) WFib
'Creamy Nutmeg' (Sc/v) ENfk EShb MHer NWad SEND SRms
'Credo' (Z) WFib
'Creeting St Peter' (Min) SAll
'Crimson Unique' (U) ♀H1c CSpe ELan ENfk MCot MHer WFib
§ ***crispum*** (Sc) GPoy
- 'Cy's Sunburst' (v) ♀H1c ECtt MHer NWsh SPet WFib
§ - 'Golden Well Sweep' (Sc/v) WFib
- 'Major' (Sc) WFib
- 'Peach Cream' (Sc/v) ENfk WFib
- 'Prince Rupert' (Sc) NWsh
- 'Variegatum' (Sc/v) ♀H1c ECtt ENfk GBin GPoy MHer NWsh SAll SPet SRms WCot WFib
crithmifolium MHer
'Crock O Day' (I/d) ECtt SAll
'Crocodile' (I/C/d) ♀H1c ECtt ELan MHer MNHC NWad WFib
'Crowfoot Rose' (Sc) WFib
'Crystal Palace Gem' (Z/v) ECtt SAll WFib
cucullatum WFib
- 'Flore Pleno' (d) MHer WFib
'Cupid' (Min/Dw/d) WFib
§ 'Czar' (Z/C) SCoo
'Dainty Maid' (Sc) ECtt ENfk
'Dale Queen' (Z) WFib
'Dame Anna Neagle' (Dw/d) SAll
'Dark Red Irene' (Z/d) SAll WFib
'Dark Secret' (R) CSpe WFib
'Dark Venus' (R) WFib
'David John' (Dw/d) SAll
'Davina' (Min/d) WFib
'Deacon Arlon' (Dw/d) ECtt SAll
'Deacon Avalon' (Dw/d) WFib
'Deacon Barbecue' (Z/d) SAll WFib
'Deacon Birthday' (Z/d) SAll
'Deacon Bonanza' (Z/d) SAll WFib
'Deacon Clarion' (Z/d) SAll WFib
'Deacon Constancy' (Z/d) SAll
'Deacon Coral Reef' (Z/d) SAll WFib
'Deacon Fireball' (Z/d) SAll WFib
'Deacon Gala' (Z/d) SAll WFib
'Deacon Golden Bonanza' (Z/C/d) WFib
'Deacon Golden Lilac Mist' (Z/C/d) WFib
'Deacon Jubilant' (Z/d) SAll
'Deacon Lilac Mist' (Z/d) WFib
'Deacon Mandarin' (Z/d) WFib
'Deacon Minuet' (Z/d) ECtt SAll WFib
'Deacon Peacock' (Z/C/d) WFib
'Deacon Picotee' (Z/d) SAll WFib
'Deacon Regalia' (Z/d) SAll
'Deacon Romance' (Z/d) SAll
§ 'Deacon Summertime' (Z/d) SAll WFib
'Deacon Sunburst' (Z/d) SAll
'Deacon Trousseau' (Z/d) SAll
'Deborah Miliken' (Z/d) ♀H1c WFib
'Decora Impérial' (I) SAll
'Decora Lavender' see *P.* 'Decora Lilas'
§ 'Decora Lilas' (I) ECtt
'Decora Mauve' see *P.* 'Decora Lilas'
'Decora Pink' see *P.* 'Decora Rouge'
'Decora Red' see *P.* 'Decora Rouge'
§ 'Decora Rose' (I) ECtt
§ 'Decora Rouge' (I) ECtt
'Deerwood Angel Wings' (A) WFib
'Deerwood Darling' (Min/v/d) WFib
'Deerwood Lavender Lad' (Sc) ENfk MHer WFib
'Deerwood Lavender Lass' (Sc) MCot MHer SRms
'Deerwood Pink Puff' (St/d) WFib
'Delightful' (R) WFib
'Delli' (R) ♀H1c MHer MPtG NPer WFib
'Denebola' (Min/d) SAll
denticulatum MHer
§ - 'Filicifolium' (Sc) ELan ENfk MCot MHer NWsh SAll SPet WFib
'Diana Louise' (Z/d) WFib
'Diana Palmer' (Z/d) SAll WFib
'Diane' (Min/d) SAll
'Dibbinsdale' (Z) ♀H1c SAll
dichondrifolium (Sc) SAll WFib
'Dick Key' (Z/d) WFib
'Didi' (Min) SAll
'Display' ambig. (Dw/v) WFib
'Distinction' (Z) SAll SPoG WFib
'Dodd's Super Double' (Z/d) WFib
'Dolly' (R) WFib
'Dolly Varden' (Z/v) ♀H1c ECtt SAll WFib
'Don's Helen Bainbridge' (Z/C) WFib
'Don's Richard A. Costain' (Z/C) WFib
'Don's Silver Wedding' (d) SAll
'Don's Stokesley Gem' (Z/C) WFib
'Don's Swanland Girl' (Min) SAll
'Doris Hancock' (R) WFib
'Doris Shaw' (R) ELan WFib
'Dorothy Baker' (R) WFib
'Double New Life' (Z/d) WFib
'Double Pink' (R/d) WFib
'Dovedale' (Dw/C) WFib
'Downlands' (Z/d) WFib
'Dragon's Breath' (Z/St) SAll
'Dresden Pink' (Dw) MHer
'Dresden White' (Dw) WFib
'Dubonnet' (R) WFib
'Duchess of Devonshire' (U) WFib
'Duke of Buckingham' (Z/d) SAll WFib
'Duke of Devonshire' (Z/d) SAll
'Duke of Edinburgh' see *P.* 'Hederinum Variegatum'
'Dunkery Beacon' (R) WFib
§ 'Dwarf Miriam Baisey' (Min) SAll
'Dwarf Miriam Read' see *P.* 'Dwarf Miriam Baisey'
'E. Dabner' (Z/d) WFib
'East Sussex' (Dw/C) SAll
§ 'Eastbourne Beauty' (I/d) WFib
echinatum MHer
- 'Album' WFib
'Eclipse' (Dw/d) ECtt
'Eden Gem' (Min/d) SAll WFib
'Edith Stern' (Dw/d) SAll
'Edmond Lachenal' (Z/d) WFib
'Edward Hockey' (Z) WFib
'Eileen Postle' (R) ♀H1c WFib
'Elaine Ward' (R) WFib

ELBE SILVER ('Pensil') (I) ♀H1c	SCoo
'Electra' (Z/d)	SAll
'Elizabeth Read' (Dw)	SAll
'Elizabeth Taylor' (Z)	WFib
'Ella Jane' (Z/d)	WFib
'Ellen Gray' (v)	SAll
'Elmsett' (Dw/C/d)	ECtt SAll WFib
'Els' (Dw/St)	WBrk
'Els' (1870)	SAll
'Elsi' (I × Z/d/v)	SAll WFib
'Elsie Gillam' (St)	WFib
'Embassy' (Min)	WFib
EMILIA ('Pactina'[PBR]) (Z)	SSea
'Emma Hössle'	see *P.* 'Frau Emma Hössle'
'Emma Jane Read' (Dw/d)	WFib
'Emma Louise' (Z)	WFib
'Emperor Nicholas' (Z/d)	WFib
'Encore' (Z/d/v)	SAll
endlicherianum	MHer SPhx WCot XEll
'Endsleigh' (Sc)	WFib
'Erwarton' (Min/d)	SAll
'Escapade' (Min/d)	SAll
'Eskay Gold' (A)	WFib
'Eskay Jewel' (A)	WFib
'Eskay Ruby' (A)	MHer
'Eskay Sugar Candy' (A)	WFib
'Eskay Verglo' (A)	WFib
EVENING GLOW	see *P.* 'Bergpalais'
'Evka'[PBR] (I/v)	ECtt SCoo
exstipulatum	MHer SVen
'Fair Ellen' (Sc)	MHer WFib
'Fairlee' (Dw)	WFib
'Fairy Lights' (Dw/St)	SAll
'Fairy Orchid' (A)	SPet WFib
'Fallen Angel' (Z/St)	ECtt SAll
'Fandango' (Z/St)	SAll WFib
'Fanny Eden' (R)	WFib
'Fantasia' white-flowered (Dw/d) ♀H1c	WFib
'Fareham' (R) ♀H1c	WFib
'Faye Brawner' (Z/St)	SAll
'Fern Mint' (Sc)	SRms
'Feuerriese' (Z)	SAll
'Fiat Queen' (Z/d)	WFib
'Fieldings Unique' (U)	SPet
'Fiery Sunrise' (R)	WFib
'Fifth Avenue' (R)	WFib
'Filicifolium'	see *P. denticulatum* 'Filicifolium'
'Fir Trees Catkins' (A)	MHer
'Fir Trees Ellie'	MPtG
'Fir Trees Fiesta' (R) ♀H1c	ECtt MPtG
'Fir Trees Hayley' (R)	WFib
'Fir Trees Mark' (R/Dec/v) ♀H1c	MPtG
'Fir Trees Muffin' (Sc) ♀H1c	MPtG
'Fir Trees Pearl Anniversary' (Z/C)	WFib
'Fir Trees Silver Wedding' (Z/C/d)	WFib
'Firebrand' (Z/d)	SAll
'First Blush' (R)	WFib
FIRST YELLOW ('Pacyell'[PBR]) (Z/d)	WFib
'Fleur d'Amour' (R)	WFib
'Fleurisse' (Z)	WFib
(Flower Fairy Series) FLOWER FAIRY BERRY ('Sweberry'[PBR]) (Z)	SSea
- FLOWER FAIRY VELVET ('Swevel'[PBR]) (Z)	SSea
- FLOWER FAIRY WHITE SPLASH ('Swewhi'[PBR]) (Z)	SSea
fragrans	ECtt ENfk SAll SPet SRms
Fragrans Group (Sc)	GPoy MCot MHer NWsh WFib WGwG
§ - 'Fragrans Variegatum' (Sc/v) ♀H1c	MCot NWsh SPet SPoG WFib
- 'Snowy Nutmeg'	see *P.* (Fragrans Group) 'Fragrans Variegatum'
'Fragrant Frosty' (Sc/v) **new**	MHer
'Fraiche Beauté' (Z/d)	WFib
'Francis Gibbon' (Z/d)	WFib
'Francis Parrett' (Min/d) ♀H1c	WFib
'Frank Headley' (Z/v) ♀H1c	ECtt EShb MCot NPer SAll SCoo SPoG WFib WOld
§ 'Frau Emma Hössle' (Dw/d)	SAll WFib
'Freak of Nature' (Z/v)	MHer SAll WFib
'Frensham' (Sc)	ENfk MHer NWsh WFib
'Freshwater' (St/C)	WFib
'Friary Wood' (Z/C/d)	WFib
'Friesdorf' (Dw/Fr)	MCot MHer WBrk WFib
'Fringed Apple' (Sc)	WFib
'Fringed Aztec' (R) ♀H1c	MHer WFib
'Frosty' misapplied	see *P.* 'Variegated Kleine Liebling'
'Frosty Petit Pierre'	see *P.* 'Variegated Kleine Liebling'
'Fruity' (Sc)	SRms
frutetorum	MHer
fruticosum	WFib
fulgidum	MCot MHer SAll WFib
'Gabriel' (A)	WFib
'Galilee' (I/d)	SAll
GALLERIA SUNRISE ('Sunrise') (R)	SAll
'Galway Star' (Sc/v) ♀H1c	MHer WFib
'Ganther' (Dec)	WFib
'Gareth Mark Pratt' (Z/C)	WFib
'Garland' (Dw/d)	SAll
'Garland' (R)	WFib
'Garnet' (Min)	NPri
'Garnet Rosebud' (Min/d)	SAll WFib
'Garnet Wings' (R)	WFib
'Gartendirektor Herman' (Dec) ♀H1c	ELan MHer MPtG WFib
'Gaudy' (Z)	WFib
'Gemini' (Z/St/d) ♀H1c	WFib
'Gemma' (R)	SAll
'Gemstone' (Sc) ♀H1c	ENfk MHer SPet WFib
'Genie' (Z/d)	SAll WFib
'Gentle Georgia' (R)	WFib
'Georgia' (R)	WFib
'Georgia Peach' (R)	WFib
'Georgina Blythe' (R) ♀H1c	WFib
'Gerald Wells' (Min)	SAll
'Giant Butterfly' (R)	WFib
gibbosum	CSpe MHer WFib
'Gillian Shaw' (R)	WFib
'Glacis'[PBR] (Quality Series) (Z/d)	SSea
'Gladys Evelyn' (Z/d)	WFib
'Gladys Weller' (Z/d) ♀H1c	WFib
glaucum	see *P. lanceolatum*
'Gleam' (Z/d)	SAll
§ ***glutinosum***	WFib
'Goblin' (Min/d)	SAll
'Goesta' (Z/d)	SSea
GOLDEN ANGEL	see *P.* 'Sarah Don'

'Golden Brilliantissimum' (Z/v)	WFib
'Golden Chalice' (Min/v)	WFib
'Golden Clorinda' (U/Sc/C)	NWsh SEND SPet WFib
'Golden Ears' (Dw/St/C) ♀H1c	NPer WFib
'Golden Edinburgh' (I/v)	WFib
'Golden Harry Hieover' (Z/C)	SAll
'Golden Lilac Gem' (I/d)	WFib
'Golden Princess' (Min/C)	WFib
'Golden Square' (Dw/St)	WFib
'Golden Staphs' (Z/St/C)	MHer SAll
'Golden Stardust' (Z/St)	SAll
'Golden Tears' (Min/Z/St/C/d)	ECtt
'Golden Well Sweep'	see *P. crispum* 'Golden Well Sweep'
'Good Vibrations' (Min/Z/St/d)	SAll
'Gooseberry Leaf'	see *P. grossularioides*
'Gosport' (Z/v)	WFib
'Grace Thomas' (Sc) ♀H1c	MHer WFib
'Grace Wells' (Min)	WFib
'Grand Slam' (R) ♀H1c	WFib
'Grandad Mac' (Dw/St) ♀H1c	MPtG
grandiflorum	MCot MHer WFib
graveolens L'Hér.	see *P.* 'Graveolens'
graveolens ambig.	SEND
graveolens *sensu* J.J.A. van der Walt	WFib
§ 'Graveolens' (Sc)	ENfk GPoy MHer SAll SVen WBrk WFib
'Great Blakenham' (Min)	SAll
'Great Bricett' (Dw/d)	SAll
'Green Eyes' (I/d)	MHer
'Greetings' (Min/v)	SAll WFib
§ 'Grenadier' (Z)	SAll
'Grey Lady Plymouth' (Sc/v)	CPbh MCot MHer NWsh WFib
'Grey Sprite' (Min/v)	WFib
§ ***grossularioides***	MHer
§ 'Hannaford Star' (Z/St)	WFib
'Hansen's Pinkie' (Dec)	WFib
'Hansen's Wild Spice' (Sc)	NWsh WFib
'Happy Appleblossom' (Z/v/d)	SAll
'Happy Thought' (Z/v) ♀H1c	ECtt MCot SAll SCoo WFib WHil
'Harbour Lights' (R)	WFib
'Harewood Slam' (R)	WFib
'Harlequin Pretty Girl' (I × Z/d)	SAll WFib
'Harlequin Rosie O'Day' (I)	ECtt WFib
'Harvard' (I/d)	WFib
'Hazel' (R)	WFib
'Hazel Cherry' (R)	WFib
'Hazel Dean' (R)	ECtt
'Hazel Glory' (R)	WFib
'Hazel Gypsy' (R)	WFib
'Hazel Peach' (R)	WFib
'Hazel Star' (R)	WFib
'Hazel's Finale' (Dec)	WFib
§ 'Hederinum Variegatum' (I/v)	ECtt WFib
'Helen Bainbridge' (Z/C)	SAll
'Helen Christine' (Z/St) ♀H1c	MHer WFib
'Hemley' (Sc)	SAll
'Henry Weller' (A) ♀H1c	WFib
'Hermanus Show' (Sc)	WFib
'Hermione' (Z/d)	WFib
'Highfields Always' (Z/d)	SAll
'Highfields Appleblossom' (Z)	SAll
'Highfields Attracta' (Z/d)	WFib
'Highfields Ballerina' (Z/d)	SAll
'Highfields Candy Floss' (Z/d)	ECtt SAll WFib
'Highfields Charisma' (Z/d)	SAll
'Highfields Choice' (Z) ♀H1c	WFib
'Highfields Dazzler' (Z)	SAll
'Highfields Delight' (Z)	WFib
'Highfields Fancy' (Z/d)	SAll
'Highfields Festival' (Z/d) ♀H1c	ECtt WFib
'Highfields Flair' (Z/d)	SAll WFib
'Highfields Melody' (Z/d)	WFib
'Highfields Orange' (Z)	SAll
'Highfields Pink' (Z)	SAll WFib
'Highfields Pride' (Z)	WFib
'Highfields Prima Donna' (Z/d)	SAll
'Highfields Salmon' (Z/d)	SAll
'Highfields Serenade' (Z)	SAll
'Highfields Snowdrift' (Z)	WFib
'Highfields Sugar Candy' (Z/d)	SAll
'Highfields Supreme' (Z)	SAll
'Highfields Symphony' (Z)	SAll WFib
'Highfields Vogue' (Z)	SAll WFib
'Hilda's Memory' (Dw/Z/d)	WFib
'Hills of Snow' (Z/v)	MHer SAll WFib
'Hindoo' (R × U) ♀H1c	WFib
hispidum	MHer
'Hit Parade' (I/d)	WFib
'Hitcham' (Min/d)	WFib
'Holbrook' (Dw/C/d)	WFib
'Honeywood Lindy' (R)	WFib
'Honeywood Suzanne' (Min/Fr)	SAll
HOT SPOT RIA ('Ria'PBR) (Z)	SAll
'House and Garden' (R)	ECtt
'Hula' (R × U)	WFib
'Ian Read' (Min/d)	SAll
'Ice Cap' (Min)	SAll
'Icing Sugar' (I/d)	WFib
ignescens	WFib
'Immaculatum' (Z)	WFib
'Imperial Butterfly' (A/Sc) ♀H1c	ENfk MPtG SPet SRms WFib
ionidiflorum	CSpe EShb MCot MHer MNHC SRms WAvo
'Irene' (Z/d)	WFib
'Irene Cal' (Z/d)	WFib
'Irene Toyon' (Z)	WFib
'Islington Peppermint' (Sc)	SPet SRms WFib
'Ivalo' (Z/d)	WFib
'Ivory Snow' (Z/d/v)	WFib
'Jacey' (Z/d)	SAll
'Jack of Hearts' (I × Z/d)	WFib
'Jack Phillips' (Z/d)	WFib
§ 'Jackie' (I/d) ♀H1c	SAll WFib
'Jackie Gall'	see *P.* 'Jackie'
'Jackie Totlis' (Z/St)	WFib
'Jackpot Wild Rose' (Z/d)	WFib
'Jacqui Caws' (Dw)	SAll
'Jane Innes' (I/d)	WFib
'Janet Hofman' (Z/d)	WFib
'Janet James' (Dw/Z/d)	SAll
'Janet Kerrigan' (Min/d)	WFib

'Jayne' (Min/d)	SAll
'Jayne Eyre' (Min/d)	WFib
'Jean Bart' (I)	SAll
§ 'Jeanne d'Arc' (I/d)	WFib
'Jer'Rey' (A)	WFib
'Jessica' (Z/d)	SAll
'Jip's Bishops Wood' (Dw/d)	WFib
'Jip's Desert Poppy' (Z/Min)	WFib
'Jip's Eleanor Renton' (Dw/d)	WFib
'Jip's Freda Burgess' (Z/C/d)	SAll
'Jip's Little Lady' (Dw)	WFib
'Jip's Megan' (Z/C/D)	ECtt
'Jip's Pippin' (Dw)	WFib
'Jip's Proud Sentinel' (Dw/d)	WFib
'Jip's Sky Gipsy' (Dw)	WFib
'Jip's Twilight' (Dw)	WFib
'Joan Fontaine' (Z)	WFib
'Joan Morf' (R) ♀H1c	WFib
'Joan of Arc'	see *P.* 'Jeanne d'Arc'
'John Squires' (Z/C/d)	SAll
'John's Angela'	SAll
'Joy' (R) ♀H1c	CSpe ECtt WFib
'Joy Lucille' (Sc)	NWsh
'Judith Thorp' (R)	SAll
'Julie Smith' (R)	WFib
'Juniper' (Sc)	WFib
'Just Beth' (Z/C/d)	WFib
'Just Jip' (Dw/Z)	WFib
'Just Joss' (Dw/d)	WFib
'Just William' (Min/C/d)	WFib
'Kamahl' (R)	WFib
'Karl Hagele' (Z/d)	WFib
'Karmin Ball'	WFib
'Karrooense'	see *P. quercifolium*
'Katie Hillier' (R)	WFib
'Kaufman's Bonfire' (R)	WFib
'Keepsake' (Min/d)	SAll WFib
'Kenny's Double' (Z/d)	ECtt WFib
'Kerensa' (Min/d)	WFib
'Kesgrave' (Min/d)	WFib
'Kewense' (Z)	EShb WFib
'Key's Unique' (U)	WFib
'Kimono' (R) ♀H1c	ECtt
'King Edmund' (R) ♀H1c	WFib
'King of Denmark' (Z/d)	SAll WFib
'King Solomon' (R)	WFib
'King's Ransom' (R)	WFib
§ 'Kleine Liebling' (Min)	WFib
'Kyra' (Min/d)	SAll
'La France' (I/d) ♀H1c	ECtt SAll WFib
'La Jolla' (Z/d)	WFib
'La Paloma' (R)	WFib
§ 'Lachskönigin' (I/d)	WFib
'Lady Alice of Valencia'	see *P.* 'Grenadier'
'Lady Ilchester' (Z/d)	WFib
'Lady Love Song' (R)	WFib
'Lady Mary' (Sc)	MHer SRms WFib
'Lady Mavis Pilkington' (Z/d)	WFib
'Lady Plymouth' (Sc/v) ♀H1c	CPbh CSpe ECtt ELan ENfk GLog MCot MHer NWad NWsh SAll SEND SPet SRms WFib WGwG
§ 'Lady Scarborough' (Sc)	ENfk MHer SRms WFib
laevigatum	MHer
'Lancastrian' (Z/d)	ECtt WFib
§ ***lanceolatum***	MHer
'Lara Ballerina' (Sc/d) ♀H1c	SPet SRms
'Lara Candy Dancer' (Sc) ♀H1c	MAsh NWsh SPet WFib
'Lara Jester' (Sc)	ECtt ENfk NWsh WFib
'Lara Starshine' (Sc) ♀H1c	ENfk MHer SPet SRms WFib
'Lara Waltz' (R/d)	WFib
'Laurel Hayward' (R)	WFib
'Lauren Alexandra' (Z/d)	WFib
'Lavender Grand Slam' (R) ♀H1c	SAll
'Lavender Lindy' (Sc)	NWsh WCot WFib
'Lavender Sensation' (R)	WFib
'Lawrenceanum'	WFib
laxum	WFib
'L'Élégante' (I/v) ♀H1c	MCot MHer SAll WFib
'Lemon Air' (Sc)	WFib
'Lemon Crisp'	see *P. crispum*
'Lemon Fancy' (Sc) ♀H1c	MHer NWad NWsh SAll SPet WFib
'Lemon Kiss' (Sc)	CSpe NWsh WFib
'Lemon Meringue' (Sc)	WFib
'Letitia' (A)	ENfk
LILA COMPAKT-CASCADE	see *P.* 'Decora Lilas'
LILAC ('Paclilac'PBR) (I)	SSea
LILAC CASCADE	see *P.* 'Roi des Balcons Lilas'
'Lilac Gem' (Min/I/d)	ENfk
'Lilian Pottinger' (Sc) ♀H1c	ENfk MHer NWsh WFib
'Lilian Woodberry' (Z)	WFib
'Limoneum' (Sc)	ENfk MHer SPet WFib
'Lincolnshire Lady' (R)	ECtt
'Lipstick' (St)	WFib
'Lisa' (Min/C)	WFib
'Lisa Jo' (St/v/Dw/d)	WFib
'Little Alice' (Dw/d) ♀H1c	SAll WFib
'Little Gem' (Sc)	ENfk MHer WFib
'Little Jip' (Z/d/v) ♀H1c	SAll WFib
'Little Spikey' (St/Min/d)	MHer WFib
'Lizzie Hillier' (R)	WFib
'Lollipop' (Z/d)	WFib
'Lord Baden-Powell'	see *P.* 'Colonel Baden-Powell'
'Lord Bute' (R) ♀H1c	CSpe ECtt MCot MHer MPtG NPer SPet SVen WFib WGwG
'Lord de Ramsey'	see *P.* 'Tip Top Duet'
'Lord Roberts' (Z)	WFib
'Lottie Lungburgh' (Z/St)	WFib
'Lotusland' (Dw/St/C) ♀H1c	ECtt SPoG WFib
I 'Louise' (R) ♀H1c	ECtt MPtG WFib
'Love Song' (R/v)	WFib
'Lucy Gunnett' (Z/d/v) ♀H1c	ECtt WFib
'Lyewood Bonanza' (R)	WFib
'Lyric' (Min/d)	WFib
'Mabel Grey' (Sc) ♀H1c	CSpe ECtt ENfk MHer MNHC NPer NWsh SAll SPet WFib
§ 'Madame Auguste Nonin' (U/Sc)	ENfk MHer NWsh SAll SPet WFib
'Madame Crousse' (I/d) ♀H1c	WFib
'Madame Layal' (A) ♀H1c	MHer WFib
'Madame Margot'	see *P.* 'Hederinum Variegatum'
'Madame Recamier' (Z/d)	ECtt
'Madame Salleron' (Min/v)	SAll
'Magda' (Z/d)	SAll
magenteum	MHer
'Magnum' (R)	WFib
'Majestic' (Z/d)	WFib
'Mandarin' (R)	ECtt SAll
'Mangles' Variegated' (Z/v)	WFib
'Maple Leaf' (Sc)	NWsh
'Maréchal MacMahon' (Z/C)	ENfk
'Margaret Soley' (R) ♀H1c	WFib
'Margaret Thorp'	SAll
'Margaret Waite' (R)	WFib

	Name	Suppliers
	'Margery Stimpson' (Min/d)	WFib
	'Marie Rudlin' (R)	SAll
	'Marie Thomas' (Sc)	SBch
	MARIMBA ('Fisrimba'[PBR])	SCoo
	'Marion Saunders' (Dec)	WFib
	'Mariquita' (R)	WFib
	'Mark' (Dw/d)	WFib
	'Marmalade' (Min/d)	SAll
	'Marquis of Bute' (R/v)	MHer SPet
	'Martha Parmer' (Min)	SAll
	'Martin Parrett' (Min/d)	WFib
	'Mary Harrison' (Z/d)	WFib
	'Maureen' (Min)	SAll
I	'Maureen' Hoddinott (Z/d)	MHer
	'Mauve Beauty' (I/d)	WFib
	'Maxime Kovalevski' (Z)	WFib
	'Maxine Colley' (Z/d/v)	SAll
	'May Day' (R)	WFib
	'May Magic' (R)	WFib
	'Meadowside Dark and Dainty' (St)	WFib
	'Meadowside Fancy' (Z/d/C)	SAll
	'Meadowside Mahogany' (Z/C)	SAll
	'Meadowside Midnight' (St/C)	WFib
	'Medley' (Min/d)	WFib
	MELOCHERRY ('Pacmel'[PBR]) (Tempo Series) (Z/d)	SSea
	MELOSILVER ('Penber') (Tempo Series) (Z/d/v)	SAll
	'Memento' (Min/d)	SAll WFib
	'Mendip' (R)	WFib
	'Mendip Barbie' (R) ♀H1c	MPtG
	'Mendip Candy Floss' (R)	WFib
	'Mendip Royale' (R)	WFib
	'Meon Maid' (R)	WFib
	'Mere Casino' (Z)	WFib
	'Mexican Beauty' (I)	WFib
	'Mexicana'	see *P.* 'Rouletta'
	'Mexicanerin'	see *P.* 'Rouletta'
	'Michael' (A) ♀H1c	MHer SPet
	'Michelle West' (Min)	WFib
	'Mike West' (St)	WFib
	MILLENNIUM DAWN (Dw)	SAll
	'Millfield Gem' (I/d)	WFib
	'Millfield Rose' (I/d)	SAll
	'Mini Czech' (Cas/Min)	ECtt SAll WBrk
	'Minnie' (Z/d/St)	WBrk WFib
	'Minstrel Boy' (R)	WFib
	'Minx' (Min/d)	WFib
	'Miriam Basey'	see *P.* 'Dwarf Miriam Baisey'
	'Miss Burdett Coutts' (Z/v)	MHer WFib
	'Miss Muffett' (Min/d)	WFib
§	'Miss Stapleton'	MHer WFib
	'Misterioso' (R)	WFib
	'Misty Morning' (R)	WFib
	'Mixed Blessings' (Min/C)	SAll
	'Modesty' (Z/d)	WFib
	'Mohawk' (R)	WFib
	'Mole'	see *P.* 'The Mole'
	'Molly' (A)	ENfk
	'Monique McEwan' (Z/St)	WFib
	'Monsieur Ninon' misapplied	see *P.* 'Madame Auguste Nonin'
§	'Monsieur Ninon' (U)	WFib
	'Mont Blanc' (Z/v)	SAll WFib
	'Montague Garabaldi Smith' (R)	WFib
	'Monty's Magic' (R)	ECtt ELan
	'Moon Maiden' (A)	WFib
	MOONLIGHT VIOLINO (Moonlight Series) (Z)	SSea
	'Moor' (Min/d)	SAll
	'More's Victory' (U/Sc)	WFib
	MORNING SUN ('Pacmorsu'[PBR]) (Green Leaf Series) (Z)	SAll
	'Morval' (Dw/C/d) ♀H1c	SAll WFib
	'Morwenna' (R)	MHer WCot WFib
	'Mosaic Gay Baby' (I/v/d)	WFib
	'Mr Henry Cox' (Z/v) ♀H1c	MHer SAll WFib
	'Mr Wren' (Z)	ECtt ELan EShb SAll WFib
	'Mrs Cannell' (Z)	WFib
	'Mrs Farren' (Z/v)	MCot
	'Mrs G.H. Smith' (A) ♀H1c	ECtt SPet WFib
	'Mrs J.C. Mappin' (Z/v) ♀H1c	ECtt
	'Mrs Kingsbury' (U)	WFib
	'Mrs Martin' (I/d)	WFib
	'Mrs McKenzie' (Z/St)	WFib
	'Mrs Morf' (R)	ECtt
	'Mrs Parker' (Z/d/v)	ECtt SAll WFib
	'Mrs Pollock' (Z/v)	ECtt ELan MCot NEgg SAll SCoo WBrk WFib
	'Mrs Quilter' (Z/C) ♀H1c	ECtt SAll WBrk WFib
	'Mrs Salter Bevis' (Z/Ca/d)	SAll
	'Mrs W.A.R. Clifton' (I/d)	WFib
	multibracteatum	WFib
	multiradiatum	WFib
	mutans	WFib
§	'Mutzel' (I/v)	SAll
	'My Chance' (Dec)	WFib
§	***myrrhifolium*** var. ***coriandrifolium***	MHer WFib
	'Mystery' (U) ♀H1c	ECtt WFib
	'Narina' (I)	SCoo
	'Needham Market' (A)	ENfk SPet
	'Neil Jameson' (Z/v)	SAll
	'Nellie Nuttall' (Z)	WFib
	NEONA ('Pacneon'[PBR]) (Z)	SSea
	'Nervous Mabel' (Sc) ♀H1c	MHer WFib
	'Nettlestead' (Dw)	SAll
	'Newbridge' (St/Min/d)	SAll
	'Newchurch' (Z/St)	WFib
	'Nicor Star' (Min)	WFib
	'Noel' (Z/Ca/d)	ECtt SAll
	'Noele Gordon' (Z/d)	SAll WFib
	'Occold Embers' (Dw/C)	SAll
	'Occold Shield' (Dw/C/d) ♀H1c	ECtt MHer NEgg SAll WBrk WFib
	'Occold Tangerine' (Z)	WFib
	'Occold Volcano' (Dw/C/d)	WFib
	odoratissimum (Sc) ♀H1c	ENfk GPoy MHer SAll SPet SRms WFib
	'Odyssey' (Min)	WFib
	'Old Spice' (Sc/v)	ENfk SPet WFib
	'Oldbury Duet' (A/v) ♀H1c	MHer SPet
	'Olivia' (R)	WFib
	'Opera House' (R)	WFib
	'Orange Fizz' (Sc) ♀H1c	MHer NWsh SPet SRms WFib
	'Orange Imp' (Dw/d)	SAll
	'Orange Parfait' (R)	WFib
	'Orange Splash' (Z)	SAll
	'Orangeade' (Dw/d)	SAll WFib
	'Orangesonne' (Z/d)	SAll
	'Orchid Clorinda' (Sc)	WFib
	'Orchid Paloma' (Dw/d)	ECtt WFib
	'Orion' (Min/d)	WFib
	'Orsett' (Sc) ♀H1c	GLog SAll
	otaviense	WFib

'Our Flynn' (Z/St)	WFib
'Our Gynette' (Dec)	SAll SPet
'Our Henry' (Dw/d)	WFib
PAC cultivars	see under selling name
'Pagoda' (Z/St/d)	MHer SAll WFib
'Paisley Red' (Z/d)	WFib
'Pamela Vaughan' (Z/St)	WFib
'Pampered Lady' (A)	SPet
panduriforme	WFib
papilionaceum	ELan MCot MHer WFib
'Parisienne' (R) ♀H1c	WFib
'Party Dress' (Z/d)	WFib
'Pat Hannam' (St)	WFib
'Paton's Unique' (U/Sc) ♀H1c	ECtt ELan ENfk MCot MHer SAll SPet SVen WCot WFib
'Patricia Andrea' (Z/T) ♀H1c	NPer SAll WFib
patulum	WFib
'Paul Crampel' (Z) ♀H1c	MCot MHer WFib
'Paul West' (Min/d)	NWad SAll SBch
'Pauline Harris' (R)	WFib
'Peace' (Min/C)	WFib
'Peach Princess' (R)	ECtt
'Pegasus' (Min)	SAll
'Peggy Franklin' (Min)	SAll
'Peggy Sue' (R)	SAll
PELFI cultivars	see under selling name
peltatum	WFib
'Penny' (Z/d)	WFib
'Penny Lane' (Z)	CSma WFib
'Pensby' (Dw)	WFib
'Peppermint Lace' (Sc)	NWsh
'Peppermint Scented Rose' (Sc)	MSCN
'Perfect' (Z)	WFib
'Pershore Princess'	WAvo WBrk
'Petals' (Z/v)	SPoG
'Peter Beard' (Dw/d)	SAll
'Peter Godwin' (R)	WFib
'Peter's Choice' (R)	WFib
'Petit Pierre'	see *P.* 'Kleine Liebling'
'Phyllis Richardson' (R/d)	SAll WFib
'Phyllis Variegated' (U/v)	ECtt ENfk MHer SAll SPet WCot WFib
'Pink Aurore' (U)	WFib
'Pink Bonanza' (R)	WFib
'Pink Capitatum'	see *P.* 'Pink Capricorn'
§ 'Pink Capricorn' (Sc)	ECtt ENfk NPri NWsh SAll SRms WFib
'Pink Champagne' (Sc)	MHer
'Pink Dolly Varden' (Z/v)	ECtt WFib
'Pink Fondant' (Min/d)	WFib
'Pink Gay Baby'	see *P.* 'Sugar Baby'
'Pink Happy Thought' (Z/v)	ECtt SAll WFib
'Pink Needles' (Min/St)	MHer WFib
'Pink Pandora' (T)	WFib
'Pink Pet' (U)	ECtt
'Pink Rambler' (Z/d)	WFib
'Pink Rosebud' (Z/d)	WFib
'Playboy Blush' (Dw)	SAll
'Playmate' (Min/St)	WFib
'Plum Rambler' (Z/d)	ECtt EShb WBrk WFib
'Polka' (U) ♀H1c	SPet WFib
POLKA (Z/d)	SAll
'Pompeii' (R)	WFib
'Poquita' (Sc)	MHer SRms
'Porchfield' (Min/St)	WBrk
praemorsum	WFib
'Preseli Lottie' (Z/d)	WFib
'Preston Park' (Z/C)	WFib
'Pretty Polly' (Sc)	WFib
'Prim' (Dw/St/d)	WFib
'Prince of Orange' (Sc) ♀H1c	ECtt ENfk GPoy MCot MHer MPtG NPri NWsh SPet SRms WFib
'Princeanum' (Sc) ♀H1c	WFib
'Princess Abigail' (Dw/d)	ECtt WFib
'Princess Alexandra' (Z/d/v)	SAll
'Princess Josephine' (R)	WFib
'Princess of Balcon'	see *P.* 'Roi des Balcons Lilas'
'Princess of Wales' (R)	WFib
'Princess Virginia' (R/v)	WFib
'Priory Salmon' (St/d)	EShb
'Priory Star' (St/Min/d)	WFib
pseudoglutinosum	WFib
'Pulsar Salmon Splash' (Pulsar Series) (Z)	CRos LRHS NRHS
'Pungent Peppermint' (Sc)	SRms
'Purple Rogue' (R)	WFib
'Purple Unique' (U/Sc)	ECtt ENfk MCot MHer SPet SVen WFib
'Pygmalion' (Z/d/v)	WFib
'Quantock' (R)	WFib
'Quantock Angelique' (A)	SPet
'Quantock Butterfly' (A)	SPet
'Quantock Candy' (A) ♀H1c	ELan SPet
'Quantock Clare' (A)	SPet
'Quantock Double Diamond'	MPtG
'Quantock Double Dymond' (A/d) ♀H1c	WFib
'Quantock Kendy' (A) ♀H1c	MPtG
'Quantock Kennedy'	MPtG
'Quantock Kirsty' (A) ♀H1c	SPet
'Quantock Marjorie' (A) ♀H1c	SPet
'Quantock Matty' (A) ♀H1c	MPtG
'Quantock Perfection' (A) ♀H1c	MPtG SPet WFib
'Quantock Sally' (A/d)	SPet
'Quantock Ultimate' (A) ♀H1c	ECtt SPet
'Queen Esther' (Z/d/St)	SAll
'Queen of Denmark' (Z/d)	SAll WFib
'Queen of Hearts' (I × Z/d)	WFib
quercifolium (Sc)	ECtt ELan GPoy WFib
quinquelobatum	WFib
radens (Sc)	ENfk WFib
'Radula' (Sc) ♀H1c	ELan MHer SAll SPet SRms WFib
'Radula Roseum' (Sc)	WFib
'Ragamuffin' (Dw/d)	SAll
'Rager's Star' (Dw)	SAll
(Rainbow Series) RAINBOW NEON ('Genraineon') (I)	SSea
– RAINBOW WHITE ('Genrawhite') (Rainbow Series) (I)	SSea
'Raspberry Sundae' (R)	SAll
'Ray Bidwell' (Min)	WFib
'Red Admiral' (Min/d/v)	SAll
§ 'Red Black Vesuvius' (Min/C)	MHer WFib
'Red Cascade' (I) ♀H1c	SAll WFib
'Red Gables'	WAvo
'Red Ice' (Min/d)	SAll
'Red Pandora' (Z/T) ♀H1c	SAll WFib
'Red Pimpernel' (Z/T)	WFib
'Red Pimpernella'	SAll
'Red Rambler' (Z/d)	SAll WBrk WFib
'Red Robin' (R)	ENfk WCot
'Red Silver Cascade'	see *P.* 'Mutzel'
'Red Spider' (Dw/Ca)	WFib

Name	Suppliers
'Red Startel' (Z/St/d)	WFib
'Red Susan Pearce' (R)	WFib
'Red Witch' (Dw/St/d)	MHer SAll WBrk WFib
§ RED-MINI-CASCADE ('Rotemica') (I)	SAll
'Redondo' (Dw/d)	SAll
'Reflections' (Z/d)	WFib
'Reg 'Q'' (Z/C)	ECtt
'Regina' (Z/d) ♀H1c	ECtt SAll WFib
'Rembrandt' (R)	SAll WFib
'Renate Parsley' ♀H1c	MHer WFib
reniforme	MHer WFib
'Reunion Rose' (Sc)	WFib
'Richard Collins' (St)	SAll
'Richard Gibbs' (Sc)	ENfk MHer SPet
'Richard Key' (Z/d/C)	WFib
'Rietje van der Lee' (A)	ENfk WFib
'Rigel' (Min/d)	SAll
'Rimfire' (R) ♀H1c	MHer NWad WFib
'Rio Grande' (I/d)	MHer SAll WFib
'Rita Scheen' (A/v)	SPet
'Rober's Lemon Rose' (Sc)	ENfk MHer SEND SPet SRms WBrk WFib
'Rober's Salmon Coral' (Dw/d)	SAll
'Robert Fish' (Z/C)	ECtt SCoo
'Robert McElwain' (Z/d)	WFib
'Robin' (R)	ECtt
'Robin' (Sc)	SAll
'Robin's Unique' (U)	WFib
'Robyn Hannah' (St/d) ♀H1c	MHer MPtG
'Rogue' (R)	WFib
§ 'Roi des Balcons Lilas' (I)	SAll SSea
'Roller's Echo' (A)	WFib
'Roller's Pioneer' (I/v)	ENfk SAll
'Roller's Satinique' (U)	MHer
'Rollison's Unique' (U)	MHer WFib
'Rookley' (St/d) ♀H1c	MPtG
'Rosa della Sera' (St)	SAll
'Rose Bengal' (A)	ENfk SPet
'Rose Eye' (Dw)	WFib
'Rose of Amsterdam' (Min/d)	WFib
'Rose Silver Cascade' (I)	ECtt MCot MHer SAll
'Rosebud Supreme' (Z/d)	WFib
'Rosina Read' (Dw/d)	SAll
'Rosita' (Dw/d)	SAll
ROSITA ('Pacsita'PBR) (Z)	SSea
'Rosmaroy' (R)	WFib
'Rosy Dawn' (Min/d)	WFib
'Rote Mini-cascade'	see *P.* RED-MINI-CASCADE
§ 'Rouletta' (I/d)	WFib
'Royal Ascot' (R)	SPet
(Royal Series) ROYAL CANDY CANE ('Klep01028') (I)	SSea
- ROYAL LAVENDER ('Klepp07196'PBR) (Royal Series) (I)	SSea
- ROYAL RED ('Kleroder'PBR) (I)	SSea
'Royal Norfolk' (Min/d) ♀H1c	SAll
'Royal Oak' (Sc) ♀H1c	CPbh ECtt ENfk MCot MHer MNHC NWad NWsh SAll SPet SPoG SRms SVen WFib
§ 'Royal Purple' (Z/d)	WFib
'Royal Sovereign' (R)	WFib
'Royal Surprise' (R) ♀H1c	MPtG
'Ruby' (Min/d)	WFib
'Rushmere' (Dw/d)	WFib
'Rushmoor Golden Rosebud' (Z)	ECtt WFib
'Rushmoor Mrs Eve Scott' (Z/d)	ECtt WFib
SAILING ('Klesail') (Z/d)	SSea
'Saint Elmo's Fire' (St/Min/d)	MHer WFib
SAINT MALO ('Guisaint') (I)	ECtt
'Salmon Beauty' (Dw/d)	WFib
§ 'Salmon Irene' (Z/d)	WFib
'Salmon Queen'	see *P.* 'Lachskönigin'
SALMON QUEEN ('Pacsalque'PBR) (Z)	SSea
'Salmon Slam' (R)	SAll
salmoneum	WFib
'Samantha' (R)	WFib
'Samantha Stamp' (Dw/C/d)	WFib
SAMELIA ('Pensam'PBR) (Dark Line Series) (Z/d)	SSea
'Sammi Brougham' (Dw/Z)	WFib
'Sancho Panza' (Dec)	CSpe WFib
'Sandra Lorraine' (I/d)	WFib
SANGRIA NOVA ('Gendana'PBR) (Z)	SSea
'Sanguineum'	CSpe
'Santa Maria' (Z/d)	SAll
§ 'Sarah Don' (A/v)	ECtt WFib
'Sarah Jane' (Sc)	WFib
'Sassa'PBR (Quality Series) (Z/d)	SSea
'Satsuki' (R) ♀H1c	ECtt
'Saxifragoides'	WFib
'Scarlet Gem' (Z/St)	WBrk WFib
'Scarlet Pet' (U) ♀H1c	ECtt ENfk NWsh SPet
'Scarlet Rambler' (Z/d)	ECtt EShb WFib
'Scarlet Unique' (U)	CSpe MCot MNHC WFib
schizopetalum	MHer WFib
'Schottii' ♀H1c	CPbh MHer WFib
'Scottow Star' (Z/C)	WFib
'Seaview Silver' (Min/St)	WFib
'Seaview Sparkler' (Z/St)	WFib
'Secret Love' (Sc)	SRms
'Seeley's Pansy' (A)	MHer
'Sefton' (R) ♀H1c	WFib
'Shannon'	WFib
'Shaun Jacobs' (Min/d)	SAll
'Shimmer' (Z/d)	SAll
§ 'Shottesham Pet' (Sc)	ECtt ENfk MCot MHer NWad NWsh SPet SRms
sidoides ♀H1c	CPbh CSpe EAJP ECtt ENfk IPot MCot MHer SAll SChr SPhx SPlb SVen WAvo WFib WHer WKif
- 'Sloe Gin Fizz'	CSpe
'Silver Blazon' (Z/Dw/C/v)	WFib
'Silver Delight' (v/d)	WFib
'Silver Kewense' (Dw/v)	WFib
'Silver Snow' (Min/St/d)	WFib
'Silver Wings' (Z/v)	SAll
'Simplicity' (Z)	SAll
'Skelly's Pride' (Z)	WFib
'Skies of Italy' (Z/C/d)	WFib
'Snow Flurry' (Sc)	WFib
'Snowbaby' (Min/d)	WFib
'Snowdrift' (I/d)	SAll WFib
'Snowflake' (Min)	see *P.* 'Atomic Snowflake'
'Snowstorm' (Z)	WFib
'Sofie'	see *P.* 'Decora Rose'
'Solferino' (A)	ENfk
SOLO ('Guillio') (Z/I)	SAll
'Something Else' (Z/St/d)	SAll

'Something Special' (Z/d) ♀H1c	SAll WFib
SOPHIE CASADE	see *P.* 'Decora Rose'
'Sophie Dumaresque' (Z/v) ♀H1c	WFib
'Sophie Emma' (Z)	WFib
'Sophie Marion' (Dw/Z)	WFib
'South American Bronze' (R) ♀H1c	WFib
'South American Delight' (R)	SAll
'Southern Peach' (Min/d)	SAll
'Southern Rosina' (Dw)	WFib
'Spanish Angel' (A) ♀H1c	MHer SPet WFib
SPANISH WINE BURGUNDY ('Pacswibu') (Z)	SSea
'Sparkler' (Z)	SAll
'Spellbound' (R)	WFib
'Spital Dam' (Dw/d)	SAll WFib
'Spitfire' (Z/Ca/d/v)	ECtt SAll WFib
§ 'Splendide' ♀H1c	CPbh CSpe MHer SWvt WFib
'Spot-on-bonanza' (R) ♀H1c	ECtt WFib
'Springfield Black' (R)	MCot SAll
'Springtime' (Z/d)	WFib
'Stadt Bern' (Z/C) ♀H1c	CSpe SAll
× ***stapletoniae***	see *P.* 'Miss Stapleton'
'Star Flecks' (St) ♀H1c	SAll
'Startel Salmon' (Z/St)	MHer
'Stella Vernante' (Z/St/Dw)	SAll
'Stellar Arctic Star'	see *P.* 'Arctic Star'
'Stellar Hannaford Star'	see *P.* 'Hannaford Star'
'Stewart Meehan' (R)	WFib
'Stolen Kisses' (Min/D)	SAll
'Strawberry Fayre' (Dw/St)	WFib
'Stringer's Souvenir' (Dw/d/v)	SAll
§ 'Sugar Baby' (DwI)	MHer SAll WFib
'Summer Cloud' (Z/d)	WFib
SUMMER RAIN (mixed) (I) <u>**new**</u>	NPri
'Summertime' (Z/d)	see *P.* 'Deacon Summertime'
'Sun Rocket' (Dw/d)	WFib
'Sundridge Moonlight' (Z/C)	WFib
'Sundridge Surprise' (Z)	WFib
SUNFLAIR ROSE ('Genrose') (Sunflair Series) (I/d)	SAll
'Sunraysia' (Z/St)	WFib
'Sunset Snow' (R)	SAll WFib
'Sunspot Petit Pierre' (Min/v)	WFib
'Sunstar' (Min/d)	WFib
'Supernova' (Z/St/d)	WFib
'Surcouf' (I)	WFib
'Susan Hillier' (R)	WFib
'Susan Payne' (Dw/d)	MHer SAll
'Susan Pearce' (R)	SAll
'Susie' (Z/C)	WFib
'Susie 'Q'' (Z/C)	SAll
'Sussex Gem' (Min/d)	SAll WFib
'Swainham Mellow Yellow' (Z)	SAll
'Swanland Lace' (I/d/v)	WFib
'Swedish Angel' (A)	WFib
'Sweet Mimosa' (Sc) ♀H1c	CPbh ECtt ELan ENfk MCot MHer NWsh SAll SPet SRms WFib WGwG
'Sweet Sixteen' (R)	WFib
'Sweet Sue' (Min)	SAll
'Swiss Star' (Z/St)	SAll
'Sybil Holmes' (I/d)	ECtt WFib
'Tammy' (Dw/d)	SAll WFib
'Tangerine' (Min/Ca/d)	SAll
'Tara Caws' (Z)	WFib
tetragonum	EShb MHer WFib
'The Boar' (Fr) ♀H1c	EShb MCot WFib
'The Culm' (A)	MHer WFib
'The Czar'	see *P.* 'Czar'
'The Joker' (I/d)	WFib
'The Marchioness of Bute' (R)	MHer SAll SPet WFib
§ 'The Mole' (A)	WFib
'The Tamar' (A)	MHer
'The Yar' (Z/St)	WFib
'Thomas Earle' (Z)	WFib
'Tinker West' (Z/St/Dw)	WFib
§ 'Tip Top Duet' (A) ♀H1c	MHer WFib
'Tirley Garth' (A)	WFib
tomentosum (Sc) ♀H1c	CPbh CSpe ENfk EShb GLog GPoy MCot MHer NWad NWsh SAll SPet WFib
- 'Chocolate'	see *P.* 'Chocolate Peppermint'
TOMMY ('Pactommy') (I)	SSea
tongaense	WFib
'Topscore' (Z/d)	WFib
'Tornado' (R) ♀H1c	WFib
'Torrento' (Sc)	MHer NWsh SPet SRms WFib
'Tortoiseshell' (R)	WFib
'Tracy' (Min/d)	SAll
transvaalense	CPbh
tricolor misapplied	see *P.* 'Splendide'
tricolor Curt.	CPbh
tricuspidatum	WFib
trifidum	WFib
'Triomphe de Nancy' (Z/d)	WFib
triste	MHer WFib
'Trudie' (Dw/Fr)	MHer SAll WFib
'Turkish Coffee' (R)	WFib
'Turkish Delight' (Dw/C)	WFib
'Turtle's Surprise' (Z/d/v)	WBrk
'Turtle's White' (R)	SAll
'Two Dees' (Dw/d)	SAll WFib
'Uncle Ernie' (Z/C)	SAll
'Unique Aurore' (U)	MHer
'Unique Mons Ninon'	see *P.* 'Monsieur Ninon'
'Urchin' (Min/St)	WFib
'Ursula Key' (Z/c)	WFib
'Ursula's Choice' (A)	WFib
'Val Merrick' (Dw/St)	WFib
'Valentine' (Z/C)	WFib
'Vancouver Centennial' (Dw/St/C) ♀H1c	ECtt MHer NEgg SAll SCoo SPoG SSea WFib
'Vandersea' (Sc)	MCot MHer
'Variegated Clorinda' (Sc/v)	WFib
'Variegated Fragrans'	see *P.* (Fragrans Group) 'Fragrans Variegatum'
§ 'Variegated Kleine Liebling' (Min/v)	WFib
'Variegated Petit Pierre' (Min/v)	MHer WFib
'Vectis Glitter' (Z/St) ♀H1c	SAll WBrk WFib
'Vectis Imp' (Min/Z)	SAll
'Vectis Pink' (Dw/St)	WFib
'Vectis Purple' (Z/d)	WFib
'Vectis Spider' (Dw/St)	SAll
'Vectis Starbright' (Dw/St)	SAll WFib
'Vectis Volcano' (Z/St)	WFib
'Venus' (Min/d)	SAll
'Vicki Town' (R)	WFib
'Vicky Claire' (R)	WFib
VICKY ('Pacvicky'[PBR]) (I)	SSea

'Village Hill Oak' (Sc)	SAll
'Vina' (Dw/C/d)	WFib
violareum misapplied	see *P.* 'Splendide'
'Viscossisimum' (Sc)	MHer
viscosum	see *P. glutinosum*
'Vivat Regina' (Z/d)	WFib
'Voodoo' (U) ♀H1c	CPbh CSpe ECtt MCot MHer SPet WCot WFib
'Wallis Friesdorf' (Dw/C/d)	WFib
'Wantirna' (Z/v) ♀H1c	ECtt SAll
'Warrenorth Coral' (Z/C/d)	WFib
'Waveney' (Min)	SAll
'Wayward Angel' (A)	SPet
'Wedding Royale' (Dw/d)	SAll WFib
'Welling' (Sc)	ENfk MHer SPet WFib
'Wendy Jane' (Dw/d)	WFib
'Wendy Read' (Dw/d)	SAll WFib
'Westdale Appleblossom' (Z/C/d)	ECtt MHer SAll WFib
'Westside' (Z/d)	MHer WFib
'Westwood' (Z/St)	WFib
'Whisper' (R)	WFib
'White Bird's Egg' (Z)	WFib
'White Boar' (Fr)	CSpe ECtt EShb WFib
'White Bonanza' (R)	WFib
'White Butterfly' (Z/C)	SAll
'White Chiffon' (R)	SAll
'White Eggshell' (Min)	WFib
'White Feather' (Z/St)	MHer
'White Unique' (U)	SPet WFib
'Wild Spice' (Sc)	SAll
'Wilhelm Kolle' (Z)	WFib
'Wilhelm Langath' (Z/v)	ECtt EShb SCoo WBrk
'Willa' (Dec)	WFib
'Winford Festival'	SAll
'Winnie Read' (Dw/d)	SAll
'Wirral Moonlight' (Z/C/d)	WFib
'Wolverton' (Z)	WFib
'Yale' (I/d) ♀H1c	WFib
'Yan le Grounch' (Z/C)	WFib
'Yhu' (R)	WFib
'York Florist' (Z/d/v)	ECtt SAll
'Yvonne' (Z)	WFib
'Zena' (Dw)	SAll
'Zinc' (Z/d)	WFib
zonale	WFib
'Zulu King' (R)	WFib
'Zulu Warrior' (R)	WFib

Peliosanthes (*Asparagaceae*)

arisanensis B&SWJ 3639	WCru
caesia B&SWJ 5183	WCru
teta subsp. ***humilis*** RWJ 10044	WCru

Pellaea (*Pteridaceae*)

falcata	EShb ISha
ovata	SPlb WCot
paradoxa 'Glowstar'	ISha
rotundifolia ♀H2	CAby CLAP CRos EShb EUJe ISha LEdu LLWG LRHS NRHS WBor WCot

Peltandra (*Araceae*)

undulata	see *P. virginica* (L.) Schott
§ ***virginica*** (L.) Schott	LLWG NPer
- 'Snow Splash' (v)	EWat

Peltaria (*Brassicaceae*)

alliacea	CSpe LEdu WCot

Peltiphyllum see *Darmera*

Peltoboykinia (*Saxifragaceae*)

§ ***tellimoides***	CElw GCal MPnt NBir WFar WMoo WPnP
watanabei	CElw CPla CSpe CWld EBee EThi GEdr GPSL IMou LEdu MMrt NLar SPad WCru WMoo WPnP

Pennellianthus see *Penstemon*

Pennisetum ✿ (*Poaceae*)

× ***advena*** 'Fireworks'PBR (v)	CBcs CRos EPfP LRHS MAsh NRHS SCob SWvt
§ - 'Rubrum' ♀H3	CBcs CBct CExl CKno CRos CWCL EMOT EShb LCro LOPS LRHS MAsh NRHS NWsh SCoo SMad SRot SWvt
§ ***alopecuroides***	CAco CBcs CBod CRos ECha EPfP EWhm LRHS NGdn NRHS SCob SLim SPer SPlb SWvt XLum XSen
- AUTUMN WIZARD	see *P. alopecuroides* 'Herbstzauber'
- 'Black Beauty'	CKno CSpe EUJe SMHy SSut WHoo
- 'Cassian's Choice' ♀H3	CKno EHoe EWes GWyn ILea NCGa SHar
- 'Caudatum'	CKno
- 'Dark Desire'	CKno CRos EPfP LEdu LRHS NRHS
- 'Foxtrot'	EPPr
- 'Gelbstiel'	CKno CRos ELon EPfP LRHS NRHS
- 'Goldstrich'	SAko XSen
- 'Hameln'	Widely available
- 'Hameln Gold'PBR	CKno WTor
§ - 'Herbstzauber'	CBod CKno EHoe ELon NLar XLum XSen
- 'Little Bunny'	CBod CKel CRos CSde EBee EHoe ELan ELon EPfP EUJe EWTr GCal LRHS LSRN MAsh NGdn NRHS SCob SMea SWvt XSen
- 'Little Honey' (v)	ELon IKil LRHS XLum XSen
- 'Magic'	CBod EBee ELon MAsh SMea
- 'Moudry'	CBod CExl CSde EBee EHoe ELon EPPr EPfP EShb EUJe LRHS MAvo NLar XLum
- 'Piglet'PBR	EBee
- 'Red Head'	CBod CKno CMea CRos EBee ELon EPfP EUJe EWes LRHS LSun MAvo NRHS NSti SMad SMea SPoG WCot XSen
- f. ***viridescens***	CBod CRos ELan ELon EPPr EShb EUJe LEdu LRHS NRHS SCob SMad SPtp WPtf XLum XSen
- 'Weserbergland'	CKno EBee EHoe ELon SAko
- 'Woodside'	CKno EHoe SMad XLum
clandestinum	EShb
compressum	see *P. alopecuroides*
'Fairy Tails'	CKno CRos EBee ELon EPPr EPfP EUJe LPla LRHS MAsh MBel NDov NRHS SMHy SMea SPoG WCot WHoo
flaccidum	EPPr
glaucum 'Purple Majesty'	CSpe SWvt
incomptum	EHoe XLum
longistylum misapplied	see *P. villosum*
macrourum	CBod CKno CRos CSam CSde CSpe EAJP EBee ECha EHoe EPPr EPfP EUJe LEdu LRHS MAvo MNrw NDov NRHS NWsh SEND SMHy SMad SPtp WArt WPGP
- 'Short Stuff'	CKno

	massaicum 'Red Bunny Tails'	CChe LRHS NRHS SRms
	- 'Red Buttons'	see *P. thunbergii* 'Red Buttons'
	orientale ♀H4	CKno CRos CSde CSpe EAJP ECha EHoe EPfP LRHS LSun MRav NBir NRHS NWsh SEND SPer SRkn SWvt WKif XLum
	- 'Flamingo'	CRos NRHS
	- 'Karley Rose'PBR	CKno CPar CSpe ECrN EHoe EUJe EWes IMou IPot LRHS MAvo NDov NLar NRHS SCob SMad SWvt WPGP
I	- 'Robustum'	EBee EPPr MAvo WPGP
	- 'Shogun'	CKno CRos CSam EPfP LRHS NRHS SMHy
	- 'Tall Tails'	CRos EHoe EPPr EWes IKil LRHS NDov NRHS SMea XLum
	'Paul's Giant'	EBee ELon EUJe XLum
	purpureum	SRms
	rueppellii	see *P. setaceum*
§	***setaceum*** ♀H3	EAJP EPfP LCro LOPS LSun SWvt WCot
	- 'Rubrum'	see *P.* × *advena* 'Rubrum'
	- 'Sky Rocket'PBR (v)	CRos EPfP LRHS NRHS
	- 'Summer Samba'	CRos LRHS NRHS
	thunbergii	CAby CBod CRos GKev LRHS NRHS
§	- 'Red Buttons'	CElw CKno CRos EHoe ELon EPPr EPfP EShb LEdu LRHS MAsh MAvo MGos NRHS SMHy SMea SPoG SSut WAvo WHoo
	VERTIGO ('Tift-8'PBR)	CBct CBod
§	***villosum*** ♀H3	CAby CBod CExl CKel CKno CRos CSpe EAJP ECha EHoe ELan EPPr EPfP EShb EUJe LCro LEdu LOPS LRHS LSRN NRHS SEND SMad SMea SPer SPhx SRms WAvo XLum XSen
	- 'Cream Falls'	CBod IKil

pennyroyal see *Mentha pulegium*

Penstemon ✿ (*Plantaginaceae*)

	'Abberley'	WJam
	'Abbotsmerry'	ECtt EPfP LLHF MBNS MCot NLar SLon
§	'Alice Hindley' ♀H4	CBar CRos CSpe CTri EAJP ELan EPfP LRHS LSRN MCot MRav NBir NRHS SCob SLon SPer SRms SWvt WAvo WBrk WCFE WCot WHoo WJam WKif XLum
	alpinus	GWyn
	'Amy Gray'	WAvo WBrk WJam
§	'Andenken an Friedrich Hahn' ♀H5	Widely available
§	***angustifolius***	CSpe
	'Apple Blossom' misapplied	see *P.* 'Thorn'
	'Apple Blossom' ♀H3	Widely available
	'Arabesque Appleblossom'	CRos LRHS NRHS
	'Arabesque Pink'	CRos LRHS MHol NRHS
	'Arabesque Red'	CRos LRHS NRHS
	'Arabesque Violet'	CRos LRHS MHol NRHS
	arizonicus	see *P. whippleanus*
	'Ashton'	WAvo WJam
	attenuatus subsp. ***militaris***	SPlb
	'Audrey Cooper'	CMac MBNS WJam
	'Avon Belle'	WHrl
	'Axe Valley Penny Mitchell'	ECtt
	azureus	GKev
	'Barbara Barker'	see *P.* 'Beech Park'
§	***barbatus***	CFis SPer SRms SSut XSen
	- 'Coccineus'	CAby CSpe GBin MBNS NAln WJam XLum
	- 'Iron Maiden'	LRHS WJam
	- orange-flowered	SPlb
	- Pinacolada Series	CRos LRHS NRHS
	- - 'Pinacolada Dark Rose'	CRos LRHS NRHS
	- - 'Pinacolada Rosy Red'	CRos LRHS NRHS
	- - 'Pinacolada White'	CRos LRHS NRHS SRms
	- var. ***praecox***	MBNS SRot
	- - f. ***nanus*** 'Rondo'	CRos EAJP LRHS NRHS
	'Beckford'	EWes LLHF MBNS WJam
§	'Beech Park' ♀H4	EBee ELan EMor EPfP LRHS WJam
	'Bisham Seedling'	see *P.* 'White Bedder'
	'Blackberry' **new**	WArt
	'Blackbird'	Widely available
	'Blue Riding Hood'PBR (Riding Hood Series)	SPoG
	'Blue Spring' misapplied	see *P. heterophyllus* 'Blue Spring'
	'Blueberry Taffy'PBR	CRos ECtt LRHS NRHS
	'Bodnant'	LLHF MBNS WAvo WBrk WHoo WHrl
	'Boysenberry Taffy'PBR **new**	CRos LRHS NRHS
	'Bredon'	MBNS WAvo WJam
	'Bubblegum' (Ice Cream Series)	CAby CBod
	'Burford Purple'	see *P.* 'Burgundy'
	'Burford Seedling'	see *P.* 'Burgundy'
	'Burford White'	see *P.* 'White Bedder'
§	'Burgundy'	CBod CMac ECtt GMaP LRHS NBir NPer NRHS SRms WAvo WJam XLum
	caeruleus	see *P. angustifolius*
§	***campanulatus***	CRos EPot EWes GKev IMou LRHS NRHS SHar SRms
	- PC&H 148	SDys
	- ***pulchellus***	see *P. campanulatus*
	- 'Roseus' misapplied	see *P. kunthii*
	'Candy Pink'	see *P.* 'Old Candy Pink'
	cardinalis subsp. ***regalis***	GKev
	cardwellii	EWes
	'Castle Forbes'	GMaP MBNS SRms WJam
	'Cathedral Rose'	EBee ELan EPfP LRHS
	'Catherine de la Mare'	see *P. heterophyllus* 'Catherine de la Mare'
	'Centra'	MBNS WJam
	centranthifolius	SIgm
	'Charles Rudd'	ECtt ELan ELon EPfP LSRN MBNS NLar SRms SWvt WHrl WJam
§	'Cherry' ♀H3	ECtt MBNS NAln SHar WJam
	'Cherry Ripe' misapplied	see *P.* 'Cherry'
§	'Chester Scarlet' ♀H3	ECtt MBNS NAln WCFE WJam WKif
	'Choirboy'	EWes
	clutei	LLHF
	cobaea	CSpe
	'Comberton'	MBNS WAvo WJam
	confertus	CTri EBee EPot GKev MMuc
	- RCB/MO A-7	WCot
	'Connie's Pink' ♀H4	MBNS SRms WAvo
	'Coral Sea'	WFar
	'Cottage Garden Red'	see *P.* 'Windsor Red'
§	'Countess of Dalkeith'	ECtt ELan GBin MCot MRav SHar SRms SWvt WAvo WCFE WJam
	'Craigieburn Taffeta'	WJam
	cristatus	see *P. eriantherus*
*	***cyananthus*** var. ***utahensis***	WCot
	'Dark Towers'PBR	CAbb CRos CWGN EBee ECtt EMor EPfP EUJe LRHS MBNS MHol MNrw

		NAst NHpl NPri NRHS SLon SPad SPoG WCot WJam
	davidsonii	EPot EWes GCrg GEdr WOld
	- var. ***davidsonii***	WAbe
	- var. ***menziesii*** 'Microphyllus'	CPBP EPot GCrg GEdr NWad WAbe
	- var. ***praeteritus***	GEdr
	- 'Silverwells'	EPot GEdr
	'Dazzler'	SWvt WJam
	'Delfts Blue Riding Hood'PBR (Riding Hood Series)	LCro LOPS NPri
	'Devonshire Cream'	MBNS WJam
	diffusus	see *P. serrulatus*
	digitalis	MBNS SRms
§	- 'Husker Red'	Widely available
	- 'Isa'	WCot
	- 'Joke'	MAvo
	- 'Mystica'	CRos EBee LRHS NRHS SRms
	- 'Purpureus'	see *P. digitalis* 'Husker Red'
	discolor pale lavender-flowered	NBir
§	'Drinkstone Red'	EHrv MBNS SDys WJam
	'Drinkwater Red'	see *P.* 'Drinkstone Red'
	(Elgar Series) 'Elgar Crown of India'	WCot
	- 'Elgar Firefly'	WCot
	- 'Elgar Light of Life'	WCot
	- 'Elgar Nimrod'	WCot
	'Ellenbank Amethyst'	NAln SDys
	'Ellenbank Cardinal'	NAln WKif
	'Ellwood Red Phoenix'	MBNS WJam
	'Elmley'	MBNS WAvo WBrk WJam
§	***eriantherus***	SPlb
	ETNA ('Yatna') (Volcano Series)	CRos ECtt EPfP LRHS MBNS NRHS SAll SRms WJam
	euglaucus	EBee GKev
§	'Evelyn' ♀H4	ECha ELan EPfP LRHS LSRN MBNS MCot MHer MRav SPer SPoG SRms SWvt WAvo WBrk WJam WKif WSHC XLum
	'Fanny's Blush'	SWvt
	'Firebird'	see *P.* 'Schoenholzeri'
	'Flame'	MBNS WAvo WJam
	'Flamingo'	CPla CRos EAJP ECtt ELon EPfP EWes GBin LRHS MBNS NLar SGbt SHar SRms SWvt WJam
§	***fruticosus*** var. ***scouleri*** ♀H4	MAsh
	- - 'Albus' ♀H4	WAbe
	- - 'Amethyst'	WAbe
	FUJIYAMA ('Yayama'PBR)	CChe CRos ECtt EPfP LRHS MAvo NRHS SAll SLon SPad SRms SWvt WJam
	'Garden Red'	see *P.* 'Windsor Red'
	'Garnet'	see *P.* 'Andenken an Friedrich Hahn'
	gentianoides B&SWJ 10271	WCru
	'Geoff Hamilton'	ECtt MBNS NLar SLon SPoG WAvo WJam
	'George Elrick'	LLHF WHoo
§	'George Home' ♀H3	EWes GBin MBNS SRms WJam
	'George Moon'	SPad
	'Gilchrist'	ECtt
	glaber	EWld SPlb WJam WKif
	- 'Roundway Snowflake'	SHar SRms
	'Gloire des Quatre Rues'	XLum
	'Grape Taffy'PBR	CRos LRHS NRHS
	hallii	EPot EWes SPlb
	hartwegii 'Albus'	SHar SIgm SRms WJam
	- 'Picotee Red'	CRos LRHS NRHS
§	***heterophyllus***	LRHS MSCN NBir SRkn SRms
	- 'Blue Gem'	CElw
§	- 'Blue Spring'	CRos CSpe EPfP LRHS MRav NRHS
§	- 'Catherine de la Mare' ♀H4	CRos EBee ELan GBin LRHS LSRN NBir NRHS SCob SHar SPer SWvt WKif WSpi XLum
	- 'Electric Blue'	CBod CRos LRHS MHol NDai NRHS SLon WFar
	- 'Heavenly Blue'	Widely available
	- 'Jeanette'	CMea
	- 'True Blue'	see *P. heterophyllus*
	- 'Züriblau'	EBee SPlb WHil
§	'Hewell Pink Bedder' ♀H4	CBod CRos EPfP GBin GPSL LRHS MBNS MRav NAln NCou NRHS SHar SRms SWvt WHil
	hidalgensis	WCot
	'Hidcote Pink' ♀H3	Widely available
	'Hidcote Purple'	SHar WHoo XLum
	'Hidcote White'	MHer SWvt WBrk
	'Hillview Pink'	SLon XLum
§	***hirsutus***	EBee WJam XLum
	- 'Blue Foam'	GWyn
	- var. ***pygmaeus***	CMea EDAr GKev NHpl NRya SPlb SRms WHoo
*	- - f. ***albus***	WHoo
	- - 'Purpureus'	WAbe
	aff. ***hirsutus*** new	WJam
	'Hopleys Variegated' (v)	SWvt
	'Hot Pink Riding Hood'PBR (Riding Hood Series)	CRos LCro LOPS LRHS NRHS
	'James Bowden'	MBNS
	JEAN GRACE ('Penbow')	CSpe ECtt
	'John Booth'	MBNS
	'John Nash' misapplied	see *P.* 'Alice Hindley'
	'John Nash'	SRms
	'Juicy Grape' (Ice Cream Series)	CPla SAll SCob WCot
	'June'	see *P.* 'Pennington Gem'
	'Jupiter'	XLum
	KILIMANJARO ('Yajaro') (Volcano Series)	CRos EPfP LRHS SLon SRms WFar
	'King George V'	Widely available
	'Knight's Purple'	ECtt
§	***kunthii***	MAsh
§	***laetus*** subsp. ***roezlii***	EPot GCrg MAsh
§	'Le Phare'	WJam XLum
	'Lilac and Burgundy'	MBNS SHar SRms SWvt
	'Lilac Frost'	LLHF
	linarioides 'Marilyn Ross'	ECtt
	- subsp. ***sileri***	WJam
	'Lord Home'	see *P.* 'George Home'
	lyallii	GAbr GWyn MPie SRms WCot
	'Lynette'	MBNS SBch
	'Macpenny's Pink'	CMac MBNS WAvo WJam XLum
	'Madame Golding'	MBNS NAln XLum
	'Margery Fish' ♀H3	CFis ECtt EWes
	'Maurice Gibbs' ♀H3	CBcs ECtt EPfP EWes LSRN MBNS NGBl SRms WJam
	'Melting Candy' (Ice Cream Series)	WCot
	mensarum	LRHS
	Mexicali hybrids (Carillo Series) 'Carillo Purple'	CRos LRHS NRHS
	- - 'Carillo Red'	CRos LRHS NRHS
	× ***mexicanus*** 'Sunburst Amethyst'	ECtt ELan SRms XLum
	- 'Sunburst Ruby'	EBou ELan
	'Midnight'	ECtt ELan EMor EWTr GBin MBNS MRav MSwo SEND SHar SWvt WCFE WJam XLum

'Miniature Bells' **new**	MEch
'Modesty'	MBNS SRms
'Mother of Pearl'	CBcs CRos CTri ELan EMor EPfP GBin GMaP LRHS LSRN MBNS MCot MSwo MWat NAln SHar SRms SWvt WJam
'Mrs Miller'	MBNS WJam
'Mrs Morse'	see *P.* 'Chester Scarlet'
'Mrs Oliver'	EWes
multiflorus	EBee WJam
§ 'Myddelton Gem'	MWat SRms WJam
'Myddelton Red'	see *P.* 'Myddelton Gem'
newberryi f. ***humilior***	EPot
§ - subsp. ***sonomensis***	GCrg SRms WAbe
'Newbury Gem'	MBNS SHar SWvt WJam
'Oaklea Red'	GBin WJam
§ 'Old Candy Pink'	SWvt WJam
'Osprey' ♀H3	CMac CMea CRos CWGN ECtt ELan EMor EPfP EWes GBin LRHS MBNS NBir SHar SRms SWvt WJam
ovatus	CMac SPhx SRms WJam WKif
aff. ***ovatus*** **new**	WJam
'Overbury'	ECtt SRms WAvo WBrk WJam
'Papal Purple'	MAsh MBNS MHer NBir SHar SRms WJam XLum
'Patio Bells Pink'	CRos
'Patio Wine'	WAvo
'Peace'	GBin MBNS
§ 'Pennington Gem' ♀H3	CTri MHer NBir SHar SRms SWvt
- 'Pensham Amelia Jane'	CAby CRos CWGN ECtt ELon EPau EPfP GWyn LRHS LSRN MAsh MBNS MTis NLar NRHS SAll SLon SPer SRms SWvt WCot WJam
- 'Pensham Anniversary'	WJam
- 'Pensham Arctic Fox'	CSpe ECtt LRHS SLon SPoG
- 'Pensham Arctic Sunset'	WJam
- 'Pensham Avonbelle'	MBNS SRms
- 'Pensham Bilberry Ice'	MBNS SWvt
- 'Pensham Blackberry Ice'	ECtt MBNS SLon SRms
- 'Pensham Blueberry Ice'	ECtt MBNS SAll SWvt
- 'Pensham Capricorn Moon'	ECtt
- 'Pensham Charlotte Louise'	ECtt ELon SRms
- 'Pensham Czar'	Widely available
- 'Pensham Eleanor Young'	CRos ECtt EPfP LRHS MBNS SLon SWvt WJam
- 'Pensham Freshwater Pearl'	SRms WHoo
- 'Pensham Great Expectations'	ECtt
- 'Pensham Jessica Mai'	ECtt SPer SRms SWvt WJam
- 'Pensham Just Jayne'	CRos ECtt ELon EPfP LRHS LSRN MBNS NRHS SAll SLon SRms SWvt WBrk WHoo WSpi XLum
- 'Pensham Kay Burton'	EPfP
- 'Pensham Laura'	Widely available
- 'Pensham Loganberry Ice'	MBNS SLon
- 'Pensham Miss Wilson'	SRms
- 'Pensham Plum Jerkum'	CAby CDor CRos CWGN EBee ECrN ECtt ELon EPfP LCro LOPS LRHS MBNS MCot MHer MPie NLar NRHS SAll SCob SLon SPer SRms SWvt WHil WHoo
- 'Pensham Raspberry Ice'	CRos MBNS SLon
- 'Pensham Son of Raven'	WAvo WBrk WJam
- 'Pensham Tayberry Ice'	CRos ECtt MBNS SLon SRms WJam
- 'Pensham Ted's Purple'	WCFE
- 'Pensham Victoria Plum'	CElw SHar WHoo
- 'Pensham Wedding Bells'	SRms
- 'Pensham Wedding Day'	CRos EBee ECrN EPfP LRHS LSRN MBNS MCot NLar NRHS SAll SCob SLon SPer SPoG WHoo WJam
- 'Pensham Westminster Belle'	ECtt LBuc MTis WHil
(PepTalk Series) 'Pep Talk Cerise' **new**	NPri
- 'Pep Talk Hot Pink' **new**	NPri
- 'Pep Talk Pink' **new**	NPri
- 'Pep Talk Purple' **new**	NPri
'Pershore Anniversary'	WAvo
'Pershore Carnival'	SRms WAvo WHrl WJam
'Pershore Fanfare'	WAvo WHrl WJam
'Pershore Festival'	WAvo WJam
'Pershore Pink Necklace'	SRms SWvt WAvo WHrl WJam
'Phare'	see *P.* 'Le Phare'
(Phoenix Series) PHOENIX APPLEBLOSSOM 09 ('Peni Ablos09')	CRos LRHS NRHS
- PHOENIX LAVENDER ('Peni Laver')	CRos LRHS NRHS
- PHOENIX MAGENTA 09 ('Peni Mag09')	CRos LRHS NRHS
- PHOENIX PINK ('Pheni Pinka')	CRos LRHS NRHS
- PHOENIX RED ('Pheni Reeda'PBR)	CRos LRHS NRHS
- PHOENIX ROSE ('Penharros'PBR)	CRos LRHS NRHS
- PHOENIX VIOLET 09 ('Peni Vio09'PBR)	CRos EPfP LRHS NRHS
'Phyllis'	see *P.* 'Evelyn'
pinifolius ♀H4	CBod CMea CRos CTri ELon EMor EPot GCrg GKev LRHS MAsh MMuc NRHS SRms WHoo WJam WThu
- 'Mersea Yellow'	CMea CRos ELan EPfP GCrg GKev LRHS MAsh MHer MMuc NLar NRHS SIgm SPlb SRms WIce WJam XLum
- 'Wisley Flame' ♀H4	EPfP EPot EWes GCrg GKev MBNS MHer NHpl SCob SIgm
'Pink Bedder'	see *P.* 'Hewell Pink Bedder', 'Sutton's Pink Bedder'
'Pink Endurance'	MBNS WHal WJam
'Port Wine' ♀H3	CMea CTri ELon EPfP GMaP LRHS MWat NBir SPer SPoG SWvt WAvo WHrl WJam WKif
'Powis Castle'	ECtt WBrk WJam
'Prairie Twilight'PBR	MHol
procerus	GKev
var. ***brachyanthus***	
§ - var. ***formosus***	GCrg WAbe
- 'Hawkeye'	CPBP
§ - 'Roy Davidson' ♀H5	CMea EPot WAbe
- var. ***tolmiei***	EPot GCal GEdr GKev WAbe
pseudospectabilis **new**	XSen
pubescens	see *P. hirsutus*
pulchellus Greene	see *P. procerus* var. *formosus*
pulchellus Lindl.	see *P. campanulatus*
'Purple and White'	see *P.* 'Countess of Dalkeith'
'Purple Bedder'	CMac CRos ELan EPfP GBin LRHS LSRN MWat NBir NRHS SPoG SRkn SRms SWvt WJam XLum
'Purple Passion'	CElw CRos EBee ELan ELon EPfP LRHS NRHS SCob
'Purple Riding Hood'PBR (Riding Hood Series)	CRos LCro LOPS LRHS NPri NRHS
'Purple Sea'	MHol WFar
'Purpureus Albus'	see *P.* 'Countess of Dalkeith'

'Raven' ♀H3	Widely available
'Razzle Dazzle'	SPlb SRms WCot WJam
'Red Ace'	WJam
'Red Emperor'	WJam
'Red Knight'	MBNS
'Red Riding Hood'[PBR] (Riding Hood Series)	CRos EPfP LCro LOPS LRHS NPri NRHS SPoG
RED ROCKS ('P008S')	GBin WCot
'Red Sea'	MHol WFar
'Rich Purple'	MBNS SPlb XLum
'Rich Ruby' ♀H3	CAby CFis CRos EHrv ELan EPfP EWes LRHS NAln NBir NRHS SHar SPlb SPtp SWvt WJam XLum
'Ridgeway Red'	WJam
roezlii Regel	see *P. laetus* subsp. *roezlii*
roezlii ambig.	MAsh
'Roger Skipper'	ECtt
'Ron Sidwell'	WAvo WBrk WJam
'Rosy Blush'	MBNS SPlb
'Roy Davidson'	see *P. procerus* 'Roy Davidson'
'Royal White'	see *P.* 'White Bedder'
'Rubicundus' ♀H4	CRos ELan EPfP LRHS LSRN MBNS NRHS SWvt WBor WJam
'Ruby' misapplied	see *P.* 'Schoenholzeri'
'Ruby Candle'	ECtt
rupicola ♀H5	NSla
- 'Conwy Lilac'	WAbe
- 'Conwy Rose'	EPot GCrg WAbe WThu
'Russian River'	ECtt EPfP LRHS SPlb SWvt XLum
rydbergii	SPlb
'Samsong'	WCFE
saxosorum new	CPBP
§ 'Schoenholzeri' ♀H4	Widely available
scouleri	see *P. fruticosus* var. *scouleri*
§ ***serrulatus***	EWes GKev XLum
- 'Albus'	WArt
'Sherbourne Blue'	WAvo WCot WJam
'Sissinghurst Pink'	see *P.* 'Evelyn'
'Six Hills'	EPot SDys WAbe WOld
smallii	CRos EBee EMor EPPr EPfP EWes LRHS LSRN MHer NRHS SPhx
'Snow Storm'	see *P.* 'White Bedder'
'Snowflake'	see *P.* 'White Bedder'
sonomensis	see *P. newberryi* subsp. *sonomensis*
'Sour Grapes' misapplied	see *P.* 'Stapleford Gem'
'Sour Grapes' ambig.	CAby CBcs CDor CTri EHoe MJak MSCN NGdn SAll SCob SPoG WArt WCAu
§ 'Sour Grapes' M. Fish ♀H4	CMac CRos CWld EBee ECha ELan EPau EPfP GBin GMaP LCro LOPS LRHS LSRN MSwo NLar NRHS SEND SHar SPer SPtp SRms WBrk WJam WKif
'Southgate Gem'	GKev GWyn MBNS MHCG MWat SRms SWvt WAvo
'Souvenir d'Adrian Regnier'	MBNS MHCG
'Souvenir d'André Torres' misapplied	see *P.* 'Chester Scarlet'
spectabilis	CSpe
§ 'Stapleford Gem' ♀H4	CFis CMac EWTr LRHS MRav SHar SRms SWvt WBrk WFar WHoo
'Storm'	WHrl
'Strawberries and Cream' (Ice Cream Series)	EAJP EBee EMor EPfP MTis NLar SAll SCob WCot WHil
'Strawberry Fancy'	SRms
'Strawberry Fizz'	SRms
strictus	EBee GKev MBNS MMuc SPhx WJam XSen
STROMBOLI ('Yaboli')	CTri
§ 'Sutton's Pink Bedder'	MBNS
'Sweet Cherry' (Ice Cream Series)	CPla ECtt WCot
tall, pink-flowered	see *P.* 'Welsh Dawn'
teucrioides	CPBP
'The Juggler'	ECtt MBNS SWvt
§ 'Thorn'	ECtt LRHS MWat NBir SRms SWvt WAvo WHrl WJam
'Threave Pink'	ECtt MRav SHar SRms SWvt WAvo WJam
'Thundercloud'	ECtt WAvo WBrk WJam
'Tiger Bell Coral'	NChi
'Torquay Gem'	MBNS WJam
'True Sour Grapes'	see *P.* 'Sour Grapes' M. Fish
'Tubular Bells Red'	MHol
uintahensis	CPBP
'Vanilla Plum' (Ice Cream Series)	EMor
venustus	WKif
- purple-flowered	SBrt
VESUVIUS ('Yasius') (Volcano Series)	CRos EPfP LRHS NRHS SLon SRms WFar WJam
virgatus 'Blue Buckle'	EMor GEdr SPlb WFar
'Watermelon Taffy'[PBR] (Taffy Series)	CRos ECtt EMor LRHS NRHS
§ 'Welsh Dawn'	MBNS
§ ***whippleanus***	GEdr LRHS MMuc SPlb
§ 'White Bedder' ♀H3	Widely available
'Whitethroat' Sidwell	MBNS WHoo WJam
I 'Whitethroat' purple-flowered	WCot
'Willy's Purple'	ECtt
§ 'Windsor Red'	CTri ECtt EPfP LRHS MBNS SCob SLon SRms SWvt WAvo WBrk WCot WJam
'Woodpecker'	ECtt EMor IPot MAvo MBNS SRms WAvo WBrk WHoo WHrl

Pentaglottis (*Boraginaceae*)

§ ***sempervirens***	EPfP SRms WSFF

Pentapanax see *Aralia*

Pentapterygium see *Agapetes*

Pentas (*Rubiaceae*)

lanceolata	CCCN EShb

Penthorum (*Saxifragaceae*)

sedoides	LLWG

Peperomia (*Piperaceae*)

ferreyrae	EShb

pepino see *Solanum muricatum*

peppermint see *Mentha* × *piperita*

Pericallis (*Asteraceae*)

× ***hybrida*** Senetti Series	NPer NPri SPoG
- - SENETTI BLUE BICOLOR ('Sunseneribuba'[PBR])	MGos SPoG
- - SENETTI BLUE ('Sunsenebu'[PBR])	SPoG
- - SENETTI MAGENTA BICOLOR ('Sunsenereba'[PBR])	MGos SPoG
- - SENETTI MAGENTA ('Sunsenere'[PBR])	SPoG
§ ***lanata*** (L'Hér.) B. Nord.	CHll EShb
- Kew form	CSpe

Perilla (*Lamiaceae*)

frutescens	WJek
§ - var. ***crispa*** ♀H3	CLau CSpe
- var. ***nankinensis***	see *P. frutescens* var. *crispa*
- var. ***purpurascens***	CLau WJek

Periploca (*Apocynaceae*)

graeca	CBcs CPla EBee MGil
sepium	CExl

Pernettya see *Gaultheria*

Perovskia (*Lamiaceae*)

abrotanoides	XLum
atriplicifolia	CDul CMea ELan LSun MGil MHer MNHC WKif
- 'Blue Shadow'	CRos LRHS NLar NRHS
'Blue Haze'	GCal
'Blue Spire' ♀H5	Widely available
'Filigran'	CBod CKel CRos CWld ELan EPfP GBin LRHS MBel NLar NRHS SPoG WGrn WGwG WSpi XSen
'Hybrida'	GCal LRHS
LACEY BLUE ('Lisslitt'PBR)	CKel CRos EBee EMor EPfP IPot LCro LOPS LPla LRHS MAsh NLar NRHS SCob SWvt
'Little Spire'PBR	CBcs CBod CKel CMac CMea CRos CSBt CSpe EBee ECrN EHoe EMor EPfP EWes GMaP LCro LOPS LRHS LSRN MAsh MAvo MCot NLar NRHS SCob SPer SPoG SRkn WCAu WSpi
'Longin'	CKel LRHS XLum
SILVERY BLUE ('Lissvery'PBR)	CRos EMor LRHS NLar NRHS WNPC XSen

Persea (*Lauraceae*)

americana	CCCN
- 'Hass' (F)	SVic
indica	CCCN
- B&SWJ 12535	WCru
japonica B&SWJ 12789	WCru
thunbergii B&SWJ 12747	WCru

Persicaria (*Polygonaceae*)

B&SWJ 11268 from Sumatra	WCru
§ ***affinis***	CBcs CSBt GAbr MSCN NBro SCob WArt WFar WMoo
- 'Darjeeling Red' ♀H6	Widely available
- 'Dimity'	see *P. affinis* 'Superba'
- 'Donald Lowndes' ♀H6	Widely available
- 'Kabouter'	EBee GBin GWyn NLar SCob WBor
§ - 'Superba' ♀H6	Widely available
alata	see *P. nepalensis*
alpina ♀H6	CBct CRos CSpe EBee ECha ECtt EHoe EPPr EWhm GBin GMaP GQue IPot LEdu LRHS MAvo MHol MRav NDov NRHS SMad SPoG WCot WPnP WSpi WWtn
amphibia	EWat LLWG XLum
§ ***amplexicaulis***	CBre CCBP CKno ELan EWes GMaP ILea MBel MCot NChi WBor WBrk WFar WMoo WRHF WWtn XLum
- 'Alba'	Widely available
- 'Amethyst'	CKno LPla
- 'Ample Pink'	MAvo
- 'Anouk'	EBee
- 'Atrosanguinea'	CBod CKno CMac CRos CTri ECha ELan ELon GLog LRHS MMuc MRav NBir NLar NRHS SEND SPer SRms SWvt WFar WOld XLum
- 'Betty Brandt'	GWyn
- 'Black Adder'	ELon
- 'Blackfield'PBR	Widely available
- 'Clent Charm'	MHCG NChi WOut
- 'Cottesbrooke Gold'	ECtt EWhm MAvo
- 'Dikke Floskes'	CAby CBct CBod CKno EBee ECtt ELon EPPr GBin LRHS MAvo MHol SRms WBrk WCot WHoo
- 'Early Pink Lady'	ELon WMoo
- 'Eastfield' (v)	WCot WFar
- 'Fascination'	ELon WCot
- 'Fat Domino'PBR	CBct CBod CKno CRos EBee ECtt EHoe EMor GBin GQue IKil ILea IPot LPla LRHS MAvo MBel MCot MHol MNrw MSCN NCou NDov NLar NRHS SCob SHeu SPoG WCAu WCot
- 'Fat White'	ELon
- 'Firedance'	CAby CKno ECtt EHoe ELon EPPr GBin GQue IPot NDov SMHy SPhx SRms WCot WFar
- 'Firetail'	Widely available
- 'Golden Arrow' (v)	CAby CBct CRos EBee ECtt ELon EMor EUJe GBin LRHS MBel NEoE NRHS SCob SPoG SRms WFar WHil WMoo WPnP
- 'High Society'	CKno GBin SPoG SRms WCAu WMoo
- 'Inverleith'	CBct CBod CBre CKno CRos EBee ECha ECtt ELon GBin GMaP GQue LRHS MAvo MBel MHer MMuc NBir NGrd NRHS SCob SPoG WCAu WMoo WPnP WWFP
I - 'Jo and Guido's Form'	ELon NLar WCAu WFar
- 'JS Caliente'PBR	CBod CKno ECtt ELon EMor GQue LRHS LSun MNrw NBir SAko SCob SHar SHeu SRms WCot WPnP WSpi
- 'JS Delgado'	CKno EBee ELon MNrw SHeu SRms
- 'Lisan'	ELon MNrw
- ORANGE FIELD ('Orangofield'PBR)	CBct CBod CKno CMea CRos EBee ECtt ELon EMor EPPr EPfP EShb EWTr GMaP GQue IKil LRHS MHol MJak MNrw NDov NLar NRHS SAko SCob WBor WCAu WHoo WMoo WWtn
- var. ***pendula***	EBee ELon GBin IMou NBir SMHy WFar WMoo
- - HWJK 2255	WCru
- 'Pink Elephant'	see *P.* 'Pink Elephant'
- 'Pink Knot'	CRos LRHS NRHS
- 'Pink Lady'	MPie
- 'Pink Mist' **new**	WGoo
- 'Rosea'	Widely available
- 'Rowden Gem'	EBee ELon GBin IPot WCAu WMoo WOut
- 'Rubie's Pink'	ECha
- 'September Spires'	NDov WGoo
- 'Seven Oaks Village'	EBee GBin SCob
- 'Summer Dance'	CKno EBee ECtt ELon EPPr SMHy
- TAURUS ('Blotau')	CElw CKno CRos CSam ECha ECtt ELon EPPr IPot LRHS MCot NLar NRHS NSti SCob SMHy SRkn SRms WCAu WFar WHoo
- 'White Eastfield'	CKno NLar SAko WCAu
§ ***bistorta***	GBin GPoy MHer MMuc NBir NGrd NLar SEND SRms WArt WFar WOut

- subsp. ***carnea***	CBod CRos EBee ECha EHoe ELon EPPr EWhm GBin LRHS MBNS MMuc NBir NBro NDov NRHS WCot WMoo WWtn
- 'Hohe Tatra'	CBod CRos EBee ECtt EMor EPPr GMaP IPot LRHS LSun MBel MHol NCou NDov NRHS SPoG WCot WFar
- 'JS Calor'[PBR]	EBee GQue
- 'Superba' 🏆H7	Widely available
campanulata	CBod CElw EBee ECha ECtt EHoe EMor GAbr GMaP IFro MAvo MMuc MRav NEgg NSti SPer WFar WMoo WOut WWFP WWtn
- Alba Group	CElw MPie WMoo
- 'Madame Jigard'	GBin
- 'Rosenrot'	CBre ILea NBir WOld
- 'Southcombe White'	GBin
§ ***capitata***	XLum
- 'Pink Bubbles'	CPla EHoe ELon LPot NBir SWvt
chinensis B&SWJ 11268	WCru
dshawachischwilii	LPla SMHy
emodi	GKev NAln
× ***fennica*** 'Johanniswolke'	EBee GBin IPot
* ***hydropiper*** var. ***rubra***	WJek
'Indian Summer'	EBee GCal LPla WCot WFar
* ***kahil***	GBin WCot
microcephala	EWes MHer
- 'Dragon's Eye'[PBR]	EBee WNPC
- 'Red Dragon'[PBR]	Widely available
milletii	CRos EBee LRHS MAvo NDov NRHS WCru
§ ***mollis***	WPGP
neofiliformis	EShb
§ ***nepalensis***	CExl EMor EPPr EShb IMou
'October Pink'	CSam SMHy
§ ***odorata***	CLau ENfk GPoy MHer MNHC NGrd SPre SRms WHer WJek WTre
orientalis	CSpe SPhx
- 'Variegata' (v) **new**	CSpe
§ 'Pink Elephant'	CKno CSam ELon EMor EPPr EWTr GBin ILea MNrw NDov NLar SAko SCob SHeu SRms WCAu WFar WHoo WSpi
polystachya	see *P. wallichii*
'Red Baron'	ECtt EMor EPPr
§ ***runcinata***	EBee MMuc NBir WMoo WWtn
- 'Purple Fantasy'	CBod CPla ECtt ELan EMor EShb EUJe IKil LPla MAvo MBel MHol MNrw NSti SCob SMad WFar WMoo WNPC
scoparia	see *Polygonum scoparium*
'Silver Dragon'[PBR]	CBct CBod EMor EUJe LPla LSun MAvo MBel NSti SMad SPoG WCot
tenuicaulis	CBre EHrv GBin SBch SBrt WCru WMoo WWtn
§ ***tinctoria***	WSFF
§ ***vacciniifolia*** 🏆H5	Widely available
§ ***virginiana***	GCal LEdu LSun WMoo WWtn
- 'Alba'	EPPr
- var. ***filiformis***	CAby CBod CSam CSpe ELan LEdu MBel MPie NChi SBrt SPoG SRkn SWvt WAul WCot
- - 'Ballet'	WCot
- - 'Batwings'	SPtp
- - 'Compton's Red'	CBod CSam ECha ECtt EMor EPPr EShb EUJe MAvo SBrt WAul WCot WFar
- - 'Guizhou Bronze'	LEdu
- - 'Lance Corporal'	CMac CMea EHoe EPPr EShb EUJe GBin LPot MAvo NLar
- - 'Moorland Moss'	WMoo
- Variegated Group (v)	ECha EShb MBNS WCot WMoo
- - 'Painter's Palette' (v)	CBod CMac CRos EBee ECha ECtt EHoe ELan EMor EPPr EShb EUJe GWyn LRHS MHol MRav NBid NRHS NSti SMad SPer SRms SWvt WAul WCot WMoo XLum
§ ***wallichii***	CSpe MMuc NLar SEND WCot WMoo WWtn XLum
§ ***weyrichii***	GCal NBir NBro NLar WFar WMoo WWtn XLum

persimmon see *Diospyros virginiana*

persimmon, Japanese see *Diospyros kaki*

Petalostemon see *Dalea*

Petamenes see *Gladiolus*

Petasites (*Asteraceae*)

albus	GPoy MHer NSti
fragrans	ELan LLWG SRms WHer XLum
§ ***frigidus*** var. ***palmatus***	NLar WCot
- - 'Golden Palms'	EUJe WBor WCot
hybridus 'Variegatus' (v)	XLum
japonicus	CAgr CBcs CFGn GPoy
- var. ***giganteus***	ECha EPfP EUJe LEdu MBel WCru
§ - - 'Nishiki-buki' (v)	CMac EBee ECha EUJe EWld GQue LEdu MHer NBir NSti SMad WBor WFar XLum
- - 'Variegatus'	see *P. japonicus* var. *giganteus* 'Nishiki-buki'
palmatus	see *P. frigidus* var. *palmatus*
paradoxus	EWld LEdu MBel WCot WFar WPGP

Petrea (*Verbenaceae*)

volubilis	CCCN

Petrocallis (*Brassicaceae*)

lagascae	see *P. pyrenaica*
§ ***pyrenaica***	WAbe
- white-flowered	WAbe

Petrocoptis (*Caryophyllaceae*)

pyrenaica	EWes SRms

Petrocosmea ✿ (*Gesneriaceae*)

barbata	WDib
begoniifolia	WAbe WDib
coerulea	WDib
§ ***cryptica***	WAbe WDib
- 'Yumebutai'	WDib
flaccida	WDib
'Fluffer Nutter'	WDib
forrestii	WAbe WDib
grandiflora	WAbe WDib
- 'Crème de Crûg'	WCru
'Ht-2'	WDib
iodioides 🏆H1c	WDib
kerrii	WCot WDib
'Keystone's Angora'	WDib
'Keystone's Bantam'	WDib
'Keystone's Barnswallow'	WDib
'Keystone's Belmont'	WDib
'Keystone's Blue Jay'	WDib
'Keystone's Magic'	WDib
mengliangensis	WDib

minor	WDib
parryorum	WDib
'Paul Kroll'	WDib
'Rosemary Platz'	WDib
rosettifolia misapplied	see *P. cryptica*
sericea	WDib

Petromarula (*Campanulaceae*)

pinnata	EBee

Petrophytum (*Rosaceae*)

caespitosum	CMea SIgm WAbe
§ ***hendersonii***	WAbe

Petrorhagia (*Caryophyllaceae*)

saxifraga 🏆H4	CSpe EPPr GLog MBel NLar NSla SRms WMoo XLum

Petroselinum (*Apiaceae*)

§ ***crispum***	CLau EMor ENfk GPoy MJak MNHC NPol NPri SPoG SRms
- 'Bravour' 🏆H6	LRHS MHer NRHS
- 'Champion Moss Curled'	SVic
- French	CCBP CLau EMor ENfk LCro LOPS MHer MNHC NPri SPoG SRms
- 'Italian'	see *P. crispum* var. *neapolitanum*
- 'Laura'PBR **new**	CLau
- 'Moss Curled' 🏆H6	CHby CRos EKin LRHS MCtn NRHS NRob SRms
§ - var. ***neapolitanum***	CLau ENfk LCro LOPS SPoG SRms SVic
§ - var. ***tuberosum***	CLau SRms SVic
hortense	see *P. crispum*
tuberosum	see *P. crispum* var. *tuberosum*

Petteria (*Papilionaceae*)

ramentacea	CPla EBtc

Petunia (*Solanaceae*)

'Buzz Purple' (Designer Series) **new**	NPri
(Cascadias Series) CASCADIAS RIM MAGENTA ('Dcas298'PBR)	NPri
- CASCADIAS RIM VIOLET	NPri
'Dark Heart' (Ovation Series) **new**	NPri
(Easy Wave Series) EASY WAVE BERRY VELOUR ('Pas982903') **new**	NPri
- EASY WAVE BLUE ('Pas320593')	NPri
- EASY WAVE BUBBLEGUM	see *P.* (Easy Wave Series) EASY WAVE PINK PASSION
- EASY WAVE BURGUNDY STAR ('Pas760702')	NPri
- EASY WAVE BURGUNDY VELOUR ('Pas933562')	NPri
- EASY WAVE NEON ROSE ('Pas760700')	NPri
§ - EASY WAVE PINK PASSION ('Pas882697')	NPri
- EASY WAVE PLUM VEIN ('Pas739163')	NPri
- EASY WAVE RED VELOUR ('Pas933560')	NPri
- EASY WAVE SILVER ('Pas1016992')	NPri
- EASY WAVE VIOLET ('Pas760717')	NPri
- EASY WAVE WHITE ('Pas760712')	NPri
exserta	CSpe WCot
'Fanfare Hot Rose' (Fanfare Series)	NPri
NIGHTSKY ('Kleph15313')	NPri
patagonica	SPlb WAbe
(Shock Wave Series) SHOCK WAVE CORAL CRUSH ('Pas803824') **new**	NPri
- SHOCK WAVE YELLOW ('Pas1003475')	NPri
(Surfinia Series) SURFINIA BLUE ('Sunblu')	NPri
- SURFINIA HOT PINK 06 ('Sunrovein'PBR)	NPri
- SURFINIA PURPLE ('Shihi Brilliant') 🏆H2	NPri
- SURFINIA SNOW **new**	NPri
(Tumbelina Series) TUMBELINA CANDYFLOSS ('Kercan'PBR) (d)	NPri
- TUMBELINA MARIA (d) **new**	NPri
- TUMBELINA PRISCILLA ('Kerpril'PBR) (d) 🏆H1c	NPri

Peucedanum (*Apiaceae*)

* ***aromaticum***	IMou
litorale	see *Kitagawia litoralis*
longifolium	WCot
officinale	CRos CSpe GBin LRHS NRHS SPhx SPlb SPtp
ostruthium	GPoy LEdu
- 'Daphnis' (v)	CSpe EBee ECha EWhm LEdu MAvo MNrw NChi NGrd NLar WAvo WCFE WCot WHrl WSHC XLum
rablense	LEdu NDov
verticillare	CRos CSam CSpe EBee EMor GBin GWyn IMou LEdu LPla LRHS MBel NRHS SBrt SPhx WCot WKif WSHC

Phacelia (*Boraginaceae*)

bolanderi	CPla EWes GEdr
californica	EBee
tanacetifolia	LCro WSFF

Phaedranassa (*Amaryllidaceae*)

viridiflora	WCot

Phaedranthus see *Distictis*

Phaenocoma (*Asteraceae*)

prolifera	SPlb

Phaenosperma (*Poaceae*)

globosa	CSam CSpe ECha EHoe EPPr EShb GCal GQue LRHS MMuc NWsh WCot WPGP WWtn XLum

Phaiophleps see *Olsynium*

nigricans	see *Sisyrinchium striatum*

Phalaris (*Poaceae*)

arundinacea	MBNS SCob SPlb SVic
- 'Elegantissima'	see *P. arundinacea* var. *picta* 'Picta'
- var. ***picta***	CDul CTri MJak NBir NPer WFar XLum
- - 'Arctic Sun' (v)	CKno EBee EPPr EShb GBin LLWG LRHS MAsh MMuc NEoE SEND SPoG

- - 'Aureovariegata' (v) MRav NPer WMoo XLum
- - 'Feesey' (v) ♀H7 Widely available
- - 'Luteopicta' (v) EPPr MMuc XLum
§ - - 'Picta' (v) CBod CRos ELan EPfP GBin LRHS MMuc NRHS SEND SPer WMoo
- - 'Streamlined' (v) EPPr NWsh
- - 'Tricolor' (v) EHoe

Phanerophlebia ✿ (*Dryopteridaceae*)

caryotidea see *Cyrtomium caryotideum*
falcata see *Cyrtomium falcatum*
fortunei see *Cyrtomium fortunei*

Pharbitis see *Ipomoea*

Phaseolus (*Papilionaceae*)

caracalla see *Cochliasanthus caracalla*

Phedimus see *Sedum*

Phegopteris (*Thelypteridaceae*)

§ ***connectilis*** CBdn CLAP EFer LEdu
decursive-pinnata CBdn CBod CRos EBee LEdu LRHS MMuc NRHS SEND WFib WPnP
hexagonoptera CBdn

Phellodendron (*Rutaceae*)

amurense CBcs CCCN CDul CMCN EPfP GBin LMaj MBlu WBor
- B&SWJ 11000 WCru
japonicum B&SWJ 11175 WCru

Phemeranthus (*Portulacaceae*)

sediformis GKev
- 'Zoe' GKev

Phenakospermum (*Strelitziaceae*)

guianense XBlo

Pherosphaera ✿ (*Podocarpaceae*)

fitzgeraldii CKen WPav WThu

Philadelphus ✿ (*Hydrangeaceae*)

SDR 2823 CExl
SDR 4862 GKev
SDR 4946 CExl
'Atlas' (v) NLar
'Avalanche' CExl MMuc NLar SRms
'Beauclerk' ♀H6 CBod CCCN CDul CKel CTri EBee ECrN EPfP LRHS MGos MMuc MRav NLar NWea SCob SLim SMad SPer SRms SWvt WSpi
'Belle Étoile' ♀H6 Widely available
'Bialy Sopel' CCCN WAvo
'Bicolore' NLar WAvo WSpi
'Bouquet Blanc' MRav NLar SGol SRms WCFE
brachybotrys MRav
'Buckley's Quill' (d) CAby EBee EPfP EWes LRHS MRav SMad SWvt
'Burfordensis' MMuc MRav SEND WSpi
coronarius CBcs CBod CDul CWld EPfP LBuc LRHS MRav NWea SPer WSpi
- 'Aureus' ♀H6 Widely available
- 'Bowles's Variety' see *P. coronarius* 'Variegatus'
§ - 'Variegatus' (v) ♀H6 CMac CRos ELan ELon EPfP EWTr GBin LPot LRHS MGil MGos MMuc MRav MSwo NBir NLar SPer SPoG SRms WAvo WCFE WCot WFar WKif WSHC WSpi
coulteri SBrt WPGP
'Coupe d'Argent' MRav
'Dainty Lady'[PBR] GBin LRHS SLon
'Dame Blanche' (d) ECrN EPfP MRav NLar WFar
delavayi EPfP EWTr GBin LEdu LLHF NLar SPer WPGP WSpi
- var. ***calvescens*** MRav SPtp
- - BWJ 8005 WCru
- f. ***melanocalyx*** CBod EPfP MRav SChF WPGP
- - B&L 12168 EBee WPGP
- - 'Nyman's Variety' ♀H6 CExl CTho WKif WPGP
aff. ***delavayi*** SBrt
'Enchantement' (d) MRav
'Erectus' CKel CSBt EBee ELan ELon EPfP LRHS MRav NLar SBrt SPer SPoG WAvo WSpi
'Étoile Rose' WAvo
'Falconeri' MRav
'Frosty Morn' (d) CBcs EPfP EShb LEdu MBlu MMuc MRav NLar SEND SPer SPoG
incanus B&SWJ 8616 WCru
§ 'Innocence' (v) ♀H6 CAgr CExl CMac CRos CTsd EHoe ELan EPfP LRHS MAsh MGos MMuc MRav MSwo NEoE NRHS SEND SGol SPad SPer SPoG SRms WFar WSHC
'Innocence Variegatus' see *P.* 'Innocence'
§ ***insignis*** MRav
karwinskianus F&M 152 WPGP
'Lemoinei' CBcs CBod CDul CTri MGos NWea SCob SGol WSpi
lewisii CExl SPhx
- L 1896 CExl
- 'Snow Velvet' CAby EPfP LLHF LRHS
- 'Waterton' WAvo WSpi
'Limestone' MRav
'Little White Love' new SGol
maculatus 'Mexican Jewel' CBcs CExl CRos EBee ELan ELon EPfP GBin LEdu LRHS NLar SChF SMad SPad WGob WKif WPGP WSHC
- 'Scented Storm' EBee WPGP
- 'Sweet Clare' ♀H5 CRos EPfP LCro LOPS LRHS NRHS SPoG WSpi
madrensis EBee MRav
- F&M 326 WPGP
'Manteau d'Hermine' (d) ♀H6 Widely available
'Marjorie' NLar
mexicanus GCal
- B&SWJ 10253 WCru
- 'Rose Syringa' CExl SBrt WPGP
mexicanus* × *palmeri EBee WPGP
microphyllus CAby CDul CKel CMCN CTho CTri EBee ELan ELon EPfP GBin LRHS MAsh MGos MRav NLar SLon SPer SPoG WFar WKif WSHC
- var. ***occidentalis*** NLar
'Minnesota Snowflake' (d) CBcs CRos ELon EPfP EWes LRHS LSRN MMuc MRav NLar NRHS SEND SGol WFar
'Mont Blanc' CBcs GKin MRav NLar
'Mrs E.L. Robinson' (d) CMac CRos ELon EPfP GLog LLHF LRHS MGos MNHC NEgg NRHS WAvo WCFE
myrtoides B&SWJ 10436 WCru
'Natchez' (d) CMac ELon LLHF NLar SCob
'Oeil de Pourpre' MRav
palmeri EBee WPGP
'Patricia' WAvo
pekinensis CExl NLar

'Perryhill'	MRav
'Polar Star'	ELon NLar WKif
purpurascens	CExl CJun EBee EPfP EWes GLog LEdu LLHF MGos MRav NLar SChF WPGP
- BWJ 7540	WCru
'Purpureomaculatus'	ELon LLHF MAsh MRav NLar WPGP
satsumi	NLar
- B&SWJ 10811	WCru
- B&SWJ 11004	WCru
schrenkii	NLar
- B&SWJ 8465	ESwi WCru
sericanthus	NLar
§ 'Silberregen' 𝕐H6	CDul CKel CMac CRos EBee ELan ELon EPfP EWTr GBin LEdu LRHS MAsh MGos MMuc MRav NEoE NGdn NLar SEND SGol SMad SPoG SRms SWvt
SILVER SHOWERS	see *P.* 'Silberregen'
'Snowbelle' (d)	CCCN CKel CRos EPfP LRHS MAsh NGdn NLar NPri NRHS SPoG SRms SWvt
'Snowgoose'	LRHS SGol
'Souvenir de Billiard'	see *P. insignis*
'Starbright'PBR	CAby CBcs CCCN CKel CRos EBee EPfP LRHS MAsh MMrt NRHS SCob SPoG
subcanus	CExl
- L 524	CExl
'Sybille' 𝕐H6	CDul CKel CMac CRos ECrN EPfP LRHS MRav MSwo NAln SRms WKif WSpi
tomentosus	CExl
- B&SWJ 2707	WCru
- GWJ 9215	WCru
'Velléda'	WAvo
'Virginal' (d)	Widely available
'Voie Lactée'	LLHF MRav NLar WSpi
WHITE ROCK ('Pekphil') 𝕐H6	CMac CRos EBee EPfP LLHF LRHS LSRN MRav NLar SPer
'Yellow Cab'	EBee
'Yellow Hill'	CMac EPfP LRHS

Philesia (*Philesiaceae*)

buxifolia	see *P. magellanica*
§ ***magellanica***	CExl CRHN GEdr GGGa ITim MGil SIgm WCru WSHC
- 'Rosea'	CRHN EPfP

Phillyrea (*Oleaceae*)

angustifolia	CBcs CBod CDul CMCN CRos CSpe EBee ELan ELon EPfP EShb EUJe LRHS MGos MRav NLar SEND SPer WPGP WSHC XSen
- f. ***rosmarinifolia***	CCCN CCoa CExl ELan
- - 'French Fries'	EBee EPfP WPGP
decora	see *Osmanthus decorus*
§ ***latifolia***	CBcs CBod CDul CKel CRos CTho CTsd EBee ELan EPfP EUJe LRHS NLar SArc SEND WPGP XSen
media	see *P. latifolia*

Philodendron (*Araceae*)

'Angra dos Reis'	see *P. cordatum*
§ ***angustisectum*** 𝕐H1a	XBlo
bipennifolium	SPlb
bipinnatifidum 𝕐H1c	XBlo
corcovadense	XBlo
§ ***cordatum***	XBlo
elegans	see *P. angustisectum*
erubescens 'Red Emerald'	XBlo
* ***radiatum***	XBlo
var. ***pseudoradiatum*** 'Simmonds'	
* ***rubrum***	XBlo
scandens 𝕐H1a	EUJe LCro LOPS
- 'Green Emerald'	XBlo
- 'Mica'	XBlo
tripartitum	XBlo
xanadu	LCro LOPS XBlo

Philotheca (*Rutaceae*)

§ ***myoporoides***	LRHS MPkF

Phlebodium (*Polypodiaceae*)

§ ***aureum*** 𝕐H1b	CSpe SPlb WCot
- var. ***areolatum***	EShb
- 'Blue Star'	ISha
- 'Glaucum'	CSpe WCot
pseudoaureum	ISha LEdu WCot

Phleum (*Poaceae*)

phleoides	CRos LRHS NRHS
pratense	EHoe WSFF

Phlomis ✿ (*Lamiaceae*)

alpina	SPlb
* ***anatolica***	CRos ELan LRHS
- 'Lloyd's Variety'	see *P. grandiflora* 'Lloyd's Silver'
anisodonta white-flowered	XSen
armeniaca	XSen
atropurpurea	GKev IMou
- BWJ 7922	WCru
bourgaei	XSen
- NJM 12.008	WPGP
bovei subsp. ***maroccana***	SEND WHal XLum
breviflora HWJCM 250	WCot WCru
capitata	XSen
cashmeriana	CBod CFis CRos EBee ECha EHoe EPfP GCal ILea LRHS MCot MHol NQui NRHS SMad WArt WAvo WCFE WSpi
chrysophylla 𝕐H5	CRos ECha ELan EPfP LRHS MAsh MRav NLar WCFE WSpi XSen
cretica	SVen
× ***cytherea***	XSen
'Edward Bowles'	CDul CKel CRos EBee ECha EPfP GBin LRHS LSRN MNHC MRav NLar SEND SIgm SWvt WAvo WSpi XSen
* 'Elliot's Variety'	CExl
fruticosa 𝕐H5	Widely available
- white-flowered	CBcs
aff. ***fruticosa***	WSpi
grandiflora	EBee EPfP MMuc MNrw SEND XSen
- NJM 10.014	WPGP
§ - 'Lloyd's Silver' 𝕐H5	CRos CSam ELan GBin LRHS MAsh NLar SHar SPer
herba-venti	XSen
italica	Widely available
lanata	CRos CSde EBee EPfP LRHS SBrt SCob WCFE XSen
- 'Pygmy'	XSen
'Le Sud'	WCot XSen
leucophracta	SVen
libanotica new	EBee
longifolia	CBod CKel CRos EBee EPfP LRHS MNrw SEND SPer WPGP XSen
- var. ***bailanica*** 𝕐H4	CRos CSam EPfP LRHS NRHS XLum

- var. ***longifolia***	WSpi
lychnitis	SIgm XSen
lycia	XSen
- NJM 10.016	WPGP
macrophylla	SPhx
× ***margaritae***	XSen
'Marina' new	XSen
monocephala	XSen
pratensis	CPla
purpurea	CBod CExl CRos ELan EPfP LRHS MAsh MMuc NBir NRHS SEND WCot XSen
I - 'Alba'	CBod ELan EPfP EWTr GBin GCal GMaP LRHS MMrt XSen
- subsp. ***caballeroi***	XSen
§ ***russeliana*** ♀H6	Widely available
- PAB 7444	LEdu
- 'Dappled Shade' (v)	WCot
samia Boiss.	see *P. russeliana*
samia L.	CBod CMac CRos LRHS MMrt MMuc MNrw NBir NGdn NLar NRHS SAko SBrt SEND XSen
- JMT	EPPr
- 'Green Glory'	WCot
taurica	CSpe SEND
× ***termessi***	XSen
'Toob'	WPGP
'Tramuntana' new	XSen
tuberosa	CAby CBcs CBod CPou CRos EHoe ILea LEdu LRHS LSRN MMuc MPnt NGdn NRHS SPhx WArt WCAu WCFE WPtf XLum XSen
- 'Amazone' ♀H5	CBod CKno EBee ECha EHrv EPfP GBin GMaP LCro LOPS LPla MBel MNrw MRav MSCN NBid NDov NGBl NSti SCob SMad SPer SRms WCAu WCot WFar WHil WSHC WSpi
- 'Bronze Flamingo'	CMac CRos EMor EPfP GBin LRHS MBel MNrw MPnt MRav NLar SPoG SPtp WSpi
viscosa misapplied	see *P. russeliana*

Phlox ✿ (*Polemoniaceae*)

adsurgens 'Alba'	WFar
- 'Wagon Wheel'	CBor CRos ECtt EWes GCrg LRHS NHpl NRHS SPlb SRms SRot WIce
amplifolia	WCot XLum
- 'Winnetou'	IPot
× ***arendsii*** 'Andrew'	WCot
- 'Autumn's Pink Explosion'	WCot
- 'Babyface'	ELon NGdn NLar
- 'Casablanca'	NDov
- 'Dylan'	WCot
- 'Eyecatcher'	NBro
- 'Gary'	WCot
- 'Hesperis'	ECha ELon GBin GWyn LRHS MAvo MNrw MTis NDov NLar SPhx WHil
- 'Luc's Lilac' ♀H7	ECtt EPPr LLHF MCot MPie NBro NDov NEgg NGdn NSti SGbt SPhx WAul WCot
§ - 'Miss Jill' (Spring Pearl Series)	ELan EPfP WCot
§ - 'Miss Karen' (Spring Pearl Series)	EBee ELan NBro
§ - 'Miss Mary' (Spring Pearl Series) ♀H7	CRos EBee ECtt ELan EPfP ILea LRHS NRHS SRkn WRHF
§ - 'Miss Wilma' (Spring Pearl Series)	EBee ELan EPfP
- 'Paul'	MNrw WCot WSHC
- 'Ping Pong'	SGbt
- 'Pink Attraction'	LRHS NBro NRHS
- 'Utopia' ♀H7	CSpe EBee ELon IMou NDov SPhx WCot
austromontana	EPot NWad
bifida 'Alba'	LLHF
- 'Ralph Haywood'	ECtt EPot
- 'Thefi'	ECtt
borealis	see *P. sibirica* subsp. *borealis*
caespitosa	CMea EWes
- subsp. ***pulvinata***	see *P. pulvinata*
- 'Zigeunerblut'	CMea CPBP ECtt EPot GCrg ITim NWad SIgm WAbe WHal WHoo
canadensis	see *P. divaricata*
carolina subsp. ***angusta***	NAln
- 'Bill Baker'	see *P. glaberrima* 'Bill Baker'
- 'Magnificence'	EBee EWes GWyn NAln SMad SPlb WCot
- 'Miss Lingard' ♀H6	CBod CDor CRos CSam EAJP ECtt GBee LRHS MMuc MRav MTis MWat NBir NGdn NLar NRHS NSti WCAu WCot
'Chattahoochee'	see *P. divaricata* subsp. *laphamii* 'Chattahoochee'
colubrina	GKev
'Daniel's Cushion'	see *P. subulata* 'McDaniel's Cushion'
diffusa	EPot
§ ***divaricata*** ♀H5	SPlb
- 'Blue Dreams'	ECtt MNrw WFar
- 'Blue Perfume'	EBee ECtt GWyn LCro LOPS NBro XLum
- 'Charles'	XLum
- 'Clouds of Perfume'	Widely available
- 'Dirigo Ice'	CRos LRHS NRHS SAko WSHC
- 'Fuller's White'	CWCL
- subsp. ***laphamii***	CWCL EBee EWes WFar
§ - - 'Chattahoochee' ♀H5	Widely available
- 'May Breeze'	CRos CWCL EAJP ECtt EHrv GMaP LRHS MAsh MNrw MSCN NRHS WSHC
- 'Plum Perfect'	ECtt
- 'White Perfume'	CRos CWCL EBee EPfP EWes ILea LRHS MAsh MMrt MTis NDov NLar NRHS SPoG WAul WFar XLum
douglasii	SRms
- 'Apollo'	CBor CPBP CTri ECtt
- 'Boothman's Variety' ♀H5	ECtt ELan GCrg ITim SRms
- 'Crackerjack' ♀H5	CMea CRos CTri EBou ECtt ELan ELon EPot EUJe GAbr GCrg GKev GMaP ITim LRHS MAsh MHol NBir NEgg NHol NHpl NRHS NSla SPoG WIce
- 'Eva'	CBor CRos EBou ECtt ELon GCrg GMaP ITim LRHS LSRN MAsh MHol NBir NHpl NLar NRHS NSla NWad WIce
- 'Georg Arends'	CBor ECtt
- 'Ice Mountain'	CBor CMea ECtt ELan EPot GKev NAln NEgg NHol NWad SPoG SRot WFar
- 'J.A. Hibberson'	EPot EWes GCrg NWad
- 'Lilac Cloud'	ECtt
- LILAC QUEEN	see *P. douglasii* 'Lilakönigin'
§ - 'Lilakönigin'	CTri
- 'Napoleon'	ECtt EPot ITim NWad
- 'Ochsenblut'	CBor CRos CSma ECtt GCrg LLHF LRHS NLar NRHS NWad SIgm WIce
- 'Red Admiral' ♀H5	EBou ECtt ELan EPfP EWes GMaP MHol NWad WCFE WFar
- 'Rose Cushion'	EWes GCrg

	Plant	Suppliers
	- 'Rosea'	ELan MMuc NHpl
	- 'Sprite'	SRms
	- 'Tycoon'	see *P. subulata* 'Tamaongalei'
	- 'Waterloo'	CPBP CRos EBou ECtt EPot LRHS NRHS
I	- 'White Admiral'	CRos CTri ECtt ELan GBin LRHS LSRN MHol NRHS
	drummondii SURPHLOX PINK ('Sunphlopin') **new**	MHol
	'Flare'	see *P. paniculata* 'Neon Flare'
§	***glaberrima*** 'Bill Baker' ♀H6	CSam ECha ECtt EPPr EPfP GMaP IKil MAsh MNrw NBir NGdn NSti SIgm WCAu WFar WPtf XLum
	- 'Morris Berd'	EBee WFar WSHC
	'Goliath'	WHlf
	hendersonii	WAbe
	hoodii	WAbe
	'Jeff's Pink'	ECtt
	'Kelly's Eye' ♀H5	CRos EBou ECtt EPot GCrg LRHS NBir NRHS SPoG
	kelseyi 'Lemhi Purple'	CPBP EPot WAbe
	- 'Rosette'	NWad
	LIGHT PINK FLAME ('Bareleven'PBR)	CBod ECtt LRHS SPoG
	LILAC FLAME ('Barten'PBR)	CRos LRHS NRHS
	maculata 'Alba'	SAko WAul
	- 'Alpha' ♀H6	CRos CSam CWCL EBee ECha ECtt EMor EPfP GMaP ILea LEdu LRHS NLar NRHS SGbt SPer SWvt WCAu WFar WSHC XLum
	- AVALANCHE	see *P. maculata* 'Schneelawine'
	- 'Delta'	CRos EAJP EBee LRHS NLar NRHS SAko SGbt SPer SRkn SWvt
	- 'Natascha' ♀H6	CMac CRos CSam EBee ECtt EPfP EWes GMaP LRHS LSRN NAln NCGa NGdn NHol NLar NRHS NWad SAko SGbt SMad SPer SRkn SWvt WCAu WFar WHil WTyc
	- 'Omega' ♀H6	CExl CMac EBee ECtt EWTr ILea LEdu MCot MMuc MNrw MPie NCGa NGdn NLar SGbt SPer SWvt WCAu WFar WSpi
	- 'Reine du Jour'	CSam NDov SPhx
	- 'Rosalinde'	CRos ECtt GBin LRHS MCot NLar NRHS SAko SWvt WSHC
§	- 'Schneelawine'	CRos LRHS NRHS SPlb WSpi
	'Millstream'	see *P. × procumbens* 'Millstream'
	'Minnie Pearl'	EWes LPla NDov WCot
	nivalis 'Nivea'	WAbe
	paniculata	LEdu NBid NDov WCot
	- (Adessa Series) 'Adessa Pink Star' **new**	NRHS WHil
	- - 'Adessa Rose Eye' **new**	WHil
	- - 'Adessa Special Deep Purple' **new**	WHil
	- - 'Adessa Special Fire' **new**	WHil
	- - 'Adessa Special Lilac Twist' **new**	WHil
	- 'Aida'	EBee
	- var. ***alba***	WCot
	- 'Alba Grandiflora' ♀H7	GMaP MNrw NChi WCot WHoo
	- 'Alexandra'PBR	LCro LOPS
	- 'All in One'	MAvo
	- 'Amethyst' misapplied	see *P. paniculata* 'Lilac Time'
	- 'Amethyst' Foerster	CRos ELon GBin GWyn LRHS MRav MTis NBir NLar WCAu WMoo
	- 'André'	LRHS NRHS
	- 'Anne'	CSam
	- 'Argus'	ECtt
	- 'Auslese D. Bach'	CSam

	Plant	Suppliers
	- 'Balmoral'	CMac EBee ECtt ELon NCou NEgg NSti SWvt
	- 'Becky Towe'PBR (v) ♀H7	ECtt EMor MHer MHol MNrw NEgg NHol SMad SPoG WCot
	- 'Blauer Morgen'	XLum
	- 'Blue Boy'	CRos EBee ECtt ELan ELon EMor EPfP GMaP GWyn LRHS NBir NEgg NRHS SWvt WCAu WFar
	- 'Blue Evening'	EBee LCro LOPS NLar
	- BLUE FLAME **new**	NPri
	- 'Blue Paradise'	Widely available
	- 'Blushing Bride'	SRms
	- 'Bonny Maid'	MAvo
	- 'Border Gem'	CAby CBcs CBod CMac ECtt ELon EShb LRHS MRav MTis SWvt WBrk WCot WHrl
	- 'Bosvigo Pink'	ELon MAvo SHar
	- 'Brigadier'	CBod CTri EBee ECtt ELan LRHS MAvo NEgg NGdn SPer SRms WHrl
	- 'Bright Eyes'	Widely available
	- 'Butonik' **new**	ELon
	- 'Cardinal'	MTis NDov
	- 'Caroline van den Berg'	SRms
	- 'Charlotte'	WGoo
	- 'Cheriton'	CRos EBee NRHS
	- 'Chintz'	CRos LRHS MRav NRHS SRms
	- 'Cinderella'	ECtt
	- 'Cleopatra'	MSCN NLar SPad WHlf
	- COMPACT LILAC	see *P. paniculata* SWEET SUMMER FAVOURITE
	- COMPACT ROSE WHITE	see *P. paniculata* SWEET SUMMER CANDY
§	- 'Cool of the Evening'	NAln
	- 'Cool Water'	WHlf
	- CORAL FLAME ('Barsixtytwo'PBR) (Flame Series)	CBod CMac EUJe MHol NLar SCob SRkn WHil
	- 'Coral Queen'	SRms
	- 'Cosmopolitan'PBR	MNrw NLar
	- COUNT ZEPPELIN	see *P. paniculata* 'Graf Zeppelin'
	- 'Danielle' ♀H7	LRHS NRHS SHar
	- 'Darwin's Choice'	see *P. paniculata* 'Norah Leigh'
	- 'David' ♀H7	Widely available
	- 'David's Lavender' ♀H7	CRos ELon IPot LRHS NRHS WSpi
	- 'Delilah'PBR	CWGN ECtt NHpl
	- 'Discovery'	EHrv EShb EWes LRHS MRav NEgg NRHS SHar
	- 'Dodo Hanbury-Forbes'	MNrw
	- 'Drakon' **new**	ELon
	- 'Dresden China'	SHar
	- 'Duchess of York'	MNrw
§	- 'Düsterlohe'	CRos CSam CSpe EBee ECtt ELon EMor GBin GQue GWyn ILea IPot LPla LRHS MHer MRav MTis NBir NDov NLar NRHS NSti SPer SRkn SRms WCAu WCot WSpi XLum
	- 'Early Light Pink'	IPot
	- 'Eclaireur' misapplied	see *P. paniculata* 'Düsterlohe'
	- 'Eclaireur' Lemoine	MAvo
	- 'Eden's Flash'	CElw ECtt MPie
	- 'Eden's Smile'	ECtt
	- 'Edentuin'	IPot
	- 'Elisabeth' (v)	LSRN NWad
	- 'Elizabeth Arden'	ECtt ELon MTis
	- 'Elizabeth Campbell'	CRos GCal LRHS NRHS
	- 'Ending Blue'	MAvo
	- 'Etoile de Paris'	see *P. paniculata* 'Toits de Paris' Symons-Jeune
	- 'Europa'	EBee ECtt ELan IPot NBir NGdn NLar SPer WCAu

Plant	Suppliers
- 'Eva Cullum' ♀H7	CBod CRos CSam EBee ECtt EHrv ELan ELon EPfP GMaP GWyn LRHS MArl MHer NHpl NRHS SAko SPer WCAu WCot
- 'Eva Foerster' ♀H7	CRos EBee GWyn LRHS NRHS XLum
- 'Eventide'	CMac CRos CSam ECtt EPfP LRHS MArl MAvo MBel MNrw MRav MWat NRHS SPer WFar WHrl
- 'Ferris Wheel'	EBee ECtt
- 'Flamingo' ♀H7	EBee ECtt ELon SWvt XLum
- 'Fondant Fancy'[PBR]	NLar
- 'Franz Schubert' ♀H7	CDor CRos CSam EBee ECtt ELan EMor EPfP EWTr GBin GWyn ILea LCro LRHS MAvo MCot MTis MWat NBir NChi NGdn NLar NRHS NSti SPer SWvt WCot WFar WHoo WMoo
§ - 'Frau Alfred von Mauthner'	GKev
- 'Fujiyama'	see *P. paniculata* 'Mount Fuji'
- 'Glebe'	CSam
- 'Goldmine'[PBR] (v)	CRos LRHS MHol MNrw NHpl NRHS SMad SPoG SRms WCot WTor
§ - 'Graf Zeppelin'	ECtt ELon MTis NHol NLar SRms XLum
- 'Grenadine Dream'[PBR] ♀H7	CRos CWGN LRHS MNrw NHpl NRHS WCot
- 'Grey Lady' ♀H7	CRos LRHS MNrw NRHS WGoo
- 'Harlequin' (v)	CMac CWGN ECha ECtt ELon GBee MHol NEgg WCot
- 'Herbstwalzer'	IPot WCot
- 'Ice Cream'	CWGN ELon
- 'Irene Mast'	CSam
- 'Iris'	MNrw SRms WCot
- 'Jade'	ECtt ELon EMor GBin GQue LRHS MHol MNrw NLar NSti WCot WHil
- 'Jeana'	MBel MNrw
- 'Jeff's Blue'	EBee MHol WCot
- 'Judy'	GBin LSRN
§ - 'Juliglut'	CRos ELon LRHS NRHS WCot
- JULY GLOW	see *P. paniculata* 'Juliglut'
- 'Junior Bouquet'	MHol NLar
- 'Junior Dream'	NLar
- 'Katherine'	CRos IPot LRHS NLar NRHS
- 'Katja'[PBR]	IPot
- 'Kirchenfürst'	CElw CRos LCro LOPS LRHS MTis NBir NLar NRHS SAko WCAu
- 'Kirmesländler'	ECtt IPot NLar SAko
- 'Ksenija' **new**	ELon
- 'Lady Clare'	SRms
- 'Landhochzeit'	NAln
- 'Larissa'	LCro LOPS
- 'Laura'	see *P. paniculata* 'Uspekh'
§ - 'Lavendelwolke'	GCal LRHS NBir NLar WCot
- LAVENDER CLOUD	see *P. paniculata* 'Lavendelwolke'
- 'Le Mahdi' ♀H7	MTis NLar SRms WBor
- 'Lichtspel'	LPla NDov SPhx
§ - 'Lilac Time'	CBod CElw CRos ECtt EPfP GMaP LRHS MMuc MTis NLar NRHS SPer SWvt WSpi
- 'Little Boy'	CElw ELon MNrw NLar SGbt WHil
- 'Little Laura'	CBod ECtt LSRN MNrw NLar WCot WHoo
- 'Little Princess'	ELon NLar
- 'Little Sara'	NDov
- 'Lizzy'[PBR]	NLar
- 'Logan Black'	GCal SHar WSHC
- MAGICAL DREAM	see *P. paniculata* SWEET SUMMER DREAM
- MAGICAL FAVORITE	see *P. paniculata* SWEET SUMMER FAVOURITE
- MAGICAL SURPRISE	see *P. paniculata* SWEET SUMMER SURPRISE
- 'Manoir d'Hézèques'	WCot
- 'Mary Christine' (v)	LRHS MAvo NBid NRHS
- 'Maude Stella Dagley'	ELon
- 'Mia Ruys'	MArl
- 'Mies Copijn'	MTis
- 'Mike's Favourite'	EBee
- 'Milly van Hoboken'	MAvo WKif
- 'Miss Holland'	ELon NGdn SGbt XLum
- 'Miss Jill'	see *P. × arendsii* 'Miss Jill'
- 'Miss Karen'	see *P. × arendsii* 'Miss Karen'
- 'Miss Kelly'	EHrv EShb NLar
- 'Miss Mary'	see *P. × arendsii* 'Miss Mary'
- 'Miss Pepper' ♀H7	CRos CWCL ECtt ELon LRHS MMuc NGdn NLar NRHS
- 'Miss Universe'	ELon
- 'Miss Wilma'	see *P. × arendsii* 'Miss Wilma'
- 'Monica Lynden-Bell' ♀H7	CAby CDor CWGN EBee ELon GBin GMaP GWyn LRHS LSun MBel MHol MNrw MPie MRav NBid NChi NDai NDov NLar NSti SGbt SMad WAul WCot WKif
- 'Monte Cristallo'	GBin GWyn
- 'Mother of Pearl' ♀H7	GQue GWyn IPot LRHS NEgg WSpi
§ - 'Mount Fuji'	Widely available
- 'Mount Fujiyama'	see *P. paniculata* 'Mount Fuji'
- 'Mrs A.E. Jeans'	SRms
- 'Nadia'[PBR]	LRHS NRHS
- 'Natural Feelings'[PBR] (Feelings Series)	NLar
§ - 'Neon Flare' (Neon Series)	CWGN ECtt
- 'Newbird'	EBee ECtt SRms
- 'Nicky'	see *P. paniculata* 'Düsterlohe'
- 'Nirvana'	CSam
§ - 'Norah Leigh' (v) ♀H7	Widely available
- 'Oljenka' **new**	ELon
- 'Orange Perfection'	see *P. paniculata* 'Prince of Orange'
- 'Othello'	CSam ECtt ELon NGdn WHoo
- 'Otley Choice'	CRos CSam EBee ECtt GBin GWyn LRHS MRav NCou NLar NRHS NSti WHrl
- 'Otley Purple'	MHer NCou
- 'P.D. Williams'	WCot
- 'Pallas Athene'	IPot
- 'Pastorale'	WCot
- (Peacock Series) PEACOCK CHERRY RED ♀H7	CRos LRHS NRHS WCFE WTor
- - PEACOCK LILAC ♀H7	CRos LRHS NRHS
- - PEACOCK NEON PURPLE ♀H7	CRos LRHS NRHS
- - PEACOCK PURPLE BICOLOR	CRos LRHS NRHS
- - PEACOCK WHITE ♀H7	CRos LRHS NRHS WTor
- 'Peppermint Twist'	CRos CWGN EBee ELon GWyn LRHS MHol MNrw MSCN NEgg NLar NRHS SWvt WFar WHil
- 'Picasso'	CWGN ECtt IPot
- 'Pina Colada'[PBR]	CWGN EBee ECtt NPri WFar
- PINK EYE FLAME ('Barthirtyfive'[PBR]) ♀H7	CRos EPfP LRHS NRHS SCob SPoG SRkn SRms
- 'Pink Lady'[PBR]	WFar
- 'Pink Posie' (v)	WCot
- PINK RED EYE FLAME ('Barthirtyfour')	SPoG
- 'Pinky Hill'	WCot
- 'Polarstern'	CSam
- 'Popeye'	IPot LPla WCot

- 'Prime Minister' ELon
§ - 'Prince of Orange' ♀H7 CBcs CBod CRos CSam EBee ECtt EMor EPfP EUJe LPla LRHS MAvo MHol MJak MRav MWat NEgg NLar NRHS SGbt SPer SRms SWvt WBor WCAu WCot XLum
- 'Prospero' ♀H7 CElw CSpe EBee GWyn MRav NBid
- PURPLE EYE FLAME ('Barthirtythree'PBR) ♀H7 CRos LLHF LRHS NRHS SRkn SWvt WFar
- 'Purple Kiss'PBR CWGN ECtt MHol NHpl NLar NPri WFar
- 'Purple Paradise' LRHS NRHS
- 'Rainbow' ELon NLar
- 'Raving Beauty' NRHS
- 'Red Caribbean' ECtt NLar NPri
- 'Red Feelings' (Feelings Series) CBod CWld LRHS NRHS
- 'Red Flame' CRos CWGN ECtt EPfP LRHS MHol MNrw NPri NRHS SAko SRkn WFar
- 'Red Riding Hood' see *P.* × *arendsii* 'Miss Mary'
I - 'Reddish Hesperis' MAvo
- 'Rembrandt' CBod CExl CRos ELon EPfP GBin LCro LOPS LRHS NRHS WCAu XLum
- 'Rijnstroom' CBcs ECha ECtt ELon MArl NAln NLar SCob WBrk WCAu
- 'Robert Poore' ECtt ELon
- 'Roberta' LCro LOPS
- 'Rosa Goliath' CSam
- 'Rosa Pastell' ♀H7 CAby CDor CEnd CSpe ECtt EHrv ELon EMor GBin GQue IPot LRHS MAvo MHol MPie MSCN MTis NBid NDov NLar SPer SPtp WAul WCot
- 'Rowie' NBid
- 'Sandringham' CRos EHrv LRHS MArl MRav NBir NCou NRHS SPer SWvt
§ - 'Schneerausch' LPla SPhx
- 'Septemberglut' CRos EBee EPfP LRHS NRHS
- 'Shockwave' (v) WCot
- 'Skylight' NBro
- SNOWDRIFT see *P. paniculata* 'Schneerausch'
- 'Spätsommer' IPot
- 'Speed Limit 45' WCot
- 'Spitfire' see *P. paniculata* 'Frau Alfred von Mauthner'
- 'Starfire' ♀H7 Widely available
I - 'Stars and Stripes' LRHS NRHS
- 'Steeple Bumpstead' WCot
I - 'Stellata' CRos LRHS NRHS
- 'Sterling Brocade' (v) WCot
- 'Sternhimmel' LPla MTis
- 'Strawberry Daiquiri'PBR WFar
§ - (Sweet Summer Series) SWEET SUMMER CANDY ('Ditosdre'PBR) MAsh
§ - - SWEET SUMMER DREAM ('Ditomdre'PBR) MAvo NLar WCAu
- - SWEET SUMMER FANTASY ('Ditopur'PBR) IKil WCAu WTor
§ - - SWEET SUMMER FAVOURITE ('Ditomfav'PBR) ♀H7 NLar WCAu
- - SWEET SUMMER QUEEN ('Ditoran'PBR) IKil NLar
§ - - SWEET SUMMER SURPRISE ('Ditomsur'PBR) ECtt WCAu
- - SWEET SUMMER WINE ('Ditowine'PBR) ECtt IKil IPot MAvo NLar
- 'Swizzle' CWGN ECtt NPri WFar
- 'Tatjana'PBR EBee IPot
- 'Tenor' CRos CTri CWCL ECtt ELon EPfP EWTr GBin LEdu LRHS MJak NLar NRHS SCob SRms SWvt WCAu WMoo WSHC
- 'Tequila Sunrise'PBR EBee ECtt MNrw
- 'The King' ♀H7 EBee ECtt MAvo NLar WSHC WSpi
- 'Tiara'PBR (d) EBee ECtt LRHS MPie NGdn SWvt WCot
- 'Toits de Paris' misapplied see *P. paniculata* 'Cool of the Evening'
§ - 'Toits de Paris' Symons-Jeune WCot WSHC
- 'Twister' EBee MNrw WFar
- 'Uralskie Skazy' **new** IPot
§ - 'Uspekh' ♀H7 Widely available
- 'Valentina'PBR EBee
- 'Veg Plot Pink' SMHy
- 'Veg Plot White' SMHy
- 'Velvet Flame' ♀H7 CRos LRHS NRHS WHrl
- 'Vintage Wine' MNrw
- 'Violetta Gloriosa' ELon
- 'Visions' ♀H7 CRos LRHS NRHS WHil
- 'Volcano Betty' MNrw
- 'Watermelon Punch' ECtt NLar NPri WFar
- 'Wendy House' ECtt MAvo MNrw NHol
- 'White Admiral' ♀H7 CBcs CElw CRos EBee ECtt ELan ELon EMor EPfP GKev GMaP LRHS MHer MNrw MWat NAln NEgg NLar NRHS SCob SPer SPhx SRms SWvt WCAu WJam XLum
- WHITE FLAME ('Bartwentynine'PBR) ♀H7 CDor CRos CWGN ECtt EPfP IPot LBuc LRHS NLar NRHS SCob SWvt WCot
- 'White Pepper' **new** MAvo
- 'Wilhelm Kesselring' CRos EBee ECtt ELon LRHS MTis NChi NRHS WBor
- 'Willow Lodge' SHar
- 'Windsor' EBee ECtt EMor EPfP NCou NDov NEgg NHol SRms SWvt WCAu
- (Younique Series) YOUNIQUE BICOLOR ('Versbicolor') MAsh WFar
- - YOUNIQUE MAUVE **new** LCro LOPS MAsh
- - YOUNIQUE OLD BLUE ('Versoldblue') WFar
- - YOUNIQUE OLD CERISE ('Verscerise') WFar
- - YOUNIQUE OLD PINK ('Versoldpink') WFar
- - YOUNIQUE OLD PURPLE WFar
- - YOUNIQUE WHITE LEdu MNrw WFar

'Peppermint Candy' WFar
'Petticoat' CMea CSma ECtt SIgm WIce
PINK FLAME ('Bartwelve'PBR) CMea CRos EPfP LLHF LRHS NLar NPri NRHS SCob SRkn SRms WHil
'Pride of Rochester' CRos EBou ECtt LRHS NRHS
§ × ***procumbens*** 'Millstream' ♀H5 ECtt
- 'Variegata' (v) EBou ECha ECtt SRot
§ ***pulvinata*** SPlb WAbe
PURPLE FLAME ('Barfourteen'PBR) CRos EPfP GWyn LRHS NRHS SCob SRkn SRms WFar WHil
× ***rugelii*** EWld
'Sherbet Cocktail'PBR CWGN EBee NHol
§ ***sibirica*** subsp. ***borealis*** CPBP WAbe
'Sileniflora' GCrg WAbe
'Smokey' **new** WHlf

	Name	Suppliers
	'Special Purple Star' (Adessa Series)	NRHS
	stolonifera	MNrw
I	- 'Alba'	EPfP NLar WFar WKif
	- 'Ariane'	ECha ECtt MCot MNrw
	- 'Blue Ridge' ♀H6	CExl CRos ECha ECtt EPfP LRHS LSRN MHol MRav SIgm SRms WFar
	- 'Fran's Purple'	ECtt EWld MNrw NBro WAvo WBrk WFar
	- 'Home Fires'	CRos ECtt EPfP LEdu LRHS MNrw NBro SPlb
	- 'Janusz'	NWad
	- 'Montrose Tricolor' (v)	NBro
	- 'Pink Ridge'	XLum
	- 'Purpurea'	EPfP LEdu
	subulata 'Alexander's Surprise'	CMea CRos ECtt EPfP EPot LRHS MAsh NBir NRHS SIgm
	- 'Amazing Grace'	CRos CTri CWCL ECtt EPfP EWes IPot LRHS NRHS NWad SPoG WHoo WIce
	- 'Apple Blossom'	GKev NHol SPoG SRms
	- 'Atropurpurea'	EPfP SPoG XLum
	- 'Bavaria'	CBor CMea CRos ECtt EPfP IPot LLHF LRHS MBel NRHS WIce
	- BEAUTY OF RONSDORF	see *P. subulata* 'Ronsdorfer Schöne'
	- 'Blue Eyes'	see *P. subulata* 'Oakington Blue Eyes'
	- 'Bonita'	CRos ECtt EPot GCrg GWyn LRHS MAsh NRHS WHoo WIce
	- 'Bressingham Blue Eyes'	see *P. subulata* 'Oakington Blue Eyes'
	- 'Candy Stripe'	see *P. subulata* 'Tamaongalei'
	- 'Cavaldes White'	ECtt
	- 'Coral Eye'	ECtt
	- 'Daisy Hill'	XLum
	- 'Drumm'	see *P. subulata* 'Tamaongalei'
	- (Early Spring Series) EARLY SPRING LIGHT PINK **new**	NSla
	- - EARLY SPRING PURPLE ('Barseventyfour'[PBR])	CRos LRHS NRHS
	- - EARLY SPRING WHITE ('Barseventythree') **new**	NSla
	- 'Emerald Cushion'	CTri EBou ECtt ELon EPfP LRHS MHol NHol NHpl NLar NSla SGbt WCFE WTor XLum
	- 'Emerald Cushion Blue'	CExl CRos CTri EBou ECtt ELan EPfP LRHS MAsh MHCG MHol NBir NRHS SPlb SPoG WCAu
	- 'Fort Hill'	ECtt
	- 'G.F. Wilson'	see *P. subulata* 'Lilacina'
	- 'Holly'	EPot ITim NHol NWad
	- 'Kimono'	see *P. subulata* 'Tamaongalei'
§	- 'Lilacina'	CMea ECha MAsh
§	- 'Maischnee'	CTri ECtt GCrg MAsh SPlb
	- 'Marjorie'	EBou ECtt GKev MHer NAln NBir SPoG WRHF
	- MAY SNOW	see *P. subulata* 'Maischnee'
§	- 'McDaniel's Cushion' ♀H6	CBod CExl CRos CTri EBou ECha ECtt EDAr ELan ELon EPfP EPot EUJe GMaP LRHS MAsh MMuc NLar NRHS SPlb SPoG WCAu WHil WHoo WIce
	- 'Mikado'	see *P. subulata* 'Tamaongalei'
	- 'Millstream Daphne'	ECtt LLHF
	- 'Moerheimii'	IPot
	- 'Moonlight'	SIgm
	- 'Nettleton Variation' (v)	CRos EBou ECtt ELon EPot EWes LRHS MMuc NRHS SPoG SRms WHoo
§	- 'Oakington Blue Eyes'	CTri GWyn SRms
	- 'Purple Beauty'	CMea CRos ECtt EPfP GMaP LLHF LRHS NRHS NWad SIgm SPoG WCFE WHoo XLum
	- 'Red Wings' ♀H5	ECtt EPfP MHol SRms
§	- 'Ronsdorfer Schöne'	ECtt EPfP NBir
	- 'Samson'	LSRN WOld
	- 'Scarlet Flame'	CMea EBou ECtt ELon EMor EPfP EPot MAsh MHol NHol NHpl WCAu WHoo
	- 'Snow Queen'	see *P. subulata* 'Maischnee'
	- 'Snowflake'	GCrg
§	- 'Tamaongalei'	CBod CMea CRos CTri EBou ECtt ELan ELon EWes GKev LRHS MAsh MHol MMuc NHic NRHS NWad SIgm WCFE WFar WHil WIce XLum
	- 'Temiskaming'	CRos CTri ECtt EWes LRHS MBel NRHS SRms WSHC
	- 'White Delight'	CMea ECtt ELan ELon EPfP SPoG WCAu
	- 'Winifred'	NEgg
	(Sweet Summer Series) SWEET SUMMER OCEAN ('Ditoocean'[PBR]) **new**	IKil
	- SWEET SUMMER SENSATION ('Ditosse'[PBR])	IKil WCAu
	- SWEET SUMMER SNOW ('Ditosnow'[PBR]) **new**	IKil
	'Swirly Burly'	MTis
	'Tiny Bugles'	CPBP SIgm
	VIOLET FLAME ('Barsixtyone'[PBR])	CBod CDor CMea EPfP EUJe LPla LRHS LSun MAvo MHol NHic NLar NPri SCob SPer SPoG WCot WHil WRHF
	WHITE EYE FLAME ('Barsixty'[PBR])	CDor CRos CWGN EPau EPfP EUJe IPot LRHS NLar NPri NRHS SCob
	'White Kimono'	CRos LRHS NRHS
	'Zwergenteppich'	CBor CRos EPfP LRHS NRHS SPoG

Phoenix (*Arecaceae*)

	Name	Suppliers
	canariensis ♀H2	CBcs CExl EPfP EUJe SArc SEND SPlb SPoG
	dactylifera 'Mazafati' **new**	XBlo
	reclinata	XBlo
	roebelenii ♀H1b	CDTJ EUJe LCro LOPS
	- 'Multistem'	XBlo
	theophrasti	CPHo

Phormium ✿ (*Hemerocallidaceae*)

	Name	Suppliers
§	'Alison Blackman'[PBR]	CBcs CBod CRos EBee EMOT EPfP EUJe LRHS LSRN MAsh MGos MJak NLar NRHS SCob SCoo SEND SPoG SWvt
	'Amazing Red'	SCob SPer
	'Apricot Queen' (v)	CAbb CBcs CCCN CRos CSBt EMOT EPfP LCro LOPS LRHS LSRN MGos NLar NRHS SCob SEND SPer SPoG
	BACK IN BLACK ('Seilack'[PBR])	CBcs CPla CRos EUJe LRHS MMrt NRHS SCob WFar
	'Black Adder'[PBR]	CBcs CRos EBee EPfP EUJe ILea LBuc LRHS LSRN MAsh MJak NRHS SCob SEND SPer SPoG
	'Black Rage'	CBcs EPfP EUJe
	BLACK VELVET ('Seivel'[PBR])	CRos CSpe EUJe LRHS MJak MSwo
	'Bronze Baby'	CBcs CCCN CRos CSBt EBee ELan EMOT EPfP EUJe LRHS LSRN MGos MSwo NLar NRHS SCob SLim SPer SPoG SWvt
	'Buckland Ruby'	EBee
	'Chocomint'[PBR]	CBod ELan EUJe NLar

	colensoi	see *P. cookianum*
§	***cookianum***	GAbr SArc SCob
	- 'Alpinum Purpureum'	see *P. tenax* 'Nanum Purpureum'
	- subsp. ***hookeri*** 'Cream Delight' (v) ♀H4	CAbb CBcs CCCN CEnd CRos CSBt EBee EMOT EPfP EUJe LRHS LSRN MAsh MGos MSwo NRHS SCob SCoo SGol SWvt WFar
	- - 'Tricolor' (v) ♀H4	CBcs CBod CChe CDTJ CDul CRos CSBt EBee ELan EMOT EPfP EUJe LCro LOPS LRHS MGos MMuc NRHS SAko SArc SCob SEND SGol SLim SPer SPoG SRms SWvt WFar
	'Crimson Devil'	CBcs CRos LRHS NRHS
	'Dark Delight'	CBcs
	'Duet' (v) ♀H3	CBcs CCCN EPfP EUJe SEND SWvt
	'Dusky Chief'	CSBt EBee
	'Evening Glow' (v)	CBcs CCCN CRos EMOT EPfP EUJe LRHS LSRN MGos NLar NRHS SCob SPoG SRms SWvt
	'Firebird'	EUJe LSRN SWvt
	'Flamingo' (v)	CBcs CCCN CDTJ CRos EMOT EPfP EUJe LRHS MGos MHol NLar NRHS SCob SLim SPoG
	'Gold Ray' (v)	CBcs CRos EPfP EUJe LRHS MJak NRHS SCob SCoo SWvt
	'Gold Sword' (v)	CBcs CCCN CRos CSBt EPfP LRHS MJak NEgg SCob
	'Golden Alison'	see *P.* 'Alison Blackman'
	'Green Sword'	CCCN
	'Jack Spratt' (v)	EHoe SWvt
	'Jester' (v)	CBcs CBod CCCN CChe CKel CRos CSBt ELan EMOT EPfP EUJe LRHS LSRN MAsh MGos MJak MSwo NEgg NRHS SCob SCoo SLim SPoG SRkn SRms
	'Limelight'	SEND SWvt
§	'Maori Chief' (v)	CRos CSBt EMOT EPfP LRHS SWvt WFar
§	'Maori Maiden' (v)	CCCN CDul CRos CTri EBee EPfP LRHS MSwo NRHS SRms SWvt
§	'Maori Queen' (v)	CBcs CCCN CDTJ CDul CRos EBee ELan EPfP EUJe ILea LCro LOPS LRHS MGos MSwo NRHS SCob SCoo SEND SPer SWvt WFar
§	'Maori Sunrise' (v)	CBcs CCCN CPla CRos IArd LCro LOPS LRHS LSRN MGos NRHS SCob SCoo SLim SRms SWvt
	'Margaret Jones'PBR	CCCN LSRN
	'Moonraker'PBR	CBcs MHol
	'Pink Panther' (v)	CAbb CBcs CCCN CDul CRos EMOT EPfP LRHS LSRN MGos NLar NRHS SCob SPoG SRms
	'Pink Stripe' (v)	CBcs CBod CRos CSBt EPfP LCro LOPS LRHS MAsh MGos MJak NRHS SCob SPoG SWvt
	'Platt's Black'	CCCN CRos EMOT EPfP LCro LOPS LRHS LSRN MGos MSwo NBir NLar NRHS SCob SLim SPer SPoG SSta SWvt WFar
	'Rainbow Chief'	see *P.* 'Maori Chief'
	'Rainbow Maiden'	see *P.* 'Maori Maiden'
	'Rainbow Queen'	see *P.* 'Maori Queen'
	'Rainbow Sunrise'	see *P.* 'Maori Sunrise'
	'Red Sensation'	EUJe LSRN
	'Sundowner' (v) ♀H3	CBcs CCCN CDul CRos CSBt EBee EMOT EPfP EUJe LCro LOPS LRHS MAsh MGos MJak NBir NEgg NRHS SCob SCoo SEND SLim SPer SPoG SWvt
	'Sunset' (v)	CBcs CCCN CSBt SWvt
	'Surfer Bronze'	CCCN
	'Surfer Green'	CCCN
	'Sussex Velvet'	SCoo SLim
	tenax	CAco CAgr CBcs CDul CFGn CRos CTsd ECrN EPfP EUJe LCro LOPS LRHS MGos MSwo NGdn NPri NRHS SArc SCob SEND SGol SPer SPlb SPoG SWvt
	- 'All Black'	MGos SCoo
	- 'Bronze'	CTsd SWvt
	- 'Co-ordination' (v)	CBcs CCCN EMOT
	- 'Croce di Malta' **new**	SArc
	- 'Joker' (v)	CBcs CBod EBee EUJe NLar
*	- ***lineatum***	SEND
§	- 'Nanum Purpureum'	SArc
	- Purpureum Group ♀H4	CBod CDul CRos EBee ELan EPfP EUJe LRHS MGil MJak MMuc MSwo NLar NRHS SCob SEND SGol SLim SLon SPer SPlb WFar XLum
	- 'Thumbelina'	CCCN
	- 'Tiny Tiger' (v)	EPfP
	- 'Variegatum' (v) ♀H5	CDTJ CPla EBee EPfP EUJe MGos MMuc NPri SArc SCob SEND SRms
	- 'Yellow Queen' (v)	WFar
	variegated (v)	SCob
	'Wings of Gold'	ELan
	'Yellow Wave' (v) ♀H4	CAbb CBcs CChe CDul CEnd CKel CRos EBee ELon EPfP EUJe LRHS LSRN MAsh MGos MJak MSwo NEgg NRHS SCob SEND SLim SPer SPoG SWvt

Photinia ✿ (*Rosaceae*)

	arbutifolia	see *Heteromeles salicifolia*
	arguta var. ***arguta*** KR 10738	WPGP
	beauverdiana	CJun NLar
	var. ***notabilis***	
	CORALLINA ('Bourfrits'PBR)	LPra
	davidiana	CMac CTri ELan EPfP GKev IDee MGil MRav NLar SCob SPer SPtp SRms SVen WPav
	- PAB 8097	LEdu
	- 'Palette' (v)	CBcs CDul CMac EHoe ELan ELon EPfP EUJe LRHS MAsh MGos MMuc MSwo NEgg NLar SCob SGol SMad SPer SPoG SRms SWvt WFar WMat
	- Salicifolia Group **new**	WPav
	- var. ***undulata*** 'Fructu Luteo'	MMuc MRav
	- - 'Prostrata'	CMac CTri MRav NLar WCFE
	× ***fraseri***	LPra WTSh
I	- 'Atropurpurea Nana'	CBcs MGos
	- 'Birmingham'	CMac EWes SRms
	- 'Canivily' ♀H5	CEnd CRos LRHS MGos NLar NRHS SGol
*	- 'Ilexifolium'	ESwi
	- 'Little Red Robin'	Widely available
	- 'Louise' (v)	CRos CSBt EBee EUJe LBuc LRHS MAsh MGos MHed MJak NRHS WFar
	- MAGICAL VOLCANO ('Kolmavoca'PBR)	LRHS MAsh SGol SMad SPoG
	- PINK MARBLE ('Cassini') (v) ♀H5	CAco CBcs CEnd CRos EBee ECrN ELan EMOT EPfP EUJe LBuc LCro LOPS LRHS MAsh MGos MJak MMuc MSwo NLar NRHS SCob SGbt SGol SLim SLon SPer SPoG SRms
	- 'Red Robin' ♀H5	Widely available

– 'Red Select'	WFar
– 'Robusta'	CMac EPfP LRHS SRms SWvt
I – 'Robusta Compacta'	LSRN
glabra	SArc
§ – 'Parfait' (v)	CMac EBee MAsh SLon
– 'Pink Lady'	see *P. glabra* 'Parfait'
– 'Rubens'	CRos EPfP LRHS MAsh MRav
– 'Variegata'	see *P. glabra* 'Parfait'
lasiogyna	CMCN
lucida	WCru
microphylla B&SWJ 11837	WCru
– HWJ 564	WCru
niitakayamensis CWJ 12435	WCru
'Redstart'	CMac ELan EPfP LRHS MMuc NLar SLon SPer SWvt WFar
§ ***serratifolia***	CBcs CMCN EPfP NLar SArc SEND SPer WFar WPGP
– var. ***ardisiifolia*** NMWJ 14513 new	WCru
– CRUNCHY ('Rev100'PBR)	LBuc
– CURLY FANTASY ('Kolcurl'PBR)	LRHS MAsh MRav NLar
– 'Jenny'	NLar WFar
– PINK CRISPY ('Oploo5'PBR)	ELan SPoG
serrulata	see *P. serratifolia*
SUPER HEDGE ('Branpara'PBR)	GBin LRHS MSwo WFar
'Super Red'	CAby CSBt NLar
villosa	CTho EPfP WPav
– B&SWJ 8665	WCru
– var. ***coreana*** B&SWJ 8789	WCru
– var. ***laevis***	CExl EPfP WPGP
– – B&SWJ 8877	WCru
– f. ***maximowicziana***	CJun NLar
* – var. ***zollingeri*** B&SWJ 8903	WCru

Phragmites (*Poaceae*)

sp.	CHab
from Sichuan, China	EPPr
§ ***australis***	CBen CHab CWat NMir SVic WMAq WPnP XLum
– subsp. ***australis*** var. ***striatopictus***	EPPr
– – 'Variegatus' (v)	CWat EPPr LLWG MMuc MPie NBir SEND SMad WWtn XLum
– subsp. ***humilis***	CHab
– subsp. ***pseudodonax***	EPPr
communis	see *P. australis*

Phuopsis (*Rubiaceae*)

§ ***stylosa***	CBod CCBP CTri EBee EBou ECha ELan ELon EPPr EPfP GAbr GMaP MHer MHol MMuc NBid NBir NBro NChi NSti SEND SRms SWvt WCAu WWFP XLum
– 'Purpurea'	EBee MNrw MRav NChi

Phycella (*Amaryllidaceae*)

cyrtanthoides	WCot

Phygelius (*Scrophulariaceae*)

aequalis	MRav
– ***albus***	see *P. aequalis* 'Yellow Trumpet'
– 'Aureus'	see *P. aequalis* 'Yellow Trumpet'
– 'Cream Trumpet'	see *P. aequalis* 'Yellow Trumpet'
– 'Indian Chief'	see *P.* × *rectus* 'African Queen'
– 'Sani Pass'	ELon MHer SCob SPer SPlb
– 'Trewidden Pink' ♀H4	CRos ELan ELon GBin LRHS MHer NRHS SWvt XLum
§ – 'Yellow Trumpet' ♀H4	CSBt CTca ELan ELon EPfP GKev GMaP LSRN MAsh MGil MMuc NAln SEND SGbt SLim SWvt WAvo
(Candy Drops Series) CANDY DROPS CREAM ('Kerphycrem'PBR)	NGBl SCob
– CANDY DROPS SALMON ORANGE ('Kerphysalm'PBR)	SRms
capensis	CHll CTri MGil MHer SRms WOut WRHF
'Golden Gate'	see *P. aequalis* 'Yellow Trumpet'
Logan form	GBin
NEW SENSATION ('Blaphy'PBR)	EPfP MRav SCob SRms SWvt
'Passionate'PBR	NLar
§ × ***rectus*** 'African Queen' ♀H4	CTri ECrN ELan EPfP LRHS MGil MRav MSwo NBir NGdn SEND SPlb SWvt WAvo WKif XLum
– 'Bridgetown Beauty'	GCal
– 'Devil's Tears' ♀H4	CBcs CPla MMuc NEgg SCob SEND SLim SWvt
– 'Ivory Twist'	ELon SPer
– 'Jodie Southon'	ELon SDys WCot
– 'Moonraker'	CAby CBcs CBod CHll CTri ELan ELon EPfP GBin GWyn MAsh MGil MHer MRav NGdn NLar SCob SEND SPer SPlb SRms WKif XLum
– 'Salmon Leap' ♀H4	CBcs CBod CRos CTri ELan EPfP LRHS LSRN MBNS MGos MRav NEgg NRHS SCob SLim SPlb SRms SWvt
– (Somerford Funfair Series) SOMERFORD FUNFAIR APRICOT ('Yapapr')	SWvt
– – SOMERFORD FUNFAIR CORAL ('Yapcor'PBR)	CRos EPfP LRHS MAsh NLar NRHS SCob SLim SRkn SWvt
– – SOMERFORD FUNFAIR CREAM ('Yapcre'PBR)	CRos EPfP LRHS NLar NRHS SLim SPoG SWvt
– – SOMERFORD FUNFAIR ORANGE ('Yapor'PBR)	CPla CRos EPfP EUJe LRHS MAsh NLar NRHS SLim SRms SWvt
– – SOMERFORD FUNFAIR WINE ('Yapwin')	CAby CChe CDul CRos ECrN ELan EPfP LRHS MAsh MBNS NRHS SCob SLim SPoG SWvt
– – SOMERFORD FUNFAIR YELLOW ('Yapyel'PBR)	CChe CRos EPfP LRHS MAsh NAln NRHS SLim SWvt
§ – 'Winchester Fanfare'	GBin GWyn MGos MRav NLar SCob SEND SLim SWvt
– 'Winton Fanfare'	see *P.* × *rectus* 'Winchester Fanfare'
'Rory'PBR	SRms
SNOW QUEEN ('Crosnoque'PBR) (Croftway Series)	SCob

Phyla (*Verbenaceae*)

lanceolata	LLWG
§ ***nodiflora***	ECha MHer SRms XSen
– 'Alba'	MMuc SEND
§ – var. ***canescens***	XLum
– var. ***rosea***	SRot

Phylica (*Rhamnaceae*)

arborea	LRHS
pubescens	CPbh

× *Phylliopsis* (*Ericaceae*)

'Coppelia' ♀H5	EPot ITim
hillieri 'Askival'	EPot GKev WThu

- 'Pinocchio' EPot GEdr GKev WThu
- 'Sugar Plum' CCCN GEdr SWvt WThu
'Hobgoblin' ITim
'Mermaid' EPot ITim
'Puck' EPot
'Sprite' EPot ITim
'Swanhilde' WThu

Phyllitis see *Asplenium*

scolopendrium see *Asplenium scolopendrium*

Phyllocladus ✿ (*Podocarpaceae*)

aspleniifolius WPav
trichomanoides CBcs CDul NWad WThu
var. ***alpinus***
- - 'Blue Blades' new MGil SAko
- - 'Highland Lass' new MGil
- - 'Highlander' new MGil SAko

Phyllodoce (*Ericaceae*)

aleutica WThu
§ - subsp. ***glanduliflora*** 'Flora Slack' WThu
- - white-flowered see *P. aleutica* subsp. *glanduliflora* 'Flora Slack'
caerulea japonica see *P. nipponica*
- 'Murray Lyon' WThu
empetriformis WThu
§ ***nipponica*** WThu
'Peach' NLar WThu

Phyllostachys ✿ (*Poaceae*)

angusta ERod MWht
arcana 'Luteosulcata' ERod MMuc MWht XCre
§ ***atrovaginata*** CBdn ERod SGol XCre
aurea ♀H6 Widely available
- 'Albovariegata' (v) EPfP ERod LRHS MWht SPoG XCre
- 'Flavescens Inversa' ERod MWht XCre
- 'Holochrysa' CDTJ CJun ERod MMuc MWht NLar XCre
- 'Koi' CDTJ ERod MWht SGol XCre
aureocaulis see *P. aureosulcata* f. *aureocaulis*, *P. vivax* f. *aureocaulis*
aureosulcata ERod WMoo XCre
- f. ***alata*** see *P. aureosulcata* f. *pekinensis*
§ - f. ***aureocaulis*** CAbb CBcs CBdn CBod CDul CJun CRos CTsd ELon EMOT ENBC EPfP EUJe GCal LCro LOPS LRHS LSRN MGos MSwo MWht NRHS SArc SCob SEWo SGol SPoG SWvt XCre
- 'Harbin' ERod XCre
- 'Harbin Inversa' ERod
- 'Lama Tempel' CDTJ CJun XCre
§ - f. ***pekinensis*** XCre
- f. ***spectabilis*** ♀H6 Widely available
bambusoides CDTJ ERod
- 'Allgold' see *P. bambusoides* 'Holochrysa'
- 'Castillonii' ♀H5 CBcs CBct ENBC ERod EUJe EWes LEdu MMuc MWht SEND XCre
- 'Castillonii Inversa' ENBC ERod LEdu MWht XCre
- 'Castillonii Variegata' (v) ERod
§ - 'Holochrysa' ♀H5 CDTJ ERod MMuc MWht SEND WPGP XCre
- 'Kawadana' (v) ERod
- f. ***lacrima-deae*** CDTJ
- 'Marliacea' ERod XCre
- 'Sulphurea' see *P. bambusoides* 'Holochrysa'
- 'Tanakae' CDTJ XCre
bissetii ♀H5 CAbb CAgr CBcs CBdn CBod CCVT CDul CRos EMOT ENBC EPfP ERod EUJe LCro LOPS LRHS MAvo MBrN MGos MMuc MSwo MWht NLar NRHS SEND SGol SPlb WPGP XCre
circumpilis XCre
congesta misapplied see *P. atrovaginata*
decora ERod MMuc MWht
dulcis CBdn CFGn EPfP ERod MWht XCre
§ ***edulis*** CAgr CBct ERod SPlb XCre
§ - 'Heterocycla' XBlo
- f. ***pubescens*** see *P. edulis*
flexuosa CBcs MWht SGol
glauca EPfP ERod MWht XCre
- f. ***yunzhu*** ERod MWht XCre
heteroclada 'Solid Stem' misapplied see *P. purpurata* 'Straight Stem'
heterocycla see *P. edulis* 'Heterocycla'
- var. ***pubescens*** see *P. edulis*
humilis CBdn ENBC ERod EUJe MMuc MWht SEND XCre
iridescens ♀H5 ERod MWht XCre
kwangsiensis XCre
lithophila ERod
lofushanensis XCre
makinoi ERod
mannii ERod MWht
nidularia ERod
nigra ♀H6 Widely available
- 'Boryana' CCVT CEnd EPfP ERod MGos MMuc MWht SEND SWvt WMoo XCre
- 'Hale' CBct MWht
- f. ***henonis*** ♀H5 CBdn ENBC ERod MMuc MWht NLar SEND SGol WPGP XCre
- 'Megurochiku' ERod MWht XCre
- f. ***punctata*** ENBC ERod MAvo MMuc SEND WMoo
- 'Tosaensis' ERod
nuda ERod MWht XCre
- f. ***localis*** ERod MWht
parvifolia ERod MWht
platyglossa ERod XCre
praecox XCre
f. ***prevernalis*** new
- f. ***viridisulcata*** ERod XCre
prominens ERod XCre
propinqua ERod MWht
§ ***purpurata*** 'Straight Stem' MWht
reticulata new XCre
robustiramea new XCre
rubromarginata ERod MMuc MWht
'Shanghai 3' ERod
stimulosa ERod MWht XCre
sulphurea 'Houzeau' ERod MMuc SEND
§ - f. ***sulphurea*** ERod XCre
- 'Sulphurea' see *P. sulphurea* f. *sulphurea*
§ - f. ***viridis*** ERod XCre
violascens CAgr ERod MWht XCre
virella XCre
viridiglaucescens CAgr CDTJ ERod MMuc MWht SEND WCot XCre
viridis see *P. sulphurea* f. *viridis*
vivax ENBC EPfP ERod EUJe MWht NLar XCre
§ - f. ***aureocaulis*** ♀H5 CAbb CAgr CBcs CBdn CCVT CDul CEnd ENBC EPfP ERod EUJe LEdu LRHS LSRN MGos MMuc MWht NLar SCob SEND SGol WPGP XCre
- - 'Huangwenzhu' CDTJ ERod MWht XCre
- 'Katrin' LEdu
* - 'Sulphurea' XBlo

Phymatosorus (*Polypodiaceae*)

diversifolius	see *Microsorum diversifolium*

Phymosia (*Malvaceae*)

§ ***umbellata***	EBee LRHS WPGP

Phyodina see *Callisia*

Physalis (*Solanaceae*)

alkekengi ♀H7	CTri EPfP NBir NLar SWvt
- var. ***franchetii***	CBcs CMac CRos CSBt CTri EBee ECha ELan EPfP ILea LCro LOPS LRHS MBel MNrw NBir NBro NEgg NRHS SPer SPoG SRms WFar WOld
- - dwarf	CRos LRHS NLar NRHS
- - 'Gigantea'	CBct CBod CRos CWld LRHS LSun NLar NRHS SPlb WFar
- - 'Gnome'	see *P. alkekengi* var. *franchetii* 'Zwerg'
- - 'Variegata' (v)	EWes LEdu SEND WPGP
§ - - 'Zwerg'	CDor CRos EBee EBou ELon EUJe LRHS LSun NRHS
- 'Halloween King'	EBee NLar
- 'Halloween Queen'	NLar
edulis	see *P. peruviana*
§ ***peruviana*** (F)	CCCN CSpe SPlb SVic

Physaria (*Brassicaceae*)

alpina	SPlb
didymocarpa	CPla
saximontana	GKev

Physocarpus (*Rosaceae*)

capitatus 'Tilden Park'	EBee SGol
LITTLE DEVIL	see *P. opulifolius* 'Donna May'
'Midnight'	GBin LRHS MAsh MMrt NEoE WFar WMoo
opulifolius AMBER JUBILEE ('Jefam'PBR)	ELan LCro LOPS NEoE
- 'Angel Gold'	CRos LRHS MAsh NPri NRHS SPoG
- 'Anny's Gold'PBR	EBee SRms
- 'Burning Embers'	SRms
- 'Chameleon'	CKel EBee EMil GBin LBuc NEoE SGol WMoo
- COPPERTINA	see *P. opulifolius* DIABLE D'OR
- 'Dart's Gold' ♀H7	Widely available
§ - DIABLE D'OR ('Mindia'PBR)	CBar CBod CKel CRos EBee EPfP LCro LOPS LRHS LSRN MAsh MBlu MGos MPkF NEgg NLar NOra NRHS SGbt SGol WCot WMoo
- 'Diabolo'PBR ♀H7	Widely available
§ - 'Donna May'PBR	ELan EPfP EShb MAsh NEoE SCob WFar
- 'Firebrand'	NEoE
§ - LADY IN RED ('Tuilad'PBR) ♀H7	Widely available
- LITTLE ANGEL ('Hoogi016'PBR)	CWGN LCro LOPS SPad SPoG
§ - 'Luteus'	MRav WMoo
- MIDNIGHT ('Jonight'PBR)	CBcs MGil
- 'Red Baron'	WFar
- RUBY SPICE	see *P. opulifolius* LADY IN RED
- SUMMER MOON ('Tuimon')	CBcs NEoE SGol WMoo
- SUMMER WINE ('Seward'PBR)	CKel EBee EPfP EWes LRHS MAsh NLar WSpi
- TINY WINE ('Smpotw')	MAsh MPkF NLar
ribesifolius 'Aureus'	see *P. opulifolius* 'Luteus'

Physochlaina (*Solanaceae*)

orientalis	GEdr

Physoplexis (*Campanulaceae*)

§ ***comosa*** ♀H6	CPBP EPot

Physostegia (*Lamiaceae*)

angustifolia	NBre
I 'Aquatica'	LLWG
§ ***virginiana***	CBod CSBt CTri GMaP ILea MBel NHic SRms WCFE WJam WOld
- 'Alba'	CAby CMac CSBt CTri EAJP EBee EHrv ELon EMor GAbr GMaP LEdu SPlb WArt WOut XLum
§ - 'Crown of Snow'	CRos EBee EPfP GWyn LRHS MHer MRav NRHS SWvt WJam WMoo
- 'Crystal Peak White'	CBod EBee LRHS WFar
- 'Miss Manners'	CBod EBee ECtt LRHS MPie NBre NGdn NLar NRHS
- 'Olympic Gold' (v)	NWad
- 'Pink Manners'	NLar STPC
- 'Rose Crown'	SPer
- 'Rose Queen'	CBod CTri EAJP EMor NBre WFar
- 'Rosea'	CRos EPfP GJos GPSL GWyn LRHS LSun MMuc NChi NCou NGdn NRHS SHar SPoG SWvt WFar WHrl
- SCHNEEKRONE	see *P. virginiana* 'Crown of Snow'
- 'Snow Queen'	see *P. virginiana* 'Summer Snow'
§ - var. ***speciosa*** 'Bouquet Rose'	CBod CMac CRos EBee ECha EHrv EPfP LEdu LRHS MRav NBir NLar NRHS SGbt SPer SRms SWvt WCAu WMoo WRHF XLum
- - ROSE BOUQUET	see *P. virginiana* var. *speciosa* 'Bouquet Rose'
- - 'Variegata' (v)	CBod CMac EBee ECtt EHoe EHrv ELan ELon EPfP GLog MRav NBir NGdn NHol SPer SPoG SRms WCAu WCot WFar XLum
§ - 'Summer Snow' ♀H7	CBcs CCBP CRos ECha ELan EPfP LRHS NGBl NLar NRHS SPer SRms WCAu WCot
- 'Summer Spire'	EHrv
- 'Vivid' ♀H7	CAby CBod CMac CRos ECha ELan ELon EMor EPfP LRHS MHer MNrw MPie MRav NEgg NGBl NHol NLar NRHS SPer SPlb SRms WAul WCAu WCot WHil WWtn XLum

Phyteuma (*Campanulaceae*)

balbisii	see *P. cordatum*
betonicifolium	WHoo
charmelii	GEdr WHoo
comosum	see *Physoplexis comosa*
§ ***cordatum***	GJos
halleri	see *P. ovatum*
hemisphaericum	GEdr NSla
humile	WThu
nigrum	GEdr NBid SBrt WBor WCot
orbiculare	CPla GEdr GJos
§ ***ovatum***	SPlb
scheuchzeri	EBee EBou EDAr EPfP EWld GEdr GJos GWyn MMrt SMad SPad SRms WArt WCot WIce WRHF XLum
sieberi	GJos
spicatum	GEdr GJos NBro
- subsp. ***coeruleum***	GJos

Phytolacca (*Phytolaccaceae*)

acinosa	EWld SBrt WHil

	- HWJ 647	WCru
§	***americana***	CAby CBcs CCBP EBee ELan EMor EPfP ESwi EUJe GPoy MBNS MHer MPie NChi SPlb SRms
	- B&SWJ 8817A	WCru
	- 'Silberstein' (v)	EBee MHol WHer
	bogotensis B&SWJ 14221	WCru
	clavigera	see *P. polyandra*
	decandra	see *P. americana*
	dioica	CExl SPlb
	esculenta	LEdu SEND
	icosandra B&SWJ 8988	WCru
	- Purpurascens Group B&SWJ 11251	WCru
	japonica B&SWJ 3005	NBid WCru
	- B&SWJ 3522	WCru
	octandra B&SWJ 9514	WCru
§	***polyandra***	EUJe GAbr NBid NBro SRms
	rivinoides B&SWJ 10264	WCru
	rugosa B&SWJ 10263	WCru

Picea ✿ (*Pinaceae*)

§	***abies***	CCVT CDul CLnd CMac CPer CSBt CTho CTri EPfP GQue LBuc LPra MJak MMuc NEgg NWea SCoo SEND SPoG WMou WTSh
	- 'Acrocona' ♀H7	CAco LRHS NLar
	- 'Archer'	CKen
	- 'Aurea'	CAco
	- 'Bago'	CKen
	- 'Barus'	NLar
	- 'Brunn'	NLar
	- 'Capitata'	CKen
	- 'Clanbrassiliana' ♀H7	CKen ELan LRHS NWad
	- Columnaris Group	LRHS NEgg
I	- 'Congesta'	CKen
	- 'Crippsii'	CKen
I	- 'Cruenta'	CKen
	- 'Cupressina'	CKen
	- 'Diffusa'	CKen MGil
	- 'Dumpy'	CKen NHol
	- 'Excelsa'	see *P. abies*
	- 'Fahndrich'	CKen CMen
	- 'Formanek'	SAko
	- 'Four Winds'	CKen
	- 'Frohburg'	CKen EUJe LRHS NEgg
	- 'Gold Drift'	CAco NLar
	- 'Gold Finch'	NLar
	- 'Gregoryana'	CKen
	- 'Hasin'	SAko
	- 'Heartland Gem'	CKen
	- 'Honey Pot' **new**	NLar
	- 'Horace Wilson'	CKen CMen
	- 'Humilis'	CKen
	- 'Hystrix'	CMen LRHS NLar NWad
	- 'Inversa' ♀H7	CDul CKen MBlu SLim
	- 'J.W. Daisy's White'	see *P. glauca* var. *albertiana* 'J.W. Daisy's White'
	- 'Jana'	CKen NLar
	- 'Jermyns Broom No. 1'	CKen
	- 'Kral'	CKen
	- 'Krenek'	NLar
	- 'Lemon Drop' **new**	NLar
	- 'Little Gem' ♀H7	CKen CMen ELan EUJe GEdr LRHS MAsh MGos NHol NLar NWad NWea SCoo SLim
	- 'Marcel'	CKen
	- 'Mini Kalous'	CKen
	- 'Nana Compacta'	CKen CMen MAsh
	- 'Nidiformis' ♀H7	CKen CMac CMen CSBt CTri EUJe LRHS MGil MGos NWea SGol SRms
	- 'Norrköping'	CKen
	- 'Ohlendorffii'	CKen
	- 'Pachyphylla'	CKen
	- 'Parsonsii' **new**	SAko
	- 'Pseudomaxwellii'	LRHS
	- 'Pumila'	WCFE
	- 'Pusch'	CKen CMen NLar
	- 'Pygmaea'	CKen NWad
	- 'Reflexa'	CAco NEgg
	- 'Remontii'	NWea
	- 'Ripley Broom' **new**	CKen
	- 'Roseospicata' **new**	NLar
	- 'Rydal' ♀H7	CAco CBcs CDul CKen LRHS MAsh NEgg NLar
	- 'Saint Mary's Broom'	NEgg
	- 'Spring Fire'	CKen
	- 'Tompa'	NLar
	- 'Tutsberg'	NLar
	- 'Typner'	CKen NLar
	- 'Vermont Gold'	CKen LRHS NLar
	- 'Wagner'	NLar
	- 'Wichtel'	CKen
	- WILL'S DWARF	see *P. abies* 'Wills Zwerg'
§	- 'Wills Zwerg'	ELan LRHS NLar
§	***alcoquiana*** var. ***alcoquiana***	SLim
	- var. ***reflexa***	MPkF
	asperata	CDul
	- 'Mongolei'	NLar
	bicolor	see *P. alcoquiana* var. *alcoquiana*
I	- 'Prostrata'	NEgg
	breweriana ♀H7	CAco CDul CMac CTho EPfP GKin IDee LEdu LRHS MBlu MGos MJak NEgg NLar NWea SLim SSta WCFE WTSh
	- 'Kohout's Dwarf'	CKen NLar
	engelmannii	CAco CDul
	- 'Bush's Lace'	NLar
	- 'Cienega' **new**	CKen
	- 'Compact'	SLim
	- subsp. ***engelmannii***	CKen
	- 'Jasper'	CKen NLar
	farreri	CAco
	glauca	CDul SWvt
	- var. ***albertiana*** ALBERTA BLUE ('Haal'PBR)	CKen LRHS
	- - 'Alberta Globe' ♀H7	CAco EUJe GKin LRHS MAsh MGil MGos NEgg NHol NWad SCoo SPoG
	- - 'Conica' ♀H7	CBcs CMac CSBt EPfP EUJe LCro LOPS LRHS MAsh MGil MGos MMuc NEgg NHol NLar NWea SEND SGol SPer SPoG SRms SWvt WCFE
	- - 'Gnome'	CKen
§	- - 'J.W. Daisy's White' ♀H7	CBcs CKen ELan EPfP EUJe GKin LRHS MAsh MGos NHol NLar NWea SCoo SLim SPoG
	- - 'Laurin' ♀H7	CKen NWad
	- - 'Lilliput'	CKen NLar NWad NWea SPoG
	- - 'Piccolo'	CKen NEgg NLar NWad
	- - 'Sander's Blue'	CAco CBod CKen EPfP GKin LCro LOPS LRHS NLar NRya SAko SPoG
	- - 'Tiny'	CKen NWad
	- 'Arneson's Blue Variegated' (v)	CKen MAsh SLim
	- 'Biesenthaler Frühling'	CKen
	- 'Blue Planet'	CKen

	- 'Blue Teardrop'	NLar
	- 'Coerulea'	EUJe NEgg
	- 'Cy's Wonder'	CKen
	- 'Dendroforma Gold'	CKen NLar
	- 'Eagle Rock' **new**	NLar
	- 'Echiniformis' ♀H7	CKen LRHS MGil NLar
	- 'Goldilocks'	CAco CKen NLar
	- 'Iseli Broom' **new**	CAco
	- 'Jalako Gold'	LRHS
I	- 'Julian Potts Monstrosa'	NLar
	- 'Milford' **new**	CKen
§	- 'Nana'	CKen
	- 'Pendula'	CKen SLim
	- 'Pixie'	CKen
	- 'Pixie Dust'	CKen
	- 'Rainbow's End' (v)	CKen NLar
	- 'Spring Surprise'	CKen
	- 'Zuckerhut'	LRHS
	glehnii 'Sasanosei'	CKen
	- 'Shimezusei'	CKen
	jezoensis	CAco CKen CMen NWea
	- 'Aurea'	SLim
	- subsp. ***hondoensis***	CMen
	- 'Marianbad'	CKen
	- 'Mariánské Làzně'	NLar
	- 'Yatsabusa'	CKen CMen
	koraiensis	CDul
	kosteri 'Glauca'	see *P. pungens* 'Koster'
	koyamae	NWea
	- 'Bedgebury Cascade'	SLim
	likiangensis	CAco CDul CMCN EBtc EPfP NLar
	- var. ***balfouriana***	see *P. likiangensis* var. *rubescens*
§	- var. ***rubescens***	LRHS SLim WHor
	mariana	EPfP NWea
	- 'Austria Broom'	CKen
	- 'Bill Archer'	NWad
	- 'Blue Teardrop'	CKen
	- 'Fastigiata'	CKen
	- 'Nana' ♀H7	CKen CMac CMen EPfP EUJe GEdr MGos MMuc NHol NWad NWea SCoo SLim SPoG
I	- 'Pygmaea'	CKen NWad
	meyeri	CTho EPfP
	morrisonicola	CKen
	obovata var. ***coerulea***	EPfP
	omorika ♀H7	CBcs CCVT CDul CJun CMCN CPer CTho EPfP EWTr EWhm LBuc LPra MMuc NLar NWea SEND SEWo WCFE
	- 'Berliner's Weeper' witches' broom	NLar
	- 'Cinderella'	NLar
	- 'De Ruyter'	NEgg
	- 'Elegance' **new**	SAko
	- 'Frohnleiten'	CKen
	- 'Frondenberg'	CKen
	- 'Halone'	CKen
	- 'Karel'	CKen LRHS
	- 'Minimax'	CKen
	- 'Nana' ♀H7	LRHS NEgg SLim WCFE
	- 'Pendula' ♀H7	CAco LRHS MBlu SSta
	- 'Pendula Bruns'	CAco MBlu NLar SAko SLim SMad
	- 'Pévé Tijn'	LRHS NLar
	- 'Pimoko'	CKen NEgg NLar SLim
	- 'Pygmy'	CKen
	- 'Schneverdingen'	CKen SAko
	- 'Tijn'	CKen SLim
	- 'Treblitsch'	CKen NLar SAko SLim
	orientalis ♀H7	CDul WThu
	- 'Aurea' (v) ♀H7	ELan MJak SMad
	- 'Aureospicata'	CAco CTho MAsh MBlu MJak NEgg
	- 'Bergman's Gem'	CKen
	- 'Golden Start'	NEgg SLim
	- 'Gowdy Gold'	NLar
	- 'Juwel'	CKen NLar
	- 'Kenwith'	CKen
	- 'Mount Vernon'	CKen NLar
	- Nana Group	GKin
	- 'Pévé Tiny Gold'	CKen NLar
	- 'Professor Langner'	CKen NLar
	- 'Shadow's Broom'	CKen CMen NEgg
§	- 'Silver Seedling'	NLar
	- 'Skylands' ♀H7	CKen ELan MAsh NEgg NLar SLim
	- 'Spring Grove'	NLar
	- 'Sulphur Flush'	see *P. orientalis* 'Silver Seedling'
	- 'Tom Thumb'	CAco CKen NLar
	- 'Wittboldt'	CKen LRHS
	pungens	CCVT LMaj NWea
	- 'Anton'	NLar
	- 'Blaukissen'	CKen NLar
	- 'Blue Diamond'	LRHS MJak SPoG
	- 'Blue Pearl'	CKen
	- 'Donna's Rainbow'	NLar
	- 'Edith' ♀H7	CAco CDul CKen NEgg NLar NOra SCoo SEWo SLim WMat
	- 'Erich Frahm'	CAco CCVT MAsh NLar NOra SCoo SPoG WMat
	- 'Fat Albert' ♀H7	CAco CCVT LMaj LRHS NEgg NLar NWea SLim SPoG
	- 'Frieda'	SLim
	- Glauca Group	CAco CCVT CDul CMac CPer EWTr LPra MMuc NWea SCoo SPoG WMou WTSh
	- - 'Glauca Pendula'	CAco
	- - 'Glauca Procumbens'	CKen
§	- - 'Glauca Prostrata'	SLim
I	- - 'Globosa' ♀H7	CAco CBcs CCVT CKen CSBt EPfP LRHS MAsh NEgg NHol SCoo SLim SPoG
	- - 'Hoopsii' ♀H7	CAco CDul EPfP GKin LRHS MAsh MGos MJak NEgg NWea SCoo SPoG SWvt WMat
	- - 'Iseli Fastigiate'	CAco CCVT GKin LRHS NEgg SCoo SLim SPoG
§	- - 'Koster'	EPfP MAsh SPoG
	- - 'Moerheimii'	CDul
	- - 'Oldenburg'	NEgg SLim
	- 'Glauca Globosa'	see *P. pungens* (Glauca Group) 'Globosa'
	- 'Globe'	CKen CMen
I	- 'Globosa Viridis'	CAco
	- 'Gloria'	CKen SLim
	- 'Hermann Naue' **new**	CKen
	- 'Lucky Strike'	CAco CKen LRHS MAsh NLar
	- 'Maigold' (v)	CKen LRHS NLar SLim
	- 'Montgomery'	CKen
	- 'Mrs Cesarini'	CKen NLar SLim
	- 'Niemitz'	NLar
	- 'Nimetz'	CKen
	- 'Porcupine' **new**	NLar
	- 'Prostrata'	see *P. pungens* 'Glauca Prostrata'
	- 'Saint Mary's Broom'	CKen
	- 'Snowkiss'	NEgg
	- 'The Blues'	CKen NLar
	- 'Thuem'	NEgg
	- 'Waldbrunn'	CKen NLar
	- 'Yvette'	NLar
	purpurea	EPfP LRHS
	schrenkiana	CMCN
	sitchensis	CAco CPer LPra MMuc NWea WTSh

	- 'Nana'	NLar
	- 'Papoose'	CAco SLim
	- 'Pévé Wiesje'	NLar
	- 'Silberzwerg'	CKen SAko SLim
	- 'Strypemonde'	CKen NEgg
	- 'Tenas'	CKen SLim SPoG
	smithiana	CAco CTho EPfP
	- 'Sunray'	LRHS NLar SLim
	wilsonii	CKen

Picrasma (*Simaroubaceae*)

	ailanthoides	see *P. quassioides*
§	***quassioides***	CMCN EBee EPfP WPGP

Picris (*Asteraceae*)

	echioides	see *Helminthotheca echioides*

Picrorhiza (*Plantaginaceae*)

	kurrooa	GPoy LEdu

Pieris (*Ericaceae*)

	'Balls of Fire'	CMac
	'Bert Chandler'	CMac WSpi
	'Brouwer's Beauty'	LRHS SPoG
	'Firecrest' ♀H5	GKev NLar
	'Flaming Silver' (v) ♀H5	Widely available
	'Forest Flame' ♀H5	Widely available
	formosa B&SWJ 2257	WCru
	- var. ***forrestii*** 'Charles Michael'	CExl
	- - 'Jermyns'	CMac MRav
	- - 'Wakehurst' ♀H5	CCCN CDul CExl CMac CRos CTri ELon EPfP GKin LMil LRHS MAsh MGos MRav NWea SAko SCob SPer WHor WSpi
	HAVILA ('Mouwsvila') (v)	CCCN CMac MAsh NWad
	japonica	CMac CPla
	- 'Bisbee Dwarf'	WThu
	- 'Bonfire' ♀H5	CCCN CRos ELan LRHS MAsh MGos MPkF NRHS SCob SLim SPer SPoG
	- 'Carnaval' (v) ♀H5	CCCN CMac CRos CSBt ELan ELon EMOT EShb LBuc LRHS LSRN MAsh MGos NLar NPri NRHS SCob SCoo SLim SPoG SWvt WFar
§	- 'Christmas Cheer'	CMac EPfP LSRN
	- 'Cupido'	LRHS MAsh NLar SLim WFar WGwG
	- 'Debutante' ♀H5	CBcs CRos ELan GKin LRHS MAsh MGos NLar SCob SCoo SWvt WFar
	- 'Don'	see *P. japonica* 'Pygmaea'
	- 'Dorothy Wyckoff'	LSRN SSta
	- 'Erik'	IArd NLar SAko
	- 'Flaming Star'	SWvt
	- 'Flamingo'	CMac
I	- 'Katsura' PBR	CBcs CMac CRos ELan EPfP GKin LBuc LMil LRHS LSRN MAsh MBlu MGos MJak NEgg NHol NLar NRHS SCob SCoo SLim SPer SPoG SWvt WFar
	- 'Little Heath' (v)	CBcs CEnd CMac CRos CSBt ELan ELon EMOT EPfP GEdr GKev GKin LRHS MAsh MGos NEgg NHol NLar NPri NRHS NWad SCob SLim SPer SPoG SRms SWvt WFar
	- 'Little Heath Green'	CCCN CMac ELon GKin MAsh MGos MMuc NEgg SCob SPer SPoG SWvt WFar
	- 'Minor'	GKev NWad WFar WThu
	- 'Mountain Fire' ♀H5	CAco CBcs CRos CTri ELon EMOT EPfP GBin GKev GKin GWyn LRHS LSRN MAsh MGos MSwo NHol NLar NPri NRHS SCob SCoo SLim SPer SPlb SPoG SRms SWvt WFar
	- 'Passion' PBR	CBcs CEnd CKel CRos CSBt EBee EPfP LCro LOPS LRHS LSRN MAsh MNHC NLar NRHS SAko SCob SPer
	- 'Pink Delight' ♀H5	CRos EMOT LMil LRHS LSRN MAsh MRav SRms
	- 'Prelude' ♀H5	CRos CSBt LMil LRHS MAsh
	- 'Purity' ♀H5	CBcs CCCN CMac EMOT MAsh MGos NEgg NLar SArc SLim SPer SWvt WFar
§	- 'Pygmaea'	NWad WThu
	- 'Ralto' PBR	CRos LRHS MAsh MRav NLar NRHS SPoG
	- RALTO ROSE ('Opstal10')	MPkF
	- RED MILL ('Zebris')	CEnd SLim SPer
	- 'Sarabande' ♀H5	MAsh SCob SPer
	- 'Scarlett O'Hara'	CSBt NLar
	- Taiwanensis Group	CMac GKin NLar SRms WFar
	- 'Temple Bells'	CSBt
	- 'Valley Rose'	CSBt ELan GKin MAsh NLar
	- 'Valley Valentine' ♀H5	CBcs CMac CRos CSBt EPfP LCro LMil LOPS LRHS LSRN MAsh MGos MJak MNHC MPkF NHpl NRHS SAko SCob SCoo SLim SPer SPoG SWvt WFar
	- 'Variegata' misapplied	see *P. japonica* 'White Rim'
	- 'Variegata' ambig.	LMil SCob SPer
	- 'Variegata' (Carrière) Bean (v)	CRos LRHS NRHS
	- 'Wada's Pink'	see *P. japonica* 'Christmas Cheer'
	- 'White Cascade'	NLar
	- 'White Pearl'	CMac
§	- 'White Rim' (v)	CMac MAsh SPlb
	- 'William Buchanan'	NWad WThu
	- var. ***yakushimensis***	NLar
	nana	WThu
	'Tilford'	CMac

Pilea (*Urticaceae*)

	libanensis	EShb

Pileostegia (*Hydrangeaceae*)

	viburnoides	CBcs CCCN CDul CKel CMac CRHN CRos EBee ELan ELon EPfP EUJe EWTr GCal LRHS MGil MGos MMuc MRav NLar SArc SEND SLon SPer SPoG SSta WCot WPGP WSHC WSpi
	- B&SWJ 3565	WCru
	- B&SWJ 3570 from Taiwan	WCru
	- B&SWJ 7132	WCru
	- variegated (v)	LRHS

Pilgerodendron (*Cupressaceae*)

	uviferum	IDee

Pilosella (*Asteraceae*)

§	***aurantiaca***	CBor EBou ELan GJos IRos LEdu LPot LRHS MHer MNHC NBid SPhx SRms WCot WHer WMoo WOut WSFF
§	- subsp. ***carpathicola***	MMuc SEND
§	***officinarum***	NRya XSen

Pimelea (*Thymelaeaceae*)

	coarctata	see *P. prostrata*

ferruginea	SVen
oreophila	WThu
§ ***prostrata***	EPot EWes
tomentosa	LRHS

Pimpinella (*Apiaceae*)

anisum	SVic
major	LEdu
- 'Rosea'	Widely available
saxifraga	CHab EBou WSFF
siifolia	WHil
tripartita	SPhx
- PAB 6112	LEdu WPGP
- PAB 7261	WPGP

pineapple see *Ananas comosus*

pineapple guava see *Acca sellowiana*

Pinellia (*Araceae*)

cordata	CAby LEdu WCru XLum
pedatisecta	GKev MRav
pinnatisecta	see *P. tripartita*
ternata	EBee GEdr GKev NLar
- B&SWJ 3532	WCru
§ ***tripartita***	CExl GKev WCot
- B&SWJ 1102	WCru
- 'Purple Face'	WCru

Pinguicula (*Lentibulariaceae*)

ehlersiae	SPlb
grandiflora ♀H4	EECP EWld GKev NRya
vulgaris	WHer

pinkcurrant see *Ribes rubrum* (P)

Pinus ✿ (*Pinaceae*)

albicaulis	CAco
- 'Flinck'	CKen
- 'Nana'	see *P. albicaulis* 'Noble's Dwarf'
- 'No 3'	CKen
§ - 'Noble's Dwarf'	CKen
aristata ambig.	CAco LRHS SAko SEND
aristata Engelm.	CAco CDul CMCN CMen WHor
- 'Bashful'	CKen
- 'Cecilia'	CKen
- 'Kohout's Hexe' new	CAco
- 'Kohout's Mini'	CKen
- 'Sherwood Compact'	CKen MAsh SLim
arizonica var. ***cooperi*** new	CAco
armandii	CAco CDul CMCN EPfP LRHS
attenuata	CAco
austriaca	see *P. nigra* subsp. *nigra*
ayacahuite	CAco CKen
balfouriana new	CAco
- dwarf	CKen
banksiana	CAco
- 'Chippewa'	CKen
I - 'Compacta'	CKen
- 'Manomet'	CAco
- 'Neponset'	CKen
- 'Schneverdingen'	CKen NEgg NLar
- 'Shoodic'	NLar
bhutanica	CAco WPGP
- KR 10358	WPGP
brutia	CAco
- var. ***eldarica***	CAco
- - multi-stemmed	CAco
- var. ***pityusa***	CAco
bungeana	CAco CMCN EPfP MBlu MGil SAko
- 'Diamant'	CKen
- 'June's Broom'	CKen
canariensis	CAco
cembra	CAco CAgr CDul EPfP LRHS MCoo MJak
- 'Barnhourie'	CKen
- 'Blue Mound'	CKen
- 'Compacta Glauca'	NLar
- 'Inverleith'	CKen
- 'Jermyns'	CKen
- 'King's Dwarf'	CKen
- 'Ortler'	CKen
- 'Stoderzinken 8'	NLar
- 'Stricta'	CKen LRHS
- witches' broom	CKen
cembroides	CAco
- NJM 09.022A	WPGP
- 'Fancy Nancy'	CKen
clausa new	CAco
contorta	CAco CBcs CDul CPer LPra SPlb
- 'Asher'	CKen LRHS NLar
- 'Chief Joseph' ♀H7	CAco CKen MAsh NLar
- 'Frisian Gold'	CAco NLar
- var. ***latifolia***	CAco CDul
- var. ***murrayana*** new	CAco
- 'Spaan's Dwarf'	CAco CKen
- 'Taylor's Sunburst'	CAco CKen NLar
coulteri	CAco EPfP WPGP
densata new	CAco
densiflora	CAco CDul EBtc
- 'Alice Verkade' ♀H7	CAco CMen LRHS MAsh NEgg NLar WFar
I - 'Bedgebury Sport Broom' new	CKen
- 'Golden Ghost'	NLar
- 'Haybud'	CAco
- 'Jim Cross'	CKen
- 'Kim'	NLar
- 'Low Glow'	CAco CKen LRHS NEgg NLar SLim SPoG
- 'Oculus-draconis' (v)	CAco SLim
- 'Pendula'	CKen MBlu MGil NEgg SLim
- 'Pumila'	LRHS
I - 'Pygmaea'	WHor
- 'Pygmy'	EUJe
- 'Rata'	NLar
- 'Umbraculifera'	CAco CMen MAsh
× ***densithunbergii*** 'Jane Kluis' ♀H7	CAco CMen LRHS NLar SLim SPoG
§ ***devoniana***	CAco
durangensis new	CAco
echinata new	CAco
edulis	CAco CMCN
- 'Juno'	CKen
elliottii	CAco
- var. ***densa***	CKen
engelmannii	CAco CDul
- 'Glauca'	CAco
fenzeliana	CAco CKen
flexilis	CAco CDul
- 'Cesarini Blue'	NLar
- 'Cow Creek'	NLar
- 'Damfino'	CAco
- 'Firmament'	NOra SLim WMat
- var. ***flexilis***	CAco
- 'Glenmore Dwarf'	CKen
- 'Lil Wolf'	NLar
- 'Nana'	CKen
- var. ***reflexa*** new	CAco
- 'Ririe'	CKen MAsh

	- 'Tara Mae'	NLar
	- 'Tarryall'	CKen
	- 'Tinby Temple'	CAco
	- 'Vanderwolf's Pyramid'	CAco
	- WB No 1	CKen
	- WB No 2	CKen
	gerardiana	CAco
	glabra	CAco
	greggii	CDul EBtc
	griffithii McClell.	see *P. wallichiana*
	halepensis	CAco CDul SEND XSen
§	***hartwegii***	CAco
§	***heldreichii***	CAco CDul EPfP NOra SLim WMat
	- 'Aureospicata'	NLar
	- 'Compact Gem' ♀H7	CKen EUJe LRHS NEgg SLim
	- 'Dolce Dorme'	CKen
	- 'Emerald Arrow'	NLar
	- 'Green Pyramid'	NLar
	- 'Groen'	CKen
	- var. ***leucodermis***	see *P. heldreichii*
	- - 'Irish Bell'	CKen NLar
	- - 'Pirin No 3' **new**	SAko
	- 'Malink'	CKen EUJe
	- 'Pygmy'	CKen
	- 'Satellit' ♀H7	CKen MAsh NEgg NLar SLim
	- 'Schmidtii'	see *P. heldreichii* 'Smidtii'
§	- 'Smidtii' ♀H7	CKen CMen LRHS MAsh NEgg NLar SLim SPoG
	- 'Zwerg Schneverdingen'	CKen SLim
	× ***holfordiana***	CAco EBee EPfP WPGP
	jeffreyi	CAco CTho
	- 'Joppi'	CAco CKen NLar SLim
	- 'Misty Lemon'	NLar
	kesiya	CAco
	koraiensis	CAco LEdu
	- 'Baishan' **new**	NLar
	- 'Bergman'	CKen LRHS
	- 'Blue Ball'	CAco CKen NLar
	- 'China Boy'	NLar
	- 'Compacta Glauca'	CAco
	- 'Dongling' **new**	NLar
	- 'Dragon Eye'	CKen SLim
	- 'Jack Corbit'	CKen WFar
	- 'Shibamichi' (v)	CKen
	- 'Silver Lining'	CAco
	- 'Silveray'	CAco
	- 'Silvergrey'	CKen
	- 'Sommersonne' **new**	NLar
	- 'Spring Grove'	CKen NLar
	- 'Tong Hua'	NLar
	- 'Tsingtao' **new**	NLar
	- 'Winton'	CKen NLar
	lambertiana	CAco
I	- 'Glauca' **new**	CAco
	latteri	CAco
	lawsonii **new**	CAco
	leiophylla **new**	CAco
	leucodermis	see *P. heldreichii*
	longaeva	CAco
	magnifica	see *P. devoniana*
	'Marie Bregéon'[PBR]	LRHS
	massoniana	CAco
	maximartinezii	CAco
	maximinoi **new**	CAco
	monophylla	CAco EBtc
	- 'Tioga Pass'	CAco
	- 'Wrinkle'	NLar
	montezumae misapplied	see *P. hartwegii*
	montezumae ambig.	CAco
	montezumae Lamb.	CAco SArc WPGP
	- NJM 09.016	WPGP
	- var. ***montezumae*** **new**	CAco
	- 'Sheffield Park'	CAco SLim
	monticola	CAco
	- 'Crawford'	NLar
	- 'Ondulata'	NLar
	- 'Pendula'	CKen
	- 'Pygmy'	see *P. monticola* 'Raraflora'
§	- 'Raraflora'	CKen
	- 'Strobicola'	CAco CDul EPfP
	- 'Windsor Dwarf'	CKen
	mugo	CBcs CDul CNWT EPfP LPra MGos MJak SCob
	- 'Allgäu'	CKen
	- 'Alpen Hexe'	CAco NLar
	- 'Benjamin'	CKen LRHS NLar
	- 'Bisley Green'	NLar
	- 'Bonita'	LRHS
	- 'Bonsai Kramer' **new**	NLar
	- 'Brownie'	CKen
	- 'Carsten' ♀H7	CAco CKen ELan EPfP LRHS MAsh NEgg NLar SCoo SLim SPoG
	- 'Corley's Mat'	CKen NLar
	- 'Devon Gem'	NEgg
	- 'Dezember Gold'	SLim
	- 'Flanders Belle'	SLim
	- 'Frohlings Gold'	CAco
	- 'Gnom'	CAco CDul ELan EPfP GKin LRHS MGos NEgg SCoo
	- 'Gold Star'	CMen
	- 'Goldcoin Weis' **new**	CAco
	- 'Golden Glow'	CAco SLim SPoG
	- 'Hesse'	SCoo
	- 'Hoersholm'	CKen
	- 'Hulk'	CKen
	- 'Humpy' ♀H7	CAco CKen CMen MAsh NEgg SCoo SLim
	- 'Ironsides'	CKen NLar
	- 'Jacobsen'	CKen NLar
	- 'Janovsky'	CKen
	- 'Kajo Schommer' **new**	CAco
	- 'Kalus' **new**	CAco
	- 'Kissen' ♀H7	CKen EPfP NHol SLim
	- KLOSTERGRUN	see *P. mugo* 'Klosterkötter'
§	- 'Klosterkötter'	CAco LRHS
	- 'Kobold'	NEgg
	- 'Krauskopf'	CKen
	- 'Laarheide'	SPoG
	- 'Laurin'	CKen
	- 'Lemon'	NLar
	- 'Little Gold Star' **new**	CKen
	- 'March'	CKen
	- 'Mini Mini' **new**	CKen
	- 'Mini Mops'	CKen SLim
	- 'Minikin'	CKen
	- 'Mops' ♀H7	CAco CDul CMen EPfP LRHS MAsh MBlu MGos NEgg SCob SCoo SLim SPoG
	- 'Mops Gold' **new**	NLar
	- 'Mops Midget'	CMen MAsh NEgg
	- var. ***mughus***	see *P. mugo* subsp. *mugo*
§	- subsp. ***mugo***	CAco CDul CSBt SCob SGol
	- - 'Milky Way'	CAco CKen NLar
	- 'Mumpitz'	CKen LRHS
	- 'Nerost'	NLar
	- 'Northern Lights'	CKen
	- 'Ophir' ♀H7	CAco CBcs CKen CMen ELan EPfP LRHS MAsh MGos NEgg SCob SCoo SLim SPoG SSta
	- 'Pal Maleter' (v)	CAco SCoo SLim SPoG

	- 'Paul's Dwarf'	CKen
	- 'Picobello'	LRHS MAsh NHol NLar SLim
	- 'Piggelmee'	CAco CKen
	- 'Pincushion'	LRHS
	- Pumilio Group	CAco ELan EPfP LRHS MGos MMuc NLar SEND WMoo
	- - 'David Compressa' **new**	SAko
	- - 'Emerald Dwarf'	NLar
	- 'Rio' **new**	CAco
	- 'Rock Garden'	NLar
	- var. ***rostrata***	see *P. mugo* subsp. *uncinata*
	- subsp. ***rotundata*** 'Ježek'	CKen MAsh NLar
	- 'Rushmore'	CKen
	- 'Ruze'	LRHS
	- 'Sandy'	NLar
	- 'Sherwood Compact'	NLar SLim
	- 'Sherwood Compact No 5' **new**	SAko
	- 'Spaan'	CKen
	- 'Sunshine' (v)	CAco CKen NLar
	- 'Suzi'	CKen NLar
	- 'Suzy Hexe'	NWad
	- 'Trompenburg'	NEgg
	- 'Tuffet'	CAco CKen LRHS NHol SLim
	- 'Uelzen'	CKen LRHS
§	- subsp. ***uncinata***	CAco IDee
	- - 'Etschtal'	CKen
	- - 'Grüne Welle'	CKen NLar
	- - 'Heideperle'	NLar
	- - 'Kostelnicek'	CKen NLar
	- - 'Leuco-like'	CKen
	- - 'Offenpass'	CKen
	- - 'Paradekissen'	CKen NLar
	- - 'Süsse Perle'	CKen
	- 'Varella'	LRHS NLar SCoo SLim
	- 'Veverka' **new**	CAco
	- 'White Tip'	CKen
	- 'Winter Gold'	CAco ELan EPfP LRHS MGos MJak NHol SSta
	- 'Winter Sun'	CAco LRHS MAsh NLar
	- 'Winzig'	CKen
	- 'Wolf' **new**	CAco
	- 'Yellow Tip' (v)	NHol
	- 'Zundert'	CKen SPoG
	- 'Zwergkugel'	CKen NLar SAko
	muricata	CAco CDul CPer EBtc
	nigra	CAco CBcs CDul CLnd CMac CTri EMOT EPfP EUJe EWTr LPra LRHS MAsh MGos SGol
	- var. ***austriaca***	see *P. nigra* subsp. *nigra*
	- 'Bambino'	CKen
	- 'Black Prince' ♀H7	CAco CKen EUJe NEgg NOra WMat
	- 'Bobo'	CKen
	- 'Brepo'	CAco
	- var. ***calabrica***	see *P. nigra* subsp. *laricio*
	- var. ***caramanica***	see *P. nigra* subsp. *pallasiana*
	- 'Cebennensis Nana'	CKen
	- var. ***corsicana***	see *P. nigra* subsp. *laricio*
	- subsp. ***dalmatica***	CAco
	- 'Frank'	CKen
	- 'Green Tower'	LRHS NLar
	- 'Helga'	NLar
	- 'Hornibrookiana'	CKen
	- 'Karaca Ball'	CAco
	- 'Komet'	NLar SAko
§	- subsp. ***laricio***	CAco CCVT CDul CMac CNWT MMuc SEND
	- - 'Aurea'	MBlu
	- - 'Bobby McGregor'	CKen
	- - 'Globosa Viridis'	NEgg

	- - 'Goldfinger'	NLar
	- - 'Pygmaea'	CKen NEgg
	- - 'Wurstle'	CKen
	- subsp. ***maritima***	see *P. nigra* subsp. *laricio*
	- 'Moran'	NLar
	- 'Moseri'	CAco CKen NEgg NLar
	- 'Nana'	LRHS
§	- subsp. ***nigra***	CAco CCVT CLnd CNWT CPer CTho ECrN LMaj LPra LRHS MMuc SCob SEND SEWo SGol
	- - 'Birte'	CKen
	- - 'Bright Eyes'	NEgg
	- - 'Helga'	NLar
	- - 'Schovenhorst'	CKen
	- - 'Skyborn'	CKen
	- - 'Strypemonde'	CKen NEgg
	- - 'Yaffle Hill'	CKen
	- 'Obelisk'	CKen NLar
	- 'Ola'	CKen
	- 'Oregon Green'	CKen NLar
§	- subsp. ***pallasiana***	CAco
	- 'Pierrick Bregéon'[PBR]	LRHS
	- 'Richard'	CKen NLar SLim
	- 'Spielberg'	LRHS
	oocarpa	CAco EBtc
	- var. ***oocarpa*** **new**	CAco
	palustris	CAco
	parviflora	CAco NEgg SPlb
	- 'Aaba-jo'	CKen
	- 'Adcock's Dwarf' ♀H7	CAco CKen NEgg SLim
	- 'Al Fordham'	CKen
	- 'Aoi'	CKen CMen NLar
	- 'Ara-kawa'	CKen CMen
	- 'Atco-goyo'	CKen
	- Azuma-goyo Group	CKen CMen LRHS
I	- 'Baasch's Form'	CKen MGil
	- 'Bergman'	CAco MAsh
	- 'Blue Angel'	CAco MBlu
	- 'Blue Giant'	CDul IArd MBlu
	- 'Bonnie Bergman' ♀H7	CAco CDul CKen EPfP LRHS NHol
	- 'Bunty' **new**	CAco MGil
	- 'Catherine Elizabeth'	CKen NLar
	- 'Dai-ho'	CKen
	- 'Daisetsusan'	CKen
	- 'Debbie' **new**	NLar
	- 'Dougal'	CKen
	- 'Floppy Joe'	NLar
	- 'Fukai' (v)	CAco CKen NHol
	- 'Fukiju'	CKen
	- Fukushima-goyo Group	CKen CMen
	- 'Fuku-zu-mi'	CKen
	- 'Fu-shiro'	CAco CKen
	- 'Gemstar'	CKen
	- 'Gin-sho-chuba'	CKen
	- Glauca Group	CAco LRHS MAsh MBlu NEgg SGol
	- - 'Glauca' ♀H7	CAco
I	- 'Glauca Nana'	CKen
	- 'Goykuri'	CAco CKen LRHS
	- 'Gyok-kasen'	CKen
	- 'Gyo-ko-haku'	CKen
	- 'Gyokusen Sämling'	CKen
	- 'Gyo-ku-sui'	CKen CMen
	- 'Hagaromo Seedling'	CAco CKen CMen
	- 'Hakko'	CKen
	- 'Hatchichi'	CAco CKen
	- 'Ha-tzumari'	NLar
	- 'Hobbit'	NWad
	- 'Ibo-can'	CKen CMen
	- 'Ichi-no-se'	CKen
	- 'Iri-fune'	CKen

	– Ishizuchi-goyo Group	CKen NLar
	– 'Jade Tiers'	LRHS
	– 'Jim's Mini Curls'	CKen NLar
	– 'Ka-ho'	CKen
	– 'Kanrico'	CKen
	– 'Kanzan'	CKen
	– 'Kin-po'	CKen NLar
	– 'Kiyomatsu'	CKen
	– 'Kobe'	CKen
	– 'Kokonoe'	CAco CKen CMen
	– 'Kokuho'	CKen
	– 'Kusu-dama'	CKen
	– 'Little Hedgehog'	CKen
	– 'Lorraine'	CKen
	– 'Masami'	CKen
	– 'Meiko'	CKen CMen
	– 'Michinoku'	CKen
	– 'Momo-yama'	CKen NLar
	– 'Myo-jo'	CKen
	– Nasu-goyo Group	CKen
	– 'Negishi' ♀H7	CAco CKen CMen LRHS MAsh NEgg SLim
	– 'Nellie D.'	NLar
	– 'Ogon-goyo'	CKen
	– 'Ōgon-janome'	CAco CKen MAsh NEgg SLim
	– 'Ossorio Dwarf'	CKen
	– 'Perido'	NLar
	– 'Regenhold'	CKen
	– 'Richard Lee'	CKen MAsh NLar
	– 'Ryo-ku-ho'	CKen
	– 'Ryu-ju'	CKen
	– 'Sa-dai-jin'	CKen
	– 'San-bo'	CKen
§	– 'Saphir'	CKen
	– 'Schoon's Bonsai'	LRHS NHol
	– 'Setsugekka'	CKen SAko
	– 'Shika-shima'	CAco CKen
	– Shikoku-goyo Group	LRHS
	– 'Shimada'	CKen
	– 'Shin Sen'	LRHS
	– 'Shin Sho'	LRHS
	– Shiobara-goyo Group	CKen
	– 'Shizukagoten'	CKen SLim
	– 'Shu-re'	CKen
	– 'Sieryoden'	CKen
	– 'Smout'	CKen
	– 'Tani-mano-uki'	CKen
	– 'Tayo-nishiki' **new**	CAco
	– 'Tempelhof'	CAco
	– 'Tenysu-kazu'	CAco CKen LRHS MAsh NLar
	– 'Tokyo Dwarf'	CKen
	– 'Tsai's Cushion'	CAco
	– 'Walker's Dwarf'	CKen
	– 'Watnong'	CKen
	– 'Zelkova'	CMen
	– 'Zui-sho'	CKen
	patula ♀H5	CAco CBcs CCCN CDul CHll CMCN ECre EPfP EUJe IDee SArc SCoo SLim SPlb SPoG WMat WPGP
	peuce	CAco CDul EPfP SEND
	– 'Arnold Dwarf'	CKen
	– 'Cesarini'	CKen NLar
	– 'Daniel'	CKen NLar
	– 'Harlekin'	NLar
	– 'Thessaloniki Broom'	CKen
	'Pichounet'	NLar
	pinaster	CAco CBcs CDul CPer EPfP MMuc SEND
	pinea ♀H5	CAco CAgr CCVT CDul CLnd CTho EPfP EUJe LMaj LPra MGos MMuc SArc SCoo SEND SEWo SGol SPlb WPGP XSen
	– 'Queensway'	CKen
	ponderosa	CAco CMCN EPfP LRHS
	– SDL2	NLar
	pseudostrobus	CAco
	pumila	CAco
	– 'Blue Note' **new**	NLar
	– 'Buchanan'	CKen
	– 'Dwarf Blue'	CAco NHol
	– 'Glauca' ♀H7	CKen
	– 'Globe'	SLim
	– 'Jeddeloh'	CKen
	– 'Pinocchio'	CKen
	– 'Säntis'	CKen
	– 'Saphir'	see *P. parviflora* 'Saphir'
	pungens	CAco CDul
	radiata	CAco CBcs CBod CCVT CCoa CDul CLnd CMCN CMac CNWT CPer CSBt CSde CTho ECrN ELan EPfP EUJe MMuc SArc SCoo WMat
	– Aurea Group	CAco ELan NEgg SCoo SLim SPoG WMat
	– – 'Aurea' ♀H5	CAco CKen LRHS NOra
	– 'Bodnant'	CKen
	– 'Marshwood' (v)	CKen
	resinosa	CAco
	– 'Don Smith'	CKen
	– 'Joel's Broom'	CKen
	– 'Nana'	CAco
	– 'Quinobequin'	CKen
	roxburghii	CAco
	sabineana	CAco
	× ***schwerinii***	CAco CKen
	– 'Wiethorst' ♀H7	CAco CKen LRHS NLar WMat
	sibirica 'Blue Smoke'	CKen
	– 'Mariko'	CKen
	strobiformis	CAco
	– 'Coronado'	CKen
	– 'Loma Linda'	CKen SLim
	strobus	CAco CBcs CCVT CDul CMen EPfP LMaj LPra LRHS MGos MMuc SEND
§	– 'Alba'	SLim
	– 'Amelia's Dwarf'	CKen
	– 'Angel Falls'	CKen NLar
	– 'Anna Fiele'	CKen NEgg
	– 'Beal's Starry Night' **new**	NLar
	– 'Bergman's Mini'	CKen LRHS
	– 'Bergman's Pendula Broom'	CKen
I	– 'Bergman's Sport of Prostrata'	CKen
	– 'Beth'	CKen
	– 'Bloomer's Dark Globe'	CKen
	– 'Blue Shag' ♀H7	CAco LRHS NLar NWad SCoo SLim
	– 'Bob's Wishes' **new**	NLar
	– 'Brevifolia'	CAco CKen SArc
	– 'Cesarini'	CKen
	– 'Contorta'	CAco
	– 'Densa'	CKen
	– 'Diablo'	NLar
	– 'Ed's Broom'	CKen
	– 'Elf'	NLar
	– 'Elkins Dwarf'	CKen LRHS NEgg
	– 'Fastigiata'	CDul CKen MBlu
	– 'Golden Candles'	NLar
	– 'Golden Showers'	NLar
	– 'Green Curls'	CKen
	– 'Green Twist'	CAco CKen NLar
	– 'Greg'	CKen

	– 'Ground Hugger'	NLar
	– 'Hershey'	CKen
	– 'Hillside Gem'	CKen
	– 'Horsford'	CKen
	– 'Horsford Sister'	CKen
	– 'Jamaican Curls'	CKen
	– 'Joe's Best Blue'	NLar
	– 'Julian Pott'	CKen
	– 'Julian's Dwarf'	CKen
	– 'Krügers Lilliput'	LRHS NLar NWad
	– 'Louie'	CKen MAsh NLar
	– 'Macopin'	LRHS WFar
	– 'Mary Butler'	CKen NLar
	– 'Mary Sweeny' **new**	NLar
	– 'Merrimack'	CKen
	– 'Minima' ♀H7	CKen LRHS MBlu NEgg SLim SPoG
	– 'Minuta'	CKen LRHS
	– 'Nana'	see *P. strobus* Nana Group
§	– Nana Group	NEgg SEWo
	– 'Nana Compacta'	NEgg
	– 'Niagara Falls'	CKen NLar
	– 'Nivea'	see *P. strobus* 'Alba'
	– 'Northway Broom'	CKen
	– 'Paul Waxman'	NLar
	– 'Pendula'	CAco CKen LRHS MBlu MGil
I	– 'Pendula Broom'	CKen
	– 'Pygmaea'	LRHS MGil
I	– 'Radiata Aurea'	NEgg
	– 'Reinshaus'	CKen
	– 'Sayville'	CKen
	– 'Sea Urchin'	CAco CKen MAsh NLar SLim
	– 'Secrest'	LRHS
	– 'Smokey Hollow'	NLar
	– 'Squiggles'	NLar
	– 'Stowe Pillar'	NLar SLim
	– 'Tiny Kurls'	CAco CKen LRHS MAsh NLar
	– 'Torulosa'	CAco MBlu
	– 'Uncatena'	CKen
	– 'Verkade's Broom'	CKen NEgg
	– 'White Mountain'	CAco MBlu SAko
	sylvestris	Widely available
	– 'Abergeldie'	CKen
	– 'Alderly Edge'	CMen
	– 'Andorra'	CKen
	– 'Anny's Wintersun'	NLar
	– Aurea Group	CDul CKen CMen ELan MBlu NEgg SLim SSta WMat
	– 'Avondene'	CKen
	– 'Bergfield'	CMen
	– 'Beuvronensis' ♀H7	CAco CMen NEgg SLim
	– 'Buchanan's Gold'	CKen
	– 'Burghfield'	CMen
	– 'Candlelight'	NLar
	– 'Chantry Blue'	CNWT LRHS MAsh MGos NEgg NOra SCoo SLim SPoG WMat
	– 'Clumber Blue'	CKen
	– 'Denny Boy'	NLar
	– 'Dereham'	CKen LRHS NLar
	– 'Doone Valley'	CKen NEgg
	– 'Edwin Hillier'	NEgg NOra WMat WPGP
	– Fastigiata Group	CAco CEnd CKen CLnd CMen LRHS SCoo SLim WCFE
	– 'Frensham' ♀H7	CKen MAsh
	– 'Globosa'	CAco
	– 'Gold Coin' ♀H7	CAco CDul CKen EPfP MAsh NEgg SPoG
	– 'Gold Medal'	CAco CKen
	– 'Grand Rapids'	CKen
	– 'Green Penguin'	NLar
	– 'Gwydyr Castle'	CKen
	– 'Hillside Creeper'	CKen
	– 'Humble Pie'	CKen LRHS
	– 'Isaszeg' **new**	CAco
	– 'Jeremy'	CKen NEgg
	– 'John Boy'	CMen
	– 'Kenwith'	CKen
	– 'Lodge Hill'	CMen MAsh NEgg SLim
	– 'Longmoor'	CKen
	– 'Martham'	CKen CMen
	– 'Meffen Gold' **new**	NLar
	– 'Mitsch Weeping'	CKen
	– Nana Group	CAco
	– 'Nana' misapplied	see *P. sylvestris* 'Watereri'
	– 'Nana Compacta'	CMen
§	– 'Nisbet's Gem'	CKen CMen
	– 'Padworth'	CMen
	– 'Piskowitz'	CKen
	– 'Pixie'	CKen
I	– 'Prostrata'	NEgg SLim
	– 'Repens'	CAco CKen
	– 'Saint George'	CKen
	– 'Sandringham'	NLar
	– 'Saxatilis'	CAco CKen CMen
	– 'Scott's Dwarf'	see *P. sylvestris* 'Nisbet's Gem'
	– 'Sentinel'	CKen
	– 'Skjak I'	CKen
	– 'Skjak II'	CKen
	– 'Spaan's Slow Column'	CKen SLim
	– 'Tage'	CKen
	– 'Tanya'	CKen
	– 'Tilhead'	CKen
	– 'Treasure'	CKen
	– 'Trefrew Quarry'	CKen LRHS
	– 'Trollguld'	CAco CKen LRHS NLar
	– 'Umbraculifera'	NEgg
§	– 'Watereri'	CNWT LMaj LRHS SCob SCoo
	– 'Westonbirt'	CKen CMen
	– 'Wintergold'	NEgg
	– 'Wittichenau'	CKen
	– 'Xavery'	NLar
	tabuliformis	CAco
	taeda	CAco CDul
	taiwanensis	CAco CDul EPfP
	tecunumanii **new**	CAco
	teocote	CAco
	thunbergii	CAco CDul CLnd CMen ELan MMuc
	– 'Akame'	CKen CMen
	– 'Akame Yatsabusa'	CMen
	– 'Aocha-matsu' (v)	CAco CKen CMen
	– 'Arakawa-sho'	CKen CMen
	– 'Banshosho'	CAco CKen CMen
	– 'Beni-kujaku'	CAco CKen CMen
	– 'Compacta'	CKen CMen
	– var. ***corticosa*** 'Fuji'	CMen
	– – 'Iihara'	CMen
	– 'Dainagon'	CKen CMen
	– 'Eechee-nee'	CKen
	– 'Hayabusa'	CMen
	– 'Iwai'	CMen
	– 'Janome' (v)	CAco CMen
	– 'Katsuga'	CMen
	– 'Kotobuki'	CAco CKen CMen NLar
	– 'Koyosho'	CMen
	– 'Kujaku'	CAco CKen CMen
	– 'Kyokko'	CKen CMen
	– 'Kyushu'	CAco CKen CMen
	– 'Maijima'	LRHS
	– 'Mikawa'	CMen MBlu
	– 'Miyajuna'	CKen CMen

- 'Nishiki-ne'	CAco CKen CMen
- 'Nishiki-tsusaka'	CMen
- 'Ogi-matsu'	CKen
- 'Ôgon'	CAco CMen LRHS NLar
- 'Porky'	CKen CMen
§ - 'Sayonara' ♀H7	CAco CMen MAsh NEgg
- 'Senryu'	CKen CMen
- 'Shinsho'	CAco CKen CMen
- 'Shio-guro'	CAco CKen CMen
- 'Suchiro'	NEgg
- 'Suchiro Yatabusa'	CKen CMen
- 'Sunsho'	CKen CMen
- 'Taihei'	CKen CMen
I - 'Thunderhead' ♀H7	CAco CKen CMen SLim
- witches' broom	CKen
- 'Yatsubusa'	see *P. thunbergii* 'Sayonara'
- 'Ye-i-kan'	CKen
- 'Yoshimura'	CAco CMen
- 'Yumaki'	CAco CKen CMen
torreyana	CAco CBcs
uncinata	see *P. mugo* subsp. *uncinata*
virginiana	CAco
- 'Driscoll'	NLar
- 'Wate's Golden'	CKen
§ ***wallichiana*** ♀H6	CAco CCVT CDul CKen CMCN CNWT CTho EPfP EUJe IDee LMaj LPra LRHS MBlu MGil MGos MJak MMuc NEgg NHol NLar NOra SBir SEND SEWo SGol SLim WMat WPGP
- 'Densa Hill'	LMaj LRHS NLar
- 'Frosty'	CKen
- 'Nana' ♀H6	CKen LRHS MGil NLar SCoo SLim
- 'Umbraculifera'	MAsh
- 'Winter Light'	NLar
- 'Zebrina' (v)	CAco LRHS MBlu NHol NLar
yunnanensis	CAco LRHS

Piper (*Piperaceae*)

auritum	GPoy LEdu
betle	GPoy
excelsum	see *Macropiper excelsum*
heydei B&SWJ 10445	WCru

Piptanthus (*Papilionaceae*)

forrestii	see *P. nepalensis*
laburnifolius	see *P. nepalensis*
§ ***nepalensis***	CBcs CDul CRos CSBt CSpe EBee ELan EPfP EWld IDee LRHS MGil MGos MPie MSCN NBid NLar SBrt SPer SRms WAvo
aff. ***nepalensis***	SWvt

Pistacia (*Anacardiaceae*)

atlantica	XSen
chinensis	CBcs EBee EBtc EPfP WPGP XSen
lentiscus	CBcs EUJe LRHS SEND SVen XSen
terebinthus	XSen
- NJM 11.004	WPGP
vera	CBcs CTsd

Pistia (*Araceae*)

stratiotes	LCro LLWG LOPS NPer SCoo
- variegated (v) **new**	LLWG

Pitavia (*Rutaceae*)

punctata	IArd IDee

Pitcairnia (*Bromeliaceae*)

bergii	CHll
heterophylla	WCot
pungens	WCot
recurvata	WCot
ringens	WCot

Pittosporum ✿ (*Pittosporaceae*)

adaphniphylloides	CBcs
anomalum	CCCN CTsd ELon SEle
'Arundel Green' (f) ♀H4	CKel CRos ELon EPfP LRHS LSRN MAsh NRHS SCob SLim SPer SWvt
'Bicton Silver' (m/v) **new**	CCCN
buchananii	SVen
'Collaig Silver'	CRos EPfP LRHS MAsh NRHS SLim
coriaceum	CBrP
crassifolium	CBcs CCCN CCoa CSde CTsd IDee
- 'Variegatum' (v)	CBcs CBod CCCN CKel MGil WAvo
'Crinkles' (f)	SVen
dallii	CCCN SPlb
daphniphylloides	ELan WPGP
- B&SWJ 6789	WCru
- CWJ 12404	WCru
- RWJ 9913	WCru
eugenioides	CCoa CMCN CSam CSde SEND
- 'Platinum' (v)	CCCN
- 'Variegatum' (v) ♀H4	CBcs CCCN CDul CKel CMac CRos CSde ELan EPfP EUJe IArd LRHS MGos NLar NRHS SAko SCob SEND SLim SVen WAvo
'Garnettii' (v) ♀H4	Widely available
glabratum	WPGP
- var. ***neriifolium*** B&SWJ 11685	WCru
heterophyllum	CBod ECrN EPfP EWes LRHS MMrt SEND
- variegated (v)	CCCN CRos EBee EBtc EPfP LRHS WSHC
illicioides	WPGP
var. ***angustifolium***	
- - B&SWJ 6771	WCru
- - RWJ 9846	WCru
- var. ***illicioides*** B&SWJ 6712	WCru
- - PAB 9004	LEdu WPGP
× ***intermedium***	SWvt
- 'Craxten' (f)	CCCN EBee
'Nanum Variegatum'	see *P. tobira* 'Variegatum'
napaulense	WCru
oblongilimbum DJHV 06137	WCru
'Oliver Twist'	CRos EPfP LRHS LSRN MAsh NRHS SCob SCoo SSta
omeiense	EWes
- VdL 80626	EBee WPGP
patulum	WPGP
phillyreoides	CTsd
ralphii	CCCN CMCN CTsd
- 'Green Globe'	EUJe
- 'Variegatum' (v)	CCCN LRHS WPGP
'Saundersii' (v)	SCoo
tenuifolium	Widely available
- 'Abbotsbury Gold' (f/v)	CAbb CBcs CBod CCCN CKel CMac CPer CRos CSde CTri EHoe ELan EPfP EUJe EWes LRHS MAsh MGil MGos MSwo NRHS SCob SEND SGbt SGol SLim SPer SWvt WAvo
- 'All Gold' **new**	CKel
- 'Atropurpureum'	CBcs ELan
- 'Brockhill Compact'	CCCN CKel EMil LRHS SAko
- 'Cornish Mist'	CTsd

- 'County Park'	CCCN EUJe SRms
- 'County Park Dwarf'	MAsh
- 'County Park Green'	ELon
- 'Elizabeth' (m/v)	CBcs CMac CRos EHoe EPfP EUJe IArd LRHS LSRN MAsh MGos MRav MSwo NRHS SCob SCoo SEND SGol SLim SNig SPer SPoG SRms
- EMERALD DOME ('Minpitto'PBR)	SArc
- 'French Lace'	CBcs CCCN CCoa CSde ELan WFar
- 'Gold Star'	CBcs CBod CKel CRos CSde EHoe ELan EPfP LRHS MAsh MGos NRHS SCob SCoo SEle SLim SPer SPoG SRms SWvt WFar
- 'Golden King'	CCCN CKel CMac CPer CRos CSBt EPfP LRHS MAsh MGos NRHS SLim SRms
- 'Golf Ball'PBR	CBcs CKel CRos EPfP EUJe GBin LCro LOPS LRHS LSRN MGos NRHS SCob SGbt SPer SPoG SWvt WFar
- 'Green Thumb'	CCCN CMac EBee
- 'Irene Paterson' (m/v) ♀H4	Widely available
- 'James Stirling'	CCCN SEND
- 'John Flanagan'	see *P. tenuifolium* 'Margaret Turnbull'
- 'Limelight' (v)	CBcs CCCN CKel CRos CSBt EBee EPfP EUJe LRHS LSRN SLim SPoG
- 'Loxhill Gold'	CCCN CCoa CRos LRHS NRHS SGol
§ - 'Margaret Turnbull' (v)	CRos EPfP EWes LRHS MGos SGol
- 'Marjory Channon' (v)	CRos EPfP LRHS NRHS
- 'Moonlight' (v)	CBcs CBod LRHS MRav SCob
- 'Mountain Green'	CMac
- 'Nutty's Leprechaun'	CBod CCCN
- 'Pompom'	CCCN CKel CRos EMil LRHS LSRN NRHS
- 'Purpureum' (m)	CBar CCCN CMac CRos CSBt CTri EPfP EUJe GBin LRHS LSRN MAsh MGil MMuc NEgg NRHS SAko SCob SEND SPer SPoG SRms WAvo WFar WSHC
- 'Silver Magic' (v)	CBcs CRos EPfP EUJe LRHS NRHS SCob SEle SRkn
- 'Silver Princess' (f)	CKel
- 'Silver Queen' (f/v) ♀H4	Widely available
- 'Silver Sheen' (m)	CBcs CMac CRos LRHS NRHS SWvt
- 'Stevens Island'	CBcs CCoa
- 'Stirling Gold' (f/v)	EWes
- 'Tandara Gold' (v)	CBcs CCCN CKel CMac CRos CSBt EBee ELan ELon EPfP EUJe LRHS MAsh MGil MGos NRHS SCob SCoo SEND SRms WAvo
- 'Tiki' (m)	CCCN
- 'Tom Thumb' ♀H4	Widely available
- 'Tresederi' (f/m)	CCCN CTsd
- 'Variegatum' (m/v)	CBcs CKel CPer CRos CSBt EBee ELon LCro LOPS LRHS LSRN MGos MSwo NRHS SArc SCob SEND SGbt SLim SWvt WFar
- 'Victoria' (v)	CBcs CBod CCCN CRos EBee LRHS LSRN WFar
- 'Warnham Gold' (m) ♀H3	CBcs CCCN CKel CMac CRos CSde EBee ELan EPfP EUJe LRHS MAsh MGos NRHS SLim SPoG SRms SVen
- 'Wendle Channon' (m/v)	CCCN CMac CRos CSBt EPfP LRHS MAsh SGol WSHC
- 'Wrinkled Blue'	CBcs CBod CRos EPfP LRHS MAsh MRav MSwo NRHS SPoG SWvt
tobira ♀H4	CBcs CBod CCht CDul CKel CMac CRos CSde CTsd ELan EPfP EUJe EWTr LRHS LSRN MGos MMuc MRav SArc SCob SEND SPer SPoG SRms SVen WAvo WKif WSHC
- B&SWJ 12758	WCru
* - 'Nanum'	CAco CBcs CCCN CCoa CKel CMac CRos ELan EPfP EUJe LRHS MGos SCob SLim SPer SPoG XSen
§ - 'Variegatum' (v) ♀H4	CBcs CCCN CDul CMac CRos CSde ELan EPfP EUJe LRHS LSRN MGos NLar SArc SCob SEND SLim SLon SPer SPoG WSHC
'Trim's Hedger'	CBod
truncatum	CCCN CExl
undulatum	WAvo
viridiflorum	EShb

Plagianthus (*Malvaceae*)

betulinus	see *P. regius*
lyallii	see *Hoheria lyallii*
§ ***regius***	CBcs IArd

Plagiorhegma see *Jeffersonia*

Plantago (*Plantaginaceae*)

coronopus	CAgr
holosteum	GKev
lanceolata	CAgr CHab WSFF
major	GPoy WSFF
- 'Atropurpurea'	see *P. major* 'Rubrifolia'
- 'Bowles's Variety'	see *P. major* 'Rosularis'
- 'Brenda'	CNat
- 'Purple Perversion' **new**	CSpe
- 'Rosenstolz'	NChi
§ - 'Rosularis'	CBre CFis CSpe LEdu NBro SRms WHer
§ - 'Rubrifolia'	CBod CSpe EShb LLWG MMuc NBid SHar SRms WMoo WSFF XLum
- 'Tony Lewis'	CNat
media	CHab MHer
nivalis	EDAr GEdr
rosea	see *P. major* 'Rosularis'
subulata	EDAr
triandra 'Wanaka'	IMou

Platanthera (*Orchidaceae*)

bifolia	NLAp
chlorantha	NLAp

Platanus ✿ (*Platanaceae*)

sp.	LPra
× ***acerifolia***	see *P.* × *hispanica*
§ × ***hispanica*** ♀H6	CBcs CCVT CDul CLnd CMCN ECrN ELan EMOT EPfP LMaj LPra MGos MMuc NWea SArc SCob SEND SEWo SGol SPer WMat WMou WTSh
- 'Pyramidalis'	LMaj
orientalis	CCVT CDul CLnd CMCN EPfP SCob WPGP
- PAB 346	LEdu
§ - f. ***digitata*** ♀H6	CCVT CDul CLnd CMCN CTho EBee EMOT EPfP ERod WMou
- var. ***insularis***	SMad WPGP
- 'Laciniata'	see *P. orientalis* f. *digitata*
- 'Minaret'	CDul EMOT WMou
- 'Mirkovec'	EPfP IArd

Platycarya (*Juglandaceae*)

strobilacea	CMCN

Platycerium (*Polypodiaceae*)

	alcicorne misapplied	see *P. bifurcatum*
§	***bifurcatum*** ♀H1b	CCCN XBlo
	grande hort.	see *P. superbum*
§	***superbum*** ♀H1a	CCCN EShb

Platycladus (*Cupressaceae*)

§	***orientalis*** 'Aurea Nana' ♀H6	CDul CKen CMac CSBt ELan EMOT EPfP LBee LPra LRHS MAsh MGos NWad SGol SLim SPoG WCFE
	- 'Autumn Glow'	CKen
	- 'Beverleyensis'	NLar
	- 'Conspicua'	CKen CSBt EMOT
	- 'Elegantissima'	LRHS
	- 'Flame'	LRHS
	- 'Franky Boy' ♀H6	NLar SPoG
	- 'Golden Pygmy'	CKen
	- 'Kenwith'	CKen
	- 'Meldensis'	CTri
	- 'Miller's Gold'	see *P. orientalis* 'Aurea Nana'
	- 'Minima Glauca'	CKen
I	- 'Pyramidalis Aurea'	LBee LRHS
	- 'Rosedalis'	CKen CSBt EMOT EPfP LBee MAsh SLim
	- 'Sanderi'	WCFE
	- 'Shirley Chilcott'	MAsh
	- 'Southport'	LBee LRHS
	- 'Summer Cream'	CKen

Platycodon (*Campanulaceae*)

	grandiflorus ♀H5	CBod CTri CTsd ECha EPfP GKev MHer NAln SRms
	- 'Albus'	EPfP GKev SPer SWvt
	- Apoyama Group ♀H5	WHoo WThu
	- - 'Fairy Snow'	EBou WHoo
	- (Astra Series) 'Astra Blue'	CRos CSpe EPfP LRHS NRHS SPoG SRot
	- - 'Astra Pink'	SPoG
	- - 'Astra White'	SPoG
	- 'Fuji Blue'	WHoo XLum
	- 'Fuji Pink'	MRav SWvt WHoo XLum
	- 'Fuji White'	WHoo
	- 'Hakone'	MRav
	- 'Hakone Blue'	EPfP LSun NBre
	- 'Hakone Double Blue' (d)	SRms
	- 'Hakone White'	EPfP LSun MRav WRHF
	- 'Mariesii' ♀H5	CAby CSBt EPfP MRav NBir NEgg SPer SPlb SRms SWvt WAul WHoo WSHC
	- MOTHER OF PEARL	see *P. grandiflorus* 'Perlmutterschale'
§	- 'Perlmutterschale'	MRav
	- pink-flowered	GKev
	- ***pumilus***	GKev
	- 'Sentimental Blue'	XLum
	- 'Shell Pink'	see *P. grandiflorus* 'Perlmutterschale'
	- 'Willy'	XLum
	- 'Zwerg'	NBre

Platycrater (*Hydrangeaceae*)

	arguta	WCru WPGP
	- B&SWJ 6266	WCru

Plectranthus (*Lamiaceae*)

	ambiguus 'Nico'	CSam
	amboinicus	CCBP MNHC SAll
	argentatus ♀H1c	CSam CSpe CTsd EUJe EWld GCal IDee MCot MPie SEND SRkn WKif
	- 'Hill House' (v)	CHll CSam EShb MPie
	- 'Silver Shield'	EShb
	behrii	see *P. fruticosus*
	caninus	SPoG
	ciliatus	CPbh EShb SRkn
	- 'Sasha' (v)	CCCN CHll CSam ECtt EShb EUJe MPie
	coleoides 'Variegatus'	see *P. madagascariensis* 'Variegated Mintleaf'
	Cuban oregano	CSam
	ernstii	EWld
§	***fruticosus***	CPbh CSam
	- 'Behr's Pride'	CSam
	- 'James' ♀H2	CSam WKif
	madagascariensis	WKif
§	- 'Variegated Mintleaf' (v) ♀H1c	CSam MNHC SRms
	MONA LAVENDER ('Plepalila'PBR) ♀H1c	WKif
	neochilus	CSpc
§	***oertendahlii*** ♀H1c	CPbh CSam EBak EUJe
	ornatus variegated (v)	EUJe
	sinensis	CRos LRHS NRHS
	Swedish ivy	see *P. oertendahlii*
	'Velvet Elvis'PBR **new**	NAst
	zuluensis	CPbh EWld GCal SRkn WBor

Pleioblastus (*Poaceae*)

	akebono	see *P. argenteostriatus* 'Akebono'
§	***argenteostriatus*** 'Akebono'	ERod
§	- f. ***pumilus***	ERod GMaP MMuc MWht NLar NWad SPlb XCre
	auricomus	see *P. viridistriatus*
	- 'Vagans'	see *Sasaella ramosa*
	chino f. ***angustifolius***	see *P. chino* 'Murakamianus'
	- f. ***elegantissimus***	CBcs EPfP ERod EShb MMuc SEND WMoo
	- var. ***hisauchii***	ERod MWht XCre
§	- 'Murakamianus'	XCre
	fortunei	see *P. variegatus* 'Fortunei'
	'Gauntlettii'	see *P. argenteostriatus* f. *pumilus*
	glaber 'Albostriatus'	see *Sasaella masamuneana* 'Albostriata'
	gramineus	XCre
§	***hindsii***	ERod XCre
	humilis var. ***pumilus***	see *P. argenteostriatus* f. *pumilus*
	juxianensis **new**	XCre
	kongosanensis 'Aureostriatus' (v)	MWht
	linearis	ERod EShb MCot MWht WMoo
	longifimbriatus	see *Sinobambusa intermedia*
	oleosus	XCre
§	***pygmaeus***	CDul CTri EHoe ELan ENBC EUJe GMaP MBrN NAln SCob SGol SPer SRms WMoo XCre
§	- 'Distichus'	MJak WMoo XCre
§	- 'Mirrezuzume'	CExl
*	- var. ***pygmaeus*** 'Mini'	MMuc WCot
§	***simonii***	CAgr CRos LRHS MMuc MWht NRHS SEND SPoG XBlo
	- 'Variegatus' (v)	CBcs CRos LRHS NRHS SPer SPoG XCre
§	***variegatus*** (v) ♀H6	CBcs CBod CDul CRos ELan ELon ENBC EPfP EUJe GMaP LEdu LRHS MBrN MJak MWht NRHS SCob SLim SPlb SWvt WFar WMoo XBlo XCre
§	- 'Fortunei' (v)	CTsd MMuc SEND SGol
	- 'Tsuboii' (v)	CAbb CDTJ ERod EUJe MBrN SGol WMoo

§ ***viridistriatus*** ♀H5 CBcs CBod CDul CExl CKel CRos ECha ELon EPfP ERod GMaP LEdu LRHS MJak MMuc MRav MWht NRHS NWsh SCob SEND SGol SPer SRms WFar WMoo XBlo XCre
- f. ***variegatus*** (v) CTsd SWvt WMoo

Pleione (*Orchidaceae*)

sp. NDav
Alishan gx 'Merlin' LYaf
- 'Mother's Day' GEdr LYaf
- 'Mount Fuji' GKev LYaf
Anstice Harris gx LYaf
Asama gx 'Red Grouse' GEdr LYaf
Ascension gx **new** LYaf
Askia gx GEdr
- 'Cinnabar' **new** GKev
aurita GEdr GKev
× ***barbarae*** GKev LAma LYaf
Barcena gx LYaf
Berapi gx 'Purple Sandpiper' LEdu LYaf WPGP
Betty Arnold gx 'Firefinch' **new** LYaf
Bonobo gx LYaf
Brigadoon gx 'Stonechat' LEdu WPGP
Britannia gx 'Doreen' LEdu LYaf WPGP
§ ***bulbocodioides*** CExl GEdr GKev LYaf
- 'New Forest' GEdr
§ - 'Yunnan' GEdr GKev
Burnsall gx GEdr
Captain Hook gx LYaf
Caroli gx 'Cape Robin' LYaf
chunii GEdr GKev LAma
Confirmation gx LYaf
Eastfield gx 'Purple Emperor' LYaf
Eiger gx LYaf
El Pico gx 'Pheasant' LYaf
Erebus gx 'Redpoll' GEdr
Fancy Pants gx **new** LYaf
formosana ♀H3 EPot GKev LAma LCro LEdu LOPS LRHS MHer NHpl NRHS SDeJ WFar WPGP
- Alba Group GKev WFar
- - 'Claire' LEdu LYaf WPGP
- - 'Snow Bunting' LEdu LYaf WPGP
- 'Blush of Dawn' NHpl
- 'Greenhill' LYaf
- 'Pitlochry' LYaf
- (Pricei Group) 'Oriental Grace' LYaf
- - 'Oriental Splendour' LYaf
- 'Snow White' CExl LEdu LYaf WPGP
forrestii EPot GKev LAma NHpl
Gerry Mundey gx GEdr GKev
- 'Tinney's Firs' LYaf
Glacier Peak gx LYaf
§ ***grandiflora*** GKev LAma LYaf
Harlequin gx 'Norman' LYaf
Hekla gx 'Locking Stumps' GEdr
- 'Partridge' GEdr
- 'Partridge' × **Zeus Weinstein gx** GEdr
humilis GKev LYaf
- orange-red-flowered GKev
- purple-flowered GKev
Irazu gx 'Cheryl' GEdr
Jake Butterfield gx LYaf
- 'Kingfisher' **new** LYaf
Jorullo gx 'Long-tailed Tit' GEdr LYaf
Katmai gx 'Crossbill' LYaf
Keith Rattray gx 'Kelty' LYaf
Kelut gx LYaf
Kenya gx 'Bald Eagle' LYaf
- 'Wood Owl' **new** LYaf
Kohala gx LYaf
Krakatoa gx LYaf
- 'Wheatear' LYaf
Lascar gx 'Dipper' LYaf
- 'Purple Finch' LYaf
Leda gx 'Golden Pipit' **new** LYaf
- 'Palm Thrush' **new** LYaf
Lhasa gx 'Blushes' LYaf
limprichtii ♀H2 GKev LEdu LYaf
maculata LYaf
Mageik gx 'Black Kite' LYaf
Mandalay gx 'Purple Rain' LYaf
- 'Strawberry Fields' LYaf
Marion Johnson gx 'Bubs' LYaf
- 'Oxpecker' LYaf
- 'Whinchat' LYaf
Matupi gx CJun
Mauna Loa gx 'Glossy Starling' LYaf
Mawenzi gx LYaf
Michael Butterfield gx LYaf
Novarupta gx 'Raven' LYaf
Orinoco gx 'Gemini' GEdr
Orizaba gx GEdr
- 'Fish Eagle' LYaf
pinkepankii see *P. grandiflora*
Piton gx EPot LYaf
§ ***pleionoides*** GKev LYaf
pogonioides misapplied see *P. pleionoides*
pogonioides (Rolfe) Rolfe see *P. bulbocodioides*
Quizapu gx 'Peregrine' LYaf
Rakata gx 'Blackbird' MHer
- 'Locking Stumps' GEdr
- 'Redwing' LYaf
- 'Shot Silk' GEdr LYaf
- 'Skylark' LEdu WPGP
Red Colobus gx LYaf
Riah Shan gx **new** GKev
'Rossini' GKev
Salek gx 'Eagle Owl' LYaf
Santa Maria gx 'Nightjar' LYaf
Santorini gx LYaf
- 'Yellow Wagtail' LYaf
saxicola GKev
Semeru gx LYaf
Shantung gx NHpl
- 'Double Cream' LYaf
- 'Ducat' LYaf
- 'Gerry Mundey' LYaf
- 'Muriel Harberd' ♀H3 GEdr
- 'Silver Anniversary' LYaf
Shasta gx LYaf
Sinope gx LYaf
Sirena gx LYaf
Sorea gx GEdr GKev
Soufrière gx GEdr
speciosa Ames & Schltr. see *P. pleionoides*
Steve James gx 'Plum Perfection' LYaf
Stromboli gx 'Fireball' CExl EPot LEdu WPGP
Suswa gx 'Sand Plover' **new** LYaf
Taal gx 'Red-tailed Hawk' LYaf
× ***taliensis*** LYaf
Tibesti gx LYaf

Tolima gx 'Moorhen' LEdu LYaf WPGP
Tongariro gx CPBP EPot GEdr GKev LCro LEdu LOPS LRHS MHer MNrw NRHS WPGP
Ueli Wackernagel gx 'Pearl' GKev LYaf
'Verdi' GKev
Versailles gx 'Bucklebury' GEdr LEdu WPGP
- 'Muriel Turner' GEdr
Vesuvius gx 'Leopard' LYaf
- 'Phoenix' EPot LYaf
- 'Tawny Owl' GEdr
Volcanello gx 'Honey Buzzard' GEdr LYaf
- 'Song Thrush' LYaf
Whakari gx LYaf
- 'Dusky Sunbird' LYaf
- 'Mountain Pipit' LYaf
Wharfedale gx 'Pine Warbler' LYaf
yunnanensis misapplied see *P. bulbocodioides* 'Yunnan'
yunnanensis ambig. GEdr GKev LAma

Pleomele see *Dracaena*

Pleurospermum (*Apiaceae*)

sp. NAln
SDR 7941 GKev
SDR 7985 GKev
benthamii B&SWJ 2988 WCru
camtschaticum B&SWJ 12627 WCru
yunnanense BWJ 7952A WCru

plum see *Prunus domestica*; also AGM Fruit Section

Plumbago (*Plumbaginaceae*)

§ ***auriculata*** ♀H2 CBcs CCCN CSBt CSpe CTri CWCL EBak ELan EPfP EShb EUJe MGil MRav SEND SPer SPoG SRms WAvo WFib
- f. ***alba*** ♀H2 CBcs CCCN CRHN EPfP EShb IDee SEND WFib
- 'Crystal Waters' CCCN CSam EShb
- dark blue-flowered CRHN WFib
- (Escapade Series) 'Escapade Blue' CWGN EShb SPre
- - 'Escapade White' EShb
capensis see *P. auriculata*
larpentiae see *Ceratostigma plumbaginoides*

Plumeria (*Apocynaceae*)

sp. WSFF
rubra ♀H1b CCCN XBlo
- 'Golden Glow' XBlo
- 'Velvet Red' XBlo

Poa (*Poaceae*)

alpina SMea XLum
chaixii EPPr
cita IMou
labillardierei CKno CRos CWCL EBee ECha EHoe ELan ELon EPPr EPfP EShb IMou LRHS MBel MMuc NRHS SEND XLum
pratensis CHab

Podalyria (*Papilionaceae*)

calyptrata SPlb
sericea SPlb

Podanthus (*Asteraceae*)

ovatifolius SVen

Podocarpus ✿ (*Podocarpaceae*)

acutifolius LRHS
alpinus R. Br. ex Hook. f. CDul
andinus see *Prumnopitys andina*
'Autumn Shades' (m) NLar
'Blaze' (f) LEdu
chilinus see *P. salignus*
'Chocolate Box' (f) ELan LRHS MAsh NLar SLim
'County Park Fire'PBR (f) ♀H6 CBcs EMOT EPfP GEdr LRHS MAsh MGos NHol NLar SCoo SLim SRms SWvt WFar
cunninghamii see *P. laetus*
dacrydioides see *Dacrycarpus dacrydioides*
'Flame' (m) EMOT GEdr NLar SLim
'Guardsman' LRHS
hallii see *P. laetus*
henkelii CBcs
'Jill' (f) CBcs
§ ***laetus*** 'Roro' (m) CBcs
lawrencei CBcs
- 'Blue Gem' (f) CJun EPfP LRHS MAsh MMuc SCoo SLim WFar WThu
- 'Purple King' NLar
- 'Red Tip' LRHS
macrophyllus CTsd SArc WPGP
- 'Aureus' CBcs
nivalis CBcs CDul SRms WThu
- 'Bronze' GCal
- 'Green Queen' (f) CBcs
- 'Jack's Pass' (m) EMOT LRHS
- 'Kilworth Cream' (m/v) ♀H6 CBcs EMOT LRHS NHol SAko SLim SWvt
- 'Livingstone' (f) CBcs
- 'Otari' (m) MAsh
- 'Ruapehu' (m) MGil
'Red Embers' (f) EMOT SCoo SLim
§ ***salignus*** ♀H5 CBcs CDul CExl EPfP EUJe IDee LRHS MGil SArc SLim WPGP WPav WSHC WThu
'Spring Sunshine' (f) CBcs
totara CBrP LEdu WPGP
- 'Aureus' CBcs LRHS
- 'Pendulus' LRHS MGil WFar
'Young Rusty' (f) CBcs LRHS MAsh SLim WFar

Podophyllum (*Berberidaceae*)

aurantiocaule CBct CExl EBee GGGa
- subsp. ***aurantiocaule*** GEdr
§ ***delavayi*** CBct CDTJ CExl WSHC
difforme CBct LEdu
emodi see *Sinopodophyllum hexandrum* var. *emodi*
- var. ***chinense*** see *Sinopodophyllum hexandrum* var. *chinense*
hexandrum see *Sinopodophyllum hexandrum*
- var. ***chinense*** see *Sinopodophyllum hexandrum* var. *chinense*
'Kaleidoscope' (v) CBct EBee ECtt ELan EMor ESwi EUJe IPot MBNS MHol MPnt NHpl NLar WCot WFar
peltatum CAby CBct CBro CWCL EBee EHrv EMor EPfP EWld GBin GEdr GKev GPoy ILea LAma LEdu NLar NSti SPhx SPtp WCru WPGP WPnP
pleianthum ♀H4 CAby CBct GCal GEdr WCru WPGP
- B&SWJ 282 from Taiwan WCru

	- var. ***album***	GEdr
	- short	WCru
	veitchii	see *P. delavayi*
	versipelle	LEdu WCru
	- 'Spotty Dotty'[PBR] (v) ♀H4	Widely available
	- subsp. ***versipelle***	GKev

Podranea (*Bignoniaceae*)

§	***ricasoliana*** ♀H1c	CBcs EShb SPoG WBor

Pogonatherum (*Poaceae*)

*	***distichum***	XBlo

Pogonia (*Orchidaceae*)

	sp.	NDav
	ophioglossoides	GKev

Pogostemon (*Lamiaceae*)

§	***cablin***	EOHP GPoy
	patchouly	see *P. cablin*

Polanisia (*Capparaceae*)

	dodecandra	SPhx

Polemonium ✿ (*Polemoniaceae*)

	ambervicsii	see *P. pauciflorum* subsp. *hinckleyi*
	'Apricot Beauty'	see *P. carneum* 'Apricot Delight'
	archibaldiae ♀H5	NBir SRms WSHC
	'Blue Pearl'	CRos EBee ELan EPfP EWld GJos LRHS MAsh MHol NBro NGdn NLar NRHS SPer WFar WGwG WSpi
§	***boreale***	GBin NPol SWvt WMoo
	- 'Heavenly Habit'	EAJP GJos
	brandegeei misapplied	see *P. pauciflorum*
§	***brandegeei*** Greene	GKev
	- subsp. ***mellitum***	see *P. brandegeei* Greene
§	***caeruleum***	Widely available
	- subsp. ***amygdalinum***	see *P. occidentale*
	- - 'Album'	see *P. caeruleum* subsp. *caeruleum* f. *album*
	- 'Bambino Blue'	CRos SWvt
	- BRISE D'ANJOU ('Blanjou'[PBR]) (v)	CMac CMea CRos ECtt ELan EMor EPfP EShb EWes LRHS MAsh MHol NBir NGdn NPri NRHS SCob SPer SPoG SWvt
	- subsp. ***caeruleum***	GKev
§	- - f. ***album***	CBre CCBP CRos CWCL EBee ECha EHrv ELan EPfP GBin GKev IFro LRHS MBNS MBel MHer MRav NAln NBro NGBl NRHS SGbt SPer SPoG SRms WBrk WCAu WMoo WSpi
	- - - 'White Pearl'	GWyn
	- 'Days of Thunder'	EBee
I	- f. ***dissectum***	NPol
	- 'Filigree Clouds'	NLar
	- 'Filigree Skies'	MWat NGdn NLar
§	- subsp. ***himalayanum***	WArt WMoo
	- - CC 7325	EWld
	- 'Humile'	see *P.* 'Northern Lights'
	- 'Larch Cottage' (v)	NPol
	- 'Sky Blue'	MBel
	- 'Snow and Sapphires' (v)	CWGN ECtt MPnt NPer NPol SWvt
	- 'Southern Skies'	NPol
	- subsp. ***vulgare***	NPol
	- white-flowered	GJos MMuc
	carneum	CElw CRos CTri ECha EWTr LRHS NPol NRHS WMoo
§	- 'Apricot Delight'	EMor GJos GMaP MNHC MNrw NGdn NPol SGbt SRms WSpi
	cashmerianum	see *P. caeruleum* subsp. *himalayanum*
	'Churchills'	CBre NPol WSHC
	confertum	LLHF
	'Dawn Flight'	NPol
	'Eastbury Purple'	CElw NPol
	'Elworthy Amethyst'	CElw EBee NPol
	flavum	see *P. foliosissimum* var. *flavum*
	foliosissimum misapplied	see *P. archibaldiae*
	foliosissimum A. Gray	NPol
	- var. ***albiflorum***	see *P. foliosissimum* var. *alpinum*
§	- var. ***alpinum***	NPol
	- 'Cottage Cream'	LEdu NPol WCot WFar
§	- var. ***flavum***	NPol
	- var. ***foliosissimum***	NPol WSpi
	- 'Scottish Garden'	NPol
	- 'White Spirit'	NPol
	'Glebe Cottage Lilac'	CDor EBee NBir NPol
	'Glebe Cottage Violet'	NPol
	'Hannah Billcliffe'	CElw ECtt MBrN NChi NPol WFar
	'Heaven Scent'[PBR]	CRos CWld EBee ECtt EMor LRHS NDov NLar NPri NRHS WCAu WGrn
§	'Hopleys'	EBee GCal MNrw NChi
	× ***jacobaea***	EPPr EWes WCot
	'Katie Daley'	see *P.* 'Hopleys'
	'Lambrook Mauve'	Widely available
	liniflorum	NAln
	'Mary Mottram'	NPol
	mellitum	see *P. brandegeei* Greene
	'North Tyne'	NChi NPol NWad
§	'Northern Lights' ♀H7	Widely available
	'Norwell Mauve'	MNrw NPol WBrk WFar
§	***occidentale***	NPol
§	***pauciflorum***	EBou ECtt ELan IFro LPot NAln NBir WMoo
§	- subsp. ***hinckleyi***	GKev NPol NQui
§	- subsp. ***pauciflorum***	NPol
	- silver-leaved	see *P. pauciflorum* subsp. *pauciflorum*
	- 'Sulphur Trumpets'	SWvt
	- subsp. ***typicum***	see *P. pauciflorum* subsp. *pauciflorum*
	'Pink Beauty'	EBee ECtt ELan EPfP NGdn NPol
	pulchellum Salisb.	see *P. reptans*
	pulchellum Turcz.	see *P. caeruleum*
	pulcherrimum misapplied	see *P. boreale*
	- 'Tricolor'	see *P. boreale*
	pulcherrimum Hook.	NBro
	- subsp. ***pulcherrimum***	LLHF
§	***reptans***	CBod CFis GPoy MHer NBro NPol SRms WMoo
	- 'Album'	see *P. reptans* 'Virginia White'
	- 'Blue Ice'	NPol
	- 'Jacob's Gold' (v)	CRos EBee ELan EMor NRHS
*	- 'Sky Blue'	NBro
	- 'Stairway to Heaven'[PBR] (v)	Widely available
	- 'Touch of Class'[PBR] (v)	CPar CWGN EMor EWTr MBel MHol NLar NPri SPoG
§	- 'Virginia White'	CBre EWes MAvo NChi NPol
	- 'White Pearl'	MHol
	'Ribby'	NPol
	× ***richardsonii*** misapplied	see *P.* 'Northern Lights'
	× ***richardsonii*** Graham	see *P. boreale*
	'Sapphire'	CBre CRos LRHS NRHS
	'Sonia's Bluebell'	CWCL ECtt EPPr EWes EWld MNrw MPie NDov NLar NPol NSti SBch WFar
	'Sunnyside Storm'	NPol
	'Theddingworth'	NPol

	viscosum	GKev LLHF NPol SPlb
	- f. ***leucanthum***	NPol
	yezoense	NBre NPol WFar
	- var. ***hidakanum***	GAbr NPol
	- - BRESSINGHAM PURPLE ('Polbress')	Widely available
	- - 'Halfway to Paradise'	SCob WGrn
	- - 'Purple Rain'	Widely available

Polianthes (*Asparagaceae*)

	elongata	WCot
	tuberosa	CBcs CCCN GKev LCro LOPS XLum
	- 'Cinderella'	GKev
	- 'Golden Harvest'	GKev
	- 'Pink Sapphire'	GKev WCot
	- 'Sensation'	GKev SDeJ
	- 'Super Gold'	SDeJ
	- 'The Pearl' (d)	CBor GKev LAma SDeJ WCot XLum
	- 'Yellow Baby'	GKev

Poliomintha (*Lamiaceae*)

	bustamanta	NBir SPhx

Poliothyrsis (*Salicaceae*)

	sinensis	CBcs EBtc EPfP

Pollia (*Commelinaceae*)

	japonica	ESwi EWes WCot

Polygala (*Polygalaceae*)

	'Africana'[PBR]	CPbh
	africana 'Nana'	LRHS
	calcarea	WAbe
	- Bulley's form	EPot WFar
	- 'Lillet' ♀H5	CRos EPot GEdr LLHF LRHS NRHS WAbe
	chamaebuxus	see *Polygaloides chamaebuxus*
§	× ***dalmaisiana*** ♀H2	CAbb CCCN CKel CSde CSpe CTsd ECre ELan GBin LRHS SEND WAbe WCFE
	'Dolomite'	GAbr GEdr
	myrtifolia ♀H2	CCCN CPbh GBin LRHS MGos SAdn SPlb
	- BIBI PINK ('Polylap')	SAdn
	- 'Grandiflora'	see *P.* × *dalmaisiana*
	'Purple Passion'	CCCN LRHS
	virgata	CCCN ELan

Polygaloides (*Polygalaceae*)

§	***chamaebuxus*** ♀H4	GKev LLHF MAsh MGos NLar NSla NWad SRms WIce WThu
I	- ***alba***	NLar WAbe
§	- 'Grandiflora' ♀H5	CBcs EPfP EPot GAbr GEdr GKev MAsh MGil MGos NBir NHpl NSla SPlb SPoG SRot WAbe WIce
	- 'Kamniski'	EPot
	- 'Loibl'	EPot WFar
	- 'Purpurea'	see *P. chamaebuxus* 'Grandiflora'
	- 'Rhodoptera'	see *P. chamaebuxus* 'Grandiflora'

Polygonatum ✿ (*Asparagaceae*)

	SBQE 310	LEdu MAvo
	acuminatifolium 'Ogon'	EBee
	altelobatum B&SWJ 286	WCru
	- B&SWJ 1886	WCru
	annamense B&SWJ 9752	WCru
	arisanense B&SWJ 271	WCru
	- B&SWJ 3839	WCru
§	***biflorum***	CPou CRos CWCL EBee ECtt ELan EMor EPfP GBin GKev GMaP ILea LRHS MAvo MSCN NLar NRHS NWad SPoG SWvt WCru WFar WJam WPnP XLum
	- dwarf	CRos LRHS NRHS
	brevistylum B&SWJ 2421 **new**	WCru
	canaliculatum	see *P. biflorum*
	cathcartii B&SWJ 2429	WCru
	- yellow-flowered B&SWJ 2412	WCru
	cirrhifolium	EBee EMor EPot GAbr GEdr GKev LEdu MAvo MNrw NHpl NWad WCru WPGP
	- ARGS 320	EPPr
	- from China	WCru
	- red-flowered	NLar
	commutatum	see *P. biflorum*
	costatum B&SWJ 6599	WCru
	cryptanthum	EBee WCru
	curvistylum	CAby CAvo CBct EHrv EPPr GEdr GKev ILea IMou LEdu MAvo NLar NRya WCru WFar WSHC
	cyrtonema misapplied	see *Disporopsis pernyi*
	cyrtonema Hua	WCru
	- B&SWJ 271	LEdu MAvo
*	***desoulavyi*** var. ***yezoense*** B&SWJ 764	WCru
	falcatum misapplied	see *P. humile*
	falcatum A. Gray	EBee NHpl NRya
	- B&SWJ 1077	EHrv WCru
	- B&SWJ 5054	WCru
	- 'Shikoku Silver'	LEdu SMHy WCru
	- 'Silver Mist' **new**	LEdu
	- 'Variegatum'	see *P. odoratum* var. *pluriflorum* 'Variegatum'
	'Falcon'	see *P. humile*
	filipes	EBee EHrv EPPr LEdu WCru
	fuscum	WCru
	geminiflorum	CBct LEdu WCru WFar
	- McB 2448	GEdr
	giganteum	see *P. biflorum*
	glaberrimum	CAvo
	'Golden Gift'	CBct LPla SMHy
§	***graminifolium***	CAby CBct CPBP EPPr IMou WCru WThu
§	***hirtum***	CAby CBct CRos EMor EPPr LEdu LRHS NRHS WCru
	- 'Robustum'	WCru
	hookeri	CAby CBct CExl CPBP CRos EBee EHrv EPPr EPot EWld GBin GEdr GKev GMaP GQue ITim LEdu LRHS NAln NBid NHpl NLar NRHS NRya NSla NWad SPhx SPtp WCru WFar
§	***humile***	CBct CWCL EAJP EBee EHrv ELan EMor EPPr EPfP EPot GCal GEdr GKev ITim LEdu MAvo MHer NGdn NLar SCob SPtp SWvt WBor WCru WHil WPGP WTor XLum
I	- 'Variegatum' (v)	CMac GKev WCot
§	× ***hybridum*** ♀H7	Widely available
	- 'Bere'	LEdu WPGP
	- 'Betberg'	CAvo CBct CSpe ECha EHrv ELon EPPr IMou LEdu MAvo NBir WCot WFar
	- 'Flore Pleno' (d)	WHer
	- 'Nanum'	CBct MRav WCot
	- 'Purple Katie'	MAvo
§	- 'Striatum' (v)	Widely available

- 'Variegatum'	see *P.* × *hybridum* 'Striatum'
- 'Wakehurst'	EHrv LEdu
- 'Weihenstephan'	EPPr GCal LEdu
- 'Welsh Gold' (v)	CAvo EBee
inflatum	GEdr WCru
- B&SWJ 922	WCru
involucratum	WCru
- B&SWJ 4285	WCru
japonicum	see *P. odoratum*
kingianum	IMou LEdu
- yellow-flowered B&SWJ 6545	WCru
- - B&SWJ 6562	WCru
'Langthorn's Variegated' (v)	ELan
lasianthum	MAvo SMHy WCru
- B&SWJ 671	WCru
latifolium	see *P. hirtum*
maximowiczii	EPPr LEdu WCru WPGP
mengtzense f. ***mengtzense*** HWJ 588	WCru
- - HWJ 861 new	LEdu WCru
- f. ***tonkinense*** B&SWJ 8246	LEdu WCru
- - HWJ 551	WCru
- - HWJ 567	WCru
- - HWJ 573	CBct WCru
- - HWJ 861	LEdu
'Multifide'	EBee GKev
multiflorum misapplied	see *P.* × *hybridum*
multiflorum L.	CAby CAgr CBcs CHab CMac CSBt CWCL ECha EMor EWTr GAbr GBin GCal GKev LSun MHol MNHC MRav NGdn NLar SPlb SRms SWvt WCAu WCru WFar WHer WMoo XLum
- CC 4572	WCot
- 'Flore Pleno' (d)	WFar
- ***giganteum*** hort.	see *P. biflorum*
- 'Ramosissima'	LEdu SMHy WCru
- var. ***ramosum***	LEdu
* ***nanum*** 'Variegatum' (v)	CBcs
nodosum	WCru
§ ***odoratum***	CAvo CBct CBro CTsd EBee EHrv EPfP GKev GMaP LEdu NAln NBid NLar NRya SCob WCru WJam
- RBG 93-101	EBee
- 'Byakko' (v)	GEdr
- 'Dusky Bere'	WPGP
§ - dwarf	EBee LEdu
- 'Flatmate'	LEdu WCru
- 'Flore Pleno' (d)	CAby CAvo EHrv LEdu MHer WCot WHoo
- 'Georgia'	WPGP
- 'Grace Barker'	see *P.* × *hybridum* 'Striatum'
- Kew form	EPot
- 'Koryu'	GEdr
- var. ***odoratum***	GKev
§ - var. ***pluriflorum*** 'Variegatum' (v)	Widely available
- 'Pruhonice' new	EBee IMou
- 'Red Stem'	EHrv LEdu MAvo WCru
- 'Silver Wings' (v)	CBct ECha EHrv IPot LEdu NBir NLar WFar
- var. ***thunbergii***	IMou WCru
- - 'Variegatum' (v)	CWld
- 'Triglav' new	MAvo
- 'Ussuriland'	EBee EPPr GCal LEdu MAvo
- 'Ussuriland Roundleaf'	EBee GCal LEdu MAvo
officinale	see *P. odoratum*
oppositifolium B&SWJ 2537	WCru
§ ***orientale***	CAvo CBct GKev
§ - S&F 364 new	WCot
pluriflorum	see *P. graminifolium*
polyanthemum	see *P. orientale*
prattii	EBee GKev ILea WCru
- CLD 325	LEdu
pubescens	CBct EHrv LEdu WCru WThu
pumilum	see *P. odoratum* dwarf
punctatum ambig.	CBct GEdr LEdu NBid WPGP
punctatum Royle ex Kunth B&SWJ 2395	CBct WCru
racemosum	CBct IMou
roseum	EMor EPPr GKev LLHF SMHy WCru
sewerzowii	EMor EPPr
sibiricum	CAvo CBct GEdr WCru WFar
- DJHC 600	EBee LEdu MAvo WPGP
singalilense	WCru
stenanthum B&SWJ 5727	LEdu WCru
- B&SWJ 11425	WCru
stenophyllum	IMou WCru
stewartianum	EBee EPPr ILea MAvo NRya
tessellatum PAB 8336	LEdu
verticillatum	CBct CBro CRos EBee ECha EPPr EPfP GEdr GKev LEdu LRHS MNrw MRav NRHS SMad WCru WFar WPGP WWtn
- B&SWJ 2147	WCru
- CLD 1308	EPPr
- PAB 2455	LEdu
- 'Giant One'	IMou XEll
- 'Himalayan Giant'	EMor EPPr MAvo WPnP
- 'Krynica'	LEdu WPGP
* - 'Roseum'	CAvo LRHS
- 'Rubrum'	CAby CBct CRos CSpe EHrv EMor EPPr EThi GEdr ILea LEdu LRHS MAvo MBel NBid NChi NLar NRHS WCot WCru WHoo
- 'Serbian Dwarf'	CBct GEdr GKev LEdu WPGP
aff. ***verticillatum***	CSpe
yunnanense	CBct EBee LEdu WPGP
zanlanscianense	CBct EBee EHrv IMou LEdu WCru

Polygonum (*Polygonaceae*)

affine	see *Persicaria affinis*
amplexicaule	see *Persicaria amplexicaulis*
aubertii	see *Fallopia baldschuanica*
baldschuanicum	see *Fallopia baldschuanica*
bistorta	see *Persicaria bistorta*
capitatum	see *Persicaria capitata*
compactum	see *Fallopia japonica* var. *compacta*
equisetiforme misapplied	see *P. scoparium*
filiforme	see *Persicaria virginiana*
forrestii	EBee GKev
molle	see *Persicaria mollis*
multiflorum	see *Fallopia multiflora*
odoratum	see *Persicaria odorata*
polystachyum	see *Persicaria wallichii*
runciforme	see *Persicaria runcinata*
§ ***scoparium***	EPPr ESwi EWes SDys SVen WFar WOld XLum
tinctorium	see *Persicaria tinctoria*
vacciniifolium	see *Persicaria vacciniifolia*
weyrichii	see *Persicaria weyrichii*

Polylepis (*Rosaceae*)

australis	CBcs EBee IDee IMou LEdu
- tall	WPGP

Polymnia (*Asteraceae*)

sonchifolia 'Red China'	WPGP

Polypodiodes (*Polypodiaceae*)

	formosana	WCot

Polypodium ✿ (*Polypodiaceae*)

	aureum	see *Phlebodium aureum*
	australe	see *P. cambricum*
	californicum new	EBee
§	***cambricum***	CLAP EFer WCot WFib
	- GG 20131	SMHy
	- 'Barrowii'	CLAP WAbe WFib WGwG
	- 'Bob's Choice'	WCot
I	- 'Cambricum' 🏆H7	GCal WAbe
	- 'Conwy'	EBee WFib
	- 'Cristatum'	EBee WFib
	- (Cristatum Group) 'Grandiceps Fox' 🏆H7	MRav WFib
	- 'Hornet'	WFib
	- 'Macrostachyon'	GBin NBid WFib
	- 'Oakleyae'	EBee EWld SMHy WCot
	- 'Omnilacerum Oxford'	EBee
	- Pat's form new	EBee
	- 'Prestonii'	CLAP WCot WFib
	- Pulcherrimum Group	SDys WAbe
	- - bifid	EBee
	- - 'Pulcherrimum Addison'	EBee GBin LEdu WCot WFib WPGP
	- - 'Pulchritudine'	LLWG WCot
	- 'Richard Kayse' 🏆H7	CLAP EShb EWes SMHy WAbe WCot WFib WPGP
	- Semilacerum Group	EFer
	- - 'Carew Lane'	WFib
	- - 'Falcatum O'Kelly'	WCot
	- - 'Robustum'	EBee WFib
	- 'Whilharris' 🏆H7	SMHy WAbe WCot
I	× ***coughlinii*** bifid	WFib
	formosanum	SPlb
	glycyrrhiza	EMor GPoy SMHy WFib
	- bifid	see *P.* × *coughlinii* bifid
	- 'Lawrence Crocker'	WCot
	- 'Longicaudatum' 🏆H7	EFer EShb WBrk WCot WFib
	- 'Malahatense'	CLAP
	- 'Malahatense' (sterile)	EBee WCot WPGP
	glycyrrhiza × ***scouleri*** new	EBee
	guttatum	SPlb
	interjectum	EFer EMor EShb MRav WCot
	- 'Glomeratum Mullins'	WFib
	macaronesicum	WCot
	× ***mantoniae***	CLAP WFib
	- 'Bifidograndiceps'	NBid WFib
	- 'Cornubiense' 🏆H7	CLAP EShb EWld LEdu NBid NBir SMHy
	pseudoaureum 'Virginia Blue'	CRos LRHS NRHS
	scouleri	CBdn CRos EBee EFer EShb ISha LRHS MRav NBro NRHS WCot WPGP
	vulgare	Widely available
	- 'Bifidocristatum'	CAby CBdn CLAP CWCL ELon EMor EPfP EUJe GBin GCal GEdr ISha LEdu LLWG MGos MRav NLar SEND WBrk WCot WMoo
	- 'Bifidomulticeps'	WCot
*	- 'Congestum Cristatum'	SRms
	- 'Cornubiense Grandiceps'	GCal SRms
*	- 'Cornubiense Multifidum'	WCot
	- 'Elegantissimum'	NBid WFib
	- 'Parsley'	WCot
	- 'Trichomanoides Backhouse'	CLAP GCal WAbe WFib
	- 'Whitley Giant'	CAby CBod EBee ECtt EMor ESwi EUJe GBin GEdr GQue ISha ITim LEdu LLWG LPla LSun MHol MMuc MPie NBid NCou SEND SMad WArt WCot WPnP

Polypompholyx see *Utricularia*

Polyspora (*Theaceae*)

§	***axillaris***	CCCN CHll EBee LRHS
	- CWJ 12363	WCru
	longicarpa B&SWJ 11704 new	WCru
	- WWJ 11604	WCru
	- WWJ 11894 new	WCru
	speciosa B&SWJ 11708 from Vietnam	WCru
	- B&SWJ 11750	WCru
	- WWJ 11934	WCru

Polystichum ✿ (*Dryopteridaceae*)

	acrostichoides	CDTJ CLAP CRos EBee EMor ERod GBin IBal LEdu LRHS NBro NLar NRHS WCot WPGP XLum
	aculeatum 🏆H7	CKel CLAP CRos ECha EFer ELan EMor ERod EShb GBin GMaP IBal LCro LEdu LRHS MGos MMuc NBid NEgg NLar NRHS SCob SPoG SRms SWvt WFib WMoo XLum
I	- Densum Group	EFer
	- 'Portia'	WFib
	andersonii	CLAP EMor WCot
	biaristatum new	WPGP
	bissectum	CExl
	braunii	CBcs CDor CLAP CMac CRos CWCL EMor EPfP GMaP IBal IKil LRHS NBid NBro NLar NRHS SPoG WFib WPnP XLum
	caryotideum	see *Cyrtomium caryotideum*
	× ***dycei*** 🏆H6	CLAP CRos EBee ISha LRHS NRHS
	falcatum	see *Cyrtomium falcatum*
	falcinellum	EBee
	fortunei	see *Cyrtomium fortunei*
	imbricans	CLAP
	interjectum	MRav
	luctuosum	ISha
	makinoi	CCCN CLAP CRos EMor EUJe GBin IBal ISha LLWG LRHS NBid NBro NEgg NRHS SPlb WCot WFib WMoo
	mayebarae	CBdn CLAP EBee ISha
	munitum 🏆H7	Widely available
	neolobatum	CBdn CLAP EBee LLHF WCot WFib
	- BWJ 8182	WCru
	polyblepharum 🏆H7	Widely available
	- 'Jade'	EBee LRHS
	proliferum misapplied	see *P. setiferum* Acutilobum Group
	proliferum (R. Br.) C. Presl	CLAP LBuc WAbe WFib WPGP
*	- ***plumosum***	SWvt
	rigens	CBdn CBod CLAP CRos CWCL EFer ELon EMOT EMor EPau IBal ISha LEdu LRHS NBro NLar NRHS SRms SRot WFib
	setiferum 🏆H7	Widely available
§	- Acutilobum Group	CRos ECha EHrv EMOT EMor EUJe GMaP IBal LLWG LRHS NRHS SCob SPad SPer SRms WMoo WPGP XLum
	- Congestum Group	CDor CKel CLAP EHrv ELon EMOT EMor EUJe EWTr GBin NBro NEgg NHol NLar SPer SRms WFib

	- - 'Congestum'	CRos CWCL ELan EMOT EPPr EPfP EPot ERod GEdr IBal IKil ISha LEdu LRHS MRav NBir NEgg NGdn NHol NRHS SPad SPoG WMoo XLum
	- 'Cristatopinnulum'	CLAP WPGP
	- Cristatum Group	CLAP EHrv SRms
	- - 'Multifidum Polydactylum' **new**	LEdu
	- (Decompositum Group) 'Proliferum'	CWCL
	- Divisilobum Group ♀H7	CLAP EBee EFer ELan MCot MGos SRms WAbe WFar WFib WHoo WPGP
	- - 'Caernarfon'	EBee
	- - 'Dahlem'	CKel CRos EBee ECha ECtt EFer ELan ELon EMOT EMor EPfP EUJe GMaP IBal LRHS LSRN NBid NEgg NRHS SPer WFib WMoo WPtf XLum
	- - 'Divisilobum Densum' ♀H7	EHrv EPfP MRav NBir
	- - 'Divisilobum Grandiceps'	CLAP
	- - 'Divisilobum Iveryanum' ♀H7	CLAP EFer SRms WFib
	- - 'Divisilobum Laxum'	EBee
§	- - 'Divisilobum Wollaston'	CDTJ CKel CLAP CRos CWCL ECtt EMor IBal ISha LEdu LRHS MGos MRav NBid NLar NRHS WCot WMoo
	- - 'Herrenhausen'	Widely available
	- - 'Proliferum'	EUJe
	- Foliosum Group	EFer
	- 'Gracile'	MRav NBir
§	- 'Gracillimum'	CLAP
	- 'Grandiceps'	EFer
	- GREEN LACE	see *P. setiferum* 'Gracillimum'
	- 'Hamlet'	WFib
	- 'Helena'	WFib
	- 'Hirondelle'	SRms
	- Lineare Group	WFib
	- Multilobum Group	SRms WFib
	- 'Othello'	WFib
	- Perserratum Group	NBid WFib
	- 'Plumo-Densum'	see *P. setiferum* Plumosomultilobum Group
	- 'Plumosodensum'	see *P. setiferum* Plumosomultilobum Group
	- Plumosodivisilobum Group	EBee ECha MPnt NBid NBro SMHy WAbe WFib WRHF
	- - 'Baldwinii'	WFib
	- - 'Bland'	WFib
§	- Plumosomultilobum Group	CDor CKel CWCL EBee EMor EPfP EUJe GEdr GQue IBal ISha LCro LOPS LPla MCot MGos NBir NLar SMad WCot WFib WHoo WMoo
I	- - 'Plumosomultilobum Densum'	CAby CLAP CRos ECtt EUJe IBal LLWG LRHS LSun MBel MSCN NRHS SCob SMad WBrk WCot WFar
	- Plumosum Group	CMac CRos CSpe EFer ELon EMor EPfP LLWG LRHS MJak NRHS SArc SRot
	- - dwarf	CSBt
*	- ***plumosum grande*** 'Moly'	SRms
	- Proliferum Group	see *P. setiferum* Acutilobum Group
	- 'Proliferum Wollaston'	see *P. setiferum* (Divisilobum Group) 'Divisilobum Wollaston'
	- 'Pulcherrimum Bevis' ♀H6	CBdn CLAP CRos EBee EFer ELon EShb ESwi IKil ISha ITim LEdu LRHS MCot MMuc MPie NRHS SArc SEND SWvt WFib WPGP
	- (Pulcherrimum Group) 'Pulcherrimum'	ISha
	- (Rotundatum Group) 'Cristatum'	CLAP ISha
	- 'Smith's Cruciate'	MRav WFib
	- 'Wakeleyanum'	EFer SRms
	'Spiny Holly' **new**	CLAP
	tsussimense ♀H6	Widely available
	- 'K Rex'	CRos NRHS
	xiphophyllum	CLAP WPGP

Polyxena see *Lachenalia*

Pomaderris (*Rhamnaceae*)

apetala	CExl
elliptica	CExl

pomegranate see *Punica granatum*

Poncirus see *Citrus*

Ponerorchis see *Hemipilia*

Pontederia (*Pontederiaceae*)

	cordata ♀H5	CBen CWat EPfP EWat LCro LOPS MWts NPer SPlb WMAq WPnP WWtn XLum
	- f. ***albiflora***	CWat EPfP EWat LLWG XLum
§	- var. ***lancifolia***	CBen EWat LLWG MNrw MWts NPer WWtn
	- pink-flowered	LLWG
	- 'Sunsplash' (v)	LLWG
	lanceolata	see *P. cordata* var. *lancifolia*

Populus ✿ (*Salicaceae*)

	× ***acuminata***	WMou
	alba	CBcs CCVT CDul CLnd CMac CPer CTho CTri ECrN EMOT EPfP LBuc LPra MMuc NWea SCob SEWo SGol SPer WMou WTSh
	- 'Bolleana'	see *P. alba* 'Pyramidalis'
§	- 'Pyramidalis'	WMou
§	- 'Raket'	CCVT CTho ECrN ELan NWea SPer
	- 'Richardii'	EBtc WCot WMou
	- ROCKET	see *P. alba* 'Raket'
§	'Balsam Spire' (f)	CDul CPer CTho NWea WMou
§	***balsamifera***	CCVT CLnd CSBt CTri GAbr LPra SPer WCot
	- 'Vita Sackville West'	MBlu
	× ***canadensis***	ECrN
§	- 'Aurea' ♀H6	CDul ECrN SPer WMat WMou
	- 'Aurea' × (× ***jackii*** 'Aurora')	CCCN ELan WFar
	- 'Columbia'	WMou
	- 'Eugenei' (m)	WMou
	- 'Robusta' (m)	CCVT CDul CLnd LBuc NWea WMou
	- 'Serotina' (m)	WMou
	× ***canescens***	CLnd LPra WMou
	- 'Tower'	WMat
	deltoides 'Fuego'	SGol
	- 'Purple Tower'PBR	CBcs CDul CLnd EBee ELan EPfP IArd LRHS MBlu MMuc NOra SLim WCot
	× ***generosa*** 'Beaupré'	WMou
	glauca	SPtp WPGP
	- KR 3993	WPGP

- MF 20088 WPGP
× ***jackii*** 'Aurora' (f/v) CBcs CCVT CDul CMac CSBt CTsd MGos MMuc NWea SPer WFar WMou
lasiocarpa CBcs CExl CMCN CTho EPfP IArd IDee MBlu SGol SMad WMou WPGP
- (m/f) WPGP
maximowiczii SPtp WMou
nigra CDul CHab CPer CTho CTri CTsd LPra SCob WSFF
- (f) ECrN MMuc
- (m) MMuc
- subsp. ***betulifolia*** CCVT CDul CHab CLnd NWea WMou
- - (f) EBtc WMou
- - (m) EBtc WMou
§ - 'Italica' (m) ♀H6 CCVT CDul CLnd CMac CPer CSBt CTho CTri ECrN ELan EMOT LBuc LPra MGos MMuc NWea SEWo SPer WMou
- 'Pyramidalis' see *P. nigra* 'Italica'
purdomii SPtp WPGP
'Serotina Aurea' see *P.* × *canadensis* 'Aurea'
simonii 'Fastigiata' WMou
szechuanica WMou
§ - var. ***tibetica*** WMou
tacamahaca see *P. balsamifera*
'Tacatricho 32' see *P.* 'Balsam Spire'
tomentosa WMou
tremula CCVT CDul CFGn CHab CLnd CMac CPer CTho CTri ELan EWTr GAbr LBuc LMaj LPra MJak MMuc NWea SCob SEWo SPer WMou WSFF WTSh
§ - 'Erecta' ♀H7 CEnd CLnd EMOT MBlu MMuc WMat WMou
- 'Fastigiata' see *P. tremula* 'Erecta'
- 'Pendula' (m) CEnd CTho WMou
trichocarpa CDul SPer
- 'Fritzi Pauley' (f) CDul CTho WMou
violascens see *P. szechuanica* var. *tibetica*
× ***wilsocarpa*** 'Beloni' WPGP
wilsonii WPGP
yunnanensis WMou

Portulaca (*Portulacaceae*)

grandiflora SVic
oleracea ENfk SSim SVic
- var. ***aurea*** MNHC

Portulacaria (*Didiereaceae*)

afra EShb
- 'Variegata' (v) EShb SSim

Potamogeton (*Potamogetonaceae*)

crispus CWat LLWG WMAq WSFF
malainus LLWG
natans LLWG WSFF XLum
perfoliatus LLWG
schweinfurthii XBlo

potato see AGM Vegetables Section

Potentilla ✿ (*Rosaceae*)

alba CTri ECha ELan GCal LPot MBel MRav NChi NWad SPer WSHC
alchemilloides CMac
ambigua see *P. cuneata*
ancistrifolia var. ***dickinsii*** GEdr
anserina CAgr MHer NMir WHer XLum
- 'Golden Treasure' (v) NSti
anserinoides WMoo
arbuscula misapplied see *P. fruticosa* 'Elizabeth'
- 'Beesii' see *P. fruticosa* 'Beesii'
'Arc-en-ciel' Widely available
argentea SPlb WFar XLum
arguta EBee
argyrophylla see *P. atrosanguinea* var. *argyrophylla*
atrosanguinea Widely available
§ - var. ***argyrophylla*** CDor CSam CWCL EBee EBou ECha ELan EPfP GCal GKev GPSL MMuc MRav NBir NBro NChi NLar SRms WMoo XLum
- - 'Golden Starlit' CBod EDAr SVic
§ - - 'Scarlet Starlit' CAby CBod CDor CRos EBou EDAr EPfP LRHS LSun NEoE NRHS SVic
- var. ***leucochroa*** see *P. atrosanguinea* var. *argyrophylla*
* - 'Sundermannii' LLHF NWad SBrt
aurea ECtt GBin WOut
- 'Aurantiaca' NLar
§ - 'Goldklumpen' ECtt MRav NEoE
- 'Plena' (d) NRya
'Blazeaway' CRos ECtt EPfP GCal LRHS MArl MAvo MBNS MBel NEoE NGdn NRHS SRms
calabra ECha EWes
§ ***cinerea*** CTri LLHF
§ ***crantzii*** CMea EBou SRms
- 'Nana' see *P. crantzii* 'Pygmaea'
§ - 'Pygmaea' ECtt NBir
§ ***cuneata*** ♀H6 GKev
davurica 'Abbotswood' see *P. fruticosa* 'Abbotswood'
dombeyi IMou
'Emilie' (d) CWCL ECtt GCal GWyn IKil IPot MBNS MBel MNrw MTis NEoE NLar SWvt WBor WFar
§ ***erecta*** GPoy MNHC SRms
eriocarpa CPBP EPot GCrg NRHS NSla WAbe WIce
'Esta Ann' CMac ECtt LRHS MArl MBNS MNrw MSCN NLar NRHS WCAu
'Etna' CRos CWCL ECtt ELan ELon GCal LRHS MNrw NBir NLar NRHS WFar WHrl WMoo WPtf
'Everest' see *P. fruticosa* 'Mount Everest'
'Fireflame' EBee NLar WMoo
fissa MNrw NBir NLar SPhx
'Flambeau' (d) CWCL ECtt ELon EPfP EShb ILea IPot LRHS MArl MAvo MRav NChi NGdn NLar NRHS NSti WCAu WMoo XEll
'Flamboyant' (d) EBee IPot
'Flamenco' CRos CSam CTri ECtt ELon IPot LRHS MArl MBNS MMrt MRav NBir NCGa NRHS WFar WMoo
fragariiformis see *P. megalantha*
fruticosa LBuc NWea
§ - 'Abbotswood' ♀H7 Widely available
- 'Annette' NEoE NLar
- 'Apple Blossom' CKel
- var. ***arbuscula*** hort. see *P. fruticosa* 'Elizabeth'
- 'Argentea Nana' see *P. fruticosa* 'Beesii'
- 'Baby Bethan'PBR (d) LLHF
§ - 'Beesii' CRos EMil EPfP LRHS MAsh NRHS SIgm
- 'Bewerley Surprise' WFar
- 'Bo-Peep' CEnd CRos EBee LRHS LSRN NRHS WFar

	Name	Suppliers
	- 'Chelsea Star' ♀H7	CKel CMac CRos EPfP LRHS LSRN MAsh NRHS SPoG
	- 'Clotted Cream'	SGbt
	- var. ***dahurica*** 'Hersii'	see *P. fruticosa* 'Snowflake'
	- 'Dakota Sunrise'	WFar
	- DANNY BOY ('Lissdan'PBR)	CKel CRos EBee EMil LCro LOPS LRHS MAsh NEoE NRHS SLon SPad SPoG
	- 'Daphne'	NWad
	- 'Dart's Golddigger'	CTri
	- 'Daydawn'	CBcs CBod CMac CRos CTri ELan EPfP LRHS MAsh MMuc MRav MSwo NBir NEgg NLar NRHS NWad SGol SLim SPer SRms SWvt WFar WMoo
	- 'Farreri'	see *P. fruticosa* 'Gold Drop'
	- 'Glenroy Pinkie'	MRav
§	- 'Gold Drop'	CMac NHol
	- 'Golden Dwarf'	WMoo
	- 'Goldfinger'	CAco CAgr CBod CChe CKel CRos CSBt EMOT EPfP LRHS MAsh MGos MJak MMuc MRav MSwo NEgg NRHS SCob SCoo SLim SPer SPlb SPoG WFar WMoo XSen
	- GOLDKUGEL	see *P. fruticosa* 'Gold Drop'
	- 'Goldstar'	CBod CRos IArd LRHS MMuc NPri NRHS SCob SEND SLim SLon SNig SRms WFar
	- 'Goldteppich'	LBuc
	- 'Grace Darling'	EPfP EWes NBir NEgg SWvt WMoo
	- 'Groneland' ♀H7	CRos ELan EPfP LRHS MAsh NRHS SCoo SPoG
	- 'Hopleys Orange' ♀H7	CKel CRos CSBt EPfP EWes LRHS NHol NPri NRHS SCob SGbt SGol SNig SRms WFar WMoo
	- 'Hurstbourne'	NEoE
	- 'Jackman's Variety' ♀H7	CRos EPfP LRHS MAsh SCob SRms
	- 'Katherine Dykes'	CDul CRos CTri EBee EPfP GKin LRHS LSRN MAsh NEgg NRHS NWea SCob SCoo SGbt SLim SPer SRms WAvo WFar WMoo
	- 'King Cup' ♀H7	CRos EPfP LRHS MAsh
§	- 'Klondike'	CBcs CSBt
	- 'Kobold'	NLar
	- 'Lemon and Lime'	see *P. fruticosa* 'Limelight'
§	- 'Limelight' ♀H7	CKel CRos CSBt EBee EPfP GKin LRHS MAsh MRav MSwo NEoE NRHS NWad SRms WAvo WFar
	- 'Lovely Pink'	see *P. fruticosa* 'Pink Beauty'
§	- 'Maanelys'	CSBt NWea SPer WMoo
	- 'Macpenny's Cream'	CMac SRms
§	- 'Manchu'	CMac MRav SCob SPer SRms WCFE
	- MANGO TANGO ('Uman'PBR)	CKel CRos CSBt EMOT EPfP LRHS LSRN MAsh NEoE NLar NRHS SGol SPoG WFar
§	- MARIAN RED ROBIN ('Marrob'PBR) ♀H7	CRos ELan EPfP GKin LCro LOPS LRHS MAsh MRav MSwo NPri NRHS NWea SCoo SLim SLon SPer SRms SWvt
	- 'McKay's White'	NLar
	- 'Medicine Wheel Mountain' ♀H7	CKel CRos EBee ELan EWes IArd LRHS MAsh MRav MTin NEoE NLar NRHS NWad SCob SCoo SGol SLim SPer SPoG
	- MOONLIGHT	see *P. fruticosa* 'Maanelys'
§	- 'Mount Everest'	CTri MMuc NWea SLon
	- 'Nana Argentea'	see *P. fruticosa* 'Beesii'
	- 'New Dawn'	CBcs EMOT GKin MAsh
	- 'Orangeade'	CRos EPfP LRHS MAsh NLar SCoo SPoG
*	- 'Peachy Proud'	NEoE
§	- 'Pink Beauty'PBR ♀H7	Widely available
	- PINK PARADISE ('Kupinpa'PBR)	SNig
	- 'Pink Pearl'	WFar
	- 'Pink Queen'	NLar
	- 'Pink Whisper'	NEoE SRms
	- 'Pretty Polly'	CRos ELan EPfP LRHS MSwo NHol NLar NWad WFar
	- 'Primrose Beauty' ♀H7	Widely available
§	- PRINCESS ('Blink')	CBcs CDul CKel CRos EBee ELan EPfP LRHS MAsh MJak MRav NRHS SCob SCoo SGol SLim SRms WFar WMoo
	- var. ***pumila***	GKev WAbe
	- 'Red Ace'	Widely available
	- 'Red Lady'PBR	CRos EBee ELan EMOT EPfP LRHS MAsh NEoE NHol NRHS SCob SPoG WMoo
	- RED ROBIN	see *P. fruticosa* MARIAN RED ROBIN
	- 'Red Surprise'	WFar
	- Rhodocalyx Group	GCal
	- 'Royal Flush'	NWad
	- 'Snowbird'	NEoE SLim WFar
§	- 'Snowflake'	CBcs
	- 'Sommerflor' ♀H7	CAco CRos EPfP LRHS MAsh NRHS
	- 'Sophie's Blush'	MRav NWea
§	- (Sulphurascens Group) 'Elizabeth'	CBcs CDul CMac CRos ECrN EPfP LRHS LSRN MGos MJak MSwo NHol NWea SCob SGol SLim SPer SRms SWvt WCFE WFar WMoo
	- - 'Longacre Variety'	CMac CTri IArd MSwo NLar NWea
	- 'Sunset'	CBcs CMac GKin LSRN MJak NBir NWea SCob SCoo SLim SPer SRms WFar WMoo
	- 'Tangerine'	CBcs CBod CDul CKel CMac CRos CTri EPfP LPot LRHS MAsh MGos MJak MMuc MRav MSwo NBir NHol NRHS NWea SCob SLim SPer SPlb SRms SWvt WFar WMoo
	- 'Tilford Cream'	CKel CRos CSBt CTri EBee ELan EPfP GKin LRHS LSRN MJak MRav MSwo NBir NEgg NHol NRHS SCob SGbt SGol SLim SNig SPer SRms WCFE WFar
	- 'Tom Conway'	CMac SRms
	- var. ***veitchii***	CSBt
	- 'Vilmoriniana'	CKel CMac CRos CTri ELan EPfP GCal LRHS MAsh MRav NLar SPer SPoG SWvt WKif WSpi
	- 'Whirligig'	CMac
	- 'White Lady'PBR	NEoE
	- 'William Purdom'	WAvo
	- 'Yellow Bird' ♀H7	CRos LRHS MAsh
	'Gibson's Scarlet' ♀H7	Widely available
§	***glandulosa*** subsp. ***nevadensis***	CTri MAsh
	'Gloire de Nancy' (d)	EBee IKil MRav NBir NChi NLar
	'Gold Clogs'	see *P. aurea* 'Goldklumpen'
	'Herzblut'	NLar
	hippiana	EBee
	× ***hopwoodiana***	CMea CSpe CWCL EBee ECha ECtt ELan EPPr GCal GMaP IKil ILea MBel MNrw MRav NBir NChi NDai NDov NLar SCob SPer WCAu WFar WMoo
	× ***hybrida*** 'Jean Jabber'	EBee GLog MRav NEoE NLar WFar
	hyparctica	GJos
	'Jack Elliot'	NEoE
	kurdica	XLum

	'Light My Fire'	EBee ECtt LLHF MAsh MBNS MNrw
	'Mandshurica'	see *P. fruticosa* 'Manchu'
§	***megalantha***	CBod CBro CRos EAJP EBou ECtt EDAr ELan EPfP GCal GQue LEdu LRHS MAsh MBNS MRav NBir NBro NRHS NSti SGbt SPer SRms SRot WMoo XLum
	- 'Gold Sovereign'	CRos EBee LRHS NEoE
	'Melton Fire'	EPfP GJos GKin GPSL MNrw NBir WHrl WMoo
	micrantha 'Purple Haze'	LEdu
	- 'Purple Heart'	WPGP
	'Monarch's Velvet'	see *P. thurberi* 'Monarch's Velvet'
	'Monsieur Rouillard' (d)	CElw CMac CRos CSam ECtt LRHS MArl MCot MNrw MPie MRav NGdn NLar NRHS WHoo
	'Mont d'Or'	EBee MRav NLar
	nepalensis	CRos EHoe LRHS NBro NChi NRHS XLum
	- 'Helen Jane'	CDor GBin GJos GQue LEdu MHer NBir NHol NLar NWad WArt WFar WHrl WMoo WPtf
§	- 'Miss Willmott'	Widely available
	- 'Ron McBeath'	CDor CKno CRos CWCL ECtt ELan EPfP GAbr GBin ILea LRHS MAvo MRav NHol NLar NRHS NSti SGol SPer SRkn SRms SWvt WGwG WHoo WMoo WPtf
	- 'Roxana'	ELan GJos MRav NBro WMoo
	- 'Shogran'	CRos EBou GJos LRHS NChi NHol NLar NRHS WPtf
§	***neumanniana***	CPBP MAsh NBir
	- 'Goldrausch'	IMou MRav XLum
§	- 'Nana'	EBou ECtt EPot GCrg MAsh NRya NWad SPlb SRms WFar WHoo WIce WMoo XLum
	nevadensis	see *P. glandulosa* subsp. *nevadensis*
	nitida	EPot MAsh WAbe
	- 'Rubra'	CMea EDAr GCrg GEdr NBir WAbe
	palustris	CWat EBee EWat LLWG MWts NLar WMoo XLum
	parvifolia 'Klondike'	see *P. fruticosa* 'Klondike'
	pedata	NChi XLum
	'Pink Panther'	see *P. fruticosa* PRINCESS
	porphyrantha	GEdr GJos LLHF
	recta	CBod SRms XLum
	- 'Alba'	GMaP NEgg WPtf
	- 'Citrina'	see *P. recta* var. *sulphurea*
	- 'Macrantha'	see *P. recta* 'Warrenii'
§	- var. ***sulphurea***	CMea EAJP EPPr GAbr GWyn MCot MNrw NBir NLar NSti NWad SPhx SRkn WBrk WCAu WHal WHoo WHrl WJam WMoo WPtf XLum
§	- 'Warrenii'	CCBP CRos CSBt EPfP GMaP LRHS MRav NBir NEgg NRHS SHar SPer SRms WHal WHrl WMoo XLum
	'Roxanne' (d)	CRos LRHS MHer
	rupestris	CMea ECha EPPr GCal LSun MHer NSti WCAu WFar WHal WPtf
	- 'Nana' **new**	WPtf
	× ***russelliana***	CRos LRHS NRHS
	'Scarlet Starlet'	see *P. atrosanguinea* var. *argyrophylla* 'Scarlet Starlit'
	speciosa	EWes
	sterilis	WHer WSFF
*	***sundermanii***	WHrl
	tabernaemontani	see *P. neumanniana*
	thurberi	CMea CRos LRHS NLar NRHS SPhx WHrl WMoo XLum
§	- 'Monarch's Velvet'	Widely available
	tommasiniana	see *P. cinerea*
	× ***tonguei*** ŸH5	Widely available
	tormentilla	see *P. erecta*
	tridentata	see *Sibbaldiopsis tridentata*
	'Twinkling Star'	EBee NEoE WPtf
	verna misapplied	see *P. neumanniana*
	- 'Pygmaea'	see *P. neumanniana* 'Nana'
	'Versicolor Plena' (d)	NLar
	villosa	see *P. crantzii*
	'Vogue'	EBee MBNS
	'Volcan'	CAby CWCL ECtt EWes IKil MAvo NChi WCAu WFar WHal
	'White Queen'	GLog MRav SHar SRms
	'William Rollisson' ŸH7	Widely available
	willmottiae	see *P. nepalensis* 'Miss Willmott'
	'Yellow Queen'	CMac CRos CTri GKin GMaP LPot LRHS MNrw MRav NLar NRHS SPer SRms WCAu

Poterium see *Sanguisorba*

	sanguisorba	see *Sanguisorba minor*

Prangos (*Apiaceae*)

	ferulacea	WCot

Pratia (*Campanulaceae*)

§	***angulata*** 'Treadwellii'	ECha ECtt SPlb SRms WFar WHal
	montana	see *Lobelia montana*
§	***pedunculata***	CTri EBou ECha ECtt EDAr ELan EPfP LLWG LSun MAsh NHpl SIgm SPlb SRms SRot WIce WMoo
I	- 'Alba'	CBod EWes NHpl SRms WFar WIce
	- 'County Park'	CExl CMea CSpe CTri EBou ECha ECtt EDAr ELan ELon GAbr GWyn LLWG MAsh NHpl SPlb SPoG SRms SRot WFar WIce WMoo XLum
	- 'White Stars'	LLWG

Preslia see *Mentha*

Primula ✿ (*Primulaceae*)

	(Si)	MAsh
	acaulis	see *P. vulgaris*
	'Adrian Jones' (Au)	EPot ITim NWad
	'Alan Robb' (Pr/Prim/d)	ECtt NGdn
	'Alexina' (*allionii* hybrid) (Au)	NHar
§	***allionii*** (Au)	NSum WAbe
	- HNG 12	ITim
	- 'Agnes' (Au)	ITim
	- 'Aire Waves'	see *P.* × *loiseleurii* 'Aire Waves'
	- 'Allen Charm' (Au)	ITim
	- 'Allen Moonbeam' (Au)	GAbr GAgs ITim NHar
	- 'Anna Griffith' (Au)	CPBP WAbe
	- 'Apple Blossom' (Au)	GKev NHpl
	- 'Archer' (Au)	ITim
	- 'Ares' (Au)	NHar
	- 'Aries Violet' (Au)	ITim NHar
	- 'Bill Martin' (Au)	EPot ITim
	- 'Blood Flake' (Au)	ITim
	- 'Blush' (Au)	CPBP
	- 'Broadwell No 4' (Au)	CPBP
	- 'Cherry' (Au)	CPBP WAbe
	- 'Chivalry' (Au)	CPBP WAbe
	- 'Circe's Flute' (Au)	NHar
	- 'Cissie' (Au)	CPBP ITim NHar
	- 'Crowsley Variety' (Au)	ITim
	- 'Crusader' (Au)	EPot
	- 'Crystal' (Au)	CPBP
	- 'Daniel Burrow' (Au)	CPBP
	- 'David Philbey' (Au)	CPBP

	- 'Eliza' (Au)	EPot
	- 'Elizabeth Baker' (Au)	ITim
	- 'Elizabeth Burrow' (Au)	ITim WAbe
	- 'Elizabeth Earle' (Au)	ITim
	- 'Eureka' (Au)	CPBP EPot LLHF WAbe
	- 'Eveline Burrow' (Au)	WAbe
	- 'Fanfare' (Au)	MAsh NHar
I	- 'Forma' (Au)	XBar
	- 'Gilderdale Glow' (Au)	CPBP GKev NHar
	- 'Giuseppi's Form'	see *P. allionii* 'Mrs Dyas'
	- 'Grandiflora' (Au)	GKev ITim WAbe
	- 'Hartside 6' (Au)	ITim
	- 'Hazey' (Au)	ITim
	- 'Hemswell' (Au)	NHpl
	- 'Henry Burrow' (Au)	WAbe
	- 'Herald' (Au)	ITim
	- 'Hocker Edge' (Au)	ITim NWad
	- 'Horwood' (Au)	ITim
	- 'Isobel' (Au)	LLHF
	- 'Joe Elliott' (Au)	ITim
	- 'Kate Evans' (Au)	CPBP
	- 'Lepus' (Au)	WAbe
	- 'Lucy' (Au)	NHar
	- 'Malcolm' (Au)	ITim
	- 'Marion' (Au)	XBar
	- 'Marjorie Wooster' (Au)	CPBP XBar
	- 'Martin' (Au)	ITim
	- 'Mary Berry' (Au)	CPBP EPot NWad
§	- 'Mrs Dyas' (Au)	NWad
	- 'Neon' (Au)	CPBP
	- 'Neptune's Wave' (Au)	NHar
	- 'New Dawn' (Au)	ITim
	- 'Peace' (Au)	NHar
	- 'Peggy Wilson' (Au)	EPot GKev NWad WThu
	- 'Pennine Pink' (Au)	CPBP
	- 'Phoebe's Moon' (Au)	ITim NHar
	- 'Pink Ice' (Au)	LRHS
	- 'Pinkie' (Au)	WAbe
	- 'Raymond Wooster' (Au)	GKev NWad
	- 'Snowflake' (Au)	CPBP GKev WSHC
	- 'Steven Burrow'	CPBP
	- 'Timsbury Glow' (Au) **new**	CPBP
	- 'Tranquillity' (Au)	CPBP ITim NWad
	- 'Viscountess Byng' (Au)	CPBP
	- 'William Earle' (Au)	CPBP ITim XBar
	allionii* × *auricula misapplied 'Blairside Yellow'	NSum
	allionii* × *auricula misapplied 'Old Red Dusty Miller' (Au)	NWad WFar
	allionii × 'Lismore Jewel' (Au)	CPBP
	allionii × 'Lismore Treasure' (Au)	ITim NHpl
	allionii* × *pubescens (Au)	NHpl
	allionii* × *pubescens 'Harlow Car' (Au)	WFar
	allionii × 'Snow Ruffles' (Au)	ITim
	allionii × 'White Linda Pope' (Au)	NHpl NWad
	alpicola (Si) $\mathbb{Y}^{H7}$	CAby CTsd CWCL EPot GAbr GKev GQue MMuc NAln NBid NChi NGdn NSum NWad WTyc XBar
	- var. ***alba*** (Si)	CPla CTsd GAbr GKev NBid
§	- var. ***alpicola*** (Si)	EBee GKev NAln
	- hybrids (Si)	GEdr NHpl WMoo
	- 'Kevock Sky' (Si)	GKev
	- var. ***luna***	see *P. alpicola* var. *alpicola*
	- var. ***violacea*** (Si)	EBee EWld GAbr GKev MNrw NAln NBid NWad
	- - wine-red-flowered (Si)	GKev NAln
	'Altaica'	see *P. elatior* subsp. *meyeri*
	altaica grandiflora	see *P. elatior* subsp. *meyeri*
	amoena	see *P. elatior* subsp. *meyeri*
	'Amy Smith' (Pr/Prim)	GAbr
	angustifolia (Pa)	GKev WAbe
	anisodora	see *P. wilsonii* var. *anisodora*
	× ***anisodoxa*** 'Kevock Surprise' (Pf)	GKev NAln
	'Annemijne' (Pr/Poly)	WCot
	apoclita (Mu)	GKev XBar
	× ***arctotis***	see *P.* × *pubescens*
	aurantiaca (Pf)	CPla EBee GKev NAln NHpl XBar
	- 'Harperley Pink' (Pf) **new**	NHpl
	aureata (Pe)	NHar WAbe
	auricula L. (Au) $\mathbb{Y}^{H5}$	CRos EDAr EWld GKev LRHS MAsh NRHS NSla SPer SPlb SPoG WRHF
	- subsp. ***bauhinii*** (Au)	GKev
	auricula misapplied (Au)	EBou ECha LRHS NRHS
	- A74 (Au)	MMuc SEND
	- K85 (Au/S)	SPop
I	- '1-2-3' (Au)	EBee
	- '2nd Vic' (Au/S)	SPop
	- 'Abdor' (Au/St)	NDro SPop
	- 'Abundance' (Au/A)	NDro
	- 'Achates' (Au/A)	WAln
	- 'Admiral' (Au/A)	WAln
	- 'Adrian' (Au/A)	GAgs ITim NDro SPop WHil XBar
	- 'Adrienne' (Au/A)	SPop
	- 'Adrienne Ruan' (Au/A)	NDro WAln
	- 'After Glow' (Au/St)	NDro SPop
	- 'Aga Khan' (Au/A)	NDro WAln
	- 'Agamemnon' (Au/A)	GAgs LLHF SPop
	- 'Airy Fairy' (Au/S)	NDro SPop
	- 'Alamo' (Au/A)	SPop
	- 'Alan Ravenscroft' (Au/A)	SPop WHil
	- 'Albert Bailey' (Au/d)	GAbr GAgs ITim NDro SPop WFar WHil XBar
	- 'Alchemist' (Au/S)	NDro SPop
	- 'Aldgate' (Au/S)	NDro
	- 'Alexandra Georgina' (Au/A)	SPop WAln
	- 'Alf' (Au/A)	GAgs NDro NSum WHil
	- 'Alfred Charles' (Au/A)	SPop WAln
	- 'Alice' (Au/d)	NDro
	- 'Alice Haysom' (Au/S)	ELan GAbr GAgs ITim NDro SPop WHil XBar
	- 'Alicia' (Au/A)	GAbr GAgs NDro NSum SPop XBar
	- 'Alien' (Au/S)	NDro SPop
	- 'Alison' (Au/S)	NDro
	- 'Alison Jane' (Au/A)	GAgs NDro SPop WHil XBar
	- 'Alison Rose' (Au/B)	NDro
	- 'Alison Telford' (Au/A)	WHil
	- 'All Gold' (Au/d)	SPop
	- 'Allard' (Au/A)	WAln
	- 'Allegro' (Au/A)	WAln
	- 'Alloway' (Au/d)	WAln
	- 'Almand' (Au/d)	WAln
	- 'Almondbury' (Au/S)	NDro SPop
	- 'Amanda' (Au/d)	SPop
	- 'Amazon' (Au/St)	SPop
	- 'Amber Light' (Au/S)	SPop WAln
	- 'Amber Valley' (Au/S) **new**	SPop
	- 'Amersham' (Au/S) **new**	NDro
	- 'Amicable' (Au/A)	GAgs NDro NSum SPop WHil
	- 'Amie Rosalind' (Au/B) **new**	NDro
	- 'Amore' (Au/St)	GAgs NDro SPop
	- 'Amy Nuttall' (Au/A)	SPop

- 'Ancient Order' (Au/A) WAln
- 'Ancient Society' (Au/A) GAgs NDro NSum SPop WHil XBar
- 'Andrea Julie' (Au/A) GAgs NDro SPop WHil
- 'Andrew Hunter' (Au/A) GAgs NDro NSum SPop
- 'Andy Cole' (Au/A) NDro SPop WAln
- 'Angel Eyes' (Au/St) NDro SPop WHil
- 'Angel Islington' (Au/S) NDro
- 'Angela Gould' (Au/B) NDro SPop WHil XBar
- 'Angela Grace' (Au/d) XBar
- 'Angela Short' (Au/St) SPop
- 'Angostura' (Au/d) EBee SPop WHil
- 'Ann Brookes' (Au/d) WAln
- 'Ann Taylor' (Au/A) WAln
- 'Anna' (Au/B) NDro
- 'Anne Hyatt' (Au/d) NDro SPop
- 'Anne Swithinbank' (Au/d) WAln
- 'Annie Tustin' (Au/S) SPop
- 'Ansells' (Au/S) SPop WAln
- 'Antoc' (Au/S) SPop
- 'Anwar Sadat' (Au/A) GAgs NDro NSum WHil
- 'Apple Blossom' (Au/B) NDro WHil
- 'Applecross' (Au/A) GAgs NDro NHpl NSum SPop WHil
- 'Apricot Truffle' (Au/d) SPop
- 'April Moon' (Au/S) GAgs NDro SPop WHil
- 'Aquarius' (Au/d) SPop
- 'Arab Prince' (Au/A) WAln
- 'Arab Queen' (Au/A) WAln
- 'Arabian Night' (Au/A) NDro WAln
- 'Arapaho' (Au/A) SPop WAln
- 'Arctic Fox' (Au/A) WAln WHil
- 'Argentine' (Au/S) SPop XBar
- 'Argus' (Au/A) GAgs ITim LSun NDro NSum NWad SPop WHil XBar
- 'Arlene' (Au/A) WAln
- 'Armorique' (Au/d) **new** XBar
- 'Art Deco' (Au/B) NDro WAln
- 'Arthur Delbridge' (Au/A) NDro WHil
- 'Artwork' (Au/S) **new** NDro
- 'Arundell' (Au/S/St) EBee ITim NDro NSum SPop WFar WHil XBar
- 'Arwen' (Au/A) SPop
- 'Ascot Gavotte' (Au/S) NDro
- 'Ashcliffe Gem' (Au/A) NDro WAln
- 'Astolat' (Au/S) EBee GAgs NDro NHpl SPop WHil XBar
- 'Athene' (Au/S) ITim NDro SPop
- 'Atlantic' (Au/S) NDro NEgg SPop
- 'Aubergine' (Au/B) NDro

I - 'Aubergine' (Au/d) SPop

- 'Audacity' (Au/d) NDro WAln
- 'Audrey' (Au/S) NDro SPop
- 'Aurora' (Au/A) EDAr NSum SPop WAln
- 'Austin' (Au/A) NDro SPop WAln
- 'Autumn Fire' (Au/A) SPop
- 'Autumn Glow' (Au/d) SPop
- 'Autumn Gold' (Au/B) NDro
- 'Autumn Jewels' (Au/d) **new** XBar
- 'Avon Angel' (Au/d) SPop
- 'Avon Bunny' (Au/d) SPop
- 'Avon Buster' (Au/d) SPop
- 'Avon Carrier' (Au/d) SPop
- 'Avon Citronella' (Au/d) SPop XBar
- 'Avon Eclipse' (Au/d) SPop
- 'Avon Elegance' (Au/d) SPop
- 'Avon Khaki' (Au/d) SPop
- 'Avon Toro' (Au/d) SPop
- 'Avon Twist' (Au/d) SPop
- 'Avonwick' (Au/B) NDro
- 'Avril' (Au/A) NDro SPop WAln WHil
- 'Avril Hunter' (Au/A) GAgs ITim MHer NDro NSum WHil XBar
- 'Awesome' (Au/St) SPop
- 'Aztec' (Au/d) WAln
- 'Baby Blue' (Au) NDro WHil
- 'Bacchante' (Au/d) SPop WAln
- 'Bacchus' (Au/A) GAgs NDro WHil
- 'Baggage' (Au/St) GAgs ITim NDro SPop WHil
- 'Bailey Boy' (Au/B) NDro
- 'Bakerloo Line' (Au/S) **new** NDro
- 'Baker's Boy' (Au/d) SPop
- 'Ballynahinch' (Au) ITim
- 'Baltic Amber' (Au/d) GAgs NDro SPop WAln WHil XBar
- 'Bank Error' (Au/S) NDro SPop WAln
- 'Barbara Mason' (Au) WAln
- 'Barbarella' (Au/S) NDro SPop XBar
- 'Barber's Pole' (Au/St) NDro
- Barnhaven Border hybrids (Au/B) XBar
- Barnhaven doubles (Au/d) GAbr NSum XBar
- 'Barr Beacon' (Au/A) ITim NDro
- 'Bartl' (Au/A) EBee
- 'Basilio' (Au/S) NDro
- 'Basuto' (Au/A) GAgs ITim NDro SPop WHil
- 'Beatrice' (Au/A) CTri GAgs NDro NHpl SPop WFar WHil WIce XBar
- 'Beauty of Bath' (Au/S) WAln
- 'Beckminster' (Au/A) WAln
- 'Bedford Lad' (Au/A) NDro
- 'Beechen Green' (Au/S) ITim SPop
- 'Beeches Variegated' (Au/A/v) EBee WFar
- 'Belgravia Gold' (Au/B) NDro
- 'Bellamy Pride' (Au/B) NDro SPop
- 'Belle Zana' (Au/S) GAgs NDro SPop
- 'Bellini' (Au/d) XBar
- 'Ben Lawers' (Au/S) SPop
- 'Ben Wyves' (Au/S) NDro SPop
- 'Bendigo' (Au/S) NDro SPop WAln
- 'Bengal Rose' (Au/S) SPop
- 'Benny Green' (Au/S) NDro SPop XBar
- 'Beppi' (Au/B) NDro WHil
- 'Bessie' (Au/d) XBar
- 'Best Wishes' (Au/F) NDro
- 'Bethan McSparron' (Au/B) NDro
- 'Betty Sherriff' (Au/B) **new** GAbr
- 'Betty Stewart' (Au/A) WAln
- 'Betty Wilson' (Au/St) NDro SPop
- 'Bewitched' (Au/A) NDro WAln
- 'Big Thrill' (Au) **new** WFar
- 'Bilbao' (Au/A) WAln
- 'Bilbo Baggins' (Au/A) NDro SPop WAln
- 'Bill Bailey' (Au/d) NDro
- 'Bill Bray' (Au/A) **new** SPop
- 'Bilton' (Au/S) SPop
- 'Bingley Folk' (Au/B) NDro SPop
- 'Bingley Snowflake' (Au/B) NDro
- 'Bisto' (Au/S) SPop WAln
- 'Bitterne Beauty' (Au/d) SPop
- 'Bitterne Bounty' (Au/d) SPop
- 'Bitterne Buttercup' (Au/d) SPop
- 'Bitterne Delight' (Au/d) SPop
- 'Bitterne Nighthawk' (Au/d) SPop
- 'Bitterne Primrose' (Au/d) SPop
- 'Bizarre' (Au) NDro
- 'Black Adder' (Au/S) SPop
- 'Black Diamond' (Au/d) SPop WHil XBar
- 'Black Jack'[PBR] (Au/d) CAby CWCL ECtt GBin MHol NHpl NLar WIce WTor

- 'Black Knight' (Au/d) SPop
- 'Blackberry Crush' (Au) NDro
- 'Blackfield' (Au/S) SPop
- 'Blackhill' (Au/S) ITim NHpl SPop
- 'Blackpool Rock' (Au/St) CWCL NDro SPop XBar
- 'Blairside Yellow' (Au/B) LLHF NDro NSla
- 'Blakeney' (Au/d) SPop
- 'Blossom' (Au/A) SPop XBar
- 'Blossom Dearie' (Au/St) SPop
- 'Blue Angel' (Au/S) SPop
- 'Blue Bella' (Au/B) NDro SPop
- 'Blue Belle' (Au/B) NDro
- 'Blue Bonnet' (Au/A/d) GAgs NDro WAln
- 'Blue Boy' (Au/S) NDro SPop WHil
- 'Blue Chip' (Au/S) GAbr NDro SPop WHil
- 'Blue Cliff' (Au/S) NDro SPop WAln
- 'Blue Fire' (Au/S) SPop
- 'Blue Frills' (Au/d) NDro WAln
- 'Blue Heaven' (Au/A) NDro SPop
- 'Blue Jean' (Au/S) SPop
- 'Blue Lace' (Au/A) WAln
- 'Blue Merle' (Au/B) NDro
- 'Blue Mist' (Au/B) NDro
- 'Blue Night' (Au/B) ITim
- 'Blue Nile' (Au/S) SPop
- 'Blue Ridge' (Au/A) NDro SPop WAln
- 'Blue Skies' (Au/St) NDro SPop
- 'Blue Veil' (Au/S) SPop
- 'Blue Velvet' (Au/B) GAbr GQue LLHF NDro NHpl SPop WHil XBar
- 'Blue Wave' (Au/d) CBor SPop
- 'Blue Waves' (Au/B) NDro
- 'Blue Yodeler' (Au/A) NDro NSum SPop WFar WHil XBar
- 'Blue Yonder' (Au/S) ITim WAln
- 'Blush Baby' (Au/St) EBee GAgs NDro NSum NWad SPop WHil XBar
- 'Blyth Spirit' (Au/A) NDro SPop WAln XBar
- 'Bob Dingley' (Au/A) SPop
- 'Bob Lancashire' (Au/S) ITim NDro SPop XBar
- 'Bokay' (Au/d) WAln
- 'Bold Tartan' (Au/St) NDro SPop
- 'Bolero' (Au/A) SPop WAln
- 'Bonafide' (Au/d) SPop WAln
- 'Bonanza' (Au/S) SPop WAln
- 'Bookham Firefly' (Au/A) GAgs NDro SPop WHil
- 'Border Bandit' (Au/B) GAbr NDro SPop XBar
- 'Border Beauty' (Au/St) NDro
- 'Border Blue' (Au/B) NDro
- 'Border Patrol' (Au/B) ITim NDro
- 'Border Tawny' (Au/B) NDro
- 'Boromir' (Au/A) NDro SPop WAln
- 'Bournebrook' (Au/A) WAln
- 'Bowen's Blue' (Au/B) NDro SPop
- 'Bradford City' (Au/A) CFis EBee GAgs NDro SPop WFar WHil XBar
- 'Bradmore Bluebell' (Au/B) GAbr NDro
- 'Bramley Rose' (Au/B) SPop
- 'Bramshill' (Au/S) NDro
- 'Bran' (Au/B) NDro
- 'Brandaris' (Au/A) WAln
- 'Branston' (Au/d) XBar
- 'Brasso' (Au/S) NDro SPop WAln XBar
- 'Brazen Hussy' (Au/d) WAln
- 'Brazil' (Au/S) EBee GAbr GAgs NDro SPop WHil
- 'Brazos River' (Au/A) GAgs NDro SPop
- 'Breckland Joy' (Au/A) NDro WAln
- 'Brenda's Choice' (Au/A) GAgs NDro NSum SPop
- 'Brenda's Dilemma' (Au/S) NDro
- 'Brentford Bees' (Au/St) NDro
- 'Brickmaker' (Au/d) SPop
- 'Bright Eyes' (Au/A) XBar
- 'Bright Ginger' (Au/S) NDro SPop WAln
- 'Brigitte' (Au/A) **new** XBar
- 'Brimstone and Treacle' (Au/d) SPop WAln
- 'Brixton' (Au/S) NDro
- 'Broad Gold' (Au/A) NDro SPop XBar
- 'Broadwell Gold' (Au/B) NDro NSum SPop
- 'Brocade' (Au/St) NDro
- 'Brompton' (Au/S) SPop
- 'Brookfield' (Au/S) GAbr NDro NHpl SPop WHil XBar
- 'Broughton' (Au/S) NDro SPop
- 'Brown Ben' (Au/A) SPop WFar WHil
- 'Brown Bess' (Au/A) GAbr GAgs ITim SPop WHil
- 'Brown Sugar' (Au/d) SPop
- 'Brownie' (Au/B) GAbr GAgs NBir NDro NSum SPop WHil XBar
- 'Brownie Guider' (Au/B) NDro
- 'Brownie Point' (Au/B) NDro
- 'Brunhilde' (Au/B) NDro
- 'Bucks Green' (Au/S) GAbr NDro SPop
- 'Buffy' (Au/St) NDro
- 'Buoyance' (Au/A) WAln
- 'Burnished Gold' (Au/d) WAln
- 'Bush Baby' (Au/B) NDro
- 'Buttercup' (Au/d) SPop
- 'Buttermere' (Au/d) WAln
- 'Butterscotch' (Au/d) SPop
- 'Butterwick' (Au/A) GAbr GAgs ITim NDro NEgg SPop XBar
- 'C.F. Hill' (Au/A) SPop
- 'C.G. Haysom' (Au/S) NDro SPop WHil
- 'C.W. Needham' (Au/A) GAgs ITim NDro SPop XBar
- 'Cadiz Bay' (Au/d) WAln
- 'Café au Lait' (Au/A) XBar
- 'Calico' (Au/d) **new** XBar
- 'Callisto' (Au/d) SPop
- 'Calypso' (Au/d) NDro SPop WAln
- 'Cambodunum' (Au/A) NDro NSum SPop WFar WHil
- 'Camelot' (Au/d) NDro SPop WFar WHil XBar
- 'Cameo' (Au/A) NHpl
- 'Cameo Beauty' (Au/d) NDro SPop
- 'Camilla' (Au/A) WAln
- 'Candy Stripe' (Au/St) NDro SPop
- 'Cannelle' (Au/d) XBar
- 'Cappela' (Au/d) SPop WAln
- 'Caramel' (Au/A) WAln
- 'Cardinal Red' (Au/d) NDro SPop
- 'Cardington' (Au/A) WAln
- 'Carioca' (Au/A) WAln
- 'Carmel' (Au/d) GAbr NDro SPop WAln
- 'Carnaval' (Au/B) XBar
- 'Carne' (Au/d) NDro
- 'Carnival' (Au/A) WAln
- 'Carole' (Au/A) SPop WHil
- 'Carousel' (Au/B) NDro
- 'Carreras' (Au) NDro
- 'Carsa Wakes' (Au/d) NDro SPop WAln
- 'Carzon' (Au/A) NDro
- 'Caslon' (Au/A) SPop
- 'Catherine Wheel' (Au/St) NDro SPop
- 'Catta Ha' (Au/d) NDro
- 'Celtic One' (Au/St) NDro SPop
- 'Ceri Nicolle' (Au/B) NDro
- 'Chaffinch' (Au/S) GAbr GAgs NDro SPop
- 'Chamois' (Au/B) GAbr NDro WHil
- 'Chanel' (Au/S) SPop WAln
- 'Chantilly Cream' (Au/d) NDro
- 'Charisma' (Au/St) **new** NDro
- 'Charles Bronson' (Au/d) GAgs NDro SPop WAln XBar

- 'Charles Rennie' (Au/B) NDro SPop WHil XBar
- 'Charlie's Aunt' (Au/A) NDro WAln
- 'Charlotte' (Au/B) NDro
- 'Charlotte Brookes' (Au/d) SPop WAln
- 'Checkmate' (Au/d) SPop WAln XBar
- 'Cheeky' (Au/d) SPop
- 'Chelsea Bridge' (Au/A) GAgs NDro SPop WHil
- 'Chelsea Girl' (Au/d) NDro
- 'Cheops' (Au/A) GAgs NDro NEgg NSum SPop XBar
- 'Cherille' (Au/S) NDro
- 'Cherry' (Au/S) NDro SPop
- 'Cherry Picker' (Au/A) GAgs NDro SPop
- 'Chestnut' (Au/B) NDro
- 'Cheyenne' (Au/S) GAbr GAgs NDro SPop
- 'Chiffon' (Au/S) GAbr GAgs NDro NSum SPop
- 'Chiquita' (Au/d) NDro SPop
- 'Chirichua' (Au/S) WAln
- 'Chloë' (Au/S) NDro NHpl SPop
- 'Chloris' (Au/S) SPop
- 'Choir Boy' (Au/A) WAln
- 'Chorister' (Au/S) EBee GAbr GAgs ITim NDro NSum SPop WHil
- 'Chyne' (Au) NDro
- 'Cicero' (Au/A) WAln
- 'Cinders' (Au/St) NDro SPop
- 'Cindy' (Au/A) NDro
- 'Cinnamon' (Au/d) GAgs ITim NDro SPop WFar WHil XBar
- 'Ciribiribin' (Au/A) WAln
- 'Citron-Ella' (Au/d) SPop
- 'Clara' (Au/d) SPop WFar
- 'Clare' (Au/S) NDro SPop
- 'Classy Stripe' (Au/St) ITim
- 'Clatter-Ha' (Au/d) NSum SPop WHil
- 'Claud Wilson' (Au/St) NDro SPop
- 'Claudia Taylor' (Au) SPop
- 'Cleft Stick' (Au) NDro
- 'Clipper' (Au/S) SPop
- 'Cloth of Gold' (Au/A) NDro SPop
- 'Clotted Cream' (Au/B) NDro
- 'Clouded Yellow' (Au/S) GAbr NDro SPop WHil
- 'Cloudy Bay' (Au/B) GAbr NDro WCot
- 'Cloverdale' (Au/d) WAln
- 'Clunie' (Au/S) NDro SPop XBar
- 'Cobbydale Orange' (Au/B) **new** NDro
- 'Cobden Meadows' (Au/A) SPop WAln
- 'Cocoa' (Au/d) XBar
- 'Coffee' (Au/S) NDro SPop WFar WHil
- 'Coffee and Cream' (Au/d) SPop
- 'Colbury' (Au/S) NDro
- 'Coleman' (Au/d) SPop
- 'Colonel Champney' (Au/S) NDro SPop
- 'Colonel Mustard' (Au/d) **new** NDro XBar
- 'Comet' (Au/S) NDro NSum
- 'Connaught Court' (Au/A) LLHF NDro
- 'Connie' (Au/S) SPop
- 'Conquistador' (Au/A) NDro WAln
- 'Conservative' (Au/S) NDro
- 'Consett' (Au/S) SPop WHil
- 'Cooks Hill' (Au/d) WAln
- 'Cooper's Gold' (Au/B) NDro
- 'Coppi' (Au/A) NDro SPop
- 'Coral' (Au/S) ITim
- 'Corn Dolly' (Au/S) SPop
- 'Cornish Cream' (Au/B) NDro
- 'Cornmeal' (Au/S) GAgs NDro SPop WHil XBar
- 'Corntime' (Au/S) SPop WAln
- 'Corporal Jones' (Au/S) SPop
- 'Corrie Files' (Au/d) SPop WAln
- 'Cortez Silver' (Au/S) SPop
- 'Cortina' (Au/S) GAgs ITim NDro SPop WHil
- 'Countdown' (Au/St) SPop
- 'County Park Red' (Au/B) NDro
- 'Coventry Street' (Au/S) NDro NSum SPop
- 'Crackling Rosie' (A/d) WAln
- 'Craig Dhu' (Au/B) SPop
- 'Craig Nordie' (Au/B) NDro
- 'Craig Vaughan' (Au/A) NDro NSum SPop XBar
- 'Cranborne' (Au/A) SPop WAln
- 'Crecy' (Au/A) SPop WAln WHil
- 'Cressida' (Au/d) SPop
- 'Crimple' (Au/S) NDro SPop WHil
- 'Crimson Black' (Au/B) SPop
- 'Crimson Glow' (Au/d) EBee ITim LCro LOPS NDro NSum SPop WHil XBar
- 'Crimson Maid' (Au/d) SPop
- 'Crinoline' (Au/S) NDro SPop
- 'Cuckoo Fair' (Au/S) ECtt GAgs NDro SPop WFar
- 'Cuddles' (Au/A) NDro SPop WAln
- 'Curry Blend' (Au/B) NDro NWad SPop WHil
- 'Cutie Pie' (Au/St) NDro SPop
- 'Cuttlefish' (Au/St) SPop
- 'Cyrn Las' (Au/St) SPop
- 'D.S.J.' (Au/S) NDro
- 'Daftie Green' (Au/S) NDro
- 'Daisy Wood' (Au/d) **new** SPop
- 'Dakota' (Au/S) SPop
- 'Dales Red' (Au/B) GAgs NDro NHpl NSum SPop WHil
- 'Damerham' (Au/A) SPop
- 'Dan Tiger' (Au/St) GAgs SPop WHil
- 'Daniel' (Au/d) **new** XBar
- 'Daniel' (Au/A) NDro SPop WAln
- 'Daniel T. Taylor' (Au/A) NDro WAln
- 'Daphnis' (Au/S) NDro SPop
- 'Darent Tiger' (Au/St) NDro SPop XBar
- 'Dark Eyes' (Au/d) GAgs NDro NSum SPop WHil
- 'Dark Lady' (Au/A) WAln
- 'D'Artagnan' (Au/B) NDro
- 'Darth Vader' (Au/d) XBar
- 'David Beckham' (Au/d) NDro SPop WAln
- 'Day by Day' (Au/St) NDro SPop
- 'Deal' (Au/S) NDro
- 'Deckchair' (Au/St) NDro SPop
- 'Dedham' (Au/d) WAln
- 'Del Boy' (Au/A) SPop WAln
- 'Delicious' (Au/St) SPop
- 'Delilah' (Au/d) ITim NDro NSum SPop WFar WHil
- 'Denise' (Au/S) WAln
- 'Denna Snuffer' (Au/d) GAbr NDro SPop
- 'Derek's Fanfare' (Au/St) **new** NDro
- 'Derrill' (Au/B) NDro SPop
- 'Derwent Water' (Au/S) **new** NDro
- 'Deuce of Hearts' (Au/St) NDro
- 'Devon Cream' (Au/d) GAgs NDro SPop XBar
- 'Devon's Road' (Au/S) **new** NDro
- 'Diamond' (Au/d) SPop
- 'Diamond Dust' (Au/B) NDro
- 'Diane' (Au/A) NDro
- 'Dick Rogers' (Au/B) NDro
- 'Dido' (Au/B) XBar
- 'Digby' (Au/d) NDro WAln
- 'Digit' (Au/d) NDro WAln
- 'Dilemma' (Au/A) SPop
- 'Dill' (Au/A) NDro NSum SPop WHil
- 'Dilly Dilly' (Au/A) NDro SPop

- 'Divint Dunch' (Au/A) LLHF NDro SPop WHil
- 'Doctor Duthie' (Au/S) SPop
- 'Doctor Lennon's White' (Au/B) GAbr MHer NDro NWad SPop WHil XBar
- 'Doctor Woolhead' (Au/S) SPop
- 'Dolly' (Au/B) NDro
- I - 'Dolly Mixture' (Au/B) new XBar
- 'Dolly Viney' (Au/d) WAln
- 'Don Carlos' (Au/d) XBar
- 'Donhead' (Au/A) GAgs ITim NDro SPop WHil
- 'Donn' (Au/d) SPop WAln
- 'Donna Clancy' (Au/S) NDro XBar
- 'Dorado' (Au/d) SPop WAln
- 'Doreen Stephens' (Au/A) NDro
- 'Doris Jean' (Au/A) NDro SPop
- 'Doublet' (Au/d) GAgs NDro NSum SPop WHil
- 'Doubloon' (Au/d) XBar
- 'Doublure' (Au/d) GAbr NDro SPop WHil
- 'Douglas Bader' (Au/A) GAgs ITim NDro NSum SPop WHil
- 'Douglas Black' (Au/S) CPla GAbr GAgs NDro SPop WHil
- 'Douglas Green' (Au/S) NDro SPop
- 'Douglas White' (Au/S) SPop
- 'Dovedale' (Au/S) NDro SPop
- DOWNTOWN DOUBLES (Au/d) SPop
- 'Doyen' (Au/d) ITim NDro NHpl SPop WAln WHil
- 'Dragon's Hoard' (Au/A) WAln
- 'Drax' (Au/A) SPop WAln
- 'Dream' (Au/St) SPop
- 'Dreamcatcher' (Au/S) new SPop
- 'Dreamweaver' (Au/S) SPop
- 'Dubarii' (Au/A) NDro SPop WAln
- 'Duchess of Malfi' (Au/S) SPop
- 'Duchess of York' (Au) LLHF
- 'Duke of Edinburgh' (Au/B) NDro
- 'Dusky Girl' (Au/A) NDro WAln
- 'Dusky Maiden' (Au/A) GAbr GAgs NDro NSum SPop WHil
- 'Dusky Yellow' (Au/B) NDro
- 'Dusty Miller' (Au/B) EBee NBir
- 'Eastern Promise' (Au/A) GAgs NDro NSum SPop WHil
- 'Eaton Dawn' (Au/S) SPop XBar
- 'Ed Spivey' (Au/A) NDro
- 'Eddy Gordon' (Au/A) WAln
- 'Eden Alexander' (Au/B) NDro
- 'Eden Amethyst' (Au/B) NDro SPop
- 'Eden Aramis' (Au/B) NDro
- 'Eden Blue Star' (Au/B) GAbr GAgs NDro NSum SPop WFar
- 'Eden Bonanza' (Au/B) SPop
- 'Eden Bramley' (Au/B) NDro
- 'Eden Brownie' (Au/B) SPop
- 'Eden Carmine' (Au/B) MHer NDro SPop XBar
- 'Eden Cynthia' (Au/B) SPop
- 'Eden Dark Eyes' (Au/B) NDro SPop
- 'Eden David' (Au/B) NDro SCob SPop WFar WHil
- 'Eden Ensign' (Au/B) SPop WFar
- 'Eden Fanfare' (Au/B) NDro WFar
- 'Eden Glow' (Au/B) NDro SPop
- 'Eden Goldfinch' (Au/B) NDro SPop WFar
- 'Eden Grace' (Au/B) SPop
- 'Eden Greenfinch' (Au/B) NDro SPop XBar
- 'Eden Lilactime' (Au/B) NDro WFar
- 'Eden Midas' (Au/B) SPop
- 'Eden Moonlight' (Au/B) NDro SPop WHil
- 'Eden Porthos' (Au/B) NDro
- 'Eden Rhiann' (Au/B) NDro SPop
- 'Eden Royalty' (Au/B) new WFar
- 'Eden Ruby Star' (Au/B) new NDro
- 'Eden Simon' (Au/B) new NDro
- 'Eden Sunrise' (Au/B) NDro
- 'Eden Surprise' (Au/B) NDro
- 'Edinburgh' (Au/A) WAln
- 'Edith Major' (Au/d) NDro SPop WHil
- 'Edward Sweeney' (Au/S) WAln
- 'Eggborough' (Au/A) SPop
- 'Eglinton' (Au) NDro NSum SPop
- 'Eileen K' (Au/S) NDro
- 'El Dorado' (Au/d) new SPop
- 'El Zoco' (Au/S) SPop
- 'Elara' (Au/d) SPop
- 'Elegance' (Au/S) SPop WFar
- 'Elf Star' (Au/A) NSum SPop WAln
- 'Eli Jenkins' (Au) WAln
- 'Elizabeth Ann' (Au/A) NDro SPop
- 'Ellen Thompson' (Au/A) NDro SPop WHil XBar
- 'Ellie May' (Au/S) XBar
- 'Elsie May' (Au/A) ITim NDro SPop WHil
- 'Elsinore' (Au/S) SPop
- 'Emberglow' (Au/d) SPop WAln
- 'Embley' (Au/S) NDro NHpl SPop
- 'Emery Down' (Au/S) NDro SPop
- 'Emmett Smith' (Au/A) NDro SPop WAln
- 'Ems Blue' (Au/B) WAln
- 'Ems Choice' (Au/B) WAln
- 'Ems Funny Face' (Au/B) NDro
- 'Enigma' (Au/S) SPop
- 'Enlightened' (Au/A) NDro
- 'Envy' (Au/S) WAln
- 'Erica' (Au/A) NDro NSum SPop WHil XBar
- 'Erjon' (Au/S) NDro SPop
- 'Error' (Au/S) NDro
- 'Eschman Starflower' (Au/S) WHil
- 'Esso' (Au/S) WAln
- 'Ethel' (Au) CBor NDro
- 'Ethel Wild' (Au/d) SPop
- 'Ethel Wilkes' (Au/d) WAln
- 'Etna' (Au/S) NDro
- 'Europa' (Au/d) SPop
- 'Euston Road' (Au/S) NDro
- 'Eve Guest' (Au/A) NDro SPop WAln
- 'Eventide' (Au/S) SPop
- 'Everest Blue' (Au/S) GAbr GAgs NDro SPop XBar
- 'Excalibur' (Au/d) GAgs NDro NSum SPop
- 'Exhibition Blau' (Exhibition Series) (Au/B) WHil
- 'Eye Candy' (Au/St) SPop
- 'Eyeopener' (Au/A) NDro NSum SPop WHil
- 'Fabuloso' (Au/St) NDro SPop
- 'Fairy' (Au/A) WAln
- 'Fairy Light' (Au/S) NDro SPop
- 'Fairy Queen' (Au/S) NDro
- 'Falcon' (Au/S) SPop
- 'Falstaff' (Au/d) WAln
- 'Fanciful' (Au/S) NDro SPop WHil XBar
- 'Fancy Free' (Au) SPop
- 'Fancy Pants' (Au/S) NDro SPop
- 'Fandancer' (Au/A) WAln
- 'Fandango' (Au/St) NDro
- 'Fanfare' (Au/S) NDro WHil
- 'Fanny Meerbeck' (Au/S) GAbr NDro SPop WHil
- 'Fantasia' (Au/d) SPop
- 'Faro' (Au/S) NDro SPop
- 'Favourite' (Au/S) GAbr GAgs ITim NDro SPop WHil XBar
- 'Fearless' (Au/S) WAln
- 'Femme Fatale' (Au/St) NDro
- 'Fen Tiger' (Au/St) SPop
- 'Fenby' (Au/S) SPop

- 'Fennay' (Au/S) NSum
- 'Ferrybridge' (Au/A) NDro WAln
- 'Fiddler's Green' (Au/d) NDro NWad SPop WCot XBar
- 'Figaro' (Au/S) NDro SPop XBar
- 'Figurine' (Au/d) WAln
- 'Finchfield' (Au/A) NDro WAln
- 'Fine Art' (Au/S) NDro
- 'Finlay Thomas' (Au/S) SPop
- 'Finley' (Au/B) NDro
- 'Firecracker' (Au) SPop WAln
- 'Firenze' (Au/A) SPop
- 'Firsby' (Au/d) NDro SPop WHil
- 'First Green' (Au/St) SPop
- 'First Lady' (Au/A) SPop WAln WFar
- 'First Light' (Au/B) NDro SPop
- 'Fishtoft' (Au/d) SPop
- 'Fitzroy' (Au/d) SPop
- 'Fleecy' (Au/S) SPop
- 'Fleet Street' (Au/S) GAgs NDro SPop WFar WHil
- 'Fleminghouse' (Au/S) NDro SPop
- 'Flirty' (Au/St) NDro
- 'Florence Baker' (Au/S) NDro
- 'Florence Brown' (Au/S) SPop
- 'Fluffy Duckling' (Au/S) NDro SPop
- 'For You' (Au/St) NDro SPop
- 'Forest Beech' (Au/d) SPop
- 'Forest Bordeaux' (Au/d) SPop
- 'Forest Bracken' (Au/d) GAbr SPop
- 'Forest Burgundy' (Au/d) SPop
- 'Forest Burnt Gold' (Au/d) SPop
- 'Forest Cappuccino' (Au/d) GAgs SPop
- 'Forest Coffee' (Au/d) NDro WHil
- 'Forest Duet' (Au/d) NDro SPop WFar
- 'Forest Fire' (Au/d) GAbr NSum SPop
- 'Forest Garnet' (Au/d) **new** WHil
- 'Forest Glade' (Au/d) SPop
- 'Forest Glow' (Au/d) SPop
- 'Forest Gorse' (Au/d) SPop
- 'Forest Heath' (Au/d) SPop
- 'Forest Lemon' (Au/d) SPop WHil
- 'Forest Lime' (Au/d) SPop
- 'Forest Pecan' (Au/d) SPop
- 'Forest Pines' (Au/S) SPop
- 'Forest Purple Plum' (Au/d) NDro
- 'Forest Rose' (Au/d) SPop
- 'Forest Shade' (Au/d) SPop WHil
- 'Forest Sunburst' (Au/d) SPop
- 'Forest Sunfire' (Au/d) SPop
- 'Forest Sunlight' (Au/d) SPop
- 'Forest Sunshine' (Au/d) SPop
- 'Forest Twilight' (Au/d) SPop WHil
- 'Foundling' (Au) ITim
- 'Foxfire' (Au/A) WAln
- 'Foxy' (Au/B) **new** NDro
- 'Fradley' (Au/A) NDro WAln WFar WHil
- 'Frances' (Au/d) SPop
- 'Françoise' (Au/d) XBar
- 'Frank Bailey' (Au/d) SPop WAln
- 'Frank Crosland' (Au/A) NDro NSum SPop WHil
- 'Frank Faulkner' (Au/A) WAln
- 'Frank Hemmingway' (Au/B) **new** NDro
- 'Frank Jenning' (Au/A) NDro WAln
- 'Fred Booley' (Au/d) LLHF NDro NSum SPop WFar WHil XBar
- 'Fred Livesley' (Au/A) WAln
- 'Freestyle' (Au/B) WAln
- 'Fresco' (Au/A) SPop WAln
- 'Freya' (Au/S) NDro SPop XBar
- 'Fridl' (Au) **new** EBee
- 'Friends of Ashwood' (Au/S) NDro
- 'Friskney' (Au/d) SPop WAln
- 'Frittenden Yellow' (Au/B) SPop
- 'Frosty' (Au/S) NDro SPop
- 'Fuller's Red' (Au/S) ITim NDro SPop WHil XBar
- 'Funny Valentine' (Au/d) NSum SPop WHil
- 'G.L. Taylor' (Au/A) NDro
- 'Gaia' (Au/d) SPop WHil
- 'Gail Atkinson' (Au/A) SPop WAln
- 'Galatea' (Au/S) SPop
- 'Galator' (Au/A) WAln
- 'Galen' (Au/A) SPop
- 'Ganymede' (Au/d) SPop WAln
- 'Gary Pallister' (Au/A) SPop WAln
- 'Gas Lane' (Au/A) SPop
- 'Gay Crusader' (Au/A) GAbr NDro NSum SPop WFar WHil
- 'Gazza' (Au/A) WAln
- 'Gee Cross' (Au/A) NDro NSum SPop
- 'Geldersome Green' (Au/S) NDro SPop
- 'Geldersome Green No. 2' (Au/S) ITim
- 'Gemini' (Au/S) NDro SPop
- 'Generosity' (Au/A) GAgs NDro NSum WHil
- 'Geoffrey Bick' (Au/A) SPop
- 'Geordie' (Au/A) SPop WAln
- 'George Edge' (Au/B) NDro
- 'George Harrison' (Au/B) NDro
- 'George Jennings' (Au/A) NDro SPop
- 'George Swinford's Leathercoat' (Au/B) NDro
- 'Geronimo' (Au/S) GAbr NDro SPop
- 'Gild Green' (Au/S) NDro
- 'Gimli' (Au/A) WAln
- 'Ginger Spice' (Au/B) NDro
- 'Girl Guide' (Au/S) SPop WHil
- 'Gizabroon' (Au/S) CBor CFis EBee GAbr NDro NEgg NLar SPop WHil XBar
- 'Glazebrook' (Au/S) SPop
- 'Gleam' (Au/S) EDAr LLHF NDro NSum SPop WHil XBar
- 'Glencoe' (Au/S) NDro SPop
- 'Gleneagles' (Au/S) NDro
- 'Glenelg' (Au/S) GAbr ITim NDro NSum SPop WHil XBar
- 'Glenluce' (Au/S) NDro SPop
- 'Gloire de Dijon' (Au/S) XBar
- 'Gnome' (Au/B) GAbr NDro
- 'Goeblii' (Au/B) NDro SPop WHil XBar
- 'Gold Seal' (Au/d) SPop
- 'Gold Seam' (Au/A) WAln WHil
- 'Gold Star' (Au/St) NDro SPop
- 'Golden Boy' (Au/A) NDro NSum SPop WAln
- 'Golden Chartreuse' (Au/d) NDro SPop
- 'Golden Fleece' (Au/S) NDro SPop
- 'Golden Girl' (Au/A) SPop WAln
- 'Golden Glory' (Au/A) NDro WAln
- 'Golden Harvest' (Au/A) SPop
- 'Golden Hill' (Au/S) ITim SPop
- 'Golden Hind' (Au/d) GAbr GAgs NDro NSum SPop WHil
- 'Golden Splendour' (Au/d) GAgs ITim NDro NSum SPop WFar WHil
- 'Golden Wedding' (Au/A) GAgs NDro SPop WAln WHil
- 'Goldie' (Au/S) NDro
- 'Goldwin' (Au/A) NDro NSum
- 'Gollum' (Au/A) NDro SPop WAln WFar
- 'Good Report' (Au/A) NDro NSum SPop WFar WHil
- 'Goody Goody' (Au/St) NDro SPop
- 'Googie' (Au/d) SPop

– 'Gordon Files' (Au/S) WAln
– 'Gorey' (Au/A) NDro SPop WHil
– 'Gorgeous George' (Au/St) SPop
– 'Grabley' (Au/S) NDro SPop
– 'Grace Ellen' (Au/S) NDro SPop
– 'Gracie Lou' (Au/B) new NDro
– 'Grandad's Favourite' (Au/B) NDro SPop
– 'Grasmere' (Au/d) NDro SPop
– 'Green Café' (Au/S) SPop
– 'Green Finger' (Au/S) SPop
– 'Green Heart' (Au/S) SPop
– 'Green Isle' (Au/S) GAbr NDro SPop XBar
– 'Green Jacket' (Au/S) NDro SPop
– 'Green Lane' (Au/S) XBar
– 'Green Meadows' (Au/S) SPop
– 'Green Mustard' (Au/S) NDro SPop
– 'Green Parrot' (Au/S) GAbr
– 'Green Shank' (Au/S) NDro SPop WHil XBar
– 'Greenfield's Fancy' (Au) EBee
– 'Greenheart' (Au/S) SPop
– 'Greenpeace' (Au/S) GAbr GAgs NDro SPop XBar
– 'Grenache' (Au/B) XBar
– 'Greswolde' (Au/d) SPop
– 'Greta' (Au/S) GAbr GAgs NDro SPop WGwG WHil XBar
– 'Gretna Green' (Au/S) SPop
– 'Grey Bonnet' (Au/S) SPop
– 'Grey Cloud' (Au/B) NDro WHil
– 'Grey Day' (Au/S) NDro
– 'Grey Friar' (Au/S) SPop
– 'Grey Hawk' (Au/S) NDro SPop
– 'Grey Ladywood' (Au/d) SPop
– 'Grey Lag' (Au/S) NSum SPop WHil XBar
– 'Grey Monarch' (Au/S) GAbr SPop WHil XBar
– 'Grey Owl' (Au/S) NDro SPop
– 'Grey Shrike' (Au/S) NDro SPop
– 'Grizedale' (Au/S) SPop
– 'Groupie' (Au/St) SPop
– 'Grüner Veltliner' (Au/S) GAbr SPop
– 'Guinea' (Au/S) GAbr ITim NDro SPop
– 'Gwai Loh' (Au/B) NDro
– 'Gwen' (Au/A) NDro SPop WAln XBar
– 'Gwen Baker' (Au/d) NDro SPop WAln
– 'Gwenda' (Au/A) NDro SPop WAln WHil
– 'Gypsy Boy' (Au/A) WAln
– 'H Old Gold' (Au/S) NDro
– 'Habanera' (Au/A) NDro NSum SPop WFar
– 'Haffner' (Au/S) NDro SPop
– 'Hallmark' (Au/A) NDro WAln
– 'Handsome Lass' (Au/St) GAgs NDro SPop XBar
– 'Hannah' (Au/A) WAln
– 'Harlequin' (Au/B) NDro
– 'Harmony' (Au/B) NDro NSum XBar
– 'Harry Armitage' (Au/B) NDro
– 'Harry Hotspur' (Au/A) GAgs NDro NSum SPop WFar WHil
– 'Harry 'O'' (Au/S) NDro SPop
– 'Harthorpeburn' (Au/B) NDro
– 'Harvest Glow' (Au/S) NDro SPop WFar WHil
– 'Harvest Gold' (Au/S) NDro
– 'Havana' (Au/d) SPop WAln
– 'Hawkwood' (Au/S) EBee GAgs NDro NEgg WHil XBar
– 'Hazel' (Au/B) NDro XBar
– 'Hazel' (Au/A) NDro SPop WHil
– 'Headdress' (Au/S) SPop
– 'Heady' (Au/A) GAgs NDro SPop WHil XBar
– 'Heart of Gold' (Au/A) NDro SPop WAln
– 'Hearts of Oak' (Au/A) WAln
– 'Heaven Scent' (Au) NDro WHil
– 'Hebers' (Au) NDro SPop WAln
– 'Helen' (Au/S) NDro SPop WHil
– 'Helen Barter' (Au/S) NDro NSum WHil
– 'Helen Ruane' (Au/d) GAgs GKev GQue SPop WFar
– 'Helena' (Au/S) NDro SPop WAln WHil
– 'Helena Brown' (Au/S) SPop
– 'Helena Dean' (Au/d) SPop WAln
– 'Helluinn' (Au/d) SPop
– 'Henry's Bane' (Au/St) NDro SPop
– 'Her Nibs' (Au/St) NDro SPop
– 'Herbert Dawson' (Au/d) new SPop
– 'Hermia' (Au/A) SPop WHil
– 'Hetty Woolf' (Au/S) GAbr NDro SPop
– 'Hew Dalrymple' (Au/S) NDro SPop
– 'Highland Park' (Au/A) GAgs NDro SPop WHil
– 'Hillhook' (Au/A) NSum WAln
– 'Hillview Hermes' (Au/S) WHil
– 'Hinton Admiral' (Au/S) GAbr GAgs NDro WHil XBar
– 'Hinton Fields' (Au/S) EBee GAbr NDro NEgg SPop WFar WHil
– 'Hobby Horse' (Au/St) ITim
– 'Holyrood' (Au/S) GAbr ITim NDro NHpl XBar
– 'Honey' (Au/d) GAbr NDro NEgg NSum SPop
– 'Honeydawn' (Au/B) NDro
– 'Hopleys Coffee' (Au/d) GAbr NDro SPop WAln
– 'Hopton Gem' (Au/B) NDro
– 'Hot Chocolate' (Au/d) SPop
– 'Howard Telford' (Au/A) SPop
– 'Hughie' (Au/A) WAln
– 'Humphrey' (Au/S) WAln
– 'Hunter's Moon' (Au/d) new SPop
– 'Hurstwood Midnight' (Au) XBar
* – 'Hyacinth' (Au/S) EBee
– 'Iago' (Au/S) SPop
– 'Ian Greville' (Au/A) NDro SPop
– 'Ibis' (Au/A) WAln
– 'Ice Cap' (Au/d) SPop
– 'Ice Maiden' (Au/A) GAbr NDro NSum SPop WHil
– 'Icon' (Au/St) SPop
– 'Idmiston' (Au/S) GAbr GAgs NDro SPop WHil XBar
– 'Ilona' (Au/d) SPop
– 'Imari Stripe' (Au/St) WHil
– 'Immaculate' (Au/A) GAgs NDro NSum SPop WHil
– 'Impassioned' (Au/A) SPop XBar
– 'Imperturbable' (Au/A) NDro SPop
– 'Indian Love Call' (Au/A) GAbr GAgs ITim NDro SPop WHil
I – 'Innominata' (Au/S) NDro
– 'Innsworth' (Au/A) SPop WAln
– 'Iris Scott' (Au/A) ITim NDro
– 'Isabel' (Au/S) WAln
– 'Isabella' (Au/A) NDro WAln
– 'Jac' (Au/S) SPop
– 'Jack Dean' (Au/A) GAgs SPop WFar WHil XBar
– 'Jack Horner' (Au) NDro
– 'Jack Redfern' (Au/A) NDro
– 'Jaffa' (Au/A) NDro NSum WAln
– 'James Arnot' (Au/S) GAbr NDro XBar
– 'James Wattam' (Au/S) NDro
– 'Jane' (Au/S) WAln
– 'Jane Myers' (Au/d) WAln WHil
– 'Janet Watts' (Au/B) NDro
– 'Janie Hill' (Au/A) SPop XBar
– 'Jb' (Au) GAbr
– 'Je t'Adore' (Au/St) NDro
– 'Jealous Lover' (Au/St) SPop
– 'Jean Fielder' (Au/A) NDro SPop WAln
– 'Jean Jacques' (Au/A) NDro SPop WAln
I – 'Jean Jacques' (Au/d) XBar
– 'Jean Walker' (Au/B) SPop

– 'Jean-Claude' (Au/d) **new**	XBar
– 'Jeannie Jingles' (Au/St)	SPop
– 'Jeannie Jingles II' (Au/St)	NDro
– 'Jeannie Telford' (Au/A)	SPop
– 'Jeff Scruton' (Au/A)	SPop WAln
– 'Jenny' (Au/A)	NDro NRya SPop WFar
– 'Jersey Bounce' (Au/A)	ITim NDro SPop
– 'Jesmond' (Au/S)	SPop
– 'Jilting Jessie' (Au/St)	NDro SPop
– 'Joan Butler' (Au)	SPop
– 'Joan Curtis' (Au/d)	SPop
– 'Joan Elliott' (Au/A)	WAbe
– 'Joanne' (Au/d)	NDro
– 'Joanne' (Au/A)	GAbr GAgs NDro SPop
– 'Joe Perks' (Au/A)	GAgs ITim NDro WHil XBar
– 'Joel' (Au/S)	GAgs ITim NDro SPop XBar
– 'Johann Bach' (Au/B)	NDro SPop
– 'John Hart' (Au/A)	NDro
– 'John Stewart' (Au/A)	SPop
– 'John Wayne' (Au/A)	GAbr NDro SPop WHil
– 'John Woolf' (Au/S)	NDro
– 'Jonathon' (Au/A)	NDro WAln
– 'Jorvik' (Au/S)	SPop
– 'Joy' (Au/A)	LLHF NDro NSum NWad SPop WHil XBar
– 'Joyce' (Au/A)	GAbr NDro NSum WFar WHil XBar
– 'Judith Borman' (Au/d)	NDro SPop
– 'Julia' (Au/S)	SPop
– 'Julia Jane' (Au/B)	NDro
– 'Julie Nuttall' (Au/B)	GAbr GAgs NDro NSum SPop WHil
– 'June' (Au/A)	NDro NSum SPop
– 'Jungfrau' (Au/d)	NDro SPop WAln
– 'Jupiter' (Au/S)	SPop
– 'Jupp' (Au/d)	EBee EWTr
– 'Jura' (Au/A)	WAln
– 'Just Steven' (Au/A)	SPop WAln
– 'Justin Case' (Au/B)	NDro WAln
– 'K S' (Au/S)	NDro
– KALEIDOSCOPE (mixed) (Au) **new**	EDAr
– 'Karen Cordrey' (Au/S)	EBee GAbr GAgs GKev NDro NSum SPop WHil
– 'Karen McDonald' (Au/A)	NDro SPop
– 'Kate Haywood' (Au/B)	NDro WHil
– 'Ken Chilton' (Au/A)	GAgs NDro SPop WHil
– 'Kenco' (Au/d)	SPop
– 'Kentucky Blues' (Au/d)	NDro SPop WAln
– 'Kercup' (Au/A)	SPop
– 'Kerry' (Au/A)	GAgs SPop WAln
– 'Kersey' (Au/S)	NDro SPop
– 'Kevin' (Au/A)	SPop WAln
– 'Kevin Keegan' (Au/A)	NDro NSum SPop WHil
– 'Key West' (Au/A)	NDro SPop WAln
– 'Khachaturian' (Au/A)	NDro SPop WAln
– 'Kilby' (Au/A)	GAgs NDro NSum SPop
– 'Kim' (Au/A)	NDro SPop WHil
– 'Kimberworth Boy' (Au/A)	NDro WAln
– 'Kincraig' (Au/S)	SPop
– 'King George' (Au/d)	WAln
– 'Kingcup' (Au/A)	GAgs NDro SPop
– 'Kingfisher' (Au/A)	GAgs NDro SPop WHil
– 'Kingpin' (Au/St)	NDro
– 'Kiowa' (Au/S)	SPop
– 'Kirklands' (Au/d)	ITim NDro SPop WHil
– 'Kitterford Cross' (Au/B)	NDro
– 'Knights' (Au/S)	SPop
– 'Kohinoor' (Au/A)	WHil
– 'Koho' (Au/d)	SPop
– 'Königin der Nacht' (Au/St)	NDro SPop WHil
– 'Lady Daresbury' (Au/A)	NDro SPop WHil XBar
– 'Lady Day' (Au/d)	SPop WAln
– 'Lady Diana' (Au/S)	NDro
– 'Lady Emma Monson' (Au/S)	NDro SPop
– 'Lady Joyful' (Au/S)	NDro
– 'Lady of the Vale' (Au/A)	NDro SPop WAln
– 'Lady Penelope Sitwell' (Au/St) **new**	NDro SPop
– 'Lady Zoë' (Au/S)	GAgs LLHF NDro SPop
– 'Laguna' (Au/d)	SPop
– 'Lambert's Gold' (Au/B)	GAbr SPop
– 'Lambrook Gold' (Au/B)	NDro
– 'Lamplugh' (Au/d)	NSum SPop WHil
– 'Lancelot' (Au/d)	SPop
– 'Landy' (Au/A)	NDro SPop
– 'Langley Park' (Au/A)	NDro SPop WHil
– 'Laphroaigh' (Au/S)	WAln
– 'Laptop' (Au/St)	SPop
– 'Lara' (Au/A)	NDro SPop
– 'Laredo' (Au/A)	WAln
– 'Larry' (Au/A)	GAgs LLHF NDro SPop WFar XBar
– 'Late Romantic' (Au/d)	CDor ECtt GAbr GBin MHol NHpl NLar WIce WTor
– 'Lavender and Old Lace' (Au/d)	SPop
– 'Lavender Hill' (Au/St)	NDro
– 'Lavender Lady' (Au/B)	NDro NEgg
– 'Lavender Ridge' (Au/B)	NDro WAln
– 'Lavenham' (Au/S)	SPop WAln
– 'Laverock' (Au/S)	NBir NEgg WHil
– 'Laverock Fancy' (Au/S)	GAbr GAgs NDro SPop XBar
– 'Lazy River' (Au/A)	NDro WAln
– 'Leather Jacket' (Au/B)	GAbr WHil
– 'Leathercoat' (Au/B)	SPop
– 'Lechistan' (Au/S)	GAgs NDro SPop WHil
– 'Lee' (Au/A)	NDro WAln
– 'Lee Clark' (Au/A)	NDro WAln
– 'Lee Paul' (Au/A)	GAgs NDro NSum SPop WHil
– 'Lee Sharpe' (Au/A)	NDro NSum SPop WAln
– 'Legolas' (Au/A)	SPop WAln
– 'Leicester Square' (Au/S)	NDro
– 'Lemmy Getatem' (Au/d)	SPop
– 'Lemon Drizzle' (Au/S)	WAln
– 'Lemon Drop' (Au/S)	GAgs ITim NDro SPop
– 'Lemon Ice' (Au/S)	WAln
– 'Lemon Ridge' (Au/B)	WAln
– 'Lemon Sherbet' (Au/B)	GAbr GAgs NDro SPop WHil
– 'Lemon Sorbet' (Au)	NDro
– 'Lemon Zest' (Au/d)	WAln
– 'Lent Rise' (Au/S) **new**	SPop
– 'Lepton Jubilee' (Au/S)	GAbr NDro SPop WAln
– 'Leroy Brown' (Au/A)	WAln
– 'Lester' (Au/d)	SPop WAln WHil
– 'Leverton' (Au/d)	SPop
– 'Lewis Telford' (Au/A)	SPop
– 'Lichfield' (Au/A/d)	SPop
– 'Light Fantastic' (Au/S)	NDro SPop
– 'Light Hearted' (Au/A)	NDro SPop XBar
– 'Light Music' (Au/d)	WAln
– 'Likely Lad' (Au/St)	SPop
– 'Lila' (Au/S)	NDro SPop WAln
– 'Lilac Domino' (Au/S)	GAbr GAgs NDro NEgg NWad SPop WHil
– 'Lilac Ladywood' (Au/d)	SPop WFar
– 'Lilac Mist' (Au/d)	XBar
– 'Lillian Hill' (Au/A)	WAln
– 'Lillibet' (Au/A)	NDro
– 'Lima' (Au/d)	SPop WAln
– 'Limaki' (Au/d)	SPop

- 'Lime 'n' Lemon' (Au) ITim NDro
- 'Lime Ridge' (Au) WAln
- 'Limelight' (Au/A) NDro SPop
- 'Limelight' (Au/S) NDro SPop
- 'Lincoln Biscuit' (Au/d) SPop
- 'Lincoln Bullion' (Au/d) NDro SPop XBar
- 'Lincoln Charm' (Au/d) SPop
- 'Lincoln Chestnut' (Au/d) NDro SPop XBar
- 'Lincoln Consort' (Au/d) SPop
- 'Lincoln Cuckoo' (Au/d) NDro
- 'Lincoln Elf' (Au/d) SPop
- 'Lincoln Gem' (Au/d) SPop
- 'Lincoln Glow' (Au/d) SPop
- 'Lincoln Halo' (Au/d) SPop
- 'Lincoln Harmony' (Au/d) SPop
- 'Lincoln Imp' (Au/d) NDro
- 'Lincoln Imperial' (Au/d) NDro SPop
- 'Lincoln Major' (Au/d) SPop
- 'Lincoln Melody' (Au/St/d) NDro XBar
- 'Lincoln Poacher' (Au/d) NDro
- 'Lincoln Pride' (Au/d) SPop
- 'Lincoln Storm' (Au/d) SPop
- 'Lincoln Whisper' (Au/d) NDro
- 'Linda' (Au/A) SPop WAln WHil
- 'Lindley' (Au/S) NDro SPop
- 'Ling' (Au/A) GAbr NDro SPop
- 'Linnet' (Au/B) NDro
- 'Lintz' (Au/B) NDro SPop WHil
- 'Linze 2' (Au/S) NDro
- 'Lisa' (Au/A) GAgs NDro SPop WFar WHil XBar
- 'Lisa Clara' (Au/S) GAgs NDro NHpl SPop WFar XBar
- 'Lisa's Smile' (Au/S) NDro SPop WHil
- 'Little Bo Peep' (Au) NDro
- 'Little Rosetta' (Au/d) GAbr GAgs NDro NSum WHil
- 'Lizzie Files' (Au/A) SPop WAln
- 'Lockyer's Gem' (Au/B/St) NDro NEgg
- 'Lofty' (Au/St) NDro
- 'Lolita' (Au/St) GAgs NDro SPop WHil XBar
- 'Lord Saye and Sele' (Au/St) CWCL GAbr NDro NEgg NSum NWad SPop WHil XBar
- 'Lothlorien' (Au/A) WAln
- 'Louis' (Au/d) XBar
- 'Louisa Woolhead' (Au/d) SPop
- 'Louise Jordan' (Au/A) NDro SPop
- 'Love Nest' (Au/S) SPop
- 'Lovebird' (Au/S) GAbr NDro NHpl SPop XBar
- 'Lowther Show' (Au/St) **new** NDro
- 'Lucia' (Au/B) XBar
- 'Lucy Locket' (Au/B) EBee GAbr ITim LCro NDro NEgg NSum SPop WHil
- 'Ludlow' (Au/S) GAbr NDro SPop
- 'Lunar Eclipse' (Au/d) CBod MHol NLar WTor
- 'Lune Tiger' (Au/St) NDro SPop
- 'Lupy Minstrel' (Au/S) NDro SPop WAln
- 'Lusty Lad' (Au/St) SPop
- 'Lynn' (Au/A) SPop WAln
- 'Lynn Cooper' (Au/S) SPop
- 'MacWatt's Blue' (Au/B) GAbr NDro NWad SPop WHil
- 'Macy the Cat' (Au/S) WHil
- 'Madelaine Palmer' (Au/d) SPop
- 'Maggie' (Au/S) NDro NSum SPop
- 'Magnolia' (Au/B) WHil
- 'Mamba' (Au/S) SPop
- 'Mamm-Gozh' (Au/d) **new** XBar
- 'Mandarin' (Au/A) GAbr GAgs NDro NSum SPop WFar WHil XBar
- 'Manka' (Au/S) SPop
- 'Marble Arch' (Au/S) NDro
- 'Mardi Gras' (Au/d) WAln
- 'Margaret' (Au/S) GAbr NDro
- 'Margaret Faulkner' (Au/A) GAbr SPop XBar
- 'Margaret Irene' (Au/A) SPop
- 'Margaret Martin' (Au/S) ITim NDro SPop
- 'Margaret Merril' (Au) GAbr
- 'Margery Thompson' (Au/d) SPop
- 'Margot' (Au/S) WAln
- 'Margot Fonteyn' (Au/A) GAbr SPop WHil
- 'Mariandl' (Au/A) EBee
- 'Marie Crousse' (Au/d) CFis CMea ITim NDro SPop WCot WFar WHil
- 'Marie Pierre' (Au/d) XBar
- 'Marion Tiger' (Au/St) SPop
- 'Mark' (Au/A) GAbr GAgs NDro SPop
- 'Marmalade' (Au/d) SPop
- 'Marmion' (Au/S) GAgs ITim NDro WHil XBar
- 'Mars Bars' (Au/St) NDro
- 'Martha Livesley' (Au/A) WAln
- 'Martha's Choice' (Au/A) WAln
- 'Martin Luther King' (Au/S) NDro WHil XBar
- 'Mary' (Au/d) GAbr NDro SPop WAln
- 'Mary Poppins' (Au/S) NDro
- 'Mary Taylor' (Au/S) NDro SPop
- 'Mary Zach' (Au/S) NDro SPop WAln WHil
- 'Marylebone' (Au/S) NDro
- 'Matthew Yates' (Au/d) GAbr GAgs ITim NDro NHpl SPop WCot WHil
- 'Maureen Millward' (Au/A) NDro SPop
- 'May' (Au/A) NDro NSum
- 'May Booley' (Au/d) SPop
- 'Mazetta Stripe' (Au/S/St) GAbr GAgs NDro NWad SPop WHil
- 'Meadow Sweet' (Au/S) NDro
- 'Meadowlark' (Au/A) ITim NDro SPop WHil
- 'Medallist' (Au/St) **new** SPop
- 'Meg' (Au/d) SPop
- 'Megan' (Au/d) SPop WAln
- 'Mehta' (Au/A) NDro SPop WAln
- 'Mellifluous' (Au/A) WHil
- 'Melody' (Au/S) NDro SPop
- 'Menin' (Au/d) SPop
- 'Mere Peppermint' (Au/S) SPop
- 'Merlin' (Au/S) EBee NSum WFar
- 'Merlin Stripe' (Au/St) CWCL NDro SPop WHil XBar
- 'Merridale' (Au/A) GAbr SPop WHil
- 'Mersey Tiger' (Au/S) GAgs ITim NDro NSum SPop WHil XBar
- 'Metis' (Au/d) SPop
- 'Mexicano' (Au/A) NDro WAln
- 'Michael' (Au/S) SPop WAln WHil
- 'Michael Wattam' (Au/S) NDro SPop
- 'Mick' (Au/A) WHil
- 'Midland Marvel' (Au/St) NDro SPop
- 'Midnight' (Au/A) WAln
- 'Mikado' (Au/S) NSum SPop WHil XBar
- 'Milkmaid' (Au/A) NSla WMAq
- 'Millicent' (Au/A) NDro NSum SPop WHil
- 'Millicent Betsy' (Au/d) SPop
- 'Millie Redfern' (Au/d) SPop
- 'Mink' (Au/A) NDro
- 'Minley' (Au/S) GAbr GAgs NBir NDro NEgg SPop WIce
- 'Minotaur' (Au/A) SPop
- 'Minstead' (Au/S) SPop
- 'Minstrel' (Au/S) ITim NDro SPop
- 'Minty' (Au/St) NDro SPop
- 'Mipsie Miranda' (Au/d) SPop
- 'Mirabella Bay' (Au/A) SPop WAln
- 'Miranda' (Au/d) SPop

- 'Mirandinha' (Au/A) NDro SPop
- 'Miriam' (Au/A) SPop
- 'Mish Mish' (Au/d) NDro WHil
- 'Miss Bluey' (Au/d) NDro SPop WAln XBar
- 'Miss Jones' (Au/St) NDro SPop
- 'Miss Muffet' (Au/S) WAln
- 'Miss Newman' (Au/A) NDro NSum SPop
- 'Miss Otis' (Au/S) SPop
- 'Miss Pinky' (Au/d) NDro SPop
- 'Miss Teak' (Au/S) **new** NDro
- 'Mist' (Au/S) WAln
- 'Misty' (Au/d) SPop
- 'Mojave' (Au/S) GAbr GEdr ITim NDro NEgg NHpl NSum SPop WHil XBar
- 'Mollie Langford' (Au/A) NDro SPop WHil
- 'Mondeo' (Au/A) WAln
- 'Monet' (Au/S) NDro
- 'Moneymoon' (Au/S) GAbr NDro SPop WHil
- 'Monk' (Au/S) NDro SPop WHil XBar
- 'Monmouth Star' (Au/St) NDro WHil
- 'Moon Fairy' (Au/S) NDro SPop
- 'Moondance' (Au/d) WAln
- 'Moonglow' (Au/S) GAbr NDro
- 'Moonlight' (Au/S) WAln
- 'Moonrise' (Au/S) NDro SPop
- 'Moonriver' (Au/A) NDro WHil
- 'Moonshine' (Au/d) SPop WAln
- 'Moonshot' (Au/d) NDro SPop
- 'Moonstone' (Au/d) SPop WAln
- 'Moorcroft' (Au/S) **new** NDro
- 'Morello' (Au/d) XBar
- 'Morning Glory' (Au/B) WAln
- 'Morven' (Au) GAbr
- 'Moscow' (Au/S) SPop
- 'Moselle' (Au/S) NDro SPop
- 'Mossy Vale' (Au/S) SPop
- 'Mr A' (Au/S) NDro WHil
- 'Mr Bojangles' (Au/d) WAln
- 'Mr Frosty' (Au/d) SPop
- 'Mr Hollis' (Au/St) **new** NDro
- 'Mrs Cairn's Blue' (Au/B) NDro
- 'Mrs Dargan' (Au/d) NDro
- 'Mrs Harris' (Au/B) NDro
- 'Mrs L. Hearn' (Au/A) GAbr ITim NDro SPop WHil
- 'Mrs R. Bolton' (Au/A) WHil
- 'Mrs Robinson' (Au/St) NDro SPop
- 'Mrs Wilson' (Au) GAbr
- 'Muriel James' (Au/A) SPop
- 'Murray Lakes' (Au/A) NDro SPop WAln
- 'Mustard Sauce' (Au/B) NDro
- 'My Buddy' (Au/St) SPop
- 'My Delight' (Au/d) SPop
- 'My Fair Lady' (Au/A) NDro
- 'My Friend' (Au/B) GAbr NDro SPop
- 'My Sweetie' (Au/St) **new** SPop
- 'Myodeboots' (Au/A) SPop
- 'Myrtle Park' (Au/A) WAln
- 'Mystery' (Au) GAbr
- 'Nancy Dalgetty' (Au/B) NDro SPop
- 'Nantenan' (Au/S) GAbr NDro SPop
- 'Neat and Tidy' (Au/S) GAbr GAgs ITim NDro SPop XBar
- 'Nefertiti' (Au/A) NDro SPop WHil
- 'Nessun Dorma' (Au/A) NDro WAln
- 'Neville Telford' (Au/S) GAbr NDro SPop WFar
- 'Newbottle' (Au/S) SPop WHil
- 'Newsboy' (Au/A) WAln
- 'Newton Harcourt' (Au/A) SPop WHil
- 'Nicholas van Zanten' (Au/B) **new** NDro
- 'Nick Drake' (Au/d) SPop
- 'Nickity' (Au/A) GAbr GAgs ITim NDro NSum SPop WHil XBar
- 'Nicola Jane' (Au/A) SPop WAln
- 'Nigel' (Au/d) GAbr NDro
- 'Night and Day' (Au/St) SPop
- 'Nightwink' (Au/S) WAln
- 'Nil Amber' (Au) SPop
- 'Nina' (Au/A) NDro SPop WAln
- 'Nita' (Au/d) SPop WAln
- 'No 21' (Au/S) NDro SPop
- 'No Deal' (Au/S) SPop
- 'Nocturne' (Au/S) NDro NSum SPop
- 'Noelle' (Au/S) EBee GKev NDro
- 'Nona' (Au/d) NDro NSum SPop
- 'Nonchalance' (Au/A) NDro NSum SPop WHil
- 'Norma' (Au/A) NDro SPop
- 'Northern Lights' (Au/S) GAbr NDro
- 'Nureyev' (Au/A) SPop
- 'Nymph' (Au/d) GAbr GAgs NDro SPop WHil
- 'Oakenshield' (Au/A) WAln
- 'Oakes Blue' (Au/S) NDro
- 'Oakie' (Au/S) SPop
- 'Oban' (Au/S) NDro SPop XBar
- 'Odette' (Au/d) SPop WHil
- 'O'er the Moon' (Au/S) WAln
- 'Oikos' (Au/B) NDro SPop
- 'Ol' Blue Eyes' (Au/St) SPop
- 'Old Black Isle Dusty Miller' (Au/B) NDro WHil
- 'Old Buffer' (Au/St) NDro SPop
- 'Old Clove Red' (Au/B) GAbr NDro NSum NWad WHil
- 'Old Cottage Blue' (Au/B) GAbr NDro WFar
- 'Old Dublin Blue' (Au/B) NDro
- 'Old England' (Au/S) GAbr GAgs NDro SPop
- 'Old Gold' (Au/S) GAbr NDro SPop WFar
- 'Old Gold Dusty Miller' (Au/B) NDro
- 'Old Irish Blue' (Au/B) ITim NDro NEgg WCot
- 'Old Irish Green' (Au/B) GAbr NDro NSum
- 'Old Irish Scented' (Au/B) GAbr NDro NWad SPop WHil
- 'Old Irish Yellow' (Au/B) NDro NEgg NHpl
- 'Old Kent Road' (Au/S) **new** NDro
- 'Old Mustard' (Au/B) GAbr NDro SIgm SMHy
- 'Old Pink Dusty Miller' (Au/B) GAbr

§ - 'Old Purple Dusty Miller' (Au/B) GAbr
- 'Old Red Dusty Miller' (Au/B) GAbr LLHF NDro NSum SPop WFar WHil
- 'Old Red Elvet' (Au/S) GAbr SPop
- 'Old Smokey' (Au/A) NDro SPop WHil XBar
- 'Old Suffolk Bronze' (Au/B) GAbr GAgs ITim NDro WHil
- 'Old Timer' (Au/S) NDro SPop
- 'Old Yellow Dusty Miller' (Au/B) EWes GAbr NDro NWad WHil
- 'Old-Fashioned' (Au/B) NDro
- 'Oldfield' (Au/d) SPop
- 'Olivia' (Au/d) SPop
- 'Olton' (Au/A) NDro WFar XBar
- 'Optimist' (Au/St) GAbr NDro SPop
- 'Opus One' (Au/A) WAln
- 'Orb' (Au/S) SPop WHil XBar
- 'Ordvic' (Au/S) NDro
- 'Orlando' (Au/S) NDro SPop
- 'Orwell Tiger' (Au/St) GAgs NDro SPop XBar
- 'Osbaston Bullseye' (Au/St) SPop
- 'Osborne Green' (Au/B) GAbr GAgs NDro SPop WHil
- 'Osorno' (Au/d) SPop
- 'Ossett Sapphire' (Au/A) NDro SPop

- 'Otto Dix' (Au/A) SPop WAln
- 'Our Sophie' (Au/B) NDro
- 'Overdale' (Au/A) NDro NSum SPop WAln
- 'Oyster' (Au/B) NDro
- 'Paddlin' Madeleine' (Au/A) NDro WAln
- 'Pageboy' (Au/A) WAln
- 'Paleface' (Au/A) GAgs NDro NSum SPop
- 'Pall Mall' (Au/St) NDro
- 'Panache' (Au/S) WAln
- 'Pang Tiger' (Au/St) NDro SPop
- 'Paphos' (Au/d) SPop
- 'Paradise Yellow' (Au/B) GAbr NDro NEgg SPop
- 'Paragon' (Au/A) WHil
- 'Parakeet' (Au/S) NDro
- 'Paris' (Au/S) SPop
- 'Partney' (Au/d) SPop
- 'Party Animal' (Au/St) NDro SPop XBar
- 'Party Time' (Au/S) SPop
- 'Passchendaele' (Au/d) SPop
- 'Passing Cloud' (Au/d) WAln
- 'Pastures New' (Au) NDro SPop
- 'Pat' (Au/S) SPop
- 'Pat Mooney' (Au/d) NDro
- 'Patience' (Au/S) NDro
- 'Paula' (Au/A) SPop
- 'Pauline' (Au/A) NDro SPop
- 'Pavarotti' (Au/A) ITim NDro NSum SPop
- 'Paxton's Blue Eden' (Au/B) **new** NDro
- 'Pegasus' (Au/d) NDro SPop
- 'Peggy' (Au/A) GAbr ITim NSum
- 'Pendeford Yellow' (Au/B) **new** NDro
- 'Pendle Pearl' (Au/A) **new** SPop
- 'Pendle Promise' (Au/A) **new** NDro SPop
- 'People's Choice' (Au/d) SPop
- 'Pequod' (Au/A) NDro NSum SPop
- 'Perdito' (Au/S) SPop
- 'Perirot' (Au) ITim
- 'Perito Moreno' (Au/d) SPop
- 'Persephone' (Au/B) NDro
- 'Phantom' (Au/d) SPop WAln
- 'Pharaoh' (Au/A) GAbr GAgs NDro SPop XBar
- 'Phoenix' (Au/A) WAln
- 'Phyllis Douglas' (Au/A) GAgs NDro NEgg SPop WHil
- 'Piccadilly' (Au/S) NDro SPop
- 'Piccalilli' (Au/d) XBar
- 'Pierot' (Au/A) GAgs NDro NSum SPop WHil XBar
- 'Piers Telford' (Au/A) EBee GAbr NDro NEgg NSum SPop WFar WHil XBar
- 'Piglet' (Au/d) GAbr NDro SPop WHil
- 'Pikey' (Au/S) NDro SPop
- 'Pimlico' (Au/S) SPop
- 'Pimroagh' (Au/A) GAbr SPop
- 'Pink Floyd' (Au/A) SPop XBar
- 'Pink Fondant' (Au/d) NDro
- 'Pink Hint' (Au/B) NDro SPop
- 'Pink Lady' (Au/A) GAbr GAgs NSum SPop WHil
- 'Pink Lilac' (Au/A/S) NDro
- 'Pink Triumph' (Au/B) NDro WHil
- 'Pinkerton' (Au/d) SPop
- 'Pinkie' (Au/A) WHil
- 'Pinkie Dawn' (Au/B) NDro NWad SPop
- 'Pinstripe' (Au) GAbr GAgs NDro NSum SPop WHil
- 'Pioneer Stripe' (Au/S) GAbr SPop
- 'Pippin' (Au/A) GAbr GAgs NDro SPop WHil XBar
- 'Pixie' (Au/A) GAgs NDro SPop WHil
- 'Playboy' (Au/A) NDro SPop WAln
- 'Plum Pudding' (Au/d) SPop WAln
- 'Plums and Custard' (Au/B) XBar
- 'Poacher's Lady' (Au/d) NDro
- 'Poacher's Starlight' (Au/d) NDro
- 'Polar Sight' (Au/B) NDro
- 'Polestar' (Au/A) NDro NSum SPop WHil XBar
- 'Polly' (Au/B) GAgs GKev NAln NDro NSum WHil
- 'Pop's Blue' (Au/S/d) NEgg SPop
- 'Portree' (Au/S) GAbr SPop
- 'Post Master' (Au/S) WAln
- 'Pot o' Gold' (Au/S) EBee GAgs NDro NEgg SPop WHil XBar
- 'Powder and Paint' (Au/A) WAln
- 'Powder Puff' (Au/B) NDro SPop
- 'Prague' (Au/S) GAbr NBir NDro SPop
- 'Pretender' (Au/A) SPop
- 'Pretty Prop' (Au/St) SPop
- 'Pretty Purple' (Au/d) NDro SPop WAln
- 'Pride of Poland' (Au/S) SPop
- 'Prim and Proper' (Au/St) **new** SPop
- 'Prima' (Au/d) NDro
- 'Primary Red' (Au/S) SPop
- 'Prince Bishops' (Au/S) SPop WAln
- 'Prince Charming' (Au/S) GAgs NDro SPop
- 'Prince Igor' (Au/A) SPop
- 'Prince John' (Au/A) NAln NDro SPop WHil
- 'Pristine' (Au/B) WAln
- 'Proctor's Yellow' (Au/B) GAbr NDro NWad WHil
- 'Prometheus' (Au/d) GAbr ITim LLHF NDro NSum SPop WHil
- 'Prosperine' (Au/S) SPop
- 'Provence' (Au/d) **new** WHil
- 'Psyche' (Au/S) NDro SPop
- 'Ptarmigan' (Au/S) SPop
- 'Pumpkin' (Au) GAbr NHpl SPop
- 'Puppy Love' (Au/St) SPop
- 'Purbeck' (Au/B) SPop
- 'Purple Dusty Miller' see *P. auricula* 'Old Purple Dusty Miller'
- 'Purple Emperor' (Au/A) SPop
- 'Purple Flake' (Au/d) SPop
- 'Purple Glow' (Au/d) WAln
- 'Purple Haze' (Au/St) SPop
- 'Purple Heart' (Au/d) SPop
- 'Purple Knight' (Au/S) WAln
- 'Purple Lace' (Au/d) SPop
- 'Purple Lovely' (Au/St) SPop
- 'Purple Orient' (Au/d) SPop
- 'Purple Patch' (Au/d) SPop
- 'Purple Pip' (Au/d) CBod MHol NLar
- 'Purple Pompom' (Au/d) SPop
- 'Purple Prolific' (Au/B) NDro
- 'Purple Promise' (Au/B) GAbr ITim NDro SPop
- 'Purple Prose' (Au/St) SPop WHil
- 'Purple Rose' (Au/d) ITim WAln
- 'Purple Royale' (Au/B) NDro
- 'Purple Sage' (Au/S) ITim NDro SPop WHil
- 'Purple Star' (Au/d) SPop
- 'Purple Velvet' (Au/S) NDro SPop
- 'Pye Powder' (Au/S) SPop
- 'Pyrites' (Au/d) **new** SPop
- 'Quatro' (Au/d) GAgs SPop
- 'Queen' (Au/d) SPop
- 'Queen Alexandra' (Au/B) GAbr NDro WHil
- 'Queen Bee' (Au/S) GAbr GAgs NDro SPop
- 'Queen's Bower' (Au/S) SPop
- 'Quintessence' (Au/A) NDro SPop WHil
- 'R.L. Bowes' (Au/A) NDro
- 'Rab C. Nesbitt' (Au/A) SPop WAln
- 'Rabley Heath' (Au/A) GAbr GAgs ITim NDro SPop WHil

- 'Rachel' (Au/A) NDro WAln
I - 'Rachel' (Au/d) **new** XBar
- 'Rachel de Thame' (Au/S) WAln
- 'Rachel Labouchere' (Au/S) WAln
- 'Radiance' (Au/A) SPop
- 'Radiant' (Au/A) NDro
- 'Rag Doll' (Au/S) NDro
- 'Ragnald the Magnificent' (Au/S) WAln
- 'Rainy Days' (Au/B) NDro
- 'Rajah' (Au/S) GAbr GAgs NEgg NHpl SPop WHil XBar
- 'Raleigh Stripe' (Au/St) GAbr GAgs NDro SPop
- 'Rameses' (Au/A) NDro SPop
- 'Rebecca Baker' (Au/d) SPop WHil
- 'Red Admiral' (Au/S) NDro SPop WAln
- 'Red Arrows' (Au/S) SPop WAln
- 'Red Baron' (Au/S) WAln
- 'Red Beret' (Au/S) SPop
- 'Red Bordeaux' (Au/S) NDro
- 'Red Carpet' (Au/S) SPop
- 'Red Diamond' (Au/d) WAln
- 'Red Embers' (Au/S) SPop WAln
- 'Red Ensign' (Au/B) NDro
- 'Red Gauntlet' (Au/S) GAbr GAgs NDro SPop
- 'Red King' (Au/S) WAln
- 'Red Mark' (Au/A) SPop WHil XBar
- 'Red Rum' (Au/S) GAbr SPop WAln
- 'Red Sonata' (Au/S) SPop
- 'Red Spin' (Au/S) SPop
- 'Red Wire' (Au/St) NDro NSum SPop
- 'Red Wrekin' (Au/S) NDro
- 'Redcar' (Au/A) GAbr NDro
- 'Reddown Apricot' (Au/B) NDro
- 'Reddown Barley Meal' (Au/B) NDro
- 'Reddown Bat' (Au/d) SPop
- 'Reddown Dark Pink' (Au/B) **new** NDro
- 'Reddown First Swallow' (Au/B) NDro
- 'Reddown Rainman' (Au/B) NDro SPop
- 'Reddown Tickled Pink' (Au/B) NDro
- 'Redstart' (Au/S) EBee GAgs GKev ITim NDro WHil
- 'Regency' (Au/A) NDro
- 'Regency Carousel' (Au/St) SPop
- 'Regency Dandy' (Au/St) SPop
- 'Regency Emperor' (Au/St) NDro SPop WHil XBar
- 'Regency Paperchase' (Au/St) NDro SPop
- 'Regency Peppermint Tea' (Au/St) SPop
- 'Regency Saint Clements' (Au/St) NDro SPop
- 'Remus' (Au/S) ELan ITim LLHF NDro NEgg SPop WHil XBar
- 'Renata' (Au/S) SPop
- 'Rene' (Au/A) GAbr NDro SPop WHil XBar
- 'Renishaw Hall' (Au/S) SPop
- 'Renown' (Au/A) WAln
- 'Repton' (Au/S) SPop
- 'Requiem' (Au/d) WAln
- 'Reresby Sitwell' (Au/S) SPop
- 'Resi' (Au/A) WHil
- 'Respectable' (Au/A) WAln
- 'Reverie' (Au/d) SPop WAln
- 'Reynardine' (Au/d) SPop WAln
- 'Rhinegold' (Au/d) XBar
- 'Riatty' (Au/d) GAbr GAgs NDro SPop
- 'Richard Shaw' (Au/A) NDro SPop
- 'Ring of Bells' (Au/S) SPop WAln
- 'Ring of Fire' (Au/A) WAln
- 'Rintein' (Au/B) NDro
- 'Risdene' (Au/A) WAln
- 'Rivendell' (Au/A) WAln
- 'Robbo' (Au/B) GAbr NDro NWad
- 'Robert Green' (Au/S) NDro SPop
- 'Robert Lee' (Au/A) WAln
- 'Roberto' (Au/S) NDro SPop
- 'Robin Hood Stripe' (Au/St) NDro SPop
- 'Robinette' (Au/d) GAbr SPop
- 'Rock Sand' (Au/S) GAbr GAgs NDro SPop WHil
- 'Rockbourne' (Au/A) SPop
- 'Rodeo' (Au/A) GAbr SPop
- 'Rolts' (Au/S) GAbr GAgs NDro SPop WHil XBar
- 'Rondy' (Au/S) ITim SPop WHil
- 'Ronnie Johnson' (Au) WAln
- 'Rosalie' (Au) SPop
- 'Rosalie Edwards' (Au/S) SPop
- 'Rose Conjou' (Au/d) GAbr GAgs NDro SPop WHil XBar
- 'Rose Kaye' (Au/A) GAbr SPop
- 'Rose Petal' (Au/d) XBar
- 'Rosebud' (Au/S) GAbr NDro
- 'Rosemarket Rackler' (Au/B) NDro
- 'Rosemary' (Au/S) GAbr NDro SPop WHil
- 'Rosewood' (Au/d) SPop WAln
- 'Rosie' (Au/S) NDro
- 'Rostock' (Au/B) NDro
- 'Rothesay Robin' (Au/A) WAln
- 'Rouge Gorge' (Au/B) XBar
- 'Rowena' (Au/A) NDro NSum SPop WHil
- 'Roxburgh' (Au/A) NDro SPop
- 'Roy Keane' (Au/A) NSum SPop WAln
- 'Royal Mail' (Au/S) NDro SPop XBar
- 'Royal Marine' (Au/S) SPop WAln
- 'Royal Scot' (Au/S) NDro SPop
- 'Royal Velvet' (Au/S) GAbr GAgs NDro WFar WHil
- 'Ruby Hyde' (Au/B) GAbr NDro SPop
- 'Ruddy Duck' (Au/S) NDro SPop
- 'Ruff' (Au/d) **new** SPop
- 'Runwell' (Au/B) NDro
- 'Runwell Red' (Au/B) SPop
- 'Rusty Dusty' (Au) GAbr NDro
- 'Rusty Red' (Au/B) NDro
- 'Ryecroft' (Au/A) WAln
- 'Sabrina' (Au/A) WAln
- 'Saginaw' (Au/A) WAln
- 'Sailor Boy' (Au/S) NDro SPop WAln
- 'Saint Boswells' (Au/S) GAbr SPop
- 'Saint Elmo' (Au/A) GAbr GAgs SPop
- 'Saint-Émilion' (Au/d) **new** XBar
- 'Salad' (Au/S) GAbr GAgs SPop
- 'Sale Green' (Au/S) NDro SPop
- 'Sally' (Au/A) NDro
- 'Sam Brown' (Au/S) WAln
- 'Sam Gamgee' (Au/A) NDro SPop WAln
- 'Sam Hunter' (Au/A) NDro SPop
- 'Samantha' (Au/A) NDro WAln
- 'Samantha' (Au/d) NDro SPop WAln WFar XBar
- 'San Antonio' (Au/A) NDro
- 'San Gabriel' (Au/A) WAln
- 'Sanctuary Wood' (Au/d) SPop
- 'Sandhills' (Au/A) GAgs SPop WHil
- 'Sandpiper' (Au/d) SPop WAln
- 'Sandra' (Au/A) ELan GAbr GAgs NDro SPop WHil
- 'Sandwood Bay' (Au/A) GAbr NDro NEgg SPop WHil
- 'Sappho' (Au/S) SPop

- 'Sarah Gisby' (Au/d) NDro SPop
- 'Sarah Grey' (Au/d) WAln
- 'Sarah Humphries' (Au/d) WAln
- 'Sarah Lodge' (Au/d) GAbr GAgs NDro SPop WHil
- 'Sarah Suzanne' (Au/B) NDro
- 'Saruman' (Au/A) WAln
- 'Sasha Files' (Au/A) WAln
- 'Satchmo' (Au/S) SPop
- 'Satin Doll' (Au/d) SPop
- 'Satsuma' (Au/d) SPop WAln
- 'Scaraben' (Au) GAbr
- 'Schaumburg' (Au/B) NDro
- 'Schicchi' (Au/d) XBar
- 'Scipio' (Au/S) NDro SPop
- 'Scorcher' (Au/S) GAbr LLHF NDro NSum SPop WHil XBar
- 'Scrumpy' (Au/St) NDro
- 'Sea Lavender' (Au/d) WAln
- 'Sea Mist' (Au/d) SPop WAln
- 'Second Victory' (Au/S) NDro WHil XBar
- 'Seen-a-Ghost' (Au/S) NDro SPop
- 'Serendipity' (Au/B) WAln
- 'Serenity' (Au/S) SPop WHil XBar
- 'Sergeant Wilson' (Au/S) NDro SPop
- 'Serre' (Au/d) SPop
- 'Shadow Boxer' (Au/St) **new** NDro SPop
- 'Shalford' (Au/d) GAbr SPop WCot WHil
- 'Sharmans Cross' (Au/S) SPop
- 'Sharon Louise' (Au/S) NDro SPop
- 'Shaun' (Au/d) ECtt GAbr GAgs GBin MHol NHpl NLar WIce WTor
- 'Sheila' (Au/S) GAbr NDro SPop WHil
- 'Sherbet' (Au/d) SPop
- 'Shere' (Au/S) NDro NSum SPop
- 'Shergold' (Au/A) SPop WHil
- 'Sherwood' (Au/S) GAbr NDro NHpl SPop XBar
- 'Shining Hour' (Au/St) SPop
- 'Shirley' (Au/S) NDro SPop
- 'Shotley' (Au/A) SPop
- 'Show Bandit' (Au/St) NDro SPop
- 'Showtime' (Au/S) NDro SPop
- 'Sibsey' (Au/d) GAgs NDro NSum SPop WFar
- 'Sidney' (Au/A) WAln
- 'Silas' (Au/B) NDro
- 'Silbermond' (Au/B) NDro
- 'Silmaril' (Au/d) SPop WAln
- 'Silver Surfer' (Au/St) NDro
- 'Silverway' (Au/S) NDro SPop WHil
- 'Simply Red' (Au/S) NDro NSum SPop XBar
- 'Sir John' (Au/A) NDro SPop WHil
- 'Sir Prize' (Au/A) **new** SPop
- 'Sir Robert' (Au/d) GAbr SPop WAln
- 'Sir Titus Salt' (Au/S) WAln
- 'Sirbol' (Au/A) GAbr GAgs NDro NSum SPop WHil
- 'Sirius' (Au/A) GAbr MHer NDro NSum NWad SPop WHil XBar
- 'Skerne Tiger' (Au/St) SPop
- 'Skylark' (Au/A) GAbr GAgs ITim NDro SPop WHil XBar
- 'Skyliner' (Au/A) NDro
- 'Slack Top Red' (Au) NDro NSla WHil
- 'Sleeping Beauty' (Au/d) SPop
- 'Slim Whitman' (Au/A) NDro NSum SPop WHil
- 'Slioch' (Au/S) GAbr GAgs NSum SPop WHil XBar
- 'Slip Anchor' (Au/A) WAln
- 'Smart Tar' (Au/S) WAln
- 'Smoothy' (Au/St) NDro SPop
- 'Snips' (Au/St) NDro SPop
- 'Snitched' (Au/St) NDro SPop
- 'Snooty Fox' (Au/A) SPop
- 'Snooty Fox II' (Au/A) NDro
- 'Snow Maiden' (Au/d) SPop WAln
- 'Snowball' (Au/d) SPop
- 'Snowline' (Au/S) SPop
- 'Snowstorm' (Au/S) NDro SPop
- 'Snowy Owl' (Au/S) NDro SPop XBar
- 'Snowy Ridge' (Au/B) NDro
- 'Solario' (Au/S) NDro SPop
- 'Solero' (Au/St) SPop
- 'Soliloquy' (Au/B) NDro
- 'Somersby' (Au/d) SPop
- 'Soncy Face' (Au/A) SPop WHil
- 'Song of India' (Au/A) SPop
- 'Sonia Nicolle' (Au/B) NDro
- 'Sonja' (Au/S) **new** NDro
- 'Sonny Boy' (Au/A) SPop WAln
- 'Sooty' (Au/d) NDro SPop
- 'Sophie' (Au/d) SPop WAln
- 'Sophie' (Au/A) NDro SPop
- 'South Barrow' (Au/d) GAbr GAgs SPop WHil
- 'Southport' (Au/B) GAbr NDro
- 'Sparky' (Au/A) NDro SPop WAln
- 'Spartan' (Au/A) SPop WAln
- 'Spider' (Au/S) **new** NDro
- 'Splash' (Au) WHil
- 'Split Ends' (Au/St) NDro SPop
- 'Spring Meadows' (Au/S) GAbr GKev NDro NEgg SPop WHil
- 'Stafford Blue' (Au/B) NDro
- 'Standish' (Au/d) GAbr
- 'Stant's Blue' (Au/S) NDro SPop
- 'Star Spangle' (Au/St) NDro
- 'Star Wars' (Au/S) GAbr GAgs NDro SPop XBar
- 'Starburst' (Au/S) NDro
- 'Starlight' (Au/S) SPop
- 'Starling' (Au/B) GAbr NDro SPop
- 'Starsand' (Au/S) NDro
- 'Steiff' (Au/S) NDro
- 'Stella' (Au/S) SPop
- 'Stella Coop' (Au/d) NDro
- 'Stella North' (Au/A) SPop WAln
- 'Stella South' (Au/A) NDro SPop WFar
- 'Stepney Green' (Au/S) NDro
- 'Stetson' (Au/A) WAln
- 'Stirling Castle' (Au/St) NDro
- 'Stoke Poges' (Au/A) NDro
- 'Stoney Cross' (Au/S) SPop WAln
- 'Stonnal' (Au/A) SPop WHil
- 'Stormin' Norman' (Au/A) NDro SPop WHil
- 'Stormy Weather' (Au/St) SPop
- 'Strand' (Au/St) NDro
- 'Strawberry Fields' (Au/S) NDro SPop
- 'Stripe Tease' (Au/St) SPop
- 'Stripe U Like' (Au/St) NDro
- 'Striped Ace' (Au/St) NDro SPop WHil
- 'Stripey' (Au/d) NDro
- 'Stromboli' (Au/d) GAbr GAgs NDro SPop WCot XBar
- 'Subliminal' (Au/A) NDro
- 'Sue' (Au/A) SPop
- 'Sue Ritchie' (Au/d) SPop
- 'Suede Shoes' (Au/S) SPop
- 'Sugar Plum Fairy' (Au/S) GAbr GAgs NDro NSum SPop WHil
- 'Summer Sky' (Au/A) NDro SPop
- 'Summer Wine' (Au/A) NDro SPop XBar
- 'Sumo' (Au/A) GAbr GAgs NDro SPop WHil
- 'Sunflower' (Au/A/S) GAbr GAgs ITim NDro SPop WHil
- 'Sunlight' (Au/A) SPop WAln
- 'Sunlit Tiger' (Au/S) GAbr NDro
- 'Sunray' (Au/St) SPop
- 'Sunrise Beauty' (Au/S) SPop

- 'Sunspot' (Au/A) WAln
- 'Sunstar' (Au/S) NDro NSum
- 'Super Para' (Au/S) GAbr GAgs GKev NDro SPop WHil
- 'Superb' (Au/S) SPop XBar
- 'Surething' (Au/A) WAln
- 'Susan' (Au/A) NDro
- 'Susannah' (Au/d) GAgs NDro NSum SPop WFar WHil XBar
- 'Sweet Georgia Brown' (Au/A) NDro SPop WAln
- 'Sweet Lorraine' (Au/S) new NDro SPop
- 'Sweet Pastures' (Au/S) GAbr GAgs NDro SPop
- 'Swiss Royal Velvet' (Au/B) NDro
- 'S'Wonderful' (Au/St) new SPop
- 'Sword' (Au/d) GAbr NDro NSum SPop WFar XBar
- 'Symphony' (Au/A) GAgs ITim NDro SPop WHil XBar
- 'T.A. Hadfield' (Au/A) GAgs NDro SPop WHil
- 'Taffeta' (Au/S) EBee GAbr LCro LOPS NDro NSti NSum SPop WFar WHil
- 'Tall Purple Dusty Miller' (Au/B) SPop
- 'Tally-ho' (Au/A) SPop WAln
- 'Tamar Gold' (Au/d) SPop WAln
- 'Tamar Mist' (Au/d) WHil
- 'Tamino' (Au/S) NDro SPop
- 'Tango' (Au/d) NDro WAln
- 'Tarantella' (Au/A) GAbr NDro NSum SPop
- 'Tawny Owl' (Au/B) GAbr
- 'Tay Tiger' (Au/St) GAbr GAgs NDro SPop WHil XBar
- 'Taylor's Grey' (Au/S) NDro SPop
- 'Teawell Pride' (Au/d) ITim NHpl SPop WHil
- 'Ted Gibbs' (Au/A) NDro SPop WHil
- 'Ted Roberts' (Au/A) CBor ITim NDro SPop WHil
- 'Teem' (Au/S) GAbr NDro SPop XBar
- 'Telesto' (Au/d) SPop
- 'Telford's Surprise' (Au/A) WAln
- 'Temeraire' (Au/A) SPop WHil
- 'Tenby Grey' (Au/S) SPop
- 'Tenderly' (Au/St) NDro
- 'Terpo' (Au/A) GAgs NDro WAln WHil
- 'Tess' (Au/A) XBar
- 'The Argylls' (Au/St) NDro SPop
- 'The Baron' (Au/S) GAbr GAgs GKev NAln SPop WHil XBar
- 'The Bishop' (Au/S) GAgs ITim SPop WAln WHil XBar
- 'The Bride' (Au/S) NDro SPop
- 'The Cardinal' (Au/d) WAln
- 'The Chef' (Au/St) new SPop
- 'The Czar' (Au/A) GAbr NDro SPop
- 'The Egyptian' (Au/A) GAgs NDro SPop WHil
- 'The Few' (Au/St) SPop
- 'The Hobbit' (Au/A) WAln
- 'The Lady Galadriel' (Au/A) NDro
- 'The Maverick' (Au/S) SPop
- 'The One' (Au/St) new SPop
- 'The Raven' (Au/S) GAgs ITim WHil
- 'The Sculptor' (Au/St) new SPop
- 'The Sneep' (Au/A) GAbr GAgs ITim NDro SPop
- 'The Snods' (Au/S) NDro SPop
- 'The Wrekin' (Au/S) SPop
- 'Thea' (Au/B) new XBar

I - 'Theodora' (Au/S) XBar
- 'Thetis' (Au/A) SPop
- 'Thisbe' (Au/A) NDro
- 'Thou Swell' (Au/St) SPop
- 'Three Way Stripe' (St) GAbr WHil
- 'Thutmoses' (Au/A) NDro SPop WAln
- 'Tiger Tim' (Au/St) SPop
- 'Tilley' (Au/d) SPop
- 'Tim' (Au/d) GAbr ITim NDro NSum SPop
- 'Timpany Blues' (Au/B) ITim
- 'Tim's Fancy' (Au/S) NDro
- 'Tinker' (Au/S) NDro WAln
- 'Tinkerbell' (Au/S) NDro SPop
- 'Tiptoe' (Au/St) NDro SPop
- 'Titania' (Au/d) SPop
- 'Toffee Apple' (Au/d) NDro
- 'Toffee Crisp' (Au/A) GAbr GAgs NDro SPop XBar
- 'Toffee Nosed' (Au/St) NDro SPop
- 'Tomboy' (Au/S) NDro SPop
- 'Tom's Red' (Au/S) SPop
- 'Tony Bray' (Au/A) SPop
- 'Toolyn' (Au/S) GAgs NDro SPop WAln
- 'Top Cat' (Au/d) WAln
- 'Top Style' (Au/d) SPop WAln
- 'Tosca' (Au/S) CWCL GAbr GAgs NSum SPop WHil XBar
- 'Trafalgar' (Au/S) new NDro
- 'Trafalgar Square' (Au/S) GAbr GAgs NDro SPop XBar
- 'Tregor Orange' (Au/d) WCot
- 'Tregor Stripe' (Au/St) XBar
- 'Trish' (Au) GAbr
- 'Trojan' (Au/S) EBee
- 'Tromen' (Au/d) SPop
- 'Trouble' (Au/d) GAbr NDro
- 'Troy Aykman' (Au/A) NDro SPop WAln WHil
- 'Trudy' (Au/S) GAbr GAgs ITim NDro SPop WHil
- 'True Briton' (Au/S) NDro
- 'Truman' (Au/B) NDro
- 'Trumpet Blue' (Au/S) NDro SPop WAln WHil
- 'Trumpton' (Au/S) SPop
- 'Tudor Rose' (Au/S) WAln XBar
- 'Tumbledown' (Au/A) NDro
- 'Tummel' (Au/A) GAbr GAgs NDro SPop WHil
- 'Tupelo Honey' (Au/d) WAln
- 'Turnberry' (Au/S) SPop
- 'Tut Tut' (Au/A) SPop
- 'Tweedy' (Au/St) SPop
- 'Twiggy' (Au/S) GAbr NDro NSum SPop WFar XBar
- 'Two Steeples' (Au/A) SPop
- 'Typhoon' (Au/A) GAgs SPop WHil
- 'Uncle Arthur' (Au/A) WAln WHil
- 'Upper Crust' (Au/St) NDro SPop
- 'Upperfields' (Au/B) new NDro
- 'Upton Belle' (Au/S) SPop
- 'Ursula' (Au/d) WAln
- 'Ushba' (Au/d) SPop
- 'Valerie' (Au/A) ITim
- 'Valerie Clare' (Au/S) SPop WAln WHil
- 'Valiant' (Au/A) WAln
- 'Vee Too' (Au/A) NDro SPop WHil
- 'Vega' (Au/A) SPop WAln
- 'Velvet Moon' (Au/A) NSum SPop WAln
- 'Velvet Truffles' (Au/d) SPop
- 'Venetian' (Au/A) GAgs ITim NDro SPop WHil
- 'Venus' (Au/A) WAln
- 'Vera' (Au/A) EPot NDro NSum SPop WAln
- 'Vera Eden' (Au) WAln
- 'Vera Hill' (Au/A) WAln
- 'Verdi' (Au/A) SPop WAln
- 'Verity' (Au/S) SPop
- 'Vesuvius' (Au/d) GAbr NDro SPop
- 'Victoria' (Au/S) NWad SPop WAln
- 'Victoria de Wemyss' (Au/A) GAgs NDro XBar
- 'Victoria Jane' (Au/A) WAln
- 'Victoria Park' (Au/A) SPop WAln
- 'Vienna' (Au/B) NDro
- 'Violet Surprise' (Au/St) NDro

- 'Virginia Belle' (Au/St) SPop
- 'Voodoo Mama' (Au/St) NDro
- 'Vroni' (Au/A) **new** EBee
- 'Vulcan' (Au/A) NDro SPop XBar
- 'Walhampton' (Au/S) NDro SPop
- 'Walton' (Au/A) GAbr GAgs NDro SPop WHil XBar
- 'Walton Heath' (Au/d) GAbr GAgs NDro SPop WCot WFar WHil
- 'Wanda's Moonlight' (Au/d) SPop WAln
- 'Warpaint' (Au/St) NDro NSum
- 'Warwick' (Au/S) SPop
- 'Watchett' (Au/S) SPop
- 'Wedding Day' (Au/S) SPop
- 'Wentworth' (Au/A) WAln
- 'Werner Müller' (Au/B) NDro
- 'West Harrow' (Au/S) **new** NDro
- 'Westbourne Park' (Au/S) **new** NDro
- 'Wheal' (Au/S) NDro SPop
- 'Whistlejacket' (Au/S) NDro SPop
- 'White Ensign' (Au/S) GAbr GAgs NDro NWad SPop WHil
- 'White Pyne' (Au/B) NDro
- 'White Satin' (Au/S) NDro SPop
- 'White Water' (Au/A) NDro SPop WHil
- 'White Wings' (Au/S) ITim NDro NHpl NSum SPop
- 'Whoopee' (Au/A) NDro WAln
- 'Whorton's Claret' (Au/S) WAln
- 'Wichita Falls' (Au/A) NDro WAln
- 'Wide Awake' (Au/A) GAgs NDro SPop
- 'Wild and Grey' (Au/S) NDro
- 'Wilf Booth' (Au/A) SPop XBar
- 'William Gunn' (Au/d) NDro SPop WAln
- 'William of Orange' (Au/d) SPop
- 'Willow' (Au/d) SPop
- 'Willow Tree' (Au/S) WAln
- 'Wincha' (Au/S) ITim NDro NEgg SPop
- 'Windward Blue' (Au) NDro
- 'Windways Mystery' (Au/B) GAbr GAgs NDro NSum
- 'Windy Goldtop' (Au/A) WAln
- 'Winifred' (Au/B) see *P.* × *pubescens* 'Winnifred'
- 'Winifrid' (Au/A) GAgs NDro WHil
- 'Witchcraft' (Au) SPop
- 'Wonderous One' (Au/St) **new** NDro
- 'Woodlands Lilac' (Au/B) NDro WHil
- 'Woodmill' (Au/A) GAgs NDro NSum SPop WHil XBar
- 'Wookey Hole' (Au/A) NDro SPop
- 'Wor Jackie' (Au/S) SPop
- 'Wycliffe Harmony' (Au/B) NDro
- 'Wycliffe Midnight' (Au/B) GAbr ITim NDro WHil
- 'Wye Hen' (Au/St) NDro SPop
- 'Wye Lemon' (Au/S) SPop
- 'X2' (Au/S) WHil
- 'Xavier' (Au/d) EBee
- 'Yacoubi' (Au/A) SPop
- 'Yellow Ace' (Au) GAbr
- 'Yellow Hammer' (Au/S) WAln
- 'Yellow Isle' (Au/S) WAln
- 'Yellow Muff' (Au/S) NDro
- 'Yellow Ribbon' (Au) WAln
- 'Yes Indeed' (Au/St) NDro SPop
- 'Yitzhak Rabin' (Au/A) NDro SPop WHil
- 'Yorkshire Grey' (Au/S) NDro SPop
- 'Young Ian' (Au/B) **new** NDro
- 'Ypres' (Au/d) SPop
- 'Yummy' (Au/St) NDro
- 'Zambia' (Au/d) GAbr ITim NDro
- 'Zephyr' (Au/St) **new** NDro
- 'Ziggy' (Au/St) NDro
- 'Zimmer' (Au/St) SPop
- 'Zircon' (Au/S) NDro SPop
- 'Zoe' (Au/A) SPop WAln
- 'Zoe Ann' (Au/S) WAln

I - 'Zona' (Au/A) NDro

- 'Zorro' (Au/St) NDro

auriculata (Or) GKev SVic

- subsp. ***olgae*** (Or) GKev

balbisii (Au) GKev

'Barbara Midwinter' (Pr) EBee GAbr SHar WArt WCot

Barnhaven Blues Group (Pr/Prim) NSum XBar

Barnhaven doubles (Pr/Prim/d) XBar

Barnhaven Gold-laced Group see *P.* Gold-laced Group Barnhaven

Barnhaven hybrids (Pr) NSum

Barnhaven Pixies Group (Pr/Prim) **new** XBar

'Beamish Foam' (Pr/Poly) GAbr

'Beatrice Wooster' (Au) CRos GAbr LRHS NRHS WFar XBar

'Beeches' Pink' (Prim/Poly) NSum

beesiana (Pf) 🏆H6 Widely available

(Belarina Series) BELARINA AMETHYST ICE ('Kerbelpicotee'PBR) (Pr/Prim/d) CDor LRHS MHol WBor WHil WTor

- BELARINA BUTTER YELLOW ('Kerbelbut'PBR) (Pr/Prim/d) CAby CDor CExl CWCL ELon EPfP LRHS MHol NCGa NLar SRot WHil
- BELARINA BUTTERMILK ('Kerbelmilk'PBR) (Pr/Prim/d) NLar
- BELARINA COBALT BLUE ('Kerbelcob'PBR) (Pr/Prim/d) CAby CExl CWCL LRHS NHpl NLar SRot WHil
- BELARINA CREAM ('Kerbelcrem'PBR) (Pr/Prim/d) CAby CDor CExl CWCL ELon LRHS NCGa NHpl SRot WBor WCAu
- BELARINA PINK ICE ('Kerbelpice'PBR) (Pr/Prim/d) CAby CDor CWCL ELon MAvo NCGa NHpl NLar WBor WCot WHil WTor
- BELARINA ROSETTE NECTARINE ('Kerbelnec'PBR) (Pr/Prim/d) CAby CDor CExl CWCL ECtt ELon LRHS MHol NCGa NLar WHil
- BELARINA VALENTINE ('Kerbelred'PBR) (Pr/Prim/d) CAby CDor CWCL LLHF LRHS MHol NCGa NLar WCAu WHil WTor

bellidifolia (Mu) GKev NAln NGdn

beluensis see *P.* × *pubescens* 'Freedom'

bergenioides (Da) **new** GKev

'Bewerley White' see *P.* × *pubescens* 'Bewerley White'

bhutanica see *P. whitei* 'Sherriff's Variety'

bileckii see *P.* × *forsteri* 'Bileckii'

'Blindsee' (Au) CPBP EPot NHar

'Blue Ice' (Pr/Prim/d) XBar

'Blue Julianas' (Pr/Prim) NSum XBar

'Blue Riband' (Pr/Prim) GAbr LLHF SIgm

'Blue Ribbon' WFar

'Blue Sapphire' (Pr/Prim/d) GBin XBar

'Bon Accord Cerise' (Pr/Poly/d) GAbr

'Bon Accord Purple' (Pr/Poly/d) WRHF

'Bonheur' (Pr/Prim/d) **new** XBar

boothii 'Renfe' (Pe) **new** WCot

- subsp. ***repens*** (Pe) GKev MNrw

'Boothman's Ruby' see *P.* × *pubescens* 'Boothman's Variety'

Name	Suppliers
boveana (Sp)	GKev
bracteata (Bu)	EPot GKev WAbe
§ - subsp. ***dubernardiana*** (Bu)	WAbe
§ ***bracteosa*** (Pe)	ITim
brevicula SDR 4452 (Cy)	GKev
'Brittany Blue' (Pr/Prim/d)	XBar
'Broadwell Chameleon' (Au)	ITim NHar
'Broadwell Milkmaid' (Au) 🏆H5	CPBP ITim WAbe
'Broadwell Ruby' (Au)	ITim WAbe
'Broadwell Snowstorm' (Au)	ITim
'Broxbourne' 🏆H5	ITim
'Buckland Wine' (Pr/Prim)	CElw CFis EBee ECtt EPfP GAbr GEdr
bullata (Bu) **new**	GKev
× ***bulleesiana*** (Pf)	CAby CDor CRos EPfP EShb GKev GMaP GWyn LRHS MCot MWts NAln NChi NEgg NGdn NHol NLar NRHS NSum NWad SAko WFar WMoo WPnP
bulleyana (Pf) 🏆H7	Widely available
- hybrids (Pf)	GKev
burmanica (Pf)	GAbr GKev MMuc WHoo WMoo
'Butter's Bronze' (Pr/Prim)	WOut
'Butterscotch' (Pr/Prim)	NSum XBar
'Caerulea Plena' (Pr/Prim)	NBid
calderiana purple-flowered (Pe)	GKev
- subsp. ***strumosa*** (Pe)	GKev
callianatha (Cy)	GKev
'Camaieu' (Pr/Prim/d)	XBar
Candelabra hybrids (Pf)	CBre CPla GAbr ITim NBir NGdn NHpl
Candy Pinks Group (Pr/Prim)	NSum XBar
capitata (Ca)	CBcs CPla EPfP GCrg GKev LRHS NAln NHpl SCob SPer WCAu WCot
- CC 3843	SRms
- subsp. ***crispata*** (Ca)	GKev
- subsp. ***mooreana*** (Ca)	CAby CExl CTsd EDAr EPfP GJos GKev NAln NGdn NHpl NLar NSum SPlb SRot WAbe XBar
- 'Noverna Blue' (Ca)	MHol
- 'Noverna Deep Blue' (Ca)	SRms
- subsp. ***sphaerocephala*** (Ca) 🏆H5	GKev
'Captain Blood' (Pr/Prim/d)	NHpl
Carnation Victorians Group (Pr/Poly)	XBar
carniolica (Au)	GKev WCot
cawdoriana (So)	GKev
cernua (Mu)	LLHF NSum XBar
Chartreuse Group (Pr/Poly)	XBar
§ ***chionantha*** (Cy) 🏆H6	GEdr GKev NAln NBir NGdn NSum WFar XBar
- subsp. ***chionantha*** (Cy)	GKev MHol NAln
§ - subsp. ***sinoplantaginea*** (Cy)	NLar
§ - subsp. ***sinopurpurea*** (Cy)	EBee GKev NBir NSum
chungensis (Pf)	CBod CDor CRos CTsd EBee ELon EPfP GBin GKev GLog GQue GWyn IKil MHol NAln NGdn NHol NLar NSum SPtp SWvt WFar WMAq WMoo XBar
§ ***chungensis* × *pulverulenta*** (Pf)	SAko WSpi
× ***chunglenta***	see *P. chungensis × pulverulenta*
'Cisca' (Pr)	WCot
'Clarence Elliott' (Au) 🏆H5	CPBP GKev MPnt NAln NRya NWad WAbe WFar WIce WThu
'Clarissa White' (Pr/Poly)	XBar
clarkei (Or)	GKev WAbe
clusiana (Au)	GKev WAbe
- 'Murray-Lyon' (Au)	NDro NHar
cockburniana (Pf) 🏆H6	CSpe CTsd WCot XBar
- SDR 1967	EBee GKev
- 'Kevock Sunshine' (Pf)	GKev NAln
- orange-flowered (Pf)	GKev
concholoba (Mu)	GKev
'Coolock Dark Star' **new**	CPBP
'Corporal Baxter' (Pr/Prim/d)	ECtt GMaP LLHF XBar
cortusoides (Co)	CAby EBee EBou EPfP GKev
'Cottage Cream' (Pr)	SVic
Cowichan Amethyst Group (Pr/Poly)	XBar
Cowichan Blue Group (Pr/Poly)	NSum XBar
Cowichan Garnet Group (Pr/Poly)	NSum XBar
Cowichan strain (Pr/Poly)	CElw
Cowichan Venetian Group (Pr/Poly)	NSum XBar
Cowichan Yellow Group (Pr/Poly)	NSum XBar
'Coy' (Au)	ITim
'Craddock White' (Pr/Prim)	CFis
'Crème du Tregor' (Pr/Prim/d) **new**	XBar
'Crimson Velvet' (Au)	WThu XBar
crispa	see *P. glomerata*
cuneifolia (Cu)	GKev
- subsp. ***heterodonta*** (Cu)	GKev
darialica (Al)	GKev LLHF NAln
'Dark Rosaleen' (Pr/Poly)	Widely available
'David Valentine' (Pr/Poly)	CFis GAbr GEdr WCot XBar
'Dawn Ansell' (Pr/Prim/d)	CAby CBod CDor ECtt EPfP GAbr GMaP MBNS MHol MRav NBir NCGa NHpl NSum WCAu WHer WHil XBar
Daybreak Group (Pr/Poly)	XBar
'Dentelle' (Pr/Prim/d) **new**	XBar
denticulata (De) 🏆H6	Widely available
- var. ***alba*** (De)	CAby CAvo CBcs CRos CTri EBee EBou ECha EPfP GAbr GMaP GWyn LRHS LSun MBel MMuc NGdn NLar NPri NRHS SCob SGbt SPer SPoG WFar WGwG WMoo WWtn
- blue-flowered (De)	CAvo EPfP GBin GWyn LLWG NLar NPri
- 'Bressingham Beauty' (De)	CRos EBee LRHS NRHS
- var. ***cachemiriana*** hort. (De)	NWad
- 'Glenroy Crimson' (De)	EBee LLHF
- hybrids	SCob WFar XBar
- 'Karryann' (De/v)	WCot
- lavender-flowered (De)	CAby
- lilac-flowered (De)	CRos EPfP LRHS NHol NRHS SCob WTor
- 'Miss Esther' (De) **new**	NSum
- purple-flowered (De)	WMoo
- red-flowered (De)	CAby CAvo EPfP NBir SCob WMoo
- 'Rubin' (De)	CRos CWCL CWat EBee EBou EPfP GAbr GMaP LRHS MBel NChi NLar NRHS SPer SPoG SRms XLum
- 'Rubinball' (De)	NHol
'Desert Sunset' (Pr/Poly)	XBar

'Don Keefe'[PBR] (Pr/Poly)	CBcs EBee ECtt GBin LLHF MBNS MBel MHol MMuc MNrw MPie NGBl NHpl NLar NWad SCob WCot WFar WMoo
'Dorothy' (Pr/Poly)	MRav
'Double Lilac'	see *P. vulgaris* 'Lilacina Plena'
dubernardiana	see *P. bracteata* subsp. *dubernardiana*
'Duchess of York' (Pr/Poly)	ECtt GAbr LLHF MHCG NLar WCot
'Duckyls Red' (Pr/Prim)	NBir WHal
'Early Bird' (*allionii* hybrid) (Au)	ITim
'Easter Bonnet' (Pr/Prim)	LRHS MMuc SEND
edgeworthii	see *P. nana*
§ ***elatior*** (Pr) ♀H6	CAby CBod CDor CMac EPfP GAbr GJos GKev GMaP MBel MHer MHol MNHC MNrw NAln NChi NEgg NLar NPri SPer SPoG SRms SWvt WArt WBrk
- hose-in-hose (Pr/d)	NBid
- hybrids (Pr)	SPlb
- 'Magnifica' (Pr)	GKev
§ - subsp. ***meyeri*** (Pr)	SBrt
- subsp. ***pallasii*** (Pr)	GKev SPhx
- subsp. ***pseudoelatior*** (Pr)	WAbe
'Elizabeth Browning' (Pr/Poly)	ECtt GAbr WCot
'Elizabeth Killelay'[PBR] (Pr/Poly/d)	CAby CBct CBod CDor CExl CPla CWCL CWGN ECtt ELan GBin MNrw MPie NBir NEgg NGdn NHpl NLar NSum NWad SPer WCot WFar XBar
'Ethel Barker' (Au)	NWad
'Eugénie' (Pr/Prim/d)	ECtt MRav
'Fairy Rose' (Au)	NWad
farinosa (Al)	GKev NGdn SIgm
- var. ***denudata***	GKev
fasciculata (Ar)	GKev SPlb
- CLD 345	GEdr WAbe
'Feuerkönig' (Au)	NDro
'Fire Opal' (Pr/Poly)	CRos LRHS NRHS
Firefly Group (Pr/Poly)	WCot XBar
§ ***firmipes*** (Si)	LPot
§ ***flaccida*** (Mu)	GEdr GKev NAln NHpl NSum
Flamingo Group (Pr/Poly)	XBar
florindae (Si) ♀H7	Widely available
- bronze-flowered (Si)	NBir
- 'Dave's Red' (Si)	LEdu
- hybrids (Si)	CMac EHrv EShb WFar WHil WWtn XBar
- Keillour hybrids (Si)	NGdn NLar SWvt WBor
- orange-flowered (Si)	GPSL LLWG MNrw SRms WMoo WPnP
- peach-flowered (Si)	CSpe
- 'Ray's Ruby' (Si)	CTsd GEdr MNrw NBir NChi WCot WMoo
- red and copper hybrids (Si)	MWts SWvt WHoo
- 'Red Shades' (Si)	CRos NWad
- red-flowered (Si)	CSpe GBin GKev GPSL LLWG MMuc NAln NBid NLar NSum WFar
- terracotta-flowered (Si)	NGdn
Footlight Parade Group (Pr/Prim)	XBar
forbesii (Mo)	WCot
- CC 4084	CExl
forrestii (Bu)	EPot GKev
- SDR 4304	CExl
§ × ***forsteri*** (Au)	NHpl NLar
§ - 'Bileckii' (Au)	GMaP LLHF NBir NHar NSla
- 'Dianne' (Au)	GAbr GCrg GKev LLHF NRya WAbe WThu
'Francisca' (Pr/Poly) ♀H7	Widely available
'Fred Salter' (Au)	ITim NRya
frondosa (Al) ♀H5	MHol MPnt WAbe
'Frou-frou' (Pr/Prim/d)	XBar
Fuchsia Victorians Group (Pr/Poly)	CWCL XBar
'Garnet' (*allionii* hybrid) (Au)	XBar
'Garryarde Crimson' (Pr/Prim)	LLHF
'Garryarde Guinevere'	see *P.* 'Guinevere'
geraniifolia (Co)	GKev
'Gigha' (Pr/Prim)	EBee GKev MNrw WFar XBar
'Gilded Garnet' (Pr/Poly/d) **new**	NHpl
'Gilded Ginger' (Pr/Poly)	XBar
'Ginger Spice' (Au)	NDro WHil
§ ***glomerata*** (Ca)	GKev NAln XBar
'Glowing Embers' (Pf)	GKev NBir
glutinosa All.	see *P. allionii*
Gold-laced Group (Pr/Poly)	Widely available
§ - Barnhaven (Pr/Poly)	MAsh NBir XBar
- Beeches strain (Pr/Poly)	CWCL XBar
- red-flowered (Pr/Poly)	ELan XEll
'Gold-laced Jack in the Green' Barnhaven	XBar
gracilipes (Pe)	GKev
- 'Major'	see *P. bracteosa*
- 'Minor'	see *P. petiolaris* Wall.
graminifolia	see *P. chionantha*
Grand Canyon Group (Pr/Poly)	CWCL XBar
grandis (Sr)	GKev XBar
'Green Lace' (Pr/Poly)	ECtt
'Groenekan's Glorie' (Pr/Prim)	CFis EBee ECtt GAbr NBir NSum WFar
'Guernsey Cream' (Pr/Prim/d)	XBar
§ 'Guinevere' (Pr/Poly) ♀H6	Widely available
'Hall Barn Blue' (Pr/Prim)	CSam EBee ELan EWhm GEdr GMaP MHCG MMuc SEND WCot
§ ***halleri*** (Al)	GKev NAln XBar
- 'Longiflora'	see *P. halleri*
- subsp. ***platyphylla*** (Al)	GKev
handeliana × ***maximowiczii*** **new**	GKev
Harbinger Group (Pr/Prim)	CWCL XBar
Harbour Lights mixture (Pr/Poly)	XBar
Harlow Car hybrids (Pf)	CRos EPfP LRHS NAln NRHS NSla NWad WMoo XBar
Harvest Yellows Group (Pr/Poly)	CWCL XBar
helodoxa	see *P. prolifera*
'Hemswell Blush' (Au)	GKev LLHF NAln NHpl WFar
'Hemswell Ember' (Au)	CPBP ECtt
'Heritage Cream' (Pr/Prim)	EPfP
heucherifolia (Co)	EBee
- SDR 3224	GKev
hidakana (R)	GEdr
'High Point' (Au)	CPBP
hirsuta (Au)	GKev MMuc SEND
- red-flowered (Au)	EBee GKev
- subsp. ***valcuvianensis*** (Au)	EPot
- white-flowered (Au)	NRya
hirsuta × ***minima***	see *P.* × *forsteri*
hoffmanniana	NSum
hose-in-hose (Pr/Poly/d)	MNrw

	Name	Suppliers
	– Barnhaven (Pr/Poly/d)	XBar
§	Husky Series (Pr/Prim) ♀H5	SVic
	'Hyacinthia' (Au)	CAby
	ianthina	see *P. prolifera*
	incana (Al)	GKev
	Indian Reds Group (Pr/Poly)	CWCL XBar
	'Ingram's Blue' (Pr/Poly)	CFis EBee EPfP MHol
	Inshriach hybrids (Pf)	CAby SPer WBor
	integrifolia (Au)	GKev
§	'Inverewe' (Pf)	EBee GKev NBir NHpl XBar
	involucrata	see *P. munroi*
	ioessa var. ***hopeana*** (Si)	GKev
	'Iris Mainwaring' (Pr/Prim)	CFis EBee ECtt ELan LLHF MCot
	irregularis (Pe)	ITim WAbe
	'Jackie Richards' (Au)	GKev
	Jack-in-the-Green Group (Pr/Poly)	MNrw WBor WMoo
	– Barnhaven (Pr/Poly)	XBar
	– red-flowered (Pr/Poly)	MMuc WHil
	– white-flowered (Pr/Poly)	IFro
	'Jack-the-Lad' (Pr/Prim/d)	XBar
	'Janet Aldrich' (Au)	CPBP
	japonica (Pf)	CSam ECha LRHS MSCN NBro NGdn WMoo
	– 'Alba' (Pf)	CAby CBod CPla CRos CTri EPfP EShb LRHS MBel NAln NGdn NLar NRHS NWad WFar
	– 'Apple Blossom' (Pf)	Widely available
*	– 'Carminea' (Pf)	CDor GKev MSCN NBro NGdn NWad SPer WFar WRHF WWtn
	– 'Fuji' (Pf)	GKev NBro
	– hybrids (Pf)	CMac MRav NHic WFar
	– 'Jim Saunders' (Pf)	SLon
	– 'Miller's Crimson' (Pf) ♀H6	Widely available
	– 'Oriental Sunrise' (Pf)	EHrv GKev ITim XBar
	– pale pink-flowered (Pf)	ITim NSum
	– 'Postford White' (Pf) ♀H6	CBcs CCBP CDor CPla CRos CSam EBee EHrv ELan EPfP GAbr GBin GKev GMaP ITim LLWG LRHS LSRN LSun NBir NRHS SPer SPoG SRms SWvt WBor WBrk WMoo XBar
	– 'Valley Red' (Pf)	GKev NRHS
	– Violet Oriental Group (Pf)	XBar
	– violet-flowered (Pf)	GKev
	jesoana (Co)	GKev
	– var. ***pubescens*** (Co)	GKev
	'Jewel' (Pr)	GAbr
	'Joan Hughes' (*allionii* hybrid) (Au)	WAbe
	'Joanna' (Pr/Poly)	ECtt MPnt
	'Johanna' (Pu)	GCrg GKev NGdn NSum WAbe
	'John Fielding' (Pr)	CBro CElw EBee NWad
	'Jo-Jo' (Au)	CPBP ITim XBar
	juliae (Pr)	CRos EWTr GCrg GKev LRHS NBid NHpl NRHS NSum SPlb WAbe
I	– 'Millicent' (Pr)	WCot
	– white-flowered (Pr)	NSum
	'Ken Dearman' (Pr/Prim/d)	ECtt MRav NBir NHpl XBar
	kewensis (Sp) ♀H3	CPla GKev XBar
	'Kingscote' (Au)	NDro
	'Kinlough Beauty' (Pr/Poly)	CFis EBee ECtt GMaP LLHF XBar
§	***kisoana*** (Co)	CExl GEdr GKev WCru
	– var. ***alba*** (Co)	GEdr NHar XBar
	– 'Barnhaven Blush' (Co) **new**	XBar
	– 'Iyo-beni' (Co)	GEdr NHar XBar
	– 'Noushoku' (Co)	GEdr XBar
	– var. ***shikokiana***	see *P. kisoana*
	komarovii (Pr)	LEdu SPlb
	'Kusum Krishna'	EBee GEdr MAvo MBNS MHol MPie NHpl NRya NSti NWad WCot WFar
	'Lady Greer' (Pr/Poly) ♀H5	CBod CMac CSam EBee ECtt EMor EPPr EPfP GAbr GKev GMaP GWyn MCot MHer MTin NAln NChi NGdn NLar NSum SIgm WCAu WFar XBar
	'Lambrook Mauve' (Pr/Poly)	CElw CFis GAbr
§	***latifolia*** (Au)	GKev
§	***laurentiana*** (Al)	EWes GKev
	'Lea Gardens' (*allionii* hybrid) (Au)	NWad
	'Lee Myers' (*allionii* hybrid) (Au)	WFar XBar
	'Lemon and Lime'	CMea
	leucophylla	see *P. elatior*
	lilacina (Mu)	EPot GKev
	'Lilian Foster'	WArt WCot
	limbata (Cy)	GKev
	'Lindum Angelic' (Au)	NHar
	'Lindum Celebration' (Au)	NHar
	'Lindum Crepes Suzette' (Au)	ITim NHar
	'Lindum Dove' (Au) **new**	NHar
	'Lindum Finale' (Au)	ITim NHar
	'Lindum First Kiss' (Au)	ITim
	'Lindum Frosty Moon' (Au)	ITim
	'Lindum Gecko' (Au)	NHar
	'Lindum Golden Orb' (Au) **new**	NHar
	'Lindum Limelight' (Au)	ITim
	'Lindum Lyric' (Au)	NHar
	'Lindum Malcolm's Mate' (Au)	CPBP
	'Lindum Moonlight' (Au)	LLHF
	'Lindum Morning Flight' (Au)	NHar
	'Lindum Rapture' (Au)	NHar
	'Lindum Rhapsody' (Au)	LLHF
	'Lindum Storm Cloud' (Au)	NHar
	'Lindum Wedgwood' (Au)	EPot ITim NHar
	'Lingwood Beauty' (Pr/Prim)	CAby CElw CFis
	'Lismore' (Au)	NWad
	'Lismore Bay' (Au)	GKev
	'Lismore Peardrop' (Au)	EPot
	'Lismore Pink Ice' (Au)	NWad
	'Lismore Sunshine' (Au)	WThu
	'Little Egypt' (Pr/Poly)	XBar
	littoniana	see *P. vialii*
	'Lizzie Green' (Pr/Prim)	NLar
	× ***loiseleurii*** 'Aire Mist' (Au) ♀H5	EPot ITim NHpl NRya NSla NSum NWad WFar WThu XBar
§	– 'Aire Waves' (Au)	CPBP CWCL ITim NHar NRya NWad
	– 'Lismore Yellow' (Au) **new**	XBar
	– 'Pink Aire Mist' (Au)	ITim
	longiflora	see *P. halleri*
	longipes (Cy)	GKev
	lutea (Au)	GKev
	luteola (Or)	GKev LLHF NGdn NHpl NSum XBar
*	***lutescens*** **new**	CBor
	macrocalyx	see *P. veris*
	macrophylla (Cy)	GKev
	– var. ***moorcroftiana*** (Cy)	GKev
	'MacWatt's Claret' (Pr/Poly)	ECtt GAbr
	'MacWatt's Cream' (Pr/Poly)	CFis CRos EBee GEdr LEdu LLHF LRHS NLar NRHS WCot WHil

Plant	Suppliers
'Mademoiselle Zia' (Pr/Poly) **new**	XBar
magellanica (Al)	SPlb
mairei (Al)	GKev
'Maisie Michael' (Pr/Prim)	GEdr LLHF NHpl WAbe
marginata (Au) ♀^{H5}	CRos LRHS MMuc NRHS NSla NSum SEND WAbe
- 'Adrian Evans' (Au)	EPot GEdr WIce
- 'Alba' (Au)	CRos GEdr LRHS NBro NRHS NRya NWad XBar
- 'Ardfearn' (Au)	GEdr
- 'Baldock's Purple' (Au)	NRya
- 'Barbara Clough' (Au)	GEdr NRya NWad XBar
- 'Beamish' (Au) ♀^{H5}	GEdr NBro NRya NSla NWad
- 'Beatrice Lascaris' (Au)	CRos GEdr ITim LRHS NRHS NRya
- 'Bill Crow' (Au)	GEdr NRya
- 'Caerulea' (Au)	GEdr GKev ITim NRya NWad
- 'Clear's Variety' (Au)	GKev ITim LLHF
- 'Crookes Variety' (Au)	NRya
- 'Doctor Jenkins' (Au)	ITim NRya NWad
- 'Dolomites' (Au)	NWad
- 'Drake's Form' (Au)	GKev ITim NLar NRya XBar
- dwarf (Au)	CRos GEdr LRHS NRHS NRya
- 'Earl L. Bolton'	see *P. marginata* 'El Bolton'
§ - 'El Bolton' (Au)	NRya NWad
- 'Elizabeth Fry' (Au)	GEdr
- 'Grandiflora' (Au)	NWad
- 'Highland Twilight' (Au)	NSla
- 'Holden Variety' (Au)	ITim NRya NWad XBar
- 'Holly Leaf' (Au)	GEdr
- 'Ivy Agee' (Au)	NRya
- 'Janet' (Au)	GEdr LLHF NWad
- 'Johannes Holler' (Au)	ITim NRya
- 'Kesselring's Variety' (Au)	CMea ITim LLHF NWad WAbe WFar WIce XBar
- 'Laciniata' (Au)	CRos LRHS NRHS XBar
- 'Lemon Sorbet' (Au)	ITim
- 'Linda Pope' (Au) ♀^{H5}	GEdr NBir NSum WThu XBar
- 'Millard's Variety' (Au)	ITim NWad
- 'Mrs Carter Walmsley' (Au)	NRya NWad
- 'Mylene' (Au)	CPBP NRya
- 'Napoleon' (Au)	GEdr ITim NRya NWad
- 'Peggy Fell' (Au)	NWad
- 'Prichard's Variety' (Au) ♀^{H5}	GCrg GEdr GPSL ITim LLHF NRya WAbe
- 'Sheila Denby' (Au)	NRya NWad
- 'The President' (Au)	NWad
- 'Waithman's Variety' (Au)	NRya NWad
'Maria Talbot' (*allionii* hybrid) (Au)	CPBP EPot
'Marianne Davey' (Pr/Prim/d)	WKif
Marine Blues Group (Pr/Poly)	CWCL NSum XBar
'Mars' (*allionii* hybrid) (Au)	XBar
'Marven' (Au)	ITim
'Mary Anne' (Pr)	GAbr
Mauve Victorians Group (Pr/Poly)	XBar
maximowiczii (Cy)	EDAr GBin GEdr NGdn NSum
§ - var. ***maximowiczii*** (Cy)	GKev NHpl
- Red-flowered Group	see *P. maximowiczii* var. *maximowiczii*
maximowiczii* × *tangutica (Cy)	GKev
megaseifolia (Pr)	GKev
melanantha 'Moonshine' (Cy)	GKev
'Melenoc'h' (Pr/Prim/d)	XBar
Midnight Group (Pr/Prim)	CWCL XBar
'Miel' (Pr/Prim/d)	XBar
'Millstream Cream' (Au)	NLar
minima (Au)	GKev NBro WAbe
minor (Cy)	GKev
'Miss Doris' (Pr/Prim/d)	XBar
'Miss Indigo' (Pr/Prim/d)	CWCL ECtt EPfP GMaP MBNS MHol MRav NHpl NSum SPer WCAu WMoo XBar
mistassinica	see *P. laurentiana* var. ***macropoda***
miyabeana (Pf)	GKev
modesta (Al)	XBar
- var. ***faurieae*** (Al)	GKev
- var. ***samanimontana*** (Al)	GKev
'Moerheimii' (Pr/Prim)	GAbr GEdr
monticola (De)	GKev
'Moorland Apricot'	WMoo
moupinensis (Pe)	CExl
- subsp. ***barkamensis*** (Pe)	GKev
'Mrs Frank Neave' (Pr/Prim)	GAbr WFar
'Mrs McGillivray' (Pr/Prim)	GAbr
§ ***munroi*** (Ar)	GKev SIgm WAbe XBar
- subsp. ***munroi*** (Ar) CC 5311	GKev
- white-flowered (Ar)	WAbe
§ - subsp. ***yargongensis*** (Ar)	EBee GKev
muscarioides (Mu)	GKev
Muted Victorians Group (Pr/Poly)	NSum XBar
'Myline'	WThu
§ ***nana*** (Pe)	GKev NHar
'Neon Maiden' (Au) **new**	EPot
New Pinks Group (Pr/Poly)	NSum XBar
'Nightingale' (Au)	ITim
nivalis Pallas	see *P. chionantha*
nivalis ambig.	NSum
nutans Delavay ex Franch.	see *P. flaccida*
obconica subsp. ***werringtonensis***	GKev
obtusifolia (Cy)	GKev
odontocalyx 'Snow Flurry' (Da)	GKev
'Old Port' (Pr/Poly)	CSam GKev GQue NSum
Old Rose Victorians Group (Pr/Poly)	NSum XBar
(Ooh La La Series) 'Ooh La La Blood Orange' **new**	WHlf
- 'Ooh La La Pastel Pink' **new**	WHlf
'Orange Flame' (Pf) **new**	GKev
orbicularis (Cy)	GKev LLHF NAln NHpl
Osiered Amber Group (Pr/Prim)	NSum NWad XBar
palmata (Co)	GEdr
'Paris '90' (Pr/Poly)	CWCL NSum XBar
parryi (Pa)	GEdr GKev
pedemontana 'Alba' (Au)	GEdr WThu XBar
'Perle von Bottrop' (Pr/Prim)	ECtt WCot
petelotii (Ch)	WAbe
'Peter Klein' (Or)	ECtt GCrg GKev
petiolaris misapplied	see *P.* 'Redpoll'
§ ***petiolaris*** Wall. (Pe)	NHar NSum
- Sherriff's form	see *P.* 'Redpoll'
'Petticoat' (Pr/Prim/d)	ECtt NWad WCot XBar
'Pink Aire' (Au)	NSum XBar
'Pink Fairy' (Au)	ITim
'Pink Grapefruit' (Pr/Prim/d)	XBar

	Name	Suppliers
	'Pink Ice' (*allionii* hybrid) (Au)	CPBP GKev NWad XBar
	'Pink' (Primlet Series) (Pr/Prim)	LRHS NRHS
	'Pink Star' (Pr/Prim/d)	XBar
	poissonii (Pf)	CDor CFis CRos CTri EDAr EPfP GKev LRHS NGdn NHpl NRHS NSum WShi WWtn
	polyanthus (Pr/Poly)	MMuc
	polyneura (Co)	CBod GKev MHol NGdn WCot
	'Powdery Pink'	CRos LRHS NRHS
	prenantha SDR 3909 (Pf)	GKev
	Primlet Series (Pr/Prim)	SVic
§	***prolifera*** (Pf) ♀H4	CRos EPfP GKev GMaP LRHS MNrw NAln NGdn NHpl NRHS NWad SPtp WMoo XBar
	- purple-flowered B&SWJ 13951	WCru
§	× ***pubescens*** (Au) ♀H5	CAby CDor CRos LRHS MHer NGdn NRHS
	- 'A.E. Matthews' (Au)	NWad
	- 'Alba' (Au)	NSla
	- 'Balfouriana' (Au)	NWad
§	- 'Bewerley White' (Au)	EBee EPfP NDro
	- 'Blue Wave' (Au)	SPop
§	- 'Boothman's Variety' (Au)	CAby CTri EPfP GKev ITim NSla WBrk WHoo
	- 'Carmen'	see *P.* × *pubescens* 'Boothman's Variety'
	- 'Christine' (Au)	CMea GKev MHer NBir NSum WCot
	- 'Cream Viscosa' (Au)	SPlb WFar
	- 'Faldonside' (Au)	GCrg NSla NSum
§	- 'Freedom' (Au)	CTri GKev NBir NSla XBar
	- 'Harlow Car' (Au)	CMea MPnt NSum NWad
	- 'Hazel's White' (Au)	NDro
	- 'Joan Danger' (Au)	NDro
	- 'Joan Gibbs' (Au)	NHpl XBar
	- 'Lilac Fairy' (Au)	GKev ITim NWad WThu
	- 'Moonlight' (Au)	NDro
	- 'Mrs J.H. Wilson' (Au)	GCrg NRya XBar
	- 'Pat Barwick' (Au)	NDro NWad
	- 'Rufus' (Au) ♀H5	GAbr GEdr NDro WThu XBar
	- 'Sid Skelton' (Au)	NRya
	- 'Slack Top Violet' (Au)	NSla
	- 'Snowcap' (Au)	ITim XBar
	- 'The General' (Au)	CTri GEdr
§	- 'Wedgwood' (Au)	GAbr NDro NSum XBar
§	- 'Winnifred' (Au))	GAbr NDro
	pulchella (Pu)	GKev
	pulverulenta (Pf) ♀H6	Widely available
	- 'Bartley' (Pf)	WWtn
	- Bartley hybrids (Pf) ♀H6	CPla EWTr GKev GWyn NAln NHpl NSum NWad WMoo
	- 'Bartley Pink' (Pf)	CPla
	'Purple' (Primlet Series) (Pr/Prim)	CRos LRHS NRHS
	'Purple Storm' (Pr/Prim/d) **new**	XBar
	'Quaker's Bonnet'	see *P. vulgaris* 'Lilacina Plena'
	'Rachel Kinnen' (Au)	GAbr WFar XBar
	'Ramona' (Pr/Poly)	XBar
	'Raspberry Ripple' (Pr/Prim/d)	CRos LRHS NRHS XBar
	'Ravenglass Vermilion'	see *P.* 'Inverewe'
	'Red' (Primlet Series) (Pr/Prim)	CRos LRHS NRHS
	'Red Ruffles' (Pr/Poly/d)	ECtt
§	'Redpoll' (Pe)	NHar
	'Reenie' (Au) **new**	EPot
	reidii (So)	GEdr XBar
	- var. ***williamsii*** (So)	GEdr GKev
*	- - ***alba*** (So)	GEdr
	reticulata (Si)	GKev
	'Reverie' (Pr/Poly)	XBar
	'Rheniana' (Au)	NRya
	'Romeo' (Pr/Prim)	LLHF NWad WCot
	'Rose' (Primlet Series) (Pr/Prim)	CRos LRHS NRHS
	rosea (Or) ♀H5	CAby CBod EPfP GKev GLog GMaP MMuc NBid NBir NRya WPnP
	- CC 5260 **new**	MAsh
	- 'Gigas' (Or)	WMAq
	- 'Grandiflora' (Or)	CBod CMac CRos EMor EPfP GCrg GKev GPSL LRHS MBel NAln NLar SPoG SRms XLum
	'Rosemary Cottage' (Pr/Poly)	WCot
	'Rowallane Rose' (Pf)	GCal
I	'Rowena' (Pr/Prim)	CFis GAbr LLHF WCot
	'Roy Cope' (Pr/Prim/d)	NBir
	rubra	see *P. firmipes*
	'Ruby Tuesday' (Au)	NDro
	rupicola (Y)	GKev
	rusbyi (Pa)	GKev
	- subsp. ***ellisiae*** (Pa)	GKev
	'Sapphire' (Au)	XBar
§	'Schneekissen' (Pr/Prim)	CAby CBod CRos CSam CWCL EBee LLHF LRHS MHer NBro NChi NRHS SCob WFar WTor
	scotica (Al)	EMor GKev GPoy NAln NRHS NSla SPlb WAbe
	secundiflora (Pf)	ELan GAbr GKev LLWG NAln NBir NSum NWad SPlb WArt WBrk WMoo XBar
	septemloba (Co)	GKev
	serratifolia (Pf)	GKev
	sharmae (Al)	GKev
	sibthorpii	see *P. vulgaris* subsp. *sibthorpii*
	sieboldii (Co) ♀H5	EWld GKev MAsh MNrw NHpl NRHS SRms
	- 'Aiaigasa' (Co)	WFar
	- 'Aki-no-yosooi' (Co)	WFar
	- 'Andromeda' (Co)	EBee WHil
	- 'Aoba-no-fue' (Co)	CAby
	- 'Aoyagi-zome' (Co)	XBar
	- 'Arimayama' (Co)	WFar WHil
	- 'Asahi' (Co)	WFar
	- 'Asahigata' (Co)	WHil
	- 'Ayanami' (Co)	WFar
	- 'Ayasegawa' (Co)	WFar WHil
	- 'Beeches Star' (Co)	EBee
	- 'Benjamin' (Co)	WFar WHil
	- 'Bide-a-Wee Blue' (Co)	NBid
	- 'Bide-a-Wee Lace' (Co)	NBid
	- 'Bijyonomai' (Co)	GWyn WFar
I	- 'Blue Lagoon' (Co)	CRos EBee EPfP LLHF LRHS NLar NRHS WFar WHil
	- blue-flowered (Co)	WHil
	- 'Blush' (Co)	WFar WHil
	- 'Boykavitch' (Co)	WHil
	- 'Bureikou' (Co)	WFar
	- 'Carefree' (Co)	ECtt LLHF NBro NLar WFar WHil XBar
	- 'Carmine Pink' (Co)	WHil
	- 'Cherubim' (Co)	CRos EBee LRHS NRHS WHil
	- 'Daikoshi' (Co)	WFar WHil
	- 'Daiminnishiki' (Co)	WFar
	- 'Dancing Ladies' (Co)	ECtt GWyn NBro WFar WHil XBar
	- 'Dart Rapids' (Co)	WHil WSHC

- 'Duane's Choice' (Co) CAby
- 'Edasango' (Co) GWyn WFar
- 'Edomurasaki' (Co) GWyn WFar WHil
- 'Emerald Sun' (Co) **new** WFar
- 'Flamenco' (Co/d) GEdr WFar XBar
- 'Frilly Blue' (Co) CRos EBee GEdr GWyn LRHS NRHS WFar
- 'Fuji Shishi' (Co/d) XBar
- 'Fuji-jishi' (Co/d) WFar
- 'Galaxy' (Co) NBro
- 'Geisha Girl' (Co) CDor CRos CSpe EBee ECtt GEdr GWyn LRHS MRav NLar NRHS WFar WHil
- 'Gin-pukurin' (Co) CAby WFar WHil
- 'Girl of the Limberlost' (Co) WFar XBar
- 'Gloaming' (Co) XBar
- 'Gunma Niizatia' (Co) WFar
- 'Hakutsuri' (Co) WFar
- 'Hana-angya' (Co/d) XBar
- 'Hanaguruma' (Co) WFar
- 'Harutugedoric' (Co) **new** GWyn WFar
- 'Hatu-garasu' (Co) WFar
- 'Hatu-goromo' (Co) WFar
- 'Hatusugato' (Co) WFar
- 'Heart's Desire' (Co) EBee WFar
- 'Higurasi' (Co) WFar
- 'Hinokoromo' (Co) WFar
- 'Hutaezuru' (Co) WFar
- 'Inikina White' (Co) WFar
- 'Inukima Mincura' (Co) GWyn WFar
- 'Iso-botan' (Co) GEdr WFar XBar
- 'Jessica' (Co) WHil
- 'Kansenden' (Co) WFar
- 'Karakoromo' (Co) WFar
- 'Kashima' (Co) CAby WFar WHil
- 'Kiraboshi' (Co) WFar XBar
- 'Kokoroiki' (Co) GWyn WFar
- 'Komon' (Co) **new** WFar
- 'Kotobuki' (Co) GEdr
- 'Kotonoshirabe' (Co) WFar
- 'Kourohou' (Co) GWyn WFar
- 'Kurama' (Co) GWyn WFar
- 'Laced Lady' (Co) **new** WFar
- 'Lacewing' (Co) WHil
- f. ***lactiflora*** (Co) CRos GWyn LRHS NBro NRHS SRot WFar WHil
- 'Lilac Crinoline' (Co) WFar XBar
- 'Lilac Sunbonnet' (Co) EPfP LLHF WFar
- 'Makazebeni' (Co) GWyn WFar
- 'Managuruma' (Co) WFar
- 'Manakoora' (Co) CAby ECtt EHrv NBro NSum WFar XBar
- 'Mangetu' (Co) WFar
- 'Martin Nest Blue' (Co) WHil
- 'Martin Nest Pale Pink' (Co) WHil
- 'Masasino' (Co) WFar
- 'Matunoyuki' (Co) WFar WHil
- 'Miho-no-koji' (Co) WFar
- 'Mikado' (Co) CRos EBee ECtt GEdr LRHS NRHS WFar WHil
- 'Mikininonomare' (Co) GWyn WFar
- Minuet Group (Co) XBar
- 'Miyakowakare' (Co) WFar
- 'Miyuki' (Co) GWyn WFar
- 'Musashino' (Co) WHil
- 'Nankin Kazakura' (Co) GEdr WFar XBar
- 'Nirvana' (Co) WFar XBar
- 'Noboruko' (Co) WHil
- 'Nuretubame' (Co) WFar XBar
- 'Okinanotomo' (Co) WFar
- 'Okinosabi' (Co) **new** WFar
- 'Old Vienna' (Co) WFar XBar
- 'Oni-gokko' (Co) WFar XBar
- 'Oriental Beauty' (Co) **new** EBee
- 'Oshibori' (Co) GKev GWyn MNrw WFar WHil
- 'Our White' (Co) WFar WHil
- 'Pago-Pago' (Co) ECtt EHrv NBro WFar XBar
- 'Pale Moon' (Co) WFar XBar
- 'Pink Laced' (Co) GWyn WFar
- 'Pink Ladies' (Co) **new** WHil
- pink-flowered (Co) NBir NRya
- 'Purity' (Co) **new** WFar
- 'Purple Dusk' (Co) WFar XBar
- 'Rasyoumon' (Co) WFar
- 'Rock Candy' (Co) WFar
- 'Romance' (Co) NCGa XBar
- 'Saiun' (Co) WHil
- 'Sakuragana' (Co) GWyn WFar
- 'Sakura-no-miya' (Co) **new** WFar
- 'Sangoguko' GBin GKev GWyn MNrw
- 'Sato-zakura' (Co) WFar XBar
- 'Senshō' (Co) GWyn WFar
- 'Seraphim' (Co) CRos EBee LRHS NLar NRHS WFar
- 'Seto-no-ume' (Co) WHil
- 'Shibori Gasane' (Co/d) **new** XBar
- 'Shiokemuri' (Co) WHil
- 'Shiro-tombo' (Co) GEdr XBar
- 'Shirousagi' (Co) WFar
- 'Shishifunjin' (Co) WFar WHil
- 'Sikoubai' (Co) WFar
- 'Sinakatonba' (Co) GWyn WFar
- 'Sinipukurn' (Co) GWyn WFar
- 'Sinnkirou' (Co) WFar
- 'Sinseto' (Co) WFar
- 'Siritonbo' (Co) GWyn WFar
- 'Sitikenjin' (Co) WFar
- 'Snowbird' (Co) XBar
- 'Snowdrop' (Co) CBod CDor ECtt GBin GKev GWyn MBel MHol MNrw MPie NCou WCot WFar WMoo WRHF
- 'Snowflake' (Co) CRos EBee EPfP GKev GWyn LRHS NLar NRHS WFar
- 'Sōshiarai' (Co) WFar
- 'Sotodorihime' (Co) WFar
- 'Spring Song' (Co) WHil
- 'Suibijin' (Co) WFar
- 'Suiloijiw' (Co) **new** GWyn
- 'Sumida-no-hatu' (Co) GWyn WFar
- 'Sumisonegawa' (Co) WFar
- 'Sumizomegenji' (Co) WFar WHil XBar
- 'Sun Bonnets' (Co) **new** GEdr
- 'Sweetie' (Co) WFar
- 'Tagonoura' (Co) GWyn WFar WHil
- 'Tah-ni' (Co) NBro NSum WHil XBar
- 'Tokasamesi' (Co) WFar
- 'Tokimeki' (Co/d) WFar XBar
- 'Toyonoharu' (Co) GWyn WFar
- 'Trade Winds' (Co) WFar XBar
- 'Turunokegoromo' (Co) WHil
- 'Vilia' (Co) XBar
- 'Vivid Pink' (Co) WFar WHil
- 'Winter Dreams' (Co) CAby ECtt EHrv GWyn NBid NBro NSum WFar WHil
- 'Yugeshiki' (Co) **new** WFar
- 'Yukiguruma' (Co) GWyn WFar
- 'Yuuhibeni' (Co) WFar

sikkimensis (Si) ♀H6 CRos EBee GAbr GKev LRHS MMuc NGdn NRHS NSum SPoG WArt

- peach-flowered (Si) GKev
- pink-flowered (Si) GKev
- var. ***pseudosikkimensis*** (Si) GKev
- var. ***pudibunda*** (Si) GKev NAln NWad
- red-flowered (Si) GKev
aff. ***sikkimensis*** (Si) NAln NGdn
Silver-laced Group (Pr/Poly) EPfP MMuc SEND SPoG SWvt WFar XBar
- black-flowered (Pr/Poly) EMor GBin WCAu XEll
sinoplantaginea see *P. chionantha* subsp. *sinoplantaginea*
sinopurpurea see *P. chionantha* subsp. *sinopurpurea*
'Sir Bedivere' (Pr/Prim) EBee WCot
smithiana see *P. prolifera*
'Snow Carpet' see *P.* 'Schneekissen'
'Snow White' (Pr/Poly) GBin MRav
SNOWCUSHION see *P.* 'Schneekissen'
'Snowgoose' (Pr/Prim/d) **new** XBar
'Snowruffles' ITim
sonchifolia (Pe) GKev
sorachiana see *P. yuparensis*
'Sorbet' (Pr/Poly) XBar
spectabilis (Au) GKev
Spice Shades Group (Pr/Poly) XBar
× ***steinii*** see *P.* × *forsteri*
stenocalyx (Pu) GKev
stenodonta (Pf) CPla GKev
'Stradbrook Charm' (Au) CWCL EPot NRya
'Stradbrook Dainty' (Au) WFar
'Stradbrook Dream' (Au) ITim WFar
'Stradbrook Gem' (Au) EPot
'Stradbrook Lucy' (Au) GEdr ITim NWad
'Strawberries and Cream' (Pr/Prim) **new** XBar
Striped Victorians Group (Pr/Poly) NSum XBar
'Strong Beer' (Pr/Prim/d) CBod EBee ECtt EPfP GBin GEdr GWyn IKil MHol MMuc MPie NHpl NWad SAko WArt WBrk WCot WFar WKif
'Sue Jervis' (Pr/Prim/d) MRav NBir NGrd NHpl
suffrutescens (Su) WAbe
'Sundae' (Pr/Prim/d) XBar
'Sunny Evans' **new** EPot
'Sunrise' (Au) CRos LRHS NRHS
'Sunshine Susie' (Pr/Prim/d) GMaP XBar
takedana (Bu) GEdr
'Tango' (Pr/Prim) NDro XBar
tangutica (Cy) GKev
'Tantallon' (Pe) NHar
Tartan Reds Group (Pr/Prim) XBar
'Tatyana' (Pr/Prim) EBee GKev NAln
'Tawny Port' (Pr/Poly) CElw CFis EBee
'Theodora' (Pr) EBee ELan GAbr WFar
'Tie Dye' (Pr/Prim) CBod ELan IKil LLHF MHol MMrt MNrw NLar NWad SAko WCot WFar WKif
'Tinney's Moonlight' (Pe) LLHF NHar
'Tipperary Purple' (Pr/Prim) ECtt NHpl
'Tomato Red' (Pr/Prim) CAby EBee GEdr LLHF NHpl WCot WFar
'Tony' (Au) ♀H5 XBar
'Top Affair' (Au/d) WAln
'Tortoiseshell' (Pr/d) ECtt

Traditional Yellows Group (Pr) XBar
tschuktschorum (Cy) LLHF
'Val Horncastle' (Pr/Prim/d) ECtt EPfP EShb GMaP NHpl XBar
Valentine Victorians Group (Pr/Poly) XBar
× ***venusta*** (Au) GKev
'Vera Maud' (Pr) NSum XBar
§ ***veris*** (Pr) ♀H5 Widely available
- PAB 3777 LEdu NRHS
- subsp. ***columnae*** (Pr) GKev
I - 'Coronation Cowslips' (Pr) XBar
- hose-in-hose (Pr/d) EWes WBrk
- 'Katy McSparron' (Pr/d) CExl EBee ECtt GBin GEdr MHol MNrw MPie NHpl NLar NSti SAko SPer WArt WCot WFar WMoo
- 'Lady Agatha' (Pr) CAby XBar
- Lord Alfred Group hose-in-hose (Pr) XBar
- subsp. ***macrocalyx*** (Pr) NWad
- orange-flowered (Pr) WMoo
- red-flowered (Pr) NBid NGdn SPer WMoo
- 'Sunset Shades' (Pr) CDor EAJP EMor EPfP GBin NGdn NLar SWvt XEll
- subsp. ***veris*** (Pr) CPla
vernalis see *P. vulgaris*
§ ***vialii*** (So) ♀H5 Widely available
- 'Alison Holland' (So) **new** NHpl
§ ***villosa*** (Au) GKev
- var. ***cottia*** see *P. villosa*
'Vintage' (Pr/Prim/d) **new** XBar
Violet Victorians Group (Pr/Poly) XBar
viscosa All. see *P. latifolia*
§ ***vulgaris*** (Pr/Prim) ♀H7 Widely available
- var. ***alba*** (Pr/Prim) WBrk
- 'Alba Plena' (Pr/Prim/d) GAbr NSum
- 'Avoca' (Pr/Prim) NHar XBar
- 'Avondale' (Kennedy Irish Series) (Pr/Prim) CAby CBod CDor EBee LLHF MAvo MHol MNrw NCGa NHar SCob WCot
- Barnhaven Gold (Pr/Prim) XBar
- 'Blarney Castle Blush' (Pr/Prim) NHar
- 'Blarney Castle Pink' (Pr/Prim) NHar NHpl
- 'Blarney Castle Red' (Pr/Prim) NHar NHpl XBar
- 'Carrigdale' (Pr/Prim) CDor EBee NHar WCot
- 'Catherine Thompson' (Pr/Prim) **new** NBir
- 'Claddagh' (Pr/Prim) NHar NHpl WCot XBar
- Cornish pink (Pr/Prim) GKev
- DRUMCLIFFE ('K74'PBR) (Pr/Prim) ECtt EHoe ELan EMor GBin GEdr GMaP LLHF MBel MHol MNrw NHpl NLar NSti WArt WCot WFar XBar
- 'Dunbeg' (Kennedy Irish Series) (Pr/Prim) CAby CDor ELan EPfP GAbr GBin LLHF NCGa NLar SCob WCot WHil
- 'Glengarriff' (Kennedy Irish Series) (Pr/Prim) NHar NHpl SCob WCot
- 'Golden Gem' (Pr/Prim/d) WCot
- green-flowered see *P. vulgaris* 'Viridis'
- INNISFREE ('K72'PBR) (Pr/Prim) CAby CBod CDor ECtt EMor EPfP GAbr GBin GEdr GMaP GWyn LLHF MBel MMuc MNrw NHpl NLar SPad WCot WFar XBar
§ - 'Lilacina Plena' (Pr/Prim/d) GCal IFro MRav NHpl NSum WHer XBar

	- 'Lutea' (Pr/Prim)	CBor
	- 'Moneygall' (Kennedy Irish Series) (Pr/Poly/d)	NHar NHpl
	- 'Mount Juliet' (Pr/Prim)	NHar
§	- subsp. ***sibthorpii*** (Pr/Prim) ♀H5	CAby CDor CRos CSam EBee ELan ELon EMor EPfP LRHS MCot MHer MNrw MRav NBro NChi NRHS NWad SPtp SRms WFar
	- 'Taigetos' (Pr/Prim) ♀H7	CBro CExl
	- 'Tara' (Pr/Prim)	NHar NHpl
	- 'Tarragem Sparkling Ruby' (Pr/Prim/d) new	NHpl WCot
	- 'Vanilla Cream' (Pr/Prim) new	WCot
§	- 'Viridis' (Pr/Prim/d)	MNrw
	- subsp. ***vulgaris*** (Pr/Prim) ♀H5	WMAq
	waltonii (Si)	EPfP GAbr GKev MNrw NAln NLar NSum
	'Wanda' (Pr/Prim) ♀H7	CBcs CRos CTri ELan GAbr GBin GKev GQue GWyn LRHS MBel MHer MMuc NAln NBid NRya SRms WBrk WCFE WCot WGwG
	Wanda Group (Pr/Prim)	NBro SVic
	- 'Wanda Hose-in-hose' (Pr/Prim/d)	NBir
	- 'Wanda Jack-in-the-Green' (Pr/Prim)	WCot
	- 'Wanda Tomato Red' (Pr/Prim)	EMor GAbr NHpl
	wardii	see *P. munroi*
	warshenewskiana (Or)	EPot EWes GCrg GJos GKev NRya WAbe WGwG
	watsonii (Mu)	CPla GKev
	- maroon-flowered (Mu)	GKev
	'Wedgwood'	see *P. × pubescens* 'Wedgwood'
	Westonbury Mill hybrids	WWtn
	'Wharfedale Bluebell' (Au)	NBir WThu
	'Wharfedale Buttercup' (Au)	ITim NWad
	'Wharfedale Butterfly' (Au)	NWad
	'Wharfedale Gem' (*allionii* hybrid) (Au)	EPot NSla NWad WIce XBar
	'Wharfedale Ling' (*allionii* hybrid) (Au)	EPot GKev NWad XBar
	'Wharfedale Sunshine' (Au)	WFar
	'Wharfedale Superb' (*allionii* hybrid) (Au)	EPot XBar
	'Wharfedale Village' (Au)	MPnt NSla WThu
	'White Linda Pope' (Au)	GEdr NSla NWad WThu
	'White Wanda' (Pr/Prim)	GAbr XBar
	'White Waves' (*allionii* hybrid) (Au)	ITim
§	***whitei*** 'Sherriff's Variety' (Pe)	NHar
	wilsonii (Pf)	CTri GAbr LLWG NBir NGdn NWad WBrk WTyc WWtn XBar
	- SDR 7824	CRos GKev
§	- var. ***anisodora*** (Pf)	GKev GLog NAln NGdn NHpl NWad XBar
	- var. ***wilsonii*** (Pf)	GKev NAln NWad
	'Wisley Crimson'	see *P.* 'Wisley Red'
§	'Wisley Red' (Pr/Prim)	CElw
	'Woodland Walk' (Pr/Prim)	EPfP SRms
	wulfeniana (Au)	GKev
	yargongensis	see *P. munroi* subsp. *yargongensis*
	'Yellow' (Primlet Series) (Pr/Prim)	CRos LRHS NRHS
§	***yuparensis*** (Al)	GKev
	zambalensis (Ar)	GKev
	'Zebra Blue' (Pr/Prim)	EPfP

Primulina (*Gesneriaceae*)

	tabacum 'Deco'	WDib

Prinsepia (*Rosaceae*)

	sinensis	MBlu NLar SLon WSHC

Pritchardia (*Arecaceae*)

	affinis	XBlo
	pacifica	XBlo

Pritzelago see *Hornungia*

Prosartes (*Liliaceae*)

§	***hookeri***	EBee LLHF MNrw
§	- var. ***oregana***	EBee WCru
§	***lanuginosa***	CRos EMor EPPr LEdu LRHS NRHS WCru WPGP
§	***maculata***	CAby LEdu MNrw NLar WCru
§	***smithii***	EBee EPfP GKev GLog IMou LEdu LRHS MNrw NBir NLar WCru WPGP WSHC
§	***trachycarpa*** SDR 8177	GKev

Prostanthera (*Lamiaceae*)

	aspalathoides	CCCN CSde CTsd
	'Badja Peak'	CCCN CCht CKel CTsd EUJe MAsh MGil
	cryptandroides	CBcs
	cuneata ♀H4	Widely available
	- 'Alpine Gold' (v)	MAsh
	- 'Blushing Bride'	CMac LBuc
	denticulata	CTsd
*	***digitiformis***	CTsd
	incana	CTsd
	incisa	CTsd
	lasianthos	CBcs CCCN CHll CTsd SPlb SVen
	- 'Badja Point' new	CSpe
	- 'Kallista Pink'	CTsd
	- var. ***subcoriacea***	CExl
	latifolia	CTsd
	melissifolia	CTsd
§	- var. ***parvifolia***	CCCN CTsd EUJe
	'Mint Royale'	CCCN EUJe LEdu LRHS
	'Mint-Ice'	LRHS
	ovalifolia ♀H3	CCCN SEle WAvo
I	- 'Variegata' (v)	CBcs CBod CCCN CExl CKel CMac CTsd ELan EUJe LRHS MAsh MGil SEle SNig WAvo WGrn
	phylicifolia	CBcs CTsd
	'Poorinda Ballerina'	CCCN CRos CTsd EBee ELan EUJe LRHS MAsh SEle SPer SRkn
	'Poorinda Petite'	CCCN CKel CRos CTsd ELan LRHS
	rhombea	CTsd
	rotundifolia ♀H3	CAbb CBod CCCN CCht CSde CTri CTsd EBee MGil MSCN SEle SNig SPer SVen WCFE WGrn WKif
	- 'Chelsea Girl'	see *P. rotundifolia* 'Rosea'
§	- 'Rosea' ♀H3	CCCN CTsd EPfP LRHS SEND
	rugosa	CTsd
	sericea	LRHS
	sieberi misapplied	see *P. melissifolia* var. *parvifolia*
	sieberi Benth.	CPbh CTsd
I	- 'Variegata' (v)	CTsd
	spinosa	CTsd
	'Starlight' (v)	CTsd
	walteri	CBcs CCCN CSpe CTsd EBee LRHS MNHC SPhx

Protea (*Proteaceae*)

aurea	SPlb
- subsp. ***aurea***	CPbh
'Brenda' new	CKel
burchellii	SPlb
caffra	CKel
'Clark's Red'	LRHS MPkF
coronata	CPbh SPlb
cynaroides	CCCN CPbh SPlb
- 'King Pine'	CCCN CKel
- 'King Red' new	CKel
- 'King White' new	CKel
- 'Little Prince'PBR	CBcs CCCN CKel
- 'Madiba'	CCCN CKel
- 'Mini King'	CCCN CKel
- 'Mini King Autumn' new	CKel
- 'Red Rex' new	CKel
- 'White Crown'PBR	CCCN CKel
effusa	SPlb
eximia	CCCN CPbh SPlb
grandiceps	CCCN CKel CPbh SPlb
'Juliet'	CCCN CKel
lacticolor	CPbh SPlb
laurifolia	SPlb
lepidocarpodendron	CPbh
'Limelight' new	CKel
longifolia	CPbh
magnifica 'Atlantic Queen' new	CKel
'Mayday' new	CKel
'Mini King'	CCCN
nana	SPlb
neriifolia	CCCN CPbh SPlb
- 'Cream Mink' new	CKel
- 'Snowcrest'	CPbh
'Niobe' new	CKel
obtusifolia	SPlb
'Pink Crown'	MPkF
'Pink Princess' new	CKel
'Pixie' new	CKel
'Possum Magic' new	CKel
'Red Baron' new	CKel
repens	CPbh LRHS MPkF SPlb
- 'Honeyglow' new	CKel
- 'Ruby Blush'	CCCN CKel
scolymocephala	SPlb
'Sheila' new	CKel
'Southern Cross'	CCCN CKel
'Special Pink Ice'	CCCN CKel
subvestita	CPbh SPlb
susannae	CPbh SPlb
'Susara'	CCCN CKel LRHS MPkF
'Sylvia'	CCCN CKel MPkF
'Whiteknight' new	CKel

Prumnopitys ✿ (*Podocarpaceae*)

§ ***andina***	CBcs IDee WFar
elegans	see *P. andina*

Prunella (*Lamiaceae*)

§ ***grandiflora***	CHby CRos ECha ELan SRms WOut
- 'Alba'	CBod CBre EBee ECha ELan EPfP GBin GMaP NBid NLar SPer SRms WCAu WOut
- 'Altenberg Rosa'	WCAu
- 'Blue Loveliness'	CWld SWvt
- 'Blue Pearl'	MHol NCou
- 'Carminea'	EBee MRav SPer
- 'Freelander'	WHil
- 'Gruss aus Isernhagen'	GBee
- 'Loveliness'	CMac ECha ELan GMaP MRav NBro NGdn NSti SPer SPlb WCAu WFar
- 'Pagoda'	CSpe NLar
- 'Pink Loveliness'	CRos SRms WFar
- 'Rosea'	WFar
- 'Rubra'	NLar
- violet-flowered	NSti
- 'White Loveliness'	CMac SRms
incisa	see *P. vulgaris*
SUMMER DAZE ('Binsumdaz'PBR)	ECtt STPC
§ ***vulgaris***	CBod CCBP CHab CTri CWld EBou ENfk GPoy MMuc MNHC NMir SRms WHer WMoo WOut
- f. ***leucantha***	WHer
- 'Rose Pearl'	CBod EBou LSRN NHpl SRms
× ***webbiana***	see *P. grandiflora*

Prunus ✿ (*Rosaceae*)

sp.	LPra
'Accolade' (d) ♀H6	Widely available
§ 'Amanogawa' ♀H6	Widely available
amygdalus	see *P. dulcis*
armeniaca	NPri
- 'Alfred' (F)	SDea SKee SPer
- 'Bergeron' (F)	NOra WMat
- 'Bredase' (F)	ELan SDea
- 'De Nancy'	see *P. armeniaca* 'Gros Pêche'
- 'Delicot' (F)	SSFr
- 'Early Moorpark' (F)	CAgr EMOT EPfP LEdu NOra SDea SEND SLon SSFr WMat
- 'Farmingdale' (F)	SDea
- FLAVORCOT ('Bayoto'PBR) (F)	CAgr EPfP EPom MCoo NOra SKee SPer SSFr WMat
- 'Garden Aprigold' (F)	EPom SSFr WMat
- 'Goldcot' (F)	CAgr CRos CTho LRHS MCoo NOra SDea SKee SPoG SSFr WMat
- 'Golden Glow' (F)	CAgr CTho CTri EMOT EPfP EPom LRHS MCoo NOra SDea SKee SSFT WMat
- 'Goldrich' (F)	CAgr
§ - 'Gros Pêche' (F)	SVic
- 'Hargrand' (F)	CAgr SVic
- 'Harogem' (F)	CAgr
- 'Helena de Roussilon' (F) new	CAgr
- 'Hemskirke' (F)	SKee
- 'Hongaarse' (F)	ELan SDea
- 'Moorpark' (F)	CDul CHab CSBt CTri ELan EMOT LBuc MJak MRav NPri SDea SKee
- 'New Large Early' (F)	SDea SEND
- ORANGE SUMMER ('Zaitorde'PBR) (F)	EPom
- 'Petit Muscat' (F)	EPom SKee
- 'Robada'PBR (F) new	CAgr
- 'Tomcot' (F)	CAgr CTho CTri EPfP EPom LBuc LSRN MCoo NOra SKee SPer SPoG SSFr WMat
- 'Tross Orange' (F)	ELan SDea
- 'Vigama' (F)	MCoo NOra WMat
'Asano'	CLnd
avium	Widely available
- 'Alba'	SKee
- 'Alfheim' (F)	SKee
- 'Amber Heart' (F)	CArg EMOT NOra SKee WMat
- 'Belgian Rivers' (F)	SKee
- 'Bigarreau Gaucher' (F)	NOra SKee WMat
§ - 'Bigarreau Napoléon' (F)	CArg EPom LMaj LSRN NOra SKee SSFr SVic WMat

Name	Suppliers
- 'Birchenhayes'	see *P. avium* 'Early Birchenhayes'
- 'Black Eagle' (F)	SKee
- 'Black Elton' (F)	SKee
- 'Black Tartarian' (F)	SKee
- 'Bottlers'	see *P. avium* 'Preserving'
- 'Bradbourne Black' (F)	SKee
- 'Bullion' (F)	CEnd CTho
- 'Burcombe' (F)	CEnd CTho
- 'Cariad' (F)	WGwG
- CELESTE ('Sumpaca'[PBR]) (D)	CAgr CArg CFGn CMac CTri EMOT MCoo NLar NOra NWea SDea SLim SPoG WMat
- 'Cherokee'	see *P. avium* 'Lapins'
- 'Colney' (F)	CArg EPom NOra SKee SSFr WJas WMat
- 'Danelia' (D)	WMat
- 'Dun' (F)	CHab CTho WMat
§ - 'Early Birchenhayes' (F)	CEnd CTho
- 'Early Rivers' (F)	CDul CSBt EMOT IArd LSRN NOra SDea SKee SSFr SVic WMat
- 'Elton Heart' (F)	SKee
- 'Emperor Francis' (F)	SKee
- 'Fice' (F)	CEnd CTho
- 'Florence' (F)	SKee
- 'Garden Bing' (F)	EPom
- 'Giorgia' (D)	WMat
- 'Goodnestone Black' (D)	SKee
- 'Grandiflora'	see *P. avium* 'Plena'
- 'Greenstem Black' (F)	CTho
- 'Hannaford' (D/C)	CHab
- 'Hertford' (F)	NOra SKee SSFr WMat
- 'Ironsides' (F)	SKee
- 'Karina' (D)	WMat
- 'Kentish Red' (F)	SKee
- 'Knight's Early Black' (D)	CArg WMat
- 'Kordia' (D) ♀H5	CArg EPom NOra SKee WMat
- 'Kozerska' (F)	WMat
§ - 'Lapins' (F) ♀H5	CAgr CArg CDul CFGn CLnd CTho ECrN EMOT EPfP EPom MRav NLar NOra NWea SDea SKee SSFT SSFr WJas WMat WWct
- 'May Duke'	see *P.* × *gondouinii* 'May Duke'
- 'Merchant' (F) ♀H5	NOra SKee SSFT SSFr WMat WWct
- 'Mermat' (F)	SKee
- 'Merton Bigarreau' (F)	CArg NOra SKee SSFr WMat
- 'Merton Favourite' (F)	SKee
- 'Merton Glory' (F)	CAgr CArg CDul CSBt EMOT EPfP NOra SEWo SKee SLim SSFr WMat WWct
- 'Merton Premier' (F)	SVic
- 'Merton Reward'	see *P.* × *gondouinii* 'Merton Reward'
- 'Mizia' (D)	WMat
- 'Nabella' (F)	MAsh SDea WJas
- 'Napoléon'	see *P. avium* 'Bigarreau Napoléon'
- 'Noble' (F)	SKee
- 'Noir de Guben' (F)	SKee WMat
- 'Noir de Meched' (D)	SKee
- 'Octavia' (D)	WMat
- 'Old Black Heart' (F)	SKee
- 'Penny'[PBR] (F) ♀H5	CAgr CArg CTri EPom MCoo NOra SKee WMat WWct
- 'Petit Noir' (F)	CArg CLnd NOra WMat
§ - 'Plena' (d) ♀H6	Widely available
§ - 'Preserving' (F)	CTho
- 'Regina' (F)	EPom NLar NOra SKee WMat
- 'Ronald's Heart' (F)	SKee
- 'Roundel Heart' (F)	SKee WMat
- 'Sasha' (F)	MCoo
- 'Skeena'[PBR] (F)	CArg MCoo NOra WMat
- 'Small Black' (F)	CHab CTho
- STARDUST ('13-7-70, Stardust') (F)	NOra
- 'Stella' (F) ♀H5	Widely available
- 'Stella Compact' (F)	ECrN LSRN SDea
- 'Summer Sun' (D) ♀H5	CAgr CArg CLnd CMac CTho CTri EMOT EPom LBuc MAsh MCoo MGos NLar NOra SCoo SDea SKee SLim SPoG SSFT SSFr WMat WWct
- 'Summit' (F)	CLnd SKee SSFr WMat
- 'Sunburst' (D)	Widely available
- 'Sweetheart' (F) ♀H5	CAgr CArg CLnd CTri EMOT EPom LCro LMaj LOPS LRHS LSRN MAsh NOra NRHS NWea SEWo SKee SLim SPoG SVic WMat
- 'Sylvia' (F)	CAgr NOra WMat
- 'Turkish Black' (F)	SKee
- 'Ursula Rivers' (F)	SKee
- 'Van' (F)	CAgr CArg CSBt EPom NLar NOra SKee WMat
- 'Vanda'[PBR] (F)	NOra WMat
- 'Vega' (F)	CAgr CArg EMOT NOra SKee SSFr WJas WMat
- 'Waterloo' (F)	NOra SKee
- 'White Heart' (F)	CHab ECrN EMOT SKee
§ 'Beni-tamanishiki' ♀H6	CBcs NOra WMat
'Beni-yutaka' ♀H6	CBcs CCVT CTho EMOT EWTr MAsh MRav MSwo NOra NRHS SCob SCoo SLim WMat WMou
'Bilski'	WMat
'Blaze'	see *P. cerasifera* 'Nigra'
× ***blireana*** (d) ♀H6	CDul CEnd CLnd CTri EMOT EPfP MGos MRav MSwo NLar SCoo SPer SPoG
- 'Moseri' (d)	WTSh
BLUSHING BRIDE	see *P.* 'Shōgetsu'
campanulata 'Felix Jury'	EBee NOra WMat
CANDY FLOSS	see *P.* 'Matsumae-beni-murasaki'
caroliniana	LMaj LPra SArc
cerasifera (F)	CAgr CDul CFGn CHab CPer CTri ECrN EPfP EPom LBuc NWea SDea SKee SPer
- 'Countess' (F)	EPom NOra
- CRIMSON POINTE ('Cripoizam')	EBee LRHS NOra SPoG
- 'Golden Sphere' (F)	CAgr CArg CFGn CLnd CTho CTri EPom NOra SDea SKee SPer SSFr WMat
- 'Gypsy' (F)	CAgr CLnd CTho LRHS NOra SKee SSFr WMat
- 'Hessei' (v)	LRHS MRav SEle
- 'Kentish Red' (F)	MMuc SEND
§ - Myrobalan Group (F)	MRav SDea SPre SVic WMat
§ - 'Nigra' ♀H6	Widely available
- 'Pendula'	ECrN SWvt
§ - 'Pissardii'	ECrN EPfP LCro LSRN SCob SCoo SLon SWvt WFar WJas WMou
- 'Ruby' (F)	CAgr CFGn EPom SKee SPer
- 'Woodii'	CSBt
cerasus 'Maynard'	SSFr
- 'Meteor Korai'	CAgr LRHS MCoo NOra NRHS WMat
- 'Montmorency' (F)	NOra SKee
- 'Morello' (C) ♀H6	Widely available
- 'Nabella' (F)	SKee
- 'Rhexii' (d)	CDul ECrN
- 'Semperflorens'	CLnd
'Cheal's Weeping'	EBar
CHOCOLATE ICE	see *P.* 'Matsumae-fuki'

§	× ***cistena*** ♀H6	CBcs CDul CRos EBee ELan EPfP LRHS MAsh MGos MSwo NRHS SCoo SGol SPoG SWvt WCFE WFar
	- 'Crimson Dwarf'	see *P.* × *cistena*
	'Collingwood Ingram' ♀H6	EBee EBtc EPfP LRHS MBlu NOra SLim WMat
	'Cot-N-Candy' (Aprium Series)	CAgr EPom
	'Daikoku'	CBcs EBee LRHS NOra WMat
	davidiana	SPlb
	'Delma'[PBR] (F)	NOra WMat
	domestica (D/C)	CPer SPre
	- 'Angelina Burdett' (D)	CHab SDea SKee
	- 'Anna Späth' (C/D)	SKee
	- 'Ariel' (C/D)	SDea SKee
	- 'Autumn Compote' (C)	SKee
	- 'Avalon' (D)	CAgr CCVT CLnd EMOT LBuc NOra SDea SKee SSFr WMat
	- 'Belgian Greengage' (F)	CHab
	- 'Belle de Louvain' (C)	CArg CDul CHab CLnd CTri EMOT NOra SDea SKee WMat WWct
	- 'Birchenhayes' (F)	CEnd
	- 'Black Diamond'	see *P. salicina* 'Black Diamond'
	- 'Blaisdon Red' (C)	NOra SKee WMat
	- 'Blue Rock' (C/D) ♀H5	SKee
	- 'Blue Tit' (C/D) ♀H5	CAgr CTho EMOT EPom LSRN MMuc NOra SDea SEND SKee SSFr WMat WWct
	- 'Bohemian' (C)	SKee
	- 'Bonne de Bry' (D)	SKee
§	- 'Bountiful' (C)	SKee
	- 'Brandy Gage' (C/D)	SKee
	- 'Bryanston Gage' (D)	CTho SKee WMat
	- 'Burbank's Giant'	see *P. domestica* 'Giant Prune'
	- 'Burcombe' (F)	CEnd
	- 'Cambridge Gage' (D) ♀H5	Widely available
	- 'Chrislin' (F)	CTho
	- 'Coe's Golden Drop' (D)	CAgr CArg CHab CLnd ECrN EPom MGos MRav NOra NWea SDea SKee SPer WMat WWct
	- 'Conwy Castle' (F)	WMat
	- 'Count Althann's Gage' (D)	CHab SDea SKee SSFr WWct
	- 'Cox's Emperor' (C)	SKee
	- 'Cropper'	see *P. domestica* 'Laxton's Cropper'
	- 'Curlew' (C)	SDea SKee
	- 'Czar' (C) ♀H6	Widely available
	- 'Delicious'	see *P. domestica* 'Laxton's Delicious'
	- 'Denbigh' (C)	CHab WGwG
	- 'Denniston's Superb'	see *P. domestica* 'Imperial Gage'
	- 'Diamond' (C)	SKee
	- 'Dittisham Ploughman' (C)	CTho SKee WMat
	- 'Dunster Plum' (F)	CTho CTri WMat
	- 'Early Laxton' (C/D)	CHab MMuc SDea SEND SKee
	- 'Early Orleans'	see *P. domestica* 'Monsieur Hâtiff'
	- 'Early Prolific'	see *P. domestica* 'Early Rivers'
§	- 'Early Rivers' (C)	CAgr CArg CDul CFGn CHab CSBt CTho CTri ELan EMOT EPom LSRN NOra SCoo SDea SKee SPer SSFr WMat WWct
	- 'Early Transparent Gage' (C/D)	CAgr CEnd CMac CSBt CTho ECrN EMOT LBuc LRHS MCoo NOra SCoo SDea SKee SSFr WMat
	- 'Early Victoria' (C/D)	SDea
	- 'Edda' (D)	NOra WMat
	- 'Edwards' (C/D)	CTri SDea SSFr
	- 'Excalibur' (D)	CAgr EMOT EPom IArd LBuc LSRN NOra SDea SKee WMat
	- 'Finger Plum' (F)	WMat
§	- German Prune Group (C)	MCoo NOra SDea SKee WMat
§	- 'Giant Prune' (C)	EMOT MMuc SDea SEND SKee SSFr
I	- 'Godshill Big Sloe' (F)	SDea
	- 'Godshill Blue' (C)	SDea
	- 'Godshill Minigage' (F)	SDea
	- 'Gold Dust' (F)	WMat
	- 'Golden Transparent' (D)	MCoo NWea SKee
	- 'Goldfinch' (D)	MCoo MMuc SEND SKee
	- 'Gordon Castle'	NLar WMat
	- Green Gage Group	see *P. domestica* Reine-Claude Group
	- - 'Lindsey Gage' (F)	SKee
	- 'Grove's Late Victoria' (D)	SKee WWct
	- 'Guinevere' (C)	CAgr CEnd EPom LRHS MCoo NOra SKee WMat
	- 'Guthrie's Late Green' (D)	SKee
	- 'Haganta'[PBR] (F) ♀H5	CAgr MCoo NOra WMat
	- 'Herman' (D)	CAgr CEnd CMac EMOT EPom LRHS MCoo NOra SDea SKee WMat
	- 'Heron' (C)	NOra WMat WWct
§	- 'Imperial Gage' (D) ♀H5	CAgr CArg CLnd CMac CSBt CTho CTri EPom LRHS MMuc NOra SDea SEND SKee SSFT SSFr WMat
	- 'Jan James' (F)	CEnd
	- 'Jefferson' (D) ♀H5	CAgr CArg CHab CLnd EMOT NOra SDea SKee SSFr SVic WMat
*	- 'Jubilaeum' (D)	CAgr CLnd CMac EPom LBuc LRHS NOra SCoo SEWo SKee SSFr
	- 'Kea' (C)	CFGn CLnd CTho SKee WMat
	- 'Kirke's' (D)	CHab ELan NOra SDea SKee SSFr WMat
	- 'Kulinaria' (D) **new**	SPoG
	- 'Landkey Yellow' (F)	CTho WMat
	- 'Langley Gage' (D)	CAgr SDea
	- 'Late Muscatelle' (D)	SKee
	- 'Late Transparent Gage' (D)	SKee
	- 'Lawson's Golden' (D)	SKee
	- 'Laxton's Bountiful'	see *P. domestica* 'Bountiful'
§	- 'Laxton's Cropper' (C)	CHab EMOT SKee
§	- 'Laxton's Delicious' (D)	CHab
	- 'Laxton's Gage' (D)	SDea
	- 'Laxton's Jubilee' (C/D)	CEnd CSBt EMOT LCro SSFr WMat
I	- 'Liegel's Apricot'	SKee
	- 'Mallard' (D) ♀H6	NOra SKee WMat
	- 'Manaccan' (C)	CFGn CTho WMat
	- 'Manning's Greengage' (F) **new**	NWea
	- 'Manns No. 1' (C/D)	SKee WMat
	- 'Marjorie's Seedling' (C) ♀H5	Widely available
	- 'McLaughlin' (D)	SKee
	- 'Meritare' (F)	NOra WMat
	- 'Merton Gage' (D)	SKee
	- 'Merton Gem' (D)	SKee
	- 'Miraclaude' (F) **new**	EPom
	- 'Monarch' (C)	SKee
§	- 'Monsieur Hâtiff' (D)	SKee
	- (Myrobalan Group) 'Myrobalan B' (F)	WTSh
	- Old English gage	CLnd ECrN EPom
	- 'Olympia' (C/D)	SKee
	- 'Opal' (D) ♀H6	Widely available
	- 'Orleans' (C)	SKee
	- 'Oullins Gage' (C/D) ♀H5	Widely available
	- 'Pershore' (C)	CAgr CHab EMOT NOra SDea SKee WMat WWct
	- 'Pershore Emblem' (F)	WWct
	- 'Pond's Seedling' (C)	CSBt SDea
	- 'Pozegaca' (D)	SKee
	- 'President' (C)	CHab LMaj MMuc SDea SEND SKee SSFr
	- 'Priory Plum' (D)	SDea

– 'Purple Pershore' (C) ♀H5	CAgr CHab CTri IArd NEgg NOra SDea SKee WMat WWct
– 'Queen's Crown' (C/D)	WMat
– 'Quetsche d'Alsace'	see *P. domestica* German Prune Group
– 'Reeves' (C)	NOra SKee
– 'Reine-Claude Dorée'	see *P. domestica* Reine-Claude Group
§ – Reine-Claude Group (D)	ECrN ELan MMuc NOra SDea SEND SKee SLim SPer WMat
– – 'Ingall's Grimoldby Green Gage' (D)	SKee
– – 'Old Green Gage'	see *P. domestica* (Reine-Claude Group) 'Reine-Claude Vraie'
– – 'Reine-Claude de Bavais' (D)	CArg CLnd CTri NOra SDea SKee WMat
– – 'Reine-Claude de Moissac' (D)	SKee
– – 'Reine-Claude de Vars' (D)	SKee SVic
– – 'Reine-Claude Précoce Léon Hisse' (D)	SKee
– – 'Reine-Claude Rosée' (D)	SKee
– – 'Reine-Claude Tardive de Chambourcy' (D)	SKee
– – 'Reine-Claude Violette' (D)	SKee
§ – – 'Reine-Claude Vraie' (C/D)	CAgr CArg CMac CRos CSBt EMOT EPfP EPom LBuc LCro LOPS LRHS LSRN NOra NPri SDea SKee SSFT SSFr WJas WMat
§ – – 'Willingham Gage' (C/D)	EMOT LSRN NOra SKee WMat
– 'Royale de Vilvoorde' (D)	SKee
– 'Sanctus Hubertus' (D)	CTri EMOT SDea SKee WWct
– 'Seneca' (D)	EPom NOra SKee SSFr WMat
– 'Severn Cross' (D)	SSFr
– 'Stanley' (C/D)	LMaj SVic
– 'Stella' (F)	CCVT LOPS LSRN NEgg NPri SLim
– 'Stella's Star' (D)	MCoo NOra WMat
– 'Swan' (C)	NOra WMat WWct
– 'Syston White' (F)	MGos
– 'Thames Cross' (D)	CLnd NOra
– 'Transparent Gage' (D)	SKee
– 'Valor' (D) ♀H5	NOra SKee
– 'Verity' (C/D)	SKee WMat
– 'Victoria' (D) ♀H5	Widely available
– 'Violetta'[PBR] (D)	CAgr EMOT
– 'Wangenheimer Frühzwetsche' (F)	SKee
– 'Warwickshire Drooper' (C)	CAgr CHab CTho EMOT MAsh NOra SDea SKee SLon SSFr WMat WWct
– 'Washington' (D)	SDea SKee
– 'White Magnum Bonum' (C)	SDea
– 'Willingham'	see *P. domestica* (Reine-Claude Group) 'Willingham Gage'
– 'Woolaston Black' (D)	SKee
– 'Zwetschen' (C)	SDea
§ ***dulcis***	CAco CHab CLnd CTri ECrN ELan EMOT EPfP EPom LRHS MGos MMuc NWea SCoo SDea SEND SWvt
– 'Ai' (F)	CAgr
– 'Ardéchoise' (F)	CAgr
– 'Ferraduel' (F)	CAgr
– 'Ferragnès' (F)	CAgr
* – 'Phoebe' (F)	CAgr
– 'Princesse' (F)	SKee
– 'Sultane' (F)	SKee
– 'Supernova' (F)	CCCN
– 'Sweetheart' (F) **new**	LCro
– 'Tuono' (F)	CCCN
EASTER BONNET ('Comet'[PBR])	CTri LRHS
'Flavor King' (Pluot Series) (D)	CAgr WMat
'Flavour Supreme' (F)	EPom
FRAGRANT CLOUD	see *P.* 'Shizuka'
FRILLY FROCK ('Fpmspl') (v)	EBee LRHS LSRN NLar NOra NPri SPoG WMat
fruticosa	LPra WFar
– 'Globosa'	LPra
'Fugenzō' misapplied	see *P.* 'Kofugen'
§ 'Fugenzō' ♀H6	CArg CBcs CCVT CDul CLnd CMCN CMac CSBt EBar EMOT EPfP EWTr GKin LBuc LCro LMaj LOPS LPra LRHS LSRN MAsh MMuc MRav NOra SCob SEND SGol SPer WJas WMat
glandulosa 'Alba Plena' (d)	CDul CEnd CMac CSBt SGol SPlb SRms SWvt WCFE
– 'Rosea Plena'	see *P. glandulosa* 'Sinensis'
§ – 'Sinensis' (d)	CDul CEnd CExl CSBt SGol SRms
§ × ***gondouinii*** 'May Duke' (F)	SKee
§ – 'Merton Reward' (F)	SKee
grayana B&SWJ 10903	WCru
'Gyoikō'	CBcs CEnd CLnd EBee LRHS NOra WMat
'Hally Jolivette'	CEnd LRHS MAsh NOra SPoG WMat
§ 'Hanagasa' ♀H6	CBcs CEnd EMOT EPfP NLar NOra NWea WMat WMou
'Hillieri'	LPra
'Hillieri Spire'	see *P.* 'Spire'
'Hilling's Weeping'	EBee LCro LOPS SLon
himalaica	CJun LRHS NLar NOra WMat WPGP
'Hokusai' ♀H6	CBcs CDul EMOT EPfP LRHS NOra SGol WMat
HOLLYWOOD	see *P.* 'Trailblazer'
'Horinji'	CBcs EMOT NLar NOra SCoo WMat
'Howard No. 3'	WMat
'Ichiyo' (d) ♀H6	CBcs CDul CLnd EBee EPfP NOra SCoo WMat
ilicifolia subsp. ***lyonii***	WPGP
× ***incam*** 'Okamé' ♀H6	Widely available
– 'Shosar' ♀H6	CEnd SCoo SPer
incisa	CTri NEgg
– 'Beniomi'	MRav
– 'February Pink'	CJun SGol
– 'Fujimae' ♀H6	NLar WAvo
– 'Kojo-no-mai' ♀H6	Widely available
– 'Mikinori'	CEnd CJun CMac CSBt EPfP MAsh MBlu MJak NLar NOra SCoo WMat
– 'Oshidori' (d) ♀H6	CAby CMac CSBt EBee ELon EPfP LRHS MMrt MRav NLar NOra NQui SRms WMat WSpi
– 'Paean'	NLar WFar
– 'Pendula' ♀H6	LCro LOPS LRHS NOra SCoo WMat
– 'Praecox'	CSBt CTho EPfP SCoo WMat
§ – f. ***yamadei*** ♀H6	CJun MAsh WSpi
insititia (F)	MWht
– 'Abergwyngregin' (C)	NOra WMat
– 'Aylesbury Prune' (C)	NOra SKee WMat
– 'Blue Violet Damson' (C)	CAgr MCoo NOra SKee WMat
§ – 'Bradley's King Damson' (C)	CArg CLnd MCoo NLar NOra SKee WMat
– bullace (C)	LEdu NWea SDea
– 'Countess' (C)	CTri

	Name	Suppliers
	- 'Dittisham Damson' (C)	CTho WMat
	- 'Farleigh Damson' (C) 𝒴H6	CAgr CArg CHab CLnd ECrN EMOT EPfP EPom LBuc LEdu MJak NLar NOra NWea SDea SKee SPer SVic WJas WMat WWct
	- 'Godshill Damson' (C)	SDea
	- 'King of Damsons'	see *P. insititia* 'Bradley's King Damson'
	- 'Langley Bullace' (C)	CAgr CTri LEdu NOra SDea SKee WMat
	- 'Lisna' (C)	CTri WMat
	- 'Merryweather Damson' (C)	Widely available
	- 'Mirabelle Countess' (C)	EPom WMat
	- 'Mirabelle de Metz' (C)	SKee
	- 'Mirabelle de Nancy' (C)	CAgr CDul CTho EPom NOra SDea SEWo SKee WMat
	- 'Mirabelle de Nancy' red (C)	SDea
	- 'Mirabelle Ruby' (C)	CArg LRHS NOra SPoG WMat
§	- 'Prune Damson' (C) 𝒴H6	CAgr CArg CDul CHab CLnd CMac CTho CTri EMOT EPom LBuc LCro LRHS MAsh MMuc NEgg NLar NOra NWea SDea SEND SEWo SKee SPer SSFr WJas WMat WWct
	- 'Shepherd's Bullace' (C)	MCoo SKee
	- 'Shropshire Damson'	see *P. insititia* 'Prune Damson'
	- 'Small Bullace' (C)	SKee
	- 'Westmorland Prune' (C)	CHab NLar NWea
	- 'Yellow Apricot' (C)	SKee
	'Jacqueline'	LRHS NOra
	'Jō-nioi'	CDul CEnd CLnd CTho LRHS
	kansuensis new	IArd
§	'Kanzan' (d) 𝒴H6	Widely available
§	'Kiku-shidare-zakura'	Widely available
	'Kobuku-zakura'	EWTr NOra WMat
§	'Kofugen'	CSBt LRHS NOra WMat
	Korean hill cherry	see *P. verecunda*
	'Kursar'	CDul CLnd CSBt CTri EMOT EPfP EUJe GKin LRHS LSRN NWea SCoo SLim SLon SPer SSFr SWvt WMat WSpi
	laurocerasus	CBcs CCVT CDul CFGn CMac EBee ECrN ELan EPfP EShb GKin LMaj LPra MGos MHed MRav NPri NWea SArc SCob SGol SPer WMat WMoo WMou WTSh
	- 'Camelliifolia'	CMac CTri MBlu
	- 'Castlewellan' (v)	CDul CKel CTri ELon EMOT EPfP EShb MGos MRav MSwo NLar NWad SCob SPer SPoG SSta WAvo WFar WRHF
	- 'Caucasica'	CEnd ECrN LMaj NLar SCob SEND SGol
	- 'Cherry Brandy'	SCob SGol
	- ETNA ('Anbri'PBR) 𝒴H5	CBod CMac CRos EMOT LBuc LRHS MAsh NRHS SCob SWvt
	- GENOLIA ('Mariblon'PBR)	LMaj SGol
	- 'Green Marble' (v)	CTri EBee EHoe
	- 'Ivory'PBR	WMoo
§	- 'Latifolia'	LMaj WCFE
	- 'Magnoliifolia'	see *P. laurocerasus* 'Latifolia'
	- 'Mano'	LMaj
	- 'Marbled White'	see *P. laurocerasus* 'Castlewellan'
	- 'Miky'	CJun
	- 'Mount Vernon'	CTri MBlu SCob
	- 'Novita'	CBod ECrN EPfP LMaj LPra LSRN NLar NPri WMoo
	- 'Otto Luyken' 𝒴H5	CBcs CBod CCVT CDul CMac CTri EBee EHoe ELan EPfP LBuc LRHS MAsh MGos MJak MSwo NBir NEgg NLar NWea SArc SCob SGol SPer SPlb WFar
	- 'Piranha'PBR	NEoE
	- 'Rotundifolia' 𝒴H5	Widely available
	- 'Variegata' misapplied	see *P. laurocerasus* 'Castlewellan'
	- 'Variegata' ambig. (v)	SRms
	- 'Whitespot'	MMuc
	- 'Zabeliana'	CDul CMac CTri MJak MSwo NEgg NWea SCob SPer SRms
	litigiosa	EBee EMOT LRHS NOra WMat
	'Little Pink Perfection'	CNWT EPom LCro LOPS NLar NOra SCoo SPoG WMat
	lusitanica 𝒴H5	Widely available
	- subsp. ***azorica***	CExl EBee LRHS WPGP
	- 'Myrtifolia' 𝒴H5	CBar CRos CTri ECrN EPfP EShb LMaj LPra LRHS MRav NLar NOra SArc SCob SGol SLon SPoG SWvt WCFE WMat
	- 'Variegata' (v)	CBar CMac ELan ELon MGos MRav MSwo SCob SGol SPer SPoG SSta SWvt WFar WMoo
	maackii	EMOT
	- 'Amber Beauty'	CDul CLnd EBee EPfP EUJe LMaj MMuc MRav NOra SEND SGol SLon WMat
	mahaleb	CNWT
§	'Matsumae-beni-murasaki'	CBcs EBee EMOT LRHS NLar NOra WMat
	'Matsumae-beni-tamanishiki'	see *P.* 'Beni-tamanishiki'
§	'Matsumae-fuki' 𝒴H6	CBcs CDul EBee EMOT LSRN NLar NOra NRHS NWea SLim WMat
	'Matsumae-hanagasa'	see *P.* 'Hanagasa'
	maximowiczii B&SWJ 10967	WCru
	'Mount Fuji'	see *P.* 'Shirotae'
	mume	CMen ELon MMrt
	- 'Beni-chidori' 𝒴H5	CBcs CEnd CMac CSBt EBee ELan EPfP LCro LOPS LRHS MBlu NLar NOra SCob SCoo SPoG WCot WJas WMat
§	- 'Omoi-no-mama' (d)	CEnd CMen SAko
	- 'Omoi-no-wac'	see *P. mume* 'Omoi-no-mama'
	myrobalana	see *P. cerasifera* Myrobalan Group
	nigra	WMat
	nipponica var. ***kurilensis*** 'Brillant'	CBcs CRos CSBt ELon LRHS NHol NLar NRHS SPoG
	- - 'Ruby'	LSRN NEgg
	'Okame Harlequin' (v)	EMOT WMou
	'Oku-miyako' misapplied	see *P.* 'Shōgetsu'
	padus	CArg CCVT CDul CFGn CHab CLnd CMac CPer CSBt ECrN EWTr LBuc MGos MJak MMuc MSwo NLar NWea SCob SEND SEWo WMou WTSh
	- 'Albertii'	CCVT EBee NOra WMat
	- 'Colorata' 𝒴H6	CArg CDul CEnd CMac CTho EBee ECrN ELan EWTr MGos MMuc MRav NLar NPri SEND SGol SPer SWvt
	- 'Grandiflora'	see *P. padus* 'Watereri'
	- 'Le Thoureil'	LRHS MMrt
	- 'Purple Queen'	ECrN SCob SGol
§	- 'Watereri' 𝒴H6	CArg CCVT CDul CEnd CMCN CMac CTho ELan EMOT EPfP LMaj LPra MMuc NWea SEND SEWo SGol SPer WMat WMou
	'Pandora' 𝒴H6	CCVT CDul CLnd CSBt EBee EMOT EPfP EPom EWTr LCro LMaj LOPS LRHS MGos MMuc MRav MSwo

	NOra NWea SCob SCoo SEND SEWo SLim SPer SPoG SSFr WMat WMou
§ ***pendula*** f. ***ascendens*** 'Rosea' ♀H6	LRHS MRav NOra WMat
- 'Pendula Plena Rosea' (d)	NOra WMat
§ - 'Pendula Rosea'	CDul CEnd CLnd CTri EPfP NWea SCob SPer WJas
§ - 'Pendula Rubra' ♀H6	CCVT CDul CLnd CMac CSBt EBee ELan EMOT EPfP EPom LRHS MSwo NOra SCoo SLim SPer SPoG WMat
§ - 'Stellata' ♀H6	EPfP LRHS NOra SPer WMat
persica	SPre
- 'Advance' (F)	SDea
- 'Amsden June' (F)	CLnd EBtc LEdu NOra SDea SKee WMat
- 'Avalon Pride' (F)	CAgr CRos EPom MCoo NOra SKee SPoG SSFr
- 'Bellegarde' (F)	NOra SDea SKee WMat
- 'Bonanza' (F)	EPom LSRN
- 'Carman' (F)	WMat
- 'Champion' (F)	CLnd SDea
- 'Crimson Bonfire' (F)	EPom
- 'Crimson Cascade' (F)	ELan
- 'Darling' (F)	SVic
- 'Diamond' (F)	EPom
- 'Dixi Red' (F)	CAgr
- 'Doctor Hogg' (F)	SDea
- 'Duke of York' (F)	CTri SDea SKee SSFr
- 'Dymond' (F)	SDea
- 'Foliis Rubris' (F)	CDul
- 'Francis' (F)	SKee
- 'Frost' (F)	WMat
- 'Garden Lady' (F)	EPom NOra SLim WMat
- 'Gorgeous' (F)	NOra SKee WMat
- 'Hale's Early' (F)	MMuc MRav NOra SKee SLim SPer WMat
- 'Hylands' (F)	SDea
- 'Jalousia' (F)	EPom SVic
- 'Lacrima' (F)	EPom
- 'Mesembrine'PBR (F)	EPom NOra
- 'Natalia' (F)	SDea
- var. ***nectarina*** CRIMSON GOLD (F)	SDea
- - 'Earliglo' (F)	NOra WMat
- - 'Early Gem' (F)	SDea
- - 'Early Rivers' (F)	LSRN SDea WMat
- - 'Elruge' (F)	SDea
- - 'Fantasia' (F)	SDea SSFr
- - 'Fire Gold' (F)	SDea
- - 'Flavortop' (F)	SSFr
- - 'Garden Beauty' (F/d)	WMat
- - 'Honey Kist'PBR (F)	EPom
- - 'Humboldt' (F)	CAgr CDul EMOT SDea WMat
- - 'John Rivers' (F)	SDea
- - 'Lord Napier' (F)	CAgr CDul CRos CSBt CTri EMOT EPfP EPom LRHS MGos MJak MWat NOra SDea SEND SKee SLim SPer SSFT SSFr SVic WMat
- - 'Madame Blanchet' (F)	SDea SVic
- - 'Nectarella' (F)	EPom LSRN NOra SLim WMat
- - 'Pineapple' (F)	CAgr CTri LRHS NOra SDea SKee WMat
- - RUBIS ('Necta Zee'PBR) (F)	EPom
- - 'Ruby Gold' (F)	SDea
- - 'Sauzee Bel' (F)	EPom
- - 'Sauzee King' (F)	EPom
- - 'Snow Baby' (F)	EPom
- - 'Snow Queen' (F)	SSFr
- - 'Terrace Ruby' (F)	MGos WMat
- 'Peregrine' (F)	CAgr CDul CLnd CSBt CTri EMOT EPfP EPom LRHS LSRN MAsh MGos MJak MMuc NLar NOra SDea SEND SKee SLim SPer SSFT SSFr WJas WMat
- 'Redhaven' (F)	CAgr EMOT NOra SDea SKee SVic WMat
- 'Redwing' (F)	CAgr
- 'Reliance' (F)	SDea
- 'Robin Redbreast' (F)	CAgr SDea
- 'Rochester' (F)	CAgr CDul CLnd CSBt CTri EMOT EPom LRHS LSRN MGos NLar NOra SDea SKee SLim SPer SSFT SSFr WMat
- 'Sanguine de Savoie' (F)	EPom LRHS NOra WMat
- 'Saturne' (F)	CAgr CLnd EMOT EPom LRHS MAsh NOra SDea SKee SSFr WMat
- 'Springtime' (F)	SDea
- 'Terrace Amber' (F)	WMat
- 'Terrace Diamond' (F)	WMat
- 'Terrace Garnet' (F)	MGos WMat
- 'Wassenberger' (F)	SDea
× ***persicoides*** 'Ingrid' (F)	CAgr CDul CEnd CFGn ECrN EMOT MCoo MGos NOra SCoo SKee SSFr WMat
- 'Pollardii'	WJas
- 'Robijn' (F)	CAgr EPom LBuc LEdu NOra SKee SVic
- 'Spring Glow'	CCVT CDul CEnd CLnd EMOT EMil EPfP MSwo NOra NWea SCoo SEND SLim SLon WJas WMat
phaeosticta NJM 10.072	WPGP
'Pink Candy' (F)	EPom
PINK PARASOL	see *P.* 'Hanagasa'
'Pink Perfection' ♀H6	CBcs CDul CLnd CSBt ECrN ELan ELon EMOT EPfP EPom EUJe LPra LRHS MGos MSwo NOra SCob SPer SSFr WJas WMat WMou
'Pink Shell'	CLnd EPfP EPom NOra SPer SSFr WMat
PINK SNOW SHOWERS ('Pisnshzam') **new**	EPom
pissardii	see *P. cerasifera* 'Pissardii'
'Pissardii Nigra'	see *P. cerasifera* 'Nigra'
pumila var. ***depressa***	MRav SAko
'Royal Burgundy' (d) ♀H6	Widely available
rufa	CDul CJun CLnd EBtc LLHF NOra SLon WMat
§ ***salicina*** 'Black Diamond' (F)	SDea
- 'Lizzie' (F)	EPom
- 'Methley' (D)	CAgr NOra WMat
sargentii	Widely available
- 'Charles Sargent' ♀H6	CMCN LMaj LSRN MBlu
- 'Columnaris'	LRHS WMat
- 'Rancho'	CLnd LMaj MAsh SCoo SLim SPer SPoG WMat
× ***schmittii***	CBcs CCVT ECrN LMaj LRHS NOra SPer WJas WMat
'Sekiyama'	see *P.* 'Kanzan'
§ ***serrula***	Widely available
- 'Branklyn' ♀H6	CNWT EBee EPfP LRHS MGos NOra SCob
- 'Princesse Sturdza'	MBlu
- var. ***tibetica***	see *P. serrula*
serrula × ***serrulata***	WPGP
serrulata (d)	CAco LPra
- 'Erecta'	see *P.* 'Amanogawa'

	- 'Grandiflora'	see *P.* 'Ukon'
	- 'Longipes'	see *P.* 'Shōgetsu'
	- 'Miyako' misapplied	see *P.* 'Shōgetsu'
	- var. ***pubescens***	see *P. verecunda*
	- 'Rosea'	see *P.* 'Kiku-shidare-zakura'
	'Shidare-zakura'	see *P.* 'Kiku-shidare-zakura'
	'Shimizu-zakura'	see *P.* 'Shōgetsu'
	'Shirofugen' ♀H6	see *P.* 'Fugenzō'
§	'Shirotae' ♀H6	Widely available
§	'Shizuka' ♀H6	CBcs CDul EBee ECrN ELon EMOT EWTr LBuc LRHS MSwo NLar NOra SCob SCoo SLim SPer WMat WMou
§	'Shōgetsu' ♀H6	CBcs CDul CEnd CLnd CMCN CMac CSBt CTho ELan EMOT EPfP EPom LMaj LRHS LSRN MAsh MMuc NEgg NLar NOra SCob SEWo SLim SPer WMat WMou
	SNOW FOUNTAINS ('Snofozam') **new**	SPer
	'Snow Goose'	CMac CRos CTho EBee ELan EMOT EPfP EPom EUJe EWTr LRHS MBlu MMuc NEgg NLar NOra SCoo SGol SPoG WMat
	'Snow Showers'	CCVT CEnd CMac EBee ELan EMOT EPom LCro LRHS LSRN MAsh MGos NOra NPri NWea SEND SLim SPer SPoG WMat
	spinosa	CArg CCVT CDul CFGn CHab CMac CPer CTri ECrN EPfP EPom GAbr LBuc LMaj LSRN MBlu MJak NLar NPol NWea SCob SEWo SPer SPoG SVic WMat WMou WSFF WTSh
	- 'Plena' (d)	CEnd CTho MBlu
	- 'Purpurea'	CDul CTho MBlu WMou
§	'Spire' ♀H6	Widely available
	SPRING SNOW	see *P.* 'Beni-tamanishiki'
	'Spring Snow' ambig.	EMOT
	'Stefania'	WMat
	× ***subhirtella***	LPra
	- var. ***ascendens***	see *P. pendula* f. *ascendens*
	- 'Autumnalis'	Widely available
	- 'Autumnalis Rosea'	Widely available
§	- 'Dahlem'	LPra
	- 'Falling Stars'	SLon
	- 'Fukubana'	CLnd CMac ELon EMOT EPfP NLar WMat WMou
	- 'Pendula' misapplied	see *P. pendula* 'Pendula Rosea'
	- 'Pendula Rosea'	see *P. pendula* 'Pendula Rosea'
	- 'Pendula Rubra'	see *P. pendula* 'Pendula Rubra'
	- 'Plena'	see *P.* × *subhirtella* 'Dahlem'
	- 'Rosea'	see *P. pendula* f. *ascendens* 'Rosea'
	- 'Stellata'	see *P. pendula* 'Stellata'
	'Sunset Boulevard' ♀H6	CCVT CLnd ELan EMOT EPfP LMaj LRHS LSRN MGos NLar NOra WMat
	'Tai-haku' ♀H6	Widely available
	'Taoyame' ♀H6	CLnd
	tenella	ECha WCot
	- 'Alba' **new**	WFar
	- 'Fire Hill'	CSBt ELan EPfP LRHS MGos NLar SPer WCot WJas WSpi
	'The Bride' ♀H6	CBcs CDul CEnd CJun CTho EBee EMOT EPfP EPom LCro LOPS LRHS MAsh NAln NOra SChF SCoo SEWo WMat
	tibetica	see *P. serrula*
	'Tiltstone Hellfire'	EBee EMOT GBin LRHS NOra WMat
	tomentosa	EBee
§	'Trailblazer' (C/D)	CDul CEnd CLnd CMac EMOT EMil MRav MSwo SCob SKee SLon
	triloba	CBcs ECha LCro LOPS MBlu MGos
	- 'Multiplex' (d)	SRms WAvo WJas
§	'Ukon' ♀H6	CBcs CDul CLnd CMCN CMac CTho CTri EBee ECrN EMOT EPfP EWTr LCro LOPS LRHS MAsh MGos MRav NLar NOra NWea SGol SLim SPer WFar WMat
	'Umineko'	CCVT CDul CLnd ECrN LMaj MGos MMuc SEND SEWo SPer
§	***verecunda***	CLnd WJas
	- 'Autumn Glory' ♀H6	CTho
	'Victoria Willis'	WMat
	virginiana 'Schubert'	ECrN EMOT MMuc NWea
	'White Cloud'	CDul
	'Woodfield Cluster'	IArd
	yamadae	see *P. incisa* f. *yamadei*
	× ***yedoensis***	CCVT CDul CLnd CSBt EMOT LMaj MRav NOra NWea SEWo SLon SPer WMat
	- 'Ivensii'	CAco CDul CSBt EMOT EPom LMaj SCoo SPer
	- 'Pendula'	see *P.* × *yedoensis* 'Shidare-Yoshino'
	- 'Perpendens'	see *P.* × *yedoensis* 'Shidare-Yoshino'
§	- 'Shidare-Yoshino'	CCVT CDul CLnd CSBt EBee ECrN EMOT EUJe LRHS MGos MRav MSwo NWea SLim SLon SPer WMat
§	- 'Somei-Yoshino' ♀H6	CCVT CMCN CTho CTri EPfP SLim SSFr WJas
	'Yoshino'	see *P.* × *yedoensis* 'Somei-Yoshino'
	'Yoshino Pendula'	see *P.* × *yedoensis* 'Shidare-Yoshino'

Pseudocydonia (*Rosaceae*)

§	***sinensis***	CBcs CMen SEND SSta

Pseudofumaria see *Corydalis*

	alba	see *Corydalis ochroleuca*

Pseudogynoxys (*Asteraceae*)

§	***chenopodioides***	CCCN CSpe ECre SVen

Pseudolarix (*Pinaceae*)

	amabilis ♀H7	CMen CTho EPfP MBlu MPkF SLim SMad
	kaempferi (Lamb.) Gordon	see *Larix kaempferi*

Pseudomuscari see *Muscari*

Pseudopanax ✿ (*Araliaceae*)

	(Adiantifolius Group) 'Adiantifolius'	CBcs EBee SVen
	- 'Cyril Watson' ♀H3	CBcs EBee ELan SVen
	arboreus	see *Neopanax arboreus*
	chathamicus	SArc
	crassifolius	CBrP CCCN CDTJ CRos ELon EUJe GBin LRHS SArc
	- var. ***trifoliolatus***	EBee WPGP
	'Dark Star'	CBcs LRHS
	discolor	LEdu
	ferox	CBrP CDTJ CTsd EUJe GBin LRHS SCob SVen
	laetus	see *Neopanax laetus*
	lessonii	CBcs CBrP
	- 'Gold Splash' (v) ♀H3	CBcs CBod CCCN EBee ELon EPfP LRHS SEND SVen
	- 'Rangitira'	CBcs LRHS
	'Linearifolius'	IDee LEdu
	'Moa's Toes'	CAbb EUJe SCob SEND SPad WCot WPGP
	'Purpureus' ♀H3	CCCN CDTJ EBee ELon IArd IDee SEND SVen

'Sabre' CBcs CDTJ EBee ELon EPfP EUJe IDee LRHS SEND
'Trident' ♀H3 SVen
'Tuatara' CAbb CCht EUJe GBin SCob WPGP

Pseudosasa (*Poaceae*)

sp. CAco
amabilis misapplied see *Arundinaria gigantea*
- var. ***tenuis*** new XCre
cantorii new XCre
§ ***japonica*** ♀H5 CAbb CAgr CBcs CBdn CBod CRos CSBt CTsd ENBC EPfP GBin LCro LOPS LRHS MMuc MWht NLar NRHS SArc SCob SEND SPoG WCFE WFar WMoo XCre
§ - 'Akebonosuji' (v) MWht WPGP XCre
I - var. ***pleioblastoides*** MWht
- 'Tsutsumiana' ELon ERod MWht NLar XCre
- 'Variegata' see *P. japonica* 'Akebonosuji'
viridula ERod MWht XCre

Pseudotaxus (*Taxaceae*)

chienii CBcs SPtp WPGP

Pseudotsuga (*Pinaceae*)

§ ***menziesii*** CAco CBcs CDul CLnd CPer ECrN EPfP LPra MBlu MMuc NWea WTSh
- 'Bhiela Lhota' CAco CKen
- 'Blue Wonder' CKen
- 'Dandy Doug' NLar
- 'Densa' CKen
- 'Fastigiata' CKen
- 'Fletcheri' CKen
- var. ***glauca*** CAco
- 'Glauca Pendula' CAco CDul CKen LRHS MBlu
I - 'Gotelli's Pendula' CKen
- 'Graceful Grace' CKen
- 'Hillside Pride' NLar
- 'Idaho Gem' CKen NLar
- 'Julie' CKen
- 'Knaphill' LRHS
- 'Little Jamie' CKen
- 'Lohbrunner' CKen
- 'McKenzie' CKen
- 'Nana' CKen
- 'Serpentine' MBlu SMad
- 'Stairii' CKen
- 'Uwes Golden' SLim
taxifolia see *P. menziesii*

Pseudowintera (*Winteraceae*)

§ ***colorata*** CBcs CCCN CExl CMac CPla EBee GAbr GKin MRav NLar SBrt SCob SEle WFar WSHC
- 'Marjorie Congreve' CBcs GKin IArd LRHS
- 'Moulin Rouge' CBcs SEle
- 'Red Glow' CBcs
- 'Red Leopard' CAby CBcs CCht CRos LRHS MPkF NLar SEle WFar

Psidium (*Myrtaceae*)

cattleyanum see *P. littorale* var. *longipes*
guajava (F) CCCN CMCN SPlb XBlo
§ ***littorale*** var. ***longipes*** (F) CCCN XBlo

Psophocarpus (*Papilionaceae*)

tetragonolobus LCro

Psoralea (*Papilionaceae*)

aphylla SVen
* ***fleta*** SPlb
glabra SPlb
glandulosa SPlb WSHC
oligophylla SPlb
pinnata CExl

Psychotria (*Rubiaceae*)

capensis CExl

Psylliostachys (*Plumbaginaceae*)

suworowii LRHS SPhx

Ptelea (*Rutaceae*)

trifoliata CAby CBcs CDul CLnd ELan EPfP MBlu SChF SPer SRms WPGP
- 'Aurea' ♀H6 CBcs CDul CExl CJun CLnd ELan EPfP MBlu MMuc SPer WBor WPGP

Pteracanthus see *Strobilanthes*

Pteridium (*Dennstaedtiaceae*)

aquilinum XLum

Pteridophyllum (*Papaveraceae*)

racemosum GEdr LEdu NHpl WCru

Pteris ✿ (*Pteridaceae*)

cretica ♀H1c CTsd
- var. ***albolineata*** ♀H1c CBdn CRos EShb EUJe LLWG LRHS MBel NRHS WCot XBlo
- 'Mayi' (v) CRos LRHS NRHS
- 'Ouvradii' SPlb
- 'Parkeri' CBdn CRos LRHS NRHS
- 'Rivertoniana' CRos LRHS NRHS
- 'Rowei' CRos LRHS NRHS XBlo
- 'Wimsettii' CRos LRHS NRHS WCot
ensiformis 'Victoriae' EShb
gallinopes EBee
* ***staminea*** XBlo
tremula EShb NBro
tricolor EShb
umbrosa CAby CBdn CLAP CRos EUJe LLWG LRHS NBro NRHS WCot WPGP
wallichiana WCot WPGP

Pterocactus (*Cactaceae*)

hickenii F&W 10240 WCot

Pterocarya ✿ (*Juglandaceae*)

fraxinifolia CBcs CCVT CDul CMCN CTho EBee ECrN EPfP IArd IDee LMaj LPra LRHS MBlu MCoo MMuc MRav SChF WTSh
- NJM 13.007 WPGP
- PAB 13.052 LEdu
- 'Abbotsbury Giant' WPGP
macroptera var. ***insignis*** CExl EBee WPGP
× ***rehderiana*** CTho MBlu
rhoifolia CDul CMCN IArd SEND
stenoptera CBcs CDTJ CDul CMCN CTho NLar WMou
- 'Fern Leaf' ♀H6 CExl MBlu WPGP
tonkinensis WPGP

Pterocephalus (*Caprifoliaceae*)

parnassi see *P. perennis*
§ ***perennis*** CMea MHer NBir SRms WAbe WHoo
spathulatus WAbe

Pterostylis (*Orchidaceae*)

curta ♀H2 — CBro SBch

Pterostyrax (*Styracaceae*)

corymbosa — CBcs CMCN GBin MBlu NLar SMad
- CWJ 12838 — WCru
hispida ♀H5 — CAby CBcs CDul CMCN CTsd EPfP GBin MBlu MRav NLar SAko WFar WGrn WHor
psilophyllus — CMCN SPtp WPGP
- var. ***leveillei*** — WPGP
- trilobed — EBee WPGP

Ptilostemon (*Asteraceae*)

§ ***diacantha*** — CRos EBee EMor LRHS NRHS
niveus — WCot

Ptilotrichum see *Alyssum*

Ptilotus (*Amaranthaceae*)

exaltatus — SPlb

Pulicaria (*Asteraceae*)

§ ***dysenterica*** — CHab LLWG NMir WHer WSFF

Pulmonaria (*Boraginaceae*)

angustifolia ♀H6 — CTri EPfP GKev GMaP MNrw SHeu SRms
- 'Azurea' — CElw CRos ELan EPPr EPfP GBin GMaP LRHS MCot MMuc MRav NBro NGrd NLar NRHS SRms WSpi
- 'Blaues Meer' — CRos EBee ECtt LRHS MNrw NRHS NSti SGbt SHeu WSpi
- 'Munstead Blue' — MCot MRav NAln NRya SRms
'Apple Frost' — CRos LRHS NRHS SHeu
'Ballyrogan Blue' — CRos LRHS NRHS
'Barfield Regalia' — NChi NSti
'Benediction' — MAvo MNrw NSti WBrk WCot
'Beth Chatto' — CElw
'Beth's Pink' — GAbr
'Blake's Silver' — CBre CDor ECtt MAvo MHol MNrw NEgg NSti WBrk WCot WHoo WWFP
'Blauer Hügel' — NSti
'Blue Crown' — CElw EWes WBrk
'Blue Ensign' ♀H6 — Widely available
'Blue Moon' — see *P. officinalis* 'Blue Mist'
'Blue Pearl' — CRos LRHS NRHS XEll
'Bubble Gum'PBR — CDor CRos LRHS NRHS SHeu
Cally hybrid — GCal
'Cleeton Red' — MNrw
'Coral Springs' — NLar
'Cotton Cool' ♀H6 — EBee EBou ECha ECtt EShb LRHS MAvo MBNS MBel MCot MHer MRav NEgg NHol NRHS NSti NWad SGbt SHeu SSut WCAu WGwG WMoo WWtn
'Dark Vader' — CRos CWCL ECtt LRHS MNrw NCGa NRHS SHeu SPoG
'Darkling Thrush' — WBrk
'Diana Clare' ♀H6 — Widely available
'Excalibur' — ECtt NLar SHeu SRms
'Fiona' — MNrw
'Gavin Compton' (v) — MNrw
'Glacier' — EPfP NChi WCot
'High Contrast' — ECtt SHeu
'Highdown' — see *P.* 'Lewis Palmer'
'Ice Ballet' (Classic Series) — CDor EBee ECtt EMor EPfP MNrw NLar SCob SHar SHeu WCAu
'Joan Curtis' — EWld MNrw
§ 'Lewis Palmer' ♀H6 — CBro CDor CTri CWCL GCal GMaP LRHS MAvo MNrw NBir SRms WAvo WBrk WHoo
'Little Star' ♀H6 — CElw CRos EBee ECha LRHS MAvo NAln NRHS NSti SHeu WFar
longifolia — ECha ELan EPfP GKev IFro LRHS MHer NBir NLar NRHS NSti SCob SRms
§ - 'Ankum' — CElw NBir WCot
- 'Bertram Anderson' — CRos EBee ECtt EMor GMaP LRHS NBir NLar NRHS SCob SHeu SPer SRms SWvt
- subsp. ***cevennensis*** — CRos EAJP EMor ILea LRHS NLar NRHS SHeu WBrk WFar WSpi
- 'Coen Jansen' — see *P. longifolia* 'Ankum'
- 'Dordogne' — NBir
- 'Howard Eggins' — WAvo WBrk
- 'Juliett M.' **new** — XEll
'Mado' — ECha
'Majesté' — CBod CDor CRos ECha EHrv ELan EMor EPfP EWes GBin GMaP IFro LRHS MBel MRav NBir NGdn NLar NRHS NSti SCob SHeu SMad SPer SPoG SRms WCAu WCot WFar
'Marchant's Spotted Dick' — SMHy
'Margery Fish' — CDor CRos LRHS NAln NChi SHeu WBrk
'Mary Mottram' — ECtt NBir NSti SHeu WCot
'Mawson's Blue' — EWes NBir NChi SWvt WMoo
'Milky Way' — ECtt EMor EPfP SHeu SPoG
'Miss Elly' **new** — MAvo
mollis — CBod GBin GCal IMou LRHS MNrw NRHS NSti WCAu
- 'Royal Blue' — MRav
'Monksilver' — CElw
'Moonshine'PBR — CRos ECtt EPfP LRHS MAsh NRHS NSti SHeu
'Moonstone' — CElw
'Mournful Purple' — ELon
'Mrs Kittle' — CWCL GPSL IMou LRHS MRav NBir NGdn NHol NRHS NSti SHeu SSut
'Nürnberg' — CDor
officinalis — CHby NChi WBrk
- 'Alba' — WBrk
§ - 'Blue Mist' — GMaP NBir WAvo WCot WMoo
- 'Bowles's Blue' — see *P. officinalis* 'Blue Mist'
- Cambridge Blue Group — EPfP LRHS MRav NBir NGdn NRHS WCot WWtn
- 'White Wings' — NLar
OPAL ('Ocupol') — Widely available
'Pierre's Pure Pink' — CRos EBee LRHS NCGa NRHS SHeu
'Pink Haze'PBR — ECtt MHol NLar SCob SWvt
'Raspberry Splash'PBR — CBod CRos CWCL ECtt EMor EPfP GKev LCro LOPS LRHS MBel MMuc MNrw NBir NLar SCob SHeu SWvt WCAu
* 'Rowlatt Choules' — MNrw
'Roy Davidson' — CBod CDor CRos ECtt EPfP LRHS NBir NChi NHol NRHS SRms SWvt
rubra — CBcs CElw CWCL ECha ELan GAbr LCro LOPS MJak MMuc MNrw NBid NChi NSti SHeu SRms WBrk WCAu
- var. ***alba*** — see *P. rubra* var. *albocorollata*
§ - var. ***albocorollata*** — CBre CRos LRHS NBid NRHS
- 'Ann' — GBin
- 'Barfield Pink' — GCal NBir SHeu

	Name	Suppliers
	- 'Bowles's Red'	CBod CRos EHrv GPSL LRHS MNrw MRav NBir NLar NRHS WFar WGwG WWtn
	- 'David Ward' (v)	CRos CWCL ECha ECtt EHrv ELan EMor GEdr GMaP LRHS MBel MRav NBir NRHS NSti SHeu SMad SPoG SRms WCAu WCFE WCot
	- 'Rachel Vernie' (v)	NQui WAvo
	- 'Redstart'	CBod CCBP CDor CRos CSam ECtt GKev GMaP ILea LRHS MNrw MRav NAln NBir NGrd NLar SHeu SRms SWvt WBrk WFar WMoo
§	***saccharata***	ECha GMaP IFro MMuc SRms
	- 'Alba'	CElw MMuc SRms
	- Argentea Group ♀H7	CTri EPfP GMaP LRHS MMuc MRav NGdn NRHS
	- 'Clent Skysilver'	WAvo WBrk
	- 'Dora Bielefeld'	CAby CBod CRos ECha EPfP EWes GMaP IMou LRHS MNrw MRav NBir NChi NEgg NGdn NHol NRHS NSti SHeu SPer SWvt WFar WHlf
	- 'Frühlingshimmel'	CDor LPla MRav
	- 'Glebe Cottage Blue'	CElw
	- 'Leopard'	CDor CMea CRos CSam CWCL ECtt EMor EPfP GBin GMaP LRHS MBel MNrw NBir NGdn NRHS NSti SHeu SWvt WCAu WCot WGwG WHoo WSpi
	- 'Mrs Moon'	CBod CRos CTri ECtt EMor EPfP GMaP IKil LRHS NLar NRHS SHeu SPer SWvt
	- 'Old Rectory Silver'	NBir
	- 'Picta'	see *P. saccharata*
	- 'Pink Dawn'	NLar
	- 'Reginald Kaye'	ECha MAvo
	- 'Silverado'PBR	CRos ECtt LRHS NGdn NRHS SHeu SWvt
	- 'Stanhoe'	EWes
	'Saint Ann's'	CRos LRHS NRHS NSti
	'Samurai' ♀H6	CBod CWCL EUJe IMou LRHS MAvo MNrw NCGa NSti SHeu WFar
	'Silver Bouquet'PBR	CElw ECtt EPfP LCro LOPS NHpl SHeu
	'Silver Lance'	SHeu
	'Silver Shimmers'PBR	SHeu
	'Sissinghurst White' ♀H6	Widely available
	'Smoky Blue'	ECtt MRav SCob SHeu
	'Spilled Milk'	SHeu
	'Stillingfleet Meg'	CDor CRos ECtt EPfP LRHS MBNS MHer NGdn NRHS NSti NWad SHeu WCAu WCot WGwG WWtn
	'Tim's Silver'	GBin
	'Trevi Fountain'	CBod CCBP CDor CRos CWCL EBee ECha ECtt ELon EPfP EShb GKev LCro LOPS LPla LRHS LSun MHol MNrw NRHS NSti SHeu SPoG WCAu WCot WFar WHoo WPnP WSpi
	'Vera May' ♀H6	MNrw
	'Victorian Brooch'PBR	CBod CRos CWCL ECtt EPau EPfP GKev GMaP LRHS MHol MNrw NCou NRHS SHeu SPad SPoG WCAu WSpi
	'Weetwood Blue'	CRos LRHS MNrw NRHS
	'Wendy Perry'	CRos LRHS NRHS

Pulsatilla (*Ranunculaceae*)

	Name	Suppliers
	albana	CRos LLHF LRHS NRHS
	- 'Lutea'	EBee LLHF NSla
	alpina	SPlb SRms WArt
§	- subsp. ***apiifolia***	GKev IFro NRya
	- subsp. ***sulphurea*** misapplied	see *P. alpina* subsp. *apiifolia*
	ambigua	GEdr GKev
	bungeana	GKev SBrt
	campanella	EBee GEdr GKev
	caucasica	CRos EWld LRHS NRHS
	halleri ♀H5	EBee GKev WHal WSHC
	- subsp. ***slavica*** ♀H5	EPot GKev LLHF
	- subsp. ***taurica***	GEdr
	lutea	see *P. alpina* subsp. *apiifolia*
	montana	SPlb XEll
	multifida	SBrt
	occidentalis	GEdr
§	***patens***	GKev NGdn
	- subsp. ***flavescens***	GEdr GKev
	pratensis	GPoy SRms
	- subsp. ***nigricans***	EBee GEdr WAbe
	red-flowered	CTri
	rubra	CAvo CMea CRos EBou ELan EMor EPfP GBin GKev GMaP LRHS MHer NBir NGdn NLar NRHS SPad SPer SPoG SRms SRot WHoo WIce WTor
*	***serotina***	EBee GKev NAln
	subslavica	CPBP
	tatewakii **new**	NSla
	turczaninovii	EBee LLHF NSla
§	***vernalis***	CBor EPot GEdr NLar NSla WAbe XEll
	violacea	CBcs LLHF
§	***vulgaris*** ♀H5	Widely available
	- 'Alba'	CAby CAvo CRos CTsd EBee ECha ELan EPfP EShb GBin GCal GKev LRHS MBel MHer NBir NGdn NRHS SCob SPad SPer SPoG SWvt WFar WGwG WIce XEll XLum
	- 'Barton's Pink'	CRos LLHF LRHS NRHS
	- 'Blaue Glocke'	CAby CBod CRos GEdr LRHS NRHS SHar SWvt WRHF
	- blue-flowered **new**	CTri
	- 'Eva Constance'	CRos LLHF LRHS NRHS
	- 'Gotlandica'	LLHF
	- subsp. ***grandis***	CFis CRos EPot GEdr LRHS NRHS NSla SIgm
	- - 'Papageno'	CDor CSpe ELon EMor GBin GCrg GEdr IPot MBel MHol NHol NHpl NLar NSla WIce
	- Heiler hybrids	EShb LLHF MArl MRav MWat NEgg NGdn NSla SVic WGwG
	- 'Perlen Glocke'	CRos EDAr GEdr LRHS MMrt NCGa NLar NRHS WArt WIce
	- pink-flowered	GKev LLHF NSla WFar
	- (Pinwheel Series) PINWHEEL BLUE VIOLET SHADES	CRos LCro LOPS NRHS
	- - PINWHEEL DARK RED SHADES	CBod LCro LOPS
	- - PINWHEEL WHITE	LCro LOPS MHol NCGa WFar
	- RED CLOCK	see *P. vulgaris* 'Röde Klokke'
	- red-flowered	CTsd EBee GAbr SCob SGbt WFar
§	- 'Röde Klokke'	CAby CBod CRos EAJP ECtt EPfP GBin GEdr GWyn LRHS MCot NRHS SHar SWvt XEll XLum
	- ROTE GLOCKE	see *P. vulgaris* 'Röde Klokke'
	- 'Violet Bells'	EBou
	- violet-blue-flowered	CRos EPfP LRHS NRHS
§	- 'Weisse Schwan'	EBee EPfP GEdr GMaP SRot
	- 'White Bells'	NHol WFar
	- WHITE SWAN	see *P. vulgaris* 'Weisse Schwan'

Pultenaea (*Papilionaceae*)

daphnoides	SVen
juniperina	SPlb SVen

pummelo see *Citrus maxima*

Punica (*Lythraceae*)

granatum	CBcs CCCN CMCN CMen ELan EPfP LMaj SCob SEND SPre SVic SWvt
- 'Chico' (d)	CBcs
- 'Fina Tendral' (F)	CCCN
- 'Legrelleae' (F/d)	SEND
- 'Maxima Rubra' (d)	EShb
- var. ***nana*** ♀H3	CCCN CMen CRos EPfP EShb LEdu LRHS MHer SRms SVen SVic
- f. ***plena*** (d)	CBcs LRHS MRav WCFE
- - 'Flore Pleno Luteo' (d)	LRHS
- 'Provence' (F)	EPom XSen
- 'Wonderful' (F)	CAgr XSen

Puschkinia (*Asparagaceae*)

scilloides	NBir
- var. ***libanotica*** ♀H5	CAby CRos EPot ERCP GKev LAma LCro LOPS LRHS MPie NAln NRHS SDeJ SEND WShi
- - 'Alba'	EPot GKev LAma SDeJ

Puya ✿ (*Bromeliaceae*)

RH 1809	WCot
RH 2910A	WCot
RH 2961C	WCot
RH 3425B	WCot
alpestris	CCCN CPla EShb SPlb
- subsp. ***zoellneri***	CAbb CCCN CDTJ EShb SVen WCot
assurgens	WCot
berteroana new	SPlb
bicolor B&SWJ 14869 new	WCru
boliviensis	WCot
castellanosii	WCot
chilensis	CAbb CCCN CDTJ CPla LRHS SPlb SVen WCot
coerulea	CCCN CDTJ CPla CTsd SPlb
- var. ***monteroana***	WCot
dyckioides	LRHS WCot
- red-bracted	WCot
ferruginea	EUJe SPlb WCot
gilmartiniae F&W 8697	WCot
grantii B&SWJ 14819 new	WCru
harmsii	WCot
hromadnikii	SPlb
killipii B&SWJ 14801 new	WCru
laxa	SPlb WCot
lineata B&SWJ 14878 new	WCru
mirabilis	CAbb CDTJ EUJe GBin
- B&SWJ 14825 new	WCru
- B&SWJ 14827 new	WCru
aff. ***nitida*** B&SWJ 14396 new	WCru
- B&SWJ 14887 new	WCru
raimondii	WCot
santosii B&SWJ 14783 new	WCru
trianae B&SWJ 14818 new	WCru
- B&SWJ 14921 new	WCru
venusta	CCCN CDTJ CPla LRHS SPlb SVen WCot
yakespala	LRHS WCot

Pycnanthemum (*Lamiaceae*)

curvipes	LEdu
muticum	LEdu SBrt WPGP
pilosum	CLau EBou MHer SPhx WJek XLum
- 'Bees' Friend' new	MNrw
tenuifolium	NLar SBrt SPhx
virginianum	EBee SPhx

Pycnostachys (*Lamiaceae*)

urticifolia	EWes SDys

Pygmea see *Chionohebe*

Pyracantha (*Rosaceae*)

ALEXANDER PENDULA ('Renolex')	MRav MSwo SRms
angustifolia	WCFE
- KR 2481	WPGP
§ ***atalantioides***	SPlb WCFE
'Brilliant'	SCoo
coccinea 'Lalandei'	CMac
- 'Red Column'	Widely available
- 'Red Cushion'	ELan MJak MRav SArc SCob SRms
crenulata	WCFE
DART'S RED ('Interrada')	CSBt
'Fiery Cascade'	CRos EPfP LRHS NRHS SPoG WFar
gibbsii	see *P. atalantioides*
'Golden Charmer'	CDul CMac CRos EPfP LBuc LRHS MGos MSwo NEgg NLar NWea SCob SCoo SGol SPoG SRms SWvt WFar
'Golden Glow'	SGol
'Golden Paradise'	NEoE SCob SHar
'Golden Sun'	see *P.* 'Soleil d'Or'
'Harlequin' (v)	CMac SCob SGol WFar
'Knap Hill Lemon'	MBlu
koidzumii 'Victory'	ECrN NLar
'Mohave'	CMac CRos CTri ECrN ELan ELon EMOT LRHS MAsh NRHS NWea SCob SGol SLim SRms SWvt WFar
'Mohave Silver' (v)	CMac CRos ELan EShb LRHS NHol NRHS
'Navaho'	LMaj
'Orange Charmer'	CDul CMac CTri ELan LRHS MGos MJak NHol NLar NWea SCob SGol SPer SPlb WFar
'Orange Glow' ♀H6	Widely available
'Red Charmer'	NHol
'Red Star'	NRHS
rogersiana	CDul NWea
- 'Flava' ♀H6	CDul CRos CSBt EPfP LRHS MAsh NEgg NRHS NWea SPoG SWvt WAvo
'Rosedale'	CRos LRHS
SAPHYR JAUNE ('Cadaune'PBR)	CBcs CCVT CEnd CRos CSBt EBee EPfP LCro LOPS LRHS MAsh MGos MJak MRav NHol SCob SGol SPer
SAPHYR ORANGE ('Cadange'PBR) ♀H6	CBcs CCVT CEnd CMac CRos CSBt EBee ECrN EPfP LCro LOPS LRHS MAsh MGos MJak MRav NEgg NRHS SCob SCoo SGol SPer
SAPHYR PANACHE ('Cadvar'PBR) (v)	MJak
SAPHYR ROUGE ('Cadrou'PBR) ♀H6	CBcs CBod CCVT CChe CDul CEnd CMac CRos CSBt EBee ELan EPfP LCro LOPS LRHS MAsh MGos MJak MMuc MRav MSwo NRHS SCob SCoo SEND SGol SPer SRms SWvt WFar
'Shawnee'	CMac MSwo
§ 'Soleil d'Or'	CBod CDul CRos CTri ECrN ELan EMOT EPfP EUJe LRHS MAsh

	MJak MRav NLar NRHS NWea SCob SEND SEWo SGol SLim SLon SNig SPer SPlb SRms SWvt WAvo WFar
'Sparkler' (v)	CMac SCob SPoG
'Teton' 𝕐H6	CMac CRos ELan EPfP LRHS MAsh MGos MJak MSwo NRHS SCob SGol SPoG SRms WFar
'Watereri'	WSpi
'Yellow Sun'	see *P.* 'Soleil d'Or'

× *Pyracomeles* (*Rosaceae*)

vilmorinii	IDee SAko

Pyrethropsis see *Rhodanthemum*

Pyrethrum see *Tanacetum*

+ *Pyrocydonia* (*Rosaceae*)

'Danielii' (F)	SAko

Pyrola (*Ericaceae*)

rotundifolia	LEdu WHer

× *Pyronia* (*Rosaceae*)

veitchii	SAko

Pyrrosia (*Polypodiaceae*)

hastata	CMen WCot
- 'Harima Jishi'	CMen
- 'Ryujin'	CMen
- 'Shikoku Jishi'	CMen
- 'World Champion'	CMen
linearifolia 'Urakoryu Jishi'	CMen
lingua	CMen WPGP
- 'Hiryu'	CMen
- 'Ōgon Nishiki' (v)	WCot
- 'Tachiba Koryu'	CMen
polydactyla	CMen WCot
sheareri	CRos LRHS NRHS

Pyrus ✿ (*Rosaceae*)

amygdaliformis	CMCN
- W&B B-10	WCot
- var. ***cuneifolia***	CLnd
calleryana	LPra SGol
- 'Bradford'	CLnd
- 'Chanticleer'	Widely available
- 'Chanticleer' variegated (v)	CDul MAsh
- 'Redspire'	CCVT EMOT SPer
caucasica	WMat
communis (F)	CCVT CDul CTri ECrN LBuc NWea SPer SPlb WMou WTSh
- 'Abbé Fétel' (D)	SKee
- 'Bambinella' (D)	SKee
- 'Barland' (Perry)	CHab
- 'Barnet' (Perry)	CHab
- 'Baronne de Mello' (D)	CTho NOra WMat
- 'Beech Hill' (F)	CDul EBee ECrN LMaj LPra SGol SPer
- 'Belle Guérandaise' (D)	SKee
- 'Belle Julie' (D)	SKee
- 'Bellissime d'Hiver' (C)	SKee
- BENITA ('Rafzas') (F)	LCro LOPS LRHS MCoo WMat
- 'Bergamotte d'Automne' (D)	SKee
- 'Bergamotte Esperen' (D)	SKee
- 'Beth' (D) 𝕐H6	CAgr CArg CHab CMac CSBt CTri EBee ECrN EMOT EPfP EPom IArd LBuc LRHS MAsh MGos NLar NOra NPri SCob SDea SKee SLim SPer SSFT SSFr WMat
- 'Beurré Bedford' (D)	SKee
- 'Beurré Clairgeau' (C)	SKee
- 'Beurré d'Anjou' (F)	SKee
- 'Beurré d'Avalon' (D)	SKee
- 'Beurré de Beugny' (D)	SKee
- 'Beurré de l'Assomption' (D)	SKee
- 'Beurré Diel' (D)	SKee
- 'Beurré Dubuisson' (D)	SKee
- 'Beurré Dumont' (D)	CAgr
- 'Beurré Giffard' (D)	CAgr
- 'Beurré Hardy' (D) 𝕐H6	CAgr CArg CCVT CDul CFGn CLnd CMac CSBt CTri ECrN ELan EMOT EPfP EPom IArd LMaj MCoo MJak MMuc MWat NOra SCob SDea SEND SKee SPer SSFT SSFr WMat WWct
§ - 'Beurré Précoce Morettini' (D)	SDea
- 'Beurré Rance' (C/D)	SKee
- 'Beurré Six' (D)	SKee
- 'Beurré Superfin' (D) 𝕐H6	SKee SSFr
- 'Bianchettone' (D)	SKee
- 'Bishop's Thumb' (D)	SDea SKee
- 'Black Worcester' (C)	CDul CHab NOra SDea SKee WJas WMat WWct
- 'Blakeney Red' (Perry)	CHab NOra SDea SKee WMat
- 'Brandy' (Perry)	CAgr CArg CHab NOra SDea SKee SVic WMat
- 'Bristol Cross' (D)	CAgr CHab SDea SKee
- 'Butt' (Perry)	CHab
- 'Calebasse Bosc' (D)	NOra SKee
- 'Canal Red' (D)	SKee
- 'Cannock' (F)	CArg SKee WMat
- 'Catillac' (C)	CAgr CHab NOra SKee WMat
- 'Charneaux' (F)	LMaj
- 'Citron des Carmes' (C)	SKee
- 'Clapp's Favourite' (D)	CHab CTho LMaj NOra SKee SVic WMat
- 'Comte de Lamy' (D)	SKee
- 'Concorde'PBR (D) 𝕐H6	Widely available
- 'Conference' (D) 𝕐H6	Widely available
- 'Coscia' (C/D) **new**	SKee
- 'Deacon's Pear' (D)	SDea
- 'Devoe' (D)	SDea
- 'Docteur Jules Guyot' (D)	CAgr CFGn SDea
- 'Double de Guerre' (C/D)	SKee
- 'Doyenné Blanc' (F)	SKee
- 'Doyenné d'Été' (D)	MCoo SKee
- 'Doyenné du Comice' (D) 𝕐H6	Widely available
- 'Doyenné Georges Boucher' (D)	SKee
- 'Duchesse d'Angoulême' (D)	SKee
- 'Durondeau' (D)	NOra SDea SKee WMat
- 'Easter Beurré' (D)	SKee
- 'Emile d'Heyst' (D)	MCoo SKee WMat
- 'English Caillot Rosat' (D)	SKee
- 'Fertility' (D)	CLnd
- 'Fertility Improved'	see *P. communis* 'Improved Fertility'
- 'Fondante d'Automne' (D)	CAgr CTho NOra SKee WMat
- 'Forelle' (D)	SKee
- 'Garden Gem' (F)	WMat
- 'Gieser Wildeman' (F)	LMaj
- 'Gin' (Perry)	CHab WMat

- 'Glou Morceau' (D)	CAgr CArg MCoo MWat NOra SDea SKee SSFT SSFr WMat
- 'Gorham' (D) 🏆H6	CAgr CDul CTho NOra SKee SSFT SSFr WMat
- 'Green Horse' (Perry)	CHab SKee WMat
- 'Green Pear of Yair' (D)	SKee
- 'Gregoire Bordillon' (D)	SKee
- 'Hacon's Incomparable' (D)	SKee
- 'Harrow Delight' (D)	SDea
- 'Harvest Queen' (D/C)	CAgr SDea
- 'Hellen's Early' (Perry)	CArg CHab SKee WMat
- 'Hendre Huffcap' (Perry)	CAgr CHab EPom NOra SKee WMat
- 'Hessle' (D)	CAgr CHab NWea SDea SKee
- HUMBUG ('Pysanka') (D)	CArg EPom LRHS NOra SSFT WMat
§ - 'Improved Fertility' (D)	CAgr SDea SKee
- INVINCIBLE ('Delwinor') (D/C)	CAgr CArg CDul CFGn CTho EPom LBuc MCoo NOra SLim SSFT WMat
- 'Jargonelle' (D)	CAgr CDul CHab SDea SKee WMat
- 'Joséphine de Malines' (D) 🏆H6	CAgr IArd NOra SDea SKee
- 'Judge Amphlett' (Perry)	EPom NOra SKee WMat
- 'Laxton's Foremost' (D)	CAgr SKee
- 'Légipont' (F)	CAgr
- 'Louise Bonne of Jersey' (D)	CAgr CArg CFGn CLnd CMac CTri ECrN EPfP EPom IArd MGos NOra SDea SKee SSFr WMat WWct
- 'Magyar Kobak' (C)	SKee
- 'Marguérite Marillat' (D)	SDea SKee
- 'Marie-Louise' (D)	SKee
- 'Merrylegs' (Perry)	CHab
- 'Merton Pride' (D)	CAgr CArg CLnd CTho EPom MCoo NOra SDea SKee SSFr WMat
- 'Monsieur le Curé'	see *P. communis* 'Vicar of Winkfield'
- 'Moonglow' (F)	CAgr NOra SDea SKee WMat
- 'Moorcroft' (Perry)	SKee
- 'Morettini'	see *P. communis* 'Beurré Précoce Morettini'
- 'Nouveau Poiteau' (C/D)	CAgr SKee
- 'Nuvar Celebration' (F)	SKee WMat
- 'Nye Russet Bartlett' (F)	CAgr
- 'Obelisk' (D) new	SPoG
- 'Old Home' (Perry)	WMat
- 'Oldfield' (Perry)	CHab
- 'Olivier de Serres' (D)	SKee
- 'Onward' (D)	CAgr CArg CDul CHab CLnd CTho CTri EMOT EPom IArd LRHS NOra NWea SDea SKee SSFT SSFr WMat WWct
- 'Ovid' (D)	CAgr
§ - 'Packham's Triumph' (D)	CAgr CDul CLnd CTri EMOT EPom NOra SDea SKee SSFr WMat
- 'Parsonage' (Perry)	CHab
- 'Passe Crassane' (D)	SKee
- 'Pear Apple' (D)	CHab SDea
- 'Penrhyn' (D)	WGwG WMat
- 'Pero Nobile' (D)	SKee
I - 'Petite Poire' (D)	EPom SVic
- 'Pitmaston Duchess' (C/D)	MCoo SDea SKee WMat WWct
- 'Précoce de Trévoux' (D)	SKee
- 'Red Beurre Hardy' (C)	SKee
- 'Red Comice' (D/C)	SKee
- 'Red Pear' (Perry)	CHab WMat
- 'Red Sensation Bartlett' (D/C)	CArg EMOT EPom LBuc LRHS NOra SKee SSFT WMat
- 'Robin' (C/D)	SDea SKee WMat
- 'Santa Claus' (D)	SDea
- 'Seckel' (D)	NOra
- 'Shipova'	see × *Sorbopyrus auricularis* 'Shipova'
- 'Sierra' (D)	CAgr
- 'Snowdon Queen' (D)	CHab WGwG
- 'Sommer Blutbirne' (D)	SAko
- 'Starkrimson' (D)	SKee
- 'Swan's Egg' (D)	SKee
- 'Taynton Squash' (Perry)	NOra WMat
- 'Terrace Pearl' (D)	WMat
- 'Thorn' (Perry)	CAgr CHab EPom SKee WMat
- 'Triomphe de Vienne' (D)	SKee
- 'Triumph'	see *P. communis* 'Packham's Triumph'
- 'Uvedale's St Germain' (C)	SKee
- 'Verdi' (F)	EPom
§ - 'Vicar of Winkfield' (C)	ECrN SDea SKee
- 'Williams' Bon Chrétien' (D/C)	Widely available
- 'Williams' Red' (D/C)	NPri SKee
- 'Williams' Rouge Delbard' (F)	EPom
- 'Winnal's Longdon' (Perry)	EPom WMat
- 'Winter Nelis' (D)	CAgr CArg CHab CTri EMOT LRHS NLar NOra SDea SKee WMat WWct
- 'Woodhall' (F)	WMat
cordata	CDul CTho
elaeagnifolia	LMaj MAsh
- var. ***kotschyana***	CDul SLim
- 'Silver Sails'	CLnd CMac EBee EMOT EMil LRHS NOra SCoo WMat WPGP
× ***michauxii***	SVen
nivalis	CDul CLnd CTho EBee ECrN EPfP LEdu LMaj NWea SPer
- 'Catalia'	CLnd MAsh WMat
pashia	CBcs CMCN EBee LEdu NLar WMat
pyraster	CDul CHab CPer WCot
pyrifolia '20th Century'	see *P. pyrifolia* 'Nijisseiki'
- 'Chojuro' (F)	CAgr LEdu
- 'Hosui' (F)	CAgr LEdu SVic
- 'Kosui' (F)	SVic
- 'Kumoi' (F)	CAgr CFGn EPom MAsh MCoo SDea SKee WMat
§ - 'Nijisseiki' (F)	CDul SKee SVic
- 'Shinko' (F)	CAgr LEdu SVic
- 'Shinseiki' (F)	CAgr CFGn CLnd CTri EMOT SDea SKee SVic WMat
- 'Shinsui' (F)	SDea SKee
salicifolia	LMaj LPra
* - var. ***orientalis***	CTho
- 'Pendula' 🏆H6	Widely available

Pyrus × *Sorbus* see × *Sorbopyrus*

Qiongzhuea see *Chimonobambusa*

Quercus ✿ (*Fagaceae*)

NJM 05.013A	WPGP
acerifolia	EPfP
acherdophylla	SBir
§ ***acuta***	CBcs
acutifolia	SBir
acutifolia* × *mexicana	SBir
acutissima	CBcs CDul CMCN EPfP IArd LMaj NLar SBir SGol
- PAB 7957	LEdu

- 'Gobbler'	ESwi
- subsp. ***kingii*** NJM 13.077	WPGP
aegilops	see *Q. ithaburensis* subsp. *macrolepis*
affinis ♀H5	CMCN EPfP SBir
agrifolia	CDul CMCN EBtc LMaj
ajudaghiensis	see *Q. hartwissiana*
alba	CMCN EBtc IArd WPGP
* ***alentejana***	CMCN
aliena	CDul CMCN LEdu
- NJM 13.075	WPGP
- PAB 8972	LEdu
- PAB 13.383	LEdu
anatolica	see *Q. pubescens* subsp. *crispata*
arkansana	CDul SBir
× ***atlantica***	SBir
austrina	SBir
× ***beadlei***	see *Q.* × *saulii*
'Bear Creek Ranch'	MBlu
× ***benderi***	SBir
berberidifolia	CMCN SBir
bicolor	CDul CMCN EPfP IArd IDee LMaj MBlu WPGP
× ***bimundorum***	SBir
§ - 'Crimschmidt'	CLnd EPfP MBlu SAko SBir SGol
borealis	see *Q. rubra*
brantii	CMCN
breweri	see *Q. garryana* var. *breweri*
buckleyi	CMCN EPfP SBir
- 'Dazzling Red'	MBlu
× ***bushii***	CMCN EPfP MBlu SBir
- 'Seattle Trident'	EPfP MBlu SAko WCot WPGP
canariensis ♀H5	CMCN CTho EPfP SGol WPGP
canbyi	CMCN
candicans	SBir
× ***capesii***	SBir
castaneifolia	CMCN EBtc WMou
- 'Green Spire' ♀H6	CDul CMCN EBee EPfP MBlu SEND
cerris	CArg CBcs CCVT CDul CMCN CPer ECrN EMOT EPfP LMaj LPra MGos NWea SCob SEND SGol SPer
- 'Afyon Lace'	MBlu SBir
§ - 'Argenteovariegata' (v)	CEnd CMCN EBee ELan EPfP MAsh MBlu NWea SBir WCot
- 'Athena'	MBlu
- 'Bolte's Obelisk' **new**	MBlu
- 'Curly Head'PBR	WCot
- 'Variegata'	see *Q. cerris* 'Argenteovariegata'
- 'Wodan'	MBlu
chenii	CDul CMCN SBir
chrysolepis	CBcs CMCN EPfP
coccifera	CAco CMCN EPfP GKev LEdu SGol SVen WCot WPGP
- NJM 12.006	WPGP
- subsp. ***calliprinos***	CMCN
coccinea	CBcs CDul CLnd CMCN CTho CTri EPfP LMaj LPra MBlu MWht NEgg NWea SBir SEWo WTSh
- 'Splendens' ♀H6	CDul CEnd CMCN CTri ELan EPfP MBlu NLar SGol SPer SPoG
aff. ***coccinea***	EMOT
crassifolia	WPGP
crassipes	SBir
CRIMSON SPIRE	see *Q.* × *bimundorum* 'Crimschmidt'
crispipilis	SBir
dalechampii	SBir
dentata	CMCN IArd
- 'Carl Ferris Miller'	CBcs CDul CMCN EPfP LLHF MBlu MMuc SBir SCob WCot WHor WMou WPGP
- 'Pinnatifida'	CMCN EPfP LLHF LMaj MBlu MPkF NLar WCot
- 'Sir Harold Hillier'	CDul CMCN MBlu
- subsp. ***yunnanensis***	MBlu SBir
dolicholepis	CMCN SBir
'Doring's Zweizack'	SBir
douglasii	CDul CMCN EBtc
durata	CMCN
× ***egglestonii*** **new**	CMCN
ellipsoidalis	CDul CMCN NLar SBir SGol
- 'Hemelrijk' ♀H6	CMCN EPfP MBlu SBir
emoryi	SBir
engleriana NJM 11.028	WPGP
× ***exacta***	SBir
fabrei	SBir
faginea	WPGP
falcata	CMCN EBtc SBir WPGP
- var. ***pagodifolia***	see *Q. pagoda*
× ***fernaldii***	CMCN EPfP MBlu
'Fire Water'	MBlu
frainetto	CDul CMCN CTho EBee ECrN EPfP LMaj LPra NWea SGol SPer WMou
- 'Hungarian Crown' ♀H6	CMCN EPfP MBlu SBir
- 'Trump'	CDul CMCN MMuc
franchetii	WPGP
fruticosa	see *Q. lusitanica* Lam.
fusiformis	SBir
gambelii	CMCN EBtc MPkF
garryana	CMCN EPfP
§ - var. ***breweri***	CMCN
- var. ***fruticosa***	see *Q. garryana* var. *breweri*
georgiana	CDul CMCN SBir
germana	WPGP
gilva	CMCN SBir
glabrescens	WPGP
glandulifera	see *Q. serrata* Thunb.
glauca	CDul CMCN EPfP NLar
- from Korea	WPGP
graciliformis	CMCN
gravesii	EPfP SBir
greggii	WPGP
grisea	CMCN
§ ***hartwissiana***	EPfP
× ***hastingsii***	CMCN SBir
havardii	CMCN
× ***hawkinsiae***	SBir
× ***haynaldiana***	SBir
hemisphaerica	CDul CMCN EPfP SBir
× ***heterophylla***	CMCN EPfP SBir
× ***hickelii***	CMCN EPfP SBir
hirtifolia	WPGP
× ***hispanica***	EUJe
- 'Ambrozyana'	CDul CMCN NLar
- 'Diversifolia'	CMCN EPfP MBlu
- 'Fulhamensis'	CDul CMCN MBlu MMuc SBir SEND SGol WMou
§ - 'Lucombeana' ♀H6	CDul CMCN CSBt CTho EBee EPfP MBlu MMuc NWea SBir SPer
- 'Suberosa'	CTho
- 'Waasland Select'	NLar SGol
- 'Wageningen'	CMCN LMaj SBir
× ***humidicola*** **new**	CMCN
hypoleucoides	CMCN EPfP
ilex	Widely available
- 'Fordii'	SBir
ilicifolia	CMCN EPfP SBir
imbricaria	CBcs CDul CMCN EPfP SBir WPGP
incana Roxb.	see *Q. leucotrichophora*
§ ***incana*** Bartram	CMCN
ithaburensis	CDul

§	- subsp. ***macrolepis***	CMCN LEdu SBir
	- - 'Hemelrijk Silver'	EPfP MBlu SBir WCot WPGP
	× ***jackiana***	SBir
	kelloggii	CBcs CMCN EPfP
	× ***kewensis*** 🏆H6	CMCN SBir SEND WMou
	laevigata	see *Q. acuta*
	laevis	CMCN EPfP SBir
	'Langtry'	SBir
§	***laurifolia***	CDul CMCN EPfP SBir
	laurina	SBir WPGP
	× ***leana***	CMCN
§	***leucotrichophora***	LEdu SBir
	liaotungensis	see *Q. wutaishanica*
	× ***libanerris***	SBir
	- 'Rotterdam'	CMCN SBir
	libani	CDul CMCN EPfP SEND
	lobata	CBcs CDul CMCN
	× ***lucombeana***	see *Q.* × *hispanica* 'Lucombeana'
	- 'William Lucombe'	see *Q.* × *hispanica* 'Lucombeana'
	× ***ludoviciana***	EPfP SBir
§	***lusitanica*** Lam.	SBir
	lyrata	CMCN SGol
	- 'Arnold'	MBlu
	'Macon'	CDul
	macranthera	CDul CMCN EPfP
	- PAB 13.002	LEdu
	macrocarpa	CDul CMCN EPfP WMou WPGP
	macrocarpa × ***robur***	SBir
	× ***virginiana***	
	macrolepis	see *Q. ithaburensis* subsp. *macrolepis*
	marilandica	CDul CMCN EPfP MBlu SBir
	'Mauri'	LMaj MBlu SBir
	'Maya' 🏆H5	CBcs CDul ELan EPfP EUJe LLHF NLar SBir SGol SLim WHor WMat WMou WPGP
	× ***megaleia*** <u>new</u>	CMCN
	mexicana	CMCN SBir
§	***michauxii***	CMCN EPfP MBlu
	mohriana	SBir
	mongolica	CBcs CDul EPfP MBlu
	- subsp. ***crispula***	CMCN
	'Monument'	WCot
	muhlenbergii	CDul CMCN MBlu MPkF SBir
	- 'Dallas'	EPfP
	myrsinifolia	CBcs CMCN LMaj NLar SArc
	myrtifolia	SBir WPGP
	nigra	CDul CMCN EBtc EPfP SBir WMou
	- 'Beethoven'	MBlu SBir
I	- 'Nyewoodii'	SBir
	- 'Thierry'	MBlu
	nuttallii	see *Q. texana*
	obtusa	see *Q. laurifolia*
	oglethorpensis	CMCN SBir
	oxyodon	LEdu
§	***pagoda***	CDul CMCN SBir WPGP
	palustris 🏆H6	CAco CArg CCVT CDul CLnd CMCN CTho ELan EMOT EPfP LMaj LPra MBlu MMuc NEgg NLar NWea SBir SCob SEWo SGol SPer WMou WTSh
	- 'Flaming Suzy'	MBlu
	- 'Green Dwarf'	CMCN LCro LMaj LOPS MBlu NLar
	- GREEN PILLAR ('Pringreen')	CTho EMOT EPfP MAsh MBlu NLar NOra SGol WMat WMou
	- 'Isabel'	EPfP WHor WMat
	- 'Pendula'	CEnd CMCN
	- 'Silhouette'	SBir
	- 'Swamp Pygmy'	CMCN EPfP ESwi MBlu SCob
	- 'Windischleuba'	MBlu
	pannosa	SBir
	parvula var. ***parvula***	SBir
	pedunculata	see *Q. robur*
	pedunculiflora	see *Q. robur* subsp. *pedunculiflora*
§	***petraea***	CArg CDul CHab CLnd CPer CTri ECrN EPfP LMaj LPra MBlu NWea SCob SGol SPer WFar WMou WTSh
	- 'Acutiloba'	SBir
	- 'Laciniata'	see *Q. petraea* 'Laciniata Crispa'
§	- 'Laciniata Crispa'	CEnd CMCN EPfP MBlu
	- Mespilifolia Group	CDul
	- subsp. ***polycarpa***	WPGP
	NJM 13.025	
§	- 'Purpurea'	CMCN EPfP MBlu
	- 'Rubicunda'	see *Q. petraea* 'Purpurea'
§	***phellos***	CAco CDul CLnd CMCN EBtc ECrN EPfP EUJe LMaj MBlu NLar SBir
	- HIGHTOWER ('Qpsta')	SGol
	- var. ***latifolia***	see *Q. incana* Bartram
	phillyreoides	CBcs CDul CLnd CMCN EPfP
	polymorpha	CDul CMCN MPkF SBir WPGP
	Pondaim Group	CDul CMCN NOra WMou
	- 'Pondaim Giant'	MBlu
	pontica	CMCN EPfP LMaj MBlu
	prinoides	CMCN
	prinus misapplied	see *Q. michauxii*
§	***prinus*** L.	CMCN
	pubescens	CDul CMCN LMaj MMuc SEND
§	- subsp. ***crispata***	WPGP
	NJM 12.016	
	- - NJM 12.017	WPGP
	pumila Michx.	see *Q. prinus* L.
	pumila Walt.	see *Q. phellos*
	pungens	CMCN
	pyrenaica	CMCN EBtc MMuc SBir SEND
	- NJM 12.001	WPGP
	- 'Pendula' 🏆H6	CMCN EPfP
	rhysophylla	see *Q. rysophylla*
	× ***riparia***	SBir
§	***robur***	Widely available
	- 'Argenteomarginata' (v)	CDul CMCN MBlu
	- 'Atropurpurea'	EBtc MPkF NWea
	- 'Blue Gnome'	MBlu
	- 'Compacta'	MBlu
	- 'Concordia'	CEnd CMCN EBtc ELan EPfP MBlu NLar
	- Cristata Group	CMCN
	- 'Dissecta'	CMCN
	- 'Facrist'	CDul SBir
	- Fastigiata Group	CDul CLnd EBee ECrN IArd LPra MGos NWea SBir SCob SGol SLim SPer
	- - 'Koster' 🏆H6	CDul CMCN CMac CNWT CTri EMOT EPfP LMaj LPra MBlu MRav NWea SCob WMat
	- - 'Zeeland'	SBir
	- 'Filicifolia' misapplied	see *Q. robur* 'Pectinata'
	- 'Filicifolia' Hort. ex Loud.	CEnd
	- var. ***haas***	CDul
	- 'Irtha'	EPfP MBlu
	- 'Menhir'	IArd LLHF MBlu
§	- 'Pectinata'	EPfP MBlu
§	- subsp. ***pedunculiflora***	CMCN
	- 'Pendula'	CEnd CMCN MBlu
	- 'Purpurascens'	CDul CEnd CMCN
	- 'Purpurea'	MBlu
	- 'Raba'	CMCN
§	- 'Salfast'	MBlu NLar
	- 'Salicifolia Fastigiata'	see *Q. robur* 'Salfast'
	- 'Strypemonde'	CMCN

	- 'Timuki'	MBlu
	- 'Totem'	WHor
	- 'Tromp Dwarf'	MBlu
	- (Variegata Group) 'Fürst Schwarzenburg' (v)	MBlu
	× ***rosacea*** 'Columna'	WMou
	rotundifolia	CAgr CMCN EPfP WPGP
§	***rubra***	Widely available
	- 'Aurea'	CEnd CMCN EPfP MBlu WHor
	- 'Bolte's Gold'	MBlu NOra SMad WHor WMat
	- 'Cyrille'	SBir
	- 'Magic Fire' ♀H6	CMCN EPfP MBlu SBir
	- 'Red Queen'	EPfP MBlu
*	- 'Sunshine'	CMCN MBlu WCot
	× ***rudkinii***	EPfP
	× ***runcinata***	CMCN SBir
	rysophylla	CMCN EPfP IArd MBlu SBir WPGP
	sadleriana	CDul CMCN WPGP
	salicina	WPGP
	× ***sargentii*** 'Thomas'	CDul EPfP MBlu
	sartorii	CMCN SBir
§	× ***saulii***	CMCN SBir
	× ***schochiana***	EPfP MBlu SBir
	schottkyana	WPGP
	× ***schuettei***	SBir
	semecarpifolia	CMCN MBlu WPGP
§	***serrata*** Thunb.	CDul CMCN EPfP SBir
	- 'Herkenrode'	MBlu
	sessiliflora	see *Q. petraea*
	shumardii	CDul CLnd CMCN EPfP LMaj MBlu NLar SBir SGol
	- 'Del Rio'	MBlu
	sinuata subsp. ***breviloba***	SBir
	stellata	CDul CMCN EPfP SBir
	× ***sternbergii***	SBir
	suber	CAgr CBcs CMCN CPer CTsd ELan EMOT EPfP EUJe IArd LEdu LMaj MBlu MGos SArc SEND SPer WPGP
	- 'Sopron'	EPfP MBlu
	× ***substellata*** new	CMCN
§	***texana***	CMCN EPfP IArd NOra SBir WPGP
	- 'New Madrid'	CDul CTho EPfP ESwi LLHF MBlu SBir SPer WHor WMat WMou WPGP
	tomentella	SBir
	trojana	CDul CMCN SBir WPGP
	turbinella	CMCN
	× ***turneri***	CLnd CMCN CTho EPfP WSpi
	- 'Pseudoturneri' ♀H5	CBcs CDul ELan MBlu SEND SGol WMou
	vacciniifolia	CMCN
	variabilis	CMCN EPfP MPkF SGol
	velutina	CBcs CDul CMCN CTho EPfP NLar NWea SBir
	- 'Albertsii'	MBlu
	- 'Oakridge Walker'	MBlu
	- 'Rubrifolia'	CMCN EPfP
	'Vilmoriana'	CMCN IArd
	virginiana	CBcs CMCN SBir
	× ***warburgii***	EPfP
	× ***warei***	CMCN
	- 'Chimney Fire'	EPfP MBlu
	- KINDRED SPIRIT	see *Q.* × *warei* 'Nadler'
§	- 'Long'	EBee ELan EMOT EPfP IArd MBlu MPkF NLar NOra WMat
§	- 'Nadler'	SGol
	- REGAL PRINCE	see *Q.* × *warei* 'Long'
	- 'Riverbank Lodge'	SBir
	- 'Windcandle'	LMaj MBlu SBir
	wislizeni	CMCN NLar SBir
§	***wutaishanica***	SBir

Quillaja (*Quillajaceae*)

	saponaria	CCCN SPlb

quince see *Cydonia oblonga*; also AGM Fruit Section

Quisqualis (*Combretaceae*)

	indica	CCCN

R

Racosperma see *Acacia*

Radermachera (*Bignoniaceae*)

	sinica ♀H1b	EShb

radish see AGM Vegetables Section

Ramonda (*Gesneriaceae*)

§	***myconi*** ♀H5	EMor EWes LLHF NSla SRms WAbe
	- var. ***alba***	WThu
	- 'Jim's Shadow'	WAbe
	- 'Rosea'	LLHF
	nathaliae ♀H5	SIgm WAbe WThu
	- 'Alba'	NSla WAbe XEll
	pyrenaica	see *R. myconi*
	serbica	WThu

Ranunculus (*Ranunculaceae*)

	aconitifolius	EBee EHrv GMaP NLar SHar WFar WHal WMoo WSHC
	- Cally form new	MNrw
	- 'Flore Pleno' (d) ♀H7	Widely available
	acris	CHab NBir NMir NPer SRms WSFF
	- subsp. ***acris*** 'Stevenii'	WHal
	- 'Citrinus'	CElw EAJP EHrv EMor LLWG LPot LSun MHol WCot WHal WHrl WMoo WPtf
	- 'Flore Pleno' (d) ♀H7	CDor CWCL EBee ECha EHrv ELan EPfP GMaP LEdu LLWG LPot MCot MRav NBid NBro NGdn NRya SPoG SRms WCAu WFar WMoo WSHC XLum
	- 'Hedgehog'	MMrt MNrw
	- 'Sulphureus'	CBre EBee WCAu WHal
	alpestris	GCrg GEdr LLHF NSla WFar
	- 'Flore Pleno' (d)	GEdr
	amplexicaulis	EBee NSla WCot
	aquatilis	CWat EWat LLWG MWts WMAq WSFF
	asiaticus	ERCP
	- var. ***albus***	GKev
	- 'Aviv'	GKev
	- 'Aviv Orange'	SDeJ
	- 'Aviv Red'	LCro LOPS
	- 'Aviv Rose'	LCro LOPS
	- 'Aviv White'	LCro LOPS
	- 'Bloomingdale Pink Shades' (Bloomingdale Series)	SDeJ
	- Tolmer's hybrids (d)	GKev
§	***bulbosus*** 'F.M. Burton'	CElw NRya WCot
	- ***farreri***	see *R. bulbosus* 'F.M. Burton'
	- 'Speciosus Plenus'	see *R. constantinopolitanus* 'Plenus'
	calandrinioides ♀H5	EWes NBir SBch SBrt WAbe WThu

circinatus new	LLWG
§ ***constantinopolitanus*** 'Plenus' (d)	EBee GCal GMaP MNrw MRav NBid NBro NLar WCot WMoo WSHC
cortusifolius	CPla ECre SBrt SHar
crenatus	GEdr
ficaria	see *Ficaria verna* subsp. *verna*
flammula	CBen CHab CWat LLWG MWts
- subsp. ***minimus***	EWat
glacialis new	WAbe
gouanii	NRya
'Gowrie'	GEdr
gramineus ♀H7	CRos EBee GEdr GMaP LRHS NRHS NRya SIgm SRms WOut XEll
- 'Pardal'	WCot
hederaceus	LLWG
illyricus	WHal
kochii	GEdr GKev MNrw NRya WCot
lanuginosus	EPPr NGrd
lapponicus	GEdr
lingua	SPlb WSFF
- 'Grandiflorus'	CBen LLWG NPer WHal WMAq WPnP
lyallii	GKev
millefoliatus	CPBP WAbe
montanus double-flowered (d)	SHar WCot
- 'Miss Austria' (d)	NHpl
- 'Molten Gold' ♀H5	GCrg GEdr GMaP MMrt MRav NRya WFar
aff. ***nigrescens*** 'Cazorla' new	SBrt
nivicola	WCot
parnassiifolius	GEdr MNrw WAbe WCot
'Pauline Violet'	IFro
platanifolius	CRos EBee LRHS NRHS SBrt SMHy
× ***prietoi*** 'Moonlight'	LEdu MMrt WCot
'Purple Heart' (d)	EPfP LCro LOPS SDeJ
repens 'Buttered Popcorn' (v)	EBee
- 'Cat's Eyes' (v)	EBee
- 'Gloria Spale'	CBre
- var. ***pleniflorus*** (d)	CBre LLWG NGrd SRot
- 'Timothy Clark' (d)	CBre
seguieri	CRos GEdr LLHF LRHS NRHS WAbe
speciosus 'Flore Pleno'	see *R. constantinopolitanus* 'Plenus'
uniflorus	GEdr

Ranzania (*Berberidaceae*)

japonica	GEdr WCru

Raoulia (*Asteraceae*)

australis misapplied	see *R. hookeri*
australis ambig.	EPot GAbr GBin GKev GMaP NHpl WCot WTor
australis Hook.f. ex Raoul	ITim MAsh
§ - Lutescens Group	ECha SRot
glabra	EPot
§ ***hookeri***	CMea ECha EPot EWes MAsh SIgm SPlb SRms WAbe
× ***loganii***	see × *Leucoraoulia loganii*
lutescens	see *R. australis* Lutescens Group
petriensis	SPlb WAbe
× ***petrimia*** 'Margaret Pringle'	EPot WAbe
tenuicaulis	ECha SPlb

raspberry see *Rubus idaeus*; also AGM Fruit Section

Ratibida (*Asteraceae*)

columnifera	CBod CRos ELan EPfP LRHS NRHS
- f. ***pulcherrima***	CRos EPfP EUJe LRHS NRHS XLum
- - 'Red Midget'	CBod CRos CSpe EMor LRHS NRHS
mexicana	CRos CSam EBee ELan LRHS NRHS SPhx
pinnata	CSam CSpe EAJP EPfP LRHS NBir SPhx SPlb WCot

Raukaua (*Araliaceae*)

laetevirens new	WPGP

Ravenala (*Strelitziaceae*)

madagascariensis	SPlb XBlo

Ravenea (*Arecaceae*)

rivularis	CCCN XBlo

Rechsteineria see *Sinningia*

redcurrant see *Ribes rubrum* (R); also AGM Fruit Section

Regelia (*Myrtaceae*)

velutina	SPlb

Rehderodendron (*Styracaceae*)

indochinense B&SWJ 12115	WCru
- NJM 09.116 new	WPGP
- WWJ 11869	WCru
kwangtungense WWJ 11940	WCru
kweichowense WWJ 12019	WCru
macrocarpum	CBcs EBee WPGP
- B&SWJ 11841	WCru
- KWJ 12310	WCru
- WWJ 11952	WCru

Rehmannia (*Plantaginaceae*)

angulata misapplied	see *R. elata*
§ ***elata*** ♀H3	CBod CDor CPla CRos CSpe ELan EPfP EUJe IDee LRHS LSun MNHC NHic NRHS SDys SRms WKif XLum
henryi	CSpe EBee LRHS WHil
piasezkii	SMHy
'Polina'PBR new	CSpe
WALBERTON'S MAGIC DRAGON ('Walremadra')	CRos EHyd EPfP LBuc LCro LOPS LRHS NRHS SHar SPad SPoG

Reineckea (*Asparagaceae*)

§ ***carnea***	CAby CDor CExl CHll ECha ELan EPPr GCal GEdr GKev IMou LEdu MMuc MPie NAln NSti SDys SEND SPlb WCot WPGP XLum
- B&SWJ 4808	ELon WCru
- 'Baoxing Booty'	IMou WCru
- 'Crûg's Broadleaf'	WCru
- 'Variegata' (v)	WCot
aff. ***carnea*** from Sichuan	WCot
incurva 'Crug's Linearleaf'	WCru
yunnanense	see *R. carnea*

Reinwardtia (*Linaceae*)

§ ***indica***	CCCN CExl CHll SEle
trigyna	see *R. indica*

Remusatia (*Araceae*)

hookeriana B&SWJ 2529 — WCru
pumila — EUJe MPie
vivipara — EUJe MPie

Reseda (*Resedaceae*)

lutea — CWld SRms
luteola — CBod CHab CHby GPoy MHer MNHC WSFF

Restio (*Restionaceae*)

festuciformis — CPbh LRHS
paniculatus — CCCN CDTJ CPbh LRHS
similis — CPbh
subverticillatus — CPbh LRHS
tetraphyllus — see *Baloskion tetraphyllum*
- 'Cornish Gold' — see *Baloskion tetraphyllum* 'Cornish Gold'

Retama (*Papilionaceae*)

§ ***monosperma*** — SBrt
raetam — SPhx
sphaerocarpa — SBrt

Reynoutria see *Fallopia*

Rhamnus (*Rhamnaceae*)

alaternus — XSen
§ - 'Argenteovariegata' (v) ♀H5 — Widely available
- 'Variegata' — see *R. alaternus* 'Argenteovariegata'
cathartica — CCVT CDul CHab CLnd CPer CTri ECrN EPfP LBuc MCoo NLar NWea SEWo WMou WSFF WTSh
davurica B&SWJ 12609 — WCru
§ ***erythroxyloides*** — NLar
frangula — see *Frangula alnus*
grandifolia new — SPtp
ilicifolia — SBrt
imeretina — WCot WPGP
ludovici-salvatoris — SBrt
lycioides — SBrt
- subsp. ***oleoides*** — XSen
pallasii — see *R. erythroxyloides*
taquetii — NLar

Rhaphidophora (*Araceae*)

decursiva — XBlo

× *Rhaphiobotrya* (*Rosaceae*)

§ 'Coppertone' — LMaj SEND WPGP

Rhaphiolepis (*Rosaceae*)

sp. — IDee
× ***delacourii*** — EBee EPfP SEND
- 'Coates' Crimson' — CRos CTsd EBee ELan EPfP LRHS MAsh SEle WSHC
- ENCHANTRESS ('Moness') — CCCN CTsd ELan EPfP LRHS MAsh MRav SLon
- 'Pink Cloud' — EPfP LRHS
indica — SEND
- B&SWJ 8405 — WCru
- 'Coppertone' — see × *Rhaphiobotrya* 'Coppertone'
- SPRINGTIME ('Monme') — CBcs CRos EPfP LCro LOPS LRHS
integerrima — CMCN
minor B&SWJ 14669 new — WCru
umbellata — CBcs CBod CTri EBee ELan EPfP GBin LEdu MAsh MGil MRav SEND SLon SVen WPGP WSHC
- f. ***ovata*** B&SWJ 4706 — WCru

Rhaphithamnus (*Verbenaceae*)

cyanocarpus — see *R. spinosus*
§ ***spinosus*** — CBcs EBee EPfP LEdu MGil SPoG WPav

Rhapidophyllum (*Arecaceae*)

hystrix — CBrP CPHo

Rhapis ✿ (*Arecaceae*)

§ ***excelsa*** ♀H1b — CCCN SEND SPlb XBlo

Rhaponticum (*Compositae*)

§ ***centaureoides*** — CBod CDor CWld EBee ECha ELon EWTr GCal GQue LRHS MAvo MBel MHer MHol MTis NBid NSti SBrt SEND WCAu WCot WSpi
coniferum — WHil
§ ***exaltatum*** — SPhx

Rhazya (*Apocynaceae*)

orientalis — see *Amsonia orientalis*

Rheum ✿ (*Polygonaceae*)

Chen Yi — WCot
GWJ 9329 from Sikkim — WCru
§ 'Ace of Hearts' ♀H6 — Widely available
'Ace of Spades' — see *R.* 'Ace of Hearts'
acuminatum HWJCM 252 — WCru
- HWJK 2354 — WCru
- PAB 2487 — LEdu WPGP
alexandrae — CBct EUJe EWes GBin GCal GEdr GKev IMou MMrt NAln NLar SPlb WFar
- KGB 767 — WPGP
- SDR 2924 — EBee
altaicum PAB 1055 — LEdu
§ ***australe*** — CRos EBee GCal GEdr LRHS NBro NLar NRHS WCot WFar
- CC 7492 — GKev
- 'Pink Marble' (v) — WCot
'Cally Dwarf' — GCal
'Cally Giant' — EBee ELon EWes GCal
delavayi — GCal NLar
- BWJ 7592 — WCru WFar
emodi — see *R. australe*
'Great Bere' — LEdu WPGP
* ***henryi*** — EBee
× ***hybridum*** 'Brandy Carr Scarlet' — CTri LEdu MRav
- 'Champagne' — CAgr EPfP EPom LCro LEdu LOPS LRHS NLar NRHS SCob SKee SPer SPoG SRms SVic WMat
* - 'Champagne Rood' — NRHS
- 'Early Victoria' — SRms
- 'Fenton's Special' — CTri LEdu MRav
- 'Glaskin's Perpetual' — CAgr CRos EMor LBuc LRHS NRHS SRms SVic
- 'Grandad's Favorite' ♀H4 — CRos LRHS NRHS
- 'Hawke's Champagne' ♀H4 — WCot
- 'Holstein Bloodred' — EMor
- 'Holsteiner Blut' — NLar SCob SPoG
- 'Livingstone'PBR — EPom LCro LOPS
- 'Pink Champagne' — EPfP
- 'Raspberry Red' ♀H4 — CMac CRos EMil EPfP EPom LCro LOPS LRHS NRHS SPoG
- 'Red Champagne' — ELan EMor EPfP LBuc SCob WSpi
- 'Stein's Champagne' ♀H4 — NRob
- 'Stockbridge Arrow' — CArg CTri ECrN
- 'Strawberry' — LCro LOPS NBir

– 'Thompson's Terrifically Tasty'	EPom
– 'Timperley Early' 𝕐H4	Widely available
– 'Timperley Early 1'	SRms
– 'Victoria'	CAgr CMac CRos CTri ELan EMil EMor EPfP EPom GBin LBuc LCro LEdu LOPS LRHS LSRN MAsh MCoo MGos MHer MJak MNHC NLar NRHS SCob SDea SLim SPoG SVic WMat
– 'Vroege Engelse'	LEdu
kialense	EBee LEdu NBid NSti
nobile	GKev IMou WHil
officinale	CBct GCal
palmatum	CBcs CRos EBee ECha ELan EPfP GKev LRHS MGos MRav NGdn NRHS SCob SHar SRms
– 'Atropurpureum'	see *R. palmatum* 'Atrosanguineum'
§ – 'Atrosanguineum'	Widely available
– 'Bowles's Crimson' 𝕐H7	MRav NBid WCot
– 'Ferguson's Red'	WCot
– 'Hadspen Crimson' 𝕐H7	CBct EBee ECtt EUJe MHol MNrw NBid WCot
– var. ***palmatum***	CPla
– 'Red Herald'	CBct WCot WPGP
– 'Rubrum'	LRHS NBir NChi NRHS
– 'Savill' 𝕐H7	CBct MRav
– var. ***tanguticum***	Widely available
pumilum new	XEll
rhaponticum	NLar
ribes	WCot WCru
tanguticum	EMor
tataricum	EBee LEdu WPGP

Rhexia (*Melastomataceae*)

mariana	SBrt

Rhinanthus (*Orobanchaceae*)

minor	CHab LCro LOPS

Rhodanthe (*Asteraceae*)

§ ***anthemoides***	IMou
chlorocephala subsp. ***rosea*** 'Pierrot' new	CSpe

Rhodanthemum (*Asteraceae*)

'African Eyes'	CBod ELan EPfP MBrN MGos MHol NPri SCoo SRot SVen
§ ***atlanticum***	EWes
'Casablanca'[PBR] (Atlas Daisy Series)	CRos EPfP LRHS NPri NRHS SCoo SPoG SRot
§ ***catananche***	CCCN CPBP EPot EWes MBNS SRot WAbe
§ – 'Tizi-n-Test'	WAbe
– 'Tizi-n-Tichka'	CRos EWes LRHS NRHS WAbe
§ ***gayanum***	CCCN EWes
– 'Flamingo'	see *R. gayanum*
– 'Pretty in Pink'	CBod CMea MHol NPri SPoG
§ ***hosmariense*** 𝕐H4	CCCN CRos EBou ECha ELan EPfP GCrg GMaP LRHS MCot MHol NRHS SEND SIgm SPer SPhx SRms SRot WHoo WIce
'Marrakech' (Atlas Daisy Series)	NPri SCoo SPoG SRot

Rhodiola (*Crassulaceae*)

SSSE 10	NWad
chrysanthemifolia WJC 13669	WCru
crassipes	see *R. wallichiana*
cretinii HWJK 2283	WCru
§ ***fastigiata***	CSpe GCal WCot WThu
– BWJ 7544	WCru
§ ***heterodonta***	MRav WCot
himalensis misapplied	see *R.* 'Keston'
himalensis (D. Don) Fu	CTri
– WJC 13723	WCru
§ ***integrifolia***	SPlb
– subsp. ***integrifolia***	EDAr
§ 'Keston'	CTri
§ ***kirilowii***	CRos LRHS NRHS
– var. ***rubra***	CRos EBee EPfP LRHS NRHS
§ ***pachyclados***	CRos ECtt EPPr EPot EUJe GBin GCrg GJos GKev GMaP GWyn LRHS MHer MMuc NAln NBir NHpl NRHS NRya NWad SEND SPlb SRot SSim SWvt WCot WFar XLum
rhodantha	NLar
§ ***rosea***	Widely available
§ ***saxifragoides***	EPot LRHS NRHS SPlb
semenovii	GKev NAln NLar
sinuata HWJK 2318	WCru
– HWJK 2326	WCru
trollii	see *R. saxifragoides*
§ ***wallichiana***	NBid
– GWJ 9263	WCru
– HWJK 2352	WCru
§ ***yunnanensis*** BWJ 7941	WCru

Rhodochiton (*Plantaginaceae*)

§ ***atrosanguineus*** 𝕐H2	CBcs CCCN CSpe ELan EPfP GBee IDee LBuc NPri SPer SPoG
volubilis	see *R. atrosanguineus*

Rhodocoma (*Restionaceae*)

arida	CCCN
capensis	CAbb CBod CCCN CCht CPbh CTsd
foliosa	LRHS
gigantea	CBod CCCN CCht CPbh LRHS SPlb

Rhododendron ✿ (*Ericaceae*)

sp.	CAco GKin SEWo
'A.J. Ivens'	see *R.* 'Arthur J. Ivens'
aberconwayi	LMil SLdr
– 'His Lordship'	GGGa LMil
'Abigale' (A) new	SLdr
acrophilum (V)	GGGa
'Addy Wery' (EA)	SPer
adenogynum	GGGa LMil
adenosum	GGGa
'Admiral Piet Hein'	GGGa SSta
'Adonis' (EA/d) 𝕐H5	CBcs CMac SLdr
'Advance' (EA)	SLdr
aeruginosum	see *R. campanulatum* subsp. *aeruginosum*
'Aksel Olsen'	CTri GEdr
'Aladdin' (EA)	SLdr
'Aladdin' (*auriculatum* hybrid)	SSta
(Albatross Group) 'Albatross'	SSta
– 'Albatross Townhill Pink'	LMil
'Albert Schweitzer' 𝕐H5	CDul LMil LRHS LSRN NLar SLdr SLim SPer
albrechtii (A)	GGGa LMil
– Whitney form (A)	LMil
'Alexander' (EA) 𝕐H4	LMil LSRN SLdr
'Alice' 𝕐H5	LMil SLdr

	Alison Johnstone Group	SLdr
	- 'Alison Johnstone'	CAco GGGa LMil WThu
	'All Gold'	GGGa
	'Al's Picotee' (EA/d) new	MPkF
§	***alutaceum*** var. ***alutaceum*** Globigerum Group	GGGa
§	- var. ***russotinctum*** R 158	SLdr
§	- - Triplonaevium Group	GGGa
	amagianum (A)	LMil
	ambiguum	LMil
	- 'Golden Summit'	GGGa
	- 'Jane Banks'	LMil
	'Ambrosia' (EA)	CSBt
	'America'	SCob
	'Amity'	LMil MMuc SLdr
	Amor Group	SLdr
	'Anah Kruschke'	LCro MAsh SPoG
	'Analin'	see *R.* 'Anuschka'
	'Anchorite' (EA)	SLdr
	Angelo Group	GGGa LMil
	- 'Angelo'	LMil SLdr SSta
	'Ann Lindsay'	SLdr
	'Anna Baldsiefen'	SPoG
	'Anna Rose Whitney'	CBcs CTri EPfP LRHS LSRN MAsh MJak NPri SLim WFar
	'Annabella' (K)	SSta
	annae	GGGa LMil LRHS
	'Anne Frank' (EA)	WFar
	'Anneke' (A)	LMil LRHS MGos MMuc MPkF NHol NLar SPer SSta
	'Anniversary Gold'	NLar
	anthopogon	LMil
	- 'Betty Graham'	GGGa WThu
	- subsp. ***hypenanthum*** 'Annapurna'	GGGa ITim LMil WAbe WThu
	anthosphaerum	GGGa
	'Antilope' (Vs) ♀H6	CBcs LMil LRHS MMuc SLdr SSta
§	'Anuschka'	LMil MAsh
	anwheiense	GGGa LMil
	aperantum	GGGa
	apodectum	see *R. dichroanthum* subsp. *apodectum*
	'Apotrophia'	SLdr
	'Apple Blossom' ambig.	CMac GKin
	'Appleblossom' (EA)	see *R.* 'Ho-o'
	'Apricot Blaze' (A)	SSta
	'Apricot Fantasy'	LMil NLar SSta
	'Apricot Surprise'	CAby CTri MAsh MMuc
	'April Chimes'	WThu
	'April Showers' (A)	LMil
	'Aquamarin'	NLar
	'Arabesk' (EA)	CKel GKin MAsh MGos MPkF NLar
	arborescens (A) ♀H6	CTsd GGGa LMil
	arboreum	GGGa GKev IDee LMil SLdr
	- B&SWJ 2244	WCru
	- subsp. ***cinnamomeum*** ♀H4	GGGa LMil SLdr
	- - Sch 2049	LMil
	- - WJC 13821	WCru
	- - var. ***album***	GGGa
	- - 'Everest Reunion'	LMil
	- - var. ***roseum***	GGGa
	- - - SDR 749	GKev
	- - - 'Tony Schilling'	GKin LMil LRHS SSta
	- subsp. ***delavayi***	GGGa LMil SLdr
	- 'Rubaiyat'	LMil
§	- subsp. ***zeylanicum***	GGGa
	'Arctic Fox' (EA)	LMil
	'Arctic Tern' ♀H5	CSBt CTri LCro LMil LOPS MGos NLar NWad WThu
	'Ardeur' (EA)	NLar
§	***argipeplum***	GGGa LMil
	- 'Fleurie'	LMil
	(Argosy Group) 'Argosy'	LMil
	argyrophyllum	SLdr
	- subsp. ***argyrophyllum***	GGGa SLdr
§	- subsp. ***hypoglaucum***	GGGa
	- subsp. ***nankingense***	GGGa
	- - 'Chinese Silver' ♀H6	LMil SLdr
	arizelum	GCal GGGa LMil WPGP
	- subsp. ***arizelum*** Rubicosum Group	GGGa
	aff. ***arizelum*** KR 10420	WPGP
	'Arneson Gem' (A) ♀H6	CBcs GGGa LMil LRHS NLar
§	(Aronense Group) 'Fumiko' (EA)	CBcs CRos CSBt CTsd LCro LMil NLar SLdr WFar
§	- 'Hanako' (EA)	WFar
§	- 'Kazuko' (EA)	CKel CPla NLar
§	- 'Satschiko' (EA) ♀H5	CBcs CKel CSBt CTsd GGGa LMil LRHS NLar NPri NRHS
	'Arpège' (Vs)	LMil NLar
	'Arthur Bedford'	CSBt
§	'Arthur J. Ivens'	SLdr
	'Arthur Stevens'	SLdr
	'Asa-gasumi' (Kurume) (EA)	SLdr
	asterochnoum	GGGa
	'Astrid'	LSRN
	atlanticum (A)	GGGa LMil WFar
	- 'Seaboard' (A)	LMil
	augustinii	CBcs GGGa LMil NLar SLdr SSta
	- 'Bowood Blue'	LMil
§	- subsp. ***chasmanthum***	GGGa
	- Electra Group	LMil SLdr
§	- - 'Electra' ♀H3	GGGa
	- Exbury form	GGGa LMil
§	- subsp. ***hardyi***	GGGa NLar
*	- 'Trewithen'	GGGa LMil
I	- 'Werrington'	CExl SLdr SSta
	aureum	GGGa
	auriculatum	GGGa LMil SLdr SSta
	auriculatum × ***hemsleyanum***	GGGa
	auritum	SLdr
	austrinum (A)	LMil NLar
	'Autumn Gold'	SLdr
	(Avalanche Group) 'Avalanche'	LMil
	Avocet Group	LMil SLdr
	'Award'	LMil
	Azrie Group	SLdr
§	'Azuma-kagami' (Kurume) (EA)	LMil LRHS SLdr
	'Azurika'	MPkF
	'Azurro'	IDee LMil LRHS MMuc SLdr
	'Babette'	see *R.* (Volker Group) 'Babette'
	'Babuschka'	LMil
	'Baden-Baden' ♀H6	CMac CPla CTri GEdr GKin LCro LMil MAsh NEgg SLdr WFar
	baileyi	SLdr
	balangense	GGGa
	balfourianum	GGGa
	'Balzac' (K)	GKin LMil MAsh NEgg
	'Barbara Reuthe'	SSta
	'Barbarella'	IDee LMil LRHS
	barbatum	GGGa LMil
	- WJC 13686 new	WCru
	'Barbecue' (K)	LMil
	'Barmstedt'	MAsh
	'Barnaby Sunset'	GGGa LRHS MAsh
	'Bashful' ♀H5	CSBt MJak
§	***basilicum***	GGGa LMil

Name	Suppliers
'Bastion'	LMil
× ***bathyphyllum***	GGGa
bauhiniiflorum	see *R. triflorum* var. *bauhiniiflorum*
beanianum	GGGa
- KC 0122	GGGa
- compact	see *R. piercei*
'Beatrice Keir'	LMil SSta
'Beattie' (EA)	SLdr
(Beau Brummell Group) 'Beau Brummell'	LMil
beesianum	GGGa
'Beethoven' (Vuykiana) (EA)	SLdr
BELAMI ('Hachbela')	LMil LRHS
'Belkanto'	CAco GKin MMuc NLar SLdr
'Bellini'	LMaj LMil
'Ben Cruachan' (K)	GGGa
'Ben Lawers' (K)	GGGa
'Ben Lomond' (K)	GGGa
'Ben Morrison' (EA)	LMil
'Ben Vorlich' (K)	GGGa
'Ben Vrackie' (K)	GGGa
'Bengal'	GEdr LRHS LSRN MAsh NLar SCob SLdr SLim
'Bengal Beauty' (EA)	SLdr
'Bengal Fire' (EA)	CMac SLdr
benhallii 'Honshu Blue'	GGGa
- 'Plum Drops'	GGGa
- 'Slieve Donard'	CMac
- 'Ylva'	GGGa
'Beni-giri' (Kurume) (EA)	CMac SLdr
'Bergensiana'	SSta
'Bergie Larson' ♀H4	LMil
'Bernard Shaw'	SSta
'Bernstein'	CAco MAsh MJak
'Berryrose' (K) ♀H6	CBcs CKel CMac CSBt CTri EPfP GKin LMil LRHS MAsh MGos MJak MPkF NLar SSta WFar
'Bert's Own'	CBcs
'Betty' (Kaempferi) (EA)	SLdr
'Betty Anne Voss' (EA)	LMil LSRN MAsh SCoo SLdr
'Betty Wormald'	CMac
bhutanense	GGGa
Bibiani Group	LMil LRHS
'Bijou de Ledeberg' (Indian) (EA/v)	CMac
'Birthday Girl'	LMil LSRN MAsh
(Biskra Group) 'Biskra'	GGGa LMil
'Blaauw's Pink' (Kurume) (EA) ♀H4	CMac CSBt EPfP GKin LCro LMil LOPS MMuc SLdr SPer SPlb SPoG
'Black Knight' (EA)	SLdr
'Black Magic'	CAby CAco GKin LMil MMuc
'Black Widow'	SSta
'Blaney's Blue'	MPkF
'Blattgold' (v)	LMil
BLAUE DONAU	see *R.* 'Blue Danube'
'Blaue Jungs'	EUJe GGGa
'Blewbury' ♀H5	LMil
BLOOMBUX ('Microhirs3'PBR)	LCro LMil LOPS
'Blue Boy'	LMil
§ 'Blue Danube' (EA) ♀H3	CBcs CKel CMac CPla CRos CSBt CTri EPfP GKin LCro LMil LOPS LRHS MAsh MGos MJak NEgg NPri SLdr SLim SPer SPoG SSta WFar
Blue Diamond Group	CBcs EPfP
- 'Blue Diamond'	CSBt LRHS LSRN MAsh MJak NRHS SLdr WGwG
'Blue Monday' (EA)	SLdr
'Blue Peter' ♀H6	CAco CBcs CSBt LCro LMil LOPS MAsh NHol SSta
'Blue Pool'	LMil
Blue Ribbon Group	SLdr
'Blue Silver'	GGGa LMil MAsh
'Blue Steel'	see *R. fastigiatum* 'Blue Steel'
Blue Tit Group	CBcs CDul CMac EPfP GGGa GKev LMaj LRHS MAsh MGos NLar NRHS SCob SLdr SLim SPer SSta
Bluebird Group	CSBt SLdr
'Blueshine Girl'	SLdr
'Blutopia'	LMil LRHS
'Boddaertianum'	LMil
BOHLKEN'S JUDITHA	LMil
BOHLKEN'S KRONJEWEL	LMil
BOHLKEN'S LUPINENBERG	LMil
BOHLKEN'S LUPINENBERG LAGUNA	LMil LRHS NLar
BOHLKEN'S SNOW FIRE	GGGa LMil LRHS NLar
boothii	GGGa
- HECC 10077	GGGa
Bo-peep Group	CBcs
- 'Bo-peep'	LMil SLdr
'Boskoop Ostara'	LMil
'Boule de Neige'	CRos MAsh NLar SPer
'Bouquet de Flore' (G) ♀H6	LMil
(Bow Bells Group) 'Bow Bells' ♀H4	EPfP GEdr LMil LRHS MAsh MGos NHol NLar SLdr
'Bowjingles'	GGGa
brachyanthum subsp. ***hypolepidotum***	GGGa
§ ***brachycarpum*** subsp. ***fauriei*** B&SWJ 4326	WCru
'Brambling'	GGGa
'Brazier' (EA)	SLdr
'Bremen'	LMil
Bric-à-brac Group	CBcs
'Bright Forecast' (K)	SLdr
'Brigitte'	LSRN MAsh
'Brilliant Blue' (EA)	MAsh
'Britannia'	CSBt MJak NHol SSta
'Bronze Fire' (A)	NHol SSta
'Brown Eyes'	CAco MAsh MMuc
'Bruce Brechtbill'	GKin MAsh MMuc
§ 'Bruns Gloria'	LMil NLar
'Bruns Schneewitchen'	SSta
'Buccaneer' (Glenn Dale) (EA)	SLdr
bullatum	see *R. edgeworthii*
'Bungo-nishiki' (Wada) (EA/d)	CMac
bureavii ♀H6	CBcs GGGa LMil SSta
bureavioides	GKev
burmanicum	CBcs
Bustard Group	LMil
'Butter Brickle'	LMil NLar
'Butterfly'	SLdr
'Buttermint'	SLdr
'C.B. van Nes'	SLdr
calendulaceum (A)	GGGa LMil
- red-flowered (A)	LMil
- yellow-flowered (A)	LMil
(Calfort Group) 'Calfort'	GGGa
callimorphum	GGGa
calophytum ♀H5	GGGa LMil SLdr
calostrotum 'Gigha' ♀H4	GGGa LMil WAbe
§ - subsp. ***keleticum*** ♀H4	CRos GCal GEdr ITim LCro LOPS NSla WThu
- - R 58	GGGa LMil
§ - - Radicans Group	CCCN GEdr GGGa ITim NSla NWad WAbe WThu

	- subsp. ***riparioides***	LMil
	- subsp. ***riparium***	ITim
§	- - Nitens Group	CBcs GGGa WThu
	caloxanthum	see *R. campylocarpum* subsp. *caloxanthum*
	Calstocker Group	LMil
	camelliiflorum	GGGa
	campanulatum	GGGa GKev LMil SLdr
	- B&SWJ 13934 **new**	WCru
	- HWJCM 195	WCru
	- HWJCM 409	WCru
§	- subsp. ***aeruginosum***	GGGa LMil
	'Campfire' J.B. Gable (EA)	SLdr
	campylocarpum	GGGa LMil
§	- subsp. ***caloxanthum***	GGGa
	campylogynum	GGGa GKev LCro LMil LOPS LRHS
	- SBEC 0519	GGGa
	- 'Album'	see *R.* 'Leucanthum'
	- Charopoeum Group	WThu
	- - 'Patricia'	GEdr
	- (Cremastum Group) 'Bodnant Red'	GGGa WThu
	- Myrtilloides Group ♀H4	GGGa LMil WAbe WThu
	camtschaticum	GGGa LMil WAbe
	- red-flowered	GGGa
	canadense (A)	GGGa
	- f. ***albiflorum*** (A)	GGGa LMil
	- dark-flowered (A)	LMil
	CANDY LIGHTS ('UMinn's Candy Lights') (A)	LRHS
§	***canescens*** (A)	LMil MPkF
	'Cannon's Double' (K/d) ♀H6	CBcs GKin LMil LRHS MGos NLar SPer
	'Canzonetta' (EA/d) ♀H5	CEnd EPfP GGGa LMil LRHS MAsh NRHS SAko SLdr
	'Captain Jack'	GGGa
	'Caractacus'	SCob
	'Carat' (A)	NLar
	cardiobasis	see *R. orbiculare* subsp. *cardiobasis*
	(Carita Group) 'Golden Dream'	LMil
	Carmen Group	GKev
	- 'Carmen' ♀H5	GEdr GGGa GKin LCro LMil LOPS MAsh MMuc SLdr
	carneum	GGGa
	'Caroline Allbrook'	MAsh NLar SLdr WFar
	'Caroline de Rothschild' **new**	LMil
	'Cary Ann'	CAco CTri LRHS MAsh
	'Casablanca' (EA)	SLdr
	'Cassley' (Vs)	LMil
	catawbiense	CMCN SLdr
	'Catawbiense Album'	CAco CTri MAsh
	'Catawbiense Boursault'	LMaj SLdr
	'Catawbiense Grandiflorum'	CAco LMil MAsh
	'Caucasicum Pictum'	LMil SLdr
	'Cayenne' (EA)	SLdr
	'Cecile' (K) ♀H6	CBcs CMac CTri GKin LMil LSRN MMuc MPkF
	'Celestial' (EA)	CMac
	cephalanthum	LMil
	- subsp. ***cephalanthum*** SBEC 0751	WThu
	- - Crebreflorum Group	GGGa LMil WAbe WThu
	cerasinum	LMil
	- 'Cherry Brandy'	GGGa
	- 'Coals of Fire'	GGGa
	chaetomallum	see *R. haematodes* subsp. *chaetomallum*
	chamaethomsonii	GGGa

	championae	GGGa
	'Chanel' (Vs)	SSta
	changii	GGGa
	'Chanticleer' (Glenn Dale) (EA)	SLdr
	chapaense	see *R. maddenii* subsp. *crassum*
	charitopes	GCal LMil
	- F 25570	GGGa LMil
*	'Charlotte de Rothschild' (EA)	SLdr
	'Charlotte Foster'	GGGa
	'Charlotte Megan' (A)	LMil
	'Charme La'	GGGa
	chasmanthum	see *R. augustinii* subsp. *chasmanthum*
	'Cheer'	MAsh MMuc NEgg SPer
	'Chelsea Reach' (K/d)	LMil
	'Chelsea Seventy'	SLdr
	'Cherokee' (EA)	SLdr
	'Cherry Cheesecake'	CRos NLar
	'Cherry Drops' (EA)	EPfP MAsh SPoG
	CHERRY KISS ('Hachcher'PBR)	GGGa IDee LMil LRHS SAko
	'Chetco' (A)	LMil MGos
	'Chevalier Félix de Sauvage'	LMil
	'Chikor'	GGGa GKin MGos NLar
	'Chionoides'	SLdr
	'Chipmunk' (EA/d)	GGGa LRHS MAsh NRHS
	'Chippewa' (Indian) (EA)	CTri LMil SAko
	Choptank River Group (A)	GKev
	(Choremia Group) 'Choremia' ♀H5	LMil
	christi (V)	GGGa
	'Christina' (Vuykiana) (EA/d)	SLdr
	'Christmas Cheer' (EA/d)	see *R.* 'Ima-shojo'
	'Christmas Cheer' (*caucasicum* hybrid) ♀H5	CBcs CSBt EPfP GGGa GKin LCro LMil LOPS MAsh MGos NLar NPri SCob SLdr SPer
	'Christopher Loder'	SLdr
	ciliatum	CBcs GGGa SLdr
	- deep rose-flowered **new**	SLdr
	- white-flowered **new**	SLdr
	Cilpinense Group	CBcs
	- 'Cilpinense' ♀H3	CMac CSBt EPfP LMil LRHS MAsh MMuc NPri SLdr
	cinnabarinum	LMil SLdr
	- subsp. ***cinnabarinum*** BL&M 234	LMil
	- - Blandfordiiflorum Group	GGGa
	- - 'Nepal'	LMil
	- - Roylei Group	GGGa LMil
	- - - B&SWJ 13972 **new**	WCru
	- - - 'Vin Rosé'	LMil
	- Cinzan Group	LMil
§	- (Conroy Group) 'Conroy'	LMil
§	- subsp. ***xanthocodon***	CBcs GGGa LMil WPGP
§	- - Concatenans Group	GGGa LMil SLdr
	- - - KW 5874	LMil
	- - Purpurellum Group	GGGa SLdr
	'Cinzia' (K)	GGGa
	circinnatum	GGGa
	citriniflorum	LMil
	- R 108	LMil
	- var. ***citriniflorum***	LMil
	- var. ***horaeum***	GGGa
	clementinae	GGGa
	- F 25705	LMil
	- subsp. ***aureodorsale***	GKev
	'Cliff Garland'	LMil

	'Coccineum Speciosum' (G) ♀^{H6}	CMac LMil LRHS SSta
	'Cockatoo' (K)	LMil
	coeloneurum	GGGa LMil
	- EGM 334	LMil
	'Colin Kenrick' (K/d)	LMil
	collettianum	GGGa
	'Colonel Coen'	MMuc
	Colonel Rogers Group	SLdr
	columbianum	SLdr
	'Colyer' (EA)	SLdr
	Comely Group	SLdr
	comisteum C 6541	GGGa
	concatenans	see *R. cinnabarinum* subsp. *xanthocodon* Concatenans Group
	concinnoides	GGGa
	concinnum	GGGa
	- Pseudoyanthinum Group ♀^{H5}	GGGa
	'Connie' (Kaempferi) (EA)	SSta
	'Conroy'	see *R. cinnabarinum* 'Conroy'
	'Contina'	LMil
	'Conversation Piece' (EA)	CEnd SLdr
	'Coral Seas' (V)	GGGa
	'Corany' (A)	LMil NLar
	coriaceum	GGGa LMil
	'Corneille' (G/d)	CSBt LMil LRHS
	'Coronation Day'	LMil
	'Cosmopolitan'	CDul CRos LCro LOPS MGos MMuc NLar SPer SPoG
	'Cotton Candy'	LMil
	'Countess of Athlone'	CMac
	'Countess of Haddington'	CBcs LMil LRHS
	Cowslip Group	CTri LMil MAsh MGos
	- 'Cowslip' ♀^{H4}	CRos EPfP LRHS NLar
	coxianum	GGGa
	'Crane' ♀^{H5}	CRos EPfP GGGa IDee LMil LRHS MAsh
	crassum	see *R. maddenii* subsp. *crassum*
	'Cream Crest'	CRos GKin NLar SLim
	'Creamy Chiffon'	CAco WGwG
	crenulatum	GGGa
	crinigerum	GGGa LMil
	'Crinoline' (EA)	SLdr
	Crossbill Group	CBcs SLdr
	'Crosswater Belle'	LMil NLar
	'Crosswater Red' (A) ♀^{H6}	LMil
	cubittii	see *R. veitchianum* Cubittii Group
	cucullatum	see *R. roxieanum* var. *cucullatum*
	cumberlandense (A)	GGGa LMil
	- 'Sunlight'	LMil
	'Cunningham's Blush'	SGol
	'Cunningham's White'	CAco CBcs CDul CTri ELan EPfP EUJe GGGa LCro LMil LOPS LRHS MAsh MGos MMuc NHol NLar NPri SArc SCob SLdr SLim SPer SPoG SSta
	'Cupcake' Thompson	GGGa
	'Curlew' ♀^{H5}	CMac GEdr GKin LMil MAsh MJak MMuc NHol SLdr WThu
	cyanocarpum	GGGa
	'Cynthia' ♀^{H6}	CBcs CMac CSBt GGGa LMil LSRN NEgg SLdr SSta
	'Dairymaid'	LMil
	'Daisetsuzan' (EA)	MPkF
	(Damozel Group) 'Damozel'	LMil
	'Dartmoor Pixie'	WThu
	'Dartmoor Shepherd's Delight'	SSta
	dauricum 'Album'	see *R. dauricum* 'Hokkaido'

§	- 'Hokkaido'	LMil
	- 'Mid-winter' ♀^{H6}	GGGa LMil
	davidii	GGGa LMil NEgg
	davidsonianum ♀^{H5}	CMac GGGa LMil
	- Bodnant form	LMil
	- 'Caerhays Blotched'	GGGa
	- 'Ruth Lyons'	LMil
	'Daviesii' (G) ♀^{H6}	CBcs CDul CEnd CRos CSBt CTho CTri ELan EPfP GKin LCro LMil LOPS LRHS MAsh MMuc MPkF NLar NPri SPer SPoG SSta
	'Daybreak' (EA/d)	see *R.* 'Kirin'
	'Dear Barbara'	LSRN
	'Dear Grandad' (EA)	CTri LMil LSRN
	'Dear Grandma' (EA)	LMil LSRN
	'Dearest' (EA)	LMil LRHS MAsh NPri NRHS
	'Debutante'	SSta
	decorum ♀^{H6}	CBcs GGGa IDee LMil LRHS SLdr
	- subsp. ***cordatum*** C&H 7132	GGGa
§	- subsp. ***diaprepes***	GCal
	- - 'Gargantua'	SLdr
	- pink-flowered	GGGa
§	***degronianum*** subsp. ***degronianum***	LMil
	- subsp. ***heptamerum*** 'Ho Emma'	LMil LRHS
	- 'Rae's Delight'	LMil
	dekatanum	GGGa
	deleiense	see *R. tephropeplum*
	'Delicatissimum' (O) ♀^{H5}	GGGa GKin LRHS MPkF
	'Delta'	MGos MMuc SCob SLdr SLim WFar
	dendrocharis	LMil
	- Cox 5016	GGGa WAbe
	- GLENDOICK GEM ('Gle002')	GGGa
*	'Denny's Rose' (A)	LMil SSta
	'Denny's Scarlet'	NHol SSta
	'Denny's White' (A)	LMil NHol SSta
	denudatum	LMil
	- EGM 294	LMil
	'Devisiperbile' (EA)	SLdr
	Diamant Group lilac-flowered (EA)	LMil
§	- red-flowered (EA)	SLdr
	'Diamant Rot'	see *R.* Diamant Group red-flowered
I	'Diana'	SLdr
	'Diana van Herzeele'	SCob
	diaprepes	see *R. decorum* subsp. *diaprepes*
	dichroanthum	GGGa LMil
§	- subsp. ***apodectum***	GGGa LMil
§	- subsp. ***scyphocalyx***	GGGa LMil
	- subsp. ***septentrionale***	GGGa
	didymum	see *R. sanguineum* subsp. *didymum*
	'Diorama' (Vs)	SSta
	discolor	see *R. fortunei* subsp. *discolor*
	diversipilosum 'Milky Way'	GGGa
	'Doc'	CBcs CMac SLdr SSta
	'Doctor Arnold W. Endtz'	SSta
	'Doctor H.C. Dresselhuys'	MMuc
	'Doctor M. Oosthoek' (M)	GKin
	'Doctor Reiger'	NLar
	'Dominik'	GGGa
	'Dopey' ♀^{H5}	CAco CBcs EPfP GGGa LMil LRHS MAsh MGos MJak NHol NLar SCob SLdr SLim SSta
	'Dora Amateis' ♀^{H6}	CAco CBcs GGGa GKev LMil LRHS MAsh MGos MMuc NPri NRHS SAko SLdr SLim SPer WThu

Name	Suppliers
Dormouse Group	LMil MAsh
'Dorothy Hayden' (EA)	SLdr
'Dörte Reich'	GGGa
'Dotella'	GGGa SSta
'Double Beauty' (Vuykiana) (EA/d)	SSta
Dragonfly Group	SSta
'Drake's Mountain'	MJak
'Dreamland' ♀H5	CBcs CRos EPfP LCro LMil LOPS LRHS MAsh MGos MMuc NLar NRHS SCob SLdr SLim SPoG SSta WFar
'Driven Snow' (EA)	SLdr
'Dufthecke'	see *R.* WHITE DUFTHECKE
'Dufthecke Yellow'	LMil
'Dusty Miller'	MAsh MJak MPkF SLdr WFar
'Earl of Donoughmore'	SSta
'Easter Parade' (EA)	SLdr
eastmanii (A)	GGGa
'Ebony Pearl'	SLdr
eclecteum	GCal GGGa LMil
§ ***edgeworthii*** ♀H3	CBcs GGGa LMil MPkF
'Edith Bosley'	LRHS NLar SLdr SPer
'Edna Bee' (EA)	LMil SLdr
'Egret' ♀H4	GEdr GGGa LMil NSla SLdr
'Eiger'PBR (EA) **new**	CRos
'Eileen'	LMil
'El Camino'	SLdr
(Eleanore Group) 'Eleanore'	SLdr
'Electra'	see *R. augustinii* 'Electra'
elegantulum	LMil
(Elisabeth Hobbie Group) 'Elisabeth Hobbie' ♀H5	LMil NLar SLdr
'Elizabeth' (EA)	CMac CSBt EPfP SLdr
Elizabeth Group	CBcs LMil MAsh SLdr
§ - 'Creeping Jenny'	GGGa SLdr
- 'Elizabeth'	CDul CTri LRHS LSRN NHol NRHS
'Elizabeth Jenny'	see *R.* 'Creeping Jenny'
'Elizabeth Red Foliage'	CTri GGGa LMil MAsh NLar SLdr
'Elsie Lee' (EA/d) ♀H5	CEnd CSBt EPfP LMil MAsh SLdr WFar
'Emasculum'	SLdr
'Endsleigh Pink'	LMil
eriocarpum 'Gumpō' (EA)	CMac SLdr
eriogynum	see *R. facetum*
'Eruption'	NLar
'Esmeralda'	CMac
'Esther May' (A)	SSta
'Etna' (EA)	SLdr
'Etta Burrows'	GGGa SLdr
'Eucharis' (Glenn Dale) (EA)	MPkF SCob
'Eunice Ann' (A)	SSta
'Europa'	SSta
'Eurydice'	LMil
'Evelyn Hyde' (EA)	SLdr
'Everbloom' (EA)	SLdr
'Everitt Hershey' (A)	SLdr
EVERRED ('851C'PBR)	GGGa
exasperatum	GGGa
- KW 6855	LMil
Exburiense Group	MMuc
'Exbury Calstocker'	CKel LMil
excellens	GGGa LMil
eximium	see *R. falconeri* subsp. *eximium*
'Explorer' (EA)	MJak
'Exquisitum' (O) ♀H5	CTho GGGa GKin LMil
exquisitum	see *R. oreotrephes* Exquisitum Group
'Extraordinaire'	LMil SSta
faberi	GGGa

Name	Suppliers
(Fabia Group) 'Fabia' ♀H3	CBcs CMac GGGa GKin LMil SLdr
§ - 'Fabia Tangerine'	CMac
- 'Fabia Waterer'	LMil
§ ***facetum***	GGGa LMil LRHS
'Faggetter's Favourite' ♀H5	LMil LRHS SLdr SSta
Fairy Light Group	LMil LRHS SLdr
faithae CGG 14142	GGGa
falconeri ♀H4	GGGa IDee LMil NEgg SLdr
- KR 10420 **new**	WPGP
- WJC 13825 **new**	WCru
§ - subsp. ***eximium***	GGGa GKev LMil
'Falling Snow'	SAko
'Fanal' (K)	NLar
'Fantastica' ♀H6	CAco ELan GGGa LMil MAsh MGos MJak MMuc NLar NPri SLim SPoG
fargesii	see *R. oreodoxa* var. *fargesii*
fastigiatum	GEdr LMil NSla SLdr WAbe
- SBEC 0804	GGGa WThu
- SDR 7990	GKev
§ - 'Blue Steel' ♀H6	CRos CTri GKin LMil LRHS MAsh NPri NRHS SLdr SPlb WAbe
- 'Indigo Steel'	GGGa
'Fastuosum Flore Pleno' (d) ♀H6	CBcs CMac CSBt GGGa IDee LMil SLdr SPer SSta
faucium	GGGa
fauriei	see *R. brachycarpum* subsp. *fauriei*
'Favorite' ambig. (EA)	SLdr
'Fawley' (K)	SLdr
'Fay Norman'	LMil
'Fedora' (Kaempferi) (EA)	CTsd
ferrugineum	IDee LMil LRHS
'Feuerwerk' (K)	MMuc NLar
fictolacteum	see *R. rex* subsp. *fictolacteum*
'Fire Bird'	SLdr
'Fire Rim'	LRHS MAsh
'Fireball' (K) ♀H6	CBcs CKel CTri EPfP GGGa GKin LMil LRHS MAsh MGos MMuc NLar NPri SPer SPoG
'Fireball' (hybrid)	MJak
'Firecracker' (A)	LRHS MAsh
'Fireglow' (EA)	GKin LMil
'Firelight' (hybrid)	GKin LMil NLar SPer
§ 'Firestorm'	LSRN NLar NPri
'Flaming Gold'	LRHS LSRN MAsh SLdr
'Flanagan's Daughter'	LMil MAsh
Flava Group	see *R.* Volker Group
flavidum	GGGa MMuc
fletcherianum 'Yellow Bunting'	GGGa
floccigerum	LMil
- bicoloured	GGGa
floribundum	GGGa LMil
'Florida' (EA/d) ♀H4	CKel CMac LMil SLdr
'Flower Arranger' (EA)	LMil MAsh SCoo
formosum	CBcs
§ - var. ***formosum*** Iteaphyllum Group	GGGa
- - 'Khasia'	GGGa
- var. ***inaequale***	GGGa
forrestii subsp. ***forrestii***	LMil
- - Repens Group	GKev LMil
- - - 'Seinghku'	GGGa
- Tumescens Group	GGGa WThu
Fortune Group	SLdr
fortunei ♀H5	GGGa LMil SLdr
§ - subsp. ***discolor*** ♀H5	CBcs LMil NLar
- - (Houlstonii Group) 'John R. Elcock'	LMil
- - var. ***kwangfuense*** AC 5208	LMil

	Name	Suppliers
	– 'Mrs Butler'	see *R.* 'Sir Charles Butler'
	fragariiflorum	GGGa
	'Fragrant Memories'	LMil
	'Fragrant Star' (A)	LRHS MPkF
	'Fragrantissimum' ♀H3	CBcs CEnd CMac CSBt CTsd GGGa IDee LMil LRHS MPkF MRav NLar SLdr
	'Fraseri' (M)	LMil
	'Fred Peste' ♀H4	LMil MGos MMuc SLdr SLim
	(Fred Wynniatt Group) 'Fred Wynniatt'	LMil
	'Fred Wynniatt Stanway'	see *R.* 'Stanway'
	'Freya' (R/d)	LMil LSRN
	'Fridoline' (EA)	SAko
	'Frigate' (EA)	SLdr
	'Frilly Lemon' (Ad)	EPfP LRHS MPkF
	'Frosted Orange' (EA)	LMil MAsh
	'Frosthexe'	WAbe
	'Frühlingszauber'	SLdr
	'Fulbrook'	LMil
	fulgens	GGGa LMil
	fulvum ♀H5	GCal GGGa IDee LMil LRHS SSta
	'Furnivall's Daughter' ♀H5	CAco CDul CMac CSBt GGGa IDee LMaj LMil MMuc NHol SLdr SPer SSta
	fuyuanense	GGGa
	'Gabrielle Hill' (EA)	MAsh SLdr
	'Gaiety' (Glenn Dale) (EA)	LMil SLdr
	galactinum	GGGa LMil
	'Galathea' (EA)	MMuc
	'Gandy Dancer'	CAco SLdr
	'Garden State Glow' (EA/d)	SLdr
	'Gartendirektor Glocker'	CMac GGGa LMil MGos NLar SLim
	'Gartendirektor Rieger' ♀H5	CBcs GGGa LMil NLar
	'Geisha Lilac'	see *R.* 'Hanako'
	'Geisha Orange'	see *R.* 'Satschiko'
	'Geisha Pink'	see *R.* 'Momoko'
	'Geisha Purple'	see *R.* 'Fumiko'
	'Geisha Red'	see *R.* 'Kazuko'
	'Gena Mae' (A/d)	GGGa SLdr
	'General Practitioner'	CMac SLdr
	'General Wavell' (EA)	CMac
	'Gene's Favourite'	SSta
	genestierianum	GGGa
	'Geoffroy Millais'	LMil
	'Georg Arends' (A)	EPfP LMil LRHS MAsh NLar
	'George Hyde' (EA)	EPfP LRHS LSRN MAsh SCoo
§	× ***geraldii***	SLdr
	'Germania'	CBcs LRHS MAsh MGos NPri SCob SPoG SSta
	Gertrud Schäle Group	CTri
	Gibraltar Group	LMil WFar
	'Gibraltar' (K) ♀H6	CBcs CDul CKel CSBt CTri EPfP GGGa GKin LMil LRHS MAsh MGos MJak MPkF NHol NLar SLim SPer SSta
	'Gilbert Mullie' (EA)	LMil NLar SLim SSta
	'Gillian Bramley'	SLdr
	'Ginger' (K)	LMil
	'Ginny Gee' ♀H5	CBcs CPla CRos EPfP GEdr GGGa GKin LMil LRHS MAsh MGos NEgg NLar NRHS NSla NWad SSta WFar
§	'Girard's Hot Shot' (EA)	LRHS MPkF NRHS SSta
§	'Girard's Variegated Hot Shot' (EA/v) ♀H4	CKel CPla GGGa MAsh NEgg SLdr SPoG
	'Gislinde' (A)	SAko
	'Glacier' (EA)	SLdr
	glanduliferum	GGGa SLdr
	– 'Peter the Great'	LMil
	glaucophyllum	GGGa LMil
	– Borde Hill form	LMil
	– 'Deer Dell'	LMil
§	– subsp. ***tubiforme***	GGGa
	GLENDOICK BUTTERSCOTCH ('Gle003')	GGGa
	GLENDOICK CRIMSON ('Gle004') (EA)	GGGa
	GLENDOICK DOVE ('Gle025')	GGGa
	GLENDOICK DREAM ('Gle005') (EA)	GGGa
	GLENDOICK ERMINE ('Gle006') (EA)	GGGa
	GLENDOICK FLAMINGO ('Gle026')	GGGa
	GLENDOICK GARNET ('Gle008') (EA)	GGGa
	GLENDOICK GLACIER ('Gle009') (EA)	GGGa
	GLENDOICK GOBLIN ('Gle010') (EA)	GGGa
	GLENDOICK GOLD ('Gle011')	GGGa
	GLENDOICK MYSTIQUE ('Gle014')	GGGa
	GLENDOICK PETTICOATS ('Gle015')	GGGa
	GLENDOICK ROSEBUD ('Gle022') (EA)	GGGa
	GLENDOICK SHERBET ('Gle029')	GGGa
	GLENDOICK SNOWFLAKES ('Gle001') (EA)	GGGa
	GLENDOICK SORBET ('Gle028')	GGGa
§	'Glendoick Tanager'	GGGa
	GLENDOICK VANILLA ('Gle017')	GGGa
	GLENDOICK VELVET ('Gle018')	GGGa
	'Glenna'	GGGa
	'Gletschernacht'	SAko
	glischrum	GGGa
	– subsp. ***glischroides***	GGGa LMil
§	– subsp. ***rude***	GGGa LMil LRHS
	globigerum	see *R. alutaceum* var. *alutaceum* Globigerum Group
	'Gloria'	see *R.* 'Bruns Gloria'
	'Glory of Littleworth' (Ad)	LMil
	'Glory of Penjerrick'	SLdr
	'Glowing Embers' (K)	CTri GKin LMil LRHS MAsh MGos MMuc NHol NLar SLim SPer SSta
	'Goblin'	SLdr
	'Gog' (K)	CSBt
§	'Goldbukett'	GGGa
	GOLDEN BOUQUET	see *R.* 'Goldbukett'
	'Golden Coach'	CAco
	'Golden Eagle' (K) ♀H6	CBcs CKel CRos GKin LMil LRHS MGos MJak NLar SLdr SPer WFar
	GOLDEN EVEREST ('Hachgold'[PBR])	GGGa LMil
	'Golden Flare' (A)	CBcs GKin NEgg
	'Golden Fleece'	LMil
	'Golden Gate'	CSBt MGos MMuc NLar SLdr
	(Golden Horn Group) 'Golden Horn'	SLdr
	'Golden Lights' (A)	GKin NEgg NLar
	'Golden Princess'	LMil
	'Golden Ruby'	CBcs
	'Golden Splendour'	LMil
	'Golden Sunset' (K) ♀H6	EPfP LMil LRHS MAsh MPkF WFar

'Golden Torch' ♀H5	CBcs CDul EPfP LCro LMil LOPS LRHS MAsh MGos MJak NLar NPri SLdr SLim SPer SPoG
'Golden Wedding'	CBcs LMil LRHS LSRN MAsh MJak SLdr
'Golden Wit'	MAsh MMuc NEgg
'Golden Wonder'	MAsh
'Goldflimmer' (v)	EPfP GGGa LRHS MAsh MGos MJak NLar NPri SCob SLim SPer SPoG WFar
'Goldika'	LMil
GOLDINETTA ('Hachinetta')	IDee LMil
'Goldkrone' ♀H5	ELon GGGa MAsh SPer SPoG SSta
'Goldsworth Orange'	CAco CMac LRHS SLdr
'Goldsworth Yellow'	CSBt
'Goldtopas' (K)	CTri EPfP GGGa GKin LMil LRHS
'Gomer Waterer' ♀H6	CBcs CDul CMac CSBt EPfP GGGa LCro LMil LOPS LRHS MAsh MGos MJak NLar SCob SLdr SPer SPoG SSta
'Gorbella'	CRos
Gowenianum Group (Ad)	LMil LRHS MGos SPer
'Grace Seabrook' ♀H5	CBcs CSBt CTri GGGa MMuc SLdr SPer
'Graf Lennart'	GGGa
GRAFFITO ('Hachgraf')	GGGa LMil
'Graham Thomas'	LMil
'Grand Slam'	MMuc
grande	CBcs GGGa IDee LMil LRHS
- WJC 13804 **new**	WCru
gratum	see *R. basilicum*
'Graziella'	GGGa LRHS MGos MPkF SPoG SSta WFar
'Greensleeves'	LMil
'Greenway' (Kurume) (EA)	MPkF SLdr
griersonianum	GGGa LMil
- F 30392	LMil
griffithianum B&SWJ 2425	WCru
'Gristede' ♀H5	LMil LRHS NLar SSta
groenlandicum	LMil NLar SPer WGob WSHC
- 'Compactum'	LRHS NLar
- 'Helma'	GBin LRHS NLar
- 'Lenie'	NLar
(Grosclaude Group) 'Grosclaude'	LMil
'Grumpy'	EPfP LMil LRHS MAsh SCob
'Guillemot' **new**	GGGa
'Gwenda' (EA)	CTri SLdr
'Gwendoline' (A)	SSta
(Gwillt-king Group) 'Gwillt-king'	CBcs
habrotrichum	GGGa LMil
'Hachmann's Brasilia'	SSta
'Hachmann's Charmant'	GGGa SAko
'Hachmann's Constanze'	LMil
'Hachmann's Eskimo'	CAco LMil SLdr
'Hachmann's Feuerschein'	SAko
'Hachmann's Junifeuer'	SSta
HACHMANN'S KABARETT ('Hachkaba')	CRos LMil NLar
'Hachmann's Mamamia'	SAko
'Hachmann's Marlis' ♀H6	LMil LRHS
§ 'Hachmann's Metallica'	GGGa LMil LRHS
§ 'Hachmann's Orakel'	GGGa LMil LRHS SSta
HACHMANN'S PICOBELLO ('Hachpico'PBR)	LMil
'Hachmann's Pinguin'	SSta
§ 'Hachmann's Polaris' ♀H7	CBcs CRos LMil
'Hachmann's Porzellan' ♀H6	LMil MPkF
§ 'Hachmann's Rokoko' (EA)	CEnd LMil SSta
'Hachmann's Sunny Boy'	LMil LRHS
haematodes	GGGa LMil
§ - subsp. ***chaetomallum***	GGGa LMil
- subsp. ***haematodes***	LMil
'Halfdan Lem' ♀H5	CBcs GKin LMil LRHS MGos MMuc NLar SLim SPer SPoG SSta
'Halopeanum'	GGGa LMil
'Hamlet' (M)	LMil
'Hammondii'	LMil
'Hampshire Belle'	LMil LRHS SSta
hanceanum 'Canton Consul'	GGGa
- Nanum Group ♀H5	CBcs GGGa
'Hanger's Flame' (A)	LMil
'Hank Windsor'	CAco
HANS HACHMANN ('Hachhans')	LMil
'Hansel'	MAsh MMuc
'Hardijzer Beauty' (Ad)	SLdr
'Hardy Gardenia' (EA/d)	SSta
hardyi	see *R. augustinii* subsp. *hardyi*
'Harkwood Red' (EA)	SLdr
Harmony Group	SLdr
'Harry Tagg'	SLdr
Harry White's hybrid (A)	SSta
'Haru-no-sono' (EA)	MPkF
'Harvest Moon' (K)	NLar SSta
'Hatsu-giri' (EA)	CMac LCro LMil LOPS SLdr SSta
(Hawk Group) 'Crest' ♀H3	CBcs GGGa LMil SSta
'Heather Macleod' (EA)	SLdr
'Heidi'PBR (EA)	SLdr
'Helen Close' (Glenn Dale) (EA)	SLdr
'Helen Curtis' (EA)	SLdr
'Helena Evelyn' (A)	LMil
'Helene Schiffner'	SSta
heliolepis	GGGa LMil
- var. ***fumidum***	see *R. heliolepis* var. *heliolepis*
§ - var. ***heliolepis***	GGGa GKev
hemitrichotum SDR 4237	GKev
hemsleyanum	LMil SLdr
'Herbert' (EA)	CMac MGos NLar SLdr SLim
'High Sheriff'	CBcs
'High Summer'	LMil LRHS NLar
'Hilda Margaret'	SSta
'Hinamayo'	see *R.* (Obtusum Group) 'Hinomayo'
'Hino-crimson' (Kurume) (EA) ♀H5	CBcs CMac CSBt CTri GKin LMil MAsh MGos MPkF NHol NLar SLdr SPer SPoG SSta
'Hinode-giri' (EA)	CBcs CMac CSBt CTsd SLdr SPer
'Hino-scarlet' (EA)	CBcs
hippophaeoides	CBcs GKev LMil WFar
- 'Bei-ma-shan'	see *R. hippophaeoides* 'Haba Shan'
§ - 'Haba Shan' ♀H6	GGGa IDee LMil WThu
hirsutum	LMil WAbe
hirtipes	GGGa
hodgsonii	LMil SLdr
- B&SWJ 2195A	WCru
'Holden'	MAsh
'Homebush' (K/d) ♀H6	CBcs CKel CMac CTri EPfP GBin LMil LRHS MAsh MGos MJak MMuc NLar SPer SPoG SSta
'Honey Butter'	MGos NLar SLim
'Honeysuckle' (K)	NHol SSta
§ 'Ho-o' (Kurume) (EA)	SLdr
hookeri	LMil
- Tigh-na-Rudha form	GGGa
'Hoppy'	CBcs LMil MAsh MGos MMuc NLar SLdr SLim SPer

	'Horizon Lakeside'	GGGa
	'Horizon Monarch' ♀H4	CAco CBcs CRos GGGa GKin LMil LRHS MGos NLar SLdr SLim SPer SSta WFar
	'Hortulanus H.Witte' (M)	SSta
	'Hot Flush'	LMil
	'Hot Shot'	see *R.* 'Girard's Hot Shot'
	'Hot Shot Variegated'	see *R.* 'Girard's Variegated Hot Shot' (EA/v)
	'Hotei'	CAco CSBt EPfP GKin LMil MAsh NEgg NHol SLdr SSta
	(Hotspur Group) 'Hotspur' (K)	MMuc
	- 'Hotspur Red' (K) ♀H6	EPfP GKin LMil MAsh MMuc MPkF NEgg
	huanum	GGGa LMil
	- EGM 316	LMil
	'Hugh Koster'	SLdr
	aff. ***huidongense***	LMil
	'Huisman's Sun Star' (A)	LMil
	'Hullaballoo'	LMil
	Humming Bird Group	GEdr IDee LMil SLdr
	'Hussar'	LMil
	'Hydon Dawn' ♀H5	CBcs IDee LMil LRHS NLar SLdr SSta
	'Hydon Hunter' ♀H5	CBcs SSta
	'Hydon Velvet'	CBcs GGGa LMil LRHS MMuc NLar SLdr
	hyperythrum	GGGa LMil
	hypoglaucum	see *R. argyrophyllum* subsp. *hypoglaucum*
	'Ice Cube'	MMuc SLdr
	'Iceberg'	see *R.* 'Lodauric Iceberg'
	(Idealist Group) 'Idealist'	LMil
	'Ightham Yellow'	SLdr
§	'Ilam Melford Lemon' (A)	LMil
§	'Ilam Ming' (A)	LMil
	'Ilam Violet'	CMac LMil
	'Imago' (K/d)	LMil
§	'Ima-shojo' (Kurume) (EA/d)	CMac LRHS SLdr
	impeditum	CBcs CSBt ELan GEdr GKev LCro LOPS MGos NAln SCob SLdr SSta
	- 'Blue Steel'	see *R. fastigiatum* 'Blue Steel'
	- 'Indigo'	GKin
	- 'Pygmaeum'	WAbe WThu
	- 'Select'	MJak
	imperator	see *R. uniflorum* var. *imperator*
	(Impi Group) 'Impi'	LMil
	indicum (EA)	CTsd
§	- 'Macranthum' (EA)	SLdr
	INKARHO LILAC DUFTHECKE ('Rhodunter 149'[PBR])	LMil
	insigne ♀H6	GGGa LMil
	Intrifast Group	GGGa
	'Irene Koster' (O) ♀H5	CKel CRos CTho ELan GGGa GKin LMil MGos MPkF NLar SLim SPer
	'Irohayama' (Kurume) (EA) ♀H5	CBcs CEnd CMac EPfP LMil LRHS MAsh NPri NRHS
	irroratum	LMil SLdr
	- 'Polka Dot'	GGGa LMil
	- subsp. ***yiliangense*** EGM 339	LMil
	'Isabel'	NPri
	'Isabel' (EA)	MAsh
	iteaphyllum	see *R. formosum* var. *formosum* Iteaphyllum Group
	'Ivette' (Kaempferi) (EA)	CMac
	'Izumi-no-mai' (EA)	SLdr
	'J.C. Williams'	CBcs

	'J.M. de Montague'	see *R.* 'The Honourable Jean Marie de Montague'
	'Jackwill'	SAko
	(Jalisco Group) 'Jalisco Janet'	SLdr
	- 'Jubilant'	LMil
	'James Burchett' ♀H6	LMil LRHS NLar SSta
	'James Gable' (EA)	MAsh SLdr
	Janet Group	LMil
	'Janet Rhea' (EA)	SLdr
	japonicum (A. Gray) J.V. Suringar	see *R. molle* subsp. *japonicum*
	- var. ***pentamerum***	see *R. degronianum* subsp. *degronianum*
	jasminiflorum (V)	GGGa
	'Jason'	LMil
	'Jean Marie Montague'	see *R.* 'The Honourable Jean Marie de Montague'
	'Jeff Hill' (EA)	SLdr
	'Jenny'	see *R.* 'Creeping Jenny'
	'Jeritsa'	LMil
	'Jessica Rose' (A)	LMil
	'Jim Russell' (*ciliicalyx* hybrid)	GGGa
	'Joanna'	CBcs
	'Jock'	SLdr
	Jock Group	CBcs
	'Jock Brydon' (O) ♀H6	GGGa LMil
	'Johann Sebastian Bach' (EA)	SLdr
	'Johanna' (EA) ♀H5	CEnd CKel CTri EPfP LMil LRHS MAsh MGos MPkF NEgg NHol NLar NPri NRHS SLdr SPer
	'John Cairns' (Kaempferi) (EA)	CMac SLdr
	'John Walter'	SCob
	johnstoneanum	CBcs GGGa SLdr
	- NJM 12.068	WPGP
	- 'Double Diamond' (d)	LMil
	'Jolie Madame' (Vs) ♀H6	CKel EPfP GKin LMil LRHS MAsh MGos MMuc MPkF NLar NPri SPer WFar
	'Joseph Hill' (EA)	CEnd NLar
	'Jubilee'	SLdr
	'July Giant'	SLdr
	'June Fire' (A)	GGGa SSta
	'Juniduft' (A)	GGGa
	kaempferi (EA)	LMil SLdr
§	- 'Mikado' (EA)	LMil SLdr
	- orange-flowered (EA)	CMac
	'Kalinka'	LMil MAsh MGos SPoG WFar
	'Karen Triplett'	LMil
	'Karin'	MJak
	'Karl Naue'	GGGa SSta
	KARMINKISSEN ('Hachkarmin')	LMil
	'Kasane-kagaribi' (EA)	SLdr
	'Kathleen' van Nes (EA)	SLdr
	'Katisha' (EA)	SLdr
	'Katy Watson'	SSta
	'Keija' (EA)	SLdr
	keiskei compact	ITim
	- var. ***ozawae*** 'Yaku Fairy' ♀H5	LMil WThu
	keleticum	see *R. calostrotum* subsp. *keleticum*
	'Ken Janeck'	GGGa
	aff. ***kendrickii*** KR 10359	WPGP
	'Kentucky Minstrel' (K)	MPkF
	'Kermesinum' (EA)	CTri LRHS MAsh MGos NLar NWad SLdr SLim
I	'Kermesinum Rosé' (EA) ♀H5	CRos CSBt LMil LRHS NLar SLdr SLim
	kesangiae	GGGa GKev LMil

	- var. ***album***	GGGa
	keysii	GGGa LMil
	(Kilimanjaro Group) 'Kilimanjaro'	LMil
	'Kimbeth'	GGGa
	'King George' Loder	see *R.* 'Loderi King George'
	kingianum	see *R. arboreum* subsp. *zeylanicum*
	'Kings Ride'	LMil
§	'Kirin' (Kurume) (EA/d)	CBcs LMil SLdr
	'Kirin' (Tsutsuji) (EA) **new**	MPkF
	kiusianum (EA)	LMil WAbe
I	- 'Album' (EA)	LMil WAbe
	- 'Hillier's Pink' (EA)	LMil
	- var. ***kiusianum*** (EA)	SLdr
	'Kleiner Prinz' (EA)	SAko
	'Klondyke' (K) ♀H6	CAby CBcs CRos CSBt CTri EPfP GGGa GKin LCro LMil LOPS LRHS MAsh MGos MMuc MPkF NLar NPri SLdr SPer
	'Kluis Sensation' ♀H5	CAco CBcs CMac CSBt SLdr SSta
	'Kluis Triumph'	SSta
	'Knap Hill Apricot' (K)	LMil
	'Knap Hill Red' (K)	LMil
	'Koichiro Wada'	see *R. yakushimanum* 'Koichiro Wada'
	'Kokardia'	LMil SAko
	kongboense	GGGa
	'Königstein' (EA)	LMil MGos SSta
§	'Koningin Emma' (M)	LMil
	'Koningin Wilhelmina' (Vuykiana) (EA)	SLdr
	'Koromo-shikibu' (EA)	GGGa MPkF
	'Koromo-shikibu White' (EA)	GGGa
	'Koster's Brilliant Red' (M)	CKel SSta
	'Kromlauer Parkperle'	SAko
§	'Kure-no-yuki' (Kurume) (EA/d)	CEnd LMil
	kyawii	GGGa
	'La Ola' (EA)	SAko
	(Lactcombei Group) 'Robert Keir'	SLdr
	lacteum	GGGa LMil
	'Lady Alice Fitzwilliam' ♀H3	CBcs CMac ECre GGGa GKin LMil
	(Lady Chamberlain Group) 'Salmon Trout'	LMil LSRN
	'Lady Clementine Mitford' ♀H6	CBcs CSBt LMil MMuc SLdr SPer
	'Lady Dark' (EA)	SAko
	'Lady de Rothschild'	LMil
	'Lady Eleanor Cathcart'	SLdr
	'Lady Elphinstone' (Kufume) (EA)	SLdr
	'Lady Louise' (EA)	SLdr
	'Lady Montagu'	LMil
	'Lady Romsey'	LMil
	laetum (V)	GGGa
	Lamellen Group	LMil
	lanatoides	GGGa
	lanatum	GGGa LMil
	'Langworth'	MMuc
	lanigerum	LMil
	lapponicum Parviflorum Group	GGGa
	'Lapwing' (K)	NLar SLdr
	'Laramie'	GGGa
	'Lavender Brilliant' (EA)	SLdr
	'Lavender Girl' ♀H6	LMil LRHS NLar SLdr SSta
	'Le Progrès'	IDee LMil LRHS
	'Ledifolium'	see *R.* × *mucronatum*

	'Ledifolium Album'	see *R.* × *mucronatum*
	'Lee's Dark Purple'	CAco LMil MJak
	'Lee's Scarlet'	LMil
	'Lemon Dream'	CRos LMil LRHS MAsh MGos NLar NPri NRHS SLim
*	'Lemon Drop' (A)	GGGa
	'Lemonora' (M)	CBcs GKin
	'Lem's 45'	SLdr
	'Lem's Cameo' ♀H5	GGGa LMil LRHS SSta
	'Lem's Monarch' ♀H4	CBcs CDul GGGa IDee LMil LRHS MMuc SLdr SSta
	'Lem's Tangerine'	LMil
	'Lemur' (EA)	GGGa LMil NLar WThu
	'Leni'	LRHS MAsh NRHS
	'Leo' (EA)	SLdr
	'Leo' (hybrid)	CMac
	'Leonardslee Giles'	SLdr
	'Leonardslee Primrose'	SLdr
	'Leonore'	LMil
	lepidostylum	CBcs CMac GGGa LMil WFar
	lepidotum	GGGa
	- var. ***album***	GGGa
	- yellow-flowered McB 110	WThu
§	***leptocarpum***	GGGa
§	'Leucanthum'	GGGa WThu
	leucaspis	CBcs SLdr
	'Leuchtpolster'	SAko
	'Lila Pedigo'	MMuc SLdr
	'Lilac Time' (EA)	SLdr
	'Lilactina'	SLdr
	'Lily Marleen' (EA)	CTri
	'Linda' ♀H5	CMac EPfP GGGa LMil LSRN MAsh MJak SCob SLdr
	'Linda Stuart' (EA)	GGGa
	lindleyi	GGGa MPkF
	- 'Geordie Sherriff'	GGGa
	'Linearifolium'	see *R. stenopetalum* 'Linearifolium'
	'Lingot d'Or' (A)	MPkF
	'Lionel's First'	LMil
	Lionel's Triumph Group	LMil
	'Little Beauty' (EA)	SLdr
	'Loch Arkaig'	GGGa
	'Loch Awe'	GGGa LMil
	'Loch Earn'	GGGa
	'Loch Faskally'	GGGa
	'Loch Laggan'	GGGa
	'Loch Leven'	GGGa
	'Loch Morar'	GGGa
	lochiae (V)	GGGa
	Lodauric Group	SLdr
§	- 'Lodauric Iceberg'	LMil LRHS
	Loderi Group	SLdr
	- 'Loderi Fairy Queen'	SLdr
	- 'Loderi Game Chick'	LMil SLdr
	- 'Loderi Georgette'	SLdr
	- 'Loderi Helen'	LMil SLdr
§	- 'Loderi King George' ♀H5	CBcs GGGa GKin LMil LRHS SLdr SPer SSta
	- 'Loderi Patience'	SLdr
	- 'Loderi Pink Coral'	LMil SLdr
	- 'Loderi Pink Diamond' ♀H4	CBcs LMil SLdr
	- 'Loderi Pink Topaz'	SLdr
	- 'Loderi Pretty Polly'	SLdr
	- 'Loderi Princess Marina'	SLdr
	- 'Loderi Sir Edmund'	LMil SLdr
	- 'Loderi Sir Joseph Hooker'	SLdr
	- 'Loderi Titan'	SLdr SSta
	- 'Loderi Venus' ♀H5	IDee LMil SLdr SSta
	- 'Loderi White Diamond'	SLdr

	'Loder's White' ♀H5	CMac LMil SSta
	longesquamatum	GGGa
	longipes	GGGa LMil
	- EGM 336	LMil
	- var. ***chienianum***	LMil
	'Lord Roberts' ♀H6	CAco CBcs CDul CMac CSBt CTri ELan GGGa LCro LMil LOPS MAsh MGos MJak MMuc NHol NLar SLdr SLim SPer SSta
	'Louis Pasteur'	SCob
	'Louisa' (EA)	MAsh NLar
	'Louise Dowdle' (Glenn Dale) (EA)	LMil SLdr
	'Lovely William'	CMac IDee LMil NLar SLdr
	'Lucy Lou'	GGGa
	ludlowii	GGGa
	'Lullaby' (EA)	SLdr
	luteiflorum	GGGa
	lutescens	CBcs CMac CTsd LMil SLdr
	- 'Bagshot Sands' ♀H3	GGGa LMil SLdr
	- 'Exbury'	CExl
	luteum (A)	Widely available
	- 'Golden Comet' (A)	GGGa
*	'Mac Ovata'	CMac
	macabeanum ♀H4	GGGa GKev GKin IDee LMil LRHS NEgg SLdr SSta
	- NAPE 052	GGGa
	macabeanum* × *wardii	GGGa
	macgregoriae (V)	GGGa
	macranthum	see *R. indicum* 'Macranthum'
	macrophyllum B&SWJ 9561	WCru
	macrosmithii	see *R. argipeplum*
	'Macrostemon' (EA)	MPkF
	maculiferum	GGGa
	'Madame Ad. van Hecke' (EA)	CTri GKin LMil MAsh MGos SLim
	'Madame Albert van Hecke' (EA)	CKel NLar SLdr
	'Madame de Bruin'	SLdr
	'Madame Galle'	SLdr
	'Madame Masson' ♀H6	CAco CDul CTri ELan EPfP LMil LRHS LSRN MAsh MGos MMuc NLar NPri SPer SSta WFar
	maddenii	CBcs LMil SAko
§	- subsp. ***crassum***	CBcs CExl GGGa
§	- subsp. ***maddenii*** Polyandrum Group	CBcs GGGa
	'Magic Flute' (EA)	LRHS MAsh NRHS
I	'Magic Flute' (V)	LMil SCoo
	magnificum	GKev
	magniflorum	GGGa
	'Maharani'	GGGa
	'Mai-ogi' (EA)	SAko
	'Maischnee' (EA)	GGGa
	'Maja' (G)	SSta
§	***makinoi*** ♀H5	GGGa LMil MMuc SSta
	- 'Fuju-kaku-no-matsu'	MGos
	mallotum	GGGa LMil
	'Manda Sue'	NLar
	'Mandarin Lights' (A)	NLar
	'Manderley'	LMil
	'Maraschino' (EA)	MPkF SAko
	'Mardi Gras'	CRos MGos NEgg
	Margaret Dunn Group	CAco
	'Maria Elena' (EA/d)	MGos NLar SLdr
	'Marie Fortie'	CRos MGos NLar
	'Marie Hoffman'	LMil
	'Marilee' (EA)	EPfP LRHS MAsh NLar SLdr
	'Marinja' (EA)	LMil
	'Marinus Koster'	SSta
	'Marion Street'	LMil
	'Markeeta's Prize' ♀H4	CAco EPfP GGGa LMil LRHS MAsh MGos MMuc NLar NPri SLdr SLim
	'Marlies' (A)	NLar
	'Marmot' (EA)	MMuc
	'Marsalla'	LMil SAko
	'Martha Isaacson' (Ad)	LMil SLdr
	'Martha Wright'	EPfP GGGa LRHS MAsh NPri
	'Maruschka' (EA) ♀H5	CRos GGGa LMil LRHS MAsh NLar SAko
	'Mary Desby' (EA)	CEnd
	'Mary Forte'	SCob
	'Mary Helen' (Glenn Dale) (EA)	LMil LRHS MAsh MGos NLar NRHS SCoo SLdr SLim
	'Mary Poppins' (A)	GKin LMil LSRN MGos MPkF NEgg NLar SCoo SLdr SLim
	'Marylou'	IDee LMil LRHS
	(Matador Group) 'Matador'	GGGa LMil SLdr
	'Mathie' (A)	SSta
	maximum	GGGa
§	'Maxwellii' (EA)	CMac SLdr
	May Day Group	CBcs CDul MGos
	- 'May Day' ♀H3	CMac MMuc SLdr
	'Mayor Johnstone'	CTri EPfP MAsh NPri
	meddianum	LMil
	var. ***atrokermesinum*** F 2649	
	Medusa Group	SLdr
	megacalyx	GGGa
	'Megan' (EA)	LSRN MAsh SLdr WGwG
	megaphyllum	see *R. basilicum*
	megeratum	GGGa
	- KR 9426	LMil
	- 'Bodnant'	GGGa ITim NWad WAbe WThu
	mekongense	GCal
	- var. ***mekongense*** Rubroluteum Group	see *R. viridescens* Rubroluteum Group
	'Melford Lemon'	see *R.* 'Ilam Melford Lemon'
	'Melina' (EA/d)	LMil
	'Melle'PBR **new**	MPkF
	'Melrose Flash'	GGGa
	'Melville'	SSta
	'Merganser' ♀H4	CAco GGGa LMil SLdr
	'Merlin' (Glenn Dale) (EA)	LMil
	METALLICA	see *R.* 'Hachmann's Metallica'
	metternichii var. ***pentamerum***	see *R. degronianum* subsp. *degronianum*
	'Mi Amor'	GGGa LMil
	'Michael Hill' (EA)	MAsh
	'Michiko' (EA)	SAko
	micranthum	LMil LRHS
	microgynum	GGGa
	microleucum	see *R. orthocladum* var. *microleucum*
	micromeres	see *R. leptocarpum*
	'Midnight Beauty'	LMil LRHS SAko
	'Midnight Mystique'	GGGa SSta
	'Midsummer'	MMuc SLdr
	'Midsummer Coral' (A) **new**	LMil
	'Midsummer Girl' (A) **new**	LMil
	'Midsummer Mermaid' (A)	LMil MAsh
	'Midsummer Moon' (A) **new**	LMil
	'Midsummer Rose' (A) **new**	LMil
	'Midsummer Star' (A) **new**	LMil
	'Midsummer Wedding' (A) **new**	LMil
	'Mikado' (EA)	see *R. kaempferi* 'Mikado'
	'Millennium' (A)	LRHS

	Name	Suppliers
	'Millennium Gold'PBR	LMil
	'Milton' (R)	LMil
	'Mimi' (Kaempferi) (EA)	CMac
	'Ming'	see *R.* 'Ilam Ming'
	miniatum CER 9927	GGGa
	minus	CBcs
	- var. ***minus*** (Carolinianum Group) 'Epoch'	LMil
	Mishmiense Group KR 10716	WPGP
	'Moerheim' ♀H5	CBcs EPfP LRHS MAsh MMuc NPri SLim
§	'Moerheim's Pink'	GGGa LMil SLdr
	(Mohamet Group) 'Mohamet'	LMil
	'Moidart' (Vs)	LMil NLar
	'Moira Salmon' (EA)	SLdr
§	***molle*** subsp. ***japonicum*** (A)	LMil NEgg
	Mollis, orange-flowered (M)	GKin SRms
	- pink-flowered (M)	GKin SRms
	- red-flowered (M)	GKin
	- yellow-flowered (M)	GKin SRms
	'Molly Ann'	LSRN
	'Molten Gold' (v)	GGGa IDee LMil LRHS MAsh
§	'Momoko' (EA)	LRHS WFar
	monanthum	GGGa
	'Monsieur Marcel Ménard' ♀H6	CBcs CDul CRos EPfP GGGa LMil LRHS MAsh MGos NLar NPri SCob SLdr SSta WFar
	montroseanum	GGGa LMil SLdr
	Moonstone Group	CMac
	- 'Moonstone Pink'	SLdr
	- 'Moonstone Yellow'	SLdr
§	'Morgenrot'	MMuc NLar WFar
	morii	GGGa
	'Morning Cloud'	EPfP LRHS MAsh MGos NHol NLar SLim SSta
	MORNING RED	see *R.* 'Morgenrot'
	'Moser's Maroon'	CBcs GGGa LSRN MMuc NLar SLdr WFar
	'Mother of Pearl'	SLdr
	'Mother's Day' (Kurume) (EA) ♀H4	CDul CKel CMac CSBt CTri EPfP GKin LCro LMil LOPS LRHS LSRN MAsh MGos MJak NEgg NHol NLar NPri NRHS SCob SLdr SLim SPer SPoG SSta WFar
§	***moulmainense***	CMCN
	'Mount Everest'	LMil LRHS SSta
	'Mount Rainier' (A)	LRHS MPkF
	'Mount Saint Helens' (A)	LMil NLar SLim SPer
	'Mount Seven Star'	see *R. nakaharae* 'Mount Seven Star'
	moupinense	GGGa SLdr
	- 'Fulmar'	GGGa
	'Mrs A.T. de la Mare' ♀H6	LMil SSta
	'Mrs Betty Robertson'	CMac GBin SLdr
	Mrs C. Whitner Group	SLdr
	'Mrs Charles E. Pearson' ♀H6	CSBt LMil SLdr SSta
	'Mrs Davies Evans'	LMil SSta
	'Mrs Emil Hager' (EA)	SLdr
	'Mrs Furnivall' ♀H6	GGGa
	'Mrs G.W. Leak'	CSBt GGGa
	'Mrs J.C. Williams' ♀H6	LMil
	'Mrs J.G. Millais'	LMil
	'Mrs James Horlick'	CAco
	'Mrs T.H. Lowinsky' ♀H6	CBcs CDul CMac GGGa GKin LMil LRHS MAsh MGos MMuc NLar SLdr SLim SPer
§	× ***mucronatum*** (EA)	MPkF SLdr
	mucronulatum	CBcs
	- B&SWJ 786	WCru
	- B&SWJ 8657	WCru
	- var. ***albiflorum***	LMil SLdr
	- var. ***chejuense***	see *R. mucronulatum* var. *taquetii*
	- 'Cornell Pink' ♀H5	GGGa
§	- var. ***taquetii***	GGGa
	'Muffet' (EA)	SLdr
	'Mulroy Cream'	LMil
§	***multiflorum*** var. ***purpureum***	CKel GGGa
	'Mum'	LMil
	'Nabucco' (A)	GGGa MMuc NLar SLdr
	nakaharae (EA) ♀H5	SLdr
	- 'Mariko' (EA)	EPot WThu
§	- 'Mount Seven Star' (EA) ♀H5	GGGa ITim LMil NWad SLdr WThu
§	- orange-flowered (EA)	LMil LRHS MAsh NRHS SLdr
	- pink-flowered (EA)	MPkF SLdr
	'Nakahari Orange'	see *R. nakaharae* orange-flowered
	'Nancy Evans' ♀H5	CRos CSBt EPfP GGGa GKin LMil LRHS LSRN MAsh MGos NLar NPri SLdr SLim SSta
	'Nancy of Robinhill' (EA)	CKel
	'Nanki Poo' (EA)	SLdr
	'Naomi' (EA)	SLdr
	(Naomi Group) 'Exbury Naomi'	LMil
	- 'Naomi Nautilus'	LMil
	- 'Naomi Pink Beauty'	LMil
	- 'Naomi Stella Maris'	LMil
	'Narcissiflorum' (G/d) ♀H6	GKin LMil MPkF NLar
	'Naselle'	LMil
	'Ne Plus Ultra' (V)	GGGa
	NEGLIGÉ ('Hachneg'PBR) (EA)	LMil
	neriiflorum	GGGa LMil
	- CN&W 906	LMil
§	- subsp. ***phaedropum*** KR 9308	LMil
	'Newcomb's Sweetheart'	LMil
	'Niagara' (Glenn Dale) (EA) ♀H5	CMac LMil SLdr
	'Nico' (EA)	CMac LMil LRHS MAsh
	'Nicola' (EA)	LSRN
	'Night Sky' ♀H5	CRos EPfP GGGa LMil LRHS MGos NLar SLdr
	nigroglandulosum	GGGa
	nipponicum	GGGa
	'Nishiki' (EA)	CMac
	nitens	see *R. calostrotum* subsp. *riparium* Nitens Group
	nitidulum var. ***omeiense***	GGGa WThu
	nivale subsp. ***boreale*** Ramosissimum Group	GGGa
§	- subsp. ***nivale***	GKev ITim NWad
	niveum ♀H5	GGGa LMil
	- B&SWJ 2611	WCru
	- B&SWJ 2659	WCru
	- B&SWJ 2675	WCru
	Nobleanum Group	GGGa LMil SLdr SSta
	- 'Nobleanum Coccineum'	CMac LMil SLdr
	- 'Nobleanum Venustum'	CAco LMil SSta
	Nobleanum Album Group	CMac GGGa LMil SLdr SSta
	(Norderney Group) 'Oudijk's Sensation'	MAsh MMuc SLdr
	'Nordlicht' (EA)	SLdr
	'Noriko' (EA)	SLdr
	'Northern Hi-Lights' (A)	CRos GKin LMil LRHS MGos MPkF NLar SLim SPer

	'Nova Zembla'	CAco CBcs CTri EPfP EUJe GGGa LCro LMil LOPS LRHS MAsh MGos MMuc MPkF NEgg SCob SLim SPer SSta
	'Nuccio's Blue Moon' (EA)	LMil MPkF SLdr
	nudiflorum	see *R. periclymenoides*
	nuttallii	GGGa LMil
	nymphaeoides CGG 14027	GGGa
	'Oban'	EPot GEdr ITim NSla
	Obtusum Group (EA)	SLdr
	- 'Amoenum' (EA/d)	CBcs CMac CSBt CTsd LMil SLdr SPer
	- 'Amoenum Coccineum' (EA/d)	SLdr SSta
§	- 'Hinomayo' (EA) 🏆H5	CBcs CMac CTri EPfP GKin LMil SLdr
	occidentale (A)	GKin LMil SLdr
	- SIN 1830	GGGa
	ochraceum 🏆H5	GGGa LMil
	- C&H 7042	LMil
	'Odee Wright'	CAco LRHS MAsh
	'Oi-no-mezame' (Kurume) (EA)	SLdr
	'Old Port'	LMil
	oldhamii (EA) B&SWJ 3742	WCru
	'Olga' 🏆H5	LMil SSta
	'Olga Niblett' (EA)	SSta
	oligocarpum	GGGa
	'Opossum' (EA)	GGGa
	ORAKEL	see *R.* 'Hachmann's Orakel'
	'Orange Beauty' (Kaempferi) (EA)	CBcs GGGa MAsh SLdr
	'Orange King' (EA) 🏆H5	CRos LMil MGos SLdr SPoG
	'Orangeade' (K)	LRHS MPkF
	orbiculare 🏆H5	GGGa LMil SLdr
§	- subsp. ***cardiobasis***	GGGa
	'Orchid Lights'	MAsh
	'Oregon' (EA)	SLdr
	Oregonia Group	LMil
	oreodoxa	LMil
§	- var. ***fargesii*** 🏆H6	GGGa LMil
	- var. ***oreodoxa***	GGGa LMil
	oreotrephes 🏆H5	LMil
	- SDR 5027	GKev
	- 'Bluecalyptus'	GGGa
§	- Exquisitum Group	SLdr
	- 'Pentland'	GGGa LMil
	'Orion' ambig.	NLar
§	***orthocladum*** var. ***microleucum***	GGGa WThu
	'Osaraku Seedling' (EA)	EPfP LRHS MPkF
	'Osmar' 🏆H5	GGGa
	'Ostara'	CBcs
	'Oudijk's Favorite'	SLdr
	pachysanthum 🏆H5	GGGa GKev GKin LMil SLdr
	- 'Crosswater'	LMil LRHS
	pachytrichum	GGGa
	'Palestrina' (Vuykiana) (EA) 🏆H5	CBcs CDul CMac CSBt EPfP GKin MAsh MJak MMuc MPkF SLdr SPer SSta
	paludosum	see *R. nivale* subsp. *nivale*
	'Pancake'	CMac
	'Panda' (EA) 🏆H5	CSBt CTri EPfP GGGa LMil LRHS MAsh SLdr SSta
	'Parfait' (EA)	LMil
	'Parkfeuer' (A) 🏆H6	GGGa
	parmulatum	LMil
	- KW 5876	LMil
	- 'Ocelot'	GGGa
	parryae AM (*roseatum*)	GGGa
	'Patty Bee' 🏆H5	CBcs CSBt CTri EPfP GEdr GGGa LMil LRHS MAsh MGos NLar NPri NSla SLim SSta
	'Peach Blossom'	see *R.* 'Saotome'
	'Pearl Betteridge'	LMil
	'Peep-bo' (EA)	SLdr
	'Peeping Tom'	NHol SSta
	'Peggy'	LMil
	pemakoense	GGGa WThu
	'Pemakofairy'	WThu
	pendulum	GGGa
	'Penheale Blue' 🏆H5	CTsd GKin LMil
	'Penjerrick'	GGGa
	'Penny Tomlin'	SSta
	pentaphyllum (A)	GGGa
	'Peppermint Candy'	LMil
	'Peppina'	GGGa LMil
	'Percy Wiseman' 🏆H5	CBcs CDul CRos EPfP GGGa GKin LCro LMil LOPS LRHS MAsh MGos MJak NEgg NLar SCob SLdr SLim SPer SSta WFar
§	***periclymenoides*** (A)	GGGa GKev LMil
	'Persil' (K) 🏆H6	CAby CBcs CKel CSBt CTri ELan EPfP GGGa GKin LMil LRHS MAsh MJak MMuc NEgg NHol NLar SCoo SLdr SPer SSta WFar
	'Peter Bee'	LMil
	'Peter Chapell'	GGGa
	'Peter Gable' (EA)	SLdr
	'Peter John Mezitt'	see *R.* (PJM Group) 'Peter John Mezitt'
	'Peter Koster' (hybrid)	GKin
	petrocharis	GGGa
	PETTICOAT ('Hachpett') (EA)	LMil
	'Pfauenauge'	GGGa LMil
	phaedropum	see *R. neriiflorum* subsp. *phaedropum*
	phaeochrysum var. ***phaeochrysum*** C 12529	GGGa
	'Phalarope'	CCCN GEdr
	'Phyllis Korn'	LMil NLar SAko
§	***piercei***	GGGa LMil
	'Pine Marten' (EA)	GGGa
	pingianum	GGGa
	'Pink and Sweet' (A)	LRHS MPkF
	'Pink Bride'	SLdr
	'Pink Cameo'	CAco
	'Pink Cherub' 🏆H6	LMil MAsh
I	'Pink Delight' (K)	GKin MMuc
	'Pink Drift'	CSBt GEdr LMil NSla
	'Pink Gin'	LMil
	'Pink Mimosa' (Vs)	SLdr
	'Pink Pancake' (EA) 🏆H4	CBcs EPfP LMil LRHS MAsh MPkF NPri SLdr
	'Pink Pearl' (EA)	see *R.* 'Azuma-kagami'
	'Pink Pearl' (hybrid) 🏆H4	CBcs CDul CSBt CTri GGGa LMil MAsh MMuc SLdr SPer SSta
	'Pink Pebble' 🏆H5	CExl ELon MAsh
	'Pink Perfection'	CMac SLdr
	'Pink Polar Bear'	LMil
	'Pink Sunset'	LMil
	'Pintail'	GGGa LMil LRHS MAsh
	'Pipit'	GGGa
	'Pippa' (EA)	CMac
§	(PJM Group) 'Peter John Mezitt'	NLar
	platypodum	LMil
	- CGG 14005	GGGa
	'Pleasant White' (EA)	LCro LMil LOPS NLar

Name	Suppliers
'Plover'	GGGa
pocophorum	GGGa
var. ***pocophorum***	
'Point Defiance'	SPer
'Polar Bear' (EA)	CAco SLdr
Polar Bear Group	LMil
- 'Polar Bear'	CSBt GGGa GKin LMil LRHS SLdr
'Polaris' (EA)	MJak NLar
'Polaris'	see *R.* 'Hachmann's Polaris'
'Polarnacht'	CBcs GGGa IDee LMil LRHS NLar SLdr
poluninii KR 8231	LMil
polyandrum	see *R. maddenii* subsp. *maddenii* Polyandrum Group
§ ***polycladum*** Scintillans Group	GGGa
'Polyroy'	GGGa
ponticum	CAco CDul CMac CTri NHol WFar
- 'Filigran'	LMil
- 'Roseum'	SGol
§ - 'Variegatum' (v)	CAco CMac CRos EPfP MAsh MGos NLar NPri SCob SLdr SPer SPoG SRms
- 'Ville d'Orléans' **new**	CKel
populare KC 0126	GGGa
'Praecox' ♀H6	CBcs CSBt GBin GGGa GKev GKin LCro LMil LOPS LRHS MAsh MGos MJak NLar NPri SLdr SLim SPoG
Praecox Group	MJak
praestans	GGGa GKin LMil
prattii	GGGa
preptum	GGGa
'President Roosevelt' (v)	CMac CSBt EPfP GKin MAsh MJak NPri SLdr SPoG SSta
'Pridenjoy'	LMil LRHS
primuliflorum ♀H5	WAbe
- 'Doker-La'	GGGa LMil WAbe
'Prince Camille de Rohan'	LMil
'Princess Alice'	CBcs SLdr
'Princess Anne' ♀H6	CBcs CMac ELon IDee LCro LMil LOPS MGos NHpl SLdr SLim SPer SPoG SSta
'Princess Margaret of Windsor' (K)	LMil
principis	GGGa LMil
- 'Lost Horizon'	IDee LMil LRHS
prinophyllum (A)	GGGa LMil
- 'Philip Holmes' **new**	LMil
'Prins Bernhard' (EA)	MAsh SLdr
'Prinses Juliana' (Vuykiana) (EA)	SLdr
'Prinses Máxima'	LMil
'Professor Hugo de Vries'	SLdr
pronum	GGGa
- R.B. Cooke form	GGGa
- Towercourt form	GGGa
proteoides	GGGa
protistum	GCal GGGa
prunifolium (A)	GGGa LMil
pseudochrysanthum ♀H6	GGGa LMil
- dwarf RWJ 9807	WCru
pseudociliipes	GGGa
Psyche Group	see *R.* Wega Group
'Ptarmigan' ♀H6	GEdr GGGa GKev LMil WThu
pudorosum	GGGa
'Pulchrum Maxwellii'	see *R.* 'Maxwellii'
pumilum	GGGa WAbe WThu
- SDR 7413	GKev
'Purple Cushion' (EA)	EPfP LMil LRHS MAsh NPri NRHS
'Purple Gem'	MGos

Name	Suppliers
'Purple Passion'PBR	LMil LRHS LSRN NLar SLdr SPer
'Purple Queen' (EA/d)	MAsh
'Purple Splendor' (Gable) (EA)	CMac SGol SLdr
'Purple Splendour'	CBcs CSBt LMil MGos MMuc NEgg SSta
'Purple Triumph' (Vuykiana) (EA) ♀H5	LMil SLdr
'Purpurkissen' (EA)	LMil
'Purpurtraum' (EA) ♀H5	CKel LMil
qiaojiaense NN 0903	GGGa LMil
'Quail'	GGGa
'Queen Alice'	CRos NLar
'Queen Elizabeth II'	LRHS
QUEEN EMMA	see *R.* 'Koningin Emma'
'Queen Mary'	SSta
Queen of Hearts Group	LRHS
quinquefolium (A)	GGGa LMil SLdr
RABATZ ('Hachraba')	GGGa LMil SAko
racemosum ♀H6	LMil
- BWJ 7811	WCru
- 'Rock Rose' ♀H5	EPfP LMil SLdr
'Racoon' (EA)	GGGa LMil
radicans	see *R. calostrotum* subsp. *keleticum* Radicans Group
'Ramapo' ♀H6	CPla CRos GGGa LMil LRHS MAsh MGos NRHS SLdr SLim SPer
'Rasputin'	EUJe SSta
'Razorbill' ♀H5	GGGa GKin LMil NLar SLim
recurvoides	GGGa LMil SLdr
- Keillour form	GGGa
'Red and Gold'	EPfP GGGa LRHS NPri
'Red Dawn'	LRHS NRHS
'Red Delicious'	LMil SLdr
'Red Diamond'	see *R.* Diamant Group red-flowered
'Red Heart' **new**	LMil
'Red Jack'	CDul MGos MMuc SCob SPoG SSta
'Red Pimpernel' (EA)	SLdr
'Red Wood'	GGGa
'Redwings' (EA)	SLdr
'Reich's Signifikant'	SAko
Remo Group	CMac
'Rennie' (A)	MMuc
'Renoir' ♀H5	CSBt LMil
reticulatum (A)	LMil LRHS
'Reuthe's Purple'	WThu
'Rêve d'Amour' (Vs)	SSta
'Rex' (EA)	MAsh
rex ♀H5	GGGa GKin LMil SLdr
- EGM 295	LMil
§ - subsp. ***fictolacteum*** ♀H4	GGGa GKin LMil SLdr
'Rhododendronpark Graal-Müritz'	SSta
'Ria Hardijzer' (Ad)	LMil
'Ribbon Candy' (A)	LRHS MPkF
rigidum	GGGa
- 'Album'	LMil
'Ring of Fire'	LMil LRHS
'Ripe Corn'	LMil
ririei	GGGa
'Robert Croux'	SLdr
'Robert Seleger'	GGGa GKin LMil MAsh
'Robert Whelan' (A)	SSta
'Robin Hill Frosty' (EA)	SLdr
'Robin Hill Gillie' (EA)	SLdr
'Robinette'	MAsh
'Rocket'	CAco CRos LRHS MAsh MGos MMuc SLim SPer SPoG
'Roehr's Peggy Ann' (EA)	LMil MPkF
'Rokoko'	see *R.* 'Hachmann's Rokoko'

Name	Suppliers
Rosalind Group	CMac
- 'Rosalind'	WFar
'Rosalinda' (EA)	SLdr
'Rosata' (Vs) ♀H5	GGGa SSta
'Rose Bud'	CBcs CKel CSBt CTri WThu
'Rose Elf'	WThu
'Rose Glow' (A)	SSta
'Rose Greely' (Gable) (EA) ♀H5	NLar SLim SPer
'Rose Haze' (Vs)	SSta
'Rosebud' (EA/d)	CMac SLdr SSta
'Rosemary Hyde' (EA)	SLdr
roseum	see *R. canescens*
'Roseum Elegans'	CAco LCro LMaj LOPS LRHS MAsh MMuc NLar SCob SLim
ROSINETTA ('Hachrosi') (EA)	LMil
'Rosy Dream'	MAsh MMuc
'Rosy Fire' (A)	LMil
rothschildii	GGGa LMil SLdr
rousei (V)	GGGa
roxieanum	GGGa LMil
§ - var. ***cucullatum***	GGGa GKev
- var. ***oreonastes*** ♀H5	GGGa LMil
- var. ***parvum***	GGGa
'Royal Command' (K)	CBcs CTri GKin LMil
'Royal Lodge' (K)	MPkF
'Royal Windsor'	LMil
'Roza Stevenson'	SLdr
'Rubicon'	GGGa SLdr
rubiginosum ♀H6	GGGa LMil
rubroluteum	see *R. viridescens* Rubroluteum Group
'Ruby Hart'	GGGa LSRN
RUBY WEDDING	see *R.* 'Firestorm'
rude	see *R. glischrum* subsp. *rude*
rugosum Sinclair 240 (V)	GGGa
rushforthii	GGGa
russatum ♀H6	GGGa LMil SLdr
- blue-black-flowered	LMil
Russautinii Group	SLdr
russotinctum	see *R. alutaceum* var. *russotinctum*
'Rwain'	NLar
'Ryde Heron' (EA)	SLdr
'Sabina' (EA)	SLdr
'Sacko'	GGGa LMil NLar SLim
'Saffron Queen'	CBcs CTsd LMil LRHS MPkF
'Sahara' (K)	SLdr
'Saint Kew'	SLdr
'Saint Merryn' ♀H5	CBcs MJak
'Saint Tudy'	SLdr
'Saint Valentine' (V)	GGGa
'Sakata Red' (EA)	SLdr
'Salmon Sander' (EA)	SLdr
'Salmon's Leap' (EA/v)	CMac ELan LMil LRHS MAsh SSta
saluenense	LMil SLdr WThu
'Sammetglut'	CAco
'Samuel Taylor Coleridge' (M)	GKin
sanguineum	LMil
§ - subsp. ***didymum***	GGGa SLdr
- subsp. ***sanguineum*** var. ***haemaleum***	GGGa LMil
- - var. ***sanguineum*** F 25521	LMil
'Santa Maria' (EA) ♀H5	LMil LSRN NEgg NLar SSta
santapaui (V)	GGGa
§ 'Saotome' (EA)	SLdr
'Sappho'	CAco CBcs CMac GGGa GKin LMil LRHS NEgg NLar SLdr SPer SSta
sargentianum	GGGa WAbe WThu
- 'Whitebait'	ITim
(Sarled Group) 'Sarled' ♀H5	GGGa ITim LMil WThu
'Satan' (K) ♀H6	CKel LMil LRHS NLar SPer SSta
Satsuki Group (EA)	ITim SLdr
- 'Gumpo Pink' (EA)	SLdr
- 'Gumpo Pink & White' (EA)	SLdr
- 'Gumpo White' (EA)	LRHS MAsh NRHS SPoG
'Saturnus' (M)	GKin
saxifragoides (V) new	CRos LRHS
§ ***scabrifolium*** var. ***spiciferum***	CMac SLdr
'Scarlet Wonder' ♀H6	CBcs CDul CRos CSBt EPfP GEdr GKev GKin LMil LRHS MAsh MGos MJak MMuc NHpl NPri SPer WFar
schlippenbachii (A)	CBcs CMCN GGGa LMil SLdr
'Schneekrone' ♀H6	GGGa IDee LMil LRHS
SCHNEEPERLE ('Hachschnee') (EA) ♀H5	LMil LRHS NRHS
scintillans	see *R. polycladum* Scintillans Group
'Scintillation' ♀H6	ELan GGGa LMil MAsh MGos MMuc NLar SLdr SPer
scopulorum	GGGa SLdr
'Scout' (EA)	MAsh SLdr
scyphocalyx	see *R. dichroanthum* subsp. *scyphocalyx*
'Seaview Sunset'	GGGa MGos
seinghkuense	GGGa LMil
- CCH&H 8106	LMil
semnoides	LMil
'Sennocke'	LMil
'September Red'	LMil
'September Song' ♀H4	GGGa LMil MAsh NHol
serotinum	GGGa LMil LRHS
serpyllifolium (A)	CBcs CTsd
'Shamrock' ♀H6	ELon EPfP GEdr LRHS MAsh MGos NEgg NSla SLim SPoG WFar WThu
'Sheila' (EA)	CSBt MAsh NPri
'Shelley' (EA)	LMil LSRN
sherriffii	GGGa
'Shiko' (EA)	MAsh
'Shiko Lavender' (A)	LMil SPoG
Shilsonii Group	LMil
'Shin-sekai' (Kurume) (EA/d)	SLdr
sidereum	GCal GGGa
siderophyllum	GGGa
sikangense	GGGa
- var. ***exquisitum***	GGGa
§ 'Silberwolke' ♀H6	IDee LMil MAsh WFar
SILVER CLOUD	see *R.* 'Silberwolke'
'Silver Edge'	see *R. ponticum* 'Variegatum'
'Silver Glow' (EA)	CMac
'Silver Jubilee' ♀H4	LMil
'Silver Moon' (Glenn Dale) (EA)	SLdr
'Silver Queen' (EA)	CKel MPkF SPoG
'Silver Sixpence'	EPfP LRHS LSRN MJak MMuc SLdr
'Silver Skies'	LMil
'Silver Slipper' (K) ♀H5	CBcs GKin LCro LMil LOPS NHol SSta WFar
'Silver Sword' (EA/v)	CKel EPfP SPoG
'Silvester' (Kurume) (EA)	CTri LMil LRHS MAsh SLdr
simsii (EA)	CMac SLdr
sinofalconeri	GGGa LMil
- KR 7342	LMil
- SEH 229	LMil
sinogrande ♀H4	ELon GCal GGGa GKev GKin IDee LMil LRHS NEgg
- KR 4027	LMil
§ 'Sir Charles Butler'	LMil
'Sir Charles Lemon' ♀H4	CBcs GGGa LMil LRHS MAsh

	'Sir Robert' (EA)	MAsh
	'Sleeping Beauty'	WAbe
	'Sleepy'	CBcs MAsh NHol
	smirnowii	GGGa LMil LRHS
	smithii	see *R. argipeplum*
	'Sneezy' 🏆H5	CBcs EPfP GGGa LCro LMil LOPS LRHS MAsh MGos MJak MMuc MPkF SLdr SLim SSta
	'Snipe'	CTri GEdr LMil LRHS MAsh MGos MMuc NLar NRHS SLdr SLim SPer WThu
	'Snow Crown' (*lindleyi* hybrid)	MAsh
	'Snow Hill' (EA) 🏆H5	CEnd LMil
	'Snow Lady'	CBcs CTsd EPfP GEdr GKin MAsh SLdr
	'Snow Pearl'	EPfP MAsh NPri
	Snow Queen Group	LMil
	- 'Snow Queen'	LMil
	'Snowbird' (A)	CBcs CDul CTho
	'Snowflake' (EA/d)	see *R.* 'Kure-no-yuki'
	'Snowwhite' (EA)	CRos MGos NLar SLdr
	'Soir de Paris' (Vs) 🏆H6	CEnd CSBt GGGa GKin LMil NHol SSta WFar
	(Solent Group) 'Drury Lane' (K)	LMil
	'Solidarity'	CAco CBcs SLdr SSta
	'Solway' (Vs)	LMil
	'Sonata'	GGGa
	'Sonatine'	IDee LMil LRHS
	'Songbird'	GEdr LMil LRHS SLdr
	sororium (V)	LMil
	- KR 3085	LMil
	souliei	LMil
	- deep pink-flowered	GGGa
	'Souvenir de D.A. Koster'	SLdr
	'Souvenir of Anthony Waterer'	SSta
	'Souvenir of W.C. Slocock'	MMuc NLar
	'Spek's Orange' (M)	GKin
	sphaeranthum	see *R. trichostomum*
	sphaeroblastum	GGGa
	- var. ***wumengense***	GGGa
	spiciferum	see *R. scabrifolium* var. *spiciferum*
	'Spinner's Glory'	MAsh
	spinuliferum	GGGa
	'Spitfire'	NHol SSta
	'Spring Morning'	SSta
	'Spring Pearl'	see *R.* 'Moerheim's Pink'
	'Spring Rose'	SLdr
	'Spring Sunshine'	LMil
	'Squirrel' (EA) 🏆H5	CRos GGGa GKin LMil LRHS MAsh NLar SLdr SLim
	'Stadt Essen'	IDee LMil LRHS SLdr
	stamineum	GGGa
§	'Stanway'	LMil
	'Starbright Champagne'	MAsh SSta
	'Statuette'	SAko
	stenaulum	see *R. moulmainense*
§	***stenopetalum***	CBcs CMac GBin LMil LRHS MPkF
	'Linearifolium' (EA)	SLdr
	stenophyllum	see *R. makinoi*
	stewartianum	GGGa
	'Stewartstonian' (EA)	CMac LCro LOPS
	'Stoat' (EA)	NLar
	'Stopham Girl' (A)	LMil
	'Stopham Lad' (A)	LMil
	'Strategist'	SLdr
	'Strawberry Cream'	EPfP GGGa LRHS
	'Strawberry Ice' (K) 🏆H6	CBcs CSBt ELan GGGa GKin MMrt
	'Strawberry Sundae'	MMuc NEgg SLdr
	strigillosum	GGGa
	subansiriense	GGGa
	suberosum	see *R. yunnanense* Suberosum Group
	'Suga-no-ito' (Kurume) (EA)	SLdr
	'Summer Blaze' (A)	SLdr
	'Summer Dawn'	LMil
	'Summer Fragrance' (A) 🏆H6	LMil SSta
	'Summer Snow'	SAko
	'Summer Sorbet'	LMil
	'Summer Wind'	GGGa
	'Sun Chariot' (K)	CBcs
	'Sun Star' (EA)	GGGa LMil
	Sunkist Group	SLdr
	'Sunspray'	SSta
	'Sunte Nectarine' (K) 🏆H6	GKin MPkF NLar
	suoilenhensis	CMCN
	- NVD 18	GGGa
	'Surprise' ambig. (EA)	CTri SLdr
	'Surprise' B.Y. Morrison (EA)	LMil
	'Surrey Heath'	CBcs EPfP LMil LRHS MGos MJak MMuc SLdr SLim SPer
	'Susan' (EA)	NLar SSta
	'Susan' J.C. Williams	LMil
	'Susannah Hill' (EA)	SLdr
	sutchuenense	GGGa LMil
	- var. ***geraldii***	see *R.* × *geraldii*
	'Swamp Beauty'	MMuc
	'Swansong' (EA)	CMac
	'Swift' 🏆H4	EPfP GEdr GGGa LMil LRHS MAsh MMuc NRHS SLdr
	'T.S. Black' (EA)	SLdr
	taggianum	GGGa
	'Talavera'	LMil
	taliense	LMil
	- SBEC 0350	GGGa
	- 'Honigduft'	LMil NLar
	Tally Ho Group	LMil
	'Tamanini' (EA) **new**	MPkF
	'Tama-no-utena' (EA)	SLdr
	TANAGER	see *R.* 'Glendoick Tanager'
	'Tangerine'	see *R.* 'Fabia Tangerine'
	'Tapestry'[PBR] **new**	LMil SPer
	tapetiforme	GGGa
	'Taurus' 🏆H5	CAco CBcs CRos GKin IDee LMil LRHS MAsh MMuc SAko SLdr
	taxifolium (V)	GGGa
	'Teal'	GEdr
	'Ted Millais'	LMil
	'Teddy Bear'	LMil SSta
	Temple Belle Group	SLdr
§	***tephropeplum***	GGGa
	- Deleiense Group	see *R. tephropeplum*
	'Tequila Sunrise'	LRHS NLar
I	'Tequila Sunrise' USA	LMil
	'Terracotta'	LMil LRHS NLar
	'Terra-cotta Beauty' (EA)	NWad WThu
	(Tessa Group) 'Tessa'	CMac
	'Thai Gold' (V)	LRHS
	thayerianum	GGGa
§	'The Honourable Jean Marie de Montague' 🏆H4	CRos GGGa GKin LMil MAsh MGos MMuc NLar SPer SSta
	'The Marquis of Lansdowne'	LMil
	'Thomas David' (A)	LMil
	thomsonii	GGGa LMil
	- B&SWJ 2638	WCru
	- WJC 13737 **new**	WCru
	- subsp. ***lopsangianum***	GGGa
	'Thor'	GGGa

	Name	Suppliers
	'Tibet'	LMil
	'Tidbit' ♀H3	CMac GGGa LMil SLdr
	'Tinkerbird'	EPfP GGGa LMil MAsh MGos NLar NPri
	'Tinner's Blush'	CBcs
	titapuriense	GGGa
	'Titian Beauty'	CBcs CSBt ELan EPfP GGGa LMil LRHS MAsh MGos MMuc NEgg NLar NRHS SAko SLdr SLim SPer SPoG
	'Titness Park'	LMil
	'Tit-Willow' (EA)	LRHS MAsh NRHS SCoo SLdr
	tomentosum	WThu
	'Too Bee'	GEdr
	'Torchlight' (EA) ♀H5	LMil MGos
	'Toreador' (EA)	SLdr
	'Torridon' (Vs)	LMil
	Tortoiseshell Group	NLar SCob
	- 'Champagne' ♀H3	CBcs CSBt LMil MAsh NLar NPri SPer
	- 'Tortoiseshell Orange' ♀H3	CBcs CDul CRos CSBt LMil LRHS MGos NLar SCob SLim SPer SSta
	- 'Tortoiseshell Wonder' ♀H3	EPfP LRHS MAsh
	'Toucan' (K)	CSBt LMil LRHS MPkF
	'Tower Beauty' (A)	LMil
	'Tower Dainty' (A)	GGGa LMil
	'Tower Daring' (A)	GGGa
	'Tower Dexter' (A)	LMil
	'Tower Dragon' (A)	LMil
	traillianum	GKev LMil
	'Tree Creeper'	GGGa LMil LRHS
	'Trewithen Orange'	SLdr
	trichanthum	GGGa
	- 'Honey Wood'	LMil SLdr
	trichocladum	GKev
§	***trichostomum***	GGGa WAbe
	- Ledoides Group	LMil
	triflorum	GGGa LMil
§	- var. ***bauhiniiflorum***	CMac
	trilectorum	GGGa
	'Tri-Lights' (A) **new**	MPkF
	triplonaevium	see *R. alutaceum* var. *russotinctum* Triplonaevium Group
	'Tromba'	GGGa IDee LMil LRHS SAko
	'Tropic Glow' (V) **new**	LRHS
	tsariense	GGGa LMil
	- var. ***trimoense***	LMil
	- - KW 8288	LMil
	tubiforme	see *R. glaucophyllum* subsp. *tubiforme*
	'Tuffet' (EA)	LMil SLdr
	'Tunis' (K)	EPfP MAsh NPri
	'Turnstone'	GGGa
	'Umpqua Queen' (K)	MPkF
	ungernii	GGGa
§	***uniflorum*** var. ***imperator***	GGGa
	'Unique' (G)	CBcs EPfP GGGa MMuc SPer
	'Unique' (*campylocarpum* hybrid)	MAsh SLdr
	uvariifolium SDR 5149	GKev
	- 'Reginald Childs'	LMil
	valentinianum	GGGa SLdr
	- var. ***oblongilobatum***	GGGa
	'Van'	LMil LRHS MGos NLar SLim
	'Van Nes Sensation'	LMil
	Vanessa Group	LMil
	- 'Vanessa Pastel' ♀H4	CMac GGGa LMil SLdr SSta
	vaseyi (A) ♀H5	CBcs GGGa LMil
	- 'White Find'	GGGa
	- white-flowered (A)	LMil
	'Vayo' (EA)	SLdr
§	***veitchianum*** Cubittii Group	CBcs GGGa
	- 'Doi Inthanon'	GGGa
	venator	GGGa
	'Venetia' (K)	SSta
	vernicosum	GGGa
	vernicosum* × *wardii SDR 5026	GKev
	'Veryan Bay'	LMil
	'Vida Brown' (Kurume) (EA/d)	CMac SLdr
	'Vinecourt Dream' (M)	GKin NLar SLdr
	'Vinecourt Duke' (A/d)	GKin MMuc NEgg NLar
	'Vineland Dream' (K/d)	GKin
	'Vintage Rosé' ♀H5	LMil MMuc SSta
	'Violetta' (Glenn Dale) (EA)	SLdr
	'Violette Funken'	LMil
	'Virginia Richards'	MAsh SCob SLdr
	viridescens 'Doshong La'	GGGa LMil
§	- Rubroluteum Group	SLdr
	viscidifolium	GGGa
	viscosum (A) ♀H6	CBcs CMac CTho GGGa LMil LRHS MGos MMrt MMuc NLar SLdr SPer
	- 'Grey Leaf' (Vs)	LMil
	- f. ***rhodanthum*** (A)	LMil
	- 'Roseum' (Vs)	LMil
	'Viscount Powerscourt'	SLdr
	'Viscy' ♀H5	CDul CRos GKin IDee LMil LRHS MMuc SLdr
§	Volker Group	EPfP IDee LMil LRHS NLar NRHS
§	- 'Babette'	LMil
	'Vollblut'	SSta
	'Vulcan' ♀H4	GGGa IDee LMil LRHS SCob
	'Vuyk's Rosyred' (Vuykiana) (EA) ♀H6	CBcs CDul CMac CTri GKin LMil MAsh NHol NWad SLdr SPer SPoG WFar
	'Vuyk's Scarlet' (Vuykiana) (EA) ♀H6	CBcs CDul CMac CSBt CTri CTsd GKin LRHS MAsh NHol NPri NRHS NWad SLdr SPer SPlb SSta
	'W.F.H.' ♀H3	LMil SLdr
	WALKÜRE ('Hachwalk')	IDee LMil LRHS
	wallichii	GGGa GKev LMil
	'Wallowa Red' (A)	CKel MMuc MPkF
	'Wally Miller'	MAsh
	'Walter's Pinwheel' (EA)	GGGa
	'Wanna Bee'	LMil
	wardii	GGGa LMil LRHS
	- L&S 5679	GGGa
	- var. ***puralbum***	GGGa
	'Ward's Ruby' (EA)	SLdr
	wasonii	LMil
	- yellow-flowered	GGGa
	'Water Baby' (A)	LMil
	'Water Girl' (A)	GGGa LMil
	'Water Pixie' **new**	LMil
	'Waterfall'	SLdr
	'Wee Bee' ♀H5	CBcs EPfP GEdr GKin LMil LRHS MAsh MGos MJak NLar SAko SLim SSta WThu
§	Wega Group	SLdr
	'Weinlese'	SAko
	'Wendy'	MAsh
	'Western Lights' (A)	LRHS MPkF
	'Westminster' (O)	LMil
	'Weston's Innocence' (A)	MPkF
	'Weston's Lollipop' (A) **new**	MPkF
	'Weston's Pink Diamond' (d)	LMil
	'What a Dane'	GGGa
	'Whidbey Island'	LMil

'Whisperingrose'	LMil
'White Brocade'	SSta
§ WHITE DUFTHECKE ('Rhodunter 48'PBR)	LMil
'White Frills' (EA)	LRHS MPkF SLdr
'White Gold'	GGGa
'White Jade' (EA)	SLdr
'White Lady' Indian (EA)	SLdr
'White Lights' (A) ♀H7	CTri
'White Pearl' (EA)	LSRN
'White Perfume' (A)	SSta
'White Prince' (EA/d)	MPkF
'White Rosebud' (EA)	CKel SSta
'White Swan' (hybrid)	LMil
'White Wings'	SLdr
'Whitestone'	GGGa SSta
'Whitethroat' (K/d) ♀H6	EPfP LMil LRHS MMrt MMuc SSta
'Whitney's Dwarf Red'	MMuc
'Whitney's Orange'	SLdr
'Wigeon'	LMil
wightii	GGGa
'Wild Ginger'	GGGa
'Wilgen's Ruby'	CSBt MGos SLdr SLim SPer
'Wilgen's Surprise'	SCob
'Willbrit'	CBcs MAsh MMuc SLdr
'William Fortescue'	LMil
williamsianum ♀H5	CBcs GGGa LMil SLdr
- Caerhays form	CExl
- white-flowered **new**	CBcs
'Willy' (Kaempferi) (EA)	LMil SLdr
wiltonii ♀H5	GGGa LMil
'Wine and Roses'PBR	CBcs GGGa
Winsome Group	CMac GGGa MAsh
- 'Winsome' ♀H3	CBcs GKin MGos NLar NPri SLdr SSta
'Winston Churchill' (M)	SSta
'Witchery'	GGGa
'Wombat' (EA) ♀H5	CTri EPfP GGGa LMil LRHS MAsh MGos NLar NPri SLdr
wongii	CMac GGGa
'Woodcock'	SLdr
'Wren' ♀H5	GEdr GGGa GKev LMil MAsh WThu
xanthocodon	see *R. cinnabarinum* subsp. *xanthocodon*
xanthostephanum	GGGa
'XXL'	LRHS SSta
'Yaku Angel'	LMil SAko
'Yaku Incense'	LMil MAsh MMuc
'Yaku Prince'	MAsh MMuc SLdr
yakushimanum ♀H5	GKin LMil MAsh NHol SArc SLdr SPer SSta
- from Exbury	CMac
- FCC form	see *R. yakushimanum* 'Koichiro Wada'
§ - 'Koichiro Wada' ♀H6	CBcs CExl CMac CRos ELan GGGa IDee LMil LRHS NLar SAko SLdr
- 'Schneekissen'	SAko
yaoshanense	GGGa
'Yellow Hammer' ♀H5	CAco CBcs CDul CMac ELan GGGa GKin NLar SLdr
Yellow Hammer Group	SPer SSta
'Yellow Petticoats'	SSta
yuefengense	GGGa LMil
yunnanense	GGGa GKev LMil
- 'Openwood' ♀H3	LMil
- pink-flowered	GGGa
- 'Red Throat'	SLdr
- red-blotched	LMil
§ - Suberosum Group	SLdr
- white-flowered	GGGa
zaleucum	GGGa LMil SLdr
- Flaviflorum Group	GGGa
zeylanicum	see *R. arboreum* subsp. *zeylanicum*

Rhodohypoxis ✿ (*Hypoxidaceae*)

'1000 Cranes'	IBal LEdu
'Andromeda'	EWes IBal
'Ann Brazier'	NWad
baurii ♀H3	CAvo CCCN IBal MAsh NBir NSla SPoG WAbe WAvo WIce
- 'Alba'	CRos EWes IBal LRHS NRHS WFar
- 'Albrighton'	CTri EWes GEdr NBir NHol NHpl NWad WAbe
- 'Apple Blossom'	EWes GKev IBal ITim LBee LEdu NHol NWad SRot WFar
- 'Badger'	ITim NWad WAbe
- var. ***baurii***	EWes LRHS
- 'Bridal Bouquet' (d)	EWes GEdr IBal NHol WFar
- 'Caro'	EWes
- 'Charlotte'	EWes
- 'Coconut Ice'	EWes LEdu
- var. ***confecta***	CElw EWes GEdr IBal NHol NWad WFar WTor
- 'Daphne Mary'	EWes
- 'David Scott'	EWes
- 'Dawn'	CAby CPla EWes GEdr GKev IBal NAln SDys WAbe
- 'Douglas'	EPfP EWes GEdr GKev IBal LEdu NBir NHol NHpl NWad WAvo WPGP
- 'Dulcie'	EWes GEdr IBal WAbe
- 'Emily Peel'	EWes GKev IBal ITim
- 'Eva-Kate'	EWes IBal ITim
- 'Fred Broome'	CRos EWes GEdr GKev IBal LEdu NHol NWad WFar
- 'Goliath'	EWes IBal
- 'Harlequin'	CAby EWes GEdr IBal ITim NHol NWad SRot
§ - 'Helen'	EPot EWes GEdr GKev IBal LEdu NHol NHpl NWad WAbe WPGP
- 'Jeanette'	EWes IBal
- 'Kitty'	EWes IBal WFar
- 'Lily Jean' (d)	CAby CPla CRos CTri EPfP EWes GEdr GKev IBal ITim LRHS NHpl NWad WFar XEll
- 'Luna'	EWes
- 'Margaret Rose'	EWes IBal NHol
- 'Mars'	CRos EWes GKev IBal LEdu LRHS NBir NHol NRHS WFar WPGP
- 'Monique'	EWes
- 'Pearl'	LRHS
- 'Perle'	EWes GEdr IBal LRHS NHol NWad
- 'Picta' (v)	EWes GKev IBal LEdu NHol NHpl NWad WAbe
- 'Pink Pearl'	EWes IBal NHol
- var. ***platypetala***	CWCL EPfP EWes GEdr GKev IBal NHol NHpl NWad WAvo XEll
- - Burtt 6981	EWes
- var. ***platypetala*** × ***milloides***	IBal LLHF NHol NWad
- 'Rebecca'	EWes
- 'Red King'	EWes IBal
- red-flowered	LRHS SPlb
- 'Ruth'	ELon EWes GEdr GKev IBal NHol SDeJ WFar
- 'Susan Garnett-Botfield'	CRos EWes GEdr IBal LRHS NHpl
- 'Tetra Pink'	CAby EWes GEdr IBal NHol NWad
- 'Tetra Red'	EWes GEdr GKev IBal NHol NWad SDeJ SRot WFar
- 'The Bride'	EWes GEdr

– white-flowered	LRHS
baurii* × *milloides	SRot
'Betsy Carmine'	CCCN GEdr IBal NWad WFar
'Bright Eyes' (d)	EWes
'Burgundy'	IBal
'Butterfly Wings'	NWad
'Candy Stripe'	EWes GEdr NWad
'Carina'	EWes
'Caroline'	EWes IBal WFar
'Cathy'	EWes IBal
'Confusion'	EWes LEdu NHol NHpl NWad
'Dainty Dee' (d)	EWes
deflexa	CRos EPot EWes GKev IBal ITim LEdu LRHS NHol NHpl NRHS NSla NWad WAbe WFar WPGP WTor
'Donald Mann'	EWes GEdr IBal ITim LLHF NHol SRot
'Dusky'	EWes GEdr GKev IBal NWad
'E.A. Bowles'	EWes IBal NHpl NRHS NSla WFar
'Ellicks'	IBal
'Flashing Ruby'	GEdr
'Forge Robies'	EWes
'Garnett'	EWes NWad WFar
'Gemma'	EWes
'Goya' (d)	CAby NHpl
'Great Scot'	EWes GEdr GKev IBal NHpl NWad WAbe
'Hebron Farm Biscuit'	see *Hypoxis parvula* var. *albiflora* 'Hebron Farm Biscuit'
'Hebron Farm Cerise'	see × *Rhodoxis* 'Hebron Farm Cerise'
'Hebron Farm Pink'	see × *Rhodoxis hybrida* 'Hebron Farm Pink'
'Hinky Pinky'	GEdr NWad
'Holden Rose' (d)	IBal NHol NWad WFar
'Hope' (d)	IBal
'Indy'	IBal
'Jupiter'	GEdr NWad
'Kiwi Joy' (d)	CRos EWes GEdr GKev IBal LLHF NHol NHpl NWad SDeJ
'Knockdolian Red'	GEdr IBal NHol NWad WFar
'Lisette'	EWes
'Louise'	IBal
'Midori'	EWes GEdr IBal NWad SDys WFar
milloides	CAby CPla CRos EWes GEdr GKev IBal ITim LBee LEdu LRHS NHol NHpl NRHS NWad WAbe WFar WPGP XEll
– 'Claret'	CAby CElw CRos CSam ELon EPot EWes GEdr GKev IBal ITim LLHF LRHS NHol SDys SRot WAbe WFar WTor
– 'Claudia'	CRos EMor GWyn NRHS
– 'Damask'	CRos EWes GKev IBal LRHS SDys SRot
– 'Donaldson'	SRot
– 'Drakensberg Snow'	EWes
– giant	WFar
– 'Susan'	EWes
'Monty'	EWes GEdr IBal NWad WAbe
'Mystery'	EWes IBal NHol
'Naomi'	EWes
'New Look'	EWes GEdr IBal LLHF NHpl NWad
'Ori Zuru'	GEdr
'Origami'	IBal LEdu
'Pat Lacey'	EWes IBal
'Paula'	IBal
'Pink Ice'	GEdr IBal NBir NWad
'Pink Star'	LRHS
'Pinkeen'	EWes LLHF
'Pinkie'	IBal SDys WFar
'Pintado'	CAby CRos EWes GEdr GKev IBal LEdu LRHS NRHS NWad SDys WFar
'Raspberry Ice'	IBal NHol NWad WFar
'Rosalie'	IBal
'Rosie Lee'	EWes
'Ruby Giant'	GEdr LRHS WFar
'Shell Pink'	EWes IBal NHol NWad
Slack Top hybrids	NSla
'Snow'	EWes
'Snow White'	EWes NHol
'Starlett'	EWes NHol
'Starry Eyes' (d)	EWes IBal WFar
'Stella'	CCCN CRos EPot EWes GEdr GKev IBal LRHS NHol NHpl NWad SDys WFar
'Sunburst'	GEdr NWad
'Telios'	IBal
'Tetra Rose'	GEdr
'Tetra White'	see *R. baurii* 'Helen'
thodiana	EWes GEdr IBal NHol NHpl NWad WAbe WFar
TWINKLE STAR MIXED	LRHS
'Two Tone'	EWes
'Venetia'	CMea GKev IBal NHol NWad
'Westacre Picotee'	EWes
'Wild Cherry Blossom'	EWes IBal

Rhodohypoxis × *Hypoxis*

R. baurii* × *H. parvula	see × *Rhodoxis hybrida*

Rhodoleia (*Hamamelidaceae*)

championii B&SWJ 11603	WCru
– FMWJ 13155	WCru
– WWJ 11858	WCru
aff. ***henryi*** B&SWJ 11782	WCru
– DJHV 0640	WCru
parvipetala FMWJ 13422	WCru
– WWJ 11866	WCru
– WWJ 11943	WCru

Rhodophiala (*Amaryllidaceae*)

rosea	GKev

Rhodora see *Rhododendron*

Rhodotypos (*Rosaceae*)

kerrioides	see *R. scandens*
§ ***scandens***	CExl CRos EBee ELan EPfP GBin IDee LEdu LRHS MGil MMrt MMuc MNrw NHol NLar NQui SBrt SEND SLon SPoG WAvo WCru

× *Rhodoxis* ✿ (*Hypoxidaceae*)

'Abigail'	EWes IBal WFar
'Anne Crock'	EWes IBal
'Aurora'	EWes IBal WFar
'Betsy'	CPBP EWes
'Bloodstone'	EWes IBal NHol NWad
FAIRYTALE ('Hil200802'PBR)	SPad
'Fanny'	EWes
'Hebron Farm Biscuit'	see *Hypoxis parvula* var. *albiflora* 'Hebron Farm Biscuit'
§ 'Hebron Farm Cerise'	CCCN CElw CRos EWes GEdr GKev IBal LEdu LRHS NRHS SDys SRot WFar
'Hebron Farm Rose'	IBal LLHF
§ ***hybrida***	EWes
– 'Aya San'	EWes GKev IBal LRHS WFar

- FAIRY KISSES ('Im201208') new — SPad
§ - 'Hebron Farm Pink' — CAby CElw CPla CRos EWes GEdr GKev IBal LRHS NHol SRot WFar
- 'Hebron Farm Red Eye' — CCCN EWes GKev IBal
- 'Pink Stars' — IBal
- 'Ruby Giant' — EWes GEdr IBal
- 'White Stars' — EWes
'Jenny' — EWes
'Little Pink Pet' — EWes IBal WFar
'Otterlo Ruby' — EWes GKev WFar
'Pink Glow' — IBal
'Pink Tips' — IBal
'Red Flyer' — EWes IBal
'Ria' — EWes
'Sandra' — EWes
'Sandy' — EWes GKev
'Sonja' — GKev
'Sue' — EWes WFar
'Summer Pink' — IBal
(Summer Stars Series) — IBal
'Summer Stars Candy' new
- 'Summer Stars Peppermint' new — IBal WFar
- 'Summer Stars Pink Blush' new — IBal
- 'Summer Stars Pinky' new — IBal
- 'Summer Stars Ruby' new — IBal

Rhoeo see *Tradescantia*

Rhoicissus (*Vitaceae*)

digitata — EShb

Rhombophyllum (*Aizoaceae*)

dolabriforme new — SSim

Rhopalostylis (*Arecaceae*)

sapida — CBrP

rhubarb see *Rheum × hybridum*; also AGM Vegetables Section

Rhus (*Anacardiaceae*)

ambigua — see *Toxicodendron orientale*
aromatica — CAgr CDul EBtc MMrt NLar
chinensis — CMCN IDee
copallinum — EBtc
coriaria — NLar
cotinus — see *Cotinus coggygria*
glabra — CBcs EBtc EPfP SPer
hirta — see *R. typhina*
incisa — SPlb
potaninii — EBee EPfP NLar WPGP
× ***pulvinata*** (Autumn Lace Group) 'Red Autumn Lace' ♀H5 — MBlu MRav SPer
radicans — see *Toxicodendron radicans*
succedanea — see *Toxicodendron succedaneum*
toxicodendron — see *Toxicodendron radicans*
typhina — CAgr CBcs CDul CLnd CMac ELan EMOT EPfP GKin LCro LMaj LOPS MAsh MGos MMuc NEgg NHol NLar NWea SCob SEND SGol SLim SPer SSta WFar
§ - 'Dissecta' ♀H6 — CBar CBcs CDul CLnd ELan EPfP EUJe LMaj MGos MJak MMuc MRav NEgg NLar NWea SArc SCob SEND SGol SLim SPer WFar
- 'Laciniata' hort. — see *R. typhina* 'Dissecta'
- RADIANCE ('Sinrus') ♀H6 — CRos LRHS MAsh MBlu NLar SPoG
- TIGER EYES ('Bailtiger'PBR) ♀H6 — ELan EPfP EUJe MAsh MGos SCob SGol SMad SWvt
verniciflua — see *Toxicodendron vernicifluum*

Rhynchospora (*Cyperaceae*)

colorata — LLWG LRHS MPkF NPer SBrt
latifolia — CKno

Ribes ✿ (*Grossulariaceae*)

alpinum — CExl EPfP MRav MWht NWea SPer SRms WSpi
- 'Aureum' — EHoe NEgg
americanum 'Variegatum' (v) — NWad
aureum misapplied — see *R. odoratum*
aureum ambig. — CAgr NWea
§ × ***beatonii*** — CDul CExl CKel CSBt CSde CWld EBee ECrN EShb LEdu LRHS MMuc NLar SBrt SGol SLim SPer SPoG SRms WAvo WCot WFar
'Ben Hope'PBR (B) — CAgr CSBt EPom NPri SCoo SWvt
'Black Velvet' (D) — CAgr MCoo
californicum — SBrt
cereum — GEdr SBrt
× ***culverwellii*** (F) — CAgr CCCN CTri EPom LBuc LCro LEdu LOPS NLar NWea SDea SVic SWvt WMat
divaricatum — CAgr LEdu
gayanum — LEdu NLar
glaciale PAB 3004 — LEdu
× ***gordonianum*** — see *R. × beatonii*
griffithii — CBod WCot
- GWJ 9331 — WCru
- PAB 4871 — LEdu
jostaberry — see *R. × nidigrolaria*
laurifolium — CBcs CDul CEnd CExl CRos CTri EBee ELan EWes IDee LRHS MMuc MRav NLar SChF SCob SMad SPer WCFE WFar
- (f) — CMac EPfP SBrt SRms
- (m) — EPfP SBrt
- 'Mrs Amy Doncaster' — CBcs CMac CRos EBee LEdu LRHS NLar NRHS SEle SPoG SRms WBor WCot WGob WPGP WSpi
- Rosemoor form — EPfP LRHS NLar SPoG WCot
longeracemosum — GGGa SBrt
menziesii — CHll EWes NQui WCot
nevadense new — SBrt
§ × ***nidigrolaria*** (F) — LBuc
nigrum (B) PAB 3755 — LEdu
- 'Baldwin' (B) — CFGn CTri EPfP MAsh NLar SDea SLim SPer SSFr WMat
- 'Barchatnaja' (B) — CAgr
- 'Ben Alder' (B) — CAgr EPom LRHS SCoo SDea
- 'Ben Connan'PBR (B) ♀H6 — Widely available
- 'Ben Gairn'PBR (B) — CAgr MCoo MMuc
- 'Ben Lomond'PBR (B) — CAgr CFGn CSBt CTri EMOT EPfP LBuc LSRN MAsh MGos MJak MNHC MRav NEgg NLar NPri NWea SDea SKee SPer SPoG SRms SSFr SVic WMat
- 'Ben More' (B) — CAgr NPri
- 'Ben Nevis' (B) — CAgr CTri EMOT SDea SKee SPer
- 'Ben Sarek' (B) — Widely available
- 'Ben Tirran' (B) — CAgr CSBt EPom LBuc LRHS LSRN MAsh MGos NLar NPri SCoo SDea SRms SWvt WMat

- 'Big Ben'PBR (B) ♀H6 CArg CFGn CRos EHyd EPfP EPom LBuc LCro LOPS LRHS LSRN MNHC NRHS SKee SPer SPoG WMat
- 'Black Reward' (B) CAgr
- 'Boskoop Giant' (B) CAgr ELan NEgg SLim
- 'Byelorussian Sweet' (B) CAgr
- 'Cassis Blanc' (B) CAgr
- 'Ebony' (B) CArg CMac CRos EPom LRHS NPri NRHS SVic
- 'Hystawneznaya' (B) CAgr LEdu
- 'Jet' (B) CAgr NEgg
- 'Kosmicheskaya' (B) CAgr
- 'Pilot Alexander Mamkin' (B) CAgr
- 'Polar' (B) CAgr
- 'Seabrook's' (B) CAgr
- 'Titania' (B) CPer EMOT LRHS MCoo NLar WMat
- 'Vertti' (B) CAgr
- 'Wellington XXX' (B) CAgr EMOT LBuc LEdu NWea SSFr

§ ***odoratum*** CBcs CDul CKel CMac CRos CSBt CTho EBee ECrN ELan ELon EPfP LRHS MGos MMuc MNrw MRav NLar NWea SCob SPer SPoG SRms
- 'Black Pearl' SVic
- 'Crandall' CAgr LEdu

orientale PAB 7066 LEdu

'Pink Perfection' CMCN

praecox CBcs MMuc SEND

rubrum 'Blanka' (W) CAgr CArg CMac CPer
- 'Cascade' (R) CAgr
- 'Cherry' (R) CAgr
- 'Gloire de Sablons' (P) EPom SPer
- 'Jonkheer van Tets' (R) ♀H6 CAgr CRos CSBt EMOT EPfP EPom GQue IArd LRHS LSRN MAsh MCoo NLar NPri NRHS NWea SDea SEND SKee SLim SPer SRms SSFr WMat
- 'Junifer' (R) CAgr CRos EPom LEdu LRHS NRHS SKee
- 'Laxton's Number One' (R) CAgr CFGn CTri EPfP EPom LCro LEdu LOPS LRHS LSRN MNHC NLar NWea SDea SLim SPer SPoG SRms SSFr WMat
- 'Lisette' (R) LRHS
- 'Red Lake' (R) ♀H6 CAgr CFGn CTri ECrN ELan EPfP EPom LBuc LEdu MGos MJak NEgg NLar NPri SDea SGol SKee SPer SPoG SSFr WMat
- 'Redstart' (R) CAgr CFGn CTri LBuc MAsh MMuc SKee WMat
- 'Rolan' (R) CAgr EMOT
- 'Rondom' (R) CAgr CPer SDea SVic
- ROSA SPORT (P) **new** LRHS
- 'Rosetta' (R) CAgr
- 'Rotet' LEdu
- 'Rovada' (R) CAgr CArg CFGn CMac CRos CSBt EMOT EPom LBuc LEdu LRHS LSRN MAsh NLar NPri NRHS SDea SKee SPoG SVic WMat
- 'Roxby Red' (R) LEdu
- 'Stanza' (R) ♀H6 CAgr EMOT SDea SEND

§ - 'Versailles Blanche' (W/C) CAgr CFGn CRos CSBt CTri EPfP EPom GQue LBuc LCro LOPS LRHS LSRN MGos MJak MMuc NPri NRHS SDea SKee SLim SPer SSFr WMat
- 'Weisse Langtraubige' (W) CAgr
- 'White Dutch' (W) EMOT
- 'White Grape' (W) ♀H6 CTri LEdu
- 'White Pearl' (W) ELan EMOT SDea SVic
- WHITE VERSAILLES see *R. rubrum* 'Versailles Blanche'

sanguineum CDul NEgg
- 'Brianjou' SRms
- 'Brocklebankii' CExl CMac EPfP MRav NLar SChF SCob SPer SRms WCFE WSHC
- 'Carneum' CRos LRHS NRHS
- 'Elkington's White' CDul CKel CRos ECrN EMil EPfP EWTr LBuc LCro LOPS LRHS LSRN MAsh MGos NLar NRHS NSti SCoo SLon SRms WBor WHlf WSpi
- 'King Edward VII' Widely available
- 'Koja' ♀H6 CBod CRos ELon EPfP GBin LEdu LRHS LSRN MAsh MGos MMuc NLar NRHS SCoo SEle SGol SPoG SRms WCot WFar
- 'Lombartsii' ♀H6 CRos EPfP LRHS MRav NRHS
- 'Pink Rain' LRHS
- 'Poky's Pink' ♀H6 CRos ECrN EWTr LLHF LRHS MAsh MRav SPoG SRms
- 'Pulborough Scarlet' Widely available
- 'Red Bross' CRos EPfP LRHS MAsh SWvt
- 'Red Pimpernel' CRos CSBt EPfP LRHS MAsh MBNS NRHS SRms SWvt WFar
- 'Somerset White' LRHS MAsh
- 'Tydeman's White' CExl CSBt ELan EPfP NLar NWea WSpi
- var. ***variegata*** CMac
- WHITE ICICLE ('Ubric') ♀H6 CBcs CRos CTri EBee ECtt EPfP EShb EWTr GBin LRHS MAsh MBlu MHer MRav MSwo NBir NLar NRHS SCob SPer SPoG SRms SWvt WCFE WCot WFar WMoo

speciosum ♀H4 CBcs CDul CEnd CKel CRos CTri EBee ELan ELon EPfP EWes GCal LRHS LSRN MGos MMuc MRav NLar NRHS SBrt SCob SEND SPer SPoG SWvt WAvo WBor WCFE WCot WFar

uva-crispa 'Annelii' (F) CAgr
- 'Captivator' (C) CFGn CMac CRos CSBt EMOT EPom LBuc LRHS MAsh MCoo MNHC NLar NRHS SDea SGol SKee SPoG WMat
- 'Careless' (C/D) ♀H6 CFGn CSBt CTri EPom LSRN MAsh MGos MJak SDea SPer WMat
- 'Early Sulphur' (D) CTri ELan SDea
- EASYCRISP LADY SUN (F) LRHS
- 'Greenfinch' (C) ♀H6 CAgr
- 'Hinnonmäki' (F) CAgr LBuc NPri SDea SPer
- 'Hinnonmäki Grön' (D) CAgr CMac CPer CSBt ECrN EMOT LRHS LSRN MAsh MRav NPri SDea SKee
- 'Hinnonmäki Gul' (D) CAgr CMac EPfP EPom LBuc LEdu LRHS MAsh MGos NRHS SDea SKee SPer SSFr SVic WMat
- 'Hinnonmäki Röd' (C/D) CAgr CFGn CMac CPer CRos ECrN EMOT EPfP EPom LBuc LCro LEdu LOPS LRHS LSRN MAsh MCoo MNHC MRav NLar NRHS SDea SKee SPer SPoG SSFr SVic WMat
- 'Howard's Lancer' (C/D) SDea
- 'Invicta' (C/D) ♀H6 Widely available
- 'Jubilee' (C/D) LBuc
- 'Jubilee Careless' (C/D) EPom
- 'Keepsake' (C/D) SDea
- 'Langley Gage' (D) MCoo
- 'Larell' (C/D) CAgr
- 'Leveller' (D) ♀H6 MCoo NWea SDea SPer
- 'London' (C/D) CTri NWea

– 'Martlet' (F)	MCoo SLim
– 'May Duke' (C/D)	SDea
– 'Mucurines' (D)	CAgr
– 'Pax' PBR (D)	CAgr SDea SLim SSFr SVic
– 'Pixwell' (C)	SGol
– 'Redeva' PBR (D)	CAgr
– 'Rokula' PBR (C/D)	ELan LRHS MCoo WMat
– 'Spinefree' (C)	CAgr
– 'Whinham's Industry' (C/D) ♀H6	LBuc LSRN MGos MMuc NEgg NPri SDea SEND SPer
– 'Whitesmith' (C/D)	CTri LSRN MCoo NWea SDea
– 'Xenia' (D)	CArg CFGn CRos EPfP EPom LEdu LRHS MCoo NRHS SPoG WMat
valdivianum	WCot WFar
viburnifolium	CBcs LRHS NLar SBrt SEND
'Worcesterberry' (C)	CHab IDee SDea

Richea (*Ericaceae*)

dracophylla	CBrP

Ricinus (*Euphorbiaceae*)

communis	CDTJ SPlb
– 'Carmencita' ♀H1c	NGBl SDys
– 'Carmencita Pink'	CDTJ
– 'Carmencita Red'	CDTJ
– 'Dominican Republic'	CDTJ
– 'Gibsonii'	CDTJ
– 'Impala'	CDTJ
– 'New Zealand Black'	CDTJ CSpe SDys
– 'Zanzibariensis' ♀H1c	CDTJ

Ridolfia (*Apiaceae*)

segetum	LRHS SPhx

Rigidella see *Tigridia*

orthantha	see *Tigridia orthantha*

Riocreuxia (*Apocynaceae*)

torulosa	CCCN SPlb

Robinia (*Papilionaceae*)

§	***hispida***	CDul CEnd CLnd ELan EMOT EPfP EWTr MBlu SPer
	– var. ***fertilis***	SBrt
	– var. ***kelseyi***	CDul EWes WSpi
	– 'Macrophylla'	CEnd
§	– var. ***rosea***	LSRN
	– 'Rosea' misapplied	see *R. hispida*, *R. hispida* var. *rosea*
	– 'Rosea' ambig.	CBcs EBee
	× ***margaretta*** CASQUE ROUGE	see *R.* × *margaretta* 'Pink Cascade'
§	– 'Pink Cascade'	CDul CEnd ELan EMOT EPfP LPra MAsh MGos NOra SCoo SEND SGol SPer WMat
	pseudoacacia	CAgr CCVT CDul CPer ELan EMOT LBuc LPra MCoo MMuc SCob SEND SGol SPlb
	– 'Bessoniana'	CDul ELan EMOT EPfP LPra
	– 'Fastigiata'	see *R. pseudoacacia* 'Pyramidalis'
	– 'Frisia'	CBcs CDul CEnd CTri EBee ECrN ELan EMOT EPfP LPra LRHS LSRN MGos MJak MRav MSwo NLar NOra NPri SCob SEND SGol SLim SPer WJas WMat WTSh
	– 'Inermis' hort.	see *R. pseudoacacia* 'Umbraculifera'
§	– 'Lace Lady' PBR	CSBt ECrN ELan EPfP LBuc LRHS MAsh MGos MJak NLar SCoo SPer SPoG WMat
	– 'Monophylla Fastigiata'	LPra
	– 'Myrtifolia'	SMad
§	– 'Pyramidalis'	LPra
	– 'Rozynskiana'	CDul
	– 'Tortuosa'	CEnd EBee EBtc LPra SPer
	– 'Twisty Baby'	see *R. pseudoacacia* 'Lace Lady'
§	– 'Umbraculifera'	CDul ECrN LMaj LPra LSRN SArc SCob
	× ***slavinii*** 'Hillieri' ♀H6	CDul CEnd EBee ELan EMOT EPfP EUJe LSRN MAsh MBlu NLar SLon SPer WSpi

Rochea see *Crassula*

Rodgersia ✿ (*Saxifragaceae*)

CLD 1432	CExl
aesculifolia ♀H6	Widely available
– SSSE 36	SMHy
– green bud	IBlr
– var. ***henrici***	CRos GCal GLog LRHS MRav NBro NHic NRHS SGbt SPer WBor WHoo WMoo
– – KW 21015	WCru
– – 'Cherry Blush'	EPfP GWyn SPad WFar
– – hybrid	ITim NLar XLum
– 'Red Dawn'	IBlr
– 'Red Leaf'	EWTr GCal WPnP
'Badenweiler'	CRos ECha LRHS NRHS
'Blickfang' ♀H7	CRos EBee IBlr LRHS MMrt NRHS
'Bloody Mary'	ECtt IMou MHol SCob WFar
'Borodin'	EBee
'Bronze Peacock'	CPla EBee ECtt EMor EUJe GBin LCro LLWG LOPS MHol MJak MPkF NAst NEoE NLar SCob SEle SHeu SMad SPad SPoG WTor
Cally strain	GCal
'Dark Pokers'	CBod EBee ECtt LRHS NLar SRms WFar
'Die Anmutige'	IMou
'Die Schöne'	EBee NLar
'Die Stolze'	IMou LEdu
'Elfenbeinturm'	IBlr
'Fascination'	IBlr
'Grande Blanche'	CRos NRHS
'Herkules'	EBee ECha ECtt ELon EUJe GBin GMaP GWyn LEdu LRHS MBNS MMuc NLar NQui NRHS WCot WPnP
'Irish Bronze' ♀H7	CAby CBod CRos ECtt ELan EMor EPfP EShb GPSL GQue LEdu LRHS LSRN MBel MWts NRHS SMad WMoo WPnP
'Koriata'	IBlr
'Kupfermond'	EBee IBlr NBir SMHy
'La Blanche'	EBee ECtt ELon LEdu LRHS MHol NAst NLar NRHS WPnP
'Maigrün'	IBlr
nepalensis	CRos EBee LEdu LRHS NRHS WPGP
– EMAK 713	IBlr
– HWJK 2140	WCru
– 'High Flier'	WCru
'Parasol'	CBro CMac CRos IBlr LRHS NBir NHol NRHS NWad WWtn
pinnata	CRos CTri EBee EHrv EPau EPfP EWTr GMaP IBlr ITim LEdu LRHS LSRN MBel MGos MRav NHol NRHS SCob SMad SRms WMoo WPnP WWtn XLum
– B&SWJ 7741A	CBcs WCru
– L 1670	CExl ELan IBlr
– 'Alba'	EMor GCal IBlr LRHS NRHS

- 'Buckland Beauty' ♀H7	CRos EBee EPfP IBlr LRHS NRHS WMoo
- 'Cally Coral'	EBee GCal
- 'Cally Salmon'	EWes GCal IBlr IMou
- 'Candy Clouds' (d)	EBee NLar
- 'Chocolate Wing'	Widely available
- 'Crûg Cardinal'	CRos EBee GCal LRHS NLar NRHS SHeu WCru
- 'Elegans' ♀H7	CAby CBod CDor CRos EBee EHoe ELan EPfP GKev GMaP IBlr LEdu LRHS MHol MRav NEgg NHol NRHS NWad SPoG SRms SWvt WCFE
- 'Fireworks'[PBR]	EBee ECtt ELan EPfP IMou NLar SPer
- 'Hanna'	SHeu
- 'Jade Dragon Mountain'	EBee GCal IBlr
- 'Maurice Mason' ♀H6	CExl EBee ECtt GKev IBlr NLar
- 'Mont Blanc'	IBlr
- Mount Stewart form	IBlr
- 'Panache'	IBlr
- 'Perthshire Bronze'	IBlr
- 'Pink Beauty'	EBee
- pink-flowered	WCru
- 'Rosea'	IBlr
- 'Shangri-La'	WCru
- 'Snow Clouds'	CBod EBee
- 'Superba' ♀H7	Widely available
- white-flowered	WCru
pinnata* × *sambucifolia	IBlr
podophylla	Widely available
- B&SWJ 10818	WCru
- B&SWJ 10823	WCru
- 'Braunlaub'	EUJe NBro WMoo WPnP
- 'Bronceblad'	IBlr
- 'Crûg's Colossus'	WCru
- Donard selection	IBlr
- 'Rotlaub' ♀H7	EBee EUJe IBlr IMou WBor WMoo
- 'Smaragd'	CRos EShb GCal IBlr LRHS MRav NBir NLar NRHS
purdomii hort.	CMac CRos GCal LRHS NRHS WCot WPGP
'Reinecke Fuchs'	IBlr
'Rosenlicht'	CRos LRHS NRHS
'Rosenzipfel'	IBlr
sambucifolia	CBcs CMac CRos GCal ILea LEdu LRHS MCot MMuc NBir NEgg NLar NRHS NSti SEND SPer WFar WMoo WPnP XLum
- B&SWJ 7899	WCru
- dwarf, pink-flowered	IBlr
- dwarf, white-flowered	IBlr
- large, red-stemmed	NBir
- 'Mountain Select'	EBee GCal
'Stoke Gabriel'	EBee
tabularis	see *Astilboides tabularis*

Roemeria (*Papaveraceae*)

hybrida	CSpe

Rohdea (*Asparagaceae*)

delavayi	WCot
japonica	CMac WCot WPGP
- B&SWJ 4853	WCru
- B&SWJ 5091	WCru
- 'Godaishu' (v)	WCot
- 'Gunjaku' (v)	WCot
- 'Lance Leaf'	LEdu WPGP
- long-leaved	WCot
- 'Miyakonojo' (v)	WCot
- 'Talbot Manor' (v)	CBct WCot WPGP
- 'Tama-jishi' (v)	WCot
- 'Tuneshige Rokujo' (v)	WCot
tonkinensis HWJ 562	WCru
watanabei B&SWJ 1911	WCru

Roldana (*Asteraceae*)

§ ***cristobalensis***	CSpe WCot
§ ***petasitis***	WCot

Romanzoffia (*Boraginaceae*)

californica	EBee
§ ***sitchensis***	CTri
suksdorfii Greene	see *R. sitchensis*
unalaschcensis	SRms

Romneya (*Papaveraceae*)

coulteri ♀H5	Widely available
§ - 'White Cloud' ♀H5	CBct CExl EBee EPfP MRav SChF WPGP WSpi
× ***hybrida***	see *R. coulteri* 'White Cloud'

Romulea (*Iridaceae*)

bulbocodium var. ***crocea***	EPot
- var. ***leichtliniana***	GKev
ligustica var. ***rouyana***	GKev
linaresii subsp. ***graeca***	GKev
ramiflora	CExl
requienii	GKev
tempskyana	EPot GKev

Rosa ✿ (*Rosaceae*)

NJM 11.048 from Guizhou, China	WPGP
NJM 11.077 from Guizhou, China	WPGP
NJM 11.079 from Guizhou, China	WPGP
90TH CELEBRATION ('Tan10558') (HT) **new**	MFry
'À Longs Pédoncules' (Ce)	EBls
'A. Mackenzie' (S)	EBls
A SHROPSHIRE LAD ('Ausled'[PBR]) (S) ♀H6	CArg CGro CKel CRos CTri EPfP LBuc LRHS MAus NAln NEgg NLar NRHS SCob SPer SPoG SSea
A WHITER SHADE OF PALE ('Peafanfare'[PBR]) (HT) ♀H6	CKel CSBt ECnt ESty LSRN MAus MFry MJak MRav SPer SSea
ABBIE'S ROSE (F)	LSRN
'Abbotswood' (*canina* hybrid)	EBls
ABIGAILE ('Tanelaigib') (F)	LSRN
ABRACADABRA ('Korhocsel') (HT)	ESty
ABRAHAM DARBY ('Auscot') (S)	CBod CKel CRos CTri EPfP LSRN MAsh MAus MJak MRav NAln NEgg NLar SCob SEND SPer
ABSENT FRIENDS ('Dicemblem'[PBR]) (F)	ESty WBor
ABSOLUTELY FABULOUS ('Wekvossutono'[PBR]) (F) ♀H6	CArg CBod CGro CSBt EBls ECnt ELon EPfP ESty LBuc LRHS LSRN MAsh MFry MJak MRav MWat NPri SCoo SPad SPer SPoG
abyssinica	LEdu
acicularis var. ***nipponensis***	EBls
'Adam' (ClT)	EBls LSRN
'Adam Messerich' (Bb)	EBls NLar
ADAM'S ROSE ('Wekromico') (F)	LSRN

Name	Suppliers
'Adélaïde d'Orléans' (Ra) ♀[H6]	CArg CRHN EBls LRHS MAus NLar SEND SPer
'Agatha' (G)	EBls
AGATHA CHRISTIE ('Kormeita'[PBR]) (ClF)	EPfP LBuc LRHS LSRN MAsh
'Agathe Incarnata' (D × G)	EBls
'Aglaia' (Ra)	CPou EBls EWTr MAus
'Agnes' (Ru)	CBcs CTho EBls EPfP EWTr IArd MAus MCot MRav NLar SPer
'Aimée Vibert' (N)	EBee EBls ELon MAus MRav NLar SPer
'Alain Blanchard' (G)	CPou EBls EWTr MAus
ALAN TITCHMARSH ('Ausjive'[PBR]) (S)	LCro LOPS LSRN MAsh MAus NAln SPer
× ***alba*** (A)	EBls
§ - 'Alba Maxima' (A) ♀[H6]	EBls EWTr MAus MRav NLar SEND SPer WFar WHer
§ - 'Alba Semiplena' (A) ♀[H6]	EBls EPfP GBin MAus NLar SPer WHer
- CELESTIAL	see *R.* 'Céleste'
- 'Maxima'	see *R.* × *alba* 'Alba Maxima'
'Albéric Barbier' (Ra) ♀[H5]	CArg CGro CRHN CSBt CTri EBls ECnt ELan EPfP LCro LOPS MAus MCot MFry MRav MSwo MWat NLar NWea SCob SEND SMad SPer WHer
'Albertine' (Ra) ♀[H6]	Widely available
'Alchymist' (ClS)	CKel CPou CRHN CRos EBls ELon EPfP ESty LRHS MAus MRav NAln NLar SPer
ALDEN BIESEN ('Lengrati') (HM) **new**	WKif
ALDERLEY PARK ('Frygladiator') (F) **new**	MFry
ALEC'S RED ('Cored') (HT)	CArg CBcs CKel CTri EBls LSRN MAus MJak MRav MWat SPer SPoG
ALEXANDER ('Harlex') (HT) ♀[H6]	CGro EBls LSRN MAus MRav SPer SSea
'Alexander Hill Gray' (T)	EBls
'Alexandre Girault' (Ra) ♀[H6]	CBod CRHN EBls LBuc LRHS MAus NRHS SPer WHer
'Alfred Colomb' (HP)	EBls
'Alfred de Dalmas' misapplied	see *R.* 'Mousseline'
ALFRED SISLEY ('Delstrijor'[PBR]) (S)	CBod ESty MRav NLar
'Alfresco'[PBR] (ClHT)	MSwo
§ 'Alibaba'[PBR] (Cl) ♀[H6]	CGro CSBt ECnt EPfP ESty EUJe LRHS LSRN MAsh MFry MRav MWat NPri SPer SPoG SSea
ALICE FAYE ('Seaodd') (Min)	ESty
'Alida Lovett' (Ra)	CRHN EBls MAus
ALISON ('Coclibee'[PBR]) (F)	LSRN
'Alison Wheatcroft' (F)	EBls
ALISSAR, PRINCESS OF PHOENICIA ('Harsidon'[PBR]) (S)	CPou GBin NLar
'Alister Clark' (F)	EBls
§ 'Alister Stella Gray' (N) ♀[H5]	EBls EPfP ESty MAus MMuc NEgg NLar SPer SSea WBor
ALL AMERICAN MAGIC ('Meiroylear'[PBR]) (HT)	ESty
ALL MY LOVING ('Fryrisky') (HT)	LRHS MAsh MFry
'Allen Chandler' (ClHT)	EBls MAus
'Allgold' (F)	EBls SCob
ALNWICK CASTLE	see *R.* THE ALNWICK ROSE
'Aloha' (ClHT) ♀[H6]	CArg CBcs CGro CKel CTri EBee EBls ELon EPfP ESty EWTr LRHS MAsh MAus MCot MJak MRav NLar SCob SPer SPoG WSpi
alpina	see *R. pendulina*
'Alpine Sunset' (HT)	CTri EBls ELon MRav MWat SCob SPer SPoG
altaica misapplied	see *R. spinosissima* 'Grandiflora'
altaica Willd.	see *R. spinosissima*
ALTISSIMO ('Delmur') (Cl)	CBod CKel EBls EWTr MAsh MAus SPer SSea
ALWAYS REMEMBER ME ('Macpadspo') (HT) **new**	LSRN
ALWAYS YOU ('Webalways') (HT)	ESty
'Amadis' (Bs)	EBls MAus
AMANDA ('Beesian') (F)	EBls ESty LSRN
'Ambassador Nogami' (S)	EBls
AMBER COVER ('Poulbambe'[PBR]) (Towne & Country Series) (GC)	EUJe
AMBER QUEEN ('Harroony') (F) ♀[H6]	CArg CKel CSBt CTri EBls ELan IArd MAsh MAus MFry MRav SPer
AMBER SWEET DREAM ('Fryritz') (Patio)	CKel CSBt MFry MRav
amblyotis RBS 0262	NLar
'Amélia'	see *R.* 'Celsiana'
AMELIA ('Poulen011'[PBR]) (Renaissance Series) (S)	ECnt LSRN
'American Pillar' (Ra)	CArg CBcs CKel CRHN CRos CSBt CTri EBls ECnt ELan EPfP LRHS MAsh MAus MFry MMuc MRav MSwo NAln NLar SCob SPer SPoG WBor
AMETHYST QUEEN ('Raw1074') (F) **new**	ESty
AMNESTY INTERNATIONAL ('Delcreja') (Cl) **new**	ESty
'Amy Robsart' (RH)	EBls MAus
ANABELL ('Korbell') (F)	LSRN
'Anaïs Ségalas' (G)	MAus
'Andersonii' (*canina* hybrid)	EBls
§ 'Anemone' (Cl)	CPou EBls EWTr MAus NLar
anemoniflora	see *R.* × *beanii*
anemonoides	see *R.* 'Anemone'
ANGEL EYES ('Albravo') (HT) **new**	LRHS MAsh
ANGELA ('Grifgela')	LSRN
ANGELA RIPPON ('Ocaru') (Min)	CSBt
'Angela's Choice' (F)	LSRN
'Angèle Pernet' (HT)	EBls
ANISLEY DICKSON ('Dickimono') (F)	SPer
ANN ('Ausfete'[PBR]) (S)	LSRN
ANN HENDERSON ('Fryhoncho') (F)	LSRN MFry
ANNA FORD ('Harpiccolo') (Min/Patio) ♀[H5]	SPer
'Anna Olivier' (T)	EBls
'Anna Pavlova' (HT)	EBls
ANNA ZINKEISEN ('Harquhling') (S)	EBls
ANNE BOLEYN ('Ausecret'[PBR]) (S)	CRos EPfP LRHS MAsh MAus NAln NEgg NRHS SCoo
'Anne Dakin' (ClHT)	MAus
ANNE HARKNESS ('Harkaramel') (F)	MAus SPer
ANNE MARIE LAING ('Jospink') (F)	EBls
'Anne of Geierstein' (RH)	EBls

	Name	Suppliers
	'Anne Watkins' (HT)	EBls
	'Anne-Marie de Montravel' (Poly)	EBls
	ANNE'S ROSE ('Frynippy'[PBR]) (F) **new**	LSRN MFry
	ANNIVERSARY WALTZ ('Raw237') (HT)	ESty
	ANNIVERSARY WISHES ('Noa140721') (F) **new**	MAsh
	'Anthony' (S)	EBls
	ANTIQUE '89 ('Kordalen'[PBR]) (ClF)	EBls MAsh
	ANTIQUE ('Antike') (F)	CBod CPou
	APHRODITE ('Tan00847'[PBR]) (S) ♀H6	ELon ESty LSRN MRav
	APHRODITE ('Tanetidor') (HT) **new**	CArg
	apothecary's rose	see *R. gallica* var. *officinalis*
	'Apple Blossom' (Ra)	EBls SHar
	APPLE BLOSSOM ('Noamel') (GC)	EShb
	'Applejack' (S)	EBls
	'Apricot Nectar' (F)	MAus
	'Apricot Silk' (HT)	CTri EBls SPer
	APRICOT SUNBLAZE ('Savamark') (Min)	CSBt
	ARC ANGEL ('Fryorst') (HT)	MFry
	'Archduke Charles' (Ch)	EBls
	'Archiduc Joseph' misapplied	see *R.* 'Général Schablikine'
	'Archiduchesse Elisabeth d'Autriche' (HP)	EBls
	ARCHIE MOSS ('Dickumon') (S)	IDic
	'Arctic Circle' (HT) **new**	ESty
	'Ardoisée de Lyon' (HP)	EBls
	'Ards Rover' (ClHP)	EBls
	'Arethusa' (Ch)	EBls NLar
§	***arkansana*** var. ***suffulta***	EBls
	ARMADA ('Haruseful') (S)	EBls
	'Arthur Bell' (F) ♀H6	CArg CGro CRos CSBt CTri EBls EPfP ESty EUJe IArd LRHS LSRN MAsh MAus MJak MRav MSwo MWat NEgg NPri SCob SPer SPoG SSea WBor
	'Arthur de Sansal' (DPo)	EBls MAus NLar
	arvensis	CCVT CDul CHab CLnd CPer EBls LBuc MAus MMuc NWea SCob WTSh
§	'Aschermittwoch' (Cl)	EBls
	ASCOT ('Tan01757'[PBR]) (HT) **new**	ESty MFry
	ASH WEDNESDAY	see *R.* 'Aschermittwoch'
	'Assemblage des Beautés' (G)	MAus
	'Astra Desmond' (Ra)	EBls MNrw
I	'At Peace Rose' (HT)	LSRN
	ATLANTIC STAR ('Fryworld'[PBR]) (F)	MFry
	ATTLEBOROUGH ('Beaat') (ClHT)	EBls
	AUDREY WILCOX ('Frywilrey') (HT)	ESty MFry
	'Auguste Gervais' (Ra)	EBls MAus
	'Auguste Roussel' (Cl)	EBls
	'Augustine Guinoisseau' (HT)	EBls
	Austrian copper rose	see *R. foetida* 'Bicolor'
	Austrian yellow	see *R. foetida*
	'Autumn' (HT)	LSRN
	'Autumn Delight' (HM)	EBls NLar
	AUTUMN FIRE	see *R.* 'Herbstfeuer'
	'Autumn Sunset' (ClS)	EBls MCot
	'Autumnalis'	see *R.* 'Princesse de Nassau'
	AVEC AMOUR ('Tan04341'[PBR]) (HT)	ESty
	'Aviateur Blériot' (Ra)	CRHN EBls
	'Avon' (HT)	CBod
	AVON ('Poulmulti'[PBR]) (GC)	EBls MRav SPer
	AWAKENING ('Probuzení') (ClHT)	CRos CWld EBee EBls LRHS MAsh MSwo NLar
	'Ayrshire Splendens'	see *R.* 'Splendens'
	'Baby Albéric' (Poly)	EBls
	'Baby Faurax' (Poly)	EBls MAus
	BABY LOVE ('Scrivluv'[PBR]) (Min/Patio)	MAus
	BABY MASQUERADE ('Tanba') (Min)	CBod CGro MRav MWat SPer
	BABYFACE ('Rawril'[PBR]) (Min)	ESty
	'Ballerina' (HM/Poly) ♀H6	CArg CBod CDul CGro CKel CRos CSBt CTri EBee EBls ECnt ELan EPfP ESty LRHS LSRN MAsh MAus MFry MJak MRav MSwo NAln NEgg NLar NPri SCob SPer SPoG SSea
	BALMORAL ('Poulcas027'[PBR]) (Palace Series) (Patio) **new**	MAsh
	'Baltimore Belle' (Ra)	CPou CRHN EBls MAus NLar
	banksiae (Ra)	CPou SNig SRms
	- ***alba***	see *R. banksiae* var. *banksiae*
§	- var. ***banksiae*** (Ra/d)	CBod CDul CHll CKel CPou CRHN CRos CSBt CTri CWld EBls ELan EPfP IMou LCro LOPS LRHS MAus SCob SEND SLon SPer WCot XSen
	- 'Lutea' (Ra/d) ♀H5	Widely available
	- 'Lutescens' (Ra)	CHll EBls WPGP
	- var. ***normalis*** (Ra)	CSBt CSam EBls EPfP MAus SLon WCot WHer WPGP
I	- 'Rosea' (Ra)	NLar SPer
	'Bantry Bay' (ClHT)	CArg CBod CSBt EBls ELan LSRN SCob SLon SPer
	BARAKURA ('Beajap') (GC/S)	EBls
	BARBARA ('Raw1050')	LSRN
	BARBARA ANN	see *R.* SCENT FROM HEAVEN
	BARBARA AUSTIN ('Austop'[PBR]) (S)	MAus SCob
	BARBRA STREISAND ('Wekquaneze') (HT) **new**	LSRN
	'Baron de Wassenaer' (CeMo)	EBls
	'Baron Girod de l'Ain' (HP)	EBee EBls ELon LSRN MAus NEgg NLar SPer
	'Baroness Rothschild' (HT)	see *R.* BARONNE EDMOND DE ROTHSCHILD
	'Baroness Rothschild' ambig.	see *R.* BARONNE EDMOND DE ROTHSCHILD, CLIMBING BARONNE EDMOND DE ROTHSCHILD
	BARONESSE ('Tan97094'[PBR]) (F) **new**	MFry
§	'Baronne Adolph de Rothschild' (HP)	EBls
§	BARONNE EDMOND DE ROTHSCHILD ('Meigriso') (HT)	MAus
	'Baronne Prévost' (HP)	EBls MAus
	BAROQUE FLOORSHOW ('Harbaroque'[PBR]) (S)	CKel MRav
	BARRY STEPHENS ('Horcabellero') (HT)	LSRN

Name	Suppliers
BATHSHEBA ('Auschimbley') (Cl) **new**	CSBt ESty MAus
§ × ***beanii*** (Ra)	EBls
BEATRIX POTTER ('Beafolly') (S)	EBls
'Beau Narcisse' (G) ♀H7	MAus
BEAUTIFUL BRITAIN ('Dicfire') (F)	EBls SCob
'Beauty of Rosemawr' (ClT)	EBls
BEAUTY STAR	see *R.* LIVERPOOL REMEMBERS
'Belinda' (HM)	EBls LSRN
§ BELLA ('Pouljill'PBR) (Renaissance Series) (S)	CPou LSRN
BELLA CHRISTINA ('Mandella') (F)	LSRN
BELLA DIANA ('Mandiana') (F)	LSRN
'Belle Amour' (A × D)	CBod CPou EBls GBin MAus
'Belle de Crécy' (G)	CPou CTri CWld EBee EBls MAsh MAus MNrw NLar NPri SMad SPer
'Belle des Jardins' misapplied	see *R.* × *centifolia* 'Unique Panachée'
BELLE EPOQUE ('Adasilthe'PBR) (HT)	SCob
BELLE EPOQUE ('Fryyaboo'PBR) (HT)	ESty MFry SCob
BELLE HAPPINESS ('Meileodevin'PBR) (Cl)	SSea
'Belle Isis' (G)	EBls MAus
'Belle Lyonnaise' (ClT)	EBls
'Belle Poitevine' (Ru)	CPou
'Belle Portugaise' (ClT)	EBls MAus
'Belle Vichyssoise' (N)	EBls
§ 'Belvedere' (Ra) ♀H6	CPou EBee MAus NLar SPer WBor
BENITA ('Dicquarrel') (HT)	IDic
BENJAMIN BRITTEN ('Ausencart'PBR) (S)	CGro CRos EPfP ESty LBuc LRHS MAsh MAus NAln NEgg NRHS SCob SPer
§ 'Bennett's Seedling' (Ra)	EBls
BERKSHIRE ('Korpinka'PBR) (GC) ♀H6	EBls SCob SSea
BERYL JOYCE ('Tan96145'PBR) (HT)	CKel ESty LSRN MRav
BEST IMPRESSION ('Tan04247'PBR) (HT) **new**	ECnt ESty MFry
BEST OF FRIENDS ('Pouldunk'PBR) (HT)	LSRN
BEST WISHES ('Chessnut'PBR) (ClHT/v)	LSRN
'Betty Sherriff' (Cl)	GBin
'Betty Uprichard' (HT)	EBls
'Betty's Smile' (HT)	LSRN
'Bewitched' (HT)	LSRN MAsh
BIANCO ('Cocblanco') (Patio/Min)	MAus
BIDDULPH GRANGE ('Frydarkeye') (S)	MFry
BIENVENUE ('Delrochipar') (Cl)	ESty
BIG PURPLE ('Stebigpu') (HT)	ECnt
BILLET DOUX ('Delrosar') (S)	ESty
BIRTHDAY BOY ('Tan97607'PBR) (HT)	CBod ESty LSRN MRav SCob SCoo SPoG
BIRTHDAY GIRL ('Meilasso'PBR) (F)	CBod CGro CKel CSBt EPfP ESty LSRN MAsh MFry MJak MRav MWat SCoo SPoG SVic
BIRTHDAY SURPRISE ('Guesyoga') (F)	ESty
BIRTHDAY WISHES (Patio)	see *R.* SHRIMP HIT (Patio)
BIRTHDAY WISHES ('Guesdelay') (HT)	CTri LRHS LSRN NRHS SSea
'Bishop Darlington' (HM)	EBls
BLACK BEAUTY ('Korfleur') (HT)	MAus
'Black Jack' (Ce)	see *R.* 'Tour de Malakoff'
'Black Prince' (HP)	EBls
BLACKBERRY NIP ('Somnip'PBR) (HT)	ELon
'Blairii Number One' (Bb)	EBls
'Blairii Number Two' (ClBb)	CArg EBls MAus NEgg NLar SPer
'Blanche de Belgique' (A)	EBls
'Blanche Double de Coubert' (Ru) ♀H7	CArg CBcs CBod CDul CKel CSBt CTho CTri EBee EBls ECnt ELan EPfP EWTr LBuc LCro LOPS LSRN MAus MFry MSwo NEgg NLar SCob SEND SPer WKif
'Blanche Moreau' (CeMo)	EBls MAus SPer
'Blanchefleur' (Ce × G)	CPou EBls MAus
blanda	EBls
'Blesma Soul' (HT)	CSBt
'Blessings' (HT)	CArg CBcs CSBt CTri EBls LBuc LSRN MAsh MAus MGos MJak MRav MWat NAln SCob SPer
'Bleu Magenta' (Ra) ♀H6	CBod CRHN EBls ELan GBin IArd MAus NLar SEND
BLOOM OF RUTH ('Harmedley'PBR) (HT)	CSBt ECnt LSRN
'Bloomfield Abundance' (Poly)	CPou EBls MAus MMuc NLar SPer
'Bloomfield Courage' (Ra)	CBod EBls
'Bloomfield Dainty' (HM)	EBls
'Blossomtime' (Cl)	SPer
BLUE DIAMOND (HT) **new**	MFry
BLUE FOR YOU ('Pejamblu'PBR) (F) ♀H6	CGro CRos EBls ECnt ELan ELon EPfP ESty GBin LBuc LRHS MAsh MAus MFry NPri NRHS SCob SCoo SMad SPoG SSea
BLUE MOON ('Tannacht') (HT)	CTri EBls ELan MGos MJak MRav SCob SPer SPoG
BLUE PETER ('Ruiblun') (Min)	ESty
BLUEBERRY HILL ('Wekcryplag') (F)	EBls
BLUESETTE ('Lenmau') (F)	EBls
'Blush Boursault' (Bs)	EBls MMuc
'Blush Damask' (D)	EBls
'Blush Hip' (A)	MAus
'Blush Noisette'	see *R.* 'Noisette Carnée'
'Blush Rambler' (Ra)	CSBt EBls ELan EPfP LBuc MAsh MAus MMuc
'Blushing Lucy' (Ra) ♀H6	CPou CRHN MNrw NLar SPer
BLYTHE SPIRIT ('Auschool'PBR) (S)	MAsh MAus NEgg SCob
'Bobbie James' (Ra) ♀H6	CArg CRos CTri EBee EBls EPfP EWTr LRHS MAus MNrw MRav MSwo NEgg NLar NRHS SCob SPer SSea WFar
'Bobby Charlton' (HT)	LSRN
BOBBY DAZZLER ('Smi133-02') (F)	ESty MRav
BOLLYWOOD ('Poulbt010') (HT) **new**	MFry
'Bon Silène' (T)	EBls
BONICA ('Meidomonac') (GC) ♀H6	Widely available
§ BONITA ('Poulen009'PBR) (Renaissance Series) (S)	ECnt

BOOGIE-WOOGIE ('Poulyc006'PBR) (Courtyard Series) (ClHT)	ECnt LRHS MAsh
BORN AGAIN	see *R.* RENAISSANCE
BOSCOBEL ('Auscousin'PBR) (S)	CRos ECnt EPfP ESty LBuc LRHS MAsh MAus NAln NRHS SCob
'Botzaris' (D)	EBls
'Boule de Neige' (Bb)	CBcs CTri EBls ECnt ELan EPfP LCro LOPS LRHS LSRN MAus MRav NLar NRHS SPer
'Bouquet d'Or' (N)	EBls MAus NLar
'Bouquet Tout Fait' misapplied	see *R.* 'Nastarana'
BOWLED OVER ('Tandolgnil'PBR) (F) ♀H6	ESty
§ ***bracteata*** (S)	CRHN EBls ECre EWes MAus SSea
BRAVE HEART ('Horbondsmile') (F)	MAus MRav
BREATH OF LIFE ('Harquanne'PBR) (ClHT)	EBee EBls ELan MAus MFry MRav SPer
BREATHTAKING ('Hargalore'PBR) (HT)	ESty
'Breeze Hill' (Ra)	EBls
'Brenda Colvin' (Ra)	EBls
'Brian's Star' (F)	LSRN
BRIDE AND GROOM ('Smi10-98') (HT)	CKel ESty LSRN MRav SCoo
BRIDE ('Fryyearn'PBR) (HT)	LSRN MFry MRav MWat
BRIDGE OF SIGHS ('Harglowing'PBR) (Cl)	ECnt ESty LBuc LRHS MAsh MFry SPoG
BRIGHT AND BREEZY ('Dicjive') (F)	ECnt
BRIGHT AS A BUTTON ('Chewsumsigns'PBR) (S) ♀H5	CKel CSBt EBee ESty GBin LRHS MAsh NLar SLon SPer
BRIGHT FIRE ('Peaxi'PBR) (ClHT)	CKel MSwo
BRIGHT FUTURE ('Kirora'PBR) (Cl)	ELon ESty
BRIGHT IDEAS ('Horcoffdrop') (Cl)	CGro CWld EBls EPfP LRHS MAsh NPri
BRIGHT SMILE ('Dicdance') (F/Patio)	MAus
BRILLIANT SWEET DREAM ('Frysassy') (Patio)	CSBt ECnt MFry
BRITANNIA ('Frycalm'PBR) (HT) ♀H6	MFry
BROADLANDS ('Tanmirsch'PBR) (GC)	NLar
BROTHER CADFAEL ('Ausglobe'PBR) (S)	CArg CKel CRos CTri LRHS MAsh MAus NAln NEgg NLar NRHS SCob SCoo SPer SSea
BROWN VELVET ('Maccultra') (F)	SPer
BROWNIE	see *R.* CHOCOLATE RIPPLES
§ ***brunonii*** (Ra)	CExl CPou EBls EWes MAus
- CC 7290	EWld
- KR 10350	WPGP
- PAB 3083	LEdu
§ - 'La Mortola' (Ra)	EBls MAus NLar SPer
BRUSH-STROKES ('Guescolour') (F)	ESty
'Buff Beauty' (HM) ♀H6	CArg CGro CKel CRos CSBt CTri EBee EBls ECnt EPfP LCro LOPS MAsh MAus MCot MRav MSwo MWat NEgg NLar SCob SEND SPer WCFE WFar
'Bullata'	see *R.* × *centifolia* 'Bullata'
§ 'Burgundiaca' (G)	EBls MAus
Burgundian rose	see *R.* 'Burgundiaca'
§ BURGUNDY ICE ('Prose'PBR) (F)	CArg CBod CKel CSBt EBee EBls EPfP ESty LBuc LCro LOPS LRHS MAsh MFry MRav MSwo MWat NRHS SCob SCoo SMad SPer SPoG SSea
'Burgundy Iceberg'PBR	see *R.* BURGUNDY ICE
'Burgundy Rose'	see *R.* 'Burgundiaca'
burnet, double pink	see *R. spinosissima* double, pink-flowered
- double white	see *R. spinosissima* double, white-flowered
BURNING DESIRE ('Frysizzle') (F) **new**	MFry
BUTTERCUP ('Ausband'PBR) (S)	CRos EPfP LRHS MAus
BUXOM BEAUTY ('Korbilant'PBR) (HT) ♀H6	CArg EPfP LRHS LSRN MAsh SSea
'C.F. Meyer'	see *R.* 'Conrad Ferdinand Meyer'
§ ***caesia*** subsp. ***vosagiaca***	LEdu
CAFÉ AU LAIT ('Simgrey') (F)	ESty
californica (S)	MAus
- 'Plena'	see *R. nutkana* 'Plena'
'Callisto' (HM)	MAus
'Camayeux' (G)	CPou EBls ECnt MAus NLar SPer
CAMBRIDGESHIRE ('Korhaugen'PBR) (GC)	CBod CTri EBls MAus NLar SPer SSea
CAMELOT ('Tan05372'PBR) (Cl)	ESty
'Cameo' (Poly)	EBls
CAMILLE PISARRO ('Destricol') (F)	ESty
'Canary Bird'	see *R. xanthina* 'Canary Bird'
CANDY KISSES ('Simwatu') (HT) **new**	ESty
CANDY LAND ('Wekrosopela'PBR) (Cl)	ECnt ESty
canina (S)	CArg CBod CCVT CDul CGro CHab CLnd CPer CTri EBls ECrN EPfP EPom LBuc LCro LOPS MAus MJak MMuc MRav NLar NWea SCob SEWo SPer WMat WMou WOut WTSh
'Cantabrigiensis' (S) ♀H6	EBls MAus NLar SPer
CANZONETTA ('Noa84497d') (F)	MAsh
CAPEL MANOR ('Beajammie') (Cl)	EBls
'Capitaine Basroger' (CeMo)	MAus
'Capitaine John Ingram' (CeMo)	CArg EBls MAus NLar
CAPRICIA ('Poulren024'PBR) (S)	NLar
'Captain Christy'	see *R.* 'Climbing Captain Christy'
'Captain Hayward' (HP)	EBls
'Captain Scarlet' (ClMin)	ESty
'Cardinal de Richelieu' (G)	CArg CBcs CPou CTri CWld EBls EPfP LCro LOPS LRHS MAsh MAus MCot MRav MSwo NEgg NLar SCob SMad SPoG
CAREFREE DAYS ('Meirivoui'PBR) (Patio) ♀H6	EPfP LBuc LRHS MAsh MFry NPri NRHS SPoG SSea
CARIAD ('Auspanier'PBR) (HM)	MAus
CARIBBEAN DAWN ('Korfeining'PBR) (Patio)	MAsh MFry
CARING FOR YOU ambig.	LSRN
'Carmen' (Ru)	EBls

	'Carmenetta' (S)	EBls
	'Carol' (F)	see *R.* 'Carol Amling'
§	'Carol Amling' (F)	LSRN
	CAROL ANN ('Peapost') (F)	LSRN
	'Caroline Testout'	see *R.* 'Madame Caroline Testout'
	CAROLINE VICTORIA ('Harprior'PBR) (HT)	LSRN
	CAROLYN KNIGHT ('Austurner'PBR) (S)	CRos EPfP LCro LOPS LRHS LSRN MAsh MAus NAln NRHS
	CARRIS ('Harmanna'PBR) (HT)	MAsh NRHS
§	CASINO ('Macca') (ClHT)	CTri EBls ELon MRav SPer
	'Castle Apricot'	see *R.* LAZY DAYS
	'Castle Cream'	see *R.* PERFECT DAY
	'Castle Peach'	see *R.* IMAGINATION ('Pouldron')
	'Castle Shrimp Pink'	see *R.* FASCINATION
	'Castle Yellow'	see *R.* SUMMER GOLD
	'Catherine Mermet' (T)	EBls
	'Catherine Seyton' (RH)	EBls
§	'Cécile Brünner' (Poly) ♀H5	CKel CTri EBee EBls ELan LSRN MAus MMuc NLar NWea SPer SSea
	CECILY GIBSON ('Evebright') (F)	ESty
	CELEBRATION 2000 ('Horcoffitup'PBR) (S)	MAus
	CELEBRATION TIME	see *R.* CINCO DE MAYO
§	'Céleste' (A) ♀H6	CTri EBls EPfP EWTr GBin MAus NAln NLar SEND SPer
	'Célina' (CeMo)	EBls GBin LSRN
	'Céline Forestier' (N)	CArg CPou EBee EBls EWTr MAus NLar SEND SPer
§	'Celsiana' (D) ♀H7	CPou EBls LSRN MAus NLar SPer
	CENTENAIRE DE LOURDES ('Delge') (F)	EBls
	CENTENARY ('Koreledas'PBR) (F)	MAsh
§	× ***centifolia*** (Ce)	EBls MAus SPer
§	- 'Bullata' (Ce)	EBls MAus
§	- 'Cristata' (Ce) ♀H6	CArg EBls LEdu MAus NLar SPer
§	- 'De Meaux' (Ce)	EBls MAus NLar SPer
§	- 'Muscosa' (CeMo)	EBls LEdu MAus
	- 'Parvifolia'	see *R.* 'Burgundiaca'
§	- 'Shailer's White Moss' (CeMo)	CBod EBls MAus
	- 'Spong' (Ce)	EBls MAus
§	- 'Unique' (Ce)	EBls EWTr MAus NLar
§	- 'Unique Panachée' (Ce)	CPou EBls MAus
	'Centifolia Variegata'	see *R.* × *centifolia* 'Unique Panachée'
	CENTRE STAGE ('Chewcreepy'PBR) (S/GC) ♀H6	MAsh MAus
	'Cerise Bouquet' (S) ♀H6	EBls MAus NLar WSpi
	CHAMPAGNE CELEBRATION ('Frylimbo') (HT) **new**	MFry
	CHAMPAGNE CELEBRATION ('Simluck') (F) **new**	ESty
§	CHAMPAGNE MOMENT ('Korvanaber'PBR) (F) ♀H6	CArg CBcs CGro CRos CSBt EBls ECnt ELan ELon EPfP ESty LBuc LRHS LSRN MAsh MAus MFry MGos MJak MRav NPri NRHS SMad SPoG SSea
	'Champion of the World' (Bb)	EBls
	'Champneys Pink Cluster' (China hybrid)	EBls MAus SCob
	CHANDOS BEAUTY ('Harmisty'PBR) (HT) ♀H6	CGro CKel CRos ECnt ELon EPfP ESty LBuc LRHS LSRN MAsh MFry MRav NAln SPoG SSea
	'Chanelle' (F)	EBls
	Chapeau de Napoléon	see *R.* × *centifolia* 'Cristata'
	'Chaplin's Pink Climber' (Cl)	EBls
	CHARDONNAY ('Simtely') (F) **new**	ESty
	CHARISMA ('Jelroganor') (F)	CGro MAsh NPri NRHS
	CHARISMA ('Noa16071'PBR) (HT) **new**	SPoG
	CHARLES AUSTIN ('Ausles') (S)	MRav
	CHARLES DARWIN ('Auspeet'PBR) (S)	CGro CRos EPfP LBuc LRHS MAsh MAus NAln NEgg NLar NRHS SCob SCoo SPer
	'Charles de Mills' (G) ♀H6	CKel CTri EBls ECnt ELan EPfP EWTr GBin LCro LOPS LRHS LSRN MAus MCot MRav MSwo NLar SMad SPer WHer
	CHARLES DICKENS ('Raw1064') (HT) **new**	ESty
	'Charles Gater' (HP)	EBls
	'Charles Lefèbvre' (HP)	EBls
	'Charles Mallerin' (HT)	EBls
	CHARLES RENNIE MACKINTOSH ('Ausren') (S)	MAus NEgg
	CHARLIE'S ROSE ('Tanellepa') (HT) ♀H6	ESty LSRN
	CHARLOTTE ('Auspoly'PBR) (S) ♀H6	CRos ELan EPfP ESty LBuc LCro LOPS LRHS LSRN MAus MJak NAln NEgg NLar NRHS SCob SCoo SPer
	CHARLOTTE VIELI ('Diclooker') (F)	IDic
	CHARMANT ('Korpeligo'PBR) (Min)	MAsh MFry
	CHARTERED ('Diclingo') (F)	IDic
	CHARTREUSE DE PARME ('Delviola') (S)	CPou ESty MRav NLar
	CHATSWORTH ('Tanotax'PBR) (Patio/F) ♀H6	SPer
	CHECKMATE ('Diclanky') (Cl)	IDic MRav
§	CHEEK TO CHEEK ('Poulslas'PBR) (Courtyard Series) (ClMin)	LRHS MAsh
	CHEERFUL CHARLIE ('Cocquimmer'PBR) (F)	LSRN MRav
	CHERIE	see *R.* SONGS OF PRAISE
	CHERRY BONICA ('Meipeporia'PBR) (S)	CRos ECnt
	CHERRY BRANDY '85 ('Tanryrandy'PBR) (HT)	CSBt
	CHERRY GIRL ('Korkosieb'PBR) (F) **new**	MAsh
	CHERRY HINTON ('Dicprolong') (S) **new**	IDic
	CHESHIRE ('Fryelise'PBR) (HT)	MFry
	CHESHIRE ('Korkonopi'PBR) (County Rose Series) (S)	MAus
	'Cheshire Life' (HT)	MAus
	'Chevy Chase' (Ra)	EBls LRHS MAsh MCot
	'Chewton Rose' (S)	EBls
	CHIANTI ('Auswine') (S)	EBls MAus NLar
	CHICAGO PEACE ('Johnago') (HT)	CArg EBls SCob
	CHILD OF ACHIEVEMENT	see *R.* BELLA
	CHILD OF MY HEART ('Beapeace') (HT)	EBls

'Chinatown' (ClF) ♀H6	CArg CTri EBls LRHS MAsh MAus MRav NPri SCob SPer
chinensis misapplied	see *R.* × *odorata*
chinensis Jacq. (S)	EBls
- 'Mutabilis'	see *R.* × *odorata* 'Mutabilis'
- 'Old Blush'	see *R.* × *odorata* 'Pallida'
- 'Semperflorens'	EBls
- var. ***spontanea***	WPGP
- 'White Beauty'	WCot
CHLOE ('Poulen003'PBR) (Renaissance Series) (S)	CBod CPou ECnt LSRN NLar
'Chloris' (A)	EBee MMuc
CHOCA MOCHA ('Simcho') (F)	ESty
§ CHOCOLATE RIPPLES ('Simstripe') (Cl)	ESty
CHOIR OF ANGELS	see *R.* OUR JANE
CHRIS ('Kirsan'PBR) (ClHT)	CArg ESty LSRN MAus
CHRISTIAN DIOR ('Meilie') (HT)	EBls
CHRISTOPHER ('Cocopher') (HT)	LSRN
CHRISTOPHER MARLOWE ('Ausjump'PBR) (S)	MAsh MAus
§ 'Chromatella' (N)	EBls MAus
'Chrysler Imperial' (HT)	EBls
'Chuckles' (F)	ESty
CIDER CUP ('Dicladida') (Min/Patio)	MAus
§ CINCO DE MAYO ('Wekcobeju'PBR) (F) ♀H6	CKel MRav
'Cinderella' (Min)	CSBt NLar
'Cinderella' (Ra)	MAsh
'Cinderella' ambig.	LRHS
CINDERELLA ('Korfobalt') (ClS)	CPou EUJe
cinnamomea misapplied	see *R. majalis*
'Circus' (F)	EBls
CITY LIGHTS ('Poulgan'PBR) (Patio)	CSBt
CITY LIVERY ('Harhero 2000') (F)	EPfP LBuc LRHS MAsh
CITY OF BELFAST ('Macci') (F)	EBls
CITY OF CARLSBAD	see *R.* HANKY PANKY
'City of Leeds' (F)	SPer
CITY OF LONDON ('Harukfore') (F)	CSBt EBls SPer
CITY OF YORK	see *R.* 'Direktör Benschop'
CLAIR MATIN ('Meimont') (ClS)	CPou EBls MAus NLar
CLAIRE AUSTIN ('Ausprior'PBR) (S)	CRos EPfP ESty LBuc LRHS MAus NAln NLar NRHS SCob SCoo SPoG
'Claire Jacquier' (N)	EBls MAus SPer
CLAIRE MARSHALL ('Harunite'PBR) (F)	ELon ESty
CLAIRE ROSE ('Auslight'PBR) (S)	LSRN
'Clarence House' (Cl)	EBls ELan LRHS MAsh
CLARET ('Frykristal'PBR) (HT) ♀H6	ECnt EPfP ESty MFry MRav
CLAUDE MONET ('Delstrirocrem') (Cl) **new**	ESty
CLAUDE MONET ('Jacdesa') (HT)	ESty
'Clementina Carbonieri' (T)	CPou EBls NLar
CLEO ('Beebop') (HT)	LSRN
CLEOPATRA ('Korverpea'PBR) (HT)	LRHS MAsh
'Cliff Richard' (F)	ESty LSRN
'Climbing Alec's Red' (ClHT)	SPer
'Climbing Allgold' (ClF)	EBls
'Climbing Arthur Bell' (ClF)	CGro CSBt CTri ELon ESty MAsh MSwo NPri SCob SPer SPoG SSea
'Climbing Ballerina' (Ra)	CSBt
§ CLIMBING BARONNE EDMOND DE ROTHSCHILD ('Meigrisosar') (ClHT)	CSBt
CLIMBING BETTINA ('Mepalsar') (ClHT)	EBls
'Climbing Blessings' (ClHT)	EBls
'Climbing Blue Moon' (ClHT)	ELan ELon ESty
§ 'Climbing Captain Christy' (ClHT)	EBls MAus
'Climbing Cécile Brünner' (ClPoly) ♀H5	CArg CSBt CTri EBls ECnt EPfP LSRN MAus MRav NLar SCob SEND SPer SSea
'Climbing Christine' (ClHT)	MAus
'Climbing Château de Clos-Vougeot' (ClHT)	EBls MAus
§ 'Climbing Columbia' (ClHT)	EBls EShb SPer
'Climbing Crimson Glory' (ClHT)	CBod CPou EBls EPfP MAsh MAus
§ 'Climbing Devoniensis' (ClT)	CPou EBls
'Climbing Ena Harkness' (ClHT)	CRos CTri EBls MAus MRav SEND SPer SPoG
'Climbing Étoile de Hollande' (ClHT) ♀H5	CKel CSBt CTri EBls EPfP EUJe LBuc LCro LOPS MAus MJak MRav NPri SMad SPer SPoG SSea WBor
'Climbing Fashion' (ClF)	EBls
'Climbing Frau Karl Druschki' (ClHP)	EBls
'Climbing General MacArthur' (ClHT)	EBls
§ 'Climbing Golden Dawn' (ClHT)	EBls
'Climbing Home Sweet Home' (ClHT)	LSRN
'Climbing Iceberg' (ClF) ♀H5	Widely available
'Climbing Jazz'	see *R.* THAT'S JAZZ
'Climbing Josephine Bruce' (ClHT)	EBls
§ 'Climbing Lady Hillingdon' (ClT) ♀H4	CArg CKel CWld EBls ELan EPfP EUJe EWTr LBuc LRHS LSRN MAus MRav NEgg NLar SPer
'Climbing Lady Sylvia' (ClHT)	CKel CSBt EBls EPfP LRHS LSRN MAsh MAus NRHS SPer
'Climbing Little White Pet'	see *R.* 'Félicité Perpétue'
'Climbing Madame Abel Chatenay' (ClHT)	MAus
'Climbing Madame Butterfly' (ClHT) ♀H6	EBls MAus
'Climbing Madame Caroline Testout' (ClHT)	CPou CTri EBls MAus MRav SPer
§ 'Climbing Madame Edouard Herriot' (ClHT)	MAus
'Climbing Masquerade' (ClF)	CBod CGro CPou CTri EBls ELan MAus MRav NEgg SCob SPer SSea
'Climbing Mrs Aaron Ward' (ClHT)	EBls
'Climbing Mrs Herbert Stevens' (ClHT)	EBls EPfP LRHS MAsh MAus MRav SEND SPer

	'Climbing Mrs Sam McGredy' (ClHT)	CArg CSBt EBls MAus NLar
	'Climbing Niphetos' (ClT)	EBls MAus
	'Climbing Ophelia' (ClHT)	EBee EBls MAus SPer
	CLIMBING ORANGE SUNBLAZE ('Meiji Katarsar'[PBR]) (ClMin)	SPer
§	'Climbing Paul Lédé' (ClT)	EBls MAus
	'Climbing Picture' (ClHT)	EBls
§	'Climbing Pompon de Paris' (ClMinCh)	CTri EBls MAus MNrw MRav SEND SPer
	'Climbing Roundelay' (Cl)	EBls
	'Climbing Ruby Wedding' (ClHT)	LSRN
	'Climbing Shot Silk' (ClHT) ♀[H6]	CKel EBls SPer
§	'Climbing Souvenir de la Malmaison' (ClBb)	CPou EBls MAus SPer
	'Climbing Talisman' (ClHT)	EBls
	'Climbing The Queen Elizabeth' (ClF)	EBls MAsh
	'Climbing White Cloud'	see *R.* WHITE CLOUD ('Korstacha')
	'Cloth of Gold'	see *R.* 'Chromatella'
	CLOUD NINE ('Fryextra'[PBR]) (HT)	MFry
	'Clytemnestra' (HM)	EBls
	COCO ('Korferse') (F)	LSRN
	'Coconut Ice' (HT)	SCob
	COLCHESTER BEAUTY ('Cansend') (F)	ECnt
§	'Colonel Fabvier' (Ch)	EBls MAus NLar
	colonial white	see *R.* 'Sombreuil'
	'Columbia' (HT)	CPou
	'Columbian'	see *R.* 'Climbing Columbia'
	'Commandant Beaurepaire' (Bb)	CPou EBls MAus
	common moss	see *R.* × *centifolia* 'Muscosa'
	'Compassion' (ClHT) ♀[H6]	Widely available
*	'Compassionate' (F)	MRav
	'Complicata' (G)	CPou CTri EBls EPfP EWTr LRHS MAus MRav NLar SCob SEND SMad SPer
	'Comte de Chambord' misapplied	see *R.* 'Madame Boll'
	COMTE DE CHAMPAGNE ('Ausufo'[PBR]) (S)	MAus
	'Comtesse Cécile de Chabrillant' (HP)	CPou EBls MAus
	'Comtesse de Lacépède' misapplied	see *R.* 'Du Maître d'Ecole'
§	'Comtesse de Murinais' (DMo)	EBls MAus
	'Comtesse d'Oxford' (HP)	EBls
§	'Comtesse du Caÿla' (Ch)	EBls MAus
	'Comtesse O'Gorman' (HP)	EBls
	'Comtesse Vandal' (HT)	EBls
	'Conditorum' (G)	EBls LEdu
	CONGRATULATIONS ('Korlift') (HT)	CBcs CBod CKel CSBt EBls ECnt IArd LSRN MAus MGos MRav SCob SPer SVic
§	'Conrad Ferdinand Meyer' (Ru)	EBee EBls SPer
	'Constance Spry' (ClS) ♀[H6]	CArg CBod CTri EBee EBls EPfP EWTr LCro LOPS LRHS MAus MMuc MRav MSwo NAln NEgg NLar NRHS SCob SEND SPer
§	'Cooperi' (Ra)	CRHN EBls EPfP EWTr MAus SSea WKif WPGP
	Cooper's Burmese	see *R.* 'Cooperi'

'Copenhagen' (ClHT)	EBls
COPPER LIGHTS ('Simhigh') (HT)	ESty
'Coral Cluster' (Poly)	EBls MAus
'Coral Creeper' (ClHT)	CRHN EBls
'Coral Dawn' (ClHT)	EBls
CORAL GEM ('Simplan') (HT)	ESty
CORAL PALACE	see *R.* IMAGINATION ('Pouldron')
CORAL SWEET DREAM ('Fryrader') (Patio) **new**	MFry
'Coralie' (D)	EBls
CORDELIA ('Ausbottle'[PBR]) (S)	MAus
'Cornelia' (HM) ♀[H6]	CArg CBcs CBod CGro CTri EBee EBls EPfP EWTr IArd LRHS LSRN MAsh MAus MCot MRav MWat NLar SCob SMad SPer
CORONATION STREET ('Wekswetrup') (F)	LSRN
CORVEDALE ('Ausnetting'[PBR]) (S)	MAus
'Coryana' (S)	EBls
corymbifera (S)	EBls
'Cosimo Ridolfi' (G)	EBls
COSMOPOLITAN ('Simgrid') (HT)	ESty
cottage maid	see *R.* × *centifolia* 'Unique Panachée'
COTTAGE MAID ('Poulspan') (S)	MAus
COTTAGE ROSE ('Ausglisten'[PBR]) (S)	LSRN
COUNTESS CELESTE	see *R.* IMAGINATION ('Pouldron')
COUNTESS OF WESSEX ('Beacream') (S)	EBls LRHS MAsh NRHS
COUNTRY MUSIC ('Harcheer') (S) **new**	LSRN
COUNTY OF YORKSHIRE ('Korstarnow'[PBR]) (GC) ♀[H6]	ESty
'Coupe d'Hébé' (Bb)	EBls MAus
COURAGE ('Poulduf'[PBR]) (HT)	ECnt
'Cramoisi Picotée' (G)	MAus
'Cramoisi Supérieur' (Ch)	EBls MAus
CRANFORD ('Frylustre') (HT) **new**	MFry
CRAZY FOR YOU ('Wekroalt'[PBR]) (F) ♀[H6]	EBls ESty LBuc LRHS LSRN MAsh
CREAM ABUNDANCE ('Harflax'[PBR]) (Abundance Series) (F)	SSea
CREAM DREAM ('Koromtar') (HT)	CTri
CREAMCRACKER ('Dicorigin') (F)	IDic
CRÈME CARAMEL ('Frynesca') (HT) **new**	MFry
CRÈME DE LA CRÈME ('Gancre'[PBR]) (ClHT)	CKel CRos CSBt EBls ECnt ELan ESty LRHS MAus MRav SPer SPoG SSea
'Crépuscule' (N)	EBee EBls EWTr MAus NLar
crested moss	see *R.* × *centifolia* 'Cristata'
CRICRI ('Meicri') (Min)	MAus
CRIMSON CASCADE ('Fryclimbdown'[PBR]) (ClHT) ♀[H6]	ESty EUJe LBuc MAsh MFry MRav MSwo SPer SPoG SSea
crimson damask	see *R. gallica* var. *officinalis*
'Crimson Descant' (ClHT)	ECnt

	Name	Suppliers
	'Crimson Glory' (HT)	CArg CTri EBls
	'Crimson Shower' (Ra)	CArg CBod CKel CRos CTri ELan EWTr LRHS MAus MBNS MMuc MRav MSwo NAln NEgg NLar SEND SPer WHer
	Crimson Sweet Dream ('Frynogo') (Patio)	CSBt ECnt ESty MFry
	'Cristata'	see *R.* × *centifolia* 'Cristata'
	Crocus Rose ('Ausquest'[PBR]) (S) ♀H6	CBod CKel CRos EPfP LCro LOPS LRHS MAus MRav NAln NEgg NLar NRHS SCob SPer
	Crown Princess Margareta ('Auswinter'[PBR]) (S) ♀H6	CRos ELan EPfP ESty LBuc LRHS MAsh MAus NAln NEgg NLar NRHS SCob SCoo SPer SPoG
	cuisse de nymphe	see *R.* 'Great Maiden's Blush'
	'Cupid' (ClHT)	EBls EWTr MAus SPer
I	'Cutie' (Patio)	ESty
	cymosa	EBls
	- 'Rebecca Rushforth'	WPGP
	'Cynthia Brooke' (HT)	EBls
	Dacapo ('Poulcy012'[PBR]) (Courtyard Series) (ClPatio)	ECnt
	'D'Aguesseau' (G)	MAus
	'Daily Mail'	see *R.* 'Climbing Madame Edouard Herriot'
	Daily Sketch ('Macai') (F)	ESty
	'Dainty Bess' (HT)	EBls MAus
	'Dainty Maid' (F)	EBls
	'Daisy Hill' ('Macrantha' hybrid) ♀H7	EBls
	× ***damascena*** var. ***bifera***	see *R.* × *damascena* var. *semperflorens*
	- 'Kazanlik' (D)	EBls
§	- 'Professeur Émile Perrot' (D)	LEdu MAus WFar
§	- var. ***semperflorens*** (D) ♀H6	CPou EBls MAus MCot NLar SSea
	- 'Trigintipetala' misapplied	see *R.* × *damascena* 'Professeur Émile Perrot'
§	- 'Versicolor' (D)	EBls MAus SSea
	'Dame Edith Helen' (HT)	EBls
	Dame Wendy ('Canson') (F)	MAus
	'Danaë' (HM)	EBls MAus
	Dancing Queen ('Fryfestoon') (ClHT) ♀H6	CArg ECnt EUJe LRHS LSRN MAsh MFry MRav
	Dancing Sunset ('Guesunusal') (ClHT) **new**	ESty
	Daniel ('Webwhite') (HT)	ESty
	Danny Boy ('Dicxcon'[PBR]) (Patio)	IDic LSRN
	Danse des Sylphes ('Malcair') (Cl)	EBls
	'Danse du Feu' (ClF)	CArg CBcs CKel CSBt CTri EBls ELan EUJe LRHS MAsh MAus MRav MWat SCob SPer
	'Daphne' ambig.	EBls LSRN
	Dapple Dawn ('Ausapple') (S)	MAus
	Darcey Bussell ('Ausdecorum'[PBR]) (S) ♀H6	CGro CRos CSBt ECnt ELan EPfP ESty LBuc LCro LOPS LRHS LSRN MAsh MAus MGos NAln NLar NRHS SCob SPer SPoG
	'Darling Jenny' (HT)	LSRN
	David Whitfield ('Gana'[PBR]) (F)	LSRN
	davidii (S)	EBls MAus WPav

	Name	Suppliers
	David's Star ('Hordadstar') (HT)	LSRN
	Dawn Chorus ('Dicquasar'[PBR]) (HT) ♀H6	CSBt EPfP ESty LRHS MAsh MFry MJak MRav SCob SPer SPoG SSea
	'Daybreak' (HM)	CTri EBls EWTr MAus NLar
	'De la Grifferaie'	EBls
	'De Meaux'	see *R.* × *centifolia* 'De Meaux'
	'De Meaux, White'	see *R.* 'White de Meaux'
§	'De Resht' (DPo) ♀H7	CArg CBod CKel CPou CTri EBls ECnt EPfP LBuc LRHS MAsh MAus MCot MRav NLar NPri SPer
	Dear Barbara ('Rawbar') (HT)	LSRN
	Dear Dad ('Smi87-02') (HT) **new**	ESty
	'Dear Daughter' (F)	ESty
	Dear Joan ('Rawjo') (F)	LSRN
§	Dear Margaret ('Raw293') (HT)	LSRN
	Dear Michael ('Raw1065') (F)	LSRN
	'Dearest' (F)	CArg CTri SCob SPer
	'Debbie Thomas' (HT)	LSRN
	Deb's Delight ('Legsweet'[PBR]) (F)	LSRN
	'Debutante' (Ra) ♀H7	CBod CRHN EBls EWTr MAus
	'Deep Secret' (HT)	CArg CBcs CGro CKel CSBt CTri EBls ECnt ELan EPfP ESty LBuc LRHS MAsh MCot MFry MJak MRav MWat NAln NPri SCob SPer SSea
	'Deidre Hall' (HT)	LSRN
	'Delambre' (DPo)	MAus
	Delightful ('Curspoglo') (ClMin) **new**	ESty
	Della Balfour ('Harblend'[PBR]) (ClHT)	EBls
	Dentelle de Malines ('Lenfiro') (S)	MAus
	'Deschamps' (N)	EBls
	Desdemona ('Auskindling') (HM)	CGro CRos LRHS MAsh MAus NRHS
	'Designer Sunset' (Patio)	MAsh
§	'Desprez à Fleur Jaune' (N)	EBls IArd LRHS MAus NEgg SPer
	'Deuil de Paul Fontaine' (Mo)	EBls
	'Devoniensis' (ClT)	see *R.* 'Climbing Devoniensis'
	Diamond ('Korgazell'[PBR]) (Patio) ♀H6	EPfP LSRN
	Diamond Anniversary ('Morsixty') (Min)	CRos LSRN
	'Diamond Celebration' (HT)	LSRN
	Diamond Days Forever ('Fryjess'[PBR]) (F)	ECnt LSRN MFry
	Diamond Days ('Hartribe'[PBR]) (HT)	ESty LSRN MFry MRav SPoG
	Diamond Eyes ('Wekwibypur') (Min)	ECnt ESty
	'Diamond Jubilee' (HT)	CSBt EBls
	Diamond Jubilee ('Tan022260') (HT) **new**	CArg ELan
	'Diamond Wishes'	see *R.* Misty Hit
	Diana ('Tananaid'[PBR]) (HT)	LSRN
	Dick's Delight ('Dicwhistle') (GC)	LSRN
	Dienie Stewart ('Dicpraise') (F)	IDic
	Dioressence ('Deldiore') (F)	ESty
§	'Direktör Benschop' (Cl)	EBls EUJe MCot

DIXIELAND LINDA ('Beadix') (ClHT) EBls LRHS MAsh
DIZZY HEIGHTS ('Fryblissful'PBR) (ClHT) ♀H6 MAus MFry MRav SPer
'Docteur Grill' (T) EBls
'Doctor Edward Deacon' (HT) EBls
'Doctor Huey' (Cl) CRHN EBls
DOCTOR JO ('Fryatlanta'PBR) (F) MFry
'Doctor W. Van Fleet' (Ra) EBls MAus
DOLCE VITA ('Delcentoran') (F) ESty
DOLLY ('Poulvision') (F) LSRN
'Don Charlton' (HT) NEgg
'Donald Prior' (F) EBls
'Doncasteri' EBls MAus
DONNA ('Pekcoupamaple') (HT) LSRN
'Doreen' (HT) LSRN
'Doris Tysterman' (HT) CTri EBls MAus SPer
DOROTHY ('Cocrocket'PBR) (F) LSRN MRav
DOROTHY HOUSE ('Fryniffi') (F) **new** MFry
'Dorothy Perkins' (Ra) CArg CBod CRHN CTri EBls LBuc MAsh MAus MRav NPer SCob SPer WHer
'Dorothy Wilson' (F) EBls
'Dortmund' (S) ♀H7 EBls MAus NLar SPer
DOUBLE DELIGHT ('Andeli') (HT) CBod EBls ELan ESty LSRN SPer SSea
DOUGLAS ('Cocfresco') (F) LSRN
DREAM LOVER ('Peayetti'PBR) (Patio) ESty
'Dreaming Spires' (Cl) MSwo SPer
'Dresden Doll' (MinMo) EBls
§ 'Du Maître d'Ecole' (G) EBls MAus WHer
DUBLIN BAY ('Macdub') (ClF) ♀H6 CArg CBod CGro CKel CRos CSBt CTri EBee EBls ECnt ELan ELon EPfP EUJe IArd LRHS LSRN MAsh MCot MFry MRav MSwo MWat NLar NPri SPer SPoG SSea WBor
'Duc de Guiche' (G) ♀H7 EBls EPfP MAus MMuc NLar SPer WHer
DUCHESS OF CORNWALL ('Tan97157') (HT) ♀H6 CKel CSBt EBee EBls ESty MFry MRav MWat SCob
'Duchess of Portland' see *R.* 'Portlandica'
DUCHESS OF YORK see *R.* SUNSEEKER
'Duchesse d'Angoulême' (Ce × G) ♀H7 EBls MAus
'Duchesse d'Auerstädt' (N) EBls
'Duchesse de Brabant' (HT) EBls
'Duchesse de Buccleugh' (G) EBls MAus
§ 'Duchesse de Montebello' (G) ♀H7 CBod CPou EBls EWTr GBin MAus NLar SPer
'Duchesse de Rohan' (Ce × HP) EBls
'Duchesse de Verneuil' (CeMo) MAus
'Duke of Edinburgh' (HP) EBls MAus
DUKE OF EDINBURGH (Patio) see *R.* THE GOLD AWARD ROSE
'Duke of Wellington' (HP) CPou EBls
'Duke of Windsor' (HT) SPer
'Dundee Rambler' (Ra) MAus
DUNHAM MASSEY ('Beajelly') (S) EBls LRHS MAsh
'Dunwich Rose' (SpH) CBod EBls EPfP MAus NLar SCob WCot
§ 'Duplex' (S) EBls MAus
'Dupontii' (S) ♀H6 EBls EWTr MAus NLar SPer
'Dupuy Jamain' (HP) EBls
'Dusky Maiden' (F) CBod EBls EWTr MAus
'Dutch Gold' (HT) CArg ELon MAus
DWARF FAIRY ('Korweenu') (Min) MAsh
DYNAMIC DUO ('Fryvogue') (F) ECnt ESty
'E.H. Morse' see *R.* 'Ernest H. Morse'
'Easlea's Golden Rambler' (Ra) ♀H5 CArg CGro EBls ESty MAus MRav NEgg NLar
§ EASY DOES IT ('Harpageant'PBR) (F) ♀H6 CBod CKel ECnt ESty LRHS MAsh MRav NLar
EASY GOING ('Harflow'PBR) (F) ♀H6 IArd MAsh
§ EBB TIDE ('Weksmopur'PBR) (F) CBod CSBt ECnt ELon ESty LRHS MAsh SPoG
ecae (S) EBls MAus
'Éclair' (HP) EBls WBor
'Eddie's Crimson' (*moyesii* hybrid) LSRN
'Eddie's Jewel' (*moyesii* hybrid) EBls LSRN MAus
EDEN ROSE '88 ('Meiviolin') (ClHT) CPou EBls MAsh SPer
'Edith Bellenden' (RH) EBls
EDITH HOLDEN ('Chewlegacy') (F) EBls
'Edward Hyams' (*persica* hybrid) MAus
EDWARD'S ROSE ('Smi73/7/97') (F) ESty LSRN MRav MWat
eglanteria see *R. rubiginosa*
EGLANTYNE ('Ausmak'PBR) (S) CKel CRos ELan EPfP LCro LOPS LRHS MAsh MAus MRav NAln NRHS SCob SPer SSea
'Eleanor' (Patio) LSRN
ELEANOR ('Poulberin'PBR) (S) CPou ECnt LSRN
'Elegance' (ClHT) EBls
§ ***elegantula*** 'Persetosa' (S) EBls MAus NLar SPer
§ ELINA ('Dicjana') (HT) ♀H6 EBls ECnt LSRN MAus MJak MRav SPer
'Elizabeth Harkness' (HT) EBls MAus SPer
'Elizabeth Harwood' (Cl) EBls
ELIZABETH OF GLAMIS ('Macel') (F) CTri EBls SPer
ELIZABETH STUART ('Maselstu') (Generosa Series) (S) LSRN
ELLE ('Meibderos'PBR) (HT) LSRN
ELLEN ('Auscup') (S) LSRN
'Ellen Willmott' (HT) EBls SPer
'Elmshorn' (S) EBls
ELOISE ('Kirsandra'PBR) (HT) LSRN
ELVIS ('Adablarop'PBR) (HT) **new** LSRN
EMILIA MARIA see *R.* LA ROSE DE MOLINARD
EMILY ('Ausburton') (S) LSRN
'Emily Gray' (Ra) CRHN EBee EBls LBuc LSRN MAsh MAus MRav NLar NPri SCob SPer WHer
EMILY VICTORIA ('Boshipeacon') (F) LSRN
'Empereur du Maroc' (HP) EBee EBls MAus

	'Ena Harkness' (HT)	CKel CTri EBee EBls ELan LBuc LRHS NRHS
	ENCHANTRESS ('Tan97281'^{PBR}) (HT)	EBee
§	'Enfant de France' (HP)	EBls LSRN
	ENGLAND'S ROSE ('Auslounge'^{PBR}) (S)	CRos MAus
	ENGLISH GARDEN ('Ausbuff') (S)	CArg CTri LSRN
	'English Miss' (F)	CArg CKel CPou EBee EBls ECnt LRHS MAsh MAus MFry MJak MRav MWat SPer SPoG
	ENGLISH SONNET	see *R.* SAMARITAN
	'Eos' (*moyesii* hybrid)	EBls MAus
	'Erfurt' (HM)	EBee EBls MAus SPer
§	'Ernest H. Morse' (HT)	CSBt CTri EBls SPer
	ESCAPADE ('Harpade') (F) ♀H6	EBls MAus
	ESPECIALLY FOR YOU ('Fryworthy'^{PBR}) (HT) ♀H6	CKel CSBt ESty LSRN MFry SCob SSea
	ESSEX ('Poulnoz'^{PBR}) (GC)	CKel EBls SCob SPer
	'Etain' (Ra)	ECnt
§	'Étendard' (ClHT)	EBls MRav NLar SPer SPoG
	ETERNAL FLAME ('Korassenet'^{PBR}) (F)	MAsh
	ETERNITY ('Moai150097') (F)	CGro
	ETERNITY ('Ricity') (Min)	LRHS
	ETERNITY ('Twoetern') (HT)	MAsh
	'Ethel' (Ra)	CPou EBls LSRN NLar
	'Étoile de Hollande' (HT)	CArg CBod CTri EBls ELan ELon EUJe EWTr LBuc LRHS LSRN MAsh MBNS MCot MJak MMrt NEgg NLar SCob WSpi
	'Etoile de Lyon' (T)	EBls
	'Eugène Fürst' (HP)	EBls
	'Eugénie Guinoisseau' (Mo)	CPou EBls
	EUPHRATES ('Harunique') (*persica* hybrid)	EBls
	'Euphrosyne' (Ra)	MAus
	'Eva' (HM)	EBls
	'Evangeline' (Ra)	EBls MAus
	EVE RUGGIEN ('Adarylop') (HT) **new**	LSRN
	EVELYN ('Aussaucer'^{PBR}) (S)	CArg CKel CRos CSBt EPfP ESty LSRN NEgg NLar SLon
§	EVELYN FISON ('Macev') (F)	CSBt CTri EBls LSRN MAus SPer
	'Evelyn May' (HT)	EBls LRHS LSRN MAsh NRHS
	'Everest Double Fragrance' (F)	EBls
	'Excelsa' (Ra)	CBod CSBt CTri EBls EPfP IArd LBuc MAsh MRav SCob SPoG WBor
	EYE OF THE TIGER ('Chewbullseye') (S)	CRos EBee ELan ESty LRHS MAsh NPri NRHS SMad SPoG
	EYEOPENER ('Interop') (S/GC)	EBls
	EYES FOR YOU ('Pejbigeye') (F) ♀H6	CGro CKel CRos CSBt CWld EBee EPfP ESty GBin LRHS MAsh MFry NLar NPri NRHS SLon SPer SPoG WKif
	'F.E. Lester'	see *R.* 'Francis E. Lester'
§	'F.J. Grootendorst' (Ru)	CBod EBls NEgg SPer WHer
	FAB AT 50 ('Woraunt') (F)	LSRN
	FABULOUS AT 40 ('Webcountry') (F)	LSRN
	FABULOUS AT 50 ('Rawfabsal') (F)	LSRN
	FABULOUS AT 65 ('Raw1041') (F)	LSRN
	FABULOUS AT 70	LSRN
	FABULOUS AT 80 ('Rawcox') (F)	LSRN
	FAB-U-LOUS! ('Forfab') (HT)	ESty
	'Fabvier'	see *R.* 'Colonel Fabvier'
	FAIR EVA ('Seaeva') (Ra/GC)	ESty
	'Fairy Rose'	see *R.* 'The Fairy'
	FAITHFUL FRIEND ('Beachallenge') (S)	EBls LSRN
	FALSTAFF ('Ausverse'^{PBR}) (S)	CArg CRos CSBt EPfP LCro LOPS LRHS LSRN MAsh MAus MBNS MJak MRav MSwo NAln NEgg NLar NRHS SCob SPer SSea
	'Fantin-Latour' (Ce) ♀H6	CArg CTri EBls ECnt ELan EWTr LEdu LRHS MAus MCot MMuc MRav NAln NEgg NLar SEND SMad SPer
	fargesii hort.	see *R. moyesii* var. *fargesii*
	farreri f. ***persetosa***	see *R. elegantula* 'Persetosa'
§	FASCINATION ('Poulmax'^{PBR}) (F) ♀H6	CArg LRHS MAsh MFry SPer
	'Fashion' (F)	EBls
	FATHER'S FAVOURITE ('Gandoug'^{PBR}) (F)	LSRN
	fedtschenkoana misapplied	MAus SPer
	fedtschenkoana Regel	EBls
	FÉE DES NEIGES	see *R.* ICEBERG
	'Felicia' (HM) ♀H6	CArg CKel CSBt CTri EBee EBls ECnt ELan LRHS MAsh MAus MCot MMuc MRav MSwo NLar SEND SPer SSea WKif
	'Félicité Parmentier' (A × D) ♀H6	CArg EBls EPfP LRHS MAus NLar SPer
§	'Félicité Perpétue' (Ra) ♀H6	CArg CBcs CBod CTri EBls ELan EPfP EWTr LRHS MAus MCot MRav MSwo MWat NEgg NLar SEND SPer SSea WFar
	'Fellemberg' (ClCh)	EBee EBls MAus
	FELLOWSHIP ('Harwelcome'^{PBR}) (F) ♀H6	EBls MAus SCob SSea
	'Ferdinand Pichard' (Bb) ♀H6	Widely available
	FERDY ('Keitoli'^{PBR}) (GC)	EBls SPer
I	'Fern's Rose' (F)	LSRN
	ferruginea	see *R. glauca* Pourr.
	FESTIVAL ('Kordialo'^{PBR}) (Patio)	CGro MRav SPer
	FESTIVE JEWEL ('Beacost') (S)	EBls EPfP LRHS MAsh
	FIGHTING TEMERAIRE ('Austrava'^{PBR}) (S)	CRos EPfP LBuc LRHS MAus NAln NRHS SSea
§	***filipes*** 'Kiftsgate' (Ra) ♀H6	CArg CBcs CBod CGro CKel CSBt CTri EBls ECnt ELan EPfP GKin LEdu LRHS MAsh MAus MFry MRav MWat NEgg NLar NRHS NWea SCob SEND SPer SSea WBor WKif
	filipes × ***glauca***	MAus
§	'Fimbriata' (Ru)	CPou EBls LEdu MAus NLar SPer
	FIONA ('Meibeluxen') (S/GC)	EBls LSRN MSwo
	'Firecracker' (F)	EBls
	FIRESTAR	see *R.* EASY DOES IT
	FIRST GREAT WESTERN ('Oracharpam'^{PBR}) (HT)	CSBt ELon ESty

	Name	Suppliers
	'First Love' (HT)	EBls
	'Fisher and Holmes' (HP)	EBls MAus
	FLAMINGO ('Simref') (F)	ESty
	FLIRT ('Korkopapp'PBR) (F)	MAsh
	FLIRT ('Korvondra') (F) **new**	MFry
	'Flora' (HT)	MAus
	'Flora' (Ra)	EBls
	'Flora McIvor' (RH)	EBls
	FLOWER CARPET AMBER ('Noa97400a'PBR) (GC) ♀H6	CGro CRos CSBt EBls EPfP EUJe LBuc LRHS MAsh NPri NRHS SPoG
	'Flower Carpet Coral'PBR (GC) ♀H6	CRos CSBt EBls EPfP LBuc LRHS LSRN MAsh NPri NRHS
	FLOWER CARPET GOLD ('Noalesa'PBR) (GC)	CGro CRos EBls ECnt LBuc LRHS MAsh NPri NRHS SPoG
	FLOWER CARPET PINK	see *R.* PINK FLOWER CARPET
	FLOWER CARPET PINK SUPREME ('Noa168098f') (GC)	EBls
	FLOWER CARPET RED VELVET ('Noare'PBR) (GC/S) ♀H6	CGro CRos EBls ELan EPfP LBuc LCro LOPS LRHS MAsh NPri NRHS SCoo SSea
	FLOWER CARPET RUBY (GC)	CRos EBls EPfP EUJe LBuc LRHS LSRN MAsh NPri NRHS SPoG
	FLOWER CARPET SCARLET ('Noa83100b'PBR) (GC) ♀H6	CRos EBls LBuc LRHS MAsh NRHS
	FLOWER CARPET SUNSET ('Deseo') (S)	CGro CRos EPfP LRHS MAsh NPri
§	FLOWER CARPET SUNSHINE ('Noason'PBR) (GC) ♀H6	CBod CRos EBls LCro LOPS LRHS MAsh NPri NRHS SCoo SPer SSea
	FLOWER CARPET WHITE ('Noaschnee'PBR) (GC) ♀H6	CGro CRos CTri EBls ECnt EPfP EUJe LCro LOPS LRHS LSRN MAsh MAus NPri NRHS SCoo SPer SPoG SSea
	FLOWER POWER ('Frycassia'PBR) (Patio) ♀H6	CKel CSBt ECnt ESty LRHS MAsh MAus MFry MRav NPri SPoG
	FLOWER POWER GOLD ('Fryneon') (Patio)	CSBt ECnt ESty LRHS MAsh MFry NPri NRHS SPoG
§	***foetida*** (S)	EBls MAus SPer
§	- 'Bicolor' (S)	EBls MAus NLar SPer
§	- 'Persiana' (S)	EBls MAus
	foliolosa	EBls
	'Follette' (Cl)	EBls
	FOND MEMORIES ('Kirfelix'PBR) (Patio)	ESty LSRN SCoo
	FOR YOU WITH LOVE ('Fryjangle') (Patio)	LSRN MAsh MFry
	FOR YOUR EYES ONLY ('Cheweyesup') (S)	CArg CBod CGro CKel CRos CSBt EBee ECnt ELon EPfP ESty LBuc LRHS LSRN MAsh MFry MRav NLar NPri NRHS SCoo SMad SPoG
	FORGET ME NOT ('Coccharm'PBR) (HT)	ESty
	forrestiana (S)	EBls MAus WPav
	× ***fortuneana*** (Ra)	EBls
	Fortune's double yellow	see *R.* × *odorata* 'Pseudindica'
	'Fountain' (S)	EBls MAus
	FOXY LADY ('Simmem') (HT)	ESty
	FRAGONARD ('Delparviro'PBR) (HT)	ESty
	FRAGRANT BEAUTY ('Smi152-1-4') (HT)	ESty
	FRAGRANT CLOUD ('Tanellis') (HT)	CArg CBcs CRos CTri EBls ELan ELon EPfP LBuc LRHS MAsh MAus MGos MRav MWat SPer SPoG
	'Fragrant Delight' (F) ♀H6	CArg CKel CSBt EBls ELan MAus MJak MRav MWat SCob SPer
	FRAGRANT DREAM ('Dicodour') (HT)	ESty SSea
	FRAGRANT MEMORIES ('Korpastato'PBR) (HT)	CSBt
	FRAGRANT PLUM ('Aroplumi') (HT)	ESty
	'Fragrant Silk'	SSea
	'Francesca' (HM)	EBls EWTr LSRN MAus NLar SPer
	FRANCINE AUSTIN ('Ausram') (S/GC)	MAus NEgg
	'Francis Copple' (S)	EBls
	'Francis Dubreuil' (T)	EBls
§	'Francis E. Lester' (HM/Ra) ♀H6	CRHN CRos CSam EBee EBls ELan EPfP EWTr LRHS MAus MCot MMuc NLar NRHS SEND SPer SSea
	× ***francofurtana*** misapplied	see *R.* 'Impératrice Joséphine'
	- 'Empress Josephine'	see *R.* 'Impératrice Joséphine'
	'François Juranville' (Ra) ♀H6	CArg CHll CRHN EBee EBls EPfP LRHS MAus MMuc MRav NLar SEND SLon SPer WFar WHer
§	'Frau Karl Druschki' (HP)	EBls MAus
	'Fred Loads' (F) ♀H7	EBls MAus MCot
	FREDDIE MERCURY ('Batmercury') (HT)	ESty LSRN NEgg
	FREE SPIRIT ('Fryjeru'PBR) (F) ♀H6	ECnt MFry
	FREEDOM ('Dicjem') (HT) ♀H6	CArg CKel CTri EBls ECnt MAus MJak MRav SCob SPer
	FREEDOM ('Tan97544') (HT)	CKel MWat
	'Frensham' (F)	CBcs EBls SSea
	FRIEND FOR LIFE ('Cocnanne'PBR) (F) ♀H6	LSRN MRav
	FRIENDS FOREVER ('Korapriber') (F) ♀H6	CSBt EPfP LSRN MAsh
	FRIENDSHIP OF STRANGERS ('633D9') (Cl)	EBls
	FRILLY CUFF ('Beajingle') (S)	EBls LRHS MAsh
	'Fritz Nobis' (S) ♀H7	CArg CPou EBls MAus NLar SPer
	FROTHY ('Macfrothy'PBR) (Patio)	ECnt ESty
	'Fru Dagmar Hastrup' (Ru) ♀H7	CArg CBcs CBod CDul CKel CSBt CTri EBee EBls ECnt ELan EPfP EWTr LBuc LRHS MAsh MAus MFry MSwo NEgg NLar SCob SEND SPer
	'Frühlingsanfang' (SpH)	EBls
	'Frühlingsduft' (SpH)	EBls
	'Frühlingsgold' (SpH) ♀H7	CArg CTho EBls ELan EWTr MAus NLar NWea SPer
	'Frühlingsmorgen' (SpH) ♀H7	EBls MAus SMad SPer
	'Frühlingsschnee' (SpH)	EBls
	'Frühlingszauber' (SpH)	EBls
	'Fulgens'	see *R.* 'Malton'
§	***gallica*** (G)	EBls
§	- var. ***officinalis*** (G) ♀H7	CBod CRos CTri EBls EPfP GPoy LEdu LRHS MAsh MAus MHer MNHC MRav NLar SPer SRms WFar WHer
	- 'Velutiniflora' (G)	EBls
§	- 'Versicolor' (G) ♀H7	CArg CKel CSBt CTri CWld EBee EBls ECnt EPfP EWTr GPoy LEdu LRHS LSRN MAsh MAus MCot MHer MNHC MRav MWat NAln NLar NRHS NSti SMad SPer SSea WBor WKif

Name	Suppliers
GALWAY BAY ('Macba') (ClHT)	CArg CBod CPou CRos EBls LRHS MAsh NLar SPer
GARDEN OF ROSES	see *R.* JOIE DE VIVRE
GARDEN PARTY ('Kormollis') (F)	EBls
'Gardeners' Glory'PBR (ClHT) 🏆H6	CArg CSBt CWld ECnt EPfP ESty EUJe LRHS MAsh MFry MRav NPri SPoG
GARDENERS' JOY ('Beadrum') (S)	EBls
'Gardenia' (Ra)	EBls MAus MMuc MSwo NLar SPer
'Garnette Carol'	see *R.* 'Carol Amling'
'Garnette Pink'	see *R.* 'Carol Amling'
'Gaujard'	see *R.* ROSE GAUJARD
'Gelbe Dagmar Hastrup'	see *R.* YELLOW DAGMAR HASTRUP
GEMINI ('Jacnepal') (HT)	ESty
'Général Jacqueminot' (HP)	EBls MAus
'Général Kléber' (CeMo) 🏆H7	EBls MAus
§ 'Général Schablikine' (T)	EBls MAus MCot NLar
GENESIS ('Fryjuicy'PBR) (Patio)	CGro ECnt MFry MRav
gentiliana misapplied	see *R.* 'Polyantha Grandiflora'
gentiliana H. Lév. & Variot	see *R. multiflora* var. *cathayensis*
GENTLE HERMIONE ('Ausrumba'PBR) (S)	CGro CRos ELan EPfP LBuc LRHS MAsh MAus NAln NLar NRHS SCob SPer SPoG
GENTLE TOUCH ('Diclulu') (Min/Patio)	CKel CSBt MRav SPer
GEOFF HAMILTON ('Ausham'PBR) (S)	EBee EPfP LSRN MAsh MAus MBNS NAln NEgg SCob SPer SSea
'Geoffrey Smith' (Cl)	LSRN NDal
'Georg Arends' (HP)	EBls MAus
GEORGE ('Simetna') (F)	ESty
GEORGE BEST ('Dichimanher'PBR) (Patio) 🏆H6	ESty IDic LSRN
'George Dickson' (HT)	EBls
'George Vancouver' (S)	EBls
GEORGE'S PRIDE ('Manpride') (Min) **new**	LSRN
'Georges Vibert' (G)	EBls MAus
'Geranium' (*moyesii* hybrid) 🏆H6	CArg CBcs CKel CTri EBls ELan EPfP IArd MAus MRav NLar SCob SPer
GERBE D'OR	see *R.* CASINO
'Gerbe Rose' (Ra)	EBls MAus WHer
GERTRUDE JEKYLL ('Ausbord'PBR) (S) 🏆H6	Widely available
'Ghislaine de Féligonde' (HM) 🏆H5	CBod CKel CSam EBls EPfP ESty EWTr LRHS MAsh MAus MCot NLar SEND SPer WBor
GHITA	see *R.* MILLIE
§ GIARDINA ('Tan97289'PBR) (Cl)	ESty
gigantea	WPGP
gigantea × longicuspis	WPGP
GIGGLES ('Frynoodle'PBR) (Patio)	MFry SCoo
GINGER SYLLABUB ('Harjolina'PBR) (ClHT)	CKel CPou ECnt ESty MRav SPer SPoG
GIPSY BOY	see *R.* 'Zigeunerknabe'
giraldii (S)	EBls
GISELA'S DELIGHT ('Horpink') (S)	EBls
GLAD TIDINGS ('Tantide') (F)	CTri EBls MRav MWat SPer
GLAMIS CASTLE ('Auslevel'PBR) (S)	CArg CTri LCro LOPS NEgg SCob SCoo
glauca Vill. ex Lois.	see *R. caesia* subsp. *vosagiaca*
glauca ambig.	EWTr MHer MSwo SCob
§ ***glauca*** Pourr. (S) 🏆H7	CSBt CSpe CTri EBls ECnt ELan ELon EPfP GBin LEdu LRHS MAus MMuc MRav MWat NEgg NLar NWea SEND SGol SPer SPoG SSea WCot WMoo
'Glenfiddich' (F)	CArg CTri LSRN MAus SPer
'Glenn Dale' (Cl)	CPou
GLOBAL BEAUTY ('Tan 94448') (HT)	EBee ECnt ELon MFry MRav
'Gloire de Bruxelles' (HP)	EBls
'Gloire de Dijon' (ClT)	CArg CGro CKel CSBt CTri EBee EBls ECnt ELan LCro LOPS LSRN MAus MRav MWat NEgg NLar NWea SCob SPer
'Gloire de Ducher' (HP)	EBls MAus
'Gloire de France' (G) 🏆H7	CArg EBls MAus NLar WHer
'Gloire de Guilan' (D)	CPou MAus
'Gloire des Mousseuses' (CeMo)	CPou EBls MAus
'Gloire du Midi' (Poly)	MAus
'Gloire Lyonnaise' (HP)	CPou EBls MMuc
'Gloria Mundi' (Poly)	EBls NEgg
GLORIANA ('Chewpope'PBR) (ClMin)	CArg CKel ECnt ESty EUJe MAsh MAus MRav MWat SPer SPoG SSea
'Glory of Edzell' (SpH)	MAus
'Glory of Seale' (S)	SSea
GLOWING AMBER ('Manglow') (Min)	ESty
'Goethe' (Mo)	EBls
GOLD CHARM ('Chewalbygold') (Cl)	MAsh
GOLD SPICE ('Frymega') (F) **new**	MFry
'Goldbusch' (RH)	EBls
'Golden Angel' (Min) **new**	MAsh
'Golden Anniversary' (Patio)	SPer SSea
'Golden Autumn' (HT)	LSRN
GOLDEN BEAUTY ('Clebeau') (Min)	CKel LRHS
GOLDEN BEAUTY ('Korberbeni'PBR) (F) 🏆H6	CArg CKel CPou MAsh MFry
GOLDEN BERYL ('Manberyl') (Min)	LSRN
GOLDEN CELEBRATION ('Ausgold'PBR) (S) 🏆H6	CArg CBod CGro CKel CRos CSBt CTri ECnt EPfP ESty LCro LOPS LRHS LSRN MAsh MAus MMuc MRav MSwo NAln NLar NRHS SCob SLon SPer SPoG SSea
'Golden Chersonese' (S)	EBls MAus
'Golden Dawn' (HT)	MAsh
'Golden Dawn' (ClHT)	see *R.* 'Climbing Golden Dawn'
GOLDEN FUTURE ('Horanymoll'PBR) (ClHT) 🏆H6	MAus
GOLDEN GATE ('Korgolgat'PBR) (ClHT) 🏆H6	ECnt EPfP LRHS MAsh MAus NRHS SSea
'Golden Glow' (Cl)	EBls
GOLDEN JEWEL ('Tanledolg'PBR) (F/Patio)	ESty
GOLDEN JUBILEE ('Cocagold') (HT)	CArg EBls MRav
GOLDEN MELODY ('Irene Churruca') (HT)	EBls
GOLDEN MEMORIES ('Korholesea'PBR) (F) 🏆H6	CArg CSBt EBls LBuc LRHS MAsh MGos MRav NPri SCoo

	Name	Suppliers
	GOLDEN MOMENT ('Smi-99-2-04') (HT)	ESty MRav
	'Golden Moss' (Mo)	EBls
	GOLDEN OLDIE ('Fryescape'PBR) (HT)	MFry
	'Golden Rambler'	see *R.* 'Alister Stella Gray'
	'Golden Salmon Supérieur' (Poly)	EBls
	'Golden Showers' (Cl)	Widely available
§	GOLDEN SMILES ('Frykeyno'PBR) (F) ♀H6	CArg CKel CRos ECnt ESty LRHS LSRN MAsh MFry NPri
	GOLDEN WEDDING ('Arokris'PBR) (F)	Widely available
	GOLDEN WEDDING ANNIVERSARY (F)	LSRN
	'Golden Wedding Celebration' (F)	LSRN
	'Golden Wings' (S)	CArg CPou CTri EBls ELan GBin MAus MCot MRav MSwo MWat NLar SPer
	'Goldfinch' (Ra)	CArg CBod EBee EBls ELan EPfP EWTr MAsh MAus MRav NAln NEgg NLar SEND SPer WFar
	GOLDSTAR ('Candide') (HT)	ECnt
	GOOD AS GOLD ('Chewsunbeam'PBR) (ClMin)	CSBt ECnt ESty MFry SPer
	GORDON SNELL ('Dicwriter') (F)	IDic
	GORDON'S COLLEGE ('Cocjabby'PBR) (F) ♀H6	CSBt
	GORGEOUS GIRL ('Forshow') (HT) **new**	ESty
	GORGEOUS ('Poulpmt009'PBR) (HT)	LRHS MAsh NPri
	'Grace Abounding' (F)	LSRN
	GRACE ('Auskeppy'PBR) (S) ♀H6	CRos CSBt EPfP ESty LBuc LRHS LSRN MAsh MAus NAln NEgg NLar NRHS SCob SPer SSea
	'Grace Darling' (T)	EBls
	GRACE DE MONACO ('Meimit') (HT)	EBls
	'Graciously Pink' (Min)	MAsh
	GRAHAM THOMAS ('Ausmas') (S) ♀H6	Widely available
I	'Granada' Lindquist (HT)	EBls
	GRANDE AMORE	see *R.* MY VALENTINE ('Korcoluma')
	'Grandma' (F)	LSRN
	GRAND-MÈRE JENNY ('Grem') (HT)	EBls
	'Grandpa Dickson' (HT)	CArg EBls MAsh MAus SPer
	GRANNY'S FAVOURITE (Patio/F)	LSRN
	GREAT EXPECTATIONS ambig.	EBee
	GREAT EXPECTATIONS ('Lanican') (HT)	CBcs
	GREAT EXPECTATIONS ('Mackalves'PBR) (F)	EPfP IArd MRav SPer
§	'Great Maiden's Blush' (A) ♀H7	EBls LEdu MRav NLar
	GREAT NORTH EASTERN ROSE (F)	see *R.* SIR GALAHAD
	'Great Ormond Street' (F)	EBls
	'Great Western' (Bb)	EBls
	GREENALL'S GLORY ('Kirmac') (F/Patio)	CKel MAus MRav
	GREETINGS ('Jacdreco'PBR) (F)	CArg LBuc MAsh
	GRETA HIT ('Poulpah076') (Patio) **new**	MAsh
	'Grimpant Cramoisi Supérieur' (ClCh)	EBls
	'Grootendorst'	see *R.* 'F.J. Grootendorst'
	'Grootendorst Supreme' (Ru)	MMrt
	'Gros Chou de Hollande' (Bb)	EBls
	GROSVENOR HOUSE (HT)	LRHS
	'Grosvenor House Rose' (S)	MAsh
	GROUSE ('Korimro') (S/GC)	EBls MAus NLar SEND SPer
	GROUSE 2000 ('Korteilhab') (GC) ♀H6	MAus
	'Gruss an Aachen' (Poly) ♀H6	EBls EPfP EWTr MCot MJak NLar SPer
	'Gruss an Teplitz' (China hybrid)	EBls MAus NLar SPer
	'Guinée' (ClHT)	CArg CBod CKel CRos CSBt CTri EBls ELan EPfP EWTr MAus MRav MSwo MWat NLar SPer WCot WKif
	GUIRLANDE ROSE ('Velwichba') (Ra)	EBls
	'Gustav Grünerwald' (HT)	EBls
	GUY SAVOY ('Delstrimen'PBR) (F)	EBls ESty MRav
	GUY'S GOLD ('Harmatch'PBR) (HT)	LRHS MAsh SPoG
	GWENT ('Poulurt'PBR) (GC)	CSBt EBls SCob SEND SPer SSea
	gymnocarpa	EBls
	GYPSY BOY	see *R.* 'Zigeunerknabe'
	'Hakuun' (F/Patio)	MAus
	HALLÉ ('Fryelectric'PBR) (HT)	MFry
	'Hamburger Phönix' (Ra)	EBls
	HAMPSHIRE ('Korhamp'PBR) (GC)	MAus
	HÄNDEL ('Macha') (ClHT)	CBcs CBod CGro CKel CSBt CTri EBls ELan EPfP LBuc MAsh MFry MRav NEgg NLar NPri SPer SPlb SSea
§	HANKY PANKY ('Wektorcent'PBR) (F)	CGro EBls ESty MAsh MRav
	HANNAH GORDON ('Korweiso') (F)	EBls MAsh SPer
	'Hansa' (Ru)	EBls LBuc MAus NLar SPer
	HANSESTADT ROSTOCK ('Tan04603'PBR) (F) **new**	MFry
	'Happenstance' (GC)	EBls
	HAPPY 60TH BIRTHDAY **new**	LSRN
	HAPPY 70TH BIRTHDAY ('Rawday') (F)	LSRN
	HAPPY 80TH BIRTHDAY **new**	LSRN
	HAPPY ANNIVERSARY ambig.	CRos EPfP SSea
	HAPPY ANNIVERSARY ('Bedfranc'PBR) (F)	LSRN MWat NPri
	HAPPY ANNIVERSARY ('Delpre') (F)	CRos CTri LRHS MAsh MRav NRHS SPoG
	'Happy Birthday' (Min/Patio)	ESty LCro LOPS LSRN SSea
	HAPPY COUPLE ('Simreg') (F) **new**	ESty
	HAPPY DAYS ('Harquad'PBR) (S)	MRav
	HAPPY GARDENING ('Smi89-2-04') (HT) **new**	ESty
	HAPPY GOLDEN WEDDING	see *R.* GOLDEN SMILES
	'Happy Memories' (F)	EBls MAsh
	HAPPY PEARL WEDDING (HT) **new**	MFry

HAPPY RETIREMENT ('Tantoras'PBR) (F) ♀H6	CBcs EBls EPfP ESty LBuc LSRN MAsh MFry MRav NPri SCoo SPoG SSea
HAPPY RUBY WEDDING ('Frynoble'PBR) (HT)	CBcs CRos MAsh MFry NPri
HAPPY SILVER WEDDING ('Frysilva') (F)	CRos EPfP LSRN MAsh MFry
× ***harisonii*** (SpH)	EBls
§ - 'Harison's Yellow' (SpH)	MAus
§ - 'Lutea Maxima' (SpH)	MAus
§ - 'Williams' Double Yellow' (SpH)	EBls MAus
HARLOW CARR ambig.	CKel CRos LRHS NRHS SCob
HARLOW CARR ('Aushouse'PBR) (S)	CKel CRos EPfP LBuc LSRN MAsh MAus MRav NAln SCob SCoo SPer
HARPER ADAMS ('Fryflash'PBR) (F)	MFry
'Harpippin' (ClHT) **new**	LRHS
'Harry Edland' (F)	SMad
'Harry Maasz' (GC/Cl)	EBls
'Harry Wheatcroft' (HT)	CArg SPer
HARVEST FAYRE ('Dicnorth'PBR) (F)	SPer
HAVANA HIT ('Poulpah032'PBR) (Patio)	EPfP MAsh MFry NPri
'Havering Rambler' (Ra)	ELon
HAYDOCK PARK ('Fryjak'PBR) (F) **new**	MFry
'Hazel Le Rougetel' (Ru)	EBls WFar
'Headleyensis' (S)	EBls MAus SPer
HEART OF GOLD ('Coctarlotte'PBR) (HT) ♀H6	ECnt ESty MRav
HEART'S DESIRE ('Raw1063') (F) **new**	ESty
HEATHCLIFF ('Ausnipper'PBR) (S)	CRos CSBt EPfP ESty LBuc MAsh NAln NLar
'Heather Muir' (*sericea* hybrid) (S)	EBls
HEATHER ('Poulcot007') (S) **new**	LSRN
§ 'Hebe's Lip' (D × RH)	MAus
'Helen Knight' (*ecae* hybrid) (S)	EBls ESty MAsh MAus
'Helen Traubel' (HT)	EBls
HELENA ('Poulna'PBR) (Renaissance Series) (S)	LSRN
helenae	CTri EBee EBls GBin GLog MAus NLar SPer WPGP
HELEN'S TRUST ('Taytrust') (HT)	LSRN
hemisphaerica (S)	EBls MAus
§ 'Henri Martin' (CeMo) ♀H7	CBod CTri EBls LEdu MAus NEgg NLar SPer
HENRI MATISSE ('Delstrobla') (HT)	ESty MRav SPoG
'Henry Kelsey' (Cl/S)	EBls
'Henry Nevard' (HP)	EBls MAus
'Her Majesty' (HP)	EBls
§ 'Herbstfeuer' (RH)	CPou EBls NLar SPer
'Here's Sam' (HT)	LSRN
HERITAGE ('Ausblush') (S)	CBod CKel CRos CTri EBee ELan EPfP MJak MRav NEgg NLar SCob SPer
'Hermosa' (Ch)	EBls MAus NLar
HERO ('Aushero') (S)	MAus
HERTFORDSHIRE ('Kortenay'PBR) (GC) ♀H6	MAus SCob SEND SPer

'Hiawatha' (Ra)	EBls
× ***hibernica***	EBls MAus
'Hidcote Gold' (S)	EBls MAus
§ 'Hidcote Yellow' (Cl)	EBls EWTr SPer
HIGH FLIER ('Fryfandango'PBR) (ClHT)	MFry
HIGH HOPES ('Haryup'PBR) (ClHT)	CGro EPfP EUJe LBuc MAsh MAus SPer SSea
'Highdownensis' (*moyesii* hybrid) (S)	EBls ELan MAus
HIGHFIELD ('Harcomp') (ClHT)	MAus
HIGHGROVE ('Hornightshade') (Cl)	EBls LRHS MAsh NPri
'Hillieri' (*moyesii* hybrid)	EBls MAus
'Hippolyte' (G)	MAus
HOLE-IN-ONE ('Horeagle') (F)	LSRN
holodonta	see *R. moyesii* f. *rosea*
holy rose	see *R.* × *richardii*
'Home Sweet Home' (HT)	EBls
HOME SWEET HOME ('Sim2008/10') **new**	ESty
'Homère' (T)	EBls
HOMMAGE À BARBARA ('Delchifrou'PBR) (HT)	CBod EBee ESty MRav WKif
HONEY BUNCH ('Cocglen'PBR) (F)	CKel MRav
HONEY DIJON ('Weksproulses'PBR) (F)	ESty
HONEYBUN ('Tan98264'PBR) (Patio)	ESty
'Honorine de Brabant' (Bb) ♀H6	CPou EBls EWTr LEdu MAus NLar SPer
HOPE AND GLORY ('Tan01360'PBR) (HT)	MFry
'Horace Vernet' (HP)	EBls
HORATIO NELSON ('Beahor') (S)	EBls
horrida	EBls
'Horstmanns Rosenresli' (F)	EBls
HOT CHOCOLATE ('Wekpaltlez') (F) ♀H6	CArg CGro CKel CRos CSBt CWld EBee EBls ECnt ELan ELon EPfP ESty GBin LBuc LRHS MAsh MFry MJak MRav SMad SPad SPer SPoG SSea WBor
HOT PRINCESS ('Tantocnirp') (HT)	ESty
HOUSE BEAUTIFUL ('Harbingo') (Patio)	MRav MWat
'Hovyn de Tronchère' (HT)	EBls
'Hugh Dickson' (HP)	CPou EBls LSRN MAus NLar
hugonis	see *R. xanthina* f. *hugonis*
- 'Plenissima'	see *R. xanthina* f. *hugonis*
HUMANITY ('Harcross'PBR) (F)	MRav MWat
Hume's blush	see *R.* × *odorata* 'Odorata'
HUMMINGBIRD ('Tynpam') (F)	ESty
'Hunter' (Ru)	EBls
HYDE HALL ('Ausbosky'PBR) (S)	CRos LRHS MAus NAln SCob
ICE CREAM ('Korzuri'PBR) (HT) ♀H6	CArg ECnt ESty MAus MFry MRav SCob SPer SPoG
§ ICEBERG ('Korbin') (F) ♀H6	Widely available
'Ilse Krohn Superior' (Cl)	EBls
§ IMAGINATION ('Pouldron'PBR) (F)	MAsh NRHS

IMOGEN ('Austritch') (S) **new**	CSBt ESty LRHS MAsh MAus NRHS
IMPÉRATRICE FARAH ('Delivour') (HT)	ESty
§ 'Impératrice Joséphine' (Gn) ♀^{H7}	EBls EWTr NLar
IN MEMORY OF	LSRN
IN MEMORY OF MY CAT ('Webyum') (HT)	LSRN
IN MEMORY OF MY DOG ('Rawbark') (F)	LSRN
INDIAN SUMMER ('Harwigwam') (ClMin)	ELon MJak
INDIAN SUMMER ('Peaperfume'^{PBR}) (HT) ♀^{H6}	CKel CSBt LBuc MFry MRav MWat
INDIANNA MAE ('Beacrunch') (S)	EBls
'Indigo' (DPo)	CPou EBls MAus
INFINITY ('Frytropic') (HT)	CArg LRHS MAsh
INGRID ('Maning') (Patio) **new**	LSRN
INGRID BERGMAN ('Poulman'^{PBR}) (HT) ♀^{H6}	CBod CTri EBls ECnt EPfP LSRN MFry MGos MRav SPer
'Inspiration' (ClHT)	EPfP MAsh
INSPIRE ('Frytempo') (HT)	CSBt ECnt
'Intermezzo' (HT)	EBls
INVINCIBLE ('Runatru') (F)	MFry
'Ipsilanté' (G)	EBls MAus
'Irene Av Danmark' (F)	EBls
'Irène Watts' (Ch)	CArg CPou EBls EWTr LSRN NLar
'Irene's Delight' (HT)	ESty LSRN
IRIS ('Coczero') (HT)	LSRN
IRIS ('Ferecha') (HT)	LSRN
IRISH EYES ('Dicwitness'^{PBR}) (F) ♀^{H6}	CArg CGro EBee ESty IArd MAsh MJak MRav NAln SCoo SPer
IRISH WONDER	see *R.* EVELYN FISON
'Isabel'	LSRN
ISABELLA ('Poulisab'^{PBR}) (Renaissance Series) (S)	CPou CTri ECnt NLar
'Isabella Sprunt' (HT)	EBls
ISN'T SHE LOVELY ('Diciluvit'^{PBR}) (HT) ♀^{H6}	CArg EBls ELan ESty IDic LSRN
'Ispahan' (D) ♀^{H6}	CArg EBls EPfP LRHS MAus NEgg NLar WFar
IT'S MAGIC! ('Frynote') (F) **new**	MFry
IVOR'S ROSE ('Beadonald') (S)	EBls LRHS MAsh
IVORY ROMANTICA ('Meisabeyla'^{PBR}) (HT)	LSRN
'Ivory Silk' (Min)	LSRN
'Jack Hume' (ClHT)	ESty
JACK WOOD ('Frydabble'^{PBR}) (F)	MFry
JACK'S WISH ('Kirsil') (HT)	LSRN
§ × ***jacksonii*** 'Max Graf' (GC/Ru)	MAus NLar
- RED MAX GRAF	see *R.* ROTE MAX GRAF
'Jacky's Favorite' (F)	LSRN
Jacobite rose	see *R.* × *alba* 'Alba Maxima'
JACQUELINE DU PRÉ ('Harwanna') (S) ♀^{H6}	CArg CKel EBls ECnt ESty GBin LSRN MAus MCot MRav NLar SEND SLon SPer
'Jacques Cartier' misapplied	see *R.* 'Marchesa Boccella'
JAM AND JERUSALEM ('Frymojo'^{PBR}) (F)	CGro CKel LRHS MAsh MFry MRav MWat
'James Bourgault' (HP)	EBls
JAMES GALWAY ('Auscrystal'^{PBR}) (S)	CRos CSBt EPfP ESty LBuc LRHS LSRN MAsh MAus NAln NEgg NRHS SCob SCoo SSea
'James Mason' (G)	EBls MAus
'James Mitchell' (CeMo)	EBls MAus
'James Veitch' (DPoMo)	MAus
JANET ('Auspishus'^{PBR}) (S)	LSRN MAus
'Janet B. Wood' (Ra)	EBls
'Janet's Pride' (RH)	EBls
§ 'Japonica' (CeMo)	MAus
§ JARDINS DE BAGATELLE ('Meimafris') (HT)	LSRN MRav
JASMINA ('Korcentex'^{PBR}) (ClHT)	CBod CPou ESty LBuc LRHS MAsh
'Jaune Desprez'	see *R.* 'Desprez à Fleur Jaune'
JAYNE AUSTIN ('Ausbreak'^{PBR}) (S)	MAus SPer
JAZZ (ClF)	see *R.* THAT'S JAZZ
'Jazz' (F)	LSRN
JEAN ('Cocupland'^{PBR}) (Patio)	LSRN
'Jean Mermoz' (Poly)	MAus
'Jean Rosenkrantz' (HP)	EBls
'Jeanne de Montfort' (CeMo)	EBls MAus
JEANNE MOREAU ('Meidiaphaz') (HT)	CSBt ESty
'Jenny Duval' misapplied	see *R.* 'Président de Sèze'
'Jenny Wren' (F)	EBls
JENNY'S ROSE ('Cansit') (F)	ECnt LSRN
'Jens Munk' (Ru)	EBls NLar
'Jersey Beauty' (Ra)	EBls
JILL'S ROSE ('Ganjil'^{PBR}) (F)	LSRN
JILLY JEWEL ('Benmfig') (Min)	LSRN
JIVE ('Poulyc009'^{PBR}) (Cl)	LSRN
JOAN ('Raw1019')	LSRN
JOAN BEALES ('Beaagile') (S)	EBls
'Joanna Hill' (HT)	EBls
'Jocelyn' (F)	LSRN
JOCKEYS ROSE ('Frynadia') (HT) **new**	MFry
JOHANN WOLFGANG VON GOETHE ROSE	see *R.* PURE POETRY ('Tan04179')
'John Cabot' (S)	EBls
'John Gwilliam'	MAvo MHCG
'John Hopper' (HP)	EBls MAus
JOHN INNES ('Beafickle') (S)	EBls
JOHN WILLAN ('Fryeager') (HT)	MFry
§ JOIE DE VIVRE ('Korfloci 01'^{PBR}) (Patio/S) ♀^{H6}	CArg CGro CPou CSBt EBee EBls ELan EPfP ESty EWTr GBin LRHS MAsh MFry MRav NLar NPri SPer SPoG
§ JOSEPHINE ('Weksiamia') (HT)	LSRN
'Josephine Bruce' (HT)	CBcs CTri EBls LSRN
'Joseph's Coat' (ClS)	CBod CKel EBls IArd
JOY VIELI ('Dickaramel') (F)	IDic
JUBILÉ PAPA MEILLAND ('Meiceazar') (HT) **new**	CSBt
'Jubilee Celebration' (F)	CBod EPfP LRHS NRHS
JUBILEE CELEBRATION ('Aushunter'^{PBR}) (S)	CKel CRos CSBt EBee LBuc LRHS MAus NAln NLar NRHS SPer SPoG
JUDE THE OBSCURE ('Ausjo'^{PBR}) (S)	CRos EPfP ESty LBuc LRHS MAsh MAus MGos NAln NEgg NRHS SCob SPer
'Julia's Rose' (HT)	EBls LSRN MAus
'Juliet' (HP)	EBls

	JULIO IGLESIAS ('Meistemon'[PBR]) (F)	ESty LSRN
	'July Racecourse' (Patio) **new**	MFry
	'Juno' (Ce)	EBls NLar
	'Juno' (Ch)	CPou MAus
	JUST FOR YOU ('Moryou') (Min)	LSRN
	JUST JANE ('Raw1046') (F) **new**	LSRN
	'Just Jenny' (Min)	LSRN
	'Just Joey' (HT) 🏆H6	CArg CBcs CBod CKel CSBt CTri EBls ECnt ELan ELon IArd LSRN MAus MFry MJak MRav NAln NEgg SCob SPer SPoG SSea
	JUST ROBERT ('Raw1075') (F) **new**	LSRN
	JUST STEVE ('Raw890')	LSRN
	'Justice of the Peace' (F) **new**	MFry
	'Karlsruhe' (Cl)	EBls
	'Kassel' (ClF)	EBls
	'Kasteel Hex' (S)	EBls
	'Katharina Zeimet' (Poly)	CKel CTri EBls MAus
	'Kathleen' (HM)	EBls LSRN
	'Kathleen Ferrier' (F)	EBls
	'Kathleen Harrop' (Bb)	CKel EBee EBls EWTr MAus MMuc MSwo NLar SEND SPer
	KATHLEEN JANE ('Horcoed') (S/F)	LSRN
	KATHLEEN'S ROSE ('Kirkitt') (F)	LSRN
	KATHRYN ('Rawkat')	LSRN
	'Katie' (ClF)	LSRN
	KATIE'S ROSE ('Horrapture') (F) **new**	LSRN
	'Kazanlik' misapplied	see *R.* × *damascena* 'Professeur Émile Perrot'
	KEEP SMILING ('Fryflorida') (HT) 🏆H6	CGro EBls MAsh MFry MRav SPoG
	KEEPSAKE ('Kormalda') (HT)	ESty
	'Keith Maughan' (Cl)	EBls LRHS MAsh
§	KENT ('Poulcov'[PBR]) (Towne & Country Series) (S/GC) 🏆H6	CBod CKel CSBt EBls ECnt ELan EPfP ESty GBin LCro LOPS LSRN MFry MMuc MRav MSwo NLar SCob SEND SPer SPoG SSea
	KEW GARDENS ('Ausfence'[PBR]) (S) 🏆H6	CBod CKel CRos EBee EPfP LBuc LRHS MAus MRav NAln NLar NRHS SCob SPer SSea
	'Kew Rambler' (Ra)	CBod CRHN EBee EBls MAus NLar SLon SPer
	'Kiftsgate'	see *R. filipes* 'Kiftsgate'
	'Kiftsgate Superior' (S)	EBls
	'Killarney' (HT)	EBls
	'Kim' (Patio)	LSRN
	KIND REGARDS ('Peatiger') (F)	LSRN
	KING'S MACC ('Frydisco'[PBR]) (HT) 🏆H6	MAus MFry
	'King's Ransom' (HT)	CSBt EBls MRav SPer
	KISSES OF FIRE ('Chewmultiseek') (Cl)	ECnt MRav NLar SSea
	KITTY ('Beaarty') (S)	EBls
	× ***kochiana***	CPou EBls
	KOLO ('Poulcy033'[PBR]) (Courtyard Series) (Cl)	ECnt
§	'Königin von Dänemark' (A) 🏆H7	CArg CBod EBls EPfP LCro LOPS LRHS LSRN MRav NAln NEgg NLar SPer
§	'Kordes' Magenta' (S/F)	EBls
	'Kordes' Robusta'	see *R.* ROBUSTA
	'Kordesii' (S)	EBls
	KORONA ('Kornita') (F)	SPer
	'Korresia' (F) 🏆H7	CArg CBod CSBt CTri EBee EBls ECnt EPfP LRHS MAsh MAus MFry MJak MRav NWea SCob SPer SPoG
	KRONENBOURG ('Macbo') (HT)	EBls
	'Kronprinzessin Viktoria von Preussen' (Bb)	EBls MAus
	L.D. BRAITHWAITE ('Auscrim'[PBR]) (S)	CArg CBod CRos CTri ELan EPfP LRHS MAus MBNS MJak NAln NLar SCob SPer SSea
	'La Belle Sultane'	see *R.* 'Violacea'
	'La France' (HT)	EBls
	'La Mortola'	see *R. brunonii* 'La Mortola'
	'La Noblesse' (Ce)	EBls
	'La Perle' (Ra)	CRHN
	'La Reine' (HP)	EBls
	'La Reine Victoria'	see *R.* 'Reine Victoria'
§	LA ROSE DE MOLINARD ('Delgrarose'[PBR]) (S) 🏆H6	CArg CPou ESty MRav NLar
	LA ROSE DE PETIT PRINCE ('Delgramau') (F)	ESty
	'La Rubanée'	see *R.* × *centifolia* 'Unique Panachée'
	LA SÉVILLANA ('Meigekanu') (F/GC)	EBls MSwo SPer WCot
	'La Ville de Bruxelles' (D) 🏆H7	EBls MAus NLar SPer
	LACE ('Frymoody') (HT) **new**	LSRN MFry
	'Lady Alice Stanley' (HT)	EBls
	'Lady Anne' (F)	LSRN
	'Lady Barnby' (HT)	EBls
	'Lady Belper' (HT)	EBls
	'Lady Curzon' (Ru)	EBls
	'Lady Elgin'	see *R.* THAÏS
	LADY EMMA HAMILTON ('Ausbrother'[PBR]) (S) 🏆H6	CGro CRos EPfP ESty GBin LBuc LRHS MAus NAln NRHS SCob SCoo SPer
	'Lady Gay' (Ra)	CBod EBee WBor
	'Lady Godiva' (Ra)	MAus
	'Lady Hillingdon' (T)	EBls MAsh MWat
	'Lady Hillingdon' (ClT)	see *R.* 'Climbing Lady Hillingdon'
	LADY MARMALADE ('Hartiger'[PBR]) (F)	CArg CGro CKel CSBt CWld ESty LBuc LRHS MAsh MFry MRav NPri SCoo SMad SPer SPoG
	'Lady Mary Fitzwilliam' (HT)	EBls
	LADY MITCHELL ('Haryearn') (HT)	ECnt
	'Lady Oaksey' (HT) **new**	MFry
	LADY OF MEGGINCH ('Ausvolume'[PBR]) (S)	MAus
	LADY OF SHALOTT ('Ausnyson'[PBR]) (S) 🏆H6	CRos ECnt ELan EPfP LBuc LCro LOPS LRHS MAsh MAus NAln NLar NRHS SCob SSea
	LADY PENELOPE ('Chewdor'[PBR]) (ClHT)	CSBt MFry
§	'Lady Penzance' (RH)	CTho EBls
	'Lady Romsey' (F)	EBls
	LADY ROSE ('Korlady') (HT)	MAsh
	LADY SALISBURY ('Auscezed'[PBR]) (S)	CRos EPfP LBuc LRHS MAus NRHS SCob SCoo
	'Lady Sylvia' (HT)	EBls LSRN MAus NEgg SPer
	'Lady Waterlow' (ClHT)	EBls MAus SPer WSpi
	laevigata (Ra)	EBls MAus MMuc

Name	Suppliers
- 'Anemonoides'	see *R.* 'Anemone'
'Lafter' (S)	EBls
'Lagoon' (F)	EBls
LAGUNA ('Koradigel'PBR) (ClHT)	MAsh
L'AIMANT ('Harzola'PBR) (F) ♀H5	MAus MRav
LALANDE DE POMAROL ('Delcherot') (F)	ESty
L'ALHAMBRA	see *R.* GIARDINA
'Lamarque' (N)	CPou EBls MAus
LANCASHIRE ('Korstesgli'PBR) (GC) ♀H6	CKel ECnt ELan ESty LSRN MAus MRav MSwo SSea
LANCELOT ('Tan03542'PBR) (Cl)	ESty
§ 'Lanei' (CeMo)	EBls
latibracteata	EBls
LAURA FORD ('Chewarvel'PBR) (ClMin) ♀H5	CKel EBls ELan LRHS MAsh MAus MGos MRav NAln SPer SPoG SSea
'Laura Louisa' (Cl)	EBee EBls EWTr LRHS MAsh
'Laure Davoust' (Ra)	CPou EBls MMuc NLar
LAVENDER ICE ('Tan04249'PBR) (F)	ESty MAsh SPoG WSpi
'Lavender Jewel' (Min)	MAus
'Lavender Lassie' (HM)	CPou EBls MAus NLar SPer
'Lavender Pinocchio' (F)	EBls WKif
LAVINIA	see *R.* LAWINIA
§ LAWINIA ('Tanklewi') (ClHT) ♀H6	CSBt LRHS MAsh SPer
'Lawrence Johnston'	see *R.* 'Hidcote Yellow'
laxa	EBls
§ LAZY DAYS ('Poulkalm'PBR) (F)	ECnt MAsh
'Le Rêve' (Cl)	EBls
LE ROUGE ET LE NOIR ('Delcart') (HT)	ESty
'Le Vésuve' (Ch)	CPou EBls MAus
LEAH TUTU ('Hornavel') (S)	CWld EBls ESty LRHS MAsh
LEANDER ('Auslea') (S)	MAus
LEAPING SALMON ('Peamight'PBR) (ClHT) ♀H6	CArg CGro CSBt EBee ELon ESty LSRN MAus MRav SPer WSpi
'Leda' (D)	CArg EBls EWTr MAus SPer
LEGENDS	see *R.* JOSEPHINE
'Lemon Pillar'	see *R.* 'Paul's Lemon Pillar'
LÉONARDO DE VINCI ('Meideauri'PBR) (F)	CSBt
'Léonie Lamesch' (Poly)	EBls
'Léontine Gervais' (Ra)	CRHN EBls MAus
'Leo's Eye' (Ra)	CPou EPfP NLar WFar
LESLIE'S DREAM ('Dicjoon') (HT)	IDic
LET FREEDOM RING ('Wekearman') (HT) **new**	ESty
LET THERE BE LOVE ('Frysoda') (F)	MAsh MFry
LET'S CELEBRATE ('Fryraffles'PBR) (F) ♀H5	CWld EPfP ESty LBuc LRHS MAsh MFry MRav NPri NRHS SPoG
'Leverkusen' (ClF) ♀H6	CArg CBod CKel EBls EWTr MAus MRav NLar SEND SPer
'Leveson-Gower' (Bb)	EBls
'Ley's Perpetual' (ClT)	CArg EBls
× ***lheritieriana*** (Bs)	EBls
LICHFIELD ANGEL ('Ausrelate'PBR) (S) ♀H6	CRos EPfP LBuc LRHS MAsh MAus NAln NLar NRHS SCob SCoo
LICHTKÖNIGIN LUCIA ('Korlillub') (S)	EBls SSea
LIFE BEGINS AT 40! ('Horhohoho') (F)	LSRN
LIGHT FANTASTIC ('Dicgottago') (F) ♀H6	CArg EPfP MAsh MFry
LIGHTNING STRIKE ('Raw967') (F)	ESty
LILAC BOUQUET ('Chewlilacdays') (Cl) **new**	ESty SSea
'Lilac Charm' (F)	EBls
LILAC WINE ('Dicmulti') (F) ♀H5	CGro CSBt IDic MRav
LILIANA ('Poulsyng'PBR) (S)	CPou EBee ECnt LSRN SLon
LILLI MARLENE ('Korlima') (F)	CTri EBee EBls SPer
LINCOLN CATHEDRAL ('Glanlin'PBR) (HT)	MJak SPer
LINCOLNSHIRE POACHER ('Glareabit') (HT)	ESty NEgg
'Lincolnshire Yellow Belly' (F)	ESty
LION'S FAIRY TALE	see *R.* CHAMPAGNE MOMENT
LIONS INTERNATIONAL ('Frycharm'PBR) (HT)	MFry
LISA ('Kirdisco') (F)	LSRN
LITTLE AMY ('Battamy') (Min)	LSRN
LITTLE DUET ('Guesbliss') (F)	ESty
'Little Emily' (Patio) **new**	LSRN
'Little Fin' (Min) **new**	LSRN
'Little Flirt' (Min)	ELan MAus
'Little Gem' (DPMo)	EBls MAus
LITTLE JACKIE ('Savor') (Min)	LSRN
LITTLE RAMBLER ('Chewramb'PBR) (MinRa) ♀H6	CArg CSBt EBls ECnt ELan ESty LRHS MAus MFry MGos MMuc MRav NAln NRHS SCoo SPer SSea
'Little White Pet'	see *R.* 'White Pet'
§ LIVERPOOL REMEMBERS ('Frystar'PBR) (HT)	MFry
LIVING DAYLIGHTS ('Fryradical') (F) **new**	MFry
LOCHINVAR ('Ausbilda'PBR) (S)	MAus NAln
'Lolabelle'	CPou EBee EWTr SPer
'Long John Silver' (Cl)	EBls ELan MAus SSea
longicuspis misapplied	see *R. mulliganii*
§ ***longicuspis*** Bertol. var. ***sinowilsonii*** (Ra)	EBls GCal MAus
LOOK GOOD... FEEL BETTER ('Poulcas034'PBR) (Castle Series) (Poly)	EPfP LRHS
LORD BYRON ('Meitosier') (ClHT)	ESty
'Lord Penzance' (RH)	CPou EBls NLar SPer
LORNA ('Cocringer') (F)	LSRN
LOTS OF LOVE ('Forchriso') (F)	ESty
'L'Ouche' misapplied	see *R.* 'Louise Odier'
'Louis Gimard' (CeMo)	MAus
'Louis Philippe' (Ch)	EBls
'Louis XIV' (Ch)	CBod EBls MCot
LOUISE CLEMENTS ('Clelou') (S)	EBls MCot
'Louise D'Arzens' (N)	EBls
§ 'Louise Odier' (Bb)	CBod CKel CTri EBls ECnt EPfP IArd LRHS LSRN MAus MCot MRav NLar SMad SPer

	Name	Suppliers
	LOVE & PEACE ('Baipeace'PBR) (HT) ♀H7	ESty
	LOVE KNOT ('Chewglorious'PBR) (ClMin) ♀H6	CArg CRos CSBt ECnt EPfP ESty LRHS MAsh MRav SSea
	LOVELY BOY ('Simjas') (HT) **new**	ESty
§	LOVELY BRIDE ('Meiratcan'PBR) (Patio)	CRos EPfP LRHS MAsh NRHS SPoG
	LOVELY LADY ('Dicjubell'PBR) (HT) ♀H6	CKel CSBt EBls ECnt ESty LSRN MAus MRav SPer SSea
	LOVELY MEIDILAND	see *R.* LOVELY BRIDE
	'Lovers' Meeting' (HT)	MJak MRav SPer
	LOVESTRUCK ('Dicommatac') (F) **new**	CSBt ESty
	LOVING MEMORY ('Korgund81') (HT)	CArg CBod CGro CKel CSBt EBls ECnt ESty IArd LSRN MAsh MFry MGos MRav MWat NPri SPer SPoG SSea SVic
	LOVING MUM	see *R.* SHOWSTAR
	LOWTHORPE DELIGHT ('Dicgoofy') (F)	IDic
	lucieae	EBls EWTr GCal MAus
	- 'Cally Anemone' (Ra)	MAus
	LUCKY! ('Frylucy') (F) ♀H6	CArg CSBt EBls EPfP ESty LBuc LRHS LSRN MAsh MFry MGos MRav NPri NRHS SCoo SPer SPoG
	LUCY ('Kirlis') (F)	LSRN
	LULLABY ('Kenfrilpin') (Cl)	ESty
	LUSCIOUS LUCY ('Tucklucy') (Patio)	LSRN
	'Lutea Maxima'	see *R.* × *harisonii* 'Lutea Maxima'
	LYDA ROSE ('Letlyda') (S)	EBls
	'Lykkefund' (Ra)	CKel EBls MAus
	'Ma Perkins' (F)	EBls
	'Mabel Morrison' (HP)	EBls MAus
	Macartney rose	see *R. bracteata*, *R.* THE MCCARTNEY ROSE
	MACMILLAN NURSE ('Beamac') (S)	EBee EBls ELan ESty LRHS MAsh MCot NRHS
	MACON ROUGE ('Frynova') (HT) **new**	MFry
	'Macrantha' (Gallica hybrid)	EBls MAus
	macrophylla (S)	MAus WPav
	- B&SWJ 2603	WCru
	- GWJ 9306	WCru
§	- 'Master Hugh' (S)	EBls MAus
	'Madame Abel Chatenay' (HT)	EBls
	'Madame Alfred Carrière' (N) ♀H5	Widely available
	'Madame Alice Garnier' (Ra)	CPou CRHN EBls SPer
	'Madame Antoine Mari' (T)	CPou EBls
	'Madame Bérard' (ClT)	EBls
§	'Madame Boll' (DPo)	CArg CKel EBls ESty EWTr MAsh MCot MRav MSwo NLar SMad
	'Madame Butterfly' (HT)	EBls
§	'Madame Caroline Testout' (HT)	CTri EBls
	'Madame de la Roche-Lambert' (DPMo)	CPou EBls MAus
	'Madame de Sancy de Parabère' (Bs)	EBls MAus
	'Madame Driout' (ClT)	CPou
	'Madame Ernest Calvat' (Bb)	CPou EBls
	'Madame Eugène Résal' misapplied	see *R.* 'Comtesse du Caÿla'
§	'Madame Grégoire Staechelin' (ClHT) ♀H6	CArg CTri EBls ECnt ELan EPfP EWTr LCro LOPS LRHS LSRN MAsh MAus MRav MSwo NEgg NLar NRHS SCob SPer SPlb
	'Madame Hardy' (D) ♀H7	CPou CSBt EBls ECnt EPfP LRHS LSRN MAus MRav MSwo MWat NEgg NLar SCob SPer WFar
	'Madame Isaac Péreire' (ClBb)	CArg CSBt CTri EBls ECnt EPfP GBin LCro LOPS MAus MCot MRav MSwo NLar SCob SMad SPer WFar
	'Madame Jules Gravereaux' (ClT)	EBls MAus
	'Madame Knorr' (DPo) ♀H7	CPou EBee ECnt EPfP SPer
	'Madame Knorr' misapplied	see *R.* 'Madame Boll'
	'Madame Laurette Messimy' (Ch)	CPou
	'Madame Lauriol de Barny' (Bb)	EBls MAus MRav NLar
	'Madame Legras de Saint Germain' (A × N)	CPou EBls EWTr MAus NLar
	'Madame Louis Laperrière' (HT)	EBls
	'Madame Louis Lévêque' (DPMo)	CPou EBls EWTr NLar
	'Madame Pierre Oger' (Bb)	CArg CTri EBls ECnt MAus NLar SPer
	'Madame Plantier' (A × N)	CArg CPou EBls MAus NLar SCob SPer WFar
	'Madame Scipion Cochet' (HP)	CPou
	'Madame Victor Verdier' (HP)	EBls
	'Madame Zöetmans' (D)	MAus
	'Madeleine Seltzer' (Ra)	EBls
	'Magenta' (S/F)	see *R.* 'Kordes' Magenta' (S/F)
	MAGIC CARPET ('Jaclover'PBR) (S/GC) ♀H6	CKel EBls ELan MAus MRav MSwo SPer
	MAGIC MOMENT ('Forrusty') (HT)	ESty
	'Magna Charta' (HP)	EBls
	MAGNETIC EYES ('Dicmimic') (S) **new**	IDic
	'Magnifica' (RH)	EBls
	MAID MARION ('Austobias'PBR) (HM)	EPfP LSRN MAsh MAus
	'Maid of Kent'PBR (Cl)	LSRN MAus NLar SCob SCoo SPer
	'Maiden's Blush' (A)	CArg CTri ELan EWTr LEdu MAsh MAus SPer WHer
	'Maiden's Blush, Great'	see *R.* 'Great Maiden's Blush'
	'Maigold' (ClPiH) ♀H6	CArg CBcs CBod CGro CRos CTri EBls ELan EPfP EWTr LRHS MAsh MAus MCot MRav MSwo NAln NLar SCob SMad SPer WBor
§	***majalis***	EBls
	Maltese rose	see *R.* 'Cécile Brünner'
§	'Malton' (China hybrid)	EBls
	MALVERN HILLS ('Auscanary'PBR) (Ra) ♀H5	CRos CSBt EPfP ESty LRHS MAsh MAus NAln NLar SCob SPer
	'Maman Cochet' (T)	EBls
	MAMMA MIA! ('Fryjolly'PBR) (HT) ♀H6	ECnt EPfP ESty LRHS MAsh MFry MRav SPoG
	'Mandarin' (F)	CKel SSea
	MANDARIN ('Korcelin'PBR) (Min)	ESty MRav
	'Manettii' (N)	EBls
	MANHATTAN BLUE ('Tanettahn') (F) **new**	MFry
	'Manning's Blush' (RH)	EBls MAus

	Name	Suppliers
	'Mannington Cascade' (Ra)	EBls
	'Mannington Mauve Rambler' (Ra)	EBls ESty
	MANY CONGRATULATIONS ('Forshelly') (F)	ESty
	MANY HAPPY RETURNS ('Harwanted'[PBR]) (F) ♀H6	CBcs CBod CGro CKel CRos CSBt EBls ECnt ELan EPfP LRHS LSRN MAsh MFry MGos MJak MRav MWat NPri NRHS SCob SPer SSea SVic
	'Marbrée' (DPo)	MAus
	'Märchenland' (F)	MAus
§	'Marchesa Boccella' (DPo) ♀H7	CArg CPou CTri EBls EPfP LRHS MAsh NAln NLar NPri SPer SSea WHer
	'Marchioness of Salisbury' (HT)	EBls
	'Maréchal Davoust' (CeMo)	LEdu MAus
	'Maréchal Niel' (N)	EBls EShb MAus NLar SPer
	MARGARET (HT)	see *R.* DEAR MARGARET
	'Margaret' (HT)	LSRN
	MARGARET GREVILLE ('Beajoker') (S) **new**	EBls
	MARGARET MERRIL ('Harkuly') (F)	CArg CBcs CGro CKel CSBt CTri EBee EBls ELan EPfP ESty IArd LCro LOPS LRHS LSRN MAsh MAus MFry MJak MRav MWat NAln NPri SCob SPer SPoG SSea
	'Marguerite Hilling' (S)	CTri EBls MAus MCot MSwo NLar SPer
	'Marie Bugnet' (Ru)	EBls
	'Marie Louise' (D)	EBls MAus
	'Marie Pavič' (Poly)	CPou MAus NLar
	'Marie van Houtte' (T)	EBls
	'Marie-Jeanne' (Poly)	EBls MAus
	MARIGOLD SWEET DREAM ('Fryprospa') (Patio)	ECnt MFry
	MARINETTE ('Auscam'[PBR]) (S)	MAus
	MARJORIE FAIR ('Harhero') (Poly/S) ♀H6	EBls ELan EPfP MAus MRav
	'Marlena' (F/Patio)	MAus
	'Martha' (Bb)	EBls LSRN
	'Martin Frobisher' (Ru)	EBls MAus
I	'Mary' (Poly)	LSRN
	MARY BERRY ('Harupon') (HT) **new**	ESty LRHS
	'Mary Manners' (Ru)	EBls
	MARY ROSE ('Ausmary') (S)	CKel CRos CSBt CTri ELan EPfP LRHS LSRN MAsh MAus MJak MRav NAln NLar NRHS SCob SLon SPer SPoG SSea WKif
	'Mary Wallace' (Cl)	EBls MAus
	'Masquerade' (F)	CTri EBls ELan MRav NLar SPer
	'Master Hugh'	see *R. macrophylla* 'Master Hugh'
	MATAWHERO MAGIC	see *R.* SIMPLY THE BEST
	MATCHMAKER ('Dicnarrow') (F)	CSBt IDic
	'Maude Elizabeth' (GC)	EBls
	'Maurice Bernardin' (HP)	EBls
	MAURICE UTRILLO ('Delstavo') (HT)	ESty
	'Max Graf'	see *R.* × *jacksonii* 'Max Graf'
	'Maxima'	see *R.* × *alba* 'Alba Maxima'
	MAXIMA ROMANTICA ('Meikerira'[PBR]) (HT)	MAsh
	'May Queen' (Ra)	CBod CPou CRHN CRos EBee EBls MAus MRav NLar SEND
	'McCartney Rose'	see *R.* THE MCCARTNEY ROSE
	'McGredy's Sunset' (HT)	EBls
	'McGredy's Yellow' (HT)	EBls
§	MEDLEY RUBY ('Noa140715'[PBR]) (Min)	MAsh SPoG
	'Meg' (ClHT)	CArg CKel EBee EBls EWTr LSRN MAus MCot MMuc NLar SPer
	'Meg Merrilies' (RH)	EBls
	MELINA	see *R.* SIR HARRY PILKINGTON
	MEMORY LANE ('Peavoodoo'[PBR]) (F)	LSRN
	'Merlot' (Min)	LSRN
	'Mermaid' (Cl) ♀H5	CArg CBcs CDul CSBt CTri EBls EPfP LRHS MAus NLar NRHS SCob SEND SPer SSea
§	'Mevrouw Nathalie Nypels' (Poly)	CArg CTri EBls MAus MMuc MRav NLar SPer
	'Michèle Meilland' (HT)	EBls MAus
	× ***micrugosa***	EBls MAus
	- 'Alba'	EBls MAus
	MIDDLESBOROUGH FOOTBALL CLUB ('Horflame') (HT)	LSRN
	MIDNIGHT BLUE ('Wekfabpur') (S)	EBls ESty
	MIDNIGHT ROSE ('Simdamo') (F)	ESty
	MIDSUMMER ('Tan02280'[PBR]) (F) **new**	MFry
§	MILLIE ('Poulren013'[PBR]) (Renaissance Series) (S) ♀H6	CArg CBcs CGro EBls ECnt ELan ESty LRHS LSRN MAsh MFry NLar NPri NRHS SPoG
	MILLIONAIRE ('Peazara') (F)	LSRN
	MINERVA ('Visancar') (F)	CSBt ESty
	'Minnehaha' (Ra)	EBls MAus SSea
	mirifica stellata	see *R. stellata* var. *mirifica*
	MISCHIEF ('Macmi') (HT)	LSRN SPer
	MISS ALICE ('Ausjake'[PBR]) (S)	LSRN
	'Miss Edith Cavell' (Poly)	EBls MAus
	MISS SCARLET ('Forbright') (Cl)	ESty
§	'Mister Lincoln' (HT)	EBls MJak SPer
§	MISTY HIT ('Poulhi011'[PBR]) (PatioHit Series) (Patio)	CGro CRos EBls ECnt LSRN MAsh NRHS
	'Misty Moon' (F) **new**	ESty
	MITSOUKO ('Delnat') (HT)	ESty
	MODERN SLAVERY ('Dicpowwow') (F) **new**	IDic
	MOLINEUX ('Ausmol'[PBR]) (S) ♀H6	CRos EPfP LRHS LSRN MAsh MAus NAln NRHS SCob SPer
	'Molly Sharman-Crawford' (HT)	EBls
	MOM ('Rawtoks') (F) **new**	LSRN
	MOMENT IN TIME ('Korcastrav'[PBR]) (F) ♀H6	CArg CSBt EBee ECnt MAsh MRav NPri SPer SPoG
	MONICA BELLUCCI ('Meimonkeur'[PBR]) (HT)	ELon ESty
	'Monique' (HT)	EBls
	MONSIEUR PÉLISSON	see *R.* 'Pélisson'
	MOODY BLUE ('Fryniche') (HT)	ECnt MAsh MFry MRav MWat
	'Moonlight' (HM)	CArg CKel CTri EBls MAus MRav MSwo SPer
	MOORCROFT ('Guesyearn') (F)	ESty
	'Morletii' (Bs)	EBls MMuc SEND
	'Morning Jewel' (ClF) ♀H7	SPer
	MORNING MIST ('Ausfire') (S)	CRos EPfP LBuc LRHS MAsh MAus SPer SSea
§	'Morsdag' (Poly/F)	LSRN SCob SPer SVic

	Name	Suppliers
	MORTIMER SACKLER ('Ausorts'[PBR]) (S) ♀H6	CKel CRos EPfP LBuc LRHS MAus MMuc NAln NRHS SCob SCoo SPer SSea
	moschata (Ra)	CPou EBls MAus SSea
	- 'Autumnalis'	see *R.* 'Princesse de Nassau'
	- var. ***nepalensis***	see *R. brunonii*
	MOTHER'S DAY	see *R.* 'Morsdag'
I	'Mother's Day'	MJak
	MOTHER'S JOY ('Horsiltrop') (F)	LSRN
	MOULIN ROUGE ('Simmarg') (HT) **new**	ESty
	MOUNT AORANGI ('Sanaran') (HT)	ESty
	MOUNTAIN SNOW ('Aussnow') (Ra)	LRHS MAus
	MOUNTBATTEN ('Harmantelle') (F) ♀H6	CKel EBls ELan MAus MRav MWat SPer SPoG
§	'Mousseline' (DPoMo)	CArg CPou EBls MAus MCot SPer
	'Mousseuse du Japon'	see *R.* 'Japonica'
	moyesii (S)	CDul CTri EBee EBls ELan EWTr GKev MAus NAln NEgg NWea SPer
§	- var. ***fargesii*** (S)	EBls
	- ***holodonta***	see *R. moyesii* f. *rosea*
§	- f. ***rosea*** (S)	EBls
	'Mr Bluebird' (MinCh)	MAus
	'Mr Lincoln'	see *R.* 'Mister Lincoln'
	'Mrs Anthony Waterer' (Ru)	EBls MAus NLar SPer
	'Mrs Arthur Curtiss James' (ClHT)	MMuc NLar
	MRS DOREEN PIKE ('Ausdor'[PBR]) (Ru)	MAus
	'Mrs F.W. Flight' (ClF)	EBls
	'Mrs Honey Dyson' (Ra)	CPou EWTr
	'Mrs John Laing' (HP)	EBls MAus NLar SPer
	'Mrs Oakley Fisher' (HT)	EBls EWTr MAus MCot SMad SPer
	'Mrs Paul' (Bb)	EBls MAus
	'Mrs Sam McGredy' (HT)	CPou EBls NEgg
	'Mrs Yamada' (Bb)	EBls
§	***mulliganii*** (Ra)	EBls EPfP GKin MAus SPer
	multibracteata (S)	CBcs EBls GLog MAus
	multiflora (Ra)	EBls MAus
	- 'Carnea' (Ra)	EBls
§	- var. ***cathayensis*** (Ra)	EBls
§	- 'Grevillei' (Ra)	EBls MAus MCot MMuc SPer WFar
	- 'Platyphylla'	see *R. multiflora* 'Grevillei'
	- var. ***watsoniana***	see *R. watsoniana*
	MUM IN A MILLION	see *R.* MILLIE
	MUMMY	see *R.* NEWLY WED
	'München' (HM)	EBls
	mundi	see *R. gallica* 'Versicolor'
	MUNSTEAD WOOD ('Ausbernard'[PBR]) (S) ♀H6	CBod CGro CRos CTri ECnt ELan EPfP EShb ESty GBin LBuc LCro LOPS LRHS LSRN MAsh MAus MBNS NAln NLar NRHS SCob SPer SPoG SSea WSpi
	murielae	EBls
	'Murjami'	EBls
	'Muscosa Alba'	see *R.* × *centifolia* 'Shailer's White Moss'
	'Mutabilis'	see *R.* × *odorata* 'Mutabilis'
	MY BROTHER ('Raw1056') (F)	ESty
	MY DAD ('Boselftay'[PBR]) (F)	CBcs CBod EBls LSRN
	'My Darling Husband' (F)	LSRN
	'My Darling Wife' (F)	LSRN
	MY GIRL ('Tan00798'[PBR]) (HT)	MFry
	'My Joy' (HT)	LSRN
	MY MUM ('Webmorrow'[PBR]) (F)	CBcs ESty LSRN SCob
	MY NAN ('Fornan') (HT) **new**	ESty
	MY SISTER ('Raw1052') (F)	ESty
§	MY VALENTINE ('Korcoluma'[PBR]) (HT) ♀H6	CSBt LBuc LSRN
	MY VALENTINE ('Mormyval') (Min)	EBls LSRN MAsh
	MYRIAM ('Cocgrand') (HT)	LSRN
	MYSTERIOUS ('Simpansy') (F)	ESty
	MYSTERY GIRL ('Dicdothis'[PBR]) (HT)	ECnt
	NANCY ('Poulninga') (Renaissance Series) (S)	CPou LSRN
	NANCY JEAN ('Ricnancy') (Patio) **new**	LSRN
	'Naomi' (HT)	CPou LSRN MAsh
	'Narrow Water' (Ra) ♀H6	CArg CPou EBls EWTr GBin
§	'Nastarana' (N)	EBls NLar
	NATALIE ('Poulren014'[PBR]) (Renaissance Series) (S)	ECnt LSRN
	NATANIA ('Dicseduce') (F) **new**	IDic
	NATASHA RICHARDSON ('Harpacket'[PBR]) (F)	CKel MRav
	'Nathalie Nypels'	see *R.* 'Mevrouw Nathalie Nypels'
	'National Trust' (HT)	CArg CTri EBls IArd MFry MJak SPer
	NATURAL BEAUTY ('Rogscriv') (HT)	SSea
	NELSON'S JOURNEY ('Beaflirt') (S)	EBls
	'Nelson's Pride' (F)	EBls
	'Nestor' (G)	EBls MAus
	'Nevada' (S)	CArg CTri EBls ECnt EPfP EWTr GBin IArd LEdu MAus MRav MWat NLar SPer
	NEVER FORGOTTEN ('Gregart') (HT)	LSRN
	NEW ARRIVAL	see *R.* 'Red Patio'
	NEW BEGINNINGS ('Korprofko'[PBR]) (F) ♀H5	CBod ELan LSRN MAsh
§	'New Dawn' (Cl) ♀H7	Widely available
	'New Home'	LSRN
§	NEWLY WED ('Dicwhynot'[PBR]) (Patio) ♀H6	LSRN SSea
	NEWS ('Legnews') (F)	MAus
	NEWSFLASH ('Kendutch'[PBR]) (F) ♀H5	CBod ESty
	NICE DAY ('Chewsea'[PBR]) (ClMin)	CTri EPfP ESty MAsh MRav NAln SPer SPoG SSea
	'Nicola' (F)	LSRN
	NIGHT LIGHT ('Poullight'[PBR]) (Courtyard Series) (Cl)	ECnt
	NIGHT OWL ('Wekpurosot') (Cl)	ECnt ESty EWTr GBin LRHS MRav NLar SPer SPoG
	NINA ('Mehnina'[PBR]) (S)	LSRN
	NINA ('Poulren018'[PBR]) (Renaissance Series) (S)	ECnt
	nitida	EBls MAus NWea SPer
	NOBLE ANTONY ('Ausway'[PBR]) (S)	CRos EPfP MAus NAln NRHS SCob
§	'Noisette Carnée' (N) ♀H7	CArg CKel CPou CRos CTri EBee EBls EPfP LEdu LRHS MAsh MBNS MCot MRav MWat NLar NRHS SPer SSea WBor

	Name	Suppliers
	NORFOLK ('Poulfolk'^{PBR}) (GC)	CBod CKel CTri EBls ESty MSwo NLar SCob SPer
	NORTHAMPTONSHIRE ('Mattdor'^{PBR}) (GC)	EBls
	'Norwell'	MNrw
	'Norwich Castle' (F)	EBls
	NORWICH CATHEDRAL ('Beacath') (HT)	EBls
	'Norwich Pink' (S)	MAus
	NORWICH THEATRE ROYAL ('Beacalm') (S)	EBls
	'Norwich Union' (F)	EBls
	NOSTALGIA ('Savarita') (Min)	CBod CGro EPfP LBuc LRHS MAsh MAus
§	NOSTALGIA ('Taneiglat'^{PBR}) (HT) ♀^{H6}	CSBt EBee EBls ECnt ESty MFry MRav SMad SPer SPoG SSea
	NOSTALGIE	see *R.* NOSTALGIA ('Taneiglat')
	'Notre-Dame de Calais' (Cl)	EBls LRHS MAsh
	'Nova Zembla' (Ru)	EBls
	'Nozomi' (ClMin/GC)	CBod CKel CTri EBls ELan ESty MAus NLar SPer
	'Nuits de Young' (CeMo) ♀^{H7}	CArg EBls EPfP MAus NLar
	'Nur Mahal' (HM)	CArg EBls MAus
	NURSE TRACEY DAVIES ('Frykookie'^{PBR}) (F) ♀^{H6}	MAsh MFry
	nutkana (S)	EBls MAus
§	- var. ***hispida*** (S)	EBls
§	- 'Plena' (S/D) ♀^{H7}	EBls MAus NLar WHer
	'Nymphenburg' (HM)	EWTr SPer
	'Nyveldt's White' (Ru)	EBls MAus
	OCTAVIA HILL ('Harzeal'^{PBR}) (F)	CBod MRav MWat NLar SPer
§	× ***odorata***	CPou EBls
	- 'Fortune's Double Yellow'	see *R.* × *odorata* 'Pseudindica'
	- 'Hume's Blush Tea-scented China' (Cl)	EBls
§	- 'Mutabilis' (Ch) ♀^{H5}	Widely available
§	- 'Ochroleuca' (Ch)	CPou
I	- 'Odorata' (Ch)	EBls
	- old crimson China (Ch)	EBls
§	- 'Pallida' (Ch)	CPou EBls EPfP EWTr LRHS MAus MWat NLar SPer SSea
§	- 'Pseudindica' (ClCh)	EBls IArd MAus
§	- Sanguinea Group (Ch)	EBls SEND XSen
	- - 'Bengal Crimson' (Ch) ♀^{H5}	CPou CRHN CRos ECre EPfP EWTr LRHS LSRN NRHS SLon SPoG WAvo WCFE WCot WKif
	- - 'Bob's Beauty' (Ch)	WCot
§	- 'Viridiflora' (Ch)	CPou EBee EBls LEdu MAus SLon SMad SPer WCot WHer
	ODYSSEY ('Franski'^{PBR}) (F)	ESty
	'Oeillet Flamand'	see *R.* 'Oeillet Parfait'
§	'Oeillet Parfait' (G)	MAus
	officinalis	see *R. gallica* var. *officinalis*
	OH WOW! ('Wekspitrib'^{PBR}) (Cl)	ECnt ESty SSea
	old blush China	see *R.* × *odorata* 'Pallida'
	old cabbage	see *R.* × *centifolia*
	OLD JOHN ('Dicwillynilly') (F)	LSRN
	old pink moss rose	see *R.* × *centifolia* 'Muscosa'
	OLD PORT ('Mackati'^{PBR}) (F)	ELon ESty IArd
	old red moss	see *R.* 'Henri Martin', *R.* 'Lanei'
	old velvet moss	see *R.* 'William Lobb'
	'Old Velvet Rose'	see *R.* 'Tuscany'
	old yellow Scotch (SpH)	see *R.* × *harisonii* 'Williams' Double Yellow'
	OLIVIA ROSE AUSTIN ('Ausmixture'^{PBR}) (S)	CRos CSBt ELan EPfP ESty GBin LRHS MAsh MAus NAln NRHS SPoG
	OLIVIA ('Wekquahofa') (HT)	LSRN
	'Olympic Flame' (F)	EPfP MAsh
	'Omar Khayyám' (D)	EBls MAus NLar
	omeiensis	see *R. sericea* subsp. *omeiensis*
	OPEN ARMS ('Chewpixcel'^{PBR}) (ClMin) ♀^{H6}	CRos EBls EPfP ESty LBuc MAsh MAus MFry MMuc SMad SPer SSea
	'Ophelia' (HT)	EBls NLar
	ORANGE BLOSSOM SPECIAL ('Smi52/02') (ClMin)	ESty
	'Orange Sensation' (F)	CTri MAus
§	ORANGE SUNBLAZE ('Meijikatar'^{PBR}) (Min)	CSBt SPer
	'Orange Triumph' (Poly)	EBls
	'Orangeade' (F)	SCob
	ORANGES AND LEMONS ('Macoranlem'^{PBR}) (F)	CArg CBod CSBt EBls ESty MAus SSea WBor
	OTHELLO ('Auslo'^{PBR}) (S)	SPer
	OUR BETH ('Beacarol') (S)	EBls LRHS LSRN MAsh
	'Our Dream' (Patio)	LRHS MAsh
	OUR GEORGE ('Kirrush') (Patio)	LSRN
	OUR HILDA ('Lancoro') (F)	LSRN
§	OUR JANE ('Horengland') (F)	LSRN
	OUR JUBILEE ('Coccages') (HT)	ESty
	'Our Millie' (HT) **new**	LSRN
	OUR MOLLY ('Dicreason') (GC/S)	IDic LSRN SPer
	OUT OF THE BLUE ('Simblue') (F)	ESty
	OXANA ('Dicovadatop') (F) **new**	IDic
	OXFORDSHIRE ('Korfullwind'^{PBR}) (GC) ♀^{H6}	SCob SSea
	'Pablito' (Min)	MMuc
	PANACHE ('Poultop'^{PBR}) (Patio/Min)	ECnt LRHS MFry NPri
	'Papa Gontier' (T)	CPou
	PAPA MEILLAND ('Meisar') (HT)	CSBt CTri EBls SPer SSea
	PAPER ANNIVERSARY (Patio)	LSRN
	PAPI DELBARD ('Delaby') (ClHT)	CArg EWTr LSRN MRav NLar
	'Papillon' (Ch)	EBls
I	'Parade' (Cl) ♀^{H6}	CArg CKel EBls LSRN MAus MFry NLar
	'Parkdirektor Riggers' (Cl)	CBod EBls GBin MAus NLar SCob SPer
	Parks's yellow China	see *R.* × *odorata* 'Ochroleuca'
	Parson's pink China	see *R.* × *odorata* 'Pallida'
	PARTRIDGE ('Korweirim') (GC)	EBls MAus SPer
	parvifolia	see *R.* 'Burgundiaca'
	PAS DE DEUX ('Poulhult'^{PBR}) (Courtyard Series) (ClF)	MAsh
	PASCALI ('Lenip') (HT)	CArg CBcs CTri EBls MAus MJak SCob SPer
	PASTELLA ('Tan98130') (F) **new**	ESty MFry
	PAT AUSTIN ('Ausmum'^{PBR}) (S)	CArg CBod CRos CTri EPfP LSRN MAsh MBNS MRav NAln NEgg NLar SCob SEND SPer
	PATRICIA MAY ('Dicscenic') (F) **new**	IDic

- 'Paul Crampel' (Poly) — EBls
- 'Paul Lédé' (ClT) — see *R.* 'Climbing Paul Lédé'
- PAUL MCCARTNEY (HT) — see *R.* THE MCCARTNEY ROSE
- 'Paul Neyron' (HP) — EBls EWTr MAus SPer
- 'Paul Noël' (Ra) — CRos CWld LSRN MAus
- 'Paul Ricault' (Ce × HP) — EBls MAus
- PAUL SHIRVILLE ('Harqueterwife'PBR) (HT) — CKel EBls MAus SPer
- 'Paul Transon' (Ra) ♀H6 — CPou CRHN CRos EBee EBls EPfP EWTr MMuc NEgg NLar SEND SPer WHer
- 'Paul Verdier' (Bb) — EBls
- 'Paula's Rose' (Patio) — LSRN
- § 'Paulii' (Ru/GC) — EBls MAus WSpi
- 'Paulii Alba' — see *R.* 'Paulii'
- 'Paulii Rosea' (Ru/GC) — MAus
- 'Paul's Early Blush' (HP) — EBls
- 'Paul's Himalayan Musk' (Ra) ♀H6 — Widely available
- § 'Paul's Lemon Pillar' (ClHT) — CArg CKel EBls ELon EPfP LRHS MAus NLar SPer
- 'Paul's Scarlet Climber' (Cl/Ra) — CArg EBee EBls LBuc LRHS MAsh MAus MJak MRav MSwo MWat NPri SPer WBor
- 'Paul's Single White Perpetual' (Ra) — CTri EBls NLar
- PAWS ('Beapaw') (S) — EBls
- 'Pax' (HM) — CPou EBls MAus WKif
- PEACE ('Madame A. Meilland') (HT) ♀H6 — CArg CBcs CKel CRos CSBt CTri EBls ECnt ELan EPfP ESty LCro LOPS LRHS LSRN MAsh MAus MFry MRav MWat NAln NEgg NPri NRHS SCob SPer SPoG SSea
- 'Peach Grootendorst' (Ru) — CPou
- PEACHY ('Macrelea') (HT) — MAsh MFry SPoG
- PEARL ('Korterschi'PBR) (F) ♀H6 — MAsh MRav MWat
- PEARL ('Wekpearl') (HT) — CRos CSBt
- PEARL ANNIVERSARY ('Whitston'PBR) (Min/Patio) — CBod CKel ESty LBuc LSRN MRav MWat SSea SVic
- PEARL DRIFT ('Leggab') (S) — EBls MAus MCot MSwo SPer
- PEAUDOUCE — see *R.* ELINA
- PEGASUS ('Ausmoon'PBR) (S) — MAus
- § 'Pélisson' (CeMo) — EBls
- § ***pendulina*** — EBls MAus WOut
- - 'Nana' — NWad
- 'Penelope' (HM) ♀H5 — CArg CKel CSBt CTri EBee EBls ECnt ELan EPfP EWTr LRHS LSRN MAus MCot MFry MNrw MRav NLar SCob SPer SSea
- 'Penelope Hobhouse' (HM) — EBls
- PENNY LANE ('Hardwell'PBR) (ClHT) ♀H6 — CArg CGro CSBt EBls ECnt ECrN EPfP EUJe LBuc LRHS MAsh MAus MFry MRav NLar SCoo SPer SPoG SSea
- PENNY LANE ('Talpen') (Min) — EWTr MSwo
- PENSIONER'S VOICE ('Fryrelax'PBR) (F) — MFry
- × ***penzanceana*** — see *R.* 'Lady Penzance'
- PEPPERMINT SPLASH — see *R.* RACHEL LOUISE MORAN
- PERENNIAL BLUE ('Mehv9601') (Ra) ♀H6 — EBls ELon ESty MRav SCob SSea
- PERENNIAL BLUSH ('Mehbarbie'PBR) (Ra) ♀H6 — CArg CKel ELan ESty MRav

- § PERFECT DAY ('Poulcrem') (F) — ECnt
- PERFECT GENTLEMAN ('Raw1059') (F) **new** — ESty
- PERFECT HARMONY ('Tangustedv') (HT) — ESty
- PERFECT PET ('Smi122-2-04') (F) — ESty
- 'Pergolèse' (DPo) — EBls
- 'Perle des Jardins' (T) — EBls
- § 'Perle d'Or' (Poly) ♀H6 — EBls EWTr MAus NLar SPer
- PERPETUALLY YOURS ('Harfable'PBR) (Cl) — CGro MRav
- Persian yellow — see *R. foetida* 'Persiana'
- PETER BEALES ('Cleexpert') (S) — EBls
- PETER PAN ('Chewpan'PBR) (Min) ♀H6 — EPfP MAus MFry
- PETER PAN ('Sunpete') (Patio) — MAsh
- 'Petite de Hollande' (Ce) — EBls MAus NAln NLar SPer
- 'Petite Lisette' (Ce × D) — MAus NLar
- 'Petite Orléannaise' (Ce) — EBls
- PHAB GOLD ('Frybountiful'PBR) (F) — MFry
- 'Pharisäer' (HT) — EBls
- PHEASANT ('Kordapt') (GC) — EBls MAus SPer
- PHILLIPA ('Poulheart'PBR) (S) — LSRN
- PHOEBE (Ru) — see *R.* 'Fimbriata'
- ***phoenicea*** — EBls
- 'Phyllis Bide' (Ra) ♀H6 — CArg CKel CRos EBls ELan EPfP EWTr IArd LCro LOPS LRHS MAus MCot MSwo NLar SMad SPer SSea WKif
- PICCADILLY ('Macar') (HT) — CSBt CTri SPer
- 'Picture' (HT) — EBls
- PIERRE CARDIN ('Meilolipo'PBR) (HT) — ESty
- PIGALLE '84 ('Meicloux') (F) — SCoo
- 'Pilgrim' — see *R.* THE PILGRIM
- ***pimpinellifolia*** — see *R. spinosissima*
- - 'Altaica' — see *R. spinosissima* 'Grandiflora'
- - double yellow-flowered — see *R.* × *harisonii* 'Williams' Double Yellow'
- - 'Harisonii' — see *R.* × *harisonii* 'Harison's Yellow'
- - 'Lutea' — see *R.* × *harisonii* 'Lutea Maxima'
- PINK ABUNDANCE ('Harfrothy'PBR) (Abundance Series) (F) — CArg
- PINK BELLS ('Poulbells') (GC) — CGro EBls SPer
- 'Pink Bouquet' (Ra) — CRHN
- PINK CHAMPAGNE ('Forchamp') (Cl) — ESty
- PINK CHAMPAGNE ('Frysamba') (F) — MAsh MFry
- 'Pink Cloud' (ClHT) — ELan
- 'Pink Favorite' (HT) — SCob SPer
- PINK FIZZ ('Poulycool') (ClPatio) — ECnt
- § PINK FLOWER CARPET ('Noatraum'PBR) (GC) ♀H6 — CGro CRos CSBt CTri EBls ECnt ELan EUJe LCro LOPS LRHS LSRN MAsh NPri NRHS SCoo SEND SPer SPoG SSea
- 'Pink Garnette' — see *R.* 'Carol Amling'
- 'Pink Grootendorst' (Ru) — EBls EPfP LEdu MAus NEgg NLar SPer
- 'Pink Gruss an Aachen' (F) — EBls
- § PINK HIT ('Poultipe'PBR) (Min/Patio) — EBls ECnt LRHS LSRN MAsh NRHS

	Name	Suppliers
	PINK MARTINI ('Tan04608'[PBR]) (HT)	ESty MFry MRav
	pink moss	see *R.* × *centifolia* 'Muscosa'
	'Pink Parfait' (F)	EBls SPer
	PINK PERFECTION ('Korpauvio'[PBR]) (HT) 🏆H5	CSBt ECnt EPfP LRHS MAsh SSea
	'Pink Perpétué' (Cl)	CArg CBod CSBt CTri EBls ECnt ELan ELon EPfP LBuc MAus MFry MRav MWat NLar SPer SPoG SSea
	'Pink Prosperity' (HM)	EBls MAus
	'Pink Showers' (ClHT)	MSwo
	PINK SKYLINER ('Franwekpink'[PBR]) (ClS)	EBls
	PINOCCHIO ('Rosenmärchen') (F)	EBls
	PIPPIN ('Beajaffa') (S)	EBls MAsh
	PIROUETTE ('Poulyc003'[PBR]) (ClS)	ECnt MAsh
	PLAYTIME ('Morplati') (F)	MAus
	PLEINE DE GRÂCE ('Lengra') (S)	EBls LEdu MAus
	'Plentiful' (F)	EBls
	POETRY IN MOTION ('Harelan'[PBR]) (HT)	CArg EBls
	POLAR STAR ('Tanlarpost') (HT)	CArg CSBt EBls ECnt MFry SPer
	'Polly' (HT)	EBls LSRN
§	'Polyantha Grandiflora' (Ra)	EBls MAus SVic WBor
	pomifera	see *R. villosa* L.
	POMPADOUR ('Deldour') (F)	ESty
	'Pompon Blanc Parfait' (A)	EBls MAus
	'Pompon de Bourgogne'	see *R.* 'Burgundiaca'
	'Pompon de Paris' (ClMinCh)	see *R.* 'Climbing Pompon de Paris'
	'Pompon de Paris' (MinCh)	SCob SSea WAbe WKif
	'Pompon Panaché' (G)	MAus
	POMPONELLA ('Korpompan'[PBR]) (F) 🏆H6	CWld MAsh
	PORT SUNLIGHT ('Auslofty'[PBR]) (HM) 🏆H6	CRos EPfP ESty LRHS MAus NAln NLar NRHS
	Portland rose	see *R.* 'Portlandica'
§	'Portlandica' (Po)	CTri EBls SPer
	prairie rose	see *R. setigera*
	prattii	EBls
	'Precious Amber' (F)	MAsh
	'Precious Gold' (F)	MAsh
	PRECIOUS LOVE ('Kirlowo'[PBR]) (F)	MAsh
	'Precious Memories' (Min)	LSRN
	PRECIOUS MEMORIES ('Dichello'[PBR]) (F)	ESty
	'Precious Platinum' (HT)	MJak SPer
	PRECIOUS TIME ('Oramarpa'[PBR]) (HT)	ESty
§	'Président de Sèze' (G) 🏆H6	CArg CPou EBls MAus NLar SPer
	'President Herbert Hoover' (HT)	EBls
	PRETTY IN PINK ('Dicumpteen'[PBR]) (GC) 🏆H6	ECnt
	PRETTY JESSICA ('Ausjess') (S)	CGro LSRN MRav SPer
	PRETTY LADY ('Scrivo'[PBR]) (F) 🏆H6	MAus
	PRETTY POLLY ('Meitonje') (Min) 🏆H6	CKel EPfP ESty LRHS MAsh MFry MRav SPoG SSea
	PRIDE OF ENGLAND ('Harencore'[PBR]) (HT)	EBls
	'Pride of Reigate' (HP)	EBls
	'Prima Ballerina' (HT)	CArg CTri EBls EPfP LRHS MAsh SPer
	primula	EBls MAus NLar SPer
	primula* × *rugosa	MJak
	'Prince Camille de Rohan' (HP)	CBod EBls MAus
	'Prince Charles' (Bb)	EBls MAus WKif
	PRINCE JARDINIER ('Meitroni'[PBR]) (HT) 🏆H6	CArg ESty LSRN
	PRINCESS ('Korspobux'[PBR]) (HT)	ECnt
	PRINCESS ALEXANDRA OF KENT ('Ausmerchant'[PBR]) (S)	CRos CSBt EPfP EShb ESty LRHS MAsh MAus NAln NRHS SPer
	PRINCESS ALEXANDRA ('Pouldra'[PBR]) (Renaissance Series) (S) 🏆H6	CTri ECnt ESty EWTr NLar
	PRINCESS ALICE ('Hartanna') (F)	LSRN
	PRINCESS ANNE ('Auskitchen'[PBR]) (S) 🏆H6	CGro CRos CSBt ECnt EPfP LBuc LRHS MAus NAln NRHS SCob
	'Princess Louise' (Ra)	EBls
	'Princess of Wales' (HP)	MWat
	PRINCESS OF WALES ('Hardinkum'[PBR]) (F) 🏆H6	EBls MJak MRav SPer
§	'Princesse de Nassau' (Ra)	CPou EBls MAus
	'Princesse Louise' (Ra)	EBls
	'Princesse Marie' misapplied	see *R.* 'Belvedere'
	'Princesse Marie' Jacques (Ra)	EBls
	'Pristine' (HT)	MAus
	'Prolifera de Redouté' misapplied	see *R.* 'Duchesse de Montebello'
	PROPER JOB ('Tan02733'[PBR]) (HT)	ECnt ELon ESty MFry
	'Prosperity' (HM) 🏆H6	CTri EBee EBls GBin MAus MCot MRav NLar SPer
	PROSPERO ('Auspero') (S)	NLar
§	PURE POETRY ('Tan04179') (HT)	EBee ELon ESty MFry
	'Purezza' (Ra)	EBls NLar
	'Purity' (ClHT)	CBod
	PURPLE EDEN	see *R.* EBB TIDE
	PURPLE PRINCE ('Simpurple') (HT)	ESty
	PURPLE SKYLINER ('Franwekpurp'[PBR]) (ClS)	EBls LRHS MAsh MCot NPri SPer SPoG
	PURPLE TIGER ('Jacpurr'[PBR]) (F)	ESty
	quatre saisons	see *R.* × *damascena* var. *semperflorens*
	'Quatre Saisons Blanche Mousseuse' (DMo)	CPou EBls MAus NLar
	QUEEN ANNE ('Austruck'[PBR]) (S)	EPfP ESty LSRN MAus
	QUEEN ELIZABETH	see *R.* 'The Queen Elizabeth'
	QUEEN MOTHER ('Korquemu'[PBR]) (Patio) 🏆H6	CSBt EBls ELan EPfP MAus MJak MRav SPer
	'Queen of Bourbons' (Bb)	EBls LEdu NLar
	QUEEN OF DENMARK	see *R.* 'Königin von Dänemark'
	QUEEN OF SWEDEN ('Austiger'[PBR]) (S)	CGro CRos ECnt EPfP LBuc LRHS MAsh MAus NAln NRHS SCob SPer
	'Rachel' (HT)	CArg CPou LRHS LSRN MAsh NLar NPri

Name	Suppliers
RACHEL ('Booyol') (S)	EBee
RACHEL ('Tangust'[PBR]) (HT) ♀[H6]	CSBt EBls EPfP ESty MFry MRav SPoG SSea
§ RACHEL LOUISE MORAN ('Jacdrama'[PBR]) (HT)	ELon ESty
RAINBOW MAGIC ('Dicxplosion'[PBR]) (Patio)	MJak
'Rambling Rector' (Ra) ♀[H6]	Widely available
RAMBLING ROSIE ('Horjasper'[PBR]) (Ra) ♀[H6]	CArg CBod CKel CRos CSBt EBls ECnt EPfP ESty EWTr GBin LSRN MAsh MAus MFry MSwo NAln NLar SSea
'Ramona' (Ra)	EBls
RASPBERRY CREAM TWIRL ('Meiteratol'[PBR]) (ClHT) **new**	MAsh
RASPBERRY QUEEN ('Tanneidol') (F) **new**	MFry
'Raspberry Royale' (F/Patio) ♀[H6]	EPfP MAsh SPoG
'Raubritter' ('Macrantha' hybrid)	CBod CPou EBls EWTr MAus SPer
RAYMOND BLANC ('Delnado') (HT)	EBee LSRN MRav NLar
'Raymond Carver' (S)	EBls LRHS MAsh
REBECCA (Patio)	ESty LSRN
'Rebecca Claire' (HT)	LSRN
REBECCA MARY ('Dicjury'[PBR]) (F)	IDic
RED ABUNDANCE	see *R.* SONGS OF PRAISE
RED BELLS ('Poulred') (Min/GC)	EBls
RED BLANKET ('Intercell') (S/GC)	EBls MAus SPer
RED COAT ('Auscoat') (F)	MAus
RED DEVIL ('Dicam') (HT)	CArg
RED EDEN ROSE ('Meidrason'[PBR]) (Cl)	ESty
RED FINESSE ('Korvillade'[PBR]) (F) ♀[H6]	CArg MAsh
'Red Grootendorst'	see *R.* 'F.J. Grootendorst'
RED LETTER DAY ('Beajackdaw') (S)	EBls LRHS MAsh NRHS
'Red Max Graf'	see *R.* ROTE MAX GRAF
red moss	see *R.* 'Henri Martin'
RED NEW DAWN	see *R.* 'Étendard'
RED PARFUM DE PROVENCE ('Meiafone'[PBR]) (HT)	ESty
§ 'Red Patio' (F/Patio)	LSRN
RED RASCAL ('Jacbed') (S/Patio)	CKel CSBt MFry
red rose of Lancaster	see *R. gallica* var. *officinalis*
'Red Wing' (S)	EBls MAus
REDOVA ('Poulcy030'[PBR]) (Courtyard Series) (Cl)	ECnt
REGENSBERG ('Macyoumis'[PBR]) (F/Patio)	EBls LEdu MAus MFry SPer
'Reine des Violettes' (HP) ♀[H6]	CPou EBls ELon EPfP EWTr GBin IArd LCro LOPS LSRN MAsh MAus NLar NPri SMad SPer
'Reine Marie Henriette' (ClHT)	CPou EBls
'Reine Olga de Wurtenberg' (N)	EBls
§ 'Reine Victoria' (Bb)	EBls LCro LOPS MAus NLar SPer
§ REMEMBER ('Poulht001'[PBR]) (HT) ♀[H6]	EBls ECnt EPfP LRHS MAsh NRHS SPoG
REMEMBER ME ('Cocdestin') (HT) ♀[H6]	CArg CGro CSBt EBls ECnt EPfP ESty IArd LCro LOPS LRHS LSRN MAsh MAus MFry MGos MRav MWat NEgg SCob SPer SPoG
REMEMBRANCE ('Harxampton'[PBR]) (F)	CArg CRos EBls EPfP ESty LBuc LRHS LSRN MAsh MFry MJak MRav MWat NPri NRHS SCob SPer SPoG
§ RENAISSANCE ('Harzart'[PBR]) (HT)	CArg CKel CSBt MJak
'René André' (Ra)	CPou CRHN EBls MAus NLar
'René d'Anjou' (CeMo)	MAus
RÉPUBLIQUE DE MONTMARTRE ('Delparfrou') (F)	ESty
'Rescht'	see *R.* 'De Resht'
'Rêve d'Or' (N)	EBls MAus MMuc SPer
'Réveil Dijonnais' (ClHT)	EBls MAus
RHAPSODY IN BLUE ('Frantasia'[PBR]) (S) ♀[H6]	Widely available
RICHARD PORSON ('Beajuniper') (S)	EBls
§ × ***richardii***	EBls MAus NLar
RICK STEIN ('Tan96205'[PBR]) (HT)	LSRN
'Rita' ambig. **new**	WKif
'Rival de Paestum' (T)	MAus
'River Gardens'	NPer
ROALD DAHL ('Ausowlish') (S) **new**	CRos CSBt ESty LRHS MAus NRHS
ROB ROY ('Cocrob') (F)	EBls SPer
ROBBIE BURNS ('Ausburn') (SpH)	MAus
'Robert le Diable' (Ce × G)	EBls MAus SPer
'Robert Léopold' (Mo)	EBls
'Robin Hood' (HM)	CBod EBls
ROBIN REDBREAST ('Interrob') (Min/GC)	EBls
§ ROBUSTA ('Korgosa') (Ru)	EBls
ROCK & ROLL ('Wekgobnez') (HT)	CSBt ESty LSRN
'Roger Lambelin' (HP)	CPou EBls MAus SPer
ROMANCE ('Tanezamor'[PBR]) (S)	LSRN
ROMANZE ('Tan03434'[PBR]) (HT) **new**	CArg
'Rosa Mundi'	see *R. gallica* 'Versicolor'
ROSARIUM UETERSEN ('Kortersen') (ClHT)	EBls
'Rose à Parfum de l'Haÿ' (Ru)	CTri EBls
'Rose Ball' (S)	EBls LRHS MAsh
§ 'Rose d'Amour' (S) ♀[H6]	EBls
'Rose de Meaux'	see *R.* × *centifolia* 'De Meaux'
'Rose de Meaux White'	see *R.* 'White de Meaux'
'Rose de Rescht'	see *R.* 'De Resht'
ROSE DES CISTERCIENS ('Delarle') (HT)	ESty
'Rose des Maures' misapplied	see *R.* 'Sissinghurst Castle'
'Rose d'Hivers' (D)	EBls
'Rose du Maître d'Ecole'	see *R.* 'Du Maître d'Ecole'
'Rose du Roi' (HP/DPo)	EBls MAus
'Rose du Roi à Fleurs Pourpres' (HP)	EBls MAus
ROSE FOR ELAINE ('Rawdenqueen') (HT)	LSRN
§ ROSE GAUJARD ('Gaumo') (HT)	CArg EBls LRHS MAsh
ROSÉE DE MATIN ('Evematch'[PBR]) (S)	EBls
'Rose-Marie Viaud' (Ra)	CPou EBee EBls MAus MMuc

ROSEMARY HARKNESS ('Harrowbond') (HT)	ESty MJak SPer
'Rosemary Rose' (F)	EBls SPer
ROSEMOOR ('Austough'[PBR]) (S) ♀H6	CRos LBuc LRHS MAsh MAus NRHS SPer
'Roseraie de l'Haÿ' (Ru) ♀H7	Widely available
ROSIE ('Benros') (Min)	LSRN
'Rosy Cheeks' (HT)	MAsh
ROSY CUSHION ('Interall') (S/GC)	CKel EBls EWTr LRHS MAus MCot NLar SPer WKif
'Rosy Mantle' (ClHT)	CSBt EBls SPer
§ ROTARY SUNRISE ('Fryglitzy') (HT)	CSBt MFry
§ ROTE MAX GRAF ('Kormax') (GC/Ru)	CBod CDul CKel EBls NLar
'Roundelay' (HT)	EBls
roxburghii	CBcs LEdu MAus
- PAB 7331	LEdu
- var. ***hirtula*** (S)	EBls
- f. ***normalis*** (S)	EBls
- 'Plena'	see *R. roxburghii* f. *roxburghii*
§ - f. ***roxburghii*** (d)	MAus
'Royal Air Force' (HT)	ELan
§ ROYAL BROMPTON ROSE ('Meivildo') (HT)	ESty
ROYAL COPENHAGEN	see *R.* REMEMBER ('Poulht001')
'Royal Gold' (ClHT)	EBls
'Royal Highness' (HT)	EBls
ROYAL JUBILEE ('Auspaddle'[PBR]) (S)	CRos CSBt EPfP LCro LOPS MAus SCob SPer
'Royal Occasion' (F)	SPer
ROYAL WILLIAM ('Korzaun') (HT) ♀H6	CArg CSBt CTri EBls ELan LBuc LRHS LSRN MAsh MAus MFry MJak MRav MWat NAln NPri SCob SPer
§ ***rubiginosa***	CCVT CDul CPer CTho EBls GPoy IFro LBuc MAus MRav NWea SPer WMoo WMou WTSh
rubra	see *R. gallica*
rubrifolia	see *R. glauca* Pourr.
'Rubrotincta'	see *R.* 'Hebe's Lip'
rubus (Ra)	MAus
RUBY ANNIVERSARY ('Harbonny'[PBR]) (Patio)	CGro CKel CRos CSBt EBls ELan ELon ESty LBuc LCro LOPS LRHS LSRN MAsh MFry MRav MSwo MWat NAln SCob SCoo SPer SPoG SSea SVic
RUBY CELEBRATION ('Peawinner'[PBR]) (F) ♀H6	CBod CKel EBls ESty MRav MWat
RUBY ROMANCE	see *R.* MEDLEY RUBY
RUBY RUBY	see *R.* RUBY SLIPPERS
§ RUBY SLIPPERS ('Weksactrumi') (Min)	LRHS MAsh NRHS SPoG
'Ruby Wedding' (HT)	CArg CBcs CKel CRos CSBt CTri EBee EBls ECnt ELan EPfP IArd LRHS LSRN MAsh MAus MFry MGos MJak MRav MWat NAln NRHS SCob SPer SVic
'Ruby Wedding Anniversary' (F)	LSRN
rugosa (Ru)	CArg CBod CDul CFGn CGro CLnd CPer CTri ECrN EPfP EPom LBuc LRHS MAus MRav NWea SCob SGol SPlb WMat WMou WTSh
- 'Alba' (Ru)	Widely available
- 'Rubra' (Ru)	CBcs CBod CCVT CDul CGro CTho CTri EBee ELan EPfP EPom LBuc LCro LOPS NWea SCob SEWo SPer SPoG SSea SVic
- var. ***ventenatiana*** (Ru)	EBls
'Rugosa Atropurpurea' (Ru)	EPom
'Ruhm von Steinfurth' (HP)	EBls
'Rumba' (F)	CBod ELan
'Rural England' (Ra)	EBls LRHS MAsh
RUSHING STREAM ('Austream') (GC)	MAus
'Russelliana' (Ra)	CBod EBls MAus NLar
'Sadler's Wells' (S)	EBls
'Safrano' (T)	EBls
SAINT BONIFACE ('Kormatt') (F/Patio)	CSBt
SAINT EDMUNDS ROSE	see *R.* BONITA
SAINT ETHELBURGA ('Beabimbo') (S)	EBls LRHS MAsh MCot
Saint John's rose	see *R.* × *richardii*
Saint Mark's rose	see *R.* 'Rose d'Amour'
'Saint Nicholas' (D)	EBls MAus
'Saint Prist de Breuze' (Ch)	EBls
SAINT SWITHUN ('Auswith'[PBR]) (S)	CRos EPfP ESty LRHS MAsh MAus NAln NLar NRHS SCob SPer SSea
'Salet' (DPMo)	CPou EBls MAus NLar
'Sally Holmes' (S) ♀H6	CPou EBee EBls ECnt EPfP MAus MFry MRav NLar SEND SLon SPer
SALLY KANE ('Frygroovy'[PBR]) (HT)	MFry MRav
SALLY'S ROSE ('Canrem') (HT)	ECnt LSRN
SALSA	see *R.* CHEEK TO CHEEK
SALVATION ('Harlark'[PBR]) (F)	ESty
§ SAMARITAN ('Harverag'[PBR]) (HT)	CSBt
sancta	see *R.* × *richardii*
'Sander's White Rambler' (Ra) ♀H6	CRHN CRos CSam CTri EBee EBls EPfP EWTr LRHS MAus MSwo NRHS SPer WFar
SANDRA ('Koreinek') (HT)	LSRN
SANDRA ('Poulen055'[PBR]) (Renaissance Series) (S)	LSRN NLar
SANDRINGHAM ('Beamolly') (S)	EBls
'Sandringham Centenary' (HT)	EBls
'Sanguinea'	see *R.* × *odorata* Sanguinea Group
SARAH (HT)	see *R.* JARDINS DE BAGATELLE
'Sarah van Fleet' (Ru)	CBod CTri EBee EBls GBin IArd MAus MMuc MRav MSwo NEgg NLar SPer
SARAH, DUCHESS OF YORK	see *R.* SUNSEEKER
SAVOY HOTEL ('Harvintage') (HT)	CArg EBls MAus MFry SPer
'Scabrosa' (Ru) ♀H7	CBod EBls ECnt EPfP LBuc MAsh MAus MCot NLar NWea SPer
SCARBOROUGH FAIR ('Ausoran') (S) ♀H6	CRos MAus MMuc
SCARLET FIRE	see *R.* 'Scharlachglut'
SCARLET GLOW	see *R.* 'Scharlachglut'
SCARLET HIT ('Poulmo'[PBR]) (PatioHit Series) (Min/Patio)	EBls ECnt LRHS LSRN NRHS
SCARLET PATIO ('Kortingle'[PBR]) (Patio)	CRos MAsh MFry SPoG
SCARLET QUEEN ELIZABETH ('Dicel') (F)	EBls
§ SCENT FROM HEAVEN ('Chewbabaluv') (Cl)	CGro CRos CSBt EBee ECnt ESty EUJe LCro LOPS MAsh MFry MWat SPoG SSea
SCENTED CARPET ('Chewground'[PBR]) (GC) ♀H6	ECnt ELan MAus

SCENTED GARDEN ('Chewscentity') (S)	CSBt ESty SSea
SCENTED MEMORY ('Poulht002'PBR) (HT)	ECnt
SCENTIMENTAL ('Wekplapep'PBR) (F)	CBod EBls EPfP ESty MAsh MRav SSea
'Scentsation' (Min)	CKel
SCENT-SATION ('Fryromeo'PBR) (HT)	CKel MFry MRav MWat SPoG
SCEPTER'D ISLE ('Ausland'PBR) (S)	CRos CSBt EPfP LBuc LRHS LSRN MAsh MAus NAln NLar NRHS SCob SCoo SPer
§ 'Scharlachglut' (ClS)	CPou EBls EPfP MAus SPer
SCHLOSS BAD HOMBURG	see *R.* 'Alibaba'
SCHNEEWITTCHEN	see *R.* ICEBERG
§ 'Schneezwerg' (Ru) ♀H7	EBls MAus NLar SPer
'Schoolgirl' (ClHT)	CArg CBcs CBod CTri EBls ELan EPfP EUJe LBuc LRHS MAsh MFry MMrt MRav MSwo MWat NEgg NPri SPer SSea
'Scintillation' (S/GC)	MAus
Scotch rose	see *R. spinosissima*
Scotch yellow (SpH)	see *R.* × *harisonii* 'Williams' Double Yellow'
'Seagull' (Ra) ♀H6	CArg CRos CTri EBls ECnt EPfP LEdu LRHS LSRN MAsh MRav MWat NLar SCob SLon SMad SPer WHer
'Seale Pink Diamond' (S)	SSea
'Seale White Rambler' (Ra) **new**	SSea
SEALED WITH A KISS ('Simwhat') (HT)	ESty
'Sealing Wax' (*moyesii* hybrid)	CPou EBls EWTr NLar
SELFRIDGES ('Korpriwa') (HT)	ESty
'Semiplena'	see *R.* × *alba* 'Alba Semiplena'
sempervirens (Ra)	EBls
sericea (S)	MAus
- var. ***morrisonensis*** B&SWJ 7139	WCru
§ - subsp. ***omeiensis***	LEdu WPGP
- - BWJ 7550	WCru
- - PAB 2883	LEdu
- - f. ***pteracantha*** (S)	CBcs CKel CTri EBls ELan EPfP EWTr IDee LEdu MAus NLar NWea SCob SPer
'Serratipetala' (Ch)	EBls
§ ***setigera***	EBls MAus
setipoda	EBls MAus
seven sisters rose	see *R. multiflora* 'Grevillei'
SEVENTH HEAVEN ('Fryfantasy'PBR) (HT)	MFry
SEXY REXY ('Macrexy') (F)	CArg CBcs EBls LSRN MAsh MAus MRav SCob SMad SPer SPoG
'Shailer's White Moss'	see *R.* × *centifolia* 'Shailer's White Moss'
SHANTY ('Tan96191') (F) **new**	ESty MFry
SHARIFA ASMA ('Ausreef'PBR) (S)	CBod EBee LSRN MSwo NEgg NLar SPer
SHEILA'S PERFUME ('Harsherry') (F) ♀H6	CArg EBls ECnt EPfP ESty LSRN MAsh MFry MRav SPer SPoG
SHINE ON ('Dictalent'PBR) (Patio) ♀H6	CSBt ECnt MFry
'Shot Silk' (HT)	CKel EBls
SHOWMEE MUSIC ('Chewdaybell') (GC)	MAsh
SHOWMEE SUNSHINE ('Kenveron') (GC)	MAsh
§ SHOWSTAR ('Smi36-1-02') (HT)	CSBt ESty
SHOWTIME ('Baitime') (ClS)	MAsh SPoG
'Showtime' Lindquist (HT)	EBls
§ SHRIMP HIT ('Poulshrimp'PBR) (Patio)	EBls ECnt MAsh MFry SPoG
'Shropshire Lass' (S)	MAus SPer
SHROPSHIRE STAR ('Chewsummit') (ClS)	ESty SSea
SIGHTSAVER ('Fryaffair'PBR) (HT)	MFry
SILVER ANNIVERSARY ambig.	CArg CGro CRos LSRN NAln
SILVER ANNIVERSARY ('Jaclav') (HT)	CKel MJak
SILVER ANNIVERSARY ('Meiborfil') (HT)	ELon
SILVER ANNIVERSARY ('Poulari'PBR) (HT) ♀H6	CBod CRos CSBt EBls ECnt ELan LCro LOPS LRHS LSRN MAsh MAus MFry MGos MRav MWat NAln NPri NRHS SCoo SPer SPoG SSea
SILVER CELEBRATION ('Guescloud') (F) **new**	ESty
'Silver Jubilee' (HT)	CArg CBcs CTri EBls IArd LRHS MAsh MAus MFry MRav NRHS SCob SPer
'Silver Lining' (HT)	CKel
'Silver Moon' (Cl)	EBls
SILVER SHADOW ('Frystereo'PBR) (HT)	ECnt ESty MFry
'Silver Wedding' (HT)	CBcs CKel CTri EBls ELan IArd MJak MRav MSwo MWat NEgg SCob SPer SVic
'Silver Wedding Celebration' (F)	ESty LSRN
SILVER WISHES	see *R.* PINK HIT
SIMBA ('Korbelma') (HT)	LSRN
'Simone' (HT)	CPou EBee
SIMPLY GORGEOUS ('Formaui') (HT)	ESty
SIMPLY SALLY ('Harpaint'PBR) (Patio)	LSRN
§ SIMPLY THE BEST ('Macamster'PBR) (HT) ♀H6	CArg CGro CKel CSBt EBls ELan EPfP ESty LRHS LSRN MAsh MAus MFry MGos MJak MRav NPri NRHS SCob SCoo SPer SPoG
sinowilsonii	see *R. longicuspis* var. *sinowilsonii*
'Sir Cedric Morris' (Ra)	EBls NLar SSea
'Sir Frederick Ashton' (HT)	EBls
'Sir Galahad' deep pink-flowered (F)	CKel
§ SIR GALAHAD ('Hareasy') (F) **new**	MWat
'Sir Galahad' white-flowered	see *R.* SIR GALAHAD ('Hareasy')
§ SIR HARRY PILKINGTON ('Tanema') (HT)	EBls
SIR HENRY CECIL ('Webpegasus') (F)	LSRN
SIR JOHN BETJEMAN ('Ausvivid'PBR) (S)	CRos EPfP LBuc LRHS MAsh MAus NAln NRHS
SIR JOHN MILLS ('Beadaffy') (Cl)	EBls
'Sir Joseph Paxton' (Bb)	CPou EWTr MAus
SIR PAUL SMITH ('Beapaul') (ClHT)	EBls LRHS MAsh
SIR WALTER RALEIGH ('Ausspry') (S)	MRav
SIR WALTER SCOTT ('Ausfalcon') (S)	MAus
§ 'Sissinghurst Castle' (G)	EBls MAus

Sister Elizabeth ('Auspalette'[PBR]) (S)	LSRN NAln
Skylark ('Ausimple'[PBR]) (S) ♀[H6]	CRos MAsh MAus SCob
'Skyrocket'	see *R.* 'Wilhelm'
Smarty ('Intersmart') (S/GC)	EBls MAus SPer
Smiling Eyes ('Chewrocko') (S/GC) **new**	MAsh
Snazzee ('Wekzazette'[PBR]) (F)	ECnt ESty
Snow Carpet ('Maccarpe') (Min/GC)	EBls MAus
'Snow Dwarf'	see *R.* 'Schneezwerg'
Snow Goose ('Auspom'[PBR]) (ClS)	CRos CSBt EPfP MAus NAln NLar SPer SSea
Snow Hit ('Poulsnows'[PBR]) (Min/Patio)	ECnt
'Snow Queen'	see *R.* 'Frau Karl Druschki'
Snow Queen ('Simseen') (HT)	ESty
Snowball ('Macangeli') (Min/GC)	LSRN
Snowcap ('Harfleet'[PBR]) (Patio)	ESty
'Snowdon' (Ru)	EBls MAus
Soeur Emmanuelle ('Delamo'[PBR]) (S)	CBod EBee ESty LSRN MRav
'Soldier Boy' (Cl)	CBod CPou EBls NLar
'Soleil d'Or' (S)	EBls
Soleil Vertical ('Delsov') (Cl)	ESty
§ Solo Mio ('Poulen002'[PBR]) (Renaissance Series) (S)	EBee ECnt NLar
§ 'Sombreuil' (ClT)	CArg EBls EPfP IArd LRHS MAus MRav NEgg NLar SPer
Some Like it Hot ('Gueschorus') (F) **new**	ESty
Something Special ('Macwyo'[PBR]) (HT)	ESty
Song and Dance ('Frydishy'[PBR]) (HT)	MFry
§ Songs of Praise ('Harkimono'[PBR]) (Abundance Series) (F)	EBls
Sonia	see *R.* Sweet Promise
'Sophia'	see *R.* Solo Mio ('Poulen002')
'Sophie's Perpetual' (ClCh)	CPou CTri EBls MAus SLon SPer
Sophy's Rose ('Auslot'[PBR]) (S)	CRos LBuc LSRN MAus MBNS NEgg SPer
Sorbet Fruité ('Meihestries'[PBR]) (ClF)	SSea
soulieana (Ra/S)	EBls MAus
'Soupert et Notting' (DPoMo)	CPou MAus NLar SPer
'Southampton' (F) ♀[H6]	CArg EBls LSRN SPer SSea
Southern Beauty ('Forauty') (F)	ESty
'Souvenir d'Alphonse Lavallée' (ClHP)	EBls
'Souvenir de Claudius Denoyel' (ClHT)	CArg EBls SPer
'Souvenir de François Gaulain' (T)	EBls
'Souvenir de Jeanne Balandreau' (HP)	CPou EBls
'Souvenir de la Malmaison' (ClBb)	see *R.* 'Climbing Souvenir de la Malmaison'
'Souvenir de la Malmaison' (Bb)	CArg EBls EWTr MAus MRav NLar SPer
'Souvenir de Madame Auguste Charles' (Bb)	EBls
'Souvenir de Madame Léonie Viennot' (ClT)	EBls MAus MRav NLar
'Souvenir de Pierre Vibert' (DPMo)	CPou
'Souvenir de Saint Anne's' (Bb)	EBls MAus NLar
'Souvenir d'Elise Vardon' (T)	EBls
'Souvenir du Docteur Jamain' (ClHP)	CPou CSBt EBls ELan ELon EPfP ESty LCro LOPS LSRN MAus MRav NLar SPer SPoG SSea WFar WKif
'Souvenir d'un Ami' (T)	EBls
spaldingii	see *R. **nutkana*** var. ***hispida***
'Spanish Beauty'	see *R.* 'Madame Grégoire Staechelin'
Sparkle ('Frymerlin'[PBR]) (HT)	ECnt ESty MAsh
Sparkler	see *R.* Kent
Sparkling Burgundy ('Raw1007') (F)	ESty
Sparkling Scarlet ('Meihati') (ClF)	MAsh
Special Anniversary ('Whastiluc'[PBR]) (HT) ♀[H6]	CBcs CGro CKel CRos CSBt EBls ECnt ELan ELon EPfP ESty GBin LCro LOPS LRHS LSRN MAsh MFry MJak MRav MWat NPri NRHS SCoo SPoG SSea
Special Child ('Taniripsa'[PBR]) (F/Patio) ♀[H6]	MRav SSea
'Special Dad' (HT)	CGro
'Special Daughter' (F) **new**	LSRN
Special Event ('Meibrelon') (HT)	ESty
Special Friend ('Kirspec'[PBR]) (Patio)	ESty LSRN SCob
'Special Grandad'	LSRN
Special Grandchild ('Flimika') (F)	ESty
Special Grandma (F)	ESty LSRN
Special Grandpa (F)	ESty
Special Memories ('Fortop') (F)	ESty
'Special Mum' (F)	LSRN
Special Occasion ('Fryyoung'[PBR]) (HT)	MFry MRav MWat
Special Son (F)	ESty
'Spectabilis' (Ra)	CBod CPou EBls
'Spek's Yellow' (HT)	EBls
'Spencer' misapplied	see *R.* 'Enfant de France'
'Spencer' (HP)	EBls
Spice of Life ('Diccheeky'[PBR]) (F/Patio)	EBls
§ ***spinosissima***	CArg CCCN CDul CPer CSde EBls LBuc MAus MMuc NWea SCob SGol SPer WTSh
- 'Andrewsii' ♀[H7]	EBls MAus MRav
- 'Cedric Morris' **new**	WCot
§ - double, pink-flowered	EBls WBor
§ - - white-flowered ♀[H7]	EBls ECha EWTr LEdu MAus
- 'Falkland'	EBls ECha MAus
§ - 'Grandiflora'	EBls
- 'Marbled Pink'	MAus
- 'Mary, Queen of Scots'	CPou EBls EWTr MAus NLar SRms
- 'Merthyr Mawr' **new**	WCot
- 'Mrs Colville'	EBls MAus
- 'Ormiston Roy'	MAus

- 'Single Cherry' EBls MAus
- 'William III' EBls EWes GCal MAus WCot
SPIRIT OF FREEDOM ('Ausbite'PBR) (S) CRos EPfP LRHS MAsh MAus NAln NEgg NRHS
§ 'Splendens' (Ra) EBls MMuc
SPLISH SPLASH ('Raw1020') (F) ESty
ST CLARE ('Horbamber') (F) EBls
ST HELENA ('Canlish') (F) ECnt
STAMFORD'S SANCTUARY ('Beajealous') (Cl) EBls
'Stanwell Perpetual' (SpH) ♀H7 CArg CTri EBls ELan EPfP EWTr MAus MRav NLar SPer SSea
STAR DUST ('Morstar') (Min) ELon
'Star Performer'PBR (ClPatio) CSBt ECnt EPfP ESty MAsh SPoG SSea
STARDUST ('Peavandyke'PBR) (Patio/F) ESty
STARLIGHT EXPRESS ('Trobstar'PBR) (Cl) LBuc LRHS MAsh MFry NPri SPer
STARRY EYED ('Horcoexist') (Patio) MMrt
'Stars 'n' Stripes' (Min) MAus
STELLA (HT) LSRN
stellata MAus
§ - var. ***mirifica*** MAus
'Stephen' LSRN
STRAWBERRIES AND CREAM ('Geestraw') (Min/Patio) ESty
STRAWBERRY FAYRE ('Arowillip'PBR) (Min/Patio) CGro CKel ESty MRav SPoG
STRAWBERRY HILL ('Ausrimini'PBR) (S) ♀H6 CRos CSBt ESty LRHS MAsh MAus MMuc NRHS SCoo
STRIKE IT RICH ('Wekbepmey'PBR) (HT) ♀H6 ESty MRav
§ SUE HIPKIN ('Harzazz'PBR) (HT) ESty MRav
'Suffolk' (HT) SCob
SUFFOLK ('Kormixal'PBR) (S/GC) ♀H6 CSBt EBls MAus MJak MRav SCob SPer SSea
suffulta see *R. arkansana* var. *suffulta*
SUGAR AND SPICE ('Peaallure'PBR) (Patio) MWat SPoG
SUGAR 'N' SPICE ('Tinspice') (Min) MRav
SUMA ('Harsuma') (GC) EBls ESty
SUMMER BEAUTY ('Kororbe'PBR) (F) ♀H6 CArg MAsh
SUMMER BREEZE ('Korelasting'PBR) (ClS) MAsh
SUMMER FRAGRANCE ('Tanfudermos') (Castle Series) (HT) EBls ELon
§ SUMMER GOLD ('Poulreb'PBR) (F) MAsh
'Summer Holiday' (HT) SPer
SUMMER LOVE ('Franluv') (F) CBcs
SUMMER MEMORIES ('Koruteli'PBR) (Palace Series) (F) CKel
SUMMER SONG ('Austango'PBR) (S) CRos EPfP ESty LBuc LSRN MAsh MAus NAln NRHS SCob
'Summer Sunrise' (GC) EBls
'Summer Sunset' (GC) EBls
SUMMER WINE ('Korizont'PBR) (ClHT) ♀H6 CSBt EBls ECnt EPfP LRHS MAsh SPer SPoG
SUMMERTIME ('Chewlarmoll'PBR) (ClPatio) ♀H6 CArg CSBt EBls ECnt ELan EPfP LBuc LRHS MAsh MAus MRav NPri SPer SPoG
SUN HIT ('Poulsun'PBR) (PatioHit Series) (Min/Patio) CSBt ECnt MRav SPoG
'Sunblaze' see *R.* ORANGE SUNBLAZE
SUNBLEST ('Landora') (HT) MAsh MRav SCob
'Sunfire' Barni (F) **new** ECnt
SUNNY DAY ('Savasun') (S) CBod SPer
SUNNY SKY ('Koraruli'PBR) (HT) CGro CRos CSBt ECnt ESty LBuc LRHS MAsh MFry NPri NRHS SCoo SPoG
SUNNY SKY ('Korvestavi') (HT) MWat
SUNRISE ('Kormarter'PBR) (S) EPfP ESty MAsh SPoG
SUNRISE ROSE FOR WAKEFIELD HOSPICE ('Frynoon') (F) **new** MFry
§ SUNSEEKER ('Dicracer'PBR) (F/Patio) ♀H6 MAsh MFry MRav SPoG
SUNSET BOULEVARD ('Harbabble'PBR) (F) MAsh MAus MRav SPer
SUNSET CELEBRATION see *R.* WARM WISHES
SUNSET GLOW see *R.* 'Alibaba'
SUPER DOROTHY ('Heldoro') (Ra) ♀H6 LSRN MAus SSea
SUPER ELFIN ('Helkleger'PBR) (Ra) CRos LBuc LRHS MAus MFry MRav NLar SCob SPer SSea
SUPER EXCELSA ('Helexa') (Ra) ♀H6 EBls ELan MAus SCob SSea
SUPER FAIRY ('Helsufair'PBR) (Ra) ♀H6 CKel EBee EBls ECnt MAus MFry MRav SMad SPer SSea
SUPER SPARKLE ('Helfels'PBR) (Ra) SCob SSea
§ SUPER STAR ('Tanorstar') (HT) CArg CKel EBls MRav MWat
SUPER TROUPER ('Fryleyeca'PBR) (F) ♀H6 CArg CBod CGro CSBt ECnt ELan ESty LRHS LSRN MAsh MFry MRav MWat SCoo SPer WBor WCot
'Surpasse Tout' (G) EBls MAus
§ 'Surpassing Beauty of Woolverstone' (ClHP) EBls
SURREY ('Korlanum') (GC) ♀H6 CKel CSBt CTri EBls ELan ESty LCro LOPS LSRN MAus MRav MSwo NLar SCob SPer SSea
SUSAN ('Poulsue') (S) ECnt LSRN NLar SLon
SUSAN HAMPSHIRE ('Meinatac') (HT) EBls
SUSAN WILLIAMS-ELLIS ('Ausquirk'PBR) (S) CRos EPfP LBuc LRHS MAsh MAus NLar NRHS SCob
SUSIE ('Harwhistle') (ClPatio) CGro ECnt ESty LSRN
SUSSEX ('Poulave'PBR) (GC) CSBt EBls MSwo SCob SMad SPer SSea
'Sutter's Gold' (HT) EBls
SWAN LAKE ('Macmed') (Cl) CArg CPou EBee EBls ECnt EPfP MRav NLar SPer
SWAN LAKE ('Schwanensee') (Cl) **new** MFry
SWANY ('Meiburenac') (Min/GC) EBls ESty MAus MJak MMuc MSwo SPer
SWEET CAROLINE ('Micaroline') (Min) LSRN
SWEET CHILD OF MINE (HT) ESty

	Name	Suppliers
	SWEET DREAM ('Fryminicot') (Patio) ♀H6	CArg CGro CRos CSBt CTri EBls ELan EPfP LRHS LSRN MAsh MAus MFry MJak MRav MWat SPer SPoG SSea
	SWEET DREAM CREAM ('Fryniggle'[PBR]) (F)	MFry
	'Sweet Fairy' (Min)	CSBt
	'Sweet Harmony' (HT)	EBls
	SWEET HAZE ('Tan97274'[PBR]) (F) ♀H6	CKel CSBt MRav SPer
	SWEET JULIET ('Ausleap'[PBR]) (S)	MAus MSwo SPer
	SWEET LEMON DREAM ('Fryrich') (Patio)	CTri MFry
	SWEET MAGIC ('Dicmagic'[PBR]) (Min/Patio) ♀H6	CTri EBls MRav SPoG
	SWEET MEMORIES ('Whamemo') (Patio)	CKel CTri EBls ECnt ELan EPfP ESty LRHS MAsh MRav MWat NPri NRHS SCoo SPer SPoG
	SWEET PARFUM DE PROVENCE ('Meiclusif'[PBR]) (HT) ♀H6	CArg ELan ESty LSRN
§	SWEET PROMISE ('Meihelvet') (GC)	EBls
	SWEET REMEMBRANCE ('Kirr') (HT)	SCoo
	'Sweet Repose' (F)	EBls
	'Sweet Revelation'	see *R.* SUE HIPKIN
	'Sweet Wonder' (Patio)	EPfP MAsh
	sweginzowii	GCal GLog MAus
	- 'Macrocarpa'	EBls
	'Sydonie' (HP)	CPou
	'Sylvia Dot' (F)	LSRN
	'Sympathie' (ClHT)	EBls MAsh SPer
	'Talisman' (HT)	EBls
	TALL STORY ('Dickooky') (F) ♀H6	EBee EBls NLar
	TAM O'SHANTER ('Auscerise'[PBR]) (S)	EPfP MAus
	TANGERINE TANGO ('Cheworangemane') (Cl)	SSea
	TANGO SHOWGROUND ('Chewpattens'[PBR]) (GC)	ESty
	TATTON ('Fryentice'[PBR]) (F)	EBls ESty MAus MFry MRav
§	'Tausendschön' (Ra)	EBls
	TAWNY TIGER ('Frygolly'[PBR]) (F)	MFry
	TEA CLIPPER ('Ausrover'[PBR]) (S)	MAus
	TEAR DROP ('Dicomo') (Min/Patio)	MFry SCob SSea
	TEASING GEORGIA ('Ausbaker'[PBR]) (S) ♀H6	CKel CRos ECnt EPfP ESty LBuc LRHS LSRN MAsh MAus MMuc NAln NLar NRHS SCob SCoo
	TEMPTRESS ('Korramal') (ClS) ♀H6	CGro CPou EPfP EUJe MAsh
	TENACIOUS ('Macblackpo'[PBR]) (F)	ESty
	TEQUILA SUNRISE ('Dicobey') (HT) ♀H6	CArg CGro CKel CTri EBls ELan EPfP ESty LBuc MAsh MAus MFry MJak MRav SPer SSea
	TERRACOTTA ('Meicobuis') (HT)	ESty
	TESS OF THE D'URBERVILLES ('Ausmove'[PBR]) (S)	CRos ELan EPfP EShb ESty LCro LOPS LRHS LSRN MAus NAln NEgg NLar NRHS SCob SCoo SPer SSea
	'Tessa' (F)	LSRN
	'Texas Centennial' (HT)	EBls
§	THAÏS ('Memaj') (HT)	EBls
	'Thalia' (Ra)	EBls
	THANK YOU ('Chesdeep'[PBR]) (Patio)	ESty LSRN
§	THAT'S JAZZ ('Poulnorm'[PBR]) (Courtyard Series) (ClF)	CArg ECnt LSRN MFry
	THE ALBRIGHTON RAMBLER ('Ausmobile'[PBR]) (Ra)	CGro CRos EPfP LRHS MAsh MAus NAln NLar NRHS
	THE ALEXANDRA ROSE ('Ausday'[PBR]) (S)	EPfP LBuc MAsh NAln SPer
§	THE ALNWICK ROSE ('Ausgrab'[PBR]) (S)	CRos EPfP LBuc LRHS MAsh MAus MGos NAln NLar NRHS SCob SCoo SPer SSea
	THE ANCIENT MARINER ('Ausoutcry') (S)	LRHS MAsh MAus NAln NRHS
I	'The Anniversary Rose'	CRos EBls EPfP LBuc LRHS MAsh NRHS
	THE BEE'S KNEES ('Guesbehold') (F) **new**	ESty
	'The Bishop' (Ce × G)	MAus
	THE BOSWORTH ROSE ('Raw1014') (F)	ESty
	THE CHESHIRE REGIMENT ('Fryzebedee') (HT)	MFry
	THE CHURCHILL ROSE ('Horoften') (S)	EBls LRHS MAsh
	THE COUNTRYMAN ('Ausman') (S)	EBee MAus SCob SSea
	THE COVENTRY CATHEDRAL ROSE ('Smi72-02') (F)	ESty
	THE DARK LADY ('Ausbloom'[PBR]) (S)	NEgg SPer
	THE DIAMOND WEDDING ROSE (HT)	EBls LSRN MAsh
	'The Doctor' (HT)	EBls
§	'The Fairy' (Poly) ♀H6	CArg CKel CSBt CTri EBee EBls ECnt ECrN ELan LEdu LRHS MAsh MAus MCot MFry MRav MWat NLar SCob SMad SPer SSea WBor WCFE WCot WHer
	'The Garland' (Ra) ♀H6	CArg EBee EBls EPfP LBuc MAus MCot MMuc NLar SPer
	THE GENEROUS GARDENER ('Ausdrawn'[PBR]) (S) ♀H6	CKel CRos CSBt CTri ELan EPfP EShb ESty GBin LBuc LRHS LSRN MAus MGos MJak NAln NLar NRHS SCob SCoo SPer SSea
§	THE GOLD AWARD ROSE ('Poulac008') (Palace Series) (Patio)	ECnt
	THE HERBALIST ('Aussemi') (S)	MAus
	THE HILDA OGDEN ROSE ('Korchakon') (Patio)	MAsh
	THE INGENIOUS MR FAIRCHILD ('Austijus'[PBR]) (S)	CRos EPfP MAus SCoo
	THE JACK DUCKWORTH ROSE ('Korlutmag'[PBR]) (Patio)	MAsh
	THE JUBILEE ROSE ('Poulbrido'[PBR]) (F)	ECnt
	THE LADY ('Fryjingo'[PBR]) (S)	ESty
	THE LADY GARDENER ('Ausbrass'[PBR]) (S)	CGro CRos ELan EPfP LRHS MAsh MAus NRHS
	THE LADY OF THE LAKE ('Ausherbert'[PBR]) (Ra)	CRos EPfP LRHS MAus NLar NRHS SCob SCoo
	THE LADY'S BLUSH ('Ausoscar'[PBR]) (S)	CRos EPfP LRHS MAsh MAus NAln

	THE LAKELAND ROSE ('Harspiral') (Cl)	MAsh
	THE LARK ASCENDING ('Ausursula'[PBR]) (S)	CRos LBuc LCro LOPS LRHS MAsh MAus NAln NRHS SCob SCoo SSea
	'The Margaret Coppola Rose'	see *R.* WHITE GOLD
	THE MAYFLOWER ('Austilly'[PBR]) (S) ♀H6	CRos CSBt LBuc LRHS MAsh MAus MSwo NAln NRHS SCob SPer
§	THE MCCARTNEY ROSE ('Meizeli'[PBR]) (HT)	LSRN SPer
	'The New Dawn'	see *R.* 'New Dawn'
	THE ODDFELLOWS ROSE ('Fryriviera') (F) **new**	MFry
	'The One and Only' (HT)	LRHS MAsh
	THE PAINTER ('Mactemaik'[PBR]) (F)	LSRN
	THE PERSE ROSE ('Beajargon') (S)	EBls
§	THE PILGRIM ('Auswalker'[PBR]) (S) ♀H6	CKel CRos CSBt CTri EPfP LBuc LRHS MAsh MAus MBNS MJak NAln NLar NRHS SCob SPer SPoG SSea
	THE POET'S WIFE ('Auswhirl'[PBR]) (S)	CRos CSBt ECnt EPfP ESty LRHS MAsh MAus NAln NRHS SCoo SPoG
	THE PRINCE ('Ausvelvet'[PBR]) (S)	NLar
	THE PRINCE'S TRUST ('Harholding'[PBR]) (Cl)	EBee MAsh MAus NAln SSea
§	'The Queen Elizabeth' (F)	CArg CBod CSBt CTri EBls ELan LCro LOPS LRHS LSRN MAsh MAus MFry MRav MWat SCob SPer SSea
	THE QUEEN'S JUBILEE ROSE ('Beajubilee') (S)	EBls LRHS MAsh
	THE ROTARIAN	see *R.* ROTARY SUNRISE
	'The Royal Brompton Rose'	see *R.* ROYAL BROMPTON ROSE
I	'The Rugby Rose' (HT)	LSRN
	THE SHEIKH KHALIFA ROSE ('Dickoolkid') (Patio)	IDic
	THE SHEPHERDESS ('Austwist'[PBR]) (S)	MAus NAln
	THE SIMPLE LIFE ('Hartrifle'[PBR]) (Cl)	MRav SSea
	THE TIMES ROSE ('Korpeahn') (F) ♀H6	ECnt MAus SCob SPer
	THE WAINWRIGHT ROSE ('Frylovely') (HT) **new**	MFry
	THE WEDGWOOD ROSE ('Ausjosiah'[PBR]) (ClS)	EPfP LRHS MAsh MAus NAln NRHS SCob
	THE WREN ('Kormamtiza'[PBR]) (F/Patio)	EPfP MAsh
	'Thelma' (Ra)	EBls MAus
	'Thérèse Bugnet' (Ru) ♀H7	EBls MAus
	THINKING OF YOU ('Frydandy'[PBR]) (HT) ♀H6	CGro EBls ELon EPfP ESty LSRN MAsh MAus MFry NRHS SPer SSea
	'Thisbe' (HM)	CPou EBls MAus
	THOMAS À BECKET ('Auswinston'[PBR]) (S)	CRos EPfP ESty LRHS MAsh MAus NAln NRHS
	'Thoresbyana'	see *R.*'Bennett's Seedling'
	THOUSAND BEAUTIES	see *R.*'Tausendschön'
	'Threave' (Bb)	CPou
	threepenny bit rose	see *R. elegantula* 'Persetosa'
	THUMBS UP ('Hornothing') (S)	EBls
	TICKLED PINK ('Fryhunky'[PBR]) (F) ♀H6	CArg CKel CSBt CTri EBls ELon LRHS LSRN MAsh MFry MRav SPer SPoG SSea
	TIMES PAST ('Harhilt'[PBR]) (ClHT)	CKel MRav SPoG
	'Tina Turner' (HT)	LSRN
	TINTINARA ('Dicuptight'[PBR]) (HT) ♀H6	ECnt
	'Tipo Ideale'	see *R.* × *odorata* 'Mutabilis'
	'Tipsy Imperial Concubine' (T)	EBls
	TITANIC ('Macdako'[PBR]) (F)	ESty
	'Toby Tristam' (Ra)	EBls
	TOGETHER FOREVER ('Dicecho'[PBR]) (F)	LSRN MAsh MFry
	TOGMEISTER ('Beahappy') (F)	EBls LRHS MAsh NRHS
	'Tom Marshall' (Ra)	LSRN
	'Tony Jacklin' (F)	LSRN
	TOP MARKS ('Fryministar'[PBR]) (Min/Patio)	EPfP MFry MJak MRav SCoo SPer
	TOPAZ JEWEL	see *R.* YELLOW DAGMAR HASTRUP
§	'Tour de Malakoff' (Ce)	CPou EBls NLar SPer
	TOYNBEE HALL ('Korwonder') (F)	LRHS MAsh
	TRADESCANT ('Ausdir'[PBR]) (S)	SCob
	TRADITION	see *R.* TRADITION '95
§	TRADITION '95 ('Korkeltin'[PBR]) (ClHT)	MAsh NLar
	TRANQUILITY ('Barout') (HT)	EPfP LRHS MAsh NRHS
	TRANQUILLITY ('Ausnoble'[PBR]) (S)	CRos CSBt ECnt ESty LBuc MAus NAln NLar SCob SCoo SPer
	'Treasure Trove' (Ra)	CRHN EBls MAus
	'Tricolore' (G)	EBls
	'Tricolore de Flandre' (G)	EBls MAus
	'Trier' (Ra)	CPou EBls MAus NLar
	'Trigintipetala' misapplied	see *R.* × *damascena* 'Professeur Émile Perrot'
	'Triomphe de Laffay' (Ch)	EBls
	'Triomphe de l'Exposition' (HP)	MAus
	triphylla	see *R.* × *beanii*
	'Triple Delight' (S)	LSRN
I	'Trish's Rose' (Ru)	LSRN
	TROIKA ('Poumidor') (HT)	MAsh MAus SPer
	'Tropicana'	see *R.* SUPER STAR
	TRUE FRIEND ('Smi35-2-02') (F) **new**	ESty
	'Truly Loved' (F)	LSRN MAsh
	TRULY SCRUMPTIOUS ('Smi35-4-02') (HT)	ESty MRav MWat
	TRUMPETER ('Mactru') (F) ♀H6	CArg CTri EBee ECnt IArd LBuc MAsh MAus MFry MRav MWat SPer SPoG
§	'Tuscany' (G)	EBls MAus SPer
	'Tuscany Superb' (G) ♀H7	CArg CBod CPou CRos CSBt CTri EBls ELan EPfP EWTr LCro LEdu LOPS LRHS MAus MCot MRav NAln NLar SMad SPer SSea WBor WFar WHer WKif
	TWENTY-FIFTH ('Beatwe') (F)	EBls
	TWENTY-ONE AGAIN! ('Meinimo'[PBR]) (HT)	LSRN
	TWICE IN A BLUE MOON ('Tan96138'[PBR]) (HT) ♀H6	CArg CGro CKel CSBt EBee EBls ECnt ESty MFry MRav MWat SCob SCoo SPoG SSea
	TWIGGY'S ROSE ('Harteam'[PBR]) (F)	MAsh
	TWIST ('Poulstri'[PBR]) (Courtyard Series) (ClPatio)	CArg ECnt LSRN

	Name	Suppliers
	TYNWALD ('Mattwyt') (HT)	EBee SPer
	'Ulrich Brünner'	see *R.*'Ulrich Brünner Fils'
§	'Ulrich Brünner Fils' (HP)	EBls MAus
	'Uncle Bill' (HT)	EBls
	UNCLE WALTER ('Macon') (HT)	EBls
	'Unique Blanche'	see *R.* × *centifolia* 'Unique'
	VALENCIA ('Koreklia'[PBR]) (HT)	MAus
	VALENTINE HEART ('Dicogle'[PBR]) (F) 🏆H6	CArg CSBt ELon ESty IArd LSRN MAsh MAus MFry MRav SPoG
	'Vanguard' (Ru)	EBls
	'Vanity' (HM)	EBls MAus
	'Variegata di Bologna' (Bb)	EBls EPfP EWTr MAus
	'Vatertag' (Min)	LSRN
	'Veilchenblau' (Ra) 🏆H7	Widely available
	VELVET FRAGRANCE ('Fryperdee') (HT)	CArg CSBt ECnt EPfP ESty MAus MFry MRav SPoG SSea
	'Venusta Pendula' (Ra)	MAus
	'Verschuren' (HT/v)	ESty
	versicolor	see *R. gallica* 'Versicolor'
	'Vick's Caprice' (HP)	EBls MAus NLar
	'Vicomtesse Pierre du Fou' (ClHT)	EBls MAus
	VICTORIA JOY ('Diciwill') (F)	IDic
	VICTORIA ('Simlast') (HT)	ESty
	VIKING PRINCESS	see *R.* IMAGINATION ('Pouldron')
	'Village Maid'	see *R.* × *centifolia* 'Unique Panachée'
§	***villosa*** L.	EBls
	- subsp. ***villosa***	MAus
§	'Violacea' (G)	EBls MAus
	VIOLET CLOUD ('Harquick'[PBR]) (Min)	CKel ESty MRav
	'Violette' (Ra)	CPou CRHN CRos EBls ESty EWTr MAus SPer WFar WHer
	'Violinista Costa' (HT)	EBls
	virginea	SPer
	VIRGINIA MCKENNA OBE ('Harsong') (S) **new**	LSRN
	virginiana 🏆H7	EBls GCal MAus NWea WMoo
	- 'Plena'	see *R.*'Rose d'Amour'
	'Viridiflora'	see *R.* × *odorata* 'Viridiflora'
	'Vivid' (Bourbon hybrid)	EBls
	vosagiaca	see *R. caesia* subsp. *vosagiaca*
	'Vuosaari' (Ru)	EBls
	WALTZ ('Poulkrid'[PBR]) (Courtyard Series) (ClPatio)	ECnt LSRN
	wardii var. ***culta***	MAus
	WARM WELCOME ('Chewizz'[PBR]) (ClMin) 🏆H6	CGro CKel CRos EBls ECnt ELan EPfP ESty EUJe LCro LOPS LSRN MAsh MAus MFry MRav NAln SMad SPer SPoG SSea WCot
§	WARM WISHES ('Fryxotic'[PBR]) (HT) 🏆H6	CSBt EBls ECnt EPfP LBuc LRHS LSRN MAsh MAus MFry MJak MRav MWat NRHS SCob SPer SSea
	'Warrior' (F)	SPer
	WARWICKSHIRE ('Korkandel'[PBR]) (GC)	EBls
§	***watsoniana*** (Ra)	EBls
	WB YEATS ('Dicoodles') (F)	IDic
	webbiana	MAus
	WEDDING BELLS ('Korsteflali'[PBR]) (HT)	LRHS LSRN MAsh
	WEDDING CELEBRATION ('Poulht006'[PBR]) (HT)	EBls ECnt LBuc MAsh
	'Wedding Day' (Ra)	Widely available
	'Weetwood' (Ra)	CRHN
	WEISSE WOLCKE	see *R.* WHITE CLOUD ('Korstacha')
	WELL-BEING ('Harjangle'[PBR]) (S)	CArg ELon
	'Wendy Cussons' (HT)	CTri EBls MRav MWat SCob SPer
	WENLOCK ('Auswen') (S)	SPer
	WESTERLAND ('Korwest') (S) 🏆H6	CBod EBls LRHS MRav NLar
	WHERE THE HEART IS ('Cocoplan'[PBR]) (HT)	ESty
	WHISKY MAC ('Tanky') (HT)	CBcs CGro CSBt CTri EBee EBls ELan LSRN MRav MWat SCob SPer
	'White Bath'	see *R.* × *centifolia* 'Shailer's White Moss'
	WHITE BELLS ('Poulwhite') (Min/GC)	EBls
	'White Cécile Brünner' (Poly)	EBls
§	WHITE CLOUD ('Korstacha'[PBR]) (ClHT)	ELon ESty MFry
	'White Cockade' (ClHT)	CPou EBls MSwo SPer
	WHITE COVER	see *R.* KENT
§	'White de Meaux' (Ce)	EBls MAus
	WHITE DIAMOND ('Interamon'[PBR]) (S)	ECnt
§	WHITE GOLD ('Cocquiriam'[PBR]) (F) 🏆H6	CSBt
	'White Grootendorst' (Ru)	EBls NLar
	'White Maman Couchet' (HT)	EBls
	WHITE MEIDILAND ('Meicoublan') (S/GC)	CWld LRHS MAsh
	white moss	see *R.* × *centifolia* 'Shailer's White Moss', *R.*'Comtesse de Murinais'
	'White New Dawn' (Cl)	EBls
	'White Patio' (Min/Patio)	CRos MAsh SPoG
	WHITE PERFUMELLA ('Meicalanq'[PBR]) (HT)	ELan ELon ESty LSRN
§	'White Pet' (Poly) 🏆H6	CArg CKel CTri EBee EBls ECnt ELan EPfP EWTr LRHS MAus MCot MRav MWat NLar SEND SPer SSea WKif
	white Provence	see *R.* × *centifolia* 'Unique'
	'White Queen Elizabeth' (F)	SCob
	white rose of York	see *R.* × *alba* 'Alba Semiplena'
	WHITE SKYLINER ('Franwekwhit'[PBR]) (ClS)	EBls SSea
	WHITE STAR ('Harquill') (ClHT) 🏆H5	ECnt MRav SSea
	'White Wings' (HT)	CArg EBls WKif
	wichurana	see *R. lucieae*
	'Wickwar' (Ra) 🏆H6	EBls GCal NLar
	WILD EDRIC ('Aushedge'[PBR]) (Ru) 🏆H6	ECnt LBuc MAus MMuc NAln SCob SCoo
	WILD ROVER ('Dichirap'[PBR]) (F) 🏆H6	EBls ESty MFry
	WILD THING ('Jactoose'[PBR]) (S) 🏆H6	MAsh
	WILDEVE ('Ausbonny'[PBR]) (S) 🏆H6	CRos LRHS MAus NAln NRHS
	WILDFIRE ('Fryessex') (Patio)	CArg CGro CRos ECnt ESty LRHS MAsh MAus MFry MRav SPoG
§	'Wilhelm' (HM)	CPou EBls MAus SPer
	'Will Scarlet' (HM)	MAus
	'William Allen Richardson' (N)	EBls MAus
	WILLIAM AND CATHERINE ('Ausrapper'[PBR]) (S)	CRos EPfP LCro LOPS MAsh MAus NAln SCob
	'William Baffin' (S)	EBls

'William Cobbett' (F) SSea
§ 'William Lobb' (CeMo) ♀H7 CArg CBod CKel CPou EBls EPfP LRHS MAus MCot MNrw MRav NAln NEgg NLar NRHS SMad SPer WHer WKif
WILLIAM MORRIS ('Auswill'PBR) (S) CRos CSBt NAln NEgg SCob SPer
'William R. Smith' (T) EBls
WILLIAM SHAKESPEARE ('Ausroyal') (S) MJak SCob SPer
WILLIAM SHAKESPEARE 2000 ('Ausromeo'PBR) (S) CArg CBod CKel CRos CSBt ECnt ELan EShb ESty LCro LOPS MBNS MJak MSwo NAln NEgg NLar SCob SSea
'William Tyndale' (Ra) CBod CPou
'Williams' Double Yellow' see *R.* × *harisonii* 'Williams' Double Yellow'
willmottiae EBls MAus
WILTSHIRE ('Kormuse'PBR) (S/GC) ♀H6 CBod CSBt CTri EBls ECnt ESty MRav NLar SCob SEND SLon SSea
WINCHESTER CATHEDRAL ('Auscat'PBR) (S) CArg CBod CGro CKel CRos CTri ECnt ELan EPfP LCro LOPS LRHS LSRN MAsh MAus MJak MRav MSwo NAln NEgg NLar NRHS SCob SLon SMad SPer SPoG SSea
'Windermere' (Ra) EBls
WINDFLOWER ('Auscross') (S) LBuc MAus
WINDRUSH ('Ausrush') (S) EBee MAus SPer
WINE AND DINE ('Dicuncle') (GC) EBls
WISLEY 2008 ('Ausbreeze'PBR) (S) CRos CSBt EPfP LBuc LRHS MAsh MAus NAln NRHS SCob SCoo
WITH THANKS ('Fransmoov'PBR) (HT) ELon MJak
'Woburn Abbey' (F) EBls
WOLLERTON OLD HALL ('Ausblanket'PBR) (S) CRos CSBt EPfP EShb ESty LBuc LRHS MAus NAln NLar NRHS SCob SCoo SPer
'Wolley-Dod' see *R.* 'Duplex'
WONDERFUL HUSBAND ('Raw982') (F) ESty
WONDERFUL NEWS ('Jonone'PBR) (Patio) ESty
WONDERFUL WIFE ('Raw1025') (HT) ESty
WONDERFUL YOU ('Smi 170-2-4') (HT) ESty
woodsii (S) EBls MAus
- var. ***fendleri*** EBls
- var. ***ultramontana*** EBls
'Woolverstone Church Rose' see *R.* 'Surpassing Beauty of Woolverstone'
WORCESTERSHIRE ('Korlalon'PBR) (GC) ♀H6 MAus MJak MRav SPer
'Wretham Rose' (Ce) EBls
WYMONDHAM ABBEY ('Beadevil') (ClHT) EBls LRHS MAsh
§ ***xanthina*** 'Canary Bird' (S) ♀H6 CArg CBcs CGro CKel CSBt CTho CTri EBee EBls ECnt ELan EPfP ESty LSRN MAsh MAus MFry MNrw MRav NEgg NLar SPer SPoG SSea SWvt WCFE
§ - f. ***hugonis*** CBod EBls ELan MAus NLar SPer
- - 'Flore Pleno' EBls
'Xavier Olibo' (HP) EBls
YARDLEY BAROQUE ('Beayar') (HT) EBls
'Yellow Cécile Brünner' see *R.* 'Perle d'Or'
§ YELLOW DAGMAR HASTRUP ('Moryelrug'PBR) (Ru) CBod CPou EBls MMrt NLar SCob SPer
YELLOW FLOWER CARPET see *R.* FLOWER CARPET SUNSHINE
'Yellow Mutabilis' (Ch) EBls
'Yellow Patio' (Min/Patio) CRos LRHS MAsh SPoG
yellow Scotch see *R.* × *harisonii* 'Williams' Double Yellow'
YELLOW SUNBLAZE ('Meitrisical') (Min) CSBt
'Yesterday' (Poly/FCl) ♀H6 CKel EBee EBls MAus NLar
YOKOHAMA ('Keihayokoki') (HT) EBls
'Yolande d'Aragon' (HP) EBls
York and Lancaster see *R.* × *damascena* 'Versicolor'
YORK MINSTER ('Harquest') (F) MRav
YORKSHIRE ('Korbarkeit'PBR) (GC) EBls MRav
'Yorkshire Lady' (HT) LSRN NEgg
YORKSHIRE PRINCESS ('Dicmouse') (Patio) IDic MRav
YOU ARE MY SUNSHINE ('Frykwango'PBR) (HT) ♀H6 MFry
YOU ONLY LIVE ONCE (F) **new** LSRN
YOUNG AT HEART ('Raw922') (F) ESty
YOUNG LYCIDAS ('Ausvibrant'PBR) (S) CRos CSBt EPfP LBuc LRHS LSRN MAus NAln NRHS SCob
'Your Wedding Day' (F) CGro
YOU'RE BEAUTIFUL ('Fryracy'PBR) (F) ♀H5 CGro CKel CSBt EBee ECnt ELan ESty LBuc LCro LOPS LRHS MAsh MFry MRav MWat NRHS SPer SPoG
YVES PIAGET see *R.* ROYAL BROMPTON ROSE
'Yvonne Rabier' (Poly) ♀H6 EBls EWTr MAus MRav NLar SPer
'Zéphirine Drouhin' (Bb) Widely available
§ 'Zigeunerknabe' (S) CBod EBls MAus NLar SPer WFar

Roscoea ✿ (*Zingiberaceae*)

sp. CMac
alpina CAby CBro CExl CPBP EBee EMor EPot GEdr GKev ILea NHar WCru XLum
- CC 1820 IBlr
- pink-flowered IBlr
- purple-flowered IBlr
- short WCru
alpina × ***cautleyoides*** IBlr
§ ***auriculata*** ♀H5 CAby CAvo CBct CBro CLAP EHrv EPfP EPot GCal GEdr GKev IBlr ILea LEdu MAsh MAvo NWad SChF SDeJ SPer WCru WHil
- B&SWJ 2594 WCru
- B&SWJ 2687 WCru
- GWJ 9230 WCru
- 'Anorexia' IBlr
- brown-stemmed × ***purpurea*** CJun IBlr
- early-flowering IBlr WCru
- 'Floriade' CJun EBee IBlr LPla WPGP WSHC
- green-stemmed × ***purpurea*** CJun IBlr
- late-flowering WCru
- 'White Cap' CJun EBee GKev
auriculata × ***australis*** IBlr
auriculata × ***capitata*** IBlr
auriculata × ***cangshanensis*** WCru
auriculata × ***purpurea*** WCru

australis	CSam EBee ELon GEdr LLHF MAsh MNrw WCru WThu
– pink-flowered KW 22124	IBlr
– purple-flowered KW 22124	IBlr
australis* × *humeana	IBlr
'Ballyrogan Lavender'	IBlr
'Ballyrogan White'	IBlr
× ***beesiana*** ♀H5	CAvo CBcs CBod EPfP EUJe ILea MAsh SMHy
– 'Ballyrogan Purple'	CJun IBlr
– Cream Group	CBct CJun EBee EPfP EPot IBlr LEdu MMrt NBir SDeJ WCru
– Dark Group	IBlr
– Gestreept Group	CAby CBro CLAP CMea CRos EMor EPot EUJe GEdr GKev IBlr LAma LRHS MPie NRHS SPer WCru
– – white-flowered	GKev
– 'Lemon and Lavender'	CJun IBlr
– 'Monique'	CDTJ CJun EBee EPfP IBlr WFar
– 'Moonlight'	CJun IBlr
– 'Petite Purple'	IBlr
bhutanica PAB 3826	LEdu
Blackthorn strain	IBlr WCru WHil
brandisii misapplied	see *R. tumjensis*
brandisii (King ex Baker) K. Schum.	IBlr
cangshanensis	CAby MAsh
– BWJ 7848	WCru
capitata	IBlr
cautleyoides	CAby CAvo CBro CPla CRos ECha EHrv ELon EMor EPot GEdr GKev IBlr ILea LAma LRHS MNrw NBid NGdn NHar NRHS SPer SRot WCot WCru XEll
– CLD 772	IBlr
– blue-leaved **new**	NHar
– var. ***cautleyoides*** f. ***atropurpurea***	IBlr
– – – 'Giraffe'	IBlr
– – white-flowered	CAby
– 'Crûg's Late Lemon'	WCru
– 'Doge Purple'	IBlr
– 'Early Purple'	CJun
– 'Early Yellow'	EBee
– 'Himalaya' ♀H5	WHil
– 'Jeffrey Thomas' ♀H5	CJun CRos CSam EBee ELan GCal GEdr IBlr LRHS NRHS WHil
– 'Last Emperor'	CLAP
– late, lavender-flowered	IBlr
– – yellow-flowered	IBlr
– 'Lemon Giraffe'	CJun IBlr
– mauve-flowered	WHil
– 'Pennine Purple'	IBlr NHar
– plum-flowered	IBlr
– var. ***pubescens***	CJun IBlr
– 'Purple Giant'	CJun EBee WHil
– 'Purple Queen' ♀H5	EBee GKev
– purple-flowered	CAby IBlr
– 'Reinier'	CJun GCal IBlr
– f. ***sinopurpurea***	GKev IBlr NAln
– 'Stephanie Bloom' ♀H5	EBee NHar
– 'Vanilla'	CJun LEdu
– 'Washfield Purple'	IBlr
– 'Wine Red'	MAvo WHil
– 'Yeti'	CJun
aff. ***cautleyoides***	MAsh MAvo SPlb
cautleyoides* × *humeana	IBlr
cautleyoides* × *praecox	IBlr
cautleyoides* × *scillifolia f. ***atropurpurea***	IBlr
debilis var. ***debilis***	IBlr
forrestii f. ***forrestii***	IBlr
– – pubescent	IBlr
– 'Ice Maiden'	IBlr
– f. ***purpurea***	IBlr
– f. ***purpurea* × *humeana***	IBlr
'Harvington Evening Star'	CJun CLAP CRos EBee LLHF LRHS MAsh MAvo NHar NRHS
Harvington hybrids **new**	NHar
'Harvington Imperial' **new**	NHar
'Harvington Raw Silk' ♀H5	CJun CLAP CRos EBee LEdu LLHF LRHS MAvo NHar NRHS WFar
'Harvington Royale'	CJun CRos EBee LLHF LRHS NHar NRHS
humeana	CAby CBro CRos EPot GEdr GKev LAma LRHS NHar NRHS WThu
– from Cruickshank Botanic Garden	IBlr NHar
– f. ***alba***	CJun IBlr NHar
– Forrest's form	IBlr
– 'Guincho White Stripe'	IBlr
– lavender-flowered	IBlr
– 'Long Acre Sunrise'	CJun EBee
– f. ***lutea*** ♀H5	CAby CJun GEdr IBlr
– pink-flowered	IBlr
– 'Purple Streaker'	CJun
– purple-flowered	EBee
– 'Rosemoor Plum'	CAby CJun
– 'Snowy Owl'	CJun GEdr
– 'Two Tone'	CJun IBlr
– f. ***tyria*** ♀H5	CJun
– – Inkling Group **new**	NHar
'Ice Maiden'	CJun IBlr
'Kew Beauty' ♀H5	CAby CBcs CBod CBro CExl CJun CLAP CMea CRos EMor EPfP GCal LRHS MAvo NGdn NRHS SMHy SPoG WGwG WHil WPtf
'Lavender Mist'	IBlr
'McBeath's Pink'	CRos LLHF LRHS NRHS
nepalensis	CJun
'Pallid Sun'	IBlr
'Pinky'	CMea
praecox	GEdr IBlr
procera misapplied	see *R. auriculata*
procera Wall.	see *R. purpurea*
'Purple King'	CJun
§ ***purpurea***	Widely available
– CC 1757	IBlr
– CC 3628	CExl IBlr
– HWJK 2020	WCru
– HWJK 2169	WCru
– HWJK 2175	WCru
– HWJK 2400	WCru
– HWJK 2407	WCru
– KW 13755	IBlr
– MECC 2	CJun IBlr
– MECC 10	CJun IBlr
– 'Ant Marian'	EBee GKev
– Blackthorn hybrids	CLAP NHar
– 'Bronzed Albino'	IBlr
– bronze-leaved	CAby
– 'Brown Peacock'	CAvo CJun GKev IBlr IPot MAvo NHar WCot WCru
– 'Butterfly'	GEdr GKev
– 'Cinnamon Stick'	CAbb CJun CLAP CWGN ECtt GEdr MAsh NHar
– 'Dalai Lama' ♀H4	GEdr GKev IPot WHil
– var. ***gigantea*** CC 1757	IBlr
– 'Himalayan Delight'	IBlr
– 'Julie's Glory'	EBee GKev WFar

- 'Late Lavender' IBlr
- 'Nico' CJun ELan IBlr
- 'Peacock' CJun EPot GKev IBlr WHil
- 'Peacock Eye' CJun GEdr GKev IBlr
- 'Petticoat Pink' GKev
- var. ***procera*** see *R. purpurea*
- 'Purple Dwarf' IBlr
- 'Purple Tower' IBlr
- 'Red Foot' EBee
- 'Red Gurkha' see *R. purpurea* f. ***rubra***
- 'Red Riding Hood' GEdr GKev WFar
- Royal Purple hybrids CJun MAsh NHar WPGP

§ - f. ***rubra*** ♀H4 CAby CBro CCht CJun EBee EUJe GKev IBlr IPot LLHF LRHS MAsh MNrw MSCN NHar NRHS SChF WCot WFar WHil WPGP WSHC
- - 'Gurkha Redstem' CJun CLAP SPoG WCru
- 'Salt 'n' Pepper' EBee GKev
- short IBlr
- 'Slender Wisp' IBlr
- 'Spice Island' CAbb CJun CLAP CWGN ECtt GEdr MMrt SPoG WFar
- 'Summer Snow' EBee
- tall WCru
- 'Twin Towers' GKev
- 'Typico' IBlr
- 'Vannin' CJun LEdu WCru
- 'Vincent' CJun EBee EPot GKev
- 'Wisley Amethyst' CBro CJun CRos EBee IBlr LLHF LRHS MAsh MAvo MNrw NHar NRHS WFar

'Red Neck' ♀H4 IBlr

schneideriana CJun GKev IBlr WThu
- robust form IBlr

scillifolia CBro CRos GEdr LAma LRHS NBir NRHS SDeJ SPlb
- f. ***atropurpurea*** CAby EBee EPot GCal GKev IBal IBlr WCru WThu
- black-flowered NHpl
- f. ***scillifolia*** EBee IBlr NHpl WCru WHil WThu

aff. ***scillifolia*** purple-flowered GEdr IBlr

'Summer Deep Purple' ♀H5 CJun CRos EBee LRHS NRHS

tibetica EBee GEdr GKev IBlr LLHF SPlb WCru WSHC WThu
- ACE 2538 IBlr WCru
- BWJ 7878 WCru
- aff. f. ***albopurpurea*** IBlr
- f. ***atropurpurea*** BWJ 7640 WCru
- f. ***rosea*** WCru

aff. ***tibetica*** IBlr

§ ***tumjensis*** IBlr

'Two Tone' CJun

wardii ♀H5 CExl IBlr

rosemary see *Rosmarinus officinalis*

Rosenia (*Asteraceae*)

humilis CPBP

Rosmarinus ✿ (*Lamiaceae*)

'Barwinnock Dwarf Blue' WHer

corsicus 'Prostratus' see *R. officinalis* Prostratus Group

× ***lavandulaceus*** misapplied see *R. officinalis* Prostratus Group

× ***noeanus*** XSen

officinalis Widely available
- f. ***albiflorus*** CBcs CBod CRos ECrN ENfk EPfP EWhm LRHS MHer MNHC NPol SDow SLim SPlb SPoG SRms WCFE WGwG WJek XSen
- - 'Lady in White' CRos CSBt ELan EPfP LRHS MAsh NRHS SGol SPer SPoG SRms WGwG WJek
- 'Alderney' WGwG WJek
- 'Almondsbury' WGwG
- 'Amethyst Beauty' SDow

§ - var. ***angustissimus*** 'Benenden Blue' ♀H4 CSBt ELan GPoy LRHS MBNS SGol SPer SPlb SPoG SRms WGwG WJek WSpi
- - 'Corsican Blue' CBod ELan GPoy MHer MHol MNHC SGol SRms WGwG
- 'Arp' CBod ENfk EWes SPad WGwG XSen
- 'Aureovariegatus' see *R. officinalis* 'Aureus'

§ - 'Aureus' (v) SRms WHer WJek
- 'Avicenna' WGwG
- 'Barbecue'PBR CLau ENfk EWhm SRms XSen
- 'Blue Lagoon' CBod CLau ENfk EWhm LRHS MHer MNHC SAko SRms WGwG WHer WJek
- 'Blue Rain' CBar CBod EPfP MHer MSwo NQui WGwG WHer
- 'Capercaillie' SDow WGwG
- 'Charlotte' WGwG
- 'Collingwood Ingram' see *R. officinalis* var. ***angustissimus*** 'Benenden Blue'
- 'Cottage White' WGwG WHer
- 'Farinole' MNHC SRms WGwG
- 'Fota Blue' CLau IArd LRHS MHer MNHC NPol NRHS SAko SDow SGol SRms SVen SWvt WGwG WJek
- 'Foxtail' CBod CCBP CLau ENfk LRHS SRms WJek XSen
- 'Frimley Blue' see *R. officinalis* 'Primley Blue'
- 'Genges Gold' (v) WGwG
- 'Gold Dust' (v) ENfk
- 'Golden Rain' see *R. officinalis* 'Joyce DeBaggio'
- 'Gorizia' CBod LRHS SDow SRms
- 'Green Ginger' ♀H4 CBod CLau EBee ELan EPfP GBin LEdu MGos MHer MNHC MRav MSCN NPer SAko SCob SDow SPer SPoG SRms SVen WGwG WJek
- 'Guilded' see *R. officinalis* 'Aureus'
- 'Haifa' CBod CCBP CLau CSde ENfk SRms WGwG
- 'Heavenly Blue' WGwG WHer
- 'Huntington Carpet' ECtt
- 'Iden Pillar' WGwG
- 'Jekka Blue' WJek

§ - 'Joyce DeBaggio' (v) MHer SDow WGwG WHer
- 'Ken Taylor' WGwG
- 'Kevock' WGwG
- 'Knightshayes Blue' CRos LRHS NRHS
- 'Lady in Blue' WGwG
- ***lavandulaceus*** see *R. officinalis* Prostratus Group
- 'Lilies Blue' GPoy WGwG
- 'Lockwood Variety' see *R. officinalis* (Prostratus Group) 'Lockwood de Forest'
- 'Madeline Hill' CRos LRHS
- 'Majorca Pink' CBcs CLau CRos CSBt CSpe ENfk LRHS MHer MNHC SDow SPer WGwG WHer WJek XLum XSen
- 'Marenca' CHll MNHC SRms WGwG
- 'Margaret of Pershore' WGwG
- 'McConnell's Blue' ♀H4 CRos ELan EPfP LRHS MGos MNHC NRHS SCob SDow SRms WGwG WHer WJek
- 'Miss Jessopp's Upright' ♀H4 Widely available

– 'Pointe du Raz'	CBod ELan EPfP MAsh SChF SRms WGwG WSpi
§ – 'Primley Blue'	CBcs CBod CLau CSam EBou ECtt MNHC MRav SGol SRms WGwG WJek
§ – Prostratus Group	Widely available
– – 'Capri'	CBod CRos EPfP LRHS SCob SRms WFar WJek
– – 'Freda'	WGwG
– – 'Gethsemane'	WGwG
§ – – 'Lockwood de Forest'	WGwG WHer
– – 'Rampant Boule'	CBod CLau MHer SDow SRms WGwG WJek XLum XSen
– – 'Sea Level'	MHer WGwG
– – 'Sheila Dore'	SPlb SVen
– – white-flowered	GPoy
– – 'Whitewater Silver'	LRHS SPad WJek
– 'Punta di Canelle'	XSen
§ – 'Pyramidalis'	XSen
– f. ***pyramidalis***	see *R. officinalis* 'Pyramidalis'
– ***repens***	see *R. officinalis* Prostratus Group
– 'Rex'	WGwG XSen
– 'Roman Beauty'[PBR]	CBcs CRos CSBt EBee EHoe EMor EPfP LRHS LSRN MHol MTin NRHS SAko SCob SRms SWvt WHer WSpi
– 'Roseus'	CKel CRos EBou ECrN ELan ENfk EPfP GPoy LRHS MAsh MHer MNHC NRHS SDow SEND SLim SPoG SRms SVen WAvo WGwG WJek
– 'Salem'	CBod MHer
– 'Severn Sea' ♀[H4]	CBcs CBod CLau CRos CSBt CSde CTri ECtt ELan EMor ENfk EPfP EWhm GPoy LRHS MGos MNHC MRav MSwo NRHS SLon SPer SRms SVen SVic WAvo WCFE WGwG WJek WSpi
– 'Shimmering Stars'	SDow WGwG
– 'Silver Sparkler'	WFar WGwG WHer
– SILVER SPIRES ('Wolros')	WGwG
– 'Sissinghurst Blue' ♀[H4]	CBod CKel CRos CSde EBee ECha ECrN ELan EPfP LRHS MAsh MHer MNHC MRav NRHS SDow SGol SPer SPlb SRms SWvt WGwG
– 'Sissinghurst White'	WGwG
– 'Sorcerer's Apprentice'	SDow
– 'South Downs Blue'	WGwG
– 'Spanish Snow'	WGwG
– 'Spice Island'	CBod CRos LRHS SPer XSen
– 'Sudbury Blue'	CLau EWhm SAko SDow SGol SRms SVic WGwG
– 'Sunkissed'[PBR]	SRms
– 'Trusty'	WGwG
– 'Tuscan Blue'	CBcs CBod CDul CExl CKel CRos ECha ECtt ELan EPfP EUJe LRHS MHer MSwo NEgg NRHS SDow SGol SPer SRms WAvo WGwG XSen
– 'Variegatus'	see *R. officinalis* 'Aureus'
– 'Vatican Blue'	WJek
– WILMA'S GOLD ('Wimtim01'[PBR])	CLau
– 'Wisley Blue'	WGwG
repens	see *R. officinalis* Prostratus Group

Rostrinucula (*Lamiaceae*)

dependens	CMCN EBee EPfP ESwi EWes IArd LRHS NLar SBrt SMad SPad WCFE
sinensis	CExl

Rosularia (*Crassulaceae*)

§ ***aizoon***	CRos EDAr LRHS NRHS SRms
alba	see *R. sedoides* var. *alba*
§ ***chrysantha***	CRos EDAr LRHS NHpl NRHS SPlb SRms
crassipes	see *Rhodiola wallichiana*
hirsuta	NHpl
libanotica RCB RL 20	WCot
§ ***muratdaghensis***	SPlb
pallida A. Berger	see *R. chrysantha*
pallida Stapf	see *R. aizoon*
pallida ambig.	EPot
platyphylla misapplied	see *R. muratdaghensis*
rechingeri	EDAr SRms
§ ***sedoides*** var. ***alba***	EBou EDAr NHpl SRms XLum
sempervivum	EWes WThu
§ – subsp. ***glaucophylla***	CRos LRHS NRHS SRms WHal WThu
serpentinica	WAbe
spatulata hort.	see *R. sempervivum* subsp. *glaucophylla*

Rotheca (*Lamiaceae*)

§ ***myricoides*** 'Ugandense' ♀[H1b]	CCCN CHll EShb WSFF

Rubia (*Rubiaceae*)

peregrina	EMor GPoy
tinctorum	CHab CHby EMor GPoy MNHC SRms WSFF

Rubus ✿ (*Rosaceae*)

RCB/Eq C-1	WCot
SDR 4635	GKev
acuminatus	ESwi LEdu SBrt
alceifolius Poir.	SDys
– B&SWJ 1833	WCru
arcticus	EBee ECtt EPPr LEdu SHar SRot WThu XLum
bambusarum	EBee EShb ESwi MRav WCFE WCru
'Benenden' ♀[H5]	CAby CBcs CDul CExl CKel CRos CTri CTsd EBee ECrN ELan EPfP GKin LRHS LSRN MBNS MMuc MRav NAln NEgg NLar SCob SPer SPhx WAvo WBor WCFE WMoo WSpi
'Betty Ashburner'	CAgr CBcs CDul EBee EPPr GLog MCoo MGos MRav SCob SPer SPoG WMoo XLum
biflorus ♀[H6]	LEdu MBlu MMuc SEND WPGP
'Boatsberry'	SDea
'Boysenberry' (F)	CArg LEdu LRHS NPri
boysenberry, thornless (F)	CMac LBuc LSRN NPri SDea SPer
buergeri B&SWJ 5555	WCru
caesius	WCot
calophyllus	CBcs CDul EBee WPGP
– PAB 13.171	LEdu
calycinoides Hayata ex Koidz.	see *R. rolfei*
calycinoides Kuntze	GKev MGil SGol
chamaemorus	GPoy
cockburnianus (F)	CBcs CTri ELan EPfP GKev LBuc LCro LOPS MMuc MRav MSwo NAln NLar NSti NWea SCob SMad SPer SPlb SRms WSpi
– 'Goldenvale' ♀[H5]	CBcs CDul CKel CRos EHoe ELon EPfP IFro LRHS MAsh MBlu MGos MMuc MRav MSwo NBir NEgg NLar

	NSti SCob SEND SLon SPer SPoG SRms WFar
crataegifolius	MRav
discolor new	NWea
'Emerald Spreader'	WMoo
fockeanus misapplied	see *R. rolfei*
formosensis	SBrt
- B&SWJ 1798	EBee ESwi WCru
fruticosus agg.	CArg EMOT NWea WSFF
- 'Adrienne' (B)	CAgr CFGn CHab CSBt LEdu MAsh SRms SSFr
- 'Apache' (B)	CHab LRHS MNHC SPoG
- 'Ashton Cross' (B)	LBuc SSFr
- 'Asterina' (B)	CMac EMil
- 'Bedford Giant' (B)	CHab CSBt LSRN MAsh MGos SEND SLim SSFr
- 'Black Butte' (B)	CHab EPom SDea SLon SVic
- 'Black Satin' (B)	CAgr ECrN EMOT NLar NPri SDea SVic
- 'Chester' (B)	CRos EPom LEdu LRHS NRHS SKee
- 'Godshill Goliath' (B)	SDea
- 'Helen' (B)	CAgr SDea SSFr
- 'Himalayan Giant' (B)	CHab EMOT NEgg NLar SDea
- 'Karaka Black'PBR (B)	CHab CRos LBuc LRHS NRHS SPoG SSFr SVic
- 'Loch Maree'PBR (B/d)	CHab EPom LEdu MCoo NPri SLon
- 'Loch Ness'PBR (B) ♀H6	CAgr CArg CHab CRos EMOT EPom IArd LCro LOPS LRHS LSRN NPri NRHS SCoo SDea SKee SPer SSFr SVic
- 'Loch Tay'PBR (B) ♀H6	CArg CHab CMac CRos EPom LRHS NRHS SPoG
- 'Merton Thornless' (B)	CSBt CTri ECrN EMOT LBuc LEdu LSRN MAsh MGos NPri SRms
- 'Navaho' (B)	CHab CRos LRHS NRHS SPoG
- 'Navaho Big and Early' (F)	LRHS
- 'No Thorn' (B)	SDea
- 'Obsidian' (B)	LEdu
- 'Oregon Thornless' (B)	CAgr CFGn CSBt ECrN EPfP LCro LOPS LRHS LSRN MAsh MJak MRav NLar SCoo SDea SKee SLim SPer SPoG SRms SSFr SVic WMat
- 'Ouachita'PBR (B)	CFGn EPfP LCro LOPS LRHS NRHS SKee SPoG
- 'Parsley Leaved' (B)	SDea
- 'Reuben' (B)	CFGn CHab CRos EPom LBuc LCro LOPS LRHS MCoo MNHC NRHS SKee SPoG WMat
- 'Thornfree' (B)	CAgr CFGn CTri EPfP MMuc NLar NPri SDea SLim WMat
- 'Triple Crown' (B)	CHab CMac MCoo
- 'Variegatus' (v)	CMac MBlu WCot
- 'Waldo' (B)	CAgr CFGn CRos LBuc LSRN MAsh MGos NPri SDea SRms SSFr
'Glencoe' (B)	MCoo
henryi	CBcs EBee ESwi GBin NLar SPoG WBor WCot
- var. ***henryi***	WCru
ichangensis	CBcs ESwi
idaeus	CPer GPoy
- 'All Gold' (F) ♀H6	CFGn CMac CPer EMOT EMil EPom LRHS NLar NPri SCoo SPer SRms SVic WMat
- 'Alpengold'PBR (F)	CRos LOPS LRHS MCoo SPoG
- 'Aureus' (F)	ECha LEdu MRav NBid WCot
- 'Autumn Amber' (F) new	LRHS
- 'Autumn Bliss' (F) ♀H6	Widely available
- 'Autumn Treasure'PBR (F)	EMil EPom NPri SLon SVic
- 'Black Jewel' (F)	EPfP LOPS

- 'Cascade Delight' (F)	CArg CRos CSBt EPom LBuc LOPS LRHS MAsh NRHS
- 'Chemainus' (F)	LCro LOPS
- 'Erika'PBR (F)	CRos LCro LOPS LRHS MCoo NLar NRHS WMat
- 'Fallgold' (F)	LSRN MMuc SKee
- 'Glen Ample'PBR (F) ♀H6	Widely available
- 'Glen Clova' (F)	CAgr CFGn CSBt CTri EMOT LRHS LSRN MAsh MGos NLar NPri NRHS SKee SLim SPer SPoG SRms WMat
- 'Glen Dee' (F) new	CMac
- 'Glen Doll'PBR (F)	CAgr MAsh NLar NRHS SCoo WMat
- 'Glen Fyne'PBR (F)	CAgr
- 'Glen Lyon'PBR (F)	CArg CRos CSBt ECrN LBuc MAsh MJak NPri SCoo
- 'Glen Magna'PBR (F) ♀H6	CAgr CArg CMac CSBt MAsh NPri SCoo SDea SKee SLim
- 'Glen Moy'PBR (F)	CAgr CArg CRos EMOT MAsh MGos MJak NWea SCoo SDea SKee SLim SPer
- 'Glen Prosen'PBR (F)	CAgr CRos CSBt EMOT LRHS LSRN MAsh MGos NPri SCoo SDea SKee SLim SPer SPlb SPoG SSFr WMat
- 'Glen Rosa' (F)	SDea
- 'Heritage' (F)	MAsh SCoo SGol SRms
- 'Joan J'PBR (F) ♀H6	CArg CMac EPom LBuc LSRN SPer SSFr
- 'Leo'PBR (F) ♀H6	CSBt LSRN MAsh SCoo SKee SPer SRms SSFr
- 'Malling Admiral' (F) ♀H6	CSBt CTri EMOT EPom LSRN MAsh NWea SCoo SKee SPer
- 'Malling Delight' (F)	ELan SCoo SPlb
- 'Malling Jewel' (F) ♀H6	CAgr CArg CSBt CTri EPfP EPom LBuc LSRN MAsh MJak NPri NWea SDea SKee SPer SRms
- 'Malling Minerva' (F)	CAgr EPom SVic
- 'Malling Promise' (F)	MJak SGol
- 'Octavia'PBR (F)	CAgr CArg CTri EMil EPom LBuc MAsh MCoo NLar NRHS SLim WMat
- 'Polka'PBR (F) ♀H6	CArg CRos EPfP EPom LBuc LCro LOPS LRHS LSRN MAsh MCoo MRav NRHS SCoo SKee SLim SPer SRms SSFr WMat
- RUBY BEAUTY ('Nr7'PBR) (F)	CSBt EPom LBuc LCro LOPS LSRN MGos NRHS SPoG
- 'Sanibelle' (F)	LRHS
- 'Sugana'PBR (F)	LRHS MAsh SKee
- 'Tadmor'PBR (F)	CArg CFGn CRos LCro LOPS LRHS NRHS SKee WMat
- 'Tulameen' (F) ♀H6	CAgr CArg CRos CSBt ELan EMil EPfP EPom LBuc LCro LOPS LRHS LSRN MAsh MMuc NPri NRHS NWea SCoo SEND SKee SLim SPer SPoG SRms SSFr SVic WMat
- TWOTIMER SUGANA YELLOW (F)	LRHS
- 'Zeva' (F)	SGol
- 'Zeva Herbsternte' (F)	MAsh
idaeus* × *ursinus	EMOT
illecebrosus (F)	LEdu XLum
irenaeus	LEdu LRHS SEND WHal
Japanese wineberry	see *R. phoenicolasius*
'Kenneth Ashburner'	NLar
laciniatus 'Thornless Evergreen'	MMuc
lambertianus PAB 8931	LEdu
lineatus	CBcs CDTJ CKel CRos EPfP EWes GBin LEdu LRHS MCot NLar WCru WPGP

- B&SWJ 11261 from Sumatra WCru
- PAB 13.163 LEdu
- HWJ 892 from Vietnam ESwi WCru
- HWJK 2045 from Nepal WCru
× ***loganobaccus*** (F) CFGn EMOT
- 'Brandywine' (F) SDea
- 'Ly 59' (F) ECrN EPfP MMuc SDea SEND SKee SRms
- 'Ly 654' (F) ♀H5 CRos CSBt EPom LBuc LRHS NEgg NPri NRHS SDea SPer SSFr SVic
- thornless (F) CAgr CTri EPfP EPom LEdu MJak MNHC SDea SPoG WMat
malvaceus FMWJ 13324 new WCru
'Margaret Gordon' MRav
microphyllus 'Variegatus' (v) MRav
§ ***nepalensis*** CAgr CFGn GKev LEdu WPGP
nutans see *R. nepalensis*
odoratus CAgr CBcs CDul CExl ELan EPPr EPfP EWTr LEdu MBlu NBid NLar SPer WBor
palmatus var. ***coptophyllus*** MMuc
parkeri PAB 6891 LEdu
parviflorus 'Bill Baker' LEdu
- double-flowered (d) EPPr
- 'Sunshine Spreader' LEdu
parvus LEdu
pectinellus var. ***trilobus*** SBrt
- - B&SWJ 1669B NLar WCru
peltatus NLar
pentalobus see *R. rolfei*
§ ***phoenicolasius*** CAgr CBcs CCCN CDul CFGn CKel ELan EMOT EPPr EPfP LCro LEdu LOPS LRHS MBlu MCoo MHer MRav SDea SPer SPoG SVic WBor WPGP
reflexus var. ***hui*** EShb
§ ***rolfei*** CDul MCoo NWad
- B&SWJ 3546 from Taiwan WCru
- B&SWJ 3878 from the Philippines WCru
- 'Emerald Carpet' ♀H5 CAgr NLar
rosifolius NJM 10.142 WPGP
- 'Coronarius' (d) CBod EBee ECrN EMor MHol WCot
rubrisetulosus PAB 9532 LEdu
'Rushbrook Redleaf' SBrt
saxatilis PAB 3912 LEdu
setchuenensis CMCN EPPr NLar
'Silvan' (F) MMuc SEND
spectabilis ELan EPPr LEdu MMuc MRav WOut
- 'Flore Pleno' see *R. spectabilis* 'Olympic Double'
§ - 'Olympic Double' (d) Widely available
splendidissimus B&SWJ 2361 WCru
squarrosus EBee SMad
'Sunberry' (F) CCCN LEdu SDea
swinhoei B&SWJ 1735 WCru
taiwanicola B&SWJ 317 ESwi WCru
- CWJ 12400 WCru
Tayberry Group (F) CRos CSBt CTri LRHS LSRN MGos NLar NPri NRHS SPer SRms SVic
- 'Buckingham' (F) CArg EMil EPom LBuc LCro LOPS LRHS NLar NPer SVic WMat
- 'Medana Tayberry' (F) CAgr CTri ECrN EMOT EPfP LEdu LRHS MNHC NLar NWea SDea SKee SPoG WMat
§ ***thibetanus*** ♀H6 CBcs CBod CDul CKel CMac CRos EBee ELan EPfP EWTr GBin LRHS LSRN MAsh MGos MMuc MRav MSwo NEgg NLar SCob SEND SMad SPer SPoG SWvt WMoo WSpi
- 'Silver Fern' see *R. thibetanus*
treutleri B&SWJ 2139 WCru
tricolor CAgr CBcs CBod CDul CSBt CTri ECrN ELan GKev MBlu MCoo MMuc MRav MSwo NLar SCob SGol SPer WMoo
trilobus B&SWJ 9096 WCru
'Tummelberry' (F) LRHS MCoo SVic
ulmifolius 'Bellidiflorus' (d) EPPr MRav NLar
ursinus SVic
xanthocarpus LEdu NLar XLum
'Youngberry' (F) SDea

Rudbeckia (*Asteraceae*)

alpicola EBee
AUTUMN SUN see *R. laciniata* 'Herbstsonne'
'Berlin' EBee ECtt GMaP LRHS LSun MHol NLar NRHS SCob SPer
californica CRos EBee LRHS NRHS
- B&SWJ 14105 WCru
'Copper Kettle' WHlf
deamii see *R. fulgida* var. *deamii*
'Dublin' ECtt IKil MBNS MBel MHol SCob SPer
fulgida SWvt WFar
- 'City Garden' ECtt GBin LRHS NCGa NLar SRms WFar
§ - var. ***deamii*** ♀H7 Widely available
- 'Early Bird Gold' CBod CRos CWGN EBee ECtt GBin GMaP LCro LRHS MHol NLar NRHS SAko WFar
- var. ***fulgida*** CCBP CMea EBee EPfP LEdu SPhx SPoG
- 'Little Goldstar'PBR CBod CKno CRos EBee ECtt ELan EPfP LCro LOPS LRHS MAsh MHol MTin NDov NLar NPri NRHS SCob SLon SPoG SRms WFar
§ - var. ***speciosa*** ♀H7 CRos CWCL EBee ECha ECtt ELan EPfP GBin GWyn LRHS MMuc NRHS SEND SHar SMad SPlb SPtp SRms SWvt WFar WMoo WOld WPtf XLum
- var. ***sullivantii*** 'Goldsturm' ♀H7 Widely available
- - 'Pot of Gold' CBod IKil NLar
- VIETTE'S LITTLE SUZY ('Blovi') CBod CRos LRHS NRHS SRms WFar
gloriosa see *R. hirta*
grandiflora CRos LRHS NRHS
- 'Sundance' CBod EBee SPhx
§ ***hirta*** NBir
- AUTUMN COLORS (mixed) ELan LOPS LRHS NRHS SPhx
- 'Cappuccino' ELan EPfP LRHS NRHS
- CHEROKEE SUNSET (mixed) (d) CSpe EPfP
- 'Cherry Brandy' CRos CSpe LRHS NGBl NRHS SPhx
- CHIM CHIMINEE (mixed) IKil NGBl SCob
- 'Goldilocks' SVic
- 'Indian Summer' ♀H3 CRos EPfP LRHS MHol MNHC NRHS SPhx
- 'Irish Eyes' SPhx SVic
- 'Marmalade' CRos EPfP LRHS NRHS SPhx SVic
- 'Prairie Sun' CRos ELon EPfP LRHS NGBl NRHS SPhx
- 'Sonora' NGBl

- (Sunbeckia Series) SUNBECKIA ALICIA **new** NPri
- - SUNBECKIA AMELIA **new** NPri
- - SUNBECKIA OLIVIA **new** NPri
- - SUNBECKIA SOPHIA **new** WHil
- 'Tiger Eye' SPoG
- 'Toto' ♀H3 EPfP SWvt
JULY GOLD see *R. laciniata* 'Juligold'
laciniata CKno CMac CRos CSpe EBee ELan EMor EPPr GCal GQue LEdu LRHS MNrw NDov NGBl NLar NRHS SMHy SPhx SRms WArt WCot WMoo WOld WPGP WWtn XLum
- var. ***digitata*** IMou
- 'Golden Glow' see *R. laciniata* 'Hortensia'
- 'Goldkugel' (d) ♀H7 MWat
- 'Goldquelle' (d) CBod CRos EBee ECha ECtt ELan EPfP GMaP GWyn LRHS MSCN MTis NGdn NRHS SCob SMad SPer SPoG SRms SWvt WCAu WFar XLum
§ - 'Herbstsonne' ♀H7 Widely available
§ - 'Hortensia' (d) EBee LPot MAvo MRav NGBl WBrk WCot WFar WHoo WOld
§ - 'Juligold' CBod CRos EBee ECtt LRHS MBNS MPie NEgg NGdn NRHS SPoG WBrk WSpi WWFP
- 'Starcadia Razzle Dazzle' ♀H7 EWld MAvo SAko WCot WFar
maxima CAby CBod CKno CSpe EBee ECha ELon EMor GBin GQue ILea LEdu LRHS LSun MBel MHol MMuc NDov NGBl NLar NSti SBrt SMad SPhx SPlb WCot WFar XLum
missouriensis CRos EAJP EBee GBin LRHS MMuc MNrw NRHS SPhx WArt
mollis CRos EBee LRHS NRHS
newmannii see *R. fulgida* var. *speciosa*
nitida WSpi
occidentalis CRos LRHS NChi NRHS
- 'Black Beauty'PBR EUJe WSpi
- 'Green Wizard' CBod CMac CRos EBee ECtt ELan EPfP EShb GBin GWyn LRHS MCot NRHS NSti SPer SRms WSpi
* ***paniculata*** CDor EBee LLHF NGBl WCot
'Peking'PBR EBee ECtt EPfP IKil MBNS MHol NSti SCob SPer
purpurea see *Echinacea purpurea*
speciosa see *R. fulgida* var. *speciosa*
subtomentosa CBod CRos CSam EPfP EWes GCal LEdu LRHS MMuc NDov NRHS NSti SCob SMHy WCot WOld WSpi XLum
- 'Henry Eilers' Widely available
- 'Little Henry'PBR CBod CKno EBee ECtt EMor EWTr LRHS LSRN MBNS MBel MHol NRHS NWsh SCob SPoG
- 'Loofahsa Wheaten Gold' MAvo WCot WGoo
- 'Poligny' **new** MNrw
Summerina Series LRHS SCob
- SUMMERINA BROWN ('Et Rdb 03'PBR) CKno CRos LRHS MBNS MHol NGBl NRHS NSti SPoG WCot
- SUMMERINA ORANGE ('Et Rdb 01'PBR) CRos LPla LRHS MBNS MHol NRHS SPad SPoG SRkn WCot
- SUMMERINA YELLOW ('Et Rdb 02'PBR) CRos LRHS MBNS MHol NGBl NRHS SPoG SRkn WCot
triloba ♀H6 CRos CSpe ECha ELon EMor EPfP LRHS MBel MNrw NGBl NGdn NRHS SCob SPhx WCAu WMoo WPGP WSpi
- 'Prairie Glow' CAby CBcs CDor CSpe EAJP EBee ELon EMor EWTr ILea LRHS NGBl SCob SMad SPer SPhx WCot

rue see *Ruta graveolens*

Ruellia (*Acanthaceae*)

amoena see *R. brevifolia*
§ ***brevifolia*** ECre EShb WFib
humilis EBee EShb GEdr SPhx
macrantha CCCN EShb
makoyana ♀H1b EShb
- white-flowered EShb
strepens EBee
tweediana EShb WFib

Rulingia (*Sterculiaceae*)

hermanniifolia WAbe

Rumex (*Polygonaceae*)

acetosa CAgr CHab CHby CLau EMor ENfk GPoy MCoo MHer MJak MMuc MNHC NBir SRms SVic WCot WHer WJek WSFF
- 'Abundance' CLau LEdu
- subsp. ***acetosa*** 'Saucy' (v) EBee LEdu MHol WCot
- 'De Belleville' CLau
- 'Profusion' GPoy
acetosella CAgr CHab SRms WSFF
alpinus EBee LEdu WCot WPGP
flexuosus CSpe EBee GCal LPot
hydrolapathum CBod CHab MMuc SEND SPlb WCot WSFF
patientia CHab CLau
sanguineus CLau ENfk EShb LEdu NLar NQui SRms XLum
- var. ***sanguineus*** CHby ELan EMor GQue MHer MNHC NBro NGrd WHer
scutatus CBod CHby CLau EMor ENfk GPoy MNHC NGrd SPlb SRms WJek
- subsp. ***induratus*** SEND
- 'Silver Shield' EPPr LEdu MHer NGrd SRms

Rumohra (*Dryopteridaceae*)

adiantiformis ♀H3 CCCN CRos EBee ISha LEdu LRHS NRHS SEND WFib

Ruschia (*Aizoaceae*)

putterillii SPlb
spinosa SPlb
tumidula SPlb

Ruscus ✿ (*Asparagaceae*)

aculeatus CBcs CDul CMac ELan EPfP GPoy LEdu MGil MGos MNrw NLar NWea SPlb SRms SWvt WMou WRHF
- (f) SCob WSpi
- hermaphrodite EPfP GCal MMuc SEND SMad
- var. ***aculeatus*** 'Lanceolatus' (f) GCal
- var. ***angustifolius*** (f) WCru
- - PAB 254 LEdu
- 'John Redmond'PBR ♀H5 CBcs ELan ELon EPfP EShb LRHS NHol NLar NWad SCob SLon SPer SWvt WBor WFar WSpi
* - 'Wheeler's Variety' (f/m) CJun MRav
colchicus PAB 1753 **new** LEdu
hypoglossum CMac IMou MMuc SEND WCot WSpi

× ***microglossus*** (f) B&SWJ 14041 — WCru
racemosus — see *Danae racemosa*

Ruspolia (*Acanthaceae*)

hypocrateriformis — CCCN

Ruspolia × *Ruttya* see × *Ruttyruspolia*

Russelia (*Plantaginaceae*)

§ ***equisetiformis*** ♀H1c — WFib
- 'Lemon Falls' ♀H1c — WFib
- 'Tangerine Falls' — WFib
juncea — see *R. equisetiformis*

Ruta (*Rutaceae*)

chalepensis — SPhx XLum
corsica — XLum
graveolens — CBod CDul CHab ENfk GPoy MJak MNHC SVic WJek XLum
- 'Alderley Blue' **new** — WJek
- 'Jackman's Blue' — CBcs ECrN EHoe ELan EMor EPfP EUJe GMaP GPoy MGos MHer MNHC MRav MSwo SRms SWvt WSpi XLum
- 'Variegata' (v) — MNHC MPie NPer SRms

Ruttya (*Acanthaceae*)

fruticosa — CCCN

× *Ruttyruspolia* (*Acanthaceae*)

lutea — CCCN
'Phyllis van Heerden' — CCCN

Rytidosperma (*Poaceae*)

* ***arundinaceum*** — EShb

S

Sabal (*Arecaceae*)

minor — CPHo SPlb

Saccharum (*Poaceae*)

arundinaceum — CKno
brevibarbe var. ***contortum*** — WCot
officinarum — SPlb
- purple-stemmed **new** — SPlb WCot
ravennae — EBee SMad SPlb WCot

sage see *Salvia officinalis*

sage, annual clary see *Salvia viridis*

sage, biennial clary see *Salvia sclarea*

sage, pineapple see *Salvia elegans*

Sageretia (*Rhamnaceae*)

§ ***thea*** — CMen
theezans — see *S. thea*

Sagina (*Caryophyllaceae*)

subulata — EHoe LRHS SVic WArt XLum
- var. ***glabrata*** — MAsh
§ - - 'Aurea' — CMea EBou ECha ECtt EDAr ELan GMaP MAsh MHer NHpl SPoG SRms

Sagittaria (*Alismataceae*)

australis — EWat
'Bloomin' Babe' — EWat
graminea — LLWG SBrt
- 'Crushed Ice' (v) — EWat
japonica — see *S. sagittifolia*
lancifolia — EWat LLWG
latifolia — NPer
§ ***sagittifolia*** — CWat LLWG MWts WMAq WPnP XLum
- var. ***leucopetala*** — WMAq
- - 'Flore Pleno' (d) — CWat EWat NPer WMAq XLum

Saintpaulia ✿ (*Gesneriaceae*)

'8e-Ajisai' **new** — WDib
'Aca's Red Ember' (v) — WDib
'Aca's Ronnie Redhead' — WDib
'Ae-Amur Elit' — WDib
'Alamo Quest' **new** — WDib
'Alan's Fallen Angel' (d/v) — WDib
'Alan's White Feather' — WDib
'Alchemy Yellow Star' **new** — WDib
'Allegro Appalachian Trail' — WDib
'Always Pink' — WDib
'Aly's Rosy Baby' — WDib
'Amazing Grace' — WDib
'Amethyst' — WDib
'Anouk' — WDib
'Anthoflores Edith' — WDib
'Apache Maiden' (v) **new** — WDib
'Apache Thunderbolt' — WDib
'Aussie Magic' — WDib
'Baby Brian' — WDib
'Beacon Trail' — WDib
'Beatrice Trail' — WDib
'Berry Splash' (v) **new** — WDib
'Betty Stoehr' — WDib
'Bliznecy' — WDib
'Bloomlover's Cat' (d) — WDib
'Blue Dragon' (d) — WDib
'Blue Tail Fly' — WDib
'Blushing Ivory' — WDib
'Bob Serbin' (d) — WDib
'Bob's Omega' — WDib
'Bol's Evening Holger' — WDib
'Bol's Evening Irja' — WDib
'Bourane' (v) **new** — WDib
brevipilosa — WDib
'Buffalo Hunt' (d) — WDib
'Calico Beauty' — WDib
'Candy Fountain' — WDib
'Candy Swirls' — WDib
'Cathedral' — WDib
'Cedar Creek Stormy' **new** — WDib
'Chantaspring' — WDib
'Cherokee Trail' (v) **new** — WDib
'Cherries 'n' Cream' — WDib
'Chiffon Fiesta' — WDib
'Chiffon Pageant' — WDib
'Chiffon Vesper' — WDib
'China Pink' **new** — WDib
'Cirelda' — WDib
'Country Romance' (d) — WDib
'Crimson Ice' — WDib
'Cupid's Jewel' — WDib
'Cupie Doll' **new** — WDib
'Deep Sky' — WDib
'Deer Trail' — WDib
'Definitely Darryl' **new** — WDib

'Delft' (d) WDib
'Dibley's Beate' WDib
'Dibleys Kaarina' WDib
'Dibleys Mercedes' WDib
'Dibley's Pat' WDib
'Edee's Rosebud Trail' (d) **new** WDib
'Ek Lubasha' WDib
'EK-Gost'ya iz Budushchego' **new** WDib
'EK-Sady Semiramidi' **new** WDib
'EK-Shedevr Khudozhnika' **new** WDib
'EK-Snezhnyi Bars' **new** WDib
'EK-Vrata Raia' WDib
'Emerald Love' WDib
'Ethel's Wild Side' **new** WDib
'Favorite Child' WDib
'Fire Mountain' WDib
'Flashy Angel' (v) WDib
'Flashy Trail' **new** WDib
'Flower Drum' WDib
'Frozen in Time' (v) **new** WDib
'Gecko's Vespa Vino' WDib
'Gillian' (d) WDib
'Golden Dawn' WDib
'Golden Eye' WDib
'Golden Threads' (d) **new** WDib
'Goldilocks' (d) **new** WDib
'Goluboi Tuman' WDib
'Grandmother's Halo' WDib
'Green Dragon' WDib
'Green Lace' (d) WDib
'Happy Cricket' WDib
'Heaven's A-calling' **new** WDib
'Hortense's Country Rose' (v) **new** WDib
'Hot Summer Day' WDib
'Ian-Minuet' (d) **new** WDib
'In The Pink' WDib
'Indigo Ruffles' WDib
ionantha subsp. ***grotei*** WDib
- subsp. ***ionantha*** WDib
- subsp. ***rupicola*** WDib
- subsp. ***velutina*** WDib
'Irish Flirt' (d) WDib
'Irish Laughter' WDib
'Island Breezes' WDib
'Jenny Lilac' (d) **new** WDib
'Jolly Gold' **new** WDib
'Jolly Orchid' (d) WDib
'Jolly Prize' (d) **new** WDib
'Jolly Texan' (d) WDib
'Kosmicheskaia Legenda 2' WDib
'Kostina Fantaziia' WDib
'LE-Karusel' (v) **new** WDib
'LE-Macho' **new** WDib
'Lemon Whip' (d) WDib
'Letnaya Noch' WDib
'Letnie Sumerki' WDib
'Lil Bit O'Irish' WDib
'Lilla Blaklockan' WDib
'Little Axel' WDib
'Little Seagull' WDib
'Lollipop' WDib
'Looking Glass' WDib
'Louisiana Lagniappe' WDib
'Louisiana Lullaby' (d) WDib
'Love Spots' WDib
'Lubimaia Dochka' WDib
'Luminescence' WDib
'Lyon's Minnie-HaHa' WDib
'Lyon's Plum Pudding' WDib
'Mac's Black Jack' WDib
'Mac's Blowing Bubbles' WDib
'Mac's Carnival Clown' WDib
'Mac's Circus Clown' WDib
'Mac's Glacial Grape' WDib
'Mac's Just Jeff' (d/v) WDib
'Mac's Nocturne' (d) WDib
'Mac's Rouge Rogue' WDib
'Mac's Scorching Sun' (v) **new** WDib
'Mac's Southern Springtime' (d) WDib
'Mac's Strawberry Sundae' WDib
'Mac's Tiamat' (v) **new** WDib
'Mac's Walkabout Uluru' (v) **new** WDib
'Mair' WDib
'Ma's Ching Dynasty' (d) WDib
'Ma's Easter Parade' WDib
'Midget Silver Fox' (v) **new** WDib
'Midnight Flame' (d) WDib
'Mikinda Girl' (v) **new** WDib
'Mindi Brooke' WDib
'MyJoy' (MyViolet Series) **new** WDib
'Ness' Antique Red' WDib
'Ness' Bangle Blue' WDib
'Ness' Cherry Smoke' WDib
'Ness' Crinkle Blue' (d) WDib
'Ness' Midnight Fantasy' WDib
'Ness' Orange Pekoe' WDib
'Ness' Satin Rose' WDib
'Ness' Sheer Peach' WDib
'Neverfloris' **new** WDib
'Newtown Ohio' WDib
nitida WDib
'Number 32' WDib
'Ode to Beauty' WDib
'Okie Easter Bunny' WDib
'Oksana' WDib
'Optimara Little Moonstone' WDib
'Otoe' (d) WDib
'Parnikovyi Effekt' WDib
'Pat Tracey' WDib
'Pink Mint' (d) **new** WDib
'Pink Pussycat' (v) **new** WDib
'Pink Wave' **new** LCro LOPS
'Pixie Blue' WDib
'Pixie Pink' WDib
'Podvenechnaia' (d) WDib
'Powder Keg' (d) WDib
'Powwow' (d/v) WDib
'Prancing Pony' WDib
'Purple Passion' WDib
'Rainbow's Limelight' (d) WDib
'Rainbow's Quiet Riot' WDib
'Ramblin' Amethyst' WDib
'Ramblin' Dots' WDib
'Ramblin' Lassie' WDib
'Ramblin' Sunshine' WDib
'Rare Tapestry' WDib
'Raspberry Crisp' WDib
'Rebel's Amy' WDib
'Rebel's Splatter Kake' WDib
'Red Lantern' (d) WDib
'Reflections of Spring' (d) WDib
'Rhapsodie Clementine' WDib
'Rob's Argyle Socks' (d) WDib

'Rob's Cherry Soda' (v) **new**	WDib
'Rob's Chilly Willy' (d/v)	WDib
'Rob's Dandy Lion' (d/v)	WDib
'Rob's Dust Storm' (d)	WDib
'Rob's Hot Tamale'	WDib
'Rob's Ice Ripples' (d)	WDib
'Rob's Jitterbug'	WDib
'Rob's Love Bite' (d)	WDib
'Rob's Mad Cat' (d)	WDib
'Rob's Melon Wedges' **new**	WDib
'Rob's Peedletuck'	WDib
'Rob's Pewter Bells'	WDib
'Rob's Sarsparilla' (d)	WDib
'Rob's Scrumptious'	WDib
'Rob's Shadow Magic' (d/v)	WDib
'Rob's Smarty Pants' (d)	WDib
'Rob's Twinkle Pink' (d)	WDib
'Rob's Vanilla Trail' (d)	WDib
'Rob's Wooloomooloo' (d)	WDib
'RS-Bog Solntsa' (d)	WDib
'RS-Boyarinya'	WDib
'RS-Gertsogninea'	WDib
'RS-Kabaret'	WDib
'RS-Korrida'	WDib
'RS-Romantika' **new**	WDib
'RS-Strast'	WDib
'RS-Utonchennyy-vkus' **new**	WDib
'RS-Vodevil' (v) **new**	WDib
'Ruffled Skies'	WDib
'Santa Anita'	WDib
'Sapphire Halo'	WDib
'Scarlet Ribbons'	WDib
'Senk's Arctic Fox'	WDib
'Senk's Beanstalk'	WDib
'Senk's Girl Wasp' **new**	WDib
'Shirl's Hawaiian Lei'	WDib
shumensis	WDib
'Shy Blue'	WDib
'Silverglade Beads'	WDib
'Silverglade Meadows'	WDib
'Sky Bells' (v)	WDib
'Sky Trail'	WDib
'Snow Leopard'	WDib
'Sparkleberry'	WDib
'Special Treat'	WDib
'Sultan' (d)	WDib
'Sun Sizzle'	WDib
'Sunkissed Rose'	WDib
'Taffeta Blue' (d)	WDib
'The Madam'	WDib
'Tiger' (v)	WDib
'Tina's April Fantasy'	WDib
'Top Dark Blue' **new**	LCro LOPS
'Toy Castle'	WDib
'Tula'	WDib
'Twist 'n' Shout'	WDib
'Two-w Miss Sophie' (d)	WDib
'Vallartas Campanas Moradas'	WDib
'Warm Sunshine'	WDib
'Whirligig Star'	WDib
'Wild Irish Rose'	WDib
'Wisteria' (d)	WDib
'Wrangler's Jealous Heart'	WDib
'Wrangler's Snowfield's' (v) **new**	WDib
'Yesterday's Child'	WDib

Salicornia (*Amaranthaceae*)

europaea	SVic

Salix ✿ (*Salicaceae*)

	sp.	GWyn LPra
	acutifolia 'Blue Streak' (m) ♀H6	CEnd EPfP EWes MBlu NBir NLar WMou
	– 'Pendulifolia' (m)	SGol
	'Aegma Brno' (f)	WMou
	aegyptiaca	EBtc ECrN MBlu NWea WMou
	alba	CCVT CDul CHab CLnd CPer CWiW ECrN EMOT LBuc LMaj LPra MAsh NWea SEWo SGol WMou WTSh
	– f. ***argentea***	see *S. alba* var. *sericea*
	– 'Aurea'	WMou
	– var. ***caerulea***	CAco CDul CLnd NWea WMou
	– – 'Wantage Hall' (f)	CWiW
	– 'Cardinalis' (f)	CWiW
	– 'Chermesina' hort.	see *S. alba* var. *vitellina* 'Britzensis'
	– 'Golden Ness' ♀H6	CRos LRHS MAsh MBlu NOra NRHS WFar WMat
	– 'Hutchinson's Yellow'	NLar NWea
	– 'Liempde' (m)	LPra NWea
	– 'Raesfeld' (m)	CWiW
§	– var. ***sericea*** ♀H6	CDul CLnd CTho EPfP MBlu MRav NLar NWea SPer WCot WMou
	– 'Splendens'	see *S. alba* var. *sericea*
	– 'Tristis' misapplied	see *S.* × *sepulcralis* var. *chrysocoma*
§	– 'Tristis' ambig.	CAco CLnd CTri ELan LMaj LRHS MGos MRav MSwo NLar NOra SEWo
	– var. ***vitellina***	CBod CDul CPer EMOT EPfP LBuc MBNS MMuc NLar NWea SGol SLon SRms
§	– – 'Britzensis' (m)	Widely available
§	– – 'Yelverton' ♀H6	CRos EBee EPfP LRHS NOra NRHS SPoG WFar WMat
	– 'Vitellina Tristis'	see *S. alba* 'Tristis' ambig.
	'Americana' (m)	CWiW
	amplexicaulis 'Pescara' (m)	CWiW
	amygdaloides	CWiW
	'Aokautere'	see *S.* × *sepulcralis* 'Aokautere'
§	***arbuscula***	XEll
	arenaria	see *S. repens* var. *argentea*
	aurita	MMuc NWea
	babylonica	CDul CEnd CPer ECrN LPra WMou
	– 'Annularis'	see *S. babylonica* 'Crispa'
	– 'Bijdorp'	NLar
§	– 'Crispa'	CBod CDul CRos ELan GBin LRHS MMrt NQui NSti SMad SPoG WBor WFar WGrn
	– 'Pan Chih-kang'	CWiW NLar
	– var. ***pekinensis*** 'Pendula'	IArd
§	– – 'Tortuosa' (f)	CBcs CDul CLnd CSBt ECrN ELan EMOT EPfP LPra MGos MMuc NBir NGrd NPer NWea SCob SEND SGol SLon SPer SPlb SRms WFar
*	– 'Tortuosa Aurea'	CAco LMaj LPra SGol SWvt
	'Blackskin' (f)	CWiW
	bockii	CKel CRos EBtc ESwi LRHS SDys SPlb
§	'Bowles's Hybrid'	WMou
	'Boydii' (f) ♀H7	CMea EPfP EPot GAbr GCrg GJos GKev GMaP ITim LEdu LRHS MGos NBir NRya NSla SAko WAbe WFar WThu
	candida	WFar WOut
	× ***canescens*** **new**	GKev
	caprea	CArg CBcs CCVT CDul CHab CLnd CPer CTri EPfP LBuc MJak NWea SCob SEWo SPer WMou WSFF WTSh

	- 'Black Stem'	CDul
§	- 'Kilmarnock' (m)	CBcs CCVT CDul CMac CSBt CTri ECrN ELan EMOT EPfP LCro LOPS LRHS MAsh MGos MJak MMuc NLar NRHS NWea SCob SGol SLim SPer SPoG SWvt WFar WJas
	- 'Mas' (m)	CNWT
	- var. ***pendula*** (m)	see *S. caprea* 'Kilmarnock' (m)
	- - (f)	see *S. caprea* 'Weeping Sally'
	- 'Pendula'	see *S. caprea* 'Kilmarnock', *S. caprea* 'Weeping Sally'
§	- 'Weeping Sally' (f)	WMat
	capusii	EBee WPGP
	cashmiriana	GEdr
	'Chrysocoma'	see *S.* × *sepulcralis* var. *chrysocoma*
	cinerea	CBcs CDul CPer CTri NWea SEWo WMou WTSh
	- 'Tricolor' (v)	NEoE
	'Coire Kander'	GKev
	daphnoides	CBcs CCVT CDul CLnd CMac CPer ELan EPfP MGos MMuc MSwo NWea SEND SGol SPer SRms WMou WSFF
	- 'Aglaia' (m) ♀H6	CDul CTri
	- 'Oxford Violet' (m)	ECrN NWea
§	× ***doniana*** 'Kumeti'	CWiW
	'E.A. Bowles'	see *S.* 'Bowles's Hybrid'
	× ***ehrhartiana***	CNat
§	***elaeagnos***	CCVT CTho ECrN EPfP MBrN MMuc SLon SMHy SPer WMou
§	- subsp. ***angustifolia*** ♀H6	CDul ELan EPfP MMuc MRav MSwo NLar SCob SEND SRms
	eriocephala 'American Mackay' (m)	CWiW
	- 'Kerksii' (m)	CWiW
	- 'Mawdesley' (m)	CWiW
	- 'Russelliana' (f)	CWiW
	exigua ♀H5	CBcs CDul CLnd CTho ELan EPfP EWes IDee LBuc LEdu LRHS MBlu MBrN MGos MSwo NBir NLar NWea SChF SCob SMad SPer WMou WPGP
	fargesii ♀H6	CAby CBcs CDul CEnd CExl CKel CMac CRos EBee ELan EPfP GBin LEdu LRHS MBlu MGos MMuc MRav NBid SBrt SCob SPer WCru WFar
	formosa	see *S. arbuscula*
§	× ***fragilis***	CCVT CDul CHab CLnd CPer EMOT NWea WMou WTSh
	- 'Basfordiana' (m)	CDul CLnd CTho CWiW MBNS WMou
	- 'Bouton Aigu'	CWiW
	- var. ***bullata***	LMaj
	- 'Farndon'	CWiW
	- 'Flanders Red' (f)	CWiW
	- 'Fransgeel Rood' (m)	CWiW
§	- var. ***furcata***	GCrg GKev NWad
	- 'Glaucescens' (m)	CWiW
	- 'Golden Willow'	CWiW
	- 'Jaune de Falaise'	CWiW
	- 'Jaune Hâtive'	CWiW
	- 'Laurina'	CWiW
	- 'Natural Red' (f)	CWiW
	- 'Parsons'	CWiW
	- 'Rouge Ardennais'	CWiW
	- 'Rouge Folle'	CWiW
	- 'Russet' (f)	CWiW
	× ***fruticosa*** 'McElroy' (f)	CWiW
	fruticulosa	see *S.* × *fragilis* var. *furcata*
	'Fuiri-koriyanagi'	see *S. integra* 'Hakuro-nishiki'
	furcata	see *S.* × *fragilis* var. *furcata*
	'Golden Curls'	see *S.* × *sepulcralis* 'Erythroflexuosa'
	gracilistyla	NWea WMou
§	- 'Melanostachys' (m) ♀H5	CAby CDul ECrN ELan EPfP EWTr MAsh MBNS MBlu MBrN MGos MMuc MRav NBir NEgg NLar NWea SBrt SGol SPer SRms WBor WFar
	- 'Mount Aso'	CMCN EBee LEdu NLar SBrt SMad WPGP
	× ***greyi***	NEoE
	hastata 'Wehrhahnii' (m) ♀H6	CBcs CDul CKel CMea EBee ELan EPfP GKev MAsh MBlu MJak MMuc MRav MSwo NBir NLar NWea SPer
	helvetica ♀H7	CBcs CDul CKel CMac EBee ELan EPfP MAsh MBlu MRav NBir NEgg NLar NWea SPer WFar
	herbacea	GEdr WAbe
	hibernica	see *S. phylicifolia*
	hookeriana	CDul CExl ELan MBlu MBrN MCoo NLar WCFE WMou
	incana	see *S. elaeagnos*
	integra 'Albomaculata'	see *S. integra* 'Hakuro-nishiki'
	- 'Flamingo'PBR	ELan NLar SPoG WTSh
§	- 'Hakuro-nishiki' (v) ♀H5	Widely available
	- 'Pendula' (f)	CEnd MAsh
	irrorata ♀H5	CDul EPfP MBlu MSwo NOra SCob WMat
	kinuyanagi (m)	NSti
§	***koriyanagi***	CWiW
	'Kumeti'	see *S.* × *doniana* 'Kumeti'
	'Kuro-me'	see *S. gracilistyla* 'Melanostachys'
	lanata ♀H7	CBcs CKel CMac CMea EBee ELan ELon EPfP GKev MAsh MGos NBir NEgg NLar NWea SBrt SPer WCFE
	lapponum	LEdu MMuc NLar NWea SRms
	- compact	GKev
I	***leucantha*** new	CMCN
	magnifica	CAby CDul CEnd CExl CKel ELan EPfP EUJe GBin IArd LEdu LRHS MMuc NLar NWea SMad WCot WFar WHer WHor WMou WPGP WSpi
	'Mark Postill' (f)	CAby CRos EWTr GBin LRHS MBNS MMuc NLar SAko WWFP
	matsudana 'Tortuosa'	see *S. babylonica* var. *pekinensis* 'Tortuosa'
	- 'Tortuosa Aureopendula'	see *S.* × *sepulcralis* 'Erythroflexuosa'
	'Melanostachys'	see *S. gracilistyla* 'Melanostachys'
	× ***meyeriana*** 'Lumley' (f)	CWiW
	× ***mollissima*** var. ***hippophaifolia*** 'Jefferies' (m)	CWiW
	- - 'Notts Spaniard' (m)	CWiW
	- - 'Trustworthy' (m)	CWiW
	- var. ***undulata*** 'Kottenheider Weide' (f)	CWiW
§	***myrsinifolia***	ELan MBlu MMuc NLar
	myrtilloides 'Pink Tassels' (m)	SBrt
	nakamurana var. ***yezoalpina***	CKel CRos EBee ELan EWes GKev LRHS MBlu MMuc MRav NHar NLar SBrt SSta WFar
	nigra	CDul
	nigricans	see *S. myrsinifolia*
	nivalis	see *S. reticulata* subsp. *nivalis*

pentandra	CDul CLnd LMaj NWea WMou
- 'Patent Lumley'	CWiW
§ ***phylicifolia***	NWea WMou
- 'Malham' (m)	CWiW
§ ***purpurea***	CCVT CDul CPer NWea SCob WMou
- 'Brittany Green' (f)	CWiW
- 'Continental Reeks'	CWiW
- 'Dark Dicks' (f)	CWiW NLar WSFF
- 'Dicky Meadows' (m)	CWiW
- 'Goldstones'	CWiW NLar
- f. ***gracilis***	see *S. purpurea* 'Gracilis'
§ - 'Gracilis'	MMuc NWea SCob WCot
- 'Green Dicks'	CWiW
- 'Helix'	see *S. purpurea*
- 'Howki' (m)	WMou
- 'Irette' (m)	CWiW
- 'Jagiellonka' (f)	CWiW
- var. ***japonica***	see *S. koriyanagi*
- subsp. ***lambertiana***	CWiW
- 'Lancashire Dicks' (m)	CWiW
- 'Leicestershire Dicks' (m)	CWiW
- 'Light Dicks'	CWiW
- 'Lincolnshire Dutch' (f)	CWiW
- 'Nancy Saunders' (f) ♀H6	CTho CWiW EHoe GLog LEdu MBNS MBlu MBrN MRav NBir NLar NSti SMHy WCot WGrn
I - 'Nicholsonii Purpurascens'	CRos
- 'Pendula' ♀H6	CCVT CEnd CMac ECrN MAsh MSwo
- 'Read' (f)	CWiW
- 'Reeks' (f)	CWiW
- 'Richartii' (f)	CWiW
- 'Uralensis' (f)	CWiW
pyrenaica	EWes
radinostachya KR 7622	WPGP
repens	NWea SRms
§ - var. ***argentea***	CRos ELan EWes LRHS MMuc MRav SPer WFar
- 'Armando'PBR	WFar
reticulata ♀H7	EBee EPot GCrg NBir NSla WFar
§ - subsp. ***nivalis***	EPot
retusa	NBir
rosmarinifolia misapplied	see *S. elaeagnos* subsp. *angustifolia*
rosmarinifolia L.	EPfP NLar
× ***rubens***	see *S.* × *fragilis*
× ***rubra***	CWiW
- 'Abbey's Harrison' (f)	CWiW
- 'Continental Osier' (f)	CWiW
- 'Eugenei' (m)	CDul ECrN MBlu
- 'Fidkin' (f)	CWiW
- 'Harrison's' (f)	CWiW
- 'Harrison's Seedling A' (f)	CWiW
- 'Mawdesley'	CWiW
- 'Mawdesley Seedling A' (f)	CWiW
- 'Pyramidalis'	CWiW
I 'Salix Red'	WJPR
§ × ***sepulcralis*** 'Aokautere' (m)	CWiW
- 'Caradoc'	CWiW
§ - var. ***chrysocoma*** ♀H5	Widely available
- 'Dart's Snake' (m)	ELan EPPr EShb MAsh MBrN MRav NLar WCot WFar
§ - 'Erythroflexuosa' (m) ♀H5	CBcs CBod CDul CEnd EBee ELan EMOT EPPr EPfP LRHS MAsh MGos MMuc MRav NOra NWea SCob SEND SGol SLim SPer SPoG WCFE WMat
serpyllifolia	GKev
- 'Chamonix'	NSla
serpyllum	see *S. fragilis* var. *furcata*
'Setsuka'	see *S. udensis* 'Sekka'
subopposita	EBtc ELan MGil MMuc SBrt
× ***tetrapla*** 'Hutchinson's Nigricans'	CNat
triandra	NWea WMou
- 'Black German' (m)	CWiW
- 'Black Hollander' (m)	CWiW NLar
- 'Black Maul'	CWiW
- 'Grisette de Falaise'	CWiW
- 'Grisette Droda' (f)	CWiW
- 'Long Bud'	CWiW
- 'Noir de Challans'	CWiW
- 'Noir de Touraine'	CWiW
- 'Noir de Villaines' (m)	CWiW WJPR
- 'Rouge d'Orléans'	EBtc
- 'Sarda d'Anjou'	CWiW
- 'Whissander'	CWiW
udensis 'Golden Sunshine'PBR	CKel CRos EBee EMil EPfP LRHS MAsh MMrt MPkF NEoE NRHS SPer SSta WCot
§ - 'Sekka' (m)	CBcs MBlu MMuc NBir NWea WMou
uva-ursi	WAbe
viminalis	CCVT CLnd CMac CPer EPfP LBuc MJak MMuc NWea SEWo SVic WJPR WMou WSFF
- 'Green Gotz'	CWiW
vitellina 'Pendula'	see *S. alba* 'Tristis' ambig.
'Yelverton'	see *S. alba* var. *vitellina* 'Yelverton'

Salsola (*Amaranthaceae*)

komarovii new	MNHC

Salvia ✿ (*Lamiaceae*)

CD&R 1141	SPin
CD&R 1162	SPhx
CD&R 1458	SPin
CD&R 1495	SPin
PC&H 226	SPin
from Catamarca, Argentina	SDys
absconditiflora	SPin
acerifolia	SDys SPin
acetabulosa	see *S. multicaulis*
adenophora	SPin
aethiopis	EWes SPhx WOut
I 'African Sky'	CBod CCBP CElw CSam ECre MAvo MCot MHer MPie NHic NRHS SDys SMHy SPhx SPin WGrn WOut
§ ***africana***	EBee SPin
africana-caerulea	see *S. africana*
africana-lutea	see *S. aurea*
agnes	SDys SPin
albicaulis new	SPin
'Alegría'	SDys
algeriensis	LRHS SPhx
'Allen Chickering'	SDys
altimitrata	see *S. lasiantha*
amarissima	SPin
'Amber'	IMou LPla SPin
ambigens	see *S. guaranitica* 'Blue Enigma'
'Amistad'PBR ♀H3	Widely available
'Amparito' new	XSen
ampelophylla	SDys
- B&SWJ 10751	SPin
§ ***amplexicaulis***	LPla MMuc NLar SRms XSen
amplifrons	SPin
angustifolia Cav.	see *S. reptans*
angustifolia Mich.	see *S. azurea*
'Anna'	SDys

	Name	Suppliers
	'Anthony Parker'	CSam WOut
	apiana	EWTr EWld SPhx SPin SPlb SRms SVen XSen
	(Arctic Blaze Series) ARCTIC BLAZE FUCHSIA ('Novasalfuc') new	XSen
	- ARCTIC BLAZE PURPLE ('Novasalpur') new	XSen
	- ARCTIC BLAZE RED ('Novasalred') new	XSen
	argentea ♀H4	CBcs CBod CDor CRos CSpe ECha ELan EPfP LRHS NRHS SMad SPer SPhx WKif WOut XSen
	arizonica	CSam EBee EWld GCal MAsh SDys SPin WSHC
	aspera	SPin
	atrocyanea	CSam CSpe ECre EWes MAsh MAvo MGil SDys SMHy SPin WHal WKif
	atropatana	SMHy WCot
	aucheri	SPin
§	***aurea***	CHll CSpe EBee SPin SPlb SVen XLum
	- 'Kirstenbosch'	CAby ECtt EWld NSti SDys SPin WCot WKif WOut
	aurita	SPin
	- var. ***galpinii***	SPin
§	***azurea***	SBrt SPhx SPin XSen
	- var. ***grandiflora***	SPin WCot
	bacheriana	see *S. buchananii*
	'Ballerina' new	XSen
§	***barrelieri***	ESwi SPin
	'Bee's Bliss'	XSen
	'Belhaven'	EBee GCal WOut
	benthamiana	SDys
	bertolonii	see *S. pratensis* Bertolonii Group
	bicolor	see *S. barrelieri*
	biserrata new	SPin
	'Black Knight'	MAsh SDys SPin
	blancoana	see *S. lavandulifolia* subsp. *blancoana*
	blepharophylla	ECtt MHer MSCN WAvo
	- 'Diablo'	ECtt
	- 'Painted Lady'	ECtt MAsh SDys SPin
	'Bleu Armor'PBR	NCGa SPhx XSen
	'Blue Merced'	MAvo SDys
	'Blue Moon'	SDys
	'Blue Note'PBR	CBod CMea CRos CSpe CWGN CWld EBee ECtt ELan EUJe IKil IPot LLWG LRHS MAvo MBel MHol NDov NPri NRHS SCob SEND SPoG SRkn WAvo WCot WHil
	'Blue Sky'	EWld
	bogotensis	SPin
	bowleyana	SPin
	brandegeei	SPin
	brevilabra	SPin
	brevipes	SPin
	'Bright Eyes' (Suncrest Series)	CWGN SCob
	broussonetii	EBee SPin
§	***buchananii*** ♀H2	CSam ECtt MAsh MHer MRav SDys SPin SRkn WKif
	bulleyana misapplied	see *S. flava* var. *megalantha*
	bulleyana Diels	CBcs CExl EWes GPSL MMuc NQui WHil
	- 'Blue Lips'	EBee ECtt MHol MSCN SCob
	bullulata	CSpe SPin
	- pale-blue-flowered	CSpe SDys SPin
	cacaliifolia ♀H2	CExl CWCL EBee ECtt EWld GCal MAsh MHer SDys SPin SRkn WAvo
	caerulea misapplied	see *S. guaranitica*
	caerulea L.	see *S. africana*
	caespitosa	SPin
	calolophos	SPin
	campanulata B&SWJ 9232	WCru
	- GWJ 9294	WCru
	- var. ***hirtella*** GWJ 9397	WCru
	canariensis	SPin WCot
	- f. ***albiflora***	EBee SVen
	- f. ***candidissima***	SPin
	candelabrum ♀H3	CSpe ECre EWes MHer SPhx SPin SVen WKif XSen
	canescens	XSen
	cardinalis	see *S. fulgens*
	cardiophylla	SPin
	carnea	MAsh SPin
	- from Valle de Bravo, Mexico	SDys
	caudata	SPin
	'Cavalieri d'Alto'	MAvo SPhx WHil
	'Cavaliero Celeste'	SDys
§	***chamaedryoides***	ELan MAsh SBrt SPin XSen
	- var. ***isochroma***	EBee EPfP MAsh SDys SPin WPGP XSen
	- 'Marine Blue'	MAsh MCot
	- silver-leaved	CAby CSpe SPhx SPin XLum
	chamelaeagnea	EPPr SDys SPin
	'Cherbourg' new	XSen
	'Cherry Queen'	CWGN MAsh WOut
	chiapensis	MAsh SDys SPin
	chionophylla	CElw SPin
	'Christine Yeo'	CElw EBee ECtt ELon MAsh SDys SEND SPin WAvo WGrn WHil WSHC XSen
	'Christopher Fairweather'	ECtt
	chrysophylla	SDys
	cinnabarina	SPin
	cleistogama misapplied	see *S. glutinosa*
	clevelandii	MHer SPin
	- 'Winnifred Gilman'	SDys
	clinopodioides	EBee SDys SPin
	coahuilensis misapplied	see *S. greggii* × *serpyllifolia*
	coahuilensis ambig.	MAsh SLon SPin SRkn WSHC XLum
	cocuyana B&SWJ 14861 new	WCru
	concolor misapplied	see *S. guaranitica*
	concolor Lamb. ex Benth.	CAby EBee GCal SDys SPin WSHC
	confertiflora	CAby CBcs CBod CExl CSam CSpe CWCL EBee ECre ECtt GCal IPot MAsh MHer MHol NSti SDys SPhx SPin SPlb SRkn SVen WAvo WHer WKif WPGP
	corrugata	CBcs CElw EBee ECtt GBin GCal LRHS MAsh MCot MHer SDys SPhx SPin
	'Crazy Dolls'	SDys
	'Crème Caramel'	EBee ECtt MAsh MAvo MCot SDys
	cruickshanksii	SPin
	cryptantha	SPin
	cuatrecasana	SPin
	curviflora	CElw CSam CSpe ELan EWld IPot LSvl MAsh SBch SDys SEle SPin WAvo WOut
	cuspidata subsp. ***gilliesii***	SPin
	- subsp. ***rosea*** new	SPin
	cyanescens	CMea EPot SPin XSen
	cyanicalyx	SDys SPin
	cyclostegia	CExl
	daghestanica	EBee GKev SPin
	'Dancing Dolls'	CWGN IKil SCob XSen
I	***dangitalis***	SPin
	- SDR 4332	CExl

darcyi misapplied	see *S. roemeriana*
darcyi J. Compton	CExl CHll ELan EWes MCot SDys SPin WSHC XLum
davidsonii	SPin
'Dayglo'	ECtt
densiflora new	SPin
deserta	LRHS SBrt SPhx WCot
desoleana	SPin
'Didi'	NDov
digitaloides BWJ 7777	SPin
discolor	CHll CSpe ECtt EWld GCal MAsh MHer SCob SDys SPin WAvo WKif
disermas	SPin SPlb
disjuncta	CElw SBrt SPin
dolichantha	CTsd NLar SPin WMoo
dolomitica	SPin
dombeyi	CAby CSam EBee SDys SPin WPGP
dominica	SPin
dorisiana	MAsh MHer SDys SPin SVen
'Dorset Wonder'	IPot NCGa NDov
durifolia	SPin
'Dyson's Crimson'	CSde ELan IPot MCot SDys WAul WTre
'Dyson's Gem'	CSpe MAvo SDys WTre
'Dyson's Joy' ♀H3	LCro LOPS MAvo MCot SDys WHil WKif
eigii	SPin
eizi-matudae	CSam SDys SPin
§ ***elegans***	CLau EWes EWhm GCal IDee IPot NPol NWad WHer WOut WSHC XLum XSen
- 'Golden Delicious'	CBod EMor ENfk EWes MHer NEoE SPin SRms WFar
- 'Honey Melon'	EBou ENfk MAsh SDys
- 'Scarlet Pineapple'	CBod CCBP CExl ELan ENfk EUJe EWld GPoy MCot MHer MNHC SDys SRms SVen WJek
- 'Sonoran Red'	SDys
- 'Tangerine'	CBod CLau ENfk EWhm MHer MNHC NQui SPin SRms WJek
EMBER'S WISH ('Sal 0101')	CBcs CBod CRos CSpe EBee ECtt EPfP EWld IPot LCro LOPS LRHS MAsh MCot MNrw MSCN NCGa NDov NPri NRHS SDys SEle SPin SPoG SRkn WAvo WFar WGrn
'Endless Love'	EBee NDov SRms
evansiana	SPin
'Eveline'	CKno CMac CRos CWGN EBee ECtt EPfP IPot LRHS NLar NRHS SHar SRms STPC
excelsa	SPin
exserta	EBee
fallax	see *S. roscida*
farinacea 'Midnight Candle'	LRHS NRHS
- 'Rhea'	SPoG
- 'Strata'	SPoG
'Flamenco Rose' (Suncrest Series) new	XSen
§ ***flava*** var. ***megalantha***	CAby CBod CRos EAJP EPfP LRHS LSRN NRHS SPin WArt XSen
'Flower Child'	SDys
forreri	EBee MAsh NDov SDys SPin
- 'Karen Dyson'	SDys
§ ***forsskaolii***	CBod CCBP CElw CExl CSam ELan EMor EPfP GKev MMuc MNrw MRav NChi NLar NQui NSti SAko SEND SPin SPtp WCAu WCot WMoo WPtf WTre XLum XSen
- white-flowered	EBee
§ ***fruticosa***	CRos LRHS SLon SPhx SPin SRms WTre XSen
§ ***fulgens*** ♀H3	CRos GCal MAsh SDys SPin SRkn
- from Mount Popocatépetl, Mexico	SPin
gachantivana	SPin
gesneriiflora	ECtt EWld SPin
- mountain form	ECre SDys
- 'Tequila'	SPin WOut
glabrescens B&SWJ 11152	WCru
* - var. ***robusta*** B&SWJ 11147	WCru
glechomifolia	SPin
§ ***glutinosa***	CBod CMac CRos CSpe EBee EWld GCal GWyn IMou LRHS MMuc MNrw NBro NLar NRHS NSti SPin SPtp WCAu WHil XLum XSen
gracilis	SPin
grahamii	see *S. microphylla* var. *microphylla* 'Newby Hall'
'Great Comp'	NDov SDys
greggii	CRos EPfP EWes LPot LRHS NRHS SPlb SRms WKif XLum
- CD&R 1148	SDys
- 'Alba'	WHil XLum XSen
- 'Blush Pink'	see *S. microphylla* 'Blush Pink'
- 'Caramba' (v)	LRHS
§ - 'Desert Blaze' (v)	CRos CWGN EAJP ECtt ELan EPfP LRHS MAsh MRav NRHS SDys SLon SPin SPoG WAvo WGrn XLum
- 'Devon Cream'	see *S. greggii* 'Sungold'
- 'Diane'	MAsh
- 'Emperor'	CBod CWGN CWld EBee EWTr EWes MAvo MBel SEle
- 'Flame'	CWGN WHil
- 'Icing Sugar'PBR	CBod CLau CRos CWGN CWld EBee ECtt ELan ENfk EPfP LCro LOPS LRHS MAsh MAvo MCot MHol NDov NRHS SCob SDys SEle SRkn WHil WKif
- 'Lara'	MAvo WHil
- 'Lipstick'	CExl ECtt GWyn LCro LOPS MAsh NRHS
- 'Magenta'	MAvo SPin WHil
- 'Peach' misapplied	see *S. × jamensis* 'Pat Vlasto'
- 'Peach'	CWGN EPfP MAsh SDys SPin XLum XSen
- 'Pink Preference'	MAsh SDys
- 'Raspberry Red'	XLum
- 'Sierra San Antonio'	see *S. × jamensis* 'Sierra San Antonio'
- 'Sparkler'	see *S. greggii* 'Desert Blaze'
- 'Stormy Pink'	CHll CSam CSpe ECtt EWTr IPot MAsh MAvo MCot NDov SIgm WHil WKif WTre
§ - 'Sungold'	CRos CWGN ECtt EPfP LRHS MAsh MPie SDys SPhx XSen
- variegated (v)	XSen
- yellow-flowered	XLum
greggii* × *lycioides	see *S. greggii* × *serpyllifolia*
§ ***greggii* × *serpyllifolia***	CSam CSpe SDys SPin SVen
guadalujarensis	SPin
§ ***guaranitica***	ECtt MHer SPin WKif WPGP WTre XLum XSen
- 'Argentina Skies'	CAby ECtt EPPr SDys SPin
- 'Black and Blue'	CBcs CBod CExl CMea CRos CWGN EBee ECre ECtt EMor EPfP EUJe GBin GCal ILea LCro LRHS LSRN NRHS SDys SPin SPoG SRkn SVen WAvo WHoo WPGP WSHC XSen

§	- 'Blue Enigma' 𝕐H3	CAby CBod CCBP CExl CRos CWGN EBee ECha ECtt EHrv ELan EPfP GCal LRHS MAsh MBel MGos MRav NRHS SDys SPin WGwG WSpi XLum XSen
	- 'Costa Rica Blue'	SDys
	- 'Indigo Blue'	EPfP MAsh SPin
	- 'Midnight'	CSpe
	- purple-flowered	CSam SDys
	- 'Super Trouper'	SDys
	- violet-flowered	SDys
	'Guarini'	SDys
	haematodes	see *S. pratensis* Haematodes Group
	haenkei	CElw SPin
	- 'Prawn Chorus'	MAsh
	'Hannah' **new**	MAvo
	heldreichiana	XSen
	henryi	SPin
	hians	ESwi GCal ILea SRms
	- CC 1787	CExl
	hierosolymitana	CRos EBee LRHS NRHS SBrt SPhx SPin WHil XSen
	hispanica misapplied	see *S. lavandulifolia*
	holwayi	SDys SPin
	horminum	see *S. viridis* var. *comata*
§	'Hot Lips' 𝕐H5	Widely available
	'I Cavalieri del Tau'	SDys
	inconspicua	SPin
	'Indiansummer'	SDys
	indica	LRHS SPhx
	'Indigo Spires'	CExl CHll CMea CSam CSpe CWGN ECre ECtt EPfP IMou MAsh MCot NDov SDys SEle SPhx SPin WAvo WFar WKif XLum
	interrupta	EWld MCot SPhx SPin WOut XSen
	involucrata 𝕐H3	CAby CRos IPot MCot NBro SDys SPin SVen WGrn WSHC
	- 'Bethellii' 𝕐H3	CBod CKel EBee ECtt ELan EPfP EWes EWld LRHS MAsh MHer MNrw NSti SDys SPin SRkn WFar WKif WSpi XLum
	- 'Boutin' 𝕐H3	CTsd LPla MAsh SDys SEle SPin
§	- 'Hadspen'	CHll CRHN CSam CSpe EWes GCal SPin WAvo WOut
	- 'Mrs Pope'	see *S. involucrata* 'Hadspen'
	- 'Pink Icicles'	SDys
	involucrata × ***wagneriana***	SDys
	iodantha	SPin
	iodochroa B&SWJ 10252	WCru
	× ***jamensis***	MAsh SPin WHil
	- 'Amarillo'	SDys
	- 'California Sunset'	MAsh SDys
	- 'Dark Dancer'	MAsh SDys WHil
	- 'Devantville'	XLum
	- 'Dysons' Orangy Pink'	CSpe NDov SDys
	- 'El Durazno'	XSen
	- 'Flammenn'PBR	CRos LRHS NCGa NRHS XSen
	- 'Golden Girl'	CSpe CWGN EBee WHil WSHC
	- HEATWAVE BLAZE ('Eggben005')	EBee
	- 'Heatwave Glimmer'PBR	CSpe MCot SPin
	- 'James Compton'	SIgm
	- 'Javier' 𝕐H5	CSpe EWld GBin MAsh MAvo SDys SPin
	- 'Kentish Pink'	SDys
	- 'La Luna'	CSam EPPr MAsh MPie MRav MSCN NDov WSHC XLum XSen
	- 'La Siesta'	MAsh XSen
	- 'La Tarde'	CTri MAsh
	- 'Lemon Light' **new**	XSen
	- 'Los Lirios'	CTri MCot SPin WAvo WHil
	- 'Maraschino'	CRos EPfP LRHS MAsh MBel SDys SPin SRms WHil XLum
	- 'Melen'PBR	EBee SRms XSen
	- 'Moonlight Over Ashwood' (v)	MAsh WSHC
	- 'Moonlight Serenade'	MAsh SDys
§	- 'Pat Vlasto'	SPin
	- 'Peter Vidgeon' 𝕐H5	CRos CWGN EBee ECha EPPr EPfP GBin LRHS MAsh MCot NPri NRHS SDys SPhx SPin WAvo WPGP WSHC
	- 'Pleasant Pink'	MAsh
	- 'Pluenn'PBR	CKel CRos LRHS NCGa NRHS XSen
	- 'Plum Wine'	WHil
	- 'Raspberry Royale'	CRos CWld ECtt EPfP LRHS MAsh MHer MPie NRHS SDys SPin XLum XSen
	- 'Red Velvet'	EBee ECtt MAsh MCot SDys SPhx WAvo WBrk WHrl WSHC
	- RÊVE ROUGE ('Fauresal02') **new**	XSen
	- 'Señorita Leah'	CWGN ENfk MAsh MCot NDov SDys
	- 'Shell Dancer'PBR	XSen
§	- 'Sierra San Antonio'	CRos EPfP LRHS MAsh NRHS SDys XLum XSen
	- 'Stormy Sunrise'	SDys
§	- 'Trebah'	CAby CBod ECre MAsh MCot SDys SPin WKif WSHC
	- 'Trenance'	CBod ECre ELon MHer SPin WHil
	- VIOLETTE DE LOIRE ('Barsal'PBR)	LRHS NCGa SRms XSen
	japonica var. ***formosana*** NMWJ 14469 **new**	WCru
	'Jean's Jewel'	SDys SPin
	'Jean's Purple Passion'	MAsh SDys SPin
	'Jezebel' 𝕐H3	CRos EPfP GBin LRHS NRHS SDys SPin
	'Joan'	CSam CWGN MAsh MCot MSCN SDys SPin WHil
	judaica	CMac XSen
	jurisicii	CRos EPfP LRHS NRHS WHil XLum XSen
	karwinskyi	SDys SPin
	karwinskyi × ***univerticillata***	SDys
	keerlii	SPin
	koyamae	EBee SPin
	- B&SWJ 10919	WCru
	'Krystle Pink'	WHlf
	'La Mancha'	SDys WHlf
	'Lalarsha'	CElw ELan MAsh MAvo MCot NDov SDys
	lanceolata	SPin WOut
	languidula	SPin
§	***lasiantha***	SPin
§	***lavandulifolia***	CBod CRos EBee ELan EPPr EPfP EWes GPoy LRHS MAsh MHer MNHC MRav SPin SRms WHoo WJek WKif XLum XSen
§	- subsp. ***blancoana***	ECha SPhx SPin XSen
	- subsp. ***gallica***	XSen
	- subsp. ***pyrenaeorum***	XSen
	- 'Roquefure'	XSen
	- subsp. ***vellerea***	XSen
	lavanduloides	SPin
	'Lavender Dilly Dilly'	MAvo
	lemmonii	see *S. microphylla* var. *wislizeni*
	'Lemon Pie'	SDys SPin WAvo
	leptophylla	see *S. reptans*

leucantha ♀H2	CCBP CSpe ECre ELan EWld MAsh MCot MHer MNrw MRav SPin SPlb SRkn SVen WHer WKif WOut XSen
- DANIELLE'S DREAM ('Ferpink')	SPin
- 'Eder' (v)	MAsh SDys
- 'Midnight'	CSam
- 'Purple Velvet'	CAby CSpe EBee ECtt MAsh MHer SDys SPin WAvo
- 'San Marcos Lavender'	SPin
- 'Santa Barbara'	CHll ECtt MAsh SDys
- 'White Mischief'	SPin
leucocephala	SDys SPin
leucophylla NNS 01-375	SPin
libanensis	SDys
littae	SDys SPin
'Little Azur'	SDys
longispicata	SPin
longistyla	SDys SPin SVen
LOVE AND WISHES ('Serendip6')	CBcs CBod CHll CPla CRos CSpe CWGN ECtt EPfP IPot LCro LOPS LPot LRHS MAsh MAvo MCot NCGa NCou NPri NRHS NSti SDys SPoG SRkn WAvo WCot WHil
lycioides misapplied	see *S. greggii* × *serpyllifolia*
lycioides A. Gray	CHll SDys
lyrata	EBee
- 'Burgundy Bliss'	see *S. lyrata* 'Purple Knockout'
§ - 'Purple Knockout'	CRos EPfP LPot LRHS NRHS SPin XSen
- 'Purple Vulcano'	see *S. lyrata* 'Purple Knockout'
LYRICAL BLUES ('Balyriclu'PBR) **new**	WHil
macellaria misapplied	see *S. microphylla*
macrophylla	SDys SPin
- purple-leaved	SDys
macrosiphon	SPin
'Madeline'PBR	CBod CRos CWGN EPfP EWTr GBin LCro LOPS LRHS MHol MNrw NCGa NRHS SPer SPin STPC WHil
madrensis	SDys SPin
- 'Dunham'	EWld GCal
'Magenta Magic'	CSpe SDys SPin
'Magic Potion'	CWGN
'Mas de Lunès' **new**	XSen
melaleuca B&SWJ 14863 **new**	WCru
mellifera	SPin
mexicana	SPin
- var. ***minor***	EWld SDys SPin
I ***miahuatlanensis***	SPin
§ ***microphylla***	CBod CMac CTri EWes EWhm MHer SIgm SVen WOut XLum
- CD&R 1141	SPin
- 'Belize'	IPot MAsh
- 'Blind Faith' **new**	MAvo
- 'Blue Monrovia'	LRHS NRHS
§ - 'Blush Pink'	MAvo SDys
- 'Bordeaux' **new**	CSpe
- 'Cerro Potosí' ♀H4	CElw CSpe EBee ECtt ELan ELon EShb GBin LRHS MAsh MAvo MCot MHer MSCN NPri SDys SHar SIgm SPhx SPin WCFE WHil WOut WSHC WTre XLum XSen
- 'Chalk White'	SMHy
- 'Hot Lips'	see *S.* 'Hot Lips'
- 'Kew Red'	CRos MNrw SPin WAvo WHil
I - 'Lutea'	ENfk MAsh SDys
- 'Maroon'	MAvo MCot SDys
- 'Mauve'	NDov
§ - var. ***microphylla***	CRHN CTri ECtt ELan ENfk LSRN MCot MHer MNHC MRav SEND SPin SRkn SVic XLum
- - 'La Foux'	SPhx WAvo
§ - - 'Newby Hall'	ECtt EWes LRHS NWad SPhx WSHC
- var. ***neurepia***	see *S. microphylla* var. *microphylla*
- 'Norwell'	MNrw
- 'Orange Door'	SDys
- orange-red-flowered	MRav
- 'Oregon Peach'	CRos EPfP LRHS NRHS
- 'Oxford'	SPin
- 'Pink Blush'	CAby CBod CRos ECtt ELan EPfP LRHS MAsh MCot MHer MNHC SEND SPin SRkn WAvo WHil WHoo WKif WSHC XSen
- 'Pleasant View'	WHil
- 'Robin's Pride'	SDys WHil
- 'Rodbaston Red'	WHil
- 'Rodbaston Rosy Cheeks'	MSCN WOut
- 'Ruby Star' **new**	IPot
- 'San Carlos Festival'	MAsh SDys SPin
- 'Trelawny Rose Pink'	see *S.* 'Trelawney'
- 'Trelissick Creamy Yellow'	see *S.* 'Trelissick'
- 'Trewithen Cerise'	see *S.* 'Trewithen'
- 'Wendy's Surprise'	EWld LSvl MCot SDys
- 'Wild Watermelon'	CWGN EBee ECtt EWTr EWes GPSL MAsh MAvo MHer NQui SDys WGrn WHil WHrl
§ - var. ***wislizeni***	CElw SPhx
- 'Wollerton White'	MCot MRav SDys
- 'Zaragoza'	SPin
miltiorrhiza	CSpe SPin WArt WHer XLum XSen
miniata	SPin
misella	SPin
mocinoi	SPin
moorcroftiana	SPin
moschata	SPin
muelleri misapplied	see *S. greggii* × *serpyllifolia*
muelleri ambig.	CPla CSpe NDov
'Mulberry Jam'	CAby CCBP CHll CSam EAJP ECtt ELan EPfP EWes MAsh MCot SDys SEle SPin SRkn WHil WKif WSHC
§ ***multicaulis*** ♀H3	MAsh XSen
munzii	SDys SPin
MYSTIC SPIRES BLUE ('Balsalmisp'PBR)	CSpe CWGN EPfP NRHS SCob SPin SPoG
'Nachtvlinder' ♀H5	Widely available
namaensis	SPin
nana B&SWJ 10272	SPin
- 'Curling Waves'PBR	ECtt MHol
napifolia	EBee EWTr EWes LRHS MMuc MNrw NLar
'Nazareth'	SPin
'Nel'	EBee
nemorosa	LSRN NAln NPol SPin SRms XLum XSen
- 'Amethyst' ♀H7	CRos EBee ELon EPfP GBin IKil LCro LOPS LPot LRHS MBel MHol MRav MTis NDov NRHS SCob SPer SPhx SPin SRms WCAu WCot WKif XSen
- 'Blaureiter'	EBee
- BLUE BOUQUETTA ('Alkif') **new**	NPri WNPC
- 'Blue Marvel'	CBod LRHS MHol SPoG WHil
- BLUE MOUND	see *S.* × *sylvestris* 'Blauhügel'
- 'Bordeau Steel Blue'	CRos EBee ELon LRHS NRHS SRms
- 'Caradonna' ♀H7	Widely available
- 'Caramia' **new**	CKno
- EAST FRIESLAND	see *S. nemorosa* 'Ostfriesland'

- 'Grace'	NDov
- 'Little Friesland'	CRos NRHS
- 'Lubecca' ♀H7	CRos CSam ECtt EHrv EPfP LRHS MAsh MBel NDov NEgg NGdn NLar NRHS SPer WCAu WFar XSen
- LYRICAL SILVERTONE ('Balyricsil'PBR)	WFar
- LYRICAL WHITE ('Florsalwhite') **new**	WHil
- MARCUS ('Haeumanarc'PBR)	CBod CRos CWld EBee ECtt ELan ELon EPfP EUJe LRHS LSRN MBNS MRav MTin NRHS SAko SDys SPoG WFar
§ - 'Ostfriesland' ♀H7	Widely available
- 'Pink Beauty'	CRos IKil LRHS NRHS
- 'Pink Friesland'PBR	CAby ECtt EPfP GBin GMaP NGdn NRHS SAko WSpi
- 'Plumosa'	see *S. nemorosa* 'Pusztaflamme'
§ - 'Pusztaflamme' ♀H7	EBee ECha ECtt EPfP MRav SAko
- 'Rose Queen'	CBar ELon GMaP GWyn NBir SCob SPhx WArt WCot WFar XLum XSen
- 'Rosenwein'	CDor CRos GWyn LRHS NGdn NRHS SGbt SPhx XSen
- 'Royal Distinction'	ECtt
- 'Schwellenburg'	CBod CRos ECtt EWes LCro LRHS MHol NLar NRHS SAko SCob
- (Sensation Series) SENSATION BLUE ('Florsalvioblu'PBR)	CRos LRHS NRHS
- - SENSATION BLUE IMPROVED	CRos LRHS NRHS
- - SENSATION DEEP BLUE ('Florsaldblue')	CRos EBee LRHS NRHS
- - SENSATION DEEP ROSE ('Flor Sal Roz'PBR)	CBod CNor LRHS NRHS
- - SENSATION DEEP ROSE IMPROVED	CRos LRHS NRHS SPoG
- - SENSATION PINK	CRos LRHS NRHS
- - SENSATION ROSE	CBod CRos LCro LLHF LOPS LRHS LSRN MHol MMrt NRHS SHar SRms
- - SENSATION SKY BLUE ('Flor Sal Sky')	CBod
- - SENSATION WHITE	CRos CWGN LRHS MBel MHol NRHS
§ - subsp. ***tesquicola***	NLar SPhx WFar
- 'Theodor'	ECtt
- 'Wesuwe'	ELon NDov
'Neon'	EBee NHic SPin WAvo
neurepia	see *S. microphylla* var. *microphylla*
* ***nevadensis***	SPin
nilotica	SPin
nipponica	EBee SBrt
- B&SWJ 5829	SPin WCru
- 'Fuji Snow' (v)	EBee
- var. ***trisecta***	SPin
nubicola	CExl GPoy
'Nuchi'	CRos LRHS NRHS SDys SPoG
nutans	SPhx SPin XSen
officinalis	Widely available
- 'Albiflora'	CBcs SPin WArt WJek XSen
- 'Aurea' ambig.	GPoy
- 'Berggarten' ♀H5	CBod CCBP CLau ECha EWhm GBin GCal MHer MRav SCob SPhx SPin WHer WHil WKif XLum XSen
- 'Bicolor'	SPin
- 'Blackcurrant'	CBod CLau
§ - broad-leaved	CLau EMor MHer WJek
- 'Crispa'	XSen
- 'Extrakta'	GCal
- 'Grete Stolze'	SEND XSen
- 'Grower's Friend'	CTsd
§ - 'Icterina' (v) ♀H5	Widely available
- ***latifolia***	see *S. officinalis* broad-leaved
- narrow-leaved	see *S. lavandulifolia*
- 'Nazareth'	XSen
- ***prostrata***	see *S. lavandulifolia*
- 'Purpurascens' ♀H5	Widely available
- 'Robin Hill'	LRHS NRHS
- 'Rosea'	WOut
- 'Tricolor' (v)	CBcs CBod CRos CTri EBee ELan EMor ENfk EPfP EWhm GPoy MAsh MHer MNHC MRav NHic SCob SGol SPer SPin SPoG SRms WFar WJek
- 'Variegata'	see *S. officinalis* 'Icterina'
- variegated (v)	MHer
- 'Würzburg'	XSen
ombrophila	SPin
omeiana BWJ 8062	SPin WCru
- 'Crûg Thundercloud'	WCru
oppositiflora misapplied	see *S. tubiflora*
oppositiflora ambig.	ELan SDys SPin
orbignaei	SPin
'Orchid Glow' (Suncrest Series)	CBod CWGN
'Othello'	SDys
oxyphora	CAby ELan MAsh MHer MPie SDys SPin WFar
pachyphylla	CRos LRHS NRHS XSen
'Pakhuis Pass'	SPin
pallida	SPin
'Pam's Purple'	MAsh
'Pasadena'	SDys
§ ***patens*** ♀H3	CAby CBod CRos CSpe EBee ECha ECtt EPfP IFro LCro LOPS LRHS MAsh MHer MNHC MRav NGdn SDys SEND SPer SPhx SPin SRms WFar WHil WKif WSHC WSpi
- 'Alba' misapplied	see *S. patens* 'White Trophy'
- 'Blue Angel'	CCht EPfP EWes LEdu NAln
- 'Cambridge Blue' ♀H3	CAby CExl CRos CSpe CWGN EBee ECtt EHrv ELan EPfP LRHS MAsh MHer MRav NLar NPer NRHS SDys SIgm SPer SPhx SPin WOut WSHC
- 'Chilcombe'	CAby SDys SPin WOut
- 'Dot's Delight'	CExl CSpe ECtt LRHS MAsh SDys SHar
- 'Guanajuato'	CAby CExl CSBt CSam ECtt EWes MAsh NLar SDys SHar SPin SRot WHil WKif WOut WSHC
- 'Holbrook'	CSam
- large	CSpe
- light blue-flowered	CRos LRHS NRHS
- OCEANA BLUE ('Salsyll')	EBee
- 'Oxford Blue'	see *S. patens*
- (Patio Series) 'Patio Deep Blue'	CBod CWGN EPfP SPoG WHil
- - 'Patio Sky Blue'	WHil WSpi
- 'Pink Ice'	EBee ECtt SDys WOut
- pink-flowered	SPin
- 'Royal Blue'	see *S. patens*
§ - 'White Trophy'	CExl ECtt EWes LRHS LSvl SDys SPin WOut
pauciserrata	SPin
'Peach Cobbler'	MAvo
'Peach Parfait'	EShb MAvo SDys
'Penny's Smile'	CBod CElw CMac ELon IPot MAsh MCot SDys SPhx SPin WGrn WHil WKif
'Peru Blue'	EBee SDys

	'Phyllis' Fancy'	CAby CSam CSde CSpe CWGN EBee EWes EWld LPla MAsh MCot MHer NDov NSti SDys SPhx SPin SPlb SRms WAvo
	pinguifolia	SPin
	'Pink Icing'	SPin
	'Pink Lace'	SDys
	pisidica	SPin XSen
	plectranthoides	SPin
	polystachya	SPin
	pratensis	CCBP CWld EPfP GJos MNHC MRav NHic SPin SRms WCot WOut XSen
	- W&B BGH-3	WCot
§	- Bertolonii Group	SPin
	- 'Dear Anja'	see *S.* × *sylvestris* 'Dear Anja'
§	- Haematodes Group ♀H7	MNrw SPin SRms
	- 'Indigo' ♀H7	CAby CBod CRos ECtt ELon GMaP LRHS MPie MRav NEgg NLar NRHS SPhx SPin SPoG WCot WPGP
	- 'Lapis Lazuli'	EBee EWes LPla LRHS
	- 'Pink Delight'PBR	EBee ECtt EPfP LRHS MPie NCGa NDov NRHS SRms
	- 'Rose Rhapsody' (Ballet Series)	CBod CDor EBee EPPr EPfP MMrt NLar SPhx WArt WKif XSen
	- 'Rosea'	ECha SPin
	- 'Sky Dance' (Ballet Series)	CBod NCGa
	- 'Swan Lake' (Ballet Series)	CDor EBee EPPr GWyn NLar SPhx SPlb XSen
	- 'Sweet Esmeralda' (Ballet Series)	CDor EBee NGdn SPhx XSen
	- 'Twilight Serenade' (Ballet Series)	CDor EBee EBou ECtt EPPr EPfP MWat SPhx WOut XSen
	- 'White Swan'	MWat
	procurrens	EBee SPin XSen
	prunelloides	SPin
	przewalskii	CExl CRos EWld LRHS NRHS SPin WArt
	- ACE 1157	WCru
	- BWJ 7920	WCru XLum
	pulchella	ELan SPin
	'Purple Majesty'	CHll CSam ECtt SDys WKif WSpi XLum
	'Purple Queen'	CBod CRos EAJP EBee EShb LRHS MCot NRHS SDys SEle WHil
	purpurea	LSRN
	quitensis	SPin
	'Radio Red' **new**	WGrn
	radula	EBee SPin
	'Raspberry Truffle'	SDys SPin
	raymondii	SPin
	subsp. ***raymondii*** **new**	
	recognita	CRos LRHS NRHS SPhx XSen
	recurva	SPin
	'Red Swing'PBR	CBod CRos EBee LRHS NRHS
	reflexa	SPin
	regeliana misapplied	see *S. virgata* Jacq.
	regeliana Trautv.	NBir
	regla	MAsh SDys SPin WPGP XSen
	- 'Jame'	SPin
	- 'Royal'	SPin
	repens	SPin
§	***reptans***	SBrt SPin
	- from western Texas	SDys WCot WFar
	retinervia	SPin
	rhinosima	EBee WHil
	'Ribambelle' ♀H3	EAJP IPot MAsh MCot XLum
	ringens	SPin XSen
	riparia misapplied	see *S. rypara*
	roborowskii	SPin

§	***roemeriana***	CSpe MAvo WOut
	- 'Arriba'	NHic
	- 'Hot Trumpets'	CRos LRHS NCGa NRHS
	'Rolando'	SDys SPin
§	***roscida***	SPin
	'Royal Bumble' ♀H4	Widely available
	'Royal Crimson Distinction'PBR	EBee
	rubescens	SPin
	- B&SWJ 14368	EWld WCru
	rubiginosa	SPin
	runcinata	SPin
	rutilans	see *S. elegans*
§	***rypara***	SPin
	sagittata	EBee GCal SPin
	'Salmon Dance'	CBod CRos CWGN ECtt EMor IPot LRHS MAvo NRHS WNPC
	scabra	EBee SPin WOut
	'Scarlet Spires' **new**	SPin
	schlechteri	EBee SPin
	sclarea	CBod CHby EBou ECtt ENfk GPoy MNHC SRms SVic XLum XSen
	- var. ***turkestanica*** hort.	CCBP CDor CRos CSpe EAJP ECha EHrv EPfP LRHS LSRN LSun MRav NEgg NRHS SEND SPer SPhx SRkn WKif XSen
§	- 'Vatican White'	CPla CRos CSpe EAJP EBee LRHS NAln NRHS SPhx XSen
	- white-bracted	SWvt
	scutellarioides	SPin
	selleana **new**	SPin
	semiatrata misapplied	see *S. chamaedryoides*
	semiatrata ambig.	EWld
	semiatrata Zucc.	SPin WHil
	serboana	EBee GBin SAko WKif WPGP WSHC
	- B&SWJ 10236	WCru
	'Serenade'	CBod CSam EBee ELon MHol MTis NDov WCot WHoo
	serpyllifolia	SPin
	- white-flowered	SPin
	sessei	SPin
	setulosa	SPin
	'Shame'	MAvo NCGa NDov
	'Shy Ruby'	SPin
	sikkimensis	SPin
	'Silas Dyson'	CRos CSam ECre ECtt ELon EPfP IPot LRHS MAsh MAvo MCot NCGa NDov NRHS SDys SPin SPoG WAvo WHil WKif WSHC
	'Silke's Dream'	CRos CSam ECtt EPfP LRHS MAsh MCot MPie SDys SHar SPin XSen
	'Silke's Red'	MCot SDys SPin
	sinaloensis	SPin
	'Smoke'	SDys
	somalensis	CSam EBee SPin SVen
	sonomensis	SBrt
	'Southern Belle'	SDys SPin
	spathacea ♀H4	WOut
	- 'Avis Keedy'	SPin
	sphacelioides	SPin
	spinosa	XSen
	splendens 'Go-Go Purple' **new**	CSpe
	- 'Jimi's Good Red'	CSpe SDys
	- 'Lighthouse Purple' **new**	CSpe
	- 'Red Indian'	SDys
	- 'São Borja'	CSpe SDys
	- 'Vanguard' ♀H3	NPri
§	- 'Van-Houttei' ♀H3	SDys SVen
	'Spring King' **new**	CKno

	Name	Suppliers
	squalens	SPin
	stachydifolia	SPin WPGP
	- CDPR 3071	WPGP
	- dark blue calyx	WPGP
	- lavender calyx	WPGP
§	***staminea***	SPin
	'Stephanie'	SDys SPin
	stolonifera	CAby CSam CSpe ECre MAsh MAvo MHer SDys SMHy SPin
	striata	SDys SPin
	- red-flowered	SPin
	styphelus	SDys SPin
	subpalmatinervis	SPin
	subrotunda	SDys SPin
	'Sunset Strip'	SDys
	× ***superba***	CRos EBee ECha ECtt ELan EPfP LRHS LSRN MWat NRHS SPer SRms WCAu WHoo
	- 'Adora Blue'	CRos LRHS NRHS
	- 'Adrian'	EBee ECtt EPfP LRHS LSRN NRHS SPoG WCot
	- 'Lyon Rose' **new**	EBee
§	- 'Merleau'	CRos EMor LRHS SAko
	- 'Merleau Blue'	see *S.* × *superba* 'Merleau'
	- 'Merleau Pink'	CRos LRHS
	- 'Merleau Rose'	EBee MRav SRms
*	- 'Rosea'	EBee
	- 'Rubin' ♀H7	ECtt NBre
I	- 'Superba'	CAby ECtt MRav SPhx SRkn
	× ***sylvestris***	LSRN SPin
	- APRIL NIGHT ('Dsalrs203'PBR) **new**	EAJP
§	- 'Blauhügel' ♀H7	CBod CRos CSam ECha ECtt ELan EPfP GBin GCal LRHS MArl MAvo MHol MRav NDov NPri NRHS SPer SPhx SRms WCAu WHoo XSen
§	- 'Blaukönigin'	CDor CNor CRos EPfP GMaP LBuc LRHS NGBl NLar NRHS SCob SPer SPlb SPoG SRms SWvt WCot WFar WHil XLum
	- BLUE QUEEN	see *S.* × *sylvestris* 'Blaukönigin'
§	- 'Dear Anja'	EBee ECtt IPot LCro LOPS MHol NAln NDov WCAu WCot
	- 'Deep Blue Field'PBR	IPot
	- 'Lye End'	MRav WCot
	- LYRICAL ROSE ('Balyricose'PBR) **new**	SPoG WHil
§	- 'Mainacht' ♀H7	Widely available
	- MAY NIGHT	see *S.* × *sylvestris* 'Mainacht'
	- 'Negrito'	EBee ECtt GQue NLar
	- 'Rhapsody in Blue'PBR	EPfP MBNS MHol MTis NLar WCot
	- 'Rose Queen'	CBod CMac CRos ECha ELan ELon EMor EPfP EShb LCro LOPS LRHS MHol MJak MRav NGBl NRHS NSti SCob SCoo SPer SPhx SPoG SRms SWvt XLum XSen
	- 'Rügen'	CRos ELon GQue LRHS NRHS SAko WCAu
	- 'Schneehügel'	CBod CMac CRos EBee ECha ECtt EHoe ELan ELon EPPr EPfP GMaP GWyn LCro LOPS LRHS MBNS MBel MRav MTis NAst NLar NRHS SPer WCAu XSen
	- 'Tänzerin' ♀H7	EBee ECtt ELon LRHS MTis NDov NLar SAko SPhx
	- 'Viola Klose' ♀H7	CBod CRos EBee ECha ECtt ELan EPfP EShb LCro LOPS LRHS LSRN MCot NCGa NDov NGdn NLar NRHS SAko SPin SRms WAul
	tachiei hort.	see *S. forsskaolii*
	taraxacifolia	SPin XSen
	tesquicola	see *S. nemorosa* subsp. *tesquicola*
	'Theresia'	SDys
	thymoides	SPin WHil WOut
	tianschanica	SPin
	tiliifolia	SPin SRms
	tingitana	SPin WHil
	tomentosa	EBee SPin XSen
	tortuosa	SPin
	transcaucasica	see *S. staminea*
	transsylvanica	IMou SPin SRms XSen
	- 'Blue Spire'	SRkn
	'Trebah Lilac White'	see *S.* × *jamensis* 'Trebah'
§	'Trelawney'	CBod ECtt EWld LRHS MCot MPie NRHS WGwG WHil
§	'Trelissick'	CBod LRHS MAsh MCot MHer NRHS SDys SEND SEle SPhx SPin SRkn WHil WHrl
§	'Trewithen'	CBod CExl ECre SPer SPin WHil XLum
	trijuga	SPin
	triloba	see *S. fruticosa*
	tubifera	SPin
§	***tubiflora*** ♀H2	MAsh SPin
	'Tutti Frutti' **new**	MAvo
	uliginosa ♀H4	Widely available
	- 'African Skies'	CChe NRHS SPin WAvo
	- 'Ballon Azul'	CBod CSpe EBee ELan EMor EWes LRHS MAsh SDys SEle SPin SPoG WPGP
	'Ultra Violet'	CWGN
	univerticillata	SPin
	urica	SPin
	- short	SDys
	'Valerie'	MPie SDys
	'Valle de Bravo'	SPin
	'Van-Houttei'	see *S. splendens* 'Van-Houttei'
	variana	SPin
	'Vatican City'	see *S. sclarea* 'Vatican White'
	vazquezii	SPin WOut
	verbenaca	MHer SPin WOut XSen
	- pink-flowered	WOut
	verticillata	EPfP LEdu NLar SPin WFar
§	- 'Alba'	CDor CRos EBee EMor EPfP GQue LRHS MRav NGdn NLar NRHS SPer SPin XSen
	- 'Hannay's Blue'	EPPr GMaP LPla MAvo SMHy SPhx WCAu WFar WHrl
	- 'Hannay's Purple'	ECtt EPPr
	- 'Purple Rain'	Widely available
	- 'Smouldering Torches'	EBee NDov SCob SPhx
	- 'White Rain'	see *S. verticillata* 'Alba'
	villicaulis	see *S. amplexicaulis*
	'Violin Music'PBR	CBod CRos CWGN EBee ECtt LRHS NRHS WTor
§	***virgata*** Jacq.	EBee SPin XSen
	- 'Alba' **new**	WHil
	viridis	CBod CHby MNHC SPin
	- 'Blue Denim' **new**	LOPS
	- Claryssa Series	SRms
§	- var. ***comata***	MCot
	- 'Marble Arch Blue' (Marble Arch Series)	CSpe
	viscosa ambig.	WArt
	viscosa Jacq.	SPin
	vitifolia	CSpe SDys WOut
	- B&SWJ 10236	SPin
	wagneriana	SPin
	'Waverly'	EAJP EBee EWld MAsh MHer MHol SDys SEle WOut

'Wendy's Wish'PBR CBod CRos EBee ECtt IPot LCro LRHS MAsh MAvo NDov NPri NRHS SCob SDys SPin SPoG SRkn SRms WGrn WNPC
× ***westerae*** SPin
- 'Petra' SDys
willeana SPin
yunnanensis SPin
aff. ***yunnanensis*** SPin

Salvinia (*Salviniaceae*)

natans CBen LLWG XBlo

Sambucus ✿ (*Adoxaceae*)

'Black Diamonds' NPri
caerulea see *S. nigra* subsp. *caerulea*
'Chocolate Marzipan' **new** WCot
coraensis see *S. williamsii* subsp. *coreana*
ebulus EBee EPPr LEdu NSti SMad WCot
formosana WCot
'Gate into Field' **new** WCot
* ***himalayensis*** WCot
mexicana B&SWJ 10349 WCot WCru
'Milk Chocolate' **new** SPad WCot
miquelii WCot
nigra CArg CBcs CCVT CDul CFGn CPer ECrN EPom GPoy LBuc NWea SEWo SPer SVic WMat WMou WSFF WTSh
- 'Albomarginata' see *S. nigra* 'Marginata'
- 'Ardwall' CAgr EPPr GBin GCal WCot
- 'Aurea' CBcs CDul CMac ELan EPom MMuc SPer WCot WMoo
- 'Aureomarginata' (v) ECrN ELan EPPr MMuc MRav SEND WCot WFar
- 'Bont Oosterwoldë' WCot
- 'Bradet' CAgr WCot WFar
- 'Broadway' (v) WCot
- 'Cae Rhos Lligwy' CAgr WCot WHer
§ - subsp. ***caerulea*** EBee WCot WPGP
- subsp. ***canadensis*** SPhx
- - 'Adams' (F) WCot
- - 'Aurea' NWea WCot
- - 'Johns' CAgr WCot
- - 'Maxima' SMad WCot
- - 'Rubra' WCot
- - 'York' (F) CAgr WCot
- 'Castledean' WCot
- 'Dart's Greenlace' WCot
- 'Dolomite' (v) WCot
- 'Donau' CAgr WCot
- 'Frances' (v) EPPr WCot
- 'Franzi' CAgr WCot
- 'Fructuluteo' WCot
- 'Godshill' (F) CAgr SDea WCot
- GOLDEN TOWER ('Jdeboer001') MMrt SPoG
- 'Haidegg 17' (F) CAgr
- 'Haschberg' CAgr WCot
- 'Heterophylla' see *S. nigra* 'Linearis'
- 'Hillier's Dwarf' WCot
- 'Ina' CAgr WCot
- 'Körsör' (F) WCot
- f. ***laciniata*** ♀H6 CBcs CDul CKel CRos EBee ELan EPPr EPfP GCal LRHS MBlu MMuc MRav NWea SLon SPer SPoG WCFE WCot WFar
§ - 'Linearis' MRav NLar WCot
- 'Long Tooth' CDul WCot
- 'Lutea Punctata' WCot WFar
- 'Madonna' (v) CBod LEdu LRHS MBlu MRav NLar NPol NQui SPer SPoG WAvo WCot
§ - 'Marginata' (v) CDul CMac MHer MRav WCot WFar
- 'Marion Bull' (v) CDul NLar WCot
I - 'Marmorata' NLar WCot
- 'Mint Julep' WCot
I - 'Monstrosa' WCot
- 'Nana' WCot
- 'Naomi' WCot
- 'Norfolk Speckled' (v) WCot
- 'Pingo Trail' WCot
- 'Plena' (d) WCot
- f. ***porphyrophylla*** 'Black Beauty' see *S. nigra* f. *porphyrophylla* 'Gerda'
- - 'Black Lace' see *S. nigra* f. *porphyrophylla* 'Eva'
- - BLACK TOWER ('Eiffel 1'PBR) Widely available
- - 'Blue Sheen' CRos EPfP GBin LRHS NRHS SCoo WCot
§ - - 'Eva'PBR ♀H6 Widely available
§ - - 'Gerda'PBR ♀H6 Widely available
§ - - 'Guincho Purple' CBcs CDul CKel CRos CTri EPPr EPfP LRHS MRav NLar NWea SPlb WCot WFar WMoo
- - 'Purple Pete' CDul WCot
- - 'Thundercloud' ♀H6 CDul ELon EWes GCal MAsh MNrw NEoE NLar SPhx WCot WFar WMoo
- 'Pulverulenta' (v) EPPr GCal MRav NLar NQui SPad SRms WCot WFar
- 'Purpurea' see *S. nigra* f. *porphyrophylla* 'Guincho Purple'
- 'Pyramidalis' MRav WCot
- 'Riese aus Vossloch' WCot
- 'Robert Piggin' (v) WCot
- var. ***rotundifolia*** WCot
- 'Sambu' (F) CAgr WCot
- 'Samdal' (F) CAgr WCot WFar
- 'Samidan' (F) CAgr WCot
- 'Samnor' (F) CAgr WCot
- 'Sampo' (F) CAgr WCot
- 'Samyl' (F) CAgr WCot
- 'Serenade' CRos EBee NEoE NRHS WCot
- 'Urban Lace' CAgr WCot
- 'Variegata' see *S. nigra* 'Marginata'
- f. ***viridis*** CAgr WCot
'Ocean Depths' GBin NEoE
palmensis WCot
racemosa EPfP GBin NWea WCot
- 'Altamont' WCot
- 'Aurea' EPfP WFar
- var. ***callicarpa*** WCot WFar
- 'Goldenlocks' EWes
- subsp. ***kamtschatica*** WCot
- LEMONY LACE ('Smnsrd4') **new** LRHS
- var. ***melanocarpa*** WCot
- 'Plumosa Aurea' CDul ELan EPfP MGos MJak MRav MSwo NLar NWea SRms WAvo WCot
- var. ***pubens*** WCot
§ - var. ***sieboldiana*** WCot
- 'Sutherland Gold' ♀H7 Widely available
- 'Tenuifolia' WCot
sieboldiana see *S. racemosa* var. *sieboldiana*
SUNNY DAYS ('Jonsun') CBod
tigranii WCot WFar
'Vermilion Summers' **new** WCot
WELSH GOLD ('Walfinb'PBR) CRos LRHS MAsh SPoG WCot
§ ***williamsii*** subsp. ***coreana*** WCot

Samolus (*Primulaceae*)

valerandi	LLWG

Sandersonia (*Colchicaceae*)

aurantiaca	CAvo EPot GKev LAma SDeJ

Sanguinaria (*Papaveraceae*)

canadensis	CAvo CBct CRos EPPr EPot GEdr GKev GPoy LAma LEdu LRHS MMuc NAln NHol NHpl NRHS NRya SEND SMHy SPer WAbe WPnP
- 'Jerry Flintoff'	GEdr
- f. ***multiplex*** (d)	CRos EPot IFro LRHS NBir NRHS SPhx
- - 'Plena' (d) ♀H5	CBct CRos CWCL EBee ECha ELon EMor EPfP GEdr GKev GPoy GQue LAma LRHS NHar NHol NHpl NRHS NRya NSla NSti SDeJ SPer WAbe WCot WFar WPnP XEll
- pink-flowered	GEdr
- 'Star'	GKev

Sanguisorba ✿ (*Rosaceae*)

from Japan	EBee MAvo
§ ***albiflora***	CKno EBee ELan EPfP EShb EWhm ILea LEdu LRHS MAvo MMuc MNrw MRav NDov NEoE NGdn SEND SPhx SRkn WCAu WMoo
'All Time High'	LEdu NDov
alpina	GLog MMuc SEND
'Ankum's Thums'	MTis
applanata	WCot
armena	CElw EBee EWes IMou MNrw MPie WWtn XEll
'Autumn Bliss'	EBee GMaP
'Autumn Red'	MAvo
'Beetlewings'	MAvo MTis
'Blacksmith's Burgundy'	LEdu
'Blackthorn'	CKno CMea EBee ECtt GMaP IKil LPla MAvo MBel MTis NDov NLar SMHy SPhx WCot WHoo
'Burr Blanc'	SMHy SPhx
canadensis	Widely available
- hybrid	MAvo
'Candy Floss' **new**	MAvo
'Cangshan Cranberry'	CSpe EBee ECtt GMaP IKil LPla MAvo MBel MHol NDov NSti SMHy WCot WWtn
* ***caucasica***	GBin LEdu SPhx
'Ccc'	MAvo
'Chocolate Tip'	CDor EBee ECtt EPPr IKil ILea IPot LRHS MAvo NGrd SPhx
'Coen's Cranberry'	NDov
dodecandra	EBee IPot MAvo MTis
'Foxtail'	MAvo
hakusanensis	CBod CKno CRos EBee EWhm GBin GCal GKev IFro IPot LEdu LRHS MAvo MMuc MNrw NAln NBir NBro NChi NDov NEoE NGBl NLar NRHS SPhx WArt WCAu WCot WFar WHoo
- B&SWJ 8709	WCru
- 'Lilac Squirrel'	CKno EBee ECtt GBee GMaP ILea IPot LEdu LRHS MAvo MBNS MBel MNrw MSCN MTis NDov NLar SMad SPhx WCAu WFar WTor
'Ivory Towers'	MAvo WFar
'John Coke'	EBee NLar
'Joni'	CKno MAvo
'Little Angel'	CAby CBct CKno CWGN EBee ECtt EMor EWhm MAvo MBNS MBel MHol NEoE SMad SPad SPoG WCot WFar WTor
magnifica	EWes GCal LEdu
- ***alba***	see *S. albiflora*
menziesii ♀H7	Widely available
- 'Dali Marble' (v)	EBee ECtt NLar WMoo
- 'Wake Up'	NDov
§ ***minor***	CAgr CCBP CHby CLau EBou EMor GPoy LEdu MHer MJak MNHC NMir NPol SCob SPhx SPlb SRms WHer WMoo XLum
- subsp. ***minor***	CHab
'Misbourne Pink'	LPla
'Miss Elly' **new**	MAvo
'Nettlesworth Wand'	SMHy SPhx
obtusa	Widely available
- 'Chatto'	MAvo NLar WPGP
- silver-leaved	MNrw SMHy WFar
- white-flowered	EBee EWTr GPSL MBel MTis WPGP
officinalis	CHab CKno CSpe EHoe GKev GQue MHer NAln NEoE NMir NPol SPer SPhx SRms WCAu WMoo WOut WTre
- CDC 262	EPPr LEdu SMHy SPhx
- CDC 282	CSpe SPhx
- CDC 292	MAvo WCot
- DJHC 535	LEdu
- from Mongolia	EBee
- 'Arnhem'	CDor CKno EBee ECtt EHrv EPPr ILea LEdu LRHS MTis NDov SMHy SPhx WCot
- 'Crimson Queen'	EBee ECtt GQue IPot MTis NLar
- dark-flowered	MAvo
- early-flowering	GMaP GWyn
- 'False Tanna'	WFar
- 'Lemon Splash' (v)	EBee ECtt LEdu MAvo MMrt WCot WFar WPGP
- 'Lum'	MAvo
- 'Martin's Mulberry'	EBee EWes GCal GMaP LEdu MAvo MNrw NDov
- 'Morning Select'	EBee ECtt EPPr GMaP NLar
- 'Red Buttons'	MAvo NDov
- 'Red Thunder'	CSpe EBee ECtt EPPr EWhm GMaP ILea IPot LCro LEdu LOPS LRHS MAvo MTis NDov NLar SMad WCAu WCot WGwG WPGP
- 'Shiro-fukurin' (v)	EBee ECtt EShb EWes EWhm GMaP IKil LEdu MBel MHol MNrw NLar WCot WFar WHer WSHC
- 'Tsetseguun'	LEdu LRHS MAvo SPhx WPGP
- 'White Tanna'	MBel
parviflora	see *S. tenuifolia* var. *parviflora*
pimpinella	see *S. minor*
'Pink Brushes'	CKno ECtt GBin GMaP GQue IKil ILea IMou IPot LRHS MAvo MBel MTis NGrd NLar SMad
'Pink September'	MAvo
'Pink Tanna'	Widely available
'Prim and Proper' **new**	MAvo
'Purple Tails'	MAvo MTis
'Raspberry Coulis'	MAvo
'Raspberry Mivvi'	MAvo SPhx
'Red Busby' **new**	MAvo
'Rock and Roll'	EBee ECtt EMor EPPr MBNS MTis NLar WOut
'Sangria'	MAvo
'Scapino'	MAvo
sitchensis	see *S. stipulata*

§	***stipulata***	CMac CRos EBee GCal LEdu LPla LRHS MHer MNrw NRHS
	- var. ***riishirensis***	EMor EPPr MNrw
	'Sussex Prairies Navaho' new	SPhx
	'Tanna' ♀H7	Widely available
	tenuifolia	CRos EHrv GCal IFro LRHS NChi NGBl NGrd NLar NRHS SPhx WCot
	- from Ernst Pagels	MAvo
	- var. ***alba***	Widely available
	- - CDC	GCal MRav
	- - 'Korean Snow'	GMaP LEdu LRHS SMHy SPhx SSut
	- 'Big Pink'	MAvo MNrw WFar WOut
	- 'Bordeaux'	EBee ECtt MAvo
	- 'Henk Gerritsen'	MAvo NLar WFar
§	- var. ***parviflora***	EBee LEdu MAvo NLar WPGP
	- 'Pieters'	ILea MAvo
	- 'Pink Elephant'	CKno EBee ECtt EMor EPPr EWhm GJos GMaP GQue ILea LEdu LRHS MAvo MBel MTis NLar SMad WCAu WFar WMoo
	- pink-flowered	SMHy
	- var. ***purpurea***	EBee GBin
	- 'Purpurea'	CKno EBee EPPr GQue ILea LEdu MAvo MTis SPhx WCAu WCot WPGP
	- 'Stand Up Comedian'	IMou LEdu MAvo NDov NLar WPGP
	- 'Strawberry Frost'	MAvo
	- 'Strawberry Fruli'	LEdu WPGP
	- 'Sturdy Guard'	LEdu
	- 'The Invisible'	MAvo WCAu
	- 'White Tanna'	EBee EPPr GQue LEdu MAvo MTis

Sanicula (*Apiaceae*)

europaea	CEls EMor GPoy IMou NGrd

Sansevieria (*Asparagaceae*)

bacularis 'Mikado'	LCro LOPS
cylindrica	ELan EShb
trifasciata 'Golden Hahnii' (v) ♀H1b	EShb
- 'Hahnii' ♀H1b	EShb
- var. ***laurentii*** (v) ♀H1b	LCro LOPS
- 'Moonshine' ♀H1b	EShb

Santolina ✿ (*Asteraceae*)

	sp.	CPla
	'Apple Court'	CRos LRHS
§	***chamaecyparissus***	Widely available
	- var. ***corsica*** misapplied	see *S. chamaecyparissus* 'Nana'
	- subsp. ***insularis***	XSen
	- 'Lambrook Silver'	CBod CFis CKel CRos EBee ECtt ENfk EPfP LRHS MAsh NLar NRHS SCoo XSen
	- 'Lemon Queen'	CRos ENfk EPfP EWTr EWhm LRHS MAsh MSwo NBir NLar NRHS SRms XSen
	- subsp. ***magonica***	XSen
§	- 'Nana' ♀H5	CRos EPfP LRHS MAsh MHer MRav MSwo SCob SRms XSen
	- 'Pretty Carroll' ♀H5	CBod CKel CRos EBee EBou EBtc ELan EPfP LRHS LSRN MAsh NLar SPoG WFar
	- 'Small-Ness'	CSma ELan EPfP EWes MHer NLar SWvt WHer XSen
	etrusca new	XSen
	incana	see *S. chamaecyparissus*
*	***lindavica***	XSen
	pinnata	CTri
§	- subsp. ***neapolitana*** ♀H5	ECha ELan ENfk EPfP MRav SEND
	- - cream-flowered	see *S. pinnata* subsp. *neapolitana* 'Edward Bowles'
§	- - 'Edward Bowles'	CBod CRos EBee EHoe EPfP EWhm GMaP LRHS LSRN MAvo MHer MNHC MRav MSwo NBir NLar NPer SCob SPoG SRms SVen SWvt WCFE WHer WHoo XSen
	- - 'Sulphurea'	CKel CRos EPfP LRHS MAsh SPer SPhx WKif XSen
	rosmarinifolia	CBod CRos GPoy LRHS LSun MRav NRHS SCob SEND SLon SPlb SRms WHoo
	- 'Green Fizz'	WFar
	- 'Lemon Fizz' ♀H5	CBod CPla CRos EBee ECrN EHoe ELan ELon ENfk EPfP GMaP LRHS MAsh MAvo MHer NBir NLar NRHS SCob SCoo SPer SPoG SRms SWvt WFar WHer XSen
§	- subsp. ***rosmarinifolia***	ECha ELan ENfk EPfP MHer MRav SCob SIgm SPer SRms SWvt WFar WGwG WKif XLum XSen
	- - 'Primrose Gem' ♀H5	CBcs CBod CKel CTri EAJP ECha EPfP LRHS MAsh MAvo MNHC MSwo NRHS SCob SEND SGbt SPer SRms SWvt XSen
	- - white-flowered	WHer
	SHADES OF JADE ('Sant101')	ECrN SRms
	tomentosa misapplied	see *S. pinnata* subsp. *neapolitana*
	virens	see *S. rosmarinifolia* subsp. *rosmarinifolia*
	viridis	see *S. rosmarinifolia* subsp. *rosmarinifolia*

Sanvitalia (*Asteraceae*)

AZTEKENGOLD	see *Melampodium montanum* AZTEC GOLD
procumbens misapplied	see *Melampodium montanum*

Sapindus (*Sapindaceae*)

mukorossi B&SWJ 14689 new	WCru

Saponaria (*Caryophyllaceae*)

	sp.	EWhm
	'Bressingham' ♀H5	CMea ECtt EPfP EPot GCrg MHol WAbe WIce
	Bressingham hybrid	MAsh
	caespitosa	EPot EWes
§	***intermedia***	NDov WCot
	× ***lempergii*** 'Fritz Lemperg'	NDov WCot
	- 'Max Frei'	CSam EBee ECtt ELon EMor EPPr LCro LOPS LPla MCot MRav NDov SBch SPhx WCot WOld XLum
	ocymoides ♀H5	CMea EBee ECha ECtt ELan EPfP MAsh MHol MNHC NHic NHpl NSla SEND SIgm SPlb SPoG SRms SRot WRHF XLum
	- 'Alba'	ECha NSla
	- 'Snow Tip'	NGdn WRHF
	officinalis	CBod CBre CCBP EMor ENfk GBin GPoy MHer MNHC SPlb SRms WHer WMoo WPtf WSFF
	- 'Alba'	CSam
	- 'Alba Plena' (d)	CBre MMuc NLar SEND WCAu WFar XLum
	- 'Betty Arnold' (d)	CAby EBee ECtt EMor EPPr EWes MHer WCot WGob WJam
	- 'Flore Pleno' (d)	CBod WOut
	- 'Red Splash' new	WFar

- 'Rosea Plena' (d)	CAby CBre CMac ELan EPfP LEdu MHer MMuc NBid NBir NGdn SCob SEND SPer WFar WGwG WMoo
- 'Rubra Plena' (d)	ELan EPPr EWes MMuc
× ***olivana*** ♀H5	CPBP ECtt GCrg GMaP MAsh NLar XLum
'Rosenteppich'	CPBP
sicula subsp. ***intermedia***	see *S. intermedia*
* × ***sundermannii***	CPBP
zawadskii	see *Silene zawadskii*

Saposhnikovia (*Apiaceae*)

divaricata	SPhx

Saracha (*Solanaceae*)

quitensis B&SWJ new	WCru

Sarcococca ✿ (*Buxaceae*)

confusa ♀H5	Widely available
hookeriana	ELon GKin LSRN MBlu MSwo NLar NWad SCob SGbt SWvt WFar WPGP WSpi
- B&SWJ 2585	WCru
- HWJK 2393	WCru
- HWJK 2428	WCru
- 'Daman'	CExl
- var. ***digyna***	Widely available
- - SDR 7816	GKev
- - 'Purple Stem' ♀H5	CBcs CBod CEnd CExl CJun CKel CTri EPfP EUJe GKin LCro LOPS LRHS MGos MNrw NLar SCob SCoo SPoG SRkn SWvt WCru WSpi
- - 'Schillingii'	see *S. hookeriana* var. *digyna* 'Tony Schilling'
§ - - 'Tony Schilling'	CExl CJun WCru
- var. ***hookeriana***	CJun LSRN
- - GWJ 9222	WCru
- - GWJ 9344	WCru
- - GWJ 9369	WCru
- - HWJK 2102	WCru
- - HWJK 2366	WCru
- - HWJK 2393	WCru
- - 'Ghorepani' ♀H5	CRos LCro LOPS LRHS NRHS
- var. ***humilis***	Widely available
- WINTER GEM ('Pmoore03'PBR)	CKel CRos CSBt EPfP LCro LOPS LRHS LSRN MAsh MGos MSwo NHol NRHS SLon SPoG SRkn WFar WGrn
orientalis	CBct CExl CJun CMCN CRos EBee ELan ELon EPfP IMou LEdu LRHS MAsh NLar NRHS NWad SPoG WPGP WSpi
'Roy Lancaster'	see *S. ruscifolia* var. *chinensis* 'Dragon Gate'
'Rudolph'	EPfP LLHF LRHS
ruscifolia	Widely available
- var. ***chinensis***	CJun NLar SLon WCru WPGP
§ - - 'Dragon Gate' ♀H5	CExl CJun CKel CRos EBee ELan ELon EPfP LEdu LLHF LRHS LSRN MAsh MGos NRHS SLon SPoG SWvt WCru WPGP WSpi
saligna	CBcs CJun EBee ELan EPfP LRHS MRav SLon WCru
- HWJK 2428	WCru
- MF P2056	WCru
- NJM 12.043 new	WPGP
I ***taiwaniana*** RWJ 9999	WCru
trinervia B&SWJ 9500	WCru
vagans B&SWJ 7285	WCru
- B&SWJ 9760 from Vietnam	WCru
- B&SWJ 9766 from Vietnam	WCru
aff. ***vagans*** B&SWJ 7265 from north Thailand	WCru
wallichii	CBcs CBod CExl ELon EWTr LEdu MBlu SPoG WPGP
- B&SWJ 2291	CJun WCru
- GWJ 9427	WCru
- HWJK 2425	WCru
- HWJK 2428	WCru
- PAB 13.077	LEdu
aff. ***wallichii*** NJM 12.043 new	WPGP
zeylanica B&SWJ 10199	WCru
- var. ***brevifolia*** GWJ 9480	WCru
- - GWJ 9483	WCru

Sarcopoterium (*Rosaceae*)

spinosum	SPhx SVen

Sarmienta (*Gesneriaceae*)

repens ♀H1c	CExl WAbe

Sarothamnus see *Cytisus*

Sarracenia ✿ (*Sarraceniaceae*)

sp.	CPla
× ***ahlesii***	CHew
alata	CHew EECP SHmp WSSs
- all green	SHmp
- 'Black Tube' ♀H3	WSSs
- heavily-veined	SHmp WSSs
- var. ***nigropurpurea***	WSSs
- var. ***ornata***	WSSs
- pubescent	EECP WSSs
- 'Red Lid'	EECP WSSs
- 'Red Lid' × ***flava*** red pitcher	EECP
- var. ***rubrioperculata***	WSSs
- wavy lid	SHmp WSSs
- white-flowered	WSSs
alata × ***flava*** var. ***maxima***	WSSs
× ***areolata***	CHew WSSs
× ***catesbaei***	CHew SHmp WSSs
- 'Johnny Marr'	SHmp
× ***courtii***	SHmp
'Eva' ♀H3	SHmp WSSs
× ***excellens***	WSSs
× ***exornata***	SPlb SRms
'Fiona'	SHmp
flava	LCro LOPS WSSs WTyc
- all green giant	see *S. flava* var. *maxima*
- var. ***atropurpurea***	EECP SHmp WSSs
- 'Claret'	WSSs
- var. ***cuprea***	SHmp WSSs
- var. ***flava***	CHew EECP WSSs
§ - var. ***maxima***	CHew EECP SHmp WSSs
- var. ***ornata***	CHew EECP SHmp WSSs
- var. ***rubricorpora***	CHew EECP SHmp SPlb WSSs
- - 'Burgundy'	WSSs
- var. ***rugelii***	CHew EECP SHmp SPlb WSSs
'Jedi' new	WTyc
leucophylla	CHew SHmp SPlb SRms WSSs WTyc
- from Okaloosa Co., Florida	SHmp
- var. ***alba***	WSSs
- 'Deer Park Alabama'	SHmp
- green	WSSs
- green and white	WSSs
- pubescent	WSSs
- - from Deer Park, Alabama	SHmp

	- 'Schnell's Ghost' ♀H3	SHmp WSSs
	- 'Tarnok'	WSSs
	- f. ***viridescens***	WSSs
	leucophylla × ***oreophila***	EECP
	leucophylla × (× ***popei***)	EECP
	'Lynda Butt' ♀H3	SHmp WSSs
	× ***miniata***	EECP SHmp WSSs
	minor	EECP SHmp WSSs
	- var. ***minor***	CHew
§	- 'Okee Giant'	WSSs
	- 'Okefenokee Giant'	see *S. minor* 'Okee Giant'
	- var. ***okefenokeensis***	CHew WSSs
	× ***mitchelliana***	SHmp WSSs
	- 'Juthatip Soper' ♀H3	SHmp WSSs
	- 'Rita Soper' ♀H3	SHmp
	× ***moorei***	CHew SHmp WSSs
	- 'Adrian Slack'	WSSs
	- 'Brooks's Hybrid' ♀H4	CHew EECP WSSs
	- 'Leah Wilkerson'	WSSs
	oreophila	CHew SHmp SPlb WSSs
	× ***popei***	WSSs
	psittacina	CHew EECP SHmp SRms WSSs
	purpurea	SPlb WTyc
	- subsp. ***purpurea*** ♀H6	CHew SHmp WSSs
	- - f. ***heterophylla*** ♀H6	WSSs
	- subsp. ***venosa***	CHew SHmp SPlb WSSs
	- - var. ***burkii*** ♀H3	SHmp WSSs
	× ***readei***	EECP SHmp WSSs
	× ***rehderi***	SHmp WSSs
	rubra	EECP WSSs
	- subsp. ***alabamensis*** ♀H3	CHew SHmp WSSs
	- subsp. ***gulfensis***	CHew SHmp WSSs
*	- - f. ***heterophylla***	WSSs
	- subsp. ***jonesii***	EECP SHmp WSSs
*	- - f. ***heterophylla***	WSSs
	- subsp. ***rubra***	CHew SHmp WSSs
	- subsp. ***wherryi***	CHew EECP WSSs
	- - giant	WSSs
	- - yellow-flowered	WSSs
	× ***swaniana***	SHmp SRms
	'Tara' **new**	WTyc
	'Vogel' ♀H3	SHmp WSSs
	× ***wrigleyana***	SRms WTyc

Saruma (*Aristolochiaceae*)

	henryi	CAby CPla EMor ESwi EWld GEdr GKev GLog LEdu LPla SBrt WCot WCru WFar

Sasa (*Poaceae*)

	disticha 'Mirrezuzume'	see *Pleioblastus pygmaeus* 'Mirrezuzume'
	glabra f. ***albostriata***	see *Sasaella masamuneana* 'Albostriata'
	kurilensis	MWht XCre
§	- 'Shima-shimofuri' (v)	ERod EShb
	- 'Shimofuri'	see *S. kurilensis* 'Shima-shimofuri'
	nana	see *S. veitchii* f. *minor*
§	***palmata***	LCro LOPS MMuc SArc XCre
	- f. ***nebulosa***	CBcs ENBC MWht NLar SArc WMoo XCre
	- var. ***niijimae***	MWht
*	***seikoana*** **new**	XCre
	tessellata	see *Indocalamus tessellatus*
	tsuboiana	CBcs MJak MWht NLar SGol WMoo XCre
§	***veitchii***	CBcs EHoe ENBC GQue MJak MMuc MRav MWht NLar SCob SGol WFar WMoo XCre
§	- f. ***minor***	MMuc WMoo

Sasaella (*Poaceae*)

§	***masamuneana***	CAco ENBC ERod LEdu MMuc
	'Albostriata' (v)	MWht WMoo XCre
§	***ramosa***	GBin MWht XCre

Sassafras (*Lauraceae*)

	albidum	CBcs CMCN CRos ELan EPfP LRHS MAsh NLar SLon SPoG WPGP

satsuma see *Citrus reticulata*

Satureja ✿ (*Lamiaceae*)

	biflora	WJek
	coerulea ♀H5	EWes XSen
	douglasii	CBod WJek
	- 'Indian Mint'PBR	ENfk MHer SRms
	hortensis	CBod CLau ENfk LCro LOPS MHer MNHC SRms SVic WJek
	intricata	XSen
	montana	CCBP CHby CLau EBou ELan ENfk EWhm GPoy MHer MNHC NGrd SEND SRms SVic WJek XSen
	- 'Aromakugel' **new**	IMou
*	- ***citriodora***	GPoy MHer XSen
§	- subsp. ***illyrica***	SPhx WJek XLum XSen
	- 'Purple Mountain'	GPoy MHer
	- ***subspicata***	see *S. montana* subsp. *illyrica*
	repanda	see *S. spicigera*
§	***spicigera***	CBod EBou ENfk EPot EWhm IMou LEdu MHer MMuc SPhx SRms WJek XLum XSen
*	- 'Prostrata'	CLau
	thymbra	SPhx SRms

Sauromatum (*Araceae*)

	gaoligongense	WCot
	giganteum	GKev
	guttatum	see *S. venosum*
§	***venosum***	CExl CRos EBee EPfP EShb GKev LAma LEdu LRHS NRHS SPlb WCot XLum

Saururus (*Saururaceae*)

	cernuus	CBen CBod CWat ELan LLWG WMAq WWtn XLum
	- 'Hertford Streaker' (v)	WCot
	chinensis	LLWG SBrt

Saussurea (*Asteraceae*)

	costus	GPoy
	leucophylla	GKev
	pseudoalpina	WCot

savory, summer see *Satureja hortensis*

savory, winter see *Satureja montana*

Saxegothaea ✿ (*Podocarpaceae*)

	conspicua	CBcs IDee NLar
	- weeping	WPGP

Saxifraga ✿ (*Saxifragaceae*)

	JJH 9309174	NMen
	acerifolia (5)	GCal GEdr
§	'Afrodite' (*sempervivum*) (7)	WAbe
	aizoides (9)	GKev
	- var. ***atrorubens*** (9)	EBou
	aizoon	see *S. paniculata* subsp. *paniculata*

Plant	Suppliers
'Akibare' (*fortunei*) (5) **new**	GEdr
× ***akinfievii*** (7)	NMen
'Aladdin' (× *borisii*) (7)	NMen
'Alan Hayhurst' (8)	CPBP NSla WAbe
'Alan Martin' (× *boydilacina*) (7)	EPot EWes
'Alba' ambig.	CRos LRHS NRHS
'Alba' (× *apiculata*) (7) ♀H5	MAsh NMen NRya SIgm SPlb
'Alba' (*oppositifolia*) (7)	ELan EWes GCrg ITim NWad WAbe
'Albert Einstein' (× *apiculata*) (7) ♀H5	NMen
'Albertii' (*callosa*)	see *S.* 'Albida'
§ 'Albida' (*callosa*) (8)	NWad WAbe
'Albrecht Dürer' (Lasciva Group) (7)	NMen
'Aldo Bacci' (Milford Group) (7)	NMen NSla
'Alfons Mucha' (7)	EPot
'Allendale Acclaim' (× *lismorensis*) (7)	NMen
'Allendale Accord' (7)	EPot NMen
'Allendale Andante' (× *arco-valleyi*) (7)	NMen
'Allendale Angel' (× *kepleri*) (7)	NMen
'Allendale Argonaut' (7)	CPBP NMen
'Allendale Ballad' (7)	NMen
'Allendale Bamby' (× *lismorensis*) (7)	EPot
'Allendale Banshee' (7)	NMen
'Allendale Baron' (7)	NMen
'Allendale Beau' (× *lismorensis*) (7)	CPBP
'Allendale Beauty' (7)	NMen WAbe
'Allendale Betty' (× *lismorensis*) (7)	EPot NMen
'Allendale Billows' (7)	NMen
'Allendale Bonny' (7)	EPot NSla WAbe
'Allendale Boon' (× *izari*) (7)	NMen
'Allendale Bounty' (7)	NMen
'Allendale Bravo' (× *lismorensis*) (7)	WHoo
'Allendale Cabal' (7)	NMen
'Allendale Carol' (7)	NMen
'Allendale Celt' (× *novacastelensis*) (7)	NMen
'Allendale Charm' (Swing Group) (7)	GKev ITim NMen WAbe WHoo WThu
'Allendale Chick' (7)	EPot
'Allendale Citation' (7)	NMen
'Allendale Czech' (7)	NMen
'Allendale Delight' (7)	NMen
'Allendale Desire' (7)	WAbe
'Allendale Divine' (7)	NMen
'Allendale Dream' (7)	EPot NMen
'Allendale Duo' (7)	NMen
'Allendale Eden' (7)	NMen
'Allendale Elegance' (7)	CPBP NMen WAbe
'Allendale Elf' (7)	EPot NMen WHoo
'Allendale Elite' (7)	NMen WAbe
'Allendale Enchantment' (7)	NMen
'Allendale Epic' (7)	NMen
'Allendale Fairy' (7)	WHoo
'Allendale Fame' (7)	NMen
'Allendale Fancy' (7)	NMen
'Allendale Frost' (7)	NMen WAbe
'Allendale Ghost' (7)	NMen
'Allendale Goblin' (7)	NMen
'Allendale Grace' (7)	NMen WAbe
'Allendale Host' (7)	NMen
'Allendale Ice' (7)	NMen
'Allendale Imp' (7)	NMen
'Allendale Ina' (7)	NMen
'Allendale Jinn' (7)	CPBP NMen NSla
'Allendale Jo' (7)	NMen WAbe
'Allendale Joy' (× *wendelacina*) (7)	NMen
'Allendale King' (7)	NMen
'Allendale News' (7)	NMen
'Allendale Noon' (7)	NMen
'Allendale Ruby' (7)	NMen
'Allendale Snow' (× *rayei*) (7)	EPot EWes NMen WAbe
'Alpenglow' (7)	NMen
alpigena (7)	WAbe
ALPINO EARLY LIME ('Sax20007') (15)	WFar
'Amberglow' (× *anglica*) (7)	NMen NSla
'Amberine' (× *anglica*) (7)	EPot WAbe WHoo
'Amedeo Modigliani' (7)	NMen
'Amerigo Vespucci' (Continent Group) (7)	NMen
'Andrea Cesalpino' (Renaissance Group) (7)	NMen
× ***andrewsii*** (8 × 11)	XLum
angustifolia Haw.	see *S. hypnoides*
'Anna' (× *fontanae*) (7)	EPot NSla
'Anne Beddall' (× *goringiana*) (7)	NMen
'Anneka Hope' (8)	GKev
'Antonín Dvořák' (× *arco-valleyi*) (7)	NMen
'Antonio Vivaldi' (7)	EPot NMen
'Aphrodite' (*sempervivum*)	see *S.* 'Afrodite'
× ***apiculata*** *sensu stricto* hort.	see *S.* 'Gregor Mendel'
× ***apiculata*** (7)	EBou MAsh SIgm
'Apple Blossom' (Mossy Group) (15)	ECtt NEoE NRya
'Arabella' (× *edithae*) (7)	NMen
'Aramis' (7)	NMen
§ 'Arco' (× *arco-valleyi*) (7)	EPot
× ***arco-valleyi*** *sensu stricto* hort.	see *S.* 'Arco'
× ***arendsii*** purple-flowered (15)	MMuc SPlb
'Arleta' (Southside Seedling Group) (8) **new**	WIce
'Artemis' (× *megaseiflora*) (7)	NMen
'Arthur' (× *anglica*) (7)	NMen
'Assimilis' (× *petraschii*) (7)	EPot NMen
'Athena' (7)	NMen
'Atropurpurea' (*paniculata* subsp. *cartilaginea*) (8)	GMaP NHol NSla WHoo WIce XLum
'Audrey Lowe' (*oppositifolia*) (7) **new**	WAbe
'August Hayek' (× *leyboldii*) (7)	NMen
'Auguste Renoir' (Decora Group) (7)	NSla
'Aurea Maculata' (*cuneifolia*)	see *S.* 'Aureopunctata'
'Aurea' (*umbrosa*)	see *S.* 'Aureopunctata'
§ 'Aureopunctata' (× *urbium*) (11/v)	CMac CRos CTri ECha ELan EPfP GAbr GKev GMaP LEdu LRHS MHer MPnt MRav NRHS SPer SPlb SPoG SRms WFar WMoo XLum
'Autumn Tribute' (*fortunei*) (5)	GEdr WAbe
'Ayako' (*fortunei*) (5)	GEdr

'Ayer's Rock' (7) WAbe
'Balcana' (*paniculata*) (8) EPot NSla WAbe
'Baldensis' see *S. paniculata* var. *minutifolia*
'Beatles' (Beat Group) (7) EPot NSla
§ 'Beatrix Stanley' (× *angelica*) (7) CRos LRHS MAsh NMen NRHS NWad
'Becky Foster' (× *borisii*) (7) EPot
'Bedřich Smetana' (*marginata*) (7) NMen
'Beinn Eighe' (× *concinna*) (7) NMen
'Beinne Alligin' (× *concinna*) (7) NMen
'Ben Loyal' (× *concinna*) (7) NMen WAbe
'Beni-karen' (*fortunei*) (5) **new** GEdr
'Beni-kirin' (*fortunei*) (5) **new** GEdr
'Beni-zakura' (*fortunei*) (5) **new** GEdr
'Benimine' (*fortunei*) (5) **new** GEdr
'Beni-tsukaji' (*fortunei*) (5) **new** NBro SHeu
'Beni-tsukasa' (*fortunei*) (5) ECtt GEdr NHar NHpl
'Berenika' (× *bertolonii*) (7) EPot
'Berounka' (Prominent Group) (7) NMen
'Bertramka' (× *megaseiflora*) (Holenka's Miracle Group) (7) NMen
'Beryl Bland' (Sugestivo Group) (7) WAbe
'Bettina' (× *paulinae*) (7) NMen
× ***biasolettoi*** *sensu stricto* hort. see *S.* 'Phoenix'
× ***biasolettoi*** Sünd. CRos LRHS NRHS
'Birch Yellow' see *S.* 'Pseudoborisii'
'Bizourtouse' (× *luteopurpurea*) (7) NSla
'Black Beauty' (15) ECtt GCrg MHer NWad
BLACK RUBY (*fortunei*) (5) Widely available
'Blackberry and Apple Pie' (*fortunei*) (5) 𝕐H4 CExl CRos ECtt EPfP GEdr LRHS NRHS SBch SWvt WMoo
'Blush' (*fortunei*) (5) LLHF
'Bob Hawkins' (Mossy Group) (15/v) NHol NWad
'Bohdalec' (× *megaseiflora*) (7) NMen
'Bohemia' (7) EPot NSla WAbe
'Bohemian Karst' (Prominent Group) (7) NMen
'Bohemian Paradise' (Region Group) (7) NMen
'Bohnice' (× *megaseiflora*) (7) NMen
'Bohunka' (7) NMen
× ***borisii*** *sensu stricto* hort. see *S.* 'Sofia'
'Boston Spa' (× *elisabethae*) (7) CRos ECtt GCrg LRHS MAsh MHer NLar NRHS NWad SPlb
'Boží Dar' (Sessile Group) (7) EPot
'Brailes' (× *poluanglica*) (7) NMen
'Brian Arundel' (Magnus Group) (7) NMen
'Bridget' (× *edithae*) (7) CMea CRos LRHS NRHS
'Brno' (× *elisabethae*) (7) EPot NMen
'Brookside' (*burseriana*) (7) EPot
brunoniana see *S. brunonis*
§ ***brunonis*** (1) GKev
'Bryn Llwyd' (Vanessa Group) (7) NMen WAbe
× ***burnatii*** (8) CRos LRHS NRHS NSla
burseriana (7) NMen WAbe
'Buster' (× *hardingii*) (7) EPot NMen
'Bychan' (*fortunei*) (5) WAbe
'Bürgel' (× *poluanglica*) (7) NAln
× ***caesia*** misapplied (× *fritschiana*) see *S.* 'Krain'
× ***caesia*** L. (8) SRms WAbe
§ ***callosa*** (8) 𝕐H5 CPla CRos EDAr GKev LRHS MHer MMuc NRHS SEND WAbe
§ - subsp. ***catalaunica*** (8) WAbe
- ***lingulata*** see *S. callosa*
'Candy Floss' (7) NMen
× ***canis-dalmatica*** see *S.* 'Canis-dalmatica'
§ 'Canis-dalmatica' (× *gaudinii*) (8) CRos EBou ECtt EPot GAbr GCrg GJos GQue LRHS NAln NRHS NWad SIgm WTor
§ 'Carmen' (× *elisabethae*) (7) WAbe
'Carniolica' (× *engleri*) (8) WAbe
§ 'Carniolica' (*paniculata*) (8) NBro NHol NWad WOld
carolinica see *S.* 'Carniolica' (*paniculata*)
cartilaginea see *S. paniculata* subsp. *cartilaginea*
'Castor' (× *bilekii*) (7) NMen
catalaunica see *S. callosa* subsp. *catalaunica*
'Cathy Read' (× *polulacina*) (7) NMen
cebennensis (15) CPla EPot NRya
- dwarf (15) WAbe
'Celebration' WAbe
cespitosa (15) WAbe
'Chambers' Pink Pride' see *S.* 'Miss Chambers'
'Charles Chaplin' (7) EPot NMen
'Charles Darwin' (7) NMen
CHEAP CONFECTIONS (*fortunei*) (5) ECtt GEdr LLHF MMrt MPnt NLar SBch SPoG WAul WBor WFar WMoo WOld
CHERRY PIE (*fortunei*) (5) GEdr LLHF NBir NHpl
'Cherrytrees' (× *boydii*) (7) NMen
'Chodov' (× *megaseiflora*) (Holenka's Miracle Group) (7) EPot NMen
cinerea (7) WAbe
- McB 1376 NWad
'Citronella' (7) NMen
'Claire Felstead' (7) WAbe
'Clare' (× *anglica*) (7) NHol
* 'Clare' (*paniculata*) (8) NSla
§ 'Clarence Elliott' (*umbrosa*) (London Pride Group) (11) 𝕐H5 CTri EBou ECtt EWTr EWes GBin GCal GJos GKev GMaP LSun MHer NDov NLar NRya NWad WIce
'Claude Monet' (Impressio Group) (7) CPBP NMen
'Cleo' (× *boydii*) (7) NMen
'Cloth of Gold' (*exarata* subsp. *moschata*) (15) CRos ECha ECtt ELan EPfP GCrg GWyn LRHS MAsh NEoE NHol NHpl NRHS NRya NSla NWad SPlb SPoG SRms WAbe WIce
cochlearis (8) CRos CTri LRHS MAsh NBro NRHS NSla SIgm WAbe
- hybrid (8) **new** MAsh
'Cockscomb' (*paniculata*) (8) ECtt EPot NLar NWad WAbe
columnaris × ***juniperifolia*** (7) NMen
'Combrook' (× *poluanglica*) (7) NMen
'Conwy Snow' (*fortunei*) (5) 𝕐H4 WAbe WFar WMoo

'Conwy Star' (*fortunei*) (5) — GEdr WAbe WFar
'Coolock Gem' (7) — NMen WAbe WHoo
'Coolock Jean' (7) — WAbe
'Coolock Kate' (7) ♀H5 — NSla WAbe WHoo
'Corennie Claret' — see *S.* 'Glowing Ember'
'Corona' (× *boydii*) (7) — NMen
* × ***correvensis*** — EBou GWyn
'Correvoniana' misapplied — see *S.* 'Lagraveana'
'Correvoniana' Farrer (*paniculata*) (8) — EDAr MHer MMuc SEND XLum
cortusifolia var. ***stolonifera*** (5) — CBct GCal XLum
COTTON CROCHET (*fortunei*) (5/d) — ECtt GEdr NBro SHeu WBor WFar WMoo WOld
cotyledon (8) — CRos LEdu LRHS NRHS WAbe WCFE
§ 'Cranbourne' (× *anglica*) (7) ♀H5 — CMea CRos GCrg LRHS MAsh NMen NRHS NSla WAbe
'Cream Seedling' (× *elisabethae*) (7) — NMen
'Crenata' (*burseriana*) (7) ♀H5 — CRos LRHS NRHS
'Crimscote-love' (*poluanglica*) (7) — EPot NMen
'Crimson Rose' (*paniculata*) — see *S.* 'Rosea' (*paniculata*)
'Crinoline' (7) — NMen NSla WAbe
§ ***crustata*** (8) — CPBP WAbe WThu XLum
- var. ***vochinensis*** — see *S. crustata*
CRYSTAL PINK (*fortunei*) (5/v) — CExl EBee ECtt EMor MBNS MHol NHpl WCot WFar
'Crystalie' (× *biasolettoi*) (7) — CRos LRHS NRHS
'Cultrata' (*paniculata*) (8) — NBro
'Cumulus' (7) ♀H5 — EPot NMen SIgm
§ ***cuneifolia*** (11) — IMou MHer NWad WMoo XLum
- var. ***capillipes*** — see *S. cuneifolia* subsp. *cuneifolia*
§ - subsp. ***cuneifolia*** (11) — ECtt GJos
'Cuscutiformis' (*stolonifera*) (5) — CAby CElw CExl EWld GEdr MAvo MBel MSCN SBch SRms WBor XLum
dahurica — see *S. cuneifolia*
'Dainty Dame' (× *arco-valleyi*) (7) — CRos ECtt LRHS NRHS
'Dana' (× *megaseiflora*) (Prichard's Monument Group) (7) — EPot NMen
'Darcie's Cross' **new** — EDAr
'David' (7) — NMen
'Dawn Frost' (7) — EPot NMen WIce
'Delia' (× *hornibrookii*) (7) — EPot
'Demeter' (× *petraschii*) (7) — NMen
§ 'Dentata' (× *polita*) (London Pride Group) (11) — ECha GCal LPot MPnt SMHy WBor WMoo
'Dentata' (× *urbium*) — see *S.* 'Dentata' (× *polita*)
I 'Diana' (× *lincolni-fosteri*) (7) — NMen WIce
diapensioides (7) — NSla WAbe
dinnikii (7) — WAbe
× ***dinninaris*** (7) — NSla
'Dobruška' (× *irvingii*) (7) — NMen
'Doctor Clay' (*paniculata*) (8) — CRos ECtt EPot GCrg GKev LRHS NHol NRHS NRya NSla SPlb WAbe
'Doctor Ramsey' (8) — CRos EWes LRHS NRHS NWad WAbe
'Doctor Watson' (7) — EPot
'Donald Mann' (15) — EWes
'Donatello' (7) — NMen
'Donnington Chalice' (7) — NMen
'Donnington Gold' (7) — NMen
'Dora Ross' (× *baccii*) (7) — NMen
'Drakula' (*ferdinandi-coburgi*) (7) — CPBP CRos LRHS NMen NRHS NSla
'Dulcimer' (× *petraschii*) (7) — NMen
'Earl Grey' (8) **new** — NSla
'Edgar Irmscher' (7) — NMen
'Edith' (× *edithae*) (7) — CRos LRHS NMen NRHS
'Eiga' (*fortunei*) (5) **new** — GEdr
'Elf' (7) — see *S.* 'Beatrix Stanley'
'Elf' (*exarata* subsp. *moschata*) (15) — ECtt MAsh SIgm SRms
'Elf Rose' (15) — CRos EPfP LRHS NEoE NRHS
'Eliot Hodgkin' (× *millstreamiana*) (7) — NMen
× ***elisabethae*** *sensu stricto* hort. — see *S.* 'Carmen'
'Elizabeth Sinclair' (× *elisabethae*) (7) — GKev
'Elliott's Variety' — see *S.* 'Clarence Elliott' (*umbrosa*)
'Emil Holub' (Ethography Group) (7) — EPot NMen
epiphylla BWJ 8177 (5) — WCru
§ 'Ernst Heinrich' (× *heinrichii*) (7) — NMen
'Esther' (× *burnatii*) (8) — CMea CRos EBou ECtt GMaP LRHS NRHS NSla WAbe WHoo
§ 'Eulenspiegel' (× *geuderi*) (7) — EPot NWad
'Eva Hanzliková' (× *izari*) (7) — EPot
'Excellent' (Exclusive Group) (7) — CPBP EPot NSla
'Exhibit' (Exclusive Group) (7) — NMen
fair maids of France — see *S.* 'Flore Pleno'
'Fairy' (*exarata* subsp. *moschata*) (15) — ECtt NBir NEoE
'Faldonside' (× *boydii*) (7) — MAsh WAbe
'Falstaff' (*burseriana*) (7) — NMen WAbe
× ***farreri*** (15) — WIce
× ***farreri*** hort. — see *S.* 'Reginald Farrer'
'Favorit' (× *bilekii*) (7) — NMen
§ ***federici-augusti*** subsp. ***grisebachii*** (7) ♀H5 — CRos GCrg GKev LRHS NRHS NSla WAbe WFar
'Felicity' (× *anglica*) (7) — NMen
ferdinandi-coburgi (7) — ECtt NSla WAbe
§ - subsp. ***chrysosplenifolia*** var. ***rhodopea*** (7) — CRos LRHS NRHS
- var. ***pravislavii*** — see *S. ferdinandi-coburgi* subsp. *chrysosplenifolia* var. *rhodopea*
- var. ***radoslavoffii*** — see *S. ferdinandi-coburgi* subsp. *chrysosplenifolia* var. *rhodopea*
'Findling' (Mossy Group) (15) — ECtt EPfP GCrg NWad SPoG WAbe
'Firebrand' (× *kochii*) (7) — WAbe
FIVE COLOR (*fortunei*) — see *S.* 'Go-nishiki'
'Flavescens' misapplied — see *S.* 'Lutea' (*paniculata*)
'Fleece' (15) — NHpl
§ 'Flore Pleno' (*granulata*) (15/d) — CElw EBee EWes NBir
'Flowers of Sulphur' — see *S.* 'Schwefelblüte'
fortunei (5) ♀H4 — CMac NBir SRms WAbe WFar
- B&SWJ 6346 — WCru
- f. ***alpina*** from Hokkaido (5) — WCru
- var. ***koraiensis*** B&SWJ 8688 (5) — WCru
- var. ***obtusocuneata*** (5) — GEdr GPSL LLHF WAbe
- f. ***partita*** (5) — WCru

	- var. ***pilosissima*** (5) B&SWJ 8557	WCru
	- pink-flowered (5)	WAbe
	'Forum' (× *megaseiflora*) (7)	NMen
	'Foster's Gold' (× *elisabethae*) (7)	NMen
	'Four Winds' (Mossy Group) (15)	EWes SPoG
	'Francesco Redi' (Renaissance Group) (7)	EPot
	'Francis Cade' (8)	EPot GAbr NSla WAbe
	'Franz Liszt' (7)	CPBP EPot NMen
	'Franzii' (× *paulinae*) (7)	NMen
	'Freckles'	GCrg GKev NHpl
	'Frederik Chopin' (7)	EPot
	'Friesei' (× *salmonica*) (7)	EPot NMen
	'Fumiko' (*fortunei*) (5)	WAbe
	'Funkii' (× *petraschii*) (7)	NMen
	'G.W. Gould No. 2' **new**	EPot
	'Gaiety' (15)	CRos ECtt LRHS NEoE NRHS SPoG
	'Galaxie' (× *megaseiflora*) (Holenka's Miracle Group) (7)	EPot NMen
	'Ganymede' (*burseriana*) (7)	EPot NMen
	× ***gaudinii*** (8)	XLum
	'Gelber Findling' (7)	EPot NMen SIgm
	'Gelbes Monster' (*fortunei*) (5)	EBee ECtt EMor GEdr MSCN NHpl WCot WFar
	'Gem' (× *irvingii*) (7)	CRos LRHS NRHS
	'Gemma' (× *megaseiflora*) (7)	CRos LRHS NRHS
	'Geoffrey Gould' (7)	NMen
	georgei (7)	EPot WAbe
	'Gertie Pritchard' (× *megaseiflora*)	see *S.* 'Mrs Gertie Prichard'
	× ***geuderi*** *sensu stricto* hort.	see *S.* 'Eulenspiegel'
§	× ***geum*** (11)	MRav WFar WMoo
	- Dixter form (11)	CElw ECha EWes LEdu NDov SMHy SPhx
	'Ginkgo' (*stolonifera*) (5) **new**	WFar
	'Gleborg' (Mossy Group) (15)	SPoG
	'Gloria' (*burseriana*) (7)	CRos EPot GCrg LRHS MAsh NMen NRHS NSla WIce
§	'Glowing Ember' (Mossy Group) (15)	ECtt EWes
	'Gokka' (*fortunei*) (5) **new**	NHar SHeu
	'Gold Dust' (× *eudoxiana*) (7)	GCrg NRya
	'Golden Eye' (× *poluanglica*) (7)	NMen
	'Golden Falls' (Mossy Group) (15/v)	EWes SPlb SPoG
	GOLDEN PRAGUE (× *pragensis*)	see *S.* 'Zlatá Praha'
	'Golem' (7)	CPBP
§	'Go-nishiki' (*fortunei*) (5)	GEdr
	'Gorges du Verdon' (8)	NAln
	'Goring White' (7)	NMen
	'Grace Farwell' (× *anglica*) (7)	NLar
	granulata (15)	EWes GJos NRHS
	'Gratoides' (× *grata*) (7)	EPot NMen
	'Grébovka' (× *megaseiflora*) (7)	NMen
	'Greensleeves' (*fortunei*) (5)	LLHF
§	'Gregor Mendel' (× *apiculata*) (7) ♀H5	CMea CRos ECtt LRHS NLar NRHS NSla NWad SIgm SRms WAbe WHoo
	'Gregor' (× *poluanglica*) (7)	NMen
	grisebachii	see *S. federici-augusti* subsp. *grisebachii*
	'Haagii' (× *eudoxiana*) (7)	CTri GKev
	'Hakubai' (*fortunei*) (5) **new**	GEdr
	'Hardii' (Mossy Group) (15) **new**	EBou
	'Hare Knoll Beauty' (8)	CRos EPot GCrg GKev LRHS NHol NHpl NRHS NSla WAbe WIce
	'Harlow Car' (× *anglica*) (7)	EPot NSla
	'Harlow Car' × ***poluniniana*** (7)	NMen
	'Harold Bevington' (*paniculata*) (8)	NSla
	'Harold Lloyd' (7)	NMen
	'Harry Marshall' (× *irvingii*) (7)	NWad
	'Harry Smith' (× *cimgani*) (7)	NMen
	'Harvest Moon' (*stolonifera*) (5)	WBor WFar WHer
	× ***heinreichii*** *sensu stricto* hort.	see *S.* 'Ernst Heinrich'
	'Helga Hufflepuff' (*cortusifolia*) (5) **new**	SBch
	'Helvellyn' (× *concinna*) (7) **new**	WAbe
	'Henri Rousseau' (Conspecta Group) (7)	EPot NMen
	'Hi-no-mai' (*fortunei*) (5) **new**	GEdr
	'Hi-Ace' (Mossy Group) (15/v)	NHpl SPlb
	'Highlander Red' (Mossy Group) (15)	ECtt GWyn WIce
	'Highlander Red Shades' (Mossy Group) (15)	WIce
	'Highlander White' (Mossy Group) (15)	GWyn
	'Hime' (*stolonifera*) (5)	SRms WCru
	'Hindhead Seedling' (× *boydii*) (7)	CRos LRHS NMen NRHS WAbe
	'Hiogi' (*fortunei*) (5) **new**	GEdr
	hirsuta (11)	EHrv ESwi EWld LEdu MMuc MNrw WCot WCru
§	'Hirsuta' (*paniculata*)	CPla
	'Hirsuta' (× *geum*)	see *S.* × *geum*
	'Hirtella' misapplied	see *S.* 'Hirsuta'
	'Hirtella' Ingwersen (*paniculata*) (8)	EPot
	'His Majesty' (× *irvingii*) (7)	NMen
	'Hiten' (*fortunei*) (5)	EBee GKev
	'Hocker Edge' (× *arco-valleyi*) (7)	WAbe
	'Holden Seedling' (Mossy) Group) (15	ECtt
I	'Holden Variety' (*oppositifolia*) (7)	NWad
	'Honeybunch' (Safran Group) (7)	NMen
	'Honington' (× *poluanglica*) (7)	NMen
	hostii (8)	GKev NAln NWad XLum
	- subsp. ***hostii*** (8)	XLum
	- - var. ***altissima*** (8)	EPot XLum
	- subsp. ***rhaetica*** (8)	NBro WThu XLum
	'Hsitou Silver' (*stolonifera*) (5)	WCot
	'Hunscote' (× *poluanglica*) (7)	NMen
	'Hyoseki' (*fortunei*) (5) **new**	GEdr

§	***hypnoides*** (15)	WAbe
	hypostoma (7)	WAbe
	'Iceland' (*oppositifolia*) (7)	EWes SIgm WAbe
	imparilis (5)	EHrv GEdr WCru
	'Ingeborg' (Mossy Group) (15)	CElw
	iranica (7)	CPBP EPot NMen
	'Irena' (7)	NMen
	'Irene Bacci' (× *baccii*) (7)	EPot NMen
	'Iris Prichard' (× *hardingii*) (7)	NMen
	× ***irvingii*** *sensu stricto* hort.	see *S.* 'Walter Irving'
	× ***jacggiana***	NSla
	'James' (7)	NMen NSla
	'Jan Amos Kómenský' (× *anglica*) (7)	NMen
	'Jan Neruda' (× *megaseiflora*) (7)	CPBP EPot NMen
	'Jan Palach' (× *krausii*) (7)	EPot NMen
	'Jan Preisler' (Conspecta Group) (7)	EPot
	'Jaromir' (8)	GCrg NMen NSla WAbe
	'Jaroslav Horný' (*marginata*) (7)	NMen WAbe
	'Jason' (× *elisabethae*) (7)	NMen
	'Jenkinsiae' (× *irvingii*) (7)	CMea CRos EPot LRHS MAsh MMuc NLar NMen NRHS NSla NWad SEND WAbe WIce
	'Joachim Barrande' (× *siluris*) (7)	EPot NMen
	'Jocelynne Bacci' (7)	NMen
	'Johanka' (7)	NMen
§	'Johann Kellerer' (× *kellereri*) (7)	EPot NMen
	'Johann Wolfgang Goethe' (7)	CPBP EPot
	'John Byam-Grounds' (Honor Group) (7)	EPot WAbe
	'John Tomlinson' (*burseriana*) (7)	NSla
	'Jorg' (× *biasolettoi*) (7)	EPot
	'Josef Čapek' (× *megaseiflora*) (Holenka's Miracle Group) (7)	EPot NMen
	'Joy'	see *S.* 'Kaspar Maria Sternberg'
	'Joy Bishop' (7)	NMen
	'Joyce Carruthers' (7)	NMen
	'Juliet'	see *S.* 'Riverslea'
§	***juniperifolia*** (7)	CMea GCrg SIgm SRms XLum
	'Jupiter' (× *megaseiflora*) (Holenka's Miracle Group) (7)	CPBP EPot NMen
	× ***karacardica*** (7)	NSla
	karadzicensis × ***scardica*** (7)	EPot
	'Karasin' (7)	NMen
	'Karel Čapek' (× *megaseiflora*) (Prichard's Monument Group) (7)	CRos LRHS NMen NRHS
	'Karlštejn' (× *borisii*) (7)	EPot NMen
§	'Kaspar Maria Sternberg' (× *petraschii*) (7) ♀H5	CRos LRHS NRHS
	'Kath Dryden' (7)	ECtt ITim NMen
	'Kathleen Pinsent' (8)	WAbe
	'Kathleen' (× *polulacina*) (7)	EPot NMen
	'Kath's Delight' (8)	GKev NAln
	'Katrin' (× *borisii*) (7)	NSla
	'Kawazu-beni' (*fortunei*) (5) **new**	GEdr
	'Kbley'	NMen
	× ***kellereri*** *sensu stricto* hort.	see *S.* 'Johann Kellerer'
	'Ken McGregor' (7)	NMen
	'Kestoniensis' (× *salmonica*) (7)	NMen
	'Kineton' (× *poluanglica*) (7)	NMen
	'King Lear' (× *bursiculata*) (7)	CRos LRHS NRHS
	'Kinki Purple' (*stolonifera*) (5)	EHrv EShb GBee GBin GWyn WCru WPnP
	'Kirke' (7)	NMen
	'Klondike' (× *boydii*) (7)	EPot NMen WAbe
	'Knapton Pink' (Mossy Group) (15)	ECtt NEoE SPoG WAbe WIce
	'Kokaku' (*fortunei*) (5)	LLHF
	'Kokoryu-nishiki' (*fortunei*) (5) **new**	GEdr
	'Komochi-daimonji' (*fortunei*) (5) **new**	GEdr
	'Kon Tiki' (7)	NMen
	kotschyi (7)	NSla
	kotschyi × ***wendelboi*** (7)	NMen
§	'Krain' (× *fritschiana*) (8)	SIgm WOld
	'Krákatit' (× *megaseiflora*) (Prichard's Monument Group) (7)	NMen
	'Krasava' (× *megaseiflora*) (Prichard's Monument Group) (7)	NMen
	'Labe' (× *arco-valleyi*) (7)	CMea CRos EPot LRHS NMen NRHS
	'Lady Beatrix Stanley'	see *S.* 'Beatrix Stanley'
§	'Lagraveana' (*paniculata*) (8) ♀H5	CRos GCrg LRHS NRHS SIgm WFar
	'Laka' (7)	EPot NMen
	× ***landaueri*** *sensu stricto* hort.	see *S.* 'Leonore'
	'Lantoscana' (*callosa* subsp. *callosa* var. *australis*) (8)	GKev
	'Lantoscana Superba' (*callosa* subsp. *callosa* var. *australis*) (8)	WOld
	'Laura Sinclair' (× *fallsvillagensis*) (7)	NMen
	'Lemon Puff'	NSla WIce
	'Lenka' (× *byam-groundsii*) (7)	EPot NMen
	'Leo Gordon Godseff' (× *elisabethae*) (7)	CRos LRHS NRHS NSla
	'Leonardo da Vinci' (7)	EPot WAbe
§	'Leonore' (× *landaueri*) (7)	CRos LRHS NRHS SIgm
	'Letchworth Gem' (× *urbium*) (London Pride Group) (11)	CRos GAbr GCal LRHS NRHS
	'Libuse' (7)	NMen
	'Lidice' (7)	EPot NMen WHoo
	'Lilac Time' (× *youngiana*) (7)	EPot
	lilacina (7)	NMen NSla WAbe
	'Limelight' (*callosa* subsp. *callosa* var. *australis*) (8)	NWad
	'Lincoln Foster' (8)	NWad
	lingulata	see *S. callosa*
	'Lismore Carmine' (× *lismorensis*) (7)	EPot NMen
	'Lismore Mist' (× *lismorensis*) (7)	EPot
	'Lissadell' (*callosa*) (8)	GKev NAln
*	'Little Piggy' (*epiphylla*) (5)	WCru
	'Lizzy' (7)	EPot NMen

ilonakhensis (1)	WAbe
'Lohengrin' (× *hoerhammeri*) (7)	EPot
'Lohmuelleri' (× *biasolettoi*) (7)	GKev
lolaensis (7)	WAbe
London Pride Group	LPot
longifolia (8)	CRos EPot GEdr GKev LRHS NHpl NRHS NSla XEll
- var. ***aitanica*** (8)	WAbe
'Louis Armstrong' (Blues Group) (7)	EPot NMen WAbe
LOVE ME	see *S.* 'Miluj Mne'
lowndesii (7)	WAbe
'Loxley' (× *poluanglica*) (7)	NMen
'Lutea' (*aizoon*)	see *S.* 'Lutea' (*paniculata*)
'Lutea' (*diapensioides*)	see *S.* 'Wilhelm Tell'
§ 'Lutea' (*paniculata*) (8)	EBou EHoe EPot GMaP MMuc NBro NHol NRya NSla NWad
§ 'Luteola' (× *boydii*) (7)	NMen
'Lydia' (× *hornibrookii*) (7) **new**	WAbe
macedonica	see *S. juniperifolia*
'Magna' (*burseriana*) (7)	NMen
'Maigrün' (*fortunei*) (5)	EBee
'Major Lutea'	see *S.* 'Luteola'
'Mangart' (*burseriana*) (7)	NMen
'Marcela' (× *megaseiflora*) (7)	NMen
'Marco Polo' (7)	NMen
marginata (7) ♀H5	NSla WAbe
- var. ***balcanica***	see *S. marginata* subsp. *marginata* var. *rocheliana*
- var. ***bubakii*** (7)	NMen NSla
- subsp. ***marginata*** var. ***boryi*** (7)	CRos EPot LRHS NRHS WAbe
§ - - var. ***rocheliana*** (7)	CRos EPot LRHS NRHS
'Maria Callas' (× *poluanglica*) (7)	CPBP
'Maria Luisa' (× *salmonica*) (7)	CPBP NMen
'Marianna' (× *borisii*) (7)	CMea
'Marie' (7)	NMen
'Maroon Beauty' (*stolonifera*) (5)	EBee ECtt EPPr LPot MCot NBid NBre WCot WFar
'Martin Luther' (Wittenberg Group) (7)	EPot
'Mary Golds' (Swing Group) (7)	GKev NLar NMen
× ***megaseiflora*** *sensu stricto* hort.	see *S.* 'Robin Hood'
mertensiana (6)	EHrv NBir WSHC
'Meteor' (7)	NHol NRya NSla
'Michelangelo' (Rutil Group) (7)	NMen
'Michle' (× *megaseiflora*) (7)	NMen
'Mikawa-beni' (*fortunei*) (5) **new**	GEdr
'Millstream Cream' (× *elisabethae*) (7)	NMen
§ 'Miluj Mne' (× *poluanglica*) (7)	CSma SPlb WAbe WHoo
'Minor' (*cochlearis*) (8) ♀H5	CRos GCrg GKev LRHS NRHS
'Mirko Webr' (Harmonia Group) (7)	NMen
§ 'Miss Chambers' (London Pride Group) (11)	CBod ECtt EWes GCal LPla SMHy WBrk WCot WMoo WSHC
'Moe' (*fortunei*) (5) ♀H4 **new**	GEdr
'Mollie Broom' (7)	NMen WAbe
'Mona Lisa' (× *borisii*) (7)	EPot
'Monarch' (8) ♀H5	CRos EPot EWes GAbr GCrg GKev LRHS NHpl NRHS NWad WAbe WIce
§ 'Mondscheinsonate' (× *boydii*) (7)	NMen
'Monika' (*webrii*) (7)	NMen
'Moon Beam' (× *boydilacina*) (7)	NMen
'Moonlight Sonata' (× *boydii*)	see *S.* 'Mondscheinsonate'
'Moonlight' (× *boydii*)	see *S.* 'Sulphurea'
'Morava' (7)	CPBP EPot NMen
Mossy Group (15)	MHol
- pink-flowered (15)	GAbr MMuc SPoG
- red-flowered (15)	SPoG
- white-flowered (15)	MMuc
'Mossy Triumph'	see *S.* 'Triumph'
'Mother of Pearl' (× *irvingii*) (7)	CMea NMen
'Mother Queen' (× *irvingii*) (7)	NMen
'Mount Nachi' (*fortunei*) (5) ♀H4	CRos EPfP EWes GAbr GEdr GMaP LPot LRHS NBro NHar NHpl NRHS SPlb WAbe WFar WMoo WSpi
§ 'Mrs Gertie Prichard' (× *megaseiflora*) (Prichard's Monument Group) (7)	NMen
'Mrs Helen Terry' (× *salmonica*) (7) ♀H5	CRos LRHS NMen NRHS
mutata (9)	GKev
'Myra Cambria' (× *anglica*) (7)	NMen NWad
'Myra' (× *anglica*) (7)	NMen WHoo
'Myriad' (7)	WAbe
'Myriad Seedling' (7)	EPot NMen WAbe
'Naarden' (7)	NMen
'Namiyama' (*fortunei*) (5) **new**	GEdr
'Nancye' (× *goringiana*) (7)	EPot NSla WAbe
'Neride' (7)	NMen
'Nicholas' (8)	GKev NHpl
'Nimbus' (*iranica*) (7)	NMen
'Niobe' (× *pulvilacina*) (7)	EPot NMen
'Nottingham Gold' (× *boydii*) (7)	EPot NMen NWad
'Nouhime' (*fortunei*) (5) **new**	GEdr
§ ***obtusa*** (7)	NMen
'Ogon-no-mai' (*fortunei*) (5) **new**	GEdr
'Oh Yes' (*cochlearis*) (8)	WAbe
'Old Britain' (× *boydii*) (7) **new**	EPot
'Olsany' (× *megaseiflora*) (7)	NMen
'Olympus' (× *boydilacina*) (7)	NMen
'Omar Khayyám' (7)	EPot NMen
'Opalescent' (7)	NMen
'Opatov' (× *megaseiflora*) (7)	NMen
oppositifolia (7)	GCrg MAsh NHol NSla SPlb SRms WAbe WSHC
'Orava' (7)	NMen
'Ottone Rosai' (Toscana Group) (7)	NMen
'Pablo Picasso' (Conspecta Group) (7)	EPot NMen
paniculata (8)	EDAr EPot GKev GMaP MHer NSla SPlb SRms WAbe WHoo
- from Austria **new**	CPla

- from Gorges du Verdon, France — GKev
§ - subsp. ***cartilaginea*** (8) — GKev
- subsp. ***kolenatiana*** — see *S. paniculata* subsp. *cartilaginea*
§ - var. ***minutifolia*** (8) — CPBP CRos GCrg GQue LRHS NBro NHpl NRHS NRya NSla SIgm SPlb WAbe
§ - subsp. ***paniculata*** (8) — MAsh
paradoxa (15) — CRos EPot LRHS NHol NRHS NWad
'Parcevalis' (× *finnisiae*) (7 × 9) — WAbe
'Paul Gaughin' (7) — EPot
'Paul Rubens' (7) — EPot WAbe
'Peach Blossom' (7) — NMen
'Peach Melba' (7) ♀H5 — CPBP CRos CSma EPot LRHS NHpl NLar NMen NRHS NSla WHoo
'Peachy Head' (7) — NMen
'Pearl Rose' (× *anglica*) (7) — EPot NMen
'Pearly Gates' (× *irvingii*) (7) — NMen
'Pearly King' (Mossy Group) (15) — ECtt GMaP WAbe
- variegated (15/v) — CBod GKev
× ***pectinata*** Schott, Nyman & Kotschy — see *S.* 'Krain'
'Penelope' (× *boydilacina*) (7) — CRos EPot LRHS NLar NMen NRHS NSla WHoo WThu
pensylvanica (4) — GCal IMou
'Perikles' (7) — NMen
'Peter Burrow' (× *poluanglica*) (7) — EPot NMen
'Peter Pan' (Mossy Group) (15) — CRos EBou ECtt EDAr EPfP GCrg GMaP LRHS MAsh MHer NHol NLar NRHS NWad SPoG WSHC
'Petra' (7) — EPot
§ 'Phoenix' (× *biasolettoi*) (7) — CRos LRHS NRHS
'Pierantonio Micheli' (Renaissance Group) (7) — NMen
'Pilatus' (× *boydii*) (7) — NMen
'Pink Cloud' (*fortunei*) (5) — GEdr NBro WAbe
'Pink Haze' (*fortunei*) (5) ♀H4 — GEdr WAbe
'Pink Mist' (*fortunei*) (5) — GEdr WAbe WFar WMoo
'Pink Pagoda' (*nipponica*) (5) — EBee WCot WCru WFar
'Pink Ray' (*fortunei*) (5) — LLHF
'Pink Star' (× *boydilacina*) (7) — EPot NLar NMen
'Pixie' (15) — ECtt GCrg GKev MAsh NHol NRya NWad SPoG SRms
'Pixie Alba' — see *S.* 'White Pixie'
'Plena' (*granulata*) — see *S.* 'Flore Pleno'
'Polar Drift' — CRos LRHS NRHS NSla SIgm WAbe
poluniniana × 'Winifred' (× *poluanglica*) (7) — EPot
'Pomona Sprout' (*cortusifolia*) (5) **new** — SBch
'Pompadour' (15) — NEoE
'Popelka' (*marginata* subsp. *marginata* var. *rocheliana*) (7) — CRos LRHS NMen NRHS
porophylla (7) — GKev
aff. ***porophylla*** (7) — EPot
'Portae' (× *fritschiana*) (8) — XLum
'Precious Piggy' (*epiphylla*) (5) — WCru
'Primrose Dame' (× *elisabethae*) (7) — EPot WAbe WIce
'Primulaize Salmon' (9 × 11) — GCrg WHoo
'Primuloides' (*umbrosa*) (11) — EDAr MMuc SRms SWvt

- variegated (11/v) — SRms
'Prince Hal' (*burseriana*) (7) — CRos EPot LRHS NRHS NSla
'Princess' (*burseriana*) (7) — CRos LRHS NMen NRHS NSla
'Probynii' (*cochlearis*) (8) — CPBP EPot NWad WAbe
'Prometheus' (× *prossenii*) (7) — NMen SIgm
'Prosek' (× *megaseiflora*) (7) — NMen
× ***prossenii*** *sensu stricto* hort. — see *S.* 'Regina'
§ 'Pseudoborisii' (× *borisii*) (7) — NMen
'Pseudo-valdensis' (*cochlearis*) (8) — WAbe
pubescens (15) — WAbe
'Punctatissima' (*paniculata*) (8) — NWad
'Purple Piggy' (*epiphylla*) (5) — WCru
'Purpurea' (*fortunei*) — see *S.* 'Rubrifolia'
'Purpurea' (*marginata*) (7) — NMen
'Pygmalion' (× *webrii*) (7) — NMen
'Pyramidalis' (*cotyledon*) (8) — GKev XLum
quadrifaria (7) — WAbe
'Quarry Wood' (× *anglica*) (7) — NMen
'Rachael Young' (× *borisii*) (7) — NMen
'Rachel' (8) — GKev
'Radka' (× *megaseiflora*) (7) — NMen
'Rainsley Seedling' (8) — EPot GKev NAln NBro
'Ray Woodliffe' (× *dinninaris*) (7) — WAbe
'Red Poll' (× *poluanglica*) (7) — GAbr NHpl NMen WAbe
* 'Regent' — WAbe
§ 'Regina' (× *prossenii*) (7) — NMen
§ 'Reginald Farrer' (Silver Farreri Group) (8) ♀H5 — WAbe
'Rembrandt van Rijn' (7) — EPot NMen WAbe
retusa (7) — WAbe
'Rex' (*paniculata*) (8) — CMac NWad SIgm
'River Thame' (× *polulacina*) (7) — NMen
§ 'Riverslea' (× *hornibrookii*) (7) — NMen
§ 'Robin Hood' (× *megaseiflora*) (7) — EPot NMen WHoo
'Rocco Red' (× *arendsii*) (15) **new** — CBod
'Rockrose'PBR (× *arendsii*) (15) — SPoG
'Rockwhite' (× *arendsii*) (15) **new** — WIce
'Rokujō' (*fortunei*) (5) ♀H4 — EBee NBro NEoE NLar SHeu
'Rosa Tubbs' (8) — EWTr EWes GKev
§ 'Rosea' (*paniculata*) (8) ♀H5 — GMaP GWyn MMuc NBro NRya NSla SEND SRms
'Rosemarie' (7) — NMen
'Rosina Sündermann' (× *rosinae*) (7) — CRos EPot LRHS NRHS
rotundifolia (12) — CElw EBee ECha MPnt
'Roztyly' (× *megaseiflora*) (7) — NMen
'Rubella' (× *irvingii*) (7) — NMen
'Rubin' (× *hornbrookii*) (7) — NMen
'Rubra' (*aizoon*) — see *S.* 'Rosea' (*paniculata*)
§ 'Rubrifolia' (*fortunei*) (5) ♀H4 — CMac CSpe ECha ECtt GAbr GEdr NBro NHpl SMad SWvt WBor WCot WCru WFar WMoo WPnP
* 'Ruby Red' — NEoE
* 'Ruby Wedding' (*cortusifolia*) (5) — WFar
rufescens BWJ 7510 (5) — EHrv WCru
- BWJ 7684 — GEdr WCru

Plant	Suppliers
'Rufina' (7)	NMen
'Rusalka' (× *borisii*) (7)	NMen
'Russell V. Prichard' (× *irvingii*) (7)	NMen
'Ruth Draper' (*oppositifolia*) (7) ♀H5	GCrg WAbe
'Ruth McConnell' (15)	CMea
'Ruzнyě' (× *megaseiflora*) (7)	NMen
'Saint John's' (8)	GKev WAbe
'Saint Kilda' (*oppositifolia*) (7)	GCrg NWad
× ***salmonica*** *sensu stricto* hort.	see *S.* 'Salomonii'
'Salome' (× *lincolni-fosteri*) (7)	EPot NMen
§ 'Salomonii' (× *salmonica*) (7)	SRms
sancta (7)	CRos LRHS NMen NRHS SIgm SRms
- subsp. ***pseudosancta***	see *S. juniperifolia*
- - var. ***macedonica***	see *S. juniperifolia*
'Sara Sinclair' (× *arco-valleyi*) (7)	CMea
'Šárka' (7)	CPBP NMen
sarmentosa	see *S. stolonifera*
'Satchmo' (Blues Group) (7)	EPot NMen NSla WAbe
'Saturn' (× *megaseiflora*) (7)	EPot NMen
'Saxony Red'	EPfP
'Sázava' (× *poluluteopurpurea*) (7)	NSla
§ ***scardica*** (7)	EPot NBro NMen WAbe
- var. ***dalmatica***	see *S. obtusa*
§ 'Schelleri' (× *petraschii*) (7)	EPfP NMen
§ 'Schwefelblüte' (15)	CRos GMaP LRHS NRHS
'Seissera' (*burseriana*) (7)	NMen
sempervivum (7)	NGdn WAbe
sendaica (5)	WCru
'Seren y Gwanwyn' (*oppositifolia*) (7)	WAbe
'Shaggy Hair' (*stolonifera*) (5) **new**	WFar
'Sherlock Holmes' (7)	NMen WAbe
'Shimanami' (*fortunei*) (5) **new**	EMor MNrw
'Shimmy'	WAbe
'Shiranami' (*fortunei*) (5) ♀H4	CBcs EBee ECtt ELan GEdr LSun NHpl WCot WFar
§ 'Silver Cushion' (15/v)	CPla CRos CTri ELan LRHS NHpl NRHS SPlb SPoG WAbe WIce
'Silver Hill' (*paniculata*) (8)	NSla
'Silver Maid' (× *engleri*) (8)	GCrg NSla
'Silver Mound'	see *S.* 'Silver Cushion'
'Silver Velvet' (*fortunei*) (5/v)	CSpe EBee ECtt EUJe MBNS MBel MNrw NHpl SHeu SMad WCot
'Sir Douglas Haig' (15)	NWad
'Sissi' (7)	CPBP EPot NMen WAbe
'Slack's Ruby Southside' (Southside Seedling Group) (8) ♀H5	GCrg NRHS NSla NWad SIgm WIce
'Slack's Supreme' (8)	NSla WCot
'Slavia' (7)	NMen
'Slzy Coventry' (× *proximae*) (7)	WAbe
'Smíchov' (× *megaseiflora*) (7)	NMen
'Sněhurka' (Fenomen Group) (7)	NMen
'Snowcap' (*pubescens*) (15)	NWad WAbe
'Snowflake' (Silver Farreri Group) (8) ♀H5	CRos LRHS NRHS WAbe
§ 'Sofia' (× *borisii*) (7)	EPot NMen
Southside Seedling Group (8)	CMea CRos EDAr EPfP EPot EWTr GAbr GKev GMaP LRHS MAsh MMuc NBro NHol NHpl NRHS NWad SAko SEND SMad SPoG SRms WAbe WFar WHoo WIce XLum
- 'Southside Star' (8) ♀H5	NHpl WAbe
spathularis (11)	WCot WHoo
'Splendens' (*oppositifolia*) (7) ♀H5	EBou EPfP GAbr GCrg MMuc SIgm SRms WAbe
'Spotted Dog'	see *S.* 'Canis-dalmatica'
'Sprite' (15)	SPoG
spruneri (7)	CRos LRHS NRHS
'Stansfieldii' (*rosacea*) (15)	EBou GCrg SPlb SPoG
'Starfire' (8)	GKev
'Starlight' (8)	GKev
startorii	see *S. scardica*
'Šťásek' (*dinnikii*) (7)	WAbe
stellaris (4)	WAbe
§ ***stolonifera*** (5) ♀H2	CRos CSpe CTsd EShb LRHS NBro SWvt WCot WFar WMoo WWtn
- large-flowered (5)	WCot WGrn
'Strawberry Melba' (7)	EPot NMen
'Sturmiana' (*paniculata*) (8)	SRms WOld
'Sue Drew' (*fortunei*) (5) ♀H4	LLHF
'Sue Tubbs' (8)	GKev
'Suendermannii' (× *kellereri*) (7)	CRos LRHS NMen NRHS
'Suendermannii Major' (× *kellereri*) (7)	CRos LRHS NRHS
SUGAR PLUM FAIRY ('Toujya') (*fortunei*) (5) ♀H4	EBee ECtt EShb SHeu
§ 'Sulphurea' (× *boydii*) (7)	CMea CRos LRHS MAsh NRHS NSla WHoo
'Superba' (*callosa* subsp. *callosa* var. *australis*) (8)	NSla
'Symons-Jeunei' (8)	NWad WAbe
tangutica (1)	LLHF
'Tankei' (5)	SAko
'Tenerife' (Swirly Group) (7)	EPot EWes NMen WAbe
'Tetín' (Teta Group) (7)	EPot NMen
'Thalia' (7)	NMen
'Theoden' (*oppositifolia*) (7)	CMea EWes WAbe
'Theresa Cooper' (7)	EPot
'Theseus' (7)	CPBP
'Thór Heyerdahl' (Ocean Group) (7)	EPot
tombeanensis (7)	EPot WAbe
'Torrisholme Rose' (7)	EPot NMen
TOURAN DEEP RED ('Rockred') (Mossy Group) (15)	CRos EPfP LBuc LRHS NRHS
TOURAN LARGE WHITE ('Rocklarwhi'PBR) (Mossy Group) (15)	CRos EPfP LBuc LRHS NRHS
TOURAN RED ('Saxz0006') (× *arendsii*) (15) **new**	SPoG WIce
TOURAN WHITE IMPROVED ('Saxz0004'PBR) (× *arendsii*) (15) **new**	SPoG
'Tricolor' (*stolonifera*) (5) ♀H2	EBak
trifurcata (15)	ECtt
'Tristan' (*stribrnyi*)	WAbe

§ 'Triumph' (× *arendsii*) (15) ECtt EPfP GMaP MAsh NEgg SPoG
'Tully' (× *elisabethae*) (7) NMen
'Tumbling Waters' (8) ♀H5 CRos EPot LEdu LRHS MRav NHol NHpl NRHS NSla NWad WAbe
§ 'Tvoje Píseň' (× *poluanglica*) (7) WHoo WThu
§ 'Tvůj Polibek' (× *poluanglica*) (7) EPot
§ 'Tvůj Úsměv' (× *poluanglica*) (7) ♀H5 NHpl
§ 'Tvůj Úspěch' (× *poluanglica*) (7) EPot NMen NWad
'Two Kings' (*fortunei*) (5) **new** WFar
'Tycho Brahe' (× *doerfleri*) (7) WAbe
'Tysoe' (7) EPot
'Tysoe Blush' (Blues Group) (7) **new** NSla
'Tysoe Burgundy' (Blues Group) (7) **new** CPBP NSla
'Tysoe Pink-Perfection' (Blues Group) (7) NSla
'Tysoe Splendour' (Blues Group) (7) NSla
umbrosa (11) CMac CRos EDAr EPfP GAbr LEdu LRHS LSun MMuc MRav NHic NRHS SCob SEND SPlb SPoG SRms SWvt WFar WMoo XLum
* - ***subinteger*** MMuc
× ***urbium*** (11) ♀H5 CBod CCBP CRos CTri ELan EPfP EWTr GMaP LEdu LRHS MBel MCot NRHS NSti SPer SRms WBor WCAu WHoo WSpi WTor
'Vaccariana' (*oppositifolia*) (7) SHar
'Václav Hollar' (× *gusmusii*) (7) NMen
'Vahlii' (× *smithii*) (7) NMen
'Valborg' see *S.* 'Cranbourne'
'Valentine' see *S.* 'Cranbourne'
'Valerie Keevil' (× *anglica*) (7) NMen
I 'Variegata' (*cuneifolia*) (11/v) CBod CRos EBou ECtt EPfP LRHS NHol NHpl NRHS NRya NWad SPlb SPoG WHoo WMoo
I 'Variegata' (*exarata* subsp. *moschata*) (15/v) GMaP
'Variegata' (*umbrosa*) see *S.* 'Aureopunctata'
I 'Variegata' (× *urbium*) (11/v) CRos EBee EPfP GPSL LPot LRHS MBel NLar NRHS SCob SMad SRms WFar WHoo WTor
vayredana (15) WAbe
'Večerní Hvězda' (7) CPBP WAbe
veitchiana (5) NBro WFar XLum
'Verona' (× *caroli-langii*) (7) WAbe
'Vesna' (× *borisii*) (7) NMen
'Vikos Gold' (7) EPot NMen
'Vincent van Gogh' (× *borisii*) (7) NMen
'Vítkov' (× *megaseiflora*) (7) NMen
'Vladana' (× *megaseiflora*) (7) CMea CRos EPot LRHS NMen NRHS NSla
'Vlasta' (7) NMen
'Vreny' (8) GKev
'Wada' (*fortunei*) (5) CAby CSpe ECtt ELon GKev GMaP LRHS MBel MNrw NBir NBro NHar NRHS SRms WAul WBor WCot WFar WOld WSHC WWtn
'Walpole's Variety' (8) NWad
'Walter Ingwersen' (*umbrosa*) (11) SRms
§ 'Walter Irving' (× *irvingii*) (7) ♀H5 NSla WAbe
'Walton' (× *poluanglica*) (7) NMen
'Wasperton' (× *poluanglica*) (7) NMen
'Welsh Dragon' (15) WAbe
'Welsh Red' (15) WAbe
'Welsh Rose' (15) WAbe
wendelboi (7) EPot NMen WThu
'Wendrush' (× *wendelacina*) (7) NMen
'Wendy' (× *wendelacina*) (7) NMen
'Wetterhorn' (*oppositifolia*) (7) GCrg
'Whatcote' (7) NMen
'Wheatley Lion' (× *borisii*) (7) NMen
'Wheatley Rose' (7) CRos LRHS NRHS
'White Cap' (× *boydii*) (7) NMen
'White Delight' (× *megaseiflora*) (7) CRos LRHS NRHS NSla
'White Imp' (7) NMen
§ 'White Pixie' (15) CPla EBou ECtt EDAr EPfP GCrg MAsh MHer NEoE NHol NRya NWad SPlb SPoG SRms WIce
'White Star' (*fortunei*) (5) CRos LLHF LRHS NMen NRHS
'White Star' (× *petraschii*) see *S.* 'Schelleri'
'Whitehill' (8) ♀H5 CMea CRos EBou ELan EPot GMaP LRHS NRHS NRya NSla NWad SBch WHoo WRHF
§ 'Wilhelm Tell' (× *malbyana*) (7) NMen
'William Boyd' (× *boydii*) (7) NMen WAbe
'William Shakespeare' (Blues Group) (7) EPot NMen WAbe
'Winifred Bevington' (8 × 11) CRos CSma EBou EDAr EPot GCrg GMaP LRHS MBel NBro NHpl NLar NRHS NRya NWad SBch SRms WAbe WHoo WRHF
'Winifred' (× *anglica*) (7) EPot NMen WAbe
'Winston Churchill' (15) CRos LRHS NEoE NHol NRHS NWad
I 'Winston Churchill Variegata' (15/v) NHol
'Winton' (× *paulinae*) (7) NMen
'Wisley' (*federici-augusti* subsp. *grisebachii*) (7) ♀H5 GKev
'Yellow Rock' (7) NMen NRya
YOUR GOOD FORTUNE see *S.* 'Tvůj Úspěch'
YOUR KISS see *S.* 'Tvůj Polibek'
YOUR SMILE see *S.* 'Tvůj Úsměv'
YOUR SONG see *S.* 'Tvoje Píseň'
YOUR SUCCESS see *S.* 'Tvůj Úspěch'
'Yunagi' (*fortunei*) (5) WOld
'Zbraslav' (× *megaseiflora*) (7) NMen NSla
× ***zimmeteri*** (8 × 11) NSla
'Ziva' (7) NMen
§ 'Zlatá Praha' (× *pragensis*) (7) NMen WAbe
'Zlatý Kůň' (× *laeviformis*) (7) EPot

Scabiosa (*Caprifoliaceae*)

africana CElw
- 'Jocelyn' EWes SHar
alpina L. see *Cephalaria alpina*
argentea EWes WPGP

Plant	Suppliers
- PAB 1229	LEdu
atropurpurea	LCro LOPS
- 'Ace of Spades'	ELan EPfP SCob SPhx
- 'Beaujolais Bonnets'	CRos EAJP EBee EPfP LRHS NGBl NRHS
- 'Black Knight'	CSpe LCro LOPS SPhx
§ - 'Chile Black'	CBcs CRos EAJP EHoe ELan EPfP GWyn LRHS NRHS SCob SPer SPoG SRkn SWvt
§ - 'Chilli Pepper'	LRHS
- 'Derry's Black'	SPtp
- 'Fata Morgana'	LCro LOPS
- 'Fire King'	LCro LOPS
banatica	see *S. columbaria*
'Barocca'	CRos CWGN EBee EPfP LRHS NRHS SRms WCot
'Blackberry Fool' (Dessert Series)	EPfP SCob
BLACKBERRY SCOOP ('Dblckbry') (Scoop Series) **new**	WHlf
BLUE DIAMONDS ('Kiescalibu'[PBR])	GJos MHol WFar
'Blueberry Muffin' (Dessert Series)	SCob
BURGUNDY BONNETS ('Scabon'[PBR])	LCro LOPS
§ 'Butterfly Blue'	Widely available
caucasica	CMac CRos EPfP GKev LEdu LRHS NRHS XSen
- var. ***alba***	CBcs EPfP ILea NGBl WHoo
- 'Blausiegel'	MRav
- 'Clive Greaves' ♀H4	CRos EBee ECha ELon EWTr GMaP LRHS MBNS NRHS SCob SGbt SPad SPer SRms SWvt WCAu WFar
- 'Deep Waters'	CSpe LRHS
- 'Fama'	CSpe NBir NGBl NLar SPlb SRms WFar WHoo
- 'Fama Deep Blue'	CNor LRHS MHol NAln NCGa NRHS WFar
- 'Fama White'	LRHS NRHS
- 'Goldingensis'	NGdn WHil
- House's hybrids	MHol NGdn SRms SVic
- 'Isaac House'	WFar XLum
- 'Kompliment'	WFar
- 'Miss Willmott' ♀H4	CMac CRos CSam EBee ECha ECtt EHoe EHrv GBin LRHS MArl MRav NLar NRHS SGbt SPer SWvt WCAu XSen
- 'Moerheim Blue'	EBee
- Perfecta Series	CRos GBin ILea LRHS NAln NGdn NLar NRHS SPoG
- - 'Perfecta Alba'	CBod CCBP CDor CRos ELan EPfP GBin GMaP LRHS MBel MHer MHol NAln NCGa NLar NRHS SCob SPer SPoG SPtp WArt WCAu XLum
- - 'Perfecta Blue'	CBod CDor CMac ELan EPfP GMaP MBel MHer MHol NAln WCot XLum
- - 'Perfecta Lilac Blue'	EPfP SPer
- 'Stäfa'	CBod CRos EBee ECha LRHS NCGa NEgg NLar NRHS NSti WHoo
- 'Thorp's Variegated' (v)	WCot
'Champanelle' **new**	CBor
'Chile Black'	see *S. atropurpurea* 'Chile Black'
'Chile Pepper'	see *S. atropurpurea* 'Chilli Pepper'
cinerea	SPhx
§ ***columbaria***	CCBP CFis CHab CRos CWld EBee LRHS NEgg NMir NRHS SPhx WArt WHer WSFF
* - ***alpina***	GKev

Plant	Suppliers
- 'Blue Note'[PBR]	CBod MHol NPri
- blue-flowered	NHpl
- FLUTTER DEEP BLUE ('Balfluttdelu')	MHol WHil
- FLUTTER ROSE PINK ('Balfluttropi')	CBod MHol WHil
- 'Mariposa Blue'[PBR]	CBod LRHS MHol NCGa NPri NRHS
- 'Mariposa Blush' **new**	SPad WHil
- 'Misty Butterflies'	CAby ECtt EPfP GJos MHol NCou NEgg NGdn NHic NLar SRms WFar
- 'Nana'	CRos EBee EPfP GWyn LRHS NBir NGdn NLar NRHS WCFE XLum
§ - subsp. ***ochroleuca***	CCBP CDor CKno CRos CSpe ECha EHrv EPPr LRHS MBel NAln NBir NGBl NLar SCob SHar SPhx SPoG SRms SSut WArt WBrk WCAu
- - MESE 344	EBee
- - 'Moon Dance'	CBod CDor CMea CRos CWGN EAJP EShb GBin GPSL LLHF LRHS LSun MTis NLar NRHS SAko SGbt SPoG WCot WHoo
- - 'Pixie Yellow'	NRHS
- 'Pincushion Blue'	CRos EDAr LRHS LSun NRHS
- 'Pincushion Pink'	CRos EBou EDAr GJos GWyn LRHS NGdn NRHS
- pink-flowered	MMuc
crenata **new**	EBee
cretica	SIgm XLum
drakensbergensis	ELan EWes GBin GKev IKil ILea LRHS NAln SLon WCot WPtf
gigantea	see *Cephalaria gigantea*
graminifolia	CPla CRos EBee GKev LRHS NBir NRHS SBch SPhx SRms XLum XSen
- 'Green Dome' **new**	GKev
- ***rosea***	EWes
'Helen Dillon'	ECre EWes
incisa	WOut
- 'Kudo'	CKno CRos EBee LCro LOPS LRHS MHol NCGa NRHS NSti SHar SPad SPoG
- 'Kudo White' **new**	LRHS
'Irish Perpetual Flowering'	see *S.* 'Butterfly Blue'
japonica var. ***alpina***	EBee EPfP GKev MMuc NGdn SEND SPhx SPtp WCot WFar WHoo XLum XSen
- - 'Blue Star'	EBee NBre SGbt
- - 'Ritz Blue'	CMea EPfP
- - 'Ritz Rose'	CMea
lachnophylla	GCal SPhx WCot
LAVENDER SCOOP ('Dlvndrscop') (Scoop Series) **new**	WHlf
'Little Cracker'	LRHS SCob SLon
'Little Emily'	ELon
lucida	CBod CRos EPfP IPot LRHS MMuc MRav NRHS SEND WCAu XLum
MAGIC ('Pmoore02')	NEoE
MARSHMALLOW SCOOP ('Dmarshscop') (Scoop Series) **new**	WHlf
'Midnight'	CMea
minoana	EBee
'Miss Havisham'	CElw EWes MNrw
montana Mill.	see *Knautia arvensis*
ochroleuca	see *S. columbaria* subsp. *ochroleuca*
parnassi	see *Pterocephalus perennis*
'Perpetual Flowering'	see *S.* 'Butterfly Blue'
PINK BUTTONS ('Walminipink')	CBod MBel

'Pink Diamonds' — EBee ELan EPfP MHol WFar
'Pink Mist' PBR — CBod CRos EBee ECtt ELan EPfP GBin LCro LOPS LRHS MAsh NBir NHpl NLar NRHS SCob SCoo SPer SPoG SRms WTor
'Plum Pudding' (Dessert Series) — NLar
pterocephala — see *Pterocephalus perennis*
RASPBERRY SCOOP ('Draspscop') (Scoop Series) **new** — WHlf
'Raspberry Sorbet' (Dessert Series) — SCob
rhodopensis — EBee
'Rosie's Pink' — ECtt
rumelica — see *Knautia macedonica*
'Satchmo' — see *S. atropurpurea* 'Chile Black'
stellata — SPhx
'Strawberry Parfait' (Dessert Series) — EPfP NLar SCob
succisa — see *Succisa pratensis*
tatarica — see *Cephalaria gigantea*
VANILLA SCOOP ('Dvanilscop') (Scoop Series) **new** — WHlf
'Vivid Violet' — CAbb CDor CRos CSpe EBee ECtt LBuc LRHS LSRN MHol MMuc MNrw NDov NHpl NRHS SAko WBrk WCot

Scadoxus ✿ (*Amaryllidaceae*)

membranaceus — WCot
multiflorus — CCCN LAma SDeJ
§ - subsp. ***katherinae*** 🏆H1b — WCot
§ - subsp. ***multiflorus*** — WCot
natalensis — see *S. puniceus*
§ ***puniceus*** — WCot

Scaevola (*Goodeniaceae*)

aemula 'Blue Fan' — see *S. aemula* 'Blue Wonder'
- BLUE PRINT ('Kingscablin' PBR) — NPri
§ - 'Blue Wonder' PBR — NPer SWvt
- 'Zig Zag' PBR — CCCN
BLAUER FACHER ('Saphira' PBR) — CCCN NLar
'Mini Blue' — CCCN

Sceletium (*Aizoaceae*)

tortuosum — SPlb

Schefflera ✿ (*Araliaceae*)

alpina B&SWJ 8247 — WCru
- B&SWJ 11827 — WCru
- HWJ 936 — WCru
- NJM 09.140 — WPGP
- NJM 09.157 — WPGP
- large-leaved WWJ 11999 — WCru
arboricola 🏆H1c — SEND XBlo
- 'Gold Capella' 🏆H1c — SEND XBlo
- 'Kalahari' — XBlo
brevipedicellata — CDTJ
- HWJ 870 — WCru
- KWJ 12224 — WCru
aff. ***brevipedicellata*** NJM 10.102 **new** — WPGP
§ ***chapana*** B&SWJ 11833 — WCru
- B&SWJ 11848 — WCru
- HWJ 983 — WCru
delavayi — CDTJ WCru WPGP
enneaphylla HWJ 1018 — WCru
fantsipanensis B&SWJ 11666 — WCru
- B&SWJ 11671 — WCru
gracilis HWJ 622 — WCru
- HWJ 878 — WCru
gracilis × taiwaniana — WCru
hoi B&SWJ 11747 — WCru
kornasii B&SWJ 11830 — WCru
- HWJ 918 — WCru
macrophylla B&SWJ 8210 — WCru
- B&SWJ 9788 — WCru
- B&SWJ 11842 — WCru
- WWJ 11681 — WCru
microphylla B&SWJ 3872 — WCru
multinervia B&SWJ 11727 — WCru
aff. ***myriocarpa*** B&SWJ 11828 — WCru
nova NJM 13.128 — WPGP
rhododendrifolia — CBct CDTJ CExl EBee WPGP
- GWJ 9375 — WCru
shweliensis PAB 13.216 — LEdu
taiwaniana 🏆H4 — CBct WPGP
- B&SWJ 3575 — WCru
- B&SWJ 3788 — WCru
- B&SWJ 7096 — WCru
- RWJ 10000 — WCru
- RWJ 10016 — WCru
vietnamensis — see *S. chapana*

Schima (*Theaceae*)

argentea — CBcs CCCN CExl EPfP WPGP
aff. ***argentea*** NJM 13.042 — WPGP
khasiana — WPGP
- PAB 3447 — EBee LEdu
wallichii — CExl ESwi

Schinus (*Anacardiaceae*)

latifolius — ESwi
lentiscifolius — SPlb SVen
molle — SPlb
montanus — SPlb
polygama — SPlb

Schisandra (*Schisandraceae*)

arisanensis — MBlu NLar WPGP
- B&SWJ 3050 — WCru
chinensis — CAgr CBcs CRHN GKev GPoy LEdu MSwo NLar SBrt
- B&SWJ 4204 — WCru
- B&SWJ 4611A — WCru
- B&SWJ 4611B — WCru
- 'Bere' — LEdu WPGP
- 'Sadova No.1' — CAgr
grandiflora 🏆H4 — CBcs CRos CWCL EBee ELan EPfP ESwi GBin IMou LRHS MBlu SBrt SNig
- B&SWJ 2245 — WCru WSHC
- PAB 3673 — LEdu
- WJC 13666 — WCru
- var. ***cathayensis*** — see *S. sphaerandra*
- 'Jamu' (m) — WCru
- 'Lahlu' (f/F) — WCru
aff. ***grandiflora*** WJC 13817 — WCru
grandiflora × rubriflora — MMuc WCru
henryi subsp. ***yunnanensis*** B&SWJ 6546 — WCru
incarnata BWJ 7898 — WCru
incarnata × rubriflora — WCru
lancifolia — MBlu

nigra	see *S. repanda*
perulata FMWJ 13100	WCru
aff. ***plena*** HWJ 664	WCru
propinqua	WSHC
- subsp. ***sinensis***	CMac CRHN LEdu NLar WPGP
- - BWJ 8148	WCru
repanda B&SWJ 5897	WCru
§ - B&SWJ 11455	WCru
rubriflora ♀H5	CBcs CRos CTri EPfP IMou LRHS MBlu MGos NLar NRHS SBrt SLon WCFE
- BWJ 7557	WCru
- (f)	IDee WSHC WSpi
- 'Bodnant Redberry' (f)	WCru
§ ***sphaerandra***	MBlu
- BWJ 7739	WCru
- BWJ 8082	WCru
sphenanthera	EBee MBlu NLar WSHC
- BWJ 8151	WCru

Schizachyrium (*Poaceae*)

§ ***scoparium***	CBod CKno CRos EBee EHoe EPfP LRHS NRHS XLum
- 'Blue Heaven'	CBod CKno ELon IPot MAvo NDov SAko
- 'Prairie Blues'	CBod CRos CSpe EBou ELon EPfP LRHS NRHS SMea WCot

Schizanthus (*Solanaceae*)

hookeri	CPla

Schizocarphus (*Asparagaceae*)

nervosus	WCot

Schizocodon see *Shortia*

Schizophragma (*Hydrangeaceae*)

corylifolium	NLar
fauriei	NLar
- B&SWJ 1701	WCru
- B&SWJ 6831	WCru
- B&SWJ 7052	WCru
- CWJ 12405	WCru
- CWJ 12433	WCru
hydrangeoides	CBcs CBct CBod CCCN CDul CKel CRHN CRos EBee ELan EPfP EWTr LCro LOPS LRHS MBlu MGos NRHS SGol SLim SLon SPer SPoG SWvt WCFE WSpi
- 'Brookside Littleleaf'	see *Hydrangea anomala* subsp. *petiolaris* var. *cordifolia* 'Brookside Littleleaf'
- var. ***concolor*** B&SWJ 5954	WCru
- - 'Moonlight' ♀H5	CBcs CKel CMac CRos CWGN ELan EPfP EWTr LRHS MBlu MGil MGos MMuc NLar NRHS SGol SLon SNig SPer SPoG SWvt WCru WPGP
- var. ***hydrangeoides*** B&SWJ 5489	WCru
- - B&SWJ 5732	WCru
- - 'Iwa Garami'	NLar
- - 'Roseum' ♀H5	CArg CBcs CCCN CDul CMac CRos ELan EPfP EWes IArd LRHS MBlu MGil MGos NLar SGol SLon SPer SWvt WCru WPGP
* - f. ***quelpartensis***	LRHS
- 'Rose Sensation'	CCCN CKel CRos EBee EPfP LRHS NRHS SGol SLon SPoG
- var. ***taquetii*** B&SWJ 8771	WCru
- - 'Cheju's Early'	WCru
- var. ***ullungdoense*** B&SWJ 8505	WCru
- - B&SWJ 8522	WCru
- var. ***yakushimense*** B&SWJ 6119	WCru
integrifolium ♀H5	CBcs CCCN CKel CRHN CRos EBee ELan EPfP LRHS MBlu MMuc NLar SPer WKif WPGP
- BWJ 8150	WCru
molle HWJ 1011	WCru
- WWJ 11905	WCru

Schizostylis see *Hesperantha*

Schoenoplectus (*Cyperaceae*)

§ ***lacustris***	CWat LLWG MMuc MWts
§ - subsp. ***tabernaemontani***	CSpe LLWG
- - 'Albescens' (v)	CBen CWat MMuc MNrw WHal WWtn XLum
- - 'Zebrinus' (v)	CBen CWat ELan EWat MNrw SPlb WMAq WWtn XLum

Schoenoxiphium (*Cyperaceae*)

lanceum	XBlo

Schoenus (*Cyperaceae*)

pauciflorus	LLWG WMoo

Sciadopitys (*Sciadopityaceae*)

verticillata ♀H6	CAco CBcs CDul CKen CMac CSBt EPfP GKin LRHS MBlu MGil MGos MMuc MPkF NHol NWea SAko SCoo SEND SLim SPoG SWvt
- 'Beauty Green'	NLar
- 'Dutch Mill'	NLar
- 'Firework'	CKen
- 'Globe'	CKen
- 'Gold Star'	CKen
- 'Golden Rush'	CKen
- 'Goldmahne'	CKen
- 'Grüne Kugel'	CKen MAsh NLar
- 'Jeddeloh Compact'	CKen
- 'Koja Maki'	NLar
- 'Kugelblitz'	NLar
- 'Kupferschirm'	CKen
- 'Marylin Monroe'	NLar
- 'Mecki'	CKen
- 'Megaschirm'	CKen
- 'Moonie's Mini'	NLar
- 'Mr Happy'	NLar
- 'Ossorio Gold'	CKen NLar
- 'Perlenglanz'	CKen NLar
- 'Picola'	CKen MAsh NLar
- 'Pygmy'	CKen
- 'Queen's Parasol' **new**	NLar
- 'Richie's Cream'	CKen
- 'Richie's Cushion'	CKen
- 'Shorty'	CKen
- 'Speerspitze'	CKen
- 'Star Wars'	CKen
- 'Starburst'	CKen
- 'Sternschnuppe'	CKen MAsh
- 'Tsai Cheng'	NLar
- 'Wiels Beauty'	NLar
- 'Wintergreen'	CKen

Scilla (*Asparagaceae*)

adlamii	see *Ledebouria cooperi*
× ***allenii***	see × *Chionoscilla allenii*
amethystina	see *S. litardierei*

amoena	GKev
autumnalis	CAvo CRos EPot GKev LAma LLHF LRHS NRHS WShi WThu
bifolia ♀H6	CAvo CTca EPot GKev LAma SDeJ SPhx WShi
- 'Alba'	GKev SDeJ SPhx
- 'Rosea'	CRos ERCP GKev LAma LRHS NRHS SDeJ
bithynica ♀H6	GKev WCot WShi
campanulata	see *Hyacinthoides hispanica*
caucasica	GKev
chinensis	see *S. scilloides*
greilhuberi	CAvo EPPr GKev LLHF SBch WCot
haemorrhoidalis	GKev
hohenackeri	GKev LLHF WCot WThu
- BSBE 811	WCot
§ ***hughii***	EBee
hyacinthoides	CAby EBee ERCP SIgm WCot
- 'Blue Arrow' **new**	GKev
ingridiae	GKev WCot
italica	see *Hyacinthoides italica*
japonica	see *S. scilloides*
liliohyacinthus	CAvo CBro GKev IBlr WShi
- 'Alba'	CAvo
§ ***litardierei*** ♀H6	CAby CAvo EPPr EPot ERCP GKev LAma MMuc SDeJ SEND SPhx WShi
lutea hort.	see *Ledebouria socialis*
madeirensis	WCot
- from Madeira	CHll
melaina	WCot
mesopotamica	GKev
messeniaca	GKev
- MS 38 from Greece	WCot
mischtschenkoana ♀H6	CAby CAvo CRos EPot IFro LAma LCro LOPS LRHS NRHS SDeJ WShi
§ - 'Tubergeniana' ♀H6	CMea GKev SPhx WCot
- 'Zwanenburg'	GKev
monanthos **new**	GKev
monophyllos	WArt WCot
morrisii	GKev
natalensis	see *Merwilla plumbea*
non-scripta	see *Hyacinthoides non-scripta*
nutans	see *Hyacinthoides non-scripta*
obtusifolia subsp. ***intermedia***	WCot
persica ♀H4	GKev WCot
peruviana	Widely available
- SB&L 20/1	WCot
- 'Alba'	CBro CTca CWCL ECha EPot EWes NHpl WCot XLum
- Carribean Jewels Series	CBod
- - 'Sapphire Blue' **new**	WFar
- 'Hughii'	see *S. hughii*
- var. ***venusta*** S&L 311/2	WCot
- 'White Moon'	ERCP GKev
pratensis	see *S. litardierei*
puschkinioides	GKev
ramburei	GKev
rosenii	CWCL
- 'Cloudy Sky'	WCot
§ ***scilloides***	CPBP
- B&SWJ 8812	WCru
* - 'Alba'	SDeJ
siberica ♀H6	CAby CAvo CRos CTca ELan EPfP EShb GKev LAma LCro LOPS LRHS MMuc NAln NGBl NRHS SCob SPer SPhx WBor WShi
- 'Alba'	CRos EPfP EPot GKev LAma LRHS NAln NRHS SDeJ WArt WShi
- subsp. ***armena***	GKev
- 'Enem'	GKev
- 'Spring Beauty'	CMea CRos EPot ERCP GKev LAma LRHS NRHS SDeJ SRms
'Tubergeniana'	see *S. mischtschenkoana* 'Tubergeniana'
verna	GKev WShi WThu
violacea	see *Ledebouria socialis*

Scirpus (*Cyperaceae*)

cernuus	see *Isolepis cernua*
'Green Mist'	WCot
lacustris	see *Schoenoplectus lacustris*
- 'Spiralis'	see *Juncus effusus* f. *spiralis*
maritimus	see *Bolboschoenus maritimus*
tabernaemontani	see *Schoenoplectus lacustris* subsp. *tabernaemontani*

Scleranthus (*Caryophyllaceae*)

biflorus	CPla CSma EDAr EPot EWes GBin LEdu MAsh NRHS SPlb WFar XLum
uniflorus	CPla EPot LEdu NHpl SPlb SRot XLum

Sclerochiton (*Acanthaceae*)

harveyanus	EShb

Scoliopus (*Liliaceae*)

bigelowii	CAby GCal
hallii	EWld GBin LEdu MNrw NHar

Scolopendrium see *Asplenium*

Scopolia (*Solanaceae*)

anomala HWJK 2252	WCru
- PAB 4925	LEdu
carniolica	EBee EPPr EWld GBin GPoy ILea LEdu NChi NLar NSti SPlb WCru WPGP WPav WSHC XLum
- from Poland	LEdu
§ - var. ***brevifolia***	CRos EBee EHrv EPPr EPfP EWld LEdu LRHS NRHS SPhx WCot WPGP WPav
- 'Zwanenburg'	EHrv EPPr EWes LEdu NLar SPhx WSHC XLum
hladnikiana	see *S. carniolica* var. *brevifolia*
stramoniifolia	WPav

Scorzonera (*Asteraceae*)

hispanica	SVic

Scorzoneroides (*Asteraceae*)

autumnalis	CHab CWld NMir

Scrophularia (*Scrophulariaceae*)

aquatica misapplied	see *S. auriculata*
§ ***auriculata***	CHab LLWG NMir NPer WHer
§ - 'Variegata' (v)	CAby CBcs CRos ECha ELan EPfP GCal GLog LRHS MHer NRHS NSti SHar SPer
buergeriana 'Lemon and Lime' misapplied	see *Teucrium viscidum* 'Lemon and Lime'
- 'Lemon and Lime' (v)	NEgg
macrantha	GJos SPhx
- 'Cardinal Red' **new**	SPad WHil
nodosa	GPoy WHer
- ***variegata***	see *S. auriculata* 'Variegata'
vernalis	CBgR

Scutellaria (*Lamiaceae*)

albida	EBee

§	***alpina***	GJos SPlb SRms SRot
	- 'Arcobaleno'	GEdr LLHF
	altissima	CFis ECha ELon EMor GPSL MMuc NBro NGrd SPlb WFar WWtn XSen
	'Amazing Grace'	EWes
	baicalensis	GJos GPoy MNHC SIgm
	canescens	see *S. incana*
	costaricana	CCCN EShb
	diffusa	SBch
	galericulata	CBod CHab ENfk GPoy LEdu LLWG MHer SPhx WHer
	hastata	see *S. hastifolia*
§	***hastifolia***	CTri EBou
§	***incana***	CMea CRos CSpe ELon LRHS MAvo MHol MPie NAst NRHS SPhx WCot WGob
	indica	GEdr
	- var. ***japonica***	see *S. indica* var. *parvifolia*
§	- var. ***parvifolia***	EBou EWes GEdr GMaP ITim SRot WAbe
	- - 'Alba'	LLHF WAbe
	integrifolia	SPhx WGob
	lateriflora	GJos GPoy SRms
	- PAB 3921	LEdu
	maekawae	EBee
	- B&SWJ 557A	WCru
	orientalis	WAbe
	- subsp. ***bicolor***	SIgm
	- subsp. ***pinnatifida***	SIgm
	pontica	CFis EBou SPhx
	red-flowered	CCCN
	scordiifolia	CFis CSpe ECha NRya NWad SHar SRms WFar WJam
	- 'Seoul Sapphire'	LEdu SPtp WPGP
	sevanensis	WCot
	'Sherbert Lemon'	CMea GJos
	suffrutescens	GJos XSen
	- 'Texas Rose'	CMea CSpe EBou EDAr EMor GJos LLHF NHpl SRot WAbe WHoo WIce WTor
	supina	see *S. alpina*
	tournefortii	CFis CRos EBee ECtt LRHS NRHS
*	***zhongdianensis***	EPPr WPtf

seakale see *Crambe maritima*

Sebaea (*Gentianaceae*)

rehmanii	SPlb
thomasii	WAbe
- 'Bychan'	WAbe

Securigera (*Papilionaceae*)

§	***varia***	CDor EWld GJos LEdu MMuc SEND SRms XLum

Sedastrum see *Sedum*

× *Sedeveria* (*Crassulaceae*)

'Harry Butterfield'	WCot
'Letizia'	SChr

Sedum ✿ (*Crassulaceae*)

	'Abbey Dore'	see *Hylotelephium* 'Abbey Dore'
	acre	CRos CTri EPfP GPoy LEdu LRHS MAsh MNHC NMir NRHS SCob SPlb XLum
	- 'Aureum'	EDAr EHoe ELan EPfP MAsh NHpl NLar NRya SCob SPoG SRms SSim WCot XLum
	- 'Elegans'	ECtt GCrg
	- 'Golden Queen'	CRos EBou LRHS NHpl NRHS SPlb SPoG SRms
	- 'Helvetica'	WCot
	- 'Minus'	CRos LRHS NRHS SRms
§	- subsp. ***neglectum*** var. ***majus***	NLar
	- 'Oktoberfest'	GJos
	aizoon	GCal NBre SPlb WFar XLum
	- 'Aurantiacum'	see *S. aizoon* 'Euphorbioides'
§	- 'Euphorbioides'	ECha ECtt ELan LPot MHer MMuc MRav NLar SEND SPlb
§	- subsp. ***maximowiczii***	NWad
	alatum	WFar
	albescens	see *S. forsterianum* f. *purpureum*
	alboroseum	see *Hylotelephium erythrostictum*
§	***album***	CRos GJos LRHS MMuc NBro NMir NRHS SEND SRms XLum
	- 'Coral Carpet'	EBou ECtt EPPr EPfP GCrg GFgr GKev GWyn MAsh MRav NAln NHpl NLar NRya SPoG WFar XLum
	- Faro form	EPot
	- subsp. ***teretifolium*** var. ***micranthum*** 'Chloroticum'	XLum
§	- - var. ***murale***	CRos CTri LRHS NHpl NRHS XLum
	alpestre	XLum
	altissimum	see *S. sediforme*
	anacampseros	see *Hylotelephium anacampseros*
	athoum	see *S. album*
	atlanticum	see *S. dasyphyllum* subsp. *dasyphyllum* var. *mesatlanticum*
	AUTUMN JOY	see *Hylotelephium* (Herbstfreude Group) 'Herbstfreude'
	batallae ISI 1496 new	NWad
	beauverdii subsp. ***vietnamense*** HWJ 824	WCru
	'Bertram Anderson'	see *Hylotelephium* 'Bertram Anderson'
	beyrichianum misapplied	see *S. glaucophyllum*
	brevifolium	EWes NHpl
§	- var. ***quinquefarium***	WIce
	burrito	EShb
	'Carl'	see *Hylotelephium* 'Carl'
	cauticola	see *Hylotelephium cauticola*
	chrysicaulum	EPot
	clavatum ISI 1161	NWad
	compressum	see *S. palmeri* subsp. *palmeri* tetraploid
	confusum Hemsl.	SEND
	crassipes	see *Rhodiola wallichiana*
	crassularia	see *Crassula setulosa* 'Milfordiae'
	cryptomerioides B&SWJ 054	WCru
	dasyphyllum	NBir NHpl NRya SPlb SRms WCot
§	- subsp. ***dasyphyllum*** var. ***mesatlanticum***	NBir
	- ***mucronatis***	see *S. dasyphyllum* subsp. *dasyphyllum* var. *mesatlanticum*
	dendroideum subsp. ***praealtum***	NWad SChr SEND
	divergens	GKev XLum
	douglasii	see *S. stenopetalum* 'Douglasii'
	drymarioides	NBre
	'Dudley Field'	EPot MHer
	'Eleanor Fisher'	see *Hylotelephium telephium* subsp. *ruprechtii*

	ellacombeanum	see *S. kamtschaticum* var. *ellacombeanum*
	'Elworthy Rose'	CElw
	erythrostictum	see *Hylotelephium erythrostictum*
§	***ewersii***	see *Hylotelephium ewersii*
	fabaria	see *Hylotelephium telephium* subsp. *fabaria*
	fastigiatum	see *Rhodiola fastigiata*
	floriferum	see *S. kamtschaticum* var. *floriferum*
	forsterianum	SEND SPlb XLum
	subsp. ***elegans***	
	- - 'Silver Stone'	GJos MMuc WRHF
§	- f. ***purpureum***	CPla NRya
	furfuraceum	GCrg NHpl NWad SPlb WAbe
§	***glaucophyllum***	EDAr GJos XLum
	'Gold Mound'	EUJe GWyn NHpl
	Herbstfreude Group	see *Hylotelephium* Herbstfreude Group
	hernandezii	SSim
	- FO -199	NWad
	heterodontum	see *Rhodiola heterodonta*
	hidakanum	see *Hylotelephium pluricaule*
	himalense misapplied	see *Rhodiola* 'Keston'
	hispanicum	SPlb
	- 'Blue Carpet'	EPPr MSCN NHpl SSim WGrn
	- ***glaucum***	see *S. hispanicum* var. *minus*
§	- var. ***minus***	ECtt MMuc NHpl SEND SPlb WCot WMoo
	humifusum	EPot NHpl WAbe WFar
§	***hybridum***	XLum
	- 'Czar's Gold'	GJos NGdn SIgm
	'Indian Chief'	see *Hylotelephium* (Herbstfreude Group) 'Herbstfreude'
	indicum var. ***yunnanense***	see *Sinocrassula yunnanense*
	integrifolium	see *Rhodiola integrifolia*
	'Joyce Henderson'	see *Hylotelephium* 'Joyce Henderson'
	kamtschaticum 🏆H5	EDAr GJos
	- B&SWJ 10870	WCru
§	- var. ***ellacombeanum*** 🏆H5	CRos LRHS MMuc NRHS SEND WCot XLum
	- - B&SWJ 8853	WCru
§	- var. ***floriferum***	XSen
§	- - 'Weihenstephaner Gold'	CTri EBou ECtt ELan EPfP GAbr GJos GKev GMaP LPot MAsh MHer MMuc MRav NAln NBir NSla SPlb SPoG SRms WFar XLum
	- var. ***kamtschaticum*** 'Variegatum' (v) 🏆H5	CMea CRos EAJP EBou EHoe ELan EPfP GCrg LRHS MHer MJak MMuc NHpl NRHS SIgm SPoG SRms SRot SSim SWvt WIce XLum
	'Katharine's Gold'	MNrw
	kirilowii	see *Rhodiola kirilowii*
	lanceolatum	NBre
	lineare 'Variegatum' (v)	XLum
	'Little Dove'	SBch
	'Little Missy' (v)	WFar
§	***lydium***	CTri GFgr MHer NHpl SPlb
	- 'Bronze Queen'	see *S. lydium*
	makinoi	SSim
	'Manoir de Gaudon'	WCot
	'Matrona'	see *Hylotelephium* 'Matrona'
	maweanum	see *S. acre* subsp. *neglectum* var. *majus*
	maximowiczii	see *S. aizoon* subsp. *maximowiczii*
	middendorffianum	GCrg MBrN MHer MMuc SRms SRot WHoo XLum
§	***montanum***	MMuc
	moranense	MMuc XLum
	morganianum 🏆H2	EBak EShb
	morrisonense B&SWJ 7078	WCru
	'Mr Goodbud'	see *Hylotelephium* 'Mr Goodbud'
	'Munstead Red'	see *Hylotelephium* 'Munstead Red'
	murale	see *S. album* subsp. *teretifolium* var. *murale*
	nevii misapplied	see *S. glaucophyllum*
	nevii ambig.	SPlb
	nicaeense	see *S. sediforme*
	nussbaumerianum 🏆H2 **new**	NWad
	obtusatum misapplied	see *S. oreganum*
§	***obtusatum*** A. Gray	NBro NSla
	obtusifolium var. ***listoniae***	EDAr GEdr GJos
	ochroleucum	NBre NWad WCot
	- subsp. ***montanum***	see *S. montanum*
	oppositifolium	see *S. spurium* 'Album'
§	***oreganum***	ECha GAbr GCrg GKev GMaP LPot MHer NBir SIgm SPlb SRms SRot XLum
	- 'Procumbens'	see *S. oreganum* subsp. *tenue*
§	- subsp. ***tenue***	NHol NRya NWad
§	***oregonense***	CRos LRHS MHer NRHS
	pachyclados	see *Rhodiola pachyclados*
	pachyphyllum	LPot SAll
	palmeri	MRav NBir SChr XLum
§	- subsp. ***palmeri*** tetraploid	SEND
	'Parish Plum'	SBch
	pilosum	GKev
	'Pink Dove'	SBch
	pluricaule	see *Hylotelephium pluricaule*
	polytrichoides 'Chocolate Ball'	CPBP ECtt EMor NHpl SSim
	populifolium	see *Hylotelephium populifolium*
	pulchellum	ECtt WFar
	quinquefarium	see *S. brevifolium* var. *quinquefarium*
	'Red Cauli'	see *Hylotelephium* 'Red Cauli'
	reflexum L.	see *S. rupestre* L.
	- 'Cristatum' **new**	EUJe NHpl
	- red-leaved	NHpl
	rhodiola	see *Rhodiola rosea*
	rosea	see *Rhodiola rosea*
	rubroglaucum misapplied	see *S. oregonense*
	rubroglaucum Praeger	see *S. obtusatum* A. Gray
	× ***rubrotinctum*** 🏆H3	SEND SSim
	'Ruby Glow'	see *Hylotelephium* 'Ruby Glow'
§	***rupestre*** L.	ELan GJos MMuc SEND SPhx SPlb WFar XLum
	- 'Angelina'	CKno EBou ECtt EPPr EUJe EWes IMou LPot MHer NBir NDov NHol NWad SPoG SSim WCot WGrn WIce XLum
	- 'Aureum'	WFar
	- 'Monstrosum Cristatum'	NBir SMad WCot XLum
	ruprechtii	see *Hylotelephium telephium* subsp. *ruprechtii*
	'Sandra Mottram' **new**	NWad
	sarcocaule hort.	see *Crassula sarcocaulis*
	sarmentosum	XLum
§	***sediforme***	MMuc NBre SEND SRms SSim XSen
	- B&F MA 25	WCot
	- ***nicaeense***	see *S. sediforme*
	selskianum	GJos NBre NLar SBch XLum
	- 'Goldilocks'	GJos
	sexangulare	EBou ELon EPot GFgr MHer MMuc NRya SPlb SRms XLum
	sibiricum	see *S. hybridum*
	sieboldii	see *Hylotelephium sieboldii*
	'Silvermoon'	NWad

	spathulifolium	CTri ECha EPot
	- Atropurpureum Group	GQue SRot
	- 'Aureum'	ECtt WAbe
	- 'Cape Blanco' ♀H5	Widely available
	- 'Purpureum' ♀H5	CRos CTri CWCL EBou ECtt EDAr EHoe ELan EPfP EPot GAbr GKev GMaP GWyn LRHS MBel MHer NAln NHol NHpl NRHS NRya NWad SPlb SPoG SSim WAbe WMoo XLum
	- subsp. ***yosemitense*** 'Red Raver'	CPBP
	spectabile	see *Hylotelephium spectabile*
	spinosum	see *Orostachys spinosa*
	spurium	GJos GKev MMuc NAln SEND SRms WFar XSen
§	- 'Album'	NRya XLum
	- 'Atropurpureum'	ECha WMoo XLum
	- 'Coccineum'	GJos GQue MMuc SEND
	- DRAGON'S BLOOD	see *S. spurium* 'Schorbuser Blut'
	- 'Erdblut'	CTri
	- 'Fuldaglut'	CRos CTri EBou ECtt EHoe EPPr GCrg GMaP LRHS MNrw NRHS NRya SRms WMoo
	- 'Green Mantle'	CRos ECha EPfP GAbr LRHS NRHS
	- 'John Creech'	ECtt
	- PURPLE CARPET	see *S. spurium* 'Purpurteppich'
	- 'Purpureum'	SRms SRot
§	- 'Purpurteppich'	ECtt GJos MJak MRav NBro NLar NWad SRms SVen
	- 'Roseum'	SRms
	- 'Ruby Mantle'	GKev NBro NEoE SPoG SRms SWvt WMoo XLum
§	- 'Schorbuser Blut' ♀H5	CBod CMea CRos ECtt ELan EPau EPfP GKev LPot LRHS MCot NAln NBir NDov NRHS NRya NSla SPlb SRms SSim WFar WHoo WIce XLum
I	- 'Splendens Roseum'	XLum
	- 'Summer Glory'	NLar
§	- 'Tricolor' (v)	CTri EBee EBou ECha EPfP GEdr GKev MHer MRav NAln NHol NRya NWad SPlb SPoG SSim WMoo XLum
	- 'Variegatum'	see *S. spurium* 'Tricolor'
	- 'Voodoo'	CBod CPla EBou ECtt EDAr EPfP EWes LPot MBel MHer NBro NDov NGdn XLum
	stefco	XLum
	stenopetalum	SPlb
§	- 'Douglasii'	MHer SRms
	'Stewed Rhubarb Mountain'	see *Hylotelephium* 'Stewed Rhubarb Mountain'
	stribrnyi	see *S. urvillei* Stribrnyi Group
	takesimense	XLum
	- B&SWJ 8493	WCru
	- B&SWJ 8518	WCru
	tatarinowii	see *Hylotelephium tatarinowii*
	telephium	see *Hylotelephium telephium*
	ternatum	MHer
	tetractinum 'Coral Reef'	CSpe SRms XLum
	trollii	see *Rhodiola saxifragoides*
	urvillei Sartorianum Group	MHer XLum
§	- Stribrnyi Group	XLum
	ussuriense	see *Hylotelephium ussuriense*
	valens	SPlb
	'Vera Jameson'	see *Hylotelephium* 'Vera Jameson'
	viviparum	see *Hylotelephium viviparum*
	'Washfield Purple'	see *Hylotelephium telephium* (Atropurpureum Group) 'Purple Emperor'
	'Weihenstephaner Gold'	see *S. kamtschaticum* var. *floriferum* 'Weihenstephaner Gold'
	weinbergii	see *Graptopetalum paraguayense*
	yezoense	see *Hylotelephium pluricaule*
	yunnanense	see *Rhodiola yunnanensis*

Seemannia see *Gloxinia*

Selaginella (*Selaginellaceae*)

	apoda	CTsd LRHS
	braunii	WCot
	helvetica	EBee IMou XLum
	kraussiana ♀H2	CKel CTsd ESwi NWad
	- 'Aurea'	CCCN CRos ISha LRHS NRHS
	- 'Brownii' ♀H2	CCCN ISha
	- 'Gold Tips'	CCCN CKel CRos ESwi ISha LRHS NRHS
	lepidophylla	GKev SVic
	martensii ♀H1b	CKel
	moellendorfii	CRos ELon ISha LRHS NRHS
	uncinata ♀H1b	CKel CRos ISha LRHS NRHS
	wallichii	SMad
	willdenovii **new**	ISha

Selinum (*Apiaceae*)

	CC 6869	EBee
	KWJ 12281 from northern Vietnam	WCru
	candollei HWJK 2329	WCru
	carvifolium	CExl CMac CSam ELan EMor LEdu LLWG MNrw SPhx SPtp WCot
	- HWJK 2347	WCru
	- PAB 2676	LEdu
	cryptotaenium FMWJ 13250	WCru
	- PAB 8948	LEdu
	filicifolium	MAvo MBel MHol MTis WCot WRHF
	tenuifolium	see *S. wallichianum*
§	***wallichianum*** ♀H6	Widely available
	- CC 6869	GKev
	- EMAK 886	EBee GPoy
	- HWJK 2347	WCru
	- PAB 3579	LEdu WPGP
	- PAB 8969	LEdu WPGP
	- WJC 13656 from Sikkim	WCru
	- from Bhutan **new**	WPGP
	- from Manipur **new**	WPGP

Selliera (*Goodeniaceae*)

	radicans	GAbr

Semele (*Asparagaceae*)

	androgyna	CRHN WCot

Semiaquilegia (*Ranunculaceae*)

§	***adoxoides***	GKev
	- double-flowered (d)	GKev
§	***ecalcarata*** ♀H5	CSpe CWCL EBee EWld GCal GKev MNrw NAln NGdn NHpl SRms WHal
	simulatrix	see *S. ecalcarata*
	'Sugar Plum Fairy'	CRos CSma EPfP LBuc LRHS MTis NRHS SPoG

Semiarundinaria (*Poaceae*)

§	***fastuosa*** ♀H6	CBcs CBdn CBod CJun CTsd ENBC EPfP ERod EUJe IMou MMuc MWht SArc SEND SPlb XCre
	- var. ***viridis***	ERod MWht WCru XCre

kagamiana	CBdn ENBC EPfP IMou MMuc MWht XCre
§ ***lubrica***	MWht XCre
makinoi	MWht
maruyamana	see *Sasa palmata* var. *niijimae*
nitida	see *Fargesia nitida*
§ ***okuboi***	CBdn ERod MWht XCre
villosa	see *S. okuboi*
yamadorii	ERod MWht
- 'Brimscombe'	XCre
yashadake	ERod MWht XCre
- f. ***kimmei***	CBdn CBod CRos ENBC EPfP ERod LCro LOPS LRHS MJak MMuc MWht NLar NRHS SPoG WMoo XCre

Semnanthe see *Erepsia*

Sempervivella see *Rosularia*

Sempervivum ✿ (*Crassulaceae*)

'Aalrika'	NMen
'Aaroundina'	NMen
'Abba'	CMea NMen WHal
'Achalm'	GFgr NMen
acuminatum	see *S. tectorum* var. *glaucum*
'Adamina' **new**	NMen
'Adelaar'	NMen
'Adelmoed'	NMen
'Ageet'	NMen
'Aladdin'	GEdr MSCN NMen SRms
'Alchimist'	NMen XLum
'Aldo Moro'	EDAr LBee NMen WIce XLum
'Alenco'	NMen
'Alesia'	NMen
'Alfons-Roelands'	NMen
'Alice'	MSCN
allionii	see *Jovibarba allionii*
'Allison'	GFgr
'Alluring'	NMen
'Alpha'	CMea LBee NMen SRms WHal XLum
altum	CRos LRHS NMen NRHS SPlb SRms XLum
'Amanda'	MBrN NMen SRms WHoo
'Ambergreen'	NMen
'Andinn Tunrida' **new**	NMen
andreanum	see *S. tectorum* var. *alpinum*
'Andrenor'	NMen
'Andrenor' sport	NMen
'Antiquity' **new**	WFar
'Apache' Haberer	NMen
'Apanatschi' **new**	NMen
'Apollo'	XLum
'Apollo's Frog' **new**	NMen
'Apple Blossom'	CMea NMen
'Apricot'	NMen
'Apricot Beauty' **new**	NMen
'Aqua' **new**	NMen
arachnoideum ♀H7	Widely available
- from the Abruzzi, Italy	NMen
- from Zermatt, Switzerland	XLum
- subsp. ***arachnoideum***	CPla
- 'Ararat'	SDys
- var. ***bryoides***	CRos LLHF LRHS NRHS SRms
- 'Clärchen'	MSCN NMen WAbe XLum
- cristate	XLum
* - ***densum***	EDAr EPPr GAbr WAbe
- subsp. ***doellianum***	see *S. arachnoideum* subsp. *tomentosum* var. *glabrescens*
- 'Gorges d'Héric'	EPot
- 'Laggeri'	see *S. arachnoideum* subsp. *tomentosum* (C.B. Lehm. & Schnittsp.) Schinz & Thell.
- 'Opitz'	SRms
- 'Peña Prieta'	XLum
- 'Piletina' **new**	WFar
- 'Red Wings'	NMen XLum
- 'Rheinkiesel'	XLum
- 'Rubin'	CBod NHpl SSim
- 'Rubrum'	CRos EBou ELon GKev GMaP LRHS NRHS SPlb WFar XLum
- 'Spider's Nest' **new**	WFar
- 'Spider's Web' **new**	WFar
- subsp. ***tomentosum*** misapplied	see *S.* × *barbulatum* 'Hookeri'
- subsp. ***tomentosum*** ambig.	EBou EPot GKev XLum
§ - subsp. ***tomentosum*** (C.B. Lehm & Schnittsp.) Schinz & Thell. ♀H7	CRos GCrg LRHS NPer NRHS NWad SPlb SRms WAbe
§ - - var. ***glabrescens***	SDys XLum
- - 'Minor'	SSim
- - 'Minus'	CRos EPfP LRHS NRHS
§ - - 'Stansfieldii'	CRos EPPr LRHS NRHS SRms WHal
- 'Web Cluster' **new**	WFar
§ - 'White Christmas'	MHer NMen
arachnoideum* × *montanum	see *S.* × *barbulatum*
arachnoideum* × *nevadense	SDys
arachnoideum* × *pittonii	NMen SRms WAbe
arenarium	see *Jovibarba arenaria*
'Argus Eye' **new**	NMen
'Arondina'	NMen
'Aross'	CMea NMen
'Arrowheads Red'	NMen
'Artist'	NMen
'Ashes of Roses'	MSCN NHol NMen WAbe XLum
'Astrid'	NMen
'Atlantic'	SRms
atlanticum	CMea MMuc NMen SRot
- from Oukaïmeden, Morocco	GAbr NMen SRms
- 'Edward Balls'	NMen SDys SRms WFar
'Atlantis' ambig.	NMen SRms
'Atlantis' Adams	NWad
'Atropurpureum' ambig.	EPot GAbr GEdr MBrN NMen WFar
'Attraction'	NMen
'Aureum'	see *Greenovia aurea*
'Averil'	NMen
'Baby Skrocki'	NMen
balcanicum	NMen SRms XLum
ballsii	CRos LLHF LRHS NMen NRHS SRms
- from Smólikas, Greece	NMen
- from Tschumba Petzi, Greece	SDys XLum
'Banderi'	NMen
'Banjo'	NMen
'Banyan'	CRos LRHS NMen NRHS SRms
§ × ***barbulatum***	GAbr LBee NMen SDys WHoo
§ - 'Hookeri'	CTri GCrg WAbe WHoo XLum
'Baronesse'	NMen
'Bascour Zilver'	LBee MSCN SRms WHal
'Be Mine'	MSCN
I 'Beate' G. Dillmann **new**	NMen
'Beatles Memory'	NMen
'Beaute'	NMen
'Bedazzled'	NMen

	'Bedivere'	LBee NMen SRms
	'Bedivere Crested'	NMen
*	'Bedley Hi'	NMen
	'Bella Meade'	NMen SRms
	'Bellotts Pourpre'	NMen
	'Bennerbroek'	NMen
	'Bernstein'	EDAr GFgr MHer MSCN NMen NWad WHal WIce XLum
	'Beta'	NMen WAbe XLum
	'Bethany'	CMea NMen NWad WHal
	'Bianca'	NMen
	'Big Slipper'	NMen
	'Bijou'	NMen
	'Birchmaier'	NMen
	'Bitter Chocolate'	GFgr
	'Björn'	NMen
	'Black Beauty'	EBou EPot NMen
	'Black Knight'	CMea CRos LRHS MHer NRHS SPlb SRms WHal
	'Black Mini'	GAbr GCrg GKev NAln NBir NMen SRms
	'Black Mountain'	GKev LBee NAln NMen
	'Black Rose'	NMen
	'Black Velvet'	NMen
	'Black Widow' **new**	NMen
	'Blade of Steel' **new**	NMen
	'Blauer Ritter' **new**	NMen
	'Blood Tip'	CMea CRos ELon EPfP GAbr GKev LRHS LSun MHer MMuc NAln NHol NMen NRHS NRya NWad SEND SPlb SPoG SRms WHal WHoo
	'Bloody Goose'	NMen
	'Bloody Mary'	GFgr
	'Blue Bird'	NMen
	'Blue Boy'	CRos EBou ELon EPPr EPot GCrg GFgr LBee LRHS MSCN NMen NRHS SPlb SRms WFar
	'Blue Knight'	NMen
	'Blue Time'	GCrg LLHF WHoo XLum
	'Blush'	NMen
	'Boissieri'	see *S. tectorum* subsp. *tectorum* 'Boissieri'
	'Bokkenrijders' **new**	NMen
	'Bold Chick'	NMen
	'Bombardier'	EDAr
	'Booth's Red'	NMen
	borisii	see *S. ciliosum* var. *borisii*
	borissovae	NMen SDys
	'Boromir'	NMen XLum
	'Boule de Neige'	GCrg GEdr NMen NRya
	'Bowles's Variety'	NMen
	'Braune Maus'	GFgr
I	'Braunella'	NMen
	'Brilland Red Brun' **new**	NMen
	'Britta'	NMen SDys
	'Brock'	CRos LLHF LRHS NRHS SRms
	'Bronco' ♀H5	CRos EBou ELon EPfP GAbr GBin GCrg LBee LRHS MMuc NHol NMen NRHS NRya NWad SEND SRms WBrk WCot WPGP WRHF XLum
	'Bronze Pastel'	EDAr GFgr MSCN NHpl NMen NSla SRms SRot
	'Brown Owl'	EBou SRms
	'Brownii'	GAbr NMen
	'Brunette'	GAbr
	'Brunhilde'	NMen
	bungeanum hort.	NMen
	'Burgundy'	NMen
	'Burgundy Velvet'	NMen
	'Burning Bush' **new**	WFar
	'Burnished Bronze'	NMen
	'Burnt Embers' **new**	NMen
	'Butterbur'	NMen
	'Butterfly'	NMen
	'Café'	ELon MSCN NHol NMen SRms
*	***calabricum***	NHol
	calcareum	CMea CRos EBou ECtt EPot GKev LRHS MAsh MMuc NBro NHol NHpl NMen NRHS SArc SEND SPlb SPoG SRms SRot SSim WFar XLum
	- GDJ 92.16 from Petite Ceüse, France	SRms
	- from Cleizé, France	see *S. calcareum* 'Limelight'
	- from Col Bayard, France	GAbr NMen
	- from Colle St Michel, France	SRms
	- from Petite Ceüse, France	SRot
	- from Queyras, France	NMen
	- from Triora, Italy	NMen
	- 'Benz'	SDys
	- 'Extra' ♀H5	EWes GAbr GCrg GEdr MSCN NMen SRms SRot
	- 'Greenii'	CRos ECtt LRHS MSCN NMen NRHS SPlb SRms
§	- 'Grigg's Surprise'	NMen SPlb
	- 'Guillaumes' ♀H5	CRos GFgr LBee LRHS MSCN NMen NRHS SRms SRot WHoo
§	- 'Limelight'	CMea CRos LBee LRHS NMen NRHS WHal
	- 'Monstrosum'	see *S. calcareum* 'Grigg's Surprise'
	- 'Mrs Giuseppi'	EBou GAbr GCrg GEdr LBee LSun MHer NHpl NMen SRms WAbe WFar WIce XLum
	- 'Nigricans'	NMen
	- 'Pink Pearl'	MSCN NMen SDys SPlb XLum
	- 'Sir William Lawrence' ♀H5	CMea CRos EBou ECtt EDAr GFgr LBee LRHS NMen NRHS SRms WAbe WHal WHoo WThu XLum
	'Campagha'	NMen
	'Canada Kate'	NMen
	'Cancer'	XLum
	'Candy Floss'	NMen
	cantabricum	MMuc NMen XLum
	- from Navafria, Spain	NMen
	- from San Glorio, Spain	GAbr
	- from Ticeros	XLum
	- from Valvanera, Spain	NMen
	- subsp. ***cantabricum*** from Leitariegos, Spain	GAbr
	- subsp. ***guadarramense***	see *S. vicentei* subsp. *paui*
	- - from Pico del Lobo, Spain, No 1	SRms SRot
	- subsp. ***urbionense***	GEdr SRms
	- - from El Gatón, Spain	GFgr
	'Caramel'	NMen
	'Carlo's II' **new**	NMen
	'Carmen'	GAbr NMen
	'Carneum'	NMen
	'Carnival'	NMen
	'Casablanca'	NMen
	'Caspara'	NMen
	caucasicum	CRos LRHS NMen NRHS SRms XLum
	'Cavo Doro'	NMen
	'Celon'	NMen
	'Centennial'	NMen
	charadzeae	LBee XLum
	'Cherry Frost'	NHol NMen WCAu XLum
	'Cherry Glow'	see *Jovibarba heuffelii* 'Cherry Glow'

	'Cherry Tart'	SPlb
	'Chilli Pepper'	MSCN
	'Chivalry'	NMen
	'Chocolate'	NHpl WAbe
	'Choctaw' **new**	NMen
	'Cholie'	GKev
	'Christmas Time'	NMen
	chrysanthum	SSim
	ciliosum ♀H7	CMea GEdr NMen NRya SPlb SRms
	- from Alí Butús, Bulgaria	SDys
§	- var. ***borisii***	EPPr GCal GKev NRya WAbe WFar WHal
	- var. ***borisii*** × ***ciliosum*** var. ***ciliosum***	CTri
	- var. ***galicicum*** 'Mali Hat'	NMen
	ciliosum × ***grandiflorum***	NMen
	'Cindy'	SRms
	'Circlet'	NMen
	'Claey's Fluweel'	NMen
	'Clara Noyes'	NMen
	'Clare'	MHer NMen
	'Classic Rock' **new**	NMen
	'Clemanum'	NMen
	'Cleveland Morgan'	NMen XLum
	'Climax' ambig.	EPfP WFar
	'Climax' Ford	NMen
	'Cobweb Capers'	NMen
	'Cobweb Centres'	EWes NMen
	'Colchicum'	SRms
	'Collage'	NMen
	'Collecteur Anchisi'	GFgr SDys
	'Commander Hay'	CTri EBou EWes GKev GMaP MSCN NHpl NMen NPer NRya SRms WHal XLum
	'Comte de Congae'	NMen
	'Concorde'	LBee
	'Congo'	NMen XLum
	'Corio'	NMen
	'Corona'	NMen
	'Coronet'	NMen
	'Corsair'	ELon EPPr GEdr GFgr MBrN MMuc NMen SRms WBrk WFar WOld
	'Cream Tea' **new**	GFgr
	'Crimson Velvet'	CMea GCrg LBee XLum
	'Crimson Webb'	WFar
	'Cripello'	NMen
§	'Crispyn' ♀H5	CMea CRos EPot LBee LRHS MHer MMuc MSCN NMen NRHS SEND SRms
	'Crows' **new**	NMen
	'Crucify'	NMen
	'Cupream'	NMen SRms
	'Cyclops'	NMen
	'Dakota'	EDAr NMen
	'Dallas'	GCrg NMen SRms
	'Damask'	LBee MSCN NMen
	'Dancer's Veil'	NMen
	'Danji' **new**	NMen
	'Darjeeling'	NMen
	'Dark Beauty'	CMea CRos EUJe LRHS MSCN NHol NMen NRHS SRms WAbe WCot WHal
	'Dark Cloud'	CMea GAbr LBee WHoo XLum
	'Dark Point'	MSCN NMen
	'Dark Velvet'	CMea
	davisii	NMen
	'De Kardijk'	NMen
	'Deep Fire'	NMen SRms
	× ***degenianum***	GAbr NMen XLum
	'Delta' ♀H5	NMen WHoo

densum	see *S. tectorum*
'Desert Dream' **new**	WFar
'Devil's Teeth'	MSCN
'Devon Glow'	MSCN
'Diavolo'	NMen
'Director Jacobs'	EDAr NHpl NMen
'Direktor General'	NMen
'Ditto' **new**	GFgr
'Dolle Dina's'	NMen
dolomiticum	NMen XLum
dolomiticum × ***montanum***	NBro NMen
'Donarrose'	NMen
'Dornröschen'	NMen
'Downland Queen'	NMen
'Dr Fritz Köhlein'	NMen
'Dragoness'	NMen
'Dream Catcher'	NMen
'Dyke'	CTri GCrg NMen WHal
dzhavachischvilii	NMen XLum
'Edge of Night'	SRms
'Edwardine'	NMen
'Eefje'	NMen
'El Greco'	NMen
'El Toro'	MSCN NHpl NMen
'Electra'	GBin
'Elgar'	NMen
'Elva'	NMen
'Elvis'	NMen
'Emerald Giant'	GFgr SRms
'Emerald Haze' **new**	WFar
'Emerald Lustre' **new**	WFar
'Emerson's Giant'	NMen SRms
'Emmchen'	NMen
'Engle's'	CMea CRos CTri GCrg GFgr GKev LRHS MHer MMuc MSCN NMen NRHS SEND SPlb SRms WHal
'Engle's 13-2'	NMen
'Engle's Rubrum'	LBee NMen
'Eos'	NMen
erythraeum	CRos LLHF LRHS NHpl NMen NRHS SPlb SRms WHal
- from Mesta Valley, Bulgaria	NMen
- 'Red Velvet'	NMen
'Essence of Lime'	GFgr
'Euphemia' **new**	NMen
'Evening Glow' **new**	NMen
'Excalibur'	NMen
'Exhibita'	EPPr NMen SDys SRms
'Exorna'	EDAr NMen
'Fair Lady'	NMen
'Fairy'	EPot NMen
'Fame'	SPlb
'Faramir'	NMen
'Fat Jack'	NMen
× ***fauconnetii*** 'Rubellum'	NMen
- 'Thompsonii'	SRms
'Feldmaier'	NMen WFar
'Fernwood'	NMen
'Festival'	NMen
'Fiery Furness'	NMen
'Fiesta' ambig.	NMen WHal
'Fifty One Shades' **new**	WFar
fimbriatum	see *S.* × *barbulatum*
'Finerpointe'	NMen
'Fire and Ice' **new**	NMen
'Fire Flies' **new**	NMen
'Fire Glint'	GCrg GEdr NMen SRms
'Firebird'	NMen
'Firgrove Big Bronze'	NMen
'Firgrove Early Riser'	NMen

'Firgrove Silver'	GFgr
'First Try'	NMen
flagelliforme	XLum
'Flaming Heart'	EDAr MBrN NMen
'Flaming Sword' **new**	NMen
'Flaming Web' **new**	WFar
'Flamingo'	NMen
'Flammenschwert'	NMen
'Flanders Passion'	EWes LBee NMen SRms
'Flasher'	GCrg NMen
'Fluweel'	MSCN NMen
'Forden'	GFgr MSCN NMen
'Ford's Amiability'	SDys
'Ford's Giant'	EUJe XLum
'Ford's Shadows'	SDys
'Ford's Spring'	NMen SRms
'Freckles'	NMen
'Fronika'	NMen
'Frosty'	GFgr NMen SRms
'Fuego' ♀H5	CRos GFgr LRHS NMen NRHS SRms
'Fuji'	NMen
× ***funckii***	MBrN NMen XLum
'Fuzzy Wuzzy'	NMen
'Fyke' **new**	NMen
'Galahad'	NMen
'Gallivarda' ♀H5	CRos GFgr LRHS MSCN NMen NRHS
'Gambol'	NWad
'Gamma'	LBee NMen SRms
'Garnet'	NMen
'Gay Jester'	CTri NMen WHoo
'Gazelle'	XLum
'Georgette'	NMen XLum
'Georgia Rowan'	NMen
'Gilosum'	EDAr
'Ginger Nut' **new**	NMen
'Ginnie's Delight'	NMen
'Gipsy'	NMen
giuseppii ♀H7	CRos GKev LBee LRHS MMuc NMen NRHS SRms
- from Coriscao, Spain	LBee
- from Peña Espigüete, Spain	SDys SRms
'Gizmo'	NMen
'Glaucum'	see *S. tectorum* var. *glaucum*
'Glaucum Minor' **new**	NMen
globiferum	XLum
subsp. ***globiferum*** 'Minor'	
'Gloriosum' ambig.	MSCN NMen
'Glowing Embers'	NMen WHal XLum
'Godaert'	MMuc SEND XLum
'Gog' **new**	NMen
'Goldie'	NMen
'Goldmarie' **new**	NMen
'Goldschatz' **new**	NMen
'Goovy' **new**	NMen
'Granada'	EDAr NMen
'Granat'	GBin GWyn LBee MHer NMen SRms XLum
'Granby'	SDys
'Grand Mère' **new**	NMen
grandiflorum	NMen WThu XLum
- 'Fasciatum'	NMen
'Grannie's Favourite'	NMen
'Grapetone'	NMen SDys WHal
'Gratiana' **new**	NMen
'Graupurpur'	XLum
'Green Apple'	GAbr NMen SDys
'Green Caro'	NMen
'Green Disk'	SRms
'Green Dragon'	CRos LRHS MSCN NMen NRHS SRms
'Green Gables'	EDAr
'Green Ice'	GFgr NMen
'Green Wheel' **new**	NMen
'Greenwich Time'	EDAr NMen
* ***greigii***	EPot MSCN
'Grey Dawn'	CRos LRHS NMen NRHS SRms XLum
'Grey Ghost'	NMen
'Grey Lady'	NMen
'Grey Owl'	CRos GFgr LRHS MSCN NMen NRHS SRms
'Grey Velvet'	LBee NMen
'Greyfriars'	CMea CRos EDAr LBee LRHS MSCN NMen NRHS SRms WOld
'Greyolla'	NMen
'Grünschnabel'	XLum
'Grunspur' **new**	NMen
'Gulle Dame'	CMea NMen SRms
'Gumby'	NMen
'Gwiazda'	GBin WFar
I 'Hall's Hybrid'	MSCN NBro NMen SRms
'Happy'	NMen SRms
'Harriet'	NMen
'Hart'	GFgr NMen
'Havana'	NMen
'Havendijker Splitt' **new**	NMen
'Havendijks Millenium' **new**	NMen
'Havendijks Pride'	NMen
'Hayling'	CRos EWes LRHS NMen NRHS NWad SRms SSim WFar XLum
'Heigham Red'	CRos EBou EPPr GKev LBee LRHS NAln NMen NRHS SRms WIce
'Heike'	NMen
'Helen'	EDAr GCrg GEdr NMen
'Heliotroop'	NMen SDys SRot
helveticum	see *S. montanum*
'Hermann Näpfel'	NMen
'Hester'	MBrN NBro NMen
'Hey-hey'	CRos ELon EPot LBee LRHS MBrN NMen NRHS SPlb WCot XLum
'Hidde'	NMen SPlb
'Highland Mist' **new**	NMen
'Hirsutum'	see *Jovibarba allionii*
hirtum	see *Jovibarba hirta*
'Honymoon'	NMen
'Hookeri'	see *S.* × *barbulatum* 'Hookeri'
'Hopi'	NMen
'Hortulanus Smit'	XLum
'Hot Boyz'	NMen
'Hot Peppermint'	NMen
'Hullabaloo'	EDAr NMen
'Hurricane'	GCrg NMen
'Icicle'	CMea CRos ELon LRHS MSCN NBro NHol NMen NRHS SRms
imbricatum	see *S.* × *barbulatum*
'Impact'	NMen
'Imperial'	NMen SPlb
'Infinity'	GFgr
'Inge'	see *Jovibarba heuffelii* 'Inge'
ingwersenii	NMen XLum
ingwersenii × ***pumilum***	GFgr SRms
'Irazu'	CMea CRos EPot GCrg LRHS MSCN NMen NRHS SDys SRms
'Isaac Dyson'	SDys SRot
'Isabelle'	NMen
italicum	XLum
'Itchen'	NMen

'Ivonne' NMen
'Iwo' GFgr NMen
'Jack Frost' NBro NMen XLum
'Jacquette' NMen
'Jadestern' NMen
'Janis' NMen
'Jelly Bean' GFgr NMen
'Jet Stream' ♀H5 CRos ELon LRHS MSCN NMen NRHS SDys SPlb SRms
'Jewel Case' CRos LRHS NMen NRHS SRms
'Jim Knopf' **new** NMen
I 'John Hobbs seedling No. 2' NMen
'John T' × 'Saffron' NMen
'Joke' **new** NMen
'Jolly Green Giant' NMen
'Jo's Spark' NMen
'Jubilee' CMea EDAr ELan GCrg GEdr MAsh MHer NMen SRms XLum
'Jubilee Tricolor' GCrg GEdr NHol NMen WAbe
'Jungle Fires' CMea ELon NMen SDys SRms WHoo
'Jungle Shadows' EDAr NMen NWad XLum
'Jupiter' GKev NAln XLum
'Jurrina' NMen
'Just Peachy' EPot
'Justine's Choice' NMen SRms
'Kai' **new** NMen
'Kappa' NBro NMen SDys SRot
'Karin' **new** NMen
'Katmai' GFgr NMen
'Keiko' NMen
'Kelly Jo' NBro WBrk
'Kermit' NMen
'Khaleesi' **new** WFar
'Kiara' NMen
'Kibo' NMen
'Kidlington' NMen
'Kildare' **new** NMen
'Kim' NMen
'Kimba' NMen
'Kimble' NMen
'Kimono' NMen NWad
kindingeri SRms XLum
'King George' CTri EBou GKev LBee MMuc NAln NMen SEND SRms WHal WHoo XLum
'King Lear' GBin
'Kip' CMea NMen
'Kismet' NMen
'Koko Flanel' GFgr NMen SRms
'Korspel Beauty' NMen
'Korspel Prince' NMen
'Korspel Sport' NMen
'Korspelsegietje' GAbr NMen SRms
kosaninii NMen
- from Koprivnik, Slovenia MSCN WAbe XLum
- 'Hepworth' SPlb
'Krakeling' NMen
'Kramer's Spinrad' CMea EPPr GEdr GFgr GKev MBel NAln NMen SPlb SRms WHoo WThu
'Krankii' XLum
'Krater' NMen
'Lady Di' **new** NMen
'Lady Kelly' CMea
'Lamia' **new** NMen
'Lancer' NMen
'Larissa' GFgr
'Laura Lee' MMuc SEND
'Lavender and Old Lace' CRos EPot LBee LRHS MSCN NMen NRHS SPlb SRms WIce XLum
'Lavenderspross' **new** NMen
'Le Congai' NMen
'Legolas' NMen
'Leneca' NMen
'Lennik's Glory' see *S.* 'Crispyn'
'Lennik's Sport' XLum
'Lentezon' GFgr
'Leocadia's Nephew' NMen
leucanthum XLum
'Lilac Queen' NMen
'Lilac Time' ♀H5 CMea CRos ELon EPPr EUJe GFgr LRHS MBrN MHer MSCN NMen NRHS SPlb SRms WFar WHal XLum
'Limbo' NMen
'Lion King' GFgr MSCN NMen
'Lioness' NMen
'Lipari' SRms WCot XLum
'Lipstick' GQue NMen
'Little Coffee Cup' GFgr
'Little Flirt' MSCN
'Little Rock' **new** NMen
'Lively Bug' CRos EPPr LRHS MSCN NMen NRHS SDys SRms XLum
'Lloyd Praeger' see *S. montanum* subsp. *stiriacum* 'Lloyd Praeger'
'Long Shanks' MSCN
'Lonzo' NMen SRms
'Lord Alan' GKev NAln NMen
'Lord Morton' NMen
'Louisse-Marie' NMen
'Lovely Roset' NMen
'Lucy Liu' NMen
'Ludmila' NMen
'Lumeseen' **new** NMen
'Lynn's Choice' GAbr NMen WHal
macedonicum NMen SPlb SRms XLum
'Magic Spell' NMen
'Magical' NMen
'Magnificum' GFgr NMen XLum
'Mahogany' CTri EDAr GKev LBee MHer MSCN NHol NMen SRms WHal XLum
'Maia' **new** SSim
'Maigret' GCrg NMen
'Majanka' NMen
'Majestic' LBee NMen
'Malby's Hybrid' see *S.* 'Reginald Malby'
'Maria Laach' GCrg NMen
'Marijntje' NMen
'Marjory' **new** NMen
'Marland Ruby' NMen
'Marmalade' CMea NMen
§ ***marmoreum*** CRos EPot LBee LRHS NMen NRHS SRms WHal
- from Börzöny, Hungary XLum
- from Kanzan Gorge, Bulgaria XLum
- from Okol, Albania NMen
- 'Brunneifolium' GAbr LBee NMen XLum
- subsp. ***marmoreum*** var. ***dinaricum*** MHer NMen
§ - - 'Rubrifolium' XLum
'Marshall' NMen
'Mary-Beth' NMen
'Matthew's Day Dream' GKev NAln
'Mauvine' NMen XLum
'Mayfair' EDAr NMen
'Maytime' NMen

'Meadow Blaze' **new** WFar
'Medallion' NMen
'Meelah' NMen
'Melanie' CMea MBrN NMen
'Mercury' CRos GAbr GCrg LRHS NBro NMen NRHS SRms
'Merlin' MSCN NMen
mettenianum NMen
'Mickey Mouse' NMen
'Midas' CRos LRHS NRHS SRms
'Mildred' **new** NMen
'Minaret' NMen
'Mini Frost' NMen
'Minuet' NMen
'Mira' GBin MHol
'Mixed Spice' CMea NMen
'Moerkerk's Merit' CRos GAbr LRHS NMen NRHS XLum
'Mohair' NMen
'Mona Lisa' NMen
'Mondstein' MSCN SRms
'Monseigneur Desmet' GQue
'Montage' NMen
§ ***montanum*** XLum
– from Haute-Loire, France XLum
– from Mont Aigoual, France XLum
– from Monte Tirone, Italy LBee
– from the Pyrenees XLum
– from Vallée d'Estaing, France XLum
– 'Caesar' MSCN
– subsp. ***carpaticum*** GKev
– – 'Cmiral's Yellow' WAbe WFar
– 'Rubrum' see *S.* 'Red Mountain'
– subsp. ***stiriacum*** NMen SRms XLum
§ – – 'Lloyd Praeger' GFgr NMen SDys
'More Honey' NMen
'Morning Glow' NMen WHal
'Moss Rose' **new** NMen
'Mount Hood' CRos ELon LRHS NMen NRHS SRms WHal
'Mount Usher' NMen
'Mulberry Wine' LBee NMen SRms WHoo
'Mystic' MBrN NMen
'Naemi' NMen
'Neon' NMen
'Neptune' GFgr WFar
* ***netaginatum*** XLum
nevadense NMen NRya SRms
– 'Hirtellum' SRms
'New Rose' WFar XLum
'Nico' NMen NWad SRms
'Nigrum' see *S. tectorum* 'Nigrum'
'Niobe' NMen WHal
'Nocturno' XLum
'Noir' CRos EPfP GKev LRHS MSCN NBro NMen NRHS WFar XLum
'Norbert' NMen SRms XLum
'Nörtofts Beauty' NMen
'Nouveau Pastel' CMea NMen WHal XLum
'Nova' **new** NMen
'Novalis' **new** NMen
'Oberon' NMen
'Obsession' **new** WFar
'Ockerwurz' WFar
'Octet' NMen
octopodes NBir NRya XLum
– var. ***apetalum*** EPPr GAbr MSCN NMen WHoo
'Oddity' GBin MBrN MHer NMen WFar WHal

'Ohio Burgundy' CRos LRHS MSCN NMen NRHS SRms WAbe
'Olcina' **new** NMen
'Old Man Sage' SPlb
'Old Rose' NMen
'Olivette' NMen
'Olivia' **new** NMen
'Olivine' GFgr
'Omega' NMen
'Ornatum' MHer WAbe WHal
ossetiense GAbr NMen XLum
'Othello' ♀H5 CTri EUJe GAbr GCrg NBir NMen SRms WCot WPGP XLum
'Pachamama' NMen
'Pacific Charm' NMen
'Pacific Devils Food' NMen
'Pacific Hazy Embers' NMen
'Pacific Hep' NMen
'Pacific Opal' NMen
'Pacific Purple Shadows' NMen WFar
'Pacific Sexy' NMen
'Pacific Sunset' NMen
'Pacific Thunder' NMen
'Pacific Velveteen' GFgr
'Packardian' NMen NWad
'Painted Lady' NMen
'Palissander' EDAr GAbr NMen XLum
'Pallas' XLum
'Papucchini' **new** NMen
'Passionata' NMen
'Pastel' CTri GFgr MHer
patens see *Jovibarba heuffelii*
'Patrician' LBee SRms
'Pavilion' NMen
'Peggy' NMen
'Pekinese' CRos EBou GEdr LRHS MBrN NBro NMen NRHS SRms WBrk XLum
'Peridot' GFgr
'Peterson's Ornatum' SDys
'Petsy' NMen SRms
'Phoebe' NMen
'Pilatus' CRos EPfP GAbr LRHS NRHS SRms WFar XLum
'Pine Cone' GFgr NMen
'Pineapple Punch' GFgr
'Pink Astrid' NMen
'Pink Cloud' NMen
'Pink Delight' MSCN
'Pink Flamingoes' NMen
'Pink Grapefruit' NMen
'Pink Lemonade' NMen
'Pink Mist' SRms
'Pink Puff' NMen
'Pippin' CMea NMen SRms
pittonii ♀H5 CMea EPot NMen WHal XLum
'Pixie' GFgr NMen
'Plum Frosting' GFgr MSCN
'Plum Mist' NWad
'Plumb Rose' NMen
'Pluto' NMen XLum
'Polaris' GBin NMen
'Poldark' NMen
I 'Powellii' NMen
'Prairie Sunset' GFgr NMen
'President Arsac' XLum
'Probus' NMen
'Procton' GCrg NMen
'Proud Zelda' EDAr GAbr MSCN NMen
'Pseudo-ornatum' LBee SRms
pulchellum XLum

	Name	Suppliers
	'Pumaros'	SDys
	pumilum	CRos LRHS NMen NRHS SRms
	- from Techensis, Caucasus Mountains	SRms
	- 'Sopa'	MSCN
	'Purdy'	NHpl NMen WAbe
	'Purdy's 50-6'	GAbr NMen
	'Purdy's 70-40'	NMen
	'Purdy's Big Red'	NMen
	'Purple Beauty'	GKev NMen
	'Purple Dazzler'	NMen
	'Purple Haze'	NMen
	'Purple King'	CMea SDys
	'Purple Passion'	NMen
	'Purple Queen'	CRos EDAr ELon EPPr GFgr LRHS NMen NRHS NRya SRms WFar
	'Purple Shadows'	NMen
	'Purple Violet'	NMen
	'Pygmalion'	NMen
	'Quax'	NMen
	'Queen Amalia'	see *S. reginae-amaliae*
	'Quintessence'	MSCN NMen SRms
	'Racey'	GFgr
	'Ramses'	SDys
	'Raspberry Ice'	LBee MSCN NBro NHpl NMen
	'Rauer Kulm'	NMen
	'Rauhreif'	ECtt XLum
	'Ravenheart'	MSCN
	'Rebecca'	GKev
	'Red Ace'	GCrg GEdr MBel NBro NEoE NMen WFar
	'Red Beam'	CRos LRHS NMen NRHS
	'Red Chief'	XLum
	'Red Delta'	NBir NMen WCot WPGP
	'Red Devil'	CRos ELon LLHF LRHS NMen NRHS SPlb SRms
	'Red King'	NMen
	'Red Lion'	NMen
§	'Red Mountain'	LBee LSun MMuc NMen SRms
	'Red Pink'	CMea GFgr NMen
	'Red Robin'	NMen
	'Red Spider'	EPot GCrg NBro NMen
	'Red West'	NMen
	'Regal'	NMen
	'Regensburger Clown' **new**	NMen
	'Regensburger Knirps' **new**	NMen
	reginae	see *S. reginae-amaliae*
§	***reginae-amaliae***	CRos GKev LRHS NAln NMen NRHS SRms XLum
	- from Kambeecho, Greece, No 2	SDys
	- from Sarpun, Turkey	SDys
§	'Reginald Malby'	CRos LRHS NMen NRHS SRms
	'Reinhard' ♈H5	CMea CRos EDAr ELon EPot GCrg GEdr GKev GMaP LRHS MAsh MBrN MHer MSCN NHpl NMen NRHS NRya SPlb SRms WBrk WFar WHal WHoo
	'Remus'	ELan NMen SRms
	'Rex'	NMen
	'Rhône'	LBee NMen
	'Rhubarb Crumble'	GFgr
	'Risque'	LBee
	'Rita Jane'	GFgr NMen
	'Robin'	GCrg NBro NHol NMen SRms XLum
	'Romantik Ritter' **new**	NMen
	'Ronny'	NMen
I	'Ronsdorfer Hybride' **new**	NMen
	'Roosemaryn'	EDAr
	'Rosa Mädchen'	NMen
	× ***roseum***	NMen
	'Rosie'	CMea CRos ELon EPot GAbr GEdr GMaP LBee LRHS MAsh MMuc MSCN NHol NMen NRHS SRms WBrk WHal WHoo WIce
	'Rotkopf' ♈H5	CRos GFgr LRHS MSCN NMen NRHS NWad XLum
	'Rotmantel'	NMen
	'Rotund'	GEdr MSCN
	'Royal Opera'	EDAr NMen
	'Royal Ruby'	GCrg
	'Royale'	GFgr
	'Rubellum Mahogany'	GFgr
	'Rubikon Improved'	NMen
	'Rubin'	CBod CMea CTri EBou EPfP EPot EUJe MAsh MMuc NBir NEgg NHpl NMen SPoG SRms SSim WAbe WIce XLum
I	'Rubra Ash'	NMen
I	'Rubra Ray'	MMuc SEND
	'Rubrifolium'	see *S. marmoreum* subsp. *marmoreum* 'Rubrifolium'
*	'Ruby Glow'	EDAr
	'Ruby Heart'	CBod SSim
	'Ruby Meadows' **new**	WFar
	'Russian River'	WHoo
	'Rusty'	NMen
	ruthenicum	CRos EPPr LLHF LRHS NRHS NRya SRms XLum
	- 'Regis-Fernandii'	XLum
	'Ruth's Choice' **new**	WFar
	'Samwise'	NMen
	'Sanford's Hybrid'	NMen
	'Sanne' **new**	NMen
	'Santis'	NMen
	'Sarah'	EDAr NMen
	'Sarotte'	NMen
	'Sassy Frass'	NMen
	'Saturn'	MSCN NMen SRms WFar
	schlehanii	see *S. marmoreum*
	schnittspahnii	XLum
	'Scooby' **new**	WFar
	'Sea Breeze'	GFgr
	'Sea Urchin'	GFgr
	seguieri	XLum
	'Seren'	GBin
	'Serendipity'	EDAr
	'Sharon's Pencil'	NMen
	'Sha'uri'	NMen
	'Sheila'	GAbr
	'Shepherd's Warning' **new**	WFar
	'Shirley Moore'	NMen
	'Shirley's Joy'	NMen XLum
	'Show Baby'	NMen
	'Sideshow'	NMen
	'Sigma'	NMen
	'Silberkarneol' misapplied	see *S.* 'Silver Jubilee'
	'Silberkarneol' ambig.	GFgr MMuc
	'Silberspitz'	CRos ELon LRHS MHer NBro NMen NRHS SPlb SRms
	'Silver Andre'	NMen
§	'Silver Jubilee'	CMea CRos EDAr GBin GQue LRHS NBro NMen NRHS NRya SPlb SRms XLum
	'Silver Sixpence'	GFgr
	'Silver Thaw'	CRos LRHS NRHS
	'Silverine'	EDAr
	'Simonkaianum'	see *Jovibarba hirta*
	'Simply Nightfall' **new**	SSim

'Sioux' GAbr LBee MBrN NMen WHal
'Sirius' GBin MHol NMen
'Skrocki's Beauty' GAbr NMen SRms
'Skrocki's Bronze' CRos LRHS NMen NRHS
'Smaragd' CRos LBee LRHS NMen NRHS
XLum
'Smit's Seedling' NMen
'Smokey Jet' GFgr NMen
'Snowberger' CMea EBou MSCN NMen SRms WHal
soboliferum see *Jovibarba sobolifera*
'Solamith' **new** NMen
'Solar Meadows' **new** WFar
'Sombrero' NMen
'Soothsayer' NMen
sosnowskyi NMen XLum
'Soul' NMen
'Space Dog' NMen
'Spangle' NMen
'Spangle' sport NMen
'Spartan's Sunrise' **new** WFar
'Spherette' EDAr MBrN NMen WAbe
'Spice' NMen
'Spider's Lair' ♀H5 NMen SRms
'Spinellii' NMen WThu
'Spiver's Velvet' NMen
'Sponnier' XLum
'Spring Beauty' **new** NMen
'Springmist' CRos GFgr LRHS NMen NRHS SRms
'Sprite' CRos GEdr LRHS MBel NMen NRHS SDys SRms
'Squib' MSCN NMen
stansfieldii see *S. arachnoideum* subsp. *tomentosum* 'Stansfieldii'
'Starburst' CRos LRHS NMen NRHS
'Starion' NMen
'State Fair' EDAr NMen
'Steerosentern' NMen
* ***stoloniferum*** GAbr
'Storm Chaser' GFgr
'Strawberry Sundae' NMen
'Strider' GAbr NMen
'Stuffed Olive' NMen SDys SRms SRot
'Sugary' NMen
'Sun Waves' SDys
'Sunray Desire' NMen
'Sunrise' WFar
'Super Dome' GFgr NMen
'Superama' NMen
'Svava' **new** NMen
'Sweetheart' **new** NMen
'Syston Flame' NMen
'Tamberlane' EDAr
'Tarita' NMen
§ ***tectorum*** ♀H7 CHby CTri ELan GPoy LBee MHer MNHC NMen SPlb XLum
§ – var. ***alpinum*** CRos LRHS NBro NRHS SRms
– var. ***andreanum*** XLum
– 'Atropurpureum' ELan SRms
– 'Atroviolaceum' NMen SPlb XLum
* – 'Aureum' GFgr NMen
– var. ***boutignyanum*** SRms
GDJ 94.04 from Route de Tuixén, Spain
§ – var. ***glaucum*** NMen XLum
– 'Mettenianum' XLum
– monstrose SPlb SRms
– 'Murale' GFgr XLum
§ – 'Nigrum' LBee MHer NBro SDys XLum
– 'Red Flush' EPPr MBrN NMen
– 'Royanum' ♀H7 MSCN NMen SRms
* – subsp. ***sanguineum*** EDAr SSim
– 'Sunset' CMea EDAr EWes GAbr GCrg NMen SDys WHal
– subsp. ***tectorum*** GEdr NMen
§ – – 'Boissieri' NMen
– – 'Triste' LBee NHpl NMen XLum
– 'Violaceum' EBou NMen SPlb SRms
'Teddy Bear' MSCN NMen
'Tederheid' GCrg NMen
'Telfan' NMen
'Tenburg' NMen
'Terlamen' NMen
'Terracotta Baby' CMea ELon GCrg GFgr NMen
'Thayne' NMen
'The Platters' NMen
'The Rocket' GFgr
'Thunder' NMen
'Tiger Bay' NMen
'Timmy' **new** NMen
'Tinner Bell' **new** NMen
'Tintenblut' NMen
'Tintinabulum' NMen
'Tip Top' EPot GEdr GFgr NMen
'Tipsy' **new** NMen
tissieri XLum
'Titania' NBro NMen WHal
'Tjabine' NMen
'Tommella' XLum
'Topaz' LBee NMen SRms XLum
'Tordeur's Memory' GCrg MMuc NMen SEND SRms
I 'Tourmalyi' NMen
'T'Pol' NMen
'Tracy Sue' XLum
'Traffic Lights' GFgr
'Trail Walker' LBee NMen SRms
transcaucasicum XLum
'Tree Beard' NMen
'Trine' NMen
'Tristesse' ♀H5 ECtt EDAr GAbr LBee MBrN NMen
'Trude' **new** NMen
'Truva' GFgr NMen
'Twilight Blues' CRos LRHS NMen NRHS SRms
'Twist' **new** NMen
'Twizzler' MSCN
'U4' NMen
'Udine' NMen
'Uralturmalin' NMen
'Uranus' XLum
'Urmina' NMen
× ***vaccarii*** XLum
'Van der Steen' NMen
'Vanbaelen' GAbr NMen SDys
'Vasi Petru' NMen
'Vega' CPla GBin MHol
'Venus' NMen XLum
× ***versicolor*** CPla
'Veughelen' NMen
vicentei NMen
– from Gaton, Spain CRos LBee LRHS NMen NRHS
§ – subsp. ***paui*** NSla
'Video' NMen
'Violet Queen' CMea GFgr NMen
'Virgil' EDAr GAbr GCrg MBrN MSCN NMen NWad SDys SPlb WAbe WCot WIce
'Vulcano' NMen
'Wasti' NMen
'Waterlily' GFgr NWad

'Watermelon Rind' NMen
webbianum see *S. arachnoideum* subsp. *tomentosum* (C.B. Lehm. & Schnittsp.) Schinz & Thell.
'Webbyola' NMen
'Wendy' NMen
'Westerlin' NMen
'Wheel of Fire' NMen
'Whirlpool' new GFgr
'White Christmas' see *S. arachnoideum* 'White Christmas'
'White Ladies' NMen
'Whitening' GAbr GEdr
× ***widderi*** NMen
'Wilhelm Tell' NMen
'Wine Queen' new NMen
'Winsome' NWad
'Wok' NMen
I 'Woolcott's Variety' GFgr NBir NMen SIgm SRms
wulfenii XLum
- subsp. ***juvanii*** XLum
'Xaviera' NMen
'Yanisha' NMen
'Yolanda' NMen
'Yvette' NMen
'Zaccour' NMen
'Zackenkrone' NMen
'Zannalee' new NMen
'Zelca' new NMen
zeleborii NMen WHal
'Zenith' GAbr NMen SRms
'Zenocrate' NHol WHal
'Zilver Moon' NMen
'Zilver Snowflake' NMen
'Zilver Suzanna' NMen
'Zilverprinsesje' NMen
'Zircon' EDAr NMen
'Zone' NMen
'Zorba' NMen
'Zulu' NMen

Senecio (*Asteraceae*)

articulatus see *Curio articulata*
§ ***barbertonicus*** EShb
bidwillii see *Brachyglottis bidwillii*
candicans misapplied see *Jacobaea maritima*
- ANGEL WINGS ('Senaw') new WCot
candidus new WCot
chrysanthemoides misapplied see *Euryops chrysanthemoides*
cineraria see *Jacobaea maritima*
cinerascens SVen
coccinilifera hort. see *Kleinia grantii*
compactus see *Brachyglottis compacta*
confusus see *Pseudogynoxys chenopodioides*
crassissimus EShb
cristobalensis see *Roldana cristobalensis*
doria EShb MMuc SAko WHrl
elegans SVen
ficoides see *Curio ficoides*
- 'Mount Everest' new EShb
formosoides B&SWJ 10736 WCru
- B&SWJ 14382 new WCru
formosus B&SWJ 10700 WCru
- B&SWJ 14246 new WCru
gerberifolius B&SWJ 10357 WCru
- B&SWJ 10361 WCru
'Gregynog Gold' see *Ligularia* 'Gregynog Gold'
greyi misapplied see *Brachyglottis* (Dunedin Group) 'Sunshine'
greyi Hook. f. see *Brachyglottis greyi* (Hook. f.) B. Nord.
haworthii see *Caputia tomentosa*
heritieri DC. see *Pericallis lanata* (L'Hér.) B. Nord.
hoffmannii EShb
kleiniiformis EShb EUJe
laxifolius hort. see *Brachyglottis* (Dunedin Group) 'Sunshine'
leucostachys misapplied see *S. viravira*
macrocephalus new WHil
macroglossus CHll EShb
- 'Variegatus' (v) ♀H1c EShb
maritimus see *Jacobaea maritima*
mikanioides see *Delairea odorata*
monroi see *Brachyglottis monroi*
niveoaureus WCot
- B&SWJ 14320 WCru
petasitis see *Roldana petasitis*
polyodon CKel GQue LRHS WArt WCAu WCot WFar WSHC
- S&SH 29 new NCGa
- var. ***polyodon*** GBee GBin MMuc WWFP
- var. ***subglaber*** CCCN CSpe EAJP EWes GLog MHol MNrw MPie SPhx WCFE WPGP
przewalskii see *Ligularia przewalskii*
pulcher CDTJ SBch SHar WWFP
reinoldii see *Brachyglottis rotundifolia*
rowleyanus see *Curio rowleyanus*
scandens see *Delairea odorata*
scaposus EShb
seminiveus EBee
serpens see *Curio repens*
§ ***smithii*** ELan NBid WWtn
'Sunshine' see *Brachyglottis* (Dunedin Group) 'Sunshine'
talinoides misapplied see *S. barbertonicus*
- subsp. ***cylindricus*** 'Himalaya' see *S. barbertonicus*
tanguticus see *Sinacalia tangutica*
§ ***viravira*** MCot SPhx WSHC

Senna (*Caesalpiniaceae*)

alexandrina CCCN EShb
artemisioides ♀H1b WCot
§ ***candolleana*** CCCN EBee
§ ***corymbosa*** CBcs CCCN CRHN CTri ECre
× ***floribunda*** SBrt
hebecarpa SBrt
§ ***marilandica*** EBee ELan MGil
obtusa Clos see *S. candolleana*
septemtrionalis CCCN CKel CRos LRHS SEND

Sequoia (*Cupressaceae*)

sempervirens ♀H6 CAco CBcs CCVT CDul CLnd CMCN CMen CPer CTho CTsd ECrN EPfP EWTr LMaj LPra MBlu MMuc NOra NWea SEND SGol WMat WMou WTSh
- 'Adpressa' CAco CDul MGos NWea SCoo
- 'Cantab' WMou WPav
- 'Filoli' new CAco
- 'Henderson Blue' SLim
- 'Mount Loma Prieta Spike' NLar
- 'Prostrata' EWhm WPav

Sequoiadendron (*Cupressaceae*)

giganteum ♀H6 CBcs CCVT CDul CLnd CMCN CPer CTho CTri CTsd ELan EPfP

	EWTr LPra LRHS MBlu MGil MGos MMuc NEgg NOra NWea SEND SEWo SGol SLim SPlb WFar WMat WMou WTSh
- 'Barabits Requiem'	MBlu NLar
- 'Beautiful Jop'	NLar
- 'Blauer Eichzwerg'	NLar
- 'Bultinck Yellow'	MBlu
- 'Cannibal'	NLar
- 'Chief' **new**	NLar
- 'Desperado'	NLar
- 'French Beauty'	NLar
- 'Glaucum'	CDul MBlu SLim WPGP
* - 'Glaucum Compactum'	MBlu
- 'Greenpeace'	MBlu
- 'Kyoxonera' **new**	NLar
- 'Little Stan'	NLar SLim
- 'Pendulum'	CCVT CKen ERod ESwi LRHS MBlu SLim
- 'Yellow Stone'	NLar

Serapias (*Orchidaceae*)

lingua	SChF

Sericocarpus (*Asteraceae*)

asteroides	GKev

Seriphidium see *Artemisia*

Serratula (*Asteraceae*)

bulgarica	see *Klasea bulgarica*
coronata subsp. ***insularis***	see *Klasea coronata* subsp. *insularis*
gmelinii	see *Klasea radiata* subsp. *gmelinii*
lycopifolia	see *Klasea lycopifolia*
shawii	see *S. tinctoria* var. *seoanei*
tinctoria	NLar NMir SPhx
- subsp. ***monticola*** white-flowered **new**	EBee
§ - var. ***seoanei***	CKno CMea CSam EBee ELan LEdu MCot MHer MNrw MPie MRav NBid NDov SHar SPhx SRms WCot WPGP

Serruria (*Proteaceae*)

florida	SPlb
- 'Blushing Bride' **new**	CKel
glomerata 'Lemon Honey' **new**	CKel
phylicoides	SPlb
'Pretty 'n' Pink' **new**	CKel

Sesamum (*Pedaliaceae*)

indicum	SVic

Sesbania (*Papilionaceae*)

punicea	CCCN

Seseli (*Apiaceae*)

elatum PAB 9228	LEdu SPhx
- subsp. ***osseum***	SPhx
gracile **new**	CSpe
gummiferum	CSam CSpe EAJP SMad SPhx WHil
hippomarathrum	CSpe ECha MAvo MNrw NGrd SBrt SPhx WCot WHal WHrl WWtn
§ ***libanotis***	CSam EBee EPPr GBin LEdu LRHS NLar SIgm SPhx
montanum	CSam CSpe EBee IMou LPla MAvo NDov SBrt SHar

Sesleria (*Poaceae*)

§ ***albicans***	EPPr SCob
§ ***argentea***	CKno LPla
autumnalis	CKno EBee EHoe ELon EPPr EShb EWes IMou LCro LOPS NDai NDov SCob SPhx XLum
caerulea	CBod CKno CSde EHoe ELan ELon EPfP GQue IMou LCro LEdu LOPS LRHS NDov NRHS SPhx SPoG XLum XSen
- subsp. ***calcarea***	see *S. albicans*
- 'Malvern Mop'	EBee WHrl
* ***candida***	EPPr
cylindrica	see *S. argentea*
'Greenlee'	CKno
heufleriana	EHoe EPPr IMou LPla MBel NRya SMea SPhx SPlb WCot
insularis	EBee EPPr EShb
'Morning Dew'	EBee GCal
nitida	CKno CRos EBee EHoe EUJe IMou LEdu LRHS NDov NRHS SPhx WCot XLum XSen
rigida	EHoe
sadleriana	EBee EPPr EWes

Setaria (*Poaceae*)

italica 'Red Jewel'	CSpe
macrostachya	SPhx
palmifolia ♀H2	CPla EShb EUJe MPie SBrt SPlb
- BWJ 8132	WCru
viridis	WCot

Setcreasea see *Tradescantia*

shaddock see *Citrus maxima*

Sharon fruit see *Diospyros kaki*

Shepherdia (*Elaeagnaceae*)

argentea	NLar
rotundifolia	GKev

Shibataea (*Poaceae*)

chinensis	XCre
kumasaca ♀H6	CAbb CBcs ENBC ERod GCal LEdu MJak MWht SGol XCre

Shortia (*Diapensiaceae*)

soldanelloides var. ***magna***	EPot IBlr

Sibbaldia (*Rosaceae*)

procumbens	GKev NAln

Sibbaldiopsis (*Rosaceae*)

§ ***tridentata***	GKev SBrt

Sibthorpia (*Plantaginaceae*)

europaea	CExl

Sidalcea (*Malvaceae*)

'Brilliant'	CBcs CBod CNor GBin ILea MJak MNrw MSCN NBir SPer WCAu WFar WMoo
campestris from Oregon, USA	EPPr
candida	CBod CRos CSam EBee ECtt ELan EMor EPfP GMaP GWyn ILea LRHS MBNS MMuc MRav MTis NChi

	NGBl NGdn NLar NRHS NSti SCob SPer WCAu WCot
- 'Bianca'	CBod EBee EMor EPfP NLar WFar WMoo
'Candy Girl'	CBod EBee NLar SCob WCot WFar
'Crimson King'	WFar
'Croftway Red'	CBod CRos EBee ELan LRHS MBel NBro NGdn NHol NRHS NWad SPer SWvt WFar
'Elsie Heugh' ♀H7	Widely available
LILAC CANDICE ('Midawioha')	CBod WFar
'Little Princess'PBR	CRos EBee EPfP EWes LRHS MHol MNrw NGdn NLar NRHS SCob SPoG WCot WFar
'Loveliness'	CBod EBee ECtt ELan EShb LRHS MBel MRav NBro NDov NRHS NWad SPoG WFar WGwG WMoo WWtn
malviflora	SBrt SRms
- 'Crimson Beauty'	EBee IKil
- subsp. ***purpurea***	CRos LRHS NRHS
'Monarch'	WFar
'Moorland Rose Coronet'	WFar WMoo
'Mr Lindbergh'	EBee MPie NHsp NLar WCFE
'Mrs Borrodaile'	CMac MBel MRav NBro NEoE NGdn NLar WMoo
'Mrs Galloway'	CRos LRHS NRHS
'My Love'	EBee NDov
'Oberon' ♀H7	CRos EBee LRHS MRav NRHS
oregana	NGdn
- subsp. ***spicata***	WFar WMoo
'Party Girl'	CMac CRos CSam ELan EMor EPfP LRHS MNHC MPie MRav NBro NGdn NLar NRHS SPlb SPoG WBor WFar WMoo WWtn XLum
'Purpetta'	CBod EBee ELan EPfP NEoE NGBl NLar
reptans	WFar
'Reverend Page Roberts'	MRav WCot
'Rosaly'	CBod CRos CSam EAJP EMor LRHS NHsp NLar NRHS WFar WWtn
'Rosanna'	CRos CSam EBou EMor EPfP GMaP LRHS NHsp NLar NRHS
'Rose Bud'	EBee ELan WFar
'Rose Queen'	CBod CRos EBee ECha EPPr LRHS MRav NBro NHol NRHS SHar SPer SRms WFar
Stark's hybrids	CBod CRos LRHS NRHS SRms
'Sussex Beauty'	CRos CSam EBee EMor LRHS MBel MHol MMrt MRav NAln NCGa NEgg NGdn NRHS SPoG WCot WFar WMoo
'Wensleydale'	CRos EBee LRHS NRHS WFar
'William Smith' ♀H7	CRos CSam EBee ECha ECtt EMor EPfP EWTr EWes GBin LRHS MArl MMuc MRav NBir NGdn NLar NRHS SEND SPer WFar WWtn
'Wine Red'	CBod EBee EMor EShb LRHS MMrt NEgg NGdn NRHS SPoG SWvt WGwG

Sideritis (Lamiaceae)

cypria	EBee
hyssopifolia	SIgm
phlomoides	SIgm
sericea	SIgm
syriaca	MHer XSen
- RCB UA 2	WCot

Sieversia (Rosaceae)

reptans	see *Geum reptans*

Silaum (Apiaceae)

silaus	NMir

Silene (Caryophyllaceae)

RBS	EPPr
from Uzbekistan	GCal
acaulis	EBou EDAr EPot GJos SRms WAbe WArt
§ - subsp. ***acaulis***	SPlb SRms
- 'Alba'	EWes WAbe
- 'Blush'	EDAr GCrg NRHS NSla WAbe WOld
§ - subsp. ***bryoides***	NLar
- 'Correvoniana'	NLar
- subsp. ***elongata***	see *S. acaulis* subsp. *acaulis*
- subsp. ***exscapa***	see *S. acaulis* subsp. *bryoides*
- 'Frances'	CPBP EDAr EPot GCrg ITim NLar NRHS NRya NSla WAbe
- 'Mount Snowdon'	EBou EWes NHpl NLar SPlb SPoG SRms SRot WHoo
- 'Pedunculata'	see *S. acaulis* subsp. *acaulis*
aegyptiaca	SPhx
alba	see *S. latifolia* subsp. *alba*
§ ***alpestris***	SRms SRot WArt WMoo WThu
- 'Flore Pleno' (d) ♀H7	CMea CPBP EBou EWes NRHS NSla WIce
- 'Starry Dreams'	CRos CSpe LRHS NRHS
aomorensis new	EBee
argaea	CPla
× ***arkwrightii***	see *Lychnis* × *arkwrightii*
armeria	SDys
- 'Electra'	CSpe MNHC
asterias	EBee EPPr GCal GJos MNrw SBrt
atropurpurea	see *Lychnis viscaria* subsp. *atropurpurea*
catholica	EBee
'Confetti'	CPla EAJP ECha EDAr
'Country Comet'	NChi
§ ***davidii***	GKev
delavayi	EDAr
§ ***dioica***	CBre CHab CWld EBou EMor GJos IKil LCro LOPS MHer MNHC NGrd NLar NMir SPhx SPoG SRms WMoo WOut WSFF WShi
- 'Clifford Moor' (v)	ECtt MHer NSti SCoo
- 'Compacta'	see *S. dioica* 'Minikin'
- 'Firefly'PBR (d)	CDor CMac CSpe CWCL ECtt NSti SHar SWvt WSHC
§ - 'Flore Pleno' (d)	MHer MRav NBid NBro NGdn WHoo
- 'Inane'	ELon WBor WSHC
- 'Innocence'	NGrd
- Kilmurry form, dark-leaved new	IKil
§ - 'Minikin'	MTis NGdn
- 'Purple Prince'	CBre MMuc SEND WMoo
I - 'Ray's Golden Campion'	EMor EPPr NWad SHar
- 'Rollie's Favorite'PBR	CRos EBee ECtt EMor EPfP LRHS MAsh MHol MNrw MSCN NDov NPri NRHS NSti SPoG WBor WCAu
- 'Rosea Plena' (d)	WSHC
- 'Rubra Plena'	see *S. dioica* 'Flore Pleno'
- 'Thelma Kay' (d/v)	NGdn WMoo
- 'Valley High' (v)	EBee ECtt EWes MHol WCot
elisabethae	NSla
§ ***fimbriata***	CAby CSpe EHrv ELan EMor EPPr EShb GQue GWyn ILea MCot MMrt

	MNrw MRav MWat NLar NSti WArt WCot WFar WKif WMoo WPtf WRHF WWtn
frivaldskyana	SBrt SPhx
hookeri	GBin GKev SPlb
– Ingramii Group	GKev WAbe WThu
kantzeensis	see *S. davidii*
keiskei	CPBP
– var. ***akaisialpina***	NSla
– – f. ***leucantha***	NSla
– var. ***minor***	CRos EWes LRHS NRHS WAbe
laciniata	CSpe
'Starburst' **new**	
latifolia	CHab GJos MHer MNHC NGrd NMir WOut
§ – subsp. ***alba***	CWld GJos LRHS SEND SPhx
mariana	GAbr
maritima	see *S. uniflora*
multifida	see *S. fimbriata*
noctiflora	CHab WSFF
nutans	SRms WSFF
pusilla	GJos NHpl NLar
quadridentata	see *S. alpestris*
regia	CBod EBee SBrt SPhx
rubra	see *S. dioica*
saxifraga	GKev
schafta ♀H5	CTri ECha EPfP GJos GKev MMuc MRav NBid SEND SRms WHoo XLum
– 'Abbotswood'	see *Lychnis* × *walkeri* 'Abbotswood Rose'
– 'Persian Carpet'	WRHF
– 'Shell Pink'	CPBP CRos CSam ECha ECtt EPfP EPot EWes GJos LRHS MMuc NBid NRHS NSla SEND WHoo
sieboldii	see *Lychnis coronata* var. *sieboldii*
stellata	SPhx
§ ***uniflora***	CHab EPfP MMuc NBro SPlb SRms SRot WMoo WOut
– 'Alba Plena'	see *S. uniflora* 'Robin Whitebreast'
I – 'Compacta'	SHar WArt WMoo
§ – 'Druett's Variegated' (v)	CBod CRos CTri EBou ECtt ELon EPot EWes LRHS MHer MHol NBid NHpl NRHS SPlb SPoG SRms WIce XLum
– 'Flore Pleno'	see *S. uniflora* 'Robin Whitebreast'
§ – 'Robin Whitebreast' (d)	ECha EPfP GBin LRHS NBid NBro NRHS NWad SPhx SRms SRot WMoo WSHC XLum
– 'Rosea'	ECtt GCrg GJos MHol MMuc NHpl SPlb SRot
– 'Swan Lake' (d)	SIgm
– 'Variegata'	see *S. uniflora* 'Druett's Variegated'
– WEISSKEHLCHEN	see *S. uniflora* 'Robin Whitebreast'
– 'White Bells'	CTri WKif
viridiflora	SPhx
§ ***vulgaris***	CAgr CHab MMuc MNHC NMir SPhx SRms WHer WMoo WOut
– subsp. ***maritima***	see *S. uniflora*
wallichiana	see *S. vulgaris*
'Wisley Pink'	ECtt
yunnanensis	SPhx WSHC
§ ***zawadskii***	GJos GKev MMuc NAln NWad SBrt SEND

Siler (*Umbelliferae*)

montanum	see *Laserpitium siler*

Silphium (*Asteraceae*)

integrifolium	IMou NBre SPhx WCot WOld XLum
laciniatum	CMac CSpe LEdu NBre SBrt SMad SPhx WHal XLum
perfoliatum ♀H7	CBod CRos EBee EMor GPoy IMou LEdu LPla LRHS MMuc NBre NDov NLar NRHS SEND SPhx WCot XLum
– from Great Dixter	IMou
– var. ***connatum***	SPhx
terebinthinaceum	CSpe SBrt SPhx WCot XLum
trifoliatum	EPPr SPhx WCot

Silybum (*Asteraceae*)

marianum	CRos ELan GPoy LRHS MNHC NBir NRHS SPhx SRms WArt WOut

Sinacalia (*Asteraceae*)

§ ***tangutica***	CSam GQue ILea MBel NBid NLar NSti WCot WOld WWtn

Sinapis (*Brassicaceae*)

alba	SVic

Sinarundinaria (*Poaceae*)

anceps	see *Yushania anceps*
jaunsarensis	see *Yushania anceps*
maling	see *Yushania maling*
murielae	see *Fargesia murielae*
nitida	see *Fargesia nitida*

Sinningia (*Gesneriaceae*)

* ***caerulea***	WDib
calcaria	WDib
§ ***cardinalis***	EBak WDib
– 'Innocent'	WDib
conspicua	WDib
nivalis	WDib
speciosa 'Blanche de Méru'	SDeJ
– 'Hollywood'	SDeJ
– 'Kaiser Friedrich'	SDeJ
– 'Kaiser Wilhelm'	SDeJ
– 'Mont Blanc'	EShb SDeJ
tuberosa	MCot
tubiflora	EShb LEdu WCot WKif XLum

Sinobambusa (*Poaceae*)

§ ***intermedia***	XCre
rubroligula	XCre
tootsik	XCre

× *Sinocalycalycanthus* see *Calycanthus*

Sinocalycanthus see *Calycanthus*

Sinocrassula (*Crassulaceae*)

§ ***yunnanensis***	CBod CPla EShb NHpl SPlb SSim

Sinofranchetia (*Lardizabalaceae*)

chinensis	CRHN IArd SAko WPGP WSHC
– DJHS 4117	WCru

Sinojackia (*Styracaceae*)

rehderiana	IArd
xylocarpa	CBcs CMCN IMou NLar

Sinopodophyllum (*Berberidaceae*)

§ ***hexandrum***	CBct CSpe CWCL EBee ELan EMor EPot GBin GKev GMaP GPoy GQue ILea LPla MNrw MPnt MRav NBid NBir NChi NLar SPlb WAvo WCot WPnP WSHC

- from Kangding, Mugecuo Lake, Sichuan, China **new**	SBrt
§ - var. ***chinense***	GCal GEdr GKev LEdu WCru
- - BWJ 7908	WCru
- - SDR 4409	CExl
- 'Chinese White'	CExl
§ - var. ***emodi***	EPfP ITim
- - 'Majus'	GBin WCot WHal

Sinowilsonia (*Hamamelidaceae*)

henryi	CBcs NLar

Siphocranion (*Lamiaceae*)

§ ***macranthum***	EBee EWes WPGP WSHC

Sison (*Apiaceae*)

amomum	CBre

Sisymbrium (*Brassicaceae*)

§ ***luteum***	EBee

Sisyrinchium (*Iridaceae*)

× ***anceps***	see *S. angustifolium*
§ ***angustifolium***	CWCL ECha EMor MCot NBir NChi SChF SPlb SRms WBrk
- f. ***album***	MCot NChi NLar
§ ***arenarium***	CWCL
bellum hort.	see *S. idahoense* var. *bellum*
bermudiana	see *S. angustifolium*
'Biscutella'	CBod CKno EMor EPfP GMaP ITim LEdu MHCG SPad SPlb SRot WHal WHoo WJam WKif
'Blue France'	EPot
'Blue Ice'	GPSL ITim LRHS NLar WAbe
'Blue Skies'	ITim
boreale	see *S. californicum*
brachypus	see *S. californicum* Brachypus Group
'Californian Skies'	CAby CElw CExl CKno CRos EAJP ECha ECtt GMaP LRHS NBir NDov NRHS NSla SRms SRot SWvt WAvo WKif
§ ***californicum***	CBen GWyn IMou LLWG LRHS WMAq XLum
§ - Brachypus Group	CPla CTri EBou EMor EPfP GAbr LPot MAsh NBir NLar SPlb SWvt
- 'Yellowstone'	CSBt EPfP SRms
* ***capsicum***	CExl
convolutum B&SWJ 9117	WCru
cuspidatum	see *S. arenarium*
'Devon Skies'	CElw CMea CPla CRos CWCL ECtt EWTr GCrg LRHS MEch MNrw NLar NRHS SRms SWvt WAbe WIce
douglasii	see *Olsynium douglasii*
'Dragon's Eye'	CElw CKno CMea CPBP ECtt EHoe EWes LPot MBrN MHer SCob WFar WHoo WIce
'E.K. Balls'	CAby CPBP CRos EBou ECtt EDAr EHoe ELan EMor GCrg GMaP LRHS MAsh MCot NHpl NRHS NRya NSla SMad SPoG SRms SRot SWvt WAbe WIce
graminoides	GWyn NWad
grandiflorum	see *Olsynium douglasii*
'Hemswell Sky'	ECtt EHoe GAbr NLar NRya
'Iceberg'	CAby CElw CKno EAJP ECha EWes
idahoense	CPla ECha ECtt GAbr MHer NDov NHpl SPlb SRms
§ - var. ***bellum***	CKno EBou EPfP SRms XLum
- - pale-flowered	CKno SMHy
- - 'Rocky Point'	CKno CRos CSpe EPfP EWes LRHS NRHS SPoG WFar
- var. ***macounii***	GEdr GPSL SPlb
§ - - 'Album' ♀H4	CAby CElw CMea ECtt EWes GCrg GEdr LPot WAbe WFar WIce
'Janet Denman' (v)	EDAr EWes LLHF SRot
junceum	see *Olsynium junceum*
littorale	CExl
macrocarpon misapplied	see *S. macrocarpum*
§ ***macrocarpum***	EWld
'Marchants Seedling'	SMHy
'Marion'	CMea ECtt MBrN WHoo
'May Snow'	see *S. idahoense* var. *macounii* 'Album'
montanum	NHpl
montanum* × *nudicaule	GAbr NRHS NWad SRot
'Mrs Spivey'	NBir
'North Star'	see *S.* 'Pole Star'
nudicaule	NWad
palmifolium	CAby CSpe LEdu MHer MNrw NWad SMad SPad WFar WSHC XLum
patagonicum	CExl CPla GKev
§ 'Pole Star'	NLar
'Quaint and Queer'	CCCN CExl EAJP ECha EShb LPot MBrN MNrw NBir WAvo WJam WSHC
'Raspberry'	CKno CMea
'Sapphire'	CAby CBod CCCN CKno CRos ECha ECtt EDAr EHoe ELan GCrg LPot LRHS MHol NHpl NLar SCob SPoG WGrn
§ ***striatum***	Widely available
§ - 'Aunt May' (v)	CBcs CBod CCCN CMac CRos ECha EHoe EPfP GMaP LRHS LSRN MGos MRav NHpl NRHS NSti SCob SPoG SRms SWvt WCAu WCot WPGP
- 'Variegatum'	see *S. striatum* 'Aunt May'
'Stripey'^{PBR} (v)	WCot
aff. ***unispathaceum*** B&SWJ 10683	WCru

Sium (*Apiaceae*)

sisarum	CLau GPoy LEdu MHer NDov

Skimmia ✿ (*Rutaceae*)

anquetilia	CMac
- (f)	WCru
- (m)	WCru
arborescens B&SWJ 11799	WCru
- B&SWJ 13902 **new**	WCru
- PAB 8774	LEdu
- subsp. ***nitida*** B&SWJ 8239	WCru
arisanensis B&SWJ 7114	WCru
- CWJ 12417	WCru
black-fruited B&SWJ 8259 from northern Vietnam (f/m)	WCru
× ***confusa*** 'Kew Green' (m) ♀H5	Widely available
japonica	CMac CTho MGos NWea SCob SSta WFar
- (f)	CMac CTri EPfP SRms
- B&SWJ 5053 (f)	WCru
- B&SWJ 5053 (m)	WCru
- 'Alba'	see *S. japonica* 'Wakehurst White'
- 'Attraction'	MGos
- 'Bowles's Dwarf Female' (f)	CEnd MRav MWht

- 'Bowles's Dwarf Male' (m)	EMil NWad
- 'Bronze Knight' (m)	CBod CMac MAsh MRav NLar NWad SRms
- 'Carberry' (f)	CMac
- 'Chameleon' (f)	CDul
- 'Dad's Red Dragon' (f)	CMac MAsh SRms
- 'Emerald King' (m)	WFar
- 'Finchy'[PBR] (m)	CRos EPfP LRHS MAsh NLar NRHS
- 'Foremanii'	see *S. japonica* 'Veitchii'
§ - 'Fragrans' (m) ♀H5	CMac CRos CSBt CTri EBee EPfP LRHS LSRN MAsh MGos MJak MRav NLar NRHS SCob SLim SPer SPoG SRms SWvt WFar WGwG
- 'Fragrant Cloud'	see *S. japonica* 'Fragrans'
- 'Fructu Albo'	see *S. japonica* 'Wakehurst White'
- 'Godrie's Dwarf' (m)	CRos EPfP LRHS MAsh NLar NRHS WFar
- 'Humpty Dumpty' (f)	WFar
- subsp. ***intermedia*** f. ***repens*** B&SWJ 5560	WCru
- - - B&SWJ 11165	WCru
- 'John Turner' (f)	GBin
- 'Kew White' (f)	CAby CBcs CRos ELan EPfP IArd LRHS MAsh MGos MJak MRav NHol NRHS NWad SLon SPer SSta SWvt WCFE
- LUWIAN ('Wanto') (m)	CRos LRHS NRHS
- 'Macpenny Dwarf' (m)	CMac SRms
- 'Magic Marlot'[PBR] (m/v)	CRos EBee EPfP LRHS LSRN MAsh MGos MRav NHpl NLar NRHS SCob SPoG SWvt
- 'Marlot' (m)	CRos EPfP LRHS NLar NRHS SPoG
- 'Mystic Marlot'[PBR] **new**	LRHS NRHS
- 'Nymans' (f) ♀H5	CEnd CRos CTsd ELan EPfP GBin LCro LOPS LRHS MAsh MGos MRav NRHS SCob SLim SPoG SRms SWvt
- OBSESSION ('Obsbolwi'[PBR]) (m/f)	LRHS LSRN MAsh MGos SCob
- 'Olympic Flame' (f)	CRos EPfP IArd LRHS MAsh MBlu MJak NRHS SPoG
- 'Pabella'[PBR] (f)	MAsh SPoG
- 'Pigmy' (f)	CExl
- 'Red Diamonds'	NRHS
- 'Red Princess' (f)	MAsh
- 'Red Riding Hood' (f)	CBod CRos ELan ELon LRHS MAsh NRHS NWad SLon SPer
- 'Redruth' (f)	CBcs CMac CSBt CTsd ELon MAsh SEND WAvo
§ - subsp. ***reevesiana***	CBcs CDul CMac CRos CSBt CTri ELan EPfP GBin LCro LOPS LRHS MGos MRav MSwo NLar SCob SPoG SRms SWvt
- - B&SWJ 3763	MAsh WCru
- - 'Chilan Choice' (f/m)	WPGP
- - 'Godries Little Ruby'[PBR]	EPfP NLar
- - var. ***reevesiana***	MJak
- - - B&SWJ 3544	WCru
§ - Rogersii Group	CMac CTri
- - 'George Gardner' (m)	CKel LRHS
- - 'Nana Mascula' (m)	CTri
- - 'Rockyfield Green'	MAsh
- - 'Rogersii' (f)	CMac
- 'Rubella' (m) ♀H5	Widely available
- 'Rubinetta' (m)	CBar EPfP IArd MAsh SCob SEND
- 'Ruby Dome' (m)	LRHS NWad
- 'Ruby King' (m)	CSBt IArd LSRN NLar
- 'Scarlet Dwarf' (f)	NHol WAvo
- SEDUCTION ('Redbolwi'[PBR])	MGos
- 'Snow White'[PBR] (m)	WAvo
- 'Tansley Gem' (f)	CRos LRHS MAsh MWht SPoG
- 'Temptation'[PBR] (f)	CRos ELan EPfP LRHS NRHS SCob
- 'Thereza'[PBR] (m)	EBee
§ - 'Veitchii' (f)	CBar CBcs CBod CDul CKel CMac CRos CSBt CTri EPfP LRHS LSRN MAsh MGos MJak MMuc MRav NLar NRHS SCob SEND SLim SPer SPoG SRms SWvt WCFE
§ - 'Wakehurst White' (f)	CBcs CMac CSBt CTri EBee EPfP LRHS MAsh MRav NWad SPoG SRms
- 'White Bella' (m)	CRos LRHS NRHS
- 'Winifred Crook' (f)	CRos EBee LRHS
- 'Winnie's Dwarf'	MAsh
- 'Wisley Female' (f)	CTri
laureola	CExl MRav SRms WCFE WSHC
- GWJ 9364	WCru
- 'Kew Green'	CBod CEnd NWad
- subsp. ***laureola*** HWJK 2095	WCru
- subsp. ***multinervia*** GWJ 9374	WCru
reevesiana	see *S. japonica* subsp. *reevesiana*
rogersii	see *S. japonica* Rogersii Group
'Snowman'	WCFE

Smallanthus (*Asteraceae*)

sonchifolius	LEdu
- 'Morado'	LEdu WPGP

Smilacina see *Maianthemum*

Smilax (*Smilacaceae*)

sp.	WBor
B&SWJ 6628 from Thailand	WCru
aspera	CMac ESwi LEdu WCru WPGP
china B&SWJ 4427	WCru
discotis	SEND
glaucophylla B&SWJ 2971	WCru
nipponica B&SWJ 4331	WCru
rotundifolia	LEdu
sieboldii	LEdu MRav
- B&SWJ 744	WCru

Smyrnium (*Apiaceae*)

olusatrum	CHab CSpe SPhx SRms WHer WOut WSFF
perfoliatum	CBod CSpe EBee EHrv ELan ELon EMor EPfP EWes GBin GKev LCro LEdu LOPS NBir SPhx WCot WHal WSHC
rotundifolium	WCot
- PAB 6714	LEdu WPGP

Solandra (*Solanaceae*)

grandiflora misapplied	see *S. maxima*
hartwegii	see *S. maxima*
§ ***maxima***	CCCN

Solanum (*Solanaceae*)

sp.	SVic
aerial-rooting climbing species B&SWJ 14398	WCru
atropurpureum	CDTJ SPlb WCot
betaceum (F)	CCCN EUJe SVic
- yellow-fruited (F)	SPlb
burchellii	SPlb
capsicastrum	SPlb
conchifolium hort.	see *S. linearifolium*
crispum 'Autumnale'	see *S. crispum* 'Glasnevin'

§ – 'Glasnevin' ♀H4	Widely available
dulcamara	GPoy
– 'Lucia' (v)	CNat
– 'Variegatum' (v)	CMac MAsh
jasminoides	see *S. laxum*
laciniatum	CCCN CDTJ CExl SArc SEND SPlb SVen
§ ***laxum***	CMac CRos EBee LRHS MAsh NRHS SPer SRms SWvt
– 'Album' ♀H4	Widely available
– 'Album Variegatum' (v)	SCob
* – 'Aureovariegatum' (v)	CMac EBee ELon NEgg SPlb
– 'Coldham'	MNrw SMad
– 'Crèche du Pape'	ECha LRHS SRms
§ ***linearifolium***	CSpe
lycopersicum	SVic
muricatum (F)	CCCN CHll EShb SPlb
– 'Pepino Gold' (F) **new**	EShb
pinnatum	SPlb
pseudocapsicum variegated (v)	WCot
pyracanthum	CDTJ SArc SPlb
quitoense (F)	CDTJ SPlb
rantonnetii	see *Lycianthes rantonnetii*
rigescentoides	SPlb
sisymbriifolium	SPlb
aff. ***stenophyllum*** B&SWJ 10744	WCru
villosum **new**	SVen
wendlandii	CCCN CHll

Solaria (*Alliaceae*)

sp.	GCal

Soldanella (*Primulaceae*)

alpina	CPBP GKev LLHF NSla SRms WAbe
I – 'Alba'	NSla WAbe
carpatica	LEdu LLHF SPlb WAbe
– 'Alba'	GEdr LEdu WAbe
carpatica* × *pusilla	MNrw NRya NWad WAbe WSHC
carpatica* × *villosa	LEdu
cyanaster	GAbr GBin GJos GKev GLog LEdu NHpl NQui WAbe
dimoniei	LEdu WAbe
hungarica	GEdr WAbe
minima	GAbr GEdr GJos LEdu NSla WAbe
montana	CFis CPla EMor GBin GJos GKev LEdu LLHF NLar WBor
– hybrid **new**	NSla
pindicola	GEdr LEdu
pusilla	NWad
'Spring Symphony'	CElw GCrg GEdr GMaP LEdu LLHF NHar NWad SAko SPoG
'Sudden Spring'	CElw GEdr LEdu NWad SIgm WAbe
villosa ♀H6	GAbr GBin GEdr GKev GLog GPSL LEdu NRya NWad WMoo WSHC

Soleirolia (*Urticaceae*)

soleirolii	CBod CTri EPot EUJe LLWG MMuc SCob SEND SMad SPer SPtp SVic SWvt WHer XLum
– 'Argentea'	see *S. soleirolii* 'Variegata'
§ – 'Aurea'	EPot EUJe NHpl SVic SWvt
– 'Golden Queen'	see *S. soleirolii* 'Aurea'
– 'Silver Queen'	see *S. soleirolii* 'Variegata'
§ – 'Variegata' (v)	EUJe LLWG SCob SVic

Solenopsis (*Campanulaceae*)

axillaris	see *Isotoma axillaris*

Solenostemon ✿ (*Lamiaceae*)

'Autumn Rainbow'	WDib
'Beauty of Lyons'	EShb WDib
'Brilliant' (v)	WDib
'Bronze Pagoda'	WDib
BURGUNDY WEDDING TRAIN ('Kakegawa Ce10') **new**	WDib
'Chamaeleon' (v)	WDib
'City of Sunderland'	WDib
'Combat' (v) ♀H1c	WDib
'Crimson Ruffles' (v) ♀H1c	WDib
'Dazzler' (v)	WDib
'Durham Gala' ♀H1c	WDib
'Firelight' (v)	WDib
'Gay's Delight' ♀H1c	NPri
HENNA ('Balcenna'PBR) (v) ♀H1c	ECtt NPri
'Illumination'	WDib
'Inky Fingers' (v)	WDib
'Juliet Quartermain' ♀H1c	EShb EUJe WDib
'Jupiter'	WDib
'Kentish Fire' (v)	WDib
'Kiwi Fern' (Stained Glassworks Series) (v)	WDib
'Lemon Chiffon'	WDib
'Lord Falmouth' (v) ♀H1c	WDib
'Mrs Pilkington' (v)	WDib
'Muriel Pedley' (v)	WDib
'Paisley Shawl' (v)	EShb WDib
'Peter Wonder' (v)	WDib
'Pineapple Beauty' (v) ♀H1c	WDib
'Pink Chaos' (v) ♀H1c	WDib
'Red Angel' (v)	WDib
'Red Velvet' (v)	WDib
REDHEAD ('Uf0646'PBR) ♀H1c	NPri
'Rose Blush' (v)	WDib
'Roy Pedley' (v) ♀H1c	WDib
'Royal Scot' (v) ♀H1c	WDib
'Saturn' (v)	WDib
scutellarioides CAMPFIRE ('Uf12823')	NPri WHil
'The Flume'	WDib
'Timotei'	WDib
TRUSTY RUSTY ('Uf06419'PBR) (v) ♀H1c	NPri
'Walter Turner' (v) ♀H1c	WDib
'Winsome' (v) ♀H1c	WDib
'Winter Sun' (v)	WDib
'Wisley Tapestry' (v) ♀H1c	WDib

Solidago (*Asteraceae*)

'Autumn Blaze'	WFar
BABYGOLD	see *S.* 'Goldkind'
'Ballardii'	SRms
brachystachys	see *S. cutleri*
caesia	CRos EBee EWes LRHS NBir NRHS SAko SMHy WFar
canadensis	CTri ELan SEND SPlb WBrk WHer WMoo WOld WWtn XLum
– var. ***salebrosa***	CRos EBee LRHS NRHS
– var. ***scabra***	MMuc
'Citronella'	ECtt
'Cloth of Gold'	CMac ECtt NEoE NHol SPoG SWvt WGwG
§ 'Crown of Rays'	CRos ECtt ELon EPfP GBin LRHS MRav NRHS SCob WFar
§ ***cutleri***	EBou EDAr NLar SIgm SPlb SRms WFar

'Dennis Strange'	MAvo
'Ducky'	SCob
'Early Bird'	NLar WFar
flabelliformis	WCot
§ ***flexicaulis***	GMaP SPhx WCot XLum
- 'Variegata' (v)	CBod CRos EBee ELan EShb GMaP LRHS NLar NRHS WMoo XLum
'Foxbrook Gold'	MAvo WFar
'Gardone' ♀H7	WFar
gigantea	WFar
glomerata	MMuc NLar SEND
GOLDEN BABY	see *S.* 'Goldkind'
§ 'Golden Dwarf'	SPoG SRms WPtf XLum
'Golden Fleece'	see *S. sphacelata* 'Golden Fleece'
'Golden Thumb'	see *S.* 'Queenie'
'Golden Wings'	CBre
'Goldenmosa' ♀H7	CSBt EWes GMaP SPer WFar
'Goldilocks'	SRms
§ 'Goldkind'	CBod CRos CSBt CTri EBee ECtt ELan EPfP GAbr LRHS NEgg NRHS SRms SWvt WBrk WFar WWtn
GOLDZWERG	see *S.* 'Golden Dwarf'
'Hiddigeigei' (v)	WCot WFar
hybrida	see *S.* × *luteus*
latifolia	see *S. flexicaulis*
'Laurin'	CSam NLar XLum
'Ledsham'	CBod CRos ECtt GBin LRHS NBre NRHS SPoG
'Lena'	SRms
'Linner Gold'	NBre
'Little Lemon'[PBR]	CBct EBee ELan MTin NEoE SCob
§ × ***luteus***	EBee GBin NDai SRms WFar XLum
- 'Lemore' ♀H7	CAby CBod CDor EBee ECha ELan EPPr EPfP GMaP NAln NSti NWsh SPer SPhx SPoG SRms WCot WFar WHoo XLum
ohioensis	XLum
- 'Four Seasons'	GBin
§ ***ptarmicoides***	EBee MMuc XEll XLum
§ 'Queenie'	MHer
riddellii	GJos XLum
rigida	WMoo
- 'Upright Rod'	GBin
rugosa	ECha MBNS MMuc SEND SPhx WCot WWtn
- 'Fireworks' ♀H7	CAby CBod CBre CCBP CMac CMea CRos CSam EBee ECha ECtt ELon GBin GQue ILea LRHS MAvo NLar NRHS SDys SPhx SRms WBrk WCAu WCot WFar WHoo WOld XLum
- 'Loydser Crown'	NDov
sempervirens	CRos EBee IMou LRHS NRHS WFar WOld
'Septembergold'	CSam
shortii 'Solar Cascade'	EBee WHil
'Sonnenschein'	NBre
speciosa	SPhx WCot
spectabilis var. ***confinis*** KM 27-01	EBee
§ ***sphacelata*** 'Golden Fleece'	CBcs EPfP IMou NBre SRms
spiraeifolia	EBee
STRAHLENKRONE	see *S.* 'Crown of Rays'
'Super'	WCot
SWEETY ('Barseven'[PBR])	CRos LRHS NRHS WHil
'Tom Thumb'	MRav NBir SRms
uliginosa	EShb
ulmifolia	EBee
virgaurea	GPoy MHer MMuc MNHC NLar SRms WHer
- subsp. ***alpestris*** var. ***minutissima***	GEdr IMou
- var. ***cambrica***	see *S. virgaurea* subsp. *minuta*
§ - subsp. ***minuta***	EAdr GBin GCrg MHol
§ - 'Variegata' (v)	CBre EHoe NEoE WOut
vulgaris 'Variegata'	see *S. virgaurea* 'Variegata'
'Yellow Springs'	GJos
'Yellow Stone'	EBee

× *Solidaster* see *Solidago*

hybridus	see *Solidago* × *luteus*

Sollya (*Pittosporaceae*)

fusiformis	see *S. heterophylla*
§ ***heterophylla*** ♀H3	Widely available
- 'Alba'	CBcs CCCN CFlo CKel CRos ELan EPfP LRHS NRHS SEle SLon SPoG SWvt
- 'Pink Charmer'	CBcs CKel CRos ELan EPfP LRHS SEle SPoG
- pink-flowered	CCCN CSBt SWvt

Sonchus (*Asteraceae*)

arboreus	CPla
pinnatus	SPlb

Sophora (*Papilionaceae*)

cassioides	MGil
- NJM 08.008	WPGP
§ ***davidii***	CAby CBcs CDul CExl CKel EBee ELon EPfP LEdu LRHS MBlu SBrt SEND SPoG WCot WGrn WSHC
flavescens	SBrt
fulvida	EBee WPGP
howinsula	EUJe WCot
japonica	see *Styphnolobium japonicum*
§ 'Little Baby'	CKel ELan EPfP EUJe LSRN MGil MGos SEle SPoG SWvt WGrn
macrocarpa	SWvt
microphylla	CTri MGil
molloyi 'Dragon's Gold'	CBcs EBee ELan ELon EPfP EUJe LRHS MAsh SCob SCoo SEND SEle SPoG SSta SWvt
prostrata misapplied	see *S.* 'Little Baby'
prostrata Buchanan	CMac
secundiflora	CMCN
SUN KING ('Hilsop'[PBR]) ♀H4	CBcs CDul CKel CRos CWGN ELan EPfP EUJe EWes LRHS LSRN MGos NLar NRHS SCob SCoo SLon SPer SPoG SWvt WCot
tetraptera	CBcs CDul CRos CTsd EPfP EUJe LRHS MMuc SEND SWvt WCFE
viciifolia	see *S. davidii*

Sorbaria (*Rosaceae*)

aitchisonii	see *S. tomentosa* var. *angustifolia*
arborea	see *S. kirilowii*
§ ***kirilowii***	CExl CMac MRav NLar SMad WOut
lindleyana	see *S. tomentosa*
sorbifolia	CBcs CMCN ELan MGil MMuc SCob SEND SPer SPlb WFar WSpi
- 'Sem'[PBR] ♀H5	Widely available
- var. ***stellipila*** B&SWJ 776	WCru
§ ***tomentosa***	CPla
§ - var. ***angustifolia*** ♀H5	CDul CKel CRos CTri EBee ELan EPfP LRHS MMuc MRav NBid SCob SEND SLon
- 'Sticks and Feathers' **new**	SMad

× *Sorbaronia* (*Rosaceae*)

fallax EPfP NLar
- 'Ivan's Beauty' ECrN

× *Sorbopyrus* (*Rosaceae*)

auricularis MCoo
§ - 'Shipova' (F) CAgr MAsh NOra WMat

Sorbus ✿ (*Rosaceae*)

sp. CMen LPra
NJM 09.203 WPGP
SDR 7808 GKev
adamii CMCN
alnifolia CLnd CMCN EPfP MBlu
- B&SWJ 8461 WCru
- B&SWJ 10948 WCru
- 'Red Bird' EPfP LRHS MBlu
'Amber Light' EBee NOra WMat
americana CLnd NWea
anglica CDul
'Apricot' CEnd
'Apricot Queen' CDul CLnd EBee ECrN EMOT MJak SGol WFar
aria CAco CCVT CDul CHab CLnd CPer CTri ECrN EMOT LBuc LPra MGos MMuc NWea SCob SEND SEWo SGol WMou WTSh
- 'Aurea' CLnd SPer
- 'Chrysophylla' CDul CSBt ECrN NWea
- 'Decaisneana' see *S. aria* 'Majestica'
- 'Lutescens' ♀H6 Widely available
- 'Magnifica' CLnd ECrN ELan EMOT ESwi LPra NEgg NLar NWea SEWo WJas
§ - 'Majestica' ♀H6 CCVT CDul CLnd CMac EBee ECrN EMOT LMaj LPra MRav NWea SCob WFar WJas
- 'Mitchellii' see *S. thibetica* 'John Mitchell'
- 'Quercoides' CDul
aria* × *pseudovilmorinii WPGP
arnoldiana 'Golden Wonder' see *S.* 'Lombarts Golden Wonder'
aronioides misapplied see *S. caloneura*
aronioides Rehder GKev
arranensis CDul
§ ***aucuparia*** Widely available
- 'Aspleniifolia' CBcs CCVT CDul CMCN CMac CSBt EBee ECrN EMOT EUJe LRHS MGos MJak MRav NLar NOra NRHS NWea SCob SLim WFar WJas WMat WMou
§ - 'Beissneri' CAgr CDul MRav NWea
- CARDINAL ROYAL ('Michred') CCVT CDul CLnd ECrN EMOT EWTr MMuc NEgg SCoo SEWo SLon
- 'Dirkenii' SGol WJas WMat
§ - var. ***edulis*** (F) CArg CDul CLnd LBuc LPra MGos MMuc SCob SPer
- - 'Rossica' misapplied see *S. aucuparia* var. *edulis* 'Rossica Major'
§ - - 'Rossica Major' CDul ECrN SEWo
§ - 'Fastigiata' CEnd CTri ELan EPfP GKin LMaj LPra SCob
- 'Fingerprint'PBR EMOT LRHS
- 'Hilling's Spire' CTho
- subsp. ***maderensis*** LPra MBlu
- ***pluripinnata*** see *S. scalaris* Koehne
- var. ***rossica*** Koehne see *S. aucuparia* var. *edulis*
- 'Sheerwater Seedling' ♀H6 CBcs CCVT CDul CMCN CSBt EBee ECrN ELan EMOT EPfP GKin LMaj LPra MGos MMuc MRav MSwo NWea SCob SEND SGol SPer WFar
aucuparia* × *scalaris EMOT NWea WMou
AUTUMN SPIRE ('Flanrock') ♀H6 CBcs CDul CEnd CLnd EBee ELan EMOT EPfP LRHS LSRN MAsh MGos MJak NLar NOra NPri NWea SCoo SEWo SLim SLon SPoG SWvt WMat
bissetii Yu 14299 WCru
brevipetiolata B&SWJ 11771 WCru
bulleyana NAln
- KR 2809 new WCru
- MF 96170 GKev
§ ***caloneura*** EBee EPfP LEdu MBlu SPtp WPGP
- Guiz 80 WCru
carmesina B&L 12545 EBee EPfP GKev WCru
- 'Emberglow' EBee EPfP NOra WMat
cashmiriana misapplied see *S. rosea*
cashmiriana Hedl. ♀H6 CBcs CCVT CDul CLnd CMCN CMac CTri EBee ECrN ELan EPfP GKev LRHS MBlu MGos MMuc MRav MSwo NEgg NLar NWea SGol SPer SPoG WCFE WJas WMat
aff. ***cashmiriana*** ambig. EMOT GKev LCro LOPS MAsh MJak NHol NOra WFar WTSh
- B 751 WCru
chamaemespilus WThu
'Chinese Lace' Widely available
§ ***commixta*** CBcs CDul CEnd CLnd CMCN EBee ECrN EMOT LCro LMaj LOPS MBlu MGos MJak MMuc MSwo NLar SCob SEND SGol SLim SPer WJas
- B&SWJ 10839 WCru
- B&SWJ 11043 WCru
- B&SWJ 12640 from Ulleungdo, South Korea WCru
- 'Embley' ♀H6 CBcs CCVT CDul CLnd CMCN CSBt CTho CTri ECrN ELan EPfP LCro LOPS MBlu MGos MMuc MRav NEgg NWea SCob SEND SGol SPer
- 'Ravensbill' EBee EPfP NLar NOra NWea SCoo WHCr WMat
- var. ***rufoferruginea*** B&SWJ 11486 WCru
- var. ***sachalinensis*** B&SWJ 8515 WCru
- 'Serotina' LPra
aff. ***commixta*** WTSh
conradinae Koehne see *S. esserteauana*
'Copper Kettle' ♀H6 EBee EPfP LRHS MAsh MBlu NLar NOra SCoo WHCr WMat WMou
'Coral Beauty' CLnd
corymbifera WWJ 11860 WCru
'Covert Gold' CEnd
croceocarpa CDul
cuspidata see *S. vestita*
* ***decora*** 'Grootendorst' CDul
- var. ***nana*** see *S. aucuparia* 'Fastigiata'
devoniensis CTho
- 'Devon Beauty' CAgr
discolor misapplied see *S. commixta*
discolor (Maxim.) Maxim. MBlu MJak NWea WJas
- MF 96172 MAsh
- MF 97103 WCru
domestica CDul CLnd CPer MMuc SEND
- 'Maliformis' see *S. domestica* f. *pomifera*
§ - f. ***pomifera*** LEdu
§ - f. ***pyrifera*** LEdu

	- 'Pyriformis'	see *S. domestica* f. *pyrifera*
	- 'Rosie'	CAgr
	dunnii	WPGP
	'Eastern Promise' ♀H6	CDul EMOT EPfP LCro MAsh MBlu MSwo NLar NOra NWea SCob SCoo SLim WHCr WMat WMou
§	***eburnea***	GKev
	- Harry Smith 12799	WPGP
	eleonorae new	SPtp
	ellipsoidalis C 288	GKev
	eminens	CDul CNat
	epidendron	WPGP
§	***esserteauana***	CLnd CTho
	'Ethel's Gold'	MBlu
	fansipanensis NJM 09.176	WPGP
	'Fastigiata'	see *S. aucuparia* 'Fastigiata', *S.* × *thuringiaca* 'Fastigiata'
	aff. ***filipes***	GKev
	folgneri 'Emiel' ♀H6	EPfP IArd MBlu NOra WMat
	- 'Lemon Drop'	CDul CEnd CLnd EBee EPfP MAsh MBlu NOra SCoo WMat
	foliolosa	CLnd
	forrestii ♀H6	CBcs CMCN EBee EPfP GKev IArd NLar
*	***fosteri*** MF 97103	GKev
§	***frutescens*** ♀H6	NWad
	- R 14987	EBee GKev
	fruticosa Crantz	GKev
	- 'Koehneana'	see *S. koehneana* C.K. Schneid.
	'Ghose'	CEnd CTho WMat
	glabrescens	LEdu
§	***glabriuscula***	GKev
	'Glendoick Spire'	EBee EMOT LRHS NLar NOra WHCr WMat
	'Glendoick White Baby'	NLar WMat
	glomerulata	LLHF
	'Golden Wonder'	see *S.* 'Lombarts Golden Wonder'
	gonggashanica	EPfP GEdr LRHS NAln SPtp WPGP
*	***gorrodini***	CLnd
	granulosa HWJ 1041	WCru
	'Gresgarth' new	GKev
	harrowiana	CDul LEdu LLHF LRHS WMat WPGP
	- KW 21009	WPGP
	- from Burma new	WPGP
	- from Yunnan new	WPGP
	hedlundii	CExl EBee EPfP NLar WMat WPGP
	- GWJ 9363	WCru WPGP
	- KR 1687	WPGP
	- KR 1810	WPGP
	- WJC 13806	WCru
	helenae	LRHS WPGP
	- EN 3088	EBee GKev WPGP
	hemsleyi	CBcs CDul CExl CLnd SPtp WPGP
	- 'John Bond' ♀H6	EMOT NLar NOra WHCr WMat
	× ***hostii***	CLnd
	hugh-mcallisteri CLD 310	GKev
	hupehensis misapplied	see *S. pseudohupehensis*
	- white-berried	see *S. glabriuscula*
	- 'November Pink'	see *S. pseudohupehensis* 'Pink Pagoda'
	- var. ***obtusa*** misapplied	see *S. pseudohupehensis* 'Pink Pagoda'
	- 'Rosea'	see *S. pseudohupehensis* 'Pink Pagoda'
	aff. ***hupehensis***	ECrN EMOT EWTr NWea WFar WTSh
	hybrida L. 'Gibbsii' ♀H6	ELan EPfP MAsh NOra SPer WMat
	insignis	LLHF WPGP
	intermedia	CAco CBcs CCVT CDul CLnd CPer CSBt CTho CTri ECrN ELan LMaj

		LPra MMuc NWea SEND SGol WMou
	- 'Brouwers'	CLnd ELan LPra
	japonica	CDul EBee LRHS WMat
	- B&SWJ 10813	WCru
	- B&SWJ 11048	WCru
	'Joseph Rock'	Widely available
	aff. ***karchungii***	EBee
	- AGS/ES 347	EBee WPGP
I	***keenanii*** NJM 13.050	WPGP
I	***keenanii*** × ***wattii*** NJM 13.123	WPGP
	keissleri	EBee
	- NJM 11.004	WPGP
	- NJM 11.056	WPGP
	- NJM 11.060	WPGP
	- PAB 7916	LEdu
	'Keith Rushforth'	WCru
§	× ***kewensis***	CDul CLnd SPlb
	khumbuensis	GKev
	'Kirsten Pink'	CCVT SPer
	koehneana misapplied	see *S. frutescens*
§	***koehneana*** C.K. Schneid.	CLnd CMCN ELan GKev MGil MMrt WCru
	aff. ***koehneana*** C.K. Schneid.	see *S. eburnea*, *S. tenuis*
	aff. ***koehneana*** ambig.	GEdr
	lanata misapplied	see *S. vestita*
	latifolia	NWea
	- 'Henk Vink'	CCVT
	'Leonard Messel' ♀H6	CTho EPfP MAsh NLar NOra WHCr WMat
	'Likjornaja'	EPfP LRHS
§	'Lombarts Golden Wonder'	CDul MMuc NWea SEND
*	***maculata***	NAln
	- KR 5334	EBee GKev
	matsumurana misapplied	see *S. commixta*
	matsumurana (Makino) Koehne	IArd WPGP
	megalocarpa	CJun CMCN EBee WPGP
	- var. ***cuneata***	WPGP
	meliosmifolia	SPtp
	- B&SWJ 11709	WCru
	microphylla agg.	CMCN GKev
	- GWJ 9252	WCru
	- SICH 1009	EBee
	monbeigii (Cardot.) N.P. Balakr.	CLnd MGil
	moravica 'Laciniata'	see *S. aucuparia* 'Beissneri'
	muliensis F 22177	EBee GKev
§	***munda***	WCFE
	needhamii NJM 11.005	EBee WPGP
	- PAB 9853	LEdu
	'Nevezhinskaja'	MBlu
	olivacea	EPfP GKev SPtp
	aff. ***ovalis*** H 1948	EBee
	paniculata NJM 13.067	WPGP
	- NJM 13.092	WPGP
	- PAB 9831	LEdu
	parvifructa	EBee GKev WPGP
	'Peaches and Cream'	LCro LOPS
	'Pearly King'	CTho GKev MAsh WJas
§	'Pink Pearl'	CDul EPfP
	'Pink-Ness'	EPfP MBlu NOra SCoo WMat
	pohuashanensis misapplied	see *S.* × *kewensis*
	pohuashanensis ambig.	CMCN
	porrigentiformis	CDul
	poteriifolia ♀H5	GEdr GKev

prattii misapplied — see *S. munda*
prattii Koehne var. ***subarachnoidea*** (Koehen) Rehder — see *S. munda*
§ ***pseudohupehensis*** ♀H6 — CBcs CDul CLnd CMCN CMac CTho CTri EPfP GKev GLog MMuc NWea SEND SGol SPer WJas
§ - 'Pink Pagoda' ♀H6 — Widely available
pseudovilmorinii — CBcs EBee GKev IMou LRHS NLar NOra WCru WHCr WMat
- SBEC 974 — WPGP
randaiensis — EBee SPlb WPGP
- B&SWJ 156 — WPGP
- B&SWJ 3202 — EPfP WCru
'Red Tip' — CDul
reducta ♀H5 — GBin GCal GKev MMuc NHar NHol NLar NSla SPer
aff. ***reducta*** — SRms
reflexipetala misapplied — see *S. commixta*
rehderiana misapplied — see *S. aucuparia*
rehderiana Koehne — GKev
rosea — GEdr GKev
- SEP 492 — WCru WPGP
- 'Rosiness' ♀H6 — CLnd EBee EPfP LRHS WMat
rubescens — GKev
rupicola — NWea
rushforthii KR 5789 — EBee GKev
rutilans — GKev
'Salmon Queen' — CLnd
sambucifolia — EBee GKev
sargentiana ♀H6 — CBcs CCVT CDul CEnd CLnd CMCN CMac CTho CTri EBee ECrN ELan EMOT EPfP MBlu MGos MRav MSwo NLar NOra NWea SLim SPer SPoG WMat WMou
- EGM 291 — WCru
'Savill Orange' — MMuc
scalaris ambig. — CBcs CMCN CNWT ELan MAsh MSwo NOra SPoG WMou
§ ***scalaris*** Koehne — CCVT CDul CEnd CTho CTri EPfP MBlu SPer WJas WMat
'Schouten' — ECrN MMuc
scopulina misapplied — see *S. aucuparia* 'Fastigiata'
section *Discolores* — GKev
- KR 5585 — WCru WPGP
- KR 6308 — WCru
setschwanensis — CMCN
'Showa' — GKev
subulata HWJ 925 — WCru
- KWJ 12272 — WCru
'Sunshine' — CCVT CDul CLnd EMOT LMaj MAsh MGos MMuc SEND WJas
§ ***tenuis*** — GKev
§ ***thibetica*** 'John Mitchell' ♀H6 — CAgr CDul CEnd CLnd CMCN EBee ECrN EPfP MBlu MGos NLar NOra NWea SLim SPoG WMat
aff. ***thibetica*** BWJ 7757a — WCru
thomsonii GWJ 9363 — WCru
- HWJ 984 — WCru
- WWJ 12004 — WCru
§ × ***thuringiaca*** 'Fastigiata' — CDul CLnd EBar EPfP LPra NEgg NWea SCoo WJas WMat
tianschanica — WCru
'Titan' — EPfP
torminalis — CAgr CBcs CCVT CDul CHab CLnd CMCN CMac CPer CTho CTri EBee ELan EPfP LPra MGos MMuc MRav NLar NWea SEND SEWo SPer SPoG WMou WSpi WTSh
ulleungensis B&SWJ 12640 — WCru
- 'Olympic Flame' ♀H6 — CEnd CSBt EBee EMOT EPfP GBin IArd LBuc LSRN MBlu NLar NOra NPri NWea SCoo SEWo SLim SPoG WHCr WMat WMou
§ ***vestita*** — CLnd CMCN CTho EPfP WCru
vexans — CDul
vilmorinii ♀H6 — Widely available
- 'Pink Charm' — EPfP NOra WMat
- 'Robusta' — see *S.* 'Pink Pearl'
aff. ***vilmorinii*** — EMOT GKin MJak
- KR 5095 — GKev
- KR 6453 — WCru WPGP
wardii — CBcs CDul CLnd CTho EPfP LRHS MBlu
- KR 21127 — EBee WPGP
'White Wax' — CCVT CDul ECrN EMOT EWTr MGos NWea SPer
'Wilfrid Fox' — CCVT MGos
wilmottiana — CDul
wilsoniana — CLnd LRHS
'Wisley Gold' ♀H6 — EBee EMOT LRHS NOra SCoo SLim WMat
yuana — EBee WPGP
- clone 1 — WPGP
- clone 2 — WPGP
zahlbruckneri C.K. Schneid. — WPGP

Sorghastrum (*Poaceae*)

avenaceum — see *S. nutans*
§ ***nutans*** — CBod EBou
- 'Indian Steel' — CBod EBee XLum

Soroseris (*Asteraceae*)

rosularis — GKev

sorrel, common see *Rumex acetosa*

sorrel, French see *Rumex scutatus*

Souliea see *Actaea*

Sparaxis (*Iridaceae*)

'Bright Star' — GKev
elegans — SPlb
grandiflora subsp. ***acutiloba*** — CPbh
- subsp. ***grandiflora*** — CPbh
'Moonlight' — GKev LAma
'Skyline' — GKev
'Sunshine' — GKev LAma
tricolor — CAby CGrW CPbh CPla GKev SDeJ

Sparganium (*Sparganiaceae*)

§ ***erectum*** — CWat NMir NPer WMAq WSFF XLum
ramosum — see *S. erectum*

Sparrmannia (*Malvaceae*)

africana ♀H1c — CCCN CHII ELan EShb SEND SPlb SVen

Spartina (*Poaceae*)

pectinata — SGol XLum
- 'Aureomarginata' (v) — CBod CRos CWCL EBee EHoe ELan EPfP GMaP LRHS MMuc NRHS NWsh SEND SPer WMoo WWtn XLum

Spartium (*Papilionaceae*)

junceum ♀H5 — CAco CBcs CCCN CDul CEnd CMac CWld EBee ELan ELon EPfP LRHS MGos MMuc SCob SEND SPer SRms WAvo XSen
- 'Brockhill Compact' — CKel CRos EPfP LRHS

Spartocytisus see *Cytisus*

Spathantheum (*Araceae*)

orbignyanum — GKev WCot

Spathipappus see *Tanacetum*

Spathiphyllum (*Araceae*)

wallisii — SPre
- 'Bellini' new — LCro LOPS

Spathodea (*Bignoniaceae*)

campanulata — SPlb

spearmint see *Mentha spicata*

Speirantha (*Asparagaceae*)

convallarioides — see *S. gardenii*
gardenii — CBct CDTJ EBee EHrv ELon EPPr EPfP IMou LEdu MNrw WCru WHil WPGP

Sphacele see *Lepechinia*

Sphaeralcea (*Malvaceae*)

ambigua — SPlb
'Childerley' — CMea CSpe ECtt MBNS MHol MSCN SPad SPoG WCot
coccinea — CPBP EBee SPlb
fendleri — CCCN CHll CSam CSde
'Hopleys Lavender' — CCCN SWvt
incana — CCCN CSpe MGil
- 'Sourup' — CBod EBee ECtt ELan SMHy WCot
malviflora — CDTJ
miniata — CCCN CHll
munroana — CCCN ECtt ELan SRkn
- pale pink-flowered — CSam
'Newleaze Coral' — CCCN ELan MAsh MGil MNrw SPad SPoG SRkn SWvt WBor WCot
'Newleaze Pink' — SRkn
remota — CExl LPla SPlb
umbellata — see *Phymosia umbellata*

Sphagneticola (*Asteraceae*)

§ **trilobata** — LLWG

Sphenomeris (*Dennstaedtiaceae*)

chinensis B&SWJ 6108 — WCru

Spigelia (*Loganiaceae*)

marilandica — EBee GKev ILea SMad WHil WSHC

Spilanthes (*Asteraceae*)

acmella misapplied — see *Acmella oleracea*
oleracea — see *Acmella oleracea*

spinach see AGM Vegetables Section

Spiraea (*Rosaceae*)

alba var. **latifolia** — MMuc
albiflora — see *S. japonica* 'Albiflora'
arborea — see *Sorbaria kirilowii*
§ 'Arguta' ♀H6 — Widely available
× **arguta** 'Bridal Wreath' — see *S.* 'Arguta'
betulifolia — CDul MRav SCob WFar
- var. **aemiliana** — MMuc SCob
- 'Tor' — EPPr
- 'Tor Gold'PBR — CBcs LRHS NEoE SPoG
× **billardii** misapplied — see *S.* × *pseudosalicifolia*
blumei CWJ 12829 — WCru
× **bumalda** 'Wulfenii' — see *S. japonica* 'Walluf'
callosa 'Alba' — see *S. japonica* 'Albiflora'
canescens — CExl GKin
- CC 7281 — EWld
- var. **glaucophylla** — MMuc
§ **cantoniensis** 'Flore Pleno' (d) — CBod
- 'Lanceata' — see *S. cantoniensis* 'Flore Pleno'
chamaedryfolia — GKev
× **cinerea** 'Grefsheim' ♀H6 — CAco CBcs CBod CSBt EBee ELan LBuc MMuc NLar SCob SGol SLim SPer SPlb
crispifolia misapplied — see *S. japonica* 'Bullata'
densiflora — GKev
- var. **splendens** — SBrt
DOUBLE PLAY BIG BANG — see *S.* 'Tracy'
douglasii — CMac GKev SCob
FIRST EDITIONS SUPERSTAR ('Denistar') — NEoE
formosana B&SWJ 1597 — CExl WCru
fritschiana — CMac
hayatana — GKev
- RWJ 10014 — WCru
hendersonii — see *Petrophytum hendersonii*
henryi — GKev
§ **japonica** 'Albiflora' — CBod CKel CMac CSBt CTri ECrN ELan ELon LRHS MRav MSwo NEgg NRHS NWad SCob SGbt SGol SLim SPad SPer SRms SWvt WFar
- 'Alpina' — see *S. japonica* 'Nana'
- 'Alpine Gold' — NEoE
- 'Anthony Waterer' (v) — CBcs CCVT CDul CMac CRos EBee ECrN ELan EPfP EShb LRHS MAsh MGos MRav MSwo NEgg NLar NWea SCob SCoo SGbt SGol SLim SPer SPoG SRms WFar WMoo
§ - 'Bullata' — CMac GCrg NLar WAbe
- 'Candlelight' ♀H6 — CRos CSBt ELan EPfP GBin GKin LRHS MAsh NEgg NLar SCob SCoo SGol SLim SPer SPoG SWvt WMoo
- 'Crispa' — CAco EPfP NEoE NWad WFar WGrn
- 'Dart's Red' ♀H6 — CDul ELan EPfP GKin
- DOUBLE PLAY ARTISAN ('Galen') — SPoG
- DOUBLE PLAY GOLD ('Yan') — SPoG
- 'Firelight' — Widely available
§ - 'Genpei' — CMac MAsh MJak MMuc NWea SGol SPer SPoG SRms
- 'Gold Mound' — CBar CExl CMac EBee EHoe ELan EPfP MAsh MGos MJak MMuc MRav MSwo NLar SCoo SGol SLim SPlb SRms WFar
- GOLDEN PRINCESS ('Lisp') ♀H6 — CMac CRos CTri ELan EPfP LBuc LRHS MAsh MGos NEgg NLar SCoo SGol SPer SRms SSta WFar WMoo
- 'Goldflame' — Widely available
- 'Little Princess' — CBcs CDul CMac CRos EBee ECrN ELan EShb LRHS MAsh MRav MSwo NLar NRHS NWea SCob SCoo SGol SLim SPer SRms SWvt WFar WMoo

- MAGIC CARPET ('Walbuma'PBR) (v) ♀H6 — CBcs CRos EPfP LBuc LRHS MAsh MMuc NLar NRHS SCob SCoo SPoG SRms
§ - 'Nana' ♀H6 — CMac CSBt MAsh SRms
- 'Nyewoods' — see *S. japonica* 'Nana'
- 'Shiburi' — see *S. japonica* 'Albiflora'
- 'Shirobana' misapplied — see *S. japonica* 'Genpei'
- 'Shirobana' — see *S. japonica* 'Albiflora'
- 'Stanton Gold' — WCFE
§ - 'Walluf' — CMac CTri GBin
- 'White Gold'PBR — CBod CKel CMac CRos CSBt ELan EPfP LRHS MAsh NEoE NHol NRHS NWad SCoo SPer SPoG SRms SWvt
× *margaritae* — SWvt
micrantha — CExl
nipponica — CAco CBcs
- 'Halward's Silver' — MRav NEoE
§ - 'Snowmound' ♀H6 — Widely available
- var. ***tosaensis*** misapplied — see *S. nipponica* 'Snowmound'
palmata 'Elegans' — see *Filipendula purpurea* 'Elegans'
prunifolia (d) — CBod CMac ELan EPfP MRav SPer WAvo WCFE WFar
× *pseudosalicifolia* 'Triumphans' — CDul MMuc SPer
rosthornii — GKev
salicifolia — WFar
schneideriana new — GKev
SPARKLING CHAMPAGNE ('Lonspi'PBR) — CSBt LBuc LSRN NEoE NWad SLon
tarokoensis — CMCN
thunbergii ♀H6 — CBcs CDul CMac CTri EPfP MMuc MRav NWea SBrt SCob SEND SGol SPer SRms
- 'Golden Times' — CRos LRHS SPoG
- 'Mellow Yellow' — see *S. thunbergii* 'Ōgon'
- 'Mount Fuji' — CMac MRav WFar
§ - 'Ōgon' — EPfP WFar
* - 'Variegata' (v) — SRms
§ 'Tracy' — NEoE
ulmaria — see *Filipendula ulmaria*
× *vanhouttei* — CBcs CBod CMac CTri ELan EPfP MMuc MRav MSwo SEND SLim SPer SRms WFar WMoo
- 'Gold Fountain' — CMac ELan EMil EPfP EShb LSRN MMuc NHol NLar SCoo SEND SPer WFar WMoo
- 'Pink Ice' (v) — CMac CRos EHoe EPfP LRHS MAsh MMuc MRav NLar SPer SPlb SPoG SWvt WFar
veitchii — GLog MRav
venusta 'Magnifica' — see *Filipendula rubra* 'Venusta'

Spiranthes (*Orchidaceae*)

cernua — NGdn
odorata 'Chadd's Ford' ♀H4 — CExl GKev IKil LAma LRHS MNrw NBir WSHC WTor

Spirodela (*Araceae*)

§ ***polyrrhiza*** — EWat

Spodiopogon (*Poaceae*)

sibiricus — CKno EBee EHoe EPPr GBin MBNS NDov SMad SPtp WPtf XLum

Sporobolus (*Poaceae*)

airoides — CBod CKno EBee EHoe EPPr EShb
heterolepis — CFis CKno CSpe EBee EHoe EPfP GBin LRHS NDov SMHy SMea SPtp WCot
- 'Blue Dust' — NDov
I - 'Wisconsin Strain' — EBee IMou
wrightii — CKno EPPr

Sprekelia (*Amaryllidaceae*)

formosissima — EShb GKev LAma LEdu SDeJ

squashes see AGM Vegetables Section

Stachys (*Lamiaceae*)

sp. — NAln
abchasica new — EMor
aethiopica 'Danielle' — see *S. thunbergii* 'Danielle'
§ ***affinis*** — GPoy LEdu SPlb SVic
balcanica — GKev NAln
- MESE — EBee
'Bello Grigio' — LPla MHol
betonica — see *S. officinalis*
§ ***byzantina*** — Widely available
§ - 'Big Ears' — Widely available
§ - 'Cotton Boll' — CRos ECha GBin GCal LRHS NAln SRms WFar XSen
- 'Countess Helen von Stein' — see *S. byzantina* 'Big Ears'
- 'Fuzzy Wuzzy' — CBod WFar
- gold-leaved — see *S. byzantina* 'Primrose Heron'
- large-leaved — see *S. byzantina* 'Big Ears'
- 'Limelight' — WCot XLum
§ - 'Primrose Heron' — CBod ECha GBin GKev GMaP LRHS MBel MRav NLar NRHS SPer SWvt WCAu XLum
- 'Sheila McQueen' — see *S. byzantina* 'Cotton Boll'
- 'Silky Fleece' — CBod EBou ECha ELan EPfP GWyn LRHS MMuc NBre SRms XSen
- 'Silver Carpet' — Widely available
chamissonis var. ***cooleyae*** — GBin
citrina — CMea GCal XSen
coccinea — ECtt GEdr SPhx
cretica — XSen
densiflora — see *S. monieri* (Gouan) P.W. Ball
§ ***discolor*** — CBcs CFis CMea EWes LRHS NLar SBrt WCAu WCot
germanica — CNat NBre
grandiflora — see *S. macrantha*
'Hidalgo' — CSpe SRms
lanata Jacq. — see *S. byzantina*
lavandulifolia — WAbe
- from Bolkar Dag, Turkey — SBrt
§ LILAC FALLS ('Wesstalifa') — CBod
§ ***macrantha*** — CBod CMac CRos CTri ECha EDAr GKev GLog LEdu LRHS LSRN NAln NBir NChi NLar NRHS NSti SPhx SRms WArt WCAu WCFE WCot
* - 'Alba' — ECha
- 'Ben' (v) — LEdu
- 'Hummelo' — see *S. officinalis* 'Hummelo'
- 'Morning Blush' — SPhx WFar
* - 'Nivea' — CSam NBir
- 'Robusta' ♀H7 — ELan ELon GCal LEdu MAvo MMuc NBro NGdn WCot WJam
- 'Rosea' — CElw CRos ELan GBee GMaP LRHS MArl NRHS SCob SPlb WCAu
- 'Superba' ♀H7 — CSpe ECtt EPfP GKev GMaP LEdu MAvo MRav NEgg NLar SCob SPer SRms SWvt WBor WCAu WCot WFar WMoo XLum
- 'Violacea' ♀H7 — EBee GKev NChi WCot
mexicana misapplied — see *S. thunbergii*
monieri misapplied — see *S. officinalis*
monieri ambig. — GKev NAln NLar NSti
- white-flowered — GKev

§	***monieri*** (Gouan) P.W. Ball	LEdu
*	- 'Rosea'	CBre EBee LEdu NBre NDov NLar SRms
	nivea	see *S. discolor*
	obliqua	NBre
§	***officinalis***	CCBP CHab CWld EBee EMor GPoy ILea LEdu MHer MMuc MNHC NGrd NMir NRya SRms WCot WHer WTre
	- 'Alba'	EBee EMor LEdu MArl MAvo MMuc NBro SCob WCAu
	- 'Cally Bicolor'	GCal
	- 'Cally Pink'	GCal
	- dark-flowered **new**	WHoo
	- dwarf, white-flowered	CBre GCal
§	- 'Hummelo' ♀H7	Widely available
	- 'Marchant's Pink'	SMHy
	- 'Pink Cotton Candy'	EBee STPC
	- 'Rosea'	GCal NBro SCob WCAu WFar
	- 'Rosea Superba'	ECha GWyn NBre WCot
	- 'Saharan Pink'	EBee EPfP IPot LSRN NLar
	- 'Spitzenberg'	LPla
	- 'Ukkie' **new**	EBee
	- 'Wisley White'	CAby CBre CRos ECtt LBuc LEdu LPot LRHS MHol NGrd NHpl NRHS SRms WCot WFar
	olympica	see *S. byzantina*
	ossetica	CFis EBee GEdr
	palustris	CHab EWat LLWG MCoo MMuc NLar NMir SEND SRms
	- from Islay, Hebrides	MMuc SEND
	- pale-flowered	WOut
	recta	WArt
	setifera	NBre XLum
	spicata	see *S. macrantha*
	sylvatica	CHab NMir WHer WOut WSFF
	thirkei	WCot
§	***thunbergii***	MBrN MNHC WHrl WKif
§	- 'Danielle'	CElw ECtt EPfP GJos LRHS NLar SDys SPhx SRkn SRms
	tuberifera	see *S. affinis*

Stachyurus (*Stachyuraceae*)

	chinensis	CBcs CJun CMCN CMac CTri MGos NLar
	- 'Celina' ♀H5	CJun CRos ELon EPfP GKin LRHS MGos NLar NRHS SPoG
	- 'Goldbeater'	NLar
	- 'Joy Forever' (v) ♀H5	CBcs CEnd CMac CRos EBee EPfP IArd LLHF LRHS LSRN MGos MPkF NLar NRHS SPer SPoG SSta SWvt WKif
	- 'Senna'	NLar
	- 'Wonderful Image'	NLar
	himalaicus	CBcs NLar
	- HWJCM 009	WCru
	- HWJK 2035	WCru
	- pink-flowered	see *S. himalaicus* subsp. *purpureus*
§	- subsp. ***purpureus*** HWJK 2052	WCru
	aff. ***macrocarpus*** B&SWJ 14678 **new**	WCru
	'Magpie' (v)	LRHS WFar
	praecox ♀H5	Widely available
	- B&SWJ 8898	WCru
	- B&SWJ 10899	IDee LCro WCru
	- var. ***leucotrichus***	CJun NLar
	- var. ***matsuzakii***	CJun NLar
	- - B&SWJ 2817	WCru
	- - B&SWJ 11229	WCru
	- 'Petra'	CJun
	retusus	CExl
	'Rubriflorus'	CBcs CBct CJun EBee EPfP MAsh NLar WPGP
	salicifolius	CBcs CExl CJun CKel CTho EBee EPfP IMou NLar SPoG SSta WPGP
	sigeyosii	CBcs CExl EBee SSta
	- B&SWJ 6915	WCru
	- CWJ 12420	WCru
	- RWJ 10094	WCru
	aff. ***szechuanensis***	CExl
	- BWJ 8153	WCru
	yunnanensis	CBcs CJun IArd IDee NLar WPGP WSHC

Stapelia (*Apocynaceae*)

grandiflora	SSim
marmoratum	see *Orbea variegata*
variegata	see *Orbea variegata*

Staphylea ✿ (*Staphyleaceae*)

bolanderi	CBcs NLar
bumalda	CJun LEdu NLar
- B&SWJ 11053	WCru
- B&SWJ 12744 from Korea	WCru
colchica	CBcs CDul CHll CMCN CRos ELan EPfP EWTr EWes LEdu LPra LRHS MGos MMrt MRav NLar SPer WKif WSHC
holocarpa	CBcs CJun EPfP
- 'Innocence'	CBcs LRHS
- var. ***rosea***	CJun CMCN EPfP MBlu NLar SAko SMad SWvt
pinnata	CAgr CBcs CJun EBtc EPfP MCoo NLar SEND
- PAB 8427	LEdu
trifolia	CAgr CBcs EBee EPfP WWFP

Statice see *Limonium*

sinuata	see *Limonium sinuatum*

Stauntonia (*Lardizabalaceae*)

sp.	CKel
FMWJ 13177 from northern Vietnam	WCru
aff. ***chinensis*** DJHV 06175	WCru
hexaphylla	CBcs CCCN CHll CKel CRos CTri CWGN EBee EPfP ESwi EUJe LEdu LRHS MAsh MGil NLar SAdn SNig SPer SPoG SSta
- B&SWJ 4858	WCru
- B&SWJ 14655 **new**	WCru
aff. ***libera*** KWJ 12218	WCru
aff. ***maculata*** FMWJ 13055	WCru
obovata CWJ 12353	WCru
obovatifoliola B&SWJ 3685	WCru
purpurea	WPGP
- B&SWJ 3690	WCru
yaoshanensis B&SWJ 8223	WCru
- HWJ 1024	WCru WPGP

Stegnogramma (*Thelypteridaceae*)

pozoi	EFer

Stellaria (*Caryophyllaceae*)

graminea	CHab
holostea	CHab CWld MMuc NBir NMir WHer WPtf WShi

Stemmacantha see *Rhaponticum*

Stenanthium (Melanthiaceae)

gramineum EBee EWes

Stenomesson (Amaryllidaceae)

variegatum see *Clinanthus variegatus*

Stenotaphrum (Poaceae)

secundatum 'Variegatum' (v) ♀H1c EShb XLum

Stephanandra (Rosaceae)

incisa CBcs CExl SCob
§ – 'Crispa' CBcs CBod CDul CMac CSpe CTri ELan EPfP GKin MBlu MGil MJak MRav NEgg NHol SCob SPer SRms WMoo
– 'Prostrata' see *S. incisa* 'Crispa'
tanakae CBcs CDul CExl CMac ELan EPfP EWTr MBlu MGil MRav NEgg SLon SPer SRms

Stephania (Menispermaceae)

aff. **hernandiifolia** B&SWJ 14950 **new** WCru
japonica CWJ 12823 WCru
longa KWJ 12163 WCru
rotunda EUJe
aff. **tetrandra** WWJ 11896 WCru

Stephanotis (Apocynaceae)

floribunda ♀H1a CBcs CCCN LCro LOPS

Sterculia (Malvaceae)

rupestris see *Brachychiton rupestris*

Sternbergia (Amaryllidaceae)

candida CBro
fischeriana CBro
greuteriana GKev
lutea ♀H4 CAvo CBro CRos CTri ECha ELan EPot ERCP EWes GKev LAma LCro LOPS LRHS NRHS SBch SCob SDeJ WHoo XLum
– Angustifolia Group CBro CMea WCot
sicula CBro EPot GKev
– 'John Marr' WThu

Stevia (Asteraceae)

rebaudiana CBod CGro ENfk GPoy SPre SRms WCot WJek

Stewartia ✿ (Theaceae)

gemmata see *S. sinensis*
'Korean Splendor' see *S. pseudocamellia* Koreana Group
koreana see *S. pseudocamellia* Koreana Group
monadelpha CBcs CJun CMen MBlu MPkF NLar
pseudocamellia ♀H5 Widely available
– B&SWJ 11044 from North Japan WCru
§ – Koreana Group ♀H5 CBct CDul CEnd CJun CMCN CRos EPfP GKin LRHS NLar SLim
– 'Ogisu' NLar
pteropetiolata B&SWJ 11726 WCru
– NJM 10.107 WPGP
– WWJ 11939 WCru
rostrata CBcs CJun CLnd CMCN LRHS MBlu MPkF NLar SPtp
– 'Hulsdonk Pink' CJun
serrata CJun CMCN MPkF WCru
§ **sinensis** ♀H5 CBcs CCCN CJun EPfP IArd IDee IMou LMaj MBlu MPkF NLar SAko SSta WPGP

Stigmaphyllon (Malpighiaceae)

ciliatum CCCN
littorale CCCN

Stipa (Poaceae)

F&M 248 EBee
arundinacea see *Anemanthele lessoniana*
barbata CSpe ECha EPPr EWes GBin SCob WKif XSen
brachytricha see *Calamagrostis brachytricha*
§ **calamagrostis** Widely available
– 'Allgäu' WCot
– 'Lemperg' CRos IMou LRHS NRHS
capillata CBod CRos CSpe EBee EPPr EWhm GBin GCal LRHS MBel MNrw NRHS SHar SMHy SPhx XSen
– 'Brautschleier' CBod
* – 'Lace Veil' WAvo
elegantissima CPla
extremiorientalis EPPr SEND
gigantea ♀H4 Widely available
– 'Gold Fontaene' CKno EPPr EPfP EWes MAvo MNrw NDov SMHy SMad WCot WMoo
– 'Goldilocks' CRos ECha LEdu NRHS
– 'Pixie' CRos EPfP LRHS NRHS
grandis WMoo
ichu CKno CRos LRHS MAvo NDov NRHS
joannis GCal
lasiagrostis see *S. calamagrostis*
lessingiana CExl CPla EPPr LRHS SEND SPhx WMoo
pennata CRos XSen
pseudoichu CBod CSam CSpe ELan EPPr GBin GCal LPla LRHS MAvo MBNS MBel SPtp WCot WHoo WRHF
– RCB/Arg Y-1 EBee ELon NCGa
pulcherrima EPPr GCal
robusta EPPr
splendens misapplied see *S. calamagrostis*
splendens Trin. ECha GCal SAko
stenophylla see *S. tirsa*
tenacissima CDul MAsh
tenuifolia misapplied see *S. tenuissima*
tenuifolia Steud. CMea EBee LRHS MRav NBir NBro NSti WHal WMoo XLum XSen
§ **tenuissima** Widely available
– 'Wind Whispers' CExl LEdu LRHS MBel SPtp
§ **tirsa** EWes GCal

Stoebe (Asteraceae)

alopecuroides SPlb

Stokesia ✿ (Asteraceae)

cyanea see *S. laevis*
§ **laevis** CMea CPou CRos ECha EPfP LRHS NLar NRHS SCob SPlb SRms WCAu WMoo
– 'Alba' CRos ECha ELan EPfP LEdu LRHS MRav NLar NRHS WCAu
– 'Blue Frills' **new** ECtt
– 'Blue Star' CAby CBcs CDor CRos CWGN ELan ELon EMor EPfP LEdu LRHS LSun MBel MHer MRav MSCN NAln

NRHS SGbt SPad SPer SPhx SPoG SRkn SWvt WHrl WMoo WSHC
- 'Color Wheel' CRos ECtt LRHS NRHS SCob
- 'Divinity' **new** ECtt
- 'Honeysong Purple' NLar
- 'Klaus Jelitto' CRos ECtt EMor LEdu LRHS NRHS SPoG WHrl WMoo
- 'Mary Gregory' CAby CBod CMac CNor CRos EBee ECtt EHrv ELan EMor EPfP EWTr IKil LRHS MBel MRav MSCN NLar NRHS SPer SPhx SWvt WGwG WHrl
- 'Mel's'[PBR] CRos ECtt LRHS NAst NPri NRHS
- MEL'S BLUE see *S. laevis* 'Mel's'
- 'Omega Skyrocket' CPou SRms
- 'Peach Melba' ECtt WMoo
- 'Peachie's Pick' EBee ECtt EMor WMoo
- 'Purple Parasols' CDor CMac CRos CWGN EBee ECtt EPfP IKil LEdu LRHS MBel NCGa NRHS SCob SPoG SWvt WAul WGwG WHrl WMoo
- 'Purple Pixie'[PBR] ECtt
- 'Silver Moon' CBod ECtt EMor EPfP GBin LRHS MBel NAst NRHS SPer

§ - 'Träumerei' CBod CWGN EBee ECtt EMor EPfP LRHS NLar NRHS WHrl WMoo XLum
- 'White Star' see *S. laevis* 'Träumerei'

Stranvaesia see *Photinia*

× *Stranvinia* see *Photinia*

Stratiotes (*Hydrocharitaceae*)

aloides CBen CWat EWat LCro LLWG LOPS MWts NPer SVic WMAq WPnP

strawberry see *Fragaria*; also AGM Fruit Section

Strelitzia (*Strelitziaceae*)

alba CCCN
juncea XBlo
nicolai CCCN NPer SPlb XBlo
reginae ♀H1b CAbb CBcs CCCN CTsd ELan EShb EUJe LCro LOPS NPer SChr SPlb XBlo
- 'Kirstenbosch Gold' XBlo

Streptocarpella see *Streptocarpus*

Streptocarpus ✿ (*Gesneriaceae*)

'Adele' WDib
'Alana' **new** WDib
'Albatross' CTsd WDib
'Alissa' WDib
'Amanda' Dibley WDib
'Ambiente' ♀H1c WDib
'Amy' WDib
'Anne' (d) CTsd WDib
'Anwen' WDib
'Awena' WDib
baudertii WDib
'Bella' WDib
'Bethan' ♀H1c CTsd WDib
'Bianca' WDib
'Black Gardenia' CTsd
'Black Panther' CTsd WDib
'Blue Frills' ♀H1c WDib
'Blue Gem' WDib
'Blue Leyla' see *S.* 'Leyla'
'Blue Moon' WDib
'Blue Nymph' WDib
'Boysenberry Delight' WDib
'Branwen' CTsd WDib
'Bristol's Black Bird' WDib
'Bristol's Very Best' WDib
caeruleus WDib
'Caitlin' CTsd WDib
candidus WDib
'Cappuccino' WDib
'Cariad' WDib
'Carol' WDib
'Carys' ♀H1c CTsd WDib
caulescens WDib
- var. ***pallescens*** WDib
'Celebration' WDib
'Charlotte' ♀H1c WDib
'Chloe' WDib
'Chorus Line' CTsd WDib
'Constant Nymph' WDib
'Crystal Beauty' WDib
'Crystal Blush' WDib
'Crystal Charm' WDib
'Crystal Dawn' WDib
'Crystal Ice'[PBR] ♀H1c LCro LOPS WDib
'Crystal Snow' WDib
'Crystal Wonder' WDib
cyaneus WDib
- subsp. ***polackii*** WDib
'Cynthia' WDib
'Daphne' WDib
'Dee' WDib
'Delia' WDib
'Denim' WDib
denticulatus WDib
'Diana' WDib
'Dinas' WDib
'Ds-Horus' WDib
dunnii WDib
'Elin' **new** WDib
'Elsi' CTsd WDib
'Emily' WDib
'Eve' NWad WDib
'Falling Stars' ♀H1c CTsd WDib
'Festival Wales' WDib
'Fiesta' WDib
'Fiona' WDib
floribundus WDib
'Franken Alayana' WDib
'Franken Isabella' WDib
'Franken Skye' WDib
'Franken Strawberry Fondant' WDib
'Freya' WDib
'Frosty Diamond' ♀H1c CTsd WDib
'Full Moon' WDib
gardenii WDib
glandulosissimus ♀H1c WDib
'Gloria' ♀H1c CTsd WDib
'Gold Dust' **new** WDib
'Gwen' WDib
'Hannah' ♀H1c WDib
'Harlequin Blue'[PBR] ♀H1c WDib
'Harlequin Damsel' WDib
'Harlequin Dawn' WDib
'Harlequin Delft' WDib
'Harlequin Lace'[PBR] ♀H1c WDib
'Harlequin Purple' WDib
'Harlequin Rose' WDib
'Harriet' WDib

	'Hayley'	WDib
	'Heidi'	CTsd WDib
	'Helen'	CTsd WDib
	'Hope'	WDib
	'Iona'	WDib
	'Isabella'	WDib
	'Jacquie'	WDib
	'Jennifer' ♀H1c	WDib
	'Jessica' ♀H1c	WDib
	'Joanna'	CTsd WDib
	johannis	WDib
	'Joy'	WDib
	'Karen'	WDib
	'Katie'PBR ♀H1c	WDib
	kentaniensis	WDib
	'Kim' ♀H1c	WDib
	kirkii	WDib
	'Laura' ♀H1c	WDib
§	'Leyla'PBR	WDib
	'Louise'	WDib
	'Lucy'	WDib
	'Lyndee'	WDib
	'Lynne'	WDib
	'Maassen's White'	WDib
	'Margaret' Gavin Brown	WDib
	'Marie'	WDib
	'Marion'	WDib
	'Matilda'	WDib
	'Megan'	WDib
	'Melanie' Dibley	WDib
	'Menai'	WDib
	meyeri	WDib
	'Midnight Flame'	CTsd
	modestus	WDib
	'Myfanwy'	WDib
	'Nadine' **new**	WDib
	'Natalie'	WDib
	'Nerys'	CTsd WDib
	'Nia'	CTsd WDib
	'Nicola'	CTsd WDib
	'Olivia'	WDib
	'Padarn'	WDib
	'Paula'	WDib
	'Pearl' ♀H1c	WDib
	pentherianus	WDib
	'Pink Leyla'PBR ♀H1c	WDib
	'Pink Souffle'	WDib
	'Polka-Dot Purple' ♀H1c	WDib
	'Polka-Dot Red'	WDib
	polyanthus	WDib
	subsp. ***dracomontanus***	
	primulifolius	WDib
	- subsp. ***formosus***	WDib
	prolixus	WDib
	'Purple Velvet'	WDib
	rexii	WDib
	'Rhiannon'	CTsd WDib
	'Rose Halo'	WDib
	'Rosebud'	WDib
	(Roulette Series) 'Roulette Azur'PBR ♀H1c	WDib
	- 'Roulette Cherry'	WDib
	'Rubina'PBR	WDib
	'Rubina Pink' ♀H1c	WDib
	'Ruby'	CTsd WDib
	'Ruth'	WDib
	'Sally'	WDib
	'Sandra'	WDib
	'Sarah'	WDib
	saxorum	CCCN CTsd WDib
	- compact ♀H1c	CCCN WDib
	'Scarlett'	WDib
	'Seren'	WDib
	'Sian'	WDib
	silvaticus	WDib
	'Sioned' ♀H1c	WDib
	'Snow White' ♀H1c	WDib
I	'Stella'PBR Dibleys ♀H1c	WDib
§	'Stella' Fleischle (Marleen Series) ♀H1c	WDib
	'Stephanie'	WDib
	stomandrus	WDib
	'Susan' ♀H1c	CTsd WDib
	'Sweet Melys'	WDib
	'Sweet Rosy' **new**	WDib
	'Tanga'	see *S.* 'Stella' Fleischle
	'Tanya'	WDib
	'Teleri'	WDib
	'Texas Hot Chili'	CTsd WDib
	thompsonii	WDib
	'Tina' ♀H1c	WDib
	'Titania' **new**	WDib
	'Tracey'	WDib
	'Valor'	WDib
	vandeleurii	WDib
	variabilis	WDib
	'Wawel'	WDib
	wendlandii	WDib
	'Wendy'	WDib
	'White Butterfly' ♀H1c	WDib
	'Wiesmoor Red'	WDib
	'Winifred'	WDib

Streptopus (*Liliaceae*)

	amplexifolius	EBee EHrv GBin MNrw WCru
	- var. ***papillatus***	GEdr
	roseus	WCru
	streptopoides	CRos EMor EPPr EPfP LEdu LRHS NRHS

Streptosolen (*Solanaceae*)

	jamesonii ♀H1c	CCCN CHll EBak EShb SWvt

Strobilanthes (*Acanthaceae*)

	CC 4071	CExl
	CC 4573	CExl
	angustifrons **new**	SBrt
	anisophylla	EShb SDys WSpi
	atropurpurea misapplied	see *S. attenuata*
	atropurpurea Nees	see *S. wallichii*
§	***attenuata***	CBct CBod CRos CWld EBee ECtt EMor EPfP GCal ILea ITim LEdu LRHS MBel MHer MPie MRav MSCN NCGa NChi NRHS NSti SPoG WCot WCru WMoo WOut
	- 'Blue and White'	EBee
	- 'Blue Carpet'	EBee NDov
	- 'Cally Bicolor'	GCal
	- 'Latham's Form'	WHil
	- subsp. ***nepalensis***	CHll XLum
	- 'Out of the Ocean'	WOut
	dyeriana ♀H1b	EBak EShb SPlb WCot
	flexicaulis	MHer
	- B&SWJ 354	WCru
	aff. ***inflata*** B&SWJ 7754	WCru
*	***lactea***	EShb
	nutans	CPou EBee EWld NSti SBrt XLum
	pentstemonoides	GCal
	rankanensis	EBee EPPr ILea MPie SDys SHar XLum

- B&SWJ 1771	WCru
violacea misapplied	EShb IArd
§ ***wallichii***	CMac EBee EPfP EWes EWld ILea MHer MMuc NSti SEND WCAu WCru WMoo
- PAB 8440	LEdu
- from Picton **new**	WMoo

Stromanthe (*Marantaceae*)

sanguinea 'Triostar'PBR (v)	XBlo

Strongylodon (*Papilionaceae*)

macrobotrys	CHll

Strophanthus (*Apocynaceae*)

speciosus	CCCN CHll EShb

Strumaria (*Amaryllidaceae*)

discifera subsp. ***bulbifera***	WCot

Stuartia see *Stewartia*

Stylidium (*Stylidiaceae*)

graminifolium	CTsd SPlb
- LITTLE SAPHIRE ('St116')	SRot

Stylophorum (*Papaveraceae*)

diphyllum	CFis CPou EWld GCal IMou LEdu MAvo MPie WCru WPGP WPnP WWtn
lasiocarpum	CExl CSpe EMor EPPr EWes EWld GEdr MMrt NBid WArt WCru

Styphelia (*Ericaceae*)

colensoi	see *Leucopogon colensoi*

Styphnolobium (*Papilionaceae*)

§ ***japonicum***	CBcs CDul CHab CMCN CMac CTho EPfP LMaj LPra SCob SPlb WTSh
- 'China Gold'	SPoG
- 'Pendulum'	CDul LPra NPri
- 'Regent'	LPra

Styrax ✿ (*Styracaceae*)

NJM 11.013 from Guizhou, China	WPGP
NJM 11.085 from Guizhou, China	WPGP
americanus	CBcs EPfP
- Kankakee form	WPGP
confusus	CExl
dasyanthus	CExl
faberi	CExl
formosanus var. ***formosanus***	CBcs CExl CJun EPfP MBlu WPGP
- - B&SWJ 3803	WCru
- - B&SWJ 6786	WCru
- var. ***hayatiana*** B&SWJ 6823	WCru
grandiflorus	CExl
hemsleyanus ♀H5	CBcs CExl CTho EPfP IDee IMou LEdu MBlu NLar SPtp
hookeri	CExl
japonicus	CAco CBcs CDul CEnd CExl CLnd CMCN CRos CTho CTri ELan ELon EPfP GKin LMaj LRHS MAsh MBlu MGos MMuc MRav NLar SPer SPoG WPGP
- B&SWJ 4405	WCru
- B&SWJ 8770	WCru
- B&SWJ 11078	WCru
- Guiz 216	CExl WPGP
- PAB 8366	LEdu
§ - Benibana Group	SChF WPGP
- - 'Pink Chimes'	CBcs CExl CJun CMCN ELan ESwi GKin MBlu MPkF NLar NOra SAko WMat
- 'Carillon'	CJun
- 'Evening Light'	CBcs SMad
- 'Fargesii' ♀H5	CBcs CDul CExl CJun CTho
- 'Fragrant Fountain'	LRHS MBlu MPkF
- MARLEY'S PINK PARASOL ('JLWeeping')	LRHS
- 'Pendulus'	CBcs EPfP NLar SMad WPGP
I - 'Pink Snowbell'	LRHS
- 'Purple Dress' ♀H5	CJun MBlu NLar
- 'Roseus'	see *S. japonicus* Benibana Group
- 'Snowfall'	CJun NLar
- 'Sohuksan' ♀H5	CExl CJun MBlu WPGP
aff. ***japonicus*** B&SWJ 14182 from Heuksando, South Korea **new**	WCru
limprichtii	CExl
obassia	CBcs CDul CMCN CTho EPfP LRHS MBlu NLar WGob WPGP
- B&SWJ 6023	WCru
- B&SWJ 10890	WCru
odoratissimus	CExl
officinalis	CBcs CJun
serrulatus	CExl
shiraianus	CExl WPGP
tonkinensis FMWJ 13134	WCru
wilsonii	CExl
wuyuanensis	WPGP

Succisa (*Caprifoliaceae*)

§ ***pratensis***	CAby CBod CDor CHab CMac CWld EBee EWld GWyn LEdu LLWG MAvo MHer MPie MWts NLar SBch SMHy SPhx SRms WCAu WHer WHoo WPGP WSFF WWFP XLum
- 'Alba'	EWes MHer
- 'Buttermilk'	CDor LEdu
- 'Cassop'	NRya
- 'Derby Purple'	CSpe
- early-flowering	LEdu SPhx
- 'Peddar's Pink'	EWes LLWG SPhx

Succisella (*Caprifoliaceae*)

inflexa	CSpe LEdu LRHS SPhx WCAu WFar
- 'Frosted Pearls'	CDor CElw CFis LEdu LSun MAvo MMuc NLar SHar

sugarsnap see AGM Vegetables Section (under pea)

sunberry see *Rubus* 'Sunberry'

Sutera (*Scrophulariaceae*)

Abunda Series	see *Chaenostoma* Abunda Series
Copia Series	see *Chaenostoma* Copia Series
cordata 'Snowflake'	see *Chaenostoma cordatum* 'Snowflake'
microphylla	see *Jamesbrittenia microphylla*
neglecta	see *Chaenostoma neglectum*
Scopia Series	see *Chaenostoma* Scopia Series

Sutherlandia ✿ (*Papilionaceae*)

frutescens	CBod CSpe GDun SPlb
montana	CPbh CSpe SBrt

Swainsona (*Papilionaceae*)

galegifolia	CHll

sweet cicely see *Myrrhis odorata*

sweet corn see AGM Vegetables Section

sweet pepper see *Capsicum*; also AGM Vegetables Section

Swertia (*Gentianaceae*)

bimaculata PAB 8845	LEdu
perennis	GEdr
petiolata CC 7335	GKev

Swietenia (*Meliaceae*)

mahogani	SPlb

Syagrus (*Arecaceae*)

botryophora	XBlo
§ ***romanzoffiana***	EUJe XBlo

× *Sycoparrotia* (*Hamamelidaceae*)

semidecidua	CBcs CBct CCCN CJun EBee MBlu NLar WHor
- 'Purple Haze'	CJun IArd IDee NLar
- 'Variegata' (v)	CJun

Sycopsis (*Hamamelidaceae*)

sinensis	CAby CBcs CCCN CExl CRos EBee EPfP GBin GCal LEdu LMaj LRHS MGil MMuc NLar SSta SWvt WPGP

Symphoricarpos (*Caprifoliaceae*)

albus	CDul CMac CPer MSwo NWea SCob WTSh
- 'Constance Spry'	SRms
§ - var. ***laevigatus***	LBuc
× ***chenaultii***	SRms
- 'Hancock'	CMac EBee ELan EPfP MMuc MRav MSwo NWea SCob SGol SPer WCFE
× ***doorenbosii*** 'Magic Berry'	EBee MRav NWea SGol
- 'Mother of Pearl'	CDul ELan EPfP LCro LOPS MMuc MRav NWea SCob SPer SRms
- 'White Hedge'	LBuc MMuc NWea SPer SPlb
guatemalensis B&SWJ 1016	WCru
MAGICAL CANDY ('Kolmcan'[PBR])	CRos ELan LRHS NEoE NRHS SPoG
MAGICAL GALAXY ('Kolmgala'[PBR])	CRos ELan EPfP LRHS NEoE NRHS SPoG
MAGICAL SWEET ('Kolmaswet'[PBR])	CRos LRHS NRHS SPoG
orbiculatus	SLon
- 'Albovariegatus'	see *S. orbiculatus* 'Taff's Silver Edge'
- 'Argenteovariegatus'	see *S. orbiculatus* 'Taff's Silver Edge'
- 'Bowles's Golden Variegated'	see *S. orbiculatus* 'Foliis Variegatis'
§ - 'Foliis Variegatis' (v)	CMac CTri EHoe MRav SGol
- 'George Gardiner'	CMac
§ - 'Taff's Silver Edge' (v)	SGol
- 'Variegatus'	see *S. orbiculatus* 'Foliis Variegatis'
rivularis	see *S. albus* var. *laevigatus*

Symphyandra see *Campanula*

asiatica	see *Hanabusaya asiatica*

Symphyotrichum (*Asteraceae*)

§ × ***amethystinum***	MNrw WCot
- 'Freiburg'	EPPr MNrw
'Anja's Choice'	EBee EPPr MTis WOld
'Ann Leys'[PBR]	EBee SCob WCot XEll
'Aqua Compact' (Autumn Jewels Series)	CBod EUJe NRHS
'Beauté du Nord' **new**	WCot
'Blue Butterfly'	SPhx WOld XLum
'Blütenregen'	WArt WCot WFar XEll
chilense 'Purple Haze'	EPPr
§ ***ciliolatum***	SPhx
'Claudia'	WOld
'Climax' Vicary Gibbs	LEdu MNrw WFar WOld
'Coombe Fishacre' ♀H7	EBee ECtt ELan ELon GCal GQue ILea LEdu LRHS MNrw NDov NLar SPhx SRms SWvt WArt WCAu WCot WHoo WOld WSpi
§ ***cordifolium***	SPhx XLum
- from Piney Fork	EPPr
- 'Aldebaran'	LEdu WOld
- 'Blue Heaven'	SAko
- 'Chieftain' ♀H7	LEdu MHCG MNrw SMHy SPhx WOld
- 'Elegans'	CSam EBee WOld
- 'Ideal'	NLar SPhx XLum
- 'Silver Spray'	CKno CRos ECtt ELon GMaP ILea MWat WOld XLum
- 'Sweet Lavender' ♀H7	CRos EBee LRHS NRHS WOld
- 'White Chief'	WOld
drummondii	SPhx
§ ***dumosum***	CChe CExl
- 'Biteliness'	NLar
- 'Early Blue'	ILea
- SAPPHIRE ('Kiesapphire'[PBR]) (Autumn Jewels Series)	CChe ELon LRHS LSRN MHol NCou NEgg SRkn SWvt XLum
§ ***ericoides***	NBre WOld
- 'Blue Star' ♀H7	CDor CRos LRHS NLar NRHS WOld
- 'Blue Wonder'	CBod XLum
- 'Brimstone' ♀H7	MRav WOld
- 'Cinderella'	CRos EBee LRHS NRHS NSti WOld
- 'Constance'	WOld
- 'Deep Danziger'	SPhx
- 'Erlkönig'	CBod EBee ELon EShb GCal GQue LEdu NAln NGdn NLar SWvt WCot WOld XLum
- 'Esther'	ECha ECtt ELan MMrt MNrw WOld
- 'First Snow'	WCot WFar
- 'Golden Spray' ♀H7	EBee ECtt ELon EPfP EWes GMaP GQue NLar SPer WOld
- 'Herbstmyrte'	CRos LRHS NRHS
- 'Hon. Edith Gibbs'	WOld
- 'Monte Cassino'	see *S. pilosum* var. *pringlei* 'Monte Cassino'
- 'Pink Cloud' ♀H7	CBod CRos ECtt EPfP EShb GCal GQue LEdu LRHS MBel NCGa NLar NRHS NWad SAko SHar SPhx WCAu WOld
- f. ***prostratum***	CRos EPot MRav SAko XEll XSen
§ - - 'Snow Flurry' ♀H7	CMea CSpe ECha ECtt ELon GQue IMou LEdu LPla MAvo MHol MNrw MWat NLar SAko SIgm SPhx SWvt WCot WHoo WOld XLum
- 'Rosy Veil'	NBir NGdn WOld
- 'Schneegitter'	CRos LRHS NRHS SAko SPhx WCot XSen
- 'Schneetanne'	SAko
- 'Sulphurea'	MWat

	- 'Vimmer's Delight'	ECtt LPla WArt WCot WFar
	- 'White Heather'	ECtt NLar WOld
	- 'Yvette Richardson'	CSam ECtt SMHy WOld
§	***falcatum***	WCot
	- var. ***commutatum***	WCot WOld
	foliaceum from Montana	EPPr
	- var. ***parryi***	EBee
	GRANAT ('Kiastgranat') (Autumn Jewels Series)	SPad
§	***greatae***	EBee
	'Herfstweelde'	EBee NAln SPhx WOld
	'Hill Close Blue'	MHCG
	'Hon. Vicary Gibbs' (*ericoides* hybrid)	WOld
§	***laeve***	CDor EBee LEdu NLar SPhx
	- 'Anneke Van der Jeugd'	MNrw
§	- 'Arcturus'	CElw LEdu MAvo MBel MNrw MTis NBir NCGa WCot WFar WOld XLum
	- 'Blauschleier'	EBee
	- 'Blue Bird'	WOld
§	- 'Calliope'	Widely available
	- 'Cally Compact'	GQue NLar WFar WOld
	- 'Climax'	CElw EBee ELan GCal MMuc MRav NBid NSti SEND WBrk XLum
	- var. ***geyeri***	MNrw
	- 'Glow in the Dark'	EBee EPPr LEdu MAvo MWat NCGa NLar WBrk WCot WHoo WOld
	- 'Les Moutiers'	CMea EPPr LEdu MAvo MNrw WBrk WFar WOld
	- 'Nightshade'	EPPr MAvo MNrw MTis NCGa WFar WOld WRHF
	- 'Orpheus'	LEdu MAvo MNrw WBrk WFar
	- 'Vesta'	ECtt MTis WOld
§	- 'White Climax'	CSam MNrw WCot
	- white-flowered	WBrk WOld
§	***lanceolatum*** Willd.	NCGa
	- 'Edwin Beckett'	CBre MNrw SWvt WFar WOld
§	***lateriflorum***	SWvt WOld
	- 'Bleke Bet'	WCot WFar WOld
	- 'Buck's Fizz'	ELan WOld
	- 'Chloe'	CDor CSam NCGa SPhx WCot WFar WOld
	- 'Datschi'	XLum
	- var. ***horizontalis*** ♀H7	CBod CRos CSam EBee ECha ECtt EHoe ELan ELon EPfP GQue LRHS MRav MWat NBro NCGa NGdn NRHS NWad SCob SPer SPlb SRms SRot SWvt WCAu WMoo WOld WSpi XEll
	- 'Lady in Black'	Widely available
	- 'Lovely'	CSam WArt WCot
	- 'Prince'	Widely available
	'Little Carlow' (*cordifolium* hybrid) ♀H7	Widely available
	'Little Dorrit' (*cordifolium* hybrid)	ECtt NWsh
	(Newstars Series) 'Newstars Fantasy'	MAvo WArt WCot WOld
	- 'Newstars Glory'	WArt WCot WFar
	'Nicholas'	ECtt WCot WFar WOld
	'Nineteen' **new**	MAvo
	'Noreen'	MAvo MHCG MTis WOld
§	***novae-angliae***	GKev WOld
	- 'Abendsonne'	SAko
	- 'Alex Deamon'	ELon MAvo WBrk WOld
	- 'Anabelle de Chazal'	ECtt ELon MWat WBrk WFar WOld
	- 'Andenken an Alma Pötschke'	Widely available
	- 'Andenken an Paul Gerber'	CRos ECtt ELon LRHS MAvo MNrw MTis NLar NRHS WOld

	- 'Augusta'	ELon MAvo NLar SPhx WBrk WOld
	- AUTUMN SNOW	see *S. novae-angliae* 'Herbstschnee'
	- 'Badsey Pink'	WCot
	- 'Barr's Blue'	CMac CRos EBee ECtt ELan ELon EPfP IPot LRHS MAvo MMuc MTis MWat NLar NRHS NWsh SEND SPer SRms WBrk WCAu WMoo WOld
	- 'Barr's Pink'	CMac CRos EBee ECtt ELan ELon EPfP LRHS MAvo MCot MMuc MPie MTis MWat NRHS SEND SRms WBrk WFar WOld WSFF
	- 'Barr's Purple'	ECtt WBrk WCFE WOld
	- 'Barr's Violet'	ECtt MAvo NSti SRms WBrk WCot WFar WHal WMoo WOld
	- 'Betel Nut' **new**	MAvo
	- 'Bishop Colenso'	EPPr SPhx WBrk
	- 'Blackheart'	ELon
I	- 'Brightness'	WCot
	- 'Brockamin'	EPPr MNrw WBrk WOld
	- 'Brunswick'	MAvo WFar WOld
	- 'Christopher Harbutt'	LEdu
	- 'Colwall Century'	MAvo WBrk WOld
	- 'Colwall Constellation'	ELon MAvo WBrk WOld
	- 'Colwall Galaxy'	WBrk WOld
	- 'Colwall Orbit'	ECtt ELon NWsh WBrk WOld
	- 'Connie'	MNrw
	- 'Constanze'	EBee ECtt ELon MAvo MTis
	- 'Crimson Beauty'	ECtt ELon MAvo MHCG MHer MNrw MWat SAko WBrk WFar WOld
	- 'Dapper Tapper'	ECtt ELon WCot WOld
	- 'Dark Desire' **new**	MNrw
	- 'Denise' **new**	MAvo
	- 'Early Bird'	ELon
	- 'Evensong'	ECtt LEdu MAvo MPie WBrk WOld
	- 'Festival'	MAvo WBrk
	- 'Foxy Emily'	ECtt MHCG WBrk WOld
	- 'Guido en Gezelle' **new**	MAvo
	- 'Harrington's Pink' ♀H7	Widely available
	- 'Helen Picton'	CDor CSam ECtt ELon LEdu MAvo MBrN MHer MPie MWat NLar NWsh SRms WBrk WFar WHoo WMoo WOld
	- 'Herbstflieder' **new**	EBee
§	- 'Herbstschnee'	Widely available
	- 'Hoo House' **new**	WHoo
	- 'James'	EPPr MAvo
	- 'James Ritchie'	CSam ECtt MCot MTis WHoo WOld
	- 'John Davis'	MNrw WOld
	- 'John Dickinson'	WBrk
	- 'Jon Baker'	WBrk
	- 'Kate Deamon'	ECtt WOld
	- 'Kylie'	ECtt EPPr LEdu LRHS LSRN MNrw MTis SPhx WBrk WCot WFar WOld
	- 'Lachsglut'	ELon EPPr LEdu NLar SAko WCot WOld
	- 'Ladies Day'	WOld
	- 'Little Bella'	ECtt MWat WOld
	- 'Lou Williams'	ECtt ELon MNrw MWat NLar WArt WFar WOld
I	- 'Lucida'	MAvo SPhx SRms WOld
	- 'Lucinda'	ECtt
	- 'Lye End Beauty'	CDor ECtt ELon MAvo MHer MNrw MPie MWat WBrk WCot WFar WMoo WOld
	- 'Mabelle'	MAvo NDov
	- 'Mandie's Choice'	WCot
	- 'Marina Wolkonsky'	CAby ECtt ELon EWes IPot LEdu MAvo MMrt MNrw MWat NLar

		SAko SPhx SRms WBrk WCot WFar WKif WOld
	- 'Millennium Star'	ECtt ELon WBrk WOld
	- 'Miss K.E. Mash'	ECtt NLar WBrk WCAu WFar WOld
	- 'Mrs S.T. Wright'	CAby CTri ECtt EWes LEdu MBrN MNrw NWsh WBrk WFar WOld
	- 'Mrs S.W. Stern'	WBrk WOld
	- 'Nachtauge'	SAko
	- 'Naomi'	MAvo WBrk WOld
	- 'Percy Picton'	LEdu
	- 'Pink Parfait'	CSam ECtt IKil MPie NGdn SRms WBrk WCot WFar WOld
	- 'Pink Victor'	EPPr SRms WMoo
	- 'Pontis Supreme' **new**	MAvo
	- 'Pride of Rougham'	ECtt EWes MAvo WBrk
	- 'Primrose Upward'	CAby ECtt MNrw NDov NWsh SPhx WCot WOld
	- 'Purple Cloud'	CAby CSam ECtt ELon MAvo MHer MWat NGdn WBrk WHal WOld
I	- 'Purple Dome'	Widely available
	- 'Quinton Menzies'	CAby ELon MAvo WOld
	- 'Red Cloud'	ECtt ELon LEdu MAvo MHer WBrk WOld
	- 'Rosa Sieger' ♀H7	CAby CSam ECtt ELon GMaP LEdu MAvo MNrw MTis NGdn WBor WBrk WFar WHoo WOld XLum
	- 'Rose Williams'	LEdu MPie WBrk
	- 'Röter Stern'	ECtt MPie WBrk WOld
	- 'Röter Turm'	SAko
	- 'Rougham Pink'	WBrk
	- 'Rougham Purple'	EWes
	- 'Rougham Violet'	EPPr WBrk
	- 'Rubinschatz'	EBee ECtt ELon MAvo MTis NWsh SRms WOld XLum
	- 'Rudelsburg'	EBee ECtt ELon MAvo SHar WBrk
	- 'Rudolph'	ECtt EWes
	- 'Saint Michael's'	MAvo MWat WBrk WFar WOld
	- 'Sayer's Croft'	ECtt ELon MAvo MWat SRms WBrk WCot WFar WHoo WOld
	- SEPTEMBER RUBY	see *S. novae-angliae* 'Septemberrubin'
§	- 'Septemberrubin'	CAby CBod CMea EBee ECtt ELan ELon EMor EPPr EPfP GQue LEdu LPla MAvo MBel MMuc MRav MTis NAln NSti NWsh SEND SRms WFar WOld WSpi XLum
	- 'Treasure'	CBre CRos ECtt ELon EPPr EWes LRHS MAvo NBre NRHS SPhx WBrk WOld
	- 'Vibrant Dome' PBR	CRos LRHS MNrw MTis NLar NRHS
	- 'Violet Dusk'	ELon WBrk
	- 'Violet Haze'	CMea ELon WBrk
	- 'Violetta'	CRos ECtt ELon GMaP ILea LEdu LRHS MAvo MNrw MTis NRHS SCob SPhx WBor WBrk WFar WHil WKif WOld
	- 'W. Bowman'	ECtt MNrw WBrk WOld
	- 'Warm Throng' **new**	WCot
	- 'Wineflower'	MCot MTis
	- 'Wow'	ELon
§	***novi-belgii***	WHer WMoo
	- 'Ada Ballard'	CFis CMac CRos CWld EBee EHoe LRHS LSRN NEgg NGrd NRHS WFar WMoo WOld
	- 'Albanian'	SRms WOld
	- 'Alderman Vokes'	WOld
	- 'Algar's Pride'	ECtt WFar WOld
	- 'Alice Haslam'	CBod CMac CRos ECtt ELan LRHS MHol MSCN NLar NRHS SRms WFar WOld
	- 'Angela Peel'	CRos LRHS NRHS
	- 'Anita Ballard'	WOld
	- 'Anita Webb'	NBir WOld
	- 'Anneke'	NLar WOld
	- 'Apollo'	CRos ILea LRHS MSCN MWat NLar NRHS WFar WOld
	- 'Apple Blossom'	MWat WFar WOld
	- 'Audrey'	CMac CRos GMaP LRHS LSRN MBNS NGdn SRms WFar WOld
	- 'Autumn Beauty'	WOld
	- 'Autumn Days'	WOld
	- 'Autumn Glory'	WOld
	- 'Autumn Rose'	WOld
	- 'Baby Climax'	WOld
	- BAHAMAS ('Dasone') (Island Series)	CBod CRos EPfP LRHS NEgg NPri NRHS NWsh SPoG SRms SWvt WCot
	- BARBADOS ('Dastwo') (Island Series)	CBod CRos EPfP LRHS NLar NPri NRHS SPoG SWvt WCot WFar
	- 'Beauty of Colwall'	WOld
	- 'Beechwood Beacon'	WFar
	- 'Beechwood Challenger'	MHCG MNrw MPie WOld
	- 'Beechwood Charm'	WFar WOld
	- 'Beechwood Rival'	CDor CTri WOld XEll
	- 'Blandie'	MWat WOld
	- 'Blauglut'	WFar WOld
	- 'Blue Baby'	CMac MPie
	- 'Blue Bouquet'	CTri SRms WFar WOld
	- 'Blue Boy'	WOld
	- 'Blue Danube'	WOld
	- 'Blue Eyes'	WOld
	- 'Blue Gown'	GCal GQue WOld
	- 'Blue Lagoon'	CDor CFis CMea ELan LSRN WBrk WCAu WOld
	- 'Blue Lapis'	EBee LRHS WFar
I	- 'Blue Moon'	MWat WFar WOld
	- 'Blue Patrol'	WOld
	- 'Blue Radiance'	WOld
	- 'Blue Spire'	SPhx WOld
	- 'Blue Whirl'	WOld
	- 'Boningale Blue'	WOld
	- 'Boningale White'	MHCG WFar WOld
	- 'Bridesmaid'	WOld
	- 'Bright Eyes'	WOld
	- 'Brightest and Best'	WOld
	- 'Brigitte'	CBod CDor EWTr NLar
	- 'Cameo'	WOld
	- 'Cantab'	WOld
	- 'Carlingcott'	WOld
	- 'Carnival'	CMac CRos EBee ECtt LRHS NRHS WOld
	- 'Cecily'	MWat WOld
	- 'Charles Wilson'	CFis WOld
	- 'Chatterbox'	CRos ELan EPfP LRHS MRav MWat NEgg NLar NRHS SRms WFar WOld
	- 'Chelwood'	WFar WOld
	- 'Chequers'	CBod CElw MBNS MHer NEgg SRms WFar WOld
	- 'Christina'	see *S. novi-belgii* 'Kristina'
	- 'Christine Soanes'	WOld
	- 'Cliff Lewis'	WFar WOld
	- 'Climax Albus'	see *S. laeve* 'White Climax'
	- 'Cloudy Blue'	WOld
	- 'Colonel F.R. Durham'	WOld
	- 'Coombe Gladys'	WOld
	- 'Coombe Margaret'	WOld
	- 'Coombe Radiance'	WOld
	- 'Coombe Ronald'	WOld
	- 'Coombe Rosemary'	ECtt NLar WBor WOld
	- 'Coombe Violet'	MWat WOld

- 'Countess of Dudley'	CFis WFar WOld
- 'Court Herald'	WOld
- 'Crimson Brocade'	CDor CRos ECtt ELan EPfP LRHS NLar NRHS SAko SPoG SRms SWvt WFar
- 'Dandy'	CMac CRos ELan EPfP LRHS NBir NGdn NRHS WFar WOld
- 'Daniela'	SRms WBrk WFar WOld
- 'Daphne Anne'	WOld
- 'Dauerblau'	EBee WOld
- 'Davey's True Blue'	CTri WFar WOld XLum
- 'David Murray'	WOld
- 'Dazzler'	ECtt WFar WOld
- 'Destiny'	WOld
- 'Diana'	ECtt NWsh
- 'Diana Watts'	WOld
- 'Dietgard'	MWat WFar WOld
- 'Dolly'	NBir SRms WOld
- 'Dora Chiswell'	WOld
- 'Dusky Maid'	ELon WFar WOld
- 'Elizabeth Hutton'	WFar WOld
- 'Elsie Dale'	WOld
- 'Elta'	WOld
- 'Erica'	CElw MWat WOld
- 'Ernest Ballard'	WOld
- 'Eva'	ELon SRms WOld
- 'Eventide'	CTri LSRN WOld
- 'Fair Lady'	MWat WOld
- 'Faith'	WFar WOld
- 'Farncombe Lilac'	MAvo
- 'Feckenham Rival'	WOld
- 'Fellowship' ♀H6	CAby CBod CDor CRos EAJP EBee ECtt ELon EPfP IKil LEdu LRHS MBel MMuc MNrw MWat NLar NRHS SAko SEND SHar SRms SWvt WCAu WCot WFar WOld
- 'Flamingo'	CRos LRHS NRHS SRms WOld
- 'Freda Ballard'	CRos ECtt GMaP LRHS MWat NRHS WFar WOld
- 'Freya'	CElw LSRN MWat SRms WOld WSHC
- 'Fuldatal'	MWat WFar WOld
- 'Gayborder Blue'	WFar WOld
- 'Gayborder Royal'	WFar WOld
- 'Goliath'	MWat WOld
- 'Grey Lady'	WFar WOld
- 'Guardsman'	WOld
- 'Gulliver'	SRms WBrk WFar WOld
- 'Gurney Slade'	WFar WOld
- 'Guy Ballard'	WOld
- 'Harrison's Blue'	MWat WOld
- 'Heinz Richard'	CFis ECha MHer NBir NGdn SRms WOld
- 'Helen'	ELon WOld
- 'Helen Ballard'	NBid SRms WFar WOld
- 'Herbstgruss vom Bresserhof'	CRos LRHS NBre NLar NRHS SAko WFar WOld
- 'Hilda Ballard'	WOld
- 'Ibiza'	WCot
- 'Ilse Brensell'	WOld
- 'Irene'	WOld
- 'Janet Watts'	WOld
- 'Jean'	ELon SRms WFar WOld
- 'Jean Gyte'	WOld
- 'Jeanette'	SRms WFar WOld
- 'Jenny'	CBod CRos CSBt ECtt EHoe ELan EPPr EPfP GBin GMaP LRHS LSRN MJak MRav MWat NBir NEgg NGdn NHol NRHS SGol SPer SRms SWvt WCAu WFar WGwG WMoo WOld
- 'Jollity'	WOld
- 'Jugendstil'	XLum
- 'Julia'	WOld
- 'Kassel'	SRms WFar WOld
- 'King of the Belgians'	WFar WOld
- 'King's College'	WOld
§ - 'Kristina'	CRos ECha ITim LRHS MNrw MRav NBir NRHS WFar WOld
- 'Lady Frances'	SRms WOld
- 'Lady in Blue'	CBod CRos CSBt ECtt EHoe ELan EPfP GWyn LEdu LRHS MBNS MGos MJak MWat NEgg NGdn NGrd NRHS NWad SGbt SPer SPoG SRms SWvt WCAu WFar WJam WMoo WOld
- 'Lassie'	MWat NWsh SRms WFar WOld
- 'Lavender Dream'	WOld
- 'Lawrence Chiswell'	WFar WOld
- 'Lederstrumpf'	NDov
- 'Lisa Dawn'	WFar WOld
- 'Lisette'	LEdu
- 'Little Boy Blue'	CDor SRms WOld XLum
- 'Little Man in Blue'	WOld
- 'Little Ness' **new**	WFar
- 'Little Pink Beauty'	CBod CCBP CRos ECtt ELan EPfP ITim LEdu LRHS MBNS NGdn NGrd NHol NRHS NWad SPer SRms WCAu WFar WOld
- 'Little Pink Lady'	SRms WFar WOld
- 'Little Pink Pyramid'	SRms WOld
- 'Little Red Boy'	WOld
- 'Little Treasure'	WOld
- 'Madge Cato'	SRms WOld
- 'Mammoth'	WOld
- 'Margery Bennett'	WOld
- 'Marie Ann Neil'	SRms WOld
- 'Marie Ballard'	CMac CRos CSBt CWld GMaP GQue LEdu LRHS MHer MRav MWat NGdn NHol NLar NPer NRHS SGol SPer SRms SWvt WCAu WFar WOld XLum
- 'Marie's Pretty Please'	WOld
- 'Marie-Theres'	SAko
- 'Marjorie'	LSRN WOld XLum
- 'Mauve Magic'	MWat SRms WFar WOld
- 'Melbourne Magnet'	WOld
- 'Midget'	WOld
- 'Mistress Quickly'	ECtt WFar WOld
- 'Mittelmeer'	CRos LRHS NRHS WOld XLum
- 'Mount Everest'	CDor WOld
- 'Mrs Leo Hunter'	WOld
- 'Nachtlicht'	SAko
- 'Neron'	IMou MNrw MPie NDov SHar SPhx WFar
- 'Nesthäkchen'	WOld
- 'Niobe'	WOld
- 'Norman's Jubilee'	CRos EBee EPfP LRHS MHer NBir NRHS WFar WOld
- 'Nursteed Charm'	WOld
- 'Oktoberschneekuppel'	WOld
- 'Pamela'	WOld
- 'Patricia Ballard' (d)	CBcs CBod CDor CMac CRos CSBt EBee EBou ELan EPfP GMaP LCro LOPS LRHS MHer MWat NBir NGrd NLar NPer NRHS NWad SGol SPer WCAu WFar WMoo WOld
- 'Peace'	MWat WOld
- 'Percy Thrower'	WOld
- 'Peter Chiswell'	SRms WOld

- 'Peter Harrison'	CRos EBee GMaP LRHS MHol NBir NRHS WOld XLum
- 'Peter Pan'	EWTr NLar
- 'Pink Lace'	MBNS WOld
- 'Pink Topas'	LRHS
- 'Plenty'	WOld
- 'Porzellan'	CBod CElw CFis CMea EBee ECtt LEdu MAvo MBNS MNrw NGdn NGrd NLar WCot WFar WHal WOld
- 'Pride of Colwall'	SRms WOld
- 'Priory Blush'	CElw MWat SRms WOld
- 'Professor Anton Kippenberg'	CBod CFis CRos EAJP ELan EPfP GMaP LRHS MNrw MRav NAln NDov NGrd NLar NRHS SAko SPer SRms SWvt WFar WOld XLum
- 'Prosperity'	WOld
- 'Purple Dome'	CDor CFis ECha ELan LEdu LOPS LSRN MHer MWat SCob SHar SRkn WFar WOld
- 'Purple Dream' **new**	WFar
- 'Ralph Picton'	WFar WOld
- 'Red Robin'	MWat
- 'Red Star'	SPhx
- 'Red Sunset'	SRms WOld
- 'Rembrandt'	ECtt MArl NGdn
- 'Remembrance'	MWat SRms WFar WOld
- 'Reverend Vincent Dale'	WOld
- 'Richness'	WOld
- 'Rose Bonnet'	CRos LRHS MWat NRHS SPlb WFar WOld
- 'Roseanne'	WOld
- 'Rosebud'	WOld
- 'Rosenquartz'	NLar WFar
- 'Rosenwichtel'	CDor ILea NLar SRms WOld
- 'Royal Blue'	WOld
- 'Royal Ruby'	CFis CRos EBee ECtt IPot LRHS NLar NRHS SRms WOld
- 'Royal Velvet'	WOld
- 'Rozika'	MNrw WOld
- 'Rufus'	NWsh WFar WOld
- 'Saint Egwyn'	WOld
- 'Sam Banham'	MNrw WFar WOld
- SAMOA ('Dasthree') (Island Series)	CBod CRos EPfP EUJe LRHS NEgg NLar NPri NRHS SPad SPoG SRms WCot
- 'Sandford White Swan'	MHer MWat WFar WOld
- 'Sarah Ballard'	NLar WFar WOld
§ - 'Schneekissen'	CBod CRos ECtt ELan EPfP GMaP LRHS MBNS MHer MJak NRHS SRms SWvt WFar WOld XLum
- 'Schneezicklein'	GBin GWyn
- 'Schöne von Dietlikon'	CKno CSpe IPot LEdu MWat NAln WFar WOld XLum
- 'Schoolgirl'	WOld
- 'Sheena'	WFar WOld
- 'Silberblaukissen'	WOld
- SNOW CUSHION	see *S. novi-belgii* 'Schneekissen'
- 'Snowsprite'	CBod CRos CSBt ELan LRHS MWat NLar NRHS SGbt SGol SRms WOld
- 'Sonata'	GMaP WOld
- 'Sophia'	MWat WOld
- 'Starlight'	CBod CDor ECtt ILea NLar WCAu WFar WRHF
- 'Steinebrück'	WOld
- 'Sterling Silver'	WOld
- 'Sun Queen'	WOld
- 'Sunset'	WOld
- 'Susan'	WOld
- 'Sweet Briar'	WOld
- 'Tapestry'	WOld
- 'Terry's Pride'	WFar WOld
- 'The Archbishop'	ECtt WOld XEll
- 'The Bishop'	WOld
- 'The Cardinal'	WOld
- 'The Dean'	WOld
- 'The Sexton'	WOld
- 'Thundercloud'	MWat WOld
- 'Timsbury'	SRms WOld
- TONGA ('Dasfour') (Island Series)	CRos EPfP LRHS MHol NLar NRHS NWsh SPoG SRms SWvt WCot
- 'Tovarich'	WOld
- 'Trudi Ann'	NBir WOld
- 'Twinkle'	WOld
- 'Victor'	WOld
- 'Vignem'	NSti
- 'Violet Lady'	WOld
- 'Waterperry'	MWat WBrk WOld
- 'White Ladies'	CBcs CRos ECtt GMaP IMou LCro LOPS LRHS MMuc MNrw MWat NLar NRHS WCAu XLum
- 'White Swan'	ECtt
- 'White Wings'	MWat WOld
- 'Winston S. Churchill'	CAby CDor CRos EAJP ELan EPfP GMaP IKil LEdu LRHS MBel MHer MPie MWat NEgg NRHS SPer SPlb SPoG WCAu WOld WTor
- 'Zwergenhimmel'	SAko
§ ***oblongifolium***	NWsh WOld XSen
§ - 'Fanny's'	ECtt GCal MMuc NGdn NWad SEND WOld
- 'October Skies'	EBee EWes MNrw SHar
'Ochtendgloren' (*pilosum* var *pringlei* hybrid) ♀H4	CMea CSam EBee ECtt ELon EPPr EWes MNrw NCGa NLar WHal WHoo WOld
§ 'Oktoberlicht'	CRos EPPr LRHS MNrw NCGa NRHS WHoo WOld
§ ***oolentangiense***	MMuc NLar SPhx WOld
'Orchidee'	CMea ECtt EPPr EWes MAvo MWat WOld
'Photograph' ♀H7	CRos CSam EBee ECtt EWes LEdu LRHS NCGa NRHS WOld WPGP
§ ***pilosum***	WCot WFar
§ - var. ***pringlei*** ♀H7	ECha EWes MMuc MRav NWad WOld
§ - - 'Monte Cassino'	CAby CSBt EPfP GQue LPot LRHS MBNS MRav MWat NBro SPer SPhx SRms WCAu WOld WSpi XLum XSen
- - 'October Glory'	ECtt MMuc WFar
- - 'Phoebe'	WOld
'Pink Star'	CRos EBee ECtt ELon GMaP LEdu LRHS MRav MWat NRHS NSti SPhx WCAu WOld XLum
'Pinwheel'	WCot
'Pixie Dark Eye' (*ericoides* hybrid)	EBee ECtt SMHy SRms WCot
'Pixie Red Eye' (*ericoides* hybrid)	EBee LEdu WCot WFar
'Prairie Lavender'	WOld
'Prairie Pink'	WOld
'Prairie Purple'	CDor ECtt MAvo MTis MWat SMHy SPhx WCot WFar WHoo WOld
'Prairie Violet'	WOld
'Primrose Path'	CDor ECtt LEdu MNrw NCGa SPhx WBrk WCot WOld
§ ***puniceum***	MMuc NLar XLum
'Ringdove' (*ericoides* hybrid) ♀H7	MAvo NCGa NSti SWvt WCot WOld
'Rosa Star'	WOld
'Rose Glow' **new**	EPPr

'Rose Quartz' (Autumn Jewels Series) NCou
§ × ***salignum*** WOld
– Scottish form WOld
'Sea Spray' WArt WCot
§ ***sericeum*** SPhx
shortii SPhx
'Soft Lass' WCot WOld
'Speyerer Herbstwoge' MAvo
'Star of Chesters' MWat WOld
'Sunhelene' EBee ECtt WCot
'Superstar' SPhx WHoo WOld
§ ***tradescantii*** MBNS MRav NSti SMad WBrk WCot WOld
'Treffpunkt' IMou MAvo SAko
turbinellum misapplied ♀H6 CFis CKno EPfP EWes LRHS MMuc NGdn SMHy SPhx SRkn SWvt WArt
turbinellum Lindl. CSam EBee EPfP LEdu MWat NCGa NLar NQui SSut WCot WOld WPGP
– 'El Fin' MNrw
– hybrid WOld WSpi
'Vasterival' IMou LEdu MHer MPie MTis NCGa NDov XLum
× ***versicolor*** 'Altweibersommer' **new** EBee
'Wood's Blue' CRos EPPr LRHS NRHS
'Wood's Pink' CBod CRos LRHS MTis NRHS WCAu
'Wood's Purple' CRos LRHS NRHS

Symphytum (*Boraginaceae*)

'Angela Whinfield' CBre CMea EBee LPla
asperum CCBP ECha EPPr MRav NLar WMoo
* ***azureum*** LPla MBel NChi WCAu
'Belsay Gold' NBid NBir WBor
bulbosum PAB 4886 LEdu
caucasicum CMea EBee ECha GPoy IFro LEdu NAln NLar NSti SPer SRms WHil WMoo WOut WWtn XLum
– 'Norwich Sky' CExl WBor
caucasicum × (× ***uplandicum***) **new** IFro
cordatum EMor EPPr LEdu MNrw
§ 'Goldsmith' (v) CMea EBee ECha ELan EMor EPfP GKev MHol MPie NBid NBir NEgg NLar NPer SPer SPoG WFar
grandiflorum CMac CTri GKev GPoy LEdu NAln SPer
– 'Sky-blue-pink' IFro
'Hidcote Blue' CBre CRos CTri ECha ECtt EMor EPPr EPfP LRHS MMuc NBro NEgg NRHS SCob SEND SPer SPoG SRms WGwG WMoo WOut WPnP WWtn
§ 'Hidcote Pink' CBod CBre CRos ECha ECtt EPPr LRHS MMuc MNrw NBir NRHS NSti SEND SPer SRms WCAu WFar WGwG WMoo WPnP WWtn XLum
'Hidcote Variegated' (v) CMac SRms
ibericum CAgr CBod CCBP CSam ECha EHrv EMor GKev GMaP GPoy LRHS MMuc NAln NRHS NSti SEND SRms WGwG WMoo WOut WWtn
– 'All Gold' CRos EBee ECha LRHS MNrw NRHS WMoo
– 'Blaueglocken' ECha WMoo
– dwarf IFro WMoo
– 'Gold in Spring' WFar
– 'Jubilee' see *S.* 'Goldsmith'
– 'Lilacinum' CFis WHer
– 'Variegatum' see *S.* 'Goldsmith'
– 'Wisley Blue' CBcs CBod ILea SCob WFar WMoo
'Lambrook Sunrise' CMac LEdu NBro SRms WCot WMoo
'Langthorns Pink' ELan GCal
officinale CAgr CHab ENfk GPoy MHer MNHC MNrw NPer NPri SPer SPoG SRms WCAu WHer XLum
– var. ***ochroleucum*** WHer
orientale EBee EPPr GCal MBel MNrw
peregrinum see *S.* × ***uplandicum***
'Roseum' see *S.* 'Hidcote Pink'
'Rubrum' CBod CRos EHrv ELan EPfP EWes LEdu LRHS MBel MHer MMuc NBro NLar NRHS SPer WCAu WGwG WWtn XLum
tuberosum CBre CFis CSam EPPr GPoy LEdu LPla MHer MMuc NGrd NWad WBor WCot WFar WHer WHil
§ × ***uplandicum*** CLau CTri ELan GPoy MMuc NAln SVic
– 'Axminster Gold' (v) CMea EWes NChi WCot
– 'Bocking 14' CAgr CBod CFGn CHby EOHP EShb GAbr LEdu MNHC SRms WSFF XLum
– 'Droitwich' (v) WCot
– gold-leaved **new** IFro
– 'Moorland Heather' CDor CSpe EAJP LEdu LPla LRHS MHer MMrt MNrw MPie SPhx WBor WMoo WWFP
– purple-flowered MMuc
– 'Variegatum' (v) ECtt ELan EWes GCal LRHS NBir NGdn NRHS WAvo WMoo WSpi

Synadenium (*Euphorbiaceae*)

grantii 'Rubrum' EShb

Syncarpha (*Asteraceae*)

vestita SPlb

Syncolostemon (*Lamiaceae*)

'Candy Kisses' WCot

Syneilesis (*Asteraceae*)

aconitifolia GEdr WCot WHal WHil
– B&SWJ 879 EHrv LEdu WCru
palmata GEdr
– B&SWJ 1003 WCru
– B&SWJ 11226 WCru
– B&SWJ 14671 **new** WCru
– 'Aka-fu' GEdr
– 'Kikkou-fu' GEdr
– 'Kiko' GEdr
subglabrata B&SWJ 298 WCru
– NMWJ 14528 **new** WCru
aff. ***tagawae*** B&SWJ 11191 WCot

Syngonium (*Araceae*)

podophyllum ♀H1a XBlo

Synnotia see *Sparaxis*

Synsepalum (*Sapotaceae*)

dulcificum SCit

Synthyris (*Plantaginaceae*)

laciniata EBee LLHF
missurica EBee WFar
subsp. ***missurica***
– subsp. ***stellata*** CAby CBod CMea CRos EBee ECtt EPfP EWes GAbr GBin GCal GMaP

	LEdu LRHS MAvo MMrt NBir NCGa NHpl NRHS NSti WGwG WHal WMoo WPtf WSHC WTor
pinnatifida	EBee
var. ***canescens***	
platycarpa	EBee

Syringa ✿ (Oleaceae)

afghanica misapplied	see *S. protolaciniata*
BLOOMERANG DARK PURPLE ('Smsjbp7'PBR)	LCro LOPS LSRN MAsh SGol SPoG
BLOOMERANG PINK PERFUME	see *S.* 'Pink Perfume'
BLOOMERANG PURPLE ('Penda')	CRos LRHS NRHS
× ***chinensis***	EPfP
- 'Bicolor'	WGob
- 'Saugeana'	MBlu MMuc SPer
× ***diversifolia***	NLar
emodi 'Aureovariegata'	see *S. emodi* 'Variegata'
- 'Elegantissima' (v)	CBcs CEnd CMac EBee EBtc ELan EPfP LRHS NEgg SPoG
§ - 'Variegata' (v)	CKel CRos EMil LRHS NLar
× ***hyacinthiflora*** 'Clarke's Giant'	NLar SGol
- 'Dark Night'	WGob
- 'Esther Staley' ♀H6	EPfP MRav WGob
- 'Maiden's Blush' ♀H6	SGol WGob
- 'Pocahontas' ♀H6	LRHS WGob
- 'Sweetheart' (d)	NOra WMat
JOSÉE ('Morjos 060f')	CBod CLnd ELan ELon EPfP MAsh SCob SGol SWvt WFar WGob
× ***josiflexa***	CExl
- 'Agnes Smith'	EBee LRHS NLar
- 'Bellicent' ♀H6	CEnd CMac CRos ELan EPfP IFro LRHS MAsh MMuc MRav NPri NRHS SPer SPoG SRms SWvt WAvo WCFE WFar WSpi
- 'Lynette'	NEoE
- 'Redwine'	NLar
§ - 'Royalty'	NLar
josikaea	CAco CMCN CSBt EWTr NLar SPer
komarowii	ESwi GGGa MGil
§ - subsp. ***reflexa***	CDul EPfP EWTr MBlu NLar SLon WPGP
§ × ***laciniata*** Mill.	CDul CJun CKel CRos CWCL EBee ELan EPfP LRHS MRav NLar SMad SPer WAvo WCFE WPGP
'Lark Song'	NLar
meyeri	SVen
- 'Inge'	NLar
§ - 'Palibin' ♀H5	Widely available
'Minuet'	CBcs LBuc LRHS SGol
'Miss Canada'	LRHS NLar
MISS JAPAN	EBee LRHS
oblata	CMCN
palibiniana misapplied	see *S. meyeri* 'Palibin'
patula misapplied	see *S. meyeri* 'Palibin'
patula (Palib.) Nakai	see *S. pubescens* subsp. *patula*
pekinensis	see *S. reticulata* subsp. *pekinensis*
× ***persica*** ♀H6	CExl CJun CTri EPfP EWTr MGos MRav NLar NWea SLon SPer WFar WGob
- 'Alba' ♀H6	CJun MRav WAvo WFar WGob
- var. ***laciniata***	see *S.* × *laciniata* Mill.
§ 'Pink Perfume'PBR	CRos EPfP LCro LOPS LRHS LSRN MAsh NRHS SGol SPoG
pinnatifolia	CBcs CKel GBin LRHS NLar SAko WPGP
× ***prestoniae*** 'Desdemona'	CRos EBtc LRHS MMuc
- 'Elinor' ♀H6	CKel ELan EPfP LRHS MRav
- 'Minuet'	NLar
- 'Miss Poland'	LRHS
- 'Nocturne'	WFar
- 'Royalty'	see *S.* × *josiflexa* 'Royalty'
§ ***protolaciniata***	EShb IDee NLar
pubescens subsp. ***julianae*** 'George Eastman'	MRav
- subsp. ***microphylla*** 'Superba' ♀H6	Widely available
§ - subsp. ***patula***	CMac CRos EPfP LRHS MMuc MRav NRHS SLim SVen
- - 'Miss Kim' ♀H6	CChe CKel CMac CSBt CTri CWCL EBee ECrN ELan ELon EWTr IArd LRHS LSRN MAsh MGos MJak MRav MSwo NEgg NGdn NHol NLar SCob SCoo SLim SPoG SSta WFar WGob
'Red Pixie'	CBod CMac CRos EPfP LCro LOPS LRHS MAsh MGos MMrt NRHS SCoo SNig WGob
'Red Prince'	NPri
reflexa	see *S. komarowii* subsp. *reflexa*
reticulata	CMCN MBlu
- 'Ivory Silk'	EBtc EPfP WMat
§ - subsp. ***pekinensis***	CMCN
- - 'Yellow Fragrance'	NLar
× ***swegiflexa***	CDul CExl
tomentella	EBee NWea SRms WCFE WPGP
- subsp. ***sweginzowii***	CBcs CWCL EBee EBtc GKin LLHF MMuc NLar SPer WSpi
- - 'Superba'	SGol
- subsp. ***yunnanensis***	CExl SBrt
velutina Kom.	see *S. pubescens* subsp. *patula*
villosa	SPlb
vulgaris	CAco CDul EPfP
- 'Amethyst' **new**	CBod
§ - 'Andenken an Ludwig Späth' ♀H6	Widely available
- 'Aucubifolia' (d/v)	SEND WGob
- 'Aurea'	MRav NEoE WAvo WFar
- BEAUTY OF MOSCOW	see *S. vulgaris* 'Krasavitsa Moskvy'
- 'Belle de Nancy' (d)	CBod CCCN CDul CMac ELan ELon EMOT GAbr MAsh MMuc MRav NLar SCob SEND SGol SWvt WGob
- CARPE DIEM	see *S. vulgaris* 'Evert de Gier'
- 'Charles Joly' (d) ♀H6	Widely available
- 'Comtesse d'Harcourt'	EPfP SEND SPer WGob
- 'Congo'	WGob
- 'Dappled Dawn' (v) **new**	MMrt
- 'Dark Koster'	WGob
- 'Dwight D. Eisenhower'	WGob
- 'Edward J. Gardner' (d) ♀H6	SEND
- 'Etna'	WGob
§ - 'Evert de Gier'PBR	CBcs GAbr
- 'Firmament' ♀H6	MRav SEND SPer WGob WSpi
- 'Hope'	see *S. vulgaris* 'Nadezhda'
- 'Hugo de Vries'	IArd
- 'Katherine Havemeyer' (d) ♀H6	Widely available
§ - 'Krasavitsa Moskvy' (d) ♀H6	CCVT CNWT CTri CWCL EPfP EWes MAsh MRav NLar NOra NPri SEND SGol WMat
- 'Lee Jewett Walker'	SSta
- 'Lila Wonder'PBR	ELan EPfP GAbr SPoG WGob
- 'Madame Florent Stepman'	CBod CMac CWCL ELon NLar WFar WGob
- 'Madame Lemoine' (d) ♀H6	Widely available

- 'Michel Buchner' (d)	CBcs CDul CLnd EBee ECrN ELan EMOT MBlu MGos NLar NOra SCob SCoo SLim SPer WMat
- 'Miss Ellen Willmott' (d)	IArd NLar
- 'Mrs Edward Harding' (d) ♀H6	ECrN EMOT EPfP MRav NLar NWea SPer WGob
§ - 'Nadezhda' (d)	CBod GAbr WGob
- 'Pat Pesata'	WGob
- 'Paul Thirion' (d)	CBod WGob
- 'Pavlinka' (d)	IArd
- 'Président Grévy' (d)	CBar CWCL EPfP MAsh NPri SGol SLim SPer SPoG
- 'President Lincoln'	WGob
- 'Président Poincaré' (d)	WGob
- 'Primrose' ♀H6	CBcs CCCN CMac EBee ELan ELon EPfP LRHS MAsh MGos MJak NLar NOra SCoo SEND SGol SPer SPoG WGob WMat WSpi
- 'Prince Wolkonsky' (d)	EBee ECrN ELan ELon EPfP LRHS LSRN MAsh SEND SPer WFar WGob
- 'Princesse Sturdza'	ELon
- 'Professor Hoser'	WGob
- 'Saint Margaret'	WGob
- 'Sarah Sands'	WGob
- 'Sensation' ♀H6	Widely available
- 'Souvenir de Louis Spaeth'	see *S. vulgaris* 'Andenken an Ludwig Späth'
- variegated (v)	EWes
- variegated double (d/v)	WCot
- 'Vesper'	IArd
- 'Victor Lemoine' (d)	WGob
- 'Viviand-Morel' (d)	CMac
- 'Wedgewood Blue'	WGob
- 'William Robinson' (d)	WGob
wolfii	EBtc NLar

Syzygium (*Myrtaceae*)

luehmannii	EShb
paniculatum	CExl

T

Tabernaemontana (*Apocynaceae*)

coronaria	see *T. divaricata*
§ ***divaricata***	CCCN WFib

Tacca (*Taccaceae*)

chantrieri	CCCN

Taccarum (*Araceae*)

weddellianum	WCot

Tacitus see *Graptopetalum*

Taenidia (*Apiaceae*)

integerrima	SPhx

Tagetes (*Asteraceae*)

'Cinnabar'	CSpe
erecta 'Jubilee Diamond' (Jubilee Series)	MAvo
lemmonii 'Martin's Mutant'	WCot
lucida	ENfk LEdu MHer SRms WJek WTre
patula 'Dainty Marietta' ♀H2	LCro LOPS
- 'Safari Red' (Safari Series)	LCro LOPS
tenuifolia 'Golden Gem'	LOPS
zypaquirensis B&SWJ 14840 new	WCru

Taiwania (*Cupressaceae*)

cryptomerioides	CAco IArd IDee WPGP

Talbotia (*Velloziaceae*)

§ ***elegans***	SBrt

Talinum (*Portulacaceae*)

paniculatum	CBod ELan
'Zoe'	CPBP

tamarillo see *Solanum betaceum*

tamarind see *Tamarindus indica*

Tamarindus (*Caesalpiniaceae*)

indica (F)	SPlb

Tamarix (*Tamaricaceae*)

gallica	NWea SArc SEND WSHC
hampeana	SEND
§ ***parviflora*** ♀H5	CDul CMac CRos EPfP LRHS NRHS SCob
pentandra	see *T. ramosissima* 'Rosea'
ramosissima	CCCN CTri EBee ELan EPfP MAsh SCob SLim SLon SRms WAvo
- 'Hulsdonk White'	CBcs SPer
- 'Pink Cascade' ♀H5	CAco CBcs CCCN CDul CMac CWCL EBee EPfP LCro LOPS MBlu MGos MRav NEgg SCob SEND SGbt SGol SPer SPoG SWvt
§ - 'Rosea'	CBcs ECrN
§ - 'Rubra'	EPfP SEND SLon SPer
- 'Summer Glow'	see *T. ramosissima* 'Rubra'
tetrandra ♀H5	CBcs CCVT CDul CRos CSde CTsd EBee ELan EPfP LRHS MAsh MBlu MGil MGos MRav MSwo NPer SEND SGol SPad SPer SPlb SRms SWvt WAvo
- var. ***purpurea***	see *T. parviflora*

Tanacetum ✿ (*Asteraceae*)

§ ***argenteum***	MRav
- subsp. ***canum***	SLon
§ ***balsamita***	CBod CHby CWld EBee EBou ELan ENfk EPPr GJos GPoy LEdu MHer MMuc MNHC NGrd SEND SRms WHer WJek WSFF XLum
§ - subsp. ***balsamita***	GPoy WJek
§ - subsp. ***balsamitoides***	CBod MHer SRms
- var. ***tanacetoides***	see *T. balsamita* subsp. *balsamita*
- ***tomentosum***	see *T. balsamita* subsp. *balsamitoides*
§ ***cinerariifolium***	CBod GPoy MNHC
§ ***coccineum***	SVic WFar
- 'Alfred'	MNrw
- 'Bees' Pink Delight'	NEgg
- 'Duro'	CRos EBee LRHS NRHS
- 'Eileen May Robinson'	EPfP
- 'Garden Treasure'	EBee ECtt NCGa
- 'H.M. Pike'	EBee
- 'James Kelway'	NBir
- 'Laurin'	CBod CRos EBee ECtt LRHS MHol NRHS
- 'Red Dwarf'	ECtt
- Robinson's crimson-flowered	CRos LRHS NRHS

	- - giant-flowered	CRos CTsd LRHS NRHS SRms
	- - pink-flowered	EAJP EBee EBou EPfP GMaP MHol SCob XLum
	- - red-flowered	CBod CSBt EAJP EBou EPfP EUJe GMaP GWyn LRHS MHol NRHS SPlb SWvt XLum
	- - rose-flowered	CSBt EWTr
	- 'Scarlet Glow'	NCGa
	- 'Snow Cloud'	ECtt EPfP NCGa
	- 'Vanessa'	MNrw
§	***corymbosum***	CRos EBee GCal LRHS NLar NRHS WCot
	- 'Bukke'	LEdu
	- 'Festtafel'	LEdu LPla
	densum	EPot WCFE
	- subsp. ***amani***	CRos ECha GKev GMaP LRHS SEND XSen
§	***haradjanii***	EBou MCot SBch WKif
	macrophyllum misapplied	see *Achillea grandifolia* Friv.
§	***macrophyllum*** (Waldst. & Kit.) Sch.Bip.	EBee ECtt EPPr GWyn MBel SPhx WBor
	- 'Cream Klenza'	WCot
	niveum	ECha WCot
	- 'Jackpot'	EPfP EWes SPhx SWvt
§	***parthenium***	CBod CCBP CHab CHby EMor ENfk GPoy GQue LCro LOPS MHer MNHC NPer SRms SVic WHer WTre XLum
	- 'Aureum'	CBod EBou ECha ELan EMor ENfk EWes EWhm GPoy MHer MNHC SPer SPlb SRms SWvt WCot WFar WHer WMoo XLum
	- 'Cartwheels'	MAvo
	- double white-flowered (d)	NPer SRms
	- 'Golden Ball'	WFar
	- 'Golden Moss'	XLum
	- 'Malmesbury'	WHer
	- 'Plenum' (d)	MNrw
§	- 'Rowallane' (d)	MMuc SEND WCot
	- 'Selma Star' (d)	WHer
	- 'Sissinghurst White'	see *T. parthenium* 'Rowallane'
	- 'White Bonnet' (d)	WHer
	poteriifolium	CRos EBee LRHS NRHS
	ptarmiciflorum 'Silver Feather'	SRms SVen
*	***tommansii***	CRos EBee LRHS NRHS
	vulgare	CCBP CHab CHby CMac CWld ECha ECtt ENfk GBin GPoy GWyn IRos LCro LOPS MHer MNHC NGrd SRms SVic WFar WMoo WSFF WTre XSen
	- 'All Gold'	SMad SRms
	- var. ***crispum***	EBee ENfk MHer MRav SMad SRms WFar
	- 'Gold Sticks'	CBod
	- 'Golden Fleece'	ECtt EWes LEdu MNHC NSti WCot WGrn
	- 'Isla Gold' (v)	CDor ECtt EWes LEdu MHer MMuc MRav NBid SEND WCAu WCot WFar WMoo
	- 'Silver Lace' (v)	CBre EBee EWes WFar WMoo

Tanakaea (*Saxifragaceae*)

radicans	GEdr WSHC
- B&SWJ 11407	WCru

tangelo see *Citrus × aurantium* Tangelo Group

tangerine see *Citrus reticulata* Tangerine Group

Tapiscia (*Staphyleaceae*)

sinensis	IArd

Taraxacum (*Asteraceae*)

faeroense	WCot
officinale agg.	CHab
pseudoroseum	MMuc
rubrifolium	CBre NWad

tarragon see *Artemisia dracunculus*

Tasmannia (*Winteraceae*)

§	***lanceolata***	Widely available
	- (f)	SPer
	- (m)	SPer
	- 'Mount Wellington'	GCal
	- 'Red Spice'	EPfP LRHS LSRN MPkF SEle
	- 'Suzette' (v)	LRHS MBlu SRms

Taxodium ✿ (*Cupressaceae*)

	ascendens 'Nutans'	see *T. distichum* var. *imbricarium* 'Nutans'
	distichum	Widely available
	- 'Cascade Falls'	MBlu MGos NLar NOra SAko SLim
	- 'Cave Hill'	NLar
	- 'Falling Waters'	SGol
	- var. ***imbricarium***	CMCN
§	- - 'Nutans'	CAco CBcs EPfP IArd MBlu SGol SLim WMat
	- 'Little Twister'	SLim
	- 'Minaret'	MBlu
*	- 'Pendulum'	IDee
	- 'Pévé Minaret'	CMen MGil MGos SAko SArc SCob SGol SLim
	- 'Pévé Yellow'	MBlu SLim
	- 'Schloss Herten'	NLar
	- 'Secrest'	MBlu
	- SHAWNEE BRAVE ('Mickelson')	MBlu
	mucronatum	CExl SMad
	- NJM 09.037	WPGP

Taxus ✿ (*Taxaceae*)

	baccata ♀H7	Widely available
	- 'Aldenham Gold'	CKen
	- 'Amersfoort'	NLar NWad
	- 'Argentea Minor'	see *T. baccata* 'Dwarf White'
	- 'Arngost'	NLar
	- Aurea Group	ELan SRms
I	- 'Aureomarginata' (v)	CBcs MAsh NEgg SWvt
	- 'Autumn Shades'	NLar
	- 'Bridget's Gold'	CKen
	- 'Corleys Coppertip'	CKen EBtc EMOT LRHS MMuc MRav NLar
	- 'Cristata'	CKen MBlu NLar
	- 'David'	EPfP IArd LRHS MGos NLar SLim SPoG SWvt
	- 'Dorothea'	NLar
	- 'Dovastoniana' (m or f)	CAco CDul CMac LPra NLar NWea
	- 'Dovastonii Aurea' (m or f/v)	CAco CBcs GKin LPra MBlu NLar NWea SGol SMad SRms
	- 'Drinkstone Gold' (v)	EMOT
§	- 'Dwarf White' (v)	NLar
	- 'Elegantissima' (f/v)	EMOT EPfP NEgg NWea SCoo SPoG
§	- 'Fastigiata' (f) ♀H7	Widely available
	- Fastigiata Aurea Group	CLnd CMac CTho EPfP GQue IArd LMaj LPra LRHS MAsh MGil MGos MJak NLar NWea SArc SCob SGol SRms

- 'Fastigiata Aureomarginata' (m/v) ♀H7 CDul CMac CSBt CTri EPfP LBee LPra LRHS MGos MSwo SCoo SLim SLon SPer SPoG SWvt WTSh
- 'Fastigiata Robusta' (f) CAco CSBt ELan EMOT EPfP EUJe LMaj LRHS MAsh MGos NLar SCoo SLim SPoG WMat
- 'Goldener Zwerg' MBlu
- 'Graciosa' NLar
- 'Grayswood Hill' WFar
- 'Great Column' MBlu
- 'Green Column' CKen NLar
- 'Green Diamond' CKen MBlu NLar
- 'Hibernica' see *T. baccata* 'Fastigiata'
- 'Icicle' ♀H7 CAco CBcs LRHS MAsh NHol NLar NWad
- 'Itsy Bitsy' CKen
- 'Ivory Tower' CAco CBcs CKen ELan EUJe LRHS NHol NLar NWad
- 'Jack's Gold' NLar
- 'Klitzeklein' CKen
- 'Lakatos' CAco
- 'Luca' NLar
- 'Micro' CKen MAsh NLar
- 'Nutans' CKen
- 'Papageno' NLar
- 'Pygmaea' CKen
- 'Repandens' (f) ♀H7 CDul IArd WFar WSpi
I - 'Repens Aurea' (v) ♀H7 CKen CMac EMOT EPfP NLar SCoo SLim SRms WFar WSpi
- 'Rushmore' NLar
- 'Semperaurea' (m) ♀H7 CBcs CMac LBuc LPra LRHS MAsh NLar NRya NWea SCoo SGol SLim SPoG WSpi
- 'Standishii' (f) ♀H7 CBcs CDul CKen CMac CSBt ELan EMOT EPfP EUJe GKin IArd LBee LRHS MAsh MGos MMuc MRav NEgg NHol NLar NOra NWad NWea SLim SPoG SWvt WMat
- 'Stove Pipe' CKen
- 'Summergold' (v) ELan EMOT LRHS MAsh MRav NBir NLar SCoo WSpi
cuspidata CAco CMen
- 'Aurescens' (v) CKen NLar
- 'Minuet' CKen
- 'Straight Hedge' SLim
× ***media*** 'Hicksii' (f) CDul LBuc LMaj LPra NWea SGol
- 'Hillii' LBuc
wallichiana LEdu

tayberry see *Rubus* Tayberry Group

Tecoma (*Bignoniaceae*)

capensis ♀H1c CHll CRHN GCal MGil SVen
- 'Apricot' CBcs
- 'Lutea' CBcs EPfP
- yellow-flowered **new** CHll
ricasoliana see *Podranea ricasoliana*

Tecomanthe (*Bignoniaceae*)

speciosa CRHN

Tecomaria see *Tecoma*

Tecophilaea (*Tecophilaeaceae*)

cyanocrocus ♀H3 CRos EPot GKev LAma LLHF LRHS NRHS
- 'Leichtlinii' ♀H3 CAvo CRos EPot GKev LAma LLHF LRHS NRHS SDeJ
- 'Purpurea' see *T. cyanocrocus* 'Violacea'
- Storm Cloud Group EPot LLHF
§ - 'Violacea' CAvo CRos EPot LLHF LRHS NRHS

Telekia (*Asteraceae*)

§ ***speciosa*** CMac CRos CSam CSpe ELan EPfP GJos GLog LEdu LRHS MMuc NBro NChi NLar NRHS NSti SEND SPlb WBrk WCAu WHer WMoo

Telesonix see *Boykinia*

Teline see *Genista*

Tellima (*Saxifragaceae*)

grandiflora Widely available
- 'Bob's Choice' WCot
- 'Delphine' (v) EPPr WCot XLum
- 'Forest Frost' CBod CFis CMac EHoe ELan EMor EPPr EPfP EShb LRHS MBNS MBel MPnt NLar NRHS SCob SWvt WCAu WCot WMoo
- Odorata Group CBre ECha WCot WMoo
- 'Purpurea' see *T. grandiflora* Rubra Group
- 'Purpurteppich' CRos ECha EMor EPPr GPSL LRHS MPnt MRav NAln NRHS SWvt WCot WMoo WPnP
§ - Rubra Group Widely available
- 'Silver Select' EPPr

Telopea (*Proteaceae*)

'Braidwood Brilliant' **new** CKel
§ 'Bridal Gown' CCCN CKel
'Emperor's Torch' LRHS MPkF
oreades SPlb
SHADY LADY CRIMSON ('T90101') CCCN CKel
SHADY LADY PINK **new** CKel
Shady Lady White see *T.* 'Bridal Gown'
SHADY LADY YELLOW CCCN CKel
speciosissima CCCN LRHS SPlb
I - 'Am Waratah' **new** CKel
truncata CCCN SPlb WCru

Temu see *Blepharocalyx*

Tephroseris (*Asteraceae*)

integrifolia subsp. ***capitata*** SPlb

Ternstroemia (*Pentaphylacaceae*)

chapaensis WWJ 11918 WCru
gymnanthera WCru
kwangtungensis FMWJ 13402 WCru
luteoflora FMWJ 13360 WCru

Tetracentron (*Trochodendraceae*)

§ ***sinense*** CBcs CMCN EPfP IArd MBlu WPGP
- WJC 13818 from the Himalaya **new** IDee WCru
- var. ***himalense*** see *T. sinense*

Tetradium (*Rutaceae*)

austrosinense NJM 09.215 WPGP
§ ***daniellii*** CBcs CDul CMCN CTho ELan EPfP ESwi IArd LEdu SAko SEND SPtp WGob WMat WPGP
- from Korea WPGP
§ - Hupehense Group CMCN CTho MCoo NLar
fraxinifolium PAB 9101 LEdu

	- WJC 13750	WCru
	aff. ***fraxinifolium*** WWJ 11615	WCru
	glabrifolium B&SWJ 6882	WCru
	- CWJ 12364	WCru
	ruticarpum	LEdu WPGP
	- B&SWJ 3541	WCru

Tetragonolobus see *Lotus*

Tetraneuris (*Asteraceae*)

§	***grandiflora***	CSma GKev SPlb
	scaposa	EPot

Tetrapanax ✿ (*Araliaceae*)

§	***papyrifer*** ♀H3	CBrP CDTJ ELan ESwi SEND SVen XBlo
	- B&SWJ 7135	WCru
	- NMWJ 14580 **new**	WCru
	- 'Empress'	WCru
	- 'Rex'	Widely available
	- 'Steroidal Giant'	CDTJ

Tetrapathaea see *Passiflora*

Tetrastigma (*Vitaceae*)

	obtectum	CCCN ECre EShb EWes SEND WAvo WCFE

Teucrium (*Lamiaceae*)

*	***ackermannii*** ♀H5	CMea EPot MHer SIgm WAbe WHoo WIce XSen
*	***armenum*** **new**	EBou
	aroanium	EDAr EPot SIgm XSen
	asiaticum	XSen
	botrys	MHer
	capitatum	EDAr
	chamaedrys misapplied	see *T.* × *lucidrys*
	chamaedrys L.	CBar CCBP CKel CRos ENfk EWTr GMaP GPoy GQue LEdu LRHS LSRN MCot MNHC MRav MSwo NWad SCob SEND SIgm SLim SNig SPer SPlb SRms SVen SWvt WBrk WJek XSen
	- f. ***albiflora***	ECha ELan EWes LPla
	- 'Nanum'	GMaP
	- 'Rose'	EBou SRms
	- 'Spring Gold'	LRHS
	aff. ***chamaedrys***	MGil
§	***creticum***	SPhx
	flavum	EBee EPPr GCal SBrt XSen
	fruticans	Widely available
	- 'Azureum' ♀H3	CBcs CBod CCoa CKel CRos CSde CTsd EBee ELan EPfP LRHS LSRN MRav SBrt SEND SMad SPer SPoG SRms SWvt WAvo WCFE WKif XSen
I	- 'Azureum Compactum'	CBod
	- 'Compactum'	CKel CRos ELan LRHS LSRN MGil SLim SLon SPer SPoG SWvt WAvo WCFE WPGP
	- 'Drysdale'	CCoa CKel CRos CSBt ELan LRHS SWvt
	hircanicum	CAby CCBP CElw CPla CSam EAJP EBou ECha ECtt ELan IFro LRHS LSRN MMuc MNrw NBir NWad SEND SPhx SRkn WArt WCFE WMoo XSen
	- PAB 13.341	LEdu
	- 'Paradise Delight'	CBod ECtt GWyn IKil
	- 'Purple Tails'	CBod CSpe CTsd CWld ELan EMor EPfP MHol MRav NBir NGrd SMad SRms WFar
§	× ***lucidrys***	CBcs CChe CMea CRos CSpe ECha ELan ENfk EPfP GBin LCro LPla LRHS LSRN MEch MHer MNHC MPie MRav SPer SPoG SRms SWvt WCFE WFar WHoo WJek XSen
	- 'Chedglow' **new**	CNat
	- 'Lucky Gold'[PBR]	LRHS SPoG SRms
	lucidum	GCal SLon
	marum	CTri LEdu SBrt SIgm SRms WJek XSen
	massiliense misapplied	see *T.* × *lucidrys*
	montanum	XSen
	orientale	XSen
	parviflorum **new**	EDAr
	polium	SIgm SPhx XSen
	pyrenaicum ♀H7	CMea CPBP EPot EWes GEdr SBch SIgm
	rosmarinifolium	see *T. creticum*
	scorodonia	CBod CHab MHer MNHC NLar NMir SRms WHer WJek XSen
	- 'Binsted Gold'	NSti
	- 'Crispum'	CCBP CRos EMor LEdu LRHS MHer MMuc NBro NLar NRHS SPer SRms WAvo WGrn WJek WKif
	- 'Crispum Marginatum' (v)	EBee EBou ECha EHoe EPPr EWld IKil LEdu MRav WFar
	- 'Winterdown' (v)	MPie
	subspinosum	EDAr EPot SIgm WHoo
§	***viscidum*** 'Lemon and Lime' (v)	NSti

Thalia (*Marantaceae*)

	dealbata	CBen EUJe EWat LLWG WMAq XLum

Thalictrum (*Ranunculaceae*)

	CC 4576	CExl
	Cox 6118	ITim
	from Afghanistan	see *T. isopyroides*
	actaeifolium B&SWJ 4664	WCru
	- B&SWJ 6310	WCru
	- var. ***brevistylum*** B&SWJ 8819	WCru
	- - 'Twinkling Star'	ECtt
	- compact B&SWJ 4946	WCru
	- 'Perfume Star'	CPar EBee ECtt GBin ILea LEdu MMrt NLar SCob WSpi
	adiantifolium	see *T. minus* 'Adiantifolium'
	alpinum	EPPr GEdr
	angustifolium	see *T. lucidum*
	'Anne'[PBR]	CAby CDor CKno CPar EBee ECtt EMor EWTr IKil ILea IPot LRHS MAvo MBel MHol MNrw MSCN MTis NDov NGBl NLar SAko SPoG WCot WPnP WSpi
	aquilegiifolium	Widely available
	- 'Album'	CBod CRos EBee ECha ELan EMor EPfP GBin IPot LRHS MBel MCot MMuc NBid NRHS SEND SPer SPhx SWvt WArt WCAu WFar WHlf WSpi
*	- 'Hybridum'	WMoo
	- var. ***intermedium*** B&SWJ 10965	WCru
	- 'Purpureum'	NLar NQui WWtn
	- var. ***sibiricum***	IMou
	- - B&SWJ 11007	WCru
	- 'Small Thundercloud'	GCal SMHy

- 'Thundercloud'	Widely available
baicalense	EPPr
'Black Stockings' ♀H7	Widely available
calabricum	NLar
chelidonii	EPPr
- HWJK 2216	WCru
clavatum	CAby
coreanum	see *T. ichangense*
cultratum	CRos EBee LRHS NRHS
dasycarpum	EPPr LPla SMHy WCot WPnP
§ ***delavayi***	Widely available
- BWJ 7800	WCru
- BWJ 7903	WCru
- var. ***acuminatum***	MBel
- - BWJ 7535	WCru
- - BWJ 7971	WCru
- 'Album'	Widely available
- 'Ankum' ♀H7	CRos EBee IPot LRHS MNrw NLar NRHS
- var. ***decorum***	CElw CSpe ECtt EPPr MBel WCot WCru WPGP WSHC
- - BWJ 7770	WCru
- aff. var. ***decorum***	CExl
- 'Gold Laced'	EBee ECtt NLar
- 'Hewitt's Double' (d)	Widely available
- 'Hinkley'	ECtt IPot LRHS
- var. ***mucronatum***	MBel WCru
- - DJHC 473	WCru
- purple-stemmed BWJ 7748	WCru
- 'White Cloud'	GBin
aff. ***delavayi***	NAln
diffusiflorum	EBee IMou IPot LRHS MBel MMrt WAbe WCru WSHC
dipterocarpum misapplied	see *T. delavayi*
dipterocarpum Franch.	CMac CRos EBee LRHS NRHS XLum
'Elin' ♀H7	Widely available
fendleri	GBin
- var. ***polycarpum***	IMou
filamentosum	EPPr IMou MBel WCot
- B&SWJ 777	WCru
- B&SWJ 4145	WCru
finetii	LRHS
flavum	CBod CHab CMac ELan EWld LLWG NBro NMir WFar WShi
- 'Chollerton'	see *T. isopyroides*
§ - subsp. ***glaucum***	Widely available
- - 'Ruth Lynden-Bell' ♀H7 **new**	SPoG WCot
- - 'Silver Sparkler' (v)	WCot
- - 'True Blue'	SGbt
- 'Illuminator'	CDor CElw CRos CTri EPfP LRHS MArl MRav NLar NRHS WCot WFar XEll
flexuosum	see *T. minus* subsp. *minus*
grandiflorum	GEdr
honanense BWJ 7962	WCru
§ ***ichangense***	CRos CSpe EBee ECtt EUJe GAbr GEdr IPot LEdu LRHS MBel MHol MTis NRHS NSti NWad SPad WCot WRHF
- B&SWJ 8203	WCru
- Evening Star strain (v)	CAby ECtt GBin MHol SCob
- var. ***minus*** 'Chinese Chintz'	WCru
- 'Purple Marble'	CSpe CWGN LEdu WCot
§ ***isopyroides***	CRos EBee EMor GBin GCal GKev GKin LEdu LRHS MBel MHol MRav NAln NLar NRHS NWad SHar WCot
javanicum	LEdu
- B&SWJ 9506	WCru
- PAB 9431	LEdu WPGP
- var. ***puberulum*** B&SWJ 6770	WCru
johnstonii B&SWJ 9127	WCru
kiusianum	CAby EBee ECha EHoe ELan EMor EPfP EWes GBin GEdr ITim LLWG LRHS MBel MHol MSCN NBir NGBl NHpl NLar NSla SMad SRot SWvt WAbe WCot WFar WPnP XEll
- Kew form	WSHC
koreanum	see *T. ichangense*
§ ***lucidum***	CBod CElw CExl CRos CSpe EBee ECtt EHoe ELan EShb GBin GCal IMou LEdu LRHS MHol MMuc MPie MTis NGBl NLar NQui NRHS NSti SEND SPhx WCot WPnP
minus	CRos GBin LEdu LRHS NRHS SEND
§ - 'Adiantifolium'	GBin MBel MRav NGdn SRms WSpi XLum
- var. ***hypoleucum*** B&SWJ 8634	WCru
§ - subsp. ***minus***	NBre
- var. ***sipellatum*** B&SWJ 5051	WCru
morisonii	CRos EBee LRHS NBid NRHS
'Nishiki'	GEdr
omeiense BWJ 8049	WCru
orientale	CRos EBee LRHS NRHS
osmundifolium	WCru
petaloideum	CFis EPPr
platycarpum B&SWJ 2261	WCru
podocarpum B&SWJ 14297	WCru
polygamum	see *T. pubescens* Pursh
przewalskii	WCru
§ ***pubescens*** Pursh	CRos EBee ECha GJos GMaP LRHS NDov NLar NRHS SHar SPhx
punctatum B&SWJ 1272	WCru
'Purplelicious' **new**	CBor MBel NCGa SMad
ramosum BWJ 8126	WCru
reniforme	LEdu
- B&SWJ 13969 **new**	WCru
- GWJ 9311	WCru
- HWJK 2403	WCru
- WJC 13761	WCru
rochebruneanum ♀H7	Widely available
rubescens B&SWJ 10006	WCru
rugosum	CRos LRHS NRHS
sachalinense RBS 0279	EBee EPPr NLar
shensiense	CExl
simplex var. ***brevipes*** B&SWJ 4794	WCru
sparsiflorum	GAbr
speciosissimum	see *T. flavum* subsp. *glaucum*
* ***sphaerostachyum***	CBod CElw CRos EBee EMor EPPr GAbr GPSL LRHS MBel MNrw MPie NDov NRHS WHal
'Splendide'	Widely available
SPLENDIDE WHITE ('Fr21034'PBR) ♀H7	CSpe CWCL CWGN EBee ECha ECtt ELan EMor EWTr IKil ILea IPot LCro LEdu LOPS MAvo MBel MCot MNrw NCGa NDov NHpl NLar SAko SHar STPC WCot WHil XEll
squarrosum	EBee
tenuisubulatum BWJ 7929	WCru
tuberiferum var. ***yakusimense*** B&SWJ 6094	WCru
tuberosum	CBor CElw CMea CPla CSpe EPot LLHF NDov WCot

	- 'Rosy Hardy'	WCot
	tubiferum B&SWJ 10999	WCru
	'Tukker Princess' ♀H7	EBee ECtt EWTr EWhm GBin IKil ILea MBel MHol NDov NLar SMad WCot
	uchiyamae	EBee EWld GKev WCot WPGP
	urbainii B&SWJ 7085	WCru
	'Yubari Mountains'	GEdr
	yunnanense	WCru

Thamnocalamus (*Poaceae*)

	crassinodus 'Gosainkund'	CDTJ ERod MWht
	- 'Kew Beauty' ♀H3	CDTJ EPfP ERod EUJe MBrN MWht WCot WPGP
	- 'Langtang'	CDTJ ERod MWht WPGP XCre
	- 'Merlyn'	CDTJ EPfP ERod MWht
	khasianus	see *Drepanostachyum khasianum*
	maling	see *Yushania maling*
	spathaceus misapplied	see *Fargesia murielae*
§	***spathiflorus***	EUJe
	- subsp. ***nepalensis***	ERod MWht
	tessellatus	see *Bergbambos tessellata*

Thamnochortus (*Restionaceae*)

	cinereus	CPbh
	insignis ♀H3	CPbh MPkF SPlb
	lucens	SPlb
	rigidus	CCCN

Thapsia (*Apiaceae*)

	decipiens	see *Melanoselinum decipiens*
	garganica	SBrt
	maxima	SIgm
	villosa	SHar
	- B&SWJ 14014 **new**	WCru

Thea see *Camellia*

Thelypteris (*Thelypteridaceae*)

	kunthii	CBdn CLAP EBee ELan EMor ISha LEdu WCot
	limbosperma	see *Oreopteris limbosperma*
	ovata var. ***lindheimeri***	CRos ISha LRHS NRHS
	palustris	CKel EBee EShb NBro NLar SRms WFib WPnP XLum
	phegopteris	see *Phegopteris connectilis*

Themeda (*Poaceae*)

	triandra	SMad

Thermopsis (*Papilionaceae*)

	caroliniana	see *T. villosa*
	chinensis	CRos EBee ELon GAbr LPla LRHS MHer MMuc NRHS
	fabacea	see *T. lupinoides*
	lanceolata	CAby CMea CRos EBee ELon EPfP LRHS MMuc NQui NRHS SHar SPad WCot WFar
§	***lupinoides***	CDor ECha EHrv
	macrophylla	EBee
	mollis	CExl NBid
	montana var. ***montana***	CBod CRos CWCL EBee ELan EPfP GMaP LRHS MBel MMuc NBir NGBl NGrd NRHS NSti NWad SEND SPer
	- - NNS 99-480	WCot
§	***villosa***	CRos LPla LRHS MRav NGdn NLar NRHS

Therorhodion see *Rhododendron*

Thladiantha (*Cucurbitaceae*)

	dubia	EBee SBrt WCot

Thlaspi (*Brassicaceae*)

	sp.	NGdn
	biebersteinii	see *Pachyphragma macrophyllum*
§	***cepaeifolium*** subsp. ***rotundifolium***	WAbe
	rotundifolium	see *T. cepaeifolium* subsp. *rotundifolium*

Thryptomene (*Myrtaceae*)

	baeckeacea	CCCN

Thuja ✿ (*Cupressaceae*)

	'Extra Gold'	see *T. plicata* 'Irish Gold'
§	***koraiensis***	NLar SLim WFar
	occidentalis	GPoy LPra NWea SEND
	- 'Amber Glow'	CAco CKen CSBt EMOT LRHS MAsh NHol NLar NWad SCoo SLim SPoG SRms
	- 'Anniek'PBR	CKen LRHS SPoG
	- 'Bateman Broom'	CKen
	- 'Beaufort' (v)	CKen
	- 'Brabant' ♀H7	LPra MGos MJak NLar NWea SCob SCoo SLim WMou
	- 'Brobeck's Tower' ♀H7	CKen NLar SLim
	- 'Caespitosa'	CKen
	- 'Columbia' (v)	LPra
	- 'Cuprea'	CKen
	- 'Danica' ♀H7	CDul CMac EMOT GKin LCro LOPS MAsh MGos MJak NWea SCob SCoo SLim SPoG SRms WCFE
	- 'Danica Gold'	SLim
	- 'Degroot's Spire'	CKen ELan LRHS NLar
	- 'Douglasii Aurea' (v)	CKen
	- EMERALD	see *T. occidentalis* 'Smaragd'
	- 'Ericoides'	SRms
	- 'Europa Gold' ♀H7	NLar SGol
	- 'Filiformis'	CKen SLim
	- 'Filips Magic Moment'PBR	LRHS SPoG
	- FIRE CHIEF ('Congabe'PBR)	CKen SPoG
	- 'Globosa'	ELan
I	- 'Globosa Variegata' (v)	CKen
	- 'Gold Drop'	CKen
	- 'Golden Anne'PBR	SPoG
	- 'Golden Globe'	MJak SCoo SLim
	- GOLDEN SMARAGD ('Janed Gold'PBR)	EPfP LRHS SLim SPoG WFar
	- 'Golden Tuffet' ♀H7	CKen ELan EMOT GKin LBee MPkF NWad SCob SCoo SLim SPoG
	- 'Hetz Midget' ♀H7	CKen EMOT GKin NWad SCob SCoo SLim SPlb WFar
	- 'Holmstrup' ♀H7	CBod CDul CMac LPra MAsh MGos SGol SLim SRms
	- 'Jantar'PBR	LRHS SLim SPoG
	- 'Konfettii' (v)	EMOT SLim SPoG
	- 'Linesville'	CKen
	- 'Little Gem'	SRms
	- 'Malonyana Holub'	SAko
	- 'Meineke's Zwerg' (v)	CKen
	- 'Miky'	LRHS
	- 'Milleri'	CKen
	- 'Mirjam'PBR (v)	CKen
	- 'Mr Bowling Ball'	LRHS NLar
	- 'Ohlendorffii'	CKen
	- 'Perk Vlaanderen' (v)	LRHS
I	- 'Pygmaea'	CKen

	- 'Pyramidalis Aurea'	ECrN
	- 'Recurva Nana'	NWad
	- 'Rheingold' 🏆H7	CAco CBcs CDul CMac CSBt CTri ELan EMOT GKin LBee LRHS MAsh MGos MJak MMuc NEgg NHol NWea SCob SEND SGol SLim SPlb SPoG SRms WCFE WFar
§	- 'Smaragd' 🏆H7	CCVT CDul CSBt ELan EMOT EPfP EUJe LBuc LCro LOPS LPra LRHS MAsh MGos MJak NLar NWea SCob SCoo SEWo SGol SLim SPoG SWvt WCFE
*	- 'Smaragd Variegated' (v)	CKen MAsh
	- 'Smokey'	CKen
	- 'Spiralis'	NLar
	- 'Starstruck'	LRHS SPoG WFar
§	- 'Stolwijk' (v)	SLim
	- 'Sunkist' 🏆H7	CBod CKen CMac EMOT MGos MJak NEgg SCoo SGol SRms WFar
	- 'Teddy'	EMOT EPfP LBee LRHS MAsh NHol SCoo SPoG
	- 'Tiny Tim'	CMac SGol SLim
	- 'Trompenburg'	CBod
	- 'Wansdyke Silver' (v)	CMac
	- 'Wareana'	CMac
	- 'Waterfield'	NLar NWad
	- 'Yellow Ribbon'	CKen CSBt LPra MJak SCob SGol SRms
	orientalis	see *Platycladus orientalis*
	plicata	CAco CBcs CCVT CDul CMac CPer CTho ELan EPfP NWea SCob SPer WMou WTSh
	- 'Atrovirens' 🏆H6	CDul ECrN ELan LBee LBuc LCro LOPS LPra LRHS MAsh MGos MHed MMuc NOra SCob SCoo SEND SEWo SGol SRms SWvt WAvo WMat WMou
	- 'Aurea' 🏆H6	LMaj MAsh SRms
	- 'Can-can' (v)	ELan EMOT
I	- 'Cole's Variety'	CDul
	- 'Collyer's Gold'	CDul SRms
	- 'Copper Kettle'	CKen GKin LRHS SLim
	- 'Cuprea'	CKen
	- 'Doone Valley'	CKen NWad
	- 'Excelsa'	CDul LMaj LPra WMou
	- 'Fastigiata'	CDul
	- 'Gelderland' 🏆H6	ELan EMOT EPfP LPra NEgg SCoo SLim
	- GOLDY ('4ever'[PBR])	EMOT LRHS NLar SLim SPoG
	- 'Hillieri'	CDul
	- 'Holly Turner'	SLim
§	- 'Irish Gold' (v)	CDul CMac LRHS
	- 'Martin'	SRms SWvt
	- 'Rogersii' 🏆H6	CKen CMac EMOT MAsh NHol SCoo SPoG SRms WThu
	- 'Semperaurescens' (v)	CMac
	- 'Stolwijk's Gold'	see *T. occidentalis* 'Stolwijk'
	- 'Stoneham Gold' 🏆H6	CMac GKin MAsh MGos SRms WCFE
	- VERIGOLD ('Courtapli')	MMuc SEND
	- 'Whipcord' 🏆H6	CAco CBcs CKen ELan EMOT EPfP LRHS MMuc MPkF NHol NLar SCoo SLim SPoG
	- 'Winter Pink' (v)	CKen
	- 'Zebrina' (v) 🏆H6	CAco CBcs CDul CMCN CMac CTri ELan EMOT EPfP LRHS MAsh MGos MMuc NLar NWea SCob SCoo SEND SLim SPer SPoG SWvt WAvo

Thujopsis (*Cupressaceae*)

	dolabrata 🏆H6	CAco CBcs CDul MMuc NEgg NWea SEND SWvt WFar
	- 'Aurea' (v)	CKen LRHS NLar
	- var. ***hondae***	IArd SLim
	- 'Laetevirens'	see *T. dolabrata* 'Nana'
§	- 'Nana'	CKen CMac LRHS NLar SLim SRms
	- 'Solar Flare'	LRHS SLim
	- 'Variegata' (v)	CMac GKin NLar SRms
	koraiensis (Nakai) hort.	see *Thuja koraiensis*

Thunbergia ✿ (*Acanthaceae*)

	alata	SPoG
	- 'African Sunset'	CSpe EShb
	- 'Lemon Queen'	CHll SWvt
	- 'Orange Beauty'	SWvt
*	***arborea***	CCCN
	battiscombeii	CCCN EShb
	coccinea	CCCN
	- B&SWJ 7166 **new**	WCru
	erecta	CCCN
	fragrans GWJ 9441	WCru
	grandiflora 🏆H1b	CCCN CHll WFib WSFF
	- 'Alba'	CCCN CHll
	gregorii 🏆H1b	CCCN CHll EShb WFib
	laurifolia B&SWJ 7166	WCru
	'Moonglow'	CCCN
	natalensis	CCCN EShb
	'Orange Wonder'	CCCN

Thymbra (*Lamiaceae*)

	capitata	LLHF WAbe
	spicata	SPhx

thyme, caraway see *Thymus herba-barona*

thyme, garden see *Thymus vulgaris*

thyme, lemon see *Thymus citriodorus*

thyme, wild see *Thymus serpyllum*

Thymus ✿ (*Lamiaceae*)

	sp.	NAln
	from Turkey	EWes LEdu
§	'Alan Bloom'	CRos LRHS NRHS
	'Albus'	ENfk
	'Anderson's Gold'	see *T. pulegioides* 'Bertram Anderson'
	'Aureus' ambig.	MJak
	azoricus	see *T. caespititius*
	'Bressingham'	CBod CMea CRos CTri EBou ECtt ELon EWhm GCrg GMaP GQue LEdu LRHS MHer MMuc MNHC NRHS SPlb SRms WIce
	'Caborn Wine and Roses'	CCBP ENfk SRms WJek
§	***caespititius***	GPoy MHer NRya SPlb SRms SRot WAbe WJek
	caespitosus	see *T. praecox* subsp. *praecox*
	camphoratus	ENfk EWes GCrg MHer NHpl SPhx WAbe WJek
	- 'Derry'	CSpe
§	***carnosus*** Boiss.	MHer XSen
	'Carol Ann' (v)	ENfk EWes MNHC SRms
	ciliatus	CBod XSen
	cilicicus misapplied	see *T. caespititius*
	cilicicus ambig.	MNHC SRms
	cilicicus Boiss. & Bail.	WAbe
	citriodorus misapplied	see *T.* 'Culinary Lemon'

	Name	Suppliers
	citriodorus ambig.	CTsd MMuc SRms SVic XLum
	citriodorus (Pers.) Schreb.	LEdu
	- 'Archer's Gold'	see *T. pulegioides* 'Archer's Gold'
	- 'Aureus'	see *T. pulegioides* 'Aureus'
	- 'Bertram Anderson'	see *T. pulegioides* 'Bertram Anderson'
	- 'Silver Posie'	see *T.* 'Silver Posie'
	'Coccineus'	see *T.* Coccineus Group
§	Coccineus Group ♀[H5]	CBod CTri EBou ECha ECtt ELan EMor ENfk GMaP LCro LOPS MHer MMuc MNHC NHpl NRya NSla NWad SPer SPoG SRms SRot WAbe WHoo WIce WJek XSen
	- 'Atropurpureus' Schleipfer	see *T.* 'Purple Beauty'
§	- 'Purple Beauty'	CRos ECtt EPot GCrg LRHS MHer NRHS SRms XSen
§	- 'Red Elf'	CBod GAbr GCrg MHer
	'Coccineus Major'	CMea LRHS MHer MNHC NRHS SCob SRms
	'Creeping Lemon' misapplied	see *T. pulegioides* 'Kurt'
§	'Culinary Lemon'	CBod CHby ENfk GPoy MBrN MHer MNHC NPri WJek XLum XSen
	'Dartmoor'	CBod WJek
	'Desboro'	see *T. serpyllum* 'Desborough'
	'Dillington'	ENfk
	doerfleri	XSen
	'Doone Valley' (v)	CBod CCBP CMea CRos CTri EBou ECha ELan EMor ENfk EPfP EWhm GMaP LRHS MAsh MHer MJak MMuc MNHC NBir NRHS SCob SPer SPlb SPoG SRms WFar WIce
	drucei	see *T. polytrichus* A. Kern. ex Borbás subsp. *britannicus*
	'Duftkissen'[PBR]	XSen
	'E.B. Anderson'	see *T. pulegioides* 'Bertram Anderson'
	'Elfin Pink Carpet'	MHol
	erectus	see *T. carnosus* Boiss.
	'Fragrantissimus'	CLau EBou EMor ENfk EWhm GPoy MHer MNHC SPlb WJek
	'Golden King' (v)	ECha ELan EMor ENfk LSRN MAsh MHer SRms
	'Golden Lemon' misapplied	see *T. pulegioides* 'Aureus'
	'Golden Lemon' (v)	WJek
	'Golden Queen' (v)	MHol SRms WFar
§	'Hartington Silver' (v)	CMea CRos CTri EBou ECha ECtt ENfk EPot EWes GCrg GKev LRHS MAsh MHer NAln NHpl NRHS SPlb SPoG SRms WJek
	herba-barona	CBod CLau CMea EBou ENfk GPoy GQue LEdu MHer MMuc MNHC SRms WJek
	- ***citrata***	see *T. herba-barona* 'Lemon-scented'
§	- 'Lemon-scented'	ECha GPoy LEdu MHer SRms WJek XSen
	'Highland Cream'	see *T.* 'Hartington Silver'
§	'Iden'	CBod WJek
	'Jekka'	CBod CLau EWhm MHer SRms WJek
	'Jekka's Autumn Pink' **new**	WJek
	'Jekka's Rosy Carpet' **new**	WJek
	'Kurt'	see *T. pulegioides* 'Kurt'
	'Lavender' **new**	SMHy
	'Lavender Sea'	EWes
	'Lemon Caraway'	see *T. herba-barona* 'Lemon-scented'
	'Lemon Curd'	CLau ENfk MNHC NHol SPlb SPoG SRms WJek
*	'Lemon Variegated' (v)	ENfk EPfP EWhm MNHC SPer SPoG XSen
	'Lilac Time'	ECtt ENfk EWes MHer SPlb SRms WJek
	'Lime'	LEdu
	longicaulis	CBod ECha MHer MMuc SRms
	longiflorus	XSen
	'Magic Carpet'	WArt WJek
	marschallianus	see *T. pannonicus*
	mastichina	XSen
	- 'Didi'	MHer
	membranaceus	WAbe
	micans	see *T. caespititius*
	minus	see *Calamintha nepeta*
	neiceffii	ECha
	nitens	XSen
	'Orange'	CBod LEdu SMHy SRms
§	ORANGE SPICE ('Tm95')	XSen
§	***pannonicus***	MHer
	- PAB 9021	LEdu
	'Peter Davis'	CRos ENfk GBin GCrg LRHS LSRN NBir NRHS SPoG SRms WAbe WIce WJek WTor XSen
§	'Pinewood'	MHer WJek XSen
	'Pink Ripple'	CBod CLau CMea ECtt ENfk EWes EWhm LEdu MHer MNHC SRms WHal WHoo WJek
	polytrichus misapplied	see *T. praecox*
§	***polytrichus*** A. Kern. ex Borbás subsp. ***britannicus***	CBod CTri EBou ECha EWhm GBin GMaP GPoy LEdu LOPS MBNS MHer MMuc MNHC NBir NEoE SEND SPlb SRms WHoo WJam WJek XLum XSen
§	- - 'Thomas's White' ♀[H5]	CTri
	'Porlock'	CBod CMea CSam CTri EPfP MHer SRms WHoo WJek
§	***praecox***	CWld EWhm GJos MHer NMir WArt
	- 'Albiflorus'	MRav XSen
	- subsp. ***arcticus***	see *T. polytrichus* A. Kern. ex Borbás subsp. *britannicus*
	- - 'Albus'	see *T. polytrichus* subsp. *britannicus* 'Thomas's White'
§	- subsp. ***praecox***	CTri
	prostrate	CBod EBou
	'Provence'	XSen
	pulegioides	CBod CCBP CHby CTri EBou EMor ENfk GPoy MHer NHpl SRms SRot WArt WJek WSFF
§	- 'Archer's Gold'	CCBP CRos ECtt EHoe ENfk EPfP EPot LRHS LSRN MAsh MHer MHol MNHC MRav NBir NHol NHpl NRHS SCob SRms
§	- 'Aureus' ♀[H5]	EBou ENfk GMaP MAsh SPer SPlb SRms WHoo
§	- 'Bertram Anderson' ♀[H5]	CMea CPla EBou ECha ECtt EMor ENfk EPfP GCrg GMaP MAsh MHer NBir NRya SCob SPer SPoG SRms WHoo WIce XSen
	- 'Foxley' (v)	CBod CCBP CLau ELon ENfk EPfP EWhm MHer MNHC SPlb SPoG SRms WJek
	- 'Golden Dwarf'	XSen
§	- 'Kurt'	CLau ENfk LEdu MHer SRms WJek
	- 'Sir John Lawes'	MHer
	- 'Tabor'	CBod CLau EBou ENfk EWhm MNHC SRms WGwG
	'Rainbow Falls' (v)	EPfP SRms

'Rasta' (v)	MHer XSen
'Redstart'	CBod ECha ECtt ENfk LEdu MHer SRms WJek
richardii subsp. ***nitidus*** 'Compactus Albus'	see *T. vulgaris* 'Snow White'
rotundifolius misapplied	see *T. vulgaris* 'Elsbeth'
'Ruby Glow'	ECtt EWes GCrg
serpyllum ambig.	SCob SVic XLum
serpyllum L.	EMor GJos LBuc MMuc SPlb SRms WRHF
- var. ***albus***	CRos ECha ELon GMaP GPoy LRHS MNHC NRHS SPer SRms WHoo
- 'Albus Variegatus'	see *T.* 'Hartington Silver'
- 'Amadé'	XSen
- 'Annie Hall'	CRos CSma EBou EPfP LRHS MAsh MHer MNHC NRHS SRms WCFE WJek
- 'Atropurpureus'	see *T.* (Coccineus Group) 'Purple Beauty'
- ***coccineus*** 'Minor' misapplied	see *T.* Coccineus Group
- - 'Minor' Bloom	see *T.* 'Alan Bloom'
- 'Conwy Rose'	CPBP WAbe
§ - 'Desborough'	MHer
- 'East Lodge'	MHer MNHC SRms
- 'Elfin'	ECtt EWes GCrg MRav NSla SPlb SRms SRot WAbe
- 'Goldstream' (v)	CMea CRos EBou ENfk LRHS MHer NRHS SPlb SRms WRHF
- 'Iden'	see *T.* 'Iden'
- 'Minimalist'	see *T. serpyllum* 'Minor'
- 'Minimus'	see *T. serpyllum* 'Minor'
§ - 'Minor'	CMea CRos CTri EBou ECha ECtt ENfk GCrg LRHS MHer MMuc MNHC NChi NRHS NSla SEND SPlb SRms SRot WAbe WHoo
- 'Minus'	see *T. serpyllum* 'Minor'
- 'Pink Chintz' ♀H5	CBod CCBP CRos EBou ECha ECtt EMor ENfk EPfP EPot EWhm GMaP GPoy LCro LEdu LOPS LRHS MHer MNHC NRHS NRya SPer SPlb SPoG SRms WIce WJek
- 'Purple Beauty'	see *T.* (Coccineus Group) 'Purple Beauty'
- 'Red Carpet'	ECtt GCrg NWad SRms SRot
- 'Red Elf'	see *T.* (Coccineus Group) 'Red Elf'
- 'Russetings'	CBod CTsd EBou ECtt ENfk EPfP GKev MHer MNHC NAln SCob SPoG SRms
- 'September'	MHer
- 'Snowdrift'	CCBP CMea ECtt EPfP LEdu MHer MNHC NWad SPlb SRms WCFE
- 'Variegatus'	see *T.* 'Hartington Silver'
- 'Vey'	CBod CRos CSma EWes LRHS MHer NRHS SRms
- 'Wirral White'	XSen
'Silver King' (v)	ENfk
§ 'Silver Posie'	CBar CHby CRos CTri ECtt EHoe ELan EMor ENfk EPfP EWhm LCro LOPS LRHS MAsh MHer MJak MNHC MRav NHpl NRHS SCob SPer SPlb SPoG SRms WFar
'Silver Queen' (v) ♀H5	CBcs CBod EBou ECha ELan EMor ENfk EPfP EWhm GCrg GKev GMaP LRHS MNHC NAln NHol SCob SPer SPlb SRms SVic WJek
'Spicy Orange'	see *T.* ORANGE SPICE
striatus	LEdu
§ ***vulgaris***	Widely available
* - 'Compactus'	CLau ENfk GPoy LEdu MHer MNHC MRav SPhx SRms WJek XSen
- 'Deutsche Auslese'	see *T. vulgaris*
- 'Dorcas White'	MHer
§ - 'Elsbeth'	MHer
- English, winter	SRms
- French	see *T. vulgaris*
- 'Golden Pins'	MHer
- 'Lucy'	MHer
- 'Pinewood'	see *T.* 'Pinewood'
§ - 'Snow White'	EWes
zygis	XSen

Tiarella ✿ (*Saxifragaceae*)

'Angel Wings' (Fox Series)	EMor MPnt WNPC
'Appalachian Trail'	CBcs ELan EMor MAvo MPnt NWad SHeu WFar
'Black Snowflake'	EBee MPnt SHeu
'Black Velvet'	MBel MPnt SHeu
'Braveheart'	EPfP MPnt SHeu
'Butter and Sugar'	MPnt
'Butterfly Wings'	MPnt
'Candy Striper'	MPnt SHeu
'Cascade Creeper'[PBR]	EMor LRHS MPnt NWad SHeu WNPC
collina	see *T. wherryi*
cordifolia ♀H5	CBcs CBod CMac CRos CTri ECha ELan EMor EPfP GAbr GMaP LEdu LPot LRHS MCot MGos MPnt MRav NBir NDov NRHS SCob SPer SRms SWvt WGwG WHoo WMoo XLum
- 'Glossy'	MPnt
- 'Milk Chocolate'	MPnt
- 'Oakleaf'	MPnt NBro SHeu
- 'Rosalie'	see × *Heucherella alba* 'Rosalie'
- 'Running Tapestry'	MPnt SHeu
- 'Slick Rock'	EPPr
'Crow Feather'[PBR]	MPnt NWad SHeu
'Cygnet'	CDor GBin MPnt SHeu
'Dunvegan'	MPnt
'Elizabeth Oliver'	MPnt
'Emerald Ellie' (Fox Series)	MPnt WNPC
'Fairy's Footsteps' **new**	SHeu
'Freckles'	MRav
'Happy Trails'[PBR]	EMor MPnt NWad SHeu WCot WNPC
'Inkblot'	LRHS MPnt NBro SHeu WMoo
'Iron Butterfly'[PBR] (v)	CBod CDor CMac CRos EBee ECha EHoe EPfP EUJe GMaP LRHS LSRN MAvo MBel MPnt MRav SCob SGbt SHeu SPer SPoG SRms SRot WHoo
'Iron Cross'	SPlb
'Jeepers Creepers'[PBR]	ECha EMor LRHS MJak MPnt NWad SHeu WNPC
'Martha Oliver'	MPnt
'Mint Chocolate'	CRos EHrv ELan LRHS MPnt MRav NBir NGdn NLar NRHS SHeu SWvt
'Moorgrün'	EPPr GCal SHeu
MORNING STAR ('Tntia042')	ELan MPnt SHeu SRkn SRot
'Mystic Mist'[PBR] (v)	CDor CWGN ECtt MPnt NWad SHeu SPoG
'Neon Lights'[PBR]	MAsh MPnt NBir NWad SCob SHeu SWvt WNPC
§ 'Ninja'	CRos EHrv ELan LRHS MPnt NBir NLar NRHS SWvt
'Oregon Trail'	EMor MNrw MPnt NWad SHeu WNPC
'Pacific Crest'[PBR]	EBee EMor MPnt NWad SHeu WNPC

'Pink Bouquet' CBod CMac CSpe EHrv ELan EMor IKil MBel MPie MPnt NBro NLar SHeu WFar WGwG WMoo WPnP
'Pink Brushes'[PBR] MPnt SHeu
'Pink Skyrocket'[PBR] CDor ELan EMor EPau LLHF LSRN LSun MBel MPnt NBir NGdn NHol NWad SHeu SMad SPer SPoG SWvt WCot WNPC WPnP
'Pinwheel' MPnt
'Pirate's Patch'[PBR] LLHF MPnt SHeu
polyphylla MPnt SHeu WCru
- 'Baoxing Pink' MPnt WCru
- 'Filigran' CBod ELan EPfP GQue MPnt NHol NWad SHar SHeu
'Running Tiger' MPnt
'Sea Foam' MPnt SHeu
'Simsalabim' MPnt
'Skeleton Key' MPnt
'Skid's Variegated' (v) MNrw MPnt SHeu SPoG SWvt
'Skyrocket' NLar
'Spanish Cross' MPnt SHeu
'Spring Symphony'[PBR] CBod CDor CRos ELan EMor EPfP EShb GBin GKev GMaP GWyn LCro LOPS LRHS MBel MPnt NPer NRHS NWad SHar SPoG WNPC WSHC
STARBURST ('Tntia041'[PBR]) MPnt NWad SHeu
'Sugar and Spice'[PBR] CWGN EPfP LRHS MPnt NRHS NWad SHeu WNPC
'Sunset Ridge'[PBR] EBee EMor MPnt NWad SHeu WNPC
SYLVAN LACE ('Tntiasl') (American Trial Series) new SHeu
'Tiger Stripe' EBee EPfP LRHS MPnt NBro SHeu
'Timbuktu' MAsh MPnt SHeu WFar
trifoliata MPnt MRav
- var. ***unifoliata*** MPnt
'Viking Ship' see × *Heucherella* 'Viking Ship'
§ ***wherryi*** 🏆[H5] CBcs CBod ELan ELon EMor EPfP EWld LPot LRHS MPnt NBir NBro NRya SCob SPer SPlb SWvt WPnP XLum
- 'Bronze Beauty' MPnt SHeu
- bronze-leaved SCob
- 'Green Velvet' ECha MPnt SHeu
- 'Heronswood Mist' (v) ELan MNrw MPnt SHeu SWvt
- 'Pink Foam' SHeu

Tibouchina (*Melastomataceae*)

grandifolia CCCN CRHN
'Groovy Baby' CBct CCht CSpe MHol
grossa B&SWJ 10758 new WCru
heteromalla CCCN
organensis CBcs CBod CCCN CHll CKel CSpe EUJe SEle SHeu SPoG SWvt
paratropica CBod CRHN GCal MGil
'Peace Baby' new CWGN
semidecandra misapplied see *T. urvilleana*
§ ***urvilleana*** 🏆[H2] CBcs CBct CCCN CEnd CSBt CSpe CTri CTsd EBak EMdy IDee SPer SRkn SWvt
- 'Compacta' CCCN
- 'Edwardsii' 🏆[H2] CRHN SAdn WCot
- variegated (v) CBcs CCCN CKel CSpe SPer SWvt WCot

Tigridia (*Iridaceae*)

sp. EShb
chiapensis CPla GKev
immaculata B&SWJ 10393 WCru
§ ***orthantha*** CPla
- 'Red-Hot Tiger' CAby CSpe EBee WCot WCru WSHC
pavonia CAby CExl EShb SDeJ WSHC
- 'Alba' CSpe WSHC
- 'Alba Grandiflora' GKev SDeJ
- 'Aurea' GKev
- 'Canariensis' GKev SDeJ
- 'Lilacea' CPla GKev SDeJ
- 'Speciosa' GKev SDeJ
van-houttei GKev

Tilia ✿ (*Malvaceae*)

sp. LPra
americana CLnd CMCN LPra
- 'Dentata' CDul
- 'Nova' LPra
- 'Redmond' MBlu
amurensis CMCN
- from Korea WPGP
argentea see *T. tomentosa*
begoniifolia see *T. dasystyla* subsp. *caucasica*
callidonta WPGP
§ ***caroliniana*** subsp. ***heterophylla*** CDul CMCN EBee EPfP MBlu WPGP
chinensis CMCN WPGP
- F 30558 WPGP
chingiana CDul CMCN EBee EBtc WPGP
concinna WPGP
cordata Widely available
§ - 'Böhlje' CDul LPra
- 'Dainty Leaf' CDul
- 'Erecta' see *T. cordata* 'Böhlje'
- Erecta Group LPra
- 'Greenspire' 🏆[H6] CArg CCVT CDul CLnd EBar EPfP LPra MRav NWea SCob SEWo WMat WMou
- 'Len Parvin' WPGP
- 'Rancho' EMOT LPra
- 'Roelvo' CDul
- 'Swedish Upright' CDul
- 'Winter Orange' 🏆[H6] CBcs CBod CDul CEnd CNWT EBee ECrN ELan EPfP MBlu MSwo SBir SCoo SEWo WMat
dasystyla CMCN
§ - subsp. ***caucasica*** CMCN EBee WPGP
- - A&L 16 WPGP
- - NJM 13.029 WPGP
endochrysea WPGP
× ***euchlora*** CArg CCVT CDul CLnd CMCN EBee ECrN EMOT EPfP LMaj LPra NWea SCob SEWo SPer WMat
§ × ***europaea*** CBcs CDul CLnd ELan EWTr LPra MMuc NWea SCob SEND
- 'Koningslinde' CDul
- 'Pallida' CDul CLnd LMaj LPra MBlu NWea
- 'Wratislaviensis' 🏆[H6] CDul EBtc MBlu NWea
× ***flavescens*** LPra
§ 'Harold Hillier' CMCN MBlu WPGP
henryana CBcs CDul CEnd CLnd CMCN EBee ECrN ELan EPfP ERod IArd IDee MBlu MMuc SBir SEND WMat WMou WPGP
- 'Bluebell' new MBlu
- 'Kerdalo' WPGP
- large WPGP
'Hillieri' see *T.* 'Harold Hillier'
insularis misapplied see *T. japonica*
intonsa CMCN

§	***japonica***	CDul CMCN EBee EPfP WPGP
	- 'Ernest Wilson' ♀H6	CMCN MBlu
	- large-leaved, from China	WPGP
	kiusiana	CMCN EBee EBtc MBlu WPGP
	mandshurica	CMCN EBee WPGP
	maximowicziana	CMCN EBee EPfP MBlu WPGP
	mexicana	WPGP
	- CD&R 1318	EBee WPGP
	miqueliana	CMCN MBlu
	× ***moltkei***	CMCN EBee IArd WPGP
	mongolica	CBcs CDul CMCN EBee EPfP MBlu WMou WPGP
	- 'Harvest Gold'	CBcs MBlu
	monticola	see *T. caroliniana* subsp. *heterophylla*
	nobilis KR 226	WPGP
	oliveri	CBcs CDul CMCN EBee MBlu WPGP
	aff. ***oliveri*** HRS 2808 new	WPGP
	paucicostata	WPGP
	platyphyllos	CAco CAgr CCVT CDul CFGn CHab CLnd CMCN CPer CSBt CTho CTri ECrN EMOT EPfP EWTr LBuc LPra MMuc NWea SCob SCoo SEND SPer WMat WMou WTSh
	- 'Aurea'	CDul CTho ECrN MBlu WMat
	- 'Corallina'	see *T. platyphyllos* 'Rubra'
	- 'Erecta'	see *T. platyphyllos* 'Fastigiata'
§	- 'Fastigiata'	CDul
	- 'Laciniata'	CDul CMCN CTho MBlu
§	- 'Rubra' ♀H6	CCVT CDul CLnd CTho EBar EMOT LPra NWea SEWo
	- 'Tortuosa'	LMaj MBlu WMou
	× ***stellata***	WPGP
§	***tomentosa***	CAco CDul CLnd CMCN LPra MMuc NWea SCob SCoo SEND
	- 'Brabant' ♀H6	CDul ELan EMOT EPfP LMaj LPra
	- 'Petiolaris' ♀H6	CArg CBcs CCVT CEnd CLnd CMCN CTho ECrN ELan EMOT EPfP LPra MBlu MSwo NWea SCob SPer WMou
	tuan	WPGP
	- var. ***chenmoui***	CMCN EBtc EPfP MBlu WPGP
I	'Varsaviensis'	WPGP
	× ***vulgaris***	see *T.* × *europaea*

Tilingia (*Apiaceae*)

	ajanensis B&SWJ 11202	IMou

Tillaea see *Crassula*

Tillandsia (*Bromeliaceae*)

	sp.	XBlo
	abdita	NCft
	aeranthos	NCft SChr
	- 'Bronze'	NCft
	- var. ***rosea***	NCft
	aizoides	NCft
	albertiana	NCft
	albida	NCft SPlb
	andreana	NCft
	argentea ♀H1c	LCro LOPS NCft
	argentina	NCft
	ariza-juliae	NCft
	baileyi	NCft
	- var. ***vivipara*** new	NCft
	balbisiana	NCft
	bandensis	NCft
	bartramii	NCft
	bergeri	NCft SChr SPlb
	brachycaulos	NCft
	- var. ***multiflora***	NCft
	brachycaulos × ***concolor*** new	NCft
	brachycaulos × ***schiedeana***	NCft
	bryoides	NCft
	bulbosa	NCft SPlb
	butzii	NCft
	cacticola	NCft
	caerulea	NCft
	'Califano'	NCft
	caliginosa	NCft
	capillaris	NCft
	capitata	NCft
	- 'Peach'	NCft
	- red-leaved	NCft
	caput-medusae	NCft
	caulescens × ***tenuifolia***	NCft
	chusgonensis	NCft
	compressa new	NCft
	concolor	NCft
	'Cotton Candy'	NCft
	crocata	NCft
	- 'Copper Penny'	NCft
	cyanea	LCro LOPS NCft
	diaguitensis	NCft
	duratii	NCft
	dyeriana ♀H1c	NCft
	elongata	NCft
	espinosae	NCft
	exserta	NCft
	fasciculata	NCft
	festucoides	NCft
	filifolia	NCft
	flabellata ♀H1c	NCft
	flavobracteata	NCft
	flexuosa	NCft
	floribunda	NCft
	× ***floridana***	NCft
	fresnilloensis	NCft
	fuchsii var. ***fuchsii***	NCft
	- f. ***gracilis***	NCft
	funckiana	NCft SPlb
	gardneri	NCft
	geminiflora	NCft
	grao-mogolensis	NCft
	harrisii	NCft
	'Heather's Blush'	NCft
	heteromorpha	NCft
	hondurensis	NCft
	incarnata	NCft
	intermedia	NCft
*	***ionantha*** 'Fuego'	NCft
	- 'Haselnuss'	NCft
	- var. ***ionantha***	NCft
	- var. ***maxima*** 'Huamelula'	see *T. ionantha* var. *stricta*
	- 'Peach'	NCft
	- 'Ron'	NCft
I	- 'Rosea'	NCft
	- 'Rubra'	NCft
	- var. ***scaposa***	see *T. kolbii*
	- 'Silver'	NCft
§	- var. ***stricta***	NCft
	- var. ***vanhyningii***	NCft
	ixioides	NCft
	'Jackie Loinaz'	NCft
	jucunda	NCft
	juncea	NCft
	kammii	NCft

	karwinskyana	NCft
	kautskyi	NCft
	'Kimberly'	NCft
§	***kolbii***	NCft
	lautneri	NCft
	leonamiana	NCft
	lepidosepela new	NCft
	loliacea	NCft
	lorentziana	NCft
	magnusiana	NCft
	mallemontii	NCft
	marconae	NCft
	'Maria Teresa'	NCft
	mitlaensis	NCft
	montana	NCft
	myosura	NCft
	neglecta	NCft
I	- 'Rubra'	NCft
	oaxacana	NCft
	paleacea	NCft
	paucifolia	NCft
	plagiotropica	NCft
	pohliana	NCft
	polystachia	NCft
	pruinosa	NCft
	pseudobaileyi	NCft
	pueblensis	NCft
	punctulata	NCft
	purpurea	NCft
	× ***rectifolia***	NCft
	recurvata	NCft
	recurvifolia new	NCft
	reichenbachii	NCft
	retorta new	NCft
	schiedeana	NCft
	- 'Major'	NCft
I	- 'Minor'	NCft
	schreiteri	NCft
	seideliana	NCft
	seleriana	NCft SPlb
	stellifera	NCft
	straminea	NCft
	streptocarpa	NCft
	streptophylla	NCft
	stricta var. ***albifolia***	NCft
I	- 'Amethyst'	NCft
	- 'Grey'	NCft
	- var. ***stricta*** new	NCft
	tectorum	NCft
	- caulescent	NCft
	tenuifolia	NCft
I	- 'Minima'	NCft
	tricholepis	NCft
	tricolor var. ***melanocrater***	NCft
	usneoides	NCft SHmp SPlb WSFF
	utriculata subsp. ***pringlei***	NCft
	xerographica	NCft
	xiphioiodes	NCft
	zecheri	NCft
	- var. ***cafayatensis***	NCft

Tinantia (*Commelinaceae*)

	pringlei	GEdr LEdu MNrw MPie SBrt SDys WPGP
	- AIM 77	EBee MNrw WCot
	- variegated (v)	WCot

Titanopsis (*Aizoaceae*)

	calcarea ♀H1c	CCCN SSim
	fulleri new	SSim

Titanotrichum (*Gesneriaceae*)

	oldhamii	GEdr SBrt

Tithonia (*Asteraceae*)

	rotundifolia 'Torch'	CSpe
	'Torchlight'	LRHS

Tofieldia (*Tofieldiaceae*)

	coccinea	CSpe GCal GEdr WCot WCru
	furusei	GEdr

Tolmiea (*Saxifragaceae*)

	menziesii	CMac MCot SPer XLum
	- 'Goldsplash'	see *T. menziesii* 'Taff's Gold'
	- 'Maculata'	see *T. menziesii* 'Taff's Gold'
§	- 'Taff's Gold' (v)	CBod CRos EHoe EMor NBid SPlb XLum
	- 'Variegata'	see *T. menziesii* 'Taff's Gold'

tomato see AGM Vegetables Section

Toona (*Meliaceae*)

§	***sinensis***	CAgr CBcs CTho ELan EPfP LEdu SEND WHor WPGP
	- 'Flamingo' (v)	CKel CRos CTho EPfP ESwi LCro LEdu LOPS LRHS MAsh MGos NLar NRHS SChF SGol SMad SPoG SWvt WCot WMat
	- 'Lise'	CMCN

Torenia (*Linderniaceae*)

	Summer Wave Series	CCCN

Torilis (*Apiaceae*)

	japonica	CBre

Torreya (*Taxaceae*)

	californica	CAco
	nucifera	CBcs IDee

Townsendia (*Asteraceae*)

	alpigena	CPla
§	- var. ***alpigena***	GKev
	eximia × ***parryi***	GKev
	formosa	NHpl
	hookeri	CPla
	incana	GEdr
	leptotes	GKev
	mensana	GKev
	montana	see *T. alpigena* var. *alpigena*
	parryi	GKev
	scapigera new	GEdr
	spathulata	SPlb

Toxicodendron (*Anacardiaceae*)

§	***orientale*** B&SWJ 3656	WCru
	- large-leaved B&SWJ 10884	WCru
§	***radicans***	GPoy
§	***succedaneum***	CDTJ
	- NJM 10.154	WPGP
§	***vernicifluum***	NLar

Trachelium (*Campanulaceae*)

§	***asperuloides***	SPlb WAbe
	caeruleum 'Black Knight'	CPla CSpe WCot
	jacquinii subsp. ***rumelianum***	SIgm
	lanceolatum	WCot

Trachelospermum ✿ (*Apocynaceae*)

from Nanjing, China	EShb
§ ***asiaticum*** ♀H4	Widely available
- 'Copper Tips'	MGil WAvo
- 'Golden Memories'	CBcs CExl CKel CMac CRHN CRos CWCL CWGN EBee ELan ELon EPfP LRHS LSRN NLar NRHS SLon SNig SPoG SRms SSta SWvt WCot
- 'Goshiki' (v)	EShb SEle
- 'Kulu Chirimen'	WCot
- 'Ōgon-nishiki' (v)	CRos LRHS SEle SMad SPoG
- 'Pink Showers'	CBcs CFlo
- 'Summer Sunset'	CWCL ELan ELon EPfP LRHS MGos SGol SRms WCot
- 'Theta'	LRHS WCot WFar WPGP
'Chameleon'	ELan SMad
jasminoides ♀H4	Widely available
- 'Major'	CMac CWCL EBee ELan MAsh MGil SRms
§ - var. ***pubescens*** 'Japonicum'	CBod CRHN CRos LRHS NPri SLon SPoG WBor WSHC
- STAR OF TOSCANA ('Selbra'PBR)	CRos ECtt EPfP LCro LOPS LRHS NLar NRHS SCob SPer SPoG
- 'Tricolor' (v)	LRHS SCob SEle SGol SWvt
- 'Variegatum' (v) ♀H4	Widely available
- 'Waterwheel'	CBcs CKel CMac CSde CWCL ELan ELon EShb EUJe LRHS NLar SCob SMad SWvt WSHC
- 'White Wings'	LRHS
- 'Wilsonii'	CExl CMac CRos CWCL ELan ELon EPfP EShb EUJe LRHS LSRN MGil MRav NLar SAdn SEND SLim SNig SPer SPoG SWvt WAvo WCot WPGP
majus misapplied	see *T. jasminoides* var. *pubescens* 'Japonicum'
majus Nakai	see *T. asiaticum*

Trachycarpus ✿ (*Arecaceae*)

sp.	LPra
from Manipur	CPHo
§ ***fortunei*** ♀H5	Widely available
nanus* × *wagnerianus new	SChr
princeps	CBrP EUJe
ukhrulensis NJM 13.085 new	WPGP
wagnerianus ♀H5	CBcs CBrP CCCN CDTJ CExl CPHo EPfP EUJe SArc SChr SMad WPGP

Trachymene (*Apiaceae*)

coerulea	CSpe

Trachystemon (*Boraginaceae*)

orientalis	Widely available

Tradescantia (*Commelinaceae*)

albiflora	see *T. fluminensis*
× ***andersoniana*** W. Ludwig & Rohw. nom. inval.	see *T.* Andersoniana Group
§ Andersoniana Group	WWtn
- 'Angelic Charm' (Charm Series)	CWGN ECtt
- 'Baby Doll'	XLum
- 'Baerbel'	XLum
- 'Bilberry Ice'	CDor CMac CRos EAJP ECtt EPfP GMaP IKil LRHS MBel MWat NBir NBro NGBl NGdn NLar NRHS SCob SGbt SWvt WWtn XLum
- 'Blanca'	WWtn
- 'Blue and Gold'	CBcs CRos ECtt ELon EPfP EUJe EWhm LRHS MHol MRav NCou NRHS NSti WCot WFar WGrn WHil
- 'Blue Stone'	CDor CMea CSBt ECha ECtt IKil MAvo MRav SRkn SRms WHoo XLum
- 'Blue Spider' new	MAsh
- 'Bridal Veil'	CHll SChr WDib
- 'Caerulea Plena'	see *T. virginiana* 'Caerulea Plena'
- CARMINE GLOW	see *T.* (Andersoniana Group) 'Karminglut'
- 'Charlotte'	CDor CRos ECha ECtt ELan LRHS LSRN NBro NGdn NLar NRHS WWtn XLum
- 'Concord Grape' ♀H5	CAby CKno CMac CMea CRos EBee ECtt EHoe ELan EPfP GMaP LRHS LSRN LSun MAvo MBel MGos NBro NChi NGdn NRHS NSti SCob SPer WCAu WFar WGwG WHoo WKif XLum
- 'Domaine de Courson'	ECtt XLum
- 'Euridice'	EWTr MBel
- 'Good Luck'PBR	MHol
- 'In the Navy'	NLar
- 'Innocence'	CAby CDor CNor CRos CSBt CTri ECha ECtt ELan EPfP GMaP GWyn LRHS MBel MMuc NBir NGdn NRHS NSti SCob SPer SWvt XLum
- 'Iris Prichard'	EBee GMaP NLar
- 'Isis'	CAby CRos EBee ECtt ELan EPfP GMaP LRHS MMuc MRav NBir NGdn NRHS SPer SWvt WGwG WKif WWtn
- 'J.C. Weguelin'	EPfP NBir SRms WWtn XLum
§ - 'Karminglut'	EBee ECtt EPfP GLog GMaP NBir NGdn WHoo XLum
- 'Leonora'	CBod EPfP MBel MMuc NLar SCob XLum
- 'Little Doll'	CDor CRos ECtt EPfP LRHS MPie NBro NLar NRHS XLum
- 'Little White Doll'	ECtt EPfP
- 'Lucky Charm' (Charm Series)	NLar
- 'Mac's Double' (d)	EBee IKil
- 'Mariella'	EBee
- 'Melissa'	XLum
- 'Merlot Clusters'	LSun SCob
- 'Ocean Blue'	EPfP
- 'Osprey'	CBcs CDor CRos ECha ECtt ELan GCal LRHS MBel MRav NGdn NRHS NSti SPer SRms WCAu WGwG WHoo WKif WWtn XLum
- 'Pauline'	MRav NBir NLar XLum
- 'Perinne's Pink'	CRos ECtt EPfP LRHS NRHS NSti WCAu
- 'Pink Chablis'	CRos ECtt EPfP IKil LRHS MHol NBro NLar NRHS XLum
- 'Pink Spider' new	MAsh
- 'Purewell Giant'	CMac CRos CTri LRHS NBro NLar NRHS SWvt WKif
- 'Purple Dome'	CRos ECtt EPfP GMaP LRHS MMuc MRav NBir NBro NGBl NGdn NRHS SPoG
- 'Red Grape'	CRos LRHS NRHS NSti SCob XLum
- 'Regal Charm' (Charm Series)	EBee
- 'Rubra'	CRos SCob SRms XLum
- 'Satin Doll'PBR	CBcs ECtt
- 'Sunshine Charm'PBR (Charm Series)	CRos CWCL LRHS NCou NLar NRHS WHil

	- 'Sweet Kate'	CMac CRos ECtt LRHS LSRN MBNS NBro NLar NRHS SGbt SPoG SRms XLum
	- 'Valour'	CRos CSBt EBee EPfP LRHS NRHS
	- 'Zwanenburg Blue'	CRos ECha ECtt ELan LRHS NLar NRHS SPlb SPoG XLum
	'Angel Eyes'	EBee
	blossfeldiana 'Variegata'	see *T. cerinthoides* 'Variegata'
	bracteata	SBrt
	canaliculata	see *T. ohiensis*
§	***cerinthoides*** 'Variegata' (v) ♀H1c	EShb
	crassifolia F&M 258	WPGP
§	***fluminensis***	SChr WDib
§	- 'Aurea' ♀H1c	EShb SChr
	- 'Maiden's Blush' (v)	CSpe CWCL EShb EUJe SChr SPlb SVen
	- 'Quicksilver' (v) ♀H1c	EShb NGBl
	- 'Variegata'	see *T. fluminensis* 'Aurea'
	'Green Hill'	LCro LOPS
	navicularis	see *Callisia navicularis*
§	***ohiensis***	SBrt
	pallida ♀H1c	EShb
	- 'Kartuz Giant'	EShb MPie WCot
	- 'Pale Puma'	EShb
§	- 'Purpurea' ♀H3	CBcs EOHP EShb EUJe NGBl SPlb
	pendula	see *T. zebrina*
	'Purple Sabre'	see *T. pallida* 'Purpurea'
	purpurea	see *T. pallida* 'Purpurea'
	sillamontana ♀H3	EShb MPie SChr
I	- 'Variegata' (v)	EShb
	spathacea	EShb EUJe
	- 'Versicolor'	EShb
	tricolor	see *T. zebrina*
	virginiana	NChi
	- 'Alba'	CMac GCal SRms
*	- 'Brevicaulis'	ECha NBro
§	- 'Caerulea Plena' (d)	ELan EPfP MRav NLar SPer XLum
	- 'Rubra'	SPlb
	'Yellow Hill' (v) **new**	EShb
§	***zebrina*** ♀H1c	EShb
	- ***pendula***	see *T. zebrina*
	- 'Purpusii' ♀H1c	EShb WDib
	- 'Quadricolor' (v) ♀H1c	EShb

Tragopogon (*Asteraceae*)

crocifolius	CSpe LRHS SPhx
porrifolius	CFis GCal LRHS MCot NGBl SPhx SVic WCot WTre
pratensis	NMir

Trautvetteria (*Ranunculaceae*)

carolinensis	ESwi IMou WSHC
- var. ***japonica***	GEdr WCru
- - B&SWJ 10861	WCru
- var. ***occidentalis***	EBee LEdu WCru

Trevesia ✿ (*Araliaceae*)

hardy KWJ 12217 from northern Vietnam **new**	WCru

Triadica (*Euphorbiaceae*)

sebifera	WPGP
- CWJ 12819	WCru

Trichodiadema (*Aizoaceae*)

densum ♀1c **new**	CBod SSim
intonsum	SPlb

Trichopetalum (*Asparagaceae*)

§	***plumosum***	CBro

Trichostema (*Lamiaceae*)

'Blue Bonnets'	MMuc

Tricuspidaria see *Crinodendron*

Tricyrtis (*Liliaceae*)

	B&SWJ 3229 from Taiwan	WCru
	'Abdane'	GKev
	'Adbane'	CLAP ELan EWes WGwG
	affinis B&SWJ 2804	WCru
	- B&SWJ 5645	WCru
	- B&SWJ 6182	WCru
	- B&SWJ 11169	WCru
	- B&SWJ 11442	WCru
	- 'Early Bird'	WCru
	'Amanagowa'	CLAP
	bakeri	see *T. latifolia*
	'Blue Wonder'	LBuc LRHS SPad SPer WWtn XLum
	dilatata	see *T. macropoda*
	'Empress'	CBct CDor CExl CLAP CPla ECha ELon EMor EWes LPot LRHS MHer MJak NEgg NWad SRkn SRot WWtn
	flava	CRos LRHS NRHS WCru
	formosana	CAvo CTri ECha EHrv ELan EThi GKev GLog GMaP LRHS MCot MMuc MNrw NAln SDys SRms SRot WAvo WKif
	- B&SWJ 355	WCru
	- B&SWJ 3073	WCru
	- B&SWJ 3616	CExl WCru
	- B&SWJ 3712	WCru
	- B&SWJ 6741	WCru
	- B&SWJ 6970	WCru
	- RWJ 10109	WCru
	- 'Autumn Glow' (v)	WFar
	- 'Dark Beauty'	CAby CDor CExl CLAP CWCL ECtt EHrv ELan EMor GAbr LCro LPot MBel MPnt SCob WCAu WFar WTyc
	- 'Emperor' (v)	EBee ESwi
	- 'Gilt Edge' (v)	CBct CBod CExl ECtt ELan EThi LPot MBNS NEgg NLar NWad SWvt WFar
	- f. ***glandosa*** B&SWJ 7084	WCru
	- aff. f. ***glandosa*** 'Blu-Shing Toad'	MAvo WCru
	- var. ***grandiflora*** 'W-Ho-ping Toad'	WCru
	- 'Kestrel' (v)	CBct WCot WFar
	- pale-flowered	EThi
	- 'Purple Beauty'	CRos
	- 'Samurai' (v)	CWCL EWes
	- 'Seiryu'	EBee MBel
	- 'Shelley's'	CLAP
	- 'Small Wonder'	LEdu WCru
	- 'Spotted Toad'	LEdu WCru
§	- Stolonifera Group	CAvo CBcs CDor CMac CRos EHrv ELan EMor EPfP LRHS MCot NRHS NWad SHar
	- - B&SWJ 7046	WCru
	- 'Taiwan Toad'	CExl
	- 'Taroko Toad'	WCru
	- 'Tiny Toad'	WCru
	- 'Variegata' (v)	LEdu NBir SRms WCru
	- 'Velvet Toad'	WCru

	'Golden Leopard'	EBee
§	***hirta***	CBcs CBod CDor CMac CRos CTri CTsd EMor ILea LCro LOPS LRHS MCot MJak NBro NHol NRHS SGbt SPlb SWvt WSHC
	- B&SWJ 5971	WCru
	- B&SWJ 11182	WCru
	- B&SWJ 11227	WCru
	- 'Alba'	CMac WAvo
	- 'Albomarginata' (v)	CBod CMac EWhm LRHS NEgg NRHS NSti SPoG SWvt WWtn
	- 'Golden Gleam'	WCot
	- var. ***masamunei***	WCru
	- 'Matsukaze'	CExl EWes MAvo
	- 'Miyazaki'	CFis CMac CRos ECha ECtt IPot LRHS MHer MNrw NCGa NRHS NSti SPoG WRHF WSHC WWtn XLum
	- 'Taiwan Atrianne'	CDor CLAP ECtt ELan EMor LRHS MNrw MPie NEgg NRHS NWad SGbt SPoG WCAu WWtn
	- 'Variegata' (v)	CRos CTri EBee EWes GKev LRHS NRHS WCot
	Hototogisu	CExl CRos ECha ECtt ELan LRHS MHer NHol NLar NRHS SPoG WWtn
	'Imperial Banner' (v)	CWCL
	ishiiana	EBee EHrv MAvo WCot WCru WSHC
	- var. ***surugensis***	LEdu WCru WFar
	japonica	see *T. hirta*
	'Kohaku'	EBee
	lasiocarpa	EHrv ESwi LEdu MAvo NCGa XLum
	- B&SWJ 3635	CAby CExl WCru
	- B&SWJ 6861	WCru
	- B&SWJ 7013	WCru
	- B&SWJ 7103	WCru
	- 'Royal Toad'	WCru
§	***latifolia***	CRos GKev GLog GPSL LEdu LLHF LRHS NRHS WCru WFar
	- B&SWJ 10996	CBct
	- 'Saffron'	WCru
	- 'Yellow Sunrise'	NCGa
	'Lightning Strike' (v)	CDor ECha ECtt WCot WFar
	macrantha	GAbr GLog WCru WSHC
§	- subsp. ***macranthopsis***	CAby CBct CExl WCot WCru
	- - 'Juro' (d)	WCru
	macranthopsis	see *T. macrantha* subsp. *macranthopsis*
*	***macrocarpa***	XLum
	macropoda	CRos GLog ILea LEdu LRHS MAvo MBNS
	- B&SWJ 1271 from Korea	WCru
	- B&SWJ 5013	WCru
	- B&SWJ 5556	WCru
	- B&SWJ 5847 from Japan	WCru
	- B&SWJ 6209	WCru
	- B&SWJ 8700	WCru
	- B&SWJ 8829 from Korea	WCru
	maculata HWJCM 470	WCru
	- HWJK 2010	WCru
	- HWJK 2411	WCru
	- PAB 3188	LEdu
	'Moonlight Treasure' PBR	CExl EBee NHol WCot
	nana	WCru
	- B&SWJ 11399	WCru
	ohsumiensis	CAby ECha EHrv EPot WCru
	perfoliata	LEdu WCru
	- 'Spring Shine' (v)	WCru
	pilosa	GKev LEdu
	PINK FRECKLES ('Innotripf' PBR)	CBct CDor CLAP CRos ELon EPot ESwi MPnt NCou SRot SWvt
	'Raspberry Mousse'	CWCL EPfP MBNS
	ravenii B&SWJ 3229	WCru
	- RWJ 10012	WCru
	setouchiensis	WCru
	'Shimone'	CExl ECha
	'Sinonome'	EBee IPot MNrw
	stolonifera	see *T. formosana* Stolonifera Group
	suzukii RWJ 10111	WCru
	'Taipei Silk' PBR	CLAP LOPS NCGa
	'Tojen'	CKel CLAP CRos ECha ECtt EPfP EWTr EWes GKev GPSL LRHS MNrw NRHS WCAu WWtn
	'White Towers'	CAby CAvo CBro CExl CLAP CRos ECha ECtt ELan LPot LRHS MBel MRav NCGa NEgg NRHS NSti SRms WCAu WSHC WWtn XLum

Trifolium (*Papilionaceae*)

	arvense PAB 7952	LEdu
	dubium	GAbr SPre
	incarnatum	CSpe MHer
	macrocephalum	EBee
	ochroleucon	CDor EAJP ECha ECtt EHrv ELon EWTr GBin GMaP ILea LEdu LPot MCot MPie SHar SMad SPhx WAul WCAu WFar WMoo WPGP
	pannonicum	CMea GCal MNrw SPhx WWFP
	- 'White Tiara'	GBin
	pratense	CHab MHer NMir SRms WOut WSFF
	- 'Dolly North'	see *T. pratense* 'Susan Smith'
	- 'Ice Cool'	see *T. repens* 'Green Ice'
§	- 'Susan Smith' (v)	CCCN
	repens	CRos LCro LOPS SPhx SVic WSFF
	- DARK DEBBIE ('Trifpot001' PBR) **new**	LEdu
	- 'Debbie'	LEdu
	- 'Dragon's Blood'	CMea EPPr GWyn LEdu LLWG LPot MMuc MPie NRHS SPer WPGP
	- 'Estelle' PBR **new**	LEdu
	- 'Gold Net'	see *T. pratense* 'Susan Smith'
§	- 'Green Ice'	NSti WFar
	- 'Harlequin' (v)	WCot WMoo WOut
	- 'Isabella' PBR	LEdu WPGP
	- 'Pentaphyllum'	see *T. repens* 'Quinquefolium'
	- 'Purpurascens'	CBre EPfP GQue LLWG LRHS MAsh MBNS MHer MPie NGrd NRHS SPoG WFar
§	- 'Purpurascens Quadrifolium'	CAby CMea ECha EHoe EPau EWes GAbr GWyn LEdu MCot NMir NPer NRHS SPer SPlb WFar WTor
§	- 'Quinquefolium'	XLum
	- 'Tetraphyllum Purpureum'	see *T. repens* 'Purpurascens Quadrifolium'
	- 'Wheatfen'	CNat LEdu NDov NPer
	- 'William'	CBre LEdu MMuc NDov WCot WFar WHil
	rubens	Widely available
	- 'Drama'	ELon LEdu MNrw
	- 'Frosty Feathers' **new**	CBod EAJP WOut
	- 'Peach Pink'	CSpe ELon EMor EPPr MMrt SHar SPhx WCot WHrl
	- 'Red Feathers'	CWld ELon EPPr EWes GBin GQue LSun MHol SHar SMad
	- white-flowered	CSpe
	'Spring'	LEdu
	trichocephalum	EPPr

Trigonella (*Papilionaceae*)

foenum-graecum SVic WSFF

Trillidium see *Trillium*

Trillium ✿ (*Melanthiaceae*)

albidum ♀H5 CRos CWCL EBee GEdr LAma LLHF LRHS MNrw NRHS SIgm
amabile GEdr
angustipetalum GEdr
apetalon GEdr
camschatcense CExl GEdr GKev
§ ***catesbyi*** CExl EBee EPot GEdr GKev ILea LAma LLHF MNrw NChi NWad
catesbyi* × *sulcatum GKev
cernuum GMaP LAma
chloropetalum CBro CElw CRos GAbr GEdr LPla LRHS NRHS NWad SIgm
§ - var. ***giganteum*** ♀H5 CExl GBin GKev LEdu NHar NHpl NSla SPhx WCru
- var. ***rubrum*** see *T. chloropetalum* var. *giganteum*
- white-flowered GKev
cuneatum CBcs CBct CExl CRos CWCL EHrv EPot GEdr GKev GWyn LAma LEdu LRHS MCot MNrw NBir NChi NHol NHpl NRHS NWad SDeJ WFar WPnP
decipiens GEdr
decumbens GEdr
discolor GEdr
erectum ♀H5 Widely available
- f. ***albiflorum*** CMea CRos ECha GKev LRHS MNrw NRHS NWad
- 'Beige' GKev
- red-flowered GKev NAln
erectum* × *flexipes EBee EHrv GKev MNrw NBir
flexipes CBct CRos CWCL EHrv GEdr GKev LAma LRHS MNrw NAln NHol NHpl NRHS NWad
- 'Harvington Dusky Pink' CRos LRHS NRHS
- 'Harvington Select' CRos EBee LRHS NRHS
foetidissimum GEdr
govanianum GEdr GKev LAma
gracile GEdr
grandiflorum ♀H5 Widely available
- Gothenburg pink GEdr
- 'Jenny Rhodes' LEdu
- pale pink-flowered CRos LRHS NRHS
- f. ***polymerum*** 'Flore Pleno' (d) CRos GEdr LLHF LRHS NHar NHpl NRHS
- - 'Snowbunting' (d) CRos EWes GKev LAma LEdu LRHS NRHS WThu
- f. ***roseum*** CRos CWCL GEdr GKev LRHS MNrw NRHS
- white-flowered MAvo
kurabayashii CExl CRos EBee EHrv EPot EWld GEdr GKev LRHS MNrw NRHS SIgm
lancifolium GEdr GKev
ludovicianum GEdr
luteum ♀H5 CBcs CExl CRos CWCL EBee EHrv EPfP EPot GEdr GKev ILea LAma LCro LEdu LOPS LRHS MAvo MCot MNrw MSCN NAln NBid NChi NHol NHpl NRHS NWad SDeJ WHlf WPnP
maculatum GEdr
nivale CBct GEdr WThu
ovatum 'Roy Elliott' CExl
parviflorum GEdr MNrw
pusillum CExl GEdr GKev ILea LAma LLHF MNrw NHol NHpl
recurvatum CBcs CWCL EBee EHrv EPot EUJe GEdr GKev ILea LAma LEdu NChi NHol NHpl NWad WPnP
reliquum GEdr
rivale ♀H4 CExl GEdr GKev SCob WSHC
- Purple Heart Group GEdr
rugelii EBee EHrv EWes GEdr MNrw WSHC
- Askival hybrids MNrw
rugelii* × *vaseyi EHrv EWes MNrw
sessile CExl CPla CWCL EPot GEdr GKev GWyn LAma MAvo MCot MNrw NBir NChi NWad SDeJ WKif WPnP WShi XEll
- 'Rubrum' see *T. chloropetalum* var. *giganteum*
simile CRos EBee GEdr GKev LLHF LRHS MNrw NHpl NRHS
smallii GEdr GKev
stamineum GEdr LAma
stylosum see *T. catesbyi*
sulcatum CExl CRos CWCL EBee EHrv GAbr GEdr GKev GMaP LAma LEdu LRHS MNrw NHpl NRHS
- yellow-flowered GKev
taiwanense B&SWJ 3411 WCru
tschonoskii GEdr
underwoodii GEdr
undulatum MNrw
vaseyi CRos CWCL EBee EHrv EWes GEdr GKev LAma LRHS MNrw NRHS
viridescens GEdr LAma XEll

Triosteum (*Caprifoliaceae*)

erythrocarpum EMor EWTr SMad
himalayanum GCal GEdr GKev IMou NAln WPnP WSHC
- BWJ 7907 WCru
pinnatifidum EBee EWld GCal GKev IMou

Tripleurospermum (*Asteraceae*)

§ ***maritimum*** WHer

Tripogandra (*Commelinaceae*)

serrulata 'Purple Scimitars' EShb

Tripolium (*Asteraceae*)

§ ***pannonicum*** CEls WHer

Tripsacum (*Poaceae*)

dactyloides EPPr

Tripterospermum (*Gentianaceae*)

japonicum GEdr

Tripterygium (*Celastraceae*)

doianum B&SWJ 11467 WCru
aff. ***doianum*** CWJ 12852 WCru
regelii CBcs
- B&SWJ 5453 WCru
- B&SWJ 8666 from Korea WCru
- B&SWJ 10921 WCru
wilfordii EBee LEdu
- BWJ 7852 from China WCru
- NJM 11.029 from China WPGP
- NMWJ 14466 from Taiwan **new** WCru
- WWJ 12009 WCru

Tristagma (*Alliaceae*)

	nivale	EBee

Triteleia (*Asparagaceae*)

	'4U'	EBee
	'Aquarius'	ERCP GKev
	californica	see *Brodiaea californica*
§	'Corrina'	CAvo EBee EPot ERCP GKev
	'Crystal Pink'	SDeJ
	'Double Touch' (d)	EBee GKev SDeJ WCot
	'Foxy'	EBee EPot MNrw
	grandiflora	WCot
	hendersonii	GKev
	hyacinthina	EBee GEdr GKev WCot
	- NNS 06-560	WCot
	ixioides 'Starlight'	CTri EPot ERCP GKev SDeJ
§	***laxa***	ECha
	- 'Allure'	EBee
§	- 'Koningin Fabiola'	CCBP EBee EShb GKev LAma MNrw NBir SCob SDeJ WCot
	- QUEEN FABIOLA	see *T. laxa* 'Koningin Fabiola'
	'Ocean Queen'	EBee ERCP
§	***peduncularis***	GKev WCot
	'Rudy'	CAvo CBro CMea CWCL EBee ERCP GKev MNrw SCob SDeJ WCot
	'Silver Queen'	CAvo EBee EPot ERCP GKev SDeJ WCot XEll
	'Twilight'	GKev
	uniflora	see *Ipheion uniflorum*
	'White Cloud'	GKev
	'White Sweep'	EBee

Trithrinax (*Arecaceae*)

	campestris	CBrP EUJe LRHS

Tritoma see *Kniphofia*

Tritonia (*Iridaceae*)

	crocata ♀H3	GKev
	- 'Baby Doll'	LEdu
	disticha	SMad
§	- subsp. ***rubrolucens***	Widely available
	laxifolia	CTca EPot GKev
	lineata	EBee LEdu
	- 'Parvifolia'	GKev
	pallida	SPlb
	rosea	see *T. disticha* subsp. *rubrolucens*
	securigera	LEdu
	- subsp. ***watermeyeri*** new	GKev

Trochocarpa (*Ericaceae*)

	clarkei	WThu
	gunnii	WThu
	thymifolia	WThu
	- white-flowered	WThu

Trochodendron (*Trochodendraceae*)

	aralioides	CAby CBcs CSam CTho CTsd ELan EPfP GBin GKin LRHS MBlu MGos MMuc SAko SLon SPer SSta WCot WPGP
	- B&SWJ 1651 from Taiwan	WCru
	- B&SWJ 6080 from Japan	WCru
	- CWJ 12357 from Taiwan	WCru
	- RWJ 9845 from Taiwan	WCru

Trollius (*Ranunculaceae*)

	ACE 1187	CExl
	acaulis	EWes GAbr
	altaicus	CRos EBee LRHS NRHS
	asiaticus	GKev
	buddae	CWCL EWes MRav WFar
§	***chinensis***	ECha GCal GKev GWyn NAln
	- 'Golden Queen' ♀H7	Widely available
	- 'Imperial Orange'	GWyn
	- orange-flowered	GKev NAln
	- wild-collected	GBin
	× ***cultorum***	CAby
	- 'Alabaster'	Widely available
	- 'Baudirektor Linne'	MRav NGdn
	- 'Byrne's Giant'	ECtt GBin IKil
	- 'Canary Bird'	GCal NGdn SRms WSpi
	- 'Cheddar'	see *T.* × *cultorum* 'Taleggio'
	- 'Earliest of All'	CRos CSam CWCL NGdn NLar WSHC WSpi
	- 'Etna'	CRos
§	- 'Feuertroll'	ECha ECtt MRav NEoE NGdn WSpi
	- FIREGLOBE	see *T.* × *cultorum* 'Feuertroll'
	- 'Golden Cup'	GWyn NBir NGdn
	- 'Goldquelle' ♀H7	EBee GBin GWyn
	- 'Goliath'	GWyn NLar
	- 'Helios'	CSam GBin
	- 'Lemon Queen'	CBod CRos CWCL CWat ECtt EHrv EPfP EWTr GKev GMaP GWyn LRHS MRav NLar NQui NRHS SCob SGol SPer SRms WWtn
	- 'New Moon'	CAby CBcs CDor CRos EBee EMor EPfP EShb GBin GWyn IKil LRHS MBel NChi NQui NRHS SPoG WGwG WHoo WWtn
	- 'Orange Crest'	EBee ECtt ELon EPfP GCal WWtn
	- 'Orange Globe'	GMaP
	- 'Orange Princess' ♀H7	CDor CRos CWat GWyn LCro LOPS LRHS NBro NLar NRHS SPer SRms
	- 'Orange Queen'	SWvt
	- 'Prichard's Giant'	ECtt ELan ELon NBro WCFE WSpi
§	- 'Superbus' ♀H7	CBod CRos CWCL ELan ELon EPfP GBin GMaP GWyn LRHS MHol NGdn NRHS SPer WFar WPnP WWtn
	- 'T. Smith'	ECtt NBro
§	- 'Taleggio'	CRos CWCL EAJP EMor EPfP GMaP ILea LEdu LRHS MBNS MBel MRav MTis NBro NEoE NLar NPri NRHS SPoG SRms SWvt WFar WPnP WSpi
	- 'Yellow Beauty'	GBin
	'Dancing Flame'	CMac CRos EMor LCro LOPS LRHS NEoE NRHS SHar SPoG SRms
	europaeus	CAby CBod CRos CWCL ECha ELan EPfP GBin GCal GWyn LEdu LLWG LRHS MHol MRav NAln NGdn NRHS NSti SRms SRot WCFE
	- SDR 6306	GKev
	- subsp. ***europaeus***	WFar
	- 'Lemon Supreme'	CRos EBee EMor GKev LRHS NAln NRHS WWtn
	- 'Superbus'	see *T.* × *cultorum* 'Superbus'
	farreri var. ***farreri*** new	GKev
	- var. ***major***	NAln
	- - SDR 2713	GKev
	hondoensis	LLHF NEoE
	ircuticus	EWes GKev NAln
	laxus	CPla
	- 'Albiflorus'	CExl EBee
	ledebourii misapplied	see *T. chinensis*
	macropetalus	EBee GKev NAln
	pumilus	CRos ECha ELan LLHF LRHS NLar NRHS SPer

	– ACE 1818	CExl MHer
	– 'Double Jeopardy' (d)	EBee
	ranunculoides	GEdr GKev
	vaginatus	EBee GEdr GKev
	yunnanensis ♀H6	CRos EBee GBin LRHS NAln NRHS
	– orange-flowered	CExl GKev

Tropaeolum (*Tropaeolaceae*)

	azureum	CCCN CExl CPla
	brachyceras	CCCN GKev
	ciliatum	CCCN CPla EWld NBid WCot WCru WPGP
	hookerianum	CExl
	– subsp. ***austropurpureum***	CExl
	incisum	CCCN
	lepidum	CPla
	leptophyllum new	GKev
	majus	ENfk GPoy SVic
	– Alaska Series (v) ♀H3	ENfk LCro LOPS MNHC
	– 'Black Velvet' (Tom Thumb Series)	LCro LOPS
§	– 'Darjeeling Double' (d) ♀H3	GCal
	– 'Darjeeling Gold'	see *T. majus* 'Darjeeling Double'
	– 'Empress of India'	CLau MNHC
	– 'Hermine Grashoff' (d)	CSpe GBee GCal MPie
	– Jewel Series	ENfk
	– 'Margaret Long' (d)	CSpe GBee GCal MPie
	– 'Red Wonder'	CCCN
	– Tom Thumb Series	MNHC
	pentaphyllum	CExl CRHN CSpe EBee GCal
	polyphyllum ♀H3	CCCN CWCL EBee EPot NBir SMHy WCot
	sessilifolium	EBee
	smithii	GCal WPGP
	speciosum ♀H5	Widely available
	sylvestre	EWld
	tricolor ♀H2	CAvo CCCN CRHN CWCL GCal GKev SBrt WCot XEll
	tuberosum	CAgr CEnd GKev GPoy SDeJ SPoG
	– var. ***lineamaculatum*** 'Ken Aslet' ♀H3	CAbb CAvo CBcs CCCN CKel CRos CSpe ECha ELan EPfP EPot GBin GKev IFro LAma LEdu LRHS NLar NRHS SPer WFar

Tsuga ✿ (*Pinaceae*)

	canadensis	CAco CDul EPfP LMaj LPra MMuc NWea
	– 'Abbott's Dwarf'	CKen NHol
§	– 'Abbott's Pygmy'	CKen
	– 'Bacon Cristate'	CKen
	– 'Beehive'	NLar
	– 'Betty Rose' (v)	CKen
	– 'Birkett's White'	CKen
	– 'Brandley'	CKen
§	– 'Branklyn'	CKen WCFE
	– 'Cappy's Choice'	CKen
	– 'Cinnamonea'	CKen
	– 'Coffin'	CKen
	– 'Cole's Prostrate' ♀H7	CAco CKen LRHS MAsh SLim
	– 'Creamey' (v)	CKen
	– 'Curley'	CKen
	– 'Curtis Ideal'	CKen
	– 'Dr Hornbeck'	see *T. canadensis* 'Hornbeck'
	– 'Eisburg'	SLim
	– 'Essex'	CKen
*	– 'Everitt's Dense Leaf'	CKen
	– 'Everitt's Golden'	CKen NLar
	– 'Fantana'	NHol
	– 'Greenwood Lake'	WThu
I	– 'Hebefolia' new	NLar
	– 'Hedgehog'	NLar
§	– 'Hornbeck'	CKen
	– 'Horsford'	CKen
	– 'Horstmann' No 1	CKen
	– 'Hussii'	CKen NHol
	– 'Jacqueline Verkade'	CKen NLar
	– 'Jeddeloh' ♀H7	GEdr LRHS MAsh NEgg NHol NLar SCob SGol SLim
	– 'Jervis'	CKen NHol NWad
	– 'Julianne'	CKen
	– 'Kingsville Spreader'	CKen
	– 'Little Joe'	CKen
	– 'Livingston'	SLim
I	– 'Lutea'	CKen
	– 'Many Cones'	CKen
	– 'Minima'	CKen
	– 'Minuta' ♀H7	CKen NHol
	– 'Palomino'	CKen
	– 'Pendula' ♀H7	CKen LRHS
	– 'Pincushion'	CKen NLar
	– 'Prostrata'	see *T. canadensis* 'Branklyn'
	– 'Pygmaea'	see *T. canadensis* 'Abbott's Pygmy'
	– 'Rugg's Washington Dwarf'	CKen
	– 'Snowflake'	CKen
	– 'Stewart's Gem'	CKen
	– 'Verkade Petite'	CKen
	– 'Verkade Recurved'	CKen
	– 'Von Helms' Dwarf'	CKen
	– 'Warnham'	CKen
	caroliniana 'La Bar Weeping'	CKen NLar
	– 'Planting Fields Broom'	CKen
	chinensis	CKen
	diversifolia 'Gotelli'	CKen
	dumosa	CKen
	heterophylla ♀H6	CAco CBcs CCVT CDul CPer EPfP MMuc NWea SCob SEWo SGol WFar WTSh
	– 'Iron Springs'	CKen NLar
	– 'Laursen's Column'	CKen
	– 'Ray Godfrey'	NLar
	– 'Thorsens Weeping'	CKen NLar SLim
	menziesii	see *Pseudotsuga menziesii*
	mertensiana	CAco
	– 'Blue Star'	CKen MAsh NLar
	– 'Elizabeth'	CKen
	– 'Glauca'	CKen
I	– 'Glauca Nana'	CKen
I	– 'Horstmann'	CKen
	– 'Quartz Mountain'	CKen
	sieboldii 'Baldwin'	CKen
	– 'Green Ball'	CKen NLar
	– 'Honeywell Estate'	CKen
	– 'Nana'	CKen

Tuberaria (*Cistaceae*)

	lignosa	SIgm

Tulbaghia ✿ (*Alliaceae*)

	acutiloba	CTca LEdu NHoy
	alliacea	CAvo LEdu NHoy WCot
*	***allioides***	CBro
	capensis	LEdu NBir WAvo
	capensis* × *violacea	NHoy
	'Cariad'	LEdu WPGP
	cernua CD&R 199	EBee LEdu
	cominsii	CExl CPla LEdu SBch
	capensis* × *violacea	CAvo CExl WHoo
	'Cornish Beauty'	CTca

'Cosmic'	EBee EMor EPPr LEdu NHoy WPGP
'Dark Beauty' new	NHoy
'Elaine Ann' new	NHoy
'Fairy Snow'	LEdu WCot
'Fairy Star'	CKno CTca CWGN EBee ELan EMor EShb LEdu NHoy SMHy WCot
fragrans	see *T. simmleri*
- 'Alba'	ELan EPot SDeJ
'Hazel'	EBee LEdu MHer NHoy SMHy
'John May's Special'	EShb LEdu NHoy WCot WHoo WPGP
leucantha ♀H2	CTca LEdu NHoy NWad
- H&B 11996	LEdu
ludwigiana	MHer
maritima	see *T. violacea* var. *maritima*
Marwood seedling	LEdu MHer
montana	CBor EBee LEdu MHer MPie NHoy
'Moshoeshoe'	LEdu NHoy WPGP
natalensis ♀H2	CBro CPrp GKev
- clone 2 pink-flowered B&V 421	LEdu
- pink-flowered	LPla
'Purple Eye' ♀H2	CBro CCht CKno EBee ELan EMor LEdu NHoy NPri SPoG WCot
'Scented Beauty' new	NHoy
§ ***simmleri*** ♀H3	CPrp EBee EPot EWes GKev LAma LEdu SDeJ WPnP
- 'Cheryl Renshaw'	WCot
- 'Snow Queen'	CPrp
- white-flowered	CPrp GKev
'Snow White'	SMHy WCot
verdoorniae	LEdu
violacea ♀H3	CAvo CBcs CBro CKno CMea CPrp CRos CSpe CTca ECha EHrv EPfP EPot ERCP GKev LAma LEdu MSCN NHoy SEND SPlb SSut WHoo WPGP WPnP XSen
* - 'Alba'	CKno EBee EShb MHer NHoy SChF WKif WPnP XSen
- 'Dissect White'	NHoy
I - 'Fine Form'	CKno
- 'Harry Hay'	SMHy
- 'John Rider'	NHoy
* - var. ***maritima***	EShb LEdu MHer NHoy
- 'Pallida'	CAvo CBro CTca EBee LEdu NHoy WPGP
- 'Peppermint Garlic'	LEdu
- var. ***robustior***	CAby ECha EWes NHoy
- 'Seren'	LEdu
§ - 'Silver Lace' (v) ♀H3	Widely available
- 'Variegata'	see *T. violacea* 'Silver Lace'
white-flowered	NHoy

Tulipa ✿ (*Liliaceae*)

(4)	CArg
'Abba' (2)	CArg LAma SCob SDeJ
'Absalon' (9)	GKev LAma
'Abu Hassan' (3)	CAvo ERCP LAma SDeJ
acuminata (15)	CTca ERCP GKev LAma SCob SDeJ
'Ad Rem' (4) ♀H6	SDeJ
'Addis' (14)	LAma
aitchisonii	see *T. clusiana*
'Akebono' (11)	LAma NAln SDeJ
'Alabaster' (5)	LAma
'Aladdin' (6)	CArg GKev LAma LCro LOPS SDeJ
'Aladdin's Record' (6)	LAma SDeJ
'Alba Regalis' (1)	LAma
'Albert Heijn' (13)	GKev SDeJ
albertii (15)	LAma
ALBION STAR ('Mieke Telkamp') (13)	CArg EPfP GKev SDeJ SPer
'Aleppo' (7)	SDeJ
'Alexander Pushkin'PBR (3)	LAma
'Alfred Cortot' (12) ♀H6	LAma SDeJ
'Alibi' (3)	EPfP GKev SDeJ
'Alice Leclercq' (2)	LAma
'Allegretto' (11)	LAma
altaica (15) ♀H6	LAma
amabilis	see *T. hoogiana*
'American Dream' (4)	LAma
'American Eagle' (7)	LAma SDeJ
'Ancilla' (12) ♀H6	GKev LAma SDeJ WShi
'André Rieu' (5)	LCro LOPS
'Angélique' (11) ♀H6	CAvo CTca EPfP ERCP GKev LAma LCro LOPS MJak NAln NBir SCob SDeJ SPer
'Angels Wish' (5) ♀H6	CAvo LAma SDeJ
'Annie Schilder' (3)	CAvo ERCP LAma
'Antarctica'PBR (3)	LAma NAln
'Anthony Eden' (2)	LAma
'Antoinette'PBR (5)	CAby GKev LAma LCro LOPS SDeJ
'Antraciet' (11)	ERCP LAma LCro LOPS
'Apeldoorn' (4)	CArg GKev LAma LCro LOPS SCob SDeJ
'Apeldoorn's Elite' (4) ♀H6	LAma SDeJ
'Apricot Beauty' (1) ♀H6	CAvo CTca ERCP GKev LAma LCro LOPS MCot NBir SDeJ
'Apricot Delight' (4)	GKev
'Apricot Emperor' (13)	GKev SDeJ
'Apricot Foxx' (3)	CArg EPfP GKev LAma SDeJ
'Apricot Impression'PBR (4)	LAma
'Apricot Jewel'	see *T. linifolia* (Batalinii Group) 'Apricot Jewel'
'Apricot Parrot' (10) ♀H6	ERCP GKev LAma MCot SDeJ
'Aquilla' (11)	LAma MJak SDeJ
'Arabian Beauty' (3) new	LCro LOPS SPer
'Arabian Mystery' (3)	GKev LAma NHol SDeJ
'Aria Card' (7)	LAma SDeJ
'Arma' (7) ♀H6	ERCP
armena (15)	GKev
'Artist' (8) ♀H6	ERCP GKev LAma SDeJ
'Atlantis' (5)	CArg ERCP LAma SDeJ
'Attila' (3)	GKev LAma
aucheriana (15) ♀H5	EPot LAma LLHF
australis (15)	GKev
'Aveyron' (11) new	NAln
'Avignon' (5)	SDeJ
aximensis (15)	EPot GKev LAma
'Bacchus' (7)	LAma
'Backpacker' (11)	GKev
bakeri	see *T. saxatilis* Bakeri Group
'Ballade' (6) ♀H6	CAvo ERCP GKev LAma LCro LOPS MCot SDeJ
BALLADE DREAM ('Sonnet') (6)	LAma SDeJ
'Ballade Gold' (6)	LAma
'Ballerina' (6) ♀H6	CArg CAvo CMea CTca EPfP ERCP LAma LCro LOPS MCot MJak SCob SDeJ SPer
'Banja Luka' (4)	LAma SDeJ
'Barbados' (7)	LAma SCob SDeJ
'Barcelona' (3) ♀H6	ERCP GKev LAma LCro LOPS NAln
'Baronesse' (5)	SDeJ
'Bastogne' (3)	LAma SCob
'Bastogne Parrot' (10)	LAma
batalinii	see *T. linifolia* Batalinii Group
'Beau Monde' (3) ♀H6	SDeJ
'Beauty of Apeldoorn' (4)	LAma
'Beauty of Bath' (9)	LAma

Name	Suppliers
'Beauty of Spring' (4)	GKev LAma
'Beauty Queen' (1)	LAma SDeJ
'Belcanto' (3)	LAma
'Belicia' (2)	GKev LAma NAln
'Bell Song' (7)	GKev
'Bellflower' (7)	LAma
'Bellona' (3)	LAma SDeJ
'Berlioz' (12)	LAma SDeJ
'Bessie' (5)	LAma
'Bestseller' (1)	SDeJ
§ ***biflora*** (15)	EPot ERCP GKev LAma SDeJ
- var. ***major*** (15)	GKev
bifloriformis (15)	GKev LAma
I - 'Maxima' (15)	SPhx
- 'Starlight' (15) ♀H6	GKev
'Big Chief' (4) ♀H6	LAma
'Black and White' (9)	LAma
'Black Hero' (11)	CAby CAvo ERCP GKev LAma LCro LOPS SDeJ
'Black Horse' (5)	LAma
'Black Jewel' (7)	ERCP GKev SDeJ
'Black Parrot' (10) ♀H6	CAby CArg CAvo EPfP ERCP GKev LAma LCro LOPS MJak SCob SDeJ SPer
'Black Swan' (5)	SDeJ
'Blackjack' (3)	GKev LAma
'Bleu Aimable' (5)	ERCP GKev LAma SDeJ
'Blue Beauty' (3)	LCro LOPS
'Blue Diamond' (11)	CArg CAvo ERCP LAma LCro SDeJ
'Blue Heron' (7) ♀H6	ERCP LAma LCro LOPS MCot NAln SDeJ
'Blue Parrot' (10)	CArg EPfP ERCP GKev LAma LCro LOPS NAln SCob SDeJ SPer
'Blue Ribbon' (3)	CAvo LCro LOPS
'Blue Spectacle' (11)	GKev
'Blue Wow' (11) **new**	LCro LOPS SPer
BLUEBERRY RIPPLE	see *T.* 'Zurel'
'Blumex Favourite'PBR (10)	LCro LOPS SCob
'Blushing Apeldoorn' (4)	LAma
'Blushing Beauty' (5)	LAma SDeJ
'Blushing Bride' (5)	SDeJ
'Blushing Girl' (5)	LAma SDeJ
'Blushing Lady' (5)	GKev LAma
'Boa Vista' (11) **new**	ERCP
'Border Legend' (13)	LAma
'Boston' (3)	LAma
'Boutade' (14)	NPer
'Bridesmaid' (5)	GKev LAma
'Bright Parrot' (10)	LAma
'Brilliant Star' (1)	LAma
'Brooklyn' (11)	NPer
'Brown Sugar' (3)	ERCP GKev LCro LOPS
'Bruine Wimpel' (5)	GKev LAma
'Buddy' (14)	SCob
'Bulldog' (7)	CAvo SDeJ
'Burgundy' (6)	CAvo CTca ERCP GKev LAma LCro LOPS SDeJ SPer
'Burgundy Lace' (7)	GKev LAma LCro LOPS SDeJ
'Burning Heart' (4) ♀H6	CArg LAma SDeJ
'Buttercup' (14)	SDeJ
'Café Noir' (5)	ERCP LAma LCro LOPS NHol
'Calgary' (3) ♀H6	CAvo GKev LAma LCro LOPS SCob SDeJ
'Calgary Flames' (3) ♀H6 **new**	CAvo
'Calibra' (7)	LAma
'Californian Sun' (14)	LAma
'Calypso' (14) ♀H6	CRos LAma LRHS NRHS
'Camargue' (5)	SDeJ
'Canasta' (7) ♀H6	LAma SDeJ
'Candela' (13) ♀H6	LAma SDeJ
'Candy Clouds' (2)	LAma
'Candy Club' (5)	LAma SDeJ
'Candy Prince'PBR (1)	CArg CRos LAma LRHS NRHS SDeJ
'Canova' (7)	SDeJ
'Cantata' (13)	LAma
'Cape Cod' (14)	CAvo LAma SDeJ
'Cape Town' (1) ♀H6	SDeJ
'Caractère' (3)	CArg
'Caravelle' (5)	SDeJ
'Cardinal Mindszenty' (2)	CRos ERCP LAma LRHS NRHS SDeJ
'Carlton' (2)	LAma
'Carnaval de Nice' (11/v) ♀H6	CAby CTca ERCP GKev LAma LCro LOPS SDeJ
'Carrousel' (7)	SDeJ
'Cartouche' (11)	LAma SDeJ
'Cassini' (3)	LAma SDeJ
'Catherina' (5)	LCro LOPS
'Celebration' (3) **new**	MJak
§ ***celsiana*** (15)	LAma
'Charles X' (9) **new**	GKev
'Charmeur'PBR (3)	SDeJ
'Charming Beauty' (11)	GKev
'Charming Lady' (11)	ERCP
'China Lady' (14)	SDeJ
'China Pink' (6) ♀H6	CAvo CTca ERCP GKev LAma LCro LOPS MCot SDeJ
'China Town' (8) ♀H6	CMea ERCP GKev LAma LCro LOPS SDeJ SPer
'Chopin' (12)	LAma NHol
'Christmas Dream' (1)	LAma SDeJ
'Christmas Marvel' (1)	SDeJ
'Christmas Sweet' (1)	CArg
chrysantha	see *T. montana*
'Cilesta' (2)	GKev LAma
'Cistula' (6)	SDeJ
'City Flower' (14)	LAma
'City of Vancouver' (5)	LAma SDeJ
'Claudia' (6)	CAby CArg LAma SDeJ
'Clearwater'PBR (5)	LAma SDeJ
§ ***clusiana*** (15)	EPfP ERCP GKev LAma SPer
- var. ***chrysantha*** (15) ♀H6	CExl GKev LAma LRHS NRHS WShi
- - 'Tubergen's Gem' (15)	EPot GKev LAma
- 'Cynthia' (15) ♀H6	CAby CTca EPot GKev LAma SDeJ WShi
- 'Sheila' (15)	GKev LAma
§ - var. ***stellata*** (15) ♀H6	GKev LAma
'Colour Spectacle'PBR (5)	CAby LAma
'Columbine' (5)	GKev LAma
'Comedian' (14)	LAma
'Concerto' (13)	LAma NPer SDeJ
'Continental' (3)	GKev LAma
'Cool Crystal' (7)	GKev LAma
'Copper Image' (11) **new**	GKev
'Coquette' (1)	SDeJ
'Corona' (12)	CAvo SDeJ
'Corsage' (14) ♀H6	GKev SDeJ
'Cortina' (9)	SDeJ
'Cottage Boy' (1)	LAma
'Couleur Cardinal' (3)	CAvo CRos ERCP GKev LAma LCro LOPS LRHS NRHS SDeJ
'Cream Cocktail' (4) **new**	MJak SPer
'Cream Perfection' (3)	LAma
'Creme Upstar' (11)	ERCP GKev LAma LCro LOPS SDeJ
cretica (15)	LAma LLHF
- 'Archanes' (15)	GKev IPot
- 'Chania' (15)	GKev
'Crystal Beauty' (7) ♀H6	LAma
'Crystal Star' (7)	CArg
'Cuban Night' (7)	LAma

Cultivar	Suppliers
'Cum Laude' (5)	LAma SDeJ
'Cummins' (7)	CAvo ERCP LAma LCro LOPS
'Curly Sue' (7)	ERCP LAma LCro LOPS SPer
'Czaar Peter' (14) ♀H6	NPer SDeJ
'Dallas' (7)	LAma
'Dance' (13)	SDeJ
'Danceline' (11)	GKev
'Dancing Show' (8)	LAma
dasystemon (15)	GKev LAma LLHF
'Davenport' (7)	CAby ERCP
'David Teniers' (2)	ERCP LAma SDeJ
'Daydream' (4) ♀H6	CArg GKev LAma NAln SCob SDeJ SPer
'Daytona' (7)	CAvo LAma
'Deep River' (5)	LAma
'Deshima' (3)	LAma
'Design Impression' (4)	LAma
'Diana' (1)	CArg
'Dior' (2)	LCro LOPS
'Doll's Minuet' (8)	EPfP ERCP LAma LCro LOPS SPer
'Dom Pedro' (5)	LAma
'Don Quichotte' (3) ♀H6	ERCP LAma LCro LOPS SDeJ
'Donauperle' (14)	SDeJ
'Donna Bella' (14)	SDeJ
'Dordogne' (5) ♀H6	LAma SDeJ
'Double Dazzle' (2)	LAma
'Double Flag' (11) **new**	GKev
'Double Flaming Parrot'PBR (10)	LAma
'Double Princess'PBR (2)	LAma
'Double Red Riding Hood' (14/v)	CAby GKev LAma MCot SCob SDeJ
'Double Sugar' (11)	LAma
'Dragon King' (3)	SDeJ
'Dream Touch' (11)	GKev LAma LCro LOPS
'Dreamboat' (14)	LAma
'Dreaming Maid' (3)	LAma
'Dreamland' (5) ♀H6	LAma SDeJ
dubia	GKev
'Duc van Tol Aurora' (1)	LAma
'Duc van Tol Max Cramoisie' (1)	LAma
'Duc van Tol Primrose' (1)	LAma
'Duc van Tol Red and Yellow' (1)	GKev LAma
'Duc van Tol Rose' (1)	LAma
'Duc van Tol Salmon' (1)	LAma
'Duc van Tol Scarlet' (1)	LAma
'Duc van Tol Violet' (1)	GKev LAma
'Duc van Tol White' (1)	LAma
'Early Glory' (3)	LCro LOPS
'Early Harvest' (12) ♀H6	CAvo GKev LAma SDeJ
'Easter Surprise' (14) ♀H6	GKev LAma SDeJ
'Ego Parrot' (10)	LCro LOPS
eichleri	see *T. undulatifolia*
'El Niño' (5)	NAln
'Electra' (5)	LAma NHol
'Elegans Alba' (6)	LAma
'Elegant Lady' (6)	CAvo GKev LAma MCot SDeJ
'Erna Lindgreen' (10)	LAma
'Escape'PBR (3)	LAma
'Esperanto' (8/v) ♀H6	LAma NPer SDeJ
'Esprit' (7)	LAma
'Estella Rijnveld' (10)	ERCP GKev LAma LCro LOPS MJak SDeJ
'Esther' (5)	LAma
'Eternal Flame' (2)	GKev LAma LCro LOPS WCot
'Evergreen' (3)	GKev
'Exotic Emperor' (13)	CAvo GKev LAma LCro LOPS SDeJ SPer

Cultivar	Suppliers
'Eye Catcher' (8)	LAma NAln
'Fabio' (7)	CRos LRHS NRHS
'Fairy Nymph' (5)	LAma
'Fancy Frills' (7) ♀H6	ERCP GKev LAma SDeJ
'Fancy Parrot' (10)	SDeJ
'Fantasy' (10) ♀H6	LAma
'Fashion' (12)	LAma SDeJ
ferganica (15)	GKev LAma WCot
'Fidelio' (3) ♀H6	SDeJ
* 'Finola' (11)	GKev MCot
'Fire of Love' (14)	LAma
'Fire Queen' (3) ♀H6	LAma
'First Impression' (14)	LAma
'Flair' (1)	CRos LAma LRHS NRHS SDeJ
'Flamenco' (7)	SDeJ
'Flaming Club' (5)	LAma
'Flaming Evita'PBR (2)	SDeJ
'Flaming Flag' (3)	LCro LOPS
'Flaming Jewel' (4)	LAma
'Flaming Parrot' (10)	CAby ERCP GKev LAma LCro LOPS SDeJ
I 'Flaming Purissima' (13)	CAvo GKev LAma SDeJ
'Flaming Springgreen' (8)	CAvo ERCP GKev LAma LCro LOPS SDeJ
'Flashback' (10)	ERCP LAma
'Florette'PBR (5)	LAma
'Florijn Chic' (6)	LAma
'Florosa' (8)	ERCP LCro LOPS SDeJ
'Fontainebleau' (3)	GKev SDeJ
'Formosa' (8)	LAma
'Foxtrot'PBR (2) ♀H6	ERCP GKev LAma SDeJ
'Foxy Foxtrot' (2) **new**	SDeJ
'Françoise' (3)	SDeJ
'Franz Léhar' (12)	SDeJ
'Fringed Elegance' (7) ♀H6	LAma LCro LOPS
'Fringed Family' (7)	SDeJ
'Fringed Golden Apeldoorn' (7)	LAma
'Fritz Kreisler' (12)	LAma SDeJ
'Fulton' (5)	LAma
'Für Elise' (14)	GKev SDeJ
'Gabriella' (3)	LAma
'Gaiety' (12)	SDeJ
'Gander's Rhapsody' (3)	LAma
'Garden Party' (3)	SDeJ
'Garden Show' (14)	LAma
'Gavota' (3) ♀H6	CAvo GKev LAma NHol SCob SDeJ
'Generaal de Wet' (1)	LAma LCro LOPS SDeJ
'George Hayward' (9) **new**	GKev
'Georges Grappe' (5)	LAma
'Georgette' (5)	LAma
'Gerbrand Kieft' (11) ♀H6	ERCP GKev
'Gipsy Love' (7)	SDeJ
'Girlfriend' (15)	GKev
'Giuseppe Verdi' (12)	CRos LAma LRHS NRHS
'Glodal Desire' (2) **new**	GKev
'Glück' (12) ♀H6	LAma
'Golden Apeldoorn' (4)	CArg GKev LAma LCro LOPS SCob SDeJ
'Golden Artist' (8)	GKev LAma LCro LOPS SDeJ
'Golden Emperor' (13)	GKev LAma SDeJ
'Golden Melody' (3)	SDeJ
'Golden Nizza' (11)	LAma
'Golden Oxford' (4)	LAma
'Golden Parade' (4)	LAma
'Goldwest' (14)	SDeJ
'Gordon Cooper' (4)	LAma SDeJ
'Gorilla' (7)	LAma
'Goudstuk' (12)	LAma
'Goya' (2)	LAma

	'Grand Perfection'PBR (3) ♀H6	CAvo GKev LCro LOPS SDeJ
	'Grand Style' (5) ♀H6	LAma
	'Granny Award' (11)	LAma
	'Green Eyes' (8)	SDeJ
	'Green River' (8)	LAma SDeJ
	'Green Unique' (11)	LAma
	'Green Wave' (10)	ERCP LAma LCro LOPS SDeJ
	'Greenstar' (6)	LAma
	greigii (14)	GKev LAma
	grengiolensis (15)	GKev
	'Greuze' (5)	LCro LOPS
	'Groenland' (8)	CAvo GKev LAma LCro LOPS SDeJ
	'Gudoshnik' (4)	LAma
	'Gwen'PBR (3) **new**	GKev
	hageri (15)	GKev LAma LLHF
	- 'Splendens' (15)	EPfP GKev LAma SDeJ SPhx
	'Hakuun' (4)	LAma
	'Halcro' (5) ♀H6	LAma
	'Hamilton' (7)	LAma SDeJ
	'Happy Family' (3)	LAma
	'Happy Generation' (3)	GKev LAma LCro LOPS
	'Happy Hour' (7)	ERCP
	'Havran' (3)	CAvo ERCP GKev LAma LCro LOPS
	'Heart's Delight' (12)	CArg GKev LAma SDeJ
	'Helmar' (3) ♀H6	LAma SDeJ
	'Hemisphere' (3)	CArg CAvo GKev LAma SDeJ
	'Hermitage' (3)	ERCP LAma
	heweri (15)	EPot GKev LAma
	'Hocus Pocus' (5)	LAma SDeJ
	'Holland Baby' (2)	LAma SDeJ
	'Holland Beauty'PBR (3)	MCot
	'Holland Bouquet' (3)	LAma
	'Holland Chic' (6)	CAby LAma NAln SDeJ
	'Holland Happening' (10)	LAma
	'Holland Queen'PBR (3)	LAma SDeJ
	'Hollands Glorie' (4)	LAma SDeJ
	'Hollywood' (8)	LAma
	'Hollywood Star' (8)	LAma
	'Honeymoon' (7)	CAby LAma
	'Honky Tonk' (15) ♀H6	CAvo GKev LAma LCro LOPS
§	***hoogiana*** (15)	GKev
	'Hotpants' (3)	LAma MCot SCob
	'Huis Ten Bosch' (7)	LAma
§	***humilis*** (15)	CRos GKev LAma LRHS NRHS SDeJ WShi
	- 'China Carol' (15)	GKev LAma SDeJ
	- 'Eastern Spice' (15)	LAma
	- 'Eastern Star' (15)	GKev LAma
§	- 'Lilliput' (15)	CAby CRos EPot GKev LAma LRHS NRHS
	- 'Magenta Queen' (15)	LAma
	- 'Odalisque' (15)	CRos EPot GKev LAma LRHS NRHS
	- 'Persian Pearl' (15)	CAby CAvo EPfP EPot ERCP GKev LAma LCro LOPS SCob SDeJ WTor
*	- 'Pink Charm' (15)	GKev
	- var. ***pulchella*** Albocaerulea Oculata Group (15)	EPot ERCP GKev
	- 'Rosea' (15)	GKev
	- 'Tête-à-tête' (15)	LAma
§	- Violacea Group (15)	CRos LRHS NRHS
	- - black base (15)	EPot ERCP GKev LAma
	- - yellow base (15)	EPot GKev LAma
	'Humming Bird' (8)	LAma
	'Ice Cream' (11)	GKev LAma LCro LOPS SDeJ
	'Ice Stick' (12)	GKev SDeJ
	'Ile de France' (5)	ERCP LAma LCro LOPS SDeJ
	iliensis (15)	EPot GKev LAma LLHF
	'India' (3)	LAma
	'Indian Velvet' (5)	LCro LOPS
	'Infinity' (3) **new**	LAma
	ingens (15)	GKev LAma
	'Innuendo' (3)	CRos LRHS MJak NRHS SPer
	'Insulinde' (9)	GKev LAma
	'Inzell' (3)	GKev LAma
	'Irene Parrot' (10) **new**	SDeJ
	'Ivory Floradale' (4) ♀H6	GKev LAma SDeJ
	'Jackpot' (3)	LAma SCob
	'Jacqueline' (6)	LAma LCro LOPS
	'Jan Reus' (3)	CAvo ERCP LAma LCro LOPS
	'Jazz' (6)	ERCP
	'Jewel of Spring' (4)	LAma
	'Jimmy' (3)	LAma
	'Johann Strauss' (12)	CArg LAma MJak
	'Juan' (13) ♀H6	CAvo LAma
	'Judith Leyster' (3)	LAma
	'Julia Farnese' (9) **new**	GKev
	'Juliette' (4)	LAma
	'Jumbo Beauty' (5) **new**	GKev SDeJ
	'Karel Doorman' (10)	LAma
	'Kathleen Truxton' (5)	LAma
	kaufmanniana (12)	EPot
	'Keizerskroon' (1)	LAma SDeJ
	'Kikomachi' (3)	CRos LRHS NRHS
	'Kingsblood' (5) ♀H6	ERCP LAma SDeJ
	kolpakowskiana (15) ♀H6	EPot ERCP GKev LAma LLHF WShi
	kurdica (15)	LAma
	'La Belle Époque' (2)	CAvo ERCP GKev LAma LCro LOPS SCob SDeJ
	'La Courtine' (5)	LAma
	'La Douceur' (5)	LAma
	'Lac van Rijn' (1)	GKev IPot LAma
*	'Lady Diana' (14)	GKev IPot
	'Lady Jane' (15) ♀H6	GKev IPot LAma SPhx WShi
	'Lalibela' (4)	GKev LOPS
	'Lambada' (7) ♀H6	SDeJ
	lanata (15)	GKev WCot
	'Lasting Love' (3)	CAby LAma
	'Latvian Gold' (15)	GKev
	'Le Mogol' (5)	LAma
	'Leen van der Mark' (3)	LAma
	'Lemon Giant' (14) **new**	GKev
	'Libretto Parrot' (10)	LAma SDeJ
	'Light and Dreamy' (4)	ERCP GKev LCro LOPS SDeJ
	'Lighting Sun' (4)	LAma
	'Lilac Crystal' (7)	LCro LOPS
	'Lilac Perfection' (11)	CTca ERCP GKev LAma SDeJ
	'Lilac Time' (6)	LAma
	'Lilac Wonder'	see *T. saxatilis* (Bakeri Group) 'Lilac Wonder'
	'Lilliput'	see *T. humilis* 'Lilliput'
	'Lilybeauty' (6)	LAma
	'Lilyfire' (6)	LAma SDeJ
	'Limelight' (3)	LAma
	'Lingerie' (7)	LAma SDeJ
	linifolia (15) ♀H5	CAvo EPot ERCP GKev LAma SDeJ WShi
§	- Batalinii Group (15) ♀H5	GKev
§	- - 'Apricot Jewel' (15)	ERCP GKev IPot LAma
	- - 'Bright Gem' (15) ♀H5	EPot GKev IPot LAma NPer SPhx WCot WHoo
	- - 'Bronze Charm' (15)	CAvo EPot GKev LAma SDeJ WTor
	- - 'Red Gem' (15)	GKev WCot
	- - 'Red Hunter' (15) ♀H5	ERCP GKev LAma SDeJ
	- - 'Red Jewel' (15)	LAma
	- - 'Salmon Jewel' (15)	GKev
	- - 'Yellow Jewel' (15)	GKev LAma WShi
§	- Maximowiczii Group (15)	GKev LAma

	'Lion King' (7)	SDeJ
	'Lipgloss' (3)	LAma NHol
	'Little Beauty' (15) ♀H6	CAby CAvo CRos EPfP EPot GKev LAma LCro LOPS LRHS NRHS SDeJ SPhx WCot WHoo
	'Little Princess' (15) ♀H6	CAvo CRos EPot GKev LAma LRHS NRHS SDeJ SPhx
	'Little Star' (15) ♀H6	GKev LAma
	'Long Lady' (5)	SDeJ
	'Louvre' (7) ♀H6	LAma
	'Love Song' (12)	LAma SDeJ
	'Lovely Surprise' (14)	SDeJ
§	'Lustige Witwe' (3)	LAma SDeJ
	'Lydia' (3)	LAma
	'Mabel' (9)	GKev LAma
§	'Madame Lefeber' (13)	GKev LAma LCro LOPS SDeJ
	'Madonna' (10)	EPfP LAma
	'Magic Lavender' (3)	GKev
	'Maja' (7)	LAma
	'Makassar' (3)	LAma
	'Mango Charm' (3)	GKev LAma SDeJ
	'Margarita' (2)	GKev LAma LCro LOPS
	'Marie José' (14)	SDeJ
	'Marie Louise' (5)	LAma
	'Mariette' (6)	CAby GKev LAma SDeJ
	'Marilyn' (6)	ERCP GKev LAma SDeJ
	'Marjolein' (6)	LAma
	marjolletii (15)	LAma
	'Marquis de la Coquette' (14) **new**	SPer
	'Mary Ann' (14)	LAma
	'Mata Hari' (3)	LAma
	'Match' (3)	LCro LOPS
	'Matchpoint' (7/d)	LAma SDeJ
	'Maureen' (5) ♀H6	CAvo ERCP GKev LAma LCro LOPS SDeJ
	'Maureen Double' (11)	LCro
	mauritiana 'Cindy' (15)	GKev LAma
	'Max Durand' (7) **new**	GKev
	maximowiczii	see *T. linifolia* Maximowiczii Group
	'Maytime' (6)	LAma LCro LOPS MCot SDeJ
	'Melody d'Amour' (5)	LAma
	'Menton' (5) ♀H6	ERCP GKev LAma LCro LOPS SDeJ
	'Menton Exotic' (11)	ERCP GKev
	'Merlot' (6)	CAby CAvo ERCP GKev LAma LCro LOPS
	'Merry Christmas' (1)	LAma
	'Merry Christmas Design' (1)	LAma
	MERRY WIDOW	see *T.* 'Lustige Witwe'
	'Mickey Mouse' (1)	LAma LCro LOPS
	'Miranda' (11)	LAma
	'Miskodeed' (14)	SDeJ
	'Miss Elegance' (3)	LAma
	'Mistress' (3)	LAma LCro LOPS
	'Modern Style' (5)	LAma
	'Mona Lisa' (6)	LAma SDeJ
	'Mondial'PBR (2)	LAma
	'Moneymaker' (6) ♀H6	ERCP
	'Monsella' (2)	LAma
§	***montana*** (15)	CTca EPot GKev LAma
	- yellow-flowered (15)	GKev LAma
	'Monte Carlo' (2) ♀H6	CArg LAma SDeJ
	'Montreux' (2)	LAma
	'Moonshine' (6)	LAma
	'Moonwalker' (4)	LAma
	'Mount Tacoma' (11)	ERCP GKev LAma LCro LOPS SDeJ
	'Mr Van der Hoef' (2)	LAma SDeJ
	'Mrs John T. Scheepers' (5)	LAma SDeJ
	'Muriel' (10)	ERCP
	'Nachtwacht' (2) **new**	GKev
	'National Velvet' (3)	LCro LOPS NAln SPer
	'Negrita' (3)	CArg ERCP GKev LAma LCro LOPS SCob SDeJ
	'Negrita Parrot' (10) **new**	LAma
	neustruevae (15)	EPot GKev LAma
	'New Design' (3/v)	LAma LCro LOPS
	'New Santa' (7) **new**	NAln
	'Nicholas Heyek' (3)	LCro
	'Night Club' (5)	NAln
	'Nightrider' (8)	ERCP GKev LAma LCro LOPS MCot SDeJ
	'Noranda' (7)	LAma
	'Ollioules' (4) ♀H6	GKev LAma SDeJ
	'Olympic Flame' (4) ♀H6	LAma LCro LOPS SDeJ
	'Orange Angelique' (11)	XEll
	'Orange Bouquet' (3) ♀H6	LAma SDeJ
	'Orange Cassini' (3)	LAma
	'Orange Emperor' (13) ♀H6	CAvo ERCP GKev LAma SDeJ
	'Orange Favourite' (10)	ERCP GKev LAma
	'Orange Lion' (4)	LAma
	'Orange Monarch' (3)	LAma
	'Orange Princess' (11) ♀H6	CAvo CRos CTca ERCP GKev LAma LCro LOPS LRHS NRHS SCob SDeJ
	'Orange Queen' (4)	LAma
	'Orange Sun'	see *T.* 'Oranjezon'
	'Orange Toronto' (14)	LAma
	'Oranje Nassau' (2) ♀H6	CRos LRHS NRHS
§	'Oranjezon' (4) ♀H6	ERCP LAma
	'Oratorio' (14) ♀H6	LAma SDeJ
	'Oriental Beauty' (14) ♀H6	LAma
	orithyioides	GKev
	'Orleans' (3)	GKev
	orphanidea (15)	GKev LAma
	- 'Flava' (15)	ERCP GKev LAma
§	- Whittallii Group (15) ♀H6	CAvo EPot ERCP GKev LCro LOPS SDeJ SPhx WCot WShi
	'Oscar' (3)	LAma NHol
	ostrowskiana (15)	LAma
	'Oxford' (4) ♀H6	LAma
	'Oxford's Elite' (4)	LAma
	'Page Polka' (3)	SDeJ
	'Palestrina' (3)	LAma
	'Panorama' (5)	LAma
	'Papillon' (9)	LAma
	'Parade' (4) ♀H6	LAma
	'Parrot King' (10)	SDeJ
	'Passionale' (3) ♀H6	EPfP LAma LCro LOPS SDeJ SPer
	'Paul Scherer' (3) ♀H6	CAvo ERCP GKev LAma LCro LOPS SDeJ
	'Peach Blossom' (2)	CArg CRos GKev LAma LCro LOPS LRHS NRHS SCob SDeJ
	Peacock Group	SDeJ
	'Peppermintstick' (15) ♀H6	CAvo CTca GKev LAma SCob SDeJ
	'Perestroyka' (5)	LAma SDeJ
	persica	see *T. celsiana*
	'Piccolo' (15)	LAma
	'Picture' (5)	ERCP LAma SDeJ
	'Pieter de Leur' (6)	LAma
	'Pimpernel' (8/v)	LAma SDeJ
	'Pink Diamond' (5)	CAvo ERCP GKev LCro LOPS NHol SDeJ
	'Pink Dwarf' (12)	GKev SDeJ
*	'Pink Emperor' (13)	GKev
	'Pink Impression' (4) ♀H6	CArg GKev LAma LCro LOPS SDeJ
	'Pink Sensation' (14)	SDeJ
	'Pink Star' (11)	GKev
	'Pinkeen' (13)	LAma
	'Pinocchio' (14)	CArg CRos GKev LAma LRHS NRHS SDeJ

'Pirand' (13) ♀[H6]	SDeJ
'Pittsburg' (3)	LAma LCro LOPS
'Plaisir' (14) ♀[H6]	LAma
platystigma (15)	LAma
'Poco Loco' (13)	SDeJ
polychroma	see *T. biflora*
praestans (15)	GKev SPer WShi
- 'Bloemenlust' (15)	GKev
- 'Fusilier' (15) ♀[H6]	CExl EPot GKev LAma NBir SDeJ
- 'Moondance' (15)	GKev
- 'Shogun' (15)	ERCP GKev SDeJ SPer
- 'Unicum' (15/v)	ERCP GKev LAma SDeJ
- 'Van Tubergen's Variety' (15)	GKev LAma NPer
- 'Zwanenburg Variety' (15)	GKev
'Pretty Princess' (3)	ERCP MJak SDeJ SPer
'Pretty Woman' (6)	LAma
'Princeps' (13)	LAma SDeJ
'Princesse Charmante' (14) ♀[H6]	LAma LCro LOPS
'Prinses Irene' (3) ♀[H6]	CArg CAvo CRos CTca EPfP ERCP GKev LAma LCro LOPS LRHS MCot NAln NBir NHol NRHS SDeJ
'Prinses Margriet' (3)	ERCP LAma
'Professor Einstein' (3)	LAma
'Professor Röntgen' (10)	ERCP GKev LAma LCro LOPS SDeJ
'Professor Schotel' (15)	LAma
pulchella humilis	see *T. humilis*
'Purified' (3)	GKev
§ 'Purissima' (13) ♀[H6]	CAvo GKev LAma LCro LOPS SCob SDeJ SPer
'Purple Bouquet' (3)	LAma SDeJ
'Purple Doll' (8) **new**	LAma
'Purple Dream' (6)	LAma SDeJ
'Purple Flag' (3)	LAma LCro LOPS
I 'Purple Prince' (1)	CArg
'Purple Prince' (5)	CRos LAma LCro LOPS LRHS NRHS SDeJ
'Purple Rain' (3)	LAma
'Purple Tower' (7)	ERCP
'Quebec' (14)	LAma SDeJ
'Queen of Marvel' (2)	LAma SDeJ
'Queen of Night' (5)	CAby CArg CAvo CMea CTca EPfP ERCP EUJe GKev LAma LCro LOPS MCot NAln SCob SDeJ SPer SPhx
'Queensday' (11)	LAma SDeJ
'Queensland' (7)	LAma
'Quest' (3)	LAma
'Rai' (10)	LAma SDeJ
'Rajka' (6)	GKev
'Real Time' (7)	LAma
'Recreado' (5)	CAvo ERCP LAma SDeJ
'Red Baby Doll' (2)	LAma
'Red Emperor'	see *T.* 'Madame Lefeber'
'Red Georgette' (5) ♀[H6]	CAby GKev LAma NBir SDeJ
'Red Hat' (7) ♀[H6]	LCro LOPS
'Red Impression'[PBR] (4) ♀[H6]	EPfP LAma LCro LOPS
'Red Princess' (11) ♀[H6]	ERCP LAma
'Red Revival' (1)	GKev LAma
'Red Riding Hood' (14) ♀[H6]	CArg CAvo CRos EPfP GKev LAma LCro LOPS LRHS MJak NAln NBir NRHS SCob SDeJ SPer
'Red Rover' (3)	LCro LOPS
'Red Shine' (6) ♀[H6]	CAby CAvo ERCP GKev LAma LCro LOPS SDeJ
'Red Springgreen' (8)	GKev LAma LCro LOPS SDeJ
'Red Wing' (7) ♀[H6]	LAma SDeJ
'Redwood' (14)	SDeJ
(Rembrandt Group) 'Saskia' (15)	LAma
'Rems Favourite' (3)	CAby CAvo LCro LOPS SDeJ
'Renown' (5)	LAma SDeJ
'Renown Unique' (11)	LAma
'Request' (3)	LAma
'Rex Rubrorum' (2)	LAma
rhodopea	see *T. urumoffii*
'Rococo' (10)	CAvo ERCP LAma LCro LOPS SDeJ
'Roi du Midi' (5)	LAma SDeJ
'Ronaldo' (3)	ERCP GKev LAma LCro LOPS
'Rosalie' (3)	ERCP LAma SDeJ
'Rose des Dames' (5)	LAma
'Rosy Dream' (13)	LAma SDeJ
'Roulette' (3)	LAma
'Royal Acres' (2)	LAma
'Royal Anthos' (14)	SDeJ
'Royal Elegance' (7)	LAma
'Ruud Lubbers' (14)	LAma
'Salmon Impression'[PBR] (4)	LAma SDeJ
'Salmon Parrot' (10)	LAma
'Sanne' (3) ♀[H6]	CAvo ERCP LAma SDeJ
'Santander' (7) **new**	SDeJ
'Sapporo' (6)	ERCP GKev LAma LCro LOPS
saxatilis (15)	EPfP GKev LAma LCro LOPS SDeJ
§ - Bakeri Group (15)	SCob SEND
§ - - 'Lilac Wonder' (15) ♀[H6]	CAby CAvo CExl EPot ERCP GKev LAma LCro LOPS NPer SCob SDeJ SPhx WShi WTor
'Scarlet Baby' (12)	LAma
'Schoonoord' (2)	LAma
schrenkii (15)	EPot ERCP GKev LAma
'Seadov' (3) ♀[H6]	LAma LCro LOPS SDeJ
'Sensual Touch' (7) ♀[H6]	LAma SDeJ
'Sesamstraat' (3) **new**	LCro LOPS
'Shakespeare' (12)	LAma SDeJ
'Shirley' (3)	CAby CAvo ERCP GKev LAma LCro LOPS SCob SDeJ
'Shirley Dream' (3)	LAma SDeJ
'Showtime' (14)	SDeJ
'Showwinner' (12) ♀[H6]	GKev LAma NHol SDeJ
'Silk Road' (2)	GKev
'Silver Dollar' (3)	LAma
'Silver Parrot' (10)	LAma
'Silver Standard' (1)	GKev
'Silverstream' (4)	GKev
'Slawa'[PBR] (3) **new**	CAvo GKev
'Snow Parrot' (10)	ERCP
'Snowboard' (3)	LAma
'Snowpeak' (5)	LAma
sogdiana (15)	GKev LAma
'Sorbet' (5) ♀[H6]	LAma SDeJ
sprengeri (15) ♀[H6]	CAvo CBro CExl CSpe CTca ECha ERCP GKev LAma LLHF SBrt WHal WShi
- Trotter's form (15)	WCot
'Spring Green' (8) ♀[H6]	CArg CAvo CTca EPfP ERCP GBin GKev LAma LCro LOPS MCot SCob SDeJ SPer SPhx
'Spryng' (3) ♀[H6]	SDeJ
'Starfighter' (7)	SDeJ
stellata	see *T. clusiana* var. *stellata*
'Stockholm' (2) ♀[H6]	LAma
'Stresa' (12) ♀[H6]	CRos GKev LAma LRHS NRHS SDeJ
'Striped Sail' (3)	LAma
'Strong Gold' (3) ♀[H6]	LAma SDeJ
'Stunning Apricot' (5)	GKev LAma LCro LOPS
subpraestans (15)	LAma
'Sun Dance' (14)	LAma
'Sun Lover' (11)	LAma

'Suncatcher' (3) **new**	LAma SDeJ
'Sunny Prince'[PBR] (1)	SDeJ
'Sunset Miami' (7) **new**	LAma
'Sunset Tropical' (11)	GKev
'Super Parrot' (10)	LAma
'Survivor' (5)	NAln SDeJ
'Swan Wings' (7)	ERCP GKev LAma LCro LOPS NAln SDeJ
'Sweet Desire' (2)	SDeJ
'Sweet Lady' (14)	LAma SDeJ
'Sweetheart' (13)	GKev LAma LCro LOPS MCot SDeJ
'Sweety' (3)	LAma
sylvestris (15)	CAby CAvo CSpe CTca EPfP EPot ERCP GKev LAma LCro LOPS NBir SDeJ SPhx WCot WShi
'Sylvia Warder' (14)	LAma
'Synaeda King' (6) ♀H6	LAma
'Synaeda Orange' (6)	LAma
systola (15)	GKev LAma
'Taco' (15)	GKev LAma
'Talisman' ambig.	LAma
'Tarafa' (14)	LAma SDeJ
tarda (15) ♀H6	CAvo CExl CRos EPfP ERCP GKev LAma LCro LOPS LRHS NAln NRHS SDeJ SPhx WShi
'Temple of Beauty' (5) ♀H6	GKev LAma SDeJ
'Tender Whisper' (3)	GKev
'Tennessee' (3)	LAma
'Tequila Sun' (3)	LAma
tetraphylla (15)	GKev LAma
'Texas Flame' (10)	GKev LAma SDeJ
'Texas Gold' (10)	LAma SDeJ
'The First' (12)	GKev IPot LAma
'The Lizard' (9)	GKev LAma
'Theeroos' (2)	LAma
'Tinka' (15) ♀H6	CMea GKev LAma SCob
'Tiny Timo' (15)	GKev LLHF
'Tom Pouce' (3)	LCro LOPS
'Toplips' (11)	GKev LAma SDeJ
'Topparrot' (10)	LAma SDeJ
'Toronto' (14) ♀H6	LAma SCob SDeJ
'Toronto Double' (2)	LAma SDeJ
'Toucan' (3)	LAma
'Toyota' (5)	SDeJ
'Très Chic' (6)	CAvo CTca EPfP GKev LAma LCro LOPS SPer
'Trinket' (14) ♀H6	LAma
'Tropical Dream' (3)	LAma
'Tropical Lady' (3)	LAma
tschimganica (15)	GKev LAma
- red-flowered **new**	GKev
- yellow-flowered **new**	GKev
turkestanica (15) ♀H5	CAby CAvo CExl CTca EPfP EPot ERCP GKev LAma LRHS NPer NRHS SDeJ WHoo WShi
'Turkish Delight' (14)	NPer
'Typhoon' (3)	CMea GKev LAma
'Uncle Tom' (11)	CAvo ERCP GKev LAma SDeJ
§ ***undulatifolia*** (15)	GKev WCot
'Unique de France'[PBR] (3)	CAvo
'United States' (14) ♀H6	LAma NPer
'Upstar' (11)	LAma
urumiensis (15) ♀H5	CAvo EPot GKev LAma SDeJ SPhx
§ ***urumoffii*** (15)	LAma
'Valentine' (3)	SDeJ
'Valery Gergiev' (7)	ERCP LAma SDeJ
'Van der Neer' (1)	GKev SDeJ
'Van Eijk'[PBR] (4)	GKev LAma SCob
'Vanilla Cream' (14)	NAln SDeJ
'Velvet Lily' (6)	GKev
'Verona' (2)	GKev LAma SDeJ
'Véronique Sanson' (3)	ERCP LCro LOPS SDeJ
'Victoria's Secret' (3)	GKev
'Vincent van Gogh' (7) ♀H6	LAma
violacea	see *T. humilis* Violacea Group
'Violet Beauty' (5)	GKev LAma LCro LOPS SDeJ
'Violet Bird' (8)	GKev LAma LCro LOPS SDeJ
'Virichic' (8)	ERCP LAma LCro LOPS MCot
vvedenskyi (15)	EPot GKev
- 'Bernadette' (15)	LAma
- 'Tangerine Beauty' (15) ♀H6	GKev LAma
'Wallflower' (5)	LAma
'Wapen van Leiden' (1)	LAma
'Warbler' (7)	LAma SDeJ
'Washington' (3)	GKev LCro LOPS
'Weber's Parrot' (10)	GKev LAma LCro LOPS MCot
'Wedding Gift' (11) **new**	SDeJ
'Weisse Berliner' (3)	CAby LAma
'West Point' (6)	CAvo CTca GKev LAma LCro LOPS SDeJ
'Whispering Dream' (3)	CAvo
* 'White Bouquet' (5)	LAma
'White Dream' (3)	CArg GKev LAma LCro LOPS SDeJ
'White Elegance' (6)	LAma
'White Emperor'	see *T.* 'Purissima'
'White Lieberstar' (5)	ERCP
'White Marvel' (3)	CRos GKev LAma LRHS NRHS
'White Parrot' (10)	CAvo ERCP GKev LAma LCro LOPS SDeJ
'White Sea' (13)	LAma
'White Triumphator' (6) ♀H6	CAby CArg CAvo CMea ERCP GKev LAma LCro LOPS NAln NBir SDeJ SPhx
whittallii	see *T. orphanidea* Whittallii Group
'Wildhof' (3) ♀H6	ERCP
'Wilja' (5)	GKev
§ 'Willem van Oranje' (2)	LAma SDeJ
'Willemsoord' (2)	CRos LAma LRHS NRHS SDeJ
WILLIAM OF ORANGE	see *T.* 'Willem van Oranje'
wilsoniana	see *T. montana*
'Wisley' (5) ♀H6	GKev LCro LOPS SCob
'World Expression' (5) ♀H6	LAma SDeJ
'Yellow Crown' (3)	LAma
'Yellow Flight' (3)	LAma SDeJ
'Yellow Pompenette'[PBR] (11) ♀H6	SDeJ
I 'Yellow Purissima' (13) ♀H6	LAma
'Yellow Springgreen' (8)	ERCP GKev LAma SDeJ
'Yoko Parrot' (10)	SDeJ
'Yokohama' (3)	GKev LAma MJak SCob SDeJ
'Yonina' (6)	CArg GKev LAma LCro LOPS SDeJ
'Zampa' (14) ♀H6	LAma
'Zombie' (13)	LAma
'Zomerschoon' (5)	LAma
§ 'Zurel' (3)	CArg ERCP GKev LAma SCob

tummelberry see *Rubus* 'Tummelberry'

Tunica see *Petrorhagia*

Tupistra (*Asparagaceae*)

aurantiaca	GEdr LEdu
- B&SWJ 2267	WCot WCru
- B&SWJ 2401	WCru
chinensis 'Eco China Ruffles'	WCot
grandistigma	WCot
- B&SWJ 11773	WCru
jinshanensis	WCot

urotepala HWJ 562 — WCru
wattii B&SWJ 8297 — WCru

Turnera (*Passifloraceae*)

diffusa — GPoy
  var. ***aphrodisiaca*** **new**

turnip see AGM Vegetables Section

Turpinia (*Staphyleaceae*)

ternata CWJ 12360 — WCru

Tussilago (*Asteraceae*)

farfara — GPoy MHer WHer WSFF

Tweedia (*Apocynaceae*)

§ ***coerulea*** ♀H1c — CBcs CCCN CDTJ CFlo CKel CSpe SChF SPad SPer SPhx SWvt

Typha (*Typhaceae*)

angustifolia — CBen CWat LLWG MMuc NPer SPlb WMAq WPnP
- 'Zebratails' **new** — LLWG
latifolia — CBen CWat LLWG NBir NPer SVic WMAq XLum
- 'Variegata' (v) — CWat LLWG MWts WBor WMAq
§ ***laxmannii*** — CBen LLWG WMAq WPnP XLum
lugdunensis — MWts
minima — CBen CWat LLWG MWts NPer WMAq WPnP XLum
shuttleworthii — CBen LLWG
stenophylla — see *T. laxmannii*

Typhonium (*Araceae*)

giganteum — WCot
horsfieldii — LEdu MPie
roxburghii — EBee WFar
venosum — EUJe

Typhonodorum (*Araceae*)

lindleyanum — XBlo

U

Uapaca (*Euphorbiaceae*)

kirkiana (F) — XBlo

Uccerodendron (*Hamamelidaceae*)

* ***whartonii*** B&SWJ 11706 — WCru
- FMWJ 13365 **new** — WCru
- WWJ 11933 **new** — WCru
- WWJ 11994 **new** — WCru

ugli see *Citrus* × *aurantium* (Tangelo Group) 'Ugli'

Ugni ✿ (*Myrtaceae*)

candollei — SVen
§ ***molinae*** — Widely available
- PAB 1347 — LEdu SBrt
- 'Butterball' — CBcs CKel EBee EPfP LEdu LRHS SPoG SWvt
- 'Flambeau' (v) — CAgr CBcs CBod CCht CDul CExl CKel CMac CRos CSde EBee ELan EPfP EShb LEdu LRHS MAsh MGil NLar NRHS SEle SLon SPoG SRms SWvt WPav
- 'Ka-Pow' — LCro LRHS SCob SPad WTyc
- orange-leaved — WJek
- 'Variegata' (v) — LEdu WJek
- 'Villarica Strawberry' — WPGP

Ulex (*Papilionaceae*)

europaeus — CBcs CCVT CDul CHab CMac CPer CTri ELan ELon EPfP LBuc MCoo MGil MGos MMuc NWea SCob SEWo SPer
§ - 'Flore Pleno' (d) ♀H6 — CBcs CBod CCoa CDul CMac CPla CSBt CSde ELan ELon EPfP GCal IArd MBlu MMuc NWea SCob SPer WFar WHer
- 'Irish Double' (d) — NLar
- 'Plenus' — see *U. europaeus* 'Flore Pleno'
gallii — NLar
- 'Mizen Head' — GCal

Ullucus (*Basellaceae*)

tuberosus — LEdu
- 'Beet Red' **new** — WCot

Ulmus ✿ (*Ulmaceae*)

× ***androssowii*** **new** — WPGP
bergmanniana — WPGP
carpinifolia — CDul LPra
  var. ***suberosa***
changii **new** — WPGP
chenmoui — IArd IDee WPGP
'Columella' — SAko
davidiana — WPGP
- var. ***davidiana*** — WPGP
- var. ***japonica*** — WPGP
'Dodoens' — IArd MBlu
'Frontier' — SGol WPGP
§ ***glabra*** — CDul CPer EPfP NWea SCob WTSh
- 'Camperdownii' — CMac ELan WMou
- 'Lutescens' — CTho EBee NOra NWea SEWo WMat
harbinensis **new** — WPGP
§ × ***hollandica*** 'Dampieri Aurea' ♀H7 — CDul CTho EBee ELan ELon EPfP LBuc MAsh MBlu MGos MJak MRav NLar NWea SCob SPer SPoG WMat
- 'Jacqueline Hillier' — CDul CMac CSpe EBee ELan LRHS MMuc NLar SEND SGol WCFE WFar
- 'Wredei' — see *U.* × *hollandica* 'Dampieri Aurea'
'Homestead' — WPGP
laevis — CPer WPGP
'Lobel' — CCVT CLnd LMaj
LUTÈCE ('Nanguen') — CDul SGol
× ***mesocarpa*** **new** — WPGP
minor 'Dampieri Aurea' — see *U.* × *hollandica* 'Dampieri Aurea'
montana — see *U. glabra*
'Morfeo'PBR — WMat
parvifolia — CAco CMCN CMen CTho EShb WPGP
- 'Geisha' (v) — ELan
§ - 'Hokkaido' — EWes NLar SIgm SMad WAbe WFar
- 'Pygmaea' — see *U. parvifolia* 'Hokkaido'
- 'Yatsubusa' — MRav
procera — CDul EMOT MCoo MGos WSFF
- 'Argenteovariegata' (v) — NLar
prunifolia **new** — WPGP
pumila 'Beijing Gold' — ELan NLar

'Regal'PBR	WPGP
'Sapporo Autumn Gold'	CCVT MRav SGol WCFE
szechuanica	WPGP
uyematsui	IArd WPGP
VADA ('Wanoux'PBR)	SGol
villosa	EBee WPGP

Umbellularia (*Lauraceae*)

californica	WPGP

Umbilicus (*Crassulaceae*)

§ ***oppositifolius*** 𝕐H5	Widely available
- 'Jane's Reverse' (v)	WCot
- 'Jim's Pride' (v)	ECha EHoe EUJe EWes GKev MHer MPie MRav NHpl NPer NWad SPlb SRms SRot WFar WKif WMoo WSHC WTor
rupestris	SChr SPhx WHer WShi

Uncinia (*Cyperaceae*)

* ***cyparissias*** from Chile	NBir
egmontiana	CPla CRos EPfP LRHS NRHS NWad WGrn WMoo
erinacea	GCal
rubra	CBod CChe CEnd CRos CSBt ECrN ELan EMOT EPfP EShb GCal GMaP LRHS MGos MRav NAln NAst NRHS NSti NWad SCob SGol SPad SPlb SPoG WFar WMoo
§ - 'Belinda's Find'PBR	CBct CKno CRos EBee ELan LRHS MHol NLar NPri NRHS SPoG SRms
- EVERFLAME	see *U. rubra* 'Belinda's Find'
uncinata	CBcs ECha
* - ***rubra***	CBod CKno IFro MAsh SCob SLim SRms SWvt

Uniola (*Poaceae*)

latifolia	see *Chasmanthium latifolium*

Urginea (*Asparagaceae*)

maritima	see *Charybdis maritima*

Urospermum (*Asteraceae*)

dalechampii	CCCN CSam

Ursinia (*Asteraceae*)

alpina	CPBP

Urtica (*Urticaceae*)

dioica 'Bradfield Purpler'	CNat
- 'Chedglow 2' (v)	CNat
- 'Curly-Wurly'	CNat
- 'Good as Gold'	CNat
- OGG mutant	CNat

Utricularia (*Lentibulariaceae*)

sp.	EECP
alpina	SHmp
biloba	CHew
bisquamata	SHmp
- 'Betty's Bay' 𝕐H2	CHew
calycifida	SHmp
dichotoma	CHew
exoleta R. Brown	see *U. gibba*
§ ***gibba***	EECP
heterosepala	CHew
intermedia	EECP
lateriflora	CHew
livida 𝕐H2	CHew SHmp
longifolia	SHmp
microcalyx	CHew
monanthos	CHew
nephrophylla	CHew
novae-zelandiae	CHew
paulineae	CHew
praelonga	CHew SHmp
prehensilis	CHew
reniformis	SHmp
sandersonii 𝕐H2	CHew EECP SHmp
simplex	CHew
tricolor	CHew SHmp
uniflora	CHew
warburgii	CHew
welwitschii	CHew

Uvularia (*Colchicaceae*)

grandiflora 𝕐H6	Widely available
- gold-leaved	CAby CBct
- 'Lynda Windsor'	LEdu NHsp
- var. ***pallida***	CAby CAvo CBct CRos EBee EHrv EMor EPPr EPfP EPot GBin GCal GEdr IBlr ILea LEdu LRHS MRav NCGa NHsp NRHS WCru WFar WPnP
- 'Susie Lewis'	WCru
grandiflora* × *perfoliata	NBir
perfoliata	CAby CBct CExl EBee ECha EPPr EPfP EPot GKev IBlr IMou LEdu MRav NBir NChi NHpl SPlb WCru
- tall	EPPr
sessilifolia	CBct CExl CRos EPfP GKev IMou LEdu LRHS MMrt NAln NHsp NRHS WCru
- 'Cobblewood Gold' (v)	EPPr LEdu WCru
- 'Variegata' (v)	EBee

Vaccaria (*Caryophyllaceae*)

§ ***hispanica***	SPhx
segetalis	see *V. hispanica*

Vaccinium ✿ (*Ericaceae*)

arctostaphylos	SWvt
'Berkeley' (F)	CAgr CCCN CEnd GKin LSRN MBlu SDea SPre
BLUE SUEDE ('Th-682') (F)	CBcs LCro LOPS LRHS NRHS
'Bluejay' (F)	CRos ELan LRHS MAsh NRHS SCoo SLon SPoG
'Blueray' (F)	GKin SDea
'Brigitta' (F)	CEnd CTrh EMil EPom NRHS SPoG SPre
chaetothrix	WAbe WThu
'Chandler' (F)	CAgr CArg CEnd CMac CRos CTrh EPom GKin LCro LOPS SKee SPer
consanguineum B&SWJ 10486	WCru
corymbosum (F)	CBcs MNHC SCoo SSta
- 'Aurora'PBR (F)	CTrh
- 'Blauweiss-Goldtraube' (F)	CAgr CMac CSBt EPfP GKin MAsh NLar NPri SDea SPoG SVic WTSh
- 'Blue Duke' (F)	LSRN

- 'Blue Pearl' (F)	CFGn
- 'Bluecrop' (F)	Widely available
- 'Bluegold' (F)	CRos LRHS MAsh NRHS SPoG
- 'Bluetta' (F)	CAgr CTri ELan SCoo SPoG
- 'Darrow' (F)	CAgr CFGn LRHS NRHS WMat
- 'Dixie' (F)	CSBt LEdu NLar SDea
- 'Draper'^{PBR} (F) new	CTrh
- 'Duke' (F) 🏆^{H6}	CArg CTrh ELan EPfP EPom LCro LOPS MCoo MGos SDea SPer SPre SRkn SSFr
- 'Elliott' (F)	LSRN
- 'Hardyblue' (F)	CAgr
- 'Izabel' (F) new	CFGn
- 'Jersey' (F)	CAgr CEnd CRos EPfP LRHS MAsh MGos MMuc NRHS SCoo SDea SPer SPoG SVic
- 'Legacy' (F)	NRHS
- 'Liberty'^{PBR} (F)	CFGn CRos CTrh EPfP LRHS
- 'Nelson' (F)	SCoo
- 'Nui' (F)	CEnd EPom LSRN MRav
- 'Patriot' (F)	CAgr CEnd CMac CRos CSBt CTrh ECrN EMOT EPom GKin LBuc LRHS MGos MRav NLar NPri NRHS SCoo SDea SPer SPre SSFr WMat
- 'Polaris' (F)	CEnd
- 'Reka' (F)	CAgr NPer
- 'Spartan' (F) 🏆^{H6}	CTrh EPom LCro LOPS LSRN MGos SKee
- 'Stanley' (F)	CRos EPfP LRHS NRHS SPoG
- 'Toro' (F)	CRos SPre
- 'Weymouth' (F)	SDea
crassifolium	CRos LRHS MAsh
subsp. ***sempervirens*** 'Well's Delight' (F)	
cylindraceum 🏆^{H4}	CBcs CEnd EBee NLar SSta WPGP
delavayi	LRHS MAsh NLar SSta WThu
dunalianum	WCru
var. ***caudatifolium*** B&SWJ 1716	
- var. ***megaphyllum*** HWJ 515	WCru
'Earliblue' (F)	CAgr CSBt CTrh GKin LBuc NRHS SDea SPer SPoG WMat
erythrocarpum new	CRos
floribundum	CBcs CRos LRHS MAsh
glaucoalbum 🏆^{H5}	CMac CRos EBee EPfP LRHS MAsh MBlu MRav NRHS SPoG WPGP
'Goldtraube 71'	EMOT MAsh
griffithianum	SSta
'Herbert' (F)	CAgr CTrh EPom LBuc
'Huron' (F) new	CTrh
macrocarpon (F)	CRos ELan LRHS MAsh NRHS SDea SPre SRms
- 'CN' (F)	NLar
- 'Early Black' (F)	ELan EMOT EPom GKin IDee NLar SVic WTSh
- 'Hamilton'	WThu
- 'Langlois' (F)	NLar
- 'Olson's Honkers' (F)	CAgr NLar
- 'Pilgrim' (F)	CAgr CFGn CSBt EMOT LEdu LOPS LRHS MAsh MCoo NPri SDea SPoG WMat
- 'Red Star' (F)	CTrh
- 'Stevens' (F)	CAgr
moupinense	CRos GEdr LRHS MAsh WThu
myrtillus	CAgr EPom GPoy SVic
'Northcountry' (F) new	CTrh
'Northland' (F)	CMac CRos CSBt EMOT EPfP EPom NLar NPri NRHS SCoo SDea SPoG WMat
nummularia	GEdr LRHS NLar WAbe WThu
'Osorno' (F) new	CTrh
ovatum (F)	CBcs CMac CTsd GKin WThu
- 'Pacific Spear' (F) new	SVic
- 'Thundercloud' (F)	CRos EPfP LRHS MAsh NRHS SSta
§ ***oxycoccos*** (F)	CAgr GPoy MCoo WThu
'Ozarkblue' (F)	EPom LCro LOPS NRHS SPer
pallidum	IBlr
palustre	see *V. oxycoccos*
§ 'Pink Lemonade' (F)	CRos ELan EPom LCro LOPS LRHS NPri NRHS SPer SPoG SSFr
'Pink Sapphire'	see *V.* 'Pink Lemonade'
retusum	WThu
'Rubel' (F)	NRHS
'Spring Surprise'	WAbe WThu
'Sunshine Blue' (F)	CAgr CEnd CRos CTrh ELan EPom LBuc LRHS SDea SPoG SSFr
'Tophat' (F)	CCCN LEdu
vitis-idaea	EPfP EWes GPoy SVic
- 'Aalshorst'	NLar
- 'Autumn Beauty'	NLar
- 'Compactum'	EWes
- 'Erntetraum'	NLar
- 'Ida'	LBuc
- Koralle Group 🏆^{H5}	CAgr EPot GKin NLar NWad
- 'Leucocarpa'	NLar
- subsp. ***minus***	GEdr NLar WThu
- 'Red Candy'^{PBR}	ELan EPfP LCro LOPS LRHS NLar NRHS SCob
- 'Red Pearl'	CSBt EPom MAsh

Vachellia (*Leguminosae*)

§ ***karroo***	CDTJ SPlb

Valeriana (*Caprifoliaceae*)

'Alba'	see *Centranthus ruber* 'Albus'
alliariifolia	CSam GCal GQue NBro SPhx
- PAB 3001	LEdu WPGP
arizonica	EBou
'Coccinea'	see *Centranthus ruber*
dioica	LLWG
hardwickii PAB 8999	LEdu
jatamansi	GPoy SRms
- PAB 6846	LEdu WPGP
montana	EBee LEdu MMuc NBro NRya SRms
officinalis	Widely available
- subsp. ***sambucifolia***	EMor EPPr GCal MNrw SHar
phu 'Aurea'	CBod CDor CHby CMac CRos EBee ECha EHoe ELan EPfP GKin GQue LRHS MRav NBid NBir NBro NEgg NLar NRHS NSti NWad SPer SPoG SRms WCAu WMoo
pyrenaica	EBee ECha EHrv EMor EPPr GCal LCro LOPS LRHS MHol MMuc MNrw SEND SHar SPhx WCot WHrl WMoo
wallrothii	WCot

Valerianella (*Caprifoliaceae*)

§ ***locusta***	CBod GPoy SVic
olitoria	see *V. locusta*

Vallea (*Elaeocarpaceae*)

stipularis	CTsd

Vallisneria (*Hydrocharitaceae*)

americana	XBlo
asiatica var. ***biwaensis***	XBlo

gigantea XBlo
spiralis LLWG XBlo
- 'Tortifolia' XBlo

Vallota see *Cyrtanthus*

Vancouveria (*Berberidaceae*)

chrysantha CExl EPPr EPfP GEdr GLog MRav NRya WMoo WPGP WPnP
hexandra CExl CMac ECha EMor EPPr EPfP GEdr GKev GLog ILea LEdu LRHS NBir NSti WCru WMoo WPGP WPnP
planipetala IMou WCru

Vania see *Thlaspi*

Vasconcellea (*Caricaceae*)

§ ***pubescens*** SPlb

Vellozia (*Velloziaceae*)

elegans see *Talbotia elegans*

Veltheimia ✿ (*Asparagaceae*)

§ ***bracteata*** ♀H2 CAvo CPla SBch SRms
viridifolia Jacq. see *V. bracteata*

× *Venidioarctotis* see *Arctotis*

Venidium see *Arctotis*

Veratrilla (*Gentianaceae*)

baillonii GEdr

Veratrum (*Melanthiaceae*)

album ♀H7 EBee ECha EMor GKev GPoy ILea MNrw MRav NBid WCot WCru WSHC
- PAB 537 LEdu
- 'Auvergne White' EBee GCal LEdu MNrw
- var. ***flavum*** CAby MNrw SPhx WCot WCru
- - 'Primrose Warburg' GEdr
- subsp. ***lobelianum*** GCal LEdu
- 'Lorna's Green' ♀H7 EBee GCal MNrw WCot
- var. ***oxysepalum*** WCru
californicum ♀H3 CAby EBee ECha EMor GCal LEdu MNrw NBid SMad WCru WWFP
formosanum CAby EBee MNrw WSHC
- B&SWJ 1575 WCru
- RWJ 9806 WCru
grandiflorum B&SWJ 4416 WCru
longebracteatum WCru
maackii EBee GCal MAvo MNrw SMad
- B&SWJ 5875 WCru
- green-flowered EBee GCal LEdu MNrw
- var. ***japonicum*** MNrw WCru
- var. ***maackii*** MNrw
- - B&SWJ 5831 WCru
nigrum ♀H6 CAby CBct CRos EBee ECha GCal GEdr GKev GMaP ILea LEdu LRHS MAvo MNrw MRav NBid NBir NRHS SMad SPer SPhx SPlb WCot WCru WWFP
- B&SWJ 4450 from South Korea WCru
schindleri GEdr MNrw
- B&SWJ 4068 WCru
stamineum WCru
viride EBee EWes GCal LEdu MNrw NBid WCot WCru

Verbascum (*Scrophulariaceae*)

'Apricot Sunset' SPhx
'Arctic Summer' see *V. bombyciferum* 'Polarsommer'
arcturus SVen
'Argentina' WHer
blattaria GJos NBir WHer
- f. ***albiflorum*** CPla CSpe NDov NGBl SPlb WHer WMoo
'Blue Lagoon' CWGN IKil SCob
'Blushing Bride'PBR LLHF
§ ***bombyciferum*** CBod CBre ECha ELan GMaP LRHS NGBl SCob SEND SRms
* - 'Arctic Snow' SPoG
§ - 'Polarsommer' CSpe EPfP LRHS NBir SPer
- 'Silver Lining' NPer
'Broussa' see *V. bombyciferum*
'Buttercup' CRos LRHS NRHS
'Camelot' CRos LRHS NRHS
'Caribbean Crush' CRos ECtt ELan GJos LRHS MBNS NRHS SPoG WSpi
chaixii CBod CSam ECha EPPr GAbr GJos MArl MMrt NBir WFar WMoo
- 'Album' Widely available
- 'Sixteen Candles' CBod GJos IKil IPot WFar
- 'Wedding Candles' CWld ELan GWyn NGdn SPtp WFar
'Cherry Helen'PBR EBee IKil LOPS LRHS LSRN MBNS NLar SCob
'Christo's Yellow Lightning' ♀H6 CBod EBee ECha ECtt MAvo MHol SPoG WCot
'Clementine' CBcs CRos ECtt EPfP ILea LCro LOPS LRHS MHol NAst NRHS SCob SPhx
'Coneyhill Yellow' EPPr
(Cotswold Group) 'Cotswold Beauty' CBod CSam CSpe ECtt EPfP LRHS LSun MRav NDov NGdn NRHS SHar SPer WHoo
- 'Cotswold Queen' CRos CSam CWld ECtt EPPr EPfP LCro LOPS LRHS MMrt MNHC MRav NDov NRHS SHar SPer SWvt WCAu WSpi
- 'Gainsborough' ♀H6 CBod CDor CRos ECha ECtt EPfP GMaP LCro LOPS LRHS MArl MJak MRav NLar NRHS NSti SCob SGbt SPer SPoG SWvt WCAu WGwG WHil WSpi
- 'Mont Blanc' LRHS NRHS NSti
- 'Pink Domino' ♀H6 CBod CRos CSam EBou ECtt EPPr EPfP EWTr EWhm GMaP LCro LOPS LRHS MJak MRav MWat NRHS NSti SPer SWvt WSpi
- 'Royal Highland' EBee ECtt EPfP LRHS MBNS NRHS SWvt WHoo
- 'White Domino' SPer WSpi
'Cotswold King' see *V. creticum*
§ ***creticum*** CSpe IKil WCot
'Dark Eyes'PBR CWGN ECtt LRHS NHpl SCob
delphicum GKev
§ ***densiflorum*** GJos
dumulosum ♀H4 EPot WAbe
epixanthinum ♀H5 EBee GJos
'Firedance' CBcs CWld ECtt EPfP IPot LLHF LRHS MHer NCGa NGBl NRHS NSti SHar WCAu
'Golden Wings' ♀H4 WAbe
'Guinevere' CRos LRHS NRHS
'Helen Johnson' CRos CWCL ECtt ELan EUJe LRHS LSRN MGos MRav NLar NRHS SCob SCoo SRkn SWvt WGwG WSpi

× ***hybridum*** 'Banana Custard'	NGBl WSpi
– 'Copper Rose'	LRHS
– 'Snow Maiden'	CTri CWld EPfP
'Jackie'	CRos ECtt IKil LRHS LSRN NRHS SCob SCoo
'Jester'	CBcs EBee ECtt MBNS MCot SCob SPoG WSpi
'Jolly Eyes'	ILea
'June Johnson'	CBod CWld ECtt LRHS NRHS
'Kynaston'	CBcs CBod CSam ECtt EPfP LRHS MBNS NRHS
'Lavender Lass'	IKil MHol WSpi
'Letitia' 𝕐H4	CRos EBee ECtt EPot EWes GCal LRHS NRHS SWvt WAbe WCot WIce
levanticum	GJos
'Linda'	ECtt
longifolium var. ***pannosum***	see *V. olympicum*
lychnitis	GJos NGBl SPhx
'Megan's Mauve'	WSpi
'Merlin'PBR	CBcs CRos ECtt LRHS MBNS NRHS WPtf
nigrum	CHab GJos NGdn NLar WMoo
– var. ***album***	GJos NGdn NLar WArt WMoo WSpi
§ ***olympicum***	CBcs CBod CRos ELan EPfP EWTr GJos LRHS MArl MBNS NAln NGBl NRHS SCob SRms WCAu WCot
'Petra'	LRHS SPhx
phlomoides	SPhx
phoeniceum	CBcs CSBt ELan EPfP GJos NBro SIgm SPlb SPoG WFar WMoo WSpi
* – 'Album'	CSpe GJos
– 'Flush of White'	CDor EAJP EPfP NGBl NGdn NLar SCob WArt WJam WMoo
– 'Rosetta'	CBod EPfP GWyn MCot NGBl WArt WHil
– 'Temptress White'	CBod
– 'Violetta'	CBod CSpe CTsd CWld EAJP EPPr EPfP GBin GMaP LCro LOPS LRHS MCot MHol MWat NEgg NGBl NGdn SGbt SPer SPhx WArt WCAu WCFE WFar WHil WMoo
'Pink Kisses'	CRos LRHS LSRN MBNS NRHS
'Plum Smokey'PBR	ECtt LLHF
'Primrose Path'	CRos EPfP LRHS MBNS NLar NRHS
pyramidatum	EBee SPhx
'Queen of Hearts'	CRos LRHS NRHS
'Raspberry Ripple'	GWyn LLHF MRav
roripifolium	GJos
'Rosie'	ECtt NHpl SCob
'Sierra Sunset'	IKil NLar
'Southern Charm'	EPfP GJos NQui WHil
'Spica'	LRHS
'Sugar Plum'PBR	ECtt IKil LLHF LRHS
'Summer Sorbet'	CBcs ECtt
'Temptress Purple'	CBod MHol
thapsiforme	see *V. densiflorum*
thapsus	CHab EBou ENfk GJos GPoy GQue MArl MNHC NBir NMir SEND SRms
'Tropic Sun' 𝕐H5	SPhx WHoo
'Ventnor Giant'	SVen
'Wessex'	CRos LRHS NRHS

Verbena (*Verbenaceae*)

(G)	see *Glandularia*
Aztec Series	see *Glandularia* Aztec Series
§ ***bonariensis*** 𝕐H4	Widely available
– 'Little One'	ECha GBin MAsh
– 'Lollipop'PBR	Widely available
brasiliensis misapplied	see *V. bonariensis*
chamaedrifolia	see *Glandularia peruviana*
hastata	CAby CRos CSpe EBee ECtt EPfP LEdu LRHS MArl MEch MNHC MNrw NAln NRHS NSti SCob SEle SPer SPhx SPlb SRms SWvt WFar WMoo WOut XLum
* – 'Alba'	CAby CSpe CTsd ELan EPfP GCal MBel NLar NSti SCob WFar WMoo XLum
– 'Blue Spires'	CCBP CNor EPfP IPot SCob
– f. ***rosea***	CAby CBar CBre CElw CRos CSpe EHoe ELan EPfP GKev IPot LCro LEdu LOPS LRHS MNrw MRav NAln NDov NSti SPer SPhx WBor WCAu WFar WMoo WSHC XLum
– – 'Pink Spires'	ELan EMor EPfP LRHS SCob
– 'White Spires'	GQue LPot
lasiostachys	EBee
litoralis 'Kilmurry' **new**	IKil
macdougalii 'Lavender Spires'	CSpe IPot LRHS NDov SHar SPhx SRms WTre
officinalis	EBee ENfk GPoy MHer MNHC SRms WHer WSFF WTre
– var. ***grandiflora*** 'Bampton'	Widely available
Quartz Series	see *Glandularia* Quartz Series
§ ***rigida*** 𝕐H3	Widely available
– f. ***lilacina*** 'Lilac Haze'	CMac CRos EPfP LRHS NRHS
– – 'Polaris'	CBod CMea CRos CSam CSpe EBee ELan ELon EPfP EShb GWyn LRHS LSRN NAln NRHS SCob SPer
– 'Santos'	LRHS MHol NRHS
scabridoglandulosa	see *Junellia succulentifolia*
serpyllifolia	see *Junellia micrantha*
stricta	CFis EBee EWes NDov NLar SPhx
Superbena Series	see *Glandularia* Superbena Series
venosa	see *V. rigida*

Verbesina (*Asteraceae*)

alternifolia	EBee
– 'Goldstrahl'	EMor EPPr WFar
helianthoides	CSam

Vernicia (*Euphorbiaceae*)

fordii	SPlb

Vernonia (*Asteraceae*)

angustifolia	SPhx
angustifolia × ***missurica***	SHar WCot
§ ***arkansana***	CBod CSam EBee ECha ECtt EPPr EWes GLog IPot LEdu LRHS NLar NRHS SHar SPhx WFar
– 'Alba'	EBee ECtt EWTr
– 'Betty Blindeman'	EBee LEdu MNrw
– 'Mammuth' 𝕐H7	CKno EBee ECtt ELon EMor EWes IKil ILea IPot LEdu LRHS MNrw SMad SPhx SPoG WCot WTor
baldwinii	EBee LRHS SPhx
crinita	see *V. arkansana*
fasciculata	EWes LRHS MRav NLar SPhx WCot
gigantea	EWes MMuc MNrw NLar SMad
glauca	SPhx WCot
lettermannii 'Iron Butterfly'	EBee IPot SCob SMad

missurica	LEdu SPhx
noveboracensis	EAJP EBee EWhm LEdu NDai NLar SHar SMad XLum
- 'Albiflora'	EPPr EWes
- 'White Lightning'	EBee ECha EMor EPPr ILea NDai

Veronica (*Plantaginaceae*)

amethystina	see *V. spuria* L.
'Anna'PBR	MTis
armena	EWes MHer MMuc SBch SRot XSen
(Atomic Ray Series) 'Atomic Hot Pink Ray'	EBee WFar
- 'Atomic Pink Ray'PBR	EBee
§ ***austriaca***	NBre WMoo
- dark blue-flowered	NChi
- var. ***dubia***	see *V. prostrata*
- 'Ionian Skies'	CMea EBou ECha ECtt EPPr EWTr GBin NWad SIgm SPer WIce WKif WSHC
§ - subsp. ***teucrium***	CSam EBee SRms WKif
- - 'Blue Fountain'	CRos LRHS NRHS
- - 'Crater Lake Blue' ♀H6	CDor CRos CTri EBee ECtt ELan EPfP EWld GWyn LEdu LRHS MArl MAsh MAvo MBel MHol MRav NChi NRHS SPhx SPlb SRms WCAu WCot WFar WGwG WSHC
- - 'Kapitän'	CRos ECha ECtt GCrg LRHS NGdn NRHS WFar
- - 'Knallblau'	EAJP IKil NDov WFar
- - 'Lapis Lazuli'	EBee
- - 'Royal Blue' ♀H6	CAby CCBP CRos EAJP EBee EPfP GMaP LRHS MAsh MHol NRHS NSti SRms WArt WFar WKif WMoo XLum XSen
- subsp. ***vahlii***	LLHF
'Baby Doll'PBR	MBNS SPoG
beccabunga	CHab CWat EWat GPoy LLWG MMuc MWts NPer SEND WMAq WSFF WSpi
'Bergen's Blue'	NLar SHar WSHC
BLUE BOUQUET	see *V. longifolia* 'Blaubündel'
'Blue Indigo'	MAvo MNrw NBre NGdn
'Blue Spire'	WSpi
bombycina	WAbe
- subsp. ***bolkardaghensis***	WAbe
bonarota	see *Paederota bonarota*
caespitosa subsp. ***caespitosa***	EPot WAbe
candida	see *V. spicata* subsp. *incana*
× ***cantiana*** 'Kentish Pink'	WAul WCFE WFar WMoo XLum
chamaedrys	NMir XLum
CHRISTY ('Henslerone'PBR)	ECtt EPfP LBuc MHol NEoE SCob SRot
cinerea ♀H5	SBch SBrt SIgm WHoo WSHC XSen
DARK BLUE MOODY BLUES ('Novaverblu') **new**	WHil
'Darwin's Blue'	NLar
'Ellen Mae'	ECtt EWes MNrw WCAu WCot
'Eveline'PBR	ECtt EPfP MHol NDov NHpl NLar SPer WHil
exaltata (d)	NChi WSpi
'Fairytale'PBR	CRos LRHS MBNS NGdn NRHS
'Fantasy'	MAvo NDov WGoo
filiformis	XLum
formosa	see *Parahebe formosa*
§ ***fruticans***	GJos
gentianoides	Widely available
- 'Alba'	CMea GCal LEdu NBre
- 'Barbara Sherwood' ♀H7	CRos EBee EWTr LRHS NGdn NRHS WFar
- 'Blue Streak'	IKil XLum
- 'Little Blues' **new**	ECha EDAr GKev LSun
- 'Mountain Breeze'	CRos LBuc NRHS SPoG
- 'Pallida'	LPot MMuc MRav SCob SPlb WBor XLum
- 'Robusta'	CAby CBod GBin GMaP GWyn LRHS MWat NAln NGdn NRHS WFar WHoo
- 'Tissington White'	CAby CBod CRos EAJP EPfP GMaP LEdu LRHS MCot MHol MPie MPnt MTis NBir NBro NEgg NGdn NLar NRHS NWad SHar SPoG SRms WCAu WFar
- 'Variegata' (v)	EBee ECha ELan GMaP GWyn LRHS MRav NBir NEgg NRHS NWad SPer WRHF
'Giles van Hees'	ECtt MAsh
grandis	EBee IFro LEdu MMuc NLar SEND WArt WFar WHrl WMoo WPtf XLum
'Hocus Pocus'	ECtt
incana	see *V. spicata* subsp. *incana*
* - 'Candidissima'	GCal
'Inspiration'	NBre
'Inspire Blue'	CBod CRos LBuc LPot LRHS MMuc MPnt NRHS WJam
'Inspire Pink'	CBod CRos LRHS MPnt NRHS
kellereri	see *V. spicata*
kiusiana	CMea EBee ECtt LEdu NLar NWad
* - var. ***maxima***	CAby WPtf
liwanensis	EPot IMou MNrw WHal XSen
longifolia	CMac CSBt ECha ELan MBel NSti WMoo XLum
- 'Alba'	ELan MArl MMuc SEND WArt WMoo XEll XLum
- 'Antarctica'	EBee EWTr
- 'Blaubart'	XLum
§ - 'Blaubündel'	CRos LRHS NGdn NRHS
- 'Blauer Sommer'	EBee EPfP LRHS NEgg NGdn NRHS SPer
§ - 'Blauriesin'	ELan EPfP GBin GMaP GWyn MMrt NLar NSti SAko SPer SRms WSpi XEll
- BLUE GIANTESS	see *V. longifolia* 'Blauriesin'
- 'Blue John'	ECtt EPfP MPie NBre NDov NSti
- 'Charlotte'PBR (v)	CChe CDor CSpe CWGN EBee ECtt EMor EWTr GBin GWyn LCro LOPS LRHS MBel MHol MSCN MTis NDov NGBl SCob SHar SPer SPoG WCot WFar WHil WTyc
- 'Charming Pink'	CDor LRHS NDov SAko
- 'Christa'PBR	ECtt
- 'Fascination'	CBod ECtt EHoe MSCN NEoE NGdn
- FIRST GLORY ('Alllord'PBR)	CMea LRHS MAsh MHol NRHS SPad WHil
- FIRST KISS **new**	WHlf
- FIRST LADY ('Alllady'PBR)	CBod LRHS MAsh NRHS
- FIRST LOVE ('Alllove'PBR)	CMea CRos EBee EPfP LRHS MNrw NGdn NPri NRHS SPad SRms WHil
- 'Foerster's Blue'	see *V. longifolia* 'Blauriesin'
- 'Incarnata'	CRos EBee LRHS NRHS
- 'Joseph's Coat' (v)	NBre
- 'Lilac Fantasy'	MRav NSti
- 'Marietta'PBR	CBod CDor CRos ECtt EMor EWTr LCro LOPS LRHS MBel MHol MTis NCou NRHS SPer SPoG SRms WCot WHil WHoo WPnP WRHF WTyc

	- 'Melanie White'	SPer WHil WPnP
	- 'Oxford Blue'	CBar CBod
	- 'Pacific Ocean'PBR	NAln
	- 'Pink Eveline'PBR	EBee ECtt EPfP MHol NDov NGdn NLar STPC
	- pink-flowered	CMac
	- 'Rose Tone'	GJos WMoo
	- 'Schneeriesin'	CRos EBee ECha ECtt EPfP EWTr GBin GMaP LRHS MRav MTis NAst NBir NLar NRHS SAko SPer
	lyallii	see *Parabebe lyallii*
	'Martje'	XLum
	montana 'Corinne Tremaine' (v)	NBir SRms
	officinalis	GJos XLum
	oltensis	CPBP EPot ITim SIgm WAbe
	orchidea	see *V. spicata* subsp. *orchidea*
	orientalis subsp. ***orientalis***	EPot
	ornata	MAvo
	'Pacific Ocean'	ECtt NLar
	pectinata	ECtt
	- 'Rosea'	EWes XSen
	peduncularis 'Oxford Blue'	see *V. umbrosa* 'Georgia Blue'
	perfoliata	see *Parabebe perfoliata*
	petraea 'Madame Mercier'	EBou SRot XLum
	'Pink Damask'	CSpe ECtt ELan ELon EPfP GMaP MCot MRav MTis NGdn NLar SDys SRms WHoo
	'Pink Harmony'	MHol NGBl
	PINK MOODY BLUES ('Novaverpin') (Moody Blues Series) **new**	MHol WHil
	pinnata	SBrt
	- 'Blue Feathers'	WArt
	(Plumosa Series) PLUMOSA AMETHYST PLUME	MHol WFar
	- PLUMOSA BLUE PLUME	MHol
	- PLUMOSA LAVENDER PLUME	CWGN EBee EPfP
	porphyriana	MAsh MMuc NLar SAko
	prenja	see *V. austriaca*
§	***prostrata*** ♀H5	CBod CMea CSpe CTri ECtt EPfP GCrg GJos GKev LRHS MAsh MHol NEgg NHol SRms WHoo WIce WMoo
	- 'Aztec Gold'PBR	CMac
§	- 'Blauspiegel'	CPBP SIgm
	- BLUE MIRROR	see *V. prostrata* 'Blauspiegel'
	- 'Blue Sheen'	CRos ECtt EPfP LRHS MAsh NBir NRHS
	- GOLDWELL ('Verbrig') (v)	EBee ECtt EPPr SRot WFar
	- 'Lavender Mist'	CRos LRHS NRHS
	- 'Lilac Time'	CRos EBou ECtt LRHS MAsh NBir NHol NRHS SRms WHil WIce WRHF WTor
	- 'Little Nell'	ECtt
	- 'Loddon Blue'	SRms WCot
	- 'Mrs Holt'	CRos EBou ECtt GCrg LRHS MHer NBir NLar NRHS NWad SRms WHoo WJam
	- 'Nana'	CPBP EBou ECtt EPot EWes GCrg WAbe
	- 'Nestor'	CTri ECtt SRms WPtf XLum
	- 'Rhapsody in Blue'	CRos NRHS
	- 'Spode Blue' ♀H5	CMac CMea CRos CTri ECtt EUJe GCrg GKev GMaP GWyn LRHS MHer MMuc NRHS SPoG SRms
	- 'Trehane'	CAby CRos EBou ECtt EPfP GBin GCrg LRHS MAsh MHer MHol NEgg NRHS NRya NWad SPlb SPoG SRms WIce
	'Purpleicious Harmony'PBR	CBod EBee GBin MBel MTis SPer WFar WHil
	repens	NEoE SPlb
	'Rosalinde'	NGdn
	'Royal Pink'	MRav NLar
	rupestris	see *V. prostrata*
	saturejoides	CPBP SRms
	saxatilis	see *V. fruticans*
	schmidtiana 'Nana'	GAbr GKev
	selleri	see *V. wormskjoldii*
	'Shirley Blue' ♀H6	ELan EPfP EWTr ILea LCro LOPS LSRN MHer MJak MMuc SEND SPer SPhx SRms WCAu WCFE WSpi
§	***spicata***	CRos CSam ELan EPfP GJos LBuc LRHS MRav NBid NRHS SCob SRms WBrk WFar WJam WMoo WShi XLum
	- 'Alba'	CBcs EBee EPfP GJos LRHS MRav NLar WFar XLum
§	- 'Blaufuchs'	CSam
	- BLUE FOX	see *V. spicata* 'Blaufuchs'
§	- 'Erika'	ECtt EPfP GBin NBid NBir NGdn
§	- 'Glory'PBR	CBcs CDor CRos CWGN ECtt ELan LCro LOPS LRHS MBel MMrt MTis NPri NRHS SCob SPer SPoG WCot WHoo
	- 'Heidekind'	CBod CBor EBee EBou ECha ELan EPot GCrg GKev NBir NGdn SRms SRot WCAu WHoo WIce XLum
	- 'High Five'PBR	CBod EBee
	- subsp. ***hybrida***	WHer
I	- - 'Elaine's Form'	WCot
§	- 'Icicle'	EBee SCob WCAu
§	- subsp. ***incana*** ♀H4	EBou EHoe ELan EPfP MMuc SPlb SRms WCFE WMoo XSen
	- - 'Nana'	NBir SRms
	- - 'Silver Carpet'	ECtt LRHS MBel MRav NRHS WAul WSpi
	- - 'Wendy'	GCal
	- 'Nana Blauteppich'	NLar
§	- subsp. ***orchidea***	SRms
	- 'Pink Goblin'	ELan EPfP WArt
	- 'Pink Marshmallow' **new**	MSCN SRkn
	- 'Pink Panther'PBR	WCot
	- RED FOX	see *V. spicata* 'Rotfuchs'
	- 'Romiley Purple'	EBee SPer WSpi
	- 'Rosalind'	NLar
	- ***rosea***	see *V. spicata* 'Erika'
§	- 'Rotfuchs'	CBcs CBod CRos ECtt ELan ELon EMor EPfP GWyn LCro LOPS LRHS MBel MHer MRav NBid NBir NGdn NRHS SCob SPer SPoG SRms WCAu WCFE WFar WMoo
	- 'Royal Candles'	see *V. spicata* 'Glory'
	- 'Sightseeing'	GJos NBir SRms
	- SNOW CANDLES ('Joca128') **new**	LCro LOPS
	- subsp. ***spicata*** 'Nana'	XSen
	- 'Total Eclipse'PBR	EMor
	- 'Twilight'PBR	ECtt EPfP NLar
	- 'Ulster Blue Dwarf'	CRos EBee EPfP GMaP IMou LRHS MAvo NBid NGdn NRHS WCAu XLum

- YOUNIQUE BABY WHITE ('Versbabywhite') new — MBNS
§ ***spuria*** L. — SEND
stelleri — see *V. wormskjoldii*
subsessilis 'Blaue Pyramide' — WPtf
'Summer Breeze' new — NBro
'Sunny Border Blue' — EBee GWyn IKil MHol NLar
teucrium — see *V. austriaca* subsp. *teucrium*
thessalica — WHal
thymoides — SIgm
- subsp. ***pseudocinerea*** — SIgm
§ ***umbrosa*** 'Georgia Blue' ♀H5 — Widely available
urticifolia — SBrt
virginica — see *Veronicastrum virginicum*
'White Icicle' — see *V. spicata* 'Icicle'
whitleyi — MMuc
§ ***wormskjoldii*** — EBou GCrg GKev MBrN MMuc SRms

Veronicastrum ✿ (*Plantaginaceae*)

'Adoration' — CSpe EBee ECtt ELon EPPr GBin IPot LCro LOPS LRHS MBel MHol NDov NLar SMHy SPhx WCot WFar WSpi
axillare — IMou
brunonianum — GCal WSHC
japonicum — WCru
var. ***australe*** B&SWJ 11009
latifolium — WCot
- BWJ 8158 — EPPr ESwi NWad WCru WSHC
'Red Arrows' — Widely available
sibiricum — CKno CRos EBee ECha EPfP EShb GCal ILea LRHS MMuc NRHS SEND SHar SRms WMoo WSpi WWtn XLum
- BWJ 6352 — NLar WCru WFar
- 'Kobaltkaars' — SMHy
- var. ***yezoense*** — IMou WHoo
- - RBS 0290 — EPPr NEoE WFar
villosulum — EWes IMou NBid NBro WSHC XLum
§ ***virginicum*** — CKno CTri EBee ECtt EMor GPoy MAvo NBir NLar SRms WFar WJam WMoo WSpi WWtn XLum
- 'Album' ♀H7 — Widely available
- 'Apollo' — Widely available
- 'Cupid' — EBee ECtt EMor EPfP EWTr EWes GBin GMaP ILea LEdu LRHS MNrw NDov SHar WMoo WSpi
- 'Diane' — CBod EBee ECtt ELon EMor EPPr EPfP EWhm GMaP ILea IPot LEdu LRHS MAvo MCot MPie MTis NCGa NDov NLar SHar SPhx SWvt WCAu WMoo WSpi
- 'Du Jardin' new — LEdu
- 'Erica' — Widely available
- 'Fascination' — Widely available
- var. ***incarnatum*** — see *V. virginicum* f. *roseum*
- 'Klein Erica' — CBod
- 'Lavendelturm' ♀H7 — Widely available
- 'Pointed Finger' — CMea GCal GMaP LEdu LRHS NLar SPhx
§ - f. ***roseum*** — CBod CRos ECha ELan EMor EPPr GMaP GQue LRHS MHol MJak MRav NBro NDov NRHS SGbt SPhx SWvt WBor WHrl WKif WMoo WSpi XLum
- - 'Pink Glow' — Widely available
- 'Spring Dew' — CBre ILea LEdu LRHS MBel MNrw NBid NBro NEoE NGBl NLar SPhx WCAu WSpi
- 'Temptation' — EBee EPPr GMaP ILea IPot LEdu LRHS MAvo MRav MTis NBro NCGa NEoE NLar SPhx

Verschaffeltia (*Arecaceae*)

splendida — XBlo

Vesalea (*Caprifoliaceae*)

§ ***floribunda*** ♀H4 — CBcs CDul CExl CKel CMac CRos CSde ECre EHyd ELan ELon EPfP LRHS MAsh MGil MRav NLar SAko SGbt SPer SPoG SRms WCot

Vestia (*Solanaceae*)

§ ***foetida*** — CBcs CCCN CExl CKel CRos CTsd EBee ELan ELon EWld LRHS MGil MNrw MPie SBrt SEND WHil WPav
lycioides — see *V. foetida*

Viburnum ✿ (*Adoxaceae*)

sp. — LPra
NJM 11.008 new — WPGP
acerifolium — NWad
alnifolium — see *V. lantanoides*
atrocyaneum — CBod CExl CJun EWTr NWad SBrt WFar
- B&SWJ 7272 — EPfP WCru
- HIRD 113 — WPGP
betulifolium — CBcs CExl CJun CMCN EBee ELan EPfP EWes GKev GKin SAko WPGP
- f. ***aurantiacum*** — CJun
- 'Hohuanshan' — SSta WCru
bitchiuense — CJun NLar
× ***bodnantense*** — CMac CTri CWld EBee WFar
- 'Charles Lamont' ♀H6 — Widely available
- 'Dawn' ♀H6 — Widely available
- 'Deben' ♀H6 — CKel EPfP NLar SPer
brachyandrum B&SWJ 5784 — WCru
bracteatum — NLar
buddlejifolium — CKel CMac EBee EBtc EPfP EWes LRHS MMuc WCru
× ***burkwoodii*** — Widely available
- 'Anika' — NLar
- 'Anne Russell' — Widely available
- 'Chenaultii' — MRav
- 'Compact Beauty' — CJun WSpi
- 'Conoy' — CJun MAsh
- 'Fulbrook' — CRos EPfP LEdu LRHS MAsh NLar SSta
- 'Mohawk' ♀H6 — CEnd CJun CRos ELan EPfP LEdu LRHS MAsh MGos NLar NRHS SCob SCoo SWvt WCFE WSpi
- 'Park Farm Hybrid' ♀H6 — CExl CKel CMac CRos CTri EBee ELan ELon EPfP LEdu LRHS MAsh MGos MRav NHol NLar SPer SPoG SRms SSta SWvt WKif WSpi
calvum — CExl
aff. ***calvum*** WWJ 12012 — WCru
× ***carlcephalum*** ♀H6 — CAby CBcs CDul CEnd CMac CRos CTri ELan ELon EPfP GKin LCro LMaj LOPS LRHS MAsh MBlu MGos MRav MSwo NRHS SCob SEND SGol SPer SPoG SWvt

- 'Cayuga' ♀H5	ELon MAsh WSpi
- 'Van der Maat'	NLar
carlesii	CBcs CCVT CDul CMac CTri ELon EPfP EWTr GKin LSRN MBlu MGos MRav MSwo SCob SEWo SGol SLim SPer SRms WFar
- B&SWJ 8838	WCru
- 'Aurora' ♀H6	Widely available
- 'Charis'	CJun WKif WPGP
- 'Compactum'	CJun MAsh NLar SSta
- 'Diana' ♀H6	CAby CEnd CJun CMac CRos EBee ELon EMil EPfP LRHS LSRN MAsh MBlu NLar SCob SPer SPoG SSta WCFE WPGP WSpi
- 'Marlou'	CJun NLar
cassinoides	CJun WPGP
'Chesapeake'	CDul CJun EWes MMuc NLar SEND
chingii	CJun WCru WPGP
'Chippewa'	CJun
cinnamomifolium ♀H5	CBcs CExl CRos CSde ELan EPfP LMaj LRHS MAsh NLar SBrt SCob SEND SLon SPer SPoG WCot WSHC WSpi
costaricanum B&SWJ 10477	WCru
cotinifolium	CExl
- CC 4541	CExl NLar
cylindricum	CRos EPfP LEdu LRHS NLar WCru WPGP WPav
- B&SWJ 6479 from Thailand	WCru
- B&SWJ 7239	WCru
- B&SWJ 9719 from Vietnam	WCru
- HWJCM 434 from Nepal	WCru
- 'Chino-Crûg'	WCru
davidii ♀H5	Widely available
- (f)	CAby CBcs CMac CSBt ELan EPfP EWTr MAsh SPer SPoG SRms WCFE
- (m)	CAby CBcs CMac CSBt ELan EPfP SGbt SPer SPoG SRms
- 'Angustifolium'	CJun NLar WPGP
dentatum	EBtc
- AUTUMN JAZZ	see *V. dentatum* 'Ralph Senior'
- BLUE MUFFIN ('Christom')	SGol
- CHICAGO LUSTRE	see *V. dentatum* 'Synnestvedt'
- 'Moonglow'	NLar
- 'Morton'	SSta
- PATHFINDER ('Patzam') **new**	SSta
- var. ***pubescens*** 'Longifolium'	SSta
§ - 'Ralph Senior'	NLar
§ - 'Synnestvedt'	NLar
- 'White and Blue'	CJun NLar
dilatatum	EBtc
- B&SWJ 5844	WCru
- B&SWJ 8734	WCru
- B&SWJ 10830	WCru
- PAB 6831	LEdu
- 'Asian Beauty'	SSta
- CARDINAL CANDY ('Henneke')	NLar SSta
- 'Iroquois'	SSta
- 'Michael Dodge'	MBlu
- 'Sealing Wax'	NLar
'Emerald Triumph'	CJun
erosum B&SWJ 8735	WCru
- B&SWJ 8893	WCru
- B&SWJ 11083	WCru
erubescens	CJun NLar
- HWJK 2163	WCru
- VdL 4122	WPGP
- var. ***gracilipes***	CJun EPfP LLHF
- 'Ward van Teylingen'	NLar
'Eskimo' ♀H5	CBcs CCVT CMac CRos CSBt EBee ELan EPfP LRHS MAsh MBNS MBlu MGos SAko SCob SCoo SGol SLim SPoG SRms SSta SWvt
fansipanense B&SWJ 8302	WCru
- KWJ 12239	WCru
§ ***farreri*** ♀H6	CBcs CBod CDul CMCN CRos CSBt CTri EBee ELan EPfP EWTr LBuc LEdu LRHS LSRN MGos MRav MSwo NLar NWea SCob SGol SPer SWvt
- 'Album'	see *V. farreri* 'Candidissimum'
§ - 'Candidissimum'	CDul CExl CKel CMac ELan EPfP LRHS MRav NLar SGol SPer SPoG SRms SWvt WAvo
- 'December Dwarf'	CJun MMrt NLar
- 'Farrer's Pink'	CExl CJun NLar
- 'Nanum'	CJun CMac CRos EBtc ELan EPfP LRHS MAsh MBrN MRav WAvo
foetens	see *V. grandiflorum* f. *foetens*
foetidum	IArd
- var. ***rectangulatum*** B&SWJ 1888	WCru
- - B&SWJ 3451	WCru
formosanum CWJ 12460	WCru
fragrans Bunge	see *V. farreri*
'Fragrant Cloud'	SWvt
furcatum ♀H6	EPfP GKin IArd IDee LRHS NLar SAko
- B&SWJ 5939	WCru
- B&SWJ 10880	WCru
× ***globosum*** 'Jermyns Globe'	CJun CMac EPfP MRav NLar SCob SEND SGol SLon SPoG WFar
grandiflorum	NLar
- 'De Oirsprong'	NLar
§ - f. ***foetens***	LRHS
harryanum	EBtc EWTr IArd IDee NLar WCru WPGP WSHC
henryi	CJun EPfP IArd IDee WCFE
× ***hillieri*** 'Winton' ♀H6	CBcs CJun CKel CMac CRos EBee EPfP IArd LRHS LSRN MGos NLar NRHS SGol SLon SPoG SVen WFar WPGP WSpi
hoanglienense	EBee
- B&SWJ 8281	WCru
- HWJ 934	WCru
- KWJ 12283	WCru
- PAB 7833	LEdu
hupehense MF 93087 **new**	SSta
'Huron'	NLar
ichangense	CJun NLar
japonicum	CExl EBee
- B&SWJ 5968	WCru
× ***juddii***	Widely available
kansuense	CExl
- BWJ 7737	WCru
koreanum B&SWJ 4231	WCru
lantana	CCVT CDul CHab CLnd CMac CNWT CPer CTho CTri ECrN ELan EPfP EShb EWTr LBuc MMuc NWea SCob SEWo SPer SVic WMat WMou WTSh

	- 'Aureum'	EHoe EPfP MAsh MBlu NLar
	- var. ***discolor***	NLar
	- 'Mohican'	NLar
	- 'Xanthocarpum'	SWvt WFar
§	***lantanoides***	SSta
	aff. ***lautum*** B&SWJ 10290	WCru
	'Le Bois Marquis'[PBR]	CKel CRos EMil EPfP EShb EUJe LRHS LSRN MAsh MGos SGol SPoG WCot
	lentago	CMac EPfP
	lobophyllum	NLar
	luzonicum B&SWJ 3637	WCru
	- var. ***formosanum*** B&SWJ 3585	WCru
	- var. ***oblongum***	LLHF
	- - B&SWJ 3549	WCru
	- var. ***sinuatum*** B&SWJ 4009	WCru
	macrocephalum	CJun SLon SSta
	- 'Sterile'	CJun SSta
	mariesii	see *V. plicatum* f. *tomentosum* 'Mariesii'
	mullaha B&SWJ 2251A	WCru
	- GWJ 9227	WCru
	aff. ***mullaha*** GWJ 9388	WCru
	nervosum HWJK 2241	WCru
	- HWJK 2373	WCru
	nudum	EPfP IDee
	- BRANDYWINE ('Bulk')	SSta WPGP
	- 'Pink Beauty'	CBod CJun CKel CRos ECrN EPfP LCro LOPS LRHS LSRN MMrt NRHS SGol SPoG SSta SWvt WFar WGob WPGP WSpi
	- 'Winterthur'	CJun NLar SSta
	obovatum new	SBrt
	odoratissimum misapplied	see *V. odoratissimum* var. *awabuki*
	odoratissimum Ker Gawl.	EBee
	- RWJ 10046	WCru
	- var. ***arboricola*** B&SWJ 6913	WCru
§	- var. ***awabuki***	CExl ECre ELon EPfP LEdu LRHS MBlu MGos NLar SEND SGol SLim SPer WCot
	- - B&SWJ 8404	ESwi WCru
	- - B&SWJ 11374 from Wabuka, Japan	WCru
	- - 'Emerald Lustre'	CBcs LRHS WFar
	aff. ***odoratissimum*** B&SWJ 3913 from the Philippines	WCru
	oliganthum 'Kyo Kanzashi'	WPGP
	'Oneida'	CJun
	opulus	Widely available
§	- var. ***americanum***	NLar
	- - 'Phillips'	CAgr
	- - 'Wentworth'	CAgr
	- 'Amy's Magic Gold'	NLar
	- 'Apricot'	NLar
	- 'Aureum'	CMac CRos EHoe ELan EPfP LRHS MAsh MGos MMuc MRav NEgg NLar SCob SPer SPoG WCFE WMoo
	- var. ***calvescens*** B&SWJ 10544	WCru
	- 'Compactum' ♀H6	CBcs CDul CMac CRos CTri EBee ELan EPfP GKev LRHS LSRN MAsh MGos MMuc MRav MSwo NLar NPer SCob SCoo SGbt SGol SPer SPoG SWvt WMoo WPGP WSpi
	- 'Fructuluteo'	CMCN SCob SGol
*	- 'Harvest Gold'	SCoo SGol SLim
	- 'Lady Marmalade'	NLar
	- 'Nanum'	ELan EPfP EPot EShb GBin MRav NLar NWad
	- 'Notcutt's Variety' ♀H6	MAsh
	- 'Park Harvest'	CAby CDul CKel CRos EBee EBtc LRHS MAsh NLar SMad SWvt
§	- 'Roseum' ♀H6	Widely available
	- 'Sterile'	see *V. opulus* 'Roseum'
*	- 'Sterile Compactum'	SWvt
	- 'Sylvie'	NLar
	- 'Xanthocarpum' ♀H6	CBcs CDul CExl CMac CRos CTho EBee ELan EPfP EShb GBin LRHS MAsh MGos MMuc MRav MSwo NLar SCob SGol SLon SPer SPoG SRms SWvt WAvo WFar WSpi
	parviflorum	LLHF
	parvifolium	EPfP NLar
	- B&SWJ 3375	WCru
	- B&SWJ 6768	WCru
	phlebotrichum B&SWJ 11058	WCru
	- B&SWJ 11470	WCru
	pichinchense B&SWJ 10660	WCru
	plicatum	CTri
	- 'Nanum'	see *V. plicatum* f. *tomentosum* 'Nanum Semperflorens'
§	- f. ***plicatum***	EWTr SChF
	- - 'Grandiflorum'	CBcs CCCN CMac EPfP LRHS NLar SCob SPer SPoG WCFE
	- - 'Mary Milton'	CJun ELan IArd NLar SSta
	- - 'Pink Sensation'	CJun GBin NLar
	- - 'Popcorn' ♀H6	CExl CJun CKel CMac CRos ECrN ELan EPfP EShb LRHS LSRN MAsh NHol NLar SGol SPoG SSta
	- - 'Rosace'	CRos EPfP LRHS MBlu NLar NRHS SAko
	- - 'Rotundifolium'	IArd MAsh MGos MRav NLar WFar
	- - TRIUMPH ('Trizam')	NLar
	- 'Sterile'	see *V. plicatum* f. *plicatum*
§	- f. ***tomentosum***	IBal SGol SPoG
	- - 'Cascade' ♀H6	CJun CKel EWTr LRHS SAko WSpi
	- - 'Dart's Red Robin'	ECtt LLHF MAsh
	- - 'Elizabeth Bullivant'	CRos EPfP LRHS NRHS
	- - KILIMANJARO ('Jww1'[PBR])	CRos EBee EPfP EUJe GBin LCro LOPS LRHS LSRN MBlu MGos MThu NEoE NLar NRHS SGol SPer SPoG WMoo WSpi
	- - KILIMANJARO SUNRISE ('Jww5')	CBcs CRos CSBt LCro LOPS LRHS MGos NRHS SCoo SPer WHlf
	- - 'Lanarth'	CBcs CCCN CDul CExl CKel CMac CRos CSBt CTri ELan EPfP EShb LRHS LSRN MAsh MBlu MGos NLar SCob SCoo SGol SPer SWvt WSpi
§	- - 'Mariesii' ♀H6	Widely available
	- - 'Molly Schroeder'	NLar SSta
§	- - 'Nanum Semperflorens'	CBcs CDul CMCN CMac CMea CRos EMOT EPfP EShb LRHS MGos NLar NRHS SGol SPoG WFar
	- - 'Pink Beauty' ♀H6	CBcs CCCN CDul CJun CKel CMac CRos EBee ELan EPfP EWTr LCro LOPS LRHS LSRN MAsh MBlu MGos MRav NEgg NLar SCob SGol SPer SPoG SWvt WFar WKif WSHC WSpi

- - 'Rowallane'	NLar
- - 'Saint Keverne'	ELan GKin
- - 'Shasta'	CDul CJun CKel CMCN EMOT EPfP EWTr LRHS MMrt NLar SGol WFar WSpi
- - 'Shoshoni'	NLar SGol WPGP WSpi
- - 'Summer Snowflake' Υ[H6]	CBar CCCN CEnd CKel CRos CWGN ECrN EMOT EPfP EShb LRHS MAsh MSwo NLar NRHS SGol SPer SPoG WFar
- 'Watanabe'	see *V. plicatum* f. *tomentosum* 'Nanum Semperflorens'
'Pragense' Υ[H6]	CBcs CDul CJun CMCN EPfP LRHS MGos NHol NLar SPer
propinquum	WFar
- CWJ 12395	WCru
- CWJ 12426	WCru
- var. ***propinquum*** Guiz 222	WPGP
prunifolium	EBtc SGol WCru
- 'Mrs Henry's Large'	CJun EPfP NLar
× ***rhytidophylloides*** 'Alleghany'	NLar
- DART'S DUKE ('Interduke')	WCFE
- 'Willowwood'	CKel CRos ELan LRHS MAsh NLar SCob SPer
rhytidophyllum	CBcs CDul CKel CMac CNWT EBee ECrN EPfP LMaj LRHS MGos MJak MMuc MSwo NEgg NLar SCob SEND SGol SPer SRms SWvt WCFE WSFF
- 'Roseum'	CExl SWvt
- 'Wisley Pink'	MAsh
'Royal Guard'	CJun
sambucinum	EBee
- HWJ 838	WCru
- var. ***tomentosum*** HWJ 733	WCru
sargentii B&SWJ 8695	WCru
- f. ***flavum***	NLar
- 'Onondaga' Υ[H6]	Widely available
semperflorens	see *V. plicatum* f. *tomentosum* 'Nanum Semperflorens'
§ ***setigerum***	EBee EPfP IDee NLar
- BWJ 8409	WCru
- 'Aurantiacum'	NLar
sieboldii	EBtc
- B&SWJ 2837	WCru
- CWJ 12808	WCru
- 'Seneca'	LRHS NLar
subalpinum	NLar
taitoense CWJ 12406	WCru
taiwanianum B&SWJ 3009	WCru
- CWJ 12467	WCru
ternatum	EPfP
theiferum	see *V. setigerum*
tinoides B&SWJ 10612	WCru
tinus	Widely available
- 'Bewley's Variegated' (v)	EBee SCob SPer
I - 'Compactum'	SWvt
- 'Eve Price' Υ[H4]	Widely available
- 'French White' Υ[H4]	CBod CCCN CDul CKel CMac CPer EBee ELan EMOT EPfP EWTr LCro LOPS MGos MRav NLar SAko SCob SCoo SLim SRms SWvt
- 'Gwenllian' Υ[H4]	Widely available
- 'Israel'	LRHS MBNS
- 'Ladybird'	CKel
- 'Lisarose'[PBR]	CBar CBcs EBee EPfP LCro LOPS LSRN MAsh MGos NLar SPoG SWvt WSpi
- 'Little Bognor'	NLar
- 'Lucidum'	CBcs CCoa CSde EPfP LMaj LPra NLar SGol
- 'Lucidum Variegatum' (v)	CMac SLim WFar
* - 'Macrophyllum'	EPfP LRHS NLar SWvt
- 'Peter's Purple'	CRos EPfP LRHS NRHS SPoG
- 'Pink Prelude'	SCob
- 'Purpureum'	CBcs CKel CSBt EHoe ELon EMOT EPfP MAsh MGos MSwo NEgg NLar SCob SCoo SGol SLim SPer WFar
- SPIRIT ('Anvi'[PBR])	CRos CSBt ELan EPfP LRHS MAsh MMrt NEoE NLar NRHS NWad SCob SCoo SPoG SWvt
- 'Spring Bouquet'	CJun MAsh
- subsp. ***subcordatum***	see *V. treleasei*
- 'Variegatum' (v)	CMac CRos CTri EBee EHoe ELan EPfP LRHS MAsh MGos NEgg NLar NPol NRHS SCob SGol SLim SPoG SRms SWvt WFar
tomentosum	see *V. plicatum* f. *tomentosum*
§ ***treleasei*** B&SWJ 12544	WCru
trilobum	see *V. opulus* var. *americanum*
triphyllum B&SWJ 10757	WCru
- B&SWJ 14298	WCru
utile	WThu
aff. ***venustum*** B&SWJ 10477	WCru
wrightii	EPfP IArd IDee MRav NLar
- B&SWJ 5871	WCru
- var. ***stipellatum*** B&SWJ 5856	WCru
- - B&SWJ 8780A	WCru

Vicia (*Papilionaceae*)

americana	EBee
cracca	CHab NMir SPhx WSFF
oroboides	EBee
sativa	CHab

Vigna (*Papilionaceae*)

angularis new	SVic
caracalla	see *Cochliasanthus caracalla*
radiata new	SVic

Villaresia see *Citronella*

Vinca (*Apocynaceae*)

difformis	CBod CFis CSpe CTri ECha IDee LPla SPer SRms WAvo WHer XLum
- 'Alba'	CCBP CDor CSam
- Greystone form	CExl EBee EPPr SEND
- 'Jenny Pym'	CBod CChe CDor CExl CMac CRos CSam EBee EPPr EPfP EWes EWld LRHS MBNS NLar SBch SEND SPoG SRms WAvo WOut WRHF
- 'Ruby Baker'	CKel EPPr EPfP EWes NChi SPoG WAvo WFar
- subsp. ***sardoa***	CBod CKel CRos CSpe EPPr EPfP EWes LRHS WCot WFar
- 'Snowmound'	CBod CRos CSBt LRHS MRav NLar SPoG SWvt WAvo
herbacea RCB UA 21	WCot
'Hidcote Purple'	see *V. major* var. *oxyloba*
major	CBcs CBod CDul CFGn CSBt ELan EShb GPoy LBuc LCro LPot MAsh MGos MJak MSwo NPol NWea SCob SGbt SGol SLim SPer SRms WFar WMoo XLum XSen

	- 'Alba'	CMac
	- subsp. ***balcanica***	IMou XLum
	- 'Elegantissima'	see *V. major* 'Variegata'
	- var. ***hirsuta*** misapplied	see *V. major* var. *oxyloba*
§	- subsp. ***hirsuta*** (Boiss.) Stearn	CMac WCot XLum
§	- 'Maculata' (v)	CBcs CKel CSBt ECrN EShb GWyn LRHS MSwo SCob SEND SGol SLim SPer SPoG SWvt WAvo WMoo WOut
§	- var. ***oxyloba***	CBod CCBP CExl CFis CKel CRos CTri ECha ELan EPPr EPfP LPot LRHS MRav SCob SRms WAvo WHer
	- var. ***pubescens***	see *V. major* subsp. *hirsuta* (Boiss.) Stearn
	- 'Surrey Marble'	see *V. major* 'Maculata'
§	- 'Variegata' (v) ♀H6	Widely available
	- 'Wojo's Jem' (v)	CAby CBod CMac CPla CRos ELan EPfP EWes LRHS MGos NCou NLar NRHS SCob SWvt WAvo WCot WMoo
	minor	CBar CBcs CDul CRos CSBt ELan GAbr GBin GKin GPoy LCro LOPS LRHS MAsh MGos MJak NRHS NWea SCob SLim SVic WFar XLum
	- f. ***alba***	CBcs CBod CDul CMac CRos ECha EMOT EPPr EPfP EWTr LCro LOPS LRHS LSRN MAsh MBel NLar NRHS SCob SGol SPer WCot WFar WOut XLum
§	- - 'Alba Variegata' (v)	CBar CExl EHoe IFro LSRN NEoE NWad SRms WCot WFar WHoo WOut WWtn
	- - 'Gertrude Jekyll'	Widely available
	- 'Alba Aureovariegata'	see *V. minor* f. *alba* 'Alba Variegata'
§	- 'Argenteovariegata' (v) ♀H6	CBcs CDul CMac CSBt CSam CTri ECha ELan ELon EMOT EPfP LRHS MGos MJak MMuc MSwo NChi NRHS SCob SGol SLim SPer SRms WFar
§	- 'Atropurpurea' ♀H6	Widely available
	- 'Aurea'	CBod
I	- 'Aureomarginata' (v)	EBou WMoo
§	- 'Aureovariegata' (v)	CBcs CMac CRos EBee ELan EPPr EPfP GAbr MGos MJak MRav NWea SGol SLim SPer SPlb
§	- 'Azurea Flore Pleno' (d) ♀H6	CKel CMac CRos CTri ECha EPPr EPfP GAbr GBin IFro LRHS MAsh MRav NChi NLar NRHS SLim SPer SPoG SRms SWvt WFar WHoo WKif WMoo XLum
*	- 'Blue and Gold' (v)	EPPr SCob
	- 'Blue Drift'	EWes MSwo
	- 'Bowles's Blue'	see *V. minor* 'Bowles's Variety'
	- 'Bowles's Purple'	CBod CTsd GMaP NCou SPer
§	- 'Bowles's Variety' ♀H6	Widely available
	- 'Burgundy'	SRms
	- 'Caerulea Plena'	see *V. minor* 'Azurea Flore Pleno'
	- 'Dartington Star'	see *V. major* var. *oxyloba*
	- 'Double Burgundy'	see *V. minor* 'Multiplex'
	- 'Evelyne'[PBR] (v)	WFar
	- 'Flower Power'	EPPr
	- GREEN CARPET	see *V. minor* 'Grüner Teppich'
§	- 'Grüner Teppich'	SGol WFar
	- 'Halstenbek'	XLum
	- 'Illumination' (v)	Widely available
	- 'Josefine'	MHol NLar
	- 'La Grave'	see *V. minor* 'Bowles's Variety'
	- 'Marie'	EPPr MBel NLar
	- 'Mrs Betty James' (d)	WCot
§	- 'Multiplex' (d)	EPPr GBin LBuc MSwo SGol SLim SRms WOut
	- 'Purpurea'	see *V. minor* 'Atropurpurea'
	- 'Ralph Shugert' (v) ♀H6	CExl CKel CMac CRos ELon EMOT EPPr EPfP EWes LCro LOPS LRHS MAsh MGos MJak NLar NPri NRHS SCob SCoo SEle SGol SPoG SRms WFar WMoo
	- 'Rubra'	see *V. minor* 'Atropurpurea'
	- 'Sabinka'	EPPr
	- 'Silver Service' (d/v)	MRav WFar
	- 'Snowdrift'	EPPr
	- 'Variegata'	see *V. minor* 'Argenteovariegata'
	- 'Variegata Aurea'	see *V. minor* 'Aureovariegata'
	- 'White Gold'	NEoE
	- 'White Power'	EPPr EWes

Vincetoxicum (*Apocynaceae*)

cretaceum PAB 3432	LEdu
forrestii	CExl
fuscatum	IMou
hirundinaria	EBee EPPr GPoy LEdu
nigrum	EBee GCal NChi WCot

Viola ✿ (*Violaceae*)

	'Ada Segre' (Vt)	CGro
	'Admiral Avellan'	see *V.* 'Amiral Avellan'
	'Admiration' (Va)	WGoo
	adunca var. ***minor***	see *V. labradorica* ambig.
§	***alba***	EWes
	'Alethia' (Va)	GBee SDys WGoo
	'Alice Kate' (Va)	WGoo
	'Alice Witter' (Vt)	CGro LLHF SHar
*	'Alison' (Va)	NDov WGoo
	'Amelia' (Va)	WGoo
§	'Amiral Avellan' (Vt)	CGro
	'Amy' (Va)	EVic
	'Annaleisia' (Vt)	CGro
	'Annette Ross' (Va)	GBee GWyn NDov WGoo
I	'Annie' (Vt)	CGro LLHF
	'Ardross Gem' (Va)	WGoo
	'Arkwright's Ruby' (Va)	MAsh
	arvensis	CHab
	'Ashvale Blue' (dPVt)	CGro
	'Aspasia' (Va) ♀H5	GAbr GWyn MAsh WGoo
	'Avril Lawson' (Va)	GBin GKev NAln SHar WGoo
	'Barbara' (Va)	ECtt WGoo
	'Baroness de Rothschild' misapplied	see *V.* 'Baronne Alice de Rothschild'
	'Baroness de Rothschild' ambig. (Vt)	CGro WHer
§	'Baronne Alice de Rothschild' (Vt)	CDor SHar WCot
	'Beatrice' (Vtta)	WGoo
	'Becky Groves' (Vt)	CGro
	'Beetroot' (Vt)	CGro
§	'Belmont Blue' (C)	CRos CSam CSpe CTri EBee ELon EWes GBin GCal GKev GMaP IPot LCro LOPS LRHS MAsh MCot MHer MRav NAln NBir NDov SCob SHar SPer SPhx WCAu WFar WGoo WSpi
§	***bertolonii***	CRos WGoo
	'Beshlie' (Va) ♀H5	WGoo
	biflora	EWld MNrw
	'Blackout'[PBR] (C)	ECtt MHol
	'Blue Butterfly' (C)	GWyn
	'Blue Carpet' (Va)	LRHS NRHS
	'Blue Horns' (C)	ELon
	'Blue Moon' (Celestial Series) (C)	MAsh WGoo

	Name	Suppliers
	BLUE MOON ('Smev1') (Va)	GWyn
	'Blue Moonlight' (C)	MPie
	'Blue Sails' (Va)	EVic
	'Blue Tit' (Va)	ECtt
	'Bonny' (Va)	EVic
	'Boughton Blue'	see *V.* 'Belmont Blue'
	'Bournemouth Gem' (Vt)	CDor CGro
§	'Bowles's Black' (T)	CSpe EPfP EShb LEdu NBro SRms
	brevistipulata var. ***hidakana***	GEdr WFar
	- var. ***laciniata***	GEdr
	'Bruneau' (dVt)	ECtt LEdu WCot WFar
*	'Bryony' (Vtta)	WGoo
	bubanii	CPla GKev
	'Bullion' (Va)	WGoo
	'Burncoose Yellow' (Va)	WGoo
	'Buttercup' (Vtta)	ECtt GWyn MHol SDys SPoG WGoo
	'Butterpat' (C)	MAsh NDov SHar WFar WGoo
	'Buxton Blue' (Va)	WGoo
	'Candy' (Vt)	CGro EBee
	canina	EMor NBro
	'Carol' (Vt)	CGro
	'Carol Loxton' (Vt)	CGro EBee
	'Catalina'	CGro
	CELESTIAL TWILIGHT ('Smev3') (C)	EBee MHol
§	***chaerophylloides*** var. ***sieboldiana***	SBrt
	- - pink-flowered	SBrt
	'Charles William Groves' (Vt)	CGro ELon
	'Charles Winston Groves' (Vt)	CGro
	'Charlotte' (Va)	GWyn WGoo
	'Chloe' (Vtta)	CGro
	'Christie's Wedding' (Vt)	CGro
	'Christmas' (Vt)	CGro
	'Clementina' (Va) 🏆H5	MRav WGoo
	'Cleo' (Va)	GWyn WGoo
	'Clive Farrell' (Vt)	MNrw
	'Clive Groves' (Vt)	CGro ELon
	'Coeur d'Alsace' (Vt)	CGro CLAP EBee ECtt GBin GMaP NLar SHar SRms WHal XLum
	'Colette' (Va)	WGoo
	'Colombine' (Vt)	CAby CGro MAsh NAln
	'Columbine' (Va)	CRos ECtt EPfP GMaP GWyn LRHS MHer MHol NBir NDov NRHS SPer SPoG WFar WGoo WTor
§	'Conte di Brazza' (dPVt)	GWyn NLar SHar WHer
	'Copperfield' (P)	CRos NRHS
	'Cordelia' (Vt)	CDor
	cornuta 🏆H5	CAby CDor CElw CMea GKev GWyn LRHS MMuc MNrw NBir NBro SCob SHar SRms WGoo WHoo
	- Alba Group (C) 🏆H5	Widely available
	- 'Alba Minor' (C)	CMea EPfP EWes MTin NBro NDov NRHS NSla SPhx WFar
	- 'Blaue von Paris' (C)	GWyn
	- blue-flowered	MHer
	- 'Cleopatra' (C)	MNrw MPie SPhx
	- 'Clouded Yellow' (C)	GWyn MNrw WFar
	- 'Gypsy Moth' (C)	GWyn SPhx
	- 'Icy But Spicy' (C)	EWTr GWyn IPot MAsh MRav NDov WGoo
	- Lilacina Group (C)	ECha MRav WPtf
	- 'Maiden's Blush' (C)	NAln WFar
	- 'Mark's Dainty' (C)	MPie
	- 'Minor' (C)	CSam EPfP MAsh NBro NDov NSla WGoo
	- 'Netta Statham' (C)	MPie WGoo
	- 'Pale Apollo' (C)	WFar
	- Purpurea Group (C)	CMea ECha
	- 'Rosea' (C)	ECha
	- 'Spider' (C)	GWyn MAsh MNrw MPie SDys WFar WGoo
	- 'Swallowtail' (C)	GWyn
	- 'Ulla' (C)	WHer
	- 'Victoria's Blush' (C)	CDor CElw CSpe ELon EWTr GMaP LRHS MAsh MPie NBir NDov SHar SPhx WGoo
	- 'Violacea' (C)	MAsh MPie
	corsica	CMea CPBP CSpe SPhx WOut
	'Covent Garden' (Vt)	CGro
§	***cucullata*** 🏆H5	SRms
§	- 'Alba' (Vt)	CBro CGro NBir SRms
*	- 'Striata Alba' (Vt)	NBro
	'Curlylocks'	ECtt
	'Czar'	see *V.* 'The Czar'
§	'Czar Bleu' (Vt)	CGro
	'Daisy Smith' (Va)	WGoo
	'Danielle Molly'	WGoo
	'Dawn' (Vtta)	CAby CBod CMea ECtt EPfP GBin GMaP GWyn NDov NLar SPoG WFar WGoo WTor
	'Delicia' (Vtta)	GWyn NDov SPhx WGoo
	'Des Charentes' (Vt)	CGro
	'Desdemona' (Va)	GKev GWyn WGoo
	'Devon Cream' (Va)	NAln WGoo
	'Diana Groves' (Vt)	CGro
	'Dick o' the Hills' (Vt)	CGro
	dissecta var. ***sieboldiana***	see *V. chaerophylloides* var. *sieboldiana*
	'Donau' (Vt)	CGro WCot WFar
	'Double White' (dVt)	CGro WHer
	'Duchesse de Parme' (dPVt)	CGro GMaP GWyn NLar SRms WHer
	'D'Udine' (dPVt)	CGro ECtt SRms WCot WHer
	'Dusk'	WGoo
	'E.A. Bowles'	see *V.* 'Bowles's Black'
	'Eastgrove Blue Scented' (C)	NAln SDys WGoo
	'Eastgrove Ice Blue' (C)	WGoo
	'Elaine Quin' (Va)	ECtt GWyn NDov NEgg NLar SPoG WGoo WKif
§	***elatior***	EPPr MNrw SBrt WArt
	'Eliza May Groves' (Vt)	CGro
	'Elizabeth' (Va)	WGoo
	'Elizabeth Lee' (Vt)	WCot
	'Elliot Adam' (Va)	WGoo
	'Emperor Magenta Red' (Vt)	EMor LEdu
	erecta	see *V. elatior*
	'Eris' (Va)	WGoo
	'Etain' (Va)	CAby CBod CRos ECtt ELan EPfP GMaP GWyn IPot LRHS MAsh MHol NEgg NLar NRHS SCob SPoG WFar WGoo WIce
*	'Fantasy'	WGoo
	'Fee Jalucine' (dVt)	CGro
	'Fiona' (Va)	MCot SPhx WGoo
	'Fiona Lawrenson' (Va)	WGoo
	'Florence' (Va)	GWyn NDov WGoo
	'Foxbrook Cream' (C)	MAsh WGoo
	'Francesca' (Va)	WGoo
	'Freckles'	see *V. sororia* 'Freckles'
	'Fred Morey' (Vt)	CGro
	glabella	SBrt
	'Gladys Findlay' (Va)	WGoo
	'Glanmore' (Vt)	WCot WFar
*	'Glenda'	WGoo
	'Glenholme' (Va)	GWyn MAsh NAln

	Name	Suppliers
	'Gloire de Verdun' (PVt)	CGro
	'Governor Herrick' (Vt)	CGro ECtt EHrv LLHF WCot WFar
	gracilis 'Lutea' (Va)	CSam
	- 'Major' (Va)	WGoo
	'Grey Owl' (Va)	WGoo
	'Grovemount Blue' (C)	CMea
	'Gustav Wermig' (C)	MAsh WGoo
	'Heartthrob' (v)	ECtt GEdr MNrw NBir NHpl NPri SPoG WBrk WHil WNPC
*	'Heaselands' (C)	SMHy
§	***hederacea***	CExl CTsd GQue GWyn SCob SRms WFar
§	'Helen Mount' (T)	GWyn
	'Helena' (Va)	GWyn WGoo
	'Hespera' (Va)	WGoo
	heterophylla subsp. ***epirota***	see *V. bertolonii*
*	'Hetty Gatenby'	WGoo
	'Holdgate'	WGoo
	'Hopleys White' (PVt)	CGro
	'Hudsons Blue'	CElw MNrw
	'Huntercombe Purple' (Va) ♀H5	CRos LRHS MAsh NBir NRHS SCob WGoo WHal WKif
	'Iden Gem' (Va)	ECtt WGoo
	'Inverurie Beauty' (Va) ♀H5	GBin GMaP GWyn NAln SDys WGoo WKif
	'Irish Elegance'	see *V.* 'Sulfurea'
	'Irish Molly' (Va)	ECtt ELan EPfP EShb GWyn MAsh NAln NEgg SPer SPoG WFar WGoo WIce WTor
	'Isabel' (Va)	SRms WGoo
	'Isabella' (Vt)	CGro EBee
	'Isobel'	MAsh
	'Ivory Queen' (Va)	GWyn MRav NAln SPhx WFar WGoo
	'Jack Sampson' (Vt)	EBee
	'Jackanapes' (Va) ♀H5	EBee ECtt ELan GWyn LRHS MAsh NLar NRHS SPer SPoG WGoo WTor
	'Jane Mott' (Va)	NAln
	'Janet' (Va)	EBee GWyn LSRN SDys SPoG
	'Janette' (Va)	NDov WGoo
	'Jean Jeannie' (Va)	GWyn NDov WGoo
	'Jeannie Bellew' (Va)	ECtt WGoo
	'Jennifer Andrews' (Va)	GWyn WGoo
	'Jenny Dickson'	CElw
	'Joanna' (Va)	WGoo
	'John Raddenbury' (Vt)	CGro
	'Johnny Jump Up'	see *V.* 'Helen Mount'
	jooi	CPla CSpe EPfP SIgm WAbe
	'Josephine' (Vt)	CGro
	'Josie' (Va)	GWyn WGoo
	'Joyce Gray' (Va)	WGoo
	'Joyce Mary Paul' (Vt)	CGro
	'Judy Goring' (Va)	ECtt GBee SPhx
	'Julian' (Va)	ECtt GWyn NAln WGoo
	'Jupiter' (Va)	GWyn WCot
	'Karpatenfrühling' (C)	WArt
	'Katerina' (Va)	WGoo
	'Kerry Girl' (Vt)	CGro
	'Kim' (Vt)	CGro
	'Kimberley's Alice' (Vt)	EBee
	'Kitten'	MAsh SDys SPhx WGoo
	'Kitty White' (Va)	GWyn NAln SDys SPhx
§	'Königin Charlotte' (Vt)	CGro CRos EMor EPfP GBin GMaP LRHS MHer NLar SRms WCAu WCot
	labradorica misapplied	see *V. riviniana* Purpurea Group
	- ***purpurea***	see *V. riviniana* Purpurea Group
§	***labradorica*** ambig.	CBod CTri EHrv EWTr GWyn NHpl SCob WCAu WHer
	'Lady Hume Campbell' (dPVt)	CGro WHer
	'Lady Jane' (Vt)	CGro
	'Lavender Lady' (Vt)	CGro
	'Lees Blue' (Vt)	CGro
	'Lees Peachy Pink' (Vt)	CGro MNrw
	'Letitia' (Va)	MAsh MNrw MRav SDys WGoo
	'Lianne' (Vt)	CGro LLHF SRms WCot
	'Lindsay'	WGoo
	'Lisa Tanner' (Va)	GWyn WGoo
	'Little Angel' (Va)	ECtt
	'Little David' (Vtta) ♀H5	CTri ECtt MCot NDov WGoo
	'Lord Plunket' (Va)	WGoo
§	'Lord Primrose' (Celestial Series) (Va)	MHol
	'Lorna Cawthorne' (C)	MAsh SDys WGoo
	'Louisa' (Va)	GWyn WGoo
	'Lucy' (Va)	MAsh
§	***lutea***	SHar WGoo
	- subsp. ***elegans***	see *V. lutea*
	'Luxonne' (Vt)	CGro
	'Lydia Groves' (Vt)	CBod CDor CGro LLHF SRms WCot
	'Lydia's Legacy' (Vt)	CGro
	'Madame Armandine Pagès' (Vt)	CGro
	'Madeleine Mary Groves' (Vt)	CGro
	'Maggie Mott' (Va) ♀H5	ECha ECtt GWyn MAsh MRav WFar WGoo
	'Magic' (C)	NDov WGoo
	mandshurica f. ***albiflora***	SBrt
	- 'Fuji Dawn' (v)	GWyn WCot
	- f. ***plena*** (d)	GEdr
	- - white-flowered	GEdr
	mandshurica × ***patrinii***	SBrt
	'Margaret' (Va)	ECtt WGoo
	'Marie-Louise' (dPVt)	CGro GWyn SHar
I	'Mars'	LSRN WSpi
	'Martin' (Va) ♀H5	CAby CBod CMea ECha ECtt EPfP GMaP GWyn LRHS LSRN MAsh MCot MHer MHol NDov SPer SPoG WFar WGoo
	'Mary Mouse'	WGoo
	'Mauve Haze' (Va)	WGoo
	'Mauve Radiance' (Va)	WGoo
	'May Mott' (Va)	WGoo
	'Mayfly' (Va)	ECtt
	'Melinda' (Vtta)	WGoo
	'Mercury' (Va)	WGoo
	'Milkmaid' (Va)	NBir
	(Miracle Series) 'Miracle Bride White' (Vt)	CBod MHol SHar WFar
	- 'Miracle Classy Pink' (Vt)	CBod MHol SHar WFar
	- 'Miracle Ice White' (Vt)	CBod NLar SHar
	- 'Miracle Intense Blue' (Vt)	WFar
	- 'Miracle Vanilla White' (Vt)	SHar
	'Miss Brookes' (Va)	WGoo
	'Misty Guy' (Vtta)	MAsh WGoo
	'Molly Sanderson' (Va) ♀H5	CAby CPla CRos ECha ECtt ELan EPfP GWyn LRHS MAsh MHer NEgg NLar NRHS SCob SPer SPlb SPoG SRms WFar WGoo WIce
	'Moonlight' (Va) ♀H5	CRos ELan LRHS NRHS WGoo
	'Morwenna' (Va)	ECtt GWyn MAsh MCot NDov WGoo
	'Mrs Lancaster' (Va)	CAby EBee ECtt ELan GMaP GWyn LSRN NAln NBir NLar NWad SDys SPoG WFar WGoo WTor
	'Mrs Pinehurst' (Vt)	CGro EBee GMaP GWyn SRms

	Name	Suppliers
	'Mrs R. Barton' (Vt)	CDor CGro SRms WHil
	'Myfawnny' (Va)	CRos LRHS NDov NRHS SDys WFar WGoo WSpi
	'Neapolitan'	see *V.* 'Pallida Plena'
	'Netta Statham'	see *V.* 'Belmont Blue'
	'Nora' (Va)	ECtt NDov WGoo
	'Norah Leigh' (Va)	WGoo
	obliqua	see *V. cucullata*
	odorata (Vt)	CBcs CBod CGro CHab EBee EBou GPoy LCro LRHS MRav NGrd NMir SEND SRms SVic WJek WOut
	- 'Alba' (Vt)	CGro CLAP EBee ELan EMor EPfP LEdu MHer SEND SRms WCAu WFar
	- 'Alba Plena' (dVt)	EHrv
	- 'Amethyst Witch' (Vt)	CGro
	- apricot-flowered	see *V.* 'Sulfurea'
	- 'Bethan Davies' (d/Vt)	WCot
	- 'Christopher William Groves' (Vt)	CGro
	- 'Copper Pennies' (Vt)	CGro
	- 'Cyclops' (Vt)	CGro
	- 'Dawnie' (Vt)	CGro EBee
	- deep violet-flowered (Vt)	SPtp
	- 'Double Rose' (d)	WCot
	- var. ***dumetorum***	see *V. alba*
	- 'Elsmeer' (Vt)	ECtt WCot
	- 'Empress Augusta' (Vt)	CGro
	- 'Explorateur Dybowski' (Vt)	CGro
	- 'Hungarian Beauty' (Vt)	EBee LCro LOPS
	- 'Katy' (Vt)	CLAP
	- 'King of Violets' (dVt)	ECtt SHar SPer
	- 'Lees Ivory' (Vt)	CGro
	- 'Little Plum' (Vt)	CGro
	- 'Melanie' (Vt)	CDor CGro CLAP MNrw WArt WCot
	- 'Mrs R.O. Barlow' (Vt)	CLAP WCot WSHC
	- 'Piddle Pink' (Vt)	CGro
	- pink-flowered	see *V. odorata* Rosea Group
	- 'Princess Thirza' (Vt)	CGro
	- ***rosea***	see *V. odorata* Rosea Group
§	- Rosea Group (Vt)	CBod CDor MRav SEND SPer SRms WCot
	- 'Stonehill Shadow' (Vt)	WOut
	- 'Sulphurea'	see *V.* 'Sulfurea'
	- 'Vin d'André Thorp' (Vt)	CGro ECtt LEdu WCot
I	- 'Violett Charm' (Vt)	WCot
	- 'Wismar' (Vt)	WCot
	'Olive Edwards' (Va)	WGoo
	'Opéra' (Vt)	LLHF
	'Orchid Pink' (Vt)	CGro EBee GMaP LEdu MNrw
	orientalis	GEdr
§	'Pallida Plena' (dPVt)	CGro WHer
	palustris	EWat LLWG NLar WHer WSFF WShi
	'Pamela Zambra' (Vt)	CGro SHar WSHC
	papilionacea	see *V. sororia*
	'Parchment' (Vt)	CGro EBee GWyn
	'Parme de Toulouse' (dPVt)	CGro EWTr GWyn NLar WHer XLum
	'Pasha' (Va)	ECtt GWyn SDys
	'Pat Creasy' (Va)	NDov WGoo
	'Pat Kavanagh' (C)	MAsh WGoo
	'Patience'	WGoo
	'Patricia Lillington' (Va)	GWyn
	pedata	MPie WAbe
	- 'Bicolor' (Vt)	WAbe
	pedatifida white-flowered	GEdr WArt
	pensylvanica	see *V. pubescens* var. *eriocarpa*
	'Peppered-palms' (Vt)	EHrv
	'Perle Rose' (Vt)	CGro EHrv SHar
	'Petra' (Vtta)	GWyn SPhx WGoo
	phalacrocarpa	SBrt
	'Phyl Dove' (Vt)	WCot
	'Pickering Blue' (Va)	WGoo
	pinnata	CTri SBrt
	'Primrose Dame' (Va)	ECtt WGoo
	'Primrose Pixie' (Va)	WGoo
	'Prince Henry' (T)	MNHC
	'Prince John' (T)	MNHC
	'Princess Diana' (Vt)	EBee
	'Princess Mab' (Vtta)	WGoo
	'Princess of Prussia' (Vt)	CGro WCot
	'Princess of Wales'	see *V.* 'Princesse de Galles'
§	'Princesse de Galles' (Vt)	CGro CTri
§	***pubescens*** var. ***eriocarpa***	SRms
	'Purple Wings' (Va)	WGoo
	QUEEN CHARLOTTE	see *V.* 'Königin Charlotte'
	'Raven' (Va)	LRHS SPhx WGoo
	'Rebecca' (Vtta)	CAby CBod CDor CRos ECtt ELan EPfP EShb GKev GMaP GWyn IPot LRHS LSRN MAsh MCot MHol NBir NDov NEgg NLar NRHS SDys SPer SPoG WFar WGoo WHer WIce
	'Red Charm' (Vt)	CGro
	'Red Giant' (Vt)	CBod CGro EHrv LEdu MBNS MPie
	'Red Lion' (Vt)	CGro
	'Reine des Blanches' (dVt)	EBee ECtt LEdu SRms WCot
	'Reine des Neiges' (Vt)	CDor CGro EMor
	reniforme	see *V. hederacea*
	riviniana	GJos MMuc WHer WOut WSFF WShi
	- dark pink-flowered	MMuc WOut
§	- Purpurea Group	CBcs CBod CMac EBee ECha EHoe EPfP EWes LPot MHer MPie MRav MWat NBir NRya NSti SPer SPhx SPlb SRms WFar WJam WJek WMoo
	- 'Rosea'	WJek
	- white-flowered	EWes IFro
	'Roem van Aalsmeer' (C)	GBin
	'Roscastle Black' (Va)	CMea CSma EPfP GBee GWyn MAsh NDov WGoo WSpi
	'Royal Elk' (Vt)	CGro
	'Royal Robe' (Vt)	CGro
	'Rubra' (Vt)	EPfP SVic WArt XLum
*	***rupestris rosea***	CTri IFro WHer
	sagittata	LPot
	'Saint Helena' (Vt)	CGro
	'Sally' (Vtta)	CGro
	selkirkii Pursh ex Goldie	WThu
	- 'Variegata' (v)	XEll
	septentrionalis	see *V. sororia*
	'Serena' (Va)	WGoo
	'Sherbet Dip' (Va)	WGoo
	'Sidborough Poppet'	EWes
	'Silver Samurai' (Vt)	WCot
	'Smugglers' Moon' (Va)	ECtt GWyn WGoo
	somchetica	WCot
	'Sophie' (Vtta)	WGoo
	Sorbet Series	NPri
§	***sororia***	CBod ECha GWyn MNrw NBir NBro SCob SPhx WGwG
*	- 'Albiflora' 🏆^{H6} (Vt)	EAJP EMor EPPr EPfP LEdu LRHS LSun MRav NLar SCob SPhx WCFE WJek
	- 'Dark Freckles' (Vt)	CGro EBee EMor NLar NRya SPhx WFar
§	- 'Freckles' (Vt)	Widely available
	- 'Hungarian Beauty' (Vt) **new**	SPer

– 'Priceana' (Vt)	CBod EMor LEdu MPie MRav NBir SHar SPlb WCot WGwG
– 'Sorority Sisters' (mixed) (Vt)	NChi SVic
– 'Speckles' (Vt/v)	WCot
– 'Sweet Emma' (Vt)	SPhx
* 'Spencer's Cottage'	WGoo
STARRY NIGHT	see *V.* 'Lord Primrose'
'Steyning' (Va)	WGoo
stojanowii	CSpe LLHF
§ 'Sulfurea' (Vt)	CDor CLAP EBou EHrv EMor MRav WCot
'Sundowner' (Va)	ECtt
'Sunny Jim' (Va)	EVic
'Susan Chilcott' (Vt)	CGro
'Susanne Lucas' (Vt)	CGro
'Susie' (Va)	GWyn WFar WGoo
'Swanley White'	see *V.* 'Conte di Brazza'
'Sweetheart' (Va)	EVic
'Sybil' (SP)	WGoo
'Thalia' (Vtta)	GWyn
§ 'The Czar' (Vt)	CBre SHar WCot
'Tiger Eyes' (Va)	CMea SPoG
'Titania' (Va)	EBee
'Tom Tit' (Va)	ECtt WGoo
'Tony Venison' (C/v)	ELon EPfP GWyn MHol NEgg NLar WFar WGoo WHer
tricolor	CBod CHab ENfk EPfP EWhm GJos GPoy LCro LOPS MHer MNHC NGrd SRms
– 'Sawyer's Black'	ENfk WJek
vaginata	GEdr
verecunda B&SWJ 604a	WCru
§ – var. ***yakusimana***	WThu
'Victoria'	see *V.* 'Czar Bleu'
'Victoria Cawthorne' (C)	MAsh NDov WFar WGoo
'Violacea' (C)	MAsh
'Virginia' (Va)	GWyn WGoo
'Vita' (Va)	ECtt SRms WGoo
'Wasp' (Va)	ECtt
'White Ladies'	see *V. cucullata* 'Alba'
'White Pearl' (Va)	SPhx WGoo
'White Perfection' (C)	GWyn
'White Swan' (Va)	MAsh WFar
'White Witch' (Vt)	EBee
'Winifred Jones' (Va)	GKev WGoo
'Wisley White'	CRos EWTr LRHS
× ***wittrockiana*** Cool Wave Series (P) **new**	NPri
– Matrix Series (P)	NPri
– 'Viking Northern Lights' (Viking Series) (P)	MHol
'Woodlands Cream' (Va)	GWyn WGoo
'Woodlands Lilac' (Va)	WGoo
yakusimana	see *V. verecunda* var. *yakusimana*
yezoensis	SBrt
'Zara' (Va)	WGoo
'Zoe' (Vtta)	CBod ECtt EPfP GWyn LRHS MAsh NEgg SPoG WFar WGoo

Viscaria (*Caryophyllaceae*)

vulgaris	see *Lychnis viscaria*

Visnaga (*Apiaceae*)

§ ***daucoides***	CBre CHby CSpe LRHS MNHC SPhx SRms WHal
– 'Green Mist'	LCro LOPS

Vitaliana (*Primulaceae*)

§ ***primuliflora***	GKev NRya NSla
– subsp. ***cinerea***	EPot
– subsp. ***praetutiana***	CPBP GCrg NWad

Vitex (*Lamiaceae*)

agnus-castus	CAgr CBcs CLau CMCN CSde EAJP EShb GPoy LEdu LRHS MMrt MRav NLar SLon SPer WCFE WJek XSen
– f. ***alba***	CRos LRHS MBlu NLar NRHS SPoG XSen
– – PAB 9281	LEdu
– – 'Silver Spire'	EBee ELan EMil EPfP NLar SRms WPGP
– f. ***latifolia*** ♀^{H4}	CKel CRos ECre ELan EPfP LRHS LSRN MGos MHer MNHC NLar NRHS SEND SPoG WPGP
chinensis	see *V. negundo* var. *heterophylla*
incisa	see *V. negundo* var. *heterophylla*
negundo	LEdu
§ – var. ***heterophylla***	EWes SBrt XSen
trifolia 'Purpurea'	LRHS

Vitis ✿ (*Vitaceae*)

'Abundante' (F)	WSuV
'Alden' (O/B)	WSuV
'Amandin' (G/W)	WSuV
amurensis	EPfP WSpi
– B&SWJ 4138	WCru
– B&SWJ 4299	WCru
– B&SWJ 12568	WCru
'Atlantis' (O/W)	WSuV
§ 'Aurore' (W)	CAgr WSuV
'Autumn King'^{PBR} (W/S) **new**	LEdu
'Autumn Royal' (B/S) **new**	LEdu
'Baco Noir' (O/B)	CAgr SDea WSuV
'Bata' (O/R/B)	SDea
'Beauty Seedless' (B/S)	SDea
betulifolia	EPfP
'Bianca' (O/W)	SSFr WSuV
'Birstaller Muscat' (W)	WSuV
BLACK HAMBURGH	see *V. vinifera* 'Schiava Grossa'
* 'Black Strawberry' (B)	CAgr SDea WSuV
'Blanc Seedless' (W/S)	SDea
§ 'Boskoop Glory' (O/B) ♀^{H5}	CMac EMOT LBuc SCob SCoo SDea WSuV
'Brant' (O/B) ♀^{H5}	Widely available
'Brilliant' (B)	WSuV
'Buffalo' (B)	WSuV
'Cabernet Cortis' (B)	WSuV
californica (F)	EPfP NLar
'Canadice' (O/R/S)	SDea WSuV
'Cascade'	see *V.* SEIBEL 13053
'Castel 19637' (B)	WSuV
'Chambourcin' (B)	WSuV
CLARET CLOAK ('Frovit'^{PBR}) ♀^{H5}	CBcs CBod CRos ELan EPfP EUJe GBin LRHS LSRN MAsh MBlu NLar NRHS SCoo SPer SPtp WPGP WSpi
coignetiae ♀^{H5}	Widely available
– B&SWJ 4550 from Korea	WCru
– B&SWJ 4744	WCru
– B&SWJ 8553 from Korea	WCru
– B&SWJ 10882 from Japan	WCru
– B&SWJ 10908 from Japan	WCru
– var. ***glabrescens*** B&SWJ 8537	WCru
– 'Purple Cloak'	SCob
– Sunningdale form	EBee NLar WGrn
'Dalkauer' (W)	WSuV

I	'Diamond' (B)	WSuV
	'Dutch Black' (O/B)	WSuV
	'Edwards No 1' (O/W)	WSuV
	'Eger Csillaga' (O/W)	WSuV
	'Einset' (B/S)	WSuV
	ficifolia	see *V. thunbergii*
	flexuosa B&SWJ 5568	WCru
	- B&SWJ 6304	WCru
	- var. ***choii*** B&SWJ 4101	WCru
	- var. ***parvifolia***	NLar
	- - B&SWJ 1946	WCru
	'Fragola' (O/R)	CAgr CDul CFGn CMac CTri ECha EPfP EPom LRHS MAsh MCoo MRav NLar SDea SLim SPoG SRms WMat WSpi WSuV
	'Gagarin Blue' (O/B)	CAgr EPom SDea SVen WSuV
	'Glenora' (F/B/S)	CAgr WSuV
	'Hecker' (O/W)	WSuV
	henryana	see *Parthenocissus henryana*
	'Himrod' (O/W/S)	CCCN ELan SDea WSuV
	'Horizon' (O/W)	WSuV
	inconstans	see *Parthenocissus tricuspidata*
	'Interlaken' (O/W/S)	CAgr SDea WSuV
	'Johanniter' (W)	SPre WSuV
	'Kempsey Black' (O/B)	CAgr WSuV
	'Kozmapalme Muscatoly' (O/W)	WSuV
	'Kuibishevski' (O/R)	WSuV
	'Kyoho' (B) **new**	WSuV
	LANDOT 244 (O/B)	WSuV
	LANDOT 3217 (O/B)	WSuV
	'L'Arcadie Blanche' (W)	WSuV
	'Léon Millot' (O/G/B)	CAgr CSBt LSRN SDea WSuV
	'Lucy Kuhlman' (B)	WSuV
	'Maréchal Foch' (O/B)	WSuV
	'Maréchal Joffre' (O/R)	CAgr WSuV
	'Mars' (O/B/S)	WSuV
	'Merzling' (O/W)	WSuV
	'Munson R.W.' (O/R)	WSuV
	'Muscat Bleu' (O/B)	CCCN CFGn EPom LRHS MNHC NLar SKee SLim SPoG SSFr WMat WSuV
	'Nero'PBR (O/B)	CAgr
	'New York Muscat' (O/B) ♀H5	ECrN WSuV
	'New York Seedless' (O/W/S)	WSuV
	'Niagara' (O/W)	WSuV
	'Niederother Monschrebe' (O/R)	WSuV
	OBERLIN 595 (O/B)	WSuV
	'Orion' (O/W)	WSuV
	'Paletina' (O/W)	WSuV
	'Perdin' (O/W)	WSuV
	'Phönix' (O/W)	CAgr CCCN EPom LBuc LCro LOPS LRHS LSRN MAsh MGos NLar NRHS SKee SLim SPer SPoG SPre SSFr SVic WMat WSuV
	piasezkii var. ***pagnuccii***	WCru
*	'Pink Strawberry' (O)	WSuV
	'Pirovano 14' (O/B)	SDea WSuV
§	'Plantet' (O/B)	WSuV
	'Poloske Muscat' (W)	CCCN CFGn EPom NLar WMat WSuV
	pulchra	WCru
	purpurea 'Spetchley Park' (O/B)	CAgr WSuV
	quinquefolia	see *Parthenocissus quinquefolia*
	'Ramdas' (O/W)	WSuV
	RAVAT 51 (O/W)	WSuV
	'Rayon d'Or' (O/W)	WSuV
	'Regent'PBR (O/B)	CAgr CCCN CFGn CTri EPom LCro LOPS LRHS MCoo MGos NLar SKee SLim SPer SPoG SPre SVic WMat WSuV
	'Reliance' (O/R/S)	CAgr WSuV
	'Rembrant' (R)	CAgr WSuV
	riparia	NLar
	'Romulus' (O/G/W/S)	WSuV
	'Rondo' (O/B)	CAgr CFGn LRHS SDea SPre SVic WMat WSuV
	'Saturn' (O/R/S)	CAgr WSuV
	'Schuyler' (O/B)	CAgr WSuV
	SEIBEL (F)	CRos EPfP NRHS SDea
	SEIBEL 5279	see *V.* 'Aurore'
	SEIBEL 5409 (W)	WSuV
	SEIBEL 5455	see *V.* 'Plantet'
	SEIBEL 7053 (R)	WSuV
	SEIBEL 9549 (R)	WSuV
§	SEIBEL 13053 (O/B)	CMac CRos LRHS MAsh NRHS SDea SEND SRms WSuV
	SEIBEL 138315 (R)	WSuV
	'Seneca' (W)	WSuV
	'Serena' (O/W)	WSuV
§	'Seyval Blanc' (O/W)	CAgr MAsh SDea SEND SVic WSuV
	SEYVE VILLARD ambig.	CRos LRHS NPer
	SEYVE VILLARD 12.375	see *V.* 'Villard Blanc'
	SEYVE VILLARD 20.473 (F)	NPer
	SEYVE VILLARD 5276	see *V.* 'Seyval Blanc'
	'Sirius' (B)	WSuV
	'Solaris' (O/W)	LRHS MCoo MNHC NLar WMat WSuV
	'Stauffer' (O/W)	WSuV
	'Suffolk Seedless' (B/S)	WSuV
	'Tereshkova' (O/B)	CAgr SDea WSuV
	'Thornton' (O/S)	WSuV
§	***thunbergii*** B&SWJ 4702	WCru
	'Triomphe d'Alsace' (O/B)	CAgr CSBt MCoo NPer SDea SVic WSuV
	'Trollhaugen' (O/B/S) **new**	WSuV
	'Trollinger'	see *V. vinifera* 'Schiava Grossa'
	'Vanessa' (O/R/S)	EPom SDea SVic WSuV
	'Venus' (O/B/S) **new**	LRHS SVic
§	'Villard Blanc' (O/W)	WSuV
	vinifera	LMaj LRHS
	- 'Abouriou' (O/B)	WSuV
	- 'Acolon' (O/B)	WSuV
	- 'Adelheidtraube' (O/W)	WSuV
	- 'Albalonga' (W)	WSuV
§	- 'Alicante' (G/B)	CBcs SDea WSuV
	- 'Alphonse Lavalle' (O/B/S)	WSuV
	- 'Augusta Louise' (O/W)	WSuV
	- 'Auxerrois' (O/W)	WSuV
	- 'Bacchus' (O/W)	CAgr CFGn LRHS MNHC NLar SDea SLim SVic WMat WSuV
	- 'Baresana' (G/W)	EMOT SRms WSuV
	- 'Beauty'	CAgr
	- 'Black Alicante'	see *V. vinifera* 'Alicante'
	- 'Black Beauty' (B)	SDea
	- 'Black Frontignan' (G/O/B)	WSuV
	- BLACK HAMBURGH	see *V. vinifera* 'Schiava Grossa'
	- 'Black Monukka' (G/B/S)	WSuV
	- 'Black Prince' (G/B)	CAgr WSuV
	- 'Blue Portuguese'	see *V. vinifera* 'Portugieser'
§	- 'Bouvier' (W)	WSuV
	- 'Bouviertraube'	see *V. vinifera* 'Bouvier'
	- 'Buckland Sweetwater' (G/W)	SDea SLim WSuV

- 'Cabernet Sauvignon' (O/B) — CRos EPfP LRHS MAsh MGos NPer NRHS SDea SVic WSuV
- 'Cardinal' (O/R) — WSuV
- 'Carla' (O/R) — WSuV
- 'Centennial' (O/N/S) — WSuV
- 'Chardonnay' (O/W) — CAgr CCCN CRos LRHS LSRN MAsh NPer SDea SPre SVic WSuV

§ - 'Chasselas' (G/O/W) — CRos LRHS SDea WSuV
- 'Chasselas de Fontainebleau' (G/O/W) — SVic
- 'Chasselas d'Or' — see *V. vinifera* 'Chasselas'
- 'Chasselas Rosé' (G/R) — CAgr WSuV
- 'Chasselas Rosé Royal' (O/R) — CCCN SVic
- 'Chasselas Vibert' (G/W) — WSuV
- 'Chenin Blanc' (O/W) — SVic WSuV
- 'Ciotat' (F) — EShb MRav SDea WSuV
- 'Cot Précoce de Tours' (O/B) — WSuV
- 'Crimson Seedless' (R/S) — WSuV
- 'Csabagyöngye' (O/W) — WSuV
- 'Dattier de Beyrouth' (G/W) — WSuV
- 'Dattier Saint Vallier' (O/W) — SVic WSuV
- 'Dolcetto' (O/B) — WSuV
- 'Dornfelder' (O/R) — CCCN CFGn MNHC NLar SLim SPoG SVic WMat WSuV
- 'Dunkelfelder' (O/R) — WSuV
- 'Ehrenfelser' (O/W) — WSuV
- 'Elbling' (O/W) — WSuV
- 'Exalta' (G/W/S) — CCCN WSuV
- 'Excelsior' (W) — SDea WSuV
- 'Faber' (O/W) — WSuV
- 'Fiesta' (W/S) — WSuV
- 'Findling' (W) — WSuV
- 'Flame' (R/S) — CAgr CFGn SPer SVic WMat
- 'Flame Red' (O/D) — CCCN EPom LRHS
- 'Flame Seedless' (G/O/R/S) — CMac EPom WSuV
- 'Forta' (O/W) — WSuV
- 'Foster's Seedling' (G/W) — SDea WSuV
- 'Freisamer' (O/W) — WSuV
- 'Frühburgunder' (O/B) — WSuV
- 'Gamay Hâtif des Vosges' (B) — WSuV
- 'Gamay Noir' (O/B) — SVic WSuV
- Gamay Teinturier Group (O/B) — WSuV

§ - 'Garnacha Tinta' (G/B) **new** — SVic
- 'Gewürztraminer' (O/R) — CRos LRHS MAsh NRHS SDea SVic WSuV
- 'Glory of Boskoop' — see *V.* 'Boskoop Glory'
- 'Golden Chasselas' — see *V. vinifera* 'Chasselas'
- 'Goldriesling' (O/W) — WSuV
- 'Grenache' — see *V. vinifera* 'Garnacha Tinta'
- 'Gros Colmar' (G/B) — WSuV
- 'Grüner Veltliner' (O/W) — WSuV
- 'Gutenborner' (O/W) — WSuV
- 'Helfensteiner' (O/R) — WSuV
- 'Huxelrebe' (O/W) — SVic WSuV
- 'Incana' (O/B) — ELon LRHS MRav SVen WCFE WCot WPGP WSHC
- 'Irsai Olivér' (O/W) — WSuV
- 'Juliaumsrebe' (O/W) — WSuV
- 'Kanzler' (O/W) — WSuV
- 'Kerner' (O/W) — WSuV
- 'Kernling' (F) — WSuV
- 'King's Ruby' (F/S) — WSuV
- 'Lakemont' (O/W/S) — CAgr CCCN CFGn CMac CRos CTri ELan EMOT EPfP EPom LEdu LRHS MGos MNHC NLar NRHS SDea SEWo SKee SLim SPoG SPre SSFr SVic WMat WSuV
- 'Lival' (O/B) — WSuV
- 'Macabeo' — see *V. vinifera* 'Viura'
- 'Madeleine Angevine' (O/W) — CAgr CRos LRHS LSRN MAsh NPer NRHS SDea SPoG SVen SVic WSuV
- 'Madeleine Celine' (B) — WSuV
- 'Madeleine Royale' (G/W) — WSuV
- 'Madeleine Silvaner' (O/W) — CRos CSBt LRHS MAsh NPer NRHS SDea SPoG WSuV
- 'Madresfield Court' (G/B) — WSuV
- 'Merlot' (G/B) — CRos EPfP LRHS NRHS SDea SVic WSuV

§ - 'Meunier' (B) — SVic WSuV
- 'Mireille' (F) — SDea WSuV
- 'Morio Muscat' (O/W) — WSuV

§ - 'Müller-Thurgau' (O/W) — CRos LRHS LSRN MAsh SDea SPoG SVic WSuV
- 'Muscat Blanc à Petits Grains' (O/W) — SWvt WSuV
- 'Muscat Cannon Hall' (G/W) — CHll
- 'Muscat de Lierval' (O/B) — WSuV
- 'Muscat de Saumur' (O/W) — WSuV
- 'Muscat Hamburg' (G/B) — CRos LRHS LSRN MAsh SDea SWvt WSuV
- 'Muscat of Alexandria' (G/W) — CBcs CCCN CMac CRHN CRos CTri LRHS MRav NRHS SDea SLim SRms SVic WMat XBlo
- 'Muscat Ottonel' (O/W) — WSuV
- 'Muscat Saint Laurent' (W) — WSuV
- 'Nebbiolo' (O/B) — WSuV
- 'No 69' (W) — WSuV
- 'Noblessa' (W) — WSuV
- 'Noir Hâtif de Marseille' (O/B) — WSuV
- 'Olive Blanche' (O/W) — WSuV
- 'Optima' (O/W) — WSuV
- 'Ora' (O/W/S) — WSuV
- 'Ortega' (O/W) — CCCN WSuV
- 'Parellada' (W) **new** — SVic
- 'Perle' (O/W) — WSuV
- 'Perlette' (O/W/S) — CCCN CRos EPom LRHS WSuV
- 'Petit Rouge' (R) — WSuV
- 'Picurka' (O/W/S) **new** — SVic
- 'Pinot Blanc' (O/W) — CCCN CRos LCro LOPS LRHS MAsh SVic WSuV
- 'Pinot Gris' (O/B) — SDea SVic WSuV
- 'Pinot Noir' (O/B) — CCCN SDea SVic WSuV

§ - 'Portugieser' (O/B) — WSuV
- 'Précoce de Bousquet' (O/W) — WSuV
- 'Précoce de Malingre' (O/W) — CAgr SDea
- 'Prima' (O/B) — WSuV
- 'Primavis Frontignan' (G/W) — WSuV
- 'Purpurea' (O/B) ♀H5 — Widely available
- 'Queen of Esther' (B) — SLim WSuV
- 'Regner' (O/W) — WSuV
- 'Reichensteiner' (O/G/W) — CAgr SDea SVic WSuV
- 'Rhea' (G/O/R) **new** — SVic
- 'Riesling' (O/W) — CCCN CRos LRHS MAsh SVic WSuV

- RIESLING-SILVANER	see *V. vinifera* 'Müller-Thurgau'
- 'Rotberger' (O/G/B)	WSuV
- 'Royal Muscadine' (G/O/W)	WMat WSuV
- 'Saint Laurent' (G/O/W)	SVic WSuV
- 'Sauvignon Blanc' (O/W)	CCCN LRHS NRHS SVic WSuV
- 'Scheurebe' (O/W)	WSuV
§ - 'Schiava Grossa' (G/B/D)	CMac CRHN CRos CSBt CTri ELan EMOT EPfP EPom LCro LOPS LRHS LSRN MAsh MRav NPer NRHS SCob SDea SLim SPer SPoG SPre SVic SWvt WMat WSuV
- 'Schönburger' (O/W)	SDea SVic WSuV
- 'Schwarzriesling'	see *V. vinifera* 'Meunier'
- 'Sémillon' (G/O/W)	CRos LRHS LSRN MAsh SVic
- 'Senator' (O/W)	WSuV
- 'Septimer' (O/W)	WSuV
- 'Shiraz' (B)	WSuV
- 'Siegerrebe' (O/W/D)	CAgr CRos LBuc LRHS MAsh NPer SDea SPoG SVic WSuV
- 'Silvaner' (O/W)	WSuV
- 'Spetchley Red' (O/B) ♀H5	CKel CRHN EBee MNrw NLar WAvo WCot WCru WMou WPGP WSpi
- strawberry grape	see *V.* 'Fragola'
- 'Suffolk Red' (G/R/S)	SDea SVic
§ - 'Sultana' (W/S)	CAgr SDea WSuV
- 'Syrah' (G/B) new	SVic
- 'Tempranillo Tinto' (G/O/B) new	SVic
- 'Theresa' (O/W)	SLim WSuV
- 'Thompson Seedless'	see *V. vinifera* 'Sultana'
- 'Triomphrebe' (W)	WSuV
- 'Verdejo Blanco' (G/O/W) new	SVic
§ - 'Viura' (G/W) new	SVic
- 'Vroege van der Laan' (O/W)	EMOT NLar SRms
- 'Wrotham Pinot' (O/B)	SDea WSuV
- 'Würzer' (O/W)	WSuV
- 'Zweigeltrebe' (O/B)	WSuV
* 'White Strawberry' (O/W)	WSuV
'Zalagyöngye' (W)	CAgr WSuV

Vriesea (*Bromeliaceae*)

splendens ♀H1a	SPlb XBlo

W

Wachendorfia (*Haemodoraceae*)

multiflora	SVen
thyrsiflora	CBcs CBod CExl EBee LEdu SVen WPGP

Wahlenbergia (*Campanulaceae*)

congesta	NWad
pumilio	see *Edraianthus pumilio*
rivularis 'Snow-cap'	CPla
serpyllifolia	see *Edraianthus serpyllifolius*

Waldsteinia (*Rosaceae*)

fragarioides	EBee IMou NAln
geoides	EMor EPPr MGil MMuc NEoE WMoo XLum
- 'Goldkäfer'	IMou
ternata	Widely available
§ - 'Mozaick' (v)	EBee EPPr EShb EWes NBir NEoE
- 'Variegata'	see *W. ternata* 'Mozaick'

walnut, black see *Juglans nigra*

walnut, common see *Juglans regia*; also AGM Fruit Section

Wasabia (*Brassicaceae*)

wasabi	see *Eutrema japonicum*

Washingtonia (*Arecaceae*)

× ***filibusta***	CCCN SEND SPlb
robusta	EUJe IDee SPlb XBlo

Watsonia (*Iridaceae*)

aletroides	CPbh CPrp EBee GBin GCal GKev SDeJ SVen
amatolae	IBlr
angusta	CBor CExl CPrp EBee IBlr SPlb
ardernei	see *W. borbonica* subsp. *ardernei* (Sander) Goldblatt 'Arderne's White'
'Ballyrogan Early Pink'	IBlr
beatricis	see *W. pillansii*
§ ***borbonica***	CPrp EBee
- subsp. ***ardernei*** misapplied	see *W. borbonica* subsp. *ardernei* (Sander) Goldblatt 'Arderne's White'
§ - subsp. ***ardernei*** (Sander.) Goldblatt 'Arderne's White'	CBre CExl GBin GCal IBlr
- subsp. ***borbonica***	IBlr
- 'Peach Glow'	CPrp EBee ERCP GKev SDeJ
brevifolia	see *W. laccata*
brick red-flowered	EBee LEdu WPGP
coccinea Herb. ex Baker	CPbh
'Curly Blooms'	CPbh
'Dart Sea Trout'	EBee
fourcadei	ECre GCal
fulgens	LEdu
galpinii lavender-flowered	IBlr
- pink-flowered	IBlr
galpinii × ***knysnana***	IBlr
§ ***humilis***	CPrp EBee GCal
knysnana	EBee IBlr
§ ***laccata***	CPbh
- pink-flowered	EBee
latifolia	IBlr
lepida	CPbh SPlb
× ***longifolia*** dark red-flowered	GCal
marginata	CPbh CPrp EBee
meriana	EBee ERCP GBin GKev IBlr MHer MPie SDeJ
- var. ***bulbillifera***	CPrp EBee GAbr GBin GCal IBlr WSHC
peach hybrid	CSpe
'Peachy Pink Orphan'	EBee
§ ***pillansii***	CAbb CBcs CCCN CExl CPrp CSpe EBee ECre EWld GBin IBlr ILea LEdu LRHS NCGa SVen
- apricot-flowered	CAbb LRHS
- peach-flowered	CExl
- pink-flowered	CExl CPrp IKil
- red-flowered	CExl
pink-flowered	EBee
pyramidata	see *W. borbonica*
roseoalba	see *W. humilis*
'Stanford Scarlet'	CExl CPrp EBee ELon
tabularis	CPrp IMou
transvaalensis	EBee

'Tresco Dwarf Pink' CExl CPrp EBee LEdu WPGP
Tresco hybrids CAbb CAby CExl CPbh SRkn
vanderspuyae CExl CPrp
wilmaniae CExl CPrp EBee IBlr WFar
wordsworthiana GCal
zeyheri EBee

Wattakaka see *Dregea*

Wedelia (*Asteraceae*)

trilobata see *Sphagneticola trilobata*

Weigela ✿ (*Caprifoliaceae*)

CC 1231 CExl
'Abel Carrière' CMac CTri ECtt LPot NWea SRms WCFE WFar WSpi
§ ALL SUMMER RED ('Slingco 1'PBR) CRos CWGN EPfP LCro LOPS LRHS MAsh NEoE NRHS SPoG WSpi
'Avalanche' misapplied see *W.* 'Candida'
'Avalanche' Lemoine EPfP
'Avant Garde' IDee MAsh
BLACK AND WHITE ('Courtacad1'PBR) CBcs CKel CRos CSpe CWGN EPfP LRHS LSRN MAsh NEoE NLar NRHS SCob SEle SGol SPoG
'Boskoop Glory' SPer
§ BRIANT RUBIDOR ('Olympiade') (v) CAby CBod CMac CRos EHoe EMOT LRHS MAsh MGos MMuc MRav NEgg NLar NQui SCob SGol SLim SPer SPlb SPoG WAvo WFar WSpi
'Bristol Ruby' Widely available
'Bristol Snowflake' CBod CDul CMac EPfP EWTr MBlu MHer MSwo NBir NLar SLon SRms
§ 'Candida' CTri ELan EWTr MRav NLar SGol SPer WSpi
CAPPUCCINO ('Verweig 2'PBR) MBlu NLar SGol
CARNAVAL ('Courtalor'PBR) 🏆H6 CBcs MRav SCob
'Chameleon' MPkF NEoE SGol
coraeensis 🏆H6 CHll EPfP EWld IArd IDee MBlu MGil MMrt MNrw NLar SBrt SPer
- 'Alba' CHll
CRIMSON KISSES see *W.* ALL SUMMER RED
decora B&SWJ 10834 WCru
EBONY AND IVORY ('Velda'PBR) CRos LCro LOPS LRHS NRHS SGol
'Eva Rathke' NBir NLar NWea
'Evita' MBlu
floribunda B&SWJ 10831 WCru
florida CMac EPfP
- B&SWJ 8439 WCru
- f. ***alba*** CBcs
* - 'Albovariegata' (v) CExl
- 'Bicolor' CMac ELan
- EYECATCHER ('Walweigeye') (v) **new** MMrt
- 'Foliis Purpureis' CBar CBcs CBod CDul CExl CMac CRos EHoe ELan EPfP EWTr LRHS MAsh MGos MJak MMuc MRav MSwo NEgg NLar NWea SCob SGol SLim SPer SPlb SRms SWvt WAvo
- 'Gustave Malet' CMCN
- MAGICAL RAINBOW ('Kolmagira'PBR) CRos LBuc LCro LOPS LRHS MAsh MJak MPkF NEoE NRHS SGol SPoG
- 'Milk and Honey' CRos LRHS NRHS
- MINOR BLACK ('Verweig 3'PBR) CKel EPfP EUJe LRHS MGos MPkF NBro NEoE NHol NLar SGol SPoG WMoo
- MONET ('Verweig'PBR) (v) CDul CMac CRos EBee EHoe EPfP EShb LBuc LCro LOPS LRHS LSRN MAsh MGos MJak MMrt NBro NHol NRHS SCob SGol SLim SPer SPoG SRms WFar
- MOULIN ROUGE ('Brigela'PBR) CRos ELan EPfP LRHS MAsh MGos WCot
- 'Pink Princess' CRos LRHS MSwo
- RUBIGOLD see *W.* BRIANT RUBIDOR
- SUNNY FANTASY ('Kolsunn') ECrN MPkF NEoE WHil
- 'Versicolor' CExl SLon SRms
- WINE AND ROSES ('Alexandra'PBR) 🏆H6 CBod CDul CExl CKel CRos CSBt EHoe ELan EMil EPfP EShb LRHS LSRN MAsh MGos MRav NBro NEgg NLar NRHS SCob SEle SPoG SRkn SWvt WGrn
- 'Wings of Fire'PBR CRos LBuc LRHS NRHS SCob
'Florida Variegata' (v) 🏆H6 Widely available
'Gold Rush' NLar
'Golden Candy' NEoE SCob
hortensis CExl
- B&SWJ 10808 WCru
'Hulsdonk' NLar
japonica 'Dart's Colourdream' CAby EHoe EWes MMrt MMuc SCob SEND SGol WGrn
- 'Variegated Dart's Colourdream' (v) ELon
'Jean's Gold' ELan MBlu MRav
'Kosteriana Variegata' (v) CDul CKel CRos CSBt EBee EPfP LRHS MAsh MMuc NEgg SEle SRms
'Little Red Robin' NEoE SCob WFar
'Looymansii Aurea' CExl CTri ELan EPfP NLar SGol SPer SRms WFar
LUCIFER ('Courtared'PBR) WSpi
maximowiczii CExl LLHF
§ ***middendorffiana*** CBcs CExl CMCN CMac CRos CTri EBee ELan EPfP GBin LPot LRHS MAsh MBlu MGil MMuc MRav NEgg NLar NSti NSum SBrt SChF SCob SCoo SPer SPoG WCru WFar WPGP
- 'Mango' CRos LCro LOPS LRHS NRHS
'Minuet' CRos LRHS MRav MSwo NEoE SGol
'Mont-Blanc' MAsh MMrt
NAIN ROUGE ('Courtanin'PBR) CTri NLar
'Nana Variegata' (v) CExl CRos ECrN ELon EPfP LCro LRHS MJak NLar NRHS SCob WFar
NAOMI CAMPBELL ('Bokrashine'PBR) EBee EShb NEgg NLar SGol WMoo
'Newport Red' see *W.* 'Vanicek'
PINK POPPET ('Plangen'PBR) CKel CRos CSBt ELan EMOT EPfP GBin LCro LOPS LRHS LSRN MAsh MGos MPkF NLar NRHS SCob SCoo SLim SPoG SRkn SWvt WMoo
praecox ECrN
- B&SWJ 8705 WCru
'Praecox Variegata' (v) 🏆H6 CMac CRos CTri EPfP LRHS MAsh MRav NBir NRHS SPer SPoG SRms WCFE WKif
'Red Prince' 🏆H6 CRos CWCL EBee ELan EMOT EPfP LRHS MAsh MSwo NLar SCob SGol
RUBIDOR see *W.* BRIANT RUBIDOR
RUBIGOLD see *W.* BRIANT RUBIDOR
'Ruby Anniversary' CRos LBuc LRHS NRHS SLon
'Ruby Queen'PBR CMac EPfP
RUBY WEDDING LSRN
'Rumba' CMac MRav
sessilifolia see *Diervilla sessilifolia*

'Snowflake' SRms
'Stelzneri' MMuc
subsessilis B&SWJ 1056 WCru
- B&SWJ 4206 WCru
'Suzanne' (v) EPPr MAsh
'Tango' CRos LRHS MAsh NEoE WAvo WFar
§ 'Vanicek' MBNS NWea
'Victoria' CBod CDul CMac CRos ECrN ELan EPfP LRHS MGos MSwo NBir NWad SCob SGol SPer WMoo
WHITE LIGHTNING ('Wf-2009') (v) NEoE

Weldenia (*Commelinaceae*)

candida EPot GEdr IBlr LLHF NHar SChF WCot

Westringia (*Lamiaceae*)

brevifolia SVen
§ ***fruticosa*** ♀H1c CBcs CBod CCCN CSde SRms SVen
- 'Smokie' (v) CCCN CTsd
- 'Variegata' (v) CCCN CPbh CSde SRms SVen
longifolia CCCN
rosmariniformis see *W. fruticosa*
'Wynyabbie Gem' CAbb CBod CCCN CKel CROs EBee LRHS MNHC SEND SPoG SVen

whitecurrant see *Ribes rubrum* (W); also AGM Fruit Section

Wigandia (*Boraginaceae*)

caracasana CHll

Wikstroemia (*Thymelaeaceae*)

gemmata see *Daphne gemmata*

wineberry see *Rubus phoenicolasius*

Wisteria ✿ (*Papilionaceae*)

'Betty's Dwarf Blue' NLar
§ ***brachybotrys*** SCob WSpi
§ - f. ***albiflora*** 'Shiro-kapitan' ♀H6 CAby CBcs CEnd CFlo CKel CRHN CTri CWGN EPfP LSRN MAsh MGil MGos MMuc MRav NHol NLar SEND SLau SLim WPGP WSpi
- 'Okayama' ♀H6 CKel CRos EPfP LRHS NOra NRHS SLau SPer WMat
- 'Showa-beni' ♀H6 CAby CEnd CFlo CKel CRHN CRos CTri CWGN EMil EPfP LRHS MGil MGos MMuc NLar NRHS SCoo SEND SLau SLim SPoG WPGP WSpi
* - 'White Silk' CBcs CKel CRos EBee EPfP LRHS LSRN MGos SLon SPer SPoG WSpi
'Burford' see *W. floribunda* (Macrobotrys Group) 'Burford'
'Caroline' CBcs CCCN CFlo CKel CMac CRos CWCL CWGN EMil EPfP EWTr LRHS LSRN MAsh MGos MJak MRav NLar NOra NRHS SCob SLau SMad SNig SPer SPoG SRms WMat WPGP
floribunda CBcs CRHN SCob SEWo SGol
- B&SWJ 12748 from South Korea WCru
§ - 'Alba' ♀H6 Widely available
- 'Black Dragon' see *W. floribunda* 'Russelliana'
§ - 'Domino' ♀H6 CBcs CKel CMac CRos CWGN ELon EPfP IArd LRHS LSRN MAsh MGos MMuc MRav MSwo NLar SCoo SEND SGol SLau SLim SPer SSta
- 'Ed's Blue Dragon' (d) EBee
- 'Fragrantissima' see *W. sinensis* f. *alba* 'Jako'
- 'Geisha' CAby CBcs CEnd CFlo CKel CRos ELon LRHS NRHS SEND SNig SRms WPGP
- 'Golden Dragon' EPfP
- 'Harlequin' CBcs CFlo CRos CWCL EHyd ELon LRHS MMuc SEND
- 'Hon-beni' see *W. floribunda* 'Rosea'
- 'Honey Bee Pink' see *W. floribunda* 'Rosea'
- 'Issai Perfect' CRos EHyd LRHS LSRN NLar SCoo SLon
- 'Issai-naga' NLar
- 'Jakohn-fuji' see *W. sinensis* f. *alba* 'Jako'
- 'Kimono' SLau
§ - 'Kuchi-beni' CBcs CEnd CKel CRHN CRos ELan GBin LCro LOPS LRHS LSRN MGos MRav NHol NLar SEND SLau SMad SPer SPoG SRms
- 'Lawrence' ♀H6 CBcs CEnd CFlo CKel CMac CRos CWCL CWGN EBtc EUJe LRHS NLar SLau SPoG
- 'Lipstick' see *W. floribunda* 'Kuchi-beni'
- 'Longissima' see *W. floribunda* f. *multijuga*
- 'Longissima Alba' see *W. floribunda* 'Alba'
§ - (Macrobotrys Group) 'Burford' ♀H6 CBod CEnd CFlo CKel CMac CRos CWGN EBee EMil EPfP LRHS LSRN MAsh MNHC NLar NOra SCob SCoo SEND SLau SLim SRms WMat WPGP WSpi
- - 'Hocker Edge' SLau
- 'Magenta' CRos LRHS
§ - f. ***multijuga*** ♀H6 Widely available
- - 'Cascade' CBcs SNig
- MURASAKI-NAGA see *W. floribunda* 'Purple Patches'
- 'Nana Richin's Purple' CEnd CRos LRHS SLau
- 'Peaches and Cream' see *W. floribunda* 'Kuchi-beni'
- 'Pink Ice' see *W. floribunda* 'Rosea'
§ - 'Purple Patches' WSpi
- REINDEER see *W. sinensis* f. *alba* 'Jako'
§ - 'Rosea' ♀H6 Widely available
- 'Royal Purple' see *W. floribunda* 'Russelliana'
§ - 'Russelliana' ♀H6 CBcs CEnd CFlo CKel EMil EPfP GBin NLar SGol SLau SPoG
- 'Shiro-naga' see *W. floribunda* 'Alba'
- 'Shiro-noda' see *W. floribunda* 'Alba'
- 'Snow Showers' see *W. floribunda* 'Alba'
- 'Variegata' (v) CWGN
- 'Violacea Plena' see *W. floribunda* 'Yae-kokuryū'
- 'Yae-kokuryū' (d) ♀H6 Widely available
× ***formosa*** CEnd LCro LOPS SLau SLim
- 'Black Dragon' see *W. floribunda* 'Russelliana'
- 'Domino' see *W. floribunda* 'Domino'
- 'Issai' Wada *pro parte* see *W. floribunda* 'Domino'
- 'Kokuryū' see *W. floribunda* 'Russelliana'
- 'Yae-kokuryū' see *W. floribunda* 'Yae-kokuryū'
frutescens EBee EPfP
- 'Alba' see *W. frutescens* 'Nivea'
- 'Amethyst Falls'PBR CBcs CEnd CWGN ELan EShb EUJe IArd LCro LOPS LRHS LSRN MGos SCoo SLon SPoG
- 'Longwood Purple' CRos LRHS NRHS
§ - var. ***macrostachya*** 'Aunt Dee' CWGN NLar
- - 'Blue Moon' NOra
- - 'Clara Mack' CWGN
§ - 'Nivea' CRos LRHS NRHS

Kapitan-fuji	see *W. brachybotrys*
'Lavender Lace'	CBcs CKel CRos EPfP LRHS LSRN MAsh MJak NLar SLau
macrostachya	see *W. frutescens* var. *macrostchya*
multijuga 'Alba'	see *W. floribunda* 'Alba'
sinensis	Widely available
- f. ***alba***	CAby CAco CBcs CKel CMen CRos ELan EMOT EPfP LCro LOPS LRHS LSRN MAsh MGil MGos MSwo NRHS SCob SLau SPer SPoG SRms WFar
§ - - 'Jako' ♀H6	CEnd NHol
- 'Amethyst' ♀H6	CAco CArg CBcs CBod CEnd CKel CRos EPfP LCro LOPS LRHS LSRN MAsh MGil MGos MJak NRHS SLau SLim SPer WSpi
- 'Consequa'	see *W. sinensis* 'Prolific'
- 'Cooke's Special'	see *W. sinensis* 'Prolific'
- 'Oosthoek's Variety'	see *W. sinensis* 'Prolific'
I - 'Pink Ice'	EWTr SRms
- 'Prematura'	see *W. floribunda* 'Domino'
- 'Prematura Alba'	see *W. brachybotrys* f. *albiflora* 'Shiro-kapitan'
§ - 'Prolific' ♀H6	Widely available
- 'Rosea'	CAco LSRN SCob SWvt
- 'Shiro-capital'	see *W. brachybotrys* f. *albiflora* 'Shiro-kapitan'
'Tiverton'	CBcs MJak
§ × ***valderi*** 'Murasaki-kapitan'	CEnd CKel CMac CRos CTri CWGN EBtc EMil EPfP LRHS MGil SEND
venusta	see *W. brachybotrys* f. *albiflora* 'Shiro-kapitan'
- 'Alba'	see *W. brachybotrys* f. *albiflora* 'Shiro-kapitan'
- var. ***violacea*** misapplied	see *W.* × *valderi* 'Murasaki-kapitan'

Withania (*Solanaceae*)

somnifera	GPoy

Wittsteinia (*Alseuosmiaceae*)

vacciniacea	GEdr WCru

Wodyetia (*Arecaceae*)

bifurcata	XBlo

Wollemia (*Araucariaceae*)

nobilis	CAco CDTJ CTho EPfP ESwi EUJe GBin LRHS MGos NWea SArc

Woodsia ✿ (*Woodsiaceae*)

obtusa	CDTJ CKel CLAP CRos CWCL EFer EMor EPfP IBal ISha LRHS MMuc NBro NRHS SGol SPoG SRms SRot WCot XLum
polystichoides	SRms

Woodwardia ✿ (*Blechnaceae*)

from Emei Shan, China	CLAP
fimbriata ♀H3	Widely available
orientalis	CKel CLAP CRos EMor ESwi ISha LEdu LRHS NRHS WFib WPGP
- var. ***formosana*** B&SWJ 6865	ESwi WCru
radicans ♀H3	CKel EShb EWes WFib XBlo
unigemmata ♀H4	CBdn CLAP CRos EFer EShb EWes ISha LEdu LRHS NRHS SPlb WAbe WFib WHal WPGP
virginica	CLAP CRos ISha LRHS NRHS

Worcesterberry see *Ribes* 'Worcesterberry'

Wulfenia (*Plantaginaceae*)

amherstiana	GEdr GKev LEdu
baldaccii	GKev SBrt
carinthiaca	EBee GAbr GEdr GKev LEdu NBir NLar WCot XLum
- 'Alba'	GKev
× ***schwarzii***	CDor EBee IMou LEdu WSHC

Wurmbea (*Colchicaceae*)

§ ***stricta***	WCot

Wyethia (*Asteraceae*)

amplexicaulis new	GEdr
angustifolia	SBrt
helianthoides	SBrt
mollis B&SWJ 14067	WCru

X

Xanthisma (*Asteraceae*)

§ ***coloradoense***	LLHF NRHS NSla

Xanthoceras (*Sapindaceae*)

sorbifolium ♀H7	CAgr CBcs CMCN EBee ELan EPfP IMou MBlu MGil NLar SBrt SPoG WSpi

Xanthocyparis (*Cupressaceae*)

§ ***nootkatensis***	LPra
- 'Aurea'	CAco
- 'Boyko's Sundown'	NLar
- 'Flaming Arrow' new	NLar
- 'Glauca'	CAco NWea
I - 'Gloria Polonica' (v) new	NLar
- 'Golden Waterfall'	NLar
- 'Green Arrow' ♀H7	CKen NLar NOra NWea SLim WMat
- 'Jubilee'	SLim WCFE WMat
- 'Pendula' ♀H7	CAco CCVT CDul CKen ELan EPfP LPra LRHS MAsh MBlu NEgg WCFE
- 'Sparkling Arrow'	NLar
- 'Strict Weeper'	CAco CKen NLar SLim
vietnamensis	WPGP

Xanthorhiza (*Ranunculaceae*)

simplicissima	CBcs CDul EPfP LEdu MGil NLar SDys WCot WPGP

Xanthorrhoea (*Xanthorrhoeaceae*)

australis	SPlb
fulva	SPlb
glauca	CCCN
johnsonii	CKel SPlb
preisii	SPlb

Xanthosoma (*Araceae*)

violaceum	EUJe

Xerochrysum (*Asteraceae*)

§ ***bracteatum***	SVen
§ - 'Coco'	CSpe
§ - 'Dargan Hill Monarch'	CHII CSpe SRms

Xeronema (*Xeronemataceae*)

callistemon	CBcs CBrP CCCN

Xerophyllum (*Melanthiaceae*)

tenax	CAco LRHS

Youngberry see *Rubus* 'Youngberry'

Ypsilandra (*Melanthiaceae*)

cavaleriei	CExl GEdr WCot
thibetica	CBct CExl CMil CSpe EBee EPfP ESwi GCal GEdr GKev LEdu LRHS MNrw NLar WCot WCru WSHC
- narrow-leaved	WCru

Yucca ✿ (*Asparagaceae*)

aloifolia	CCCN CDTJ SArc SCob SPlb
angustifolia	see *Y. glauca*
angustissima	SIgm
arizonica	CDTJ
baccata	CAco CAgr CCCN SIgm SPlb XSen
campestris	CDTJ XSen
carnerosana	CDTJ
cernua	WCot
constricta	CDTJ
decipiens	XSen
§ ***elata***	CCCN CTsd XSen
§ ***elephantipes*** ♀H2	CDTJ EUJe LCro LOPS SEND
- 'Jewel' (v)	EUJe SEND
- 'Puck' (v)	SEND
- variegated (v)	SEND
faxoniana	CDTJ EUJe SPlb
filamentosa	CAco CBcs CCCN CDul CKel CMac CRos CTri EBee ELan EPfP EUJe LCro LOPS LRHS LSun MCri MGos MJak MMuc MSwo SCob SEND SGol SLim SPer SPlb SRms XSen
- 'Antwerp'	GCal
- 'Bright Edge' (v) ♀H4	CBcs CDul CMac CPla CTri ELan ELon EPfP EUJe LCro LOPS LSRN MRav MSwo SChr SCob SGol SLim SPer SWvt
- 'Color Guard' (v) ♀H5	CPla EPfP EUJe MJak SChr SPoG
- 'Garland's Gold' (v)	CBcs CCCN MJak
- 'Gold Heart' (v)	EUJe
- 'Variegata' (v)	CBcs SCob SRms
filifera	EUJe SPlb
flaccida	SCob XSen
- 'Golden Sword' (v) ♀H4	CBcs CMac CRos CTsd EBee ELan EPfP GMaP LRHS LSRN MAsh MGos MSwo SCob SGol SLim SPer SRms SWvt WFar
- 'Ivory' ♀H5	CTsd ELan ELon GBin GCal GMaP LSRN MRav NLar SRms
× ***floribunda***	SArc
§ ***glauca***	EPfP SPlb SPtp WCot XSen
gloriosa ♀H5	CBcs CMac CTri EUJe GKev NAln SArc SCob SEND SPlb SWvt WFar
- 'Aureovariegata'	see *Y. gloriosa* 'Variegata'
- BRIGHT STAR ('Walbristar'[PBR]) (v) ♀H5	SCob
§ - 'Variegata' (v) ♀H5	CBcs CDul CKel CMac CRos CSBt CTsd ELan ELon EPfP EUJe GMaP LRHS MRav NRHS SArc SCob SEND SLim SPer SPlb SPoG SRms SWvt WCFE
guatemalensis	see *Y. elephantipes*
harrimaniae	SIgm WCot
linearis	see *Y. thompsoniana*
mexicana	CDTJ
mixtecana new	XSen
queretaroensis	CDTJ
radiosa	see *Y. elata*
recurvifolia ♀H5	SArc
- BANANA SPLIT ('Monvil') (v)	EBee EPfP MAsh WCot
- 'Gold Stream' (v)	WCot
rigida	CDTJ EUJe XSen
rostrata	CCCN CDTJ EUJe SArc SPlb WCot XSen
- 'Sapphire Skies'	CMac CSpe EUJe WCot
rupicola	WCot XSen
schottii	EShb
§ ***thompsoniana***	CDTJ EUJe SIgm XSen
torreyi	CDTJ SIgm
'Vittorio Emanuele II'	SMad
whipplei	CCCN CKel CRos ELan EPfP LRHS SPtp WPGP XSen
- subsp. ***whipplei*** NJM 11.001	WPGP

Yushania (*Poaceae*)

KR 7698	ERod MWht
addingtonii new	XCre
§ ***anceps***	CAgr CBcs CDul CExl ENBC MMuc MWht SEND WMoo
- 'Pitt White'	CAgr CBdn CExl MWht
- 'Pitt White Rejuvenated'	ERod
brevipaniculata	ERod
chungii	CBdn CExl ERod MWht XCre
maculata	CAgr CDul CExl ERod MWht
§ ***maling***	CExl ERod
Yunnan 5	CExl MWht

Z

Zabelia (*Caprifoliaceae*)

§ ***biflora***	LRHS
§ ***triflora***	CExl CRos CTho LRHS MMuc NLar SEND WPGP WSHC

Zaluzianskya (*Scrophulariaceae*)

JCA 15665	WAbe
elongata	SPlb
microsiphon	SPlb
ovata	CPbh CSpe CWCL EPfP EPot EWld GBin GKev LCro LOPS MHer NAln NRHS NSla SIgm SPlb SPoG SPtp WIce XEll
- 'Orange Eye'	CPBP CPbh ECtt EWes GKev NAln NHpl NRHS NSla SIgm WIce
- 'Star Balsam'	CBod CPla NCou
pulvinata	SPlb
'Semonkong'	GCal SWvt

Zamia (*Zamiaceae*)

pumila	SPlb

Zamioculcas (*Araceae*)

zamiifolia	CCCN LCro LOPS

Zantedeschia (*Araceae*)

§ ***aethiopica***	Widely available
- 'Childsiana'	CRos EBee LRHS NRHS

- 'Crowborough' ♀H4	Widely available
- 'Glencoe'	CAby CBct CBod EBee ECtt GCal MAvo MHol SPad WBrk WCot WFar WRHF WSHC
- 'Glow'	CExl CMac ECtt WAvo WGwG
- 'Green Goddess' ♀H4	Widely available
- 'Little Gem'	SMad
- 'Luzon Lovely'	WCru
- 'Marshmallow'	ECtt ELan EPfP LRHS MAsh NRHS WAvo WFar WGwG
- 'Mr Martin'	CCCN ECtt ELon SWvt WCot WFar
- 'Pershore Fantasia' (v)	CDTJ CExl WAvo WCot WFar
- 'Pink Mist'	GKev
- 'Spotted Giant'	CDTJ
- 'White Gnome'	WCot WFar
- 'White Sail'	CBod ECtt ELan LRHS MRav NGdn NRHS WGwG WPtf
albomaculata	CTca GKev LAma SPlb WPGP
'Allure'PBR	GKev
'Anneke'	CCCN SDeJ
'Apricot Glow'	CHll GKev
'Ascari'PBR	CCCN
'Auckland'PBR	SDeJ
'Black Eyed Beauty'	GKev
'Black Eyed Lady' **new**	CBod
'Black Magic'	CCCN CMac GKev SChr
'Black Pearl'	LAma
'Black Star'	see *Z.* 'Edge of Night'
'Cameo'	CCCN GKev LAma SDeJ
'Cantor'PBR	CRos LRHS NRHS
(Captain Series) 'Captain Murano'PBR	SPoG
- 'Captain Prado'PBR	CRos LRHS NRHS SPoG
- 'Captain Romance'PBR	LCro LOPS
- 'Captain Tendens'PBR	SDeJ
'Chianti'	GKev SDeJ
'Crystal Blush'	LAma SDeJ
§ 'Edge of Night'	CCCN GKev SDeJ
'Elegant Swan'PBR	SCob
elliottiana ♀H1c	CBcs CTri LAma
'Festival'PBR **new**	SRms
'Flame'	CBcs CBod CCCN GKev MSCN
'Flamingo'PBR	GKev
'Garnet Glow'	CBod LCro LOPS MHol
'Helen O'Connor'	CExl
'Hercules'	ESwi
jucunda	GKev
'Kiwi Blush'	CAby CBod CBro CCCN CExl CRos CSam CSpe CTca ELan ELon EPfP LRHS NRHS WCot WFar WGwG
'Lime Lady'	ECha
'Majestic Red'	GKev
'Mango'	EShb LAma SRms
'Mercedes'PBR	CRos LRHS NRHS
'Mozart'	CCCN SDeJ
'Nightlife'PBR **new**	SRms
'Odessa'PBR	CBod LCro LOPS MSCN SPad
'Philomena'	CRos LRHS NRHS
'Picasso'PBR	CBcs CBod CCCN EPfP GKev MSCN SDeJ
'Pink Mist'	LAma SMad
'Pink Persuasion'	GKev LAma
'Pink Royalty'	CRos NRHS
'Pot of Gold'	GKev
'Red Alert'PBR	CBod CRos MSCN NRHS SPad
'Red Sox'PBR	CCCN SDeJ
rehmannii ♀H1c	GKev LAma SDeJ SRms
'San Remo'PBR	GKev
'Sapporo'PBR	CRos LRHS NRHS
'Schwarzwalder'PBR	EShb GKev
'Summer Sun'PBR	CRos LRHS NRHS
'White Flirt'PBR **new**	CRos LRHS NRHS
'White Giant'	EWat MAvo WPGP

Zanthorhiza see *Xanthorhiza*

Zanthoxylum (*Rutaceae*)

acanthopodium GWJ 9287	WCru
- PAB 8760	LEdu
- WJC 13653	WCru
aff. ***acanthopodium*** WJC 13795 **new**	WCru
ailanthoides	CDTJ EBee
- B&SWJ 11115 from Japan	WCru
- B&SWJ 11394 from Japan	WCru
- from Taiwan	WPGP
- f. ***inermis*** RWJ 10048	WCru
americanum	ELan ESwi LEdu
armatum	CAgr
- B&SWJ 12753	WCru
- CWJ 12824	WCru
- FMWJ 13091	WCru
- NJM 11.080	WPGP
- PAB 8902	LEdu
bungeanum BWJ 8040	ESwi WCru
dissitum FMWJ 13498 **new**	WCru
fauriei B&SWJ 11080	WCru
aff. ***fauriei*** B&SWJ 11371	WCru
- B&SWJ 11523	WCru
laetum FMWJ 13175	WCru
- WWJ 11678	WCru
myriacanthum B&SWJ 11844	WCru
oxyphyllum	CMCN LEdu
- GWJ 9428	WCru
- HWJK 2131	WCru
piperitum	CAgr GPoy LEdu WJek WPGP
- B&SWJ 8543	WCru
- B&SWJ 11377	WCru
- B&SWJ 14677 **new**	WCru
- purple-leaved	CBcs CDTJ CExl EBee LEdu WPGP
schinifolium	CAgr
- B&SWJ 8593	WCru
- B&SWJ 11080	WCru
- B&SWJ 11391	WCru
- B&SWJ 14654 **new**	WCru
simulans	CAgr CBcs CDul CExl ESwi LEdu MBlu SBrt WPGP
stenophyllum	CMCN
tomentellum B&SWJ 13903	WCru
aff. ***yuanjiangense*** FMWJ 13498 **new**	WCru

Zauschneria (*Onagraceae*)

arizonica	see *Z. californica* subsp. *latifolia*
§ ***californica***	CHll CTri MBrN SLon SWvt XLum
§ - 'Dublin' ♀H4	Widely available
- 'Ed Carman'	ECha ECtt EUJe MGil MMuc
* - subsp. ***garrettii***	SDys XLum
- 'Glasnevin'	see *Z. californica* 'Dublin'
§ - subsp. ***latifolia***	XLum
§ - subsp. ***mexicana***	SRms
- 'Olbrich Silver'	ECha EWes WHoo WKif XSen
- 'Solidarity Pink'	WAbe

- 'Western Hills' ♀H4	CFis CTri ECha EPfP EPot EWld MHer MMuc MRav SEND SIgm SPhx SRms SWvt WHoo XLum
§ **cana**	ECha
- from Santa Lucia Mountains, California	SBrt
- ***villosa***	see *Z. californica* subsp. *mexicana*
I 'Pumilio'	EPot NRHS
§ ***septentrionalis***	WAbe

Zea (*Poaceae*)

mays 'Variegata' (v) **new**	CSpe

Zebrina see *Tradescantia*

Zelkova ✿ (*Ulmaceae*)

abelicea	CMCN LRHS MBlu
carpinifolia	CDul CMCN SPlb WPGP
- PAB 13.047	LEdu
- NJM 13.014 from Azerbaijan	WPGP
- NJM 13.016 from Azerbaijan	WPGP
'Kiwi Sunset'	EPfP WMat
serrata ♀H6	CBcs CCVT CDul CLnd CMCN CMen EBee ECrN ELan EShb GQue LMaj LPra MGos MMuc NWea SEND SGol WHCr WMou
- B&SWJ 8491 from Korea	WCru
- 'Goblin'	CJun MBlu NLar
- 'Green Vase'	LMaj MBlu SCob
- 'Green Veil'	IDee
- 'Kiwi Sunset' PBR	CDul MGos NOra NWea SPoG
- 'Luminifera'	MBlu
- 'Musashino'	ESwi SGol
- 'Ogon'	EPfP SGol
- 'Urban Ruby'	LMaj
- 'Variegata' (v)	CJun CMac MBlu NLar SGol
× ***verschaffeltii***	CMCN EPfP IArd MBlu

Zenobia (*Ericaceae*)

pulverulenta	CBcs CMac CRos ELan EPfP LRHS MAsh MBlu MGil MGos SCob SLon SSta
- 'Blue Sky'	CBcs CBct CDul CMCN CRos EPfP LRHS MAsh MBlu MGos MPkF NLar SCob SPer SPoG SSta WPGP
- f. ***nitida***	CMac NLar
- 'Raspberry Ripple'	CBcs CRos LRHS MAsh NLar NRHS SPoG SSta
- 'Viridis'	NLar

Zephyranthes (*Amaryllidaceae*)

candida	CAby CBro CRos EBee EPot EShb EWld GKev LAma LRHS NRHS SChF SDeJ WAvo
citrina	CExl EShb GKev LAma SDeJ
'Krakatau'	WCot
La Bufa Rosa Group	CExl WCot
robusta	see *Habranthus robustus*
rosea	GKev SDeJ

Zigadenus (*Melanthiaceae*)

elegans	CRos EDAr GAbr IMou LEdu LRHS MAvo MHer NRHS SMad WSHC

Zingiber ✿ (*Zingiberaceae*)

clarkei	CTsd
mioga	CAgr CSpe CTsd EBee GPoy IMou LEdu LRHS SChr SPlb SRms WPGP
- 'Crûg's Zing'	LEdu MAvo SBrt WCru WPGP
- 'Dancing Crane' (v)	CMac LEdu SRms WPGP
- 'White Feather'	CTsd LEdu WPGP
officinale	GPoy SPlb SPre

Zinnia (*Asteraceae*)

DAHLIA-FLOWERED MIXED	LCro LOPS
elegans	SVic
- (Benary's Giant Series) 'Benary's Giant Lime'	CSpe
- - 'Benary's Giant Scarlet' **new**	CSpe
- 'Queen Lime Red' (Queen Series) (d) **new**	CSpe
'Red Spider'	CSpe

Zizia (*Apiaceae*)

aptera	SPhx
aurea	LRHS SBrt SPhx WSHC XLum

Ziziphus (*Rhamnaceae*)

§ ***jujuba*** (F)	CBcs MBlu
- 'Lang' (F)	CAgr
- 'Li' (F)	CAgr
sativa	see *Z. jujuba*

Zosima (*Apiaceae*)

absinthifolia	WCot

30
ANNIVERSARY
EDITION
RHS Award
of Garden Merit
Vegetables

AWARD OF GARDEN MERIT VEGETABLES

This is a directory of vegetables offered by nurseries participating in *RHS Plant Finder 2017* that have been awarded an RHS Award of Garden Merit (AGM). It does not represent a complete list of AGM vegetables.

Entries are accompanied by a short description and the relevant hardiness rating for the UK. **Hardiness ratings** are explained on p.39. The figures to the left of the rating indicate the year the Award of Garden Merit was made.

Vegetables present some nomenclatural peculiarities that may require explanation. Cultivars that are repeatedly raised by different growers, while retaining their essential characteristics, can become recognisably different. These strains are referred to as maintenances and are often distinguished by the use of **maintenance names** which exist separately from the cultivar name. Here maintenance names appear after the cultivar name separated by a dash following The Vegetable Seed (England) Regulations 2002.

ASPARAGUS (*Asparagus officinalis*)

01 H4 **'Backlim'**
F_1 hybrid; consistently high yield of large spears.
EPom

93 H4 **'Connover's Colossal'**
Early; heavy yield of good quality spears. Reconfirmed after trial 2001 and 2012.
EKin ELan LCro LOPS LSRN MCtn MNHC NRob SEND SVic

12 H4 **'Dariana'**
Bred in France. Sound yield of straight, green spears and tight buds of excellent flavour.
SDea

01 H4 **'Gijnlim'**
F_1 hybrid; early. Consistently high yield of mid-green spears with purple tips. Reconfirmed after trial 2012.
CRos EKin EPom LCro LOPS LRHS NRob SDea

12 H5 **'Guelph Millennium'**
Bred in Canada. Excellent cold tolerance. Lateness helps to avoid frost damage. Sound yield of slender stems with pleasing flavour.
EPom LCro LOPS NRob

AUBERGINE (*Solanum melongena*)

95 H1c **'Bonica'**
F_1 hybrid. Early-cropping, good quality, attractive glossy black fruits are a good size. Plants are tall, but also strong and vigorous. Reconfirmed after trial 2008.
MCtn

BASIL (*Ocimum basilicum*)

12 H1c **'Lemonade'**
Compact, even plant growing to c.30cm. Aromatic with a sherbet-lemon scent and taste. Fine leaves: keeled as young foliage. Flowers are white, and attractive to bees. Plants hold well and show good disease- and weather-resistance. Previously listed as basil (× *africanum*).
SRms

12 H1c **'Mrs Burns' Lemon'**
Tall, upright, neat habit, growing to c.60cm. Fine, mid-green leaves, aromatic and intensely lemon-scented. Flowers white, and attractive to bees.
EKin MCtn SRms WJek

BEANS

BROAD BEANS (*Vicia faba*)

95 H5 **'Aguadulce'**
Dark green foliage, showing some variability. Long pods; the highest yielding in the trial. May also be sold as 'Aquadulce'. November-sown.
CHby

93 H5 **'Aquadulce Claudia'**
Not too tall; a good compact plant. An early crop when spring-sown, but can also be sown in November. One of the most reliable cultivars for overwintering. Reconfirmed after trial 1999, 2011.
EKin LCro LOPS MCtn NRob

11 H3 **'De Monica'**
Short pods; well filled. Good ratio of seed to

pod; excellent cropping.
EKin MCtn

93 H3 **'Express'**
Quick to mature, with well-filled pods.
Spring-sown.
EKin MCtn

11 H3 **'Giant Exhibition Longpod'**
Smooth, slender pods of good length; long cropping period.
EKin MCtn NRHS NRob

93 H3 **'Imperial Green Longpod'**
Green-seeded, with long smooth pods; good green colour and flavour; particularly good for freezing. Reconfirmed after trial 1999, 2011.
Spring-sown.
EKin MCtn

99 H3 **'Masterpiece Green Longpod'**
Slender, well-filled pods; stands well; good green colour and flavour; suitable for freezing; reconfirmed after trial 2011.
Spring-sown.
EKin LCro LOPS

11 H3 **'Robin Hood'**
Green-seeded; 3–5 seeds per pod. Good yield. Dwarf cultivar, ideal for containers and small gardens.
MCtn

93 H3 **'The Sutton'**
Dwarf compact plants, with nice flavour; ideal for smaller gardens or containers and windy situations. Reconfirmed after trial 1999, 2011.
Spring-sown.
EKin LCro LOPS NRob SVic

99 H4 **'Witkiem' - Manita**
Traditional 'Witkiem' type; sets well. Good early yield, with uniform pods; reconfirmed after trial 2011. Spring-sown.
CHby EKin LRHS NRHS

Climbing French beans (*Phaseolus vulgaris*)

00 H2 **'Cobra'** (round)
Very high early yield; long, fleshy; very attractive; reconfirmed after trial 2008.
CHby EKin LCro LOPS MCtn NRob

93 H2 **'Eva'** (round)
Very early. Long straight fleshy pods, wider-podded than other round varieties. Reconfirmed after trial 2000 and 2008.
CHby

08 H2 **'Golden Gate'** (flat)
Good crop of golden, fleshy, flat pods with a sweet, fresh flavour.
CHby

93 H2 **'Hunter'** (flat)
Attractive long stringless pods. Slow to show seed development. Reconfirmed after trial 2000 and 2008.
EKin MCtn NRob

08 H2 **'Limka'** (flat)
Consistently high yields of good quality, flat, light green pods with a good flavour.
CHby

Dwarf French beans (*Phaseolus vulgaris*)

93 H2 **'Annabel'**
Dark green colour, compact habit, fine foliage, tender fleshy-tasting pods. Reconfirmed after trial 1996 and 2010.
EKin MCtn

01 H2 **'Safari'**
Short, slim, mid-green, round, attractive pods. Low yields.
EKin LRHS MCtn NRHS

93 H2 **'Sprite'**
Heavy yield, with long, dark green pods.
CRos EHyd EKin LOPS LRHS MCtn NRHS

10 H2 **'Stanley'**
Mid- to dark green colour; tender and sweet. Taller plant. Uniform and picks over long period.
MCtn

96 H2 **'The Prince'**
Excellent yield; straight pale green pods.
EKin NRob

Runner beans (*Phaseolus coccineus*)

93 H2 **'Achievement'**
Maincrop with long, smooth, slender pods.
MCtn

06 H2 **'Benchmaster'**
Long, fairly straight beans, good yield; reconfirmed after trial 2013.
EKin

06 H2 **'Celebration'**
High yield of attractive, straight, smooth, good quality, fleshy pods with good colour and flavour. Flowers are a decorative pink. Reconfirmed after trial 2013.
EKin

99 H2 **'Desiree'**
Stringless pods with thick fleshy walls.
EKin MCtn

99 H2 **'Enorma'**
Late; long, smooth, slender pods.
CHby CRos EHyd EKin LRHS NRHS

13 H2 **'Firestorm'**
Hybrid of runner and French bean parentage. Excellent yield, slender, smooth-skinned, fleshy pods. Self-setting.
EKin

99 H2 **'Lady Di'**
Attractive, blemish-free, long, slender pods.
CHby EKin LCro LOPS MCtn

93 H2 **'Liberty'**
Very long pods; a popular show variety.
NRob

13 H2 **'Moonlight'**
Hybrid of runner and French bean parentage; grown commercially. Very high yielding. Easy to pick; leaves pedicel behind on picking. Smooth, fleshy pods, of good length. Self-setting.
CRos EHyd EKin LRHS MCtn NRHS

99 H2 **'Red Rum'**
Good early and late yield; slim, straight, stringless pods of medium length. Reconfirmed after trial 2006, 2013.
EKin MCtn

06 H2 **'St George'**
Bicolour variety; prized for ornamental value. Some French bean parentage. Popular commercial variety; easy to pick, leaving pedicel behind. Slender beans, straight, pale green. Reconfirmed after trial 2013.
CHby

99 H2 **'White Emergo'**
Late; smooth, tender, uniform pods, with good colour.
CHby

99 H2 **'White Lady'**
Late; very fleshy pods. Reconfirmed after trial 2006, 2013.
CHby EKin LCro LOPS LRHS MCtn NRHS

Beetroot (*Beta vulgaris*)

05 H3 **'Alto'** (round red root)
F_1 hybrid; early. Cylindrical, uniform, smooth roots with very good internal colour. Potential to bulk up well.
EKin

93 H3 **'Boltardy'**
Good bolting resistance.
EKin LCro LOPS MCtn SVic

93 H3 **'Forono'** (long red root)
Open-pollinated. Cylindrical, with fairly smooth skins and roots of moderate uniformity; good internal colour. Slow to bulk up. Reconfirmed after trial 2005.
EKin

93 H3 **'Pablo'** (round red root)
F_1 hybrid; very early. Uniform roots with very smooth skins; very good internal colour and freedom from internal rings. Appears to have good bolting resistance. Widely used as a show cultivar. Reconfirmed after trial 2001 and 2005.
CRos EHyd EKin LRHS MCtn NRHS NRob

01 H3 **'Red Ace'** (round red root)
F_1 hybrid; uniform roots with good flesh colour and no rings.
EKin NRob

Borecole or curly kale (*Brassica oleracea* Acephala Group)

15 H5 **'Black Magic'**
Very dark green, strap-leaved type with small blisters. Good yield.
MCtn

99 H5 **'Redbor'**
F_1 hybrid. Tall plants with open habit; strongly curled purple-green leaves. Winters well. Reconfirmed after trial 2015.
EKin LCro LOPS MCtn NRob

93 H5 **'Winterbor'**
F_1 hybrid. Tall plants with finely curled blue-green leaves; winters well. Reconfirmed after trial 1999, 2015.
EKin MCtn

Broccoli (*Brassica oleracea* Italica Group)

See under calabrese for calabrese broccoli

Purple sprouting

13 H5 **'Cardinal'**
Tidy upright plants, some variability in height, as expected for open-pollinated cultivars. Dense spears of deep purple. Good for late crop.
EKin

95 H5 **'Claret'**
F_1 hybrid. Very tall; heavy yield of dark purple spears from March through April. Reconfirmed after trial 2013.
LRHS NRHS

95 H5 **'Red Arrow'**
Early to mid-season; long cropping period. Good winter hardiness; bushy, vigorous plants. Reconfirmed after trial 2003, 2013.
EKin MCtn

White sprouting

95 H5 **'White Star'**
Good weight; late white spears for cutting in April.
EKin

Brussels sprouts (*Brassica oleracea* Gemmifera Group)

99 H5 **'Cascade'**
F_1 hybrid; late. Smooth, clean, well-spaced, fairly round sprouts. Uniform plants which stand and yield well.
EKin

93 H5 **'Igor'**
F_1 hybrid. Mid- to late season; attractive, vigorous, uniform plants producing well-spaced, solid, round, mid-green sprouts. Reconfirmed after trial 2006.
NRob

06 H4 **'Maximus'**
F1 hybrid; early to mid-season. Uniform plants, producing a good crop of mid- to dark green, smooth, solid sprouts. Reconfirmed after trial 2015.
EKin LCro

CABBAGE (*Brassica oleracea* Capitata Group)

AUTUMN – SEPTEMBER TO NOVEMBER

09 H3 **'Minicole'**
F1 hybrid. Good early autumn cultivar with attractive round heads.
EHyd LRHS NRHS NRob

09 H3 **'Red Jewel'**
F1 hybrid. Attractive. Solid, round-headed red cabbage with upright foliage and a short core. Could be grown at a closer spacing.
NRob

SAVOY – SEPTEMBER TO MARCH

01 H5 **'Tundra'**
F1 hybrid; dark green, slightly blistered leaf; heads solid and attractive. Sweet-tasting; overwinters well. Reconfirmed after trial 2007.
EKin MCtn

01 H5 **'Wintessa'**
F1 hybrid; late. Dark green well-blistered leaves, with uniform well-filled heads of good quality and flavour. Plants stand well.
EKin

JANUARY KING – NOVEMBER TO MARCH

08 H5 **'Deadon'**
Uniform, attractive 'January King' type with a flattened round head.
EKin

08 H5 **'January King 3'**
Open-pollinated. Attractive heads that develop a good colour. Good yield and long spread of cut.
EKin MCtn

WINTER HYBRID – NOVEMBER TO MARCH

08 H3 **'Kilaton'**
Late-season, large, white cabbage with claimed resistance to clubroot.
EKin

SPRING

11 H5 **'Advantage'**
Good heart. Compact, uniform, with little bolting.
MCtn

93 H5 **'Duncan'**
F1 hybrid. Pointed cabbage; mid- to dark green uniform heads with well-closed bases. A good early yield; compact neat habit; plants heart slowly to produce small, solid, well-filled heads. Reconfirmed after trial 2001, 2011 as spring greens and hearted cabbage.
LRHS NRHS

11 H5 **'Spring Hero'**
Distinctive round-headed spring cabbage for overwintering. Large, dense ball-shaped heads. Blue-grey, rugose leaves. Showing excellent winter survival.
EKin

SUMMER – JUNE TO AUGUST

93 H2 **'Derby Day'**
Early. Bright, round, mid-green, well-filled heads. Reconfirmed after trial 1998.
CHby

02 H2 **'Greyhound'**
Early-maturing; pointed; pale to mid-green; medium to large frame.
EKin MCtn

02 H2 **'Hispi'**
F1 hybrid; early. Smooth, pointed, dark green outer leaves, with good uniformity and well-filled heart.
CHby EKin LOPS LRHS NRHS NRob

93 H2 **'Stonehead'**
F1 hybrid; late. Uniform, round, mid-green heads. Also useful for cropping into the autumn from later planting.
EKin LRHS NRHS NRob

CALABRESE BROCCOLI (*Brassica oleracea* Italica Group)

03 H3 **'Belstar'**
F1 hybrid; May-sown. Mid- to late season; uniform medium-sized plants, with attractive heads and medium to small buds.
EKin

07 H3 **'Green Magic'**
Autumn-cropping; very good yield of slightly domed, good-sized heads with small beads. Known to make good sideshoots. Reconfirmed after trial 2013.
EKin MCtn

13 H2 **'Ironman'**
Domed, larger heads of blue-green, tight buds, healthy foliage.
EKin

03 H3 **'Kabuki'**
F1 hybrid; May-sown; early. Short, compact plants, producing a good crop of medium green, deep, well-rounded heads with uniform buds. Average yield of medium-sized secondaries, produced 3 to 5 weeks after the primary heads. Could be closely spaced to produce baby heads. Reconfirmed after trial

2007, 2013.
EHyd LRHS MCtn NRHS

13 H2 **'Marathon'**
Dome-shaped heads, uniform, mid-size, held high.
EKin LRHS NRHS

Carrot (*Daucus carota*)

99 H3 **'Adelaide'**
F_1 hybrid; very early. Good weight and colour; sweet-flavoured; quickly forms very smooth, stump-ended roots; almost coreless; fine tops. Ideal for successional sowings and early sowing in frames. Reconfirmed after trial 2006 and 2010 as early, suitable for containers.
EKin

06 H3 **'Amsterdam Forcing 3'**
Open-pollinated. Relatively smooth with good flesh and core colour; bulks up well. Strong foliage that does not grow too tall.
EKin MCtn

05 H5 **'Eskimo'**
F_1 hybrid; medium-length, smooth roots with good colour. Useful size, well-filled. Grows with crowns at or below ground level, so very little crown discoloration. Good overwintering cultivar. Reconfirmed after trial 2014.
EKin MCtn

99 H3 **'Flyaway'**
F_1 hybrid. Maincrop; medium-length, well-filled, stump-ended roots with good flesh and core colour. Good strong tops. Partial resistance (i.e. lack of attraction) to carrot flies. Reconfirmed after trial 2006.
EKin LCro LOPS MCtn

10 H3 **'Marion'**
Early to mature; uniform crop of slightly tapered roots with good weight. Smooth skin, deep orange flesh and good core colour. Suitable for containers.
EKin

93 H3 **'Mokum'**
F_1 hybrid. Early to mature, good weight and sweet flavour. Slightly tapering roots, well-coloured to the tip; smooth skin; almost coreless. Good for bunching. Reconfirmed after trial 2010 as early, suitable for containers.
EHyd LRHS NRHS

99 H3 **'Nairobi'**
F_1 hybrid; second early / early maincrop. Strong tops, with uniform, broader-shouldered, cylindrical, stump-ended roots. Heavy yields. Reconfirmed after trial 2006, 2014.
EKin

93 H3 **'Napoli'**
F_1 hybrid, very early maturing. Slightly tapering; good weight. Smooth skin, core and flesh deep orange. Strong tops for easy pulling; quick to bulk up. Ideal for successional sowings and early sowing in frames. Reconfirmed after trial 2010 as early, suitable for containers.
EKin

14 H3 **'Resistafly'**
A 'Nantes' type. Bred for intermediate carrot-fly resistance. Smooth skin, good uniformity, well-stumped root, good colour, nice flavour.
SVic

05 H4 **'Sugarsnax 54'**
F_1 hybrid. Very long, smooth, 'Imperator' type with roots of good internal colour. Suited to deep, light soils. Commercially used, cut into short lengths and sold as pre-packed baton carrots.
MCtn

05 H3 **'Sweet Candle'**
F_1 hybrid; short, blunt, quite smooth, well-filled, uniform roots. Good internal colour. Reconfirmed after trial 2014.
EKin LCro LOPS MCtn NRob

Cauliflower (*Brassica oleracea* Botrytis Group)

Coloured and Romanesco

05 H3 **'Graffiti'**
F_1 hybrid. Small to medium, high quality, solid curds of a very attractive amethyst colour. The colour fades a little if boiled, and is retained better if steamed. The raw curds have a good flavour and would be a colourful addition to a salad or dish of crudités. Mid-season. Reconfirmed after trial 2006.
EKin LRHS NRHS

05 H3 **'Veronica'**
F_1 hybrid; appetising light green Romanesco type. Uniform good-sized, solid, well-shaped heads.
EKin

Summer – June to mid-July

06 H3 **'Avalanche'**
Hybrid; mid-season. Attractive, high quality, medium to large, white, solid curds.
EHyd LRHS NRHS

97 H3 **'Barcelona'**
F_1 hybrid; mid-season. Deep, round, solid, well-protected curds.
EKin

06 H3 **'Flamenco'**
Hybrid; mid-season to late. Very high quality, large to medium to large, white, solid curds with good depth.
NRob

97 H3 **'Nautilus'**
F_1 hybrid; late. Vigorous plants with deep, white, well-protected curds of excellent quality.
LRHS NRHS

WINTER FOR SPRING HEADING (MATURING FROM MARCH TO MAY)

05 H5 **'Aalsmeer'**
Open-pollinated cultivar; early mid-season. Produces medium to small, cream-coloured, slightly lumpy, well-protected curds that have a good depth. This cultivar produced several multiple heads and sideshoots, many of usable quality.
EKin NRob

CELERIAC (*Apium graveolens* var. *rapaceum*)

00 H4 **'Prinz'**
Smooth, deep, white-skinned; small to medium, flattened and round; compact plant with healthy foliage. Reconfirmed after trial 2011.
CHby EKin LCro LOPS MCtn SVic

CELERY (*Apium graveolens* var. *dulce*)

93 H2 **'Celebrity'**
Self-blanching, fairly short plants, with ribbed petioles and good flavour. Reconfirmed after trial 2001.
LRHS MCtn NRHS

93 H4 **'Giant Pink' - Mammoth Pink**
Pink-tinged, green variety for blanching or earthing up; solid stems.
NRob

94 H2 **'Victoria'**
F_1 hybrid. Tall, well-filled plants with medium-green, smooth, fleshy petioles. Widely used for commercial crops. Reconfirmed after trial 2005.
EKin

CHARD (*Beta vulgaris* subsp. *cicla* var. *flavescens*)

00 H3 BRIGHT LIGHTS
Good colourful mix, including reds, yellows and whites; very ornamental and decorative.
CHby CRos EHyd LRHS NRHS NRob SVic

00 H3 **'Bright Yellow'**
Bright golden-yellow petioles and mid-green puckered leaf; uniform; sweet taste; reconfirmed after trial 2011.
MCtn NRob

11 H3 **'Canary Yellow'**
Green leaves and yellow stem; healthy blister-type attractive glossy leaf. Even stock. Taste is not bitter. No bolting in either sowing during trial.
NRob

00 H3 **'Fordhook Giant'**
Attractive shiny light green, puckered leaf with white stem and long succulent broad white petioles; old blister-leaf chard type.
EKin MCtn NRob

00 H3 **'Rhubarb Chard'**
Dark green leaves and red stem; uniform; blister-type leaf; reconfirmed after trial 2011.
EKin LCro LOPS MCtn NRob SVic

CHICORY (*Cichorium intybus*)

RADICCHIO

02 H5 **'Indigo'**
Dense round heads; very uniform with dark green outer leaves and red hearts.
LRHS NRHS

02 H5 **'Palla Rossa'**
Medium to large heads; well-filled red hearts; fairly uniform. No bolting.
CHby MCtn SRms

SUGAR LOAF

02 H5 **'Pan di Zucchero'**
Uniform plants with medium to large frames and dark green outer leaves. Hearts blanch well.
CHby MCtn

CHILLI PEPPER (*Capsicum annuum*)

06 H1c **'Apache'**
Decorative, growing to 45cm; does well in both large and small pots. Produces large crop of small, juicy, hot peppers that ripen from bright green to red and are held outwards from the stems. Reconfirmed after trial 2013.
CCCN CRos EHyd EKin LRHS NPri NRHS NRob SPre

13 H1c **'Basket of Fire'**
Multi-branched, open habit, height to c.25cm. Numerous upright fruits, maturing through cream, lemon, yellow and orange to red.
CRos EHyd EKin LRHS NRHS SPre SVic

13 H1c **'Bolivian Rainbow'**
Compact plant, height c.32cm, with mid-green foliage. Stumpy, broad-based fruit held erect. Fruit ripening cream through orange to red.
SVic

06 H1c **'Caribbean Antillais'**
Quite small, blocky, bright red fruits; aromatic and very hot, of a type widely used in South American and Caribbean cooking. Later-cropping; best sown in January and given a higher temperature to germinate.
SVic

06 H1c **'Demon Red'**
A small, ornamental plant, starred with white flowers, producing an abundant crop of tiny upward-pointing fruits that mature to dark,

bright red. Fruits are hot and used in Thai cooking. Reconfirmed after trial 2013.
CRos EHyd EKin LRHS MCtn NRHS SPre SVic

06 H1c **'Etna'**
Attractive bunches of erect, shiny peppers that mature from bright mid-green to red, carried on compact plants that are suitable for growing in pots. Large crop of very hot peppers.
CRos EHyd LRHS MCtn NRHS

06 H1c **'Filius Blue'**
Attractive, highly ornamental plants. The young leaves are mid-green, becoming very dark green with a purple flush; the plants are covered with purple, orange and bright red fruits that are spicy and hot.
NRob

06 H1c **'Fresno'**
Fairly short, upright-growing plants; very productive. The conical fruits ripen from light green to deep scarlet red, with medium thick flesh that is very hot.
LRHS NRHS

06 H1c **Habanero Group**
Very attractive, blocky, orange fruits; very hot. Plants quite compact; good yield; suitable for growing in pots. Later-cropping, it is best sown in January.
EKin NRob

13 H1c **'Hot Thai'**
Bushy yet compact habit, height to 25cm. Dainty dark green foliage. Small, hot fruits (1.5cm in length, and 1cm wide), held erect. Ideal for a windowsill.
CRos EHyd LRHS NRHS

06 H1c **'Hungarian Hot Wax'**
Conical fruits ripening from pale yellow to bright red; medium hot; very good for frying, stuffing and using in salads. One of the easiest to grow. Suitable for growing in pots.
CHby EKin LCro LOPS MCtn NRob SVic

13 H1c **'Krakatoa'**
Compact, bushy plant, with dark green foliage; height c.20cm. Erect clusters of glossy fruit, 3cm long, and 1cm across the base.
CRos EHyd LRHS NRHS

13 H1c **'Loco'**
Bushy plant, height c.25cm, cascading habit which looks especially attractive in a basket or container. Numerous oblong fruit, c.2cm long, held erect above the foliage. Ripening purple to red.
CRos EHyd LRHS NRHS

14 H1c **'Pot Black'**
Upright plant with branching habit; height c.36cm. Stem, foliage, fruit very dark purple. Fruit blocky in shape, held erect above the foliage. Interesting and unusual variety.
SVic

06 H1c **'Prairie Fire'**
Very attractive, short (20cm high), spreading plants covered in a mass of very small, very hot, upright peppers that ripen from white, through yellow and orange, to red. Ideal for pots or a windowsill. Reconfirmed after trial 2013.
CCCN CRos EHyd LRHS NRHS NRob SVic

06 H1c **'Super Chili'**
Ornamental plants; well suited to growing in pots. Produces a high yield of very hot, thin-walled fruits that are held upright and ripen from light green to orange-red.
SPre SVic

06 H1c **'Tricolor Variegatum'**
Ornamental foliage an attractive mid-green, splashed cream and purple. Small fruits mature from purple, through orange to red. Plants 70cm high with a rather spreading habit, but can be pruned to shape.
NRob

Chinese cabbage (*Brassica rapa* Pekinensis Group)

03 H3 **'Yuki'**
Barrel-shaped. Medium green, slightly savoyed outer leaves; very short internal stem; medium-sized heavy head; well-blanched.
EKin MCtn

Coriander (*Coriandrum sativum*)

14 H2 **'Calypso'**
Vigorous, bushy strong growth; holds well; good leaf yield. Ideal size for the home gardener.
EKin MCtn

14 H2 **'Confetti'**
Neat and clean, with distinct fern-like look; uniform. Ideal for smaller gardens.
EKin MCtn

Courgette (*Cucurbita pepo*)

93 H2 **'Defender'**
F_1 hybrid. A high yield of medium-sized, slender, very lightly flecked fruits.
EKin LCro LOPS MCtn

93 H2 **'Early Gem'**
F_1 hybrid; a high yield of slender, lightly speckled fruits. Easy to see on the plant.
EKin MCtn

98 H2 **'El Greco'**
F_1 hybrid. Bush type; plant of open habit with mid-green fruits.
MCtn

13 H2 **'Orelia'**
Upright plant, producing a good yield of yellow

fruits. Vigorous plants, showing good mildew resistance.
EKin

07 H2 **'Romanesco'**
Distinctive, heavily ribbed fruits that hold their flowers. Popular in Italy; the flowers are used for stuffing. Semi-trailing plants; good yield.
LCro LOPS

Cucumber (*Cucumis sativus*)

02 H1c **'Carmen'**
F_1 hybrid; standard length, dark green, slightly ribbed fruits. Reconfirmed after trial 2009.
EKin NRob

09 H1c **'Cucino'**
Smooth, small, dark green, uniform fruits with good flavour and texture. Highly productive plants
LRHS NRHS SVic

95 H2 **'Marketmore'**
Ridge cucumber. Good yield of short, attractive, dark green fruits. Grown in the open garden. Reconfirmed after trial 2001.
CHby EKin MCtn

09 H1c **'Mini Munch'**
Highly productive plants producing abundant small, crunchy, shiny-skinned fruits with good flavour.
EKin

Endive (*Cichorium endivia*)

96 H3 **'Pancalieri'**
Very strong cut-leaf type. Does not blanch well.
CHby EKin MCtn

Florence fennel (*Foeniculum vulgare*)

05 H2 **'Orion'**
F_1 hybrid; vigorous foliage; attractive, medium to large bulbs with a good shape, with few sideshoots and clean, with a bright white colour.
EKin

96 H2 **'Zefa Fino'**
Quick-maturing. Medium large, round, very uniform bulbs of excellent quality.
EKin MCtn NRob

Garlic (*Allium sativum* var. *ophioscorodon*)

04 H4 **'Early Wight'**
Very early crop (during May); good fat cloves. Hard neck; best used immediately after harvest.
NRob

04 H4 **'Germidour'**
Late-maturing, virus-free selection. Soft necks; well-packed, purple-skinned cloves.
NRob

04 H4 **'Solent White'**
Late. Soft neck; many purple-skinned, very attractive cloves, with appealing bouquet; high yield; keeps beyond Christmas (up to March). Also performed well at Harlow Carr.
EKin LCro LOPS NRob

Kohlrabi (*Brassica oleracea* Gongylodes Group)

97 H3 **'Quickstar'**
F_1 hybrid. Uniform crop of juicy, tender bulbs with a mild flavour. Medium-sized tops. Reconfirmed after trial 2006.
LRHS MCtn NRHS

Leeks (*Allium porrum*)

Early maturing

00 H4 **'Mammoth Blanch'**
A show variety suitable for December sowing, with high yields of well-shaped leeks with pale green flags, long, heavy shafts and no bolters.
EKin NRob

Late spring

09 H5 **'Blauwgroene Winter' - Atlanta**
Good open-pollinated cultivar. Dark blue-green, erect flags, with healthy foliage. Medium length of blanch.
EKin

09 H5 **'Blauwgroene Winter' - Bandit**
Good open-pollinated cultivar. Dark blue-green flags; reasonable length of blanch.
EKin

Maincrop

00 H4 **'Jolant' (Swiss Giant Group)**
For December cropping; high yield; medium to dark green flags; long, solid shafts with little bulbing and very few bolters. Low levels of rust infection. Reconfirmed after trial 2002, 2015.
EKin MCtn NRob

02 H5 **'Mammoth Pot'**
Uniform, with whole stem blanched and light green flag. High December yield. A good short garden plant.
EKin NRob

02 H5 **'Oarsman'**
F_1 hybrid; erect plant, with very straight shank, uniform, smooth; flag leaf clean. Reconfirmed after trial 2015.
EKin MCtn

Lettuce (*Lactuca sativa*)

Cos

12 H2 **'Chartwell'**
Neat, mid-size green Cos; dense, crisp heart.
EKin

93 H2 **'Little Gem'**
Small solid heads with mid-green, medium-blistered leaves. Reconfirmed after trial 1999, 2007, 2012.
CHby CRos EHyd EKin LCro LOPS LRHS MCtn NRHS NRob

99 H2 **'Little Leprechaun'**
Semi-Cos with dark red leaves.
MCtn NRob

93 H2 **'Lobjoit's Green Cos'**
Large, rather open heads, with relatively smooth mid-green leaves. Reconfirmed after trial 1999.
EKin NRob SVic

12 H2 **'Maureen'**
Uniform crop, with mid-green leaves. One of the most popular commercial 'Gem' varieties.
EKin

99 H2 **'Parris Island'**
Vigorous with pale green uniform heads; reconfirmed after trial 2007.
EKin

00 H2 **'Winter Density'**
Semi-Cos with leafy, erect habit; dark green, very uniform. Reconfirmed after trial 2007, 2012.
EKin LCro LOPS MCtn NRob

Crisphead

01 H2 **'Robinson'**
Medium to large frame, good quality solid hearts; reconfirmed after trial 2014.
NRob

Leafy

95 H2 **'Black-seeded Simpson Improved'**
Yellow-green leaves with frilled edges. Cos-like in growth.
MCtn

95 H2 **'Catalogna'**
Strong-growing oak-leaved type. Light green slightly blistered leaves.
MCtn SVic

95 H2 **'Cocarde'**
Large oak-leaved type, with bronze green-tinged leaves.
MCtn

95 H2 **'Lollo Rossa'**
Round, medium-sized plants with green-centred leaves and bronzed frilled outer leaves.
CHby CRos EKin LCro LOPS LRHS MCtn NRHS NRob

95 H2 **'New Red Fire'**
Large, with puckered light bronze outer leaves.
EKin

95 H2 **'Red Salad Bowl'**
Large oak-leaved type. Green leaves flushed with red on the edge.
CHby EKin LCro LOPS LRHS MCtn NRHS NRob

95 H2 **'Salad Bowl'**
Large open-hearted plants with light green frilled leaves.
CHby EKin LCro LOPS LRHS MCtn NRHS NRob

Mangetout see under Peas

Marrow (*Cucurbita pepo*)

97 H2 **'Tiger Cross'**
F_1 hybrid. High yield of pale-striped fruits. Claimed CMV tolerance.
EHyd EKin LRHS MCtn NRHS SVic

Melon (*Cucumis melo*)

09 H1c **'Emir'**
Good crop of netted Charentais-type fruits with orange flesh; H2 for outdoor use.
EKin MCtn

93 H1c **'Sweetheart'**
Early-ripening; globular, medium-sized, cream-coloured fruit with orange flesh.
NRob

Onions (*Allium cepa* Cepa Group)

From sets

93 H3 **'Centurion'**
F_1 hybrid. Flattened globe-shaped bulbs with straw-coloured skins of good thickness. Reconfirmed after trial 2002, 2013.
NRob

13 H3 **'Rumba'**
Uniform crop; large bulb size, globe-shaped, with brown skin. Stores well.
EKin NRob

02 H3 **'Sturon'**
Very good yield of globe-shaped, slightly high-shouldered bulbs, with good yellow-brown skins. Reconfirmed after trial 2002, 2013.
CHby EKin LCro LOPS NRob

02 H3 **'Stuttgarter'**
High yield, well-shaped, deep bulb, good skin.
EKin LCro LOPS NRob

93 H3 **'Turbo'**
Globe-shaped to slightly conical bulbs with brown skins. Some skin splitting.

Reconfirmed after trial 2013.
NRob

Maincrop bulb

93 H3 **'Golden Bear'**
F_1 hybrid; early. Thin-skinned, high-shouldered bulbs; do not store well.
MCtn NRob

95 H3 **'Rijnsburger 5' - Balstora**
Thick-skinned, dark straw-coloured bulbs; store well.
NRob

Red, globe, from seed and sets

05 H3 **'Red Baron'**
High yield of attractive, dark-skinned, globe-shaped bulbs with good internal colour. Plants in the trial grown from seed produced a higher yield and bolder bulbs than those grown from sets. Reconfirmed after trial 2013.
CHby EKin LCro LOPS LRHS MCtn NRHS NRob

Salad – non-bulbing (*Allium fistulosum*)

96 H3 **'Ishikura'**
Strong-growing; long-stemmed.
MCtn

96 H3 **'Savel'**
Long stems with a good length of blanch.
MCtn

04 H3 **'Summer Isle'**
Late; erect, vigorous, uniform plants, with a good length of blanch. Also performed well at Harlow Carr.
MCtn

Salad – traditional

04 H3 **'Lilia'**
Dark green leaves with attractive deep red base. Tends to be bulby. Also performed well at Harlow Carr.
EKin

96 H4 **'Ramrod'**
Later-cropping. Versatile cropper with medium-green leaves and a good length of blanch. Reconfirmed after trial 2004.
MCtn

93 H4 **'White Lisbon'**
Medium-green leaves with good length of blanch. Good for early and successional sowing. Reconfirmed after trial 2004.
CHby CRos EHyd EKin LCro LOPS LRHS MCtn NRHS NRob SVic

93 H4 **'Winter White Bunching'**
Strong-growing with dark green leaves. Overwinters well.
EKin

Shallot (*Allium cepa* Aggregatum Group)

01 H3 **'Golden Gourmet'**
Well-shaped, good size; high yield.
EKin LCro LOPS NRob SVic

01 H3 **'Jermor'**
Good skin, uniform shape and size; suitable for exhibition.
NRob

01 H3 **'Longor'**
Good yield and shape; also suitable for exhibition.
LCro LOPS NRob

01 H3 **'Matador'**
F_1 hybrid; thick skins, and good yield.
EKin LRHS MCtn NRHS SVic

93 H3 **'Santé'**
Attractive, reddish brown, uniform bulbs with smooth skins. Plant a month later than others to avoid bolting.
NRob

Pak choi (*Brassica rapa* Chinensis Group)

10 H3 **'Baraku'**
Good germination rate. Little bolting. Compact and uniform, attractive dark green leaf and petiole. Good size for cooking.
MCtn

10 H3 **'Red Choi'**
Good germination rate. Very little bolting. Stands well. Attractive purple leaves and tender green stem. Good hearting, uniform clean, healthy crop. Ideal size for cooking.
EKin

Parsley (*Petroselinum crispum*)

97 H6 **'Bravour'**
A reliable cropper; good stalks, well curled.
LRHS MHer NRHS

93 H6 **'Moss Curled'**
Aromatic, deeply cut, tightly curled leaves and small umbels of yellow-green flowers in summer.
CHby CRos EKin LRHS MCtn NRHS NRob SRms

Parsnip (*Pastinaca sativa*)

01 H5 **'Gladiator'**
F_1 hybrid; very smooth skin, good potential yield, uniform shape, shallow lenticels. Reconfirmed after trial 2009.
CRos EHyd EKin LCro LOPS LRHS MCtn NRHS

01 H5 **'White Spear'**
Uniform shape, shallow lenticels, smooth skin, good white colour.
NRob

Peas (*Pisum sativum*)

98 H2 **'Ambassador'**
Maincrop; medium-sized twin pods, easy to pod; good yield with even distribution.
EKin

93 H2 **'Early Onward'**
Early; high yield of blunt-ended pods borne in pairs.
EKin LCro LOPS MCtn NRob

93 H2 **'Hurst Green Shaft'**
Maincrop; heavy yield of dark green, medium-length, pointed pods. Average of nine good-flavoured peas per pod. Reconfirmed after trial 1998, 2005.
EKin LCro LOPS MCtn

05 H2 **'Jaguar'**
Early maincrop; heavy crop of mainly double pods per node. Medium-length pods have an average of seven peas per pod, with good flavour.
MCtn

97 H2 **'Kelvedon Wonder'**
Early maincrop. Long, dark green pods, with an average of 7 to 8 peas per pod. Reconfirmed after trial 2004, 2005.
EKin LCro LOPS MCtn NRob

98 H2 **'Onward'**
First of the main crop with a high yield and good flavour.
CRos EKin LRHS MCtn NRHS NRob

98 H2 **'Rondo'**
Maincrop; large, broad, straight, pointed pods.
EKin

05 H2 **'Serge'**
Maincrop; semi-leafless plants produce a heavy crop of easy-to-pick pods. Medium-length pods have an average of ten peas per pod, with good flavour.
EKin MCtn

98 H2 **'Show Perfection'**
Maincrop; an exhibition pea, very tall with long dark green pods. A high yield over a long period.
NRob

Mangetout

09 H2 **'Oregon Giant'**
Clean, healthy, mid-height plants. Attractive broad, mid-green pods.
EKin

Sugarsnap

00 H2 **'Delikett'**
Dwarf habit. Young, dark green pods stringless but soon form strings; become fleshier and sweeter with age. Very well cropped and a long season of picking. Reconfirmed after trial 2009.
EKin MCtn NRob

00 H2 **'Sugar Ann'**
Medium height. Early to crop and gives a good yield of juicy, sweet pods. Good flavour. Reconfirmed after trial 2009.
CHby EKin MCtn

00 H2 SUGAR DWARF SWEET GREEN (**'Norli'**)
Medium height. About the earliest to mature and a heavy cropper, but over a short period and so requires successional sowing. Medium height plants; good for garden use. Reconfirmed after trial 2009.
CHby MCtn

Potatoes (*Solanum tuberosum*)

First early

98 H2 **'Accent'**
A super-tasting new potato, with pale creamy yellow waxy flesh. Eelworm and common scab resistance.
EKin NRob

98 H2 **'Foremost'**
Originally 'Suttons Foremost'. Ever popular new potato with slightly waxy, firm, white, good-flavoured flesh that does not discolour or disintegrate on cooking.
EKin NRob

07 H2 **'Orla'**
Can also be used as a second early and maincrop. Good yield of round to oval creamy white tubers; flesh slightly waxy with good flavour. Popular with organic gardeners.
NRob

98 H2 **'Red Duke of York'**
Oval red sport of 'Duke of York' with moist pale yellow flesh of superb flavour. Excellent roasted, but a good all-rounder as tubers bulk up quickly if left to mature as a late second early.
EKin LCro LOPS NRob

07 H2 **'Vales Emerald'**
Very good yield of oval, pale yellow, shallow-eyed tubers with cream-coloured flesh. Reconfirmed after trial 2013 as early for container use.
NRob

07 H2 **'Vivaldi'**
Can be left to bulk up as summer baker. Good yield of oval, pale yellow, smooth-skinned tubers with creamy flesh.
EKin LCro LOPS NRob

98 H2 **'Winston'**
Bulks up quickly to produce large, even-shaped tubers. Creamy moist flesh of excellent flavour which does not discolour on cooking.
EKin NRob

SECOND EARLY

98 H2 **'British Queen'**
Heavy and uniform crop of white-skinned and floury-textured tubers of delicious flavour for all cooking purposes.
NRob

98 H2 **'Charlotte'**
Long oval variety producing yellow-skinned and waxy tubers with creamy yellow flesh of first-class flavour either hot or cold. Reconfirmed after trial 2013 as early for container use.
EKin LCro LOPS NRob

98 H2 **'Kondor'**
Large pale red-skinned oval tubers with tasty, almost waxy, yellow flesh. Very high yields. Excellent for baking.
NRob

98 H2 **'Lady Christl'**
Bulks up very quickly and is almost a first early. Long oval, shallow-eyed, pale yellow-skinned and creamy flesh which remains firm on cooking. Eelworm-resistant. Reconfirmed after trial 2007; also in 2013 after trial as early for container use.
EKin NRob

98 H2 **'Nadine'**
Exceptionally smooth skin and shallow eyes. Cream flesh with a moist, waxy texture that does not discolour on cooking. Heavy uniform yields. An exhibitor's favourite.
EKin NRob

EARLY IN CONTAINERS

13 H2 **'Casablanca'**
Clean crop, white flesh, uniform size.
EKin LCro LOPS NRob

13 H2 **'Jazzy'**
Attractive, oval, uniform crop. Yellow skin and flesh, waxy tubers with sweet taste.
EKin LCro LOPS NRob

13 H2 **'Maris Bard'**
White flesh, thin skin, good flavour and texture; fairly uniform crop.
EKin NRob

13 H2 **'Sharpe's Express'**
Heritage variety; white skin, uniform crop size. Slightly waxy, good flavour.
NRob

EARLY MAINCROP

93 H2 **'Maxine'**
Large, smooth, pale red-skinned tubers with white waxy flesh. Uniform tubers so also recommended for exhibitors. Eelworm-resistant. Reconfirmed after trial 1998.
NRob

93 H2 **'Picasso'**
One of the heaviest croppers with creamy skin and striking bright red eyes. Waxy fine-flavoured flesh, particularly when boiled. Eelworm-resistant and good resistance to common scab. Reconfirmed after trial 1998, 2014.
NRob

MAINCROP

14 H2 **'Desiree'**
Red skin, light yellow flesh, oval tubers; reliable, and still the world's most popular red.
LCro LOPS

14 H2 **'Maris Piper'**
Cream skin, cream flesh, oval tubers; a massive favourite with gardeners.
LCro LOPS

14 H2 **'Sarpo Mira'**
Red skin, white flesh, oval tubers; still the leading blight benchmark.
LCro LOPS

SALAD

98 H2 **'Charlotte'**
Long oval variety producing yellow-skinned and waxy tubers with creamy yellow flesh of first-class flavour either hot or cold. Reconfirmed after trial 2013 as early for container use.
EKin LCro LOPS NRob

03 H2 **'Cherie'**
Good yield; pink-skinned, oval tubers. Pale yellow, waxy flesh, good flavour. Reconfirmed after trial 2007.
NRob

03 H2 **'Pink Fir Apple'**
Late main crop (22 weeks from planting). Very vigorous plants; elongated, knobbly tubers; good flavour.
EKin LCro LOPS NRob SVic

03 H2 **'Ratte'**
Early main crop. Oval tubers, waxy, cream flesh; good flavour.
NRob

RADISH (*Raphanus sativus*)

08 H2 **'Pink Beauty'**
Attractive, shiny pink roots. Crunchy texture and good, sweet flavour. No pithiness.
MCtn

96 H2 **'Scarlet Globe'**
Round medium to large red roots.
EKin

96 H2 **'Sparkler'**
Slightly flattened round roots. Unique colour split: red upper with white lower skin.

Reconfirmed after trial 2013.
CHby EKin MCtn

Rhubarb (*Rheum* × *hybridum*)

03 H4 **'Grandad's Favorite'**
First early. Vigorous plants, high yield, thick, fairly sweet stem, bright colour, good leaf to stem ratio. Suitable for showing.
CRos LRHS NRHS

03 H4 **'Hawke's Champagne'**
Second early. Compact plants; high yield potential. Attractive , bright red, medium-length, uniform stems.
WCot

12 H4 **'Raspberry Red'**
First early. High quality rich red stalks. Crops heavily and reliably.
CMac CRos EMil EPfP EPom LCro LOPS LRHS NRHS SPoG

03 H4 **'Stein's Champagne'**
Maincrop. Very bold, bright red stems, with the colour along the full length. Medium vigour.
NRob

03 H4 **'Timperley Early'**
First early. Thick stems, early, high yield. Bred for forcing; performs very well outside, but even better colour when forced.
CRos CSBt CTri LRHS SLim EKin WMat EMil NPri ECrN NRob EPfP SCoo NLar LEdu LSRN MMuc LCro MJak EPom SCob NRHS LOPS EMOT EMor SDea NEgg MGos MAsh SKee ELan CMac SPer SPoG MRav

Shallot see under Onions

Spinach (*Spinacia oleracea*)

08 H2 **'Amazon'**
F_1 hybrid; resistant to mildew races 1–10. Vigorous plants that bulk well; leaves are large, round and a good glossy dark green.
MCtn

00 H2 **'Matador'**
F_1 hybrid. Thick, dark green, upright leaf.
EKin

00 H2 **'Medania'**
Open-pollinated; resistant to mildew races 1 and 3. Good yield from slower-growing plants that are slow to bolt. Slightly blistered, large round leaves. Reconfirmed after trial 2008.
EKin MCtn SVic

08 H2 **'Missouri'**
F_1 hybrid; resistant to mildew races 1–10. Heavy yield of bright, medium green leaves with an upright habit.
EKin

Spinach beet (*Beta vulgaris* subsp. *cicla* var. *cicla*)

00 H4 **'Perpetual Spinach'**
Mid- to pale green with fairly soft texture, medium vigour; uniform; stable and clean; flat leaf with good green petiole; reconfirmed after trial 2011.
CHby EKin LCro LRHS MCtn NRHS NRob SVic

Squashes (*Cucurbita* species)

Butternut

08 H2 **'Hunter'**
A very high yield of uniformly small to medium, long pear-shaped fruits with a small seed cavity. Early-ripening with orange-gold flesh.
MCtn NRob SVic

Summer

06 H2 **'Eight Ball'**
Good yield of round, green fruits; easy to see and pick from the compact, upright plants.
SVic

06 H2 **'Geode'**
Early and heavy crop of uniform, round, mid- to pale green, marbled fruits with smallish blossom end scar. Clean, healthy plants.
LRHS NRHS

06 H2 **'Peter Pan'**
Uniform crop of light-green, scallop-shaped fruits should be harvested when small.
SVic

06 H2 **'Sunburst'**
Hybrid; attractive yellow, scallop-shaped fruits. Used for "baby veg"; best harvested when small (5–6cm in diameter).
NRob

Winter

11 H2 **'Crown Prince'**
Large fruits, with blue-grey skin and excellent storage quality. Popular, reliable variety. Fruits have high flesh content, of deep orange colour and excellent flavour.
CHby EKin MCtn NRob SVic

11 H2 **'Harlequin'**
High sugar cultivar. Decorative ridged fruits, striped yellow, gold and green; mid-sized with a typical diameter 10–13cm. Good yield per plant and excellent storage quality. Plant has a semi-bush habit. Firm flesh of smooth texture and sweet flavour.
SVic

11 H2 **'Honey Bear'**
High sugar variety. Dark green, mini-acorn-shaped fruits of uniform size, typically 8–10cm

in diameter. Sweet flavour; ideal size for baking whole. Compact, bushy habit, giving a reasonable yield of fruits, with excellent storage qualities. Plant demonstrates good resistance to powdery mildew.
MCtn

11 H2 **'Kabocha Large Fruited'**
Dark green flattened fruit, typically 15 to 17cm in diameter. Good storage. Flesh is thick, sweet and smooth. Ideal for desserts.
SVic

11 H2 **'Sweet Dumpling'**
Original sweet dumpling type. Uniform crop of small fruit, approximately 9 to 10cm in diameter; ridged, cream-coloured with green stripes and mottling; sweetly flavoured orange flesh. Trailing habit, producing a good yield of fruits with excellent storage quality.
CHby EKin MCtn NRob

SUGARSNAP SEE UNDER PEAS

SWEET CORN (*Zea mays*)

03 H2 **'Earlibird'** (supersweet)
F_1 hybrid; 2nd early. Uniform cobs; good vigour. Reconfirmed after trial 2009.
EKin MCtn

03 H2 **'Lark'** (extra tender sweet)
F_1 hybrid; 2nd early. High yield of well-filled cobs with very sweet, clean flavour. Reconfirmed after trial 2009.
EKin MCtn SVic

09 H2 MIRAI WHITE M421 (**'Mirai 421W'**) (extra tender sweet)
Early. Tall plants, with well-filled cobs and very good flavour. Attractive white cobs are exceptionally tender and sweet.
LRHS

09 H2 **'Seville'** (supersweet)
Mid-season. Tall plants; attractive later-maturing cobs with good shape and straight rows of small grains.
SVic

03 H2 **'Swift'** (extra tender sweet)
F_1 hybrid; early. High yield of cobs with excellent eating quality. Good sweet flavour and tender kernels. Reconfirmed after trial 2009.
EKin MCtn

SWEET PEPPER (*Capsicum annuum* var. *annuum* Grossum Group)

05 H1c **'Corno di Toro Rosso'**
Open-pollinated; later-cropping. Long, horn-shaped, very fleshy fruits that have a good flavour. Maturing from pale green to bright red.
CHby

05 H1c **'Mohawk'**
F_1 hybrid. Medium-sized, bell-shaped fruits that ripen from dark green to bright yellow; good flavour. Dwarf-growing plants are well suited to growing in pots.
CRos EHyd EKin LRHS NRHS

05 H1c **'Redskin'**
F_1 hybrid; small to medium, blocky, bell-shaped fruits that ripen from dark green to a glossy, dark red. Compact plants give a high yield and are well suited to growing in pots.
CRos EHyd EKin LRHS NRHS

TOMATOES (*Solanum lycopersicum*)

97 H1c **'Alicante'**
Good shape; heavy crop of attractive fruits which ripen well. H2 for outdoor use.
CRos EKin LCro LOPS LRHS NRHS NRob

13 H1c **'Elegance'**
Strong plants producing high yield of large fruits. Trusses of 8–10 flavoursome fruits.
LRHS

97 H1c **'Golden Sunrise'**
Later-maturing; small yellow fruits.
EKin LCro LOPS LRHS MCtn NRHS NRob SVic

93 H1c **'Outdoor Girl'**
Early. Indeterminate, round red fruits with good flavour.
CRos EHyd LRHS MCtn NRHS NRob SVic

93 H1c **'Shirley'**
F_1 hybrid; fairly early. Uniform trusses; nice round red fruit of medium size and average flavour. Reconfirmed after trial 1997.
CRos EKin LRHS NRHS NRob SVic

93 H1c **'Tigerella'**
Interesting attractive striped fruit with quite good flavour; reconfirmed after trial 1997. H2 for outdoor use.
CHby EKin MCtn NRob SVic

97 H1c **'Vanessa'**
F_1 hybrid. High yield of greenback-free, succulent fruits with very nice flavour.
NRob

93 H1c **'Yellow Perfection'**
Indeterminate, uniform, round, pale, yellow fruit. H2 for outdoor use.
EKin

BEEFSTEAK

14 H1c **'Beefmaster'**
Multilocular; large fruit; deeply ribbed;

light, smooth taste, good yield.
EKin

03 H1c **'Costoluto Fiorentino'**
High yield; medium-sized, attractive bright red, highly ribbed, succulent fruit with good flavour.
LCro LOPS

03 H1c **'Marmande'**
High yield; large, bright red, attractive fruits, with solid flesh and good flavour.
CHby EKin MCtn

14 H1c **'Supersteak'**
Multilocular; smooth skin; good-sized fruit; nice taste, good yield.
CRos EHyd LRHS NRHS

Cherry

93 H1c **'Gardener's Delight'**
Indeterminate plants, producing long trusses of fruits of good flavour under glass or outside; reconfirmed after trial 1998. H2 for outdoor use.
CHby CRos EHyd EKin LCro LOPS LRHS MCtn NRHS NRob SVic

98 H1c **'Sun Baby'**
Good trusses of uniform, attractive, yellow fruits. H2 for outdoor use.
MCtn

07 H1c **'Sungold'**
Good yield of attractive round golden-orange fruits. Good flavour.
CHby CRos EKin LRHS MCtn NRHS NRob SVic

98 H1c **'Sweet Million'**
F_1 hybrid. Long trusses of sweet, round, bright red fruits; good yield.
CRos LRHS NRHS NRob

Plum

04 H1c **'Ildi'**
Vigorous, indeterminate plants; heavy crop of small, attractive, yellow, plum-shaped fruit.
EKin

04 H1c **'Sweet Olive'**
F_1 hybrid; very early. Very high yield from vigorous, healthy, determinate plants. Small, red, round to plum-shaped fruits, a little difficult to pick, but of good flavour.
MCtn

Turnip (*Brassica rapa* Rapifera Group)

97 H3 **'Market Express'**
F_1 hybrid; early. Uniform, medium size, smooth, round, pure white, shiny roots. Reconfirmed after trial 2004.
MCtn

04 H3 **'Primera'**
Uniform crop of flat-shaped roots with purple top and attractive smooth skin. Good internal flesh.
EHyd LRHS NRHS

30
ANNIVERSARY
EDITION
RHS Award
of Garden Merit
Fruit

Award of Garden Merit Fruit

This is a directory of fruit offered by nurseries participating in *RHS Plant Finder 2016* that have been awarded an RHS Award of Garden Merit (AGM). It does not represent a complete list of AGM fruit.

Entries are accompanied by a short description and the relevant **hardiness rating** for the UK (see p.39 for an explanation of these). The figures to the left of the rating indicate the year of the award. Cultivars particularly suitable for culinary use are flagged **(C)**, while **(D)** denotes dessert fruit.

Cultivation

All fruits are best grown in sheltered sites, with protection from spring frosts and cold winds. Brief guidance is given below on suitability for different locations, rootstocks, pollination and storage.

Location

Most of the **apple** cultivars listed here succeed all over the country, including the north of England. Those which have been found to be particularly successful in higher-rainfall and colder areas are **marked with an asterisk**; this is also used to highlight other fruits that have been found to be successful in northern regions. **Pears** crop best in sheltered warm situations; in the more exposed areas and northern counties, some pears will benefit from the protection of walls. **Plums** are susceptible to spring frosts and also need warm summers to ripen fully. Only early ripening plums can be relied upon in the shorter season of northern counties.

Currants, **gooseberries**, **raspberries** and **berry fruits** are generally satisfactory in most parts of the country, but cold winds at flowering time can be a problem. **Strawberries** can be grown all over the country, but will need some protection in exposed sites and from spring frosts. **Blueberries** are hardy plants but require light, well-drained, moisture-retentive, acid soil (pH 4.0–5.5).

Figs can crop satisfactorily in sheltered, warm situations in southern England. In northerly areas they will need protection such as a south-facing wall, or to be grown under glass or in polytunnels.

Pollination

Most tree fruits need to be pollinated by another tree of the same kind growing reasonably close by, which flowers at approximately the same time. Flowering groups are given in descriptions; for good pollination, choose cultivars from the same group, though those from adjacent groups will also serve as pollinators. **Apples** and **pears** listed as triploid are poor pollinators and require a normal (i.e. diploid) pollinator to set fruit. Gardeners should be aware that this diploid pollinator will not itself set fruit unless pollinated by another diploid tree. Many *Malus* species and crab apples, such as 'Golden Hornet' and 'Evereste', are also a good source of pollen for dessert and culinary apples. A number of the **plums** listed are self-fertile or partly self-fertile and will produce crops without a pollinator, but a pollinator is needed for all other plums. **Cherries** listed as self-fertile will crop without a pollinator, but otherwise cherries need a pollinator. Soft fruits are self-fertile, except that **blueberries** may need a pollinator.

Rootstocks

All tree fruits are grafted onto rootstocks of varying vigour. Choice of rootstock will determine the ultimate size of the tree and hence needs to be borne in mind when selecting new trees for the garden. For example, **apple trees** on 'M9' rootstock are suitable for small gardens, while those on 'M25' will produce large, standard trees. The size of the tree will also be determined by the vigour of the cultivar. It is often advisable to obtain a very vigorous cultivar, for example 'Bramley's Seedling', on a more dwarfing stock. **Apples** are available on 'M27' (very dwarfing), 'M9' (dwarfing), 'M26' (semi-dwarfing), 'MM 106' (semi-vigorous), and 'M25' (vigorous) rootstocks. **Pears** are available on 'Quince C' (dwarfing), 'Quince A' (semi-vigorous), 'BA 29' (semi-vigorous) and seedling pear (vigorous) rootstocks. Some pear cultivars are incompatible with a quince rootstock and these are sold with a pear interstock (usually 'Beurré Hardy'). **Plums** are available on 'Pixy' (semi-dwarfing) and 'Saint Julien A' (semi-vigorous) rootstocks; cherries on 'Tabel' (very dwarfing), 'Gisela 5' (dwarfing), and 'Colt' (semi-vigorous).

Storage

Early **apples** and **pears** will not store, but many more of the apple and pear cultivars listed will store to Christmas and some to the spring. This calls for good storage conditions, i.e. a cool, dark, frost-free place that is not subject to fluctuating temperatures. Often this can be achieved in sheds and garages, but in general centrally heated houses are not suitable for long-term storage.

Apple (*Malus domestica*)

98 H6 **'Alkmene'** (D)
Pollination group 2. aromatic, Cox-like flavour. Good, regular crops; some resistance to scab and mildew. Season: late Sept. to late Oct.
CAgr ECrN NOra SDea

'American Mother' *see* 'Mother'

93 H6 **'Arthur Turner'** (C)
Pollination group 3. Flavoursome cooker. Large, golden exhibition fruit. Good, regular crops; prone to mildew; some resistance to scab. Striking deep pink blossom, for which an Award of Merit was given in 1945. Season: Sept. to Nov.
CArg CCVT CHab CLnd CTri ECrN EMOT EPom LBuc MWat NOra SBdl SDea SKee SSFr WJas WMat

93 H6 **'Ashmead's Kernel'** (D)
Pollination group 4. Intense, fruit-drop flavour. Cropping erratic; prone to bitter pit. Season: Dec. to Feb.
CAgr CArg CDul CFGn CHab CLnd CRos CSBt CTho CTri ECrN EMOT EPfP EPom LBuc LRHS MAsh MRav MWat NOra NWea SBdl SDea SKee SLim SLon SSFr SSFT SVic WJas WMat WWct

93 H6 **'Belle de Boskoop'** (C/D)
Triploid. Pollination group 3. Needs little or no extra sugar when cooked; mellows to brisk eating apple. Good, regular crops; very vigorous tree. Season: Oct. to Apr.; keeps well.*
CAgr CHab ECrN MCoo NOra SBdl SCob SDea SKee

93 H6 **'Blenheim Orange'** (C/D)
Triploid. Pollination group 3. Characteristic nutty flavour. Use early for cooking. Some resistance to mildew; very vigorous tree; partial tip-bearer; light crops. Season (C): from late Sept. (D): Oct. to Dec./Jan.*
CAgr CArg CCVT CDul CHab CLnd CSBt CTho CTri EBee ECrN ELan EMOT EPfP EPom IArd LBuc LEdu LRHS MAsh MCoo MRav MWat NOra NPri NRHS NWea SBdl SCob SDea SEND SEWo SKee SPer SSFr SVic WJas WMat WWct

93 H6 **'Bramley's Seedling'** (C)
Triploid. Pollination group 3. Cooks to very sharp, savoury purée; retains acidity to spring. Heavy crops; prone to bitter pit and scab; partial tip bearer; can bear fruit parthenocarpically; tendency to be biennial if over-cropped; blossom susceptible to frost. Very vigorous tree. Season: Nov. to Mar.; stores well.*
CAgr CArg CBcs CCVT CDul CFGn CLnd CMac CRos CSBt CTho CTri ECrN ELan EMOT EPfP EPom GKin LBuc LCro LEdu LMaj LRHS LSRN MGos MJak MMuc MRav MWat NEgg NLar NOra NPri NRHS NWea SBdl SCob SDea SEND SEWo SKee SLim SPer SSFr SSFT SVic SWvt WJas WMat WWct

93 H6 **'Charles Ross'** (C/D)
Pollination group 3. Quite rich flavour; needs no sugar when cooked. Handsome exhibition fruit. Good, regular crops; hardy tree; some resistance to scab. Season: Oct. to Dec.*
CAgr CArg CCVT CDul CFGn CHab CLnd CMac CSBt CTho CTri ECrN EMOT EPom IArd LBuc LRHS LSRN MAsh MCoo MJak MRav NEgg NOra NWea SCob SDea SKee SLim SSFr SSFT WJas WMat WWct

14 H6 **'Christmas Pippin'** (D)
Pollination group 3. Medium vigour; upright spreading habit; good, regular crops. Medium sized apple of attractive appearance, flushed with colour over yellow background with some russet; crisp, juicy, sweet flesh with rich sweet sharp flavour, developing aromatic quality. Well-flavoured, good quality apple.
CArg CRos CTri EPom LBuc LCro LRHS MCoo MWat NLar NOra NPri NRHS WMat

93 H6 **'Discovery'** (D)
Pollination group 3. Bright red, crisp, juicy; keeps longer than most earlies. Ornamental tree. Good, regular crops; partial tip bearer; good resistance to scab and mildew. Season: mid-Aug. to Sept.*
CAgr CArg CBcs CCVT CDul CFGn CLnd CMac CSBt CTri EBee ECrN EMOT EPfP EPom GKin LBuc LRHS MGos MJak MRav MWat NLar NOra NPri NWea SBdl SCob SDea SKee SLim SPer SSFr SSFT SVic WJas WMat WWct

93 H6 **'Dummellor's Seedling'** (C)
Pollination group 4. Previously listed as

'Dumelow's Seedling'. Cooks to well-flavoured, juicy purée; retains acidity to spring. Good, regular crops, but fruit can be small for a cooker. Season: Nov. to Apr.*
CHab MCoo NOra SDea SKee

'Early Victoria' *see* 'Emneth Early'

93 H6 **'Edward VII'** (C)
Pollination group 6. Cooks to well-flavoured purée, not as acidic as 'Bramley's Seedling'. Large, regular, exhibition fruit. Deep pink blossom; flowers very late so escapes frosts; needs late-flowering pollinator. Good, regular crops; resistant to scab; some resistance to mildew. Season: Dec. to Apr.*
CHab EMOT NOra SDea SKee WMat WWct

93 H6 **'Egremont Russet'** (D)
Pollination group 2. Characteristic nutty flavour. Good, regular crops; fruit resistant to scab, but prone to leaf scab; very prone to bitter pit and woolly aphids. Season: Oct. to Dec.*
CAgr CArg CCVT CDul CHab CLnd CMac CRos CSBt CTri EBee ECrN ELan EMOT EPfP EPom LBuc LEdu LRHS MAsh MGos MJak MMuc MWat NLar NOra NPri NWea SBdl SDea SEND SEWo SKee SLim SPer SSFr SSFT WJas WMat WWct

93 H6 **'Ellison's Orange'** (D)
Pollination group 4. Rich, aniseed flavour. Good, regular crops; some resistance to scab, but susceptible to canker. Season: late Sept. to late Oct.
CAgr CArg CDul CHab CLnd CMac CSBt CTri ECrN EMOT EPfP EPom LBuc LRHS MMuc MWat NOra NWea SBdl SCob SDea SEND SKee SLon SPer SSFr SVic WJas WMat WWct

93 H6 **'Elstar'** (D)
Pollination group 3. Intense flavour, honeyed, crisp. Heavy regular crops. Season: late Oct. to Dec.
CCVT CLnd ECrN EMOT EPom NOra SBdl SDea SKee

93 H6 **'Emneth Early'** (C)
Pollination group 3. Codlin type, cooking to fluffy purée; needs hardly any sugar. Heavy but biennial crops; needs thinning for size. Some resistance to scab and mildew. Season: Aug. to Sept.*
CAgr CArg CHab ECrN NOra SDea WJas WMat WWct

'Epicure' *see* 'Laxton's Epicure'

93 H6 **'Fiesta'** (D)
Pollination group 3. Aromatic, Cox-like flavour. Heavy, regular crops; frost-resistant blossom; less prone to disease than Cox, but can be susceptible to scab and develop canker in some sites. Season: Oct. to Dec./Jan.*
CAgr CArg CCVT CDul CMac CTri EBee ECrN EMOT EPfP EPom LBuc LRHS MAsh MCoo MGos MMuc MRav NEgg NLar NOra NPri NWea SCoo SDea SEND SKee SLim SPer SPoG SSFr WJas WMat WWct

'Fortune' *see* 'Laxton's Fortune'

93 H6 **'Golden Noble'** (C)
Pollination group 4. Cooks to a well-flavoured purée, not as acidic as 'Bramley's Seedling'. Attractive blossom. Good, regular crops; partial tip bearer; some scab and mildew resistance. Season: Oct. to Dec. and longer.
CAgr CTri ECrN EMOT IArd MCoo NOra SDea SKee

93 H6 **'Greensleeves'** (D)
Pollination group 3. Crisp, brisk, becoming sweeter. Very precocious and heavy, regular crops; needs thinning for good fruit size. Blossom has some frost resistance. Can be susceptible to scab. Season: late Sept. to Oct.; short season once picked.
CAgr CArg CDul CMac CTri EBee ECrN ELan EMOT EPfP EPom MAsh MGos MMuc NLar NOra NWea SBdl SCob SDea SEND SKee SLim SPer SSFT SSFr WJas WMat WWct

93 H6 **'Grenadier'** (C)
Pollination group 3. Cooks to sharp purée. Heavy, regular crops; good disease resistance. Season: Aug. to Sept.*
CAgr CArg CHab CLnd CTri ECrN EMOT EPom MGos MJak MMuc NLar NOra SBdl SCob SDea SEND SKee SLon SPer SSFT SSFr WJas WMat

14 H6 **'Howgate Wonder'** (C)
Pollination group 3. Very large, late-season, heavy-cropping apple with a very mild flavour. Vigorous; fruit yellow-green flushed with red. Partially self-fertile.
CAgr CArg CCVT CDul CHab CLnd CSBt CTri EBee ECrN EMOT EPfP EPom LBuc LRHS MMuc MWat NOra NWea SBdl SDea SKee SPer SSFr SVic WJas WMat WWct

93 H6 **'James Grieve'** (C/D)
Pollination group 3. Savoury, crisp to melting flesh; when cooked keeps shape, with juicy, delicate flavour. Good, regular crops; fruit bruises easily. Prone to scab, canker; resistant to mildew; requires well-drained soil. Season: Sept. to Oct. and longer.*
CAgr CArg CBcs CCVT CDul CHab CLnd CMac CRos CSBt CTri EBee ECrN EMOT EPfP EPom LBuc LRHS LSRN MAsh MGos MJak MMuc MRav MWat NEgg

NLar NOra NPri NRHS NWea SBdl SCob SCoo SDea SEND SEWo SKee SLim SPer SSFr SSFT SVic SWvt WJas WMat WTSh WWct

93 H6 **'Jonagold'** (D)
Triploid. Pollination group 3. Attractive, crisp, honeyed taste; large fruit. Heavy, regular crops; prone to canker. Fruit can be poorly coloured, but many more colourful sports exist. Vigorous. Season: Nov. to Jan./Feb.; stores well.
CArg CLnd CTri ECrN ELan EMOT EPom IArd NLar NOra SBdl SDea SKee SPer SSFr WWct

93 H6 **'Jupiter'** (D)
Triploid. Pollination group 3. Cox-like flavour, but sharper. Heavy crops, but biennial if allowed to over-crop; fruit can be irregular shape and heavily russetted. Vigorous. Season: late Oct. to Jan.*
CAgr CArg CDul CSBt CTri ECrN EMOT LSRN MJak MRav NLar NOra NWea SBdl SDea SKee SLon SSFr WJas WMat

14 H6 **'Kent'** (D)
Pollination group 3. Good flavour; good reliable crops; keeps well. Also sold as 'Malling Kent'.
ECrN SDea

93 H6 **'Kidd's Orange Red'** (D)
Pollination group 3. Very attractive; rich aromatic, perfumed taste. Good, regular crops; fruit prone to coarse russet. Season: Nov. to Jan.
CAgr CArg CDul CMac CRos CTri ECrN EMOT EPfP EPom LBuc LRHS MWat NOra SDea SKee SLon SSFr WMat WWct

93 H6 **'King of the Pippins'** (C/D)
Pollination group 5. Well ripened, good flavour. Cooked, keeps shape, flavoursome; suited to open tarts, etc. Heavy, regular crops; upright habit; good resistance to disease; keeps well. Season: Oct. to Dec.; can store to Feb.*
CArg CFGn CHab CLnd CTri ECrN EPom LBuc MCoo NOra SDea SKee SVic

93 H6 **'King Russet'** (D)
Pollination group 3. Russetted form of 'King of the Pippins'. Improved eating quality; good distinct "russet" flavour. Not as heavy cropping. Season: Oct. to Dec.
SDea

93 H6 **'Lane's Prince Albert'** (C)
Pollination group 3. Cooks to brisk purée, not as acidic as 'Bramley's Seedling'. Large fruit. Good, regular crops; fruit easily bruised. Hardy; makes neat small tree. Resistant to scab; very prone to mildew; prone to canker on all but very well-drained soils. Season: Nov. to Mar.; stores well.*
CAgr CArg CHab CLnd CSBt CTri ECrN EMOT EPfP LRHS MGos MRav MWat NOra NWea SBdl SCoo SDea SSFr SVic WJas WMat

93 H6 **'Laxton's Epicure'** (D)
Pollination group 3. Delicate, aromatic, Cox-like flavour. Heavy, regular crops; needs thinning for size; prone to bitter pit, canker. Season: late Aug. to Sept. Awarded as 'Epicure'.*
CAgr CHab CTri ECrN EMOT SDea SKee

93 H6 **'Laxton's Fortune'** (D)
Pollination group 3. Sweet, lightly aromatic flavour; needs to colour well for good quality. Good crops, but tendency to be biennial. Fruit bruises easily, can be poorly coloured. Prone to canker, good resistance to scab. Season: Sept. to Oct. Awarded as 'Fortune'.
CArg CDul CHab CMac CSBt CTri ECrN IArd LRHS NOra SBdl SDea SKee SSFr WJas WMat WWct

14 H6 **'Limelight'** (D)
Pollination group 3. Crisp and refreshing; heavy-cropping.
CArg EBee EMOT MAsh MCoo NLar NOra SCoo SKee SSFT SSFr WMat

93 H6 **'Lord Lambourne'** (D)
Pollination group 2. Sweet, juicy, attractive flavour. Skin can become greasy when stored. Good, regular crops. Partial tip bearer; resistant to mildew. Season: late Sept. to Nov.*
CAgr CArg CDul CHab CLnd CMac CRos CSBt CTri ECrN ELan EMOT EPom LSRN MAsh MCoo MGos MWat NLar NOra SBdl SDea SKee SLon SPer SSFr WJas WMat WWct

93 H6 **'Mother'** (D)
Pollination group 5. Sweet, perfumed, distinctive flavour. Crops can be erratic, light; good resistance to scab and mildew. Season: Oct. to Dec.*
CAgr CEnd CLnd CTri ECrN SDea SKee SSFr

93 H6 **'Peasgood's Nonsuch'** (C/D)
Pollination group 3. Cooks to sweet, delicately flavoured purée; needs no or little extra sugar. Exhibition apple with large, handsome regular shape. Good, regular crops; resistance to mildew and red spider; moderate resistance to scab. Season: late Sept. to Dec.
CAgr CArg CHab ECrN EPom IArd LSRN MAsh NOra SDea SKee SLon WMat

93 H6 **'Pixie'** (D)
Pollination group 4. Intensely aromatic, Cox-like flavour, but sharper and firmer-fleshed. Good to heavy crops, but small fruit unless thinned. Season: Dec. to Mar.*
CSBt EMOT EPom LRHS MWat NOra NPri SCob SDea SKee SLon WWct

14 H6 **'Red Falstaff'** (D)
Pollination group 3. Late-season, heavy-cropping sport of 'Falstaff' with a fruity flavour and crisp, juicy flesh. Self-fertile and moderately vigorous. Skin flushed with orange-red when ripe. Season: Nov. to Jan.
CAgr CArg CCVT CDul CMac CTri EBee ECrN EMOT EPfP GKin LBuc LRHS LSRN MAsh MCoo NLar NOra NRHS SKee SLim SLon SPer SPoG SSFT WMat WWct

93 H6 **'Ribston Pippin'** (D)
Triploid. Pollination group 2. Intense, rich, aromatic flavour; more acidity and more robust than Cox. Good, regular crops; resistant to scab; prone to mildew and canker. Season: Oct. to Jan.
CArg CDul CTho CTri ECrN EMOT MCoo MRav MWat NOra NWea SDea SKee SLon SSFr WJas WMat WWct

93 H6 **'Rosemary Russet'** (D)
Pollination group 3. Sweet-sharp acid drop taste, resembling 'Ashmead's Kernel'. Crops good, regular; vigorous tree with upright habit. Season: Nov./Dec. to Mar.
CAgr CArg CHab CTho ELan MCoo NOra SDea SKee SLon SSFr WMat WWct

93 H6 **'Saint Edmund's Pippin'** (D)
Pollination group 2. Very attractive; richly flavoured when fully ripe. Good, regular crops; fruit bruises easily. Prone to mildew. Season: late Sept. to Oct.*
CHab CTho ECrN ELan EPfP MCoo NOra SDea SKee SSFr

14 H6 **'Santana'** (D)
Pollination group 4. Medium to quite vigorous tree, with upright spreading habit. Good to heavy crop, with low susceptibility to scab. Mid-season apple; picking early September and keeping well. Bright red flushed; sweet, crisp, juicy flesh; good flavour.
NOra WMat

09 H6 **'Scrumptious'** (D)
Pollination group 3. Regular cropper, good fruit size, attractive ornamental fruit. Good tree habit; easily managed. A good dessert apple: sweet, good flavour, crisp, juicy.
CAgr CArg CCVT CDul CMac CRos CSBt CTri EMOT EPfP EPom LBuc LCro LOPS LRHS LSRN MAsh NLar NOra NRHS NWea SCob SCoo SDea SEWo SKee SLim SLon SPer SPoG SSFr SSFT WJas WMat

93 H6 **'Sunset'** (D)
Pollination group 3. Aromatic, like small early Cox, but sharper. Heavy, regular crops, but small fruit. Resistant to scab; prone to mildew and canker. Season: Oct. to Dec.
CAgr CArg CCVT CDul CHab CLnd CMac CSBt CTri EBee ECrN EMOT EPfP EPom GKin LBuc LRHS LSRN MRav NOra NRHS NWea SBdl SCoo SDea SKee SLim SLon SPer SSFr SSFT SVic WJas WMat WWct

14 H6 **'Topaz'** (D)
Pollination group 4. Medium vigour, with upright spreading habit. Good crop, with resistance to scab; late season, picking in early/mid-October. Medium-sized apple; attractive appearance, red flushed over a yellow background; crisp, juicy flesh, sweet-sharp taste, can be quite sharp, mellows with keeping.
SKee

93 H6 **'Warner's King'** (C)
Triploid. Pollination group 2. Cooks to well-flavoured purée; not as acidic as 'Bramley's Seedling'. Attractive, deep pink blossom. Heavy, regular crops; fruit can be very large. Prone to bitter pit. Vigorous. Season: late Sept. to Dec.
CTri NOra SDea SKee

93 H6 **'Winston'** (D)
Pollination group 4. Aromatic and rich. Good, regular crops; fruit can be rather small; good disease resistance. Season: Dec. to Apr.; keeps very well.*
CAgr CCVT CMac CTri ECrN MCoo SDea SKee SVic WWct

93 H6 **'Worcester Pearmain'** (D)
Pollination group 3. Intense strawberry flavour when well-ripened and scarlet. Tip bearer; heavy, regular crops. Resistant to mildew; some susceptibility to canker. Season: late Sept. to Oct.
CAgr CArg CBcs CCVT CDul CFGn CHab CLnd CMac CSBt CTri EBee ECrN EMOT EPfP EPom LBuc LRHS MAsh MMuc MRav MWat NEgg NOra NWea SBdl SCoo SDea SEND SEWo SKee SLim SPer SSFr WJas WMat WWct

Blackberry (*Rubus fruticosus*)

Season extends from late July to early Sept.

93 H6 **'Loch Ness'** (D/C)
Large, well-flavoured berries. Thornless; heavy cropping; moderate vigour; hardy. Good resistance to purple blotch and botrytis, but prone to downy mildew. Reconfirmed after trial 2015.
CAgr CArg CHab CRos EMOT EPom IArd LCro LOPS LRHS LSRN NPri NRHS SCoo SDea SKee SPer SSFr SVic

15 H6 **'Loch Tay'**
No spines; has a good blackberry flavour and

shiny fruit. Healthy but not too vigorous, producing good replacement canes. Early.
CArg CHab CMac CRos EPom LRHS NRHS SPoG

Blackcurrant (*Ribes nigrum*)

Season extends from early July to mid-Aug.

95 H6 **'Ben Connan'** (C)
Large fruit; medium long strigs. Heavy crops; compact habit. Good resistance to mildew, leaf-curling midge. Season: early. Reconfirmed after trial 2012.
CAgr CFGn CMac CRos CSBt ECrN EMOT EPfP EPom LBuc LCro LOPS LRHS LSRN MAsh MGos MNHC NLar NRHS NWea SCoo SDea SEND SKee SLim SPer SPoG SRms SSFr SWvt WMat

12 H6 **'Big Ben'**
Fairly vigorous medium-sized bush, flowering early to mid-season. Fruit large and easy to pick. Good yields, showing resistance to mildew and leaf spot. Fresh fruit flavour pleasant to quite sweet; rich when cooked. Good all-round cultivar.
CArg CFGn CRos EHyd EPfP EPom LBuc LCro LOPS LRHS LSRN MNHC NRHS SKee SPer SPoG WMat

Blueberry (*Vaccinium corymbosum*)

Blueberries begin to ripen mid-July and continue to late Aug.

03 H6 **'Duke'** (D)
Good flavour, medium to large fruit. Crops well; easy to grow. Flowers late; good for frost-prone sites; partly self-fertile. Season: early.
CArg CTrh ELan EPfP EPom LCro LOPS MCoo MGos SDea SPer SPre SRkn SSFr

03 H6 **'Spartan'** (D)
Excellent flavour; medium-sized fruit. Quite good crops; not self-fertile. Vigorous; upright habit. Good autumn colour. Season: early to mid.
CTrh EPom LCro LOPS LSRN MGos SKee

Cherry (morello) (*Prunus cerasus*)

93 H6 **'Morello'** (C)
Dark red, acid cherry; excellent for preserves, tarts, etc. Regular, good crops; very attractive in blossom; self-fertile. Crops on north-facing site. Season: late July to early Aug.
CAgr CArg CCVT CDul CLnd CMac CSBt CTho CTri ECrN ELan EMOT EPfP EPom LBuc LMaj LRHS LSRN MGos MJak MMuc MWat NEgg NLar NOra NPri NRHS NWea SDea SEND SEWo SKee SLim SPer SSFr SSFT SVic SWvt WJas WMat

Cherry (sweet) (*Prunus avium*)

14 H4 **'Kordia'** (D)
Pollination group 5. mid- to late season; large to very large, true black cherry; bold appearance; excellent rich flavour. Spreading habit; can show some bare wood; medium vigour. Heavy, reliable crops; easy to grow. Not self-fertile; usually pollinated by 'Regina' or 'Sylvia' in commercial orchards; can also be pollinated by 'Summer Sun', 'Stella' (early bloom only). Blossom can be a little frost-sensitive. Good garden cherry.
CArg EPom NOra SKee WMat

14 H5 **'Lapins'**
Pollination group 4. mid- to late season; large, dark red cherry; very good flavour. Upright habit; medium vigour. Heavy, reliable crops. All-round excellent cherry; self-fertile.
CAgr CArg CDul CFGn CLnd CTho ECrN EMOT EPfP EPom MRav NLar NOra NWea SDea SKee SSFT SSFr WJas WMat WWct

95 H5 **'Merchant'** (D)
Pollination group 3. Early black cherry; well-flavoured. Regular crops. Pollination: universal donor, but not self-fertile. Season: early July. Reconfirmed 2014.
NOra SKee SSFT SSFr WMat WWct

14 H5 **'Penny'**
Pollination group 4. mid- to late season; dark red, very large, meaty cherry; excellent flavour. Upright spreading habit; medium vigour; prone to some bare wood. Crops well and regularly on Gisela 5; bred for UK conditions. Not self-fertile; pollinated by late to mid-season cultivars, e.g. 'Summer Sun', 'Skeena', 'Regina'; needs sufficient pollination to ensure heavy crops.
CAgr CArg CTri EPom MCoo NOra SKee WMat WWct

93 H5 **'Stella'**
Pollination group 4. Black cherry; large, rich, high quality. Heavy, regular crops; self-fertile. Prone to splitting in wet weather. Season: late July. Reconfirmed 2014.
CAgr CArg CDul CEnd CHab CLnd CMac CRos CSBt CTri ECrN ELan EMOT EPfP EPom LBuc LCro LMaj LRHS MAsh MGos MJak MMuc MRav MWat NLar NOra NRHS NWea SCoo SDea SEND SEWo SKee SLim SPer SPoG SSFr SSFT SVic SWvt WJas WMat WTSh WWct

04 H5 **'Summer Sun'** (D)
Pollination group 4. Late (July). Produces firm,

well-flavoured, red to black fruit. Very good crops. Some resistance to bacterial canker. Attractive, upright, spreading habit; moderate vigour. Not self-fertile. Reconfirmed 2014.
CAgr CArg CLnd CMac CTho CTri EMOT EPom LBuc MAsh MCoo MGos NLar NOra SCoo SDea SKee SLim SPoG SSFT SSFr WMat WWct

14 H5 **'Sweetheart'**
Pollination group 4. Dark red cherry; latest of the season. Good flavour; very firm fruit. Medium vigour, upright spreading habit. Heavy, regular crops; fruits moderate size. Slightly prone to canker and brown rot. Only late-season self-fertile cultivar available. Prolific blossom, making a tree exceptionally pretty in the spring. Sets dense clusters of fruits, which can be prone to botrytis/brown rot.
CAgr CArg CLnd CTri EMOT EPom LCro LMaj LOPS LRHS LSRN MAsh NOra NRHS NWea SEWo SKee SLim SPoG SVic WMat

DAMSON (*Prunus insititia*)

00 H6 **'Farleigh Damson'** (C)
Pollination group 4. Excellent flavour. Regular, heavy crops. Blossom shows some resistance to frost. Season: late Aug.
CAgr CArg CHab CLnd ECrN EMOT EPfP EPom LBuc LEdu MJak NLar NOra NWea SDea SKee SPer SVic WJas WMat WWct

98 H6 **'Prune Damson'** (C)
Pollination group 4. Larger fruits than 'Farleigh Damson', but typical damson flavour. Regular, good crops. Season: late Aug.
CAgr CArg CDul CHab CLnd CMac CTho CTri EMOT EPom LBuc LCro LRHS MAsh MMuc NEgg NLar NOra NWea SDea SEND SEWo SKee SPer SSFr WJas WMat WWct

FIG (*Ficus carica*)

93 H4 **'Brown Turkey'** (D)
Fruits regularly in the open in southern England and in many parts of the Midlands and East Anglia in a warm position. For good crop, root restriction advisable. Season: mid-Aug. to mid-Sept., depending on site.
CAby CAgr CBcs CCCN CCVT CDul CJun CRHN CRos CSBt CTho CTri CTsd EBee ECrN ELon EPfP EPom EUJe EWTr LBuc LCro LEdu LMaj LRHS LSRN MBlu MHer MJak MMuc MNHC NLar NRHS NWea SEND SEWo SGol SLim SPlb SPre NOra LOPS CFGn EMOT SSFT SDea MGos MAsh SKee CKel ELan CMac SMad WMou SPer NPer SPoG MRav SRms SSta SVic SWvt WAvo WFar WMat WPGP WTSh XSen

GOOSEBERRY (*Ribes uva-crispa*)

Season extends from early June to mid-Aug. For culinary use, pick from early June. For ripe fruit pick from about early July.

93 H6 **'Careless'** (C/D)
Green fruit. Reliable, good crops. Good for tarts, jam, etc. Prone to mildew. Season: mid.
CFGn CSBt CTri EPom LSRN MAsh MGos MJak SDea SPer WMat

94 H6 **'Greenfinch'** (C/D)
Green fruit; compact bush. Some resistance to mildew and leaf spot. Season: mid; similar to 'Careless'.
CAgr

93 H6 **'Invicta'** (C/D)
Green fruit; quite good flavour. Heavy crops; very vigorous; spreading habit; large thorns. Some resistance to mildew. Young shoots can be damaged on exposed site. Season: mid; slightly earlier than 'Careless'. Main use culinary.
CAgr CMac CRos CSBt CTri ECrN EMil EMOT EPfP EPom GBin LBuc LCro LOPS LRHS LSRN MAsh MGos MJak MMuc MNHC NEgg NLar NPri NRHS NWea SCoo SDea SEND SKee SLim SPer SPoG SSFr SVic SWvt WMat

93 H6 **'Leveller'** (C/D)
Large, yellow fruit; good dessert quality. Season: mid to late.
MCoo NWea SDea SPer

93 H6 **'Whinham's Industry'** (C/D)
Red fruit; quite good dessert quality. Heavy, reliable crops. Very susceptible to mildew. Season: mid.
LBuc LSRN MGos MMuc NEgg NPri SDea SEND SPer

GRAPE (*Vitis*)

04 H5 **'Boskoop Glory'** (D)
Black grape. Good outdoor vine for the amateur, both dessert and wine; crops reliably; disease-resistant. Moderately good flavour, but better than many shop-bought grapes. Awarded as 'Gloire de Boskoop'.
CMac EMOT LBuc SCob SCoo SDea WSuV

04 H5 **'New York Muscat'** (D)
Black grape. A good dessert Muscat with blackcurrant flavour. Disease-resistant. Best when grown on a warm site or wall.
ECrN WSuV

Hazelnut (*Corylus maxima*)

14 H6 **'Gunslebert'**
Good-sized nut; kernel fills the shell; very few blanks. Excellent flavour; very tasty. Mid-season. Regular, good crops; nuts held as large clusters of four nuts. Medium vigour tree; moderate amount of suckering. Pollinated by 'Kentish Cob', 'Cosford'. Good tree habit, with a natural goblet shape and exceptionally attractive with prolific catkins making it also an ornamental tree. A mainstay of Kent nut production. Reliable, hardy hazel nut, easy to grow in a garden situation; productive and ornamental; requires a pollinator.
CCVT CDul CMac CTri ECrN EMOT NOra SDea SPoG SRms SSFr WMat

14 H6 **'Kentish Cob'**
Good-sized nut; kernel fills the shell; very few blanks. Excellent flavour; rich and meaty. Early season, cropping before the squirrels become active. Regular, good crops. Medium vigour tree; moderate amount of suckering. Pollinated by 'Gunslebert', 'Cosford', 'Hall's Giant' ('Merveille de Bollwiller'). The main cultivar of commercial nut plantations in Kent. Reliable hazel nut, easy to grow in a garden situation; needs a pollinator.
CAgr CBcs CDul CMac CSBt CTho CTri ECrN ELan EMOT EPfP EPom IArd LBuc LRHS MGos NLar SDea SEWo SKee SLim SPer SPoG SRms SSFr SVic SWvt WMat WMou

Loganberry (*Rubus × loganobaccus*)

93 H5 **'Ly 654'** (C)
Large, dark fruit; distinctive flavour; good crops. Thornless. Season: July.
CRos CSBt EPom LBuc LRHS NEgg NPri NRHS SDea SPer SSFr SVic

Medlar (*Mespilus germanica*)

14 H6 **'Nottingham'**
Upright habit with good flavour; fruits small.
CAgr CArg CBcs CCVT CDul CEnd CFGn CHab CTho CTri EBee ECrN ELan EMOT EPfP EPom LBuc LRHS MAsh MGos MMuc NEgg NOra NPri NWea SCoo SDea SEND SEWo SKee SLim SPer SPoG SSFr SSFT SVic WJas WMat

Pear (*Pyrus communis*)

93 H6 **'Beth'** (D)
Pollination group 4. Attractive; good quality and flavour. Small fruit. Heavy, regular crops. Season: mid/late Aug. to early Sept.; short season once picked.
CAgr CArg CHab CMac CSBt CTri EBee ECrN EMOT EPfP EPom IArd LBuc LRHS MAsh MGos NLar NOra NPri SCob SDea SKee SLim SPer SSFT SSFr WMat

93 H6 **'Beurré Hardy'** (D)
Pollination group 3. Very melting and fragrant with rose-water perfume. Good, regular crops. Very hardy, vigorous tree; slow to bear; resistant to scab. Season: Nov. to Dec.*
CAgr CArg CCVT CDul CFGn CLnd CMac CSBt CTri ECrN ELan EMOT EPfP EPom IArd LMaj MCoo MJak MMuc MWat NOra SCob SDea SEND SKee SPer SSFT SSFr WMat WWct

06 H6 **'Beurré Superfin'** (D)
Pollination group 3. An excellent September-cropping cultivar for the amateur gardener, with a lovely cinnamon-russet colour and an exquisite flavour. Gives a good, consistent yield and is not over-vigorous. Mid-season.
SKee SSFr

93 H6 **'Concorde'** (D)
Pollination group 4. Sweet, buttery, fragrant flavour, similar to 'Conference', but superior. Heavy, regular crops; frost-tolerant blossom. Young trees very precocious. Season: late Oct./Nov. to Dec.
CAgr CArg CCVT CDul CMac CRos CSBt CTho CTri EBee ECrN ELan EMOT EPfP EPom IArd LBuc LCro LOPS LRHS LSRN MAsh MGos MJak MNHC MRav MWat NLar NOra NPri NWea SCob SDea SEWo SKee SLim SPer SPoG SSFr SSFT SVic WJas WMat WWct

93 H6 **'Conference'** (D)
Pollination group 3. Sweet, buttery, quite rich taste. Heavy, regular crops. Can produce fruits without pollinators, but resulting fruits often misshapen. Season: Oct. to Nov./Dec.*
CAgr CArg CBcs CCVT CDul CLnd CMac CRos CSBt CTho CTri CTsd EBee ECrN ELan EMOT EPfP EPom LBuc LCro LEdu LMaj LOPS LRHS LSRN MAsh MGos MJak MMuc MWat NLar NOra NPri NRHS NWea SCob SDea SEND SEWo SKee SLim SPer SPoG MRav SSFr SVic SWvt WJas WMat WTSh WWct

93 H6 **'Doyenné du Comice'** (D)
Pollination group 4. Very rich flavour; very juicy, buttery, perfumed. Excellent quality, but moderate crops, although older trees more regular. Vigorous tree; prone to scab. Season: Nov. to Dec. Not compatible with 'Onward'.
CAgr CArg CBcs CCVT CDul CHab CLnd CMac CSBt CTri EBee ECrN ELan EMOT EPfP EPom IArd LBuc LCro LMaj LOPS

LRHS MAsh MJak MMuc MRav MWat NLar NOra NPri NWea SCob SDea SEND SEWo SKee SLim SPer SSFr SVic WJas WMat WTSh WWct

06 H6 **'Gorham'** (D)
Pollination group 4. A beautiful green pear with a good covering of russet. Has an excellent flavour; a good reliable cropper and is readily available. Late.
CAgr CDul CTho NOra SKee SSFT SSFr WMat

93 H6 **'Joséphine de Malines'** (D)
Pollination group 3. Very rich, buttery and perfumed. Crops good, reliable, but needs warm site. Fruit easily bruised. Tip-bearer; resistant to scab. Season: Nov. to Dec./Jan.
CAgr IArd NOra SDea SKee

Plum (*Prunus domestica*)

00 H5 **'Blue Rock'** (C/D)
Pollination group 1. Quite well-flavoured blue plum. Regular, good crops; not self-fertile. Neat tree. Season: mid-Aug.
SKee

95 H5 **'Blue Tit'** (C/D)
Pollination group 5. Pleasant flavour; blue plum. Regular, good crops. Self-fertile. Season: mid-Aug.
CAgr CTho EMOT EPom LSRN MMuc NOra SDea SEND SKee SSFr WMat WWct

98 H5 **'Cambridge Gage'** (D)
Pollination group 4. Honeysweet excellent greengage quality, but more reliable than most greengages. Reasonably regular crops in favourable situations. Partly self-fertile. Season: mid-Aug.
CAgr CArg CCVT CEnd CHab CLnd CMac CTri ECrN EMOT EPfP EPom LCro LRHS LSRN MAsh MMuc MWat NOra NWea SCoo SDea SEND SEWo SKee SLim SPer SSFr WJas WMat WWct

93 H6 **'Czar'** (C/D)
Pollination group 3. Well-flavoured; early blue plum; use for jam but also moderate eating quality. Heavy, regular crops. Self-fertile. Season: mid-Aug.
CAgr CArg CCVT CDul CEnd CHab CLnd CMac CSBt CTri ECrN ELan EMOT EPfP EPom LBuc LCro LMaj LOPS LRHS MAsh MCoo MGos MJak MMuc NLar NOra NPri NWea SDea SEND SEWo SKee SLim SPer SPoG SSFr SSFT SVic SWvt WMat WWct

14 H5 **'Haganta'** (D)
Pollination group 3. Large dark blue plum, late-ripening, with good consistent crop; juicy, sweet; sugary; and stone almost free; good flavour; potential for cold storage to extend the eating season to the end of October.
CAgr MCoo NOra WMat

93 H5 **'Imperial Gage'** (C/D)
Pollination group 2. Gage quality but not as rich as 'Cambridge Gage'. Regular crops. Partly self-fertile. Season: mid-Aug.
CAgr CArg CLnd CMac CSBt CTho CTri EPom LRHS MMuc NOra SDea SEND SKee SSFT SSFr WMat

94 H5 **'Jefferson'** (D)
Pollination group 1. Yellow flushed with red; rich, gage quality. Moderate, regular crops. Not self-fertile. Season: mid- to late Aug.
CAgr CArg CHab CLnd EMOT NOra SDea SKee SSFr SVic WMat

00 H6 **'Mallard'** (D)
Pollination group 1. Medium-sized red plum; quite good flavour. Good, regular crops. Moderate vigour; not self-fertile. Season: mid- to late Aug.
NOra SKee WMat

93 H5 **'Marjorie's Seedling'** (C)
Pollination group 5. Late blue plum. Good for jam. Reliable good crops; vigorous, upright habit. Self-fertile. Season: late Sept. to early Oct.
CAgr CArg CCVT CDul CEnd CHab CLnd CMac CSBt CTho CTri ECrN EMOT EPfP EPom LBuc LCro LOPS LRHS LSRN MAsh MGos MJak MMuc MWat NEgg NLar NOra NPri NWea SCoo SDea SEND SKee SLim SPer SSFr SSFT WJas WMat WWct

95 H6 **'Opal'** (D)
Pollination group 3. Small purple plum; good flavour. Reliable, heavy crops; needs thinning. Partly self-fertile. Blossom buds very prone to bird damage. Season: early to mid-Aug.
CAgr CArg CCVT CDul CLnd CMac CRos CTri ECrN EMOT EPom LBuc LRHS LSRN MAsh MGos MMuc MWat NLar NOra NWea SCoo SDea SEND SKee SLim SPer SSFr SSFT WMat WTSh WWct

93 H5 **'Oullins Gage'** (D)
Pollination group 4. Large, yellow flushed with pink. Not typical gage quality, but quite rich. Heavy, regular crops. Partly self-fertile. Season: mid-Aug.
CAgr CArg CCVT CDul CLnd CMac CSBt CTri ELan EMOT EPfP EPom LBuc LEdu LRHS MGos MJak MMuc MRav NOra NPri SDea SEND SEWo SKee SPer SPoG SSFr SSFT SVic SWvt WJas WMat WWct

14 H5 **'Purple Pershore'** (C)
Pollination group 3. Good flavour; reliable good crops.
CAgr CHab CTri IArd NEgg NOra SDea SKee WMat WWct

95 H5 **'Valor'** (C/D)
Pollination group 2. Blue, medium-sized plum. Good quality. Moderately good, regular crops. Not self-fertile. Season: late Aug.
NOra SKee

93 H5 **'Victoria'** (C/D)
Pollination group 3. Red plum; reasonable to good eating quality; excellent for bottling, jam and tarts. Heavy, regular crops. Self-fertile. Season: mid-to late Aug.
CAgr CArg CCVT CDul CFGn CHab CLnd ELan CMac SPer SPoG MRav CRos CSBt CTho CTri CTsd ECrN EMOT EPfP EPom GKin IArd LBuc LCro LEdu LMaj LOPS LRHS LSRN MAsh MGos MJak MMuc MWat NEgg NLar NOra NPri NRHS NWea SCoo SDea SEND SEWo SKee SLim SSFr SSFT SVic SWvt WJas WMat WTSh WWct

Quince (*Cydonia oblonga*)

14 H5 **'Meech's Prolific'**
Regular crops of pear-shaped golden-yellow fruits with good flavour.
CAgr CDul CHab CLnd CTri ECrN EPom LRHS MAsh MGos MRav NLar NOra NWea SDea SKee SLim SPer SSFT SSFr WMat WWct

14 H5 **'Vranja'**
Large green pear-shaped fragrant fruits, becoming golden-yellow when ripe.
CAgr CArg CCVT CDul CEnd CHab CLnd CMac CRos CSBt CTri EBee ECrN ELan EPfP EPom EUJe EWTr LBuc LEdu LRHS LSRN MAsh MGos MMuc MRav NLar NOra NWea SDea SEND SKee SLim SLon SPer SSFr WJas WMat WWct

Raspberry (*Rubus idaeus*)

Raspberries crop from late June to early Aug. Autumn primocanes from late July to early Oct.

09 H6 **'All Gold'**
Autumn cropping. Yellow/golden-fruited; needs to be left to ripen well before the flavour is fully tasted. Yield generally peaking at the end of August and early September. An upright habit with easy-to-manage cane.
CFGn CMac CPer EMOT EMil EPom LRHS NLar NPri SCoo SPer SRms SVic WMat

93 H6 **'Autumn Bliss'** (D)
Autumn cropping. Primocane-fruiting (fruiting on current season's canes). Excellent flavour; large fruit. Good crops. Resistant to aphid vectors of virus disease and phytophthora root rot. Season: crops late July to early Oct. Reconfirmed after trial 2009.
CAgr CMac CRos CSBt CTri ECrN ELan EMOT EPfP EPom LBuc LCro LEdu LOPS LRHS LSRN MAsh MGos MJak MMuc MNHC NEgg NLar NPri NRHS NWea SCoo SDea SEND SGol SKee SLim SPer SPoG SRms SSFr SVic WMat

00 H6 **'Glen Ample'** (D)
Summer cropping. Large fruit, excellent flavour. Recommended for freezing. Heavy crops; spine-free canes. Resistant to main aphid vector of virus disease; some tolerance to phytophthora root rot; some susceptibility to leaf and bud mite. Season: mid. Reconfirmed after trial 2009.
CAgr CArg CMac CRos CSBt CTri ECrN ELan EMil EPfP EPom LBuc LCro LOPS LRHS LSRN MAsh MCoo MNHC NLar NRHS NWea SCoo SDea SKee SLim SPer SPoG SRms SSFr SVic WMat

09 H6 **'Glen Magna'** (D)
Summer cropping. A very vigorous cultivar with long, strong fruiting laterals. It has large fruit with a good flavour. Yields high with a long cropping season.
CAgr CArg CMac CSBt MAsh NPri SCoo SDea SKee SLim

09 H6 **'Joan J'**
Autumn cropping. Easy to grow and pick; upright habit; good berry size.
CArg CMac EPom LBuc LSRN SPer SSFr

93 H6 **'Leo'** (D)
Large firm fruit; excellent flavour. Good crops. Very long laterals. Season: late.
CSBt LSRN MAsh SCoo SKee SPer SRms SSFr

93 H6 **'Malling Admiral'** (D)
Summer cropping. Good quality; medium to large, attractive fruit. Consistent, moderate to good crops; tall canes; withstands wet conditions, but laterals easily damaged in exposed sites. Good disease resistance. Season: mid to late. Reconfirmed after trial 2009.
CSBt CTri EMOT EPom LSRN MAsh NWea SCoo SKee SPer

93 H6 **'Malling Jewel'** (D)
Summer cropping. Good flavour and crops. Season: early to mid. Reconfirmed after trial 2009.
CAgr CArg CSBt CTri EPfP EPom LBuc LSRN MAsh MJak NPri NWea SDea SKee SPer SRms

09 H6 **'Polka'**
Autumn cropping. Early flush of fruit

with good berry size and appearance; good upright habit with medium vigorous cane growth.
CArg CRos EPfP EPom LBuc LCro LOPS LRHS LSRN MAsh MCoo MRav NRHS SCoo SKee SLim SPer SRms SSFr WMat

09 H6 **'Tulameen'**
Summer cropping. Outstanding cultivar, with strong cane growth and upright habit. Spine-free and easily handled, with exceptional fruit quality and high yield. Less prone to pest and disease than other varieties.
CAgr CArg CRos CSBt ELan EMil EPfP EPom LBuc LCro LOPS LRHS LSRN MAsh MMuc NPri NRHS NWea SCoo SEND SKee SLim SPer SPoG SRms SSFr SVic WMat

REDCURRANT (*Ribes rubrum*)

Redcurrants crop from mid-July to early Sept.

93 H6 **'Jonkheer van Tets'** (C)
Large, handsome fruit; long strigs. Heavy crops. Season: early.
CAgr CRos CSBt EMOT EPfP EPom GQue IArd LRHS LSRN MAsh MCoo NLar NPri NRHS NWea SDea SEND SKee SLim SPer SRms SSFr WMat

93 H6 **'Red Lake'** (C)
Good quality medium to large fruit; cropping on long trusses. Prone to wind damage in exposed sites; in summer prune early. Season: mid to late.
CAgr CFGn CTri ECrN ELan EPfP EPom LBuc LEdu MGos MJak NEgg NLar NPri SDea SGol SKee SPer SPoG SSFr WMat

93 H6 **'Stanza'** (C)
Medium-sized fruit; good quality. Compact habit; heavy crops. Season: mid to late.
CAgr EMOT SDea SEND

STRAWBERRY (*Fragaria × ananassa*)

In an early season, strawberries begin to crop mid-June; in a late season, mid- to late June.

06 H6 **'Alice'**
A good consistent cropper, with a high percentage of mid to large, bright orange-red, sweet, juicy fruit. Scored well in taste tests and performed well at different geographical locations (Stafford, Kent, Dundee) in HDC trials. Has good resistance to verticillium wilt; very useful to home gardener. Mid- to late season.
CAgr CMac EPom NAln

93 H6 **'Cambridge Favourite'** (D)
Good flavour; medium size, but rather soft berries. Moderate crops; excellent resistance to disease. Good runner production. Season: mid.
CAgr CArg CMac CRos CSBt CTri EMil EPfP EPom LBuc LCro LOPS LRHS MGos MJak MMuc NAln NPri NRHS SDea SPlb

94 H6 **'Hapil'** (D)
Large glossy berries; good flavour. Heavy crops; vigorous. Susceptible to verticillium wilt. Season: early/mid. Reconfirmed after trial 2004.
CTri EMil EPfP EPom LBuc LEdu LRHS

93 H6 **'Honeoye'** (D)
Excellent flavour. Heavy crops; susceptible to verticillium wilt. Season: early. Reconfirmed after trial 2004.
CAgr CArg CRos CSBt EMil EPfP EPom LBuc LCro LEdu LOPS LRHS MMuc SPer

94 H6 **'Pegasus'** (D)
Good flavour; quite soft flesh. Good disease resistance; tolerance to verticillium wilt. Season: mid. Reconfirmed after trial 2004 and 2006.
CAgr CRos CSBt EPfP EPom LBuc LRHS NRHS

94 H6 **'Rhapsody'** (D)
Good flavour; medium to large berries. Resistant red core; some resistance to verticillium wilt and mildew. Season: late. Reconfirmed after trial 2006.
CRos LRHS LSRN NRHS

95 H6 **'Symphony'** (D)
Good flavour; bright, firm berries. Vigorous; good resistance to red core; susceptible to mildew. Good runner production. Season: mid to late. Reconfirmed after trial 2006.
CAgr CRos CSBt EPom LBuc LRHS LSRN NRHS

WALNUT (*Juglans regia*)

15 H6 **'Franquette'**
Old French variety, known since 19th century; received the designation *appellation d'origine contrôlée* in 1938 as 'Noix de Grenoble' and in 2002 as 'Noix du Perigord'; remains a main market walnut of France; long recommended for planting in UK. Tree upright with rounded crown; moderate vigour; late-leafing; tolerates disease. Good, regular crops; reliable and productive. Nuts easily husked; quite soft shell, and can be cracked with fingers; well-sealed and well-filled nut; medium size, long, oval shape. Flavour excellent. Season: quite late/late. Pollinated by 'Meylanaise', 'Ronde de Montignac', 'Fernette'; reported partially self-fertile.
CAgr EMOT NOra WMat

15 H6 **'Lara'**
French cultivar; seedling of American cultivar 'Payne'. One of the main cultivars of modern walnut plantations. Good habit, making broad spreading tree, but not very vigorous; quite early leafing out; lateral bearing; good disease resistance. Good, regular crops; reliable and productive. Nuts easily husked; medium to quite large, globose; well-sealed, well-filled; well-flavoured as fresh nut and as dried nut. Season: early. Pollinated by 'Franquette', 'Meylanaise' and 'Ronde de Montignac'.
NOra WMat

WHITECURRANT (*Ribes rubrum*)

93 H6 **'White Grape'** (D/C)
Attractive, translucent berries; good flavour.
Season: mid-July.
CTri LEdu

30
ANNIVERSARY
EDITION
Perfect
for
Pollinators

RHS Perfect for Pollinators

The plants listed below have been selected to help gardeners identify those plants that will provide nectar and pollen for bees and the many other types of pollinating insects.

Key to codes: T tree S shrub C climber B bulb / corm A annual Bi biennial H herbaceous perennial † denotes an archaeophyte (a naturalised plant introduced before 1500)

Wildflowers

Short Grass (up to 15cm)

Ajuga reptans bugle	H
Bellis perennis daisy	H
Campanula rotundifolia common harebell	H
Hippocrepis comosa horseshoe vetch	H
Lotus corniculatus bird's foot trefoil	H
Potentilla anserina silverweed	H
Potentilla erecta tormentil	H
Potentilla reptans creeping cinquefoil	H
Primula veris common cowslip	H
Prunella vulgaris selfheal	H
Ranunculus repens creeping buttercup	H
Sanguisorba minor salad burnet	H
Taraxacum officinale dandelion	H
Thymus polytrichus wild thyme	H
Thymus pulegioides large thyme	H
Trifolium pratense red clover	H
Trifolium repens white clover	H
Veronica chamaedrys germander speedwell	H

Hedges, Shrub Borders and Woodland Edges

Acer campestre field maple	S or T
Alliaria petiolata garlic mustard	Bi
Allium ursinum ramsons	B
Aquilegia vulgaris columbine	H
Ballota nigra black horehound	H
Berberis vulgaris barberry †	S
Bryonia dioica white bryony	H/C
Buxus sempervirens common box	S
Campanula trachelium nettle-leaved bellflower	H
Clematis vitalba old man's beard, traveller's joy	C
Clinopodium vulgare wild basil	H
Cornus sanguinea common dogwood	S
Crataegus monogyna common hawthorn	S or T
Cytisus scoparius common broom	S
Digitalis purpurea common foxglove	Bi
Euonymus europaeus spindle	S
Fragaria vesca wild strawberry	H
Frangula alnus alder buckthorn	S
Galium mollugo hedge bedstraw	H
Galium odoratum sweet woodruff	H
Galium verum lady's bedstraw	H
Geranium robertianum herb robert	A/Bi
Geum urbanum wood avens	H
Hedera helix common ivy	C
Helleborus foetidus stinking hellebore	H
Hyacinthoides non-scripta bluebell	B
Ilex aquifolium common holly	T
Lamium album white deadnettle	H
Lamium galeobdolon yellow archangel	H
Ligustrum vulgare wild privet	S
Lonicera periclymenum common honeysuckle	C
Malus sylvestris crab apple	T
Malva sylvestris common mallow	H
Myosotis sylvatica wood forget-me-not	H
Primula vulgaris primrose	H
Prunus avium wild cherry, gean	T
Prunus padus bird cherry	T
Prunus spinosa blackthorn, sloe	S
Ranunculus ficaria lesser celandine	H
Rhamnus catharticus purging buckthorn	S
Rosa canina dog rose	S
Rosa rubiginosa sweet briar	S
Rubus fruticosus blackberry	S
Salix atrocinerea grey willow (male forms best)	S
Salix caprea goat willow (male forms best)	S
Sanicula europaea sanicle	H
Sedum telephium orpine	H
Silene dioica red campion	H
Silene latifolia subsp. *alba* white campion	H
Smyrnium olusatrum alexanders †	Bi

Sorbus aria common whitebeam T
Sorbus aucuparia rowan, mountain ash T
Sorbus torminalis wild service tree T
Stachys officinalis betony H
Stellaria holostea greater stitchwort H
Symphytum officinale common comfrey H
Teucrium scorodonia wood sage H
Tilia cordata small-leaved lime T
Viburnum lantana common wayfaring tree S
Viburnum opulus guelder rose S
Vicia cracca common tufted vetch H
Vicia sativa common vetch H

Disturbed Ground

Agrostemma githago corncockle † A
Anchusa arvensis bugloss † A
Anthemis arvensis corn chamomile † A
Anthemis cotula stinking chamomile † A
Centaurea cyanus cornflower † A
Cichorium intybus chicory † H
Dipsacus fullonum common teasel Bi
Echium vulgare viper's bugloss Bi
Glebionis segetum corn marigold † A
Iberis amara wild candytuft A
Lamium amplexicaule henbit deadnettle † A
Matricaria recutita scented mayweed † A
Mentha arvensis corn mint H
Myosotis arvensis field forget-me-not † A/H
Onopordum acanthium cotton thistle † Bi
Papaver dubium long-headed poppy † A
Papaver rhoeas common poppy † A
Sinapis arvensis charlock † A
Sonchus arvensis perennial sowthistle H
Tussilago farfara coltsfoot H
Verbascum thapsus great mullein Bi

Flower Beds

Calluna vulgaris heather, ling S
Erica ciliaris Dorset heath S
Erica cinerea bell heather S
Erica tetralix cross-leaved heath S

Long Grass (above 50cm)

Arctium minus lesser burdock Bi
Carduus crispus welted thistle Bi
Carduus nutans musk thistle Bi
Chamaenerion angustifolium rosebay willowherb H
Cirsium arvense creeping thistle H
Cirsium vulgare spear thistle Bi
Conopodium majus pignut H
Cynoglossum officinale hound's tongue H
Daucus carota wild carrot Bi
Geranium pratense meadow cranesbill H
Heracleum sphondylium hogweed Bi
Hypericum perforatum perforate St John's wort H
Knautia arvensis field scabious H
Lathyrus pratensis meadow vetchling H
Pastinaca sativa wild parsnip Bi
Succisa pratensis devil's bit scabious H
Tanacetum vulgare tansy † H
Thalictrum flavum meadow rue H
Tragopogon pratensis goat's beard Bi
Verbascum nigrum dark mullein Bi/H

Medium Height Grass (up to 50cm)

Achillea millefolium common yarrow H
Achillea ptarmica sneezewort H
Agrimonia eupatoria agrimony H
Anthyllis vulneraria kidney vetch H
Armeria maritima thrift, sea pink H
Blackstonia perfoliata yellowwort A
Campanula glomerata clustered bellflower H
Centaurea nigra common knapweed, hardheads H
Centaurea scabiosa greater knapweed H
Centaurium erythraea common centaury Bi
Echium vulgare viper's bugloss Bi
Erigeron acris blue fleabane A/H
Filipendula vulgaris dropwort H
Helianthemum nummularium common rockrose H
Hypochaeris radicata cat's ear H
Inula conyzae ploughman's spikenard H
Leontodon autumnalis autumn hawkbit H
Leontodon hispidus rough hawkbit H
Leucanthemum vulgare ox-eye daisy H
Linaria vulgaris common toadflax H
Malva moschata musk mallow H
Ononis repens common restharrow H
Origanum vulgare wild marjoram H
Pilosella officinarum mouse-ear hawkweed H
Ranunculus acris meadow buttercup H
Ranunculus bulbosus bulbous buttercup H
Reseda lutea wild mignonette Bi/H
Rhinanthus minor yellow rattle A
Scabiosa columbaria small scabious H
Silene vulgaris bladder campion H
Solidago virgaurea goldenrod H

Ponds, Pond Margins & Wet Soils

Alisma plantago-aquatica water plantain H
Angelica sylvestris wild angelica Bi
Butomus umbellatus flowering rush H
Caltha palustris marsh marigold H
Cardamine pratensis cuckoo flower, lady's smock H
Cirsium dissectum meadow thistle H
Epilobium hirsutum great willowherb H
Eupatorium cannabinum hemp agrimony H
Filipendula ulmaria meadowsweet H
Galium palustre marsh bedstraw H
Geum rivale water avens H

Hypericum tetrapterum square-stalked St John's wort H
Iris pseudacorus yellow iris H
Lotus pedunculatus greater bird's-foot trefoil H
Lychnis flos-cuculi ragged robin H
Lycopus europaeus gypsywort H
Lysimachia nummularia creeping Jenny H
Lysimachia vulgaris yellow loosestrife H
Lythrum salicaria purple loosestrife H
Mentha aquatica water mint H
Menyanthes trifoliata bogbean H
Myosotis scorpioides water forget-me-not H
Nasturtium officinale common watercress H
Nuphar lutea yellow waterlily H
Nymphaea alba white waterlily H
Oenanthe aquatica fine-leaved water dropwort A/Bi
Oenanthe crocata hemlock water dropwort H
Persicaria amphibia amphibious bistort H
Persicaria bistorta common bistort H
Polemonium caeruleum Jacob's ladder H
Pulicaria dysenterica common fleabane H
Ranunculus aquatilis common water crowfoot A/H
Ranunculus flammula lesser spearwort H
Ranunculus fluitans river water crowfoot H
Ranunculus lingua greater spearwort H
Ranunculus sceleratus celery-leaved buttercup A
Sagittaria sagittifolia arrowhead H
Sanguisorba officinalis great burnet H
Scrophularia auriculata water figwort H
Scutellaria galericulata common skullcap H
Stachys palustris marsh woundwort H
Valeriana officinalis common valerian H
Veronica beccabunga brooklime H

Shingle – Gravel Garden

Cakile maritima sea rocket A
Crambe maritima sea kale H
Crithmum maritimum rock samphire H
Eryngium maritimum sea holly H
Glaucium flavum yellow horned poppy Bi/H
Sedum acre biting stonecrop H
Sedum album white stonecrop † H
Silene uniflora sea campion H

Garden Plants

Winter (nov – feb)

Clematis cirrhosa Spanish traveller's joy C
Crocus species crocus (winter-flowering) B
Eranthis hyemalis winter aconite B
× *Fatshedera lizei* tree ivy S
Galanthus nivalis common snowdrop B
Helleborus species and hybrids hellebore (winter-flowering) H
Lonicera × *purpusii* Purpus honeysuckle S
Mahonia species Oregon grape S
Salix aegyptiaca musk willow S
Sarcococca confusa sweet box S
Sarcococca hookeriana sweet box S
Viburnum tinus laurustinus S

Spring (mar – may)

Acer campestre Native plant; field maple S or T
Acer platanoides Norway maple T
Acer pseudoplatanus sycamore T
Acer saccharum sugar maple T
Aesculus hippocastanum horse chestnut T
Ajuga reptans Native plant; bugle H
Arabis alpina subsp. *caucasica* alpine rock cress H
Armeria juniperifolia juniper-leaved thrift H
Aubrieta species aubretia H
Aurinia saxatilis gold dust H
Berberis darwinii Darwin's barberry S
Berberis thunbergii Japanese barberry S
Bergenia species elephant ear H
Buxus sempervirens Native plant; common box S
Caltha palustris Native plant; marsh marigold H
Cercis siliquastrum Judas tree T
Chaenomeles species Japanese quince S
Cornus mas Cornelian cherry S
Cotoneaster conspicuus Tibetan cotoneaster S
Crataegus monogyna Native plant; common hawthorn S or T
Crocus species crocus (spring-flowering) B
Doronicum × *excelsum* leopard's bane H
Enkianthus campanulatus redvein enkianthus S
Erysimum species wallflower Bi
Erica carnea alpine heath S
Erica × *darleyensis* Darley Dale heath S
Erysimum 'Bredon' wallflower 'Bredon' H
Euphorbia amygdaloides Native plant; wood spurge H
Euphorbia characias Mediterranean spurge H
Euphorbia cyparissias cypress spurge H
Euphorbia nicaeensis Nice spurge H
Euphorbia epithymoides cushion spurge H
Geranium species cranesbill H
Geum rivale Native plant; water avens H
Hebe species hebe S
Helleborus species & hybrids hellebore (spring-flowering) H
Iberis saxatilis alpine candytuft H
Iberis sempervirens perennial candytuft H
Ilex aquifolium Native plant; common holly T
Lamium maculatum spotted dead nettle H
Lunaria annua honesty Bi
Mahonia species Oregon grape (spring-flowering) S
Malus baccata Siberian crab T

Malus domestica edible apple T
Malus floribunda Japanese crab T
Malus hupehensis Hupeh crab T
Malus sargentii Sargent's crab apple T
Mespilus germanica common medlar T
Muscari armeniacum Armenian grape hyacinth B
Ornithogalum umbellatum common star of Bethlehem B
Pieris formosa lily-of-the-valley bush S
Pieris japonica lily-of-the-valley bush S
Primula veris Native plant; common cowslip H
Primula vulgaris Native plant; primrose H
Prunus avium Native plant; wild & edible cherries T
Prunus domestica wild & edible plums T
Prunus dulcis almond T
Prunus incisa 'Kojo-no-mai' cherry 'Kojo-no-mai' S
Prunus insititia damson T
Prunus laurocerasus cherry laurel S
Prunus mume Japanese apricot T
Prunus padus Native plant; bird cherry T
Prunus pendula f. *ascendens* 'Rosea' flowering cherry T
Prunus persica peach T
Prunus spinosa Native plant; blackthorn S
Prunus tenella dwarf Russian almond S
Prunus × *yedoensis* flowering cherry T
Pulmonaria species lungwort H
Pyrus communis pear T
Ribes nigrum blackcurrant S
Ribes rubrum Native plant; common redcurrant S
Ribes sanguineum flowering currant S
Salix caprea Native plant; goat willow (male form only) S or T
Salix hastata 'Wehrhahnii' halberd willow 'Wehrhahnii' S
Salix lanata Native plant; woolly willow (male form only) S
Skimmia japonica skimmia S
Smyrnium olusatrum Native plant; alexanders † Bi
Stachyurus chinensis stachyurus S
Stachyurus praecox stachyurus S
Vaccinium corymbosum blueberry S

Summer (June – Aug)

Achillea species yarrow H
Actaea japonica baneberry H
Aesculus indica Indian horse chestnut (resistant to leaf-mining moth) T
Aesculus parviflora bottlebrush buckeye S
Agastache species giant hyssop H
Ageratum houstonianum flossflower A
Alcea rosea hollyhock Bi
Allium species ornamental and edibles (when allowed to flower) B
Amberboa moschata sweet sultan A
Amsonia tabernaemontana eastern bluestar H
Anchusa azurea large blue alkanet A
Anchusa capensis Cape alkanet A
Angelica archangelica angelica Bi
Angelica gigas purple angelica Bi
Angelica sylvestris Native plant; wild angelica Bi
Anthemis tinctoria dyer's chamomile H
Antirrhinum majus snapdragon A or H
Aquilegia species columbine H
Argemone platyceras crested poppy A or H
Armeria maritima Native plant; thrift H
Aruncus dioicus goat's beard (male form only) H
Asparagus officinalis common asparagus H
Astrantia major greater masterwort H
Borago officinalis borage A
Brachyglottis (Dunedin Group) 'Sunshine' brachyglottis 'Sunshine' S
Brachyglottis monroi Monro's ragwort S
Buddleja davidii butterfly bush S
Buddleja globosa orange ball tree S
Buphthalmum salicifolium yellow ox-eye H
Bupleurum fruticosum shrubby hare's ear S
Calamintha nepeta Native plant; lesser calamint H
Calendula officinalis common marigold A
Callicarpa bodinieri var. *giraldii* beautyberry S
Callistephus chinensis China aster A
Calluna vulgaris Native plant; heather S
Campanula carpatica tussock bellflower H
Campanula glomerata Native plant; clustered bellflower H
Campanula lactiflora milky bellflower H
Campanula latifolia Native plant; giant bellflower H
Campanula medium Canterbury bells Bi
Campanula persicifolia peach-leaved bellflower H
Campsis radicans trumpet honeysuckle C
Caryopteris × *clandonensis* caryopteris S
Catalpa bignonioides Indian bean tree T
Catananche caerulea blue cupidone H
Centaurea atropurpurea purple knapweed H
Centaurea cyanus cornflower † A
Centaurea dealbata mealy centaury H
Centaurea macrocephala giant knapweed H
Centaurea montana perennial cornflower H
Centaurea nigra Native plant; common knapweed H
Centaurea scabiosa Native plant; greater knapweed H
Centranthus ruber red valerian H
Centratherum punctatum Manaos beauty A
Cerinthe major 'Purpurascens' honeywort 'Purpurascens' A
Cirsium rivulare 'Atropurpureum' purple plume thistle H
Clarkia unguiculata butterfly flower A
Clematis vitalba Native plant; old man's beard, traveller's joy C
Cleome hassleriana spider flower A
Consolida ajacis giant larkspur A

Convolvulus tricolor dwarf morning glory C/A
Coreopsis species tickseed H or A
Cornus alba red-barked dogwood S
Cosmos bipinnatus cosmea A
Cosmos sulphureus yellow cosmos A
Crambe cordifolia greater sea kale H
Crataegus monogyna Native plant; common hawthorn S or T
Cucurbita pepo marrow, courgette A
Cuphea ignea cigar flower A
Cynara cardunculus including Scolymus Group globe artichoke and cardoon H
Cynoglossum amabile Chinese forget-me-not H
Dahlia species dahlia H
Delosperma floribundum ice plant H
Delphinium elatum candle larkspur H
Dianthus barbatus sweet william Bi
Dictamnus albus dittany H
Digitalis species foxglove Bi
Dipsacus fullonum Native plant; common teasel Bi
Echinacea purpurea purple coneflower H
Echinops species globe thistle H
Echium vulgare Native plant; viper's bugloss A
Elaeagnus angustifolia oleaster S
Erica cinerea Native plant; bell heather S
Erica erigena Irish heath S
Erica vagans Native plant; Cornish heath S
Erigeron species fleabane H
Eriophyllum lanatum golden yarrow H
Eryngium alpinum alpine eryngo H
Eryngium giganteum Miss Willmott's ghost Bi
Eryngium planum blue eryngo H
Eryngium × tripartitum eryngo H
Erysimum × allionii Siberian wallflower H
Erysimum 'Bowles's Mauve' wallflower 'Bowles's Mauve' S
Escallonia species escallonia S
Eschscholzia californica California poppy A
Eupatorium cannabinum Native plant; hemp agrimony H
Eupatorium maculatum Joe Pye weed H
Euphorbia cornigera horned spurge H
Euphorbia sarawschanica Zeravshan spurge H
Ferula communis giant fennel H
Foeniculum vulgare common fennel † H
Fragaria × ananassa garden strawberry H
Fuchsia species fuchsia – hardy types S
Gaillardia × grandiflora blanket flower H
Gaura lindheimeri white gaura H
Geranium pratense Native plant; meadow cranesbill H
Geranium species cranesbill (summer-flowering) H
Geum species avens (summer-flowering) H
Gilia capitata blue thimble flower A
Glebionis segetum corn marigold † A
Gypsophila elegans annual baby's breath A
Hebe species hebe S
Helenium species Helen's flower H
Helianthus annuus common sunflower A
Helianthus debilis cucumberleaf sunflower A
Heliopsis helianthoides smooth ox-eye H
Heliotropium arborescens common heliotrope A
Heracleum sphondylium Native plant; hogweed Bi
Hesperis matronalis dame's violet H
Hydrangea anomala subsp. *petiolaris* climbing hydrangea C
Hydrangea paniculata paniculate hydrangea (cultivars with many fertile flowers e.g. 'Kyushu', 'Big Ben', 'Floribunda', 'Brussels Lace') S
Hyssopus officinalis hyssop S
Iberis amara Native plant; wild candytuft A
Ilex aquifolium Native plant; common holly T
Inula species harvest daisy H
Jasminum officinale common jasmine C
Kalmia latifolia mountain laurel S
Knautia arvensis Native plant; field scabious H
Knautia macedonica Macedonian scabious H
Koelreuteria paniculata pride of India T
Lathyrus latifolius broad-leaved everlasting pea H
Laurus nobilis bay tree S
Lavandula angustifolia English lavender S
Lavandula × intermedia lavandin S
Lavandula stoechas French lavender S
Lavatera olbia tree lavatera S
Lavatera trimestris annual lavatera A
Leucanthemum × superbum Shasta daisy H
Leucanthemum vulgare Native plant; ox-eye daisy H
Liatris spicata button snakewort H
Ligustrum ovalifolium garden privet S
Ligustrum sinense Chinese privet S
Limnanthes douglasii poached egg flower A
Limonium platyphyllum broad-leaved statice H
Linaria maroccana annual toadflax A
Linaria purpurea purple toadflax H
Lobularia maritima sweet alyssum A
Lonicera periclymenum Native plant; common honeysuckle C
Lychnis coronaria rose campion Bi or H
Lychnis flos-cuculi Native plant; ragged robin H
Lysimachia vulgaris Native plant; yellow loosestrife H
Lythrum salicaria Native plant; purple loosestrife H
Lythrum virgatum wand loosestrife H
Malope trifida large-flowered mallow wort A
Malva moschata Native plant; musk mallow H
Matthiola incana hoary stock Bi
Mentha aquatica Native plant; water mint H
Mentha spicata spearmint H
Monarda didyma bergamot H
Myosotis species forget-me-not Bi
Nemophila menziesii baby blue eyes A
Nepeta × faassenii garden catmint H
Nicotiana alata flowering tobacco A
Nicotiana langsdorffii Langsdorff's tobacco A
Nigella damascena love-in-a-mist A

Nigella hispanica Spanish fennel flower A
Oenothera species evening primrose Bi
Olearia species daisy bush S
Onopordum acanthium cotton thistle Bi
Origanum 'Rosenkuppel' marjoram 'Rosenkuppel' H
Origanum vulgare Native plant; oregano, wild marjoram H
Paeonia species peony H
Papaver orientale oriental poppy H
Papaver rhoeas Native plant; common poppy † A
Parthenocissus tricuspidata Boston ivy C
Penstemon species beard-tongue T
Perovskia atriplicifolia Russian sage S
Persicaria amplexicaulis red bistort H
Persicaria bistorta Native plant; common bistort H
Phacelia campanularia Californian bluebell A
Phacelia tanacetifolia fiddleneck A
Phaseolus coccineus scarlet runner bean A
Phlomis species sage S
Phlox paniculata perennial phlox H
Photinia davidiana stranvaesia S
Phuopsis stylosa Caucasian crosswort H
Pileostegia viburnoides climbing hydrangea C
Polemonium caeruleum Native plant; Jacob's ladder H
Potentilla species cinquefoil H or S
Prostanthera cuneata alpine mint bush S
Ptelea trifoliata hop tree S
Pyracantha species firethorn S
Reseda odorata garden mignonette A
Ridolfia segetum false fennel A
Robinia pseudoacacia false acacia T
Rosa canina Native plant; dog rose S
Rosa rubiginosa Native plant; sweet briar S
Rosa rugosa Japanese rose S
Rosmarinus officinalis rosemary S
Rubus fruticosus agg. Native plant; blackberry S
Rubus idaeus Native plant; common raspberry S
Rudbeckia species coneflower H or A
Salvia species sage A or H
Sanvitalia procumbens creeping zinnia A
Scabiosa atropurpurea sweet scabious A
Scabiosa caucasica garden scabious H
Scabiosa columbaria Native plant; small scabious H
Sedum spectabile & hybrids ice plant H
Sedum telephium Native plant; orpine H
Sidalcea malviflora checkerbloom H
Solidago species goldenrod H
Sorbus aria Native plant; common whitebeam T
Sorbus aucuparia Native plant; mountain ash, rowan T
Spiraea japonica Japanese spiraea S
Stachys byzantina lamb's ear H
Stachys macrantha big sage H
Stokesia laevis Stokes' aster H
Symphoricarpos albus snowberry S
Tagetes patula French marigold A
Tamarix ramosissima tamarisk S
Tanacetum coccineum pyrethrum H
Tanacetum vulgare Native plant; tansy † H
Telekia speciosa yellow ox-eye H
Tetradium daniellii bee-bee tree T
Teucrium chamaedrys Native plant; wall germander H
Thymus species thyme S
Tilia × *europaea* common lime T
Tilia maximowicziana lime T
Tilia oliveri lime T
Tilia platyphyllos Native plant; broad-leaved lime T
Tithonia rotundifolia Mexican sunflower A
Trachymene coerulea blue lace flower A
Tropaeolum majus garden nasturtium A
Verbascum species mullein Bi
Verbena bonariensis purple top H
Verbena × *hybrida* garden verbena A
Verbena rigida slender vervain A
Veronica longifolia garden speedwell H
Veronicastrum virginicum Culver's root H
Viburnum lantana Native plant; common wayfaring tree S
Viburnum opulus Native plant; guelder rose S
Vicia faba broad bean A
Weigela florida weigelia S
Zauschneria californica Californian fuchsia S
Zinnia elegans youth and old age A

Autumn (sept – oct)

Aconitum carmichaelii Carmichael's monk's hood H
Actaea simplex simple-stemmed bugbane H
Anemone hupehensis Chinese anemone H
Anemone × *hybrida* Japanese anemone H
Arbutus unedo strawberry tree S or T
Campanula poscharskyana trailing bellflower H
Ceratostigma plumbaginoides hardy blue-flowered leadwort H
Chrysanthemum species & hybrids chrysanthemum H
Clematis heracleifolia tube clematis C
Colchicum species autumn crocus B
Crocus species crocus (autumn-flowering types) B
Dahlia species & hybrids dahlia H
Elaeagnus × *ebbingei* Ebbinge's silverberry S
Elaeagnus pungens silverthorn S
Fatsia japonica Japanese aralia S
Hedera colchica Persian ivy C
Hedera helix Native plant; common ivy C
Helianthus × *laetiflorus* perennial sunflower H
Leucanthemella serotina autumn ox-eye H
Machaeranthera tanacetifolia tansy-leaf aster A
Salvia species sage (autumn-flowering types) H
Symphyotrichum species and hybrids Michaelmas daisy H
Tilia henryana Henry's lime (one of the last to flower) T

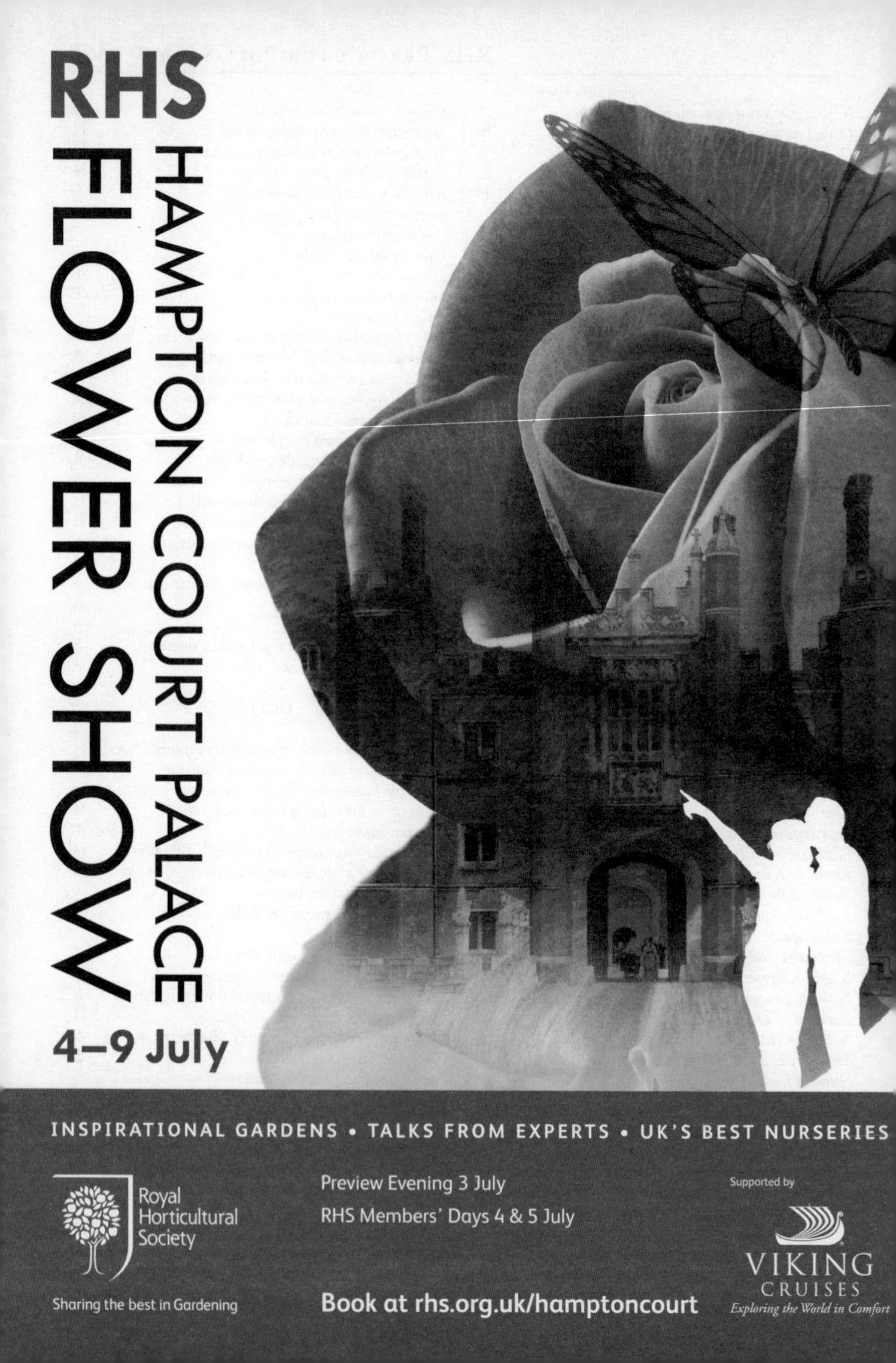

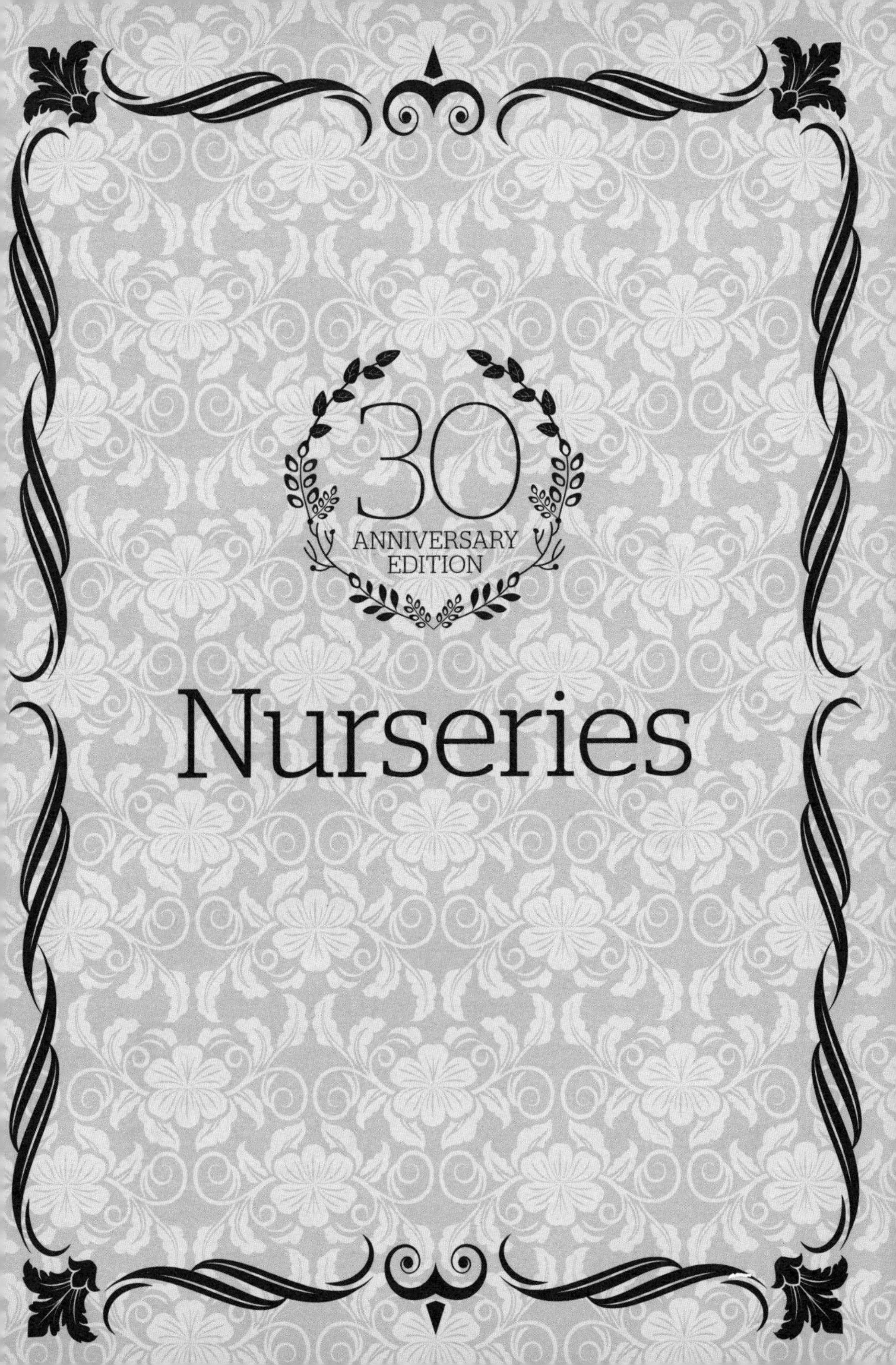

Nurseries

Nursery Codes and Symbols

The first letter of each nursery code represents the area of the country in which the nursery is situated.

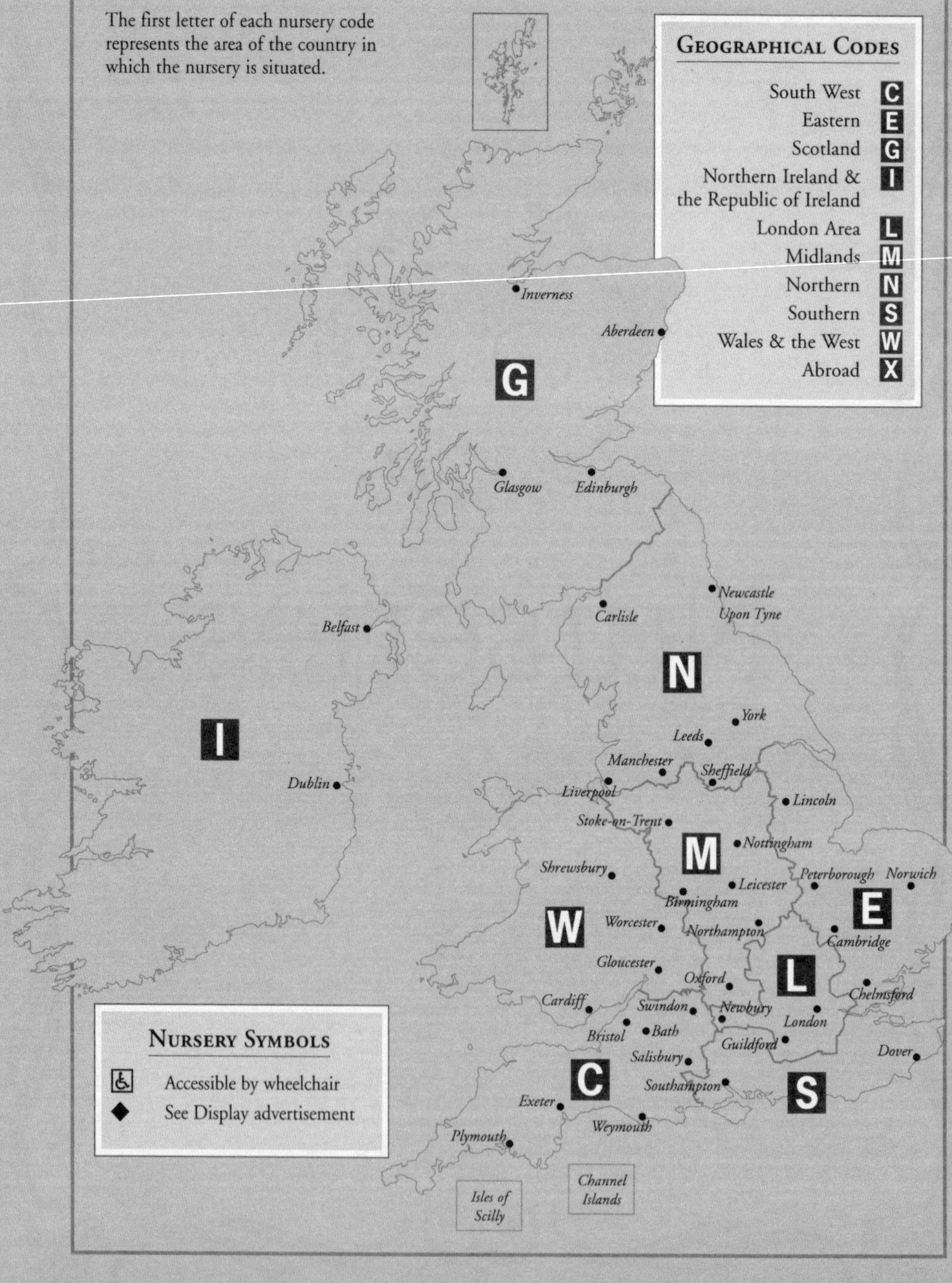

Using the Nursery Listings

Your main reference from the Plant Directory is the Nursery Details by Code listing, which includes all relevant information for each nursery in order of nursery code. The Nursery Index by Name is an alphabetical list for those who know a nursery's name but not its code and wish to check its details in the main list.

1 Nursery Details by Code

Once you have found your plant in the Plant Directory, turn to this list to find out the name, address, opening times and other details of the nurseries whose codes accompany the plant.

KEY

♿ Accessible by wheelchair ◆ See Display advertisement

A geographical code is followed by three letters reflecting the nursery's name

ESwi **Swines Meadow Farm Nursery** ♿ ◆
47 Towngate East, Market Deeping, Peterborough PE6 8LQ
Ⓣ 01778 343340
Ⓜ 07432 627766
Ⓔ ceveandsons@btconnect.com
Ⓦ www.swinesmeadowfarmnursery.co.uk
Contact: Colin Ward
Opening Times: 0900-1600 Mon-Sat, 1000-1600 Sun. Closed Jan, except by appt. only.
Min Mail Order UK: £10.00
Min Mail Order EU: £10.00
Credit Cards: All major debit/credit cards except American Express
Specialities: Hardy exotics, tree ferns, bamboos & phormiums. Wollemi pine stockist. Many specialities available in small quantities only.
Notes: Delivers to shows. Wheelchair accessible.
OS Grid Ref: TF150113

A brief summary of the plants available

Other information about the nursery

The Ordnance Survey national grid reference for use with OS maps

2 Nursery Index by Name

If you are looking for a particular nursery, use this alphabetical index to find it, note its code and then turn to the Nursery Details by Code listing for full information.

Sussex Fruit Trees	SSFT
Dan Sutton	SSut
Swallows Nursery	MSwo
Swines Meadow Farm Nursery	**ESwi**
Table Bay View Nursery	XBlo
Tan-y-Llyn Nurseries	WTan
Terrace Gardener	STrG
Thistlefield Plants and Design	EThi

How to Use the Nursery Listings

The details given for each nursery have been compiled from information supplied to us in answer to a questionnaire. In some case, because of space constraints, the entries have been abbreviated.

Nurseries are not charged for their entries and inclusion in no way implies a value judgement.

Nursery Details by Code (p.868)

Each nursery is allocated a code, for example GPoy. The first letter of each code indicates the region of the British Isles in which the nursery is situated. In this example G = Scotland. The remaining three letters reflect the nursery's name, in this case Poyntzfield Herb Nursery.

In this listing, nurseries are given in alphabetical order of code for quick referral from the Plant Directory. All of the nurseries' details, such as addresses, opening times, etc will be found in this index.

Opening Times

These are published as submitted. It is always advisable, especially if travelling a long distance, to double-check with the nursery before setting out.

Mail Order

Many nurseries offer a mail order service. This is often restricted to certain times of the year or to particular genera. Please check the **Notes** section of the nursery entry for restrictions or special conditions.

In some instances the mail order service extends throughout the European Union. Where this is the case, the minimum charge to the EU will be noted. If this is "Nmc" ("no minimum charge") please note that to send even one plant may involve the nursery in substantial postage and packaging costs. Some nurseries may not be prepared to send tender or bulky plants.

Where a nursery offers a mail order only service, this will be noted under **Opening Times** in the nursery entry. Many nurseries offer a mail order online service with some only operating in this way.

Export

This refers to mail order beyond the EU and indicates nurseries that are prepared to consider this. There is usually a substantial minimum charge and, in addition, all the costs of phytosanitary certificates and Customs have to be met by the purchaser.

Catalogue Cost

Only a small number of nurseries now offer a printed catalogue. Some may not charge or may ask for stamps to bear the cost of postage. If plant lists are available in an electronic format, some nurseries have indicated that they will email them to enquirers.

The majority of nurseries now publish their catalogues only on the internet as this is more cost-effective than producing a printed copy and enables them to reflect stock changes throughout the year.

Specialities

This is where nurseries list the plants or genera in which they specialise and any National Collections that they hold. Please note that some nurseries may charge an entry fee to visit a National Collection. Charges may also be levied to visit any garden to which the nursery is attached.

Nurseries also indicate here if they only have small quantities of individual plants available for sale or if they will propagate to order.

Notes

This section contains: information on restrictions to mail order or export; whether payment in euros is accepted; whether nurseries deliver to shows; details of partial wheelchair access; the nursery site address if this differs from the office address; and any other non-horticultural or general information.

Wheelchair Access ♿

Nurseries are asked to indicate if their premises are suitable for wheelchair users.

We use the wheelchair symbol for those nurseries that tell us their site is fully accessible. Where only partial or restricted access is offered, this is stated in the **Notes** section of the nursery's details and the nursery is not marked with the symbol.

Please note that wheelchair access does not necessarily relate to any gardens to which the nursery may be attached.

The assessment of ease of access is entirely the responsibility of the individual nursery.

Delivers to Shows

Many nurseries will deliver pre-ordered plants to flower shows for collection by customers. Contact the nursery for details of shows that they will be attending.

Payment in Euros

A number of UK nurseries will accept payment in euros. You should check with the nursery concerned before making such a payment, as some will only accept cash and some only cheques, whilst others will expect the purchaser to pay bank charges.

OS Grid Ref

Nurseries are also encouraged to provide their Ordnance Survey national grid reference for use with OS Land Ranger Series maps.

Nursery Index by Name

An alphabetical index of nurseries is included (p.949). Nurseries new to the book and those making a re-entry are shown in embolden type.

Deleted Nurseries

Every year some nurseries ask to be removed from the book. This may be a temporary measure because, for example, they are relocating or because their plant stocks are low due to adverse growing conditions, or it may be permanent following closure, sale, retirement or a change in the way they trade.

Some nurseries miss the deadline for submissions and may ask to re-enter the book in the following edition. Other nurseries do not respond at all and, as we have no current information on their trading status, they are not included in the book.

Please, never use an out of date edition

NURSERY DETAILS BY CODE

Please note that all these nurseries are listed in alphabetical order by their code. All nurseries are listed in alphabetical order by their name in the **Nursery Index by Name** on page 949.

SOUTH WEST

CAbb ABBOTSBURY SUB-TROPICAL GARDENS ♿
Abbotsbury, Nr Weymouth, Dorset
DT3 4LA
Ⓣ (01305) 871344
Ⓕ (01305) 871344
Ⓔ info@abbotsburygardens.co.uk
Ⓦ www.abbotsbury-tourism.co.uk/gardens/
Contact: David Sutton
Opening Times: 1000-1800 daily, mid Mar-1st Nov. 1000-1500, Nov-mid Mar.
Credit Cards: Access, Visa, MasterCard, Switch
Specialities: Less common & tender shrubs incl. palms, tree ferns, bamboos & plants from Australia, New Zealand & S. Africa.
Notes: Mail order of some plants is possible upon request, please phone/email for details & a quotation. Wheelchair accessible.

CAby THE ABBEY NURSERY ♿
Forde Abbey, Chard, Somerset
TA20 4LU
Ⓣ (01460) 220088
Ⓔ theabbeynursery@hotmail.com
Contact: Paul Bygrave
Opening Times: 1000-1700 7 days, 1st Mar-31st Oct.
Cat. Cost: None issued.
Credit Cards: All major credit/debit cards
Specialities: Hardy herbaceous perennials.
Notes: Wheelchair accessible.
OS Grid Ref: ST359052

CAco ACORN TREES AND SHRUBS ♿
Hilltown Farm, Rackenford, Tiverton, Devon
EX16 8DX
Ⓣ (01884) 881633
Ⓜ 07976 807510
Ⓔ goakey101@gmail.com
Ⓦ www.acorntreesandshrubs.co.uk
Contact: Grahame Oakey
Opening Times: Most days & times but by appt. only.
Min Mail Order UK: £50.00 + p&p
Min Mail Order EU: £60.00 + p&p
Cat. Cost: Full plant listing available by email only.
Credit Cards: All major credit/debit cards
Specialities: Rhododendrons. Conifer specialist, incl. very rare & long needle varieties: *Pinus montezumae*, *Pinus holfordiana*, *Pinus schwerinii* & other pendulous trees. Also dwarf and miniature conifers including a Japanese selection, all suitable for rockeries and smaller garden spaces.
Notes: Plant specimen procurement, incl. rare/large specimens, delivery & planting service. Also sells wholesale. Wheelchair accessible.

CAgr AGROFORESTRY RESEARCH TRUST
46 Hunters Moon, Dartington, Totnes, Devon
TQ9 6JT
Ⓕ (01803) 840776
Ⓔ mail@agroforestry.co.uk
Ⓦ www.agroforestry.co.uk
Contact: Martin Crawford
Opening Times: Not open. Mail order only.
Min Mail Order UK: Nmc
Min Mail Order EU: Nmc
Cat. Cost: 4 × 1st class.
Credit Cards: All major credit/debit cards
Specialities: Top & soft fruit, nut trees including *Castanea*, *Corylus*, *Juglans*, *Pinus*. Also seeds. Some plants in small quantities only.
Notes: Euro accepted.

CAni ANITA ALLEN
Shapcott Barton Estate, East Knowstone, South Molton, Devon EX36 4EE
Ⓣ (01398) 341664

Contact: Anita Allen
Opening Times: By appt. only. Garden open under NGS & Plant Heritage.
Min Mail Order UK: Nmc
Cat. Cost: 5 × 1st class & state which catalogue: Shasta daisies or *Buddleja*.
Credit Cards: None
Specialities: Nat. Collections of *Leucanthemum* × *superbum* & *Buddleja davidii* & hybrids, 70+ cvs. 80+ accurately named Shasta daisies, a few in very short supply. Also many hardy perennials. Most *Buddleja* propagated to order.
OS Grid Ref: SS846235

CArg **ASHRIDGE NURSERIES**
Grove Cross Barn, Castle Cary, Somerset
BA7 7NJ
Ⓣ (01963) 359444
Ⓕ (01963) 359445
Ⓔ support@ashridgetrees.co.uk
Ⓦ www.ashridgetrees.co.uk
Contact: Rose Hurst
Opening Times: Not open. Mail order only.
Min Mail Order UK: £20.00
Credit Cards: MasterCard, Visa
Specialities: Trees, hedging. Fruit trees & soft fruit. Roses, lavender, climbers & bulbs.

CAvo **AVON BULBS**
Burnt House Farm, Mid-Lambrook, South Petherton, Somerset
TA13 5HE
Ⓣ (01460) 242177 or 249060
Ⓔ info@avonbulbs.co.uk
Ⓦ www.avonbulbs.co.uk
Contact: C Ireland-Jones
Opening Times: Mail order only. Collection of pre-booked orders by arrangement.
Min Mail Order UK: Nmc
Min Mail Order EU: Nmc
Cat. Cost: 4 × 2nd class.
Credit Cards: All major credit/debit cards
Specialities: Some special snowdrops are only available in small quantities.
Notes: Delivers to some shows.
OS Grid Ref: ST422187

CBar **BARTERS PLANT CENTRE & NURSERY** ♿
Chapmanslade, Westbury, Wiltshire
BA13 4AL
Ⓣ (01373) 832694
Ⓕ (01373) 832677
Ⓔ plantcentre@barters.co.uk
Ⓦ www.barters.co.uk
Contact: Andrew Stone
Opening Times: 0900-1700 Mon-Sat, Mar-Oct. 0900-1630 Mon-Sat, Nov-Feb. 1000-1600 Sun (closed Sun Jul-Nov & Jan-Feb), 1000-1600 Sun, Dec only.
Cat. Cost: Online only.
Credit Cards: All major debit/credit cards except American Express
Specialities: Wide range of shrubs. Ground cover, container trees, ferns, half-hardy perennials, grasses, herbaceous & climbers. Hedging, fruit trees, old fashioned roses & bare-root stock.
Notes: Also sells wholesale. Wheelchair accessible.
OS Grid Ref: ST830480

CBcs **BURNCOOSE NURSERIES** ♿
Gwennap, Redruth, Cornwall
TR16 6BJ
Ⓣ (01209) 860316
Ⓔ info@burncoose.co.uk
Ⓦ www.burncoose.co.uk
Contact: C H Williams
Opening Times: 0830-1700 Mon-Sat & 1100-1600 Sun.
Min Mail Order UK: Nmc
Min Mail Order EU: Individual quotations for EU sales.
Cat. Cost: Free
Credit Cards: Visa, MasterCard, Maestro
Specialities: Extensive range of over 3500 ornamental trees & shrubs and herbaceous. Rare & unusual *Magnolia*, *Rhododendron*. Conservatory plants. 30 acre garden.
Notes: Also sells wholesale. Delivers to shows. Wheelchair accessible.
OS Grid Ref: SW742395

CBct **BARRACOTT PLANTS** ♿
Old Orchard, Calstock Road, Gunnislake, Cornwall PL18 9AA
Ⓣ (01822) 832234
Ⓜ 07811 207186
Ⓔ geoffandthelma@barracott.eclipse.co.uk
Ⓦ www.barracottplants.co.uk
Contact: Geoff & Thelma Turner
Opening Times: 0900-1700 Thu & Fri, Mar-end Sep. Other times by appt.
Min Mail Order UK: Nmc
Cat. Cost: 1st class stamp.
Credit Cards: None
Specialities: Herbaceous plants: shade-loving, foliage & form. *Acanthus*, *Aspidistra*, *Astrantia*, *Bergenia*, *Convallaria*, *Disporum*, *Liriope*, *Maianthemum*, *Polygonatum*, *Roscoea*, *Trillium* & *Uvularia*.
Notes: Also sells wholesale. Delivers to shows. Euro accepted. Wheelchair accessible.
OS Grid Ref: SX436702

C

CBdn **Bowden Hostas**
Cleave House, Sticklepath, Okehampton, Devon EX20 2NL
Ⓣ (01837) 840989
Ⓔ tim@bowdenhostas.com
Ⓦ www.bowdenhostas.com
Contact: Tim Penrose
Opening Times: 1000-1700 Mon-Sat, Apr-Aug. Sep-Mar, please ring before travelling.
Min Mail Order UK: Nmc
Min Mail Order EU: Nmc
Cat. Cost: Free.
Credit Cards: Visa, Access, EuroCard, Switch
Specialities: Hostas, ferns, bamboos, *Agapanthus*. Nat. Collection of modern hybrid *Hosta*.
Notes: Also sells wholesale. Exports beyond EU.
OS Grid Ref: SX640940

CBen **Bennetts Water Gardens** ♿
Putton Lane, Chickerell, Weymouth, Dorset DT3 4AF
Ⓣ (01305) 785150
Ⓔ orders@waterlily.co.uk
Ⓦ www.waterlily.co.uk
Contact: James Bennett
Opening Times: 1000-1700 Apr-Sep, Sun-Fri.
Min Mail Order UK: Nmc
Min Mail Order EU: Nmc
Credit Cards: Visa, MasterCard, JCB, Maestro
Specialities: Nat. Collection of *Nymphaea* (hardy water lilies).
Notes: Loose plants available by mail order; potted plants available in store. Wheelchair accessible.
OS Grid Ref: SY650797

CBgR **Beggar's Roost Plants**
Lilstock, Bridgwater, Somerset TA5 1SU
Ⓣ (01278) 741519
Ⓔ ro@lilstock.eclipse.co.uk
Contact: Lady Rosemary FitzGerald
Opening Times: Not open. Mail order only.
Min Mail Order UK: £10.00
Min Mail Order EU: £15.00
Cat. Cost: 3 × large 2nd class.
Credit Cards: None
Specialities: *Hemerocallis* (incl. heritage) grown in British conditions.
Notes: Mail order for specialities *Hemerocallis*, ask for list. Euro accepted.
OS Grid Ref: ST168450

CBod **Bodmin Nursery** ♿
Laveddon Mill, Laninval Hill, Bodmin, Cornwall PL30 5JU
Ⓣ (01208) 72837
Ⓕ (01208) 76491
Ⓔ bodminnursery@aol.com
Ⓦ www.bodminnursery.co.uk
Contact: Mark Lawlor
Opening Times: 0900-1700 Mon-Sat. 1000-1600 Sun.
Credit Cards: All major credit/debit cards
Specialities: Herbs, herbaceous & grasses, hardy geraniums & coastal plants. Interesting shrubs, fruit & ornamental trees.
Notes: Wheelchair accessible.
OS Grid Ref: SX053659

CBor **Border Alpines**
Chasty Court, Chasty, Holsworthy, Devon EX22 6NA
Ⓣ 01409 253654
Ⓜ 07841 021557
Ⓔ borderalpines@btinternet.com
Ⓦ www.borderalpines.co.uk
Contact: Janette Lowe
Opening Times: By appointment only
Min Mail Order UK: Nmc
Min Mail Order EU: Nmc
Cat. Cost: Online only
Credit Cards: None
Specialities: Alpines, dwarf herbaceous & specimen acers. A family-run nursery, selling a range of British-grown alpines, dwarf herbaceous and other hardy perennial plants. Experienced growers and breeders for over 30 years.
Notes: Delivers to shows.

CBre **Bregover Plants**
Middlewood, North Hill, Nr Launceston, Cornwall PL15 7NN
Ⓣ (01566) 782661
Ⓔ jenbousfield@gmail.com
Contact: Jennifer Bousfield
Opening Times: 1100-1700 Wed, Mar-mid Oct and by appt.
Min Mail Order UK: Nmc
Cat. Cost: 3 × 1st class. Plant list available as pdf download.
Credit Cards: None
Specialities: Unusual hardy perennials grown in small garden nursery. Available in small quantities only.
Notes: Mail order Oct-Mar only. Delivers to shows. Limited wheelchair access.
OS Grid Ref: SX273752

CBro **Broadleigh Gardens** ♿
Bishops Hull, Taunton, Somerset TA4 1AE
Ⓣ (01823) 286231
Ⓕ (01823) 323646
Ⓔ info@broadleighbulbs.co.uk

Ⓦ www.broadleighbulbs.co.uk
Contact: Christine Skelmersdale
Opening Times: 0900-1600 Mon-Fri for viewing only (charity donation). Orders may be collected if notice given.
Min Mail Order UK: Nmc
Min Mail Order EU: Nmc
Cat. Cost: 2 × 1st class.
Credit Cards: All major credit/debit cards
Specialities: Jan catalogue: bulbs in growth (*Galanthus, Cyclamen* etc.) & herbaceous woodland plants (trilliums, hellebores etc). Extensive list of *Agapanthus* & other South African bulbs. June catalogue: dwarf & unusual bulbs, *Iris* (DB & PC). Nat. Collection of Alec Grey hybrid daffodils.
Notes: Display garden and nursery open. Euro accepted as cash payment only. Wheelchair accessible.
OS Grid Ref: ST195251

CBrP **Brooklands Plants**
25 Treves Road, Dorchester, Dorset
DT1 2HE
Ⓣ (01305) 265846
Ⓔ cycads@btinternet.com
Ⓦ botanicalgardenphotography.com
Contact: Ian Watt
Opening Times: By appt. only for collection of plants.
Min Mail Order UK: £50.00 + p&p
Cat. Cost: Online only.
Credit Cards: None
Specialities: Cycad nursery specialising in the more cold-tolerant species of *Encephalartos, Dioon, Macrozamia* & *Cycas*. Also specialist in cold-tolerant palms as well as plants from New Zealand. Some species available in small quantities only.
Notes: Mail order available on small plants only. Euro accepted.
OS Grid Ref: SY682897

CBur **Burnham Nurseries**
Forches Cross, Newton Abbot, Devon
TQ12 6PZ
Ⓣ (01626) 352233
Ⓔ mail@orchids.uk.com
Ⓦ www.orchids.uk.com
Contact: Any member of staff
Opening Times: 1000-1600 Mon-Sun.
Min Mail Order UK: Nmc
Min Mail Order EU: £100.00 + p&p
Cat. Cost: 1 × 2nd class or online.
Credit Cards: Visa, MasterCard, Maestro
Specialities: Many types of tropical orchid species and hybrids.
Notes: Exports beyond EU, please ask for details. Delivers to shows. Euro accepted. Partial wheelchair accessiblity.
OS Grid Ref: SX841732

CCbn **Cranborne Garden Centre** ♿
Cranborne, Dorset BH21 5PP
Ⓣ (01725) 517248
Ⓔ info@cranbornegardencentre.co.uk
Ⓦ www.cranbornegardencentre.co.uk
Contact: Claire Whitehead
Credit Cards: All major debit/credit cards except American Express
Specialities: A wide selection of stock with over 400 varieties of old-fashioned and modern roses and a wide range of shrubs, climbers, herbaceous and bedding plants.
Notes: Wheelchair accessible.

CCBP **CB Plants**
Lower Severalls Nursery, Crewkerne, Somerset
TA18 7NX
Ⓣ 01460 220218
Ⓜ 07851 468430
Ⓔ catherine_bond@hotmail.co.uk]
Ⓦ www.cbplants.co.uk
Contact: Catherine Bond
Opening Times: 1000-1700 Wed-Sat. Early Mar-End Sept.
Min Mail Order UK: £5.00 + p&p
Credit Cards: All major debit/credit cards except American Express
Specialities: Nectar-rich hardy perennials and herbs all grown peat-free. Some varieties available in small quantities only.
Notes: Small nursery situated just off the A30, half a mile east of Crewkerne.

CCCN **Cross Common Nursery**
The Lizard, Helston, Cornwall
TR12 7PD
Ⓣ (01326) 290722 or 290668
Ⓔ info@crosscommonnursery.co.uk
Ⓦ www.crosscommonnursery.co.uk
Contact: Kevin Bosustow
Opening Times: 1000-1700 7 days, Apr, May & Jun. Reduced hours Mar, Jul, Aug & Sep, please phone for opening times.
Min Mail Order UK: Nmc
Cat. Cost: Online only.
Credit Cards: All major debit/credit cards except American Express
Specialities: The most southerly nursery in England, offering a wide range of unusual plants & shrubs. Tropical/sub-tropical, coastal plants & conservatory plants. Wide range of grapevines and citrus trees. Some plants available in small quantities only.
OS Grid Ref: SW704116

C

CChe **CHERRY TREE NURSERY** ♿
(Sheltered Work Opportunities Project)
off New Road Roundabout,
Northbourne, Bournemouth, Dorset
BH10 7DA
Ⓣ (01202) 593537
Ⓔ contactus@cherrytreenursery.org.uk
Ⓦ www.cherrytreenursery.org.uk
Contact: Stephen Jailler
Opening Times: 0830-1530 Mon-Fri, 0900-1500 Sat, Apr-Sep & 0900-1300 Sat, Oct-Mar. 1000-1500 Sun, Mar-Oct.
Credit Cards: All major debit/credit cards except American Express
Specialities: Hardy shrubs, perennials, climbers, grasses & bamboos.
Notes: A registered charity providing work for adults with severe and enduring mental illness. Also sells wholesale. Wheelchair accessible.
OS Grid Ref: SZ083965

CCht **CHESTNUT NURSERY** ♿
(Sheltered Work Opportunities Project)
75 Kingland Road, Poole, Dorset
BH15 1TN
Ⓣ (01202) 685999
Ⓔ info@chestnutnursery.org.uk
Ⓦ www.chestnutnursery.org.uk
Contact: Angela Mansbridge
Opening Times: 0800-1600 Mon-Fri. 1000-1600 Sat (Mar-Nov) & 1000-1500 Sat (Nov-Xmas). 1000-1500 Sun (Mar-Sep).
Credit Cards: All major credit/debit cards
Specialities: Wide variety of nectar-rich herbaceous perennials, evergreen specimen shrubs, ornamental grasses and annual bedding. Range of exotics for coastal gardens.
Notes: A registered charity providing work for adults with severe and enduring mental illness. Wheelchair accessible.
OS Grid Ref: SZ018909

CCoa **COASTAL HEDGING**
Marsh Lane Nursery, West Charleton,
Kingsbridge, Devon TQ7 2AQ
Ⓣ 01548 531734
Ⓜ 07775 201595
Ⓔ info@coastalhedging.co.uk
Ⓦ www.coastalhedging.co.uk
Contact: William Hornby
Opening Times: Viewing by appointment only
Min Mail Order UK: £4.95
Cat. Cost: Online only
Credit Cards: All major credit/debit cards
Specialities: *Griselina, Elaeagnus, Olearia.*
Notes: Euro accepted.

CCVT **CHEW VALLEY TREES** ♿
Winford Road, Chew Magna, Bristol BS40 8HJ
Ⓣ (01275) 333752
Ⓔ info@chewvalleytrees.co.uk
Ⓦ www.chewvalleytrees.co.uk
Contact: S Scarth
Opening Times: 0800-1700 Mon-Fri all year. 0800-1630 Sat. Closed Sun. Closed B/hols & Sats Jul & Aug.
Min Mail Order UK: Nmc
Cat. Cost: Free.
Credit Cards: All major credit/debit cards
Specialities: Native British & ornamental trees, shrubs, fruit trees & hedging.
Notes: Also sells wholesale. Wheelchair accessible.
OS Grid Ref: ST558635

CDor **DORSET PERENNIALS** ♿
Berkeley Perennials, Holnest, Sherborne,
Dorset DT9 5PR
Ⓣ (01963) 210643
Ⓕ (01963) 210643
Ⓔ sales@dorsetperennials.co.uk
Ⓦ www.dorsetperennials.co.uk
Contact: Dawn & Martin Preston
Opening Times: Open for collections only. Please check with nursery first.
Min Mail Order UK: Nmc
Cat. Cost: Online only.
Credit Cards: All major credit/debit cards
Specialities: An eclectic mix of hardy perennials grown. Plants for herbaceous borders & cottage gardens with a good mix of oddities to tempt the discerning.
Notes: All plants available via website. Delivers to shows. Wheelchair accessible.
OS Grid Ref: ST662090

CDoy **CARADOC DOY**
PO Box 28, Exeter, Devon EX3 0WY
Ⓣ (01392) 877225
Ⓕ (01392) 877225
Ⓔ info@caradocdoy.co.uk
Ⓦ www.caradocdoy.co.uk
Contact: Caradoc Doy
Opening Times: Open by appt. only.
Min Mail Order UK: Nmc
Cat. Cost: Online.
Credit Cards: None
Specialities: Olive trees.

CDTJ **DESERT TO JUNGLE** ♿
Henlade Garden Nursery, Lower Henlade,
Taunton, Somerset TA3 5NB
Ⓣ (01823) 443701
Ⓜ 07969 652547
Ⓔ plants@deserttojungle.com

Ⓦ www.deserttojungle.com
Contact: Rob Gudge
Opening Times: 1000-1700 Mon, Tues & Thu-Sun (closed Wed), 1st Mar-31st Oct. Thu, Fri & Sat only, Nov-Feb. Opening times may vary during RHS shows, so please phone to check.
Min Mail Order UK: Nmc
Cat. Cost: Online only.
Credit Cards: All major credit/debit cards
Specialities: Exotic-looking plants giving a desert or jungle effect in the garden. Incl. *Agave*, *Canna*, aroids, succulents, ferns, tree ferns & bamboos.
Notes: Nursery shares drive with Mount Somerset Hotel. Also sells wholesale. Delivers to shows. Wheelchair accessible.
OS Grid Ref: ST273232

CDul **Dulford Nurseries** ♿
Cullompton, Devon EX15 2BY
Ⓣ (01884) 266361
Ⓔ dulford.nurseries@virgin.net
Ⓦ www.dulford-nurseries.co.uk
Contact: Paul Rawlings
Opening Times: 0730-1630 Mon-Fri.
Min Mail Order UK: Nmc
Min Mail Order EU: Nmc
Cat. Cost: Free.
Credit Cards: All major credit/debit cards
Specialities: Native, ornamental & unusual trees, hedging & shrubs incl. oaks, maples, beech, birch, chestnut, lime, *Malus*, *Sorbus* & pines.
Notes: Wheelchair accessible.
OS Grid Ref: SY062062

CEls **Elsworth Herbs**
Farthingwood, Broadway, Sidmouth, Devon EX10 8HS
Ⓣ (01395) 578689
Ⓔ john.twibell@btinternet.com
Contact: Drs J D & J M Twibell
Opening Times: By appt. only.
Min Mail Order UK: £10.00
Cat. Cost: By email only.
Credit Cards: None
Specialities: Nat. Collection (Scientific & Reference) of *Artemisia*. Wide range of *Artemisia*, stock available in small quantities only. Orders may require propagation from Collection material, for which we are the primary reference source. Native coastal plants.
Notes: Mail order on small scale & in exceptional circumstances only. Partially accessible for wheelchairs.
OS Grid Ref: SY119881

CElw **Elworthy Cottage Plants** ♿
Elworthy Cottage, Elworthy, Nr Lydeard St Lawrence, Taunton, Somerset TA4 3PX
Ⓣ (01984) 656427
Ⓔ mike@elworthy-cottage.co.uk
Ⓦ www.elworthy-cottage.co.uk
Contact: Mrs J M Spiller
Opening Times: Most Mon & Thurs mornings, late Mar-end Aug. Please phone to check. By appt Feb-Oct.
Cat. Cost: 3 × 2nd class.
Credit Cards: None
Specialities: Unusual herbaceous plants esp. hardy *Geranium*, *Geum*, *Crocosmia*, *Epimedium*, *Monarda*, *Pulmonaria* & *Viola*. Some varieties only available in small quantities. *Galanthus* available by mail order in Feb.
Notes: Nursery on B3188, 5 miles north of Wiveliscombe, in centre of Elworthy village. Delivers to shows. Wheelchair accessible.
OS Grid Ref: ST084349

CEnd **Endsleigh Gardens Nursery** ♿
Milton Abbot, Tavistock, Devon PL19 0PG
Ⓣ (01822) 870235
Ⓕ (01822) 870513
Ⓔ info@endsleigh-gardens.com
Ⓦ www.endsleighgardens.co.uk
Contact: Adrian Steele
Opening Times: 0800-1700 Mon-Sat. 1000-1600 Sun.
Min Mail Order UK: Nmc
Cat. Cost: 2 × 1st class.
Credit Cards: Visa, Access, Switch, MasterCard
Specialities: Choice & unusual trees & shrubs incl. *Acer*, alpines, bamboos, climbers, conifers, *Cornus*, heathers, old apple & cherry varieties, *Rosa*, *Wisteria*. Grafting service. Modern fruit trees, soft fruit and good selection of perennials.
Notes: Wheelchair accessible (but no disabled toilets).
OS Grid Ref: SX398780

CExl **Exclusive Plants Nursery**
Tretawn, High Cross, Constantine, Falmouth, Cornwall TR11 5RE
Ⓣ (01326) 341496
Ⓜ 07775 811385
Ⓕ (01326) 341496
Ⓔ info@exclusiveplants.com
Ⓦ www.exclusiveplants.com
Contact: Paul Bonavia
Opening Times: W/ends or by appt. only.
Min Mail Order UK: Nmc
Min Mail Order EU: £25.00

Cat. Cost: 2 × 1st class.
Credit Cards: All major credit/debit cards
Specialities: A plantsperson's nursery, offering rare & unusual plants from around the world. Also new introductions & the best forms of our better known plants.
Notes: Euro accepted.
OS Grid Ref: SW175131

CFGn **THE FOREST GARDEN**
Penjerrick Hill, Budock Water, Falmouth, Cornwall TR11 5ED
Ⓣ (01326) 250090
Ⓔ simonmiles@theforestgarden.co.uk
Ⓦ www.theforestgarden.co.uk
Contact: Simon Miles
Opening Times: Not open. Mail order only. Will open for pre-arranged collection of plant orders.
Min Mail Order UK: £10.00
Specialities: Perennial edible forest garden & agroforestry plants. Top fruit & nut trees, soft fruit, unusual & less common perennial vegetables, tubers, fruits & herbs. Shelter belts & hedging.
OS Grid Ref: SW178030

CFen **FENTONGOLLAN FARM** ♿
Merther Lane, St Michael Penkivel, Tresillian, Truro, Cornwall TR2 4AQ
Ⓣ (01872) 520209
Ⓕ (01872) 520606
Ⓔ admin@flowerfarm.co.uk
Ⓦ www.flowerfarm.co.uk
Contact: James Hosking
Opening Times: 0900-1700 7 days, Aug-end Nov.
Min Mail Order UK: Nmc
Min Mail Order EU: Nmc
Cat. Cost: Free.
Credit Cards: All major debit/credit cards except American Express
Specialities: *Narcissus*. Importers of quality Dutch bulbs.
Notes: Also sells wholesale. Delivers to shows. Euro accepted. Wheelchair accessible.

CFis **MARGERY FISH PLANT NURSERY** ♿
East Lambrook Manor Gardens, East Lambrook, South Petherton, Somerset TA13 5HH
Ⓣ (01460) 240328
Ⓜ 07710 484745
Ⓔ enquiries@eastlambrook.com
Ⓦ www.eastlambrook.com
Contact: Tom Wild
Opening Times: 1000-1700 Tue-Sat, Feb-Oct, plus B/hol Mons & Suns Feb, May-Jul. Nov-Jan by appt.
Cat. Cost: None issued.
Credit Cards: All major credit/debit cards
Specialities: Hardy geraniums & cottage garden herbaceous plants. Stock available in small quantities only. Major collection of hardy geraniums on site.
Notes: Wheelchair accessible.
OS Grid Ref: ST431188

CFlo **FLOYDS CLIMBERS AND CLEMATIS**
36 Dowding Drive, Lower Compton, Calne, Wiltshire SN11 8QL
Ⓣ (01249) 823200
Ⓜ 07762 499416
Ⓔ sales@floydsclimbers.co.uk
Ⓦ www.floydsclimbers.co.uk
Contact: Marcel Floyd
Opening Times: Open w/ends twice a year. See website or phone for dates.
Min Mail Order UK: Nmc
Credit Cards: Paypal
Specialities: *Clematis* and climbers.
Notes: Also sells wholesale. Euro accepted. Delivers to shows.

CFst **FOREST EDGE NURSERIES**
Verwood Road, Woodlands, Wimborne, Dorset BH21 8LJ
Ⓣ (01202) 824387
Ⓕ (01202) 829564
Ⓔ info@theheathergarden.co.uk
Ⓦ www.theheathergarden.co.uk
Contact: David Edge
Opening Times: 0900-1630 Mon. Plant collection available by arrangement on other days.
Min Mail Order UK: Nmc
Cat. Cost: £2.00
Credit Cards: Paypal
Specialities: Heathers: *Calluna*, *Erica*, *Daboecia*.
Notes: Also sells wholesale. Euro accepted.

CGro **C W GROVES & SON LTD** ♿
West Bay Road, Bridport, Dorset DT6 4BA
Ⓣ (01308) 422654
Ⓔ garden@grovesnurseries.co.uk
Ⓦ www.grovesnurseries.co.uk
Contact: Becky Groves
Opening Times: 0800-1700 Mon-Sat, 1000-1600 Sun.
Min Mail Order UK: Nmc
Min Mail Order EU: £15.00 + p&p
Cat. Cost: Free.
Credit Cards: Visa, Switch, MasterCard
Specialities: Established in 1866, a family run garden centre with nursery on site specialising

in *Viola odorata*, Parma violets & roses.
Notes: Mainly violets, roses, herbs, soft fruit & grapevines by mail order. Main violet display at nursery in Feb, Mar & Apr. Will export only violet seeds beyond EU. Wheelchair accessible.
OS Grid Ref: SY466918

CGrW **The Great Western Gladiolus Nursery**
9 Ash Lane, Wells, Somerset BA5 2LT
Ⓜ 07779 273562
Ⓔ info@greatwesterngladiolus.co.uk
Ⓦ www.greatwesterngladiolus.co.uk
Contact: F Hazell
Opening Times: Mail order only. Open by appt. only.
Min Mail Order UK: Nmc
Min Mail Order EU: Nmc
Cat. Cost: 4 × 1st class (2 catalogues).
Credit Cards: Paypal
Specialities: *Gladiolus* species & hybrids, corms & seeds. Other South African bulbous plants. Only available in small quantities.
Notes: Also sells wholesale. Euro accepted.

CHab **Habitat Aid Ltd.**
Hookgate Cottage, South Brewham, Somerset BA10 0LQ
Ⓣ (01749) 812355
Ⓔ info@habitataid.co.uk
Ⓦ www.habitataid.co.uk
Contact: Nick Mann
Opening Times: Not open. Mail order only.
Min Mail Order UK: £50.00, incl. p&p.
Cat. Cost: None issued.
Credit Cards: All major credit/debit cards
Specialities: British trees, wildflowers and seeds. Local provenance seed mixes. Native aquatic plants. Cottage garden perennials. Heritage fruit trees.
Notes: Also sells wholesale. Delivers to shows.

CHby **The Herbary**
161 Chapel Street, Horningsham, Warminster, Wiltshire BA12 7LU
Ⓣ (01985) 844442
Ⓔ info@beansandherbs.co.uk
Ⓦ www.beansandherbs.co.uk
Contact: Pippa Rosen
Opening Times: May-Sep strictly by appt. only.
Min Mail Order UK: Nmc
Min Mail Order EU: Nmc
Cat. Cost: Online only.
Credit Cards: None
Specialities: Culinary, medicinal & aromatic herbs organically grown in small quantities.
Notes: Mail order for seed only. All year for organic vegetable seed & large selection of organic bean & herb seed. Also sells wholesale. Delivers to shows. Euro accepted.
OS Grid Ref: ST812414

CHew **Hewitt-Cooper Carnivorous Plants**
The Homestead, Glastonbury Road, West Pennard, Somerset BA6 8NN
Ⓣ (01458) 832844
Ⓕ (01458) 832712
Ⓔ sales@hccarnivorousplants.co.uk
Ⓦ www.hccarnivorousplants.co.uk
Contact: Nigel Hewitt-Cooper
Opening Times: Not open.
Min Mail Order UK: Nmc
Min Mail Order EU: Nmc
Cat. Cost: Online only.
Credit Cards: All major credit/debit cards
Specialities: Carnivorous plants.
Notes: Mail order all year. Euro accepted. Delivers to shows.

CHll **Hill House Nursery Ltd**
Landscove, Nr Ashburton, Devon TQ13 7LY
Ⓣ (01803) 762273
Ⓔ bluebird@hillhousenursery.com
Ⓦ www.hillhousenursery.com
Contact: Raymond, Sacha & Matthew Hubbard
Opening Times: 1100-1700 7 days, all year. Open all B/hols incl. Easter Sun. Closed Friday before Xmas Eve for two weeks. Tearoom open 1st Mar-30th Sep.
Min Mail Order UK: Nmc
Cat. Cost: None issued.
Credit Cards: Delta, MasterCard, Switch, Visa, Paypal
Specialities: 3000+ varieties of plants, most propagated on premises, many rare or unusual. The garden, open to the public, was laid out by Edward Hyams. Pioneers of glasshouse pest control by beneficial insects.
Notes: Groups welcome with prior notice. Also sells wholesale. Euro accepted. Tea room & garden wheelchair accessible, access limited in nursery.
OS Grid Ref: SX774664

CHVG **Hidden Valley Gardens** ♿
Treesmill, Nr Par, Cornwall PL24 2TU
Ⓣ (01208) 873225
Ⓔ hiddenvalleygardens@yahoo.co.uk
Ⓦ www.hiddenvalleygardens.co.uk
Contact: Mrs P Howard
Opening Times: 1000-1800 Thu-Mon (closed Tue & Wed), 20th Mar-15th Oct.

C

Please phone for directions. Garden open as nursery.
Cat. Cost: None issued.
Credit Cards: All major debit/credit cards except American Express
Specialities: Cottage garden plants, *Dahlia* & many perennials which can be seen growing in the garden. Some stock available in small quantities. Display garden.
Notes: Award-winning Garden In Cornwall 2014. Euro accepted. Wheelchair accessible.
OS Grid Ref: SX094567

CJun **JUNKER'S NURSERY**
Higher Cobhay, Milverton, Somerset TA4 1NJ
Ⓣ (01823) 400075
Ⓔ karan@junker.co.uk
Ⓦ www.junker.co.uk
Contact: Karan Junker
Opening Times: Strictly by appt. only. Contact nursery for directions (do not rely on Sat Nav).
Min Mail Order UK: Nmc
Min Mail Order EU: Nmc
Cat. Cost: Free list available by email.
Credit Cards: None
Specialities: Choice & unusual shrubs & trees incl. grafted *Acer palmatum*, *Betula*, *Cornus*, *Daphne*, *Magnolia* cvs. Also extensive collections of *Euonymus*, *Ilex*, *Liquidambar* & *Viburnum*, all grown on own roots. Many available in larger, more mature sizes. Small quantities only of some hard to propagate plants, esp. daphnes.
Notes: Extensive planted areas showing how the plants look growing in "real world" conditions. Propagate & grow all own plants with an increasing number grown naturally in open ground as well as younger plants in pots, incl. larger sizes. Limited wheelchair access.

CKel **KELWAYS PLANTS LTD** ♿
Picts Hill, Langport, Somerset TA10 9EZ
Ⓣ (01458) 250521
Ⓔ sales@kelways.co.uk
Ⓦ www.kelways.co.uk
Contact: Dave Root, Andy Martin, Simon Littlewood
Opening Times: 0900-1700 Mon-Sat, 0930-1600 Sun.
Min Mail Order UK: Nmc
Cat. Cost: Online only.
Credit Cards: Paypal
Specialities: *Paeonia*, *Iris*, *Rosa*, *Clematis*, *Dicksonia*, *Cyathea*, tree ferns, herbaceous perennials & shrubs.
Notes: Contract growing & plant sourcing service. Coffee shop. Also sells wholesale. Euro accepted. Wheelchair accessible.
OS Grid Ref: ST434273

CKen **KENWITH CONIFER NURSERY (GORDON HADDOW)** ♿
Blinsham, Nr Torrington, Beaford, Winkleigh, Devon EX19 8NT
Ⓣ (01805) 603274
Ⓔ info@kenwithconifernursery.co.uk
Ⓦ www.kenwithconifernursery.co.uk
Contact: Gordon Haddow
Opening Times: 1000-1630 Tue-Sat all year. Closed all B/hols. If travelling a long distance, please phone previous day to ensure nursery will be open.
Min Mail Order UK: £20 + p&p
Cat. Cost: Online only.
Credit Cards: Visa, MasterCard
Specialities: All conifer genera. Grafting a speciality.
Notes: Wheelchair accessible.
OS Grid Ref: SS518160

CKno **KNOLL GARDENS**
Hampreston, Wimborne, Dorset BH21 7ND
Ⓣ (01202) 873931
Ⓕ (01202) 870842
Ⓔ enquiries@knollgardens.co.uk
Ⓦ www.knollgardens.co.uk
Contact: N R Lucas
Opening Times: 1000-1700 Tue-Sat, Feb-Dec. Open B/hol Mons. See website for further details.
Min Mail Order UK: Nmc
Min Mail Order EU: Nmc
Cat. Cost: None.
Credit Cards: Visa, MasterCard
Specialities: Grasses (main specialism), flowering perennials. Nat. Collection of *Pennisetum*.
Notes: Also sells wholesale.

CLAP **LONG ACRE PLANTS** ♿
South Marsh, Charlton Musgrove, Wincanton, Somerset BA9 8EX
Ⓣ (01963) 32802
Ⓕ (01963) 32802
Ⓔ info@plantsforshade.co.uk
Ⓦ www.plantsforshade.co.uk
Contact: Nigel Rowland
Opening Times: Open by appointment only
Min Mail Order UK: £12.00 + p&p
Min Mail Order EU: £30
Cat. Cost: Catalogue available online
Credit Cards: MasterCard, Visa, Maestro
Specialities: Ferns, woodland bulbs & perennials. Marginal/bog plants. Specialises in plants for shade, carrying a wide range of

unusual and tough shade tolerant perennials and ferns.
Notes: Mail order online. Wheelchair accessible. Delivers to shows.

CLau **LAUREL FARM HERBS AND EDIBLES**
Moorland Barn, Whiddon Down, Okehampton, Devon EX20 2QL
Ⓣ (01647) 400301
Ⓜ 07905 518666
Ⓔ laurelfarmherbs@aol.com
Ⓦ www.laurelfarmherbs.co.uk
Contact: Chris Seagon
Opening Times: 1000-1700 Apr-Oct.
Min Mail Order UK: £9.95
Min Mail Order EU: 6 plants.
Cat. Cost: Online only.
Credit Cards: Visa, Paypal
Specialities: Herbs esp. rosemary, thyme, mint & sage. Also grows edible garden plants.
Notes: Also sells wholesale. Delivers to shows (payment in advance).

CLnd **LANDFORD TREES**
Landford Lodge, Landford, Salisbury, Wiltshire SP5 2EH
Ⓣ (01794) 390808
Ⓔ trees@landfordtrees.co.uk
Ⓦ www.landfordtrees.co.uk
Contact: C D Pilkington
Opening Times: 0800-1700 Mon-Thu, 0800-1530 Fri.
Cat. Cost: Free.
Credit Cards: All major debit/credit cards except American Express
Specialities: Deciduous ornamental trees.
Notes: Also sells wholesale.
OS Grid Ref: SU247201

CLoc **C S LOCKYER (FUCHSIAS)** ◆
Lansbury, 70 Henfield Road, Coalpit Heath, Bristol BS36 2UZ
Ⓣ (01454) 772219
Ⓕ (01454) 772219
Ⓔ mary@lockyerfuchsias.co.uk
Ⓦ lockyerfuchsias.co.uk
Contact: Mary Lockyer
Opening Times: 1000-1300, 1430-1700 most days, please ring.
Min Mail Order UK: 6 plants + p&p
Min Mail Order EU: £12.00 + p&p
Cat. Cost: 4 × 1st class or online
Credit Cards: All major credit/debit cards
Specialities: *Fuchsia*.
Notes: Many open days & coach parties. Also sells wholesale. Exports beyond EU. Euro accepted. Delivers to shows. Partial wheelchair access.

CMac **MAC PENNYS NURSERIES**
154 Burley Road, Bransgore, Christchurch, Dorset BH23 8DB
Ⓣ (01425) 672348
Ⓕ (01425) 673917
Ⓔ office@macpennys.co.uk
Ⓦ www.macpennys.co.uk
Contact: T & V Lowndes & S Lowndes
Opening Times: 0900-1700 Mon-Sat, 1000-1700 Sun & B/hols, except closed Xmas-New Year.
Min Mail Order UK: Nmc
Cat. Cost: A4 sae with 4 × 1st class.
Credit Cards: All major debit/credit cards except American Express
Specialities: General. Plants available in small quantities only.
Notes: Mail order available Oct-Feb incl., UK only. Also sells wholesale. Nursery partially accessible for wheelchairs.

CMCN **MALLET COURT NURSERY** ♿
Marshway, Curry Mallet, Taunton, Somerset TA3 6SZ
Ⓣ (01823) 481493
Ⓜ 07713 091521
Ⓕ (01823) 481493
Ⓔ malletcourtnursery@btinternet.com
Ⓦ www.malletcourt.co.uk
Contact: J G S & P M E Harris F.L.S.
Opening Times: 0930-1700 Mon-Fri summer, 0930-1600 winter. Sat & Sun by appt.
Min Mail Order UK: Nmc
Min Mail Order EU: Nmc
Cat. Cost: £1.50
Credit Cards: All major credit/debit cards
Specialities: Maples, oaks, *Magnolia*, hollies & other rare and unusual plants including those from China & South Korea.
Notes: Mail order Oct-Mar only. Also sells wholesale. Exports beyond EU. Euro accepted. Wheelchair accessible.

CMea **THE MEAD NURSERY** ♿
Brokerswood, Nr Westbury, Wiltshire BA13 4EG
Ⓣ (01373) 859990
Ⓔ info@themeadnursery.co.uk
Ⓦ www.themeadnursery.co.uk
Contact: Steve & Emma Lewis-Dale
Opening Times: 0900-1700 Wed-Sat & B/hol Mons, 1200-1700 Sun, 1st Feb-10th Oct. Closed Easter Sun.
Cat. Cost: 4 × 2nd class.
Credit Cards: All major credit/debit cards
Specialities: Perennials, alpines, pot-grown bulbs and grasses.

C

Notes: Wheelchair accessible.
OS Grid Ref: ST833517

CMen **Mendip Bonsai Studio**
Byways, Back Lane, Downside, Shepton Mallet, Somerset BA4 4JR
Ⓣ (01749) 344274
Ⓜ 07711 205806
Ⓔ john@mendipbonsai.co.uk
Ⓦ www.mendipbonsai.co.uk
Contact: John Trott
Opening Times: Private nursery. Visits by appt. only.
Min Mail Order UK: £15.00
Cat. Cost: None issued. Workshop lists available.
Credit Cards: All major credit/debit cards
Specialities: Bonsai, Potensai, accent plants & garden stock. Acers, conifers, incl. *Pinus thunbergii*, *Aciphylla*, *Davallia* & *Pyrrosia*. Many plants available in small numbers only. Can propagate to order. Young trees for garden or bonsai culture. Many rare & unusual ferns from Japan for 'accent' use and gardens (very limited numbers).
Notes: Education classes, lectures, demonstrations & club talks on bonsai. Stockist of most bonsai pots, related bonsai sundries & a large range of bronze figurines. Mail orders will normally be despatched late Mar-early Apr, late Sep-Oct. Delivers to shows by arrangement.

CMil **Mill Cottage Plants** ♿
Henley Mill, Henley Lane, Wookey, Somerset BA5 1AW
Ⓣ (01749) 676966
Ⓜ 07851 698759
Ⓔ millcottageplants@gmail.com
Ⓦ www.millcottageplants.co.uk
Contact: Sally Gregson
Opening Times: By appt. only. Phone for directions.
Min Mail Order UK: Nmc
Min Mail Order EU: £25.00 + p&p
Cat. Cost: Online only.
Credit Cards: All major credit/debit cards
Specialities: Rare *Hydrangea serrata* cvs, *H. aspera* cvs, *Epimedium*, shade & damp-loving plants.
Notes: Euro accepted. Wheelchair accessible.

CNat **Natural Selection**
1 Station Cottages, Hullavington, Chippenham, Wiltshire SN14 6ET
Ⓣ (01666) 837369
Ⓜ 07800 583999
Ⓔ martin@worldmutation.demon.co.uk
Contact: Martin Barber
Opening Times: Please phone first.
Min Mail Order UK: £9.00 + p&p
Min Mail Order EU: Nmc
Cat. Cost: 1 × 2nd class.
Credit Cards: None
Specialities: Unusual British natives & others. Also seed. Only available in small quantities.
Notes: Euro accepted.

CNMi **Newport Mills Nursery**
Wrantage, Taunton, Somerset TA3 6DJ
Ⓣ (01823) 490231
Ⓔ john@newportmillsnursery.net
Ⓦ www.newportmillsnursery.net
Contact: John Barrington
Opening Times: Not open. Mail order only.
Min Mail Order UK: Nmc
Min Mail Order EU: Nmc.
Cat. Cost: Free.
Credit Cards: All major credit/debit cards
Specialities: *Delphinium elatum* hybrids. English scented perpetual flowering carnations. *Dianthus*. Pinks: Exhibition, Modern & Old World.
Notes: Mail order Apr-Sep for young delphiniums in 7cm pots. Euro accepted.
OS Grid Ref: ST318234

CNor **Northbrook Nursery** ♿
47 Northbrook Road, Broadstone, Dorset BH18 8HD
Ⓣ (01202) 695256
Ⓔ marg@northbrooknursery.co.uk
Ⓦ www.northbrooknursery.co.uk
Contact: Margaret Bailey
Opening Times: 1000-1600, Wed-Fri, Apr-Oct.
Cat. Cost: None issued.
Credit Cards: Paypal
Specialities: Perennials. Plants available in small quantities only.
Notes: Delivers to shows. Wheelchair accessible.
OS Grid Ref: SZ 001947

CNWT **New Wood Trees**
Oldwood House, Aish Road, Stoke Gabriel, Totnes, Devon TQ9 6PX
Ⓣ (01803) 782666
Ⓔ info@newwoodtrees.co.uk
Ⓦ www.newwoodtrees.co.uk
Contact: Philip Nieuwoudt
Opening Times: 0900-1700 Mon-Fri.
Credit Cards: None
Specialities: Trees. Multi-stem ornamentals; small to medium sized trees and large shrubs.

Notes: Specialises in specimen trees so when a species is sold out it takes a while to replenish stocks. Also sells wholesale. Delivers to shows.
OS Grid Ref: SX847580

CPar **Parks Perennials**
242 Wallisdown Road, Wallisdown, Bournemouth, Dorset BH10 4HZ
Ⓣ (01202) 524464
Ⓜ 07977 878546
Ⓔ parks.perennials@ntlworld.com
Contact: S. Parks
Opening Times: Apr-Oct most days, please phone first.
Cat. Cost: None issued.
Credit Cards: None
Specialities: Hardy herbaceous perennials.
Notes: Delivers to shows.

CPbh **Penberth Plants**
St Buryan, Penzance, Cornwall TR19 6HJ
Ⓣ (01736) 810978
Ⓔ info@penberthplants.co.uk
Ⓦ www.penberthplants.co.uk
Contact: Jeff Rowe
Opening Times: Not open. Mail order plus sells at RHS shows. Open Days throughout the year, check website or contact nursery for dates.
Min Mail Order UK: Nmc
Min Mail Order EU: Nmc
Cat. Cost: Online only.
Credit Cards: All major credit/debit cards
Specialities: *Protea*, *Restio*, succulents and other unusual plants.
Notes: Card payment accepted at shows. Mail order through website only. Sells & delivers to shows.

CPBP **Parham Bungalow Plants**
Parham Lane, Market Lavington, Devizes, Wiltshire SN10 4QA
Ⓣ (01380) 812605
Ⓔ jjs@pbplants.freeserve.co.uk
Contact: Mrs D E Sample
Opening Times: Please ring first.
Min Mail Order UK: Nmc
Min Mail Order EU: Nmc
Cat. Cost: 2 × 2nd class.
Credit Cards: None
Specialities: Alpines.
Notes: Delivers to shows.

CPer **Perrie Hale Nursery**
Northcote Hill, Honiton, Devon EX14 9TH
Ⓣ (01404) 43344
Ⓕ (01404) 47163
Ⓔ faye@perriehale.co.uk
Ⓦ www.perriehale.co.uk
Contact: Faye Davey
Opening Times: 0800-1730 Mon-Fri, 0900-1230 Sat, Oct-Apr. Please phone first May-Sep.
Min Mail Order UK: £10.00 + VAT
Cat. Cost: Free
Credit Cards: All major debit/credit cards except American Express
Specialities: Broad-leaf trees & conifers; native & evergreen hedging for screening & amenity; soft fruit & shrubs. Family business established 1957, supplying in excess of 700,000 plants per year.
Notes: Sell bare-root stock Oct-Mar, after which pot-grown stock available. Also sells wholesale.
OS Grid Ref: ST178007

CPhi **Alan Phipps Cacti**
62 Samuel White Road, Hanham, Bristol BS15 3LX
Ⓣ (0117) 9607591
Ⓦ www.cactus-mall.com/alan-phipps/index.html
Contact: A Phipps
Opening Times: 1000-1700 but prior phone call essential to ensure a greeting.
Min Mail Order UK: £5.00 + p&p
Min Mail Order EU: £20.00 + p&p
Cat. Cost: Sae or 2 × IRC (EC only).
Credit Cards: None
Specialities: *Mammillaria*, *Astrophytum* & *Ariocarpus*. Species & varieties will change with times. Ample quantities exist in spring. Limited range of *Agave*.
Notes: Specimen-size plants not available by mail order. Euro accepted as cash only.
OS Grid Ref: ST644717

CPHo **The Palm House**
8 North Street, Ottery St Mary, Devon EX11 1DR
Ⓣ (01404) 815450
Ⓜ 07815 673397
Ⓔ george@thepalmhouse.co.uk
Ⓦ www.thepalmhouse.co.uk
Contact: George Gregory
Opening Times: Mail order only. Open by appt. only.
Min Mail Order UK: £5.00
Min Mail Order EU: £10.00
Cat. Cost: 2 × 1st class.
Credit Cards: All major credit/debit cards
Specialities: Palms.
Notes: Also sells wholesale.
OS Grid Ref: SY098955

C

CPla **Plant World Gardens and Nurseries** ♿
St Marychurch Road, Newton Abbot, Devon TQ12 4SE
Ⓣ (01803) 872939
Ⓕ (01803) 875018
Ⓔ raybrown@plant-world-seeds.com
Ⓦ www.plant-world-seeds.com
Contact: Doug De Val
Opening Times: 0930-1700 7 days a week, Apr-Oct.
Min Mail Order UK: Nmc
Min Mail Order EU: Nmc
Cat. Cost: Free.
Credit Cards: Visa, Access, EuroCard, MasterCard
Specialities: Alpines, perennials, small shrubs, succulents, herbaceous & patio plants. 4-acre garden planted as map of the world (entry charge).
Notes: Mail order for seed only (no mail order for plants). Also sells wholesale. Exports beyond EU. Wheelchair access to nursery & café only.
OS Grid Ref: SX893693

CPne **Pine Cottage Plants** ♿
Bowdens, Cleave House, Sticklepath, Okehampton, Devon EX20 2NL
Ⓣ (01769) 580076
Ⓔ sales@bowdenhostas.com
Ⓦ www.bowdenhostas.com
Contact: Tim Penrose
Opening Times: By appt. only. Please phone first.
Min Mail Order UK: £20.00
Min Mail Order EU: £20.00
Cat. Cost: 3 × 1st class.
Credit Cards: Maestro, MasterCard, Visa
Specialities: *Agapanthus*, South African bulbous plants, *Rhododendron* (species only) & other unusual plants.
Notes: Mail order *Agapanthus* from Sep-Jun. Wheelchair accessible.
OS Grid Ref: SS683099

CPou **Pounsley Plants** ♿
Pounsley Combe, Spriddlestone, Brixton, Plymouth, Devon PL9 0DW
Ⓣ (01752) 402873
Ⓜ 07770 758501
Ⓔ pou599@aol.com
Ⓦ www.pounsleyplants.com
Contact: Mrs Jane Hollow
Opening Times: Normally 1000-1600 Mon-Sat but please phone first.
Min Mail Order UK: £10.00 + p&p
Min Mail Order EU: €20.00 + p&p
Cat. Cost: Online only
Credit Cards: None
Specialities: Unusual herbaceous perennials. Comprehensive range of Old Roses & large selection of modern roses.
Notes: Mail order solely bare-root roses, Nov-Mar. Also sells wholesale. Delivers to shows. Euro accepted. Wheelchair accessible.
OS Grid Ref: SX521538

CPrp **ProperPlants.com**
Penknight, Edgcumbe Road, Lostwithiel, Cornwall PL22 0JD
Ⓣ (01208) 872291
Ⓔ sarahwilks52@gmail.com
Ⓦ www.ProperPlants.com
Contact: Sarah Wilks
Opening Times: By appt. only. Please phone or email first.
Min Mail Order UK: Nmc
Min Mail Order EU: Nmc
Cat. Cost: 2 × 1st class.
Credit Cards: All major credit/debit cards
Specialities: *Agapanthus*, *Crocosmia* & *Hesperantha*.
Notes: Also sells wholesale. Exports beyond EU. Delivers to shows.
OS Grid Ref: SX093596

CQua **Quality Daffodils**
14 Roscarrack Close, Falmouth, Cornwall TR11 4PJ
Ⓣ (01326) 317959
Ⓜ 07989 243450
Ⓕ (01326) 317959
Ⓔ rascamp@daffodils.uk.com
Ⓦ www.qualitydaffodils.com
Contact: R A Scamp
Opening Times: Not open. Mail order only. Viewing by appt. only.
Min Mail Order UK: Nmc
Min Mail Order EU: Nmc
Cat. Cost: 4 × 1st class.
Credit Cards: All major credit/debit cards
Specialities: *Narcissus* hybrids & species. Some stocks are less than 100 bulbs.
Notes: Exports beyond EU. Euro accepted.

CRea **Really Wild Flowers**
H V Horticulture Ltd, Heather Cottage, 23 New Close, Bourton, Gillingham, Dorset SP8 5DL
Ⓣ (01747) 416376
Ⓔ info@reallywildflowers.co.uk
Ⓦ www.reallywildflowers.co.uk
Contact: Grahame Dixie
Opening Times: Not open. Mail order & online only.

C

Min Mail Order UK: £10 + p&p
Cat. Cost: 3 × 1st class.
Credit Cards: All major debit/credit cards except American Express
Specialities: Native wild flowers for grasslands, woodlands & wetlands. Seeds & bulbs. Hedge plants & trees. Soil analysis services.
Notes: Credit card payment accepted for online orders only. Also sells wholesale.

CRHN ROSELAND HOUSE NURSERY
Chacewater, Truro, Cornwall TR4 8QB
Ⓣ (01872) 560451
Ⓔ clematis@roselandhouse.co.uk
Ⓦ www.roselandhouse.co.uk
Contact: C R Pridham
Opening Times: 1300-1700 Tue & Wed, Apr-Sep. Other times by appt.
Min Mail Order UK: Nmc
Min Mail Order EU: Nmc
Cat. Cost: Online only.
Credit Cards: All major credit/debit cards
Specialities: Climbing & conservatory plants. Nat. Collections of *Clematis viticella* & *Lapageria rosea*. Named *Lapageria* in short supply but occasionally available.
Notes: Garden open to the public. Credit cards accepted from mail order customers only. Delivers to shows.
OS Grid Ref: SW752445

CRos ROSEMOOR PLANT CENTRE (RHS) ♿ ◆
RHS Garden Rosemoor, Torrington, Devon EX38 8PH
Ⓣ (01805) 626842
Ⓔ rosemooradmin@rhs.org.uk
Ⓦ www.rhs.org.uk/rosemoor
Contact: Emma Van-Huysse or Sam Smith
Opening Times: 1000-1800 Mon-Sat, 1130-1730 Sun, Apr-Sep (summer). 1000-1700 Mon-Sat, 1030-1630 Sun, Oct-Mar (winter). Closed Easter Sun & Xmas Day.
Cat. Cost: None issued
Credit Cards: All major credit/debit cards
Specialities: Wide range of shrubs, herbaceous plants, roses, climbers, alpines & seasonal lines, reflecting where possible the diversity of planting in the garden. Displays of Curator's Choice, garden favourites, AGM plants & Plants for Pollinators.
Notes: Plant centre attached to RHS Garden Rosemoor. Free entry to plant centre, gift shop & restaurant. Plants subject to seasonal availability but will source plants whenever possible. Accept HTA & RHS vouchers (paper only). Wheelchair accessible.
OS Grid Ref: SS500176

CSam SAMPFORD SHRUBS ♿
Sampford Peverell, Tiverton, Devon EX16 7EN
Ⓣ (01884) 821164
Ⓔ mainpage@samshrub.co.uk
Ⓦ www.samshrub.co.uk
Contact: M Hughes-Jones & S Proud
Opening Times: 1000-1700 Wed-Fri, 29th Mar-15th Sep 2017. Closed 29th Jul-15th Aug.
Min Mail Order UK: £25.00 + carriage
Cat. Cost: Online only.
Credit Cards: All major credit/debit cards
Specialities: Plants particularly suitable for naturalistic gardening, especially herbaceous.
Notes: Mail order through website only, despatched Oct-Mar. Wheelchair accessible.
OS Grid Ref: ST043153

CSBt ST BRIDGET NURSERIES LTD ♿
Old Rydon Lane, Exeter, Devon EX2 7JY
Ⓣ (01392) 873672
Ⓕ (01392) 876710
Ⓔ sales@stbridgetnurseries.co.uk
Ⓦ www.stbridgetnurseries.co.uk
Contact: Sales Dept
Opening Times: 0900-1700 Mon-Sat, 1030-1630 Sun. Closed Xmas Day, Boxing Day, New Year's Day & Easter Sun.
Min Mail Order UK: Nmc
Cat. Cost: Free.
Credit Cards: All major credit/debit cards
Specialities: General nursery propagating a wide range of top quality plants, with two retail garden centres in the Exeter locality. Founded 1925.
Notes: Tours of the rose field during the summer and tree field during the autumn. See website for details. Mail order available, please contact for prices & carriage charges. Also sells wholesale. Wheelchair accessible.
OS Grid Ref: SX955905

CSde SEASIDE PLANTS
Marsh Lane Nursery, West Charleton, Kingsbridge, Devon TQ7 2AQ
Ⓜ 07747 661272
Ⓔ info@seasideplants.co.uk
Ⓦ www.seasideplants.co.uk
Contact: Michael Hornby
Opening Times: Not open. View by appt. only.
Min Mail Order UK: Nmc
Min Mail Order EU: Nmc
Cat. Cost: Online only.
Credit Cards: All major credit/debit cards
Specialities: Wide range, esp. coastal plants,

Elaeagnus, *Euonymus*, *Fuchsia*, grasses, *Griselinia*, *Hydrangea*, *Olearia* & *Pittosporum*.
Notes: Euro accepted.

CSgt **Strete Gate Camellias**
(office) 17 Seymour Drive, Torquay, Devon TQ2 8PY
Ⓣ (01803) 770710
Ⓜ 07964 824673
Ⓔ plants@stretegatecamellias.co.uk
Ⓦ www.stretegatecamellias.co.uk
Contact: Jeremy Wilson
Opening Times: Not open. Mail order only. Plant collection may be available by prior arrangement.
Min Mail Order UK: Nmc
Specialities: Over 400 varieties of *Camellia*, many in small quantities not listed.
Notes: Nursery at different site from correspondence address. Also sells wholesale. Delivers to shows.

CSma **Plants for Small Gardens**
Goosegate, Bridford, Exeter, Devon EX6 7LW
Ⓜ 07845 793582
Ⓔ sales@plantsforsmallgardens.co.uk
Ⓦ www.plantsforsmallgardens.co.uk
Contact: Sue Hearnden
Opening Times: Not open. Mail order online only.
Min Mail Order UK: £15.00
Cat. Cost: Online only.
Credit Cards: Paypal
Specialities: Dwarf hardy, rockery and alpine plants, all grown on our nursery in Devon. Range to suit all types of gardeners from *Aubrieta* & *Helianthemum* to more specialist plants such as kabschia saxifrages & *Meconopsis*. Good range of hardy geraniums.
Notes: Delivers to shows.

CSpe **Special Plants**
Hill Farm Barn, Greenways Lane, Cold Ashton, Chippenham, Wiltshire SN14 8LA
Ⓣ (01225) 891686
Ⓔ derry@specialplants.net
Ⓦ www.specialplants.net
Contact: Derry Watkins
Opening Times: 1000-1700 7 days Mar-Oct. Other times please ring first to check.
Min Mail Order UK: £10.00 + p&p
Cat. Cost: Free
Credit Cards: All major credit/debit cards
Specialities: Tender perennials, *Pelargonium*, *Salvia*, hardy geraniums, *Anemone*, *Erysimum*, *Papaver* & grasses. Many varieties propagated in small numbers only.
Notes: Mail order Sep-Mar only. Delivers to shows. Euro accepted.
OS Grid Ref: ST749726

CTca **Trecanna Nursery**
The Old Barn, Chilsworthy, Cornwall PL18 9PB
Ⓣ (01822) 834680
Ⓜ 07785 242148
Ⓔ mark@trecanna.com
Ⓦ www.trecanna.com
Contact: Mark Wash
Opening Times: Not open. Mail order only.
Min Mail Order UK: £22.00
Min Mail Order EU: £45.00
Cat. Cost: Online only.
Credit Cards: All major credit/debit cards
Specialities: Hardy South African plants. Good collections of *Crocosmia*, *Eucomis*, *Kniphofia*, *Watsonia*, *Crinum*, *Albuca*, nerines, *Zantedeschia*, *Lachenalia* & *Moraea*. Wide range of dry bulbs from around the globe.
Notes: Talks given to garden societies. Exports beyond EU. Delivers to shows.
OS Grid Ref: SX247733

CTho **Thornhayes Nursery**
St Andrews Wood, Dulford, Cullompton, Devon EX15 2DF
Ⓣ (01884) 266746
Ⓕ (01884) 266739
Ⓔ trees@thornhayes-nursery.co.uk
Ⓦ www.thornhayes-nursery.co.uk
Contact: K D Croucher
Opening Times: 0800-1600 Mon-Fri. 0900-1300 Sat.
Min Mail Order UK: £100
Min Mail Order EU: Price on application.
Cat. Cost: Free.
Credit Cards: All major credit/debit cards
Specialities: A broad range of forms of ornamental, amenity & fruit trees incl. West Country apple varieties and choice shrubs. A particular emphasis on disease-resistant forms for the wet and windy west.
Notes: Also sells wholesale. Euro accepted. Limited wheelchair accessible.

CTrh **Trehane Nursery** ♿
Stapehill Road, Hampreston, Wimborne, Dorset BH21 7ND
Ⓣ (01202) 873490
Ⓔ office@trehanenursery.co.uk
Ⓦ www.trehanenursery.co.uk
Contact: Lorraine Keets
Opening Times: 0830-1630 Mon-Fri all year (excl. Xmas & New Year). 1000-1600 Sat in spring & by special appt.

Min Mail Order UK: Nmc
Min Mail Order EU: Nmc
Cat. Cost: Free
Credit Cards: All major credit/debit cards
Specialities: Extensive range of *Camellia* species, cultivars & hybrids. Many new introductions. Blueberries.
Notes: Also sells wholesale. Wheelchair accessible.
OS Grid Ref: SU059000

CTri TRISCOMBE NURSERIES ♿ ◆
West Bagborough, Nr Taunton, Somerset TA4 3HG
Ⓣ (01984) 618267
Ⓔ info@triscombenurseries.co.uk
Ⓦ www.triscombenurseries.co.uk
Contact: S Parkman
Opening Times: 0900-1730 Mon-Sat.
Min Mail Order UK: Nmc
Cat. Cost: 1 × 1st class.
Credit Cards: None
Specialities: Trees, shrubs, roses, fruit, *Clematis*, herbaceous & rock plants.
Notes: Wheelchair accessible.

CTsd TRESEDERS NURSERY ♿
Wallcottage Nursery, Lockengate, St. Austell, Cornwall PL26 8RU
Ⓣ (01208) 832234
Ⓔ Treseders@btconnect.com
Ⓦ www.treseders.co.uk
Contact: James Treseder
Opening Times: 0900-1700 Mon-Sat, 1000-1600 Sun. Closed Wed.
Min Mail Order UK: Nmc
Min Mail Order EU: Nmc
Cat. Cost: Online or by email only.
Credit Cards: All major credit/debit cards
Specialities: A wide range of choice & unusual plants grown in peat-free compost. Establishing collection of *Prostanthera.*
Notes: Plants sometimes only available in small quantities. Enquiries welcome. Delivers to shows. Wheelchair accessible.
OS Grid Ref: SX034618

CWat THE WATER GARDEN ♿
Hinton Parva, Swindon, Wiltshire SN4 0DH
Ⓣ (01793) 790558
Ⓔ ben@thewatergarden.co.uk
Ⓦ www.thewatergarden.co.uk
Contact: Ben Newman
Opening Times: 1000-1700 Wed-Sun.
Min Mail Order UK: £10.00 + p&p
Cat. Cost: 4 × 1st class.
Credit Cards: Visa, Access, Switch
Specialities: Water lilies, marginal & moisture plants, oxygenators & alpines.
Notes: Also sells wholesale. Wheelchair accessible.

CWCL WESTCOUNTRY NURSERIES (NORTH DEVON) LTD
Donkey Meadow, Woolsery, Devon EX39 5QH
Ⓣ (01237) 431111
Ⓔ info@westcountry-nurseries.co.uk
Ⓦ www.westcountry-nurseries.co.uk
Contact: Sarah Conibear
Opening Times: 1000-1600 Mar-mid Jul. Closed for lunch 1300-1330. Before travelling at a weekend, please check with nursery.
Min Mail Order UK: Nmc
Cat. Cost: 2 × 1st class + A5 sae for full colour cat.
Credit Cards: All major credit/debit cards
Specialities: *Lupinus, Lewisia, Hellebore, Clematis*, cyclamen, select perennials, grasses, ferns & climbers. Nat. Collection of Lupins.
Notes: Delivers to shows.
OS Grid Ref: SS351219

CWGN WALLED GARDEN NURSERY ♿
Brinkworth House, Brinkworth, Nr Malmesbury, Wiltshire SN15 5DF
Ⓣ (01666) 826637
Ⓜ 07921 436863
Ⓔ sales@clematis-nursery.co.uk
Ⓦ www.clematis-nursery.co.uk
Contact: Fraser Wescott
Opening Times: 1000-1700, 7 days, Mar-Oct. 1030-dusk, Mon-Fri, Nov & Feb. Closed Dec & Jan.
Min Mail Order UK: £15.00
Credit Cards: All major credit/debit cards
Specialities: *Clematis* & climbers, with a selection of unusual perennials & shrubs.
Notes: Mail order UK mainland only. Wheelchair accessible.
OS Grid Ref: SU002849

CWGr NATIONAL DAHLIA COLLECTION
Varfell Farm, Long Rock, Penzance, Cornwall TR20 8AQ
Ⓣ (01736) 339276
Ⓜ 07879 337714
Ⓔ info@nationaldahliacollection.co.uk
Ⓦ www.nationaldahliacollection.co.uk
Contact: Michael Mann
Opening Times: Garden open in summer. See website or contact nursery for details.
Min Mail Order UK: Nmc
Min Mail Order EU: Nmc
Cat. Cost: Online. Contact nursery for hard copy.

Creit Cards: All major debit/credit cards except American Express
Specialities: Nat. Collection of *Dahlia*. 1600+ *Dahlia* cultivars.
Notes: See website for plant availability. Also sells wholesale. Limited wheelchair accessible.

CWiW **WINDRUSH WILLOW**
Higher Barn, Sidmouth Road, Aylesbeare, Exeter, Devon EX5 2JJ
Ⓣ (01395) 233669
Ⓕ (01395) 233669
Ⓔ windrushw@aol.com
Ⓦ www.windrushwillow.com
Contact: Richard Kerwood
Opening Times: Mail order only. Open by appt.
Min Mail Order UK: Nmc
Min Mail Order EU: Nmc
Cat. Cost: 2 × 1st class.
Credit Cards: All major credit/debit cards
Specialities: *Salix*. Unrooted cuttings available Dec-Mar.
Notes: Carrier charge £5.00. Also sells wholesale. Euro accepted.

CWld **WILD THYME**
(office) The Old Orchard, Friggle Street, Frome, Somerset BA11 5LH
Ⓣ (01373) 464417
Ⓜ 07956 888477
Ⓔ jess@wildthymeplants.co.uk
Ⓦ www.wildthymeplants.co.uk
Contact: Monica Ashman
Opening Times: Not open. Mail order only via online shop.
Min Mail Order UK: £15.00
Credit Cards: Visa, MasterCard, Maestro
Specialities: Wildflowers & fragrant plants.
Notes: Delivers to shows.

CWSG **WEST SOMERSET GARDEN CENTRE** ♿
Mart Road, Minehead, Somerset TA24 5BJ
Ⓣ (01643) 703812
Ⓕ (01643) 706476
Ⓔ wsgc@btconnect.com
Ⓦ www.westsomersetgardencentre.co.uk
Contact: Ms J K Webber
Opening Times: 0800-1700 Mon-Sat, 1000-1600 Sun.
Min Mail Order UK: Nmc
Cat. Cost: None issued.
Credit Cards: All major debit/credit cards except American Express
Specialities: Wide general range. *Clematis* & rose varieties change throughout the season.
Notes: Wheelchair accessible.

EASTERN

EACa **ALPINE CAMPANULAS (BELLFLOWER NURSERY)** ♿
Langham Hall Walled Garden, Langham, Nr Bury St Edmunds, Suffolk IP31 3EE
Ⓜ 07879 644958
Ⓔ campanulas@btinternet.com
Ⓦ www.bellflowernursery.co.uk
Contact: Sue Wooster
Opening Times: 1000-1600 Thu & Fri, mid-Mar to end Oct. Other times by appt.
Min Mail Order UK: £10.00
Cat. Cost: Online only.
Credit Cards: None
Specialities: *Campanula*. Nat. Collection of Alpine Campanulas. Most stock in small numbers only.
Notes: Hardy plant nursery & Nat. Collection within 3.5 acre Georgian Walled Garden. Groups welcome by appt. Wheelchair accessible but nursery reached by gravel paths through walled garden.
OS Grid Ref: TL978691

EAJP **A & J PLANTS**
Chappel Road, Great Tey, Colchester, Essex CO6 1JR
Ⓣ (01206) 212124
Ⓕ (01206) 212124
Ⓔ mail@aandjplants.com
Ⓦ www.aandjplants.com
Contact: Jackie Rhodes
Opening Times: Not open. Mail order only. Orders can be collected from nursery by prior arrangement.
Min Mail Order UK: Nmc
Specialities: Wide variety of choice perennials and ornamental grasses propagated on the nursery, some in small quantities.
Notes: Plant centre at Marks Hall Garden (CO6 1TG) stocked with seasonal selection of perennials & grasses. Also sells wholesale. Delivers to shows.

EBak **B & H M BAKER** ♿
Bourne Brook Nurseries, Greenstead Green, Halstead, Essex CO9 1RB
Ⓣ (01787) 476369
Contact: Clive Baker
Opening Times: 0800-1600 Mon-Fri, 0900-1200 & 1400-1600 Sat & Sun, Mar- Jun.
Cat. Cost: 2 × 1st class + 33p.
Credit Cards: All major credit/debit cards
Specialities: *Fuchsia* & conservatory plants.
Notes: Also sells wholesale. Wheelchair accessible.

EBar **Barcham Trees plc**
Eye Hill Drove, Ely, Cambridgeshire
CB7 5XF
Ⓣ (01353) 720950
Ⓔ info@barchamtrees.co.uk
Ⓦ www.barcham.co.uk
Contact: Ellen Carvey
Opening Times: Visits to the nursery by appt. only. 0900-1730 Mon-Fri.
Min Mail Order UK: Nmc
Min Mail Order EU: Nmc
Cat. Cost: £20.00
Credit Cards: All major debit/credit cards except American Express
Specialities: Large grower of containerised trees. 478 varieties available, from 10-12cm to 40cm girth.
Notes: As trees range from 3-8 metres all are despatched on lorries rather than through the mailing service. Also sells wholesale. Exports beyond EU. Delivers to shows. Euro accepted.

EBee **Beeches Nursery** ♿
Crown Hill, Ashdon, Saffron Walden, Essex
CB10 2HB
Ⓣ (01799) 584362
Ⓕ (01799) 584421
Ⓔ sales@beechesnursery.co.uk
Ⓦ www.beechesnursery.co.uk
Contact: Alan Bidwell/Kevin Marsh
Opening Times: 0830-1700 Mon-Sat, 1000-1700 Sun & B/hols.
Min Mail Order UK: £15.00
Min Mail Order EU: £20.00
Cat. Cost: Online.
Credit Cards: All major credit/debit cards
Specialities: Herbaceous specialists & extensive range of other garden plants. Rarieties available in limited numbers only.
Notes: Plants dispatched Oct-Feb only. Orders accepted throughout the year. No trees by mail order. Wheelchair accessible.
OS Grid Ref: TL586420

EBls **Peter Beales Roses** ♿ ◆
London Road, Attleborough, Norfolk
NR17 1AY
Ⓣ (01953) 454707
Ⓔ info@peterbealesroses.com
Ⓦ www.classicroses.co.uk
Contact: Tina Limmer
Opening Times: 0900-1700 Mon-Sat, 1000-1600 Sun & B/hols. Closed 25th Dec-5th Jan.
Min Mail Order UK: Nmc
Min Mail Order EU: Nmc
Cat. Cost: £5.00 outside UK.
Credit Cards: All major debit/credit cards except American Express
Specialities: Large range of perennials, shrubs, *Clematis*, climbers, ornamental trees, fruit, summer & winter bedding. Nat. Collection of Species Roses.
Notes: Display garden open all year round (free entry). New wildlife garden. Agent for Classic Garden Element iron work. Also sells wholesale. Exports beyond EU. Wheelchair accessible.
OS Grid Ref: TM026929

EBou **Boundary Nursery**
Colne Road, Bluntisham, Huntington, Cambridgeshire PE28 3LU
Ⓣ 01487 842611
Ⓔ herbsandalpines@gmail.com
Ⓦ https://boundarynursery.co.uk/
Contact: Peter Reason
Opening Times: Visitors by appointment only.
Min Mail Order UK: Nmc
Credit Cards: All major credit/debit cards
Specialities: Plants for pathways, wildflower and wildlife gardens, groundcover plants, plants for dry soil, shady areas, fragrant sensory plants, cottage plants, Mediterranean plants and low hedging. Grows alpines and rockery plants plus compact plants for pots, tubs, raised beds and the smaller garden. Also herbs, perennials, ornamental grasses and a small selection of shrubs.
OS Grid Ref: TL369752

EBtc **Botanica**
Chantry Farm, Campsea Ashe, Wickham Market, Suffolk IP13 0PZ
Ⓣ (01728) 747113
Ⓜ 07887 423964
Ⓕ (01728) 747725
Ⓔ sales@botanica.org.uk
Ⓦ www.botanicaplantnursery.co.uk
Contact: Daniel Everett
Opening Times: 0900-1700 Mon-Fri (0900-1600 in winter), 1000-1600 w/ends. Closed w/ends in Jul.
Min Mail Order UK: £30 + p&p
Cat. Cost: Online only.
Credit Cards: All major debit/credit cards except American Express
Specialities: Range of rare & unusual hardy plants. All stock is English-grown at our nursery and in non-peat based compost.
Notes: Also sells wholesale.
OS Grid Ref: TM328550

ECha **The Beth Chatto Gardens** ♿
Clacton Road, Elmstead Market, Colchester, Essex CO7 7DB
Ⓣ (01206) 822007

E

Ⓕ (01206) 825933
Ⓔ info@bethchatto.co.uk
Ⓦ www.bethchatto.co.uk
Contact: David Ward
Opening Times: 0900-1700 Mon-Sat, 1000-1700 Sun, 1st Mar-31st Oct. 0900-1600 Mon-Sat, 1000-1600 Sun, Nov-end Feb.
Min Mail Order UK: Nmc
Min Mail Order EU: Ask for details
Cat. Cost: Online only.
Credit Cards: All major debit/credit cards except American Express
Specialities: Predominantly herbaceous perennials, grasses & ferns. Many unusual for special situations.
Notes: Delivers to shows. Wheelchair accessible.
OS Grid Ref: TM069238

ECnt **CANTS OF COLCHESTER LTD**
Nayland Road, Mile End, Colchester, Essex CO4 5HA
Ⓣ (01206) 844008
Ⓕ (01206) 855371
Ⓔ enquiries@cantsroses.co.uk
Ⓦ www.cantsroses.co.uk
Contact: Angela Pawsey
Opening Times: 0900-1300, 1400-1630 Mon-Fri. Sat varied, please phone first. Sun closed.
Min Mail Order UK: Nmc
Min Mail Order EU: Nmc
Cat. Cost: Free
Credit Cards: Visa, MasterCard, Delta, Maestro
Specialities: Roses. Unstaffed rose field can be viewed dawn-dusk every day from end Jun-end Sep.
Notes: Celebrated 250 years of rose growing in 2015. Bare-root mail order end Oct-end Mar, containers Apr-Aug. Exports beyond EU. Partial wheelchair access.

ECrc **THE CROCOSMIA GARDENS**
9 North Street, Caistor, Lincolnshire LN7 6QU
Ⓣ (01472) 859269
Ⓜ 07834 725392
Ⓔ thecrocosmiagardens@live.co.uk
Ⓦ www.simplesite.com/foxsplants
Contact: Mark Fox
Opening Times: 1000-1700 Mon, Wed-Sun. Closed Tue.
Min Mail Order UK: £5.00
Min Mail Order EU: £5.00
Cat. Cost: None issued.
Credit Cards: None
Specialities: *Crocosmia*. Nat. Collection of *Crocosmia*. Available in small quantities only.
Notes: Sent bareroot only, Oct-Apr. Exports beyond EU. Euro accepted.

ECre **CREAKE PLANT CENTRE** ♿
Leicester Road, South Creake, Fakenham, Norfolk NR21 9PW
Ⓣ (01328) 823018
Ⓜ 07760 762499
Ⓕ (01328) 823018
Ⓔ trevor-harrison@btconnect.com
Ⓦ www.creakeplantcentre.co.uk
Contact: Mr T Harrison
Opening Times: 1000-1300 & 1400-1730 7 days excl. Xmas.
Cat. Cost: None issued
Credit Cards: All major credit/debit cards
Specialities: Unusual shrubs, herbaceous, conservatory plants, old roses. Hellebores. Some plants only available in small quantities.
Notes: Delivers to shows. Wheelchair accessible.
OS Grid Ref: TF864353

ECrN **CROWN NURSERY** ♿
High Street, Ufford, Suffolk IP13 6EL
Ⓣ (01394) 460755
Ⓕ (01394) 460142
Ⓔ enquiries@crown-nursery.co.uk
Ⓦ www.crown-nursery.co.uk
Contact: Jill Proctor
Opening Times: 0900-1700 (1600 in winter) Mon-Sat.
Min Mail Order UK: Nmc
Credit Cards: All major credit/debit cards
Specialities: Mature & semi-mature native, ornamental & fruit trees. Heritage fruit varieties.
Notes: Mail order for small/young stock only. Also sells wholesale. Wheelchair accessible.
OS Grid Ref: TM292528

ECtt **COTTAGE NURSERIES** ♿
Thoresthorpe, Alford, Lincolnshire LN13 0HX
Ⓣ (01507) 466968
Ⓔ bill@cottagenurseries.net
Ⓦ www.cottagenurseries.net
Contact: W H Denbigh
Opening Times: 0900-1700, 7 days 1st Mar-31st Oct. 1000-1500, Nov-Feb. Closed 15th Dec-6th Jan.
Min Mail Order UK: £15.00
Cat. Cost: Online only.
Credit Cards: Visa, MasterCard, Maestro
Specialities: Hardy perennials. Wide general range.
Notes: Wheelchair accessible.
OS Grid Ref: TF461776

EDAr **D'ARCY & EVEREST**
Meadowsweet Nursery, Pidley Sheep Lane (B1040), Pidley, Cambridgeshire PE28 3FL
Ⓣ (01480) 463570
Ⓜ 07715 374440
Ⓕ (01480) 466042
Ⓔ angela@darcyeverest.co.uk
Ⓦ www.darcyeverest.co.uk
Contact: Angela Whiting
Opening Times: Open w/ends only. Please see website or contact nursery for dates & nursery tour dates (bookable in advance only). Coach parties welcome by appt. Closed Oct-Feb.
Min Mail Order UK: £15.00 + p&p
Cat. Cost: None available.
Credit Cards: All major credit/debit cards
Specialities: Alpines & sempervivums.
Notes: Delivers to shows. Partial wheelchair access.
OS Grid Ref: TL338762

EECP **ESSEX CARNIVOROUS PLANTS**
12 Strangman Avenue, Thundersley, Essex SS7 1RB
Ⓣ (01702) 551467
Ⓜ 07957 196391
Ⓔ Mark@essexcarnivorousplants.com
Ⓦ www.essexcarnivorousplants.com
Contact: Mark Haslett
Opening Times: By appt. only.
Min Mail Order UK: Nmc
Min Mail Order EU: Nmc
Cat. Cost: 3 × 1st class or online.
Credit Cards: Paypal
Specialities: Good range of carnivorous plants. *Sarracenia, Dionaea*. Some stock available in small quantities only.
Notes: Also sells wholesale. Delivers to shows.
OS Grid Ref: TQ797875

EFer **THE FERN NURSERY** ♿
Grimsby Road, Binbrook, Lincolnshire LN8 6DH
Ⓣ (01472) 398092
Ⓔ rtimm@fernnursery.co.uk
Ⓦ www.fernnursery.co.uk
Contact: R N Timm
Opening Times: 0900-1700 Fri, Sat & Sun Apr-Oct or by appt.
Min Mail Order UK: Nmc
Min Mail Order EU: Nmc
Cat. Cost: Online only.
Credit Cards: All major credit/debit cards
Specialities: Ferns. Display garden.
Notes: Only plants in the mail order part of the catalogue can be sent mail order. Also sells wholesale. Euro accepted. Wheelchair accessible.
OS Grid Ref: TF212942

EFly **THE FLY TRAP PLANTS** ♿
Cookes Road, Thurton, Norwich, Norfolk NR14 6AE
Ⓣ (01508) 480348
Ⓜ 07769 256556
Ⓔ sales@tftplants.co.uk
Ⓦ www.tftplants.co.uk
Contact: Pauline Steward
Opening Times: By appt. only.
Min Mail Order UK: Nmc
Cat. Cost: 1 × 1st class sae
Credit Cards: Paypal
Specialities: All kinds of carnivorous plants, from *Sarracenia, Drosera, Pinguicula*, to *Utricularia* aquatic plants.
Notes: Delivers to shows. Euro accepted. Wheelchair accessible.

EHDe **HARPER & DEBBAGE**
33 The Ridgeway, Norwich, Norfolk NR1 4ND
Ⓣ (01603) 708104
Ⓜ 07889 679444
Ⓔ info@harperanddebbage.co.uk
Ⓦ www.harperanddebbage.co.uk
Contact: Kristopher Harper
Opening Times: Not open except by appt. or on Open Days. Plant collection by appointment only.
Min Mail Order UK: Nmc
Cat. Cost: Online only.
Credit Cards: All major credit/debit cards
Specialities: *Fuchsia*. Nat. Collection of Fuchsias introduced by James Lye.
Notes: Sells by mail order or at Open Days. Also sells wholesale. Attends some shows (contact nursery for details).
OS Grid Ref: TG248096

EHoe **HOECROFT PLANTS**
Severals Grange, Holt Road, Wood Norton, Norfolk NR20 5BL
Ⓣ (01362) 684206
Ⓔ hoecroft@hotmail.co.uk
Ⓦ www.hoecroft.co.uk
Contact: Jane Lister
Opening Times: 1000-1600 Thu-Sun, 1st Apr-15th Oct or by appt.
Cat. Cost: 4 × 2nd class.
Credit Cards: None
Specialities: An extensive range of coloured & variegated-leaved shrubs, herbaceous perennials & a large collection of ornamental grasses. Donation to NGS for entry to display gardens.

Notes: Nursery 2 miles north of Guist on B1110. Wheelchair accessible in most places.
OS Grid Ref: TG008289

E

EHrv **Harveys Garden Plants** ♿
Great Green, Thurston, Bury St Edmunds, Suffolk IP31 3SJ
Ⓣ (01359) 233363
Ⓔ admin@harveysgardenplants.co.uk
Ⓦ www.harveysgardenplants.co.uk
Contact: Roger Harvey
Opening Times: 0930-1630 Mon-Sat. Closed 24th Dec-1st Jan incl.
Min Mail Order UK: £25.00
Min Mail Order EU: £25.00
Cat. Cost: None issued.
Credit Cards: All major credit/debit cards
Specialities: *Helleborus*, *Anemone*, *Epimedium*, *Galanthus*, *Astrantia*, *Pulmonaria* & other herbaceous perennials, plus shade & woodland plants.
Notes: Garden design & maintenance service. Customers can buy online. Exports beyond EU. Delivers to shows. Euro accepted. Wheelchair accessible.
OS Grid Ref: TL951677

EHyd **Hyde Hall Plant Centre (RHS)** ♿ ◆
RHS Garden Hyde Hall, Rettenden, Chelmsford, Essex CM3 8ET
Ⓣ (01245) 402113
Ⓕ (01245) 400013
Ⓔ benmansfield@rhs.org.uk
Ⓦ www.rhs.org.uk
Contact: Ben Mansfield
Opening Times: 0930-1600 Mon-Sat, 1000-1600 Sun, Nov-Feb. 0930-1800 Mon-Sat, 1100 -1700 Sun, Mar-Oct. Closed Xmas Day & Easter Sun.
Credit Cards: All major credit/debit cards
Notes: Wheelchair accessible.

EIri **Irisesonline**
Slade Cottage, Petts Lane, Little Walden, Essex CB10 1XH
Ⓣ (01799) 526294
Ⓔ sales@irisesonline.co.uk
Ⓦ www.irisesonline.co.uk
Contact: Clare Kneen
Opening Times: By appt. only.
Min Mail Order UK: Nmc
Cat. Cost: Online only.
Credit Cards: None
Specialities: *Iris*. Small family-run nursery. Some varieties available in small quantities only.
Notes: Delivers to shows.
OS Grid Ref: TL546416

EKin **E W King & Co. Ltd. (Kings Seeds)**
Monks Farm, Pantling Lane, Coggeshall Road, Kelvedon, Essex CO5 9PG
Ⓣ (01376) 570000
Ⓕ (01376) 571189
Ⓔ sales@kingsseeds.com
Ⓦ www.kingsseeds.com
Contact: Andrew Tokely
Min Mail Order UK: Nmc
Min Mail Order EU: Nmc
Cat. Cost: Free
Credit Cards: All major credit/debit cards
Specialities: Vegetable, flower, grass, sweet pea and pea & bean seeds, incl. many hybrid & unusual items.
Notes: Incorporating Suffolk Herbs. Also sells wholesale. Exports beyond the EU.

ELad **Ladybird Nurseries** ♿
Gromford Lane, Snape, Saxmundham, Suffolk IP17 1RD
Ⓣ (01728) 688289
Ⓦ www.ladybirdnurseries.co.uk
Contact: Mrs M Booker
Opening Times: 0900-1700, Mon-Sat, 1000-1600 Sun.
Credit Cards: All major credit/debit cards
Notes: Wheelchair accessible.
OS Grid Ref: TM388589

ELan **Langthorns Plantery** ♿
High Cross Lane West, Little Canfield, Dunmow, Essex CM6 1TD
Ⓣ (01371) 872611
Ⓔ info@langthorns.com
Ⓦ www.langthorns.com
Contact: E Cannon
Opening Times: 1000-1700 or dusk (if earlier) 7 days. Closed Xmas fortnight.
Min Mail Order UK: £ 20.00
Cat. Cost: Online only.
Credit Cards: Visa, Access, Switch, MasterCard, Delta
Specialities: Wide general range with many unusual plants.
Notes: Mail order any plant under 4ft tall. Wheelchair accessible.
OS Grid Ref: TL592204

ELon **Long House Plants** ♿
The Long House, Church Road, Noak Hill, Romford, Essex RM4 1LD
Ⓣ (01708) 371719
Ⓔ tim@longhouse-plants.co.uk
Ⓦ www.longhouse-plants.co.uk
Contact: Tim Carter
Opening Times: 1000-1700 Fri, Sat & B/hols, 1000-1600 Sun, beginning Mar-

end Sep, or by appt.
Cat. Cost: None issued.
Credit Cards: All major credit/debit cards
Specialities: Interesting range of choice trees, shrubs, climbers, roses, grasses, herbaceous perennials & ferns. Many unusual varieties. Specialities incl. *Agapanthus*, *Aster*, *Camellia*, *Hemerocallis*, *Iris sibirica*, *Kniphofia*, *Phlox* & *Symphyotrichum*. Some plants available in small quantities.
Notes: Wheelchair accessible. Disabled toilet.
OS Grid Ref: TQ554194

EMac FIRECREST TREES & SHRUBS NURSERY ♿
Hall Road, Little Bealings, Woodbridge, Suffolk IP13 6LG
Ⓣ (01473) 625937
Ⓕ (01473) 625937
Ⓔ mac@firecrest.org.uk
Ⓦ www.firecrest.org.uk
Contact: Mac McGregor
Opening Times: 0900-1600 Mon-Fri, 1230 Sat.
Min Mail Order UK: Nmc
Cat. Cost: 2 × 1st class (bare-root only).
Credit Cards: None
Specialities: Trees & shrubs. Japanese maples. Bare-root hedging.
Notes: Also sells wholesale. Euro accepted. Wheelchair accessible.

EMal MARSHALL'S MALMAISONS ♿
Hullwood Barn, Shelley, Ipswich, Suffolk IP7 5RE
Ⓣ (01473) 822400
Ⓜ 07768 454875
Ⓔ jim@malmaisons.plus.com
Contact: J M Marshall/Sarah Cook
Opening Times: By appt. only.
Min Mail Order UK: £33.00 incl. p&p
Min Mail Order EU: £36.00 incl. p&p
Cat. Cost: 1st class sae.
Credit Cards: None
Specialities: Nat. Collections of Malmaison Carnations & Cedric Morris Irises. *Iris* stock only available in small quantities.
Notes: Also sells wholesale. Wheelchair accessible.
OS Grid Ref: TM006394

EMdy MANDY PLANTS ♿
(office) 4 Stevens Road, Little Snoring, Norfolk NR21 0GZ
Ⓣ (01328) 878144
Ⓜ 07432 112245
Ⓔ enquiries@mandyplants.com
Ⓦ www.mandyplants.com
Contact: Liz Spanton
Opening Times: By appt. only.
Min Mail Order UK: Nmc
Min Mail Order EU: £25.00
Credit Cards: Paypal, All major credit/debit cards
Specialities: *Mandevilla*, *Dipladenia*, *Lantana* & other tender perennials.
Notes: Nursery is at Little Snoring, Norfolk. Also sells wholesale. Delivers to shows. Wheelchair accessible.

EMic MICKFIELD HOSTAS ♿
The Poplars, Mickfield, Stowmarket, Suffolk IP14 5LH
Ⓣ (01449) 711576
Ⓕ (01449) 711576
Ⓔ mickfieldhostas@btconnect.com
Ⓦ www.mickfieldhostas.co.uk
Contact: Mr & Mrs R L C Milton
Opening Times: 1000-1600, Fri to Mon. Closed Tue-Thurs.
Min Mail Order UK: Nmc
Min Mail Order EU: Nmc
Cat. Cost: Online only.
Credit Cards: All major debit/credit cards except American Express
Specialities: Nat. Collection of *Hosta* containing over 2000 varieties. See website for details of cvs held & latest availability. Operates a waiting list for rarities & some limited quantity plants only available at nursery. Will divide parent plants for collectors if feasible. Expect to pay more for root divisions of mature plants.
Notes: Delivers to shows. Wheelchair accessible.
OS Grid Ref: TM136619

EMil MILL RACE GARDEN CENTRE ♿
New Road, Aldham, Colchester, Essex CO6 3QT
Ⓣ (01206) 242521
Ⓔ plantdesk@millracegardencentre.co.uk
Ⓦ www.millracegardencentre.co.uk
Contact: Annette Bayliss
Opening Times: 0900-1730 Mon-Sat, 1000-1630 Sun.
Min Mail Order UK: £9.00
Credit Cards: All major credit/debit cards
Specialities: Stock available in small quantities only.
Notes: Trees & large shrubs not sent by mail order. Wheelchair accessible.
OS Grid Ref: TL918268

EMor MOORE AND MOORE PLANTS ♿
London Road, Billericay, Essex CM12 9HR

E

Ⓣ 01277 563243
Ⓜ 07881 756252
Ⓔ contact@mooreandmooreplants.co.uk
Ⓦ www.mooreandmooreplants.co.uk
Contact: Lynne Moore
Opening Times: By appt. only. See website or contact nursery for details of Open Days.
Cat. Cost: Online only
Credit Cards: All major credit/debit cards
Specialities: Nursery stocking a large range of perennials, bulbs, ferns, grasses and herbs, especially unusual or rare varieties. *Agapanthus*, *Astrantia*, *Athyrium*, *Dryopteris*, *Echinacea*, *Geranium*, *Helenium*, *Hosta* & other plants for shaded areas. Bog garden/marginal plants. Most plants available in small numbers only.
Notes: Delivers to shows. Wheelchair accessible.

EMOT **MAIL ORDER TREES**
42 Station Road, Fordham, Ely, Cambridgeshire CB7 5LW
Ⓣ 0800 066 5972
Ⓔ info@mailordertrees.co.uk
Ⓦ www.mailordertrees.co.uk
Contact: Michael Simpson
Opening Times: Not open. Mail order only.
Min Mail Order UK: Nmc
Credit Cards: All major credit/debit cards
Specialities: Specialist fruit & ornamental tree growers, offering a range of home-grown evergreen & deciduous shrubs, climbing plants, conifers, soft fruit bushes & hedging plants to buy online.
Notes: Also sells wholesale.
OS Grid Ref: TL623701

ENBC **NORFOLK BAMBOO COMPANY**
Vine Cottage, The Drift, Ingoldisthorpe, King's Lynn, Norfolk PE31 6NW
Ⓣ (01485) 543935
Ⓜ 07970 310880
Ⓔ Lewdyer@hotmail.com
Ⓦ www.norfolkbamboo.co.uk
Contact: Lewis Dyer
Opening Times: 1000-1600 Fri & 1000-1400 Sat, Apr-Sep, or by appt.
Min Mail Order UK: £10.00 + p&p
Cat. Cost: 1 × 1st class sae for price list.
Credit Cards: None
Specialities: Bamboos.

ENfk **NORFOLK HERBS** ♿
Blackberry Farm, Dillington, Dereham, Norfolk NR19 2QD
Ⓣ (01362) 860812
Ⓕ (01362) 860812
Ⓔ info@norfolkherbs.co.uk
Ⓦ www.norfolkherbs.co.uk
Contact: Rosemary or Oliver Clifton-Sprigg
Opening Times: 0900-1700 Mon-Sat, 1000-1600 Sun, Apr-Aug. 1000-1600 Fri & Sat, Feb, Oct & Nov. 1000-1600 Wed-Sat, Mar, Sept & Dec. Closed from Xmas to end Jan. To visit at other times, please contact nursery.
Min Mail Order UK: £8.39
Cat. Cost: 2 × 2nd class.
Credit Cards: All major credit/debit cards
Specialities: Established 1986. Growers & suppliers of naturally raised culinary, medicinal & aromatic herb plants. Bay trees & scented pelagoniums.
Notes: Sells from nursery, online & at local shows. A founding member of Norfolk Nursery Network. Also sells wholesale. Delivers to shows. Wheelchair accessible.
OS Grid Ref: TF967150

ENor **NORFOLK LAVENDER** ♿
Caley Mill, Heacham, King's Lynn, Norfolk PE31 7JE
Ⓣ (01485) 570384
Ⓜ 07787 550286
Ⓕ (01485) 571176
Ⓔ info@norfolk-lavender.co.uk
Ⓦ www.norfolk-lavender.co.uk
Contact: Shelley Eagle
Opening Times: 0900-1700 7 days, Apr-Oct. 0900-1600 7 days, Nov-Mar.
Min Mail Order UK: Nmc
Cat. Cost: Free.
Credit Cards: All major debit/credit cards except American Express
Specialities: Nat. Collection of *Lavandula*, sect. *L. dentata* & *L. pterostoechas*.
Notes: Wheelchair accessible.
OS Grid Ref: TF685368

EOHP **OLD HALL PLANTS**
1 The Old Hall, Barsham, Beccles, Suffolk NR34 8HB
Ⓣ (01502) 717475
Ⓔ info@oldhallplants.co.uk
Ⓦ www.oldhallplants.co.uk
Contact: Janet Elliott
Opening Times: By appt. only. Please phone first.
Min Mail Order UK: Nmc
Min Mail Order EU: Nmc
Cat. Cost: 4 × 1st class.
Credit Cards: Paypal
Specialities: A variety of rare herbs. House plants. Some plants available in small quantities.

Notes: Paypal (overseas orders only). Euro accepted. Partial wheelchair access.
OS Grid Ref: TM396904

EOli **The Norfolk Olive Tree Company** ♿
61 Riverside Road (adjacent to the Cotswold Company), Norwich, Norfolk NR1 1SR
Ⓜ 07766 730893
Ⓔ thenorfolkolivetreecompany@gmail.com
Ⓦ www.thenorfolkolivetreecompany.co.uk
Contact: Antonia
Min Mail Order UK: Nmc
Credit Cards: All major credit/debit cards
Specialities: Olive trees.
Notes: Also sells wholesale. Wheelchair accessible. Pre-ordered plants delivered to shows. Euros accepted.

EPau **Paugers Plants Ltd**
Bury Road, Depden, Bury St Edmunds, Suffolk IP29 4BU
Ⓣ (01284) 850527
Ⓜ 07906 618603
Ⓔ enquiries@paugers-plants.co.uk
Ⓦ www.paugers-plants.co.uk
Contact: Geraldine Arnold
Opening Times: 0900-1730 Wed-Sat, 1000-1700 Sun & B/hols, 1st Mar-30th Nov.
Min Mail Order UK: Nmc
Cat. Cost: None issued.
Credit Cards: All major credit/debit cards
Specialities: Hardy shrubs & perennials in large or small quantities.
Notes: Also sells wholesale.
OS Grid Ref: TL783568

EPfP **The Place for Plants** ♿
East Bergholt Place, East Bergholt, Suffolk CO7 6UP
Ⓣ (01206) 299224
Ⓕ (01206) 299229
Ⓔ sales@placeforplants.co.uk
Ⓦ www.placeforplants.co.uk
Contact: Sara Eley
Opening Times: 1000-1700 (or dusk if earlier) 7 days. Closed Easter Sun. Garden open Mar-Oct.
Min Mail Order UK: Nmc
Cat. Cost: Online only.
Credit Cards: All major credit/debit cards
Specialities: Wide range of specialist & popular plants. Nat. Collection of Deciduous *Euonymus*. 20 acre mature garden with free access to RHS members during season (excl. Sun).
Notes: Mail order from Sep-Feb. Delivers to shows. Euro accepted. Wheelchair accessible.

EPom **Pomona Fruits Ltd**
Pomona House, 12 Third Avenue, Walton-on-the-Naze, Essex CO14 8JU
Ⓣ (01255) 440410
Ⓕ (01255) 440420
Ⓔ Info@PomonaFruits.co.uk
Ⓦ www.PomonaFruits.co.uk
Contact: Ming Yang/Claire Higgins
Opening Times: Not open. Mail order only.
Min Mail Order UK: Nmc
Cat. Cost: Free.
Credit Cards: All major credit/debit cards
Specialities: Fruit stock.

EPot **Pottertons Nursery** ♿
Moortown Road, Nettleton, Caistor, Lincolnshire LN7 6HX
Ⓣ (01472) 851714
Ⓔ sales@pottertons.co.uk
Ⓦ www.pottertons.co.uk
Contact: Robert Potterton
Opening Times: 1000-1600 Tue-Sat, Mar-Oct. By appt. only from Nov-Feb.
Min Mail Order UK: Nmc
Min Mail Order EU: Nmc
Cat. Cost: £2.00 in stamps
Credit Cards: MasterCard, Visa
Specialities: Alpines, dwarf bulbs & woodland plants.
Notes: Talks given nationally & internationally to garden clubs & societies. Group nursery tours by arrangement. Delivers to shows. Euro accepted. Wheelchair accessible.
OS Grid Ref: TA091001

EPPr **The Plantsman's Preference** ♿
Church Road, South Lopham, Diss, Norfolk IP22 2LW
Ⓣ (01379) 710810
Ⓜ 07799 855559
Ⓔ tim@plantpref.co.uk
Ⓦ www.plantpref.co.uk
Contact: Tim Fuller
Opening Times: 0930-1700 Fri, Sat & Sun Mar-Oct. Other times by appt.
Min Mail Order UK: Nmc
Min Mail Order EU: Nmc
Cat. Cost: Online only.
Credit Cards: All major credit/debit cards
Specialities: Hardy geraniums & ornamental grasses. Unusual & interesting perennials incl. shade/woodland. Some choice shrubs esp. *Caprifoliaceae*. Nat. Collection of *Molinia*.
Notes: Mail order all year except Xmas-New Year. Delivers to shows. Wheelchair accessible.
OS Grid Ref: TM041819

E

EPts **POTASH NURSERY** ♿
Cow Green, Bacton, Stowmarket, Suffolk
IP14 4HJ
Ⓣ (01449) 781671
Ⓔ enquiries@potashnursery.co.uk
Ⓦ www.potashnursery.co.uk
Contact: M W Clare
Opening Times: Pre-ordered plants can be collected by appt. only.
Min Mail Order UK: £22.50
Cat. Cost: 1 × 1st class.
Credit Cards: Visa, Delta, MasterCard
Specialities: *Fuchsia.*
Notes: Peat free. Delivers to shows. Wheelchair accessible.
OS Grid Ref: TM055656

ERCP **ROSE COTTAGE PLANTS**
Bay Tree Farm, Epping Green, Essex CM16 6PU
Ⓣ (01992) 573775
Ⓔ anne@rosecottageplants.co.uk
Ⓦ www.rosecottageplants.co.uk
Contact: Anne & Jack Barnard
Opening Times: Most Fridays Mar-Oct. Also by appt & for special events. See website for details.
Min Mail Order UK: Nmc
Min Mail Order EU: £20.00
Cat. Cost: Online only.
Credit Cards: All major debit/credit cards except American Express
Specialities: Hardy bulbs & dahlias.
Notes: Mail order for bulbs only. Delivers to shows.
OS Grid Ref: TL435053

ERod **THE RODINGS PLANTERY** ♿
Anchor Lane, Abbess Roding, Essex
CM5 0JW
Ⓣ (01279) 876421
Ⓜ 07790 020940
Ⓔ janeandandy@therodingsplantery.co.uk
Ⓦ www.therodingsplantery.co.uk
Contact: Jane & Andy Mogridge
Opening Times: 1000-1600 Wed & Sat. By appt. only. Occasional Open Days, please phone for details.
Min Mail Order UK: Nmc
Min Mail Order EU: £500.00 + p&p
Cat. Cost: 3 × 1st class.
Credit Cards: None
Specialities: Bamboos. Rare & unusual trees.
Notes: Also sells wholesale. Delivers to shows. Euro accepted. Wheelchair accessible.

ESgI **SEAGATE IRISES** ♿
A17 Long Sutton By-Pass, Long Sutton, Lincolnshire PE12 9RX
Ⓣ (01406) 365138
Ⓜ 07887 856389
Ⓔ sales@irises.co.uk
Ⓦ www.irises.co.uk
Contact: Julian Browse or Wendy Browse
Opening Times: 1000-1700 daily Apr-mid Jul. Please phone for appt. mid-Jul to Mar.
Cat. Cost: £3.50 or €8.00.
Credit Cards: Maestro, Visa, MasterCard
Specialities: Different types of *Iris*, bearded, beardless & species hybrids with about 1000 varieties in all, both historic & modern. Some only available in small quantities. Many container-grown available to callers.
Notes: Wheelchair accessible.
OS Grid Ref: TF437218

EShb **SHRUBLAND PARK NURSERIES**
Maltings Farm, Whatfield Road,
Elmsett, Ipswich, Suffolk
IP7 6LZ
Ⓣ (01473) 657012
Ⓜ 07890 527744
Ⓔ gill@shrublandparknurseries.co.uk
Ⓦ www.shrublandparknurseries.co.uk
Contact: Gill & Catherine Stitt
Opening Times: See website or contact nursery.
Min Mail Order UK: Nmc
Min Mail Order EU: Nmc
Cat. Cost: Online or free by post.
Credit Cards: All major credit/debit cards, Paypal
Specialities: Conservatory plants, succulents, hardy perennials, climbers, shrubs, ferns & grasses. Some more unusual plants may be in short supply.
Notes: Please check before visiting that nursery is open & that any plants you require are in stock. Delivers to shows.
OS Grid Ref: TM052466

ESMi **STRAIGHT MILE NURSERY GARDENS** ♿
Ongar Road, Pilgrims Hatch, Brentwood, Essex CM15 9SA
Ⓣ (01277) 374439
Ⓔ gdlsisley@aol.com
Ⓦ www.straightmile.net
Contact: David Sisley
Opening Times: 1000-1700, 7 days (but closed some Weds, phone first).
Min Mail Order UK: Nmc
Cat. Cost: Online only.
Credit Cards: All major debit/credit cards except American Express
Specialities: General nursery stock. Japanese maples, *Epimedium*. Some in small quantities only.

Notes: Delivers to shows. Wheelchair accessible.
OS Grid Ref: TQ571964

ESta **Stackyard Nurseries** ♿
Old Station Road, Mendlesham, Suffolk IP14 5RS
Ⓣ (01449) 768078
Ⓜ 07951 590057
Ⓔ karon@stackyard-nursery.com
Ⓦ www.stackyard-nursery.co.uk
Contact: Karon Sanders
Opening Times: 1000-1600 Thur-Sat.
Credit Cards: All major debit/credit cards except American Express
Specialities: Trees, shrubs and perennials.
Notes: Specialises in garden and interior design. Wheelchair accessible.

EStr **Strictly Daylilies**
2 Primes Corner, Histon, Cambridgeshire CB24 9AG
Ⓣ (01223) 236239
Ⓜ 07765 236880
Ⓔ info@strictlydaylilies.com
Ⓦ www.strictlydaylilies.com
Contact: Paula & Chris Dyason
Opening Times: Mail order only. Open gardens Fri-Sun in Jul, please phone for confirmation.
Min Mail Order UK: Nmc
Min Mail Order EU: Nmc
Cat. Cost: No charge.
Credit Cards: All major credit/debit cards
Specialities: *Hemerocallis*. Some stock available in small quantities only. Nat. Collection of *Hemerocallis* (post 2014 hybrid registrations).
Notes: Also sells wholesale. Exports beyond the EU. Delivers to shows. Euro accepted.

ESty **Style Roses** ♿
(office) Highworth, 56 Spalding Road, Holbeach, Spalding, Lincolnshire PE12 7HG
Ⓣ (01406) 424089
Ⓜ 07760 626750 or 07780 860415
Ⓕ (01406) 490006
Ⓔ mail@styleroses.co.uk
Ⓦ www.styleroses.co.uk
Contact: Margaret Styles
Opening Times: Vary, so phone for appt. before visiting.
Min Mail Order UK: Nmc
Min Mail Order EU: Nmc
Cat. Cost: Free in UK.
Credit Cards: MasterCard, Visa
Specialities: Standard & bush roses.
Notes: Nursery is at Cackle Hill Farm, Holbeach, Lincs, PE12 8AG. Bush roses available mail order to mainland UK all year round. Standard roses mail order as bare-root plants Nov-Mar, or in pots by collection from nursery/shows all year round. Export to EU Nov-Mar. Exports beyond EU subject to Plant Health Requirements (not USA). Also sells wholesale. Delivers to shows. Wheelchair accessible.

ESwi **Swines Meadow Farm Nursery** ♿ ◆
47 Towngate East, Market Deeping, Peterborough PE6 8LQ
Ⓣ 01778 343340
Ⓜ 07432 627766
Ⓔ ceveandsons@btconnect.com
Ⓦ www.swinesmeadowfarmnursery.co.uk
Contact: Colin Ward
Opening Times: 0900-1600 Mon-Sat, 1000-1600 Sun. Closed Jan, except by appt. only.
Min Mail Order UK: £10.00
Min Mail Order EU: £10.00
Credit Cards: All major debit/credit cards except American Express
Specialities: Hardy exotics, tree ferns, bamboos & phormiums. Wollemi pine stockist. Many specialities available in small quantities only.
Notes: Delivers to shows. Wheelchair accessible.
OS Grid Ref: TF150113

EThi **Thistlefield Plants and Design**
65 Westgate Street, Shouldham, Kings Lynn, Norfolk PE33 0BL
Ⓣ (01366) 347365
Ⓜ 07899 994071
Ⓕ (01366) 347365
Ⓔ paul@thistlefieldplants.co.uk
Ⓦ www.thistlefieldplants.co.uk
Contact: Paul Welford
Opening Times: Not open. Sells at plant fairs & shows only.
Min Mail Order UK: Nmc
Cat. Cost: Online only.
Credit Cards: None
Specialities: Perennials. *Tricyrtis* available in small quantities only.
Notes: Delivers to shows.

EUJe **Urban Jungle**
Ringland Lane, Old Costessey, Norwich, Norfolk NR8 5BG
Ⓣ (01603) 744997
Ⓕ (0709) 2366869
Ⓔ lizzy@urbanjungle.uk.com
Ⓦ www.urbanjungle.uk.com
Contact: Elizabeth Browne
Opening Times: 1000-1700 7 days incl

E

B/hols, 1st Feb-31st Oct. 1000-1600 Thu-Sun, Nov-Dec. Closed Jan.
Min Mail Order UK: Nmc
Min Mail Order EU: Nmc
Credit Cards: All major credit/debit cards
Specialities: Wide range of choice plants from exotic bedding to hardy evergreens.
Notes: Display gardens & living walls. Delivers to shows. Limited wheelchair access.
OS Grid Ref: TG153127

EVic **VICTORIAN VIOLAS**
85 Fulmar Road, Lincoln, Lincolnshire LN6 0RX
Ⓣ (01522) 686343
Ⓔ victorianviolasinfo@fsmail.net
Ⓦ www.victorianviolas.co.uk
Contact: Robert Chapman
Opening Times: Not open. Mail order only.
Min Mail Order UK: Nmc
Cat. Cost: Online only.
Credit Cards: None
Specialities: Hardy perennial violas (summer flowering). Named cultivars.
Notes: Also sells wholesale.

EWat **WATER GARDEN PLANTS**
Wayside Aquatics, Blackmore Road, Doddinghurst, Brentwood, Essex CM15 0HU
Ⓜ 07517 873206
Ⓔ sales@watergardenplants.co.uk
Ⓦ www.watergardenplants.co.uk
Contact: Anna Robinson
Opening Times: Mail order only. With prior notice, plants may be collected by appointment.
Min Mail Order UK: Nmc
Min Mail Order EU: Nmc
Cat. Cost: Online.
Credit Cards: All major credit/debit cards
Specialities: Range of water garden plants: waterlilies; floating plants; oxygenating plants; marginals; marsh plants. Some stock in small quantities.
Notes: Euro accepted.
OS Grid Ref: TQ585995

EWes **WEST ACRE GARDENS** ♿
Tumbleyhill Road, West Acre, King's Lynn, Norfolk PE32 1UJ
Ⓣ (01760) 755562
Ⓔ info@westacregardens.co.uk
Ⓦ www.westacregardens.co.uk
Contact: J J Tuite
Opening Times: 1000-1700 7 days 1st Feb-30th Nov. Other times by appt.
Cat. Cost: None issued.
Credit Cards: Visa, MasterCard, Delta, Switch
Specialities: Very wide selection of herbaceous & other garden plants incl. *Rhodohypoxis, Primula auricula* & *Galanthus.*
Notes: Delivers to shows. Wheelchair accessible.
OS Grid Ref: TF792182

EWhm **WALTHAM HERBS**
Willow Vale Nursery, North Kelsey Road, Caistor, Lincolnshire LN7 6SF
Ⓣ (01472) 859481
Ⓜ 07949 883091
Ⓕ (01472) 859481
Ⓔ angelasach2@aol.com
Ⓦ www.waltham-herbs.co.uk
Contact: Steve Penney
Opening Times: By appt. only. For Open Days, see website or contact nursery.
Min Mail Order UK: £3.00
Credit Cards: All major credit/debit cards
Specialities: Herbs, lavenders & perennials, also some shrubs. Peat-free & pesticide-free.
Notes: Delivers to shows.
OS Grid Ref: TA40135091

EWld **WOODLANDS**
Peppin Lane, Fotherby, Louth, Lincolnshire LN11 0UW
Ⓣ (01507) 603586
Ⓔ annbobarmstrong@btinternet.com
Ⓦ www.woodlandsplants.co.uk
Contact: Ann Armstrong
Opening Times: Flexible, but please phone or email to avoid disappointment.
Min Mail Order UK: Nmc
Min Mail Order EU: Nmc
Cat. Cost: None issued.
Credit Cards: None
Specialities: Small but interesting range of unusual plants, esp. woodland, *Codonopsis* & *Salvia*, all grown on the nursery in limited quantity. Nat. Collection of *Codonopsis.*
Notes: Mature garden, art gallery & refreshments. Euro accepted.
OS Grid Ref: TF322918

EWTr **WALNUT TREE GARDEN NURSERY**
Flymoor Lane, Rocklands, Attleborough, Norfolk NR17 1BP
Ⓣ (01953) 488163
Ⓔ info@wtgn.co.uk
Ⓦ www.wtgn.co.uk
Contact: Jim Paine & Clare Billington
Opening Times: 0900-1800 Tue-Sun Feb-Nov & B/hols.
Min Mail Order UK: Nmc
Cat. Cost: Online.
Credit Cards: All major credit/debit cards

Specialities: Flowering dogwood: *Cornus florida, C. kousa* & *C. nuttalli* cvs. Crab apple (*Malus*) cvs.
Notes: Delivers to shows.
OS Grid Ref: TL978973

Scotland

GAbr **Abriachan Nurseries** ♿
Loch Ness Side, Inverness, Inverness-shire IV3 8LA
Ⓣ (01463) 861232
Ⓔ info@lochnessgarden.com
Ⓦ www.lochnessgarden.com
Contact: Mr & Mrs D Davidson
Opening Times: 0900-1900 daily (dusk if earlier) Feb-Nov.
Min Mail Order UK: Nmc
Cat. Cost: 4 × 1st class.
Credit Cards: All major credit/debit cards
Specialities: Herbaceous perennials, old-fashioned *Primula, Helianthemum*, hardy geraniums, *Sempervivum* & *Primula auricula*.
Notes: Delivers to shows. Wheelchair access to nursery only.
OS Grid Ref: NH571347

GAgs **Angusplants**
3 Balfour Cottages, Menmuir, By Brechin, Angus DD9 7RN
Ⓣ (01356) 660280
Ⓜ 07972 026109
Ⓔ alison@angusplants.co.uk
Ⓦ www.angusplants.co.uk
Contact: Dr Alison S. Goldie & Mark A. Hutson
Opening Times: By appt. only. Please phone first.
Min Mail Order UK: Nmc
Min Mail Order EU: Nmc
Cat. Cost: 2 × 2nd large letter stamps.
Credit Cards: None
Specialities: *Primula auricula*, Nat. Collection of Alpine Auriculas.
Notes: Mail order available all year.
OS Grid Ref: NO528643

GBee **Beeches Cottage Nursery** ♿
High Boreland, Lesmahagow, South Lanarkshire ML11 9PY
Ⓣ (01555) 893369
Ⓜ 07930 343131
Ⓔ thebeeches.nursery@talktalk.net
Ⓦ www.beechescottage.co.uk
Contact: Margaret Harrison, Steven Harrison
Opening Times: 1000-1630 Wed-Sun, 1st Apr-30th Sep.
Cat. Cost: None issued.
Credit Cards: None
Specialities: Traditional & unusual hardy cottage garden perennials which can be seen growing in display gardens at 850ft. Some plants available in small quantities only.
Notes: Groups by arrangement. Wheelchair access to nursery only.
OS Grid Ref: NS837403

GBin **Binny Plants** ♿
Binny Estate, Ecclesmachan Road, Near Broxburn, West Lothian EH52 6NL
Ⓣ (01506) 858931
Ⓜ 07753 626117
Ⓔ contact@binnyplants.com
Ⓦ www.binnyplants.com
Contact: Billy Carruthers & David Wong
Opening Times: 1000-1700, 7 days. Closed over Xmas & New Year.
Min Mail Order UK: Nmc
Min Mail Order EU: Nmc
Cat. Cost: 4 × 1st class.
Credit Cards: Visa, MasterCard, EuroCard, Maestro
Specialities: Over 250 varieties of *Paeonia*, plus a good range of herbaceous perennials, grasses & ferns incl. *Astilbe, Bergenia, Geranium, Molinia, Persicaria* & *Iris*.
Notes: Also sells wholesale. Exports beyond the EU. Delivers to shows. Wheelchair accessible.
OS Grid Ref: NT050732

GCal **Cally Gardens** ♿
Gatehouse of Fleet, Castle Douglas, Kirkcudbrightshire DG7 2DJ
Ⓣ (01557) 815029 recorded information only.
Ⓔ info@callygardens.co.uk
Ⓦ www.callygardens.co.uk
Contact: Any member of staff
Opening Times: 1000-1730 Sat-Sun, 1400-1730 Tue-Fri, Easter Sat to last Sun in Sep.
Min Mail Order UK: £15.00 + p&p
Cat. Cost: 3 × 1st class.
Credit Cards: None
Specialities: Unusual perennials & grasses. Some rare shrubs, climbers & conservatory plants. 3500 varieties growing in an 2.7 acre walled garden built in the 1760s.
Notes: Also sells wholesale. Wheelchair accessible.
OS Grid Ref: NX604549

GCrg **Craigiehall Nursery**
Carnwath, Lanark, Lanarkshire ML11 8LH
Ⓣ (01555) 840027 (answering machine)
Ⓔ sales@craigiehallnursery.co.uk

Ⓦ www.craigiehallnursery.co.uk
Contact: Innes Hogg
Opening Times: Not open. Mail order only.
Min Mail Order UK: Nmc
Cat. Cost: Online only.
Credit Cards: All major credit/debit cards
Specialities: A very wide range of alpine and rock garden plants; over 500 different varieties on the nursery. Some are quite common, others much less so.
Notes: Online sales only, no telephone ordering.

GCro **CROFT 16 DAFFODILS**
16 Midtown of Inverasdale, Poolewe, Ross-shire IV22 2LW
Ⓣ (01445) 781717
Ⓔ sales@croft16daffodils.co.uk
Ⓦ www.croft16daffodils.co.uk
Contact: Duncan & Kate Donald
Opening Times: Not open. Mail order only.
Min Mail Order UK: Nmc
Min Mail Order EU: Nmc
Cat. Cost: Online only.
Credit Cards: Paypal
Specialities: Nat. Collection of Daffodils bred pre-1930. Some stocks only available in small quantities. A waiting list for *desiderata* is in operation.
Notes: Please order by mid-May for delivery in the same year. Orders unfulfilled in one season will take priority the following year. Customers outside the EU should contact nursery.
OS Grid Ref: NG822851

GDun **DUNSKEY GARDENS & MAZE** ♿
Portpatrick, Stranraer, Wigtownshire DG9 8TJ
Ⓣ (01776) 810905
Ⓜ 07899 092070
Ⓕ (01776) 810581
Ⓔ gabygardeners@btinternet.com
Ⓦ www.dunskey.com
Contact: Gabrielle Reynolds
Opening Times: 1000-1600 w/ends only Feb, 1000-1700 daily Easter-Oct. See website for details.
Credit Cards: All major credit/debit cards
Specialities: Broad range, propagated from the gardens, incl. bulbs, tender perennials, herbaceous, trees and shrubs. Available in small quantities only. Nat. Collections of *Clianthus*, *Nicotiana* & *Sutherlandia*.
Notes: Dunskey Estate walled garden & maze open to the public. Tea room. Free use of electric buggy. Wheelchair accessible.
OS Grid Ref: NX004560

GEdr **EDROM NURSERIES**
Coldingham, Eyemouth, Berwickshire TD14 5TZ
Ⓣ (01890) 771386
Ⓕ (01890) 771387
Ⓔ mail@edrom-nurseries.co.uk
Ⓦ www.edrom-nurseries.co.uk
Contact: Mr Terry Hunt
Opening Times: 0900-1700 Thu, Fri, Sat & Mon (closed Tue & Wed), 1000-1600 Sun.
Min Mail Order UK: Nmc
Min Mail Order EU: Nmc
Cat. Cost: Free.
Credit Cards: All major credit/debit cards
Specialities: *Cypripedium*, *Epimedium*, *Gentiana*, *Primula*, *Meconopsis*, *Rhodohypoxis*, *Trillium* & Japanese *Hepatica*.
Notes: Delivers to shows.
OS Grid Ref: NT873663

GFgr **FIRGROVE PLANTS**
21 South Main Street, Wigtown, Newton Stewart, Dumfries and Galloway DG8 9EH
Ⓣ (01988) 402054
Ⓜ 07749 314394
Ⓔ jenny.mackinnon@virgin.net
Contact: Jenny MacKinnon
Opening Times: Not open. Mail order only.
Min Mail Order UK: £10.50
Cat. Cost: Sae.
Credit Cards: None
Specialities: Wide range of houseleeks in small quantities.
Notes: Houseleeks by mail order Apr-mid Oct.

GGGa **GLENDOICK GARDENS LTD** ♿
Glendoick, Perth, Perthshire PH2 7NS
Ⓣ (01738) 860205
Ⓔ orders@glendoick.com
Ⓦ www.glendoick.com
Contact: Kenneth Cox
Opening Times: Nursery not open to the public. Garden centre open 0900-1730 (summer), 0900-1700 (winter) 7 days. Gardens open Apr & May, details on website or contact nursery for details.
Min Mail Order UK: £50.00
Min Mail Order EU: £100.00
Cat. Cost: £2.00.
Credit Cards: All major debit/credit cards except American Express
Specialities: Rhododendrons, azaleas and ericaceous, *Primula* & *Meconopsis*. Plants from wild seed. Many catalogue plants available at garden centre. 3 Nat. Collections.
Notes: Wheelchair access to garden centre.

GJos **Jo's Garden Enterprise** ♿
Easter Balmungle Farm, Eathie Road, by Rosemarkie, Ross-shire IV10 8SL
Ⓣ (01381) 621006
Ⓔ jos_garden_enterprise@hotmail.co.uk
Contact: Joanna Chance
Opening Times: 1000 to dusk, 7 days.
Cat. Cost: None.
Credit Cards: None
Specialities: Alpines & herbaceous perennials. Selection of native wild flowers.
Notes: Wheelchair accessible.
OS Grid Ref: NH600742

GKev **Kevock Garden Plants**
Kevock Road, Lasswade, Midlothian EH18 1HX
Ⓣ 0131 454 0660
Ⓕ 0131 454 0660
Ⓔ sales@kevockgarden.co.uk
Ⓦ www.kevockgarden.co.uk
Contact: Elea Strang
Opening Times: Not open to the public. Purchase plants by mail order or from plant stalls.
Min Mail Order UK: £30.00
Min Mail Order EU: £30.00
Cat. Cost: 3 × 1st class.
Specialities: Chinese & Himalayan plants. *Androsace*, *Daphne*, *Paeonia*, *Primula*, *Meconopsis*, *Iris*, woodland plants, alpines, rock plants, marginal & bog plants, bulbs, Sino-himalayan trees & shrubs.
Notes: Also sells wholesale. Delivers to shows.

GKin **Kinlochlaich Garden Plant Centre**
Appin, Argyll PA38 4BB
Ⓜ 07881 525754
Ⓔ fiona@kinlochlaich.plus.com
Ⓦ www.kinlochlaichgardencentre.co.uk
Contact: Fiona Hutchison
Opening Times: 1000-1700 Mar-mid Oct, 1000-1500 or by appt., mid-Oct-Feb. Happy to open if contacted by phone first.
Cat. Cost: None issued
Credit Cards: All major credit/debit cards
Specialities: Hardy shrubs, trees, azaleas, perennials. Also Gulf Stream plants such as *Tropaeolum*, *Embothrium*, *Eucryphia*, *Drymis* & more. Good selection of hardy seaside plants.
Notes: Does not offer mail order but will post where possible. Limited wheelchair access (gravel paths), wheelchair accessible toilet.

GLet **Letham Plants**
11a Letham Mains Holdings, Haddington, East Lothian EH41 4NW
Ⓣ (01620) 822350
Ⓜ 07842 211712
Ⓔ lethamplants@hotmail.co.uk
Ⓦ www.letham-plants.co.uk
Contact: Caroline Samuel
Opening Times: By appt. only.
Min Mail Order UK: Nmc
Min Mail Order EU: Nmc
Cat. Cost: Online only.
Credit Cards: All major credit/debit cards
Specialities: *Astrantia*, *Dicentra*.
Notes: Also sells wholesale. Delivers to shows. Euro accepted.
OS Grid Ref: NT487730

GLog **Logie Steading Plants** ♿
Forres, Moray
IV36 2QN
Ⓣ (01309) 611222 or 611278
Ⓕ (01309) 611300
Ⓔ panny@logie.co.uk
Ⓦ www.logie.co.uk
Contact: Mrs Panny Laing
Opening Times: 1030-1700 hours, 7 days, Mar-Xmas.
Credit Cards: All major credit/debit cards
Specialities: Unusual hardy plants, grown in Scotland for Scottish gardens. Large range of hardy geraniums, bold herbaceous plants, grasses & marginal plants.
Notes: Logie House Garden open every day. Café, farm shop, art gallery, second-hand books, antiques, whisky & wine, river walk, heritage centre. Wheelchair accessible (except river walk).
OS Grid Ref: NJ006504

GMaP **Macplants** ♿
Berrybank Nursery, 5 Boggs Holdings, Pencaitland, East Lothian
EH34 5BA
Ⓣ (01875) 341179
Ⓕ (01875) 340842
Ⓔ sales@macplants.co.uk
Ⓦ www.macplants.co.uk
Contact: Gavin McNaughton
Opening Times: 1030-1700 7 days, Mar-end Sep. 1030-1600 Mon-Fri, Oct. Closed Nov-end Feb except by appt.
Min Mail Order UK: Nmc
Cat. Cost: 4 × 2nd class.
Credit Cards: MasterCard, Switch, Visa
Specialities: Herbaceous perennials, alpines, hardy ferns, violas & grasses. *Meconopsis*. Nat. Collection of *Sanguisorba*.
Notes: Also sells wholesale. Delivers to shows. Wheelchair accessible.
OS Grid Ref: NT447703

GPer **Perthshire Heathers**
Starr Farm, Cupar, Fife KY15 4NP
Ⓜ 07734 175937
Ⓔ irene@perthshireheathers.com
Contact: Irene Lang
Min Mail Order UK: Nmc
Specialities: Heathers.
Notes: Mail order for small orders only.

GPoy **Poyntzfield Herb Nursery** ♿
Nr Balblair, Black Isle, Dingwall, Ross-shire IV7 8LX
Ⓣ (01381) 610352. Phone between 1200-1300 & 1800-1900 Mon-Sat only.
Ⓔ info@poyntzfieldherbs.co.uk
Ⓦ www.poyntzfieldherbs.co.uk
Contact: Duncan Ross
Opening Times: 1300-1700 Mon-Sat 1st Mar-30th Sep, 1300-1700 Sun May-Aug.
Min Mail Order UK: £10.00 + p&p
Min Mail Order EU: £20.00 + p&p
Cat. Cost: 4 × 1st class.
Credit Cards: All major credit/debit cards
Specialities: Over 400 popular, unusual & rare herbs esp. medicinal. Also seeds.
Notes: Mail order operates in the spring & autumn. Exports beyond the EU. Wheelchair accessible.
OS Grid Ref: NH711642

GPSL **Plants, Shoots and Leaves**
Dovecot Bungalow, Haddington, East Lothian EH41 4HA
Ⓣ (01620) 823536
Ⓜ 07885 444241
Ⓔ karen.leys@btinternet.com
Ⓦ www.plantsshootsandleaves.co.uk
Contact: Karen Payne
Opening Times: 1000-1700 1st Apr-1st Oct. Closed Mon. Please phone first.
Min Mail Order UK: £3.50
Min Mail Order EU: £6.60
Cat. Cost: Online only.
Credit Cards: All major credit/debit cards
Specialities: *Epimedium*. Hardy geraniums. Perennials and some shrubs. Some available in small quantities only.
Notes: Delivers to shows. Euro accepted. Mostly wheelchair accessible.
OS Grid Ref: NT500730

GQue **Quercus Garden Plants Ltd**
Whitmuir Farm, Lamancha, West Linton, Scottish Borders EH46 7BB
Ⓣ (01968) 660708
Ⓔ rona@quercusgardenplants.co.uk
Ⓦ www.quercusgardenplants.co.uk
Contact: Rona Peddie
Opening Times: 1000-1700 Wed-Sun.
Cat. Cost: Online only.
Credit Cards: All major credit/debit cards
Specialities: Tough plants for Scottish gardens. Wide range of plants, including old favourites and many unusual varieties of herbaceous perennials, grasses, trees, shrubs & plants for shade.
Notes: Plants are grown at 850ft above sea level, so are tough and well acclimatised to Scottish growing conditions. The majority of plants are propagated on site and grown on for a least a season. Display beds to show customers what can be grown in these challenging conditions.
OS Grid Ref: NT192512

GRid **J & I Cruickshanks** ♿
Ridgeview Nursery, Crossroad by Longridge, Fauldhouse, West Lothian EH47 9AB
Ⓣ (01501) 771144
Ⓔ enquiries@ridgeviewnursery.co.uk
Ⓦ www.ridgeviewnursery.co.uk
Contact: Alice Kyle & Andrew Cruickshanks
Opening Times: 0900-1600, 7 days.
Min Mail Order UK: Nmc
Credit Cards: None
Specialities: Rooted *Dahlia* cuttings.
Notes: Wheelchair accessible.

GWyn **Wyndford Farm Plants Ltd**
Wyndford Farm, Ecclesmachan, West Lothian EH52 6NW
Ⓜ 07871 496732
Ⓔ info@wyndfordfarmplants.com
Ⓦ www.wyndfordfarmplants.com
Contact: Adam Fleming
Opening Times: 1000-1700, 7 days.
Min Mail Order UK: Nmc
Cat. Cost: Online only.
Credit Cards: All major debit/credit cards except American Express
Specialities: Large range of perennials & shrubs, incl. large collection of *Primula sieboldii* and *Viola*.
Notes: Also sells wholesale. Delivers to shows.
OS Grid Ref: NT 059731

N. Ireland & Republic

IArd **Ardcarne Garden Centre** ♿
Ardcarne, Boyle, Co. Roscommon F52 RY61 Rep. of Ireland
Ⓣ +353 7196 67091
Ⓕ +353 7196 67341
Ⓔ info@ardcarne.ie
Ⓦ www.ardcarne.ie

Contact: James Wickham, Mary Frances Dwyer, Kirsty Ainge
Opening Times: 0900-1800 Mon-Sat, 1300-1800 Sun & B/hols.
Credit Cards: Access, Visa, American Express
Specialities: Native & unusual trees, choice perennials, roses, plants for coastal areas, fruit trees, incl. heritage Irish apple trees, vegetable plants, specimen plants & semi-mature trees. Wide general range.
Notes: Café. Groups & tours welcome. Ample free parking. Garden design & landscape service available. Euro accepted. Wheelchair accessible.

IBal **Bali-Hai Mail Order Nursery**
42 Largy Road, Carnlough, Ballymena, Co. Antrim, N. Ireland BT44 0EZ
Ⓣ 028 2888 5289
Ⓜ 07708 257164
Ⓕ 028 2888 5289
Ⓔ balihainursery@btinternet.com
Ⓦ www.mailorderplants4me.com
Contact: Mrs M E Scroggy
Opening Times: Mon-Sat by appt. only.
Min Mail Order UK: Nmc
Min Mail Order EU: Nmc
Cat. Cost: Online only.
Credit Cards: All major credit/debit cards
Specialities: Nat. Collection of *Hosta*, part planted in 1.5 acres, open to the public by appt. *Agapanthus*, *Crocosmia*, *Rhodohypoxis*, tree ferns & other perennials. Hostas grown to order.
Notes: Also sells wholesale. Export beyond EU restricted to bare-root perennials, no grasses. Euro accepted.
OS Grid Ref: D287184

IBlr **Ballyrogan Nurseries** ♿
The Grange, Ballyrogan, Newtownards, Co. Down, N. Ireland BT23 4SD
Ⓣ 028 9181 0451 (evenings)
Ⓔ gary.dunlop@btinternet.com
Contact: Gary Dunlop
Opening Times: Only open by appt.
Min Mail Order UK: £10.00 + p&p
Min Mail Order EU: £20.00 + p&p
Cat. Cost: 2 × 2nd class.
Credit Cards: None
Specialities: Choice herbaceous. *Agapanthus*, *Crocosmia*, *Rodgersia*, *Dierama*, *Erythronium*, *Roscoea* & *Watsonia*.
Notes: Also sells wholesale. Euro accepted. Wheelchair accessible.

IDee **Deelish Garden Centre**
Deelish, Skibbereen, Co. Cork P81 FD34 Rep. of Ireland
Ⓣ +353 28 21374
Ⓕ +353 28 21374
Ⓔ deel@eircom.net
Ⓦ www.deelish.ie
Contact: Bill & Rain Chase
Opening Times: 1000-1800 Mon-Sat, 1400-1800 Sun.
Min Mail Order UK: Nmc
Min Mail Order EU: Nmc
Credit Cards: Visa, MasterCard, Access, Paypal
Specialities: Unusual plants for the mild coastal climate of Ireland. Conservatory plants. Sole Irish agents for Chase Organic Seeds.
Notes: No mail order outside Ireland & UK. Euro accepted.

IDic **Dickson Nurseries**
Milecross Road, Newtownards, Co. Down, N. Ireland BT23 4SS
Ⓣ 028 9181 2206
Ⓔ mail@dickson-roses.co.uk
Ⓦ www.dickson-roses.co.uk
Contact: Colin Dickson
Opening Times: 0800-1230 & 1300-1515 Mon-Thu. 0800-1230 Fri.
Min Mail Order UK: Nmc
Min Mail Order EU: £25.00 + p&p
Cat. Cost: Free
Credit Cards: None
Specialities: Roses esp. modern Dickson varieties. Limited selection, check website or contact nursery. Most varieties available in small quantities only.
Notes: Also sells wholesale. Only glasshouses accessible for wheelchairs.

IEsk **Esker Farm Daffodils (formerly Ringhaddy Daffodils)**
38 Esker Road, Dromore, Omagh, Co. Tyrone, N. Ireland BT78 3LE
Ⓣ (028) 8289 8398
Ⓜ 07980 634423
Ⓔ eskerfarmdaffs@gmail.com
Ⓦ www.eskerfarmdaffodils.com
Contact: Dave Hardy
Opening Times: Mail order only. Not open.
Min Mail Order UK: £20.00 + p&p
Min Mail Order EU: £50.00 + p&p
Cat. Cost: £3.00 or free online.
Credit Cards: Paypal
Specialities: Daffodil bulbs, some varieties only available in small numbers.
Notes: Exports beyond EU. Euro accepted.

IFro **Frogswell Nursery**
Cloonconlan, Straide, Foxford, Co. Mayo, Rep. of Ireland
Ⓜ +353 8621 06166

Ⓔ frogswell@gmail.com
Ⓦ www.frogswellhardyplants.com
Contact: Celia Graebner
Opening Times: Feb-Oct by appt. Please phone first. Also charity Open Days & occasional on-site workshops; see website or contact nursery for details.
Credit Cards: None
Specialities: A small garden-based nursery specialising in shade & spring woodland plant incl. hybrid hellebores and hardy geraniums; unusual perennials for the Irish climate and bee and wild pollinator forage plants. All plants raised on site, some in very limited quantities, using organic fertilisers & peat-free media where possible.
Notes: Group visits & talks by arrangement. See website for location map. Euro accepted.
OS Grid Ref: M2497

IKil **Kilmurry Nursery** ♿
Gorey, Co. Wexford, Rep. of Ireland
Ⓣ +353 53 948 0223
Ⓜ +353 8681 13171
Ⓕ +353 53 948 0223
Ⓔ kilmurrynursery@hotmail.com
Ⓦ www.kilmurrynursery.com
Contact: Paul & Orla Woods
Opening Times: 0900-1700 Mon-Fri, all year round. 0900-1700 Sat Mar-Sept.
Min Mail Order UK: Nmc
Min Mail Order EU: Nmc
Cat. Cost: Online only.
Credit Cards: All major credit/debit cards
Specialities: Herbaceous perennials, grasses and ferns.
Notes: Tea rooms open during summer. Also sells wholesale. Delivers to shows. Euro accepted. Wheelchair accessible.

ILea **Leamore Nursery**
Cronroe, Ashford, Co. Wicklow A67 Y681
Rep. of Ireland
Ⓣ +353 87 227 8850
Ⓕ +353 404 70126
Ⓔ info@leamorenursery.com
Ⓦ www.leamorenursery.com
Contact: Phil Havercroft
Opening Times: Not open to the public.
Min Mail Order UK: €25
Min Mail Order EU: €25
Cat. Cost: Online only.
Credit Cards: All major credit/debit cards
Specialities: *Paeonia* & other perennials. Most items in large quantities. Itoh peonies & some more unusual items only available in small quantities.
Notes: Bare-root peonies supplied in autumn, available to order from July (on website). Founding members of the Irish Specialist Nursery Association (ISNA). Also sells wholesale. Delivers to shows. Sterling & Euro accepted.
OS Grid Ref: SG 23594 52062

IMou **Mount Venus Nursery** ♿
The Walled Garden, Mutton Lane, Dublin 16, Rep. of Ireland
Ⓣ +353 1 493 3813
Ⓜ +353 08632 18789
Ⓔ mountvenusnursery@gmail.com
Ⓦ www.mountvenusnursery.com
Contact: Oliver & Liat Schurmann
Opening Times: 1000-1800 Wed-Sat, Feb-Nov. 1100-1700 Sun, Apr-Oct.
Min Mail Order UK: €20
Min Mail Order EU: €35
Cat. Cost: Online only.
Credit Cards: All major credit/debit cards
Specialities: Specialist perennials. Grasses & bamboos. Unusual woodland plants, trees & shrubs.
Notes: Also sells wholesale. Delivers to shows. Euro accepted. Wheelchair accessible.

IPot **The Potting Shed** ♿
Bolinaspick, Camolin, Enniscorthy, Co. Wexford Y21 TD93
Rep. of Ireland
Ⓣ +353 5393 83629
Ⓔ susan@camolinpottingshed.com
Ⓦ www.camolinpottingshed.com
Contact: Susan Carrick
Opening Times: 1100-1700, Wed-Sat (incl.), Mar-Sep 2016. Other times by appt.
Min Mail Order UK: Nmc
Min Mail Order EU: Nmc
Cat. Cost: 3 × 1st class.
Credit Cards: MasterCard, Visa
Specialities: Grow a wide range of unusual, hard to find & new introductions of herbaceous perennials, ornamental grasses and *Clematis*, many of which can be seen growing to their full potential in our display beds.
Notes: Member of the Irish Specialist Nursery Assoc. (ISNA). Orders outside Ireland can only be delivered by courier, charges at cost. Delivers to shows. Euro accepted. Wheelchair accessible.

IRos **Ros Ban Wildlife Garden** ♿
Common, Raphoe, Co. Donegal, F93 HH0X
Rep. of Ireland
Ⓣ +353 74 91 45336
Ⓜ +353 8608 05214
Ⓔ Rosbangarden@gmail.com
Contact: Ann Kavanagh

Opening Times: Garden open, morning to evening, Easter to Sep.
Credit Cards: None
Notes: Plants available in season from the garden. Please check plant availability with nursery before travelling. Euro accepted. Wheelchair accessible.

ISha **SHADY PLANTS** ♿
Coolbooa, Clashmore, Youghal, Co. Cork P36 EY19 Rep. of Ireland
Ⓣ +353 24 86998
Ⓜ +353 8605 42171
Ⓔ mike@shadyplants.ie
Ⓦ www.shadyplants.net
Contact: Mike Keep
Opening Times: 1300-1700, Tue-Sat, by appt. only.
Min Mail Order UK: Nmc
Min Mail Order EU: Nmc
Cat. Cost: Online only.
Credit Cards: MasterCard, Paypal, Visa
Specialities: Specialist fern nursery based near the south coast of Ireland.
Notes: Delivers to shows. Euro accepted. Wheelchair accessible.
OS Grid Ref: 613,585

ITim **TIMPANY NURSERIES & GARDENS** ♿
77 Magheratimpany Road, Ballynahinch, Co. Down, N. Ireland BT24 8PA
Ⓣ 028 9756 2812
Ⓜ 07711 428477
Ⓔ s.tindall@btconnect.com
Ⓦ www.timpanynurseries.com
Contact: Susan Tindall
Opening Times: 1000-1730 Tue-Sat, Sun by appt.
Min Mail Order UK: £40.00 + p&p
Min Mail Order EU: £40.00 + p&p
Cat. Cost: £3.50
Credit Cards: All major debit/credit cards except American Express
Specialities: *Androsace*, *Cassiope*, *Celmisia*, *Cyclamen*, *Dianthus*, *Galanthus*, *Meconopsis*, *Hosta*, *Primula*, *Primula auricula*, *Rhodohypoxis* & *Saxifraga*.
Notes: Delivers to shows. Wheelchair accessible.

LONDON AREA

LAma **JACQUES AMAND INTERNATIONAL LTD** ♿
The Nurseries, 145 Clamp Hill, Stanmore, Middlesex HA7 3JS
Ⓣ 020 8420 7110
Ⓕ 020 8954 6784
Ⓔ bulbs@jacquesamand.co.uk
Ⓦ www.jacquesamandintl.com
Contact: Stuart Chapman
Opening Times: 0900-1700 Mon-Fri, 1000-1600 Sat.
Min Mail Order UK: Nmc
Min Mail Order EU: Nmc
Cat. Cost: 1 × 1st class.
Credit Cards: All major credit/debit cards
Specialities: Rare and unusual species bulbs esp. *Arisaema*, *Trillium*, *Fritillaria*, tulips.
Notes: Also sells wholesale. Exports beyond EU. Delivers to shows. Euro accepted. Wheelchair accessible.
OS Grid Ref: TQ154919

LAyl **AYLETT NURSERIES LTD** ♿ ◆
North Orbital Road, St Albans, Hertfordshire AL2 1DH
Ⓣ (01727) 822255
Ⓕ (01727) 823024
Ⓔ info@aylettnurseries.co.uk
Ⓦ www.aylettnurseries.co.uk
Contact: Julie Aylett
Opening Times: 0830-1730 Mon-Fri, 0830-1700 Sat, 1030-1630 Sun.
Cat. Cost: Free.
Credit Cards: All major credit/debit cards
Specialities: *Dahlia*. 2-acre trial ground and garden adjacent to garden centre.
Notes: Wheelchair accessible.
OS Grid Ref: TL169049

LBee **BEECHCROFT NURSERY** ♿
127 Reigate Road, Ewell, Surrey KT17 3DE
Ⓣ 020 8393 4265
Ⓕ 020 8393 4265
Ⓔ enquiries@beechcroft-nursery.co.uk
Ⓦ www.beechcroft-nursery.co.uk
Contact: C Kimber
Opening Times: 1000-1600 Mon-Sat, 1000-1400 Sun & B/hols. Closed Xmas-New Year week.
Cat. Cost: None issued.
Credit Cards: All major credit/debit cards
Specialities: Conifers.
Notes: Wheelchair accessible.

LBuc **BUCKINGHAM NURSERIES** ♿ ◆
14 Tingewick Road, Buckingham, Buckinghamshire MK18 4AE
Ⓣ (01280) 822133
Ⓕ (01280) 815491
Ⓔ enquiries@buckingham-nurseries.co.uk
Ⓦ www.buckingham-nurseries.co.uk
Contact: R J & P L Brown
Opening Times: 0830-1730 (1800 in summer) Mon-Sat, 1000-1600 Sun.

Min Mail Order UK: Nmc
Min Mail Order EU: Nmc
Cat. Cost: Free.
Credit Cards: Visa, MasterCard, Maestro
Specialities: Bare-rooted and container grown hedging. Fruit trees, soft fruit, trees, shrubs, herbaceous perennials, alpines, grasses & ferns.
Notes: Garden centre with restaurant. Wheelchair accessible.
OS Grid Ref: SP675333

L

LCla **Clay Lane Nursery**
3 Clay Lane, South Nutfield, Nr Redhill, Surrey RH1 4EG
Ⓣ (01737) 823307
Ⓔ claylane.nursery@btinternet.com
Ⓦ www.claylane-fuchsias.co.uk
Contact: K W Belton
Opening Times: Not open to general visitors. Pre-ordered plants can be collected by arrangement.
Min Mail Order UK: £12.00
Cat. Cost: 3 × 2nd class.
Credit Cards: None
Specialities: *Fuchsia*. Many varieties in small quantities only.
Notes: Mail order by telephone prior arangement.

LCro **Crocus.co.uk**
Nursery Court, London Road, Windlesham, Surrey GU20 6LQ
Ⓣ (01344) 578000
Ⓕ (01344) 629600
Ⓔ customerservices@crocus.co.uk
Ⓦ www.crocus.co.uk
Contact: Customer Care Team
Opening Times: Mail order only. Order lines open 24hrs, 7 days. Nursery has several Open Days a year, see website or phone for details.
Min Mail Order UK: Nmc + delivery charges.
Cat. Cost: Free.
Credit Cards: All major debit/credit cards except American Express
Specialities: Large general nursery. Perennials, shrubs, climbers, roses, bulbs, ferns & grasses.
Notes: Also sells wholesale.

LEdu **Edulis** ♿
(office) 1 Flowers Piece, Ashampstead, Reading, Berkshire RG8 8SG
Ⓣ (01635) 578113
Ⓜ 07802 812781
Ⓔ edulisnursery@gmail.com
Ⓦ www.edulis.co.uk
Contact: Paul Barney
Opening Times: 1000-1600 Tues & Wed, & by appt. Apr-Oct. Nov-Mar by appt. only. See website or contact nursery for Open Days.
Min Mail Order UK: £20.00 + p&p
Min Mail Order EU: £30.00 + p&p
Cat. Cost: Online only.
Credit Cards: All major debit/credit cards except American Express
Specialities: Unusual edibles, architectural plants, permaculture plants & many of our own collections.
Notes: Nursery is at The Walled Garden, Tidmarsh Lane, Pangbourne, RG8 8HT. Also sells wholesale. Delivers to shows. Euro accepted. Wheelchair accessible.
OS Grid Ref: SU615747

LHom **Home Farm Plants**
Home Farm, Shantock Lane, Bovingdon, Hertfordshire HP3 0NG
Ⓜ 07773 798068
Ⓔ enquiries@homefarmplants.com
Ⓦ www.homefarmplants.co.uk
Contact: Graham Austin
Opening Times: 0900-1730 Fri & Sat, 1000-1600 Sun, viewing by appt. only Mon-Thu, 1st Apr-end Oct (subject to weather conditions).
Cat. Cost: 1st class sae for list.
Credit Cards: None
Specialities: *Delphinium elatum* (over 60 varieties). Hardy perennials & seasonal cut flowers. Show area of 200+ delphiniums (contact nursery for flowering times). Some varieties only available in small quantities.
Notes: If travelling, please contact nursery to confirm plant availability. Delivers to shows. Limited wheelchair access.

LLHF **Little Heath Farm (UK)** ♿
Little Heath Lane, Potten End, Berkhamsted, Hertfordshire HP4 2RY
Ⓣ (01442) 864951
Ⓜ 07835 200789
Ⓔ lhfnursery@gmail.com
Ⓦ www.littleheathfarmnursery.co.uk
Contact: John Spokes
Opening Times: 1000-1700 or dusk if earlier, 7 days.
Cat. Cost: Online only.
Credit Cards: Visa, MasterCard
Specialities: Large range of alpines, herbaceous, shrubs, many available in small quantities only.
Notes: Delivers to shows. Wheelchair accessible.
OS Grid Ref: TL019085

LLWG **Lilies Water Gardens** ♿
Broad Lane, Newdigate, Surrey RH5 5AT
Ⓣ (01306) 631064
Ⓜ 07801 166244
Ⓔ mail@plilieswatergardens.co.uk
Ⓦ www.lilieswatergardens.co.uk
Contact: Simon Harman
Opening Times: 0900-1700 Wed-Sat, Mar-Aug. By appt. only Sep-Feb.
Min Mail Order UK: Nmc
Min Mail Order EU: Nmc
Cat. Cost: Online only.
Credit Cards: All major credit/debit cards
Specialities: Waterlilies, moist perennials, bog-garden plants, primulas, marginal plants, ferns, oxygenating plants. Pond plants, incl. submerged & free-floating, aquatic, water iris, water-garden, floating, stream & deep-water plants. Alpine, rock & creeping plants. Rushes & grasses.
Notes: Flat rate £6.50 UK delivery charge. Wheelchair accessible.

LMaj **Majestic Trees** ♿
Chequers Meadow, Chequers Hill (Junc 9, M1), Flamstead, St Albans, Hertfordshire AL3 8ET
Ⓣ (01582) 843881
Ⓕ (01582) 843882
Ⓔ info@majestictrees.co.uk
Ⓦ www.majestictrees.co.uk
Contact: Andy Miles
Opening Times: 0830-1700 Mon-Fri. 1000-1600 Sat, Nov-Feb, 1000-1700 Sat, Mar-Oct. Closed Sun, B/hols, Xmas/New Year.
Credit Cards: MasterCard, Visa, Switch, Maestro
Specialities: Semi-mature & mature containerised trees grown in airpots from 50ltr to 5000 ltr.
Notes: Also sells wholesale. Delivers to shows. Euro accepted. Disabled access by golf buggy can be arranged by appt. Wheelchair access to building.
OS Grid Ref: TL08140815

LMil **Millais Nurseries** ♿
Crosswater Farm, Crosswater Lane, Churt, Farnham, Surrey GU10 2JN
Ⓣ (01252) 792698
Ⓔ sales@rhododendrons.co.uk
Ⓦ www.rhododendrons.co.uk
Contact: David Millais
Opening Times: 1000-1700 Mon-Fri all year. Daily in spring. Please phone or see website for weekend opening in spring.
Min Mail Order UK: Nmc
Min Mail Order EU: Nmc
Cat. Cost: Free list on request. Full catalogue online.
Credit Cards: All major credit/debit cards
Specialities: Rhododendrons, azaleas, magnolias, camellias & acers. Garden open in spring.
Notes: Mail order all year. Also sells wholesale. Wheelchair accessible.
OS Grid Ref: SU856397

LOPS **RHS Plant Shop: RHSplants.co.uk** ◆
Nursery Court, London Road, Windlesham, Surrey GU20 6LQ
Ⓣ (01344) 578822
Ⓕ (01344) 629600
Ⓔ customerservices@rhsplants.co.uk
Ⓦ www.rhsplants.co.uk
Contact: Customer Care Team
Opening Times: Not open. Online mail order only.
Min Mail Order UK: Nmc
Credit Cards: All major debit/credit cards except American Express

LPai **Painshill Park Trust** ♿
Portsmouth Road, Cobham, Surrey KT11 1JE
Ⓣ 01932 868113
Ⓔ AndyMills@painshill.co.uk
Ⓦ www.painshill.co.uk
Contact: Andy Mills
Opening Times: 7 days, 1000-1800 Mar to Oct, 1000-1600 Nov to Feb. Closed Xmas Day & Boxing Day.
Cat. Cost: None issued.
Credit Cards: All major credit/debit cards
Specialities: Small selection of surplus stock of annuals and perennials grown on site, available in very small quantities only. All funds raised contribute to the continuing restoration & conservation of Charles Hamilton's landscape garden at Painshill.
Notes: Wheelchair accessible.

LPla **The Plant Specialist**
7 Whitefield Lane, Great Missenden, Buckinghamshire HP16 0BH
Ⓣ (01494) 866650
Ⓕ (01494) 866650
Ⓔ enquire@theplantspecialist.co.uk
Ⓦ www.theplantspecialist.co.uk
Contact: Sean Walter
Opening Times: 1000-1700 Wed-Sat, 1000-1600 Sun, Apr-Oct. 1000-1600 B/hol Mons.
Cat. Cost: None issued.
Credit Cards: All major credit/debit cards

Specialities: Herbaceous perennials, grasses, half-hardy perennials, bulbs.
Notes: Delivers to shows. Limited wheelchair access.

LPot **POTASH PLANTS** ♿
Potash Nursery, Drayton Parslow, Milton Keynes, Buckinghamshire MK17 0JE
Ⓣ (01296) 720578
Ⓜ 07778 398808
Ⓕ (01296) 720578
Ⓔ info@potashplants.co.uk
Ⓦ www.potashplants.co.uk
Contact: Gill Gallon
Opening Times: 0900-1730 Mon-Sat. 1030-1630 Sun.
Cat. Cost: Online.
Credit Cards: All major debit/credit cards except American Express
Specialities: Wide range of traditional and unusual hardy perennials, grasses, trees & shrubs. Some available in small quantities only.
Notes: Nursery on B4032 mid-way between Aylesbury and Milton Keynes. Also sells wholesale. Delivers to shows. Wheelchair accessible.
OS Grid Ref: SP834279

LPra **PRACTICALITY BROWN LTD**
Swan Road, Iver, Buckinghamshire SL0 9LA
Ⓣ (01753) 652022
Ⓕ (01753) 653007
Ⓔ hedge@pracbrown.co.uk
Ⓦ www.pracbrown.co.uk
Contact: Julie Rockell
Opening Times: 0800-1700 Mon-Fri. Closed B/hols. Open for viewing by appt. only.
Credit Cards: All major credit/debit cards
Specialities: Established over 30 years. Large shrubs, topiary and semi-mature trees incl. yew, holly, box, beech & hornbeam.
Notes: Also sells wholesale. Delivers to shows.
OS Grid Ref: TQ038815

LRHS **WISLEY PLANT CENTRE (RHS)** ♿ ◆
RHS Garden, Wisley, Woking, Surrey GU23 6QB
Ⓣ (01483) 211113
Ⓕ (01483) 212372
Ⓔ wisleyplantcentre@rhs.org.uk
Ⓦ www.rhs.org.uk/wisleyplantcentre
Contact: Any member of staff
Opening Times: 0900-1700 Mon-Sat, Oct-Feb. 0900-1800 Mon-Sat, Mar-Sep. 1100-1700 Sun all year, browsing from 1030.
Credit Cards: All major credit/debit cards
Specialities: Over 12,000 plants, many rare or unusual, reflecting the range of the RHS flagship garden at Wisley. Also houseplants, bedding plants, bulbs & seed potatoes, plus a range of garden sundries.
Notes: Plants subject to seasonal availability. For plants not in stock, a reservation service is operated. All plants must be collected from Wisley as no mail order. Wheelchair accessible.

LSRN **SPRING REACH NURSERY** ♿
Long Reach, Ockham, Guildford, Surrey GU23 6PG
Ⓣ (01483) 284769
Ⓜ 07884 432666
Ⓕ (01483) 284769
Ⓔ info@springreachnursery.co.uk
Ⓦ www.springreachnursery.co.uk
Contact: Nick & Lissa Hourhan
Opening Times: 7 days. 1000-1700 Mon-Sat, 1030-1630 Sun. Open B/hols. Closed 23rd Dec-2nd Jan.
Min Mail Order UK: Nmc
Min Mail Order EU: Nmc
Credit Cards: All major credit/debit cards
Specialities: Shrubs, evergreen climbers, *Clematis*, perennials, roses, grasses, ferns, bamboos, trees, hedging, soft fruit & top fruit. Plants for chalk & clay. Deer & rabbit proof plants. Specimen & acid-loving plants.
Notes: Please ring for mail order details. Also sells wholesale. Delivers to shows. Wheelchair accessible.

LSta **STAFFORD LAKE NURSERY**
Knaphill, Woking, Surrey GU21 2SJ
Ⓜ 07738 241871
Ⓔ enquiries@staffordlake.co.uk
Ⓦ www.staffordlake.co.uk
Contact: Mark Roberts
Opening Times: Open by appt. only.
Min Mail Order UK: Nmc
Specialities: Growers of hostas, dwarf conifers & hedging. Propagates as many own plants as possible. Currently selling only English hostas either out of divisions or from an English tissue culture programme.
Notes: Also sells wholesale. Attends various shows (check with nursery for details).

LSun **SUNNYSIDE NURSERY**
Upper Allotments, New Road, Northchurch, Hertfordshire HP4 1NJ
Ⓜ 07743 552154
Ⓔ philsmith2004@yahoo.co.uk
Contact: Philip Smith
Opening Times: 0900-1700 Mon-Fri. Closed Sat, Sun & B/hols. 10 or more shows during the season. Please contact nursery for details.
Cat. Cost: Availability list on request.

Credit Cards: All major credit/debit cards
Specialities: Hardy perennials, alpines & ornamental grasses. Some plants available in small quantities only.
Notes: Please phone for stock availability & updates. Trade discounts available with orders of £100+.

LSvl **SAVILL GARDENS VISITOR CENTRE** ♿
Wick Lane, Englefield Green, Egham, Surrey TW20 0UU
Ⓣ (01784) 485401
Ⓔ veronique.serre@thecrownestate.co.uk
Ⓦ www.windsorgreatpark.co.uk
Contact: Veronique Serre
Opening Times: 0930-1800 (summer), 0930-1630 (winter).
Credit Cards: All major debit/credit cards except American Express
Specialities: Woody plants, incl. Windsor magnolias, herbaceous, *Ligularia* & *Mahonia*. Available in small numbers only.
Notes: Wheelchair accessible.

LYaf **YAFFLES** ♿
Harvest Hill, Bourne End, Buckinghamshire SL8 5JJ
Ⓣ (01628) 525455
Contact: I Butterfield
Opening Times: 0900-1300 & 1400-1700. Please phone beforehand in case we are attending shows.
Min Mail Order UK: Nmc
Min Mail Order EU: £30.00 + p&p
Cat. Cost: 2 × 2nd class.
Credit Cards: None
Specialities: *Pleione*.
Notes: Only *Pleione* by mail order. Delivers to shows. Wheelchair accessible.

MIDLANDS

MArl **ARLEY HALL NURSERY** ♿
Northwich, Cheshire CW9 6NA
Ⓣ (01565) 777479
Ⓔ arleyhallplantnursery@gmail.com
Ⓦ www.arleyhallandgardens.com
Contact: Rob Groom
Opening Times: 1000-1730 Mon-Sun 1st Mar-29th Sep.
Cat. Cost: 4 × 1st class.
Credit Cards: All major credit/debit cards
Specialities: Wide range of herbaceous incl. many unusual varieties, some in small quantities. Wide range of unusual pelargoniums.
Notes: Nursery is beside car park at Arley Hall Gardens. Wheelchair accessible.
OS Grid Ref: SJ673808

MAsh **ASHWOOD NURSERIES LTD** ♿
Ashwood Lower Lane, Ashwood, Kingswinford, West Midlands DY6 0AE
Ⓣ (01384) 401996
Ⓕ (01384) 401108
Ⓔ mailorder@ashwoodnurseries.com
Ⓦ www.ashwoodnurseries.com
Contact: Karrina Gilbert & Steve Lampitt
Opening Times: 0900-1700 Mon-Sat & 0930-1700 Sun, excl. Xmas & Boxing Day.
Min Mail Order UK: Nmc
Min Mail Order EU: Nmc
Cat. Cost: 4 × 1st class.
Credit Cards: All major credit/debit cards
Specialities: Large range of hardy plants, shrubs & dwarf conifers. Roses, alpines & herbaceous plants. Also specialises in *Auricula*, *Cyclamen*, *Galanthus*, hellebores, *Hepatica*, *Hydrangea* & *Salvia*. Nat. Collection of *Lewisia*.
Notes: Tea room overlooking display garden. Ample parking. Regular events. Groups by appt. to visit private garden. Wheelchair accessible.
OS Grid Ref: SO865879

MAus **DAVID AUSTIN ROSES LTD** ♿ ◆
Bowling Green Lane, Albrighton, Wolverhampton, West Midlands WV7 3HB
Ⓣ (01902) 376300
Ⓕ (01902) 375177
Ⓔ retail@davidaustinroses.co.uk
Ⓦ www.davidaustinroses.com
Contact: Customer Services Dept
Opening Times: 0830-1800 Mon-Fri, 0830-1630 Sat, 1000-1400 Sun.
Min Mail Order UK: Nmc
Min Mail Order EU: Nmc
Cat. Cost: Free.
Credit Cards: All major credit/debit cards
Specialities: Roses. Nat. Collection of English Roses.
Notes: Also sells wholesale. Exports beyond EU. Euro accepted. Wheelchair accessible.
OS Grid Ref: SJ798042

MAvo **AVONDALE NURSERY** ♿
(office) 3 Avondale Road, Earlsdon, Baginton, Nr Coventry, Warwickshire CV5 6DZ
Ⓣ (024) 766 73662
Ⓜ 07979 093096
Ⓔ enquiries@avondalenursery.co.uk
Ⓦ www.avondalenursery.co.uk
Contact: Brian Ellis
Opening Times: 1000-1230, 1400-1700 Mon-Sat, 1030-1630 Sun, Mar-Sep. Other times by appt.
Cat. Cost: 4 × 1st class.

Credit Cards: All major credit/debit cards
Specialities: Rare & unusual perennials esp. asters, *Eryngium*, *Leucanthemum*, *Geum*, *Crocosmia*, *Sanguisorba* & grasses. Nat. Collections of *Symphyotrichum novae-angliae*, *Anemone nemorosa* & *Sanguisorba*.
Notes: Nursery is at Russell's Nursery, Mill Hill, Baginton, near Coventry CV8 3AG. Display garden open. Groups welcome. Delivers to shows. Wheelchair accessible.
OS Grid Ref: SP339751

MBel **Bluebell Cottage Nursery** ♿
Lodge Lane, Dutton, Cheshire WA4 4HP
Ⓣ (01928) 713718
Ⓔ info@bluebellcottage.co.uk
Ⓦ www.bluebellcottage.co.uk
Contact: Sue Beesley
Opening Times: 1000-1700 Wed-Sun & B/hols, 1st Apr-end Sep. By appt. only outside these dates.
Min Mail Order UK: £6.50
Cat. Cost: Online only.
Credit Cards: All major credit/debit cards
Specialities: *Achillea*, *Anthemis*, *Brunnera*, *Centaurea*, *Echinacea*, *Geranium*, *Geum*, *Lychnis*, *Persicaria*, *Potentilla*, *Sanguisorba*, *Thalictrum* & ornamental grasses. Some items stocked in small quantities.
Notes: Mail order available all year round. Mail order plants are fully established, ready to plant out. RHS Partner Garden open Apr-Sep. Refreshments available. Delivers to shows. Wheelchair accessible.
OS Grid Ref: SJ586779

MBlu **Bluebell Arboretum & Nursery** ♿
Annwell Lane, Smisby, Nr Ashby de la Zouch, Derbyshire LE65 2TA
Ⓣ (01530) 413700
Ⓕ (01530) 417600
Ⓔ sales@bluebellnursery.com
Ⓦ www.bluebellnursery.com
Contact: Robert & Suzette Vernon
Opening Times: 0900-1700 Mon-Sat & 1030-1630 Sun, Mar-Oct. 0900-1600 Mon-Sat (not Sun) Nov-Feb. Closed 24th Dec-1st Jan incl. & Easter Sun.
Min Mail Order UK: £8.95
Min Mail Order EU: Nmc
Cat. Cost: £1.50 + 3 × 1st class.
Credit Cards: Visa, Access, Switch, MasterCard
Specialities: Specialists in rare & unusual plants. Uncommon trees & shrubs. Rare *Acer*, *Betula*, *Cornus*, *Fagus*, *Magnolia*, *Liquidambar*, *Quercus* & *Tilia*. Woody climbers.
Notes: 9-acre woodland garden & arboretum surrounds nursery. RHS partner garden. Guide dogs only. Working nursery, so wear appropriate clothing & sturdy footwear when visiting. Delivers to shows. Wheelchair accessible but please call to check after wet weather.
OS Grid Ref: SK344187

MBNS **Barnsdale Gardens** ♿
Exton Avenue, Exton, Oakham, Rutland LE15 8AH
Ⓣ (01572) 813200
Ⓔ mailorder@barnsdalegardens.co.uk
Ⓦ www.barnsdalegardens.co.uk
Contact: Nick Hamilton
Opening Times: 0900-1700 Mar-May & Sep-Oct, 0900-1900 Jun-Aug, 1000-1600 Nov-Feb, 7 days. Closed 24th & 25th Dec.
Min Mail Order UK: Nmc
Min Mail Order EU: Nmc
Cat. Cost: Online only.
Credit Cards: All major credit/debit cards
Specialities: Wide range of choice & unusual garden plants but specialising in perennials.
Notes: Mail order from website or by telephone ordering only. Delivers to shows. Wheelchair accessible.
OS Grid Ref: SK912108

MBrN **Bridge Nursery** ♿
Tomlow Road, Napton-on-the-Hill, Nr Rugby, Warwickshire CV47 8HX
Ⓣ (01926) 812737
Ⓔ philipemartino@gmail.com
Ⓦ www.Bridge-Nursery.co.uk
Contact: Christine Dakin & Philip Martino
Opening Times: 1000-1600 Sat, Sun & B/hol Mons Mar-Oct. Other times by appt.
Min Mail Order UK: £10.00
Cat. Cost: Online only.
Credit Cards: All major credit/debit cards
Specialities: Ornamental grasses, sedges & bamboos. Also range of shrubs & perennials. Display garden.
Notes: Limited range available by mail order, please check with nursery. Also sells wholesale. Euro accepted. Wheelchair accessible.
OS Grid Ref: SP463625

MCms **Chrysanthemums Direct**
Holmes Chapel Road, Over Peover, Knutsford, Cheshire WA16 9RA
Ⓣ 0800 046 7443
Ⓜ 07977 312 593
Ⓔ sales@chrysanthemumsdirect.co.uk
Ⓦ www.chrysanthemumsdirect.co.uk
Contact: Martyn Flint
Opening Times: Not open. Mail order only.
Min Mail Order UK: Nmc
Min Mail Order EU: Nmc

Cat. Cost: 4 × 1st class.
Credit Cards: All major credit/debit cards
Specialities: Chrysanthemums. Young plants grown to order. Delivery within 14 days. Winner Protected Ornamental Grower of the Year at the UK Grower Awards 2015.
Notes: Delivers to shows.

MCoo **Cool Temperate**
(office) 45 Stamford Street, Awsworth, Nottinghamshire NG16 2QL
Ⓣ (0115) 916 2673
Ⓜ 07952 019376
Ⓕ (0115) 916 2673
Ⓔ phil.corbett@cooltemperate.co.uk
Ⓦ www.cooltemperate.co.uk
Contact: Phil Corbett
Opening Times: 0900-1700, 7 days. Please ring/write first.
Min Mail Order UK: Nmc
Cat. Cost: Online or via email.
Credit Cards: None
Specialities: Tree fruit, soft fruit, nitrogen-fixers, hedging, own-root fruit trees. Many species available in small quantities only.
Notes: Nursery at Newton's Lane, Cossall, Notts NG16 2YH.
OS Grid Ref: SK473433

MCot **Coton Manor Garden**
Guilsborough, Northampton, Northamptonshire NN6 8RQ
Ⓣ (01604) 740219
Ⓔ nursery@cotonmanor.co.uk
Ⓦ www.cotonmanor.co.uk
Contact: Caroline Tait
Opening Times: 1200-1730 Tue-Sat, 1st Apr-27th Sep. Also Sun Apr, May & B/hol w/ends. Other times in working hours by appt.
Cat. Cost: Online only.
Credit Cards: All major credit/debit cards
Specialities: Wide-range of herbaceous perennials (1200+ varieties), some available in small quantities only. Also many tender perennials & selected shrubs.
Notes: Garden open. Tea rooms. Garden school. Partial wheelchair access.
OS Grid Ref: SP675715

MCri **Crin Gardens**
79 Partons Road, Kings Heath, Birmingham B14 6TD
Ⓜ 07805 591475
Ⓔ cringardens@tiscali.co.uk
Ⓦ www.cringardens.co.uk
Contact: M Milinkovic
Opening Times: Not open. Mail order only.
Min Mail Order UK: Nmc
Min Mail Order EU: Nmc
Cat. Cost: 2 × 1st class + 1× 2nd.
Credit Cards: None
Specialities: Lilies. Limited stock available on first come, first served basis.
Notes: Euro accepted.

MCtn **Chiltern Seeds Ltd**
Crowmarsh Battle Barns, 114 Preston Crowmarsh, Wallingford, Oxfordshire OX10 6SL
Ⓣ (01491) 824675
Ⓔ info@chilternseeds.co.uk
Ⓦ www.chilternseeds.co.uk
Contact: Any member of staff
Opening Times: Mail order only. Normal office hours, Mon-Fri.
Min Mail Order UK: Nmc
Min Mail Order EU: Nmc
Cat. Cost: Free.
Credit Cards: All major debit/credit cards except American Express
Specialities: Large selection of wild flowers, trees, shrubs, cacti, annuals, houseplants, vegetables & herbs.
Notes: Exports beyond EU. Customer's responsibility to ensure no restrictions & special import requirements apply.

MDon **Donington Nurseries Ltd** ♿
Kings Mills, Park Lane, Castle Donington, Derbyshire DE74 2RS
Ⓣ (01332) 853004
Ⓕ (01332) 853793
Ⓔ sales@doningtonnurseries.co.uk
Ⓦ www.doningtonnurseries.co.uk
Contact: Rebecca Faulkner
Opening Times: Open daily (hours vary depending on season).
Cat. Cost: None.
Credit Cards: All major credit/debit cards
Specialities: Family-owned nursery stocking wide range of trees, shrubs, perennials & alpines. 50% of stock grown on nursery set within 4-acre former walled garden of Donington Hall. Home grown *Prunus laurocerasus* (laurel) & *Thuja* hedging available in large quantities.
Notes: Wheelchair accessible.
OS Grid Ref: SK421273

MEch **Echium World**
Edwinstowe House, High Street, Edwinstowe, Nottinghamshire NG21 9PR
Ⓜ 07957 602073
Ⓔ echiumworld@gmail.com
Ⓦ www.echiumworld.co.uk
Contact: Linda Heywood

Opening Times: Plant sales or collection from our Echium Garden Open Days: Sun 14th, 21st, 28th May & Mon 29th May 2017. Other times by appt. only.
Min Mail Order UK: £6.95
Credit Cards: Paypal
Specialities: Specialist growers & suppliers of *Echium* varieties, incl. rare & threatened plants. Also plant varieties used for complementary planting schemes in our showcase Echium Garden. Suppliers of *Echium* plants for wildlife gardens. All plants grown and cultivated at our UK nursery. Nat. Collection of *Echium* species & cvs from the Macaronesian Islands.
Notes: Exhibiting at RHS Chatsworth 7th-11th Jun 2017. Also sells wholesale.
OS Grid Ref: SK626665

M

MFry **FRYER'S ROSES AND GARDEN CENTRE** ♿
Manchester Road, Knutsford, Cheshire WA16 0SX
Ⓣ (01565) 755455
Ⓕ (01565) 653755
Ⓔ webenquiries@bluediamond.gg
Ⓦ www.fryers-roses.co.uk
Contact: Jill Kerr
Opening Times: 0900-1800 Mon-Sat & 1030-1630 Sun.
Min Mail Order UK: £6.50 (bare root)
Min Mail Order EU: Contact nursery.
Cat. Cost: Free
Credit Cards: All major debit/credit cards except American Express
Specialities: Stocks over 250 varieties of roses. New roses usually launched at RHS Hampton Court Flower Show. Bare root roses available for sale from Nov-Mar, potted roses available all year round.
Notes: Talks held throughout the year, contact nursery for information. Group bookings available. Exports beyond the EU. Wheelchair accessible.
OS Grid Ref: SJ738803

MGil **JOHN GILLIES** ♿
at Russell's Garden Centre, Mill Hill, Baginton, Warwickshire CV8 3AG
Ⓜ 07546 064961
Ⓔ enquiries@gilliesrareplants.com
Ⓦ www.gilliesrareplants.com
Contact: John Gillies
Opening Times: 1000-1700 Mon, Wed, Thurs, Fri & Sat, 1030-1630 Sun Mar-Sept. (Closed Easter Sun). 1000-1600 Wed-Sat Oct-Nov. Other times by appt.
Min Mail Order UK: Nmc
Cat. Cost: Online only.
Credit Cards: All major credit/debit cards
Specialities: A range of choice & rare plants incl., but not limited to, *Azara, Clethra, Daphne, Diostea, Embothrium, Ercilla, Iochroma, Lomatia* & *Rhapiolepis*. Most available in small quantities only.
Notes: Nursery situated on Russell's Nursery site next to Avondale Nursery. Please contact before visiting to ensure plant is currently in stock. Wheelchair accessible.
OS Grid Ref: SP337750

MGos **GOSCOTE NURSERIES LTD** ♿
Syston Road, Cossington, Leicestershire LE7 4UZ
Ⓣ (01509) 812121
Ⓔ enquiries@goscote.co.uk
Ⓦ www.goscote.co.uk
Contact: James Toone
Opening Times: 7 days, year round, apart from between Xmas & New Year.
Cat. Cost: Online only.
Credit Cards: Visa, Access, MasterCard, Delta, Switch
Specialities: Japanese maples, rhododendrons & azaleas, *Magnolia, Camellia, Pieris* & other *Ericaceae*. Ornamental trees & shrubs, conifers, fruit, heathers, alpines, roses, *Clematis* & unusual climbers.
Notes: Design & landscaping service available. Café & show garden. Also sells wholesale. Wheelchair accessible.
OS Grid Ref: SK602130

MHCG **HILL CLOSE GARDENS** ♿
Bread and Meat Close, Warwick, Warwickshire CV34 6HF
Ⓣ (01926) 493339
Ⓜ 07533 401934
Ⓔ headgardener@hcgt.org.uk
Ⓦ www.hillclosegardens.com
Contact: Gary Leaver
Opening Times: 1100-1700, 7 days, Apr-Oct. 1100-1600 Mon-Fri only, Nov-Mar.
Cat. Cost: 2 × 1st class or online.
Credit Cards: All major credit/debit cards
Specialities: Small retail nursery attached to heritage garden which is open to the public. Hold dispersed Nat. Collection of hardy *Chrysanthemum*. Also specialise in *Symphyotrichum* (asters) & *Galanthus*.
Notes: Wheelchair accessible.
OS Grid Ref: SP277647

MHed **HEDGEXPRESS** ♿
Buckland Road, Bampton, Oxfordshire OX18 2AA
Ⓣ (01993) 850979

Ⓔ info@hedgexpress.co.uk
Ⓦ www.hedgexpress.co.uk
Contact: Gavin Stevens
Opening Times: 0900-1600, Mon-Fri.
Min Mail Order UK: £100
Cat. Cost: Online only.
Credit Cards: All major credit/debit cards, Paypal
Specialities: Hedging & lavenders.
Notes: Also sells wholesale. Wheelchair accessible.
OS Grid Ref: SP322024

MHer **The Herb Nursery** ♿
Thistleton, Oakham, Rutland LE15 7RE
Ⓣ (01572) 767658
Ⓔ herbnursery@southwitham.net
Ⓦ www.herbnursery.co.uk
Contact: Peter Bench
Opening Times: 0900-1700 Mon-Sat, 1000-1600 Sun. Closed Xmas until 1st Feb.
Cat. Cost: Free with A5 sae.
Credit Cards: All major credit/debit cards
Specialities: Herbs, wild flowers, cottage garden plants, *Pelargonium*, *Thymus*, *Mentha*, *Lavandula*.
Notes: Open garden weekend 17th and 18th Jun. Wheelchair accessible.

MHol **Hollies Farm Plant Centre**
Uppertown, Bonsall, Nr Matlock, Derbyshire DE4 2AW
Ⓣ (01629) 822734
Ⓔ rbrt.wells@gmail.com
Ⓦ www.holliesfarmplantcentre.co.uk
Contact: Robert or Linda Wells
Opening Times: 0900-1700 every day except Wed.
Credit Cards: None
Specialities: Range of rare & unusual herbaceous perennials.
Notes: Garden designers welcome.

MHom **Homestead Plants**
The Homestead, Normanton, Bottesford, Nottingham, Nottinghamshire NG13 0EP
Ⓣ (01949) 842745
Ⓦ www.homesteadplants.com
Contact: Mrs S Palmer
Opening Times: By appt.
Min Mail Order UK: Nmc
Min Mail Order EU: Nmc
Cat. Cost: 2 × 2nd class.
Credit Cards: None
Specialities: Heliotropes in small quantities.
Notes: Mail order not offered year round. Please check with nursery for details.
OS Grid Ref: SK812407

MJac **Jackson's Nurseries**
Clifton Campville, Nr Tamworth, Staffordshire B79 0AP
Ⓣ (01827) 373307
Contact: N Jackson
Opening Times: 0900-1800 Mon & Wed-Sat, 1000-1700 Sun.
Cat. Cost: 2 × 1st class.
Credit Cards: None
Specialities: *Fuchsia*.
Notes: Also sells wholesale.

MJak **Jackson's Nurseries** ♿
Thorney Edge Road, Bagnall, Stoke-on-Trent, Staffordshire ST9 9LE
Ⓣ (01782) 502741
Ⓕ (01782) 504932
Ⓔ sales@jacksonsnurseries.co.uk
Ⓦ www.jacksonsnurseries.co.uk
Contact: Sales Team
Opening Times: 0800-1700 7 days, Mar-Oct. 0800-1630, Nov-Feb.
Min Mail Order UK: Nmc.
Cat. Cost: None issued.
Credit Cards: MasterCard, Visa
Specialities: Good general range.
Notes: Family-run nursery, established for over 50 years, a short distance from the Peak District. Tea room. Also sells wholesale. Wheelchair accessible.
OS Grid Ref: SJ934504

MLod **Lodge Farm Plants & Wildflowers** ♿
Case Lane, Fiveways, Hatton, Warwickshire CV35 7JD
Ⓜ 07977 631368
Ⓔ lodgefarmplants@btinternet.com
Ⓦ www.lodgefarm-plants.com
Contact: Janet Cook & Nick Cook
Opening Times: Open 7 days all year, except Xmas Day & Boxing Day.
Min Mail Order UK: Nmc
Cat. Cost: Availability list online.
Credit Cards: All major credit/debit cards
Specialities: All forms of fruit trees: bush; espalier; fan; stepovers; cordons. Soft fruit. Native trees & hedging. Ornamental trees.
Notes: Courier service to all UK. Offers online & phone sales as well as at nursery. Also sells wholesale. Euro accepted. Wheelchair accessible.
OS Grid Ref: SP223700

MMrt **Morton Nurseries Ltd** ♿
Morton, Retford, Nottinghamshire DN22 8HE
Ⓣ (01777) 702530

Ⓜ 07940 434398
Ⓔ enquiries@morton-nurseries.com
Ⓦ www.morton-nurseries.co.uk
Contact: Gill McMaster
Opening Times: 1000-1600 Mon-Fri, 1400-1700 Sat & Sun.
Min Mail Order UK: £5.00 + p&p
Cat. Cost: None issued.
Credit Cards: All major credit/debit cards
Specialities: Shrubs & perennials.
Notes: Delivers to shows. Wheelchair accessible.

MMuc **Mucklestone Nurseries** ♿
Rock Lane, Mucklestone, Nr Market Drayton, Shropshire TF9 4FA
Ⓣ (01630) 674284
Ⓜ 07714 241668
Ⓔ info@botanyplants.co.uk
Ⓦ www.botanyplants.co.uk
Contact: William & Louise Friend
Opening Times: 0930-1700 (or dusk) Wed-Sat. Closed Sat in winter. Mon & Tue by appt. only. Closed Sun. If travelling far please phone 07929 178751 or email first.
Min Mail Order UK: Nmc
Cat. Cost: Online.
Credit Cards: All major credit/debit cards
Specialities: Trees, shrubs, grasses, bamboos, rhododendrons, ferns & perennials for acid & damp soils of the north & west UK. Our nursery in Kent grows complementary range for dry, chalk & coast. Extensive grounds where plants can be seen growing. Small numbers only of each variety available.
Notes: Any plants on website or listed under nursery code SEND (in Kent) can be collected to order or sent/delivered. Evening garden tours & talks for garden groups in Staffs, Salop or Cheshire by appt., see website or phone for details. Wheelchair accessible.
OS Grid Ref: SJ728373

MNHC **The National Herb Centre** ♿
Banbury Road, Warmington, Nr Banbury, Oxfordshire OX17 1DF
Ⓣ (01295) 690999
Ⓕ (01295) 690034
Ⓔ info@herbcentre.co.uk
Ⓦ www.herbcentre.co.uk
Contact: Plant Centre Staff
Opening Times: 0900-1730 Mon-Sat, 1030-1700 Sun.
Min Mail Order UK: Nmc
Credit Cards: All major credit/debit cards
Specialities: Herbs, culinary & medicinal. Extensive selection of rosemary, thyme & lavender in particular.
Notes: Next day delivery UK mainland only, signature required. Carriage charge of £10.00 for orders valued up to £50, more for larger orders. Wheelchair accessible.
OS Grid Ref: SP413471

MNrw **Norwell Nurseries** ♿
Woodhouse Road, Norwell, Newark, Nottinghamshire NG23 6JX
Ⓣ (01636) 636337
Ⓔ wardha@aol.com
Ⓦ www.norwellnurseries.co.uk
Contact: Dr Andrew Ward
Opening Times: 1000-1700 Mon, Wed-Fri & Sun (Wed-Mon May & Jun). By appt. Aug & 23rd Oct-1st Mar.
Min Mail Order UK: £20.00 + p&p
Min Mail Order EU: £40.00
Cat. Cost: 3 × 1st class or online.
Credit Cards: None
Specialities: A large collection of over 2500 unusual & choice herbaceous perennials esp., hardy geraniums, *Geum*, pond & bog plants, cottage garden plants, *Hemerocallis*, grasses, *Trillium* & woodland plants. Nat. Collection of Hardy Chrysanthemums.
Notes: One acre garden & tea room. Talks given and garden tours. Also sells wholesale. Delivers to shows. Wheelchair accessible.
OS Grid Ref: SK767616

MPhe **Phedar Nursery**
42 Bunkers Hill, Romiley, Stockport, Cheshire SK6 3DS
Ⓣ (0161) 430 3772
Ⓔ mclewin@phedar.com
Ⓦ www.phedar.com
Contact: Will McLewin
Opening Times: Frequent but irregular. Please phone to arrange appt.
Min Mail Order UK: Nmc
Min Mail Order EU: Nmc
Cat. Cost: Online or write for printed version.
Credit Cards: None
Specialities: *Helleborus*, *Paeonia*. Limited stock of some rare items.
Notes: Exports beyond EU subject to destination & on an ad hoc basis only. Please contact nursery for details. Also sells wholesale. Euro accepted.
OS Grid Ref: SJ936897

MPie **Piecemeal Plants** ♿
Whatton House Gardens, Nr Kegworth, Loughborough, Leicestershire LE12 5BG
Ⓣ (01509) 672056
Ⓜ 07950 757444

Ⓔ nursery@piecemealplants.co.uk
Ⓦ www.piecemealplants.co.uk
Contact: Mary Thomas
Opening Times: 1300-1600 (1700 in summer) Thu & Fri, early Apr-mid Sep. For up to date details please ring or see website. Also open by arrangement throughout the year.
Cat. Cost: Online only.
Credit Cards: None
Specialities: Wide range of interesting herbaceous perennials & bulbs, many unusual, some half-hardy or tender. Majority in small quantities.
Notes: Nursery located at entrance to Whatton Gardens, off A6 between Kegworth & Hathern. Car parking in front of Whatton House at top of drive. Delivers to shows (Midland Plant Fairs). Wheelchair accessible.
OS Grid Ref: SK494242

MPkF PACKHORSE FARM NURSERY ♿
Sandyford House, Lant Lane, Tansley, Matlock, Derbyshire DE4 5FW
Ⓣ (01629) 57206
Ⓜ 07974 095752
Ⓕ (01629) 57206
Contact: Hilton W Haynes
Opening Times: 1000-1600 Tues & Wed, 1st Mar-31st Oct. Any other time by appt. only.
Cat. Cost: 2 × 1st class for plant list.
Credit Cards: None
Specialities: *Acer*, rare stock is limited in supply. Other more unusual hardy shrubs, trees & conifers.
Notes: Delivers to shows. Wheelchair accessible.
OS Grid Ref: SK322617

MPnt PLANTAGOGO.COM
Jubilee Cottage Nursery, Snape Lane, Englesea Brook, Crewe, Cheshire CW2 5QN
Ⓣ (01270) 820335
Ⓜ 07713 518271
Ⓔ info@plantagogo.com
Ⓦ www.plantagogo.com
Contact: Vicky & Richard Fox
Opening Times: Visitors are welcome by appt. only. Also Open Days (no appt. required): 1000-1600 31st Mar, 1st/2nd Apr, 6th/7th May, 29th/30th Sep, 1st Oct 2017.
Min Mail Order UK: £9.95
Min Mail Order EU: Price on application
Cat. Cost: Online only.
Credit Cards: All major credit/debit cards
Specialities: *Heuchera*, *Heucherella*, *Tiarella*, also large selection of perennials. Plants listed in the *RHS Plant Finder* are available in good quantities. Others, not listed here, are available from our collections on request. Nat. Collections of *Heuchera*, *Heucherella* & *Tiarella*.
Notes: Open days throughout the year (see above). Also sells wholesale. Delivers to shows. Limited wheelchair access.
OS Grid Ref: SJ750516

MPtG PLANTS2GARDENS LTD
The Nursery, Manor House Farm, Woodford, Kettering, Northamptonshire NN14 4ES
Ⓣ (01832) 733374
Ⓜ 07397 167539
Ⓔ customerservice@plants2gardens.com
Ⓦ www.plants2gardens.com
Contact: Lindsey Ward
Opening Times: Not open. Mail order only via website.
Min Mail Order UK: Nmc
Credit Cards: All major credit/debit cards
Specialities: Specialist propagator of regal, angel & species *Pelargonium*.

MRav RAVENSTHORPE NURSERY ♿
6 East Haddon Road, Ravensthorpe, Northamptonshire NN6 8ES
Ⓣ (01604) 770548
Ⓔ ravensthorpenursery@hotmail.com
Contact: Jean & Richard Wiseman
Opening Times: 1000-1800 (or dusk if earlier) Wed-Sat. B/hol Mons in May.
Min Mail Order UK: Nmc
Cat. Cost: None issued.
Credit Cards: Visa, MasterCard
Specialities: Huge range of perennials, shrubs & trees with numerous unusual varieties, many of which can be seen growing in the display garden. Some plants only available as dug from garden during the lifting season.
Notes: Search & delivery service for large orders, winter months only. Wheelchair accessible.
OS Grid Ref: SP665699

MSCN STONYFORD COTTAGE NURSERY ♿
Stonyford Lane, Cuddington, Northwich, Cheshire CW8 2TF
Ⓣ (01606) 888970/888128 (answerphone)
Ⓜ 07714 205177
Ⓔ stonyfordcottage@yahoo.co.uk
Ⓦ www.stonyfordcottagenursery.co.uk
Contact: Andrew Overland
Opening Times: 1000-1700 Tue-Sun & B/hol Mons 1st Feb-31st Oct.
Min Mail Order UK: Nmc
Min Mail Order EU: Nmc
Cat. Cost: None.

Credit Cards: All major credit/debit cards
Specialities: Wide range of herbaceous perennials, *Iris*, hardy *Geranium*, moisture-loving & bog plants. *Sempervivum*, *Paeonia*, candelabra *Primula*.
Notes: Also sells wholesale. Wheelchair accessible.
OS Grid Ref: SJ580710

MSwo **Swallows Nursery** ♿
Mixbury, Brackley, Northamptonshire
NN13 5RR
Ⓣ (01280) 847721
Ⓔ enq@swallowsnursery.co.uk
Ⓦ www.swallowsnursery.co.uk
Contact: Chris Swallow
Opening Times: 0900-1300 & 1400-1700 (earlier in winter) Mon-Fri, 0900-1300 Sat.
Min Mail Order UK: £19.50
Cat. Cost: 3 × 1st class (plus phone number).
Credit Cards: All major credit/debit cards
Specialities: Growing a wide range, particularly shrubs, climbers, trees & roses.
Notes: Trees not for mail order unless part of larger order. Nursery transport used where possible, esp. for trees. Also sells wholesale. Wheelchair accessible.
OS Grid Ref: SP607336

MThu **T. D. Thursfield**
Kerry Hill Nurseries, Eaves Lane,
Bucknell, Stoke-on-Trent, Staffordshire
ST2 8NA
Ⓣ (01782) 302498
Ⓜ 07977 464363
Ⓔ tdthursfield@aol.com
Contact: Susan Thursfield
Opening Times: 0900-1730 Mon-Fri, 0930-1630 Sat, 1000-1600 Sun.
Cat. Cost: None issued.
Credit Cards: All major debit/credit cards except American Express
Specialities: Traditional family nursery founded in the 1930s, currently offering broad selection of hardy nursery stock.
Notes: Also sells wholesale. Delivers to shows. Wheelchair access to main sales areas.

MTin **The Tiny Plant Company**
25 Owley Wood Road, Weaverham, Cheshire
CW8 3LF
Ⓣ (01606) 851146
Ⓔ thetinyplantco@hotmail.com
Ⓦ www.tinyplantcompany.co.uk
Contact: Matt Wood
Opening Times: Not open. Mail order only.
Min Mail Order UK: £3.00
Cat. Cost: Online only.
Credit Cards: All major credit/debit cards
Specialities: Newly-opened small nursery. All plants available in very small quantities only.
Notes: Delivers to shows.

MTis **Tissington Nursery** ♿
The Old Kitchen Gardens, Tissington,
Ashbourne, Derbyshire DE6 1RA
Ⓣ (01335) 390650
Ⓜ 07929 720284
Ⓔ info@tissington-nursery.co.uk
Ⓦ www.tissington-nursery.co.uk
Contact: Mairi Longdon
Opening Times: 1100-1700 daily, end Mar-end Sep.
Min Mail Order UK: Nmc
Cat. Cost: 4 × 1st class or online.
Credit Cards: All major credit/debit cards
Specialities: Choice & unusual perennials esp. *Achillea*, *Aster*, *Dianthus*, *Geranium*, *Geum*, *Helenium*, *Helianthus*, *Nepeta*, *Phlox*, *Salvia*, *Sanguisorba* & *Sedum*.
Notes: Delivers to shows. Wheelchair accessible.
OS Grid Ref: SK176521

MWat **Waterperry Gardens Ltd** ♿
Waterperry, Nr Wheatley, Oxfordshire
OX33 1JZ
Ⓣ (01844) 339226/254
Ⓜ 07864 678864
Ⓕ (01844) 339883
Ⓔ office@waterperrygardens.co.uk
Ⓦ www.waterperrygardens.co.uk
Contact: T Connell
Opening Times: 1000-1730 summer. 1000-1700 winter.
Min Mail Order UK: £30.00
Cat. Cost: Online only.
Credit Cards: All major credit/debit cards
Specialities: General, large range of herbaceous esp. asters, also Nat. Collection of *Saxifraga* (subsect. *Kabschia* & *Engleria*).
Notes: Also sells wholesale. Wheelchair accessible.
OS Grid Ref: SP630064

MWht **Whitelea Nursery** ♿
Whitelea Lane, Tansley, Matlock, Derbyshire
DE4 5FL
Ⓣ (01629) 55010
Ⓔ sales@uk-bamboos.co.uk
Ⓦ www.uk-bamboos.co.uk
Contact: David Wilson
Opening Times: By appt.
Min Mail Order UK: Nmc

Cat. Cost: Online only. Price list available 2 × 1st class.
Credit Cards: None
Specialities: Bamboos. Substantial quantities of 45 species/cvs of bamboo, remainder stocked in small numbers only. Limited stocks of grasses, trees & shrubs.
Notes: Mail order limited by carrier restrictions, please contact nursery or see website for details. Also sells wholesale. Wheelchair accessible.
OS Grid Ref: SK325603

MWts **WATERSIDE NURSERY**
Sharnford, Leicestershire
Ⓣ (01455) 273730
Ⓜ 07931 557082
Ⓔ info@watersidenursery.co.uk
Ⓦ www.watersidenursery.co.uk
Contact: Linda Smith
Opening Times: Mail order only.
Min Mail Order UK: Nmc
Cat. Cost: Online only.
Credit Cards: All major credit/debit cards
Specialities: Aquatics, marginal pond plants, miniature waterlilies, waterlilies, submerged oxygenating plants, bog garden plants & moisture-loving plants.

NORTHERN

NAln **THE ALNWICK GARDEN** ♿
Greenwell Road, Alnwick, Northumberland NE66 1SF
Ⓣ 01665 511350
Ⓔ Peter.edge@alnwickgarden.com
Ⓦ https://alnwickgarden.com/visit-the-alnwick-garden/the-gift-plant-shop/
Contact: Peter Edge
Opening Times: 1000-1800 Mon-Sun Apr-Oct. 1000-1600 Mon-Sun Nov-Mar. Closed Jan.
Credit Cards: All major credit/debit cards
Specialities: Wide general range including own peat-free plants propagated from Alnwick Garden. Perennials, shrubs and bulbs. David Austin roses and rare alpines from Kevock Garden Plants. Other ornamental perennials and climbers also available.
Notes: Retail plant centre with on-site nursery. Easily accessible from the town and no Alnwick Garden ticket necessary for entry. Horticultural advice available. Wheelchair accessible.
OS Grid Ref: NU189133

NAst **ASHCROFT PERENNIALS**
(office) 2 Mallee Crescent, Southport, Merseyside PR9 8NJ
Ⓣ (01704) 509257
Ⓜ 07793 710350
Ⓔ sales@ashcroftperennials.co.uk
Ⓦ www.ashcroftperennials.co.uk
Contact: Chris Ashcroft
Opening Times: 0900-1600 Mon-Fri. Sat/Sun by appt. only.
Min Mail Order UK: £8.00
Min Mail Order EU: Nmc
Cat. Cost: Online only.
Credit Cards: None
Specialities: Range of herbaceous perennials.
Notes: Nursery at The Hawthornes, Marsh Road, Hesketh Bank, Preston PR4 6XT. Mail order via website. Delivers to shows.

NBid **BIDE-A-WEE COTTAGE GARDENS** ♿
Stanton, Netherwitton, Morpeth, Northumberland NE65 8PR
Ⓣ (01670) 772238
Ⓜ 07976 559416
Ⓕ (01670) 772238
Ⓔ info@bideawee.co.uk
Ⓦ www.bideawee.co.uk
Contact: Mark Robson
Opening Times: 1330-1700 Sat & Wed, 15th Apr-30th Aug 2017. Group visits at other times, except Sun.
Min Mail Order UK: £28.00
Cat. Cost: Online only.
Credit Cards: All major credit/debit cards
Specialities: Unusual herbaceous perennials, *Agapanthus*, *Primula*, ferns, grasses. Nat. Collection of *Centaurea*.
Notes: Wheelchair accessible.
OS Grid Ref: NZ132900

NBir **BIRKHEADS SECRET GARDENS & NURSERY** ♿
Birkheads Lane, Sunniside, Gateshead, Tyne & Wear NE16 5EL
Ⓣ (01207) 232262
Ⓜ 07778 447920
Ⓕ (01207) 232262
Ⓔ birkheadsnursery@gmail.com
Ⓦ www.birkheadssecretgardens.co.uk
Contact: Mrs Christine Liddle
Opening Times: 1100-1700 Sat and Sun. 1000-1700 Wed, Thurs, Fri. Closed Mon & Tues. Pre-booked coach groups only on Tues. Open B/hol Mons through season.
Cat. Cost: None issued.
Credit Cards: All major credit/debit cards
Specialities: Hardy herbaceous perennials, grasses, hardy bulbs. Herbs. *Allium*, *Digitalis*, *Euphorbia*, *Galanthus*, *Geranium*, *Primula*, *Sedum* & *Rodgersia*.
Notes: Nursery & coffee shop wheelchair

accessible, please ring for special access directions.
OS Grid Ref: NZ220569

NBre **BREEZY KNEES NURSERIES** ♿
Common Lane, Warthill, York YO19 5XS
Ⓣ (01904) 488800
Ⓔ admin@breezyknees.co.uk
Ⓦ www.breezyknees.co.uk
Contact: Any member of staff
Opening Times: 1000-1700 7 days (open 1100 Sun), 1st Apr-30th Sep.
Credit Cards: All major credit/debit cards
Specialities: Very wide range of perennials. All can be viewed in 15-acre gardens (open 1st May-30th Sep).
Notes: Wheelchair accessible.
OS Grid Ref: SE675565

N

NBro **BROWNTHWAITE HARDY PLANTS** ♿
Fell Yeat, Casterton, Kirkby Lonsdale, Lancashire LA6 2JW
Ⓣ (01524) 271340 (after 1800 hours).
Ⓦ www.hardyplantsofcumbria.co.uk
Contact: Chris Benson
Opening Times: 1000-1700, 1st Apr-20th Sep.
Min Mail Order UK: Nmc
Cat. Cost: 3 × 1st for fern list.
Credit Cards: None
Specialities: Herbaceous perennials incl. *Geranium*, *Hosta*, *Primula*, hardy ferns, *Hydrangea paniculata* & *H. serrata* varieties.
Notes: Follow brown signs from A65 between Kirkby Lonsdale & Cowan Bridge. Mail order for *Hydrangea* & ferns. Delivers to shows. Wheelchair accessible.
OS Grid Ref: SD632794

NCft **CRAFTYPLANTS**
(office) 21 Woodgreen Drive, Radcliffe, Lancashire M26 1BF
Ⓣ 0161 820 8606
Ⓜ 07742 783631
Ⓔ sales@craftyplants.co.uk
Ⓦ www.craftyplants.co.uk
Contact: Graham Sigsworth
Opening Times: Mail order only. Not open except for nursery Open Days (see website or phone for details).
Min Mail Order UK: Nmc
Min Mail Order EU: Nmc
Cat. Cost: Online only.
Credit Cards: All major debit/credit cards except American Express
Specialities: *Tillandsia*.
Notes: Nursery at Eezitill, Startley Nook, Preston PR4 4XW. Also sells wholesale. Delivers to shows. Euro accepted. No wheelchair access.

NCGa **CATHS GARDEN PLANTS** ♿
The Walled Garden, Heaves Hotel, Levens, Cumbria LA8 8EF
Ⓣ (01539) 561126
Ⓔ cath@cathsgardenplants.co.uk
Ⓦ www.cathsgardenplants.co.uk
Contact: Rachel James
Opening Times: 0930-1700 Tues-Sat, Apr & May. For other times, please contact nursery as may be relocating during 2017.
Min Mail Order UK: Nmc
Min Mail Order EU: £25.00
Cat. Cost: Online only.
Credit Cards: All major credit/debit cards
Specialities: Herbaceous *Paeonia*. A wide range of perennials including uncommon varieties & recent introductions.
Notes: On A590 south of Kendal follow signs for Heaves. Between Levens Hall and Sizergh Castle. Delivers to shows. Wheelchair accessible.
OS Grid Ref: SD497867

NChi **CHIPCHASE CASTLE NURSERY** ♿
Chipchase Castle, Wark, Hexham, Northumberland NE48 3NT
Ⓣ (01434) 230083
Ⓜ 07575 714002
Ⓔ chipchaseplants@aim.com
Ⓦ www.chipchaseplants.com
Contact: Mark Cummings
Opening Times: 1000-1700 Thu-Sun & B/hol Mons, 1st Apr (or Easter if earlier) to end Sep.
Min Mail Order UK: Nmc
Min Mail Order EU: Nmc
Cat. Cost: A5 sae for list
Credit Cards: All major credit/debit cards
Specialities: Rare & unusual herbaceous esp. *Pulmonaria*, *Geum* & *Geranium* & some herbs. Some plants only available in small quantities.
Notes: Delivers to shows. Suitable for accompanied wheelchair users.
OS Grid Ref: NY880758

NCou **COURTYARD PLANTERS** ♿
9 Westgate, Otley, West Yorkshire LS21 3AT
Ⓣ (01943) 462390
Ⓔ katie@courtyardplanters.co.uk
Ⓦ www.courtyardplanters.co.uk
Contact: Katie Burnett
Opening Times: 0930-1700 Tue-Sat. Closed all Jan.
Cat. Cost: Online only.

Credit Cards: All major debit/credit cards except American Express
Specialities: Perennials. Plants for heavy clay soils. Peat free.
Notes: Gardening classes & workshops. Also sells wholesale. Wheelchair accessible.
OS Grid Ref: SE201455

NDai **DAISY CLOUGH NURSERIES LTD** ♿ ◆
Station Road, Scorton, Lancashire PR3 1AN
Ⓣ (01524) 793104
Ⓔ info@daisyclough.com
Ⓦ www.daisyclough.com
Contact: Jo Riding
Opening Times: 0900-1700 Mon-Sat, 1000-1600 Sun.
Cat. Cost: Online only.
Credit Cards: All major credit/debit cards
Specialities: Family run nursery with a focus on growing a wide variety of quality and unusual perennials and grasses. Over 600 different varieties. Large range of vegetable plants available from Feb onwards. Selection of trees, shrubs, and alpines, plus bedding plants grown on the nursery.
Notes: Wheelchair accessible.

NDal **DALESIDE NURSERIES LTD** ♿
Ripon Road, Killinghall, Harrogate, North Yorkshire HG3 2AY
Ⓣ (01423) 506450
Ⓕ (01423) 527872
Ⓔ contact@dalesidenurseries.co.uk
Ⓦ www.dalesidenurseries.co.uk
Contact: Any Member of Staff
Opening Times: 0830-1700 Mon-Sat, 1030-1630 Sun. Winter hours: 0830-1600 Mon-Sat (closed Sun) Jan & 0830-1630 Mon-Sat, 1030-1630 Sun, Feb.
Cat. Cost: Online only.
Credit Cards: All major debit/credit cards except American Express
Specialities: Many plants & trees not generally available. Container-grown fruit trees: apples, pears & soft fruit. Container-grown trees. Conifers, *Clematis* & hardy perennials.
Notes: Wheelchair accessible.
OS Grid Ref: SE287590

NDav **DAVE PARKINSON PLANTS**
4 West Bank, Carlton, Goole, East Yorkshire DN14 9PZ
Ⓣ (01405) 860693
Ⓜ 07773 564945
Ⓦ www.daveparkinsonplants.co.uk
Contact: Mary Parkinson
Opening Times: Not open. Mail order only. Sells at RHS & Orchid Shows.
Min Mail Order UK: £12 + p&p
Min Mail Order EU: Nmc
Cat. Cost: 1st class stamp.
Credit Cards: None
Specialities: Hardy orchids. Terrestrial South African *Disa* orchids, species & hybrids.
Notes: Delivers to shows.

NDov **DOVE COTTAGE NURSERY & GARDEN** ♿
Shibden Hall Road, Halifax, West Yorkshire HX3 9XA
Ⓣ (01422) 203553
Ⓔ info@dovecottagenursery.co.uk
Ⓦ www.dovecottagenursery.co.uk
Contact: Stephen & Kim Rogers
Opening Times: 1000-1700 Wed-Sun, 1st Mar-30th Sep & B/hols Mons. Other times by appt.
Cat. Cost: £3.00.
Credit Cards: All major credit/debit cards
Specialities: Herbaceous perennials & selected grasses, many displayed in adjoining naturalistic garden.
Notes: Wheelchair accessible.
OS Grid Ref: SE115256

NDro **DROINTON NURSERIES** ♿
Plaster Pitts, Norton Conyers, Ripon, North Yorkshire HG4 5EF
Ⓣ (01765) 641849
Ⓜ 07909 971529
Ⓔ info@auricula-plants.co.uk
Ⓦ www.auricula-plants.co.uk
Contact: Robin & Annabel Graham
Opening Times: Open days in spring, otherwise by appt. only.
Min Mail Order UK: Nmc
Min Mail Order EU: Nmc
Cat. Cost: 4 × 1st class.
Credit Cards: All major credit/debit cards
Specialities: *Primula auricula.* More than 1150 cvs of show, alpine, double & border auriculas. Limited stock of any one cultivar. Nat. Collection of *Primula auricula* (borders).
Notes: Also sells wholesale. Exports beyond EU. Delivers to shows. Wheelchair accessible.
OS Grid Ref: SE315753

NEgg **EGGLESTON HALL GARDENS** ♿
Eggleston, Barnard Castle, Co. Durham DL12 0AG
Ⓣ (01833) 650230
Ⓜ 07747 620908
Ⓔ lahock@btinternet.com
Ⓦ www.egglestonhallgardens.co.uk.
Contact: Lisa Hockham
Opening Times: 1000-1700 7 days. Closed 24th Dec to 6th Jan each year.

Cat. Cost: Online only.
Credit Cards: All major credit/debit cards
Notes: Collection from nursery only. Euro accepted. Wheelchair accessible.
OS Grid Ref: NY997233

NEoE **East of Eden Nursery** ♿
Ainstable, Carlisle, Cumbria CA4 9QN
Ⓣ (01768) 896604
Ⓜ 07788 142969
Ⓔ roger@east-of-eden-nursery.co.uk
Ⓦ www.east-of-eden-nursery.co.uk
Contact: Roger Proud
Opening Times: Mar-Oct. Days & times variable, so please phone or email before calling.
Min Mail Order UK: £10.00
Cat. Cost: None issued
Credit Cards: All major credit/debit cards
Specialities: Interesting & unusual shrubs, perennials & alpines, esp. astilbes & geums with over 60 new *Geum* cvs, bred & raised on nursery.
Notes: Delivers to shows. Wheelchair accessible.
OS Grid Ref: NY467504

NEqu **Equatorial Plant Co.**
The Dovecote, Newgate, Barnard Castle, Co. Durham DL12 8NW
Ⓣ (01833) 908127
Ⓕ (01833) 908127
Ⓔ Equatorial9@gmail.com
Ⓦ www.equatorialplants.com
Contact: Dr Richard Warren
Opening Times: Mail order only. Open by appt. only.
Min Mail Order UK: Nmc
Min Mail Order EU: Nmc
Cat. Cost: Free.
Credit Cards: Visa, Access, Paypal
Specialities: Laboratory-raised orchids only.
Notes: Also sells wholesale. Exports beyond EU. Delivers to shows. Euro accepted.

NGBl **Garden Blooms**
Fieldgate, Mill Field Road, Fishlake, Doncaster, Yorkshire DN7 5GH
Ⓣ (01302) 288145
Ⓔ info@gardenblooms.co.uk
Ⓦ www.gardenblooms.co.uk
Contact: Liz Webster
Opening Times: Open by appt. or on Open Days. Contact nursery for details.
Min Mail Order UK: Nmc
Cat. Cost: Online only.
Credit Cards: All major credit/debit cards
Specialities: Hardy & tender perennials & small range of conservatory/house plants. Some plants available in small quantities only.
Notes: Delivers to shows.
OS Grid Ref: SE659148

NGdn **Garden House Nursery** ♿
The Square, Dalston, Carlisle, Cumbria CA5 7LL
Ⓣ (01228) 710297
Ⓜ 07595 219082
Ⓔ stephickso@hotmail.co.uk
Ⓦ www.gardenhousenursery.co.uk
Contact: Stephen Hickson
Opening Times: 0900-1700 Mon-Sat, 1000-1600 Sun, mid-Mar to Oct.
Cat. Cost: Plant list online only.
Specialities: *Geranium*, *Hosta*, *Hemerocallis*, *Iris*, grasses, *Brunnera*, *Pulmonaria* & *Aconitum*.
Notes: Also sells wholesale. Wheelchair accessible.
OS Grid Ref: NY369503

NGrd **Gardener's Cottage Plants**
Gardener's Cottage, Bingfield, Newcastle-upon-Tyne, Tyne and Wear NE19 2LE
Ⓣ 01434 672594
Ⓜ 07500 895052
Ⓔ andrew@gcplants.co.uk
Ⓦ www.gcplants.co.uk
Contact: Andrew Davenport
Opening Times: 0800-1700 Thu-Sat, Apr-Oct incl.
Min Mail Order UK: £4.95
Min Mail Order EU: £9.95
Credit Cards: None
Specialities: Perennials, herbs and wildflowers. The nursery runs on sustainable and organic principles whereby all plants sold are propagated on site in peat-free composts and reycled pots.
Notes: Also sells at plant fairs. Contact nursery for details.

NHal **Halls of Heddon**
West Heddon Nurseries, Heddon-on-the-Wall, Northumberland NE15 0JS
Ⓣ (01661) 852445
Ⓕ (01661) 852398
Ⓔ enquiry@hallsofheddon.co.uk
Ⓦ www.hallsofheddon.co.uk
Contact: David Hall
Opening Times: 0900-1700 Mon-Sat 1000-1700 Sun.
Min Mail Order UK: £10.00
Min Mail Order EU: £35.00
Cat. Cost: 3 × 2nd class
Credit Cards: MasterCard, Visa, Switch, Delta

Specialities: *Chrysanthemum* & *Dahlia*.
Notes: Also sells wholesale.
OS Grid Ref: NZ122679

NHar **Hartside Nursery Garden**
Penrith Road, Alston, Cumbria CA9 3BL
Ⓣ (01434) 381372
Ⓕ (01434) 381372
Ⓔ enquiries@plantswithaltitude.co.uk
Ⓦ www.plantswithaltitude.co.uk
Contact: Mr Neil Huntley
Opening Times: 1130-1630 Mon-Fri & 1230-1600 Sat, Sun & B/hols, Mar-Jun. 1130-1600 Tue-Fri, Jul-Oct. Other times by appt. only.
Min Mail Order UK: Nmc
Min Mail Order EU: £50.00 + p&p
Cat. Cost: 4 × 1st class.
Credit Cards: All major credit/debit cards
Specialities: *Primula*, include Asiatic, petiolaries, European and allionii forms. Autumn flowering gentians.
Notes: Delivers to shows.
OS Grid Ref: NY708447

NHaw **The Hawthornes Nursery** ♿
Marsh Road, Hesketh Bank, Nr Preston, Lancashire PR4 6XT
Ⓣ (01772) 812379
Ⓔ richardhaw@talktalk.net
Ⓦ www.hawthornes-nursery.co.uk
Contact: Irene & Richard Hodson
Opening Times: 0900-1800 7 days, Mar-Jun & Thu-Sun, July-Oct. Gardens open for NGS. Check with nursery for Nat. Collection Open Day 2017.
Min Mail Order UK: £10.00
Min Mail Order EU: Nmc
Cat. Cost: None issued.
Credit Cards: None
Specialities: *Clematis*. Nat. Collection of *Clematis viticella*.
Notes: Exports beyond the EU. Euro accepted. Wheelchair accessible.

NHic **Hic Bibi Nursery**
67 Coppull Moor Lane, Coppull, Chorley, Lancashire PR7 5JB
Ⓜ 07761 000780 or 07557 363882
Ⓔ hicbibinurseries@yahoo.co.uk
Ⓦ www.hicbibinurseries.co.uk
Contact: Fern Lane
Opening Times: 0800-1700 Mon-Fri.
Min Mail Order UK: £4.95
Credit Cards: All major credit/debit cards
Specialities: *Hebe*. Herbaceous perennials.
Notes: Also sells wholesale.
OS Grid Ref: SD 56654 12846

NHip **Hippopottering Nursery**
Orchard House, East Lound, Nr Doncaster, South Yorkshire DN9 2LR
Ⓜ 07979 764677
Ⓔ hippomaples@hotmail.co.uk
Ⓦ www.hippopottering.com
Contact: Pat Gibbons
Opening Times: By appt. only & Open Days.
Min Mail Order UK: £15.00 + p&p
Cat. Cost: Online only.
Credit Cards: Visa, MasterCard
Specialities: Japanese maples: *Acer palmatum*, *A. japonicum* & *A. shirasawanum*.
Notes: Mail order to UK throughout year; to EU during winter. Delivers to shows. Wheelchair accessible in dry weather only.

N

NHol **Holden Clough Nursery** ♿
Holden, Bolton-by-Bowland, Nr Clitheroe, Lancashire BB7 4PF
Ⓣ (01200) 447447
Ⓔ info@holdencloughnursery.com
Ⓦ www.holdencloughnursery.com
Contact: Kate Lawson
Opening Times: 0900-1700 Mon-Sat, 1030-1630 Sun, incl. B/hols. Closed Xmas Day & Boxing Day.
Min Mail Order UK: Nmc
Min Mail Order EU: Nmc
Cat. Cost: 2 × 1st class.
Credit Cards: All major credit/debit cards
Specialities: Large general list incl. perennials, esp. *Crocosmia*, shrubs, dwarf conifers, alpines, heathers, grasses & ferns.
Notes: Seasonal mail order on some items. Also sells wholesale on some items. Exports beyond EU. Delivers to shows. Wheelchair accessible.
OS Grid Ref: SD773496

NHoy **Hoyland Plant Centre**
Market Street, Hoyland, Barnsley, South Yorkshire S74 0ET
Ⓣ (01226) 744466
Ⓜ 07717 182169
Ⓕ (01226) 744466
Ⓔ hoylandplantcentre@btconnect.com
Ⓦ www.somethingforthegarden.co.uk
Contact: Steven Hickman
Opening Times: Open by appt. only.
Min Mail Order UK: Nmc
Min Mail Order EU: Nmc
Cat. Cost: Free online
Credit Cards: All major credit/debit cards
Specialities: Nat. Collections of *Agapanthus* & *Tulbaghia*. Also holds a large collection of *Clivia* & *Nerine*.
Notes: Nursery sales by appointment only.

Sells by mail order or at the major flower shows. Also sells wholesale. Exports beyond the EU. Delivers to shows. Euro accepted. Top of the nursery and glasshouse accessible to most wheelchairs
OS Grid Ref: SE372010

NHpl **Harperley Hall Farm Nurseries** ♿
Harperley, Stanley, Co. Durham DH9 9UB
Ⓣ (01207) 233318
Ⓜ 07944 644126
Ⓔ enquiries@harperleyhallfarmnurseries.co.uk
Ⓦ www.harperleyhallfarmnurseries.co.uk
Contact: Gary McDermott
Opening Times: Open on set days only. See website or phone for details.
Min Mail Order UK: Nmc
Min Mail Order EU: Nmc
Cat. Cost: None issued.
Credit Cards: All major credit/debit cards
Specialities: Growers of a wide range of alpine & woodland plants, incl. *Meconopsis* & *Primula*, many of which are rare or unusual. Also growers of a wide range of autumn-flowering gentians.
Notes: Also sells wholesale. Delivers to shows. Euro accepted. Wheelchair accessible.

NHsp **Hare Spring Cottage Plants**
Church Orchard, Church Wind, Alne, York, Yorkshire YO61 1RX
Ⓜ 07792 376805
Ⓔ stella@harespringcottageplants.co.uk
Ⓦ www.harespringcottageplants.co.uk
Contact: Stella Exley
Opening Times: By appointment only
Min Mail Order UK: Nmc
Min Mail Order EU: Nmc
Cat. Cost: Online only
Credit Cards: All major debit/credit cards except American Express
Specialities: *Camassia*, *Uvularia* & *Sidalcea*. Nat. Collection of *Camassia*. Some specialist plants available in small quantities only.
Notes: Sells at & delivers to specialist plant fairs. Talks to specialist groups & societies by arrangement. Also sells wholesale. Delivers to shows. Euro accepted.

NJRG **JRG Dahlias**
22 Summerville Road, Milnthorpe, Cumbria LA7 7DF
Ⓣ (01539) 562691
Ⓔ jack@jrg-dahlias.co.uk
Ⓦ www.jrg-dahlias.co.uk
Contact: Jack Gott
Opening Times: By appt. only.
Min Mail Order UK: £10.00 + p&p
Min Mail Order EU: Price with order.
Cat. Cost: Sae: 110mm × 220mm, 2nd class.
Credit Cards: Paypal
Specialities: *Dahlia*. Some available in small quantities only.
Notes: Delivers to shows.

NLAp **Laneside Hardy Orchid Nursery** ♿
74 Croston Road, Garstang, Preston, Lancashire PR3 1HR
Ⓣ (01995) 605537
Ⓜ 07946 659661
Ⓔ jcrhutch@aol.com
Ⓦ www.lanesidehardyorchids.co.uk
Contact: Jeff Hutchings
Opening Times: By appt. to collect orders only.
Min Mail Order UK: Nmc
Min Mail Order EU: Nmc
Cat. Cost: None issued.
Credit Cards: All major credit/debit cards
Specialities: Hardy terrestrial orchids & associated composts. *Cypripedium*, *Bletilla*, *Calanthe*, *Dacylorhiza*, *Anacamptis*, *Ophrys*, *Orchis* & *Platanthera*.
Notes: Exports beyond the EU. Delivers to shows. Wheelchair accessible.

NLar **Larch Cottage Nurseries** ♿ ◆
Melkinthorpe, Penrith, Cumbria CA10 2DR
Ⓣ (01931) 712404
Ⓕ (01931) 712727
Ⓔ plants@larchcottage.co.uk
Ⓦ www.larchcottage.co.uk
Contact: Peter & Joanne Stott
Opening Times: Daily from 1000-1730 (or dusk in winter), all year round.
Min Mail Order UK: £20.00 + p&p
Min Mail Order EU: £50.00 + p&p
Credit Cards: All major credit/debit cards
Specialities: Comprehensive plant collection in unique garden setting. Rare & unusual plants, particularly shrubs, trees, perennials, dwarf conifers & Japanese maples. *Acer*, *Hamamelis*, *Magnolia* & *Cornus kousa* cvs. Old-fashioned roses, bamboo & alpines.
Notes: Terraced restaurant, art gallery and shop open everyday. RHS partner gardens open Wed-Sun throughout the summer. Please check website for details. Wheelchair accessible.
OS Grid Ref: NY315602

NMen **Mendle Nursery** ♿
Holme, Scunthorpe, North Lincolnshire DN16 3RF
Ⓣ (01724) 850864
Ⓔ annearnshaw@lineone.net
Ⓦ www.mendlenursery.co.uk

Contact: Mrs A Earnshaw
Opening Times: 1000-1600 Tue-Sun.
Min Mail Order UK: Nmc
Min Mail Order EU: Nmc
Credit Cards: Paypal
Specialities: *Jovibarba*, *Saxifraga* & *Sempervivum*.
Notes: Wheelchair accessible.
OS Grid Ref: SE925070

NMir **MIRES BECK NURSERY** ♿
Low Mill Lane, North Cave,
Brough, East Riding, Yorkshire
HU15 2NR
Ⓣ (01430) 421543
Ⓕ (01430) 421543
Ⓔ admin@miresbeck.co.uk
Ⓦ www.miresbeck.co.uk
Contact: Sue Hewitt
Opening Times: 1000-1600 7 days, 1st Mar-30th Sep. 1000-1600 Mon-Fri, 1st Oct-30th Apr.
Min Mail Order UK: Nmc
Cat. Cost: 3 × 1st class.
Credit Cards: All major debit/credit cards except American Express
Specialities: Wildflower plants of Yorkshire provenance.
Notes: Mail order for wildflower plants & plugs only. Also sells wholesale. Wheelchair accessible.
OS Grid Ref: SE889316

NNor **NORCROFT NURSERIES** ♿
Roadends, Intack, Southwaite, Carlisle,
Cumbria CA4 0LH
Ⓣ (01697) 473933
Ⓔ info@norcroftnurseries.co.uk
Ⓦ www.norcroftnurseries.co.uk
Contact: Keith Bell
Opening Times: Every afternoon excl. Mon (open B/hol) Apr-Jul, or ring for appt.
Min Mail Order UK: Nmc
Cat. Cost: 2 × 2nd class
Credit Cards: None
Specialities: Hardy herbaceous, *Dianthus*, *Aquilegia*, *Hosta*, *Papaver*.
Notes: Also sells wholesale. Euro accepted. Wheelchair accessible.
OS Grid Ref: NY474433

NOra **ORANGE PIPPIN LTD**
(office) 33 Algarth Rise, Pocklington, York,
Yorkshire YO42 2HX
Ⓣ (01759) 392007
Ⓔ trees@orangepippin.com
Ⓦ www.orangepippintrees.co.uk
Contact: Maureen Borrie
Opening Times: Not open. Mail order online only.
Min Mail Order UK: Nmc
Min Mail Order EU: Nmc
Cat. Cost: Online only.
Credit Cards: MasterCard, Visa
Specialities: Wide range of fruit trees & ornamentals, incl. traditional & modern varieties. Wide choice of rootstocks & tree forms. Fruit tree expert available most days. Website incl. extensive tasting notes & variety comparisons.
Notes: Website for ornamental trees: www.pippintrees.co.uk. Order online all year round, deliveries from Aug-Apr. Exports beyond EU (to USA).

NPer **PERRY'S PLANTS** ♿
The River Garden, Sleights, Whitby, North
Yorkshire YO21 1RR
Ⓜ 07879 498623
Ⓔ richardperry008@hotmail.co.uk
Ⓦ www.perrysplants.co.uk
Contact: Sharon & Richard Perry
Opening Times: 1000-1700 mid-March to Oct.
Cat. Cost: None published.
Credit Cards: None
Specialities: *Lavatera*, *Malva*, *Erysimum*, *Euphorbia*, *Anthemis*, *Osteospermum* & *Hebe*. Uncommon hardy & container plants & aquatic plants.
Notes: Euro accepted. Wheelchair accessible.
OS Grid Ref: NZ869082

NPol **POLEMONIUM PLANTERY**
28 Sunnyside, Trimdon Grange, Co. Durham
TS29 6HF
Ⓣ (01429) 881529
Ⓔ dandd@polemonium.co.uk
Ⓦ www.polemonium.co.uk
Contact: David or Dianne Nichol-Brown
Opening Times: By appt. only.
Min Mail Order UK: £10.00
Cat. Cost: 3 × 1st class
Credit Cards: All major credit/debit cards, Paypal
Specialities: Nat. Collections of *Polemonium*, *Collomia*, *Gilia*, *Leptodactylon* (*Polemoniaceae*) & *Hakonechloa*.
Notes: Also sells wholesale. Delivers to shows.
OS Grid Ref: NZ369353

NPri **PRIMROSE COTTAGE NURSERY** ♿
Ringway Road, Moss Nook, Wythenshawe,
Manchester M22 5WF
Ⓣ (0161) 437 1557
Ⓜ 07798 754457
Ⓔ info@primrosecottagenursery.co.uk
Ⓦ www.primrosecottagenursery.co.uk

N

Contact: Caroline Dumville
Opening Times: 0900-1730 Mon-Sat, 0930-1700 Sun (summer). 0900-1700 Mon-Sat, 0930-1700 Sun (winter).
Credit Cards: All major credit/debit cards
Specialities: Perennials, herbs, patio & hanging basket plants, always lots of new & unusual varieties. Shrubs, roses, ornamental trees, fruit trees, soft fruit bushes, bedding & vegetable plants.
Notes: Refreshments area open daily. Wheelchair accessible.

NQui **QUIET CORNER PLANTS**
(office) 20 Grove Road, Brandon, Co. Durham DH7 8AW
Ⓜ 07932 159204
Ⓔ hal@uwclub.net
Ⓦ www.quietcornerplants.co.uk
Contact: Howard Leslie
Opening Times: 1100-1700 (or sunset in winter), closed Tue & Thu.
Min Mail Order UK: Nmc
Cat. Cost: Online only.
Credit Cards: All major credit/debit cards
Specialities: Hardy herbaceous & shrubby perennials, incl. small quantities of lesser known and harder to find plants.
Notes: Nursery is at Misty Blue Farm, Rock Road, Kirk Merrington, Co. Durham DL16 7HJ. Also sells wholesale. Delivers to shows.

N

NRHS **HARLOW CARR PLANT CENTRE (RHS)** ◆
RHS Garden Harlow Carr, Crag Lane, Harlow Carr, Harrogate, North Yorkshire HG3 1QB
Ⓣ (01423) 724666
Ⓕ (01423) 569521
Ⓔ nigeleaton@rhs.org.uk
Ⓦ www.rhs.org.uk
Contact: Any member of staff
Specialities: Wide general range, particularly alpines.
Notes: Programme of free plant events throughout the year. Please ring or check website for details. Customer ordering system for plants which need to be collected from the plant centre (no mail order).

NRib **RIBBLESDALE NURSERIES** ♿
Newsham Hall Lane, Woodplumpton, Preston, Lancashire PR4 0AS
Ⓣ (01772) 863081
Ⓔ philsd@btinternet.com
Ⓦ www.ribblesdalenurseries.co.uk
Contact: Mr & Mrs Dunnett
Opening Times: 0900-1800 Mon-Sat, Apr-Sep. 0900-1700 Mon-Sat, Oct-Mar. 1030-1630 Sun.
Credit Cards: All major credit/debit cards
Specialities: Trees, shrubs & perennials. Conifers, hedging, alpines, fruit, climbers, herbs, aquatics, ferns & wildflowers. Own grown plants in peat-free compost.
Notes: Wheelchair accessible.
OS Grid Ref: SD515351

NRob **W ROBINSON & SON (SEEDS & PLANTS) LTD** ♿
Sunny Bank, Forton, Nr Preston, Lancashire PR3 0BN
Ⓣ (01524) 791210
Ⓕ (01524) 791933
Ⓔ info@mammothonion.co.uk
Ⓦ www.mammothonion.co.uk
Contact: Miss Robinson
Opening Times: 1000-1600 7 days Mar-Jun, 0800-1700 Mon-Fri Jul-Feb.
Min Mail Order UK: Nmc
Min Mail Order EU: Nmc
Cat. Cost: Free.
Credit Cards: All major credit/debit cards
Specialities: Mammoth vegetable seed. Onions, leeks, tomatoes & beans. Range of vegetable plants in the spring.
Notes: Also sells wholesale. Exports beyond EU. Delivers to shows. Euro accepted. Wheelchair accessible.

NRya **RYAL NURSERY** ♿
East Farm Cottage, Ryal, Northumberland NE20 0SA
Ⓣ (01661) 886562
Ⓔ alpines@ryal.freeserve.co.uk
Contact: R F Hadden
Opening Times: Mar-Jul by appt., please phone in advance.
Cat. Cost: Sae.
Credit Cards: None
Specialities: Alpine & woodland plants, mainly available in small quantities only. Nat. Collection of *Primula marginata*.
Notes: Also sells wholesale. Delivers to shows. Wheelchair accessible.
OS Grid Ref: NZ015744

NSla **SLACK TOP ALPINE NURSERY**
Alpine House, 22A Slack Top, Hebden Bridge, West Yorkshire HX7 7HA
Ⓣ (01422) 845348
Ⓜ 07392 856395
Ⓔ enquiries@slacktopnurseries.co.uk
Ⓦ www.slacktopnurseries.co.uk

Contact: Michael & Allison Mitchell
Opening Times: 1000-1700 Fri-Sun, Mar-Aug & B/hols. Other times by appt.
Min Mail Order UK: £20.00
Min Mail Order EU: £50.00
Cat. Cost: 2 × 1st class A5 sae or online.
Credit Cards: All major credit/debit cards
Specialities: Alpine, rockery & woodland plants.
Notes: Talks given to gardening clubs & other groups by appt. Delivers to shows. Euro accepted. Some areas of garden inaccessible for wheelchairs.
OS Grid Ref: SD977286

NSti **Stillingfleet Lodge Nurseries** ♿
Stewart Lane, Stillingfleet, York
YO19 6HP
Ⓣ (01904) 728506
Ⓔ info@stillingfleetlodgenurseries.co.uk
Ⓦ www.stillingfleetlodgenurseries.co.uk
Contact: Vanessa Cook
Opening Times: 1300-1700 Wed & Fri, 1st Apr-30th Sep. 1300-1700, 1st & 3rd Sat & Sun in each month.
Cat. Cost: Online only.
Credit Cards: All major credit/debit cards
Specialities: Foliage & unusual perennials. Hardy geraniums, *Pulmonaria*, variegated plants & grasses.
Notes: Wheelchair accessible.

NSue **Sue Proctor Plants**
69 Ings Mill Avenue, Clayton West, Huddersfield, West Yorkshire HD8 9QG
Ⓣ (01484) 866189
Ⓜ 07917 006636
Ⓔ hostas@sueproctorplants.co.uk
Ⓦ www.sueproctorplants.co.uk
Contact: Richard Proctor
Opening Times: By appt. only. Please phone first.
Min Mail Order UK: £3.50
Cat. Cost: 1st class sae.
Credit Cards: All major credit/debit cards
Specialities: *Hosta*, especially miniature hostas.
Notes: Delivers to shows.

NSum **Summerdale Garden Nursery**
Summerdale House, Cow Brow, Lupton, Carnforth, Lancashire LA6 1PE
Ⓣ (01539) 567210
Ⓔ sheals@btinternet.com
Ⓦ www.summerdalegardenplants.co.uk
Contact: Gail Sheals
Opening Times: 1000-1630 Thu, Fri & Sat, 1st Apr-31st Aug. Other times by appt. only.
Min Mail Order UK: Nmc
Cat. Cost: Online only.
Credit Cards: None
Specialities: Shade-loving perennials. *Primula*, including *P. auricula* cultivars.
Notes: Mail order for primulas only. Delivers to shows.
OS Grid Ref: SD545819

NTPC **Tree Peony Company**
Willow Cottage, Rillington, Malton, North Yorkshire
YO17 8JU
Ⓣ (01944) 758280
Ⓔ info@treepeony.co.uk
Ⓦ www.treepeony.co.uk
Contact: Thelma Scruton, Roger Scruton
Min Mail Order UK: £12.00
Min Mail Order EU: Nmc
Cat. Cost: None.
Credit Cards: None
Specialities: Tree peonies. *Paeonia suffruticosa. P.* Gansu Group. *P. rockii.*
Notes: Also sells wholesale. Euro accepted. Delivers to shows.

NTre **Treetyme**
Prospect Hill House, Kirkoswald, Penrith, Cumbria CA10 1ER
Ⓣ (01768) 800238
Ⓕ (01768) 897138
Ⓔ sales@treetyme.co.uk
Ⓦ www.treetyme.co.uk
Contact: Hugh Povey
Opening Times: Not open. Visits by appt. only. Mail order via website only.
Min Mail Order UK: Nmc
Min Mail Order EU: Nmc
Cat. Cost: Online only.
Credit Cards: None
Specialities: *Cercis.* Stock available in small quantities only. Nat. Collection of *Cercis.*
Notes: Collection from nursery available by appointment. Only accept payment by cheque, BACS or cash. Also sells wholesale.

NWad **Waddow Lodge Garden** ♿
Clitheroe Road, Waddington, Clitheroe, Lancashire BB7 3HQ
Ⓣ (01200) 429145
Ⓔ peterfoleyhcn@hotmail.co.uk
Ⓦ www.gardentalks.co.uk
Contact: Peter Foley
Opening Times: By appt. only all year. Also open under NGS 1300-1700 28th May & 16th Jul 2017 with plant sales for Plant Heritage NW Group.
Min Mail Order UK: Nmc

N

Min Mail Order EU: Nmc
Cat. Cost: Online only.
Credit Cards: None
Specialities: A developing plantsman's garden with an ever-changing & interesting plant collection. Some plants may only be available in small numbers.
Notes: Open for group visits by appt., incl. evenings. Wheelchair accessible.
OS Grid Ref: SD732434

NWea **WEASDALE NURSERIES LTD.**
Newbiggin-on-Lune, Kirkby Stephen, Cumbria CA17 4LX
Ⓣ (015396) 23246
Ⓕ (015396) 23277
Ⓔ sales@weasdale.com
Ⓦ www.weasdale.com
Contact: Andrew Forsyth
Opening Times: 0830-1730 Mon-Fri. Closed for lunch 1300-1400 Closed w/ends, B/hols.
Min Mail Order UK: Nmc
Min Mail Order EU: Nmc
Cat. Cost: Free of charge in UK or £2.00 to EU.
Credit Cards: All major credit/debit cards
Specialities: Hardy forest trees, hedging, broadleaved & conifers. Specimen trees & shrubs grown at 850ft (260m) elevation. Some rarer plants grown in small batches, so availability can't be guaranteed. Peat-free.
Notes: Mail order a speciality. Mail order Nov-Apr only. Also sells wholesale to VAT registered customers.
OS Grid Ref: NY 68986 03904

S

NWms **WOODMOSS FUCHSIAS** ♿
Woodmoss Lane Nursery, Woodmoss Lane, Scarisbrick, Ormskirk, Lancashire L40 9RJ
Ⓣ (01253) 980667
Ⓜ 07849 080248
Ⓔ woodmossfuchsia@yahoo.co.uk
Contact: Brian Houghton & Keith Middleton
Opening Times: 0900-1600 Mon-Fri, 0900-1230 Sat, Jan-end Jun. B/hols & w/ends by appt.
Min Mail Order UK: £13.50 for 6 plants.
Cat. Cost: Free, or by email.
Credit Cards: None
Specialities: *Fuchsia*. New varieties may be available in small quantities only.
Notes: Wheelchair accessible.

NWsh **WESTSHORES NURSERIES**
82 West Street, Winterton, Scunthorpe, Lincolnshire DN15 9QF
Ⓣ (01724) 733940
Ⓜ 07875 732535
Ⓔ westshnur@aol.com
Ⓦ www.westshores.co.uk
Contact: Gail & John Summerfield
Opening Times: 1st Mar-31st Oct. Please check before visiting.
Min Mail Order UK: £15.00
Cat. Cost: Online only.
Credit Cards: All major credit/debit cards
Specialities: Ornamental grasses, autumn flowering perennials & scented pelargoniums.
Notes: Wide selection of talks for gardening clubs and Hardy Plant Society groups.
OS Grid Ref: SE927187

SOUTHERN

SAdn **ASHDOWN FOREST GARDEN CENTRE & NURSERY** ♿
Duddleswell, Ashdown Forest, East Sussex TN22 3JP
Ⓣ (01825) 712300
Ⓔ victoria@ashdownforestgardencentre.co.uk
Ⓦ www.ashdownforestgardencentre.co.uk
Contact: Victoria Falletti
Opening Times: 0900-1700 winter, 0900-1700 summer.
Min Mail Order UK: Nmc
Credit Cards: All major credit/debit cards
Specialities: *Lapageria*, *Fuchsia*, conservatory climbers, unusual shrubs. Available in small quantities only.
Notes: Wheelchair accessible.
OS Grid Ref: TQ468283

SAko **AKORN AND OAKE**
18 Twyford Avenue, Southampton, Hampshire SO15 5NP
Ⓣ (023) 8034 4040
Ⓜ 07973 149404
Ⓔ stefan.rau@hotmail.co.uk
Contact: Stefan Rau
Opening Times: Open by appt. only.
Specialities: *Saxifraga*.
Notes: Delivers to shows.

SAll **ALLWOODS (HASSOCKS) LTD** ♿
London Road, Hassocks, West Sussex BN6 9NA
Ⓣ (01273) 844229
Ⓔ info@allwoods.net
Ⓦ www.allwoods.net
Contact: David & Emma James
Opening Times: Office 0900-1630 Mon-Fri. Answer machine all other times. Office closed B/hols and Xmas-New Year. Visits by prior arrangement only.
Min Mail Order UK: Nmc

Min Mail Order EU: Nmc
Cat. Cost: £2.00
Credit Cards: All major debit/credit cards except American Express. Paypal.
Specialities: Large collection of *Dianthus*, incl. hardy border carnations, pinks, perpetual flowering & spray carnations, Malmaisons & *D. allwoodii*. Unusual & collectors' geraniums & pelargoniums. *Fuchsia*, Penstemons & other garden plants. Succulents.
Notes: All listed varieties available as plugs but choice varies depending on time of year. Please phone before travelling to avoid disappointment &/or to ensure order is ready for collection. Also sells wholesale. Wheelchair accessible.

SArc ARCHITECTURAL PLANTS LTD ♿
Stane Street, North Heath, Pulborough, West Sussex RH20 1DJ
Ⓣ (01798) 879213
Ⓜ 07468 698772
Ⓔ enquiries@architecturalplants.com
Ⓦ www.architecturalplants.com
Contact: Cindy Hines
Opening Times: 0900-1700 Mon-Sat & B/hols. Closed Sun.
Cat. Cost: Free
Credit Cards: All major debit/credit cards except American Express
Specialities: Architectural plants & hardy exotics esp. rare evergreen broadleaved trees & seaside exotics, spiky plants, yuccas/agaves, climbers, topiary & bamboos.
Notes: Also sells wholesale. Delivers to shows. Wheelchair accessible (& available on site).
OS Grid Ref: TQ192262

SBch BIRCHWOOD PLANTS
(office) 10 Westering, Romsey, Hampshire SO51 7LY
Ⓣ (01794) 502192
Ⓜ 07874 678175
Ⓔ birchwoodplants@gmail.com
Ⓦ www.birchwoodplants.co.uk
Contact: Lesley Baker
Opening Times: Not open to the public. Plants can be collected by arrangement from sales & shows.
Min Mail Order UK: £15 + p&p
Min Mail Order EU: £15+ p&p
Cat. Cost: Online only.
Credit Cards: Paypal
Specialities: Alpines & drought-tolerant plants. Plants to attract bees & butterflies. Unusual plants. Predominantly growing peat-free. Nat. Collection of *Geranium nodosum*.
A small nursery only able to supply plants in small quantities.
Notes: Mail order mostly for small plants. No mail order sent Dec-Jan. Delivers to shows.
OS Grid Ref: SU333190

SBdl GROW AT BROGDALE
Brogdale Farm, Brogdale Road, Faversham, Kent
ME13 8XZ
Ⓣ (01795) 531888
Ⓕ (01795) 531710
Ⓔ fruit@brogdaleonline.co.uk
Ⓦ www.brogdaleonline.co.uk
Contact: Donna Cooper
Min Mail Order UK: Nmc
Min Mail Order EU: Nmc
Cat. Cost: £4.95
Credit Cards: Visa, MasterCard, Switch
Specialities: Over 5000 fruit varieties, most of which can be propagated to order. Holders of several Nat. Collections of Fruit.
Notes: Also sells wholesale. Exports beyond EU. Euro accepted.

SBir BIRCHFLEET NURSERIES ◆
Greenfields Close, Nyewood, Petersfield, Hampshire GU31 5JQ
Ⓣ (01730) 821636
Ⓕ (01730) 821636
Ⓔ gammoak@aol.com
Ⓦ www.birchfleetnurseries.co.uk
Contact: John & Daphne Gammon
Opening Times: By appt. only. For 2017 Open Days, please contact nursery.
Cat. Cost: 2 × 1st class.
Credit Cards: None
Specialities: Oak, beech, *Nyssa*. Nat. Collection of *Liquidambar*.
Notes: Also sells wholesale. Nursery accessible for wheelchairs in dry weather.

SBri BRICKWALL COTTAGE NURSERY
1 Brickwall Cottages, Frittenden, Cranbrook, Kent
TN17 2DH
Ⓣ (01580) 852425
Ⓜ 07714 529946
Ⓔ sue.martin@talktalk.net
Ⓦ www.geumcollection.co.uk
Contact: Sue Martin
Opening Times: By appt. only.
Min Mail Order UK: Nmc
Min Mail Order EU: Nmc
Credit Cards: None
Specialities: Hardy perennials. Stock available in small quantities only. Nat. Collection of *Geum*.

Notes: Limited wheelchair access.
OS Grid Ref: TQ815410

SBrt **Brighton Plants** ♿
New Hall Lane, Small Dole, Sussex BN5 9YJ
Ⓜ 07955 744802
Ⓔ brighton.plants@gmail.com
Ⓦ www.brightonplants.blogspot.com
Contact: Steve Law
Opening Times: Open by appt. only. Please email/phone before visiting.
Min Mail Order UK: Nmc
Min Mail Order EU: Nmc
Cat. Cost: 4 × 1st class.
Credit Cards: None
Specialities: Hardy herbaceous and woody plants. Drought-tolerant plants.
Notes: Delivers to shows. Euro accepted. Wheelchair accessible.
OS Grid Ref: TQ208132

S

SCac **Cacti & Succulents**
Hammerfield, Crockham Hill, Edenbridge, Kent TN8 6RR
Ⓣ (01732) 866295
Contact: Geoff Southon
Opening Times: Flexible. Please phone first.
Min Mail Order UK: Nmc
Cat. Cost: None issued.
Credit Cards: None
Specialities: *Echeveria* & related genera & hybrids. A large range of *Aeonium*, both species & hybrids, possibly the largest collection in the country. Many available in small quantities only.

SCam **Camellia Grove Nursery** ♿
Market Garden, Lower Beeding, West Sussex RH13 6PP
Ⓣ (01403) 891412
Ⓔ lp@hortic.com
Ⓦ www.camellia-grove.com
Contact: Chris Loder
Opening Times: 1000-1600 Mon-Sat, please phone first so we can give you our undivided attention.
Min Mail Order UK: Nmc
Min Mail Order EU: Nmc
Cat. Cost: 2 × 1st class.
Credit Cards: All major debit/credit cards except American Express
Specialities: *Camellia japonica*, *C. williamsii*, *C. sasanqua* & *C. reticulata*, from the purest white to richest red flowers.
Notes: Also sells wholesale. Exports beyond EU. Delivers to shows. Euro accepted. Wheelchair accessible.
OS Grid Ref: TQ221255

SChF **Charleshurst Farm Nursery**
Loxwood Road, Plaistow, Billingshurst, West Sussex RH14 0NY
Ⓣ (01403) 752273
Ⓜ 07736 522788
Ⓔ Charleshurstfarm@aol.com
Ⓦ www.charleshurstplants.co.uk
Contact: Clive Mellor
Opening Times: Normally 0900-1730 Fri, Sat, Sun, Feb-Oct, but please ring before travelling.
Min Mail Order UK: Nmc
Min Mail Order EU: Nmc
Cat. Cost: Online only.
Credit Cards: All major credit/debit cards
Specialities: Shrubs including some more unusual species. Good range of daphnes & Japanese maples.
Notes: Delivers to shows. Euro accepted.
OS Grid Ref: TQ015308

SChr **John Churcher**
47 Grove Avenue, Portchester, Fareham, Hampshire PO16 9EZ
Ⓣ (023) 9232 6740
Ⓜ 07717 495861
Ⓔ johnchurcher47@btinternet.com
Contact: John Churcher
Opening Times: By appt. only. Please phone or email.
Min Mail Order UK: Nmc
Min Mail Order EU: Nmc
Cat. Cost: None issued.
Credit Cards: None
Specialities: Hardy exotics for the Mediterranean-style garden, incl. palms, tree ferns, *Musa*, hedychiums, cycads, *Agave*, *Aloe*, *Opuntia* & echiums. Stock available in small quantities only.
OS Grid Ref: SU614047

SCit **The Citrus Centre** ♿
West Mare Lane, Marehill, Pulborough, West Sussex RH20 2EA
Ⓣ (01798) 872786
Ⓔ enquiries@citruscentre.co.uk
Ⓦ www.citruscentre.co.uk
Contact: Amanda & Chris Dennis
Opening Times: 0930-1600 Tue-Sat. Phone or check website for Xmas & B/hol opening times.
Min Mail Order UK: Nmc
Min Mail Order EU: Nmc
Cat. Cost: Online.
Credit Cards: Visa, MasterCard
Specialities: *Citrus* & *Citrus* relatives.
Notes: Wheelchair accessible.

SCmr **Cromar Nursery** ♿
39 Livesey Street, North Pole, Wateringbury, Maidstone, Kent ME18 5BQ
Ⓣ (01622) 812380
Ⓔ CromarNursery@aol.com
Ⓦ www.cromarnursery.co.uk
Contact: Debra & Martin Cronk
Opening Times: 0930-1630 Thu, Fri, Sat, Sun. Please check website or phone if travelling far.
Min Mail Order UK: Nmc
Min Mail Order EU: Nmc
Cat. Cost: 2 × 1st class.
Credit Cards: All major credit/debit cards
Specialities: Ornamental & fruit trees.
Notes: Wheelchair accessible.
OS Grid Ref: TQ697547

SCob **Coblands Online**
Trench Road, Tonbridge, Kent TN11 9NG
Ⓣ (01452) 742445
Ⓔ info@coblands.co.uk
Ⓦ www.coblands.co.uk
Contact: Daniel Slinger
Opening Times: 0800-1700 Mon-Sat, all year. Closed for Xmas/New Year.
Min Mail Order UK: Nmc
Min Mail Order EU: Nmc
Credit Cards: All major credit/debit cards
Specialities: Wide range of plants esp. herbaceous perennials of garden-worthiness incl. many new varieties. *Hebe*, *Hydrangea*, *Phormium*, *Brunnera*, *Echinacea*, *Epimedium*, *Heuchera*, *Hosta*, *Rudbeckia* & ferns. Wide range of established specimen plants. New introductions may be in limited supply.
Notes: Free delivery on website orders over £25. Also sells wholesale.
OS Grid Ref: TQ586487

SCog **Coghurst Camellias** ♿
Ivy House Lane, Three Oaks, Hastings, East Sussex TN35 4NP
Ⓣ (01424) 756228
Ⓕ (01424) 756228
Ⓔ rotherview@btinternet.com
Ⓦ www.rotherview.com
Contact: Wendy Bates
Opening Times: 1000-1700 7 days, Mar-Sep. 1000-1530 Tue-Sun, Oct-Mar.
Min Mail Order UK: Nmc
Min Mail Order EU: Nmc
Cat. Cost: 6 × 1st class stamps.
Credit Cards: All major credit/debit cards
Specialities: Alpines, ferns, *Camellia*.
Notes: Nursery is on the same site as Rotherview Nursery. Delivers to shows. Euro accepted. Wheelchair accessible.

SCoo **Cooling's Nurseries Ltd** ♿
Rushmore Hill, Knockholt, Sevenoaks, Kent TN14 7NN
Ⓣ (01959) 532269
Ⓕ (01959) 534092
Ⓔ Plantfinder@coolings.co.uk
Ⓦ www.coolings.co.uk
Contact: Mark Reeve or Garry Norris
Opening Times: 0900-1700 Mon-Sat & 0900-1630 Sun.
Min Mail Order UK: Nmc
Cat. Cost: None issued
Credit Cards: All major debit/credit cards except American Express
Specialities: Large range of perennials, conifers & bedding plants. Many unusual shrubs & trees. Third generation family business.
Notes: Display garden. Coffee shop. Wheelchair accessible.
OS Grid Ref: TK477610

SDay **A La Carte Daylilies**
Little Hermitage, St Catherine's Down, Ventnor, Isle of Wight PO38 2PD
Ⓣ (01983) 730512
Ⓔ andy.hyjack@googlemail.com
Ⓦ www.alacartedaylilies.co.uk
Contact: Jan & Andy Wyers
Opening Times: Mail order only. Open by appt. only. Difficult to find on an unmade private road, phone/email for directions.
Min Mail Order UK: Nmc
Min Mail Order EU: Nmc
Cat. Cost: 3 × 1st class.
Credit Cards: None
Specialities: *Hemerocallis*. Nat. Collections of Miniature & Small Flowered *Hemerocallis* & Large Flowered *Hemerocallis* (post-1960 award-winning cultivars).
Notes: Euro accepted.
OS Grid Ref: SZ499787

SDea **Deacon's Nursery** ♿ ◆
Moor View, Godshill, Isle of Wight PO38 3HW
Ⓣ (01983) 840750 (24 hrs) or (01983) 522243
Ⓕ (01983) 523575
Ⓔ info@deaconsnurseryfruits.co.uk
Ⓦ www.deaconsnurseryfruits.co.uk
Contact: G D & B H W Deacon
Opening Times: 0800-1600 Mon-Fri, May-Sep. 0800-1700 Mon-Fri, 0800-1200 Sat, Oct-Apr.
Min Mail Order UK: Nmc
Min Mail Order EU: Nmc
Cat. Cost: Free.

S

Credit Cards: All major debit/credit cards except American Express
Specialities: Over 300 varieties of apple, old & new, apricots, cherries, damsons, gages, nectarines, peaches, pears, plums. Modern soft fruit, grapes, hops, nuts & family trees.
Notes: Also sells wholesale. Exports beyond EU. Euro accepted. Wheelchair accessible.

SDeJ **P. de Jager & Sons Ltd** ♿ ◆
Church Farm, Ulcombe, Maidstone, Kent ME17 1DN
Ⓣ (01622) 840229
Ⓕ (01622) 844073
Ⓔ flowerbulbs@dejager.co.uk
Ⓦ www.dejager.co.uk
Contact: George Clowes
Opening Times: Mail order only. Orders taken from 0900-1700 Mon-Fri
Min Mail Order UK: Nmc
Min Mail Order EU: Nmc
Cat. Cost: Free
Credit Cards: All major credit/debit cards
Specialities: Wide range of all flower bulbs.
Notes: Also sells wholesale. Exports beyond EU. Euro accepted. Wheelchair accessible.

S

SDow **Downderry Nursery** ♿
Pillar Box Lane, Hadlow, Nr Tonbridge, Kent TN11 9SW
Ⓣ (01732) 810081
Ⓔ info@downderry-nursery.co.uk
Ⓦ www.downderry-nursery.co.uk
Contact: Dr Simon Charlesworth
Opening Times: 1000-1700 Thu-Sun 1st May-30th Sep & B/hols. Other times by appt.
Min Mail Order UK: Nmc
Min Mail Order EU: Nmc
Cat. Cost: None issued.
Credit Cards: Delta, MasterCard, Maestro, Visa
Specialities: Nat. Collections of *Lavandula* and *Rosmarinus*.
Notes: Euro accepted. Wheelchair accessible.
OS Grid Ref: TQ625521

SDys **Dysons Nurseries** ♿
Great Comp Garden, Platt, Sevenoaks, Kent TN15 8QS
Ⓣ (01732) 885094
Ⓜ 07887 997663
Ⓔ dysonsorders@greatcompgarden.co.uk
Ⓦ www.dysonsalvias.com
Contact: William T Dyson
Opening Times: 1100-1700 7 days 1st Apr-31st Oct. Other times by appt.
Cat. Cost: Online only.
Credit Cards: All major credit/debit cards
Specialities: Salvias & an eclectic range of choice and uncommon plants.
Notes: Delivers to shows. Wheelchair accessible.

SEle **Eleplants Nursery**
32 Framfield Road, Uckfield, East Sussex TN22 5AH
Ⓣ (01825) 760356
Ⓜ 07810 660109
Ⓔ eleplantsnursery@talk21.com
Ⓦ www.eleplantsnursery.co.uk
Contact: Martin Batchelor
Opening Times: Not open but can be visited by prior appt. only.
Min Mail Order UK: Nmc
Min Mail Order EU: Nmc
Credit Cards: All major credit/debit cards, Paypal
Specialities: Shrubs.
Notes: Exports beyond EU. Delivers to shows.

SEND **East Northdown Nurseries** ♿
George Hill Road (B2052), Margate, Kent CT10 3BN
Ⓣ (01843) 862060
Ⓜ 07714 241668 or 07714 241667
Ⓔ info@botanyplants.co.uk
Ⓦ www.botanyplants.co.uk
Contact: Louise & William Friend
Opening Times: 0900-1700 7 days, all year except Sun in winter. Closed Xmas week.
Min Mail Order UK: Nmc
Cat. Cost: Online only.
Credit Cards: All major credit/debit cards
Specialities: Chalk & coast-loving plants. Specimen shrubs & bamboos available. Complimentary range of plants for damp/acid conditions available to order from our Mucklestone Nursery (MMuc). Collection of rare Mediterranean plants.
Notes: Free consultation/advice. Plant selection service. Tea room & gardens. Close to Botany Bay. Lectures given to gardening groups in Kent. Garden tours by appt. See website or contact nursery for full list & details. Wheelchair accessible.
OS Grid Ref: TR383702

SEWo **English Woodlands** ♿
Burrow Nursery, Herrings Lane, Cross-in-Hand, Heathfield, East Sussex TN21 0UG
Ⓣ (01435) 862992
Ⓕ (01435) 867742
Ⓔ sales@englishwoodlands.com
Ⓦ www.englishwoodlands.com
Contact: Joanne Carter

Opening Times: 0800-1700 Mon-Fri. 0800-1600 Sat. Closed Sun & B/hols.
Min Mail Order UK: £25.00
Cat. Cost: Free.
Credit Cards: All major debit/credit cards except American Express
Specialities: Trees, shrubs, hedging. Phone to check plant availability before visiting.
Notes: Also sells wholesale. Wheelchair accessible.
OS Grid Ref: TQ567222

SFai FAIRWEATHER'S GARDEN CENTRE ♿
High Street, Beaulieu, Hampshire SO42 7YB
Ⓣ (01590) 612307
Ⓕ (01590) 612519
Ⓔ info@fairweathers.co.uk
Ⓦ www.fairweathers.co.uk
Contact: Sue Greaves
Opening Times: 0900-1700 7 days.
Min Mail Order UK: Nmc
Cat. Cost: None issued.
Credit Cards: Visa, MasterCard
Specialities: *Agapanthus* & *Lavandula.*
Notes: Wheelchair accessible.

SGbt GILBERT'S NURSERY ♿
Dandy's Ford Lane, Sherfield English, Romsey, Hampshire SO51 6DT
Ⓣ (01794) 322566
Ⓔ gilbertsnursery@aol.com
Ⓦ www.gilbertsnursery.co.uk
Contact: Nick Gilbert
Opening Times: 0900-1700 Tue-Sat, 1000-1630 Sun, all year round. Dahlia field open from 2nd week Aug to 2nd week Oct.
Min Mail Order UK: Nmc
Min Mail Order EU: Nmc
Cat. Cost: 2 × 1st class
Credit Cards: All major debit/credit cards except American Express
Specialities: *Dahlia.* Proper plant nursery with many unusual plants & staff happy to share their knowledge & help with plant selection.
Notes: *Dahlia* field with over 400 cvs on view (grass pathways). See above for opening times or go to www.gilbertsdahlias.co.uk. Tea room. Delivers to shows. Wheelchair accessible.

SGol GOLDEN HILL NURSERIES ♿
Lordsfield, Goudhurst Road, Marden, Kent TN12 9LT
Ⓣ (01622) 833218
Ⓜ 07826 523655
Ⓕ (01622) 832528
Ⓔ enquiries@goldenhillplants.com
Ⓦ www.goldenhillplants.com
Contact: Roger Butler
Opening Times: 0900-1700 Mon-Sat, 1st Mar-31st Oct. 0900-1600 Mon-Sat, 1st Nov-28th Feb. 1100-1600 Sun from 3rd Sun in Feb until Xmas.
Min Mail Order UK: Nmc
Cat. Cost: Online only.
Credit Cards: All major credit/debit cards
Specialities: Specimen plants, shrubs, grasses, bamboos, Japanese maples, conifers & trees.
Notes: Also sells wholesale. Euro accepted. Wheelchair accessible.

SHaC HART CANNA ♿
27 Guildford Road West, Farnborough, Hampshire GU14 6PS
Ⓣ (01252) 514421
Ⓜ 07762 950000
Ⓔ sales@hartcanna.com
Ⓦ www.hartcanna.co.uk
Contact: Keith Hayward
Opening Times: By arrangement.
Min Mail Order UK: Nmc
Min Mail Order EU: Nmc
Cat. Cost: Online only.
Credit Cards: All major credit/debit cards
Specialities: *Canna.* Nat. Collection of *Canna.*
Notes: Also sells wholesale. Euro accepted. Delivers to shows. Wheelchair accessible.

SHal HALL'S COURT NURSERY ♿
Pluckley Road, Bethersden, Ashford, Kent TN26 3ET
Ⓣ (01233) 820828
Ⓜ 07729 418275
Ⓔ info@hallscourt.co.uk
Ⓦ www.hallscourt.co.uk
Contact: Jeanette Jahnz
Opening Times: 0900-1700 every w/end, end Mar-beginning Oct. Weekdays by arrangement.
Cat. Cost: Online only.
Credit Cards: Visa, MasterCard, Maestro
Specialities: At least 90 varieties of hardy geraniums. Over 20 varieties of scented leaf pelargoniums, plus some species, zonal & ivy leaf. Perennials, grasses, hardy fuchsias, alpines, herbs & some succulents. Some plants available in small quantities only.
Notes: Small nursery, situated midway between Ashford and Tenterden in rural Kent. Euro accepted. Wheelchair accessible.
OS Grid Ref: TQ919414

SHar HARDY'S COTTAGE GARDEN PLANTS ♿
Priory Lane Nursery, Freefolk Priors, Whitchurch, Hampshire RG28 7FA
Ⓣ (01256) 896533
Ⓔ info@hardys-plants.co.uk

Ⓦ www.hardys-plants.co.uk
Contact: Rosemary Hardy
Opening Times: 1000-1700 7 days, 1st Mar-30th Sep. 1000-1600 Mon-Fri, Oct. 1000-1500 Mon-Fri, 1st Nov-28th Feb. Closed 23rd Dec-4th Jan.
Min Mail Order UK: Nmc
Cat. Cost: Online only.
Credit Cards: Visa, Access, Electron, Switch, Solo
Specialities: Wide range of herbaceous perennials incl. *Achillea, Gaura, Geum, Geranium, Hemerocallis, Heuchera, Lathryus vernus, Paeonia, Penstemon* & *Salvia.*
Notes: Accepts HTA Gift Tokens. Offers trade discount. Euro accepted. Delivers to shows. Wheelchair accessible.

S

SHeu **HEUCHERAHOLICS** ♿
Boldre Nurseries, Southampton Road, Lymington, Hampshire SO41 8ND
Ⓣ (01590) 670581
Ⓜ 07973 291062
Ⓔ jooles.heucheraholics@gmail.com
Ⓦ www.heucheraholics.co.uk
Contact: Julie Burton/Sean Atkinson
Opening Times: Visits to nursery by appt. only. Please phone first. See website or contact nursery for Open Day details.
Min Mail Order UK: Nmc
Min Mail Order EU: Please contact nursery to discuss
Cat. Cost: Online only
Credit Cards: All major credit/debit cards, Paypal
Specialities: *Heuchera, Heucherella, Pulmonaria* & *Tiarella.* Other foliage plants.
Notes: Working nursery in the New Forest. Toilet facilities. Well-behaved dogs welcome. Visits by groups can be arranged, please contact nursery for details. Delivers to shows. Wheelchair accessible.
OS Grid Ref: SZ310934

SHmp **HAMPSHIRE CARNIVOROUS PLANTS**
Stroudwood Nursery, Stroudwood Lane, Lower Upham, Southampton, Hampshire SO32 1HG
Ⓣ (023) 8047 3314
Ⓜ 07703 258296
Ⓕ (023) 8047 3314
Ⓔ sales@hantsflytrap.com
Ⓦ www.hantsflytrap.com
Contact: Matthew Soper
Opening Times: Mail order only. Open by appt. only.
Min Mail Order UK: Nmc
Min Mail Order EU: £50.00 + p&p
Credit Cards: All major credit/debit cards
Specialities: Carnivorous plants esp. *Cephalotus, Darlingtonia, Dionaea, Drosera, Heliamphora, Nepenthes, Pinguicula, Sarracenia* & *Utricularia.*
Notes: Also sells wholesale. Exports beyond the EU. Delivers to shows. Euro accepted. Partial wheelchair access.

SHyH **HYDRANGEA HAVEN** ♿
Market Garden, Lower Beeding, West Sussex RH13 6PP
Ⓣ (01403) 891412
Ⓔ lp@hortic.com
Ⓦ www.hydrangea-haven.com
Contact: Chris Loder
Opening Times: 1000-1600 Mon-Sat, please phone first so we can give you our undivided attention.
Min Mail Order UK: Nmc
Min Mail Order EU: Nmc
Cat. Cost: 2 × 1st class.
Credit Cards: All major debit/credit cards except American Express
Specialities: *Hydrangea*: mophead, lacecap & panicle. *Agapanthus.*
Notes: Also sells wholesale. Exports beyond EU. Delivers to shows. Euro accepted. Wheelchair accessible.
OS Grid Ref: TQ221255

SIgm **TIM INGRAM** ♿
Copton Ash, 105 Ashford Road, Faversham, Kent ME13 8XW
Ⓣ (01795) 535919
Ⓔ coptonash@yahoo.co.uk
Ⓦ coptonash.plus.com
Contact: Dr T J Ingram
Opening Times: 1400-1800 Wed, Thu, Fri, Mar-Oct. Other times by appt.
Credit Cards: None
Specialities: Small, specialised nursery, offering mainly alpines and spring plants. Many unusual plants available in small quantities.
Notes: Delivers to shows. Wheelchair accessible.
OS Grid Ref: TR015598

SIri **IRIS OF SISSINGHURST**
Roughlands Farm, Goudhurst Road, Marden, Kent TN12 9NH
Ⓣ (01622) 831511
Ⓔ orders@irisofsissinghurst.com
Ⓦ www.irisofsissinghurst.com
Contact: Sue Marshall
Opening Times: Contact nursery or see website for opening times.

Min Mail Order UK: Nmc
Min Mail Order EU: Nmc
Cat. Cost: Online only.
Credit Cards: None
Specialities: *Iris*, short, intermediate & tall bearded, *ensata*, *sibirica* & many species.
Notes: Euro accepted. Pre-ordered plants delivered to shows
OS Grid Ref: TQ735437

SKee **Keepers Nursery**
Gallants Court, Gallants Lane, East Farleigh, Maidstone, Kent ME15 0LE
Ⓣ (01622) 326465
Ⓔ sales@keepers-nursery.co.uk
Ⓦ www.keepers-nursery.co.uk
Contact: Hamid Habibi
Opening Times: Only on a limited number of Open Days & for collection of order by arrangement.
Min Mail Order UK: Nmc
Cat. Cost: Online only.
Credit Cards: Visa, MasterCard, Switch, Maestro
Specialities: A very large range of old & rare as well as modern fruit trees varieties. Soft fruit plants & nut trees.

SKin **Kings Barn Trees**
Kings Barn Farm, Kent Street, Cowfold, West Sussex RH13 8BB
Ⓣ (01403) 865405
Ⓜ 07908 708915
Ⓔ sales@kingsbarntrees.co.uk
Ⓦ www.kingsbarntrees.co.uk
Contact: Adrian Rumble
Opening Times: Not open. Mail order via website only.
Min Mail Order UK: £3.00
Min Mail Order EU: £9.95
Cat. Cost: Online only.
Credit Cards: All major credit/debit cards
Specialities: Mainly grow containerised trees, specialising in *Eucalyptus*. Also grow willow for sale as whips & setts during the winter/early spring. *Eucalyptus* available in small quantities only.

SLau **The Laurels Nursery**
Benenden, Cranbrook, Kent TN17 4JU
Ⓣ (01580) 240463
Ⓦ www.thelaurelsnursery.co.uk
Contact: Peter or Sylvia Kellett
Opening Times: 0800-1600 Wed-Fri, 0900-1200 Sat, Sun by appt. only.
Min Mail Order UK: £30
Cat. Cost: Free.
Credit Cards: All major credit/debit cards
Specialities: Open ground & container ornamental trees, shrubs & climbers especially birch, beech & *Wisteria*.
Notes: Mail order of small *Wisteria* only. Also sells wholesale. Euro accepted. Partly accessible for wheelchairs.
OS Grid Ref: TQ815313

SLay **Layham Garden Centre & Nursery** ♿
Lower Road, Staple, Nr Canterbury, Kent CT3 1LH
Ⓣ (01304) 813267
Ⓕ (01304) 814007
Ⓔ info@layhamgardencentre.co.uk
Ⓦ www.layhamgardencentre.co.uk
Contact: Ellen Wessel
Opening Times: 0900-1700 Mon-Sat, 1000-1630 Sun.
Min Mail Order UK: Nmc
Min Mail Order EU: £25.00 + p&p
Cat. Cost: Free.
Credit Cards: Visa, MasterCard
Specialities: Roses, herbaceous, shrubs, trees & hedging plants.
Notes: Mail order roses only. Also sells wholesale. Euro accepted. Wheelchair accessible.
OS Grid Ref: TR276567

SLBF **Little Brook Fuchsias** ♿
Ash Green Lane West, Ash Green, Nr Aldershot, Hampshire GU12 6HL
Ⓣ (01252) 329731
Ⓔ carol.gubler@ntlbusiness.com
Ⓦ www.littlebrookfuchsias.co.uk
Contact: Carol Gubler
Opening Times: 1000-1700 Wed-Sun, 1st Jan-25th Jun.
Cat. Cost: 70p + sae.
Credit Cards: All major credit/debit cards
Specialities: Fuchsias, old & new.
Notes: Nursery located off White Lane in Ash Green. Wheelchair accessible.
OS Grid Ref: SU901496

SLdr **Loder Plants** ♿
Market Garden, Lower Beeding, West Sussex RH13 6PP
Ⓣ (01403) 891412
Ⓔ sales@rhododendrons.com
Ⓦ www.rhododendrons.com
Contact: Chris Loder
Opening Times: 1000-1600 Mon-Sat, please ring first so we can give you our undivided attention.
Min Mail Order UK: Nmc
Min Mail Order EU: Nmc
Cat. Cost: 2 × 1st class.

S

Credit Cards: All major debit/credit cards except American Express
Specialities: Rhododendrons & azaleas in all sizes. Some in very limited quantities only. *Agapanthus*.
Notes: Also sells wholesale. Exports beyond EU. Delivers to shows. Euro accepted. Wheelchair accessible.
OS Grid Ref: TQ221255

SLim **LIME CROSS NURSERY** ♿
Herstmonceux, Hailsham, East Sussex BN27 4RS
Ⓣ (01323) 833229
Ⓔ info@limecross.co.uk
Ⓦ www.limecross.co.uk
Contact: Vicky Tate, Anita Green
Opening Times: 0830-1700 Mon-Sat & 1000-1700 Sun.
Min Mail Order UK: Nmc
Min Mail Order EU: £50.00
Cat. Cost: Online only.
Credit Cards: All major credit/debit cards
Specialities: Conifers, trees & shrubs, climbers.
Notes: Wheelchair accessible.
OS Grid Ref: TQ642125

SLon **LONGSTOCK PARK NURSERY** ♿
Longstock, Stockbridge, Hampshire SO20 6EH
Ⓣ (01264) 810894
Ⓕ (01264) 810924
Ⓔ longstock.park.nursery@waitrose.co.uk
Ⓦ www.leckfordestate.co.uk
Contact: Mark Pitman
Opening Times: 0900-1730 Mon-Sat, 1000-1600 Sun. Closed 25th-27th Dec & 1st Jan.
Min Mail Order UK: £15.00
Credit Cards: All major credit/debit cards
Specialities: A wide range, over 2000 varieties, of hardy trees (ornamental and fruiting), shrubs, perennials, climbers, aquatics & ferns. Extensive collection of *Penstemon*. Nat. Collections of *Buddleja* & *Clematis viticella*.
Notes: Farm shop and café on same site as nursery. Wheelchair accessible.
OS Grid Ref: SU365389

SMad **MADRONA NURSERY** ♿
Pluckley Road, Bethersden, Kent TN26 3DD
Ⓣ (01233) 820100
Ⓕ (01233) 820091
Ⓔ madrona@hotmail.co.uk
Ⓦ www.madrona.co.uk
Contact: Liam Mackenzie
Opening Times: 1000-1700 Sat-Tue, 18th Mar-31st Oct. Other times by appt.
Cat. Cost: Free
Credit Cards: All major credit/debit cards
Specialities: Unusual shrubs, conifers & perennials. *Eryngium, Colletia*.
Notes: Delivers to shows. Euro accepted. Wheelchair accessible.
OS Grid Ref: TQ918419

SMea **MEADOWGATE NURSERY**
Street End Lane, Sidlesham, Chichester, West Sussex PO20 7RG
Ⓣ (01243) 641997
Ⓜ 07736 523262
Ⓔ meadowgatenursery@tiscali.co.uk
Ⓦ www.meadowgatenursery.co.uk
Contact: David Allen
Opening Times: 1000-1700 Sat-Thurs.
Min Mail Order UK: Nmc
Credit Cards: All major credit/debit cards
Specialities: Ornamental grasses.
Notes: Also sells wholesale. Delivers to shows.
OS Grid Ref: SZ854994

SMHy **MARCHANTS HARDY PLANTS** ♿
2 Marchants Cottages, Mill Lane, Laughton, East Sussex BN8 6AJ
Ⓣ (01323) 811737
Ⓔ graham@marchantsplants.plus.com
Ⓦ www.marchantshardyplants.co.uk
Contact: Graham Gough
Opening Times: 0930-1730 Wed-Sat, Mar to Oct 2017.
Cat. Cost: 3 × 2nd class
Credit Cards: Visa, MasterCard
Specialities: Uncommon herbaceous perennials. *Agapanthus*, choice grasses, *Galanthus, Miscanthus, Molinia*.
Notes: Euro accepted. Wheelchair accessible.
OS Grid Ref: TQ506119

SMor **MOREHAVENS**
Stocks Lane, Meonstoke, Hampshire SO32 3NQ
Ⓣ (01489) 878501
Ⓔ morehavens@camomilelawns.co.uk
Ⓦ www.camomilelawns.co.uk
Contact: E. Clements
Opening Times: Mail order only. Open for collection only.
Min Mail Order UK: £20.00
Min Mail Order EU: £20.00 + p&p
Cat. Cost: Free.
Credit Cards: Paypal
Specialities: *Camomile nobile* 'Treneague' and *C. nobile* dwarf.
Notes: Also sells wholesale.

SNig **Nightingale Nursery** ♿
Gardeners Lane, East Wellow, Romsey, Hampshire SO51 6AD
Ⓣ (023) 8081 4350
Ⓔ gfnightingale4@gmail.com
Ⓦ www.nightingalenursery.co.uk
Contact: Graham Farmiloe
Opening Times: 0800-1700 Mon-Fri & open 7 days from mid-Mar to mid-Jun. 0800-1630 winter.
Cat. Cost: Free via email.
Credit Cards: All major debit/credit cards except American Express
Specialities: *Clematis*. Also climbers & wall shrubs; herbaceous; seasonal bedding; hanging baskets.
Notes: Also sells wholesale. Wheelchair accessible.

SPad **Paddock Plants**
The Paddock, Upper Toothill Road, Rownhams, Southampton, Hampshire SO16 8AL
Ⓣ (023) 8073 9912
Ⓜ 07763 386717
Ⓔ rob@paddockplants.co.uk
Ⓦ www.paddockplants.co.uk
Contact: Rob & Joanna Courtney
Opening Times: By appt. only. Please telephone in advance.
Min Mail Order UK: £10.00
Cat. Cost: Online only.
Credit Cards: All major credit/debit cards
Specialities: A family-run nursery offering an interesting range of perennials, grasses, ferns & shrubs, incl. some more unusual varieties or plants new to the UK market. All plants are grown in a peat-free medium. Some varieties grown in small quantities.
Notes: Local delivery by our own transport. Courier delivery throughout UK. Delivers to shows.
OS Grid Ref: SU383177

SPer **Perryhill Nurseries Ltd** ♿
Edenbridge Road, Hartfield, East Sussex TN7 4JP
Ⓣ (01892) 770377
Ⓕ (01892) 770929
Ⓔ sales@perryhillnurseries.co.uk
Ⓦ www.perryhillnurseries.co.uk
Contact: P J Chapman
Opening Times: 0900-1700 7 days, 1st Mar-31st Oct. 0900-1630, 1st Nov-28th Feb.
Min Mail Order UK: Nmc
Cat. Cost: Online only.
Credit Cards: Maestro, Visa, Access, MasterCard
Specialities: Wide range of trees, shrubs, perennials, roses, fruit trees, soft fruit. Unusual & rare plants may be available in small quantities.
Notes: Mail order despatch depends on size & weight of plants. Wheelchair accessible.
OS Grid Ref: TQ480375

SPet **Pettet's Nursery** ♿
Drainless Road, Eastry, Sandwich, Kent CT13 0EA
Ⓣ (01304) 613869
Ⓜ 07940 337520
Ⓕ (01304) 613869
Ⓔ pettets.nursery@btconnect.com
Ⓦ www.pettetsnursery.co.uk
Contact: Terry Pettet
Opening Times: 1000-1600 Tue-Sun, Mar-Oct. Closed Mon (except B/hol). Closed Nov-Feb.
Min Mail Order UK: £10.00
Cat. Cost: Online only.
Credit Cards: None
Specialities: *Pelargonium*: scented-leaf, decorative regal, unique, angel. *Fuchsia*.
Notes: Delivers to shows. Wheelchair accessible.

SPhx **Phoenix Perennial Plants**
Paice Lane, Medstead, Alton, Hampshire GU34 5PR
Ⓣ (01420) 560695
Ⓜ 07909 528191
Ⓕ (01420) 563640
Ⓔ marina@phoenixperennialplants.co.uk
Ⓦ www.phoenixperennialplants.co.uk
Contact: Marina Christopher
Opening Times: Open by appt. only.
Credit Cards: All major credit/debit cards
Specialities: Perennials, many uncommon & hardy, selected for beneficial insects particularly pollinators. *Agastache*, *Centaurea*, *Monarda*, *Sanguisorba*, *Sedum*, *Thalictrum*, *Verbascum*, bulbs, prairie plants, umbellifers & late-flowering perennials.
Notes: Also sells wholesale. Delivers to shows.
OS Grid Ref: SU657362

SPin **John and Lynsey's Plants** ♿
2 Hillside Cottages, Trampers Lane, North Boarhunt, Fareham, Hampshire PO17 6DA
Ⓣ (01329) 832786
Ⓔ landjpink@tiscali.co.uk
Contact: Mrs Lynsey Pink
Opening Times: By appt. only.
Cat. Cost: None issued.
Credit Cards: None

Specialities: Mainly *Salvia* with a wide range of other unusual perennials. Stock is only available in small quantities but we are happy to try & propagate anything that we have. Nat. Collection of species *Salvia*.
Notes: Wheelchair accessible.
OS Grid Ref: SU603109

SPlb **Plantbase** ♿
Sleepers Stile Road, Cousley Wood, Wadhurst, East Sussex TN5 6QX
Ⓣ (01892) 785599
Ⓜ 07967 601064
Ⓔ graham@plantbase.freeserve.co.uk
Ⓦ www.plantbase.co.uk
Contact: Graham Blunt
Opening Times: 1000-1700, 7 days all year (appt. advisable).
Min Mail Order UK: Nmc
Min Mail Order EU: Nmc
Cat. Cost: Online only.
Credit Cards: All major credit/debit cards
Specialities: Wide range of alpines, perennials, shrubs, climbers, waterside plants, herbs, Australasian, South African & South American plants in particular. Some available in small quantities only.
Notes: Delivers to shows. Euro accepted. Wheelchair accessible.

S

SPoG **The Potted Garden Nursery** ♿
Ashford Road, Bearsted, Maidstone, Kent ME14 4NH
Ⓣ (01622) 737801
Ⓦ www.thepottedgarden.co.uk
Contact: Any staff member
Opening Times: 0900-1730 (dusk in winter), 7 days. Xmas/New Year period opening times on website or answerphone.
Credit Cards: All major credit/debit cards
Notes: Mail order not available. Wheelchair accessible.
OS Grid Ref: TQ810550

SPop **Pops Plants**
Pops Cottage, Barford Lane, Downton, Salisbury, Wiltshire SP5 3PZ
Ⓣ (01725) 511421
Ⓔ pops08@btinternet.com
Ⓦ www.popsplants.com
Contact: Lesley Roberts
Opening Times: By appt. only.
Min Mail Order UK: 5 plants.
Min Mail Order EU: 5 plants.
Cat. Cost: £2.50
Credit Cards: Paypal
Specialities: *Primula auricula*, some varieties in limited numbers. Nat. Collection of Show, Alpine, Double & Striped Auriculas.
Notes: Euro accepted.

SPre **Plants4Presents** ◆
The Glasshouses, Fletching Common, Newick, Lewes, East Sussex BN8 4JJ
Ⓣ (01825) 721162
Ⓔ plants@4presents.co.uk
Ⓦ www.plants4presents.co.uk
Contact: Emily Rae
Opening Times: Not open. Mail order only.
Min Mail Order UK: Nmc
Cat. Cost: Online only.
Credit Cards: All major credit/debit cards
Specialities: Well-established nursery offering a range of unusual flowering and fruiting plants, incl. citrus trees.
Notes: Delivers to shows.

SPtp **Plantstoplants.com**
Paragon Plants, Fromefield, Church Lane, Awbridge, Romsey, Hampshire SO51 0HN
Ⓣ (01794) 341123
Ⓔ info@plantstoplant.com
Ⓦ www.plantstoplant.com
Contact: David West
Opening Times: Not open. Mail order only.
Min Mail Order UK: Nmc
Cat. Cost: Online only.
Credit Cards: All major credit/debit cards, Paypal
Specialities: Rare & hard to find garden plants of all types. *Cotoneaster* a speciality.
Notes: Mail order only through website. Orders can be collected by appt. only.

SRiv **River Garden Nurseries**
Troutbeck, Otford, Sevenoaks, Kent TN14 5PH
Ⓣ (01959) 525588
Ⓔ box@river-garden.co.uk
Ⓦ www.river-garden.co.uk
Contact: Jenny Alban Davies
Opening Times: By appt. only.
Min Mail Order UK: £10.00 + p&p
Min Mail Order EU: £50.00 + p&p
Cat. Cost: Online only.
Credit Cards: None
Specialities: *Buxus* species & cultivars. *Buxus* topiary.
Notes: Also sells wholesale. Delivers to shows.
OS Grid Ref: TQ523593

SRkn **Rapkyns Nursery** ♿
Street End Lane, Broad Oak, Heathfield, East Sussex TN21 8UB
Ⓣ (01825) 830065
Ⓜ 07771 916933

Ⓔ rapkynsnursery@hotmail.com
Ⓦ www.rapkynsnursery.co.uk
Contact: Steven Moore
Opening Times: 1000-1700 Tue, Thu & Fri, Mar-Oct incl. or by appt.
Min Mail Order UK: Nmc
Min Mail Order EU: Nmc
Cat. Cost: Online only.
Credit Cards: All major credit/debit cards
Specialities: Unusual shrubs, perennials & climbers. Asters, campanulas, *Ceanothus*, geraniums, lavenders, *Clematis*, penstemons & grasses. New collections of *Crocosmia*, *Anemone*, *Heuchera*, *Heucherella*, *Phlox*, *Coreopsis* & *Helleborus*. Extensive range of salvias.
Notes: Nursery next door to Scotsford Farm, TN21 8UB. Mail order Sep-Apr incl. Also sells wholesale. Delivers to shows. Wheelchair accessible.
OS Grid Ref: TQ604248

SRms **RUMSEY GARDENS** ♿
117 Drift Road, Clanfield, Waterlooville, Hampshire PO8 0PD
Ⓣ (023) 9259 3367
Ⓔ info@rumsey-gardens.co.uk
Ⓦ www.rumsey-gardens.co.uk
Contact: Mrs M A Giles
Opening Times: 0900-1700 Mon-Sat & 1000-1600 Sun & B/hols. Closed Xmas to New Year B/Hol.
Min Mail Order UK: £15.00
Cat. Cost: Online only.
Credit Cards: American Express, Visa, MasterCard
Specialities: Wide general range. Herbaceous, alpines, heathers & ferns. Nat. & International Collection of *Cotoneaster*.
Notes: Wheelchair accessible.

SRot **ROTHERVIEW NURSERY** ♿
Ivy House Lane, Three Oaks, Hastings, East Sussex TN35 4NP
Ⓣ (01424) 756228
Ⓔ rotherview@btinternet.com
Ⓦ www.rotherview.com
Contact: Ray & Wendy Bates
Opening Times: 1000-1700 Tue to Sun, Mar-Oct & 1000-1530 Nov-Feb.
Min Mail Order UK: Nmc
Min Mail Order EU: Nmc
Cat. Cost: 6 × 1st class.
Credit Cards: All major credit/debit cards
Specialities: Alpines. Ferns. *Camellia*.
Notes: Nursery is on same site as Coghurst Camellias. Also sells wholesale. Delivers to shows. Euro accepted. Wheelchair accessible.

SSea **SEALE ROSE GARDEN**
Seale Nurseries, Seale Lane, Seale, Farnham, Surrey GU10 1LD
Ⓣ (01252) 782410
Ⓔ catherine@sealenurseries.demon.co.uk
Ⓦ www.sealenurseries.co.uk
Contact: David & Catherine May
Opening Times: 1000-1600 Tue-Sat. Other times by appt. Please phone for winter opening times.
Cat. Cost: None issued.
Credit Cards: Visa, Access, Delta, MasterCard
Specialities: Roses & *Pelargonium*. Some varieties in short supply, please phone first.
OS Grid Ref: SU887477

SSFT **SUSSEX FRUIT TREES**
Hook Farm, Nettlesworth Lane, Heathfield, East Sussex TN21 9EN
Ⓜ 07745 379526
Ⓔ mark@sussexfruittrees.co.uk
Ⓦ www.sussexfruittrees.co.uk
Contact: Mark Piper
Opening Times: 0800-1700, 7 days.
Specialities: Grows & sells a wide range of fruit trees on various rootstocks. Some Sussex apple tree cultivars.
Notes: Also provides delivery, planting, pruning, grafting, orchard maintenance & tree sundries.

SSFr **SOUTHERN FRUIT TREES** ♿
The Old Grain Dryer Corner, Blackmoor, Hampshire GU33 6BP
Ⓣ (01420) 488822
Ⓜ 07811 253530
Ⓔ neil@southernfruittrees.co.uk
Ⓦ www.southernfruittrees.co.uk
Contact: Neil Smith
Opening Times: 0900-1600 7 days, Nov-May. Webshop open all year around.
Min Mail Order UK: Nmc
Cat. Cost: Free
Credit Cards: All major credit/debit cards
Specialities: Over 200 varieties of fruit trees, mostly home-grown, incl. bush, half-standard, cordon espalier and fan-trained fruit.
Notes: Wheelchair accessible.
OS Grid Ref: SU778335

SSim **SIMPLY SUCCULENTS**
(office) 72 Dover Road, Sandwich, Kent CT13 0BY
Ⓜ 07548 947357
Ⓔ simplysucculents@gmx.co.uk
Ⓦ www.simplysucculents.co.uk
Contact: John Chandler
Opening Times: Not open. Mail order online only.

S

Min Mail Order UK: Nmc
Cat. Cost: Online only.
Specialities: Succulents for home, garden & containers.
Notes: Online sales only.

SSta **STARBOROUGH NURSERY** ♿
Starborough Road, Marsh Green, Edenbridge, Kent TN8 5RB
Ⓣ (01732) 865614
Ⓔ starborough@hotmail.co.uk
Contact: Sales
Opening Times: 0900-1600 Thu, Fri & Sat. Closed Jan, Jul & Aug or open by appt. only. Please phone first if travelling.
Credit Cards: Visa, Access
Specialities: Rare & unusual shrubs esp. *Daphne*, *Acer*, rhododendrons & azaleas, *Magnolia* & *Nyssa*. Some plants only available in larger sizes.
Notes: Deliveries can be made at cost. Planting & landscaping services available. Wheelchair accessible.

STPC **THE PLANT COMPANY** ♿
Coolham Road, West Chiltington, Pulborough, West Sussex RH20 2LH
Ⓣ (01403) 740100
Ⓔ sales@theplantco.co.uk
Ⓦ www.theplantco.co.uk
Contact: Tim Ricketts
Opening Times: 0900-1730 Mon-Fri.
Min Mail Order UK: £8.95
Cat. Cost: Online only.
Credit Cards: All major debit/credit cards except American Express
Specialities: A range of herbaceous, shrubs and grasses.
Notes: Also sells wholesale. Delivers to shows. Wheelchair accessible.
OS Grid Ref: TQ111196

STrG **TERRACE GARDENER**
(office) Thickets, Copthall Road, Ightham, Kent TN15 9DU
Ⓣ (01732) 883776
Ⓔ info@terracegardener.com
Ⓦ www.terracegardener.co.uk
Contact: Mike McGonigle
Opening Times: Not open. Mail order only, incl. online & telephone orders.
Min Mail Order UK: Nmc
Cat. Cost: Online only
Credit Cards: All major debit/credit cards except American Express
Specialities: Patio plants & topiary trees. Container gardening. Architectural & hardy exotics. Containers & pots.

SSut **DAN SUTTON**
(office) 142 Hawks Road, Hailsham, East Sussex BN27 1NA
Ⓣ (01323) 845270
Ⓜ 07772 869645
Ⓔ suttonnursery@gmail.com
Ⓦ www.suttonnursery.co.uk
Contact: Dan Sutton
Opening Times: By appt. only.
Min Mail Order UK: £5.80.
Cat. Cost: Online only.
Credit Cards: Paypal
Specialities: Herbaceous perennials, bulbs/corms, incl. *Crocosima*, grasses, specimen bamboos, *Fargesia robusta*, *F. scabrida* & *Borinda boliana*. Coastal and drought-tolerant plants.
Notes: Nursery at Park Wood Farmhouse, Upper Dicker, Hailsham, BN27 3QL. Landscape design. Also sells wholesale.

SVen **VENTNOR BOTANIC GARDEN** ♿
Undercliff Drive, Ventnor, Isle of Wight PO38 1UL
Ⓣ (01983) 855397
Ⓔ sales@botanic.co.uk
Ⓦ www.botanic.co.uk
Contact: Chris Kidd
Opening Times: 1000-1700 7 days, all year.
Min Mail Order UK: Nmc
Min Mail Order EU: Nmc
Cat. Cost: None issued
Credit Cards: All major debit/credit cards except American Express
Specialities: Coastal, drought-tolerant, Mediterranean & southern hemisphere plants. Rare & esoteric half-hardy trees, shrubs & perennials. Nat. Collection of Hardy & Half-hardy *Puya*.
Notes: Wheelchair accessible.
OS Grid Ref: SZ548768

SVic **VICTORIANA NURSERY GARDENS** ♿
Challock, Ashford, Kent TN25 4DG
Ⓣ (01233) 740529
Ⓔ help@victoriananursery.co.uk
Ⓦ www.victoriananursery.co.uk
Contact: Serena Shirley
Opening Times: 0930-1630 (or dusk if sooner) Mon-Fri, 1030-1500 (or dusk if sooner) Sat.
Min Mail Order UK: Nmc
Cat. Cost: Free by post or online.
Credit Cards: All major credit/debit cards
Specialities: Heritage & unusual vegetable plants, seeds, fruit trees & bushes. Specialist grower of chillies & tomatoes, with annual tasting days. Also 600+ varieties of *Fuchsia*.
Notes: Also sells wholesale.

Wheelchair accessible.
OS Grid Ref: TR018501

SWhi **John Hall Plants Ltd** ♿
Whitehall Nursery, Red Lane (Off Churt Road), Headley Down, Hampshire GU35 8SR
Ⓣ (01428) 715505
Ⓜ 07714 344327
Ⓔ info@johnhallplants.com
Ⓦ www.johnhallplants.com
Contact: John Hall
Opening Times: 0900-1630 Mon-Fri, 0900-1300 Sat, by appt. only.
Min Mail Order UK: Nmc
Min Mail Order EU: Nmc
Cat. Cost: By email only.
Credit Cards: None
Specialities: *Erica, Calluna* & *Daboecia.*
Notes: Planting plans supplied. Also sells wholesale. Exports beyond EU. Euro accepted. Wheelchair accessible.
OS Grid Ref: SU837371

SWvt **Wolverton Plants Ltd** ♿
Wolverton Common, Tadley, Hampshire RG26 5RU
Ⓣ (01635) 298453
Ⓕ (01635) 299075
Ⓔ plantranch2000@hotmail.com
Contact: Julian Jones
Opening Times: 0900-1700 (or dusk Nov-Feb), 7 days. Closed Xmas/New Year.
Credit Cards: All major credit/debit cards
Specialities: Wide range of herbaceous perennials & shrubs grown on a commercial scale for the public.
Notes: Horticultural club visits welcome by prior arrangement. Also sells wholesale. Euro accepted. Wheelchair accessible.
OS Grid Ref: SU555589

Wales and the West

WAbe **Aberconwy Nursery**
Graig, Glan Conwy Conwy LL28 5TL
Ⓣ (01492) 580875
Contact: Keith & Tim Lever
Opening Times: 1000-1600 Tue-Sun Mar-Sep incl.
Cat. Cost: 2 × 2nd class.
Credit Cards: Visa, MasterCard
Specialities: Alpines, including specialist varieties, esp. gentians, dionysias, dwarf *Dianthus, Primula, Saxifraga* & dwarf ericaceous plants. Some choice shrubs & woodland plants incl. smaller ferns.
Notes: Delivers to shows.
OS Grid Ref: SH799744

WAln **L. A. Allen**
Windy Ridge, Llandrindod Wells, Powys LD1 5NY
Ⓔ leslie.allen@mypostoffice.co.uk
Contact: Les Allen
Opening Times: Mail order only. Open by prior appt.
Min Mail Order UK: Nmc
Min Mail Order EU: Nmc
Cat. Cost: 6 × 1st class.
Credit Cards: None
Specialities: All sections of *Primula auricula*: alpine auriculas, show-edged, show-self, doubles, show-stripe. Surplus plants from private collection so available in small quantities. Occasionally only 1 or 2 available of some cvs.
Notes: Also sells wholesale.

WArt **Artisan Plant Nurseries**
CLM Keder Greenhouses, Newtown, Offenham, Evesham, Worcestershire WR11 8RZ
Ⓜ 07460 661165
Ⓔ helen@artisanplantnurseries.com
Ⓦ www.artisanplantnurseries.com
Contact: Helen Lockwood
Opening Times: Open by appt. only.
Min Mail Order UK: Nmc
Min Mail Order EU: Nmc
Cat. Cost: Online only.
Credit Cards: Paypal
Specialities: Wide range of rare & unusual hardy perennials, especially many species of plants that are beneficial to wildlife. Building collections of *Primula, Digitalis, Verbascum, Salvia, Nepeta* & *Iris.*
Notes: Group visits welcome. Talks and workshops available, see website for details. Plant displays for special events, weddings, parties & festivals. Also sells wholesale. Wheelchair accessible. Delivers to shows.
OS Grid Ref: SP066462

WAul **Aulden Farm**
Aulden, Leominster, Herefordshire HR6 0JT
Ⓣ (01568) 720129
Ⓔ pf@auldenfarm.co.uk
Ⓦ www.auldenfarm.co.uk
Contact: Alun Whitehead
Opening Times: Flexible. Individuals & groups welcome. Please contact nursery. Also open for NGS.
Min Mail Order UK: £25.00
Cat. Cost: Online only.
Credit Cards: Paypal
Specialities: Nat. Collection of Siberian *Iris.*

Notes: Informal three acre country garden. Talks given. Nat. Collection of Siberian *Iris* best viewed at the end of May/Jun.
OS Grid Ref: SO462548

WAvo **Pershore College** ♿
Avonbank, Pershore, Worcestershire
WR10 3JP
Ⓣ (01386) 551177
Ⓔ avonbanknurseries@warwickshire.ac.uk
Ⓦ www.warwickshire.ac.uk/plantcentre
Contact: Josh Egan-Wyer
Opening Times: 0900-1700 Mon-Sat, 1000-1630 Sun (1600 in winter).
Cat. Cost: £3.00 incl. p&p
Credit Cards: All major debit/credit cards except American Express
Specialities: Extensive range of specialist plants incl. Nat. Collections of *Penstemon* (pre-1995 cvs) & *Philadelphus* cvs. Perennials & climbers being trialled peat-free for 2017.
Notes: Also sells wholesale. Wheelchair accessible.
OS Grid Ref: SO957447

WBor **Bordervale Plants** ♿
Nantyderi, Sandy Lane, Ystradowen, Cowbridge, Vale of Glamorgan
CF71 7SX
Ⓣ (01446) 774036
Ⓔ bordervaleplants@gmail.com
Ⓦ www.bordervale.co.uk
Contact: Claire E Jenkins
Opening Times: 1000-1700 Fri-Sun & B/hols Mar-Sep. Very often open Mon-Thu but please make an appt. on these days if travelling some distance.
Min Mail Order UK: £20.00 + p&p
Cat. Cost: 3 × 1st class.
Specialities: Unusual herbaceous perennials, trees, shrubs & roses, as well as cottage garden plants, many displayed in the 2-acre garden.
Notes: Mail order available for smaller items, subject to season. Garden open mid-May to Sep when nursery open. Also open for NGS. See website or contact nursery for details. Delivers to shows. Nursery wheelchair accessible.
OS Grid Ref: ST022776

WBrk **Brockamin Plants** ♿
Brockamin, Old Hills, Callow End, Worcestershire WR2 4TQ
Ⓣ (01905) 830370
Ⓔ stone.brockamin@btinternet.com
Contact: Margaret Stone
Opening Times: By appt. only.
Cat. Cost: Free.
Credit Cards: None
Specialities: Nat. Collections of *Symphyotrichum novae-angliae, Geranium sanguineum, G. macrorrhizum* & *G. × cantabrigiense*. Plants available in small quantities only.
Notes: Wheelchair accessible.
OS Grid Ref: SO830488

WBuc **Bucknell Nurseries** ♿
Bucknell, Shropshire SY7 0EL
Ⓣ (01547) 530606
Ⓕ (01547) 530699
Ⓔ nickcoull@yahoo.co.uk
Contact: A N Coull
Opening Times: 0800-1700 Mon-Fri & 1000-1300 Sat.
Min Mail Order UK: Nmc
Cat. Cost: Free
Credit Cards: All major credit/debit cards
Specialities: Bare-rooted hedging conifers & forest trees.
Notes: Also sells wholesale. Euro accepted. Wheelchair accessible.
OS Grid Ref: SO356736

WCAu **Claire Austin Hardy Plants**
White Hopton Farm, Wern Lane, Sarn, Newtown, Powys SY16 4EN
Ⓣ (01686) 670342
Ⓔ enquiries@claireaustin-hardyplants.co.uk
Ⓦ www.claireaustin-hardyplants.co.uk
Contact: Claire Austin
Opening Times: Mail order only. Open Day towards start of Jun. See website or contact nursery for details.
Min Mail Order UK: Nmc
Min Mail Order EU: Nmc
Cat. Cost: Free, UK only.
Credit Cards: MasterCard, Visa, Switch
Specialities: *Paeonia, Iris, Hemerocallis* & hardy plants. Nat. Collections of Bearded *Iris*.

WCFE **Charles F Ellis**
Oak Piece Nurseries, Stanway Road, Stanton, Nr Broadway, Worcestershire
WR12 7NQ
Ⓣ (01386) 584077
Ⓔ ellisplants@cooptel.net
Ⓦ www.ellisplants.co.uk
Contact: Charles Ellis
Opening Times: 1000-1600 Wed-Sun, 1st Apr-30th Sep incl.
Min Mail Order UK: £10.00
Cat. Cost: None issued.
Credit Cards: All major debit/credit cards except American Express
Specialities: Wide range of shrubs, conifers,

climbers & perennials, some unusual. All available in small quantities only.
Notes: Euro accepted.

WChG **Chennels Gate Gardens & Nursery** ♿
Eardisley, Herefordshire HR3 6LT
Ⓣ (01544) 327288
Ⓔ mark.richard.dawson60@gmail.com
Contact: Mark Dawson
Opening Times: 1000-1700 7 days Mar-Oct.
Cat. Cost: None issued.
Credit Cards: None
Specialities: Interesting & unusual cottage garden plants, grasses & shrubs.
Notes: Wheelchair accessible.

WCot **Cotswold Garden Flowers**
Sands Lane, Badsey, Evesham, Worcestershire WR11 7EZ
Ⓣ nursery: (01386) 833849 or mail order: (01386) 422829
Ⓜ 07812 833849
Ⓕ nursery: (01386) 49844
Ⓔ info@cgf.net
Ⓦ www.cgf.net
Contact: Bob Brown
Opening Times: 0900-1730 Mon-Fri &1000-1730 Sat & Sun, Mar-Sep. 0900-1630 Mon-Fri only, Oct-Feb. Closed from Xmas Eve for 10 days.
Min Mail Order UK: Nmc
Min Mail Order EU: Nmc
Cat. Cost: Free.
Credit Cards: All major debit/credit cards except American Express
Specialities: A very wide range of easy to grow & unusual perennials.
Notes: Delivers to shows. Euro accepted. Limited wheelchair access.
OS Grid Ref: SP077426

WCra **Cranesbill Nursery** ◆
1 Waverley Road, Mossley Estate, Bloxwich, Walsall, West Midlands WS3 2SW
Ⓣ (01684) 770733
Ⓜ 07500 600205
Ⓔ gary@cranesbillnursery.com
Ⓦ www.cranesbillnursery.com
Contact: Gary Carroll
Opening Times: Mail order only. Not open to the public. Collections by appt. only.
Min Mail Order UK: £12.50
Min Mail Order EU: £25.00
Credit Cards: Access
Specialities: Hardy geraniums, around 200 species & cvs. Can supply large quantities with 6-8 weeks notice. Please contact nursery for further details.
Notes: Exports beyond the EU.
OS Grid Ref: SO940378

WCru **Crûg Farm Plants** ♿
Caernarfon, Gwynedd LL55 1TU
Ⓣ (01248) 670232
Ⓜ 07774 980842
Ⓔ mailorder@crug-farm.co.uk
Ⓦ www.mailorder.crug-farm.co.uk
Contact: B and S Wynn-Jones
Opening Times: 0930-1630 Thu-Sat, 1st Sat in Apr to 2nd Sat in Sep. Or Mon-Fri by appt., all year.
Min Mail Order UK: Nmc
Min Mail Order EU: Nmc
Cat. Cost: Online only.
Credit Cards: All major credit/debit cards
Specialities: Unusual & rare inc. trees, shrubs, herbaceous & bulbous, mostly self-collected new introductions from the Far East & the Americas. Rare woody & climbers esp. *Acer*, *Araliaceae*, *Carpinus*, *Hydrangeaceae* & *Magnolia* with many other extraordinary introductions. Shade plants esp. *Asparagaceae*, *Convallariaceae*, *Liliaceae*, *Ranunculaceae* & *Saxifragaceae*. Many supplied bare-rooted. Nat. Collections of *Coriaria*, *Paris* & *Polygonatum*.
Notes: Delivery by overnight carrier for UK & Ireland. Courier for rest of EU. Delivers to shows. Wheelchair accessible.
OS Grid Ref: SH509652

WDib **Dibleys Nurseries** ♿ ◆
Llanelidan, Ruthin, Denbighshire LL15 2LG
Ⓣ (01978) 790677
Ⓕ (01978) 790668
Ⓔ sales@dibleys.com
Ⓦ www.dibleys.com
Contact: R Dibley
Opening Times: 1000-1700 Mon-Sat (closed Sun), Apr-Aug. 1000-1700 Mon-Fri, Mar, Sep & Oct.
Min Mail Order UK: Nmc
Min Mail Order EU: Nmc
Cat. Cost: Free
Credit Cards: Visa, Access, Switch, Electron, Solo
Specialities: *Streptocarpus*, *Columnea*, *Solenostemon*, *Saintpaulia* & other gesneriads & *Begonia*. Nat. Collections of *Streptocarpus*, *Saintpaulia* & *Petrocosmea*.
Notes: Also sells wholesale. Euro accepted. Delivers to shows. Wheelchair accessible.

WFar **Farmyard Nurseries** ♿
Dol Llan Road, Llandysul, Carmarthenshire SA44 4RL

Ⓣ (01559) 363389
Ⓜ 01267 220259
Ⓔ sales@farmyardnurseries.co.uk
Ⓦ www.farmyardnurseries.co.uk
Contact: Richard Bramley
Opening Times: 0900-1700 7 days, excl. Xmas Day, Boxing Day & New Year's Day.
Min Mail Order UK: Nmc
Min Mail Order EU: Nmc
Cat. Cost: None issued.
Credit Cards: Visa, Switch, MasterCard
Specialities: Large range of home grown shrubs & herbaceous perennials, incl. *Convallaria*, *Geranium*, *Helleborus*, *Impatiens* & *Primula*. Trees, shrubs, climbers, alpines, conifers & bedding plants.
Notes: Additionally sells from shop/yard in Carmarthen. Also sells wholesale. Euro accepted. Wheelchair accessible.
OS Grid Ref: SN421406

WFib **Fibrex Nurseries Ltd** ♿
Honeybourne Road, Pebworth, Stratford-on-Avon, Warwickshire CV37 8XP
Ⓣ (01789) 720788
Ⓔ sales@fibrex.co.uk
Ⓦ www.fibrex.co.uk
Contact: U Key-Davis & R L Godard-Key
Opening Times: 0900-1700 Mon-Fri, 1st Mar-31st Aug. 0900-1600 Mon-Fri, 1st Sep-28th Feb. 1030-1600 Sat & Sun, 1st Apr-25th Jun. Closed last week Dec & 1st week Jan. Closed Easter Sun & Aug B/hol Mon.
Min Mail Order UK: £10.00 + p&p
Min Mail Order EU: £20.00 + p&p
Cat. Cost: 3 × 1st class.
Credit Cards: MasterCard, Visa, Maestro
Specialities: *Hedera*, ferns, *Pelargonium*, named tuberous begonias, *Hibiscus rosa-sinensis* cvs, hardy geraniums. Nat. Collections of *Pelargonium* & *Hedera*. Plant collections subject to time of year, please check by phone.
Notes: Also sells wholesale. Delivers to shows. Wheelchair accessible.
OS Grid Ref: SP133458

WGSt **Ross Garden Store** ♿
The Engine Shed, Station Approach, Ashburton, Ross-on-Wye, Herefordshire HR9 7BW
Ⓣ (01989) 568999
Ⓕ (01989) 568157
Ⓔ sales@rossgardenstore.co.uk
Ⓦ www.rossgardenstore.com
Contact: Jane Fishwick
Opening Times: 0900-1700, Mon-Sat, incl. B/hols. 1000-1630 Sun.
Min Mail Order UK: Nmc
Credit Cards: All major credit/debit cards
Specialities: Good general range, incl. specimen Italian stock.
Notes: Café. Garden design service. Also sells wholesale. Wheelchair accessible.

WGob **The Gobbett Nursery**
Farlow, Kidderminster, Worcestershire DY14 8TD
Ⓣ (01746) 718647
Ⓔ chrislink59@gmail.com
Ⓦ www.thegobbettnursery.co.uk
Contact: C H Link
Opening Times: By appt. only.
Min Mail Order UK: £10.00
Min Mail Order EU: £50.00
Cat. Cost: None issued.
Credit Cards: None
Specialities: *Syringa*, & *Cornus*. Some varieties available in small quantities only.
Notes: Delivers to shows.
OS Grid Ref: SO648811

WGoo **Wildegoose Nursery, home of Bouts Violas** ♿
The Walled Garden, Lower Millichope, Munslow, Craven Arms, Shropshire SY7 9HE
Ⓣ (01584) 841890
Ⓜ 07798 628762
Ⓔ flowers@boutsviolas.co.uk
Ⓦ www.wildegoosenursery.co.uk
Contact: Laura Willgoss
Opening Times: 1100-1600 Fri-Sun, 31st Mar-15th Oct 2017.
Min Mail Order UK: Nmc
Min Mail Order EU: Nmc
Cat. Cost: 1st class sae.
Credit Cards: All major credit/debit cards
Specialities: *Viola*, incl. *Viola* stock from Bouts Cottage Nursery. Herbaceous perennials & grasses. Some varieties propagated in small quantities.
Notes: Delivers to shows. Wheelchair accessible.

WGrn **Green's Leaves** ♿
36 Ford House Road, Newent, Gloucestershire GL18 1LQ
Ⓣ (01531) 820154
Ⓜ 07890 413036
Ⓔ r.paul.green@hotmail.co.uk
Ⓦ www.greensleavesnursery.co.uk
Contact: Paul Green
Opening Times: By appt. only. Please phone to arrange collection of orders from house (nursery site not open).
Min Mail Order UK: £10.00 + p&p

Cat. Cost: 4 × 2nd class.
Credit Cards: None
Specialities: Range of rare & choice shrubs, also some perennials. Ornamental grasses & sedges. Coloured foliage plants.
Notes: Delivers to shows. Wheelchair accessible.
OS Grid Ref: SO732273

WGwG **Gwynfor Growers**
Gwynfor, Pontgarreg, Llangrannog, Llandysul, Ceredigion SA44 6AU
Ⓣ (01239) 654151
Ⓔ info@gwynfor.co.uk
Ⓦ www.gwynfor.co.uk
Contact: Steve & Angie Hipkin
Opening Times: Usually 1000-1800 (or sunset if earlier) Wed, Thu & Sun, all year round.
Min Mail Order UK: Nmc
Cat. Cost: Online only.
Credit Cards: All major credit/debit cards, Paypal
Specialities: Nat. Collection of *Rosmarinus* cvs. Specialist supplier of Welsh fruit trees. Classic & contemporary plants grown organically & peat-free. Some plants available in small quantities only. Rarities propagated to order.
Notes: Plants also available at local farmers' markets, plant fairs & some NGS Open Gardens. Delivers to shows.
OS Grid Ref: SN331536

WHCr **Hergest Croft Gardens**
Kington, Herefordshire HR5 3EG
Ⓣ (01544) 230160
Ⓜ 07968 435627
Ⓔ gardens@hergest.co.uk
Ⓦ www.hergest.co.uk
Contact: Stephen Lloyd
Opening Times: 1200-1730, 7 days, Apr-Oct.
Cat. Cost: None issued
Credit Cards: All major credit/debit cards
Specialities: *Acer*, *Betula* & unusual woody plants.
Notes: Limited wheelchair access.
OS Grid Ref: SO286567

WHal **Hall Farm Nursery**
Vicarage Lane, Kinnerley, Nr Oswestry, Shropshire SY10 8DH
Ⓣ (01691) 682135
Ⓔ info@hallfarmnursery.co.uk
Ⓦ www.hallfarmnursery.co.uk
Contact: Christine & Nick Ffoulkes-Jones
Opening Times: 1000-1700, Wed-Sat, 1st Mar-30th Sep 2017.
Cat. Cost: Online only.
Credit Cards: Visa, MasterCard, Electron, Maestro
Specialities: Wide range of herbaceous perennials, woodland plants, alpine & scree plants. Herbs and vegetable plants in season.
Notes: Partially accessible for wheelchairs.
OS Grid Ref: SJ333209

WHer **The Herb Garden & Historical Plant Nursery**
Frondeg, Gilfachreda, New Quay, Ceredigion SA45 9SP
Ⓣ (01545) 580893
Ⓔ corinnetremaine@gmail.com
Ⓦ www.HistoricalPlants.co.uk
Contact: Corinne Tremaine
Opening Times: By appt. only.
Min Mail Order UK: Nmc
Min Mail Order EU: Nmc
Cat. Cost: Online only.
Credit Cards: None
Specialities: Rarer herbs, rare natives & wild flowers; rare & unusual & historical perennials, old roses, heritage pinks & Parma violets.

WHil **Hillview Hardy Plants** ♿
(off B4176), Worfield, Nr Bridgnorth, Shropshire WV15 5NT
Ⓣ (01746) 716454
Ⓜ 07974 391608
Ⓕ (01746) 716454
Ⓔ hillview@onetel.net
Ⓦ www.hillviewhardyplants.com
Contact: Ingrid, John & Sarah Millington
Opening Times: 0930-1700 Mon-Sat, Mar-mid Oct. At other times, please phone first.
Min Mail Order UK: £10.00 + p&p
Min Mail Order EU: £10.00 + p&p
Cat. Cost: Online only.
Credit Cards: All major credit/debit cards
Specialities: Choice herbaceous perennials incl. *Acanthus*, *Albuca*, *Aquilegia*, *Primula auricula*, *Eucomis*, *Ixia*, South African bulbs. Nat. Collections of *Acanthus* & *Albuca*.
Notes: Also sells wholesale. Exports beyond EU. Delivers to shows. Euro accepted. Wheelchair accessible.
OS Grid Ref: SO772969

WHlf **Hayloft Plants**
Manor Farm, Pensham, Pershore, Worcestershire WR10 3HB
Ⓣ (01386) 554440 or (01386) 562999
Ⓕ (01386) 553833
Ⓔ info@hayloftplants.co.uk
Ⓦ www.hayloftplants.co.uk
Contact: Yvonne Walker
Opening Times: Not open. Mail order only.

Min Mail Order UK: Nmc
Min Mail Order EU: Nmc
Cat. Cost: Free.
Credit Cards: All major debit/credit cards except American Express
Notes: Mail order only.

WHoo **Hoo House Nursery** ◆
Hoo House, Gloucester Road, Tewkesbury, Gloucestershire GL20 7DA
Ⓣ (01684) 293389
Ⓕ (01684) 293389
Ⓔ nursery@hoohouse.co.uk
Ⓦ www.hoohouse.co.uk
Contact: Julie & Robin Ritchie
Opening Times: 1000-1700 Mon-Sat, 1100-1700 Sun. Please ring to check Nov-Jan.
Cat. Cost: 3 × 1st class.
Credit Cards: All major credit/debit cards
Specialities: Wide range of herbaceous & alpines grown peat-free. Asters, *Cyclamen*, *Geranium*, *Penstemon*, *Saxifraga* & many later-flowering varieties.
Notes: Also sells wholesale. Euro accepted. Partially wheelchair accessible.
OS Grid Ref: SO893293

WHor **Horticultural Sales** ◆
Upper Brockington, Berrington Street, Bodenham, Herefordshire HR1 3HT
Ⓣ (01568) 797747
Ⓜ 07966 635005
Ⓔ pdavies@hortsales.fsnet.co.uk
Ⓦ www.hortplants.co.uk
Contact: Peter Davies
Opening Times: Open 6 days a week. Closed Mondays.
Min Mail Order UK: Nmc
Min Mail Order EU: Nmc
Cat. Cost: Free but available by email only.
Credit Cards: All major credit/debit cards, Paypal
Specialities: Wide selection of less commonly grown shrubs, available in small quantities only.
Notes: Plant finding service. 40 years experience in trade. Also sells wholesale. Euro accepted.

WHrl **Harrells Hardy Plants**
(office) 15 Coxlea Close, Evesham, Worcestershire WR11 4JS
Ⓣ (01386) 443077
Ⓜ 07799 577120 or 07733 446606
Ⓔ mail@harrellshardyplants.co.uk
Ⓦ www.harrellshardyplants.co.uk
Contact: Liz Nicklin & Kate Phillips
Opening Times: By appt. only. Please telephone.
Min Mail Order UK: Nmc
Min Mail Order EU: Nmc
Cat. Cost: Online plant list.
Credit Cards: None
Specialities: Display gardens showcase wide range of hardy perennials, esp. *Hemerocallis* & grasses.
Notes: Nursery located off Rudge Rd, Evesham. Please phone for directions or see website. Partial wheelchair access.
OS Grid Ref: SP033443

WHwl **Howle Hill Nursery** ♿
Watersedge, Howle Hill, Ross-on-Wye, Herefordshire HR9 5SP
Ⓣ (01989) 567726
Ⓜ 07961 570409
Ⓔ enquiries@howlehillnursery.co.uk
Ⓦ www.howlehillnursery.co.uk
Contact: Andy Houghton or Luke Delaney
Opening Times: 0800-1800 Mon-Fri, 0900-1700 Sat.
Min Mail Order UK: £20
Min Mail Order EU: £50
Cat. Cost: Free or online.
Credit Cards: All major debit/credit cards except American Express
Specialities: A large selection of Japanese maples (approx. 90 cvs), ranging in size from 9cm pots to 600ltr mature specimens. Also large & expanding selection of grasses, herbaceous, conifers, exotics, trees & shrubs.
Notes: Nursery is 3 miles from Ross on Wye on the edge of the Forest of Dean, owned by award-winning garden designer, Peter Dowle. Offers plant/tree hire for special occasions, plant sourcing, complete garden design & build service. Also sells wholesale. Delivers to shows. Euro accepted. Wheelchair accessible.
OS Grid Ref: SO606206

WIce **Ice Alpines** ♿
Lye Head Road, Bewdley, Worcestershire DY12 2UW
Ⓣ (01299) 269219
Ⓕ (01562) 510003
Ⓔ icealpines@gmail.com
Ⓦ www.icealpines.co.uk
Contact: Mark Lagomarsino
Opening Times: Mail order. Open by appt. only.
Min Mail Order UK: Nmc
Min Mail Order EU: £18
Credit Cards: All major credit/debit cards
Specialities: British grown alpine & rockery plants.
Notes: Delivers to shows. Wheelchair accessible.

WJam **Green JJam Nurseries**
Badsey Lane, Knowle Hill, Evesham, Worcestershire WR11 7EL
Ⓣ (01386) 49564
Ⓜ 07980 277709
Ⓔ julia@greenjjam.co.uk
Ⓦ www.greenjjam.co.uk
Contact: Julia Mitchell
Opening Times: Open by appt. only.
Min Mail Order UK: £10.00
Credit Cards: All major credit/debit cards
Specialities: Small, family run nursery propagating and growing almost all of the plants they sell. *Penstemon*, hardy perennials and white-themed plants.
Notes: Delivers to shows.

WJas **Paul Jasper Trees**
(office) The Lighthouse, Bridge Street, Leominster, Herefordshire HR6 8DX
Ⓔ jaspertreescouk@aol.com
Ⓦ www.jaspertrees.co.uk
Contact: Paul Jasper
Opening Times: Not open. Mail order only.
Min Mail Order UK: £20.00 + p&p
Cat. Cost: Online only.
Credit Cards: All major credit/debit cards
Specialities: Full range of fruit & ornamental trees. Over 100 modern and traditional fruit tree varieties plus 100 ornamental tree varieties, all direct from the grower. Many unusual varieties of *Malus domestica* & *Prunus*.
Notes: Regular updates & notes on website. Also sells wholesale. Delivers to shows.
OS Grid Ref: SO495595

WJek **Jekka's Herb Farm** ♿
Rose Cottage, Shellards Lane, Alveston, Bristol, South Gloucestershire BS35 3SY
Ⓣ (01454) 418878
Ⓔ sales@jekkasherbfarm.com
Ⓦ www.jekkasherbfarm.com
Contact: Jekka McVicar
Opening Times: Open on specific days only. Please check website or contact nursery for dates.
Min Mail Order UK: £10.00
Min Mail Order EU: £18.00
Cat. Cost: Online only.
Credit Cards: Visa, MasterCard, Delta, Maestro
Specialities: Specialist herb farm with a herbetum containing over 300 culinary herbs. The collection contains herbs from all around the world.
Notes: Wheelchair accessible.

WJPR **JPR Environmental**
The Malt House, Standish, Stonehouse, Gloucestershire GL10 3DL
Ⓣ (01453) 822584
Ⓔ enquiries@jprenvironmental.co.uk
Ⓦ www.jprwillow.co.uk
Contact: Elizabeth Hillary
Opening Times: Not open. Mail order only. 0900-1700, Mon-Fri.
Min Mail Order UK: £6.00
Credit Cards: All major debit/credit cards except American Express
Specialities: *Salix*.
Notes: Also sells wholesale.

WKif **Kiftsgate Court Gardens** ♿
Kiftsgate Court, Chipping Camden, Gloucestershire GL55 6LN
Ⓣ (01386) 438777
Ⓕ (01386) 438777
Ⓔ anne@kiftsgate.co.uk
Ⓦ www.kiftsgate.co.uk
Contact: Mrs J Chambers
Opening Times: 1200-1800 Sat-Wed, May, Jun & Jul. 1400-1800 Sat-Wed, Aug. 1400-1800 Sun, Mon & Wed, Apr & Sep.
Cat. Cost: None issued
Credit Cards: All major debit/credit cards except American Express
Specialities: Small range of unusual plants.
Notes: Wheelchair accessible.
OS Grid Ref: SP170430

WLav **The Lavender Garden**
Ashcroft Nurseries, Nr Ozleworth, Kingscote, Tetbury, Gloucestershire GL8 8YF
Ⓣ (01453) 860356 or 549286
Ⓜ 07837 582943
Ⓔ Andrew007Bullock@aol.com
Ⓦ www.TheLavenderG.co.uk
Contact: Andrew Bullock
Opening Times: 1100-1700 Sat & Sun. Weekdays variable, please phone. 1st Nov-1st Mar by appt. only.
Min Mail Order UK: £10.00 + p&p
Min Mail Order EU: £20.00 + p&p
Cat. Cost: 2 × 1st class.
Credit Cards: All major credit/debit cards
Specialities: *Lavandula*, *Buddleja*, plants to attract butterflies. Herbs, wildflowers. Nat. Collection of *Buddleja*.
Notes: Also sells wholesale. Delivers to shows.
OS Grid Ref: ST798948

WMAq **Merebrook Water Plants**
Kingfisher Barn, Merebrook Farm, Hanley Swan, Worcestershire WR8 0DX
Ⓣ (01684) 310950

Ⓜ 07876 777066
Ⓔ enquiries@pondplants.co.uk
Ⓦ www.pondplants.co.uk
Contact: Roger Kings & Biddi Kings
Opening Times: Not open. Mail order only.
Min Mail Order UK: Nmc
Min Mail Order EU: £25.00
Cat. Cost: Online only.
Credit Cards: All major credit/debit cards
Specialities: *Nymphaea*, Louisiana irises & other aquatic plants. International Waterlily & Water Gardening Soc. accredited collection.
OS Grid Ref: SO802425

WMat **The Tree Shop at Frank P. Matthews Ltd.** ♿
Berrington Court, Tenbury Wells, Worcestershire WR15 8TH
Ⓣ (01584) 812800
Ⓕ (01584) 811830
Ⓔ treeshop@fpmatthews.co.uk
Ⓦ www.frankpmatthews.com
Contact: Steve Grosvenor
Opening Times: 0730-1700 Mon-Fri
Cat. Cost: 4 × 1st class.
Credit Cards: All major credit/debit cards
Specialities: Fruit & deciduous ornamental trees.
Notes: Also sells wholesale. Wheelchair accessible.
OS Grid Ref: SO571676

WMil **Anne Milner**
Meadow House, Baunton, Cirencester, Gloucestershire GL7 7BB
Ⓣ (01285) 643731
Ⓔ anne.milner@btinternet.com
Ⓦ www.blissiris.co.uk
Contact: Anne Milner
Opening Times: By appt. only.
Min Mail Order UK: Nmc
Min Mail Order EU: Nmc
Cat. Cost: 50p (UK) £1.00 (EU) to cover postage.
Credit Cards: None
Specialities: Nat. Collection of *Iris* (A.J. Bliss introductions). Available in small quantities only.
Notes: Euro accepted. Delivers to some shows, check with nursery.

WMon **National Collection of Monarda**
Glyn Bach, Pont Hywel, Efailwen, Pembrokeshire SA66 7JP
Ⓣ (01994) 419104
Ⓜ 07828 199303
Ⓔ carole.whittaker7@btinternet.com
Ⓦ www.glynbachgardens.co.uk
Contact: Carole Whittaker
Opening Times: Open by appt. & May-Oct for collection of orders only.
Min Mail Order UK: Nmc
Min Mail Order EU: Nmc
Cat. Cost: Online only.
Credit Cards: None
Specialities: Nat. Collection of *Monarda*. Limited stock available.
Notes: Gardens open under NGS and by appt. Talks given. If travelling some distance please contact nursery to check plant availability.
OS Grid Ref: SN132275

WMoo **Moorland Cottage Plants and Garden**
Rhyd-y-Groes, Brynberian, Crymych, Pembrokeshire SA41 3TT
Ⓣ (01239) 891363
Ⓦ www.moorlandcottageplants.co.uk
Contact: Jennifer Matthews
Opening Times: 1030-1700 daily excl. Wed 14th Mar-18th Sep.
Credit Cards: All major credit/debit cards
Specialities: Traditional & unusual hardy perennials raised outside. Many garden-worthy rarities. Cottage garden plants incl. many *Astilbe*, *Crocosmia*, *Geum*, *Geranium*, *Monarda*, *Potentilla*, *Persicaria* & *Veronicastrum*. Plants for shade incl. ferns, moisture lovers & ornamental grasses. Colourful ground cover.
Notes: New RHS partner garden with mountain & moorland views. Open for NGS from 1st May until 18th Sep.
OS Grid Ref: SN091343

WMou **Mount Pleasant Trees Ltd** ♿
Rockhampton, Berkeley, Gloucestershire GL13 9DU
Ⓣ (01454) 260348
Ⓔ info@mountpleasanttrees.com
Ⓦ www.mountpleasanttrees.com
Contact: Tom Locke & Elizabeth Murphy
Opening Times: 0830-1630 Mon-Fri, 0830-1230 Sat, Oct-Apr.
Min Mail Order UK: Nmc
Cat. Cost: Free.
Credit Cards: All major credit/debit cards
Specialities: Wide range of trees for forestry, hedging, woodlands & gardens esp. *Populus*, *Salix*, *Tilia* & *Quercus*.
Notes: Mail order available for plants under 1m in height, quotes on request, p&p quoted on individual basis. Also sells wholesale. Wheelchair accessible.
OS Grid Ref: ST654929

WNHG **New Hope Gardens** ♿
(office) The Old Chapel, Cefn Einion,
Nr Bishops Castle, Shropshire
SY9 5LF
Ⓣ Office: (01588) 630750
Ⓔ Newhopegardensmz@aol.com
Ⓦ www.newhopegardens.com
Contact: Mark Zenick
Opening Times: Open w/ends: 1000-1700 Sat & Sun, 24th/25th Jun; 1st/2nd, 8th/9th, 15th/16th, 22nd/23rd, 29th/30th Jul. Or by appt.
Min Mail Order UK: Nmc
Min Mail Order EU: Nmc
Cat. Cost: Online only. Plant list on request.
Credit Cards: All major credit/debit cards
Specialities: American bred, British grown, *Hemerocallis*. Ships bare-rooted plants. Daylily plants are growing and for sale at New Hope Gardens, Colebatch Farm, Shropshire on Open W/ends.
Notes: Wheelchair accessible.
OS Grid Ref: SO872317

WNPC **Newent Plant Centre** ♿
Little Verzons Farm, Hereford Road,
Ledbury, Herefordshire
HR8 2PZ
Ⓣ (01531) 670121
Ⓔ markmoir999@btinternet.com
Ⓦ www.newentplantcentre.co.uk
Contact: Mark Moir
Opening Times: 0900-1700 Mon-Sat, 1000-1600 Sun.
Credit Cards: All major credit/debit cards
Specialities: Extensive range of *Heuchera* & *Euphorbia*. Herbaceous perennials, climbers, shrubs, trees, alpines, herbs, roses & fruit.
Notes: Coffee shop & deli on site. Delivers to shows. Wheelchair accessible.
OS Grid Ref: SO665395

WOld **Old Court Nurseries**
Colwall, Nr Malvern, Worcestershire
WR13 6QE
Ⓣ (01684) 540416
Ⓜ 07971 522891
Ⓔ oldcourtnurseries@btinternet.com
Ⓦ www.autumnasters.co.uk
Contact: Paul, Meriel or Helen Picton
Opening Times: 1400-1700 Wed-Sat, May-Aug. 1100-1700 Wed-Sun, Aug. 1100-1700 7 days, 1st week Sep-2nd week Oct. Also by appt. May to Oct. See website or contact nursery for special Open Days.
Min Mail Order UK: Nmc
Min Mail Order EU: Nmc
Cat. Cost: Free.
Credit Cards: All major debit/credit cards except American Express
Specialities: Nat. Collection of Michaelmas Daisies. Herbaceous perennials.
Notes: Mail order sent in spring only. Display garden open Aug-Oct. See website for early season openings.
OS Grid Ref: SO759430

WOut **Out of the Common Way**
Penhyddgan, Boduan, Pwllheli, Gwynedd
LL53 8YH
Ⓣ (01758) 721577
Ⓔ ziggymen22@hotmail.co.uk
Contact: Margaret Mason
Opening Times: By arrangement.
Min Mail Order UK: Nmc
Min Mail Order EU: Nmc
Cat. Cost: A5 sae large letter rate postage or online.
Credit Cards: None
Specialities: *Labiates*, esp. *Salvia*. Also *Geranium* & *Crocosmia*. Native plants. Some plants propagated in small quantities only. Will propagate salvias to order.
Notes: Delivers to shows. Euro accepted.

W

WPav **Paviour and Davies Plants** ♿
(office) Dame School, Castle Street,
Wigmore, Herefordshire
HR6 9UA
Ⓜ 07966 580812
Ⓔ info@paviouranddaviesplants.co.uk
Ⓦ www.paviouranddaviesplants.co.uk
Contact: Mark Paviour
Opening Times: By appt. only.
Min Mail Order UK: Nmc
Cat. Cost: Online
Credit Cards: None
Specialities: Plants of Chilean and Argentinian origin together with a selection of unusual plants from Australasia. All plants propagated and grown on site. Nat. Collection of *Azara*. Some plants only available in small numbers.
Notes: Groups welcome by appt. Talks given by arrangement. Delivers to shows. Wheelchair accessible.
OS Grid Ref: SO429556

WPGP **Pan-Global Plants** ♿
The Walled Garden, Frampton Court,
Frampton-on-Severn, Gloucestershire
GL2 7EX
Ⓣ (01452) 741641
Ⓜ 07801 275138
Ⓔ info@panglobalplants.com
Ⓦ www.panglobalplants.com

Contact: Nick Macer
Opening Times: 1100-1700 Wed-Sun 1st Feb-31st Oct. Also B/hols. Closed 2nd Sun in Sep. Winter months by appt., please phone first.
Min Mail Order UK: £25.00
Min Mail Order EU: £35.00
Cat. Cost: 6 × 1st class.
Credit Cards: Maestro, MasterCard, Visa, Solo, Delta
Specialities: A serious plantsman's nursery offering a very wide selection of correctly named, rare & desirable trees, shrubs, herbaceous, bamboos, exotics, climbers, ferns etc. Specialities incl. *Magnolia*, *Hydrangea*, *Tilia*, *Betula*, *Sorbus*, *Bamboo* & *Agavaceae*.
Notes: Wheelchair accessible.
OS Grid Ref: SO750080

WPnP **Penlan Perennials** ♿
Wern Rhos, Newchapel, Boncath, Pembrokeshire SA37 0EN
Ⓣ (01239) 842260
Ⓜ 07857 675312
Ⓔ info@penlanperennials.co.uk
Ⓦ www.penlanperennials.co.uk
Contact: Richard Cain
Opening Times: Open for collection of orders & by appt..
Min Mail Order UK: Nmc
Min Mail Order EU: Nmc
Cat. Cost: Online only.
Credit Cards: All major credit/debit cards
Specialities: Aquatic, marginal & bog plants. Shade-loving & woodland perennials, ferns & hardy geraniums, all grown organically in peat-free compost.
Notes: Mail order all year, next day delivery. Secure online web ordering. Also sells wholesale. Euro accepted. Delivers to shows. Wheelchair accessible.
OS Grid Ref: SN217392

WPtf **Pantyfod Garden & Nursery**
Llandewi Brefi, Tregaron, Ceredigion SY25 6PE
Ⓣ (01570) 400564 (answering service)
Ⓜ 07473 922858
Ⓔ suepantyfod@gmail.com
Ⓦ www.pantyfodgarden.co.uk
Contact: Susan Rowe
Opening Times: 1200-1800 Sat only, mid Apr-mid Sep, nursery & garden. Other times by arrangement. Garden open under the NGS with plants for sale. Please check with NGS for Open Days.
Min Mail Order UK: Nmc
Min Mail Order EU: Nmc
Cat. Cost: Online only.
Credit Cards: Paypal
Specialities: Hardy geraniums, unusual hardy perennials, grasses, plants for moist soil, black plants, woodland plants. All plants grown largely peat-free. Many plants available in small quantities only.
Notes: Stock changes throughout the year as new varieties are added. Not all plants available for mail order. Mail order plants may be sent bare-rooted when dormant. Some listed plants ready later in the year. See website for regular updates or phone/email.
OS Grid Ref: SN654540

WRHF **Red House Farm** ♿
Flying Horse Lane, Bradley Green, Nr Redditch, Worcestershire B96 6QT
Ⓣ (01527) 821269
Ⓔ redhousenursery@googlemail.com
Ⓦ www.redhousefarmgardenandnursery.co.uk
Contact: Mrs Maureen Weaver
Opening Times: 1000-1700 Mon-Sat all year. 1000-1700 Sun & B/hols.
Cat. Cost: 2 × 1st class.
Credit Cards: None
Specialities: Cottage garden perennials.
Notes: Wheelchair accessible.
OS Grid Ref: SO986623

WSFF **Saith Ffynnon Wildlife Plants** ♿
Whitford, Holywell, Flintshire CH8 9EQ
Ⓣ (01352) 711198
Ⓕ (01352) 716777
Ⓔ jan@7wells.org
Ⓦ www.7wells.co.uk
Contact: Jan Miller
Opening Times: By appt. only.
Min Mail Order UK: Nmc
Min Mail Order EU: Nmc
Cat. Cost: 2 × 1st class (list only) or full catalogue online.
Credit Cards: All major credit/debit cards
Specialities: Plants and seeds to attract bees, butterflies & other wildlife. Natural dye plants. Nat. Collection of *Eupatorium*. Stock available in small quantities unless ordered well in advance.
Notes: Percentage of profits go to conservation. Credit cards accepted via website only. Also sells wholesale. Euro accepted. Wheelchair accessible.
OS Grid Ref: SJ154775

WSHC **Stone House Cottage Nurseries** ♿
Church Lane, Stone, Nr Kidderminster, Worcestershire DY10 4BG
Ⓜ 07817 921146
Ⓔ louisa@shcn.co.uk

Ⓦ www.shcn.co.uk
Contact: L N Arbuthnott
Opening Times: 1000-1700 Wed-Sat, early Apr-early Sep only.
Credit Cards: None
Specialities: Small general range esp. wall shrubs, climbers & unusual plants.
Notes: Wheelchair accessible.
OS Grid Ref: SO863750

WShi **Shipton Bulbs**
Y Felin, Henllan Amgoed, Whitland, Carmarthenshire SA34 0SL
Ⓣ (01994) 240637
Ⓕ (01994) 240637
Ⓔ admin@shiptonbulbs.co.uk
Ⓦ www.shiptonbulbs.co.uk
Contact: John Shipton & Astra Shipton
Opening Times: By appt. only.
Min Mail Order UK: Nmc
Min Mail Order EU: Nmc
Cat. Cost: Sae.
Credit Cards: All major credit/debit cards
Specialities: Native British bulbs. Bulbs & plants for naturalising.
Notes: Also sells wholesale. Euro accepted.
OS Grid Ref: SN188207

WSpi **Spinneywell Nursery**
Spinneywell Farm, Waterlane, Oakridge, Stroud, Gloucestershire GL6 7PH
Ⓣ (01452) 770092
Ⓜ 07986 887158
Ⓔ spinneywellsales@btconnect.com
Ⓦ www.plantproviders.co.uk
Contact: Wendy Asher
Opening Times: 0900-1700 most Sats, Mar-Oct, otherwise by prior appt. only. Also advertised Open Days. Check website or contact nursery for details.
Min Mail Order UK: £10.00 + p&p
Min Mail Order EU: £30.00 + p&p
Cat. Cost: Online only.
Credit Cards: All major credit/debit cards
Specialities: *Buxus*, *Taxus*, hellebores, euphorbias, hardy geraniums, ferns & *Hemerocallis*.
Notes: Plant sourcing service available. Mail order only. Also sells wholesale.
OS Grid Ref: SO921044

WSSs **Shropshire Sarracenias** ♿
Beaufort, Coppice Drive, Wrockwardine Wood, Telford, Shropshire TF2 7BP
Ⓣ (01952) 501598
Ⓔ mike@carnivorousplants.uk.com
Ⓦ www.carnivorousplants.uk.com
Contact: Mike King
Opening Times: By appt. only.
Min Mail Order UK: Nmc
Min Mail Order EU: Nmc
Cat. Cost: 2 × 1st class.
Credit Cards: Paypal
Specialities: *Sarracenia. Dionaea muscipula* & forms. Some stock available in small quantities only. Nat. Collections of *Sarracenia* & *Dionaea.*
Notes: Exports beyond EU. Delivers to shows. Euro accepted. Wheelchair accessible.
OS Grid Ref: SJ689085

WSuV **Sunnybank Vine Nursery (National Vine Collection)**
Cwm Barn, King Street, Ewyas Harold, Rowlestone, Herefordshire HR2 OEE
Ⓣ (01981) 240256
Ⓔ Sarah@sunnybankvines.co.uk
Ⓦ www.sunnybankvines.co.uk
Contact: Sarah Bell
Opening Times: Not open. Mail order only. Open day once a year advertised on both nursery & Plant Heritage websites.
Min Mail Order UK: £13.00 incl. p&p
Min Mail Order EU: £23.00 incl. p&p
Cat. Cost: Online only.
Credit Cards: None
Specialities: Vines. Nat. Collection of *Vitis vinifera* (hardy, incl. dessert & wine). Small quantities of 60-70 varieties available as rooted plants, the entire Collection usually available as bare wood cuttings for own propagation depending upon wood ripening this season.
Notes: Exports beyond EU by arrangement.

WTan **Tan-y-Llyn Nurseries**
Meifod, Powys SY22 6YB
Ⓣ (01938) 500370
Ⓔ info@tanyllyn-nursery.co.uk
Ⓦ www.tanyllyn-nursery.co.uk
Contact: Callum Johnston
Opening Times: By appt. only. Please phone.
Min Mail Order UK: Nmc
Cat. Cost: None issued
Credit Cards: Paypal
Specialities: Herbs, alpines, perennials.
OS Grid Ref: SJ167125

WThu **Thuya Alpine Nursery**
Glebelands, Hartpury, Gloucestershire GL19 3BW
Ⓣ (01452) 700548 (ring between 1900-2100 hours)
Ⓜ 07599 957869
Contact: S W Bond
Opening Times: 1000-dusk Sat & B/hols. 1100-dusk Sun, Weekdays appt. advised.
Min Mail Order UK: £7.00 + p&p
Min Mail Order EU: £14.00 + p&p

Cat. Cost: 4 × 2nd class.
Credit Cards: None
Specialities: Wide and changing range including rarities, available in small quantities only.
Notes: Will deliver plants to AGS shows only. Partially accessible for wheelchair users.

WTor **TORTWORTH PLANTS LTD**
Old Lodge Farm, Tortworth, Wotton-under-Edge, Gloucestershire GL12 8HF
Ⓣ (01454) 260020
Ⓕ (01454) 260020
Ⓔ info@tortworthplants.co.uk
Ⓦ www.tortworthplants.co.uk
Contact: Rebecca Flint or Tim Hancock
Opening Times: By appt. only.
Min Mail Order UK: Nmc
Cat. Cost: Online or 2 × 1st for plant list.
Credit Cards: All major credit/debit cards
Specialities: Herbaceous perennials & alpines, incl. rare & unusual.
Notes: Also sells wholesale. Partial wheelchair access. Delivers to shows.

WTre **WALLED GARDEN TREBERFYDD**
Llangasty, Brecon, Powys LD3 7PX
Ⓣ (01874) 730169
Ⓜ 07711 222700
Ⓔ alison@walledgardentreberfydd.com
Ⓦ www.walledgardentreberfydd.com
Contact: Alison Sparshatt
Opening Times: 1000-1700 daily, Apr-Oct. For Nov-Mar opening times see website or contact nursery.
Cat. Cost: Online only.
Credit Cards: All major credit/debit cards
Specialities: Old-fashioned plant nursery in a walled Victorian kitchen garden. Hardy plants grown in Wales which are structural, unusual, herbal or fragrant. Special emphasis on herbs & perennial vegetables. Many varieties propagated in small quantities only.
Notes: Events & workshops throughout the year. Contact nursery for details. Delivers to shows.
OS Grid Ref: SO128255

WTSh **TREE SHOP LTD**
Unit 16, Harts Barn, Monmouth Road, Longhope, Gloucestershire GL17 0QD
Ⓣ (01452) 832100
Ⓕ (01452) 831273
Ⓔ office@tree-shop.co.uk
Ⓦ www.tree-shop.co.uk
Contact: Helen Conneely & Lorraine Organ
Opening Times: By appt. only 0830-1600 Mon-Fri. Please phone first.
Min Mail Order UK: Nmc
Cat. Cost: Free.
Credit Cards: All major debit/credit cards except American Express
Specialities: Trees, hedging, shrubs.
OS Grid Ref: SO679185

WTyc **TY CWM NURSERY**
Penfordd, Llanybydder, Ceredigon SA40 9XE
Ⓣ (01570) 480655
Ⓔ helenwarrington@hotmail.co.uk
Ⓦ www.tycwmnursery.co.uk
Contact: Helen Warrington
Opening Times: 1000-1800, 1st Apr–31st Sep, Tue–Sun. Closed Mon. 1st Oct-31st Mar by appointment only.
Min Mail Order UK: Nmc
Min Mail Order EU: Nmc
Cat. Cost: Online only
Credit Cards: All major credit/debit cards
Specialities: Carnivorous plants & unusual perennials. Also sell shrubs, climbers, bedding, fruit and veg plants. Many items not listed available in small quantities.
Notes: Partial wheelchair access. Delivers to shows.

WViv **VIV MARSH POSTAL PLANTS** ♿
Hunkington Nurseries, Walford Heath, Shrewsbury, Shropshire SY4 2HT
Ⓣ (01939) 291475
Ⓔ mail@postalplants.co.uk
Ⓦ www.postalplants.co.uk
Contact: Mr Viv Marsh
Opening Times: Open 2 w/ends a year. Please phone or see website for details.
Min Mail Order UK: £30.00
Min Mail Order EU: £30.00
Cat. Cost: Free.
Credit Cards: All major credit/debit cards
Specialities: Specialists in *Alstroemeria*. Nat. Collection of *Alstroemeria*, viewing by appt.
Notes: Wheelchair access to tunnels but no disabled toilet.
OS Grid Ref: SJ445197

WWct **WALCOT ORGANIC NURSERY**
Lower Walcot Farm, Walcot Lane, Drakes Broughton, Pershore, Worcestershire WR10 2AL
Ⓣ (01905) 841587
Ⓜ 07780 547983
Ⓔ enquiries@walcotnursery.co.uk
Ⓦ www.walcotnursery.co.uk
Contact: Kevin O'Neill
Opening Times: 0800-1700 Mon-Fri. 1000-1300 Sat. Nov-Mar only.

Min Mail Order UK: £15.00
Cat. Cost: Free.
Credit Cards: All major credit/debit cards
Specialities: Organic fruit trees. Apples, plums, pears, cherries, quinces on different rootstocks.
Notes: Also sells wholesale. Nursery buildings accessible for wheelchairs.
OS Grid Ref: SO944461

WWFP **Whitehall Farmhouse Plants**
Sevenhampton, Cheltenham, Gloucestershire GL54 5TL
Ⓣ (01242) 820772
Ⓜ 07711 021034
Ⓔ info@wfplants.co.uk
Ⓦ www.wfplants.co.uk
Contact: Victoria Logue
Opening Times: By appt. only.
Min Mail Order UK: Nmc
Credit Cards: None
Specialities: A small nursery producing a range of interesting & easy hardy perennials for the garden. Some plants held in small quantities only.
Notes: Delivers to shows.
OS Grid Ref: SP018229

WWtn **Westonbury Mill Water Garden** ♿
Pembridge, Herefordshire HR6 9HZ
Ⓣ (01544) 388650
Ⓕ (01544) 388650
Ⓔ westonburymillnursery@gmail.com
Ⓦ www.westonburymillwatergardens.com
Contact: Richard Pim
Opening Times: 1100-1700 daily, 1st Apr-30th Sep. By appt. only at other times & to arrange collection. Please contact nursery for orders outside open season.
Specialities: Range of herbaceous plants suitable for a wide range of growing conditions, with special emphasis on plants for the water garden & bog areas. Plants available in small quantities. Seasonal availability varies as stock sells out. Contact nursery to confirm availability before travelling.
Notes: Café. Wheelchair accessible.

Abroad

XBar **Barnhaven Primroses**
Keranguiner, Plestin-les-grèves 22310 France
Ⓣ +33 2 9635 6841
Ⓜ +33 6 6124 7739
Ⓕ +33 2 9635 6841
Ⓔ info@barnhaven.com
Ⓦ www.barnhaven.com
Contact: Lynne Lawson & Rob Mitchell
Opening Times: 1400-1700 Feb-Apr. For visits outside this period, please phone first.
Min Mail Order UK: Nmc
Min Mail Order EU: Nmc
Credit Cards: Visa, MasterCard, Paypal
Specialities: *Primula*. French Nat. Collection of Barnhaven *Primula* hybrids. Certified collection of *Primula auricula* cvs. Old-fashioned and double primroses. Large collection of Asiatic and Alpine *Primula*. Seeds & plants available worldwide.
Notes: Exports beyond EU. Euro & sterling accepted. Delivers to shows.

XBlo **Table Bay View Nursery**
PO Box 12123, Mill Street, Cape Town 8010, South Africa
Ⓣ +27 21 683 5108
Ⓕ +27 21 683 5108
Ⓔ info@tablebayviewnursery.co.za
Contact: Terence Bloch
Opening Times: Mail order only. No personal callers.
Min Mail Order UK: £15.00 + p&p
Min Mail Order EU: £15.00
Cat. Cost: £3.40 (postal order)
Credit Cards: None
Specialities: Tropical & sub-tropical ornamental & fruiting plants. Self-harvested seed, predominently from our own inventory of mother stock plants.
Notes: Due to high local bank charges, cannot accept foreign bank cheques, only undated postal orders. To comply with UK import regulations, prospective buyers must register with DEFRA before placing an order. Exports beyond EU. Euro accepted.

XCre **Crea Paysage**
Lannénec, Allée De La Roselière, Ploemeur 56270, France
Ⓣ +33 02 9785 2555
Ⓜ +33 06249 25588
Ⓔ creapaysage@orange.fr
Ⓦ www.creapaysage.com/fr/
Contact: Audrey Le Borgne
Opening Times: 1000-1730 Tue-Sat (closed for lunch 1230-1330).
Min Mail Order UK: Nmc
Min Mail Order EU: Nmc
Notes: Euro accepted.

XEll **Ellebore**
La Chamotière, 61360 Saint-Jouin-de-Blavou, France
Ⓣ +33 2 3383 3772
Ⓜ +33 6802 28674
Ⓔ pepiniere.ellebore@orange.fr

Ⓦ www.pepiniere-ellebore.fr
Contact: Nadine Albouy & Christian Geoffroy
Opening Times: 1000-1800 Wed-Sat, mid-Feb to late Jun & Sep-Dec. 1500-1800 Thu, Fri & Sat, Jul, Aug & Jan to mid-Feb.
Min Mail Order UK: Nmc
Min Mail Order EU: Nmc
Cat. Cost: Free.
Credit Cards: All major credit/debit cards
Specialities: *Helleborus*. Bulbs. *Clematis*.
Notes: Also sells wholesale. Euro accepted. Delivers to shows. Exports beyond EU.

XFro **Frosch Exclusive Perennials**
Ziegelstadelweg 5, D-83623 Dietramszell-Lochen, Germany
Ⓣ +49 172 842 2050
Ⓕ +49 8027 904 9975
Ⓔ info@cypripedium.de
Ⓦ www.cypripedium.de
Contact: Michael Weinert
Opening Times: Not open. Mail order only. Orders taken between 0700-2200 hours.
Min Mail Order UK: £350.00 + p&p
Min Mail Order EU: £350.00 + p&p
Cat. Cost: Online only.
Credit Cards: None
Specialities: *Cypripedium* hybrids. Hardy orchids.
Notes: Also sells wholesale. Exports beyond EU. Euro accepted.

XHod **SCEA Hodnik**
1 Place du 19 Mars 1962, 45700 St Maurice sur Fessard, France
Ⓣ +33 02 3897 8459
Ⓕ +33 02 3897 8939
Ⓔ contact@hodnik.com
Ⓦ www.hodnik.com
Contact: André Hodnik
Opening Times: Not open except by appt. Mail order only.
Min Mail Order UK: Nmc
Min Mail Order EU: Nmc
Cat. Cost: Online only.
Credit Cards: All major credit/debit cards
Specialities: A large number of tropical & Mediterreanean plants which can be grown in a conservatory. French Nat. Collection of *Bougainvillea* & *Brugmansia*.
Notes: Weekly shipments to the UK. Euro accepted.

XLum **Lumen Plantes Vivaces**
Les Coutets, 24100 Creysse-Bergerac, Occitania, France
Ⓣ +33 5 5357 6215
Ⓔ ets.lumen@gmail.com
Ⓦ www.lumen.fr
Contact: Jordi & Amélie Tura
Opening Times: 0800-1730 Mon-Sat. Closed Sun.
Min Mail Order UK: Nmc
Min Mail Order EU: Nmc
Cat. Cost: Online only.
Credit Cards: Visa, MasterCard, Paypal
Specialities: Hardy perennials. French Nat. Collection of *Miscanthus*.
Notes: Also sells wholesale. Exports beyond EU. Delivers to shows. Euro accepted.

XPou **Koen Van Poucke** ♿
Heistraat 106, Sint-Niklaas, Oost-Vlaanderen, 9100 Belgium
Ⓣ +32 0377 77642
Ⓕ +32 0376 61698
Ⓔ kvanpoucke@skynet.be
Ⓦ www.koenvanpoucke.be
Contact: Koen Van Poucke
Opening Times: 0900-1230 & 1300-1800, Tue-Sat. Closed Sun & Mon. Closed Jul. Check website before travelling a long distance.
Min Mail Order UK: €100
Min Mail Order EU: €100
Credit Cards: None
Specialities: *Epimedium*. Also rare Asian shade plants. *Dahlia*.
Notes: Mail order Sep-Apr. Collector's garden open to the public. Delivers to shows. Euro accepted. Wheelchair accessible.

XSen **GAEC Senteurs Du Quercy** ♿
Mas de Fraysse, Escamps, Lot, 46230 France
Ⓣ +33 5 652 10167
Ⓔ contact@senteursduquercy.com
Ⓦ www.senteursduquercy.com
Contact: Frédéric Prévot
Opening Times: 1400-1800 spring & summer (excl. Aug). Other times, incl. Aug by appt.
Min Mail Order UK: Nmc
Min Mail Order EU: Nmc
Cat. Cost: €5.00
Specialities: *Salvia*, *Iris*, *Phlomis*, *Teucrium*, *Lavandula* and drought tolerant plants. French Nat. Collection of *Salvia* species.
Notes: Euro accepted. Delivers to shows. Wheelchair accessible.

Nursery Index by Name

Nurseries that are included in the *RHS Plant Finder* for the first time this year (or have been reintroduced after a significant absence) are marked in **bold type**.

Full details of the nurseries will be found in **Nursery Details by Code** on page 868. For a key to the geographical codes, see the start of **Nurseries**.

Hawthornes Nursery, The	NHaw
Hayloft Plants	WHlf
Hedgexpress	MHed
Herb Garden & Historical Plant Nursery, The	WHer
Herb Nursery, The	MHer
Herbary, The	CHby
Hergest Croft Gardens	WHCr
Heucheraholics	SHeu
Hewitt-Cooper Carnivorous Plants	**CHew**
Hic Bibi Nursery	**NHic**
Hidden Valley Gardens	CHVG
Hill Close Gardens	MHCG
Hill House Nursery Ltd	CHll
Hillview Hardy Plants	WHil
Hippopottering Nursery	NHip
Hoecroft Plants	EHoe
Holden Clough Nursery	**NHol**
Hollies Farm Plant Centre	MHol
Home Farm Plants	LHom
Homestead Plants	MHom
Hoo House Nursery	WHoo
Horticultural Sales	WHor
Howle Hill Nursery	**WHwl**
Hoyland Plant Centre	**NHoy**
Hyde Hall Plant Centre (RHS)	EHyd
Hydrangea Haven	SHyH
Ice Alpines	**WIce**
Tim Ingram	**SIgm**
Iris of Sissinghurst	SIri
Irisesonline	EIri
JPR Environmental	WJPR
Jackson's Nurseries	MJak
Jackson's Nurseries	MJac
Paul Jasper Trees	WJas
Jekka's Herb Farm	**WJek**
Jo's Garden Enterprise	GJos
John and Lynsey's Plants	SPin
JRG Dahlias	NJRG
Junker's Nursery	CJun
Keepers Nursery	SKee
Kelways Plants Ltd	CKel
Kenwith Conifer Nursery (Gordon Haddow)	CKen
Kevock Garden Plants	GKev
Kiftsgate Court Gardens	WKif
Kilmurry Nursery	**IKil**
E W King & Co. Ltd. (Kings Seeds)	EKin
Kings Barn Trees	SKin
Kinlochlaich Garden Plant Centre	GKin
Knoll Gardens	CKno
Ladybird Nurseries	ELad
Landford Trees	CLnd
Laneside Hardy Orchid Nursery	**NLAp**
Langthorns Plantery	ELan
Larch Cottage Nurseries	NLar
Laurel Farm Herbs and Edibles	**CLau**
Laurels Nursery, The	SLau
Lavender Garden, The	**WLav**
Layham Garden Centre & Nursery	SLay
Leamore Nursery	ILea
Letham Plants	**GLet**
Lilies Water Gardens	LLWG
Lime Cross Nursery	SLim
Little Brook Fuchsias	SLBF
Little Heath Farm (UK)	LLHF
C S Lockyer (Fuchsias)	CLoc
Loder Plants	SLdr
Lodge Farm Plants & Wildflowers	MLod
Logie Steading Plants	GLog
Long Acre Plants	**CLAP**
Long House Plants	ELon
Longstock Park Nursery	SLon
Lumen Plantes Vivaces	XLum
Mac Pennys Nurseries	CMac
Macplants	GMaP
Madrona Nursery	SMad
Mail Order Trees	EMOT
Majestic Trees	LMaj
Mallet Court Nursery	CMCN
Mandy Plants	EMdy
Marchants Hardy Plants	SMHy
Margery Fish Plant Nursery	CFis
Marshall's Malmaisons	EMal
Tree Shop at Frank P. Matthews Ltd., The	**WMat**
Mead Nursery, The	CMea
Meadowgate Nursery	**SMea**
Mendip Bonsai Studio	CMen
Mendle Nursery	NMen
Merebrook Water Plants	WMAq
Mickfield Hostas	EMic
Mill Cottage Plants	CMil
Mill Race Garden Centre	EMil
Millais Nurseries	LMil
Anne Milner	WMil
Mires Beck Nursery	NMir
National Collection of Monarda	WMon
Moore and Moore Plants	**EMor**
Moorland Cottage Plants and Garden	WMoo
Morehavens	SMor
Morton Nurseries Ltd	MMrt
Mount Pleasant Trees Ltd	WMou
Mount Venus Nursery	IMou
Mucklestone Nurseries	MMuc
National Dahlia Collection	CWGr
National Herb Centre, The	MNHC
Natural Selection	CNat
New Hope Gardens	WNHG
New Wood Trees	**CNWT**
Newent Plant Centre	WNPC
Newport Mills Nursery	CNMi
Nightingale Nursery	SNig
Norcroft Nurseries	NNor
Norfolk Bamboo Company	ENBC
Norfolk Herbs	ENfk
Norfolk Lavender	**ENor**

Aylett Nurseries Ltd.
North Orbital Road (A414), St. Albans,
Hertfordshire, AL2 1DH
Tel: 01727 822255

RARE OAKS

Est. over 60 years
HEDGING, TREES, SHRUBS, CONIFERS
ORNAMENTAL & FRUIT TREES
Over 200 different varieties of hedging plants and young trees to choose from plus fruit trees, soft fruit, ground cover plants etc.
Telephone or write for your FREE COLOUR BROCHURE
Buckingham Nurseries
14 Tingewick Rd, Buckingham MK18 4AE
Tel: (01280) 822133 Fax: (01280) 815491
www.hedging.co.uk

The Dingle Nurseries & Garden
We have one of the largest ranges of trees and shrubs in the country, including native trees, hedging, conifers, roses, perennials and fruit. Semi mature and standard trees are also available, as well as specimen shrubs and many rarities all at competitive prices.
Open 7 days a week 9am to 5pm.
DINGLE NURSERIES & GARDEN
Welshpool, Powys, Wales SY21 9JD
T: 01938 555145
E: info@dinglenurseryandgarden.co.uk

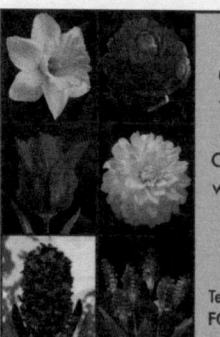

Index of Advertisers

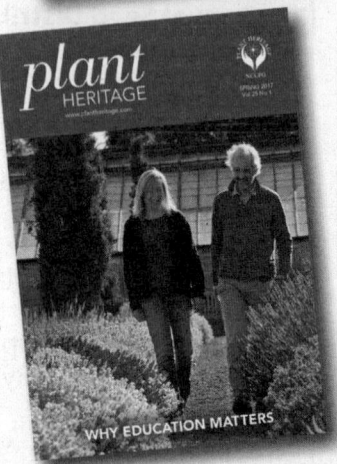